Student Quick Tips

Use this Student Quick Tips guide for a quick and easy start with McGraw-Hill Connect. You'll get valuable tips on registering, doing assignments, and accessing resources, as well as information about the support center hours.

Getting Started

TIP: To get started in Connect, you will need the following:

- Your instructor's Connect Web Address

    Sample of Connect Web Address:

    http://www.mcgrawhillconnect.com/class/instructorname_section_name

- Connect Access Code

TIP: If you do not have an access code or have not yet secured your tuition funds, you can click "Free Trial" during registration. This trial will provide temporary Connect access (typically three weeks) and will remind you to purchase online access before the end of your trial.

Registration and Sign In

1. Go to the Connect Web Address provided by your instructor
2. Click on **Register Now**
3. Enter your email address

TIP: If you already have a McGraw-Hill account, you will be asked for your password and will not be required to create a new account.

4. Enter a registration code or choose **Buy Online** to purchase access online

5. Follow the on-screen directions

TIP: Please choose your Security Question and Answer carefully. We will ask you for this information if you forget your password.

6. When registration is complete, click on **Go to Connect Now**

7. You are now ready to use **Connect**

Trouble Logging In?

- Ensure you are using the same email address you used during registration

- If you have forgotten your password, click on the "Forgot Password?" link at your Instructor's Connect Course Web Address

- When logged into Connect, you can update your account information (e.g. email address, password, and security question/answer) by clicking on the *"My Account"* link located at the top-right corner

Home (Assignments)

TIP: If you are unable to begin an assignment, verify the following:

- The assignment is available (start and due dates)

- That you have not exceeded the maximum number of attempts

- That you have not achieved a score of 100%

- If your assignment contains questions that require manual grading, you will not be able to begin your next attempt until your instructor has graded those questions

TIP: Based on the assignment policy settings established by your Instructor, you may encounter the following limitations when working on your assignment(s):

- Ability to Print Assignment

- Timed assignments – once you begin a "*timed assignment*," the timer will not stop by design

TIP: "*Save & Exit*" vs. "*Submit*" button

- If you are unable to complete your assignment in one sitting, utilize the "*Save & Exit*" button to save your work and complete it at a later time

- Once you have completed your assignment, utilize the "*Submit*" button in order for your assignment to be graded

Library

TIP: The *Library* section of your Connect account provides shortcuts to various resources.

- If you purchased ConnectPlus, you will see an *eBook* link, which can also be accessed from the section information widget of the *Home* tab

- *Recorded Lectures* can be accessed if your instructor is using *Tegrity Campus* to capture lectures. You may also access recorded lectures when taking an assignment by clicking on the projector icon in the navigation bar

- Many McGraw-Hill textbooks offer additional resources such as narrated slides and additional problems, which are accessible through the *Student Resources* link

Reports

TIP: Once you submit your assignment, you can view your available results in the *Reports* tab.

- If you see a dash (-) as your score, your instructor has either delayed or restricted your ability to see the assignment feedback

- Your instructor has the ability to limit the amount of information (e.g. questions, answers, scores) you can view for each submitted assignment

Need More Help?

CONTACT US ONLINE

Visit us at:

www.mcgrawhillconnect.com/support

Browse our support materials including tutorial videos and our searchable Connect knowledge base. If you cannot find an answer to your question, click on "Contact Us" button to send us an email.

GIVE US A CALL

Call us at:

1-800-331-5094

Our live support is available:

Mon-Thurs: 8 am – 11 pm CT
Friday: 8 am – 6 pm CT
Sunday: 6 pm   11 pm CT

—

Westmoreland County Community College

BIO 171/172

Human Anatomy & Physiology

Anatomy & Physiology
An Integrative Approach

Michael P. McKinley
Glendale Community College

Valerie Dean O'Loughlin
Indiana University

Theresa Stouter Bidle
Hagerstown Community College

Boston   Burr Ridge, IL   Dubuque, IA   New York   San Francisco   St. Louis
Bangkok   Bogotá   Caracas   Lisbon   London   Madrid
Mexico City   Milan   New Delhi   Seoul   Singapore   Sydney   Taipei   Toronto

BIO 171/172: Human Anatomy & Physiology
Westmoreland County Community College

This book is a McGraw-Hill Learning Solutions textbook and contains select material from *Human Anatomy & Physiology: An Integrative Approach* by Michael P. McKinley, Valerie Dean O'Loughlin and Theresa Stouter Bidle. Copyright © 2013 by The McGraw-Hill Companies, Inc. Reprinted with permission of the publisher. Many custom published texts are modified versions or adaptations of our best-selling textbooks. Some adaptations are printed in black and white to keep prices at a minimum, while others are in color.

5 6 7 8 9 0 BKM BKM 14 13 12

ISBN-13: 978-0-07-783560-6
ISBN-10: 0-07-783560-3
PART OF:
ISBN-13: 978-0-07-783561-3
ISBN-10: 0-07-783561-1

Learning Solutions Consultant: Robert Scanlon
Associate Project Manager: Vanessa Estrada
Printer/Binder: BookMasters, Inc.
Cover Images © 2012 JupiterImages Corporation

about the authors

MICHAEL MCKINLEY received his undergraduate degree from the University of California at Berkeley, and both his M.S. and Ph.D. degrees from Arizona State University. He did his postdoctoral fellowship at the University of California Medical School–San Francisco (UCSF) in the laboratory of Dr. Stanley Prusiner, where he worked for 12 years investigating prions and prion diseases. During this time, he became a member of the anatomy faculty at the UCSF Medical School, where he taught medical histology for 10 years while continuing to perform prion research. Concurrently, he was an author or co-author of more than 80 scientific papers. Between 1991 and 2000, Michael also participated in Alzheimer disease research and served as director of the Brain Donation Program at the Sun Health Research Institute. During this time he also taught developmental biology and genetics at Arizona State University West Campus. Since 1991, Michael has been a member of the biology faculty at Glendale Community College (GCC), and has taught undergraduate anatomy and physiology, general biology, and genetics at GCC Main Campus. In 2009, he moved to GCC North Campus, where he has been teaching anatomy and physiology courses exclusively. Mike's vast experience in histology, neuroanatomy, and cell biology greatly shaped the related content in the market-leading McKinley/O'Loughlin: *Human Anatomy,* 3rd edition textbook. Mike is an active member of the Human Anatomy and Physiology Society (HAPS). He resides in Tempe, Arizona with his wife Jan.

I am indebted to Jan (my wife), Renee, Ryan, and Shaun (my children), and Connor, Eric, Patrick, Keighan, and Aydan (my grandchildren). They are the love of my life and my inspiration always.

VALERIE DEAN O'LOUGHLIN received her undergraduate degree from the College of William and Mary, and her M.A. and Ph.D. degrees in biological anthropology from Indiana University. She is an associate professor at Indiana University School of Medicine, where she teaches human gross anatomy to medical students, basic human anatomy to undergraduates, and human anatomy for medical imaging evaluation to undergraduate and graduate students. She also teaches a pedagogical methods course and mentors M.S. and Ph.D. students pursuing anatomy education research. She is active in the Human Anatomy and Physiology Society (HAPS) and the American Association of Anatomists (AAA). She received the AAA Basmajian Award for excellence in teaching gross anatomy and outstanding accomplishments in scholarship in education. Valerie is co-author of the market-leading McKinley/O'Loughlin: *Human Anatomy,* 3rd edition textbook.

To my husband Bob and my daughter Erin: Thank you for always being there for me.

With love and thanks to my husband Jay and my daughter Stephanie for the many ways that they have supported me during this project.

TERRI STOUTER BIDLE received her undergraduate degree from Rutgers University, her M.S. degree in biomedical science from Hood College in Maryland, and has completed additional graduate coursework in genetics at the National Institutes of Health. She is a professor at Hagerstown Community College, where she teaches anatomy and physiology and genetics to pre–allied health students. Before joining the faculty in 1990, she was the coordinator of the Science Learning Center, where she developed study materials and a tutoring program for students enrolled in science classes. Terri has been a developmental reviewer and has written supplemental materials for both textbooks and lab manuals.

brief contents

contents

■ COMMUNICATION AND CONTROL

Chapter 12
Nervous System: Nervous Tissue   437

Chapter 13
Nervous System: Brain and Cranial Nerves   479

■ MAINTENANCE AND REGULATION

Chapter 18
Cardiovascular System: Blood 694

Chapter 19
Cardiovascular System: Heart 726

preface

Human anatomy and physiology is a fascinating subject. However, students can be overwhelmed by the complexity, the interrelatedness of concepts from different chapters, and the massive amount of material. Our goal in writing this textbook on anatomy and physiology was to create a book that guides students on a clearly written and expertly illustrated beginner's path through the human body. We have strived to make this book enjoyable to read, easy to understand, pedagogically efficient, and visually engaging while also assisting students in integrating concepts.

An Integrative Approach

One of the most daunting challenges that students face in mastering concepts in an anatomy and physiology course is integrating related content from numerous chapters. Understanding a topic like blood pressure, for example, requires knowledge from the chapters on the heart, blood vessels, kidneys, and how these structures are regulated by the nervous and endocrine systems. The usefulness of a human anatomy and physiology text is dependent in part on how successfully it helps students integrate these related concepts. Without this, students are only acquiring what seems like unrelated facts without seeing how they fit into the whole.

To adequately explain such complex concepts to beginning students in our own classrooms, we as teachers present multiple topics over the course of many class periods, all the while balancing these

detailed explanations with refreshers of content previously covered and intermittent glimpses of the big picture. Doing so ensures that students learn not only the individual pieces, but also how the pieces ultimately fit together. This book represents our best effort to replicate this teaching process. In fact, it is the effective integration of concepts throughout the text that makes this book truly unique from other undergraduate anatomy and physiology texts.

Our goal of emphasizing the interrelatedness of body systems and the connections between form and function necessitates a well-thought-out pedagogical platform to deliver the content. First and foremost, we have written a very user-friendly text with concise, accurate descriptions that are thorough, but don't overwhelm readers with nonessential details. The text narrative is deeply integrated with corresponding illustrations drawn specifically to match the textual explanations. In addition, we have included a set of "Integrate" features that support our theme and work together to give the student a well-rounded introduction to anatomy and physiology. **Integrate: Concept Overview** figures are one- or two-page visual summaries that aggregate related concepts in a big-picture view. These comprehensive figures link multiple sections of a chapter together in a cohesive snapshot ideal for study and review. **Integrate: Concept Connections** boxes provide glimpses of how concepts at hand will play out in upcoming chapters, and also pull vital information from earlier chapters back into the discussion at crucial points when relevant to a new topic. **Integrate: Clinical View** discussions apply concepts from the surrounding narrative to practical or clinical contexts, providing examples of what can go wrong in the human

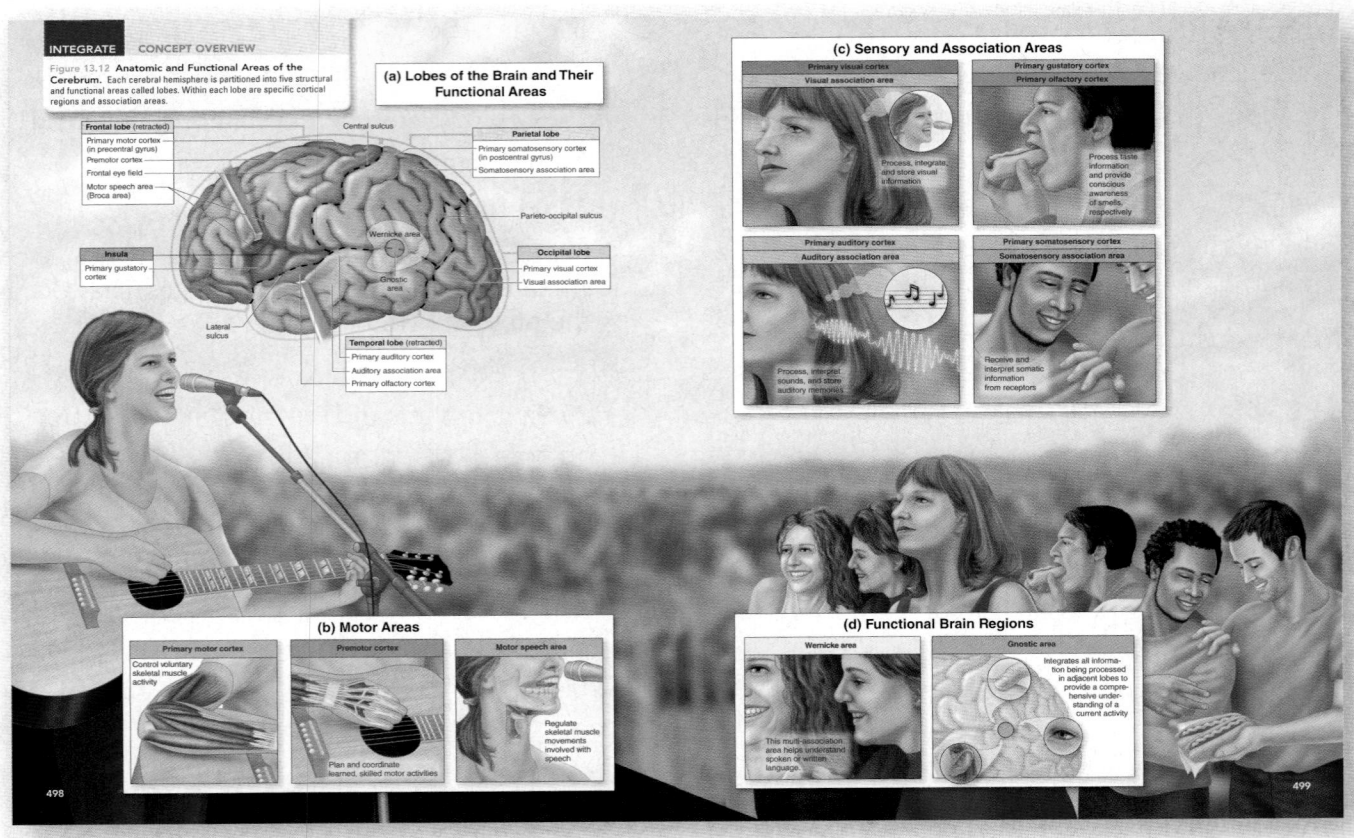

body to help crystallize understanding of the "norm." **Integrate: Learning Strategy** boxes infuse each chapter with practical study tips to understand and remember information. Learning strategies include mnemonics, analogies, and kinesthetic activities that students can perform to relate the anatomy and physiology to their own bodies. Finally, the media assets that accompany our book are tied to each section's learning objectives and previewed in the **Integrate: Online Study Tools** boxes at the end of each chapter.

Chapter Organization

In order to successfully execute an integrative approach, foundational topics must be presented at the point when it matters most for understanding. Students must have a baseline of knowledge about a given concept before it comes time to apply that information in a more complex situation. Thus, we have put a few simple "twists" on the way the following topics are typically subdivided and the order in which they are covered.

- **Chapter 2: Atoms, Ions, and Molecules** Most students taking an A&P course have limited or no chemistry background, which requires a textbook to provide a detailed, organized treatment of atomic and molecular structure, bonding, water, and biological macromolecules as a basis to understanding physiological processes.

- **Chapter 3: Energy, Chemical Reactions, and Cellular Respiration** ATP is essential to all life processes. A solid understanding of ATP furthers student comprehension of movement of materials across a membrane, muscle contractions, production of needed replacement molecules and structures in cells, action potentials in nerves, pumping of the heart, and removal of waste materials in the kidneys. This textbook elevates the importance of the key concept of ATP by teaching it early. We then utilize this knowledge in later chapters as needed, expanding on what has already been introduced rather than re-teaching it entirely.

- **Chapter 13: Nervous System: Brain and Cranial Nerves and Chapter 14: Nervous System: Spinal Cord and Spinal Nerves** Instead of subdividing the nervous system discussion into separate central nervous system (CNS) and peripheral nervous system (PNS) chapters, nervous system structures are grouped by region. Thus, students can integrate the cranial nerves with their respective nuclei in the brain, and they can integrate the spinal cord regions with the specific spinal nerves that originate from these regions.

- **Chapter 17: Endocrine System** We have organized both the endocrine system chapter and the specific coverage of the many hormones released from endocrine glands to most effectively and efficiently guide students in understanding how this system of control functions in maintaining homeostasis. Within the chapter on the endocrine system, we provide an introduction and general discussion of the endocrine system's central concepts and describe selected representative hormones that maintain body homeostasis. Details of the actions of most other hormones—which require an understanding of specific anatomic structures covered in other chapters—are described in those chapters;

for example, sex hormones are discussed in Chapter 28: Reproductive System. Learning the various hormones is facilitated by the inclusion of a "template" figure for each major hormone; each visual template includes the same components (stimulus, receptor, control center, and effectors) organized in a similar layout. In addition, information on each major hormone described in this text can be quickly accessed in the summary tables in Appendix B.

- **Chapter 21: Lymphatic System and Chapter 22: Immune System and the Body's Defense** A single chapter that discusses both the lymphatic system and immune system is overwhelming for most students. Thus, we separated the discussion into two separate chapters. The lymphatic system chapter focuses on the anatomic structures that compose the system, and provides a brief functional overview of each structure. This allows us to provide a thorough discussion and overview of the immune system in a separate chapter, where we frequently reference and integrate material from the earlier chapter.

- **Chapter 29: Development, Pregnancy, and Heredity** Coverage of heredity is included in the chapter on pregnancy and human development as a natural extension of Chapter 28: Reproductive System. This introduction will serve well as a precursor for students who follow their A&P course with a genetics course.

We Welcome Your Input!

We hope you enjoy reading this textbook, and that it becomes central to mastering the concepts in your anatomy and physiology course. This text is a product that has taken many years to complete, and comes from authors with over 70 years of combined teaching experience in anatomy and physiology. We are active classroom instructors, and are well aware of the challenges that current students face in mastering these subjects. We have taken what we have learned in the classroom and have created a textbook truly written for students.

Please let us know what you think about this text. We welcome your thoughts and suggestions for improvement, and look forward to your feedback!

Michael P. McKinley
Department of Biology
Glendale Community College
michael.mckinley@gcmail.maricopa.edu

Valerie Dean O'Loughlin
Medical Sciences
Indiana University
vdean@indiana.edu

Terri Stouter Bidle
Science Division
Hagerstown Community College
tsbidle@hagerstowncc.edu

guided tour

Fully Integrated Content and Pedagogy

Anatomy and Physiology: An Integrative Approach is structured around a tightly integrated learning system that combines illustrations and photos with textual descriptions; focused discussions with big-picture summaries; previously learned material with new content; factual explanations with practical and clinical examples; and bite-sized topical sections with multi-tiered assessment.

Unparalleled Art Program

In a visually oriented subject like A&P, quality illustrations are crucial to understanding and retention. The brilliant illustrations in *Anatomy and Physiology: An Integrative Approach* have been carefully rendered to convey realistic, three-dimensional detail while incorporating pedagogical conventions that help deliver a clear message. Each figure has been meticulously reviewed for accuracy and consistency, and precisely labeled to coordinate with the text discussions.

Blood flow

Rich Detail

Vibrant colors and three-dimensional shading make it easy to envision body structures and processes.

(a) Skeletal muscle fiber

Muscle
Fascicle
Muscle fiber
Sarcoplasmic reticulum
Triad
T-tubule Terminal cisternae
Sarcolemma
Nucleus
Myofibrils
Sarcomere
Myofilaments
Openings into T-tubules
Nucleus
Nucleus
Sarcoplasm
Mitochondrion

(b) Sarcolemma and T-tubules

Interstitial fluid
Na⁺/K⁺ pump
3 Na⁺ out
Voltage-gated Na⁺ channel
K⁺
Voltage-gated K⁺ channel
2 K⁺ in
Na⁺
Sarcolemma
Sarcoplasm
T-tubule

(c) Sarcoplasmic reticulum

SR membrane
Ca^{2+}
Ca^{2+} pump
Voltage-gated Ca^{2+} channel
Calmodulin
Calsequestrin
Sarcoplasm
Terminal cisterna

Multilevel Perspective

Microscopic structures are connected to macroscopic views to show changes in perspective between increasingly detailed drawings.

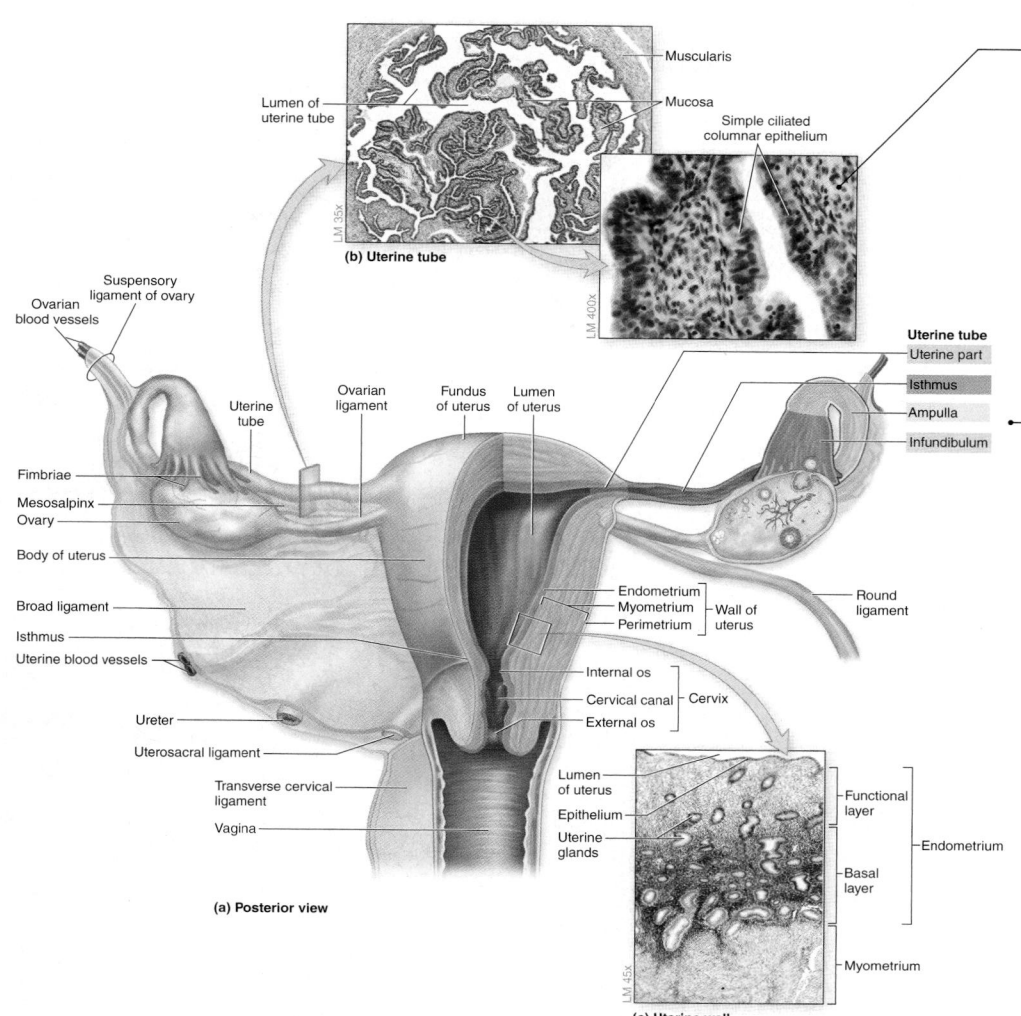

Muscularis

Mucosa

Lumen of
uterine tube

Simple ciliated
columnar epithelium

LM 35x

(b) Uterine tube

LM 400x

Photographs

Atlas-quality micrographs and cadaver images are frequently paired with illustrations to expose students to the appearance of real anatomic structures.

Suspensory
ligament of ovary

Ovarian
blood vessels

Fimbriae

Mesosalpinx

Ovary

Body of uterus

Broad ligament

Isthmus

Uterine blood vessels

Ureter

Uterosacral ligament

Transverse cervical
ligament

Vagina

Uterine
tube

Ovarian
ligament

Fundus
of uterus

Lumen
of uterus

Endometrium
Myometrium
Perimetrium

Wall of
uterus

Internal os

Cervical canal

External os

Cervix

Round
ligament

Uterine tube
Uterine part
Isthmus
Ampulla
Infundibulum

Color Coding

Many figures use color coding to organize information and clarify concepts for visual learners.

(a) Posterior view

Lumen
of uterus

Epithelium

Uterine
glands

Functional
layer

Basal
layer

Endometrium

Myometrium

LM 45x

(c) Uterine wall

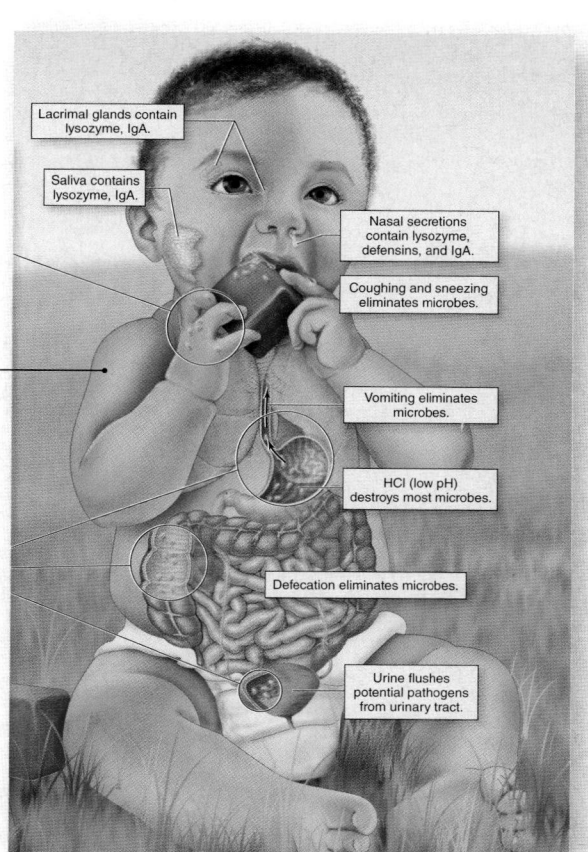

Lacrimal glands contain
lysozyme, IgA.

Saliva contains
lysozyme, IgA.

Nasal secretions
contain lysozyme,
defensins, and IgA.

Coughing and sneezing
eliminates microbes.

Vomiting eliminates
microbes.

HCl (low pH)
destroys most microbes.

Defecation eliminates microbes.

Urine flushes
potential pathogens
from urinary tract.

Real-Life Context

Illustrations include depictions of realistic people and situations to make figures more relevant and memorable.

Injury

**Damage to tissue
outside of vessel**

Integrative Visual Summaries

The groundbreaking new **Integrate: Concept Overview** figures combine multiple concepts into one big-picture summary. These striking, visually dynamic presentations offer a review of previously covered material in a creatively designed environment to emphasize how individual parts fit together in the understanding of a larger mechanism or concept.

Integrate: Concept Overview Figures

Multifaceted concepts are brought together in captivating one- or two-page visual presentations.

INTEGRATE CONCEPT OVERVIEW

Figure 20.15 **Factors That Regulate Blood Pressure.**
Three primary factors influence blood pressure: (a) cardiac output, (b) peripheral resistance, and (c) blood volume.

(a) Cardiac Output (CO)

Cardiac output is the volume of blood pumped per minute. CO is a function of heart rate (HR) and stroke volume (SV): **CO = HR × SV**.

Heart rate (HR)

Cardiac output increases. / Cardiac output decreases.

120 bpm / 65 bpm

Increased heart rate increases cardiac output and blood pressure. / Decreased heart rate decreases cardiac output and blood pressure.

Stroke volume (SV)

Cardiac output increases. / Cardiac output decreases.

Force of contraction

Increased stroke volume increases cardiac output and blood pressure. / Decreased stroke volume decreases cardiac output and blood pressure.

INTEGRATE

CLINICAL VIEW

Measuring Blood Pressure

Arterial blood pressure is measured indirectly using a **sphygmomanometer** (sfig′mō-mă-nom′ ē-ter; *phygmos* = pulse, *metron* = measure). A cuff is wrapped around the arm, and a stethoscope is placed just distal to the compressed artery, allowing a practitioner to listen for pulse sounds. The cuff is inflated until the brachial artery is completely compressed, temporarily stopping blood flow. The pressure in the cuff is then decreased as air is gradually released. Two values are recorded (e.g., 120/80), and the unit of measurement is millimeters of mercury (mm Hg).

Brachial artery / Stethoscope / Blood pressure cuff

Stretch / Recoil

Systolic pressure (e.g., 120 mm Hg) / Diastolic pressure (e.g., 80 mm Hg)

Blood flow

Systolic pressure

The "top" number of a blood pressure recording represents systolic pressure, which is pressure in the arteries when the heart contracts. This value is recorded when the first sound is heard. The sound occurs when pressure in the brachial artery is sufficient to overcome the pressure in the cuff, reestablishing blood flow.

Diastolic pressure

The "bottom" number of a blood pressure recording represents the diastolic pressure, which is the pressure in the arteries when the heart relaxes. This value is recorded when sounds are no longer heard. The absence of sound occurs when blood flow in the brachial artery is smooth because pressure in the cuff is no longer compressing the artery.

INTEGRATE CONCEPT OVERVIEW

Figure 14.11 **Differences Between Sensory and Motor Pathways.**
(a) Sensory pathways transmit ascending information to the brain, travel in the posterior and lateral funiculi of the spinal cord, and use up to three neurons to transmit this information (primary, secondary, and tertiary neurons). (b) Motor pathways transmit descending information from the brain, typically travel through the anterior and lateral funiculi of the spinal cord, and use two neurons (upper and lower motor neurons).

(a) Sensory Pathways

Nerve signals *ascend* to the brain in sensory pathways.

Most sensory pathways travel in the *posterior* and *lateral* funiculi of the spinal cord.

Posterior funiculus–medial lemniscal pathway

Spinocerebellar pathway (this pathway travels to the cerebellum and not to the thalamus)

Anterolateral pathway

Tertiary sensory neuron / Secondary sensory neuron / Primary sensory neuron

(b) Motor Pathways

Nerve signals *descend* from the brain in motor pathways.

Motor pathways tend to travel through the *anterior* and *lateral* funiculi of the spinal cord.

Upper motor neuron / Lower motor neuron

Lateral corticospinal tract / Rubrospinal tract / Medial pathway / Anterior corticospinal tract

Sensory pathways to the cerebrum use up to *three* neurons: a *primary*, *secondary*, and a *tertiary* neuron.

Tertiary neuron (cell body located in thalamus)

Thalamus

Secondary neuron (cell body located in posterior horn or a brainstem nucleus)

Primary neuron (cell body located in posterior root ganglion or a brainstem nucleus)

Motor pathways use *two* motor neurons: an *upper motor* neuron and a *lower motor* neuron.

Upper motor neuron (cell body located in cerebral cortex or a brainstem nucleus)

Lower motor neuron (cell body located in anterior horn or a brainstem nucleus)

(b) Peripheral Resistance

Peripheral resistance is the opposition to flow of blood in vessels, and is a function of vessel radius, vessel length, and blood viscosity.

Vessel radius	Vessel length	Blood viscosity
Vasoconstriction narrows vessel and forces blood through a narrower lumen, increasing peripheral resistance and blood pressure.	Longer vessels increase peripheral resistance, which raises blood pressure.	Increased viscosity creates an opposition to blood flow, increasing peripheral resistance and blood pressure.
Vasodilation widens vessel, decreasing peripheral resistance and blood pressure.	Shorter vessels decrease peripheral resistance, which lowers blood pressure.	Decreased viscosity allows blood to flow more freely through vessels, decreasing peripheral resistance and blood pressure.

(c) Blood Volume

Blood volume is a function of fluid intake and fluid output. Fluid intake increases blood volume and blood pressure. Fluid output decreases blood volume and blood pressure.

Fluid intake (~2500 mL/day)	Fluid output (~2500 mL/day)
Food and drink	Moisture in expired air
Metabolic water	Sweat and transpiration
	Urine
	Feces

Sufficient blood pressure is required to maintain adequate perfusion of systemic tissues during capillary exchange.

"It is an old adage that a 'picture is worth a thousand words' and I feel the Concept Overviews take this adage to new heights. In two pages, the author presents a chapter's worth of information [in] an easy-to-understand memorable diagram."

—William Dunscombe,
Union County College

INTEGRATE CONCEPT OVERVIEW

Figure 12.22 Events of Neuron Physiology. Neuron physiology involves specific events that occur in the four functional segments of a neuron: (1) receptive segment, (2) initial segment, (3) conductive segment, and (4) transmissive segment.

② INITIAL SEGMENT: "Trigger Zone"

Summation of EPSPs and IPSPs (not shown), includes both spatial summation of multiple presynaptic neurons and temporal summation of one presynaptic neuron quickly stimulating; determines if threshold (−55 mV) is reached.

Spatial summation

Temporal summation

③ CONDUCTIVE SEGMENT: Propagation of Action Potential

Repolarization   Depolarization

Repolarization and its propagation: Sequential opening of voltage-gated K⁺ channels that immediately follows depolarization to reestablish RMP. K⁺ moves out of axon.

Depolarization and its propagation: Sequential opening of voltage-gated Na⁺ channels in response to reaching threshold. Na⁺ moves into axon.

Labels: Action potential along presynaptic neuron axon; Dendrites; Presynaptic neuron; Graded potentials of postsynaptic neuron; ② Initial segment; Axon hillock; Postsynaptic neuron; Cell body; ① Receptive segment; Myelin sheath; Axon; ③ Conductive segment; Action potential; Diffusion of Na⁺ through axoplasm; Depolarization; Repolarization; Telodendria; ④ Transmissive segment

① RECEPTIVE SEGMENT: Establishing Graded Potentials: EPSPs and IPSPs

Excitatory neurotransmitter is released from presynaptic neuron; it binds with chemically gated cation channels; more Na⁺ enters neuron than K⁺ exits and inside becomes more positive, which is an excitatory postsynaptic potential (EPSP).

Inhibitory neurotransmitter is released from presynaptic neuron, which binds with either chemically gated K⁺ channels, and K⁺ exits neuron or to chemically gated Cl⁻ channels, and Cl⁻ enters neuron. In either case, the inside becomes more negative, which is an inhibitory postsynaptic potential (IPSP).

Labels: Excitatory neurotransmitter; Na⁺; Chemically gated cation channel; Chemically gated K⁺ channel; K⁺; Chemically gated Cl⁻ channel; Cl⁻; Inhibitory neurotransmitter; EPSP; IPSP

④ TRANSMISSIVE SEGMENT: Release of Neurotransmitter

Arrival of an action potential at the synaptic knob triggers the opening of voltage-gated Ca²⁺ channels. Ca²⁺ enters the synaptic knob, causing the subsequent release of neurotransmitter from synaptic vesicles by exocytosis.

Neurotransmitter binds with receptors of either another neuron or an effector (muscle or gland).

Labels: Ca²⁺; Voltage-gated Ca²⁺ channel; Neurotransmitter; Synaptic vesicle; Synaptic knob; Action potential

Concept Integration

Both backward and forward references are supplied throughout the text to remind the reader of the significance of previously covered material, and to foreshadow how knowledge of a topic at hand will come into play in a later discussion. Simple references appear in the flow of the text, while more detailed refreshers are presented in **Integrate: Concept Connection** boxes.

"This is a great way to allow students to integrate information from one chapter to the next, both within and between semesters."

—John Placyk,
University of Texas–Tyler

"It is very important for students to be 'connecting' one concept to another in order to build on their understanding. The 'spiral method' of instruction capitalizes on review and integrating past information. In a course like Human A&P, it is essential that the body systems are not thought of as discrete, stand-alone entities. This textbook keeps the instructors (and the students) 'on task,' processing the big picture."

—R. Christopher Harvey,
Brevard Community College

Practical and Clinical Applications

Integrating familiar contexts into the study of A&P makes seemingly abstract concepts more relevant and memorable. **Integrate: Learning Strategy** boxes provide simple, practical advice for learning the material. **Integrate: Clinical View** readings offer insight on how complex physiologic processes or anatomic relationships affect body functioning.

INTEGRATE

LEARNING STRATEGY

The mnemonic "Never let monkeys eat bananas" is a simple way to recall the leukocytes in order of their relative abundance:

Never = Neutrophil (most abundant)
Let = Lymphocyte
Monkeys = Monocyte
Eat = Eosinophil
Bananas = Basophil (least abundant)

INTEGRATE

LEARNING STRATEGY

The analogy of an archery target can help you remember the components of an osteon:

- The entire *target* represents the *osteon.*
- The *bull's-eye* of the target is the *central canal.*
- The *rings* of the target are the *concentric lamellae.*

Learning Strategies

Classroom tried-and-tested learning strategies offer everyday analogies, mnemonics, and useful tips to aid understanding and memory.

INTEGRATE

LEARNING STRATEGY

Drinking through a straw provides an easy way to demonstrate the variables that influence resistance:

- **Viscosity.** Water or soda moves through a straw more easily than does a thick vanilla milkshake.
- **Vessel length.** It is easier to drink through a relatively short straw compared with a very long, twisty straw.
- **Vessel radius.** Water can be sipped through a normal-sized straw more easily than through a hollow coffee stirrer with its smaller diameter.

Greater resistance is experienced when drinking thick liquids, using a longer straw, or using a more narrow straw. In the same way, an increase in resistance is exhibited with more viscous blood, increased total length of blood vessels, and vasoconstriction of blood vessels.

Clinical View

Interesting clinical sidebars reinforce or expand upon the facts discussed within the narrative. The clinical views are adjacent to the facts in the narrative (rather than placed at the end of the chapter) so students may immediately make connections between the narrative and real-life applications.

INTEGRATE

CLINICAL VIEW
Smoking

Smoking results in the inhalation of over 200 chemicals into the respiratory passageways of the lungs. These chemicals blacken the respiratory passageways and cause respiratory changes that increase the risk of (1) respiratory infections, including the common cold, influenza, pneumonia, and tuberculosis; and (2) cellular and genetic damage to the lungs that may lead to emphysema or lung cancer.

The deleterious effects of smoking are not limited to the respiratory system. Nicotine causes vasoconstriction in the cardiovascular system, carbon monoxide interferes with oxygen binding to hemoglobin, and the risk and severity of atherosclerosis is increased. These changes decrease blood flow, thus resulting in decreased delivery of nutrients and oxygen to cells of systemic tissues. Women who smoke during pregnancy typically have babies with lower birth weight. This condition occurs in part because the umbilical arteries vasoconstrict, decreasing blood flow to the placenta.

Smoking increases the risk of both stomach ulcers caused by *Helicobacter py*~~lori~~ ~~infection and~~

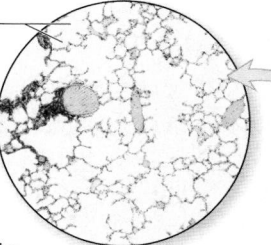

Alveoli are small, numerous, and well formed.

Alveoli are enlarged, less numerous, and contain black deposits.

Alveoli
Deposits
Enlarged alveolus

Nonsmoker's lungs: lungs are pink

Smoker's lungs: lungs are blackened

INTEGRATE

CLINICAL VIEW
Diverticulosis and Diverticulitis

Diverticulosis (dī′ver-tik′yū-lō′sis) is the presence of diverticula (small "bulges") in the intestinal lining. These are formed typically when the colon tightens and narrows in response to low amounts of fiber or bulk in the colon. **Diverticulitis** is inflammation of diverticula. Diverticulitis may be life-threatening if the diverticula rupture and the intestinal contents leak into the abdominal cavity.

An external view of the sigmoid colon and endoscopic view show diverticula.

Diverticula

Integrated Assessments

Throughout each chapter, sections begin with learning objectives and end with questions intended to assess whether those objectives have been met. Critical-thinking questions within the narrative prompt students to apply the material as they read. A set of tiered questions at the end of the chapter, as well as additional online problems, further challenge students to master the material.

 WHAT DO YOU THINK?

④ Calcium channel–blocking drugs are sometimes given to patients with heart problems. If a patient is given a Ca^{2+} channel blocker, how will this affect both heart rate and force of contraction? Explain.

What Do You Think?

These critical-thinking questions engage students in application or analysis and encourage them to think more globally about the content.

 WHAT DID YOU LEARN?

⑪ What is the function of Ca^{2+} in skeletal muscle contraction?

⑫ Describe the four processes that repeat in crossbridge cycling to cause sarcomere shortening.

⑬ What causes the release of the myosin head from actin? What resets the myosin head?

What Did You Learn?

These mini self-tests at the end of each section help students determine whether they have a sufficient grasp of the information before moving on to the next section.

CHALLENGE YOURSELF

Do You Know the Basics?

____ 1. All of following are functions of the kidney *except*

    a. gluconeogenesis, the formation of glucose from non-carbohydrate sources.

    b. release of erythropoietin to control erythrocyte prod

    c. contr

    d. prod

____ 2. When t this ref

    a. are i cavit

    b. are p cavit

    c. are s cavit

    d. have

____ 3. Which

    a. colle

    b. glom

    c. renal

    d. dista

Challenge Yourself

Assessments at the end of each chapter progress through knowledge-, application-, and synthesis-level questions. The "Can You Apply…" and "Can You Synthesize…" question sets are clinically oriented to encourage concept application, and expose students who may be pursuing health-related careers to problem solving in clinical contexts.

Can You Apply What You've Learned?

Use the following paragraph to answer questions 1–3.

Maria is 8 months pregnant. When she goes to her doctor for her checkup, the nurse takes her blood pressure. It is unusually high: 200/100 mm Hg. The nurse also collects a urine sample and detects elevated levels of protein in her urine.

1. What can account for the protein in her urine?

    a. Protein is a normal component of urine and is no cause for concern.

    b. Excessive amounts of plasma proteins are filtered at the renal corpuscle.

    c. Tubular cells produce additional protein in response to the elevated blood pressure.

    d. The tubular cells have exocytosed protein into the tubular fluid.

2. What would you predict has concentration?

    a. It has no effect.

    b. Plasma protein levels will

    c. Plasma protein levels will

    d. Plasma proteins levels wi increase.

Can You Synthesize What You've Learned?

1. A patient with cancer is treated with chemotherapy. This specific medication is eliminated by the kidney. Results from a renal plasma clearance test are higher than average. Will the medication need to be given more or less often? Explain.

2. Theoretically, which one of the following hormones could be administered to decrease blood volume: antidiuretic hormone, aldosterone, parathyroid hormone, or atrial natriuretic peptide? Explain.

Integrated Media and Textbook

Print and Digital Study Tools Connected

Each chapter ends with a listing of online tools that may be used to study and master the concepts presented.

Can You Apply What You've Learned?

1. Paramedics arrived at a car accident to find an elderly gentleman breathing erratically. He was not wearing his seat belt and had hit his head on the windshield. Given his erratic breathing, they were concerned that he had damage to the
   a. medulla oblongata.
   b. cerebral cortex.
   c. pons.
   d. spinal cord.

Use the following to answer questions 2–4.

Michelle, age 45, has been smoking for over 30 years. She now is beginning to have trouble breathing. Her physician sent her to have her respiratory function tested. The results showed that she has emphysema, which is characterized by a decreased surface area for alveolar gas exchange.

2. What component of the respiratory system is most affected in emphysema, causing her to struggle with breathing?
   a. Nasal passageways are inflamed, and less air can move into and out of the respiratory tract.
   b. Bronchi are inflamed.
   c. Bronchioles are dilated.
   d. Damage to the alveoli has occurred.

3. Since physiologic dead space is increased, she would be exhibiting
   a. increased resistance during inhaling.
   b. smaller amounts of air entering her lungs.
   c. harder and deeper breathing that leaves her feeling tired.
   d. decreased blood P_{CO_2}.

4. Blood samples were also taken. Which results might be expected for her blood respiratory gases and blood pH?
   a. decrease in P_{O_2}, increase in P_{CO_2}, decrease in blood pH
   b. decrease in P_{O_2}, decrease in P_{CO_2}, decrease in blood pH
   c. decrease in P_{O_2}, increase in P_{CO_2}, increase in blood pH
   d. increase in P_{O_2}, decrease in P_{CO_2}, increase in blood pH

5. A 10-year-old boy named Michael is playing soccer and begins to have trouble breathing. His mother takes him to the pediatrician, who suspects that he has asthma. The pediatrician recommends that Michael see a respiratory specialist, and results from his pulmonary function tests indicate that Michael does have asthma. Michael's difficulty in breathing, as a result of the asthma, is caused by
   a. inflammation of his nasal passageways.
   b. inflammation and bronchoconstriction of his bronchioles.
   c. spastic closure of his epiglottis, temporarily closing off his trachea.
   d. damage to the alveoli, resulting in decreased surface area of the respiratory membrane.

Can You Synthesize What You've Learned?

1. Tiffany had returned to her college dorm and was having difficulty breathing. She knew she was having an asthma attack. What changes are occurring in her respiratory tract to cause her difficulty in breathing? What potential changes would you predict for her blood P_{O_2} and P_{CO_2}? What substance is generally given that would result in her bronchioles dilating?

2. The nerve to the sternocleidomastoid muscle was damaged during surgery. What type of breathing will be impaired—quiet inspiration, quiet expiration, forced inspiration, or forced expiration?

3. Mark is attempting his first serious mountain climb above 8000 feet. He begins to breathe harder during his ascent, feels light-headed, and has difficulty thinking clearly. What has stimulated him to breathe harder? What effect does this have on P_{CO_2}? What potential change in blood pH can occur? Why? Does more or less oxygen reach the brain? Explain.

INTEGRATE

ONLINE STUDY TOOLS
www.mhhe.com/mckinleyap

Concept Overview Interactive: Figure 23.30 The Movement of Oxygen and Carbon Dioxide

Clinical Case Study: How the Smallest Things Become Critically Important

Interactive Questions: This chapter's content is served up in a number of multimedia question formats for student study.

LearnSmart: Topics and terminology include upper and lower respiratory tracts, lungs, pulmonary ventilation, alveolar and systemic gas exchange, gas transport, and breathing rate and homeostasis

Anatomy & Physiology Revealed: Topics include pharynx and larynx, trachea and bronchi, alveolar pressure changes, partial pressure

Animations: Topics include B Cells and Humoral Immunity

INTEGRATE

ONLINE STUDY TOOLS
www.mhhe.com/mckinleyap

Concept Overview Interactive: Figure 23.30 The Movement of Oxygen and Carbon Dioxide

Clinical Case Study: How the Smallest Things Become Critically Important

Interactive Questions: This chapter's content is served up in a number of multimedia question formats for student study.

LearnSmart: Topics and terminology include upper and lower respiratory tracts, lungs, pulmonary ventilation, alveolar and systemic gas exchange, gas transport, and breathing rate and homeostasis

Anatomy & Physiology Revealed: Topics include pharynx and larynx, trachea and bronchi, alveolar pressure changes, partial pressure

Animations: Topics include B Cells and Humoral Immunity

Concept Overviews into Digital Learning

Selected **Concept Overview Figures** from the textbook have been transformed into interactive study modules. This digital transformation process was guided by anatomy and physiology professors who reviewed the modules throughout the development process. Interactive Concept Overview Figures also have assessable, autograded learning activities in Connect®, and are also provided separately to instructors as classroom presentation tools.

Concept Overview from Textbook

Interactive Presentation Study Tool

Assessable Autograded Activity in Connect

ConnectPlus®

McGraw-Hill ConnectPlus® interactive learning platform provides:

- Auto-graded assignments
- Adaptive diagnostic tools
- Powerful reporting against learning outcomes and level of difficulty
- An easy-to-use interface
- **McGraw-Hill Tegrity®,** which digitally records and distributes your lectures with a click of a button

ConnectPlus includes the full textbook as an integrated, dynamic eBook, which you can also assign. Everything you need...in one place!

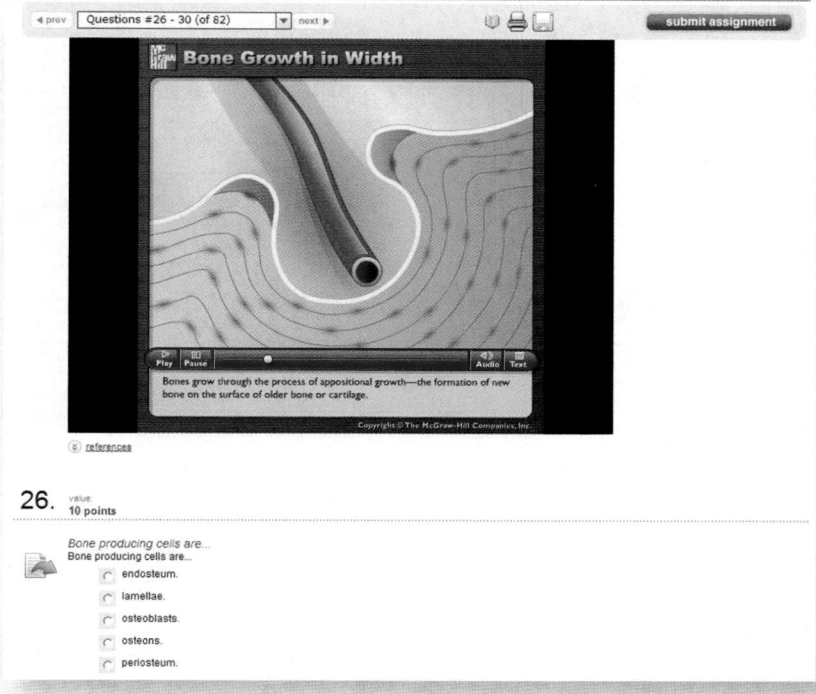

McGraw-Hill LearnSmart™

Unlike static flashcards or rote memorization, **McGraw-Hill LearnSmart™** ensures your students have mastered course concepts before taking the exam, thereby saving you time and increasing student success.

- The only truly adaptive learning system
- Intelligently identifies course content students have not yet mastered
- Maps out personalized study plans for student success

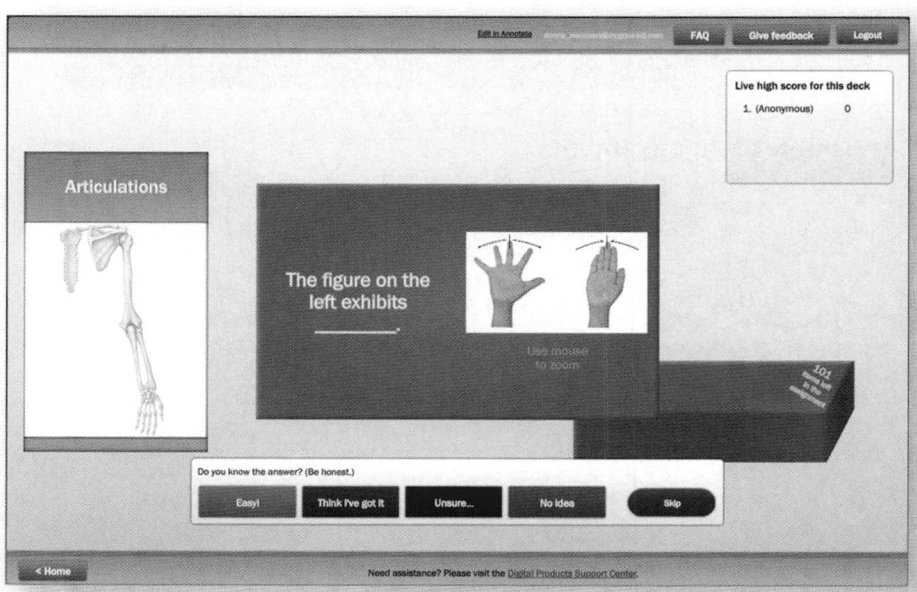

Learning Objectives and Connect®

Each Learning Objective from the textbook is tied to interactive questions in Connect, to assure that all parts of the chapters have adequate coverage within Connect assignments.

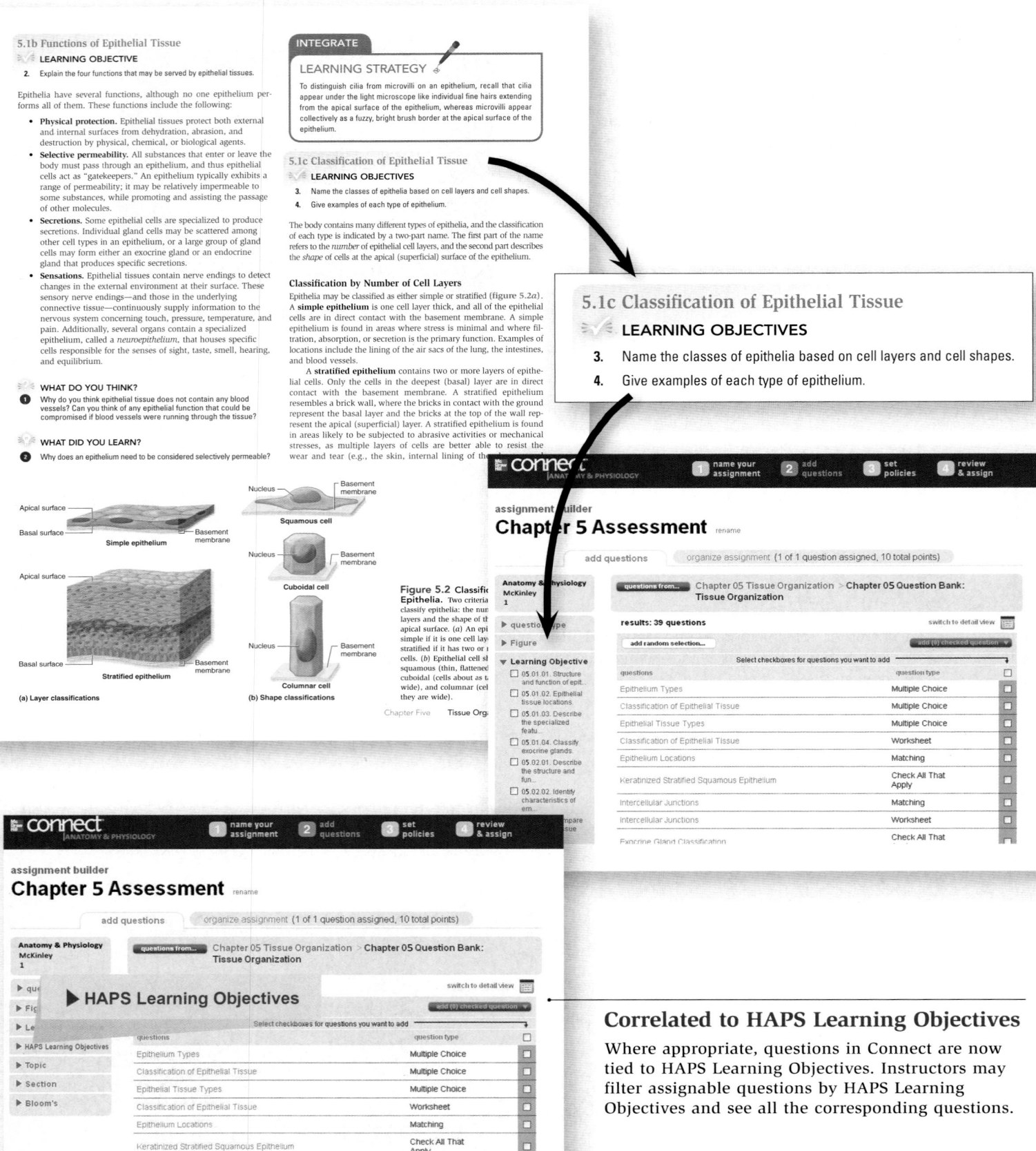

5.1b Functions of Epithelial Tissue

LEARNING OBJECTIVE

2. Explain the four functions that may be served by epithelial tissues.

Epithelia have several functions, although no one epithelium performs all of them. These functions include the following:

- **Physical protection.** Epithelial tissues protect both external and internal surfaces from dehydration, abrasion, and destruction by physical, chemical, or biological agents.
- **Selective permeability.** All substances that enter or leave the body must pass through an epithelium, and thus epithelial cells act as "gatekeepers." An epithelium typically exhibits a range of permeability; it may be relatively impermeable to some substances, while promoting and assisting the passage of other molecules.
- **Secretions.** Some epithelial cells are specialized to produce secretions. Individual gland cells may be scattered among other cell types in an epithelium, or a large group of gland cells may form either an exocrine gland or an endocrine gland that produces specific secretions.
- **Sensations.** Epithelial tissues contain nerve endings to detect changes in the external environment at their surface. These sensory nerve endings—and those in the underlying connective tissue—continuously supply information to the nervous system concerning touch, pressure, temperature, and pain. Additionally, several organs contain a specialized epithelium, called a *neuroepithelium*, that houses specific cells responsible for the senses of sight, taste, smell, hearing, and equilibrium.

WHAT DO YOU THINK?

1. Why do you think epithelial tissue does not contain any blood vessels? Can you think of any epithelial function that could be compromised if blood vessels were running through the tissue?

WHAT DID YOU LEARN?

2. Why does an epithelium need to be considered selectively permeable?

INTEGRATE

LEARNING STRATEGY

To distinguish cilia from microvilli on an epithelium, recall that cilia appear under the light microscope like individual fine hairs extending from the apical surface of the epithelium, whereas microvilli appear collectively as a fuzzy, bright brush border at the apical surface of the epithelium.

5.1c Classification of Epithelial Tissue

LEARNING OBJECTIVES

3. Name the classes of epithelia based on cell layers and cell shapes.
4. Give examples of each type of epithelium.

The body contains many different types of epithelia, and the classification of each type is indicated by a two-part name. The first part of the name refers to the *number* of epithelial cell layers, and the second part describes the *shape* of cells at the apical (superficial) surface of the epithelium.

Classification by Number of Cell Layers

Epithelia may be classified as either simple or stratified (figure 5.2*a*). A **simple epithelium** is one cell layer thick, and all of the epithelial cells are in direct contact with the basement membrane. A simple epithelium is found in areas where stress is minimal and where filtration, absorption, or secretion is the primary function. Examples of locations include the lining of the air sacs of the lung, the intestines, and blood vessels.

A **stratified epithelium** contains two or more layers of epithelial cells. Only the cells in the deepest (basal) layer are in direct contact with the basement membrane. A stratified epithelium resembles a brick wall, where the bricks in contact with the ground represent the basal layer and the bricks at the top of the wall represent the apical (superficial) layer. A stratified epithelium is found in areas likely to be subjected to abrasive activities or mechanical stresses, as multiple layers of cells are better able to resist the wear and tear (e.g., the skin, internal lining of the ...

5.1c Classification of Epithelial Tissue

LEARNING OBJECTIVES

3. Name the classes of epithelia based on cell layers and cell shapes.
4. Give examples of each type of epithelium.

Correlated to HAPS Learning Objectives

Where appropriate, questions in Connect are now tied to HAPS Learning Objectives. Instructors may filter assignable questions by HAPS Learning Objectives and see all the corresponding questions.

Anatomy & Physiology Revealed®

Anatomy & Physiology REVEALED® is an interactive cadaver dissection tool to enhance lecture and lab that students can use anytime, anywhere. Instructors can customize APR 3.0 by indicating the specific content they require in their course through a simple menu selection process. APR 3.0 does the rest. In the course-specific area of the program, students see only the instructor's designated content, and only this content appears in quiz questions.

APR contains all the material covered in an A&P course, including these three new modules:

- Body Orientation
- Cells and Chemistry
- Tissues

Tissues Module

Body Orientation Module

Cells and Chemistry Module

Presentation Center

Accessed from the *Anatomy and Physiology: An Integrated Approach* Connect website, **Presentation Center** is an online digital library containing photos, artwork, animations, and other media types that can be used to create customized lectures, visually enhanced tests and quizzes, compelling course websites, or attractive printed support materials. All assets are copyrighted by McGraw-Hill Higher Education, but can be used by instructors for classroom purposes. The visual resources in this collection include the following:

- **Art** Full-color digital files of all illustrations in the book can be readily incorporated into lecture presentations, exams, or custom-made classroom materials. In addition, all files are preinserted into PowerPoint slides for ease of lecture preparation.
- **Photos** The photo collection contains digital files of photographs from the text, which can be reproduced for multiple classroom uses.
- **Tables** Every table that appears in the text has been saved in electronic form for use in classroom presentations and/or quizzes.
- **Animations** Numerous full-color animations illustrating important processes are also provided. Harness the visual impact of concepts in motion by importing these files into classroom presentations or online course materials.

Also accessed through the *Anatomy and Physiology: An Integrated Approach* Connect website are:

- **PowerPoint Lecture Outlines** Ready-made presentations that combine art and lecture notes are provided for each chapter of the text.
- **PowerPoint Slides** For instructors who prefer to create their lectures from scratch, all illustrations, photos, tables, embedded animations, and relevant Anatomy & Physiology Revealed images are preinserted by chapter into blank PowerPoint slides.

The Presentation Center library includes thousands of assets from many McGraw-Hill titles. This ever-growing resource gives instructors the power to utilize assets specific to an adopted textbook as well as content from all other books in the library. Accessed through the instructor side of your textbook's Connect website, Presentation Center's dynamic search engine allows you to explore by discipline, course, textbook chapter, asset type, or keyword. Simply browse, select, and download the files you need to build engaging course materials. All assets are copyright McGraw-Hill Higher Education but can be used by instructors for classroom purposes. Instructors: To access Connect, request registration information from your McGraw-Hill sales representative.

Digital Lecture Capture: Tegrity McGraw-Hill Tegrity® records and distributes your lecture with just a click of a button. Students can view anytime/anywhere via computer, iPod, or mobile device. Tegrity indexes as it records your slideshow presentations and anything shown on your computer, so students can use keywords to find exactly what they want to study.

Computerized Test Bank Prepared by John Pellegrini of St. Catherine University, over 3,600 test questions are served up utilizing EZ Test software to accompany *Anatomy and Physiology: An Integrated Approach*. Diploma's software allows you to quickly create a customized test using McGraw-Hill's supplied questions, or by authoring your own questions. Diploma is a downloadable application that allows you to create your tests without an Internet connection—just download the software and question files directly to your computer.

Content Delivery Flexibility *Anatomy and Physiology: An Integrated Approach* by McKinley/O'Loughlin/Bidle is available in many formats in addition to the traditional textbook to give instructors and students more choices when deciding on the format of their A&P text. Choices include the following:

- **Customizable Textbooks: Create** Introducing **McGraw-Hill Create**™—a new, self-service website that allows you to create custom course materials—print and eBooks—by drawing upon McGraw-Hill's comprehensive, cross-disciplinary content. Add your own content quickly and easily. Tap into other rights-secured third-party sources as well. Then, arrange the content in a way that makes the most sense for your course. Even personalize your book with your course name and information. Choose the best format for your course: color print, black-and-white print, or eBook. The eBook is now viewable on an iPad! And when you are finished customizing, you will receive a free PDF review copy in just minutes! Visit McGraw-Hill Create— *www.mcgrawhillcreate.com*—today and begin building your perfect book.
- **ConnectPlus eBook** McGraw-Hill ConnectPlus® eBook takes digital texts beyond a simple PDF. With the same content as the printed book, but optimized for the screen, ConnectPlus has embedded media, including animations and videos, which bring concepts to life and provide "just in time" learning for students. Additionally, fully integrated homework allows students to interact with the questions in the text to determine if they're gaining mastery of the content, and can also be assigned by the instructor.

The **Best** of **Both Worlds**

McGraw-Hill and Blackboard®

McGraw-Hill Higher Education and Blackboard have teamed up. What does this partnership mean for you? Blackboard users will find the single sign-on and deep integration of ConnectPlus within their Blackboard course an invaluable benefit. Even if your school is not using Blackboard, we have a solution for you. Learn more at *www.domorenow.com*.

Lab Manual Options to Fit Your Course

Anatomy & Physiology Laboratory Manual by Christine Eckel, Terri Bidle, and Kyla Ross is a laboratory manual specifically developed for the McKinley/O'Loughlin/Bidle *Anatomy and Physiology: An Integrative Approach* text:

- Three versions are available including main, cat, and fetal pig.
- Each chapter opens with a set of learning objectives that are keyed to the post-laboratory worksheet to ensure student understanding of each chapter's objectives.
- The manual includes the highest-quality photographs and illustrations of any laboratory manual in the market.
- Laboratory exercises are "how-to" guides that involve touch, dissection, observation, experimentation, and critical-thinking exercises.
- In-chapter learning activities offer a mixture of labeling exercises, sketching activities, table completion exercises, data recoring, palpation of surface anatomy, and other sources of learning.
- Numerous exercises throughout the manual utilize Physiology Interactive Lab Simulations (Ph.I.L.S.) 4.0 Online to provide additional student understanding of physiology.
- Ph.I.L.S. 4.0 is included with each new laboratory manual.

Laboratory Manual for Human Anatomy & Physiology by Terry Martin is written to coincide with any A&P textbook:

- Three versions available, including main, cat, and fetal pig
- Includes Ph.I.L.S. 4.0 Online
- Outcomes and assessments format
- Clear, concise writing style

Student Supplements

McGraw-Hill offers various tools and technology products to support the textbook. Students can order supplemental study materials by contacting their campus bookstore or online at *www.shopmcgraw-hill.com.*

Instructor Supplements

Instructors can obtain teaching aids by calling the McGraw-Hill Customer Service Department at 1-800-338-3987, vising our online catalog at *www.mhhe.com,* or by contacting their local McGraw-Hill sales representative.

ACKNOWLEDGMENTS

Many people have worked with us over the last several years to produce this text. We would like to thank the many individuals at McGraw-Hill who worked with us to create this textbook. We are especially grateful to Kris Queck, our Developmental Editor, for her vision in the development of both the text and figures in this book. She is the best! The talented medical illustrators at Electronic Publishing Services developed truly remarkable and accurate illustrations for this text. In addition, we would like to thank Maria Florez, Lone Star College–Cyfair (glossary author); Dena Berg Johnson, Tarrant County College (author of answers in appendix), Christine Eckel (cadaver dissection and photography), Al Telser (photomicroscopy), Jw Ramsey (surface anatomy photography), and Mark Braun (clinical consultant). Jody Larson, Beatrice Sussman, Dorothy Wendel, and Patti Evers were our wonderful copy editors and proofreaders who helped ensure that every "i" was dotted and every "t" was crossed.

Finally, we could not have performed this effort were it not for the love and support of our families. Our families provided us with the encouragement we needed, were forgiving when our book schedules made it seem as if we were working all the time, and made sacrifices in order to see this project to fruition. Jan, Renee, Ryan, and Shaun McKinley; Bob and Erin O'Loughlin; and Jay and Stephanie Bidle—thank you and we love you! We are blessed to have you all.

We are also grateful to our Media Board of Advisors, as well as our media authors and media contributors, who have worked tirelessly to envelop this text with media-rich components for both student study and assessment, as well as for classroom presentation.

Media Advisors and Contributors

Amy Banes Berceli
Oakland University

Molly Brandel
Northeast Iowa Community College

Mark Braun
Indiana University

William M. Clark
Lonestar College–Kingwood

Elyce Ervin
University of Toledo

Lynn Gargan
Tarrant County College–Northeast Campus

Richard Griner
Augusta State University

William F. Huber
Saint Louis Community College–Forest Park

Alexander Imholtz
Prince George's Community College

Corey Johnson
University of North Carolina–Chapel Hill

Jody E. Johnson
Arapahoe Community College

Joseph D. Gar
West Kentucky Community and Technical College

Marta Klesath
North Carolina State University

Luis Labiste
Miami Dade College North

Angela Mick
Glendale Community College

Michele Monlux
Modesto Junior College

John Pattillo
Macon State College

Ximara Peckham
Long Island University–Brooklyn

John Pellegrini
St. Catherine University

Publicis Healthware International
Sarah Pugh
Shelton State Community College

Laurel Shelton
Northern Arizona University

Jill Stein
Essex County College

Rachel Tomco
Brigham Young University–Provo

Amy Way
Lock Haven University

Many instructors and students across the country have positively affected this text through their careful reviews of manuscript drafts, art proofs, and page proofs, as well as through class tests and through their attendance at focus groups and symposia. We gratefully acknowledge their contributions to this text.

Reviewers

Mike Aaron
Shelton State Community College

Abass Abdullahi
Bronx Community College–CUNY

Emily Allen
Gloucester County College

Patricia Amdumanu Ahanotu
Georgia Perimeter College

Lynn Atkins
University of Maine

Stephanie J. S. Baiyasi-Kozicki
Central Michigan University

Sarah Bales
Moraine Valley Community College

Caroline Ballard
Rock Valley College

Amy Banes Berceli
Oakland University

Jeanne K. Barnett
University of Southern Indiana

Jerry D. Barton II
Tarrant County College–South Campus

Franklyn F. Bolander, Jr.
University of South Carolina

James J. Bottesch
Brevard Community College

Danita Bradshaw-Ward
Eastfield College

Mike Brady
Columbia Basin College

Eldon J. Braun
University of Arizona

Suzanne Butler
Miami Dade College–North Campus

Dennis Burke
Bunker Hill Community College

David D. Busath
Brigham Young University

Barbara Bushman
Missouri State University

William Caldecutt
Polk State College

Joseph Bradley Caldwell
Greenville Technical College

Christie Campbell
Ozarks Technical Community College

Mickael J. Cariveau
Mount Olive College

Ken Carpenter
Southwest Tennessee Community College

Robert S. Carter
Volunteer State Community College

Roger D. Choate
Oklahoma City Community College

Ana Christensen
Lamar University

William M. Clark
Lone Star College–Kingwood

Vincent Cobb
Middle Tennessee State University

Pamela Anderson Cole
Shelton State Community College

Barbara A. Coles
Wake Technical Community College

Lisa Conley
Milwaukee Area Technical College

Jackie Conrad
Broward College

Andrew Corless
Vincennes University

Kathryn Stephenson Craven
Armstrong Atlantic State University

George Dalich
Lake Washington Institute of Technology

Juville Dario-Becker
Central Virginia Community College

Harry Davis
Gloucester County College

Mary Elizabeth Dawson
Kingsborough Community College/City University of New York

Leslie Day
Northeastern University

Mario De La Haye
Kennedy-King College

Patricia DeLeon
BMCC/CUNY

Danielle Desroches
William Paterson University of New Jersey

Sharon DeWitte
University of South Carolina

Charles J. Dick
Pasco-Hernando Community College

Pamela A. Dobbins
Shelton State Community College

Richard Doolin
Daytona State College

William E. Dunscombe
Union County College

Kash Dutta
University of New England

Angela Edwards
Trident Technical College

Abdeslem El Idrissi
College of Staten Island/City University of New York

Paul S. Emerick
Monroe Community College

Elyce Ervin
University of Toledo

Martha Eshleman
Pulaski Technical College

Sondra M. Evans
Florida State College–Jacksonville

James Ezell
J. Sargeant Reynolds Community College

Rebekah S. Faber-Starr
Northwest State Community College

Kyle W. Felling
University of Central Arkansas

Jeanette Ferguson
Columbus State Community College

Philip J. Fernandez
Glendale Community College

Jose L. Fierro
Florida Community College–Kent

Bradley J. Fillmore
Eastern Washington University

Lorraine A. Findlay
Nassau Community College

Pamela B. Fouche
Walters State Community College

Paul Florence
Jefferson Community and Technical College

Maria Florez
Lone Star College–CyFair

Carl Frailey
Johnson County Community College

Frederick R. Frank, Jr.
Volunteer State Community College

Jennifer Freed
Rio Salado College

Denise Y. Friedman
Hudson Valley Community College

Marie Gabbard
Boise State University

Purti P. Gadkari
Wharton County Junior College

Chris Gan
Highline Community College

Joseph D. Gar
West Kentucky Community and Technical College

Lynn Gargan
Tarrant County College–Northeast Campus

Anthony J. Gaudin
Ivy Tech Community College

Peter Germroth
Hillsborough Community College

Kathy Gifford
Butler Community College

Jared Gilmore
San Jacinto College–Central

Chaya Gopalan
St. Louis College of Pharmacy

Matthew W. Gosses
Owens Community College

Richard D. Griner
Augusta State University

John Hamlin
Louisiana State University–Eunice

Sandra A. Hanes
Jefferson Community and Technical College

Terry Harrison
Arapahoe Community College

R. Christopher Harvey
Brevard Community College

Gerald Heins
Northeast Wisconsin Technical College

Jean A. S. Helgeson
Collin County Community College—Spring Creek Campus

DeLoris Hesse
University of Georgia

Regina Hoffman
Midlands Technical College

Anthony Holt
University of Arkansas Community College at Morrilton

William Hoover
Bunker Hill Community College

William F. Huber
Saint Louis Community College–Forest Park

Mark J. Hubley
Prince George's Community College

Alex Imholtz
Prince George's Community College

Jean Jackson
Bluegrass Community and Technical College

Renu Jain
Houston Community College–Central College

Corey Johnson
University of North Carolina–Chapel Hill

Dena Berg Johnson
Tarrant County College–Northwest Campus

Edward Johnson
Central Oregon Community College

Jody E. Johnson
Arapahoe Community College

Lisa Johnson
Tarrant County College

Latoya Jones
West Kentucky Community and Technical College

Susanne Kalup
Westmoreland County Community College

Kristopher Kelley
University of Louisiana–Monroe

Eric Kenz
Columbus State Community College

Michael Kielb
Eastern Michigan University

Brian H. Kipp
Grand Valley State University

Michelle Klein
Prince George's Community College

Marta Klesath
North Carolina State University

Chad Knights
Northern Virginia Community College–Alexandria Campus

Tim Koneval
Mount Aloysius College

Michael Koot
Michigan State University

Elizabeth Kozak
Lewis University

Johanna Kruckeberg
Kirkwood Community College

Louis Wm. Kutcher
University of Cincinnati–Blue Ash College

Brian L. Kuyatt
Hillsborough Community College—Southshore

Luis Labiste
Miami Dade College

Cleveland Lane, Jr.
Prairie View A&M University

Michael S. LaPointe
Indiana University Northwest

Jason LaPres
Lone Star College–North Harris

Kaddee Lawrence
Highline Community College

Steve Leadon
Durham Technical Community College

Stephanie Lee
Pearl River Community College

Sarah Liechty
Ivy Tech Community College

Jerri K. Lindsey
Tarrant County College–Northeast Campus

Katherine Lockwood
University of New Hampshire

Jodi Long
Santa Fe College

Carol Mack
Erie Community College—North Campus

Elizabeth A. Maher
Ivy Tech Community College

Mara L. Manis
Hillsborough Community College

D. Barry Markillie
Cape Fear Community College–North Campus

Theresa Martin
College of San Mateo

Scott C. Mateer
Armstrong Atlantic State University

John McDaniel
Skyline College

Nicole L. McDaniels
Herkimer County Community College

Louis F. McIntyre, Sr.
Robeson Community College

Karen K. McLellan
Indiana University Purdue University–Fort Wayne

Kren J. McManus
North Hennepin Community College

Margaret McMichael
Baton Rouge Community College

Alfred P. McQueen
Hampton University

Claire Miller-Rashad
Community College of Denver

Melissa Mills
Anoka-Ramsey Community College

Scott Mittman
Essex County College

Evelyn Mobley
Chattanooga State Community College

Jane Moore
Tarrant County College–Northwest Campus

Christine Morin
Prince George's Community College

Alfredo Muñoz
University of Texas/Texas Southmost College–Brownsville

Regina Munro
Chandler-Gilbert Community College

Victor Miriel
Salisbury University

Necia Nicholas
Calhoun Community College

Linda Nichols
Santa Fe College

Jeremy Nicholson
South Plains College

Claire Oakley
Rocky Mountain College

Jorge L. Obeso
Miami Dade College–North Campus

Rami Ockaili
JSR Community College

Maria H. Oehler
Florida State College–Jacksonville

Robyn L. O'Kane
LaGuardia Community College/CUNY

Sue Caley Opsal
Illinois Valley Community College

Margaret Ott
Tyler Junior College

James F. Palmer
Southeastern Louisiana University

John Pattillo
Macon State College

Karen Payne
Chattanooga State Technical Community College

Elizabeth Pennefather-O'Brien
Medicine Hat College

Davonya J. Person
Auburn University

Marius Pfeiffer
Tarrant County College—Northeast Campus

Thomas Pilat
Illinois Central College

Julie C. Pilcher
University of Southern Indiana

John S. Placyk, Jr.
University of Texas–Tyler

Eileen Lynn Preston
Tarrant County College–Northwest Campus

Wanda Ragland
Macomb Community College

Wendy M. Rappazzo
Harford Community College

Nancy Rauch
Merritt College

Samiksha Raut
Dalton State College

Robert Rawding
Gannon University

Deborah Rhoden
Snead Community College

John Ripper
Butler County Community College

Laura H. Ritt
Burlington Community College

Caroline Clark Rivera
Tidewater Community College

Michele Robichaux
Nicholls State University

Amanda Rosenzweig
Delgado Community College

Robert W. Rothrock
Camden County College

Michael W. Ruhl
Vernon College

Amy Sandy
Columbus Technical College

Hope Sasway
Suffolk County Community College

Heidi Schutz
California Polytechnic State University

Samuel Schwarzlose
Amarillo College

Michael P. Scola
Northern Kentucky University

Marsha L. Segebarth
University of Southern Indiana

Joanne Settel
Baltimore City Community College

Kelly J. Sexton
North Lake College, DCCCD

Judith D. Shardo
Middle Tennessee State University

Marilyn M. Shannon
Indiana University/Purdue University–Fort Wayne

Donald Shaw
University of Tennessee at Martin

Jason Shaw
Brigham Young University–Idaho

Marilyn Shopper
Johnson County Community College

Colleen Sinclair-Winters
Towson University

Mark Slivkoff
Collin College

Janice Yoder Smith
Tarrant County College Northwest Campus

Joy Smoots
Cape Fear Community College

William Sproat
Walters State Community College

Laura Steele
Ivy Tech Community College Northeast

William Stewart
Middle Tennessee State University

Megan Pickering Stringer
Jones County Junior College

Steve Sullivan
Bucks County Community College

Lathi Taylor
Texas A&M University

chapter 1

The Sciences of Anatomy and Physiology

You are about to embark on an adventure into the amazing world of human anatomy and physiology. Both fields explore the workings of the incredible workings of the human body. Anatomy studies the form and structure of the body, whereas physiology examines how the body functions. Together, these applied sciences provide the basis for understanding health and human performance. The basic vocabulary of these sciences is derived from both Greek and Latin. ➡

Anatomy and physiology are two specialty disciplines that are inappropriately treated as distinctive and different. Observe the health professionals included in this photograph and appreciate that there is no clue as to their specific expertise. Anatomists often are deemed physical structure experts but clearly their investigations and research into individual organ and total body system structure must be considered with respect to a specific body system function. Physiologists study function of organs and body systems. Their work is important in our ability to "combine" body system structure and total body function. Throughout this book we will integrate both disciplines—because they truly cannot be separated. You will succeed in this field by understanding and appreciating both views of a topic.

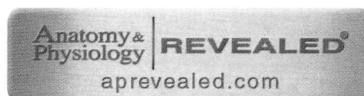

Module 1: Body Orientation

1

If you actively practice the vocabulary and descriptive terminology used in this text, your understanding and appreciation of body structure and function will be enhanced significantly. In this book, you will learn that structure and function are inseparable. You will see how the body functions normally, as well as what happens to body function and structure when injury and disease occur.

1.1 Anatomy and Physiology Compared

In this section, we compare anatomy and physiology and present the general subdivisions of these sciences.

Anatomy is the study of structure and form. The word *anatomy* is derived from the Greek word *anatome*, which means to cut apart or dissect. Anatomists are scientists who study the structure and form of organisms. Specifically, they examine the relationships among parts of the body as well as the structure of individual organs. **Physiology** is the study of function of the body parts. Physiologists are scientists who examine how organs and body systems function under normal circumstances, as well as how their functioning may be altered via medication or disease. **Table 1.1** compares how anatomists and physiologists may examine the same organs.

The sciences of anatomy and physiology are intertwined; one cannot study physiologic function without first having some understanding of anatomic form. Likewise, one cannot adequately describe and understand the anatomic form of an organ without first learning that organ's function. Throughout these chapters, we have attempted to integrate the study of anatomy and physiology, showing how form and function are interrelated.

1.1a Anatomy: Details of Form

LEARNING OBJECTIVES

1. Describe the science of anatomy.
2. List the subdivisions in both microscopic and gross anatomy.

As mentioned in the previous section, anatomy examines the structure and form of organisms. The discipline is extremely broad and can be divided into several more specific fields. **Microscopic anatomy** examines structures that cannot be observed by the unaided eye. For most of these studies, scientists prepare individual cells or thin slices of some part of the body and examine these specimens under the microscope. Microscopic anatomy has several subdivisions with two main divisions:

- **Cytology** (sī-tol′ō-jē; *cyto* = cell, *logos* = study) is the study of body cells and their internal structure.
- **Histology** (his-tol′ō-jē; *histos* = web, tissue) is the study of tissues.

Gross anatomy, also called *macroscopic anatomy,* investigates the structure and relationships of body parts that are visible to the unaided eye, such as the intestines, stomach, brain, heart, and kidneys. In these macroscopic investigations, specimens or their parts are often dissected (cut open) for examination. Gross anatomy may be approached in several ways:

- **Systemic anatomy** studies the anatomy of each functional body system. For example, studying the urinary system would involve examining the kidneys (where urine is formed) and the organs of urine transport (ureters and urethra) and storage (urinary bladder). Most undergraduate anatomy classes study anatomy using this systemic approach.
- **Regional anatomy** examines all of the structures in a particular region of the body as a complete unit. For example, one may

Table 1.1	Comparison of Anatomy and Physiology	
Organ(s)	**How Anatomists Describe the Organ(s)**	**How Physiologists Describe the Organ(s)**
Muscles of the thigh	These muscles are composed of skeletal muscle tissue and receive innervation from somatic motor neurons. These muscles include the quadriceps femoris and the hamstrings, which are designed to extend and flex the knee, respectively.	The muscles of the thigh contract voluntarily via nerve impulses from somatic motor neurons. The muscles are designed to provide enough power to move the parts of the lower limbs during a footrace.
Small intestine	The wall of the small intestine contains an innermost simple columnar epithelium, as well as two layers of smooth muscle: an inner circular layer and an outer longitudinal layer. The smooth muscle cells are spindle shaped and lack the striations seen in skeletal muscle.	The simple columnar epithelium is designed for absorption of nutrients from the small intestine. The two layers of muscle contract slowly and involuntarily to compress and move materials in the small intestine during digestion, processing, and absorption of nutrients.
Esophagus	The esophageal wall is composed of an innermost nonkeratinized stratified squamous epithelium, a middle layer of dense irregular connective tissue, and an outer layer of muscle tissue (which contains a mixture of skeletal and smooth muscle).	The esophageal wall is designed to withstand the abrasive activities associated with swallowing food. The mixture of skeletal and smooth muscle contracts sequentially, in order to propel food toward the stomach.
Blood capillaries	The blood capillary wall is composed of a thin simple squamous epithelium. Some types of capillary walls also have fenestrations (openings) between the epithelial cells.	The thin structure of the blood capillary walls promotes nutrient, gas, and waste exchange between the blood and the surrounding tissues. Fenestrated capillaries are designed to allow for additional substance exchange.

study the axillary (armpit) region of the body, and in so doing examine the blood vessels (axillary artery and vein), nerves (branches of the brachial plexus), lymph nodes (axillary lymph nodes), musculature, connective tissue, and skin. Most medical school gross anatomy courses are taught using a regional anatomy approach.

- **Surface anatomy** focuses on both superficial anatomic markings and the internal body structures that relate to the skin covering them. Health-care providers use surface features to identify and locate important landmarks, such as pulse locations or the proper body region on which to perform CPR. Most anatomy classes also instruct students on important surface anatomy locations.
- **Comparative anatomy** examines similarities and the differences in the anatomy of different species. For example, a comparative anatomy class may examine limb structure in humans, chimps, dogs, and cats.
- **Embryology** (em′brē-ol′o-jē; *embryon* = young one) is the discipline concerned with developmental changes occurring from conception to birth.

Several specialized branches of anatomy focus on the diagnosis of medical conditions or the advancement of basic scientific research. **Pathologic** (path-ō-loj′ik; *pathos* = disease) **anatomy** examines all anatomic changes resulting from disease. Both gross anatomic changes and microscopic structures are examined. **Radiographic anatomy** investigates the relationships among internal structures that may be visualized by specific scanning procedures, such as ultrasound, magnetic resonance imaging (MRI), or x-ray.

It may seem as though nothing new can be learned about anatomy—after all, the body has been much the same for thousands of years. Yet in fact, new information is being learned from ongoing anatomic studies, some of which displace the traditional thinking about the workings of various organs. Never forget that anatomy is a dynamic, changing science, not a static, unchanging one.

WHAT DID YOU LEARN?

1 What subdiscipline of anatomy may explore how the lower limb differs between humans and chimpanzees?

1.1b Physiology: Details of Function

LEARNING OBJECTIVES

3. Describe the science of physiology.
4. List the subdivisions in physiology.

Physiologists examine the function of various organ systems, and they typically focus on the molecular or cellular level to gain a complete understanding of the system's workings. Thus, a basic knowledge of chemistry is essential in understanding physiology, and that's why we've included an early chapter about chemistry.

The discipline of physiology parallels anatomy because it also is very broad and may be subdivided into smaller groups. Many specific physiology subdisciplines focus their studies on a particular body system. For example, **cardiovascular physiology** examines the functioning of the heart, blood vessels, and blood. Cardiovascular physiologists examine how the heart pumps the blood, what are the parameters for healthy blood pressure, and details of the cellular exchange mechanisms by which respiratory gases, nutrients, and wastes move between blood and body structures. Other examples include **neurophysiology** (which examines how nerve impulses travel throughout the nervous system and how nervous system

organs work), **respiratory physiology** (which studies how respiratory gases are transferred by gas exchange between the lungs and the blood vessels supplying the lungs, among other things), and **reproductive physiology** (which explores how the regulation of reproductive hormones can drive the reproductive cycle and influence sex cell production and maturation).

Pathophysiology investigates the relationship between the functioning of an organ system and disease or injury to that organ system. For example, a pathophysiologist would examine how blood pressure, contractile force of the heart, and both gas and nutrient exchange may be affected in an individual afflicted with heart disease.

All health-care professionals must understand not only how organ systems function normally, but also how pathology can affect the physiology of this system. Throughout the chapters in this book, Clinical View boxes provide you with selected pathologies and how these pathologies affect the anatomy and physiology of that system.

WHAT DID YOU LEARN?

2 What is the relationship between anatomy and physiology?

3 _____ physiology examines how the heart, blood vessels, and blood function.

1.2 Anatomy and Physiology Integrated

LEARNING OBJECTIVE

1. Explain how the studies of form and function are interrelated.

Anatomy and physiology initially may appear to be different sciences, but further reflection reveals that these two sciences are integrated, because form (anatomy) and function (physiology) are interrelated. Anatomists cannot gain a full appreciation of anatomic form without also understanding a structure's function. Likewise, physiologists cannot fully appreciate body functions without learning about the forms of the structures involved. For example, the small sacs in the lungs called *alveoli* provide a very large surface area for gas exchange, and therefore their structure contributes to respiratory function.

Integrating the disciplines of anatomy and physiology, rather than trying to separate discussion of form and function, is the easiest way to learn about both fields. Look at table 1.1 again, and note that anatomists and physiologists may be describing the organs slightly differently, but both disciplines must use information from the other field for a full understanding of the organ system. You cannot fully understand *how* the small intestine propels food and digests or absorbs nutrients unless you know about the *structure* of the small intestine wall. **Figure 1.1** compares how anatomists and physiologists examine the human body, and also shows how both sciences are integrated. Note that anatomists (left side of the figure) tend to focus on the form and structure, while physiologists (right side of figure) focus on the mechanisms and functions of these structures. However, both anatomists and physiologists understand that the form and function of structures are interrelated. Throughout this text, we integrate these disciplines so you can more easily see that anatomic form and physiologic function are inseparable.

WHAT DID YOU LEARN?

4 Compare and contrast how anatomists and physiologists describe the esophagus.

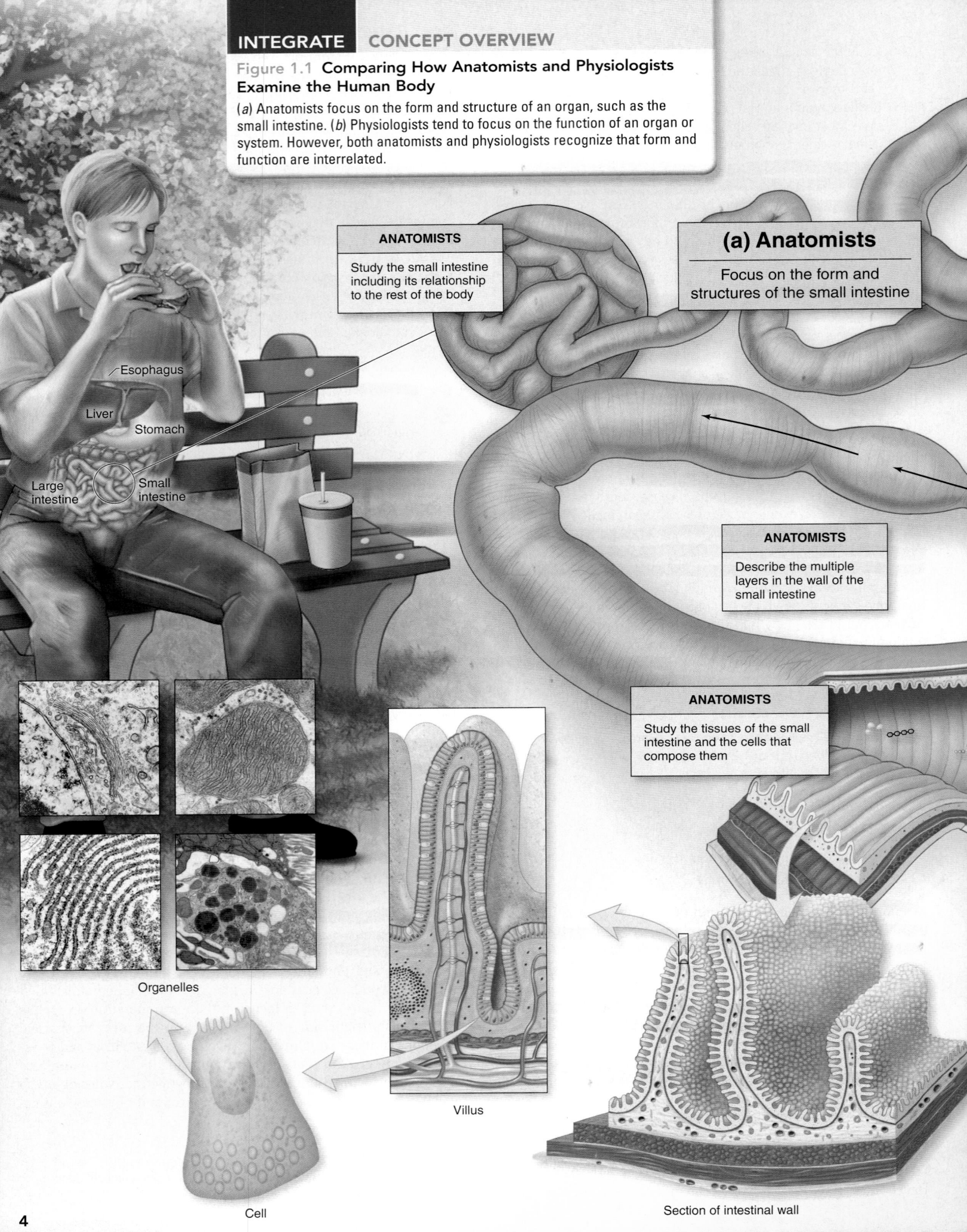

Figure 1.1 Comparing How Anatomists and Physiologists Examine the Human Body

(a) Anatomists focus on the form and structure of an organ, such as the small intestine. (b) Physiologists tend to focus on the function of an organ or system. However, both anatomists and physiologists recognize that form and function are interrelated.

ANATOMISTS

Study the small intestine including its relationship to the rest of the body

(a) Anatomists

Focus on the form and structures of the small intestine

Esophagus

Liver

Stomach

Large intestine

Small intestine

ANATOMISTS

Describe the multiple layers in the wall of the small intestine

ANATOMISTS

Study the tissues of the small intestine and the cells that compose them

Organelles

Villus

Cell

Section of intestinal wall

Peristalsis

Wave of contraction

Small intestine

Bolus

Relaxation

Propulsion of bolus forward.

(b) Physiologists

Focus on the function of the small intestine

PHYSIOLOGISTS

Examine how the muscles of the small intestine propel food through the digestive tract

Anatomists and Physiologists

Know form and function of the small intestine are interrelated

PHYSIOLOGISTS

Describe the mechanisms by which different nutrients are broken down

Protein

Carbohydrate

Fat globules

Bile salts

Monosaccharides

Amino acids

Monoglycerides

Epithelial cell of intestinal villus

PHYSIOLOGISTS

Study the mechanisms by which different nutrients are absorbed

Blood capillary

Lymphatic capillary

5

1.3 The Body's Levels of Organization

Scientists group the body's components into an organizational hierarchy of form and function. In thinking about these levels, it is helpful to know the characteristics common to living things and how each level supports these characteristics. For example, the organ system concept allows functions to be considered as an interaction between many organs.

1.3a Characteristics That Describe Living Things

LEARNING OBJECTIVE

1. List the characteristics common to all living things.

Several properties are common to all organisms, including humans:

- **Organization.** All organisms exhibit a complex structure and order. In the next section, we observe that the human body has several increasingly complex levels of organization.
- **Metabolism.** All organisms engage in **metabolism** (mĕ-tab′ō-lizm; *metabole* = change), which is defined as the sum of all of the chemical reactions that occur within the body. Metabolism consists of both **anabolism** (ă-nab′ō-lizm, *anabole* = a raising up), in which small molecules are joined to form larger molecules, and **catabolism** (kă-tab′ō-lizm; *katabole* = a casting down), in which large molecules are broken down into smaller molecules. Examples of metabolic reactions include using the cell's own energy to perform certain functions, and contracting muscles to move the body or body organs.

WHAT DO YOU THINK?

1. When you digest a meal, what type of metabolic reactions do you think you are utilizing primarily: *anabolic* or *catabolic* chemical reactions? Why?

- **Growth and Development.** During their lifetime, organisms assimilate materials from their environment and often exhibit increased size (growth) and increased specialization as related to form and function (development). As the human body grows and develops, structures such as the brain become more complex and sophisticated.
- **Responsiveness.** All organisms exhibit **responsiveness**, which is the ability to sense and react to **stimuli** (changes in the external or internal environment). A stimulus to the skin of the hands, such as an extremely hot temperature, causes the human to withdraw the hand from the stimulus so as to prevent injury or damage. Responsiveness occurs at almost all levels of organization.
- **Regulation.** An organism must be able to adjust or direct internal bodily function in the face of environmental changes. **Homeostasis** (hō-mē-ō-stā′sis; *homoios* = similar, *stasis* = standing) refers to the ability of an organism to maintain a consistent internal environment, or "steady state." When body temperature rises, the body regulates this change by circulating more blood near its surface to facilitate heat loss, and thus return the body to

homeostasis. (Homeostasis is discussed in greater depth later in this chapter.)

- **Reproduction.** All organisms produce new cells for growth, maintenance, and repair. The somatic (body) cells divide by a process called mitosis, while sex cells (called gametes) are produced by a cell division process called meiosis. The sex cells, under the right conditions, have the ability to develop into a new living organism.

WHAT DID YOU LEARN?

5. What does it mean if an organism is 'responsive', and how does this characteristic relate to the survival of this organism?

Atom Molecule

Macromolecule (e.g., DNA)   **Organelle** (e.g., Golgi apparatus)

Chemical level

1.3b The View from Simplest to Most Complex

LEARNING OBJECTIVE

2. Describe the levels of organization in the human body.

Anatomists and physiologists recognize several levels of increasingly complex organization in humans, as illustrated in **figure 1.2**. These levels, from simplest to most complex, are the chemical level, cellular level, tissue level, organ level, organ system level, and organismal level.

The **chemical level** is the simplest level, and it involves atoms and molecules. **Atoms** are the smallest units of matter. When two or more atoms combine they form a **molecule.** Examples of molecules include a sugar, a water molecule, or a vitamin. More complex molecules are called **macromolecules** and include some proteins and the deoxyribonucleic acid (DNA) molecules. Macromolecules form specialized microscopic subunits in cells called **organelles,** which are microscopic structures found within cells.

The **cellular level** consists of **cells,** which are the smallest living structures and serve as the basic units of structure and function in organisms. Cells and their components are formed from the atoms and molecules from the chemical level. The structures of cells vary widely, reflecting the specializations needed for their different functions. For example, a skeletal muscle cell may be very long and contain numerous organized protein filaments that aid in muscle contraction, whereas a red blood cell is small and has a flattened disc shape that facilitates the quick and effective exchange of respiratory gases.

The **tissue level** consists of **tissues,** which are groups of similar cells that perform common functions. There are four types of tissues. Epithelial tissue covers exposed surfaces and lines body cavities. Connective tissue protects, supports, and binds structures and

Epithelial tissue

Connective tissue

Tissue level

Cells

Cellular level

Small intestine

Organ level

Liver
Stomach
Gallbladder
Large intestine
Small intestine

Organ system level

Organismal level

organs. Muscle tissue produces movement. Finally, nervous tissue conducts nerve impulses for communication.

The **organ level** is composed of **organs,** which contain two or more tissue types that work together to perform specific, complex functions. The small intestine is an example of an organ that is composed of all four tissue types which work together to process and absorb digested nutrients.

The **organ system level** contains related organs that work together to coordinate activities and achieve a common function. For example, the organs of the digestive system (e.g., oral cavity, stomach, small and large intestine, and liver) work together to digest food particles, absorb nutrients, and expel the waste products.

The highest level of structural organization in the body is the **organismal level.** All body systems function interdependently in an **organism,** which is the living being.

Figure 1.2 Levels of Organization in the Human Body. The most simple level is the chemical level, followed by increasingly more complex levels of organization.

 WHAT DID YOU LEARN?

 6 Does a higher level of organization contain all the levels beneath it? Explain.

INTEGRATE

CONCEPT CONNECTION

Throughout future chapters, boxes like this one will highlight how various organ systems are interconnected and do not work in isolation. For example, the cardiovascular system and respiratory system work together in the transport of respiratory gases (oxygen and carbon dioxide) by the blood throughout the body.

1.3c Introduction to Organ Systems

 LEARNING OBJECTIVE

3. Compare the organ systems of the human body.

All organisms must exchange nutrients, wastes, and gases with their environment to carry on their metabolism. Simple organisms (like bacteria) may exchange these substances directly across their surface membranes. In contrast, complex, multicellular organisms require sophisticated organ systems with specialized structures and functions to perform the myriad of activities required for the routine events of life. In humans, 11 **organ systems** are commonly denoted, each composed of interrelated organs that work in concert to perform specific functions **(figure 1.3)**. A human body maintains homeostasis through the intricate interworkings of all of its organ systems. Subsequent chapters examine each of these organ systems in detail.

 WHAT DID YOU LEARN?

7 Which organ system is responsible for filtering the blood and removing the waste products of the blood in the form of urine?

Hair

Skin and associated glands

Toenails

Integumentary System (Chapter 6)
Provides protection, regulates body temperature, site of cutaneous receptors, synthesizes vitamin D, prevents water loss.

Skull

Sternum
Rib
Cartilage

Upper limb bones

Vertebrae

Sacrum

Lower limb bones

Knee joint

Skeletal System (Chapters 7–9)
Provides support and protection, site of hemopoiesis (blood cell production), stores calcium and phosphorus, provides sites for muscle attachments.

Pectoralis major muscle

Aponeurosis

Tendons

Sartorius muscle

Muscular System (Chapters 10–11)
Produces body movement, generates heat when muscles contract.

Sense organ (eye)

Central Nervous System

Brain
Spinal cord

Peripheral Nervous System

Peripheral nerves

Nervous System (Chapters 12–16)
A regulatory system that controls body movement by initiating responses to muscles, processes, and responds to sensory stimuli. Also responsible for consciousness, intelligence, memory.

Figure 1.3 Organ Systems. Major components and characteristics of the 11 organ systems of the human body are presented.
AP|R

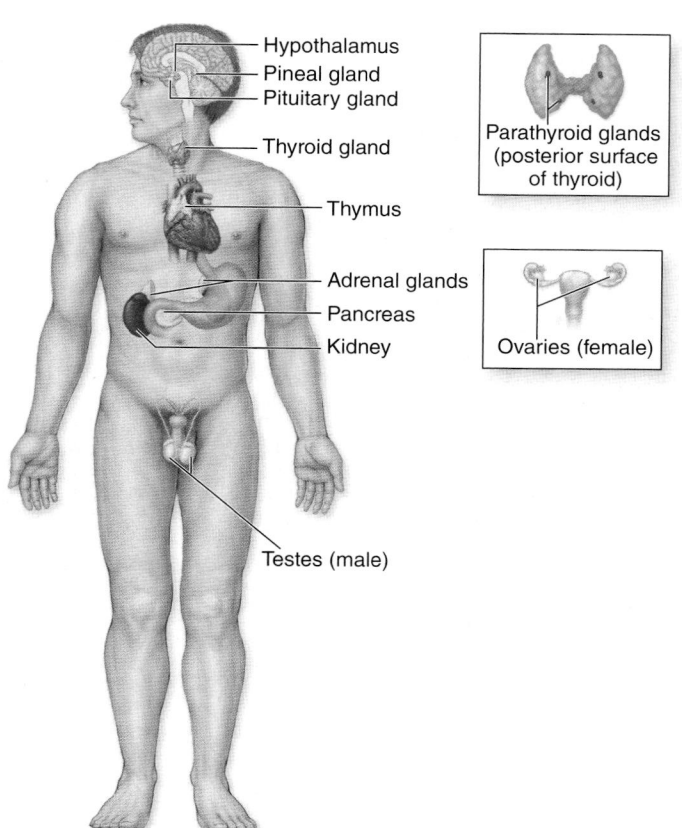

Endocrine System (Chapter 17)

Consists of glands and cell clusters that secrete hormones, which regulate development, growth and metabolism; maintain homeostasis of blood composition and volume, control digestive processes, and control reproduction.

Hypothalamus
Pineal gland
Pituitary gland
Thyroid gland
Thymus
Adrenal glands
Pancreas
Kidney
Testes (male)
Parathyroid glands (posterior surface of thyroid)
Ovaries (female)

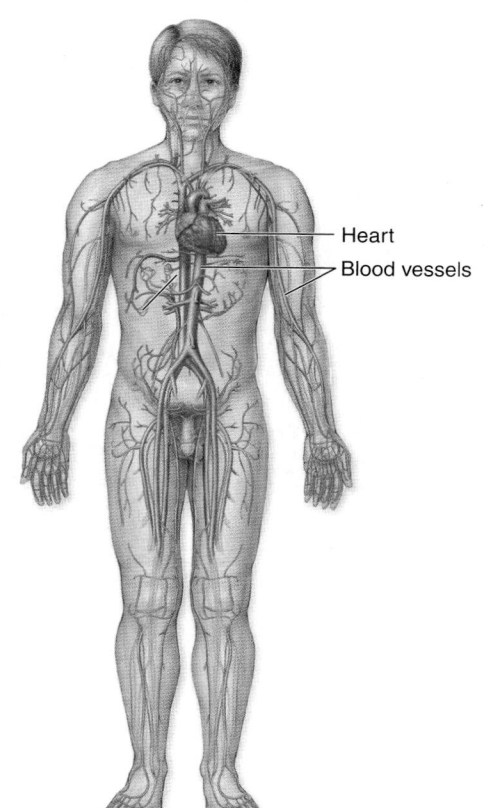

Cardiovascular System (Chapters 18–20)

Consists of the heart and blood vessels; the heart moves blood through blood vessels in order to distribute hormones, nutrients, gases, and pick up waste products.

Heart
Blood vessels

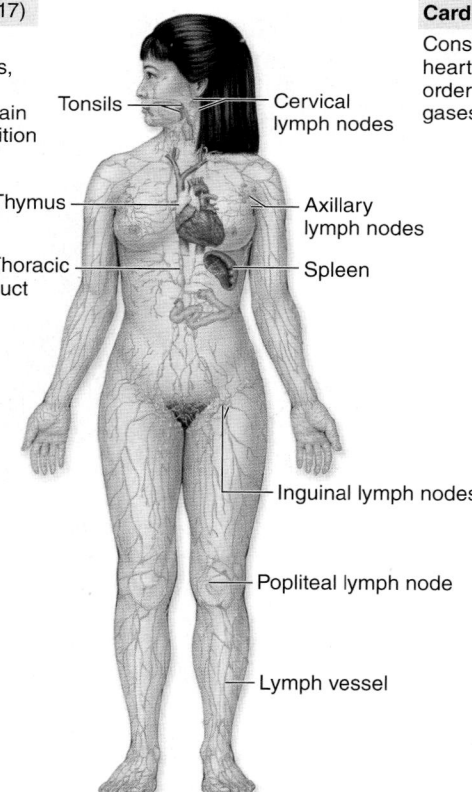

Lymphatic System (Chapters 21–22)

Transports and filters lymph (interstitial fluid transported through lymph vessels) and participates in an immune response when necessary.

Tonsils
Cervical lymph nodes
Thymus
Axillary lymph nodes
Thoracic duct
Spleen
Inguinal lymph nodes
Popliteal lymph node
Lymph vessel

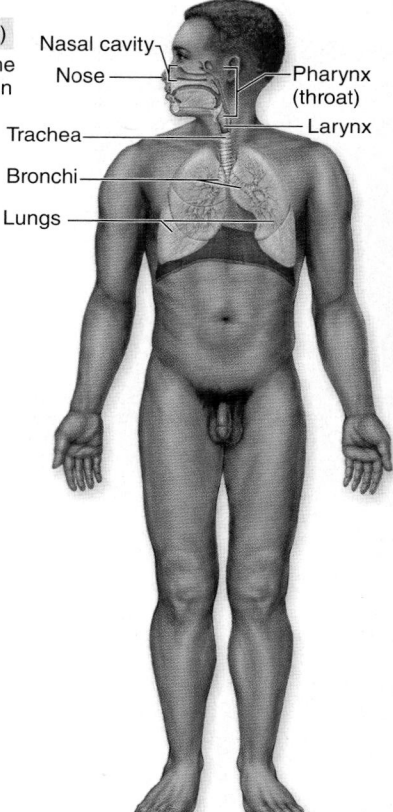

Respiratory System (Chapter 23)

Responsible for exchange of gases (oxygen and carbon dioxide) between blood and the air in the lungs.

Nasal cavity
Nose
Pharynx (throat)
Larynx
Trachea
Bronchi
Lungs

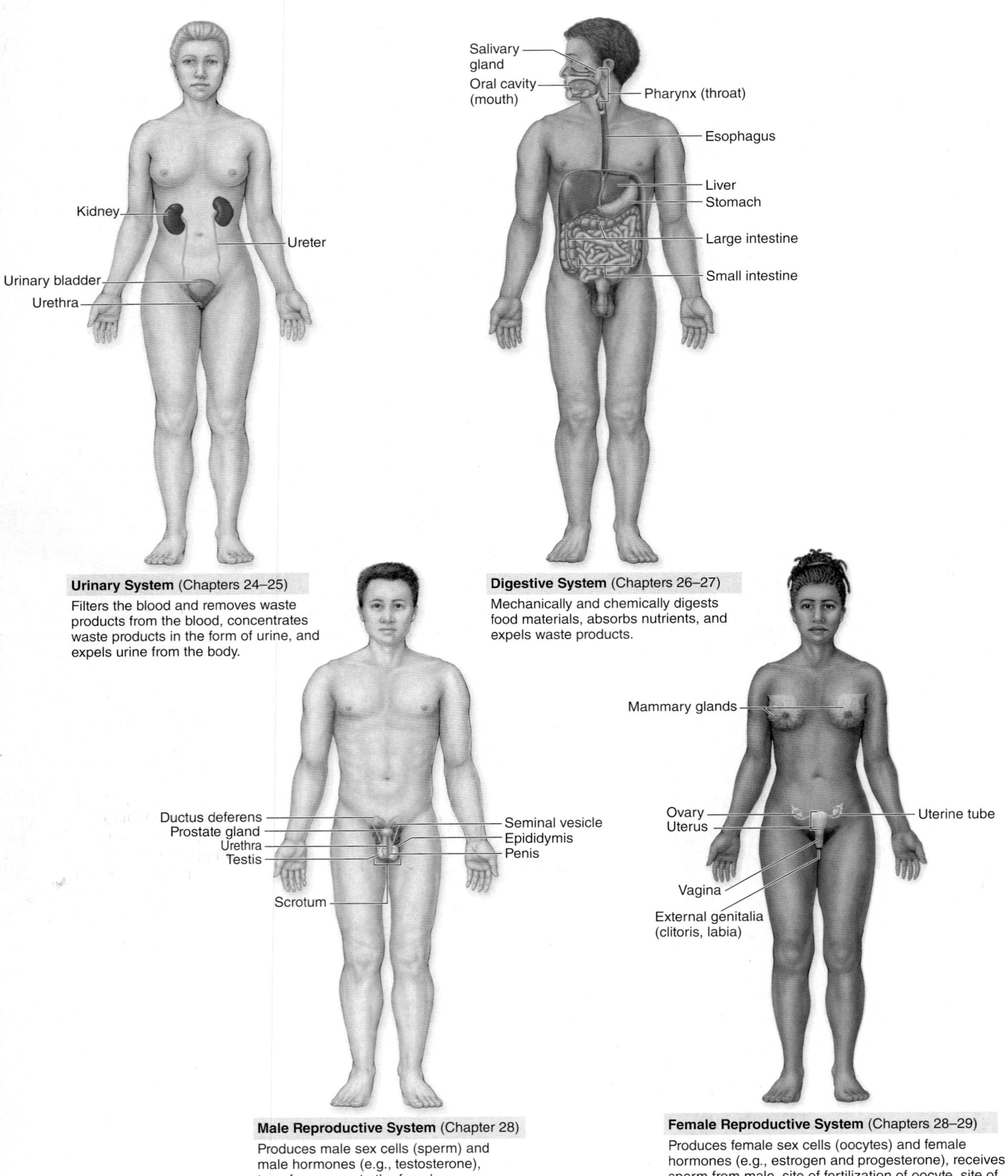

Urinary System (Chapters 24–25)

Filters the blood and removes waste products from the blood, concentrates waste products in the form of urine, and expels urine from the body.

Digestive System (Chapters 26–27)

Mechanically and chemically digests food materials, absorbs nutrients, and expels waste products.

Male Reproductive System (Chapter 28)

Produces male sex cells (sperm) and male hormones (e.g., testosterone), transfers sperm to the female.

Female Reproductive System (Chapters 28–29)

Produces female sex cells (oocytes) and female hormones (e.g., estrogen and progesterone), receives sperm from male, site of fertilization of oocyte, site of growth and development of embryo and fetus, produces and secretes breast milk for nourishment of newborn.

Figure 1.3 Organ Systems. (*continued*)

AP|R

1.4 The Language of Anatomy and Physiology

Clinicians and researchers in anatomy and physiology require a precise language to ensure that they are all discussing the same features and functions. A technical terminology has been developed that describes body position, direction, regions, and body cavities. These technical terms are different from those used in everyday conversation, because the more conversational terms often do not accurately describe location and position or identify structures. For example, the term *arm* in everyday conversation refers to the entire upper limb, but in anatomy the specific portions of the upper limb are named, and the term *arm* or *brachium* refers only to that part of the upper limb between the shoulder and the elbow.

Most anatomic and physiologic terms are derived from Greek or Latin, and we frequently provide word origins, pronunciations, and definitions of terms where appropriate throughout this text. We've used *Stedman's Medical Dictionary* (which defines all medical terms) and *Terminologia Anatomica* (which lists and categorizes the modern, proper anatomic terms) as references.

1.4a Anatomic Position

LEARNING OBJECTIVE

1. Describe the anatomic position and its importance in the study of anatomy.

Descriptions of any body region or part require a common initial point of reference. Note that terms such as "anterior" or "posterior"

INTEGRATE

LEARNING STRATEGY

Breaking a word into smaller parts can help you understand and remember its meaning. In this book, we provide word derivations for new terms following their pronunciations. For example, in the case of histology, the study of tissues, we give (*histos* = web, tissue, *logos* = study).

Many biological terms share some of the same prefixes, suffixes, and word roots, so learning the meanings of these common terms can help you figure out the meanings of unfamiliar terms. A review of prefixes, suffixes, and word roots also appears on the inside of the back cover of this book.

can be relative terms. For example, when a person is standing it would be accurate to say "the heart is superior to the stomach," yet if that person is lying down in a supine position, this statement would seem not to be true. For accuracy and clarity, anatomists and physiologists describe these parts based on the premise that the body is in what is termed the anatomic position, which is then the point of common reference. An individual in the **anatomic position** stands upright with the feet parallel and flat on the floor, the upper limbs are at the sides of the body, and the palms face anteriorly (toward the front); the head is level, and the eyes look forward toward the observer (**figure 1.4**). All of the anatomic and directional terms used in this book refer to the body in anatomic position.

(a)

(b) Coronal section

(c) Transverse section

(d) Midsagittal section

Figure 1.4 Anatomic Position and Body Planes. (*a*) In the anatomic position, the body is upright, and the forearms are positioned so the palms are facing anteriorly. A plane is an imaginary surface that slices the body into specific sections. The three major anatomic planes of reference are the (*b*) coronal, (*c*) transverse, and (*d*) midsagittal planes. AP|R

1.4b Sections and Planes

LEARNING OBJECTIVE

2. Describe the anatomic sections and planes through the body.

Anatomists and physiologists refer to real or imaginary "slices" of the body, called sections or planes, to examine the internal anatomy and describe the position of one body part relative to another. The term **section** implies an actual cut or slice to expose the internal anatomy, while the word **plane** implies an imaginary flat surface passing through the body. The three major anatomic planes are the coronal, transverse, and midsagittal planes (figure 1.4).

A **coronal** (kōr′ō-năl; *korone* = crown) **plane,** also called a *frontal plane,* is a vertical plane that divides the body or organ into *anterior* (front) and *posterior* (back) parts. When a coronal plane is taken through the trunk, the anterior portion contains the chest and the posterior portion contains the back and buttocks.

A **transverse plane,** also called a *horizontal plane* or *cross-sectional plane,* divides the body or organ into *superior* (top) and *inferior* (bottom) parts. If a transverse plane is taken through the middle of the trunk, the superior portion contains the chest and the inferior portion contains the abdomen.

A **midsagittal** (mid-saj′ĭ-tăl; *sagitta* = arrow) **plane,** or *median plane,* is a vertical plane and divides the body or organ into *left* and *right halves.* A midsagittal plane through the head will split it into a left half and a right half (each containing one eye, one ear, and half of the nose and mouth). A plane that is parallel to the midsagittal plane, but either to the left or right of the midsagittal plane, is termed a **sagittal plane.** A sagittal plane divides a structure into left and right portions that may not be equal. Although there is only one midsagittal plane, an infinite number of sagittal planes are possible.

In addition to these major planes, there are numerous minor planes called **oblique** (ob-lēk′) **planes** that pass through a structure at an angle.

Interpreting body sections has become increasingly important for health-care professionals. Technical advances in medical imaging have produced sectional images of internal body structures (figure 1.4*b*). To determine the shape of any object within a section, we must be able to reconstruct its three-dimensional shape by observing many continuous sections.

Sectioning the body or an organ along different planes often results in very different views of that organ or region. For example, different sections through the abdominal cavity exhibit multiple profiles of the long, twisted tube that is the small intestine. These sections may appear as circles, ovals, a figure eight, or maybe a long tube with parallel sides, depending on where the section was taken (**figure 1.5**). Being able to convert and interpret two-dimensional images into three-dimensional structures is especially important when comparing and understanding histologic and gross anatomic views of the same organ.

WHAT DID YOU LEARN?

8 What type of plane would separate the nose and mouth into superior and inferior structures?

Figure 1.5 Three-dimensional Reconstruction from Planes of Section. Serial sections through an object are used to reconstruct its three-dimensional structure, as in these sections of the small intestine. Often a single section, such as the plane at the lower part of this figure, misrepresents the complete structure of the object.

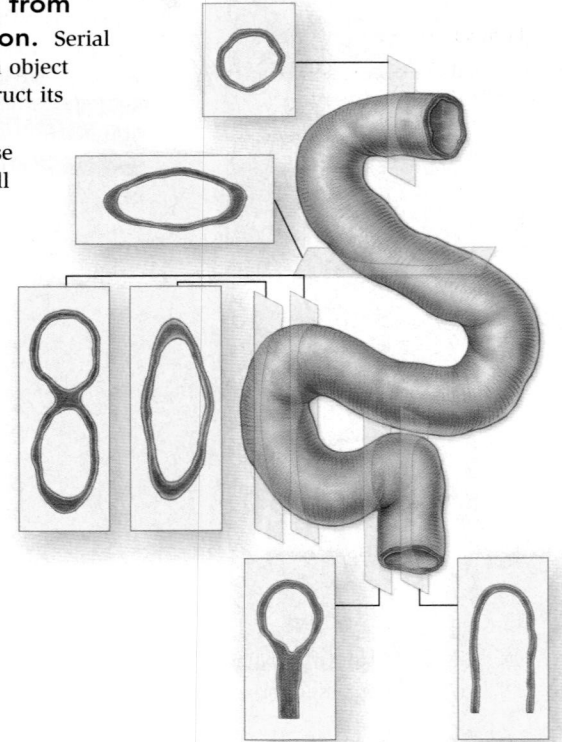

Table 1.2	Anatomic Directional Terms		
Direction	**Term**	**Meaning**	**Example**
Relative to front (belly side) or back of the body	Anterior	In front of; toward the front surface	The stomach is *anterior* to the spinal cord.
	Posterior	In back of; toward the back surface	The heart is *posterior* to the sternum.
	Dorsal	At the back side of the human body	The spinal cord is on the *dorsal* side of the body.
	Ventral	At the belly side of the human body	The umbilicus (navel, belly button) is on the *ventral* side of the body.
Relative to the head or bottom of the body	Superior	Closer to the head	The chest is *superior* to the pelvis.
	Inferior	Closer to the feet	The stomach is *inferior* to the heart.
	Cranial (cephalic)	At the head end	The shoulders are *cranial* to the feet.
	Caudal	At the rear or tail end	The buttocks are *caudal* to the head.
	Rostral	Toward the nose or mouth	The eyes are *rostral* to the back of the head.
Relative to the midline or center of the body	Medial	Toward the midline of the body	The lungs are *medial* to the shoulders.
	Lateral	Away from the midline of the body	The arms are *lateral* to the heart.
	Deep	On the inside, internal to another structure	The heart is *deep* to the rib cage.
	Superficial	On the outside	The skin is *superficial* to the biceps brachii muscle.
Relative to point of attachment of appendage	Proximal	Closest to point of attachment to trunk	The elbow is *proximal* to the hand.
	Distal	Furthest from point of attachment to trunk	The wrist is *distal* to the elbow.

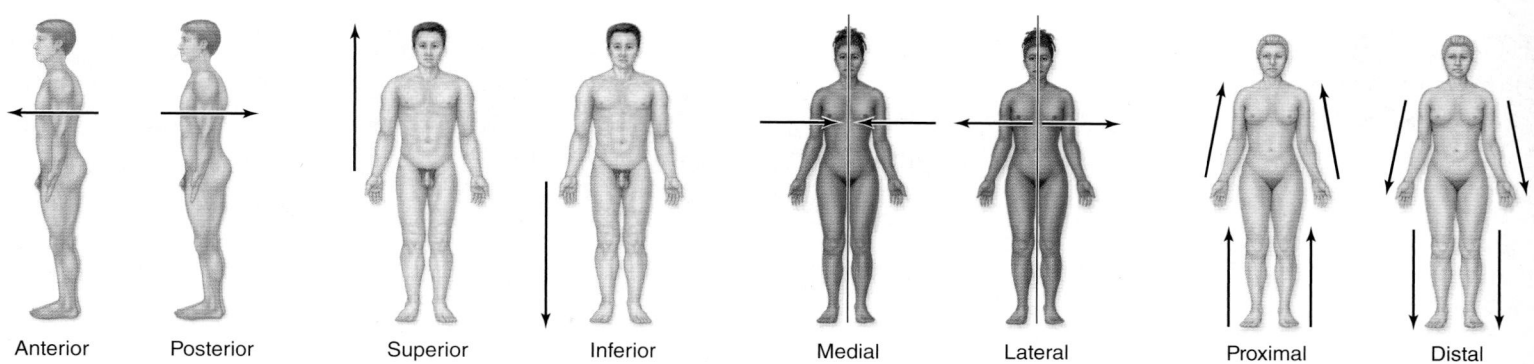

| Anterior | Posterior | Superior | Inferior | Medial | Lateral | Proximal | Distal |

Figure 1.6 Directional Terms in Anatomy. Directional terms precisely describe the location and relative relationships of body parts. (See also table 1.2.) **AP|R**

1.4c Anatomic Directions

✓ LEARNING OBJECTIVE

3. Define the different anatomic directional terms.

Once the body is in the anatomic position, we can precisely describe the relative positions of structures by using specific directional terms. These directional terms are precise and brief, and most of them have a correlative term that means the opposite. Examples include **anterior** and **posterior**, **dorsal** (toward the back) and **ventral** (toward the belly), and **proximal** (nearer to the trunk) and **distal** (farther from the trunk). **Table 1.2** and **figure 1.6** describe some commonly used directional terms. Studying the table and figure together, and referring back to these materials as needed, will maximize your understanding of anatomic directions and aid your study of anatomy throughout the rest of this book.

💡 WHAT DID YOU LEARN?

9 Which directional term would be most appropriate in the sentence "The elbow is _____ to the wrist"?

1.4d Regional Anatomy

✓ LEARNING OBJECTIVE

4. Identify the major regions of the body, using proper anatomic terminology.

The human body is partitioned into two main regions, the axial and appendicular regions. The **axial** (ak′sē-ăl) **region** includes the head, neck, and trunk; it forms the main vertical axis of the body. The **appendicular** (ap′en-dik′ū-lăr) **region** is composed of the upper and lower limbs, which attach to the axial region. Several more specific regions are located within these two main ones, and they are identified by proper anatomic terminology. **Figure 1.7** and **table 1.3**

Anterior view labels:
- Cephalic (head)
- Frontal (forehead)
- Nasal (nose)
- Oral (mouth)
- Orbital (eye)
- Buccal (cheek)
- Cervical (neck)
- Mental (chin)
- Deltoid (shoulder)
- Axillary (armpit)
- Sternal (sternum)
- Pectoral (chest)
- Mammary (breast)
- Brachial (arm)
- Antecubital (front of elbow)
- Antebrachial (forearm)
- Abdominal (abdomen)
- Coxal (hip)
- Pelvic
- Inguinal (groin)
- Carpal (wrist)
- Pubic
- Palmar (palm)
- Digital (finger)
- Femoral (thigh)
- Patellar (kneecap)
- Crural (leg)
- Tarsal (ankle)
- Pes (foot)
- Dorsum of the foot
- Digital (toe)

(a) **Anterior view**

Posterior view labels:
- Cranial (surrounding the brain)
- Auricular (ear)
- Occipital (back of head)
- Thoracic
- Vertebral (spinal column)
- Deltoid (shoulder)
- Brachial (arm)
- Olecranal (elbow)
- Abdominal (abdomen)
- Lumbar (lower back)
- Sacral
- Gluteal (buttock)
- Antebrachial (forearm)
- Dorsum of the hand
- Manus (hand)
- Femoral (thigh)
- Perineal
- Popliteal (back of knee)
- Sural (calf)
- Calcaneal (heel)
- Plantar surface (sole)

(b) **Posterior view**

Figure 1.7 Regional Terms. (*a*) Anterior and (*b*) posterior views show key regions of the body. Their common names appear in parentheses. **AP|R**

Table 1.3	Human Body Regions		Regional Name	Description
Regional Name	**Description**		Manus	Hand
Abdominal	Region inferior to the thorax (chest) and superior to the hip bones		Mental	Chin
			Nasal	Nose
Antebrachial	Forearm (the portion of the upper limb between the elbow and the wrist)		Occipital	Posterior aspect of the head
			Olecranal	Posterior aspect of the elbow
Antecubital	Region anterior to the elbow; also known as the cubital region		Oral	Mouth
			Orbital	Eye
Auricular	Visible surface structures of the ear		Palmar	Palm (anterior surface) of the hand
Axillary	Armpit		Patellar	Kneecap
Brachial	Arm (the portion of the upper limb between the shoulder and the elbow)		Pectoral	Chest
			Pelvic	Pelvis
Buccal	Cheek		Perineal	Diamond-shaped region between the legs that contains the anus and external reproductive organs
Calcaneal	Heel of the foot			
Carpal	Wrist			
Cephalic	Head		Pes	Foot
Cervical	Neck		Plantar	Sole of the foot
Coxal	Hip		Pollex	Thumb
Cranial	Skull		Popliteal	Area posterior to the knee
Crural	Leg (the portion of the lower limb between the knee and the ankle)		Pubic	Anterior region of the pelvis
			Radial	Lateral (thumb side) aspect of forearm
Deltoid	Shoulder		Sacral	Posterior region between the hip bones
Digital	Fingers or toes (also called phalangeal)		Scapular	Shoulder blade
Dorsal/ Dorsum	Back		Sternal	Anterior middle region of the thorax
Facial	Face		Sural	Calf (posterior part of the leg)
Femoral	Thigh		Tarsal	Ankle, root of the foot
Fibular	Lateral aspect of the leg		Thoracic	Chest or thorax
Frontal	Forehead		Tibial	Medial aspect of leg
Gluteal	Buttock		Ulnar	Medial aspect of the forearm
Hallux	Great toe		Umbilical	Navel
Inguinal	Groin (sometimes used to indicate the crease or junction of the thigh with the trunk)		Vertebral	Spinal column
Lumbar	Relating to the loins, or the inferior part of the back, between the ribs and pelvis			
Mammary	Breast			

identify the major regional terms and some additional minor ones. Not all regions are shown in figure 1.7.

 WHAT DID YOU LEARN?

10 The term *antebrachial* refers to which body region?

1.4e Body Cavities and Membranes

 LEARNING OBJECTIVES

5. Describe the body cavities and their subdivisions.
6. Explain the role of serous membranes in the ventral cavities.

Internal organs and organ systems are housed within enclosed spaces, or cavities. These body cavities are named either according to the bones that surround them or the organs they contain. For purposes of discussion, these body cavities are grouped into a posterior aspect and a ventral cavity.

Posterior Aspect

The **posterior aspect** of the body is different from the ventral cavity, in that the posterior aspect contains cavities that are completely encased in bone and are physically and developmentally different from the ventral cavity. The term *dorsal body cavity* has been used by others to describe this posterior aspect, but is not used here because of these differences between the ventral cavity and posterior aspect.

The posterior aspect is subdivided into two enclosed cavities (**figure 1.8a**). A **cranial cavity** is formed by the bones of the cranium, and so it also goes by the name *endocranium.* The cranial cavity houses the brain. The second cavity is the **vertebral** (ver′te-brăl) **canal,** which is formed by the bones of the vertebral column. The vertebral canal houses the spinal cord.

Ventral Cavity

The **ventral cavity** is the larger, anteriorly placed cavity in the body (figure 1.8). Unlike the posterior aspect, the ventral cavity and its subdivisions do not completely encase their organs in bone. The ventral cavity is partitioned by the diaphragm into a superior **thoracic** (thō-ras′ik) **cavity** and an inferior **abdominopelvic** (ab-dom′i-nō-pel′vik) **cavity.**

Another significant difference between the posterior aspect and the ventral cavity is that the subdivisions of the ventral cavity are lined with thin **serous membranes.** (Posterior aspect cavities have no serous membranes.) In this usage a *membrane* is a continuous layer of cells, as compared to the plasma membrane that surrounds a single cell.

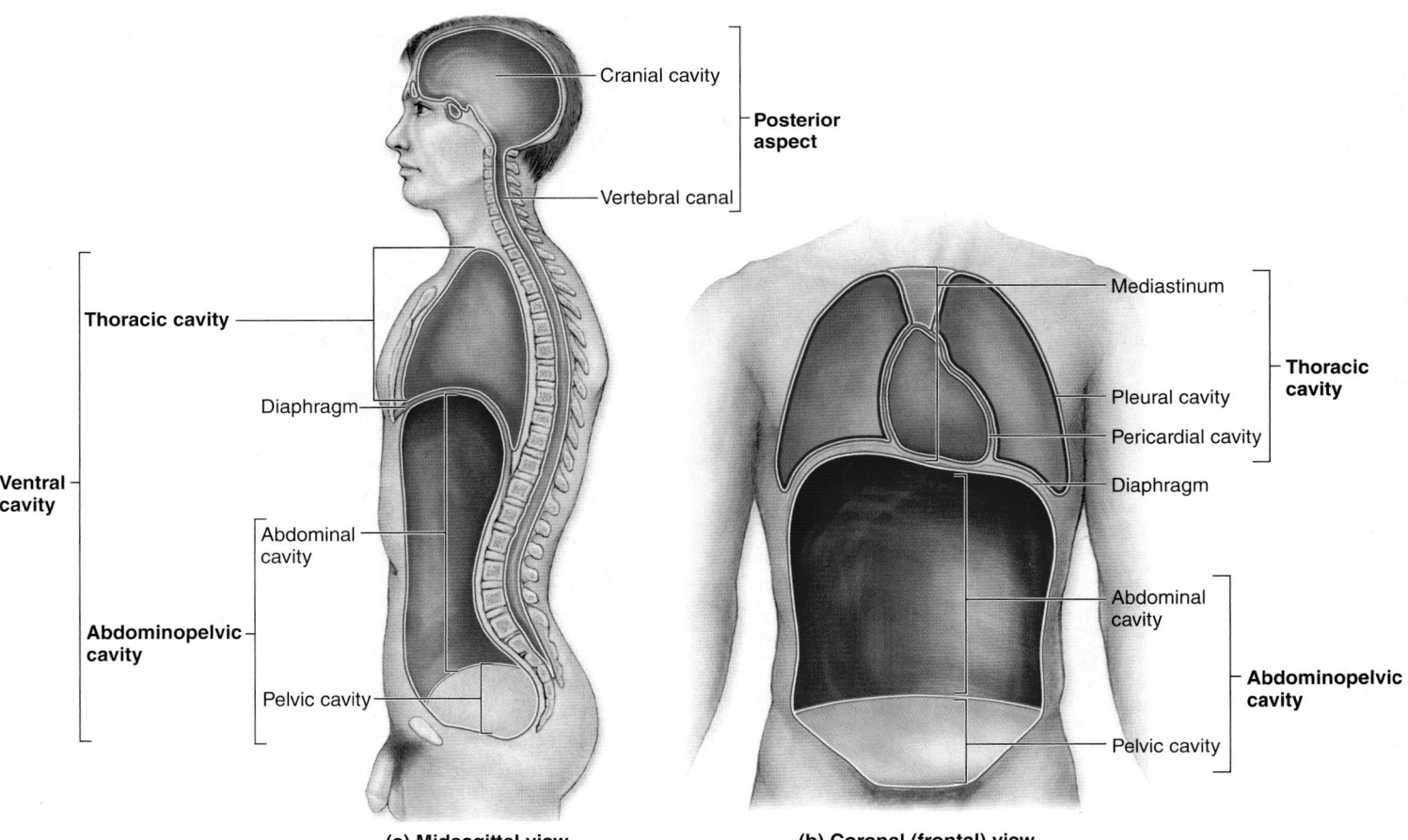

(a) Midsagittal view   **(b) Coronal (frontal) view**

Figure 1.8 Body Cavities. The body is composed of two main spaces: the posterior aspect and the ventral cavity. (*a*) A midsagittal view shows both the posterior aspect and the ventral cavity. (*b*) A coronal view shows the relationship between the thoracic and abdominopelvic cavities within the ventral cavity. AP|R

Serous membranes are composed of two layers: (1) a **parietal** (pă-rī′ĕ-tăl) **layer** that typically lines the internal surface of the body wall and (2) a **visceral** (vis′er-ăl) **layer** that covers the external surface of the organs (collectively called the **viscera**) within that cavity. Between the parietal and visceral serous membrane layers is a potential space called the **serous cavity.** Serous membranes secrete a liquid called **serous fluid** within a serous cavity. Serous fluid has the consistency of oil and serves as a lubricant. In a living human, organs (e.g., heart, lungs, intestines) are moving and rubbing against each other and the body wall. Friction caused by this constant movement is reduced by the serous fluid so the organs move more smoothly against one another and the body walls.

WHAT DO YOU THINK?

2 What do you think would happen to your body organs if there were no serous fluid between the parietal and visceral layers?

Figure 1.9a provides a helpful analogy for visualizing the serous membrane layers. The closed fist is comparable to an organ, and the balloon is comparable to a serous membrane. When a fist is pushed against the wall of the balloon, the inner balloon wall that surrounds the fist is comparable to the visceral layer of the serous membrane. The outer balloon wall is comparable to the parietal layer of the serous membrane. The thin, air-filled space within the balloon, between the two "walls," is comparable to the serous cavity. Note that the organ is not *inside* the serous cavity; it is actually *outside* the cavity and merely covered by the serous membrane.

Thoracic Cavity The median space in the thoracic cavity is called the **mediastinum** (mē-dē-as-tī′nŭm; *medius* = middle) (figure 1.8b). It contains the heart, thymus, esophagus, trachea, and major blood vessels that connect to the heart.

Within the mediastinum, the heart is enclosed by a two-layered serous membrane called the serous **pericardium** (per-ĭ-kar′dē-ŭm; *peri* = around, *kardia* = heart). The **parietal pericardium** is the outermost layer of the serous membrane and forms the sac around the heart, while the **visceral pericardium** forms the heart's external surface (figure 1.9b). The **pericardial cavity** is the potential space between the parietal and visceral layers of the pericardium, and it contains serous fluid.

The right and left sides of the thoracic cavity house the lungs, which are associated with a two-layered serous membrane called the

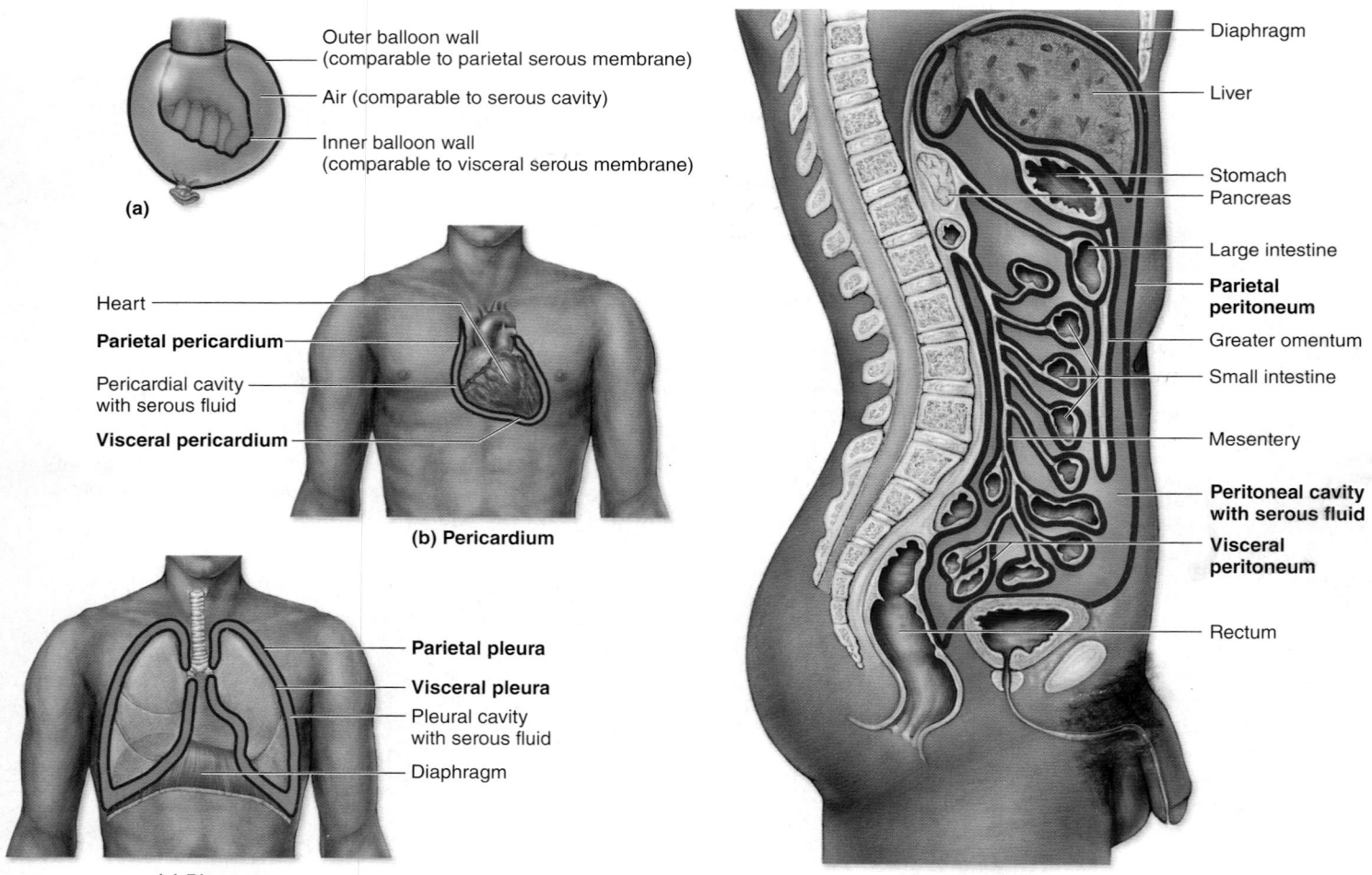

(a)

- Outer balloon wall (comparable to parietal serous membrane)
- Air (comparable to serous cavity)
- Inner balloon wall (comparable to visceral serous membrane)

(b) Pericardium

- Heart
- Parietal pericardium
- Pericardial cavity with serous fluid
- Visceral pericardium

(c) Pleura

- Parietal pleura
- Visceral pleura
- Pleural cavity with serous fluid
- Diaphragm

(d) Peritoneum

- Diaphragm
- Liver
- Stomach
- Pancreas
- Large intestine
- Parietal peritoneum
- Greater omentum
- Small intestine
- Mesentery
- Peritoneal cavity with serous fluid
- Visceral peritoneum
- Rectum

Figure 1.9 Serous Membranes in the Thoracic and Abdominopelvic Body Cavities. Serous membranes line the inside of the cavity (parietal layer) and cover the outside of an organ (visceral layer) within the cavity. (a) The parietal and visceral serous membranes are similar to the inner and outer balloon walls that wrap around a fist, where the fist represents the body organ. (b) Parietal and visceral layers of the pericardium line the pericardial cavity around the heart. (c) Parietal and visceral layers of the pleura line the pleural cavity between the lungs and the chest wall. (d) Parietal and visceral layers of the peritoneum line the peritoneal cavity that lies between the abdominopelvic organs and the body wall. AP|R

(a) Abdominopelvic regions

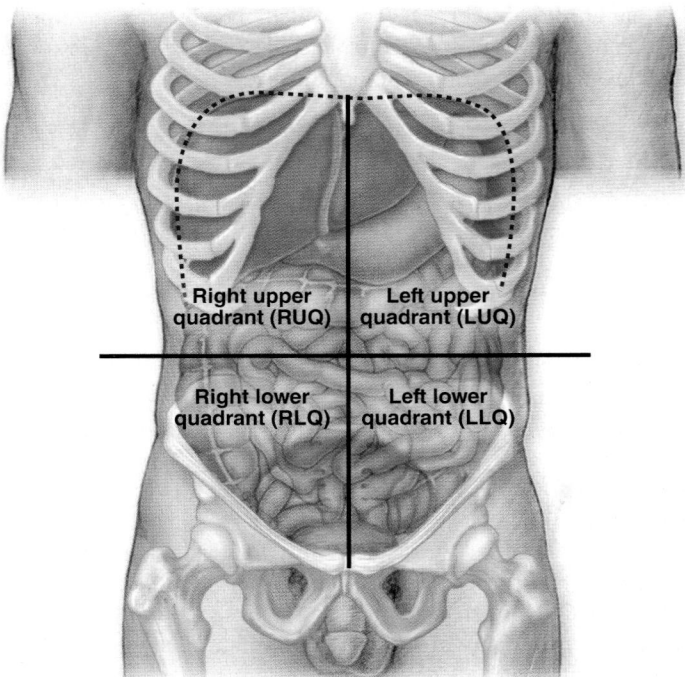

(b) Abdominopelvic quadrants

Figure 1.10 Abdominopelvic Regions and Quadrants. The abdominopelvic cavity can be subdivided into (*a*) nine regions or (*b*) four quadrants for purposes of description or identification. AP|R

pleura (ploor'ă; = a rib) (figure 1.9*c*). The **parietal pleura** is the outer layer of the serous membrane and lines the internal surface of the thoracic wall. The inner layer is the **visceral pleura,** which covers the external surface of each lung. The **pleural cavity** is the potential space between these parietal and visceral layers, and it contains serous fluid.

Abdominopelvic Cavity The abdominopelvic cavity may be subdivided into two smaller cavities by a horizontal plane at the level of the superior aspects of the hip bones. The area superior to this plane is the **abdominal cavity;** the **pelvic cavity** lies inferior to this plane where it is wedged between the two hip bones. You can locate the division between these two cavities by palpating (feeling for) the superior ridges of your hip bones. The abdominal cavity contains most of digestive system organs, as well as the kidneys and most of the ureters. The pelvic cavity contains the distal part of the large intestine, the remainder of the ureters and the urinary bladder, and the internal reproductive organs.

The **peritoneum** (per'i-tō-nē'um; *periteino* = to stretch over) is the two-layered serous membrane that lines the abdominopelvic cavity (figure 1.9*d*). The **parietal peritoneum,** the outer layer of this serous membrane, lines the internal walls of the abdominopelvic cavity. The **visceral peritoneum** is the inner layer of this serous membrane, and it covers the external surfaces of most abdominal and pelvic organs. The potential space between these serous membrane layers is the **peritoneal cavity,** and it contains and is lubricated by serous fluid.

WHAT DID YOU LEARN?

11 Which body cavity is associated with the lungs, and what are the names of its serous membranes?

1.4f Abdominopelvic Regions and Quadrants

LEARNING OBJECTIVE

7. Compare the terms used to subdivide the abdominopelvic region into nine regions or four quadrants.

To more accurately describe organ location, anatomists and healthcare professionals commonly partition the large abdominopelvic cavity into smaller compartments. Nine compartments, called **abdominopelvic regions,** are delineated by using two transverse planes and two sagittal planes. These nine regions are shown in **figure 1.10*a*** and summarized here:

- The **umbilical** (ŭm-bil'i-kăl; = navel) **region** is the middle region and is named for the umbilicus, or navel (belly button) that lies in its center.
- The **epigastric** (ep-ĭ-gas'trik; *epi* = above, *gaster* = belly) **region** is the superior region above the umbilical region.
- The **hypogastric** (hī-pō-gas'trik; *hypo* = under) **region** lies inferior to the umbilical region.
- The **right** and **left hypochondriac** (hī-pō-kon'drē-ak; *chondr* = cartilage) **regions** are inferior to the costal cartilages and lateral to the epigastric region.
- The **right** and **left lumbar regions** are lateral to the umbilical region.
- The **right** and **left iliac** (il'ē-ak; *eileo* = to twist) **regions** are lateral to the hypogastric region.

Some health-care professionals prefer to partition the abdomen more simply into four quadrants, using the umbilicus as the central point and having imaginary transverse and midsagittal planes pass through the umbilicus (figure 1.10*b*). The quadrants are named **right upper quadrant (RUQ), left upper quadrant (LUQ), right lower quadrant (RLQ),** and **left lower quadrant (LLQ)**. These quadrants, like the abdomino-pelvic regions, are used to accurately locate and describe various aches, pains, injuries, or other abnormalities.

💡 **WHAT DID YOU LEARN?**

12 If a physician makes an incision into the abdomen along a midsagittal plane, superior to the umbilicus and just inferior to the diaphragm, then the skin of the _____ abdominopelvic region was incised.

1.5 Homeostasis: Keeping Internal Conditions Stable

Have you ever noticed that your body maintains an average internal temperature of about 37°C (98.6°F), regardless of the outside temperature? Perhaps you also have noticed that the size of your pupil is altered in response to light intensity entering your eye, or that your breathing returns to normal shortly after exercise. Likewise, your heart rate, blood pressure, and blood levels of sugar (glucose) and O_2 are also regulated and maintained within certain parameters. In fact, there are hundreds of anatomic structures and physiologic processes that are continuously monitored and adjusted within your body so that they are kept within normal limits.

Homeostasis refers to the body's ability to maintain a relatively stable internal environment in response to changing internal or external conditions. Homeostasis is a central theme throughout this text, and you will be learning the appropriate details about homeostasis in each chapter. In this section, we introduce you to the general concept of homeostasis. We describe the general components of homeostatic systems, provide specific examples of these regulatory processes, and then describe the relationship of homeostasis, health, and disease.

1.5a Components of Homeostatic Systems

✔️ **LEARNING OBJECTIVES**

1. Define the components of a homeostatic system.

2. Be able to recognize each of the components in representative systems.

The body maintains homeostasis by utilizing homeostatic control systems. Three components are associated with each homeostatic system: receptor, control center, and effector **(figure 1.11)**.

Receptor

The **receptor** is the body structure that detects changes in a variable, which is either the substance or process that is regulated. A receptor typically consists of sensory nerves. These nerves may be in the skin, internal organs of the body, or specialized organs such as the eye, ear, tongue, or nose. The change in the variable is the **stimulus.** The stimulus might be a change in temperature, chemicals, or stretch in muscle.

Control Center

The **control center** is the structure that interprets input from the receptor and initiates changes through the effector. You can think of it as the "go between" for the other two components of a homeostatic system. The control center is generally a portion of the nervous system (brain or spinal cord) or an endocrine organ (such as the thyroid gland). A homeostatic system involving the nervous system provides a relatively quick means of responding to change. An example is regulating blood pressure when you rise from bed in the morning. In contrast, the endocrine system usually provides a means of a more sustained response over several hours or days through the release of hormones. An example is when the parathyroid hormone continuously regulates

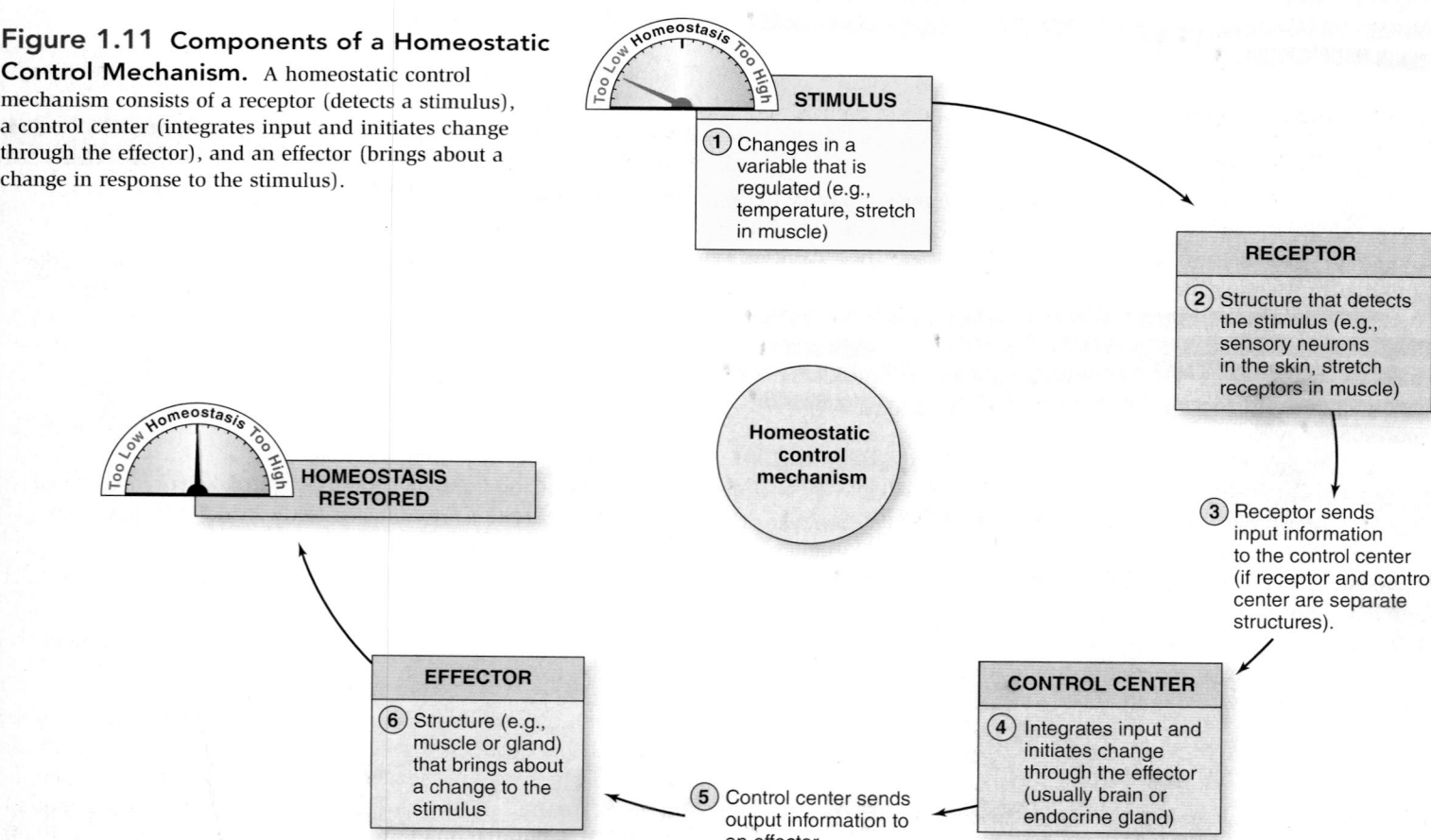

Figure 1.11 Components of a Homeostatic Control Mechanism. A homeostatic control mechanism consists of a receptor (detects a stimulus), a control center (integrates input and initiates change through the effector), and an effector (brings about a change in response to the stimulus).

STIMULUS
① Changes in a variable that is regulated (e.g., temperature, stretch in muscle)

RECEPTOR
② Structure that detects the stimulus (e.g., sensory neurons in the skin, stretch receptors in muscle)

③ Receptor sends input information to the control center (if receptor and control center are separate structures).

Homeostatic control mechanism

HOMEOSTASIS RESTORED

EFFECTOR
⑥ Structure (e.g., muscle or gland) that brings about a change to the stimulus

⑤ Control center sends output information to an effector.

CONTROL CENTER
④ Integrates input and initiates change through the effector (usually brain or endocrine gland)

blood calcium levels, a process that is essential for the normal function of both muscles and nerves. Note that the control center is sometimes the same structure as the receptor because it both detects the stimulus and causes a response to regulate it. For example, the pancreas acts as a receptor because it detects an increase in blood glucose and also acts as a control center because it releases the hormone insulin in response.

Effector

The **effector** is the structure that brings about the change to alter the stimulus. Most body structures can serve as effectors, including muscles—such as smooth muscles in the walls of air passageways (bronchioles) to regulate airflow into and out of the lungs—or glands, such as insulin-secreting cells of the pancreas.

As you view figure 1.11, notice that the response of a homeostatic system occurs through a feedback loop that includes the following:

- A stimulus
- The detection of the stimulus by a receptor
- Input information relayed to the control center (if a separate structure)
- Integration of the input by the control center and initiation of a change through effectors
- Return of homeostasis by the actions of effectors

Homeostatic control systems are separated into two broad categories based on whether the system maintains the variable within a normal range by moving the stimulus in the opposite direction, or amplifies the stimulus in the same direction. These two types of feedback control are called negative feedback and positive feedback, respectively.

 WHAT DID YOU LEARN?

 13 List and describe the three components of a homeostatic system, and give examples of each in the human body.

1.5b Homeostatic Systems Regulated by Negative Feedback

LEARNING OBJECTIVES

3. Define negative feedback.
4. Explain how homeostatic mechanisms regulated by negative feedback detect and respond to environmental changes.

Most processes in the body are controlled by negative feedback. If a homeostatic system is controlled by negative feedback, the resulting action will always be in the opposite direction of the stimulus. In this way, the variable is maintained with a normal level, or what is called its **set point.**

How a variable that is regulated by negative feedback fluctuates over time can be viewed in **figure 1.12**. Notice that the variable does not remain constant over time but rather it fluctuates, and its fluctuation occurs around the set point. If the stimulus increases, the homeostatic system is activated to cause a decrease in the stimulus until it returns to the set point. In contrast, if the stimulus decreases, the homeostatic system causes an increase in the stimulus until it returns to normal. This idea is generally better understood by describing a specific example, such as temperature regulation.

Temperature Regulation

We begin by first explaining how a negative feedback mechanism works to maintain the temperature of your home at a set point of 70°F. On a very cold day, the indoor temperature drops. This drop in temperature is detected by the thermostat. The drop in tempera-

Figure 1.12 Negative Feedback. Note that when a variable is regulated by negative feedback, the variable fluctuates around a set point (rather than being a constant).

ture is relayed through the electrical wiring of your home to the heat pump, which is then activated. The heat pump continues to heat your home until the thermostat reaches 70°F. An electrical signal is then sent from the thermostat to shut off the heat pump.

Body temperature is regulated in an analogous way to how the temperature of your home is regulated (**figure 1.13a**). If you venture outside on a cold day, body temperature may begin to drop. This decrease is detected by the sensory receptors of the skin, which send nerve impulses to the hypothalamus (a component of the brain). (The hypothalamus can also directly detect changes in body temperature by monitoring blood temperature as it passes through this region of the brain.) The hypothalamus alters nerve impulses to blood vessels in the skin to decrease the diameter of the inside opening (lumen) of the vessels, thus decreasing the amount of blood circulating to the surface of the body. As a result, less heat is released through the skin. Nerve impulses are also sent to skeletal muscles which cause shivering, and perhaps to smooth muscle associated with hair follicles of the skin, causing "goosebumps."

In contrast, on a very hot day (figure 1.13b), or when you are engaging in strenuous exercise, an increase in body temperature is detected by the sensory receptors of the skin or hypothalamus. Nerve impulses are altered to blood vessels of the skin to increase the lumen diameters of blood vessels so that additional blood is brought near the surface of the body for the release of heat through the skin. Nerve impulses are also sent from the hypothalamus to the sweat glands to initiate sweating. Both responses help cool the body by the loss of heat from its surface. In these examples, regulation occurs through the nervous system.

Other examples of homeostatic regulation through the nervous system include the withdrawal reflex in response to injury from stepping on glass or burning your hand (section 14.6), regulating heart rate and blood pressure when you exercise (section 20.5), or changing breathing rate in response to an increase in carbon dioxide levels (section 23.5).

Recall that the control center may also be the endocrine system. Examples of homeostatic systems that regulate through the endocrine system include the parathyroid gland release of parathyroid hormone in response to a decrease in blood calcium (section 7.6) or pancreas release of insulin in response to an increase in blood glucose (section 17.10).

 WHAT DID YOU LEARN?

 14 On a cold day, what are some of the strategies the body uses to conserve heat?

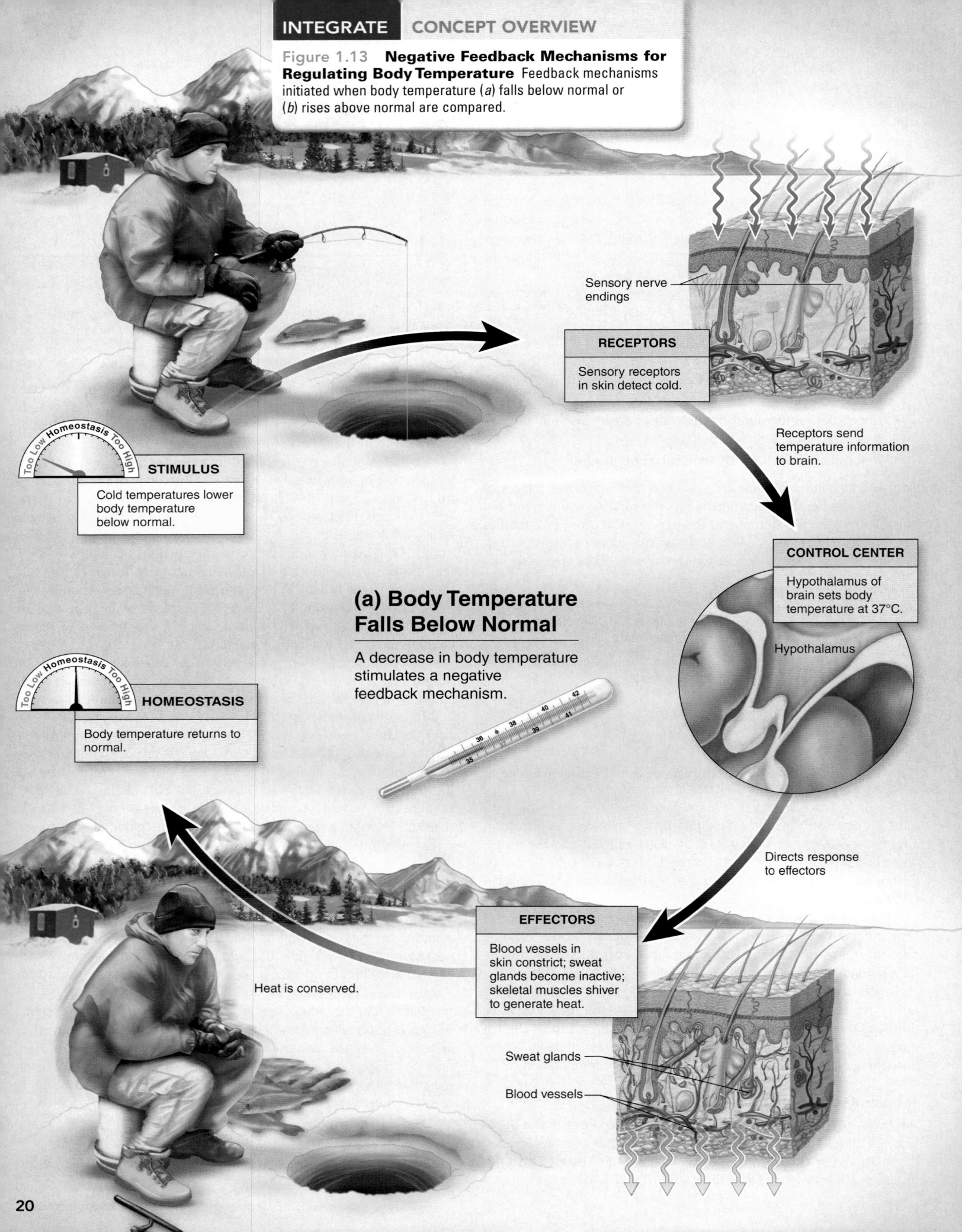

Figure 1.13 **Negative Feedback Mechanisms for Regulating Body Temperature** Feedback mechanisms initiated when body temperature (a) falls below normal or (b) rises above normal are compared.

RECEPTORS

Sensory receptors in skin detect cold.

Sensory nerve endings

Receptors send temperature information to brain.

STIMULUS

Cold temperatures lower body temperature below normal.

CONTROL CENTER

Hypothalamus of brain sets body temperature at 37°C.

Hypothalamus

(a) Body Temperature Falls Below Normal

A decrease in body temperature stimulates a negative feedback mechanism.

HOMEOSTASIS

Body temperature returns to normal.

Directs response to effectors

Heat is conserved.

EFFECTORS

Blood vessels in skin constrict; sweat glands become inactive; skeletal muscles shiver to generate heat.

Sweat glands

Blood vessels

Sensory nerve endings

RECEPTORS

Sensory receptors in skin and other organs detect heat.

Receptors send temperature information to brain.

STIMULUS

Vigorous exercise or hot temperatures raise body temperature above normal.

Too Low Homeostasis Too High

(b) Body Temperature Rises Above Normal

An increase in body temperature stimulates a negative feedback mechanism.

CONTROL CENTER

Hypothalamus of brain sets body temperature at 37°C.

Hypothalamus

Directs response to effectors

HOMEOSTASIS

Body temperature returns to normal.

Too Low Homeostasis Too High

Heat is given off.

EFFECTORS

Blood vessels in skin dilate; sweat glands secrete sweat, which, if evaporated, will cool the skin's surface.

Sweat

Sweat glands

Blood vessels

1.5c Homeostatic Systems Regulated by Positive Feedback

A homeostatic system may also be controlled by positive feedback. The stimulus here is reinforced to continue in the same direction until a climatic event occurs. Following the climatic event, the body again returns to homeostasis. Because their end result is to increase the activity (instead of initially returning the body to homeostasis), positive feedback mechanisms occur much less frequently than negative feedback mechanisms.

Figure 1.14 illustrates one example of a positive feedback mechanism in the human body, when a mother breast-feeds her baby. The baby suckling at the breast is the initial stimulus detected by sensory receptors in the skin of the nipple region. The receptors transmit this input to the control center, which is the hypothalamus of the brain. The hypothalamus signals the posterior pituitary to release the hormone oxytocin into the blood. Oxytocin is the "output" that is sent to the effector, which is the glandular tissue of the breast. Oxytocin stimulates the mammary gland to eject the breast milk. The baby feeds and the cycle repeats as long as the baby suckles. Once the baby stops suckling (and thus the initial stimulus is removed), then the cycle will stop.

Other examples of positive feedback mechanisms include the blood clotting cascade (see section 18.4) and uterine contractions involved in labor and childbirth (see section 29.6).

💡 WHAT DID YOU LEARN?

15 What is the main difference between a homeostatic system regulated by negative feedback versus positive feedback?

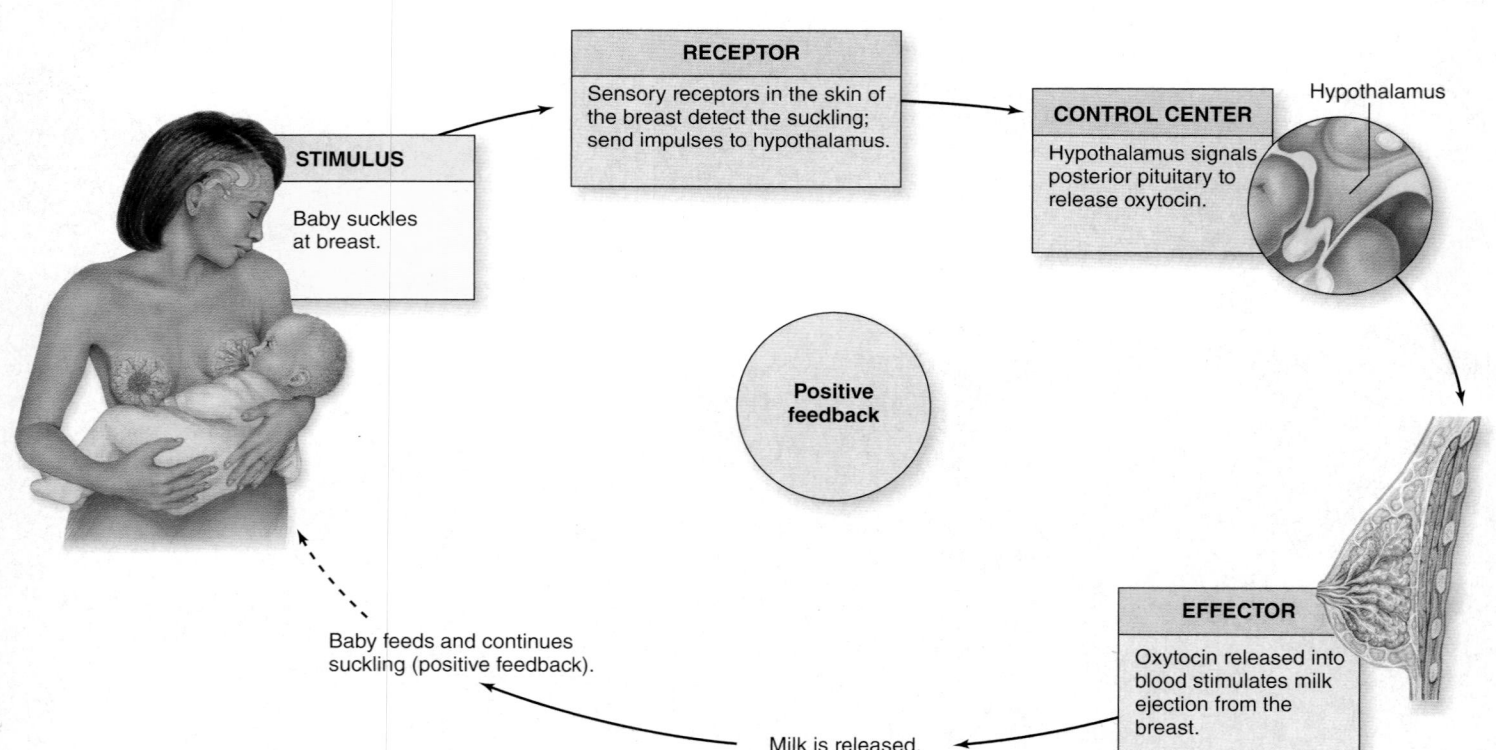

Figure 1.14 Positive Feedback. Positive feedback mechanisms often work in loops, where the initial step in the pathway is the stimulus, and the end product of the pathway is to stimulate (not turn off) the pathway activity. In this example of a mother breast-feeding her child, the stimulus of the baby suckling encourages release of hormones that stimulate the breast to secrete more breast milk.

1.6 Homeostasis, Health, and Disease

LEARNING OBJECTIVE

1. Explain the general relationship of maintaining homeostasis to health and disease.

In summary, homeostasis is a term that describes the many physiologic processes to maintain the health of the body. These characteristics are noted about homeostatic systems:

- They are dynamic.
- The control center is generally the nervous system or the endocrine system.
- There are three components: receptor, control center, and effector.
- They are typically regulated through negative feedback to maintain a normal value or set point.
- It is when these systems fail that a homeostatic imbalance or disease results, ultimately threatening an individual's survival.

Diabetes is an example of a homeostatic imbalance. Diabetes occurs when the homeostatic mechanisms for regulating blood glucose are not functioning normally, and blood glucose fluctuates out of the normal range, sometimes resulting in extremely high blood glucose readings. High blood glucose results in damage to anatomic structures throughout the body. Patients with diabetes must rely on other methods, such as diet restriction, exercise, and perhaps a medication to lower blood glucose.

Sometimes a homeostatic imbalance results when critical changes from aging or disease cause a variable that is normally controlled by negative feedback, to be abnormally controlled by positive feedback. An example is when there is extensive damage to the heart, perhaps from a heart attack. This heart is less able to pump blood to the structures of the body including the heart itself. Consequently, the heart receives reduced amounts of nutrients and oxygen. The heart becomes progressively weaker, and even less able to pump blood to the body's structure. Ultimately, the heart becomes so weak that the heart stops beating.

Treating patients generally involves determining a **diagnosis,** or the specific cause of the homeostatic imbalance. Once diagnosed, the patient is treated through the administration of medications or through other therapeutic avenues to facilitate the body in maintaining homeostasis.

Health-care practitioners also need to understand how the drugs patients are taking may affect the normal homeostatic control mechanisms. For example, one type of medication for the treatment of depression is an SSRI, which stands for selective serotonin reuptake inhibitor. Paroxetine (Paxil), fluoxetine (Prozac), and sertraline (Zoloft) are examples of SSRIs. Serotonin is a type of neurotransmitter. Normally, a neurotransmitter is released from one nerve cell in response to a nerve impulse. The neurotransmitter accomplishes its communication task, and then is taken up again by the nerve cell for future use. Some depressed individuals may have lower levels of serotonin, so an SSRI blocks the reuptake of serotonin into the nerve cell. Therefore, serotonin stays outside the nerve cell for a longer period of time and its effects are prolonged, which may elevate the mood of the patient taking the SSRI.

However, like all drugs, SSRIs come with some drawbacks. Some SSRI side effects include digestive system distress, such as nausea, upset stomach, diarrhea, or combinations of all three. As it turns out, serotonin is also used in the nerve cells of the digestive system. By tinkering with the serotonin reuptake in the brain, the drug also affects serotonin reuptake in the digestive system. Essentially, the digestive system becomes a bit more excitable due to the intake of the SSRI drug, with the symptoms just described.

Virtually all medications have some benefits and some side effects, many of which can be explained by examining the homeostatic control mechanisms with which they interact. Thus, an understanding of these mechanisms is a must for anatomists, physiologists, and health-care practitioners.

WHAT DID YOU LEARN?

16 What is an example of a disease process by which homeostasis is disrupted?

CLINICAL VIEW
Medical Imaging

Health-care professionals have taken advantage of sophisticated medical imaging techniques to extend their ability to visualize internal body structures noninvasively (e.g., without inserting an instrument into the body). Some of the most common techniques are radiography, sonography, computed tomography, digital subtraction angiography, dynamic spatial reconstruction, magnetic resonance imaging, and positron emission tomography.

Radiograph (x-ray) of the head and neck.

Radiography

Radiography (rā-dē-og'ra-fē; *radius* = ray, *grapho* = to write) is the primary method of obtaining an image of a body part for diagnostic purposes. A beam of **x-rays,** a form of high-energy radiation, penetrates solid structures within the body. X-rays can pass through soft tissues but they are absorbed by dense tissues, including bone, teeth, and tumors. Film images produced by x-rays passing through soft tissues leave the film lighter in the areas where x-rays are absorbed. Hollow organs can be visualized if they are filled with a radiopaque (rā-dē-ō-pāk; *opacus* = shady) substance that absorbs x-rays.

The term x-ray also applies to the photograph (radiograph) made by this technique. Radiography is commonly used in dentistry, mammography, diagnosis of fractures, and chest examination. Disadvantages of x-rays are that they are difficult to interpret when organs overlap in the images, and they are unable to reveal slight differences in tissue density. In addition, the radiation of an x-ray is not without risk.

Sonography

The second most widely used imaging method is **sonography** (sŏ-nog'ră-fē; *sonus* = sound; *grapho* = to write), also known as *ultrasound*. A technician slowly moves a small, hand-held device across the body's surface. This device produces high-frequency ultrasound waves and then receives

Sonogram of a fetus.

signals that are reflected from internal organs. The image produced is called a *sonogram*. Sonography is the method of choice in obstetrics, where a sonogram can examine the fetus and evaluate fetal age, position, and development. Sonography avoids the harmful effects of x-rays, and the equipment is inexpensive and portable. Until recently, its primary disadvantage was that it did not produce a very sharp image, but technological advances are now markedly improving the images produced.

When radiography or sonography fail to produce the desired images, other more detailed but much more expensive imaging techniques are available.

Computed Tomography (CT)

A **computed tomography (CT)** (tō'mō-graf-ē; *tomos* = a section) scan, previously termed a computerized axial tomography (CAT) scan, is a more sophisticated application of x-rays. A patient is slowly moved through a cylindrical, doughnut-shaped machine while low-intensity x-rays are emitted on one side the cylinder, passed through the body, collected by detectors, and then processed and analyzed by a computer. These signals produce an image of the body that is about the thickness of a dime. Continuous thin "slices" can be used to reconstruct a three-dimensional image of the body. Little overlap of organs occurs in these thin sections, and the image is much sharper than one obtained by a conventional x-ray. CT scanning is useful for identifying tumors, aneurysms, kidney stones, cerebral hemorrhages, and other abnormalities.

Computed tomography (CT) scan of the head at the level of the eyes.

Digital Subtraction Angiography (DSA)

Digital subtraction angiography (DSA) is a modified three-dimensional x-ray technique used primarily to observe blood vessels. It involves taking radiographs both prior to and after injecting an opaque medium into a blood vessel. The computer compares the before and after images, and removes or subtracts the data from the before image from the data generated by the after image, thus leaving an image that may indicate evidence of vessel blockages. DSA is useful in the procedure in which a physician directs a catheter through a blood vessel and puts a stent in the area where a blood vessel is blocked. The image produced by the DSA allows the physician to accurately guide the catheter to the blockage.

Dynamic Spatial Reconstruction (DSR)

Using modified CT scanners, a special technique called **dynamic spatial reconstruction (DSR)** provides two important pieces of medical information: (1) three-dimensional images of body organs, and (2) information about the normal organ movement as well as changes in its internal volume. Unlike traditional static CAT scans, DSR allows the physician to observe the movement of an organ. This type of observation, at slow speed or halted in time completely, has been invaluable in observations of the heart and the flow of blood through blood vessels.

Digital subtraction angiography (DSA) shows three-dimensional images of blood vessels and normal changes in these vessels.

Positron Emission Tomography (PET)

The **positron emission tomography (PET)** scan is used both to analyze the metabolic state of a tissue at a given moment in time and to determine which tissues are most active. The procedure begins with an injection of radioactively labeled glucose (sugar), which emits particles called positrons (like electrons, but with a positive charge). Collisions between a positron and electron cause the release of gamma rays that can be detected by sensors and analyzed by computer. The result is a brilliant color image that shows which tissues were using the most glucose at that moment. In cardiology, the image can reveal the extent of damaged heart tissue—because damaged heart tissue consumes little or no glucose, the damaged tissue will appear dark. PET scans have also been used to illustrate activity levels in the brain. Recently, PET scans also have been used to detect whether certain cancers have metastasized throughout the body, because cancerous cells will take up more glucose and show up as a "hot spot" on the scan. The PET scan is an example of nuclear medicine, which uses radioactive isotopes to form anatomic images of the body.

Magnetic Resonance Imaging (MRI)

Magnetic resonance imaging (MRI), previously called *nuclear magnetic resonance (NMR) imaging,* was developed as a noninvasive technique to visualize soft tissues. The patient is placed in a supine position within a cylindrical chamber that is surrounded by a large electromagnet. The magnet generates a strong magnetic field that causes protons in the nuclei of hydrogen atoms in the tissues to align. Thereafter, upon exposure to radio waves, the protons absorb additional energy and align in a different direction. The hydrogen atoms then abruptly realign themselves to the magnetic field immediately after the radio waves are turned off. This results in the release of the atoms' excess energy at different rates, depending on the type of tissue. A computer analyzes the emitted energy to produce an image of the body. MRI is better than CT for distinguishing between soft tissues, such as the white and gray matter of the nervous system.

Positron emission tomography (PET) scan of the brain of an unmedicated schizophrenic patient. Red areas indicate high glucose use (metabolic activity). The visual center at the posterior region of the brain was especially active when the scan was made.

Magnetic resonance imaging (MRI) scan of the head at the level of the eyes.

However, dense structures (e.g., bone) do not show up well in MRI. Formerly, another disadvantage of MRI was that patients felt claustrophobic while isolated in the closed cylinder. However, newer MRI technology has improved the hardware and lessened this effect.

Recent advances in MRI, called **functional MRI (fMRI),** provide the means to map brain function based on local oxygen concentration differences in blood flow. Increased blood flow relates to increased brain activity.

CHAPTER SUMMARY

- Anatomy is the study of structure and form of the human body, while physiology is the study of function of these parts.

1.1a Anatomy: Details of Form   2
- Anatomy may be subdivided into microscopic anatomy (anatomic study of materials using the microscope) and gross anatomy (the study of structures visible to the unaided eye).

1.1b Physiology: Details of Function   3
- Physiologists may examine the function of specific body systems (e.g., cardiovascular physiology) and may focus on problems or pathologies of such systems (pathophysiology).

- Form and function are interrelated. Anatomists cannot gain a full appreciation of anatomic form without first understanding the structure's function. Likewise, physiologists cannot fully appreciate body functions without learning about the structure's form.
- It is easiest to learn anatomy and physiology by integrating the two disciplines, rather than trying to separate the study of form from the study of function.

- Scientists group the body's components into an organizational hierarchy of form and function.

1.3a Characteristics That Describe Living Things   6
- All living organisms exhibit several common properties: organization, metabolism, growth and development, responsiveness, adaptation, and reproduction.

1.3b The View from Simplest to Most Complex   6
- Anatomic structure is organized in an increasingly complex series of levels: the chemical level, cellular level, tissue level, organ level, organ system level, and the organismal level.

1.3c Introduction to Organ Systems   7
- The human body contains 11 organ systems: integumentary, skeletal, muscular, nervous, endocrine, cardiovascular, lymphatic, respiratory, urinary, digestive, and reproductive.

- Clear, exact terminology accurately describes body structures and helps us identify and locate them.

1.4a Anatomic Position   11
- The anatomic position is used as a standard reference point for the human body.

1.4b Sections and Planes   12
- Three planes section the body and help describe relationships among the parts of the three-dimensional human body: the coronal plane, the transverse plane, and the midsagittal plane.

1.4c Anatomic Directions   13
- Specific directional terms indicate body structure locations.

1.4d Regional Anatomy   13
- Specific anatomic terms identify body regions.

1.4e Body Cavities and Membranes   14
- Body cavities are spaces that enclose organs and organ systems.
- The posterior aspect of the body contains the cranial cavity and the vertebral canal.
- The ventral cavity is subdivided into a thoracic cavity (which is partitioned into pleural cavities, mediastinum, and pericardial cavity) and an abdominopelvic cavity (which is partitioned into an abdominal cavity and a pelvic cavity).
- The ventral cavity is lined by thin serous membranes. A parietal layer lines the internal body wall surface, and a visceral layer covers the organs.

1.4f Abdominopelvic Regions and Quadrants   17
- Regions and quadrants are two aids for describing locations of the abdominopelvic viscera.
- There are nine abdominopelvic regions and four abdominopelvic quadrants.

- Homeostasis refers to the body's ability to maintain a relatively stable internal environment, even in the face of changing internal or external environmental factors.

1.5a Components of Homeostatic Systems   18
- The three components are the receptor (detects a stimulus), control center (interprets input from the receptor and initiates changes through the effector), and effector (the structure that brings about a change to the stimulus).

1.5b Homeostatic Systems Regulated by Negative Feedback   19
- Negative feedback mechanisms or loops are initiated by a stimulus, and the end result is to inhibit or slow down the stimulus. Most feedback mechanisms in the human body work by negative feedback.

1.5c Homeostatic Systems Regulated by Positive Feedback   22
- Positive feedback mechanisms are initiated by a stimulus, and they maintain or increase the activity of the original stimulus.

- An understanding of the concept of homeostasis is essential when understanding the structure and function of a normal, healthy body, the mechanisms of disease, and how the body reacts to pharmaceutical agents.

CHALLENGE YOURSELF

Do You Know the Basics?

_____ 1. Examining the superficial anatomic markings and internal body structures as they relate to the covering skin is called
   - a. regional anatomy.
   - b. surface anatomy.
   - c. pathologic anatomy.
   - d. comparative anatomy.

_____ 2. The _____ level of organization is composed of two or more tissue types that work together to perform a common function.
   - a. cellular
   - b. molecular
   - c. organ
   - d. organismal

_____ 3. The term _____ refers to the sum of all chemical reactions in the body.
   - a. metabolism
   - b. responsiveness
   - c. stimulus
   - d. reproduction

_____ 4. A midsagittal plane separates the body into
   - a. anterior and posterior portions.
   - b. superior and inferior portions.
   - c. right and left halves.
   - d. unequal right and left portions.

_____ 5. The term used to describe an appendage structure that is closest to its point of attachment to the trunk is
   - a. distal.
   - b. lateral.
   - c. superior.
   - d. proximal.

_____ 6. The _____ region is the anterior part of the knee.
   - a. patellar
   - b. popliteal
   - c. pes
   - d. inguinal

_____ 7. Which body cavity is located inferior to the diaphragm and superior to a horizontal line drawn between the superior edges of the hip bones?
   - a. abdominal cavity
   - b. pelvic cavity
   - c. pleural cavity
   - d. pericardial cavity

_____ 8. The _____ is the serous membrane layer that covers the surface of the lungs.
   - a. parietal pleura
   - b. visceral pericardium
   - c. visceral peritoneum
   - d. visceral pleura

_____ 9. The state of maintaining a constant internal environment within an organism is called
   - a. reproduction.
   - b. homeostasis.
   - c. imbalance.
   - d. life.

_____ 10. In a negative feedback mechanism, which of the following events does _not_ occur?
   - a. A stimulus is a change in some variable (e.g., rise in blood glucose levels).
   - b. A receptor perceives a stimulus.
   - c. The control center sends output to an effector.
   - d. The effector stimulates or increases the stimulus, so the cycle continues.

11. What are the similarities and differences between anatomy and physiology?

12. List the levels of organization in a human, starting at the simplest level and proceeding to the most complex. Give an example of a structure in each level.

13. What properties are common to all living things?

14. Name the organ systems in the human body.

15. Describe the body in the anatomic position. Why is the anatomic position used?

16. List the anatomic term that describes each of the following regions: forearm, wrist, chest, armpit, thigh, and foot.

17. What are the two body cavities within the posterior aspect, and what does each cavity contain?

18. Describe the structure and function of serous membranes in the body.

19. What are the main components in a homeostatic control system?

20. Compare and contrast negative and positive feedback mechanisms.

Can You Apply What You've Learned?

Use the following paragraph to answer questions 1–3.

Your friend Eric complains of some pain in his "belly area." You ask him to point to the precise location of the pain. He points to a region that is below his umbilicus, on the lower right side of his abdomen, and just medial to his hip bones.

1. Which abdominal quadrant contains Eric's pain?
   a. Right upper quadrant
   b. Right lower quadrant
   c. Left upper quadrant
   d. Left lower quadrant

2. You also could describe the pain as being in the _____ abdominopelvic region.
   a. right lumbar
   b. right hypochondriac
   c. right umbilical
   d. right iliac region

3. Eric goes to the doctor to determine the cause and source of the pain. The physician orders a CT scan, which shows that Eric has an enlarged and inflamed appendix (an organ associated with the digestive system). Eric asks the physician why she didn't just take an x-ray of his belly region. She explains an x-ray would not be the best diagnostic imaging tool in this case because
   a. x-ray images are more expensive to produce than CT scans.
   b. soft-tissue structures don't show up well on basic x-rays.
   c. the x-rays could inflame the appendix further and cause it to burst.
   d. x-rays now are used primarily for bone injuries only.

4. When you are outside on a hot, humid day, what body changes occur to help your body temperature return to normal?
   a. The blood vessels in your skin constrict.
   b. The sweat glands release sweat.
   c. Nerve impulses are sent to muscles to cause shivering.
   d. The smooth muscle associated with hair follicles contracts, causing goosebumps.

5. A friend just started taking Zoloft (an SSRI) and is experiencing an upset stomach and diarrhea. Your friend asks if the drug is causing her symptoms and you respond:
   a. Yes, because the drug is irritating her stomach lining and that explains her symptoms.
   b. Yes, because serotonin is located both in the brain and the digestive tract, so the drug is altering digestive system functioning.
   c. No, because the drug is supposed to elevate mood and affect brain function, and it shouldn't have any effect on the digestive system.
   d. No, because the drug is quickly absorbed from the digestive tract and does not remain in the digestive system long enough to have any effect there.

Can You Synthesize What You've Learned?

1. Lynn was knocked off her bicycle during a race. She broke some bones in her right antebrachial region, suffered an abrasion on her mental region, and had severe bruising on her right gluteal and femoral regions. Explain where each of these injuries is located.

2. Carly was stung by a bee and was taken to the emergency room because she was undergoing anaphylactic shock (e.g., her breathing became more rapid and more difficult, her heartbeat increased). She was given a shot of epinephrine, which reduced her allergic reactions and brought her breathing and heartbeat back to normal. Did the dose of epinephrine result in a negative feedback mechanism occurring, or a positive feedback mechanism occurring? Explain your answer.

3. Your grandmother is being seen by a radiologist to diagnose a possible tumor in her small intestine. Explain to your grandmother what imaging techniques would best determine whether a tumor exists, and which techniques would be inadequate for determining the placement of the tumor.

INTEGRATE

ONLINE STUDY TOOLS
www.mhhe.com/mckinleyap

Clinical Case Study: A Clinical Case of Hyperthermia in an Athlete

Interactive Questions: This chapter's content is served up in a number of multimedia question formats for student study.

LearnSmart: Topics and terminology include anatomy and physiology and details of form and function; the body's levels of organization; terminology for anatomic position, sections, and planes; homeostasis, health, and disease

Anatomy & Physiology Revealed: Topics include organ systems, planes of section, directional terms, body regions, body cavities, pleura and pericardium; abdominal quadrants and regions

Animations: Topics include DNA hybridization, lysosomes, mutations, positive and negative feedback

chapter 2

Atoms, Ions, and Molecules

We describe many fascinating physiologic processes of the human body in later chapters, including the transmission of an impulse along a nerve, the transport of oxygen in the blood, and nutrient digestion in the gastrointestinal tract. By reading and comprehending the material in this chapter on atoms, ions, and molecules—and information on energy, enzymes, and metabolism in chapter 3—you will develop a working knowledge of the basic chemical concepts needed to understand these ➡

A chemist knows about the properties and composition of matter. She is a scientist involved in the study of events that occur during experiments that have a chemical reaction. She must use the scientific method that is a body of techniques to acquire new knowledge or investigate unknown phenomena. The chemist must plan all steps in the experiment and learn how to propose a hypothesis and test it. Acquired experience permits the chemist to predict and test for specific results.

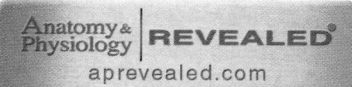
apⁿrevealed.com

Anatomy & Physiology | REVEALED

Module 2:
Cells and Chemistry

processes. We will refer back to these concepts throughout the rest of the text, so that you'll more easily see the connections between chemistry and life processes.

Our coverage of chemistry is not comprehensive. Rather, our discussion is tailored to focus primarily on chemical structures relevant to the study of anatomy and physiology, and we have included examples of their application in the human body. The general characteristics of atoms, ions, and molecules are presented in the earlier sections of this chapter. Then we describe specific molecules, including water and water mixtures, and the four major organic biological macromolecules: lipids, carbohydrates, nucleic acids, and proteins. The chapter concludes with a section devoted to proteins, the most versatile macromolecules of living systems. Now, let's embark upon an adventure to explore the body's simplest constituents: atoms and molecules.

2.1 Atomic Structure

The human body at its simplest level of organization is composed of chemical structures that include atoms, ions, and molecules. We begin our discussion on the human body's chemical composition by describing matter, atoms, elements, and the position of each element in the periodic table. This information allows us to make certain predictions regarding the chemical properties of each element, including whether and how the element forms ions and molecules.

2.1a Matter, Atoms, Elements, and the Periodic Table

LEARNING OBJECTIVES

1. Define matter, and list its three forms.
2. Describe and differentiate among the subatomic particles that compose atoms.
3. Explain the arrangement of elements in the periodic table based on atomic number.
4. Diagram the structure of an atom.

The human body is composed of **matter,** generally defined as a substance that has mass and occupies space. Matter is present in the body in three forms: solid, liquid, and gas. For example, bone is a solid, blood is a liquid, and oxygen (O_2) and carbon dioxide (CO_2) are gases.

All matter is composed of atoms. An **atom** is the smallest particle that exhibits the chemical properties of an **element.** There are 92 naturally occurring elements. Hydrogen is the smallest and lightest element; uranium is the largest and heaviest element. Technical advances both in chemistry and physics have resulted in the ability to produce "ultraheavy" elements that are larger than uranium. All elements, including the scientifically manufactured elements, are organized into chart form in the **periodic table of elements** (figure 2.1a).

Elements are grouped into major, lesser, and trace elements based on the percentage each composes by weight in the human body. Major elements comprise over 98% and lesser elements less than 1% (figure 2.1b). In comparison, trace elements appear in the body in only limited amounts (less than 0.01%). Only 12 elements occur in living organisms in greater than trace amounts: oxygen, carbon, hydrogen, nitrogen, calcium, phosphorus, sulfur, potassium, sodium, chlorine, magnesium, and iron. All of these elements except iron have atomic numbers (described shortly) between 1 and 20 in the periodic table. Consequently, our emphasis in this chapter will be on only the first 20 elements.

Note in figure 2.1a that the 12 common elements are elevated above the other elements. Each element is color-coded, and these color-codes are used throughout the text.

The Components of an Atom

Atoms are composed of three **subatomic particles:** neutrons, protons, and electrons (figure 2.2). Two major criteria differentiate subatomic particles—namely, mass and charge. The mass of an atom is expressed as the **atomic mass unit (amu)**, or dalton. (The mass of a subatomic particle is very small: consider that 1 amu is equal to 1.66×10^{-27} kilograms.)

Neutrons and protons each have a mass of 1 amu. A **neutron** is uncharged (meaning it is neutral), whereas a **proton** has a positive charge of one ($+1$). Neutrons and protons compose almost the entire mass or weight of an atom and are located at the center, or core, of the atom, called the **atomic nucleus.** The atomic nucleus contains mass because it has both neutrons and protons, and it is positively charged because of the protons.

The **electron** is the third component of an atom. An electron has a very small mass—only about 1/1800th of the mass of a proton or neutron—and makes a negligible contribution to total mass. Each electron has a negative charge of one (-1). Electrons are located at varying distances from the nucleus in regions called *orbitals*, often depicted as either an electron cloud or as discrete energy shells. Both the cloud model and shell model indicate where the electrons are most likely found.

The Periodic Table

Elements differ in the number of subatomic particles. The periodic table may be used to obtain the number of subatomic particles in an atom of a specific element. Several important parameters for each element appear in the periodic table, including the element's symbol, atomic number, and average atomic mass.

A unique **chemical symbol** has been assigned to each element. An element is usually identified either by its first letter, or by its first letter plus an additional letter that is based on its English name. For example, H is for hydrogen, C is for carbon, and O is for oxygen. If more than one element begins with the same letter, the symbol will also include a second letter written in lowercase (e.g., He for helium and Cl for chlorine). The symbol of some elements, in rare cases, is derived from their Latin name. For instance, the symbol for sodium is Na (natrium) and potassium is K (kalium).

The **atomic number** of an element indicates the number of protons in an atom of that element and is located above its symbol

(a)

Figure 2.1 Periodic Table of Elements.
(*a*) The periodic table includes all of the elements arranged in chart form. The grayed out boxes at the bottom of the table are for proposed elements that as of yet do not have sufficient evidence to support their official inclusion as elements. (*b*) Twelve of the elements that compose the human body are present in greater than trace amounts. These twelve elements are color coded in both (*a*) and (*b*), and this color scheme is used throughout the book to represent these elements.

Most Common Elements of the Human Body

Major elements (collectively compose more than 98% of body weight)			Lesser elements (collectively compose less than 1% of body weight)		
Symbol		% Body weight	Symbol		% Body weight
O	Oxygen	65.0	S	Sulfur	0.25
C	Carbon	18.0	K	Potassium	0.20
H	Hydrogen	10.0	Na	Sodium	0.15
N	Nitrogen	3.0	Cl	Chlorine	0.15
Ca	Calcium	1.5	Mg	Magnesium	0.05
P	Phosphorus	1.0	Fe	Iron	0.006

(b)

in the periodic table. Note that elements are arranged by atomic number in consecutive order within rows (figure 2.1*a*). The atomic number is designated as a subscript at the left of the chemical symbol when it is written. For example, $_1$H shows that the nucleus of a hydrogen atom has one proton, and $_6$C indicates that the carbon nucleus has six protons.

The **average atomic mass** indicates the mass of both protons and neutrons in the atomic nucleus, and it reflects the "heaviness" of an element's atoms relative to atoms of other elements. (The electrons are not included because they are so "light.") It is shown below the element's symbol on the periodic table. The average atomic mass is rounded to the nearest whole number and it is designated by a superscript to the left of the chemical symbol when it is written. For example, a sodium atom, with an atomic number of 11 and an average atomic mass of 22.99, is designated as $_{11}^{23}$Na.

WHAT DO YOU THINK?

1 How would the chemical shorthand for oxygen be written?

(a)   (b)

Nucleus: ○ Proton (+)   **Electron shells:** ○ Electron (−)
● Neutron (no charge)

Figure 2.2 General Atomic Structure. Oxygen atoms are depicted with protons and neutrons in the nucleus. Electrons are shown in both a cloud model (*a*) and an energy shell model (*b*). AP|R

LEARNING STRATEGY

To diagram an atom, the number of protons, neutrons, and electrons must be known. How these are determined can be summarized as follows:

- Proton number (p) = Atomic number
- Neutron number (n) = Atomic mass (p + n) – atomic number (p)
- Electron number (e) = Proton number (p)

Determining the Number of Subatomic Particles

The number of each type of subatomic particle is determined as follows:

- The **number of protons** is the atomic number—thus, carbon has six protons and oxygen has eight protons.

- The **number of neutrons** can be determined by subtracting the atomic number (number of protons) from the atomic mass (protons and neutrons). For example, to calculate the number of neutrons in sodium ($^{23}_{11}$Na), recognize that there are a total of 23 protons and neutrons, and the number of protons = 11; thus, sodium has 12 neutrons.

- The **number of electrons** in an atom is determined indirectly by the atomic number. This is possible because all atoms are *neutral*. The number of negatively charged electrons must equal the number of positively charged protons for an atom to be neutral. Each electron has a charge of –1 and counters the +1 charge of a proton in the nucleus—therefore, the atom has zero charge, meaning it has no net charge. Atoms that have lost or gained electron(s) do not have the same number of protons and electrons and are referred to as ions (described later).

Diagramming Atomic Structures

An atom is represented as having shells of electrons that surround the atomic nucleus. The electrons within a shell have a given energy level. Each shell can hold only a limited number of electrons. The innermost shell may hold up to two electrons and the second shell up to eight electrons. All subsequent shells have a capacity of eight electrons but may also house more than eight electrons (the conditions for when the third and higher shells hold more than eight electrons are beyond our purposes here). The electron shells closest to the nucleus must be filled prior to filling any potential shells at some greater distance from the nucleus when diagramming an atom. Figure 2.2 shows the placement of protons and neutrons within the nucleus and electrons in specific shells for the atomic structure of oxygen.

WHAT DID YOU LEARN?

1 What subatomic particles determine the mass of an atom? What subatomic particles determine the charge of an atom?

2 Diagram the atomic structure of chlorine—atomic number is 17 and the mass number is 35.

2.1b Isotopes

LEARNING OBJECTIVES

5. Describe an isotope.

6. Explain how radioisotopes differ from other types of isotopes.

CLINICAL VIEW

Medical Imaging of the Thyroid Gland Using Iodine Radioisotopes

Radioisotopes including ^{14}C, ^{32}P, and ^{123}I have been extensively used in basic biology research efforts, medical investigations, and diagnoses. Radioisotopes introduced into the body during medical procedures are used by cells in a manner similar to a substance that is a nonradioisotope (e.g., ^{12}C, ^{31}P, and ^{127}I). Thus, products of metabolic reactions that use these elements may be traced and quantified by the high-energy radiation the radioisotopes emit. Individuals who work with radioactive materials must protect themselves from the potentially damaging high-energy radiation that may harm living cells and produce genetic damage. The image below is of a thyroid gland that has taken up radioactive ^{123}I. The entire thyroid appears whitish. The darker colored area is a benign nodule that is less metabolically active than the surrounding thyroid tissue.

Thyroid gland

Benign nodule

Elements in nature usually occur as a mixture of isotopes. **Isotopes** are different atoms of the same element that have the same number of protons and electrons but differ in the number of neutrons. Isotopes exhibit essentially identical chemical characteristics but have different atomic masses.

For example, carbon exists in three isotopes: carbon-12, carbon-13, and carbon-14 **(figure 2.3)**. All isotopes of carbon have six protons in their nuclei—however, carbon-12 has six neutrons, carbon-13 has seven neutrons, and carbon-14 has eight neutrons. Generally, one isotope is usually more prevalent than the others. Carbon-12 is the most prevalent isotope for carbon.

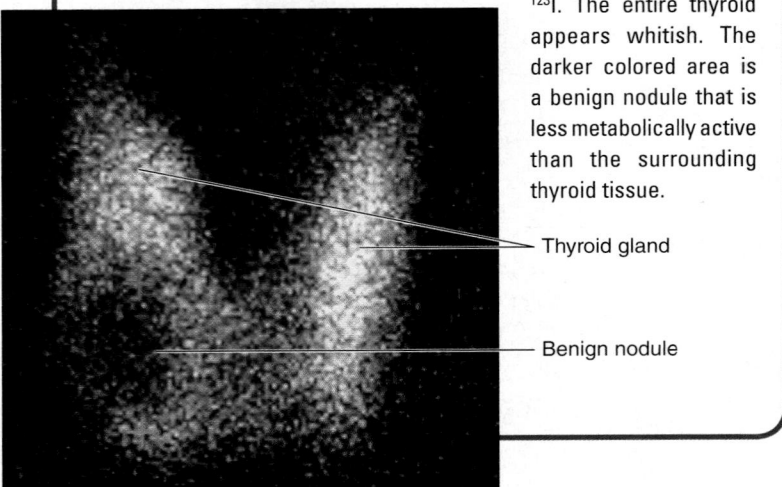

Carbon-12	Carbon-13	Carbon-14
6 protons 6 neutrons 6 electrons	6 protons 7 neutrons 6 electrons	6 protons 8 neutrons 6 electrons

Figure 2.3 The Three Most Common Carbon Isotopes.
Notice that all three carbon isotopes contain the same number of protons and electrons but have different numbers of neutrons.

The weighted average of the atomic mass for all isotopes of an element is the average atomic mass. This value is included on the periodic table below each element. The average atomic mass for carbon, for example, is 12.01 amu.

Some isotopes are referred to as **radioisotopes.** They are unstable because they contain an excess number of neutrons. Radioisotopes usually lose nuclear components in the form of high-energy radiation that includes alpha particles, beta particles, or gamma rays as they decay or break down into a more stable isotope. The time it takes for 50% of the radioisotope to become stable is its **physical half-life.** This time may vary from a few hours to thousands of years. Radioisotopes produced in a nuclear power plant, for example, have a half-life of at least 10,000 years. In comparison, the time required for half of the radioactive material (e.g., from a medical test using radioactive contrast material) to be eliminated from the body is the **biological half-life.** Biological half-life is also applied to substances that are nonradioactive, such as hormones or drugs (see section 17.4).

WHAT DID YOU LEARN?

3 Do isotopes represent the same element? Do they have the same number of protons, neutrons, or electrons? Describe a radioisotope.

2.1c Chemical Stability and the Octet Rule

LEARNING OBJECTIVES

7. Describe how elements are organized in the periodic table based on the valence electron number.

8. State the octet rule.

Recall that the periodic table is organized into rows based on atomic number. It is also organized into columns based on the number of elec-

trons in the outer shell, or what is referred to as the *valence shell.* This organization is presented in **figure 2.4**, showing the atomic structure of elements 1 to 20 arranged as they appear in a periodic table. Column IA shows hydrogen, lithium, sodium, and potassium: All the atomic structures of these elements contain one electron in their outer shell. Each consecutive column thereafter (columns IIA–VIIIA) has one additional electron in its outer shell for each element in that column. This organization allows us to make predictions about the chemical characteristics of a given element simply by its location in the periodic table.

Notice that the elements in column VIIIA each have a valence shell that is full or complete. These elements (only helium, neon, and argon are shown in figure 2.4) have an outermost shell housing eight electrons, except for helium, which has only two electrons. A complete outer shell results in chemical stability. These stable atoms are chemically inert and do not combine with other elements. The atoms in column VIIIA are referred to as *noble gases* because they do not react with the "common" elements in the rest of the periodic table.

Examine the atomic structure of the other elements of the periodic table and observe that they lack a full outer shell with eight electrons. These elements tend to lose, gain, or share electrons to obtain a complete outer shell. Chemists call this tendency the **octet rule:** Atoms obtain an outer shell with eight electrons and gain chemical stability through the loss, gain, or sharing of electrons. Not all elements follow the octet rule, but it is accurate for our purposes here. Ions are formed from the loss or gain of electrons, and covalently bonded molecules are formed by the sharing of electrons. We describe the formation of ions and covalently bonded molecules in the next two sections.

WHAT DID YOU LEARN?

4 What is the relationship of the octet rule and chemical stability?

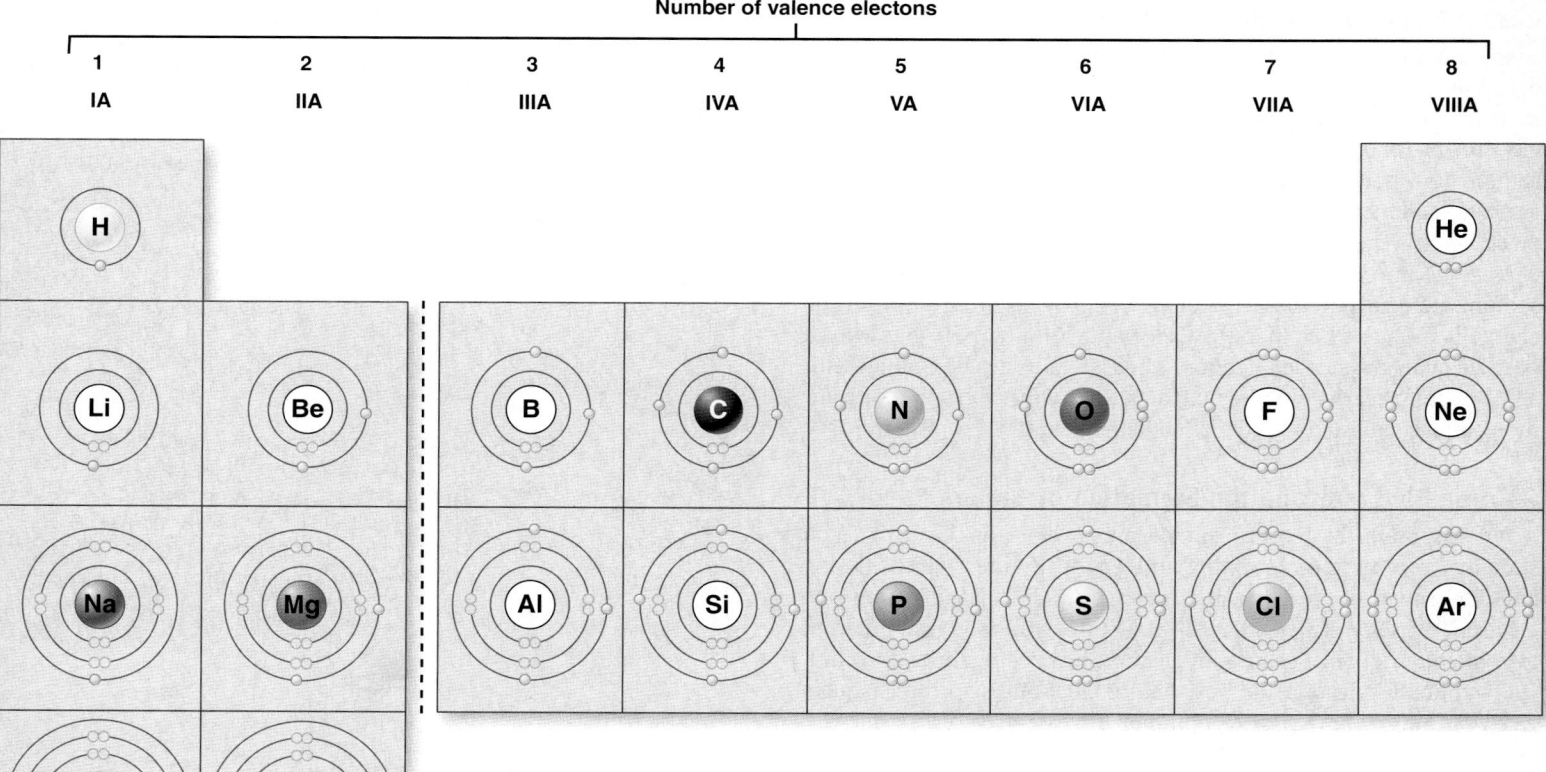

Number of valence electrons

1	2	3	4	5	6	7	8
IA	IIA	IIIA	IVA	VA	VIA	VIIA	VIIIA

Figure 2.4 Organization of the Periodic Table Based on Valence Shell Electrons. The atomic structures of elements 1 to 20 of the periodic table are depicted, showing the nucleus and electrons in energy shells. The valence shell electrons are shown in yellow. Valence shell number increases by one in each column as you move from left to right from columns IA through VIIIA.

2.2 Ions and Ionic Compounds

The body consists mostly of chemical compounds. **Chemical compounds** are stable associations between two or more elements combined in a fixed ratio. These associations are classified as either ionic compounds or molecular compounds. Here we describe ionic compounds, which are structures composed of ions that are held together in a lattice by ionic bonds. We first define ions and list some common ions of the human body, then explain how ions are formed and their charge determined, and finally we describe ionic bonds and the electrostatic interaction between ions within an ionic compound. Molecular compounds are described later in the chapter.

2.2a Ions

LEARNING OBJECTIVES

1. Define an ion.
2. List some common ions in the body.
3. Differentiate between cations and anions.
4. Describe how charges are assigned to ions.

Ions are atoms or groups of atoms with either a positive charge or a negative charge. They are produced from the loss or gain of an electron or electrons. **Table 2.1** lists the most common ions in the human body along with their significant physiologic functions—notice the diversity of body structures (e.g., nerves, muscles, liver, stomach) that require specific ions to function normally. Maintaining homeostatic blood concentration of each of these ions is critical to health and is described in section 25.3.

Losing Electrons and the Formation of Cations

A sodium atom, found in column IA of the periodic table, is a good example of an element that can reach stability by losing or donating an electron. The atomic structure of sodium (figure 2.5a) has one electron in its outer shell. By giving up or donating that electron, sodium now satisfies the octet rule and becomes stable. But is the structure still neutral? Recall that "neutral" means that the number of positively charged protons is equal to the number of negatively charged electrons. Because an electron has been donated by the sodium atom, it now has 11 protons but only 10 electrons, and the charge is calculated as follows: $11(+)$ and $10(-) = +1$. Ions with a positive charge are called **cations.** Thus, sodium ion is a cation with a $+1$ charge and is now designated as Na^+. Other examples of common cations, as listed in table 2.1, include K^+, Ca^{2+}, Mg^{2+}, and H^+.

Gaining Electrons and the Formation of Anions

A chlorine atom is a good example of an element that can reach stability by gaining or accepting an electron (figure 2.5b). Chlorine contains seven electrons in its outer shell, and by accepting one electron, stability is reached. The structure formed is now referred to as a chloride ion. Because an electron has been gained, the chloride ion has 17 protons and now has 18 electrons, and the charge is calculated as follows: $17(+)$ and $18(-) = -1$, written as Cl^-. Negatively charged ions are called **anions.** Some simple and complex anions are included in table 2.1.

Two of the common anions listed in table 2.1, bicarbonate ion (HCO_3^-) and phosphate ion (PO_4^{3-}) are composed of more than one atom and are referred to as **polyatomic ions.** These form when one or more atoms in a structure has lost or gained electrons.

Table 2.1	Common Ions in the Human Body and Their Physiologic Significance

COMMON CATIONS (POSITIVELY CHARGED IONS)

Cation	Structure	Physiologic Significance
Sodium ion	Na^+	• Most common extracellular cation • Participant in conducting electrical signals in neurons and muscle • Most important in osmotic movement of water • Sodium gradient involved in cotransport of other substances across a plasma membrane
Potassium ion	K^+	• Most common intracellular cation • Participant in conducting electrical signals in neurons and muscle • Role in glycogen storage in liver and muscle • Function in pH balance
Calcium ion	Ca^{2+}	• Hardness of bone and teeth • Muscle contraction • Exocytosis (including release of neurotransmitter) • Blood clotting • Second messenger in hormonal stimulation of cells
Magnesium ion	Mg^{2+}	• Required for ATP production
Hydrogen ion	H^+	• Concentration determines pH of blood and other fluids of the body

COMMON ANIONS (NEGATIVELY CHARGED IONS)

Anion	Structure	Physiologic Significance
Chloride ion	Cl^-	• Alters neuron responsiveness to stimulation • Component of stomach acid (HCl) • Chloride shift in erythrocytes
Bicarbonate ion	HCO_3^- $HO-\overset{\overset{\textstyle O}{\|\|}}{C}-O^-$	• Conversion of CO_2 gas to HCO_3^-, which is transported in the blood • Buffering of pH in blood
Phosphate ion	PO_4^{3-} $^-O-\overset{\overset{\textstyle O}{\|\|}}{\underset{\underset{\textstyle O^-}{\|}}{P}}-O^-$	• As $Ca_3(PO_4)_2$ it hardens bone and teeth • Component of phospholipids (membranes) • Component of nucleotides, including ATP and nucleic acids (DNA and RNA) • Most common intracellular anion • Intracellular buffer

General Rules for Assigning Charges

A general rule helps you determine which atoms gain or lose electrons and the charge that they develop. Atoms with one, two, or three electrons in the outer shell generally donate electrons and become positively charged cations. The amount of charge depends

Figure 2.5 Formation of an Ionic Bond Involving Sodium and Chloride. (*a*) A sodium atom donates an electron to a chlorine atom (*b*). (*c*) The loss of an electron from a sodium atom results in the formation of a positively charged sodium ion (Na^+), and the gain of an electron by chlorine results in the formation of a negatively charged chloride ion (Cl^-). (*d*) The NaCl ionic compound (a salt) is composed of lattice crystal formed by the electrostatic attractions between Na^+ and Cl^-. AP|R

upon the number of electrons donated—namely, one, two, or three. For example, since calcium has two electrons in its outer shell, it reaches stability by donating two negatively charged electrons, develops a charge of $+2$, and in ionic form is written as Ca^{2+}.

In comparison, atoms with five, six, or seven electrons in the outer shell tend to accept electrons and become negatively charged anions. The amount of charge depends upon the number of electrons gained to meet the octet rule criterion—namely, three, two, or one. An atom with seven electrons in the outer shell, such as chlorine, reaches stability and becomes chloride (Cl^-) when it gains one electron and develops a -1 charge.

Note that carbon (atomic number 6), with four electrons in its outer shell, neither gains nor loses electrons to become an ion. It only forms covalent bonds in molecules, as described later in the chapter.

 WHAT DO YOU THINK?

2 Can you predict the specific charge for magnesium ion (atomic number 12) based on its position in the periodic table?

Using the Periodic Table to Assign Charges

The periodic table (see figure 2.1*a*) may be used to quickly assess whether an atom will become a cation or anion and the amount and nature of its specific charge. Usually, elements on the left side (termed the "metallic" side) of the periodic table, and in column IIIA, tend to lose electrons. The specific positive charge is dependent upon the position of the element in the periodic table: Group IA = $+1$, group IIA = $+2$, and group IIIA = $+3$. In contrast, elements on the right side (conversely called the "nonmetallic" side) of the periodic table (columns VA–VIIA) tend to gain electrons. The specific amount of negative charge is as follows: Group VA = -3, group VIA = -2, and group VIIA = -1. Sometimes there are anomalies, such as iron (Fe), which is the metal in the hemoglobin molecule within red blood cells (erythrocytes). It can form more than one type of ion, either a ferrous (Fe^{2+}) or ferric (Fe^{3+}) ion.

 WHAT DID YOU LEARN?

5 List the common cations and anions of the human body, including their name and symbol.

6 On the periodic table (see figure 2.1), highlight the elements that form the common ions of the human body (do not include the polyatomic ions).

7 Explain how and why ions form based on the octet rule.

2.2b Ionic Bonds

LEARNING OBJECTIVES

5. Define an ionic bond.

6. Describe an ionic compound of NaCl.

7. List other examples of ionic compounds.

Positively charged cations and negatively charged anions may bind together by electrostatic interactions called **ionic bonds.** The structures formed are **salts.** A classic example involves the formation of common table salt from metallic atoms of sodium and nonmetallic atoms of chlorine. Each sodium atom donates one outer shell electron to a chlorine atom. The sodium atom then becomes a sodium ion (Na^+), and the chlorine atom becomes a chloride ion (Cl^-). The Na^+ and Cl^- ions are held together by ionic bonds in a precise, lattice crystal structure composing an **ionic compound** (figure 2.5*d*). NaCl is the smallest repeating structure of this ionic compound and represents its chemical formula (the chemical constituents in a compound and their ratios).

Consider also the ionic compound magnesium chloride ($MgCl_2$). Notice that the chemical formula contains one magnesium and two chloride ions. This is because magnesium, which is in column IIA on the periodic table, has two electrons in its outer shell. It becomes stable by donating one electron to each of the two chlorine atoms.

Other examples of ionic compounds include those involving polyatomic anions, sodium bicarbonate ($NaHCO_3$), and the most common ionic compound in the body, calcium phosphate, $Ca_3(PO_4)_2$, which helps harden bones and teeth. Notice that each of these examples is a combination of a common cation and common anion (table 2.1).

WHAT DID YOU LEARN?

8 Could an ionic bond form between two cations or between two anions? Explain.

INTEGRATE

LEARNING STRATEGY

As a general rule, the interaction between elements from the left side of the periodic table, which are metals (e.g., sodium, potassium, magnesium, calcium), with elements on the right side of the periodic table (e.g., chlorine, fluorine), form ionic bonds. The salt that is formed is composed of ions held together in a lattice arrangement by ionic bonds.

2.3 Covalent Bonding, Molecules, and Molecular Compounds

Instead of donating or gaining electrons to form ionic compounds that are arranged in a lattice, atoms also have the possibility of reaching stability by sharing electrons. The sharing of electrons between atoms results in a **covalently bonded molecule.** Most molecules are composed of two or more different elements and are called **molecular compounds.** Thus, molecules of carbon dioxide (CO_2) and water (H_2O) are molecular compounds. However, molecules composed of only one element are not, such as molecular oxygen (O_2) and molecular hydrogen (H_2).

Here we describe covalent bonds, the different types of covalently bonded molecules, and interactions between covalently bonded molecules, after first discussing how molecules are represented with molecular and structural formulas.

2.3a Chemical Formulas: Molecular and Structural

LEARNING OBJECTIVES

1. Define a molecular formula.
2. Describe a structural formula, and explain its use in differentiating isomers.

Molecular Formula

The chemical constituents of a molecule and their ratios are represented using a **molecular formula.** An example of a molecular formula would be carbonic acid (H_2CO_3), where the molecule contains two hydrogen atoms, one carbon atom, and three oxygen atoms.

Structural Formula

The **structural formula** of a molecule is complementary to its molecular formula and exhibits not only the numbers and types of atoms but also their arrangements within the molecule. Atoms are always arranged in a defined manner within each molecule. The molecular formula for carbon dioxide (CO_2) thus is complemented by its structural formula ($O\!=\!C\!=\!O$).

Structural formulas provide a means for differentiating **isomers,** which are molecules composed of the same number and kind of elements but arranged differently in space. Two relevant isomers in humans are glucose and galactose **(figure 2.6).** These sugar molecules both have a molecular formula of $C_6H_{12}O_6$, indicating that each molecule has six carbon, twelve hydrogen, and six oxygen atoms. However, the atoms are arranged differently in space as shown in their structural formulas. Notice the different arrangement of atoms on carbon four in the six-sided ring structure of glucose and galactose. (Sugars in a ring-structure have carbon atoms that are numbered beginning with the carbon to the right of the oxygen as carbon one, and then are numbered consecutively clockwise around the ring.) Although fructose is a five-sided ring, it is also an isomer of glucose and galactose because it contains the same number and kinds of elements, but it has a different structural arrangement.

Isomers may have very different properties from one another— therefore, structural formulas are an important piece of chemical information.

WHAT DID YOU LEARN?

9. What information about a molecule is gained by a structural formula? How does this differ from a molecular formula?

10. What is an isomer?

2.3b Covalent Bonds

LEARNING OBJECTIVES

3. Describe a covalent bond and explain its formation based on the octet rule.
4. List the four most common elements in the human body.
5. Distinguish between single, double, and triple covalent bonds.
6. Explain polar and nonpolar covalent bonds.

Glucose	Galactose	Fructose
Molecular formula		
$(C_6H_{12}O_6)$	$(C_6H_{12}O_6)$	$(C_6H_{12}O_6)$

(a)   (b)   (c)

Figure 2.6 Isomers. (*a*) Glucose, (*b*) galactose, and (*c*) fructose are isomers that share the same chemical formulas but have different structural formulas (highlighted in yellow).

The bond that is formed when atoms *share* electrons is a **covalent bond.** Covalent bonding occurs when both atoms require electrons to become stable. This takes place when the participating atoms that form the chemical bond have four, five, six, or seven electrons in the outer shell. View figure 2.4 and note that this applies to the nonmetal elements on the right side of the periodic table. (The exception is hydrogen because only two electrons are needed to complete its outermost electron shell.)

The four most common elements of the human body that form covalent bonds are oxygen (O), carbon (C), hydrogen (H), and nitrogen (N). These four elements account for over 96% of the body's weight. The simplest example of covalent bond formation occurs when hydrogen gas is formed from two hydrogen atoms. The covalent bond formation between two hydrogen atoms fills the outer shell of each atom because each hydrogen atom shares its single electron (and only two electrons are required for the first shell to be complete).

The Number of Bonds an Atom Can Form

Although hydrogen can share only one pair of electrons and thus produce one covalent bond to become stable, some elements are able to share more than one pair. The number of covalent bonds formed by an atom may be determined by examining the number of electrons needed to complete the outer shell (see figure 2.4). The atomic structure of the four most common elements that compose molecules show that hydrogen needs one electron, oxygen needs two electrons, nitrogen needs three electrons, and carbon needs four electrons. Thus, hydrogen can form one covalent bond, oxygen two, nitrogen three, and carbon can form four covalent bonds.

Single, Double, and Triple Covalent Bonds

Atoms of elements that can form more than one covalent bond also may do so through combinations of single, double, or triple covalent bonds **(figure 2.7)**. A **single covalent bond** is one pair of electrons shared between two atoms. The bond just described between two hydrogen atoms is a single covalent bond. A **double covalent bond** involves the sharing of two pairs of electrons between two atoms. An example is the double covalent bond between two oxygen atoms. The sharing of two pairs of electrons between oxygen atoms is necessary to achieve stability because each oxygen atom has only six electrons in its outer shell and needs eight electrons to satisfy the octet rule. Three pairs of electrons are shared between atoms in some molecules, forming a **triple covalent bond.** A prime example is the triple covalent

(a)

(b)

(c)

Figure 2.7 Single, Double, and Triple Covalent Bonds. Covalent bonds involve the sharing of electrons. (*a*) One pair of electrons is shared in a single covalent bond, (*b*) two pairs of electrons are shared in a double covalent bond, and (*c*) three pairs of electrons are shared in a triple covalent bond.

bond between two nitrogen atoms. The order of stability (e.g., the more energy required to break the bonds) is from least to greatest: single covalent bond, double covalent bond, triple covalent bond.

An atom of a specific element might share electrons in a variety of ways to satisfy the octet rule. For example, a carbon atom contains four electrons in the outer electron shell and thus needs four electrons to satisfy the octet rule. These four electrons can be obtained in a number of ways to form different types of molecules **(figure 2.8)**.

(a)

(b)

(c)

Figure 2.8 Carbon-Containing Molecules. Carbon can form four covalent bonds and may do so in many ways. For example, carbon can form (*a*) four single covalent bonds with four hydrogen atoms in methane; (*b*) two double bonds with oxygen atoms in carbon dioxide; and (*c*) four single covalent bonds in a more complex structure like ethanol.

Carbon Skeleton Formation

Numerous carbon atoms are sometimes bonded together to form a "carbon skeleton." Three possible arrangements may occur: a straight chain, branched chain, or a ring (**figure 2.9**). Notice that in a structural formula of a carbon chain or ring skeleton, the letter "C" is often not included in the structural formula with the understanding that a carbon atom lies where lines meet at an angle. In addition, if a carbon atom does not have its required four bonds shown in the structural formula, the additional atoms are assumed to be hydrogen atoms.

Nonpolar and Polar Covalent Bonds

Atoms share electrons in a covalent bond either equally or unequally between the atoms. How they share is determined by the relative attraction each atom has for electrons, a concept referred to as **electronegativity.** Since two atoms of the same element, such as two hydrogen atoms, two oxygen atoms, or two carbon atoms, have equal attraction for electrons, they share the electrons equally. The resultant bond is a **nonpolar covalent bond.**

Different types of atoms have varying degrees of electronegativity, or attraction for electrons, and thus may share the electrons unequally. The resultant bond is a **polar covalent bond** (an important exception will be described shortly). As a general rule, electronegativity increases both from left to right across a row of the periodic table and from bottom to top in a column (see figure 2.1a). These trends reflect that, for elements across a specific row, a greater number of protons in the nucleus of the atom are "pulling" on the electrons. For elements in a column, the elements closer to the top of the periodic table have electrons in shells closer to the nucleus (see figure 2.4). Thus, electronegativity is determined both by the number of protons in the nucleus and the proximity of the valence electron shells to the nucleus.

Consequently, for the four most common elements composing living organisms, the order of electronegativity from least to greatest is as follows: hydrogen < carbon < nitrogen < oxygen. Therefore, of these four elements, oxygen has the greatest attraction for electrons, and hydrogen has the least. The electrons, in each case, spend a greater amount of time orbiting the nucleus of the more electronegative atom.

Because electrons have a negative charge, the more electronegative atom develops a partial negative charge, and the less electronegative atom develops a partial positive charge. Partial charges are written using the Greek letter delta (δ) followed by a superscript + or − to designate the relative charge. For example, a polar covalent bond formed between oxygen and hydrogen would be assigned and written as $^{\delta-}O$—$H^{\delta+}$. Note that the term **polar** (or *dipole*) refers to the "poles" of partial electrical charges, which are analogous to poles of a magnet.

Polar bonds have varying degrees of unequal sharing of electrons. Thus, polar bonds are along a continuum with ionic bonds (which involve a complete donation of electrons) on one end and nonpolar bonds (with equal sharing of electrons) on the other.

One important exception exists to the rule that a polar bond generally forms between two different atoms. The exception is carbon bonding with hydrogen. Because the electronegativity difference between carbon and hydrogen is relatively small, a covalent bond produced between carbon and hydrogen (C—H) has approximately equal sharing of electrons and forms an essentially *nonpolar* covalent bond between them.

WHAT DO YOU THINK?

3 Assign the partial charges between nitrogen and hydrogen (N—H) in a polar covalent bond.

WHAT DID YOU LEARN?

11 Explain covalent bond formation in terms of chemical stability.

12 What type of bond (a single, double, or triple covalent bond) is formed between two oxygen atoms? Explain why this is possible.

13 Why are some covalent bonds nonpolar and others polar? Identify the exception to the rule that polar covalent bonds are formed between two different types of atoms.

Straight chain	Branched chain	Ring
		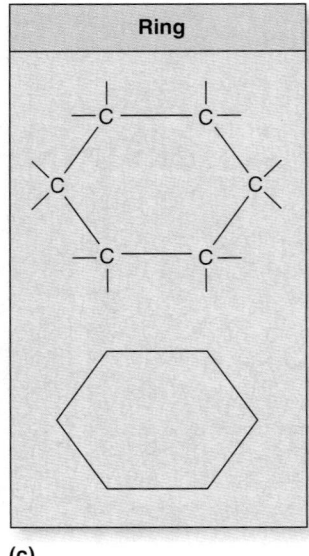
(a)	(b)	(c)

Figure 2.9 Carbon Skeleton. A carbon skeleton has three major types of arrangements including (*a*) a straight chain, (*b*) a branched chain, and (*c*) a ring. Remember the convention that a carbon is present where the lines meet at an angle.

2.3c Nonpolar, Polar, and Amphipathic Molecules

LEARNING OBJECTIVES

7. Describe the difference between a nonpolar molecule and a polar molecule.

8. Define an amphipathic molecule.

Covalent bonds may be nonpolar or polar. To determine whether an entire molecule is nonpolar or polar, the molecule as a whole is evaluated to determine the prevalence and relative strength of its nonpolar and polar bonds. The most important concept to remember is that **nonpolar molecules** contain nonpolar covalent bonds, which are bonds formed between the same elements (e.g., C—C, O—O), by C—H bonds, or both. Oxygen (O_2) and triglyceride (fat) molecules are examples of nonpolar molecules (figure 2.10).

In comparison, **polar molecules** contain polar covalent bonds. These molecules contain different elements that are bonded together, such O—H, C—O, N—H, and N—O. Water (H_2O) and glucose

($C_6H_{12}O_6$) are both polar molecules. Notice that oxygen is bonded to two hydrogen atoms in a water molecule, and several C—O and O—H bonds are within a glucose molecule. One exception to this general pattern exists: A molecule containing polar covalent bonds that extend in opposite directions can be nonpolar because the electronegativities cancel each other. Carbon dioxide ($^{\delta-}O{=}C{=}O^{\delta-}$) is an example.

Sometimes a molecule is large enough that it can have one major part that is nonpolar and another part that is polar. Molecules that contain both nonpolar and polar components are called **amphipathic** (*amphi* = both, *patheia* = feeling) **molecules**. A phospholipid molecule is an example of an amphipathic molecule.

WHAT DO YOU THINK?

4 Is a fatty acid (see figure 2.19) a nonpolar or polar molecule? Explain your answer. Would you predict that it will or will not dissolve in water?

WHAT DID YOU LEARN?

14 Are O_2 and CO_2 nonpolar or polar molecules?

(a)

(b)

(c)

Figure 2.10 Nonpolar, Polar, and Amphipathic Molecules. (*a*) Oxygen, carbon dioxide, and a triglyceride are examples of nonpolar molecules. (*b*) Water and glucose are examples of polar molecules. (*c*) A phospholipid is an example of an amphipathic molecule.

The two respiratory gases, O_2 and CO_2, are both nonpolar molecules. This chemical characteristic—and the fact that they are small in size—permits both to easily cross cell membranes. The transport of respiratory gases is discussed in other chapters of the text, including section 4.3 on membrane transport in chapter 4 (Biology of the Cell) and the exchange of O_2 and CO_2 between the blood and cells in section 23.6 in chapter 23 (Respiratory System).

2.3d Intermolecular Attractions

LEARNING OBJECTIVES

9. Describe hydrogen bonding between polar molecules.

10. List and define the intermolecular attractions between nonpolar molecules.

Molecules sometimes have weak chemical attractions to other molecules called **intermolecular** (*inter* = between) **attractions.** One important intermolecular attraction is called a hydrogen bond. A **hydrogen bond** forms between polar molecules. It is a weak attraction between a partially positive (δ^+) hydrogen atom within a molecule and a partially negative (δ^-) atom within a molecule, usually oxygen, but sometimes nitrogen. A hydrogen bond is designated in this text with a dotted or broken line. A hydrogen bond is shown in **figure 2.11** between the partially positive charge of a hydrogen atom within a glucose molecule and the partially negative charge of an oxygen atom within a water molecule. Although an individual hydrogen bond is a weak bond or attraction (approximately 5–10% the strength of a covalent bond), hydrogen bonds collectively are strong.

Other types of intermolecular attractions involve nonpolar molecules. These interactions are collectively called **van der Waals forces.** They occur when electrons orbiting the nucleus of an atom of a nonpolar molecule are, for a brief instant, distributed unequally. One portion of the atom is slightly negative and another portion is slightly positive. This momentary unequal distribution of charge in the atom induces an unequal distribution of electrons in an adjacent atom of another nonpolar molecule. Individual van der Waals forces are weak (about 1% of the strength of a covalent bond).

A third type of interaction is **hydrophobic interactions,** which results when nonpolar molecules are placed in water or another polar substance. (Hydrophobic interactions are described in detail later in the chapter.) Note that all of these attractions may also occur between different portions of a large molecule. In this case, they are more appropriately called **intramolecular** (*intra* = within) **attractions.**

Hydrogen bonds form between water molecules and have significant influence in how water molecules behave. Hydrogen bonding, van der Waals forces, and hydrophobic interactions are all important in establishing and maintaining the three-dimensional shape of complex molecules such as DNA and proteins (described later), as well as the temporary binding of molecular structures to one another, such as the binding of a hormone to a protein receptor (see section 17.5).

WHAT DID YOU LEARN?

15. What is the name of the intermolecular attraction between a partially charged hydrogen of one polar molecule with a partially negative atom of another polar molecule?

Figure 2.11 Hydrogen Bonding. A hydrogen bond formed between a partially positive charged hydrogen atom of a glucose molecule and the partially negative charged oxygen atom of a water molecule.

2.4 Molecular Structure of Water and the Properties of Water

Water is the first molecule that we examine in detail. It is appropriate to begin with water because it is the substance that composes approximately two-thirds of the human body by weight. We first look closely at the molecular structure of water molecules and then describe several important water properties. The relevance to normal body activities is included for each property.

2.4a Molecular Structure of Water

LEARNING OBJECTIVE

1. Describe the molecular structure of water and how water molecules form four hydrogen bonds.

Water is a polar molecule composed of one oxygen atom bonded to two hydrogen atoms. It exhibits polarity because there is an unequal sharing of electrons between the oxygen atom and each of the two hydrogen atoms **(figure 2.12)**. The oxygen atom is more electronegative, and it has two partial negative charges. In contrast, each hydrogen atom exhibits a single partial positive charge.

Every water molecule has the ability to form four hydrogen bonds with adjacent water molecules. This is because each hydrogen bond is formed between a partially positive hydrogen atom of one water molecule and the partially negative oxygen atom of a different water molecule. Recall from our earlier discussion of hydrogen bonds that these intermolecular attractions are individually weak but collectively very strong. Thus, hydrogen bonding between water molecules is central to the properties exhibited by water.

WHAT DID YOU LEARN?

16 What is the intermolecular bond that is significant in determining the properties of water?

Figure 2.12 Water Molecule. (*a*) A water molecule is a polar molecule due to the unequal sharing of electrons between the oxygen atom and each of the two hydrogen atoms. Partial charges are shown. (*b*) Hydrogen bonds form between the partially positive (δ^+) hydrogen atom of one water molecule with the partially negative (δ^-) oxygen atom of a different water molecule.

2.4b Properties of Water

✓ LEARNING OBJECTIVE

2. List the different properties of water and provide an example of the importance of each property within the body.

Phases of Water

Water is present in three phases, depending upon the temperature: a gas (water vapor), a liquid (water), and a solid (ice). Substances that have a low molecular mass (described later) such as water generally are present in the gaseous phase at room temperature. However, water is liquid at room temperature because hydrogen bonds hold the water molecules in the liquid phase and limit their escape into the gaseous phase. Almost all water within the human body occurs within the liquid phase, although small amounts of water are present as water vapor within the air passageways. As a liquid, water serves the following functions:

- **Transports.** Substances are dissolved in water and moved throughout the body in water-based fluids (e.g., blood and lymph).
- **Lubricates.** Water-based fluids between body structures decrease friction (e.g., serous fluid between the heart and its sac, synovial fluid within joints).
- **Cushions.** The force of sudden body movements is absorbed by water-based fluids (e.g., cerebrospinal fluid surrounding the brain and spinal cord).
- **Excretes Wastes.** Unwanted substances are eliminated in the body dissolved in water (e.g., urine, sweat).

Cohesion, Surface Tension, and Adhesion

Cohesion is the attraction between water molecules. They are inclined to "stick together" because hydrogen bonds form between these molecules. **Surface tension** is the inward pulling of cohesive forces at the surface of water. This inward attraction occurs because water molecules at the surface are pulled by hydrogen bonds in only three directions, whereas water molecules that are internal in the liquid are pulled by hydrogen bonds in four directions. **Adhesion** is the attraction between water molecules and a substance other than water. This occurs when hydrogen bonds form between water molecules and the molecules that compose those other substances.

Surface tension can be demonstrated readily. Try this experiment: First, stack two flat plates of glass, such as two clean microscope slides, and then lift them apart. Note that they are easily separated. Then repeat this experiment, but first place one or two drops of water between the slides before they are stacked. Note it is much more difficult, if not impossible, to separate the plates of glass without first wedging them apart. This is because water causes increased surface tension between the surfaces. A similar situation is experienced within the walls of the moist air sacs of the lungs (called alveoli) because opposing air sac walls will stick together. However, we produce a mixture of lipids and proteins called *surfactant* (see section 23.3) that prevents the alveoli from collapsing when we breathe out. Without surfactant (a risk of some premature infants), alveoli collapse with each breath out, and the two moist sides of the alveoli adhere to one another. The next breath in requires breaking of the surface tension within alveoli and their reinflation—a situation that requires much greater effort.

High Specific Heat and High Heat of Vaporization

Temperature is a measure of the kinetic energy, or random movement, of atoms or molecules within a substance. The relationship between temperature and kinetic energy is direct—the temperature is higher when there is a greater amount of kinetic energy in an object. Two properties of water influence water temperature: its specific heat and the heat of vaporization.

Specific heat is the amount of energy (measured in calories) required to increase the temperature of 1 gram of a substance by 1 degree Celsius (C). The specific heat of water has one of the highest values of any substance (1 calorie/gram/°C). This is because most of the energy imparted into water during heating is first used to break hydrogen bonds. Thereafter, the energy from heating increases the kinetic energy of water molecules. As we change between cool and warm environments, or generate large amounts of heat during physical exertion, much of this heat (energy) is used to break hydrogen bonds and not increase the random movement of molecules (kinetic energy) within the body. Thus, body temperature remains relatively constant.

Heat of vaporization is the energy required for the release of molecules from a liquid phase into the gaseous phase for 1 gram of a substance. Water has a high heat of vaporization because the hydrogen bonds between individual water molecules must first be broken before these molecules can be released from the liquid phase into the gaseous phase. This is the reason why sweating is an effective measure in helping to cool the body. As water molecules evaporate from the surface of the skin, excess heat is dissipated from the body.

〰 WHAT DO YOU THINK?

5 Why is sweating less effective in cooling the body on a humid day?

💡 WHAT DID YOU LEARN?

17 Which property of water contributes to the need to produce surfactant and prevent collapse of the alveoli? Which property contributes to body temperature regulation through sweating?

2.4c Water as the Universal Solvent

✓ LEARNING OBJECTIVES

3. Compare substances that dissolve in water with those that both dissolve and dissociate in water. Distinguish between electrolytes and nonelectrolytes.
4. Describe the chemical interactions of nonpolar substances and water.
5. Explain how amphipathic molecules interact in water to form chemical barriers.

Water is the **solvent** of the body, and substances that dissolve in water are called **solutes.** Water is called the **universal solvent** because most substances dissolve in it. However, not all substances dissolve completely or at all in water. The chemical properties of a substance (whether it is polar, charged, nonpolar, or amphipathic) determine how it interacts with water molecules. Here we examine the substances that dissolve in water (polar molecules and ions) and those that do not dissolve in water (nonpolar molecules) or that partially dissolve in water (amphipathic molecules).

Substances That Dissolve in Water (Polar Molecules and Ions)

Water molecules are polar. Each molecule has regions that are differently charged: $H^{\delta+}$ and $O^{\delta-}$ (see figure 2.12). Some polar molecules (e.g., glucose) and other charged substances or ions (e.g., Na^+, HCO_3^-) interact with and **dissolve** within water. In other words, they

Figure 2.13 Substance Interaction with Water. Chemical properties of the substance combined with water will determine their interaction. (*a*) Hydrophilic substances dissolve in water. Nonelectrolytes dissolve and remain intact within water as water molecules form a hydration shell around each molecule. Electrolytes, which include salts, acids, and bases, dissolve and dissociate in water to a certain extent as water molecules form hydration shells around each ion. (*b*) Hydrophobic molecules are nonpolar substances that do not dissolve in water; rather, the nonpolar molecules are "pushed" out of the water by hydrophobic exclusion. (*c*) Amphipathic molecules are unique in that the polar portion dissolves in water and the nonpolar portion does not. Cell membranes and micelles are two common arrangements formed within the body by amphipathic molecules.

disperse in the water. The substances that dissolve in water are appropriately called **hydrophilic** (meaning "water-loving"). Many water molecules surround this substance and form a **hydration shell** around it (**figure 2.13a**).

Polar molecules such as glucose and alcohol dissolve in water as a result of the hydrogen bonds that form between those molecules and water. However, here the solute remains intact as individual molecules are surrounded by water molecules.

Some substances dissolve in water but do not remain intact. These substances both dissolve and **dissociate,** meaning that they pull apart or separate. Salts are ionic compounds that both dissolve and dissociate when placed into water. When added to water, the cations and anions of the salt are pulled apart. For example, sodium chloride (NaCl) dissociates in water to form both Na^+ and Cl^- ions. Hydration shells form around each ion, causing their

separation. The water molecule's partial positive charges ($H^{\delta+}$) associate with the released anions (Cl^-) of the salt, while the water molecule's partial negative charges ($O^{\delta-}$) are united with the released cations (Na^+).

Acids and bases also dissociate in water. Hydrochloric acid (HCl) dissociates to form both H^+ and Cl^-, whereas sodium bicarbonate dissociates to form both Na^+ and HCO_3^- ions. Acids and bases are described in detail in the next section.

Substances that both dissolve and dissociate in water, such as salts, acids, and bases, can readily conduct an electric current. For this reason, they are called **electrolytes.** In contrast, substances that remain intact when introduced into water, such as glucose, do not conduct an electric current and are called **nonelectrolytes.** Maintaining normal levels of electrolytes including salts, acids, and bases is discussed in chapter 25.

Substances That Do Not Dissolve in Water (Nonpolar Molecules)

Nonpolar molecules do not dissolve in water, and so they are called **hydrophobic** (meaning "water-fearing"). The hydrogen bonds between water molecules cause the water molecules to be cohesive and attract each other; at the same time, they exclude, or "force out," the nonpolar molecules by a process called **hydrophobic exclusion** (figure 2.13b). The interaction between the molecules of the "excluded" nonpolar substance is termed **hydrophobic interaction** because it appears that these molecules are avoiding water. In this case, contact between the polar water molecules and the nonpolar substance is minimized. You can observe hydrophobic exclusion by placing a few drops of oil into water; the oil forms small spherical drops on the water's surface.

Hydrophobic substances, such as triglycerides (fats) and cholesterol, require carrier proteins to be transported within the blood because of their inability to dissolve within water. The nonpolar molecules are enclosed within the confines of the protein molecule to limit its contact with the water in the blood.

Substances That Partially Dissolve in Water (Amphipathic Molecules)

Amphipathic molecules have both polar and nonpolar regions. They do not completely dissolve, nor are they completely excluded when placed into water. Instead, the polar portion dissolves in water, and the nonpolar portion is repelled by water (figure 2.13c). Through hydrophobic exclusion, nonpolar portions become positioned in close proximity.

Recall that phospholipid molecules are amphipathic molecules. The polar heads of these molecules have contact with water, but their nonpolar tails are grouped together. This results in bilayers of phospholipids that form chemical barriers within the body. A bilayer of phospholipid molecules composes membranes of a cell (see section 4.2a). Other amphipathic molecules form a spherical structure called a *micelle*. This is a special structure within the digestive tract that is associated with the breakdown and absorption of nonpolar molecules including triglycerides (see section 26.4c).

The many functions of water in the human body are summarized in **figure 2.14**. Note that the property of water as a neutral solvent (included in this figure) is described in the next section on acidic and basic solutions.

WHAT DID YOU LEARN?

18 How does the interaction of a nonelectrolyte and water differ from the interaction of an electrolyte and water? Give examples of each.

19 How do phospholipid molecules interact with water to form a membrane?

2.5 Acidic and Basic Solutions, pH, and Buffers

Acidic and basic solutions occur specifically when an acid or base is added to water. Here we describe why water is neutral; define an acid and a base; and explain pH, neutralization, and the action of buffers.

2.5a Water: A Neutral Solvent

LEARNING OBJECTIVE

1. Describe what is formed when water dissociates.

Another property of water is that it spontaneously dissociates to form ions. The covalent chemical bond between oxygen and either of the two hydrogen atoms in a water molecule spontaneously breaks apart at a low rate (about two dissociations occur per billion water molecules). This number is about 10^{-7} ions (or 1/10,000,000 ions) per liter.

A hydrogen ion (H^+) transfers to a second water molecule during dissociation. The water molecule that picked up the extra hydrogen ion is called a *hydronium ion*, and it is represented as H_3O^+. The electron of this "transferred" hydrogen remains associated with the original water molecule, which now is deficient in one hydrogen ion but still has the

Figure 2.14 **Water as the Solvent of Body Fluids.** Water serves several critical functions within the body. It helps regulate body temperature, serves as the universal solvent, cushions, transports, lubricates, and creates high surface tension that allows body structures to cling to each other. The pH of water, a neutral substance, is changed by the addition of acid or base.

CUSHIONS

- Cerebrospinal fluid
- Skull
- Brain
- Fluid cushions against sudden movements.

REGULATES BODY TEMPERATURE

Water helps regulate body temperature due to its high specific heat and high heat of vaporization.

Heat

TRANSPORTS

Water is the fluid medium to transport substances in blood and other body fluids (e.g., blood, urine).

UNIVERSAL SOLVENT

Hydrophilic substance

CH₂OH
H   O
HO–C Glucose
HO–C   C
H   OH
C
OH

Nonelectrolytes dissolve and remain intact.

Na⁺

Cl⁻

Electrolytes dissolve and dissociate.

LUBRICATES

Fluid serves as a lubricant to decrease friction.

- Pericardial sac
- Pericardial fluid
- Heart

Hydrophobic molecules

Water molecules exclude nonpolar molecules, thus proteins are required for their transport within the body.

HIGH SURFACE TENSION

Water's high surface tension causes structures to adhere. The moist alveoli in the lungs are prevented from collapsing and adhering by surfactant.

- Alveolus
- Surfactant

Amphipathic molecules

Polar portion dissolves, nonpolar portion excluded.

Amphipathic molecules form chemical barriers (e.g., plasma membranes, micelles).

NEUTRAL pH

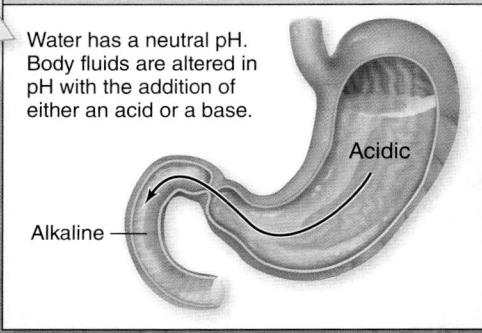

Water has a neutral pH. Body fluids are altered in pH with the addition of either an acid or a base.

- Acidic
- Alkaline

original electron. This molecule is called a *hydroxide ion* (OH⁻). This dissociation reaction is written as

$$H_2O + H_2O \longrightarrow H_3O^+ + OH^-$$

simplified to

$$H_2O \longrightarrow H^+ + OH^-$$

Equal numbers of positively charged hydrogen ions (H⁺) and negatively charged hydroxyl ions (OH⁻) are produced from the dissociation of water. Consequently, water has no net charge and is neutral.

 WHAT DID YOU LEARN?

20 Explain why water is neutral.

2.5b Acids and Bases

LEARNING OBJECTIVE

2. Explain the difference between an acid and a base.

An **acid** is a substance that dissociates in water to produce both an H⁺ and an anion. An acid increases the concentration of H⁺ free in solution (**figure 2.15**). Because H⁺ is a proton, an acid is also called a **proton donor**. The equation is as follows:

Substance A (an acid in water) $\longrightarrow$ H⁺ + Anion

Strong acids dissociate to a greater extent and produce more H⁺. Hydrochloric acid (HCl), secreted by cells lining the stomach, is a good example of a strong acid. Weak acids, such as carbonic acid (H_2CO_3) in the blood, dissociate to a lesser extent, producing fewer H⁺ ions.

In contrast, a **base** accepts H⁺ when added to a solution. Therefore, a base is also called a **proton acceptor**. A base decreases the amount of H⁺ free in solution. Thus,

Substance B (a base in water) + H⁺ $\longrightarrow$ B—H

Stronger bases, such as sodium hydroxide (NaOH), absorb more H⁺ than do weak bases, leaving less H⁺ in solution. Ammonia and bleach are effective cleaning agents because they are strong bases. Weak bases absorb less H⁺, leaving more H⁺ in solution. Bicarbonate (HCO_3^-) is one of the most important weak bases in the body; it is both transported in the blood and released into secretions from the liver and pancreas that enter the small intestine.

 WHAT DID YOU LEARN?

21 Which type of substance releases H⁺ when added to water?

2.5c pH, Neutralization, and the Action of Buffers

LEARNING OBJECTIVES

3. Define pH and explain the relative pH values of both acids and bases.

4. Explain the term neutralization, and describe how the neutralization of both an acid and a base occur.

5. Describe the action of a buffer.

The pH of a solution is a measure of the relative amounts of H⁺ it contains; it is expressed as a number between 0 and 14. pH is the inverse relationship of the logarithmic values for a given *hydrogen ion concentration* [H⁺]:

$$\text{Negative log of } [H^+] = \frac{1}{\log \text{ of } [H^+]}$$

Recall that water readily dissociates to produce 10^{-7} H⁺ and OH⁻ ions (or 1/10,000,000) per liter. If this concentration of H⁺ is placed into the formula just given for pH, then the value for the pH of water is calculated to be equal to 7.

Notice that as [H⁺] increases, for example, 10^{-6} to 10^{-5} to 10^{-4}, that pH decreases from 6 to 5 and finally to 4. Conversely, as [H⁺] decreases, 10^{-8} to 10^{-9} to 10^{-10}, the pH increases. Thus, [H⁺] and pH value are *inversely related*.

Interpreting the pH Scale

Pure water and other solutions that have equal concentrations of H⁺ and OH⁻ are neutral and have a pH of 7. Solutions with a pH below 7 are acidic, and solutions with a pH above 7 are basic, or alkaline.

Moving from one increment to another (e.g., 7 to 6) represents a 10-fold change in [H⁺]. Therefore, a pH 6 solution has a [H⁺] that is 10 times greater than pure water. Changing by two units (e.g., 7 to 5) is a 100-fold increase in [H⁺]. This relationship is accurate for changes above 7 as well, except that each increment is a 10-fold decrease in [H⁺].

Figure 2.15 pH. pH scale is a measure of the relative concentration of H⁺ and OH⁻. A neutral solution has equal amounts of H⁺ and OH⁻, acidic solutions contain greater amounts of H⁺ than OH⁻, and basic solutions contain lesser amounts of H⁺ than OH⁻. Examples of common solutions that exhibit a specific pH are shown.

WHAT DO YOU THINK?

6 If stomach acid has a pH of 2, how much more acidic is stomach acid than water (pH 7)? Predict what would happen to the stomach if it were not protected from the effects of hydrochloric acid.

Neutralization

Neutralization occurs when a solution that is either acidic or basic is returned to neutral (pH 7). The neutralization of an acidic solution is accomplished by adding a base, whereas a basic solution is neutralized by adding an acid. Thus, medications to neutralize stomach acid, such as Rolaids or Tums, must contain a base.

Buffers

A **buffer** is a single substance, or an associated group of substances, that helps prevent pH changes if either excess acid or base is added. A buffer acts either to accept H^+ from excess acid or donate H^+ to neutralize excess base. Both carbonic acid (H_2CO_3), a weak acid, and bicarbonate (HCO_3^-), a weak base, are present within the blood and serve as buffers to maintain the blood's critical pH range (7.35 to 7.45) (see section 25.5d).

WHAT DID YOU LEARN?

22 What is the general relationship of [H⁺] and pH?

23 Why are buffers important, and how do they function to help maintain pH?

2.6 Water Mixtures

Mixtures are formed from the combining or "mixing" of two or more substances. Several types of mixtures have already been described, including sugar water, salt water, and acidic solutions. Two defining features of mixtures are: (1) The substances that are mixed are not chemically changed; and (2) the substances in the mixture can be separated by physical means, such as by evaporation or by filtering. Our emphasis here is on water mixtures. We describe how water mixtures are categorized into three types and explain how solution concentration is expressed.

2.6a Categories of Water Mixtures

LEARNING OBJECTIVES

1. Compare and contrast the three different types of water mixtures.

2. Explain how an emulsion differs from other types of mixtures.

Water mixtures are placed into three categories based on the relative size of the substance mixed with water and include suspensions, colloids, and solutions **(figure 2.16)**.

- **Suspension.** A suspension occurs when material that is larger in size than 100 nanometers is mixed with water. Unlike a colloid or a solution, a suspension does not remain mixed together unless it is in motion. A suspension appears cloudy or opaque until the particles drop out of the liquid. Sand in water is an example of a suspension. Blood cells within the plasma (the liquid portion) of blood form a suspension.

- **Colloid.** A colloid is a mixture composed of protein within water, where the protein ranges in size from 1 to 100 nanometers. A colloid may appear either opaque or milky and scatters light like a suspension—but, unlike a suspension, remains mixed when not in motion. Some colloids, including gelatin and agar media (used in the microbiology laboratory), display an interesting feature—namely, they become liquid when heated but change to a gel-like state when left standing and cooled. Colloids within the body include cell cytosol and proteins within blood plasma.

- **Solution.** A solution is a homogeneous mixture in which the substance is smaller than 1 nanometer, and it dissolves in water. The water is the solvent, and the dissolved substance is the solute. Both salt water and sugar water are examples of solutions. The small size of the solutes in a solution results in a mixture with these characteristics: The solutes are not visible, do not scatter light, and do not settle if the solution is not in motion. Blood plasma is an example of a body solution, with salts, glucose, HCO_3^-, and other dissolved nonprotein substances.

A suspension composed specifically of water and a nonpolar (hydrophobic) liquid substance such as vegetable oil does not "mix" unless shaken or agitated (e.g., oil and vinegar salad dressing). The combination of water and a nonpolar liquid when forcibly mixed is classified instead as an **emulsion.** Breast milk is an example of an emulsion in the body.

INTEGRATE

CONCEPT CONNECTION

Blood exhibits all three types of mixtures: suspension, colloid, and solution. Blood is a **suspension** of formed elements that includes erythrocytes (red blood cells), leukocytes (white blood cells), and platelets within plasma (section 18.1). If blood is withdrawn from the body, the formed elements will settle out from the plasma. Blood is also a **colloid** of proteins (e.g., albumin) dissolved in plasma, and it is a **solution** of ions (e.g., Na⁺, K⁺, and Ca²⁺) and molecules (e.g., glucose and amino acids) dissolved in plasma (section 18.2).

Figure 2.16 Mixtures and Emulsions. (*a*) Mixtures include suspensions, colloids, and solutions. (*b*) An emulsion is a suspension specifically composed of water (or other polar substance) and a nonpolar liquid, such as vegetable oil, that mix only when agitated.

24 When left standing, erythrocytes (red blood cells) settle to the bottom of a tube of blood. Based on this characteristic alone, blood would be characterized as a (a) suspension, (b) colloid, or (c) solution?

25 Why is blood also considered the other two types of water mixtures?

2.6b Expressions of Solution Concentration

LEARNING OBJECTIVE

3. Explain the different ways to express the concentration of solute in a solution.

The amount of solute dissolved in a solution determines the concentration of a solution. Concentration of a solution may be expressed in several ways, including mass/volume, mass/volume percent, molarity, and molality. The units for expressing concentration are summarized in table 2.2, which includes a description, units of measurement, and an example for each.

Mass/volume is mass of solute per volume of solution. Results from a blood test are often expressed in mass/volume. **Mass/volume percent** is grams of solute per 100 milliliters of solution. For example, mass/volume percent is the unit of measurement for intravenous (IV) solutions.

Molarity is a measure of number of moles per liter of solution. A molar solution of glucose is made by placing 180.10 grams (its molecular mass) of glucose into a container and adding enough water until it measures 1 liter. (Both moles and molecular mass are described shortly.) **Molality** is the moles per kilogram of solvent. A solution of one molality is made by placing 180.10 grams of glucose into a container and adding 1 kilogram of water. Molarity and molality may be used interchangeably, subject to this caveat: The two values are the closest when the measurements are taken at 4°C. At this temperature, 1 liter of water is at its most dense, and its mass is exactly equal to 1 kilogram of water.

Molarity alters with changes in temperature (and to a limited degree with changes in pressure). When water temperature increases above 4°C, the solution expands, and molarity (moles per liter of solution) decreases slightly because it is based on volume (liter) of solution. In contrast, molality (moles per kilogram of solvent) does not alter with changes in temperature because it is based on mass (kilograms) of solvent. Consequently, molality is the more accurate of the two values. However, molality is more difficult to measure in the human body; thus, molarity—the slightly less accurate unit of concentration—is more often used.

Osmoles, Osmolarity, and Osmolality

Another means of expressing concentration is with **osmoles (osm)**, which reflects whether a substance either dissolves, or dissolves and dissociates, when placed into a solution (e.g., whether it is a nonelectrolyte or an electrolyte). It is the unit of measurement for the number of particles in solution. The term osmole generally is used to reflect the extent a solution is able to alter water movement through osmosis (a concept described in section 4.3b). If a solute dissolves but does not dissociate, such as occurs when glucose, amino acids, or proteins are placed in water, then the osmolarity = 1 osmole (osm). However, if the solute both dissolves and dissociates, such as occurs with both NaCl and $CaCl_2$, then there is a change in the number of particles after the solute is in solution. A one molar (1 M) solution of NaCl dissociates in solution to form both 1 M Na^+ and 1 M Cl^-. The osmoles of 1 M of a NaCl solution = 2 osm. What would you predict for the osmoles of $CaCl_2$? Each molecule of $CaCl_2$ dissolves into three particles: 1 Ca^{2+} and 2 Cl^-; thus, 1 M $CaCl_2$ = 3 osm.

Osmoles can be expressed as either osmolarity or osmolality. **Osmolarity** is the number of particles in a 1 liter solution, whereas **osmolality** is the number of particles in 1 kilogram of water. Osmolality more accurately reflects the osmotic movement of water in the body but it is difficult to measure. Osmolarity is a close approximation to osmolality. Although osmolarity is less

Table 2.2   Expressing Solution Concentrations

Solution Concentration	Expressed As	Unit of Measurement	Examples
Mass/volume	Mass of solute per volume of solution	µg solute/dL solution mg solute/dL solution	Normal blood concentration of iron is within the range of 40 to 150 µg/dL. Normal blood concentration of glucose is between 70 and 110 mg/dL.
Mass/volume percent	Grams of solute per 100 milliliters (mL) of solution	grams/100 mL	5% dextrose intravenous (IV) solution (D5W) has a concentration of 5 grams of dextrose (glucose) per 100 mL of solution. Physiologic saline (0.9% NaCl) has 0.9 grams of NaCl per 100 mL of solution.
Molarity	Moles of solute per liter of solution	moles solute/L solution	0.164 mol/L solution
Molality	Moles of solute per kilogram of solvent	moles solute/kg solvent	0.164 mol/kg solvent

mg = milligrams; dL = deciliters; kg = kilograms; µg = micrograms

accurate, it is often the preferred unit of measurement for the same reason that molarity is used over molality.

The range of values associated with the body is generally much smaller than osmoles and given as milliosmoles (mOsm). Note that 1 osm = 1000 mOsm. Thus, normal blood serum may be expressed as either 275 to 295 mOsm per liter or 275 to 295 mOsm per kilogram.

Moles and Molecular Mass

Notice in table 2.2 that molarity and molality are based on the number of particles in units called a **mole.** The specific value of 1 mole is 6.022×10^{23} atoms, ions, or molecules. The number of particles may seem huge, but the particles themselves are minuscule.

A mole is the mass in grams that is equal to either the atomic mass of an element or the molecular mass of a compound. For example, a mole of carbon is equal to 12.01 grams. **Molecular mass** is determined using the molecular formula and the average atomic mass for each element. To find a compound's molecular mass, multiply the number of units of each element by its average atomic mass and add together the totals. The molecular mass of glucose ($C_6H_{12}O_6$), for example, is determined as follows:

$$6 \text{ carbon atoms} \times 12.01 \text{ amu} = 72.06 \text{ amu}$$
$$12 \text{ hydrogen atoms} \times 1.008 \text{ amu} = 12.10 \text{ amu}$$
$$6 \text{ oxygen atoms} \times 15.99 \text{ amu} = 95.94 \text{ amu}$$
$$\text{Molecular mass} = 180.10 \text{ amu}$$

Thus, 1 mole of glucose ($C_6H_{12}O_6$) would be equal to 180.10 grams (with some variation due to isotopes).

 WHAT DID YOU LEARN?

 26   What are four ways solution concentration may be expressed?

2.7 Biological Macromolecules

Four classes of organic biological macromolecules (biomolecules) can be distinguished in living systems: lipids, carbohydrates, nucleic acids, and proteins. We begin this section by discussing the similarities among the four classes, then describe each class in detail.

2.7a General Characteristics

 LEARNING OBJECTIVES

1. Differentiate between an organic molecule and an inorganic molecule.
2. Describe the general chemical composition of biomolecules.
3. Define a monomer and polymer.
4. Describe the role of water in both dehydration and hydrolysis reactions in altering biomolecules.

Biomolecules are a subset of organic molecules. **Organic molecules** are defined as molecules that contain carbon. Most organic molecules are a component of living organisms or have been produced from them. All other types of molecules are **inorganic molecules** including water, salts (e.g., sodium chloride), acids (e.g., carbonic acid), and bases (e.g., sodium hydroxide).

Chemical Composition

Biomolecules always contain carbon, hydrogen, and generally oxygen. Some biomolecules may also have one or more of the following: nitrogen (N), phosphorus (P), or sulfur (S). Notice that all of these elements (except hydrogen) are clustered on the right side of the periodic table (see figure 2.1a).

The carbon component of biomolecules may simply be an individual carbon atom or numerous carbon atoms arranged in a "carbon skeleton." The structure of a carbon skeleton may be a chain, branch, or ring (see figure 2.9).

The single carbon atom or the carbon skeleton within some biomolecules only have hydrogen atoms attached. These molecules are more specifically called hydrocarbons. They are nonpolar molecules because they contain only C—C and C—H bonds. Consequently,

INTEGRATE

LEARNING STRATEGY

You can use the acronym **CLaPiN** to remember the four major classes of macromolecules—carbohydrates, lipids, proteins, and nucleic acids.

Functional Group	Structural Formula	Properties	Representative Molecules	Structural Diagram of Example Molecule
Hydroxyl	—OH	• Polar • Forms hydrogen bonds • Increases molecules' solubility in water	• Carbohydrates • Proteins • Nucleic acids • Lipids	Glucose
Carbonyl	O‖ —C—	• Polar • Forms hydrogen bonds • Increases molecules' solubility in water	• Carbohydrates • Nucleic acids	Acetaldehyde
Carboxyl (carboxylic acid)	O‖ —C—OH	• Polar • Forms hydrogen bonds • Increases molecules' solubility in water • Acts as an acid	• Proteins • Lipids	Fatty acid
Amine	H | —N—H	• Polar • Forms hydrogen bonds • Increases molecules' solubility in water • Acts as a base	• Proteins • Nucleic acids	Alanine
Phosphate	O‖ —O—P—O⁻ | O⁻	• Polar • Forms hydrogen bonds • Increases molecules' solubility in water • Forms phosphodiester bonds • Acts as an acid (shown here with hydrogens released)	• Nucleic acids • Phospholipids • ATP	Adenosine triphosphate (ATP)
Sulfhydryl	—S—H	• Forms disulfide bridge	• Proteins	Cysteine

Figure 2.17 Molecules Containing Functional Groups. When attached to a carbon skeleton, functional groups change the chemical properties of the molecules. For example, most functional groups increase the polarity of the molecule.

hydrocarbons are hydrophobic and not soluble in water. Methane gas (CH_4) is an example of a hydrocarbon.

In comparison, the single carbon atom or the carbon skeleton of other biomolecules may contain functional groups. A functional group is two or more atoms that display specific chemical characteristics. Some common examples of these groups include hydroxyl (—OH), amine (—NH_2), and carboxyl (—COOH). Almost all functional groups are polar and able to form hydrogen bonds, increasing the biomolecule's solubility in water. In addition, some functional groups may act like an acid and release H^+, such as a carboxyl group, whereas others may act like a base by binding H^+, such as an amine group. Biomolecules that contain functional groups typically have more than one within it. Important functional groups are presented in **figure 2.17**.

Polymers

Many important biomolecules are called polymers. **Polymers** are molecules that are made up of repeating subunits called **monomers,** and each monomer is either identical or similar in its chemical structure. Carbohydrates, nucleic acids, and proteins are polymers (lipids are not). Carbohydrates contain sugar monomers, nucleic acids have nucleotide monomers, and proteins are composed of amino acid monomers.

Process of Dehydration and Hydrolysis

Two processes are associated with both the synthesis and breakdown of complex biomolecules: dehydration synthesis and hydrolysis. During the synthesis of complex molecules from simpler subunits, one specific subunit loses an —H, and the other subunit loses an —OH, to form a water molecule as a new covalent bond is produced. This type of reaction is called **dehydration** (*de* = away; *hydro* = water) **synthesis** or *condensation* because the equivalent of a water molecule is "lost" from the original structures **(figure 2.18)**.

During the breakdown of complex molecules, H_2O molecules are split. An —H is added to one subunit, and an —OH is added to another subunit in the complex molecule, and the chemical bond is broken between them. Because the equivalent of water is added to digest the molecule, this process is referred to as **hydrolysis** (hī-drol′i-sis; *lysis* = to dissolve) **reaction.** We will see examples of both of these types of reactions in the following sections on biomolecules.

WHAT DID YOU LEARN?

27 Using a different color than you did for highlighting the common ions on the periodic table, highlight the six common elements that form organic molecules. Which element both (a) forms a common ion, and (b) is a common element in biomolecules?

28 What functional groups may act as an acid?

29 What defines a polymer? List the three biomolecules that are polymers and the monomers that compose them.

(a)   (b)

Figure 2.18 Dehydration and Hydrolysis. (*a*) Dehydration synthesis involves the loss of a water molecule during the formation of complex molecules from simpler components. (*b*) Hydrolysis occurs with the addition of a water molecule during the digestion of complex molecules to form simpler components.

2.7b Lipids

✔️ **LEARNING OBJECTIVES**

5. Describe the general characteristics of a lipid.
6. Identify the four types of lipids and their physiologic roles.

Lipids are the only category of biomolecules that are not polymers, because they are not formed from repeating monomers. Rather, they are a very diverse group of fatty, water-insoluble (hydrophobic) molecules that function as stored nutrients, components of cellular membranes, and hormones. Triglycerides (neutral fats), phospholipids, steroids, and eicosanoids are the four primary classes of lipids. They are summarized in table 2.3.

Triglycerides: Energy Storage

Triglycerides (trī-glis'ĕr-idz; *tri* = three), or *triacylglycerols*, are the most common form of lipids in living things. They are used for long-term energy storage in adipose connective tissue (section 5.2) and for structural support, cushioning, and insulation of the body. Adipose connective tissue deep to the skin in the abdomen, for example, serves as long-term energy storage and insulates the abdomen against heat loss. Adipose connective tissue posterior to the eye cushions the eye within the eye's bony orbit.

Table 2.3 Major Classes of Lipids*

Class	Structure	Description	Function
Triglycerides		Composed of glycerol and three fatty acids Fatty acids may be saturated or unsaturated	Long-term energy storage in adipose connective tissue Structural support, cushioning, and insulation of the body
Phospholipids		Composed of glycerol, two fatty acids, a phosphate, and various organic groups Glycerol, phosphate, and organic groups form a polar head, and fatty acids form two nonpolar tails	Major component of membranes including the plasma membrane, which forms the chemical barrier between the inside and outside of a cell
Steroids (includes cholesterol, steroid hormones, and bile salts)		Four rings composed predominantly of hydrocarbons that differ in the side chains extending from the rings	Cholesterol is a component of cell membranes and is the precursor molecule for synthesis of other steroids Steroid hormones are regulatory molecules released by certain endocrine glands Bile salts facilitate micelle formation in the digestive tract
Eicosanoids (includes prostaglandins, prostacylins, thromboxanes, and leukotrienes)		Modified 20-carbon fatty acids synthesized from arachidonic acid	Local acting signaling molecules associated with all body systems, with primary functions in the inflammatory response of the immune system and communication within the nervous system

*Glycolipids and fat-soluble vitamins are also types of lipids.

Triglycerides are formed from a glycerol molecule and three fatty acids. Glycerol is a three-carbon molecule with a hydroxyl functional group attached to each carbon. A fatty acid is composed of a long chain of hydrocarbons with a carboxylic acid functional group on one end. Triglyceride molecules form by the process of dehydration synthesis, during which the equivalent of a water molecule is lost for each fatty acid added to the glycerol: an —H from the glycerol and an —OH from the fatty acid (figure 2.19).

Fatty acids may vary in length—commonly ranging in even numbers from 14 to 20 carbons—and may differ in the number of double bonds between the carbons in the chain. The fatty acid is saturated if it lacks double bonds—that is, every carbon has the maximum number of hydrogen atoms bound to it. An unsaturated fatty acid has one double bond, and a polyunsaturated fatty acid has two or more double bonds.

Adipose connective tissue is used to store triglycerides. When conditions of excess nutrients exist, adipose connective tissue binds fatty acids to glycerol to form triglycerides in a dehydration synthesis process called lipogenesis (lĭp′o-jĕn′e-sis; lipos = fat, genesis = production). Adipose connective tissue breaks down triglycerides and releases the products into the blood when nutrients are needed. This process is a hydrolysis reaction called lipolysis (li-pol′i-sis; lysis = to break).

Phospholipids: Membranes

Phospholipids were previously described as amphipathic molecules that form chemical barriers of cell membranes. The chemical structure of a phospholipid is similar to a triglyceride, except that one end of the glycerol has a polar phosphate group with various organic groups (choline, ethanolamine, or the amino acid serine) attached to it instead of a fatty acid (see table 2.3). The glycerol, phosphate, and organic

Figure 2.19 Triglycerides. (*a*) A glycerol and three fatty acid molecules. (*b*) A triglyceride molecule. Lipogenesis occurs through a dehydration synthesis reaction that involves the removal of a water molecule between each fatty acid and a glycerol. Lipolysis is a hydrolysis reaction that splits the glycerol and three fatty acids by the addition of water at each of the fatty acids.

CLINICAL VIEW
Fatty Acids: Saturated, Unsaturated, and Trans Fats

Most naturally occurring animal fats are **saturated,** whereas most naturally occurring vegetable fats (except palm and coconut tropical oils) are **unsaturated.** You can usually distinguish between a saturated and unsaturated fat by whether it is solid (most saturated fats) or liquid (most unsaturated fats) at room temperature. Unsaturated fats are generally healthier than saturated fats—which is why we are encouraged to use olive oil instead of butter for our cooking.

Unsaturated fats are converted to saturated fats through the process of **hydrogenation.** For example, vegetable oil may be hydrogenated to form margarine. Recent studies have shown that partial hydrogenation of fatty acids may lead to the production of **trans fats.** These fats are solid at a lower temperature than their counterparts, "cis-fats." Studies have shown that trans fats in the diet increase the risk of developing lipid buildup on the inside of blood vessels (atherosclerosis), a condition that increases the risk of heart attack or stroke.

groups are polar and form the water-soluble hydrophilic part of the molecule referred to as the **hydrophilic (polar) head.** The two fatty acid molecules attached to the other carbons of the glycerol form a water-insoluble hydrophobic end called the **hydrophobic (nonpolar) tails.**

Steroids: Ringed Structures Including Some Hormones

Steroids are composed predominantly of hydrocarbons arranged in a distinct multiringed structure. A steroid has four attached carbon rings; three rings have six carbon atoms and one ring has five carbon atoms. Steroids differ in the side chains extending from their rings. Steroids include cholesterol, steroid hormones (e.g., testosterone, estrogen, and progesterone), and bile salts. Cholesterol is a component of animal cell membranes and is also the precursor used to synthesize other steroids. Cholesterol is synthesized in the liver from fatty acids and also may be obtained from eating animal products such as meat, eggs, and milk.

Eicosanoids: Locally Acting Hormones

Eicosanoids are modified 20-carbon fatty acids that are synthesized as needed from arachidonic acid, a common component of both plasma membranes (the boundary of a cell) and nuclear membranes (the boundary of the nucleus). Four classes of eicosanoids are produced and include prostaglandins, prostacyclins, thromboxanes, and leukotrienes (section 17.3b). These molecules act locally and are signaling molecules associated with all body systems: they have primary functions in the inflammatory response of the immune system and communication within the nervous system.

Other Lipids

Glycolipids—lipid molecules with carbohydrate attached—are also lipids. These molecules are associated with plasma membranes and serve several roles, including cellular binding to form tissues (section 4.2). Fat-soluble vitamins such as vitamins A, E, and K (see section 27.1b) are also lipids.

WHAT DID YOU LEARN?

30 Do lipid molecules typically dissolve in water? Explain.

31 Which class of lipids forms cell membranes? What characteristic allows it to perform this function?

2.7c Carbohydrates

LEARNING OBJECTIVES

7. Describe the distinguishing characteristics of carbohydrates.

8. Explain the relationship between glucose and glycogen.

9. Name some other carbohydrates found in living systems.

The term **carbohydrate** means "hydrated carbon." Nearly every carbon is hydrated with the equivalent of a water molecule—that is, both an —H and an —OH are usually attached to every carbon. The general chemical formula for carbohydrates is $(CH_2O)_n$, where n indicates the number of carbon atoms that are in a molecule. The number of carbon atoms typically ranges from 3–7. The least complex carbohydrates are simple sugar monomers called **monosaccharides.** All monosaccharides have between three and seven carbon atoms. Carbohydrates formed from two monosaccharides are **disaccharides,** and those with many monosaccharides are **polysaccharides.**

Glucose and Glycogen

Glucose is a six-carbon (hexose) carbohydrate that is the most common monosaccharide. It is shown here (and throughout the text) in the ring form (**figure 2.20**). Glucose is crucial to life processes because it is the primary nutrient supplying energy to cells. In fact, the brain and other nervous tissue use glucose almost exclusively as their nutrient fuel molecule. The concentration of blood glucose must be carefully maintained by homeostasis (see section 1.5) to ensure a continual, adequate energy supply for cellular activities. One way the body ensures its supply is to store excess glucose immediately following a meal. Liver and skeletal muscle tissue absorb the excess glucose—and then bind the glucose monomers together to form a polysaccharide called **glycogen** by a process called **glycogenesis**

Figure 2.20 Glucose and Glycogen. (*a*) The monomer glucose is typically shown in ring form. (*b*) Glycogen is a polysaccharide composed of multiple glucose monomers.

(a) Glucose

(b) Glycogen

Glycogenesis

Glycogenolysis

(glī'kō-jen'ĕ-sis). The glycogen polymer is shown in figure 2.20b—although only several glucose molecules are shown, glycogen may contain thousands of glucose monomers.

When blood glucose levels drop between meals, the liver hydrolyzes some of the glycogen into glucose and releases it into the blood. This process is called **glycogenolysis** (glī'kō-jĕ-nol'i-sis). Thus, the liver serves the role of a "glucose bank," storing glycogen, then breaking down glycogen as needed to release glucose. Nutrient storage and release are important in the endocrine regulation of nutrient blood levels of both triglycerides and glucose (see section 17.7).

Other Types of Carbohydrates

Other hexose monosaccharides, including galactose and fructose, are glucose isomers (**figure 2.21a**). Some monosaccharides, such as ribose and deoxyribose, are composed of five carbons. These five-carbon monosaccharides are called *pentose sugars*. The pentose sugars ribose and deoxyribose are structural components of nucleic acids, which are discussed in the following section. The only structural difference between these pentose sugars is the lack of an oxygen atom on carbon two of the deoxyribose sugar.

Disaccharides are composed of two simple sugars bonded together (figure 2.21b). The most common disaccharides are sucrose (table sugar), lactose (milk sugar), and maltose (malt sugar, which is found in sprouting grains). All three disaccharides contain a glucose monosaccharide bonded to a second hexose monosaccharide.

Polysaccharides are composed of three or more sugars. The common polysaccharide in animals is glycogen. Polysaccharides in plants include starch and cellulose, which are also composed of repeating glucose monomers. Plant starch is a major nutritional source of glucose for humans. It is found in potatoes, grains, and many other plant foods. Glucose released from the breakdown of starch within the digestive tract is absorbed into the blood. Cellulose, a structural polysaccharide of plant cell walls, however, is a source of fiber (nondigestible substances). Humans cannot digest cellulose because of the unique chemical bonds between the glucose molecules. The breakdown of both disaccharides and polysaccharides is described in section 26.4a.

 WHAT DID YOU LEARN?

32 What is the repeating monomer of glycogen? Where is glycogen stored in the body?

33 For each of the following, indicate if it is a monosaccharide, disaccharide, or polysaccharide: fructose, galactose, glucose, glycogen, lactose, maltose, starch, and sucrose.

Figure 2.21 Other Simple Carbohydrates. (*a*) Hexose monosaccharides include galactose and fructose, and pentose monosaccharides include ribose and deoxyribose. (*b*) Disaccharides include sucrose, lactose, and maltose.

(a) Nucleotide monomer

(b) Nitrogenous bases

Pyrimidines

Cytosine (C)
(both DNA and RNA)

Thymine (T)
(DNA only)

Uracil (U)
(RNA only)

Purines

Adenine (A)
(both DNA and RNA)

Guanine (G)
(both DNA and RNA)

Phosphate group

Nitrogenous base

Sugar

OH in RNA

H in DNA

Unique to RNA

5′

Phosphate group

Nitrogenous base

Ribose sugar

Nucleotide

Phosphodiester bonds

3′

OH

(c) RNA (single-stranded)

Sugar-phosphate "backbone"

Nitrogenous base

Deoxyribose sugar

Phosphate group

Nucleotide

5′

Unique to DNA

Hydrogen bonds between nitrogenous bases

3′

(d) DNA (double-stranded)

Figure 2.22 Nucleic Acids. (*a*) A general representation of a nucleotide monomer, which is composed of a pentose sugar (ribose or deoxyribose), a phosphate functional group, and a nitrogenous base. Nucleotides that contain ribose are ribonucleotides, and nucleotides that contain deoxyribose are deoxyribonucleotides. (*b*) The five nitrogenous bases. (*c*) RNA is a single-stranded nucleic acid formed from repeating units of ribonucleotides linked together by phosphodiester bonds. Ribonucleotides contain the nitrogenous bases uracil, guanine, adenine, and cytosine. (*d*) DNA is a double-stranded nucleic acid with each strand composed of repeating units of deoxyribonucleotides linked together by phosphodiester bonds. Deoxyribonucleotides contain the nitrogenous bases thymine, guanine, adenine, and cytosine. Hydrogen bonds between complementary bases (T:A and C:G) hold the two strands together. Both RNA and DNA participate in protein formation.

2.7d Nucleic Acids

✓ LEARNING OBJECTIVES

10. Describe the general structure of a nucleic acid.

11. Describe the structure of a nucleotide monomer.

12. Distinguish between DNA and RNA.

13. Name other important nucleotides.

Nucleic acids (figure 2.22) are macromolecules that store and transfer genetic or hereditary information within cells. Originally discovered within the cell nucleus, nucleic acids ultimately determine the types of proteins synthesized within cells—a process described in detail in section 4.7.

The two classes of nucleic acid are deoxyribonucleic acid (DNA) and ribonucleic acid (RNA). Both DNA and RNA are polymers composed of **nucleotide** monomers. These monomers are linked together through covalent bonds between one nucleotide monomer and an adjacent nucleotide monomer. This covalent linkage is called a **phosphodiester bond.**

The Nucleotide Monomer

A nucleotide monomer has three components: a sugar, a phosphate group, and a nitrogenous base. The sugar is a five-carbon pentose sugar (deoxyribose for DNA and ribose for RNA). A phosphate functional group is attached at carbon number five; a nitrogenous base is attached to the same sugar but at carbon number one. A **nitrogenous base** has either a single-ring or a double-ring structure that contains both carbon and nitrogen within the ring.

Five different nitrogenous bases commonly occur in nucleic acids. Single-ring nitrogenous bases are called **pyrimidines,** and they include cytosine (C), uracil (U), and thymine (T) (you can remember these bases with the acronym CUT). Double-ring nitrogenous bases are called **purines,** which include adenine (A) and guanine (G). Nitrogenous bases within either group—pyrimidines or purines—differ in the functional groups attached to the ring.

Deoxyribonucleic Acid (DNA)

Deoxyribonucleic acid (DNA) is a double-stranded nucleic acid; it can be found as a component of chromosomes within the nucleus. A small circular strand of DNA is also within the mitochondria. (These cellular components are described in chapters 3 and 4.) The nucleotides that form DNA have a deoxyribose sugar, a phosphate, and one of four nitrogenous bases: adenine, guanine, cytosine, or thymine. Notice that DNA does not contain uracil. The double strands of nucleic acid are held together by hydrogen bonds formed between complementary nitrogenous bases: thymine with adenine and guanine with cytosine.

Table 2.4	Differences Between RNA and DNA	
Characteristic	**RNA**	**DNA**
Number of strands	1	2
Sugar	Ribose	Deoxyribose
Nitrogenous base	Uracil (unique to RNA)	Thymine (unique to DNA)

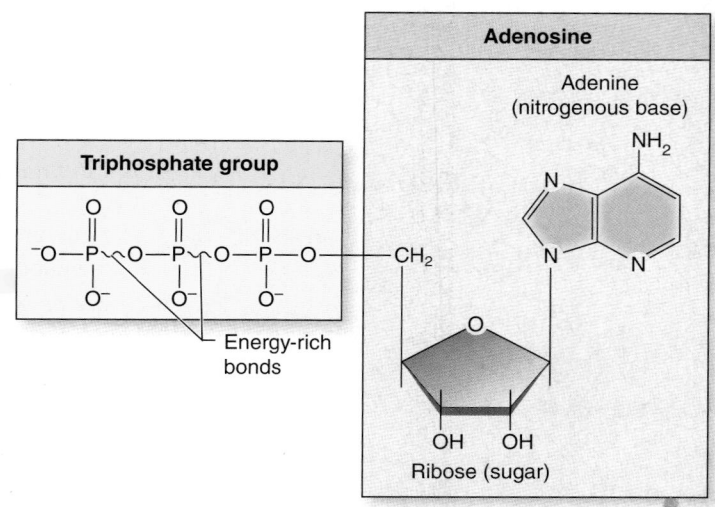

Figure 2.23 ATP. Adenosine triphosphate (ATP) is composed of the sugar ribose and the nitrogenous base adenine, which together are referred to as adenosine. Three phosphates attached to adenosine form adenosine triphosphate.

Ribonucleic Acid (RNA)

Ribonucleic acid (RNA) is a single-stranded nucleic acid located both within the cell nucleus and within the cytoplasm of the cell. The nucleotides that are part of RNA molecules are composed of the sugar ribose, a phosphate, and one of four nitrogenous bases: adenine, guanine, cytosine, or uracil. RNA does not contain thymine. **Table 2.4** compares the chemical structural differences between RNA and DNA.

Other Important Nucleotides

Several other nucleotides have key roles in cells. **Adenosine triphosphate** (a-den′ō-sēn trī-fos′fāt), or **ATP,** is composed of the nitrogenous base adenine, a ribose sugar, and three phosphate groups covalently linked **(figure 2.23)**. ATP is the central molecule in the transfer of chemical energy within cells. Biologists often refer to this molecule as the "energy currency" of a cell. The covalent phosphate bond linkages between the last two phosphate groups are unique, energy-rich bonds that release relatively large amounts of energy when they are broken.

Two other important nucleotide-containing molecules are *nicotinamide adenine dinucleotide (NAD⁺)* and *flavin adenine dinucleotide (FAD).* Both molecules participate in the production of ATP that occurs in cellular mitochondria. (ATP, NAD⁺, and FAD are discussed in more detail in chapter 3.)

💡 WHAT DID YOU LEARN?

34 What is the general function of nucleic acids?

35 What are the structural differences between RNA and DNA?

2.7e Proteins

✓ LEARNING OBJECTIVES

14. List the general functions of proteins.

15. Describe the general structure of amino acids and proteins.

Scientists estimate that more than 10,000 different proteins are synthesized by cells, and following their synthesis they function within a cell, within a plasma membrane, blood plasma, and other body fluids. Proteins serve a vast array of functions. For example, proteins

- Serve as *catalysts* (enzymes) in most metabolic reactions of the body
- Act in *defense*, which occurs, for example, when immunoglobulins (antibodies) attach to foreign substances for their elimination
- Aid in *transport*, such as hemoglobin molecules transporting respiratory gases within the blood
- Contribute to structural *support*, such as collagen, a major component of ligaments and tendons
- Cause *movement*, when myosin and actin proteins interact during contraction of muscle tissue
- Perform *regulation*, such as occurs when the peptide hormone insulin helps control blood glucose levels
- Provide *storage*, such as ferritin, which stores iron in liver cells

Table 2.5 organizes the functions of proteins into several categories providing the general function, class of protein, and examples for each.

Table 2.5	Protein Functions	
Function	**Class of Protein**	**Examples of Proteins and Their Functions**
Catalysts	Enzymes	Hydrolytic enzymes: Cleave polysaccharides
		Isomerases: Convert a molecule to its isomer
		DNA polymerase: Synthesizes DNA
		Kinases: Transfer phosphate functional groups
Defense	Immunoglobulins	Antibodies: "Tag" foreign proteins for elimination
	Cell surface antigens	Major histocompatibility complex (MHC) proteins: Serve as "self" recognition molecules
Transport	Circulating transporters	Hemoglobin: Carries O_2 and CO_2 in blood
		Transferrin: Carries iron in the blood
	Membrane transporters	Cytochromes: Participate in electron transport
		Sodium–potassium pump: Participates in establishing a resting membrane potential
		Glucose transporter: Transports glucose across plasma membranes
Support	Supporting proteins	Collagen: Forms ligaments, tendons
		Keratin: Forms hair, nails
		Fibrin: Forms blood clots
Movement	Contractile proteins	Actin: Participates in contraction of muscle fibers
		Myosin: Participates in contraction of muscle fibers
Regulation	Osmotic proteins	Albumin: Maintains osmotic concentration of blood
	Hormones	Insulin: Controls blood glucose levels
		Antidiuretic hormone (ADH): Increases water retention by kidneys
		Oxytocin: Stimulates uterine contractions and milk ejection
	Molecular chaperones	Protein disulfide isomerase: Participates in folding of proteins that involve intramolecular interactions
Storage	Metal binding proteins	Ferritin: Stores iron in liver cells
		Casein: Binds iron in breast milk
	Ion binding proteins	Calmodulin: Binds calcium ions in sarcoplasmic reticulum (SR) of muscle cells

General Protein Structure

Proteins are polymers composed of one or more linear strands of **amino acid** monomers that may number in the thousands **(figure 2.24)**. Twenty different amino acids are normally found in the proteins of living organisms. Each amino acid has both an amine ($—NH_2$) and a carboxylic acid (—COOH) functional group. Both functional groups are covalently linked to the same carbon atom, which accounts for the general name "amino acid" for these monomers. The other two covalent bonds to this carbon are a hydrogen (—H) and different side-chain structures that are simply referred to as the **R group.** The R groups distinguish different amino acids from one another. Properties of the R groups form the basis for classifying amino acids (described later).

Amino acids are linked covalently by **peptide bonds** that form during dehydration synthesis reactions between the amine functional group of one amino acid and the carboxylic acid functional group of a second amino acid. An —H is lost from the amine group and an —OH from the carboxylic acid of another amino acid. The ends of a protein are distinguished as the **N-terminal** end, which has a free amine group, and the **C-terminal** end, which has a free carboxyl group.

A strand of amino acids that includes between 3 and 20 amino acids is termed an **oligopeptide,** whereas a **polypeptide** has a strand composed of between 21 and 199 amino acids. If more than 200 amino acids are linked, the structure is called a **protein.** (We use the general term *protein*, in this text, to apply to all three types of structures.)

Proteins with carbohydrate attached are called **glycoproteins.** ABO blood groups are based on structural differences in glycoproteins within the plasma membrane of erythrocytes (see section 18.3b).

Lipids, carbohydrates, nucleic acids, and proteins are four major classes of organic biomolecules that compose the human body. They are summarized in **figure 2.25.**

 WHAT DID YOU LEARN?

36 What are the monomers of proteins and the name of the bond between them?

37 What are the names of structures that contain: 2 amino acids, 3 to 20 amino acids, 21 to 199 amino acids, and 200 or more amino acids? What general term is used to refer to any of these structures?

(a)

(b)

(c)

Figure 2.24 Proteins. (*a*) Amino acids are the monomers of proteins. (*b*) Dehydration synthesis reaction occurs as a hydrogen atom is removed from the amine of one amino acid and a hydroxyl functional group is removed from the carboxylic acid of another amino acid to form a peptide bond between two amino acids. A molecule of water is formed during the process. (*c*) The polymer protein is composed of repeating amino acid monomers that are held together by peptide bonds.

(a) Lipids | Nonpolar and amphipathic molecules with four major subclasses

Triglycerides (storage form)

Adipose connective tissue cells with fat droplets

Triglycerides are the most common form of lipid in living things. They are used for long-term energy storage, structural support, cushioning, and insulation of the body.

Glycerol

Fatty acid (saturated or unsaturated)

Blood

Fatty acid

Eicosanoids (local acting molecules)

Prostaglandins
Prostacyclins
Thromboxanes
Leukotrienes

Phospholipids

Chemical barrier of cells

Polar head

Nonpolar tails

Steroids

Component of plasma membrane

Cholesterol

Precursor for steroid hormones and bile salts

Plasma membrane

(c) Nucleic acids and nucleotides | DNA and RNA

Chromosome

DNA (polymer)

INTEGRATE CONCEPT OVERVIEW

Figure 2.25 **Organic Biomolecules.**

The four primary organic biological macromolecules include: (a) lipids, (b) carbohydrates, (c) nucleic acids, and (d) proteins.

Nucleotide (monomer)

Nitrogenous base

P Phosphate group

O

5-carbon sugar

OH

Nucleotides are monomers that make up the nucleic acid biomolecules of DNA and RNA. There are 5 different nucleotides, each with a different nitrogenous base (C,U,T,G,A).

RNA (polymer)

Nucleus

(b) Carbohydrates | Two important molecules are glucose and glycogen

Glucose (monomer)

Glycogen (polymer)

The liver stores glucose as glycogen and breaks down glycogen to glucose as needed.

Fatty acid

Blood glucose

Plasma proteins (e.g., albumin)

High energy molecules

Plasma membrane protein (e.g., channel)

Extracellular proteins (e.g., collagen)

Fatty acid and Glucose

O_2

H_2O and CO_2

Intracellular proteins (e.g., cytoskeleton)

ATP (a nucleotide)

Adenine

P P P

Triphosphate group

O

5-carbon sugar

OH OH

ATP is a nucleotide that is the central molecule in the transfer of chemical energy within cells. It is often referred to as the "energy currency" of a cell.

Energy transferred

(d) Proteins | Most diverse organic biomolecule

Proteins are macromolecules made of one or more linear strands of amino acid monomers. Proteins, once synthesized, function within the cell, plasma membrane, blood plasma, and in other body fluids.

Instructions for protein synthesis

Amino acid (monomer)

Protein (polymer)

H

H

O

N

C

C

R

Amino acids are the building blocks that form proteins. There are 20 different amino acids: they differ at their R groups.

2.8 Protein Structure

Here we describe protein structure in more depth, including categories of amino acids, amino acid sequence, and three-dimensional protein shape. We also discuss how a protein can lose its three-dimensional shape and the consequences of this occurrence.

2.8a Categories of Amino Acids

LEARNING OBJECTIVES

1. Name the categories of amino acids.
2. Distinguish between nonpolar, polar, and charged amino acids.
3. Give examples of amino acids with special characteristics.

Amino acids are organized into groups based on the chemical characteristics of their R group. They are nonpolar, polar, charged, and those having special functions (figure 2.26).

- **Nonpolar amino acids** contain R groups with either hydrogen (glycine) or hydrocarbons (alanine, valine, leucine, isoleucine, phenylalanine, and tryptophan). They tend to group with other nonpolar amino acids by hydrophobic interactions within the body's aqueous environment.

- **Polar amino acids** contain R groups with elements in addition to carbon and hydrogen (e.g., O, N, or S) (serine, threonine, asparagine, glutamine, and tyrosine). They form interactions with other polar amino acids and with water molecules.

- **Charged amino acids** can have either a negative charge or a positive charge. Those with a negatively charged R group include glutamic acid and aspartic acid, and those with a positively charged R group include histidine, lysine, and arginine. An ionic bond (electrostatic interaction) can form between an R group with a negative charge and an R group with a positive charge. Groups of amino acids that are either polar or charged are hydrophilic, and their presence increases the solubility of the protein in water.

- **Amino acids with special functions**—three amino acids have unique characteristics. The R group in proline attaches to the amine group, forming a ring. Proline amino acids cause a bend in the protein chain. The sulfhydryl functional groups of two cysteine amino acids form **disulfide covalent bonds.** These bonds are significant in stabilizing the folding of a protein (described next). Methionine is always the first amino acid positioned when a protein is synthesized (see section 4.7b), and it may or may not be removed later.

WHAT DID YOU LEARN?

38. Why is the amino acid leucine (figure 2.26) classified as a nonpolar amino acid?

INTEGRATE

LEARNING STRATEGY

The construction of proteins from amino acids is similar to the building of words from the letters of an alphabet. Just as English, Spanish, and many other languages are built upon words formed by grouping letters together, the "language of proteins" is built upon the grouping of amino acids together.

Nonpolar

Glycine (Gly)

NH$_2$—C—C—OH
H, O, H

Alanine (Ala)

NH$_2$—C—C—OH
H, O, CH$_3$

Valine (Val)

NH$_2$—C—C—OH
H, O
CH
CH$_3$ CH$_3$

Isoleucine (Ile)

NH$_2$—C—C—OH
H, O
H—C—CH$_3$
CH$_2$
CH$_3$

Leucine (Leu)

NH$_2$—C—C—OH
H, O
CH$_2$
CH
CH$_3$ CH$_3$

Phenylalanine (Phe)

NH$_2$—C—C—OH
H, O
CH$_2$

Tryptophan (Trp)

NH$_2$—C—C—OH
H, O
CH$_2$
C
HN
HC
N
H$^+$
(indole ring)

Polar

Serine (Ser)

NH$_2$—C—C—OH
H, O
CH$_2$
OH

Threonine (Thr)

NH$_2$—C—C—OH
H, O
OH—C—CH$_3$
CH$_3$

Asparagine (Asn)

NH$_2$—C—C—OH
H, O
CH$_2$
C
NH$_2$ O

Glutamine (Gln)

NH$_2$—C—C—OH
H, O
CH$_2$
CH$_2$
C
NH$_2$ O

Tyrosine (Tyr)

NH$_2$—C—C—OH
H, O
CH$_2$
OH

Charged

(–) Charge

Glutamate (Glu)

NH$_2$—C—C—OH
H, O
CH$_2$
CH$_2$
C
O O$^-$

Aspartate (Asp)

NH$_2$—C—C—OH
H, O
CH$_2$
C
O O$^-$

(+) Charge

Histidine (His)

NH$_2$—C—C—OH
H, O
CH$_2$
C
H
HC CH
N
H$^+$

Lysine (Lys)

NH$_2$—C—C—OH
H, O
CH$_2$
CH$_2$
CH$_2$
CH$_2$—NH$_3^+$

Arginine (Arg)

NH$_2$—C—C—OH
H, O
CH$_2$
CH$_2$
CH$_2$
NH
CH$_2$—NH$_2^+$
NH$_2$

Special Functions

Proline (Pro)

NH$_2^+$, O
CH$_2$ CH—C—O$^-$
CH$_2$ CH$_2$

Allows bends in protein chain

Cysteine (Cys)

NH$_2$—C—C—OH
H, O
CH$_2$
S
H

Forms disulfide bond

Methionine (Met)

NH$_2$—C—C—OH
H, O
CH$_2$
CH$_2$
S
CH$_3$

Always the first amino acid in a protein sequence (may be removed following synthesis of protein)

Figure 2.26 Amino Acids. Amino acids are categorized based on the chemical properties of the R groups. The categories include nonpolar, polar, charged, and those with special functions.

Primary structure

Linear sequence of amino acids joined by peptide bonds

(a)

Figure 2.27 Levels of Protein Structure. Amino acids bonded together form protein polymers. There are four increasingly complex levels of organization. (*a*) The primary structure is the linear sequence of amino acids in the protein. (*b*) The secondary structures of a protein may include alpha helixes and beta-pleated sheets. (*c*) The tertiary structure is the completed 3-dimensional shape or conformation of the protein, which may be a globular or fibrous protein. (*d*) A quaternary structure is formed in some complex proteins when two or more protein molecules associate to form the final protein.

2.8b Amino Acid Sequence and Protein Conformation

✓ LEARNING OBJECTIVES

4. Describe the different types of intramolecular (or intermolecular) attractions that participate in both the folding of a protein and in maintaining its three-dimensional shape.

5. Distinguish between the four structural hierarchy levels of proteins.

6. Explain what is meant by denaturation and list factors that can cause it.

We describe a protein as being composed of a linear sequence of amino acids that are bonded together through covalent peptide bonds. This sequence is called its **primary structure** (**figure 2.27a**). The protein then folds to form into its three-dimensional shape, or **conformation.** Protein conformation is crucial for its proper function.

The conformational structure of proteins has increasingly complex hierarchies, or levels, of organization beyond a protein's primary structure, including secondary, tertiary, and perhaps quaternary structural levels. These more complex structural organizations are dependent upon intramolecular attractions between the amino acids in the linear sequence for the proper folding and maintaining of a protein's conformation. The process of protein folding is assisted by specialized proteins called *chaperones* that "direct" the folding process.

Secondary structure

Structural patterns within a protein that result from hydrogen bonds formed between amino acids

Alpha helix (spiral coil)   **Beta sheet (planar pleats)**

(b)

Tertiary structure

Final 3-dimensional shape of a protein, which contains repeating secondary structures

Globular protein   **Fibrous protein**

(c)

Quaternary structure

Molecule composed of two or more separate proteins

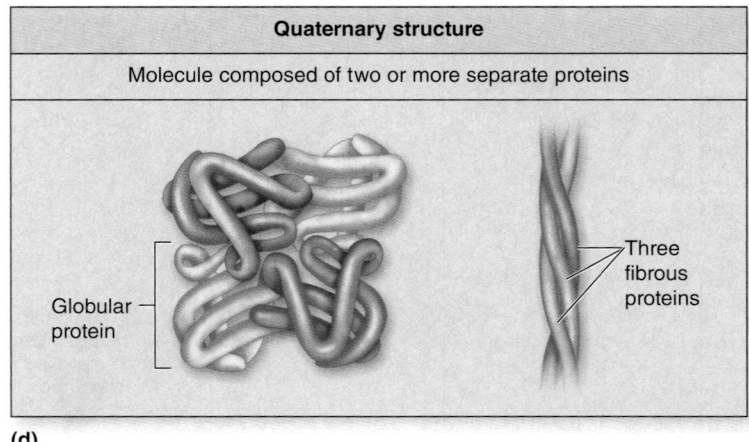

Globular protein

Three fibrous proteins

(d)

The intramolecular interactions that contribute to the final conformation of a protein are as follows:

- The primary protein structure is forced into its initial shape as hydrophobic exclusion "tucks" amino acids with nonpolar R groups into a more central location, limiting their contact with water.
- Hydrogen bonds form between polar R groups, and between the amine and carboxylic acid functional groups of closely positioned amino acids.
- Electrostatic interactions (ionic bonds) form between negatively charged and positively charged R groups.
- Disulfide bonds form between the sulfhydryl groups of two cysteine amino acids.

Higher levels of protein organization result from folding. **Secondary structures** are patterns within a protein that may repeat several times. The two distinctive secondary levels of organization are a spiral coil, called an **alpha helix** and a planar pleat arrangement, called a **beta sheet.** These secondary structures confer unique characteristics on the regions of the protein where they are found. Alpha helix gives some elasticity to fibrous proteins that are located, for example, in skin or hair. In contrast, beta sheets give some degree of flexibility to many globular proteins (e.g., enzymes).

Tertiary structure is the final three-dimensional shape exhibited by a completed polypeptide chain. Two categories of proteins—either fibrous or globular—are distinguished by their molecular shape. For example, **globular proteins** fold into a compact, often nearly spherical shape such as enzymes, antibodies, and some hormones. In comparison, **fibrous proteins** are extended linear molecules that are constituents of ligaments, tendons, and contractile proteins within muscle cells.

The **quaternary structure** of a protein is present only in those proteins with two or more polypeptide chains. The protein hemoglobin is an example because it is composed of four polypeptide chains. Each of these chains has its own primary, secondary, and tertiary structures. Only when the constituent polypeptides associate through intermolecular attractions to form the quaternary structure does the biological molecule become active. Therefore, hemoglobin is functional only when all four polypeptide chains are present in the correct association.

The normal function of a protein may also require a **prosthetic group.** These are nonprotein structures covalently bonded to the protein. The lipid heme group in the hemoglobin protein is an example of a prosthetic group.

WHAT DO YOU THINK?

7 Why might proteins be rendered nonfunctional by exposure to high temperatures?

The biological activity of a protein is usually disturbed or terminated when its conformation is changed. This is called **denaturation.** The tertiary structure of the protein is disrupted if the protein is heated or chemically altered. Usually, the loss of biological activity cannot be reversed. Denaturation may occur as a consequence of increased temperature because this increase weakens the intramolecular interactions that hold the protein in its three-dimensional shape. Alternatively, denaturation may take place in response to changes in pH.

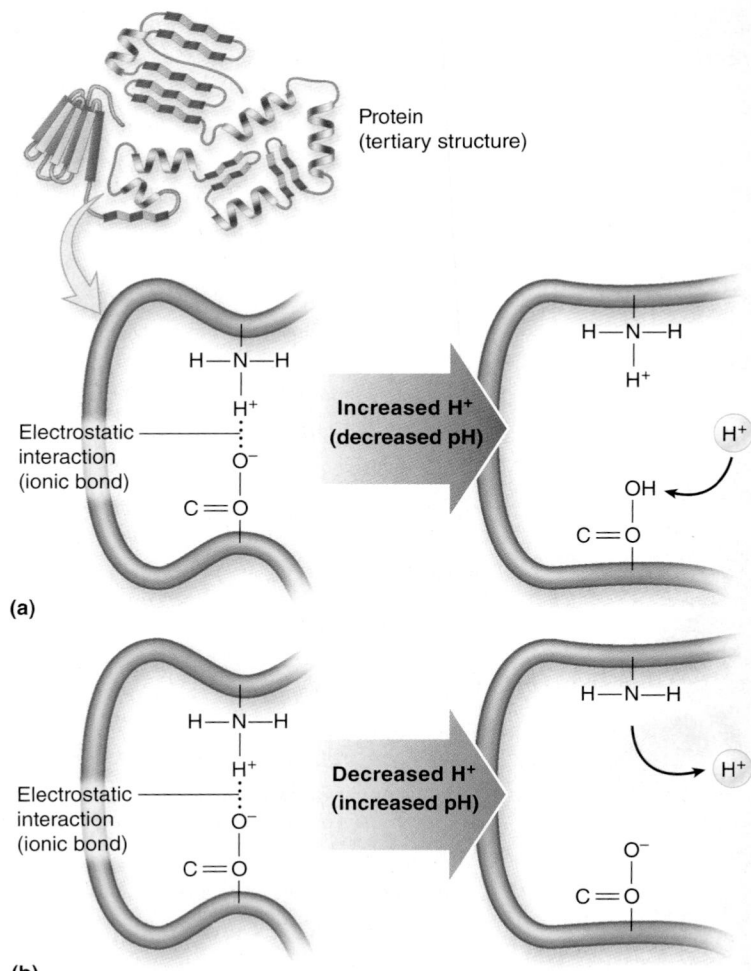

(a)

(b)

Figure 2.28 Denaturation. Proteins denature in response to (*a*) increased H$^+$ (decrease in pH) or (*b*) decreased H$^+$ (increase in pH).

Changes in pH can denature proteins because the alteration of hydrogen ion concentration [H$^+$] interferes with electrostatic interactions (and other intramolecular bonds) that hold the protein in its three-dimensional shape. If pH decreases as a consequence of an increase in [H$^+$], the excess H$^+$ binds to negatively charged R groups, as shown in **figure 2.28a.** The electrostatic interaction is disrupted because an H$^+$ attaches to the negatively charged R group, with an accompanying loss of the negatively charged R group that participated in the electrostatic interaction. If pH increases, reflecting a decrease in [H$^+$], the electrostatic interaction is disrupted because the H$^+$ that previously participated in the electrostatic interaction has been removed, as shown in figure 2.28b. For this reason, changes in blood pH out of the normal homeostatic range can be lethal (pH balance is described in section 25.5.)

WHAT DID YOU LEARN?

39 What distinguishes the tertiary and quaternary level of organization of a protein?

40 What happens to a protein when it denatures? How does a protein denature when it is exposed to higher than normal H$^+$?

- Atoms, ions, and molecules form the human body at its simplest level.

2.1 Atomic Structure 30

- Diagramming atomic structure from the periodic table provides the foundation to understand isotopes, ions, and molecules.

2.1a Matter, Atoms, Elements, and the Periodic Table 30

- An atom is the smallest particle that exhibits the chemical properties of an element.
- Atomic structure—composed of protons, neutrons, and electrons—can be drawn from the information obtained from the periodic table.

2.1b Isotopes 32

- Atoms having the same number of protons and electrons—but differing in the number of neutrons and thus atomic mass—are called isotopes.
- Unstable isotopes resulting from an excess number of neutrons are called radioisotopes.

2.1c Chemical Stability and the Octet Rule 33

- Atoms with a complete outer shell of eight electrons are chemically stable. Atoms bond to reach chemical stability.

2.2 Ions and Ionic Compounds 34

- Chemical compounds, which include ionic compounds and molecular compounds, are stable associations between two or more elements combined in a fixed ratio.

2.2a Ions 34

- An ion is a charged atom that is either positively charged or negatively charged as a result of having respectively lost or gained electrons.
- Common ions of the human body include sodium (Na^+), potassium (K^+), calcium (Ca^{2+}), magnesium (Mg^{2+}), hydrogen (H^+), chloride (Cl^-), bicarbonate (HCO_3^-), and phosphate (PO_4^{3-}).
- Cations are positively charged ions that are formed by the loss of electron(s) from atoms with one, two, or three electrons in their outer shell, or elements in columns IA, IIA, or IIIA in the periodic table, respectively.
- Anions are negatively charged ions that are formed by the gain of electron(s) by atoms typically with five, six, or seven electrons in the outer shell, or elements in columns VA, VIA, or VIIA in the periodic table, respectively.

2.2b Ionic Bonds 35

- Ionic bonds are electrostatic attractions between positively charged cations and negatively charged anions that hold the ions in a lattice crystal (or salt).

2.3 Covalent Bonding, Molecules, and Molecular Compounds 36

- A covalent bond occurs when atoms share electrons to reach chemical stability and form a molecule.
- Molecular compounds are formed by two different elements covalently bonded together.

2.3a Chemical Formulas: Molecular and Structural 36

- The molecular formula is the ratio of chemical constituents of a molecule.
- The structural formula demonstrates both the ratio of chemical constituents of a molecule and their arrangement within the molecule—and can be used to distinguish isomers.
- Isomers have the same number and kind of atoms, or molecular formula, but differ in their arrangement in space.

2.3b Covalent Bonds 36

- Covalent bonds are formed between two atoms in which both atoms have four, five, six, or seven electrons in their outer shell (except hydrogen).
- A single covalent bond is the typical covalent bond and involves the sharing of a pair of electrons. A double or triple covalent bond can be formed if both atoms, respectively, need at least two or three electrons to become stable.
- Nonpolar covalent bonds occur when the two atoms share electrons equally, as occurs between atoms of the same element, or almost equally, as occurs when hydrogen bonds to carbon. Polar covalent bonds occur between atoms of different elements that share electrons unequally.

2.3c Nonpolar, Polar, and Amphipathic Molecules 39

- Nonpolar molecules generally include those molecules composed of nonpolar bonds.
- Polar molecules generally include those molecules composed predominantly of polar bonds.
- Amphipathic molecules are large molecules that have both nonpolar and polar regions.

2.3d Intermolecular Attractions 40

- Intermolecular attractions occur between molecules, and intramolecular attractions occur between regions within large molecules.
- Hydrogen bonds occur between a partially positively charged hydrogen atom and a partially negatively charged atom of polar molecules.
- Intermolecular attractions between nonpolar molecules include van der Waals forces and hydrophobic interactions.

(continued on next page)

2.7 Biological Macromolecules (continued)	**2.7c Carbohydrates 54** • Carbohydrates are molecules with the following chemical formula: $(CH_2O)_n$. Carbohydrates exist in increasing levels of complexity that include monosaccharides, disaccharides, and polysaccharides. • Glucose is the most common monosaccharide in the human body and is used for energy. When in excess, glucose is stored as the polysaccharide called glycogen in liver and skeletal muscle tissue. • Other types of carbohydrates include the monosaccharides galactose, fructose, ribose, and deoxyribose; the disaccharides maltose, sucrose, and lactose; and the polysaccharides starch and cellulose. **2.7d Nucleic Acids 57** • Nucleic acids include deoxyribonucleic acid (DNA) and ribonucleic acid (RNA), polymers formed from nucleotide monomers. These molecules ultimately determine the type of proteins synthesized by cells. • Adenosine triphosphate (ATP) is the energy currency molecule of a cell. **2.7e Proteins 57** • Proteins serve many different functions in the body. • Proteins are polymers that differ in the number and sequence of 20 different amino acid monomers arranged in a unique linear sequence.
2.8 Protein Structure 62	• The three-dimensional structure of proteins is dependent upon the linear sequence of its amino acids. **2.8a Categories of Amino Acids 62** • The 20 amino acids can be categorized as nonpolar, polar, charged, and those with special functions. **2.8b Amino Acid Sequence and Protein Conformation 64** • Protein organization includes the primary, secondary, tertiary structures—and a quaternary structure if there are two or more protein chains. These levels of organization ultimately determine the structure and function of a protein. • Denaturation usually results in the loss of biological activity of a protein in response to the change in its three-dimensional shape that may have occurred through an increase in temperature or a change in pH.

CHALLENGE YOURSELF

Do You Know the Basics?

____ 1. Atoms composed of the same numbers of protons and electrons, but different numbers of neutrons, are called

    a. isomers.   c. isotopes.

    b. ions.   d. organic atoms.

____ 2. Substances that dissolve in water include all of the following except

    a. lipids.   c. proteins.

    b. glucose.   d. salts.

____ 3. Temperature stabilization is dependent upon which properties of water?

    a. cohesion and adhesion

    b. capillary action and adhesion

    c. specific heat and heat of vaporization

    d. cohesion and specific heat

____ 4. All of the following are accurate about H^+ concentration and pH except

    a. acids contain more H^+ than water.

    b. H^+ concentration and pH are inversely related.

    c. neutralizing an acidic solution requires that base is added.

    d. a pH of 6 is basic or alkaline.

____ 5. Blood is a mixture that is more specifically described as a

    a. suspension.   c. solution.

    b. colloid.   d. All of these are correct.

____ 6. Which organic biomolecule is not a polymer?

    a. triglyceride   c. glycogen

    b. protein   d. DNA

____ 7. Glucose is stored as which molecule within the liver and skeletal muscle tissue?

    a. starch   c. glycogen

    b. phospholipid   d. glucagon

____ 8. All of the following are common ions of the human body except

    a. Na^+.   c. Ca^{2+}.

    b. P^+.   d. Cl^-.

____ 9. Intermolecular attractions between polar molecules are

    a. hydrophobic interactions.

    b. hydrogen bonds.

    c. van der Waals forces.

    d. ionic bonds.

____ 10. When a protein permanently unfolds, it has been

    a. polymerized.   c. converted to nucleic acids.

    b. denatured.   d. made more efficient.

11. List the common ions of the human body by name, symbol, and charge.

12. Describe a polar bond and a polar molecule.

13. Diagram two water molecules and label the polar covalent bonds and a hydrogen bond.

14. Compare and contrast what occurs when a substance dissolves in water with a substance that dissolves and dissociates in water. Include examples of specific substances.

15. Define the terms acid, base, pH, and buffers.

16. Explain the units for expressing a concentration that are included in this chapter.

17. List the four organic biomolecules and the building blocks that compose them.

18. Which two organic biomolecules contain nitrogen atoms and contribute to the formation of nitrogenous waste that must be eliminated by the urinary system?

19. Describe how phospholipid molecules form the plasma membrane of a cell.

20. Explain protein denaturation, including how it occurs and the consequences in response to an increase in temperature and a change in pH.

Can You Apply What You've Learned?

1. Which property of water is significant in children born prematurely because it causes the air sacs to collapse in the lungs, making breathing difficult?

   a. specific heat   c. surface tension
   b. water reactivity   d. capillary action

2. A young boy playing outside on a very hot day has become dehydrated. When he enters the house, he appears lethargic. The mother is a nurse and becomes concerned that he may be experiencing a fluid and electrolyte imbalance. Electrolytes include all of the following *except*

   a. sodium ion.   c. potassium ion.
   b. glucose.   d. chloride ion.

3. A young woman has noticed that her thyroid appears enlarged. One of the diagnostic procedures used to produce an image of her thyroid requires this type of substance that emits high-energy radiation.

   a. ions   c. radioisomers
   b. radioisotopes   d. isomers

4. The condition of rickets involves bones that have insufficient amounts of this common ion, resulting in the bones bending under a child's weight.

   a. Na^+ c. Cl^-
   b. K^+ d. Ca^{2+}

5. The hormone insulin is a _____ composed of repeating units of amino acids and cannot be administered orally because the enzymes of the gastrointestinal tract will break the peptide bond through the process of hydrolysis, releasing individual amino acids.

   a. nucleic acid   c. protein
   b. glycogen   d. steroid

Can You Synthesize What You've Learned?

1. An individual is exposed to high-energy radiation. Which biomolecule that regulates the process of protein synthesis may have been mutated?

2. The lab results from a diabetic patient show a lower than normal pH (a condition referred to as acidosis). Explain the change in H^+ concentration in the blood, and describe how this change may affect the folding of proteins in the blood plasma (and elsewhere).

3. A patient is given a new drug that decreases blood sugar levels. This drug is regulating which specific molecule?

chapter 3

Energy, Chemical Reactions, and Cellular Respiration

All living organisms require energy. In humans, energy is needed to power muscle, pump blood through the body, absorb nutrients from the gastrointestinal tract, and exchange respiratory gases. Energy is also required both to synthesize new molecules for maintenance, growth and repair, and to establish cellular ion concentrations. Here we discuss the chemical principles of energy, chemical reactions, enzymes, and metabolic pathways. Many of these concepts are then integrated to describe the metabolic pathway that breaks ➡

Biochemists study results of chemical processes involving biomolecules, the specific products produced and their affects in living organisms. They must know the building blocks (monomers) of biomolecules and how they function in chemical reactions and metabolism. Human illnesses are studied by medical biochemists. This biochemist is performing tests on blood samples to determine if a bacterial infection is present in hospital patients.

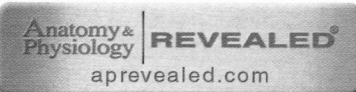

Module 2:
Cells and Chemistry

down glucose molecules. It is during the breakdown of glucose (and other fuel molecules) that energy is released to synthesize adenosine triphosphate (ATP). ATP is the molecule that serves as the "energy currency" of a cell for movement, synthesis, and for all other energy-requiring cellular processes.

3.1 Energy

Energy is defined as the capacity to do work. Energy differs from matter in that it has no mass and does not take up space It is invisible except for the effects it has on matter. This section describes the two major states of energy, the various forms of energy, and physical laws that govern energy.

3.1a States of Energy

LEARNING OBJECTIVE

1. Describe the two states of energy.

Energy exists in two states: potential energy and kinetic energy. **Potential energy** is the energy of position or stored energy. **Kinetic energy** is the energy of motion. Potential energy can be converted or changed to kinetic energy and vice versa. For example, water at the top of a dam has potential energy because of its position; when the water falls over the dam it now has kinetic energy

because of its motion. The kinetic energy of falling water can be harnessed to do work if it drives a water wheel at the bottom of the dam.

A bow and arrow also provides an example of an energy conversion from potential energy to kinetic energy. When the arrow is pulled back in the bow, it has potential energy because of the tension of the bowstring. This potential energy is converted to kinetic energy as the string is released and the arrow flies. The kinetic energy of the flying arrow can do work when it knocks an apple from a tree.

Potential energy is exhibited in cells of living organisms when a concentration gradient exists across the plasma membrane, which is the boundary between the inside and outside of a cell (**figure 3.1a**). Sodium ion (Na^+) concentration typically is greater outside the cell than inside. This difference in Na^+ concentration across the membrane is analogous to the water at the top of a dam because it represents potential energy. The movement of Na^+ from a high concentration outside the cell to where there is less Na^+ inside the cell is an example of kinetic energy. Like water falling over a dam, the kinetic energy of Na^+ movement may be

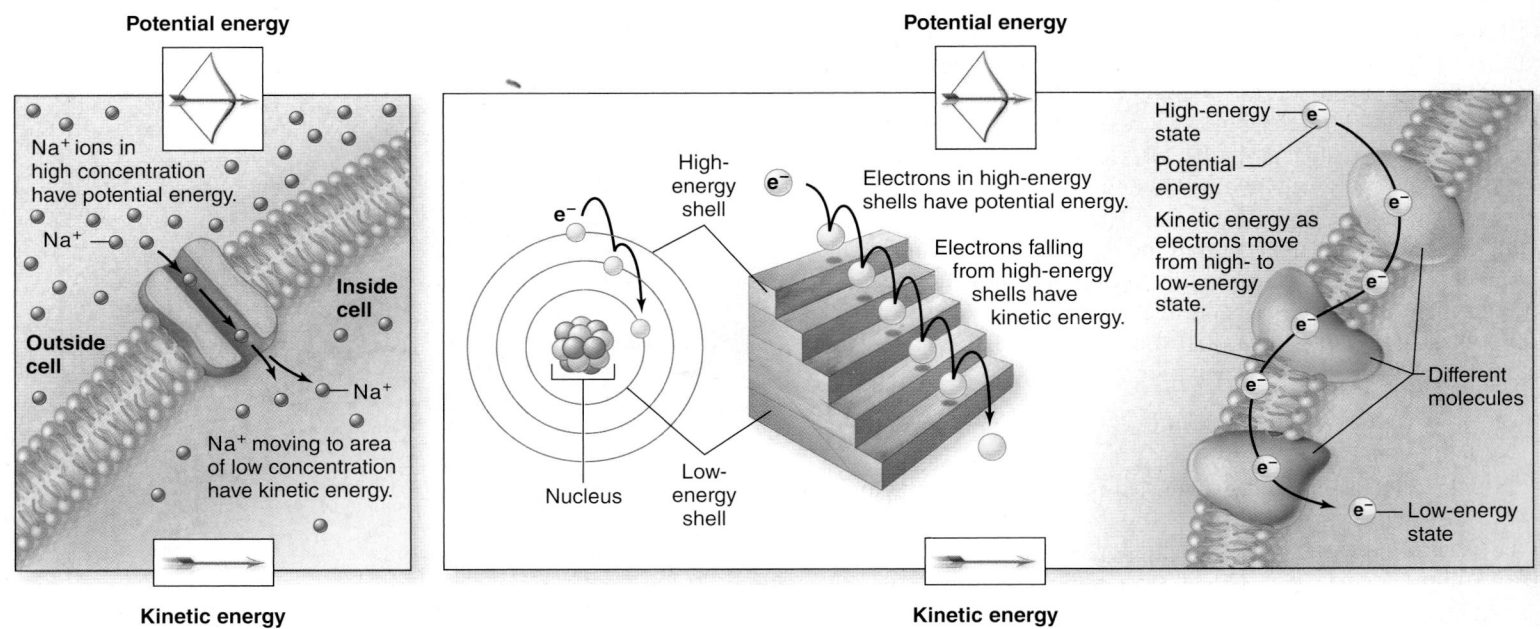

(a) Concentration gradients

(b) Movement of electrons

Figure 3.1 Conversion of Potential Energy to Kinetic Energy. Potential energy that is converted to kinetic energy may be harnessed to do work. (*a*) The Na^+ gradient across the plasma membrane has potential energy that changes to kinetic energy when Na^+ moves down the gradient. (*b*) A high-energy electron has potential energy and may be converted to kinetic energy either in the same atom or be transferred to different molecules as the electron "falls" from high-energy shells to low-energy shells.

harnessed to do work. You will see applications of this principle both in this chapter and in later chapters (e.g., section 24.6).

Potential energy is also exhibited by the position of electrons in electron shells relative to an atom's nucleus (figure 3.1*b*). Electrons can move from a higher-energy shell to a lower-energy shell. Note that when electrons move during a chemical reaction, they may do so either within the same chemical structure or from one chemical structure to another (e.g., in the electron transport chain of a mitochondrion, a cell organelle that synthesizes ATP). The kinetic energy of electron movement can be harnessed to do work—movement of electrons is critical to the formation of ATP molecules.

Note that potential energy has the ability, or *potential,* to do work because of its position. Potential energy must be converted to kinetic energy to be actively engaged in doing work.

 WHAT DID YOU LEARN?

 Both the movement of Na$^+$ down its concentration gradient and the movement of an electron from a higher energy to a lower energy state are examples of (a) potential energy or (b) kinetic energy?

3.1b Forms of Energy

LEARNING OBJECTIVES

2. Describe chemical energy (one form of potential energy) and the various forms of kinetic energy.

3. List the three important molecules that function primarily in chemical energy.

Potential and kinetic energy exist in several forms. We first describe chemical energy, which is one form of potential energy, and then describe several forms of kinetic energy.

Chemical Energy (A Form of Potential Energy)

Chemical energy is one form of potential energy. **Chemical energy** is the energy stored in a molecule's chemical bonds. Chemical energy is the most important form of energy in the human body. It specifically is used for the energy-requiring processes of movement, synthesis of molecules, and establishment of concentration gradients. The chemical bonds of all molecules have chemical energy. This energy is released when bonds are broken during chemical reactions.

Three important molecules in the human body function primarily in chemical energy storage: triglycerides, glucose, and adenosine triphosphate (ATP). These molecules differ in their chemical structure, where they are stored, and the length of time each generally stores energy. Recall the following from chapter 2:

- Triglycerides are involved in long-term energy storage in adipose connective tissue.
- Glucose is stored in the liver and muscle tissue in the form of the polymer glycogen.
- ATP is stored in all cells in limited amounts and is produced continuously and used immediately for cells' energy-requiring processes.

Note that protein also stores chemical energy and can be used as a fuel molecule. However, as described in section 2.7e, proteins are primarily important as the structural and functional components of the body.

Kinetic Energy Forms

Other forms of energy—electrical, mechanical, sound, radiant, and heat—exist as kinetic energy.

Electrical energy is the movement of charged particles. Examples include electricity, which is the movement of electrons along a wire, and the propagation of an impulse by a neuron due to the movement of ions across its plasma membrane.

Mechanical energy is exhibited by an object in motion. Examples of mechanical energy include muscle contraction for walking and the pumping action of the heart to circulate blood.

Sound energy occurs when the compression of molecules that move in a solid, liquid, or gas is caused by a vibrating object, such as the head of a drum or the vibration of the vocal cords. The sense of hearing is initiated when sound waves cause vibration of the tympanic membrane (eardrum) in the ear.

Radiant energy is the energy of electromagnetic waves traveling in the universe. Radiant energy consists of a spectrum of different energy forms that vary in wavelength and frequency (**figure 3.2**). The higher the frequency in the spectrum, the greater the amount of radiant energy associated with it. Gamma rays have the highest amount of radiant energy, whereas radio waves have the lowest. All forms of radiant energy with a frequency higher than visible light (gamma rays, x-rays, and ultraviolet [UV] light) have sufficient energy to penetrate the body and mutate (change) the DNA of living organisms. Cells of the skin normally protect themselves from everyday UV light exposure by producing the pigment melanin (section 6.1a). This process commonly darkens skin color and is referred to as tanning. Visible light is a lower frequency radiant energy that is detected by retinal cells of the eye. This

Figure 3.2 The Electromagnetic Spectrum. Different forms of radiant energy are represented on an electromagnetic spectrum. The forms of energy are arranged from highest energy (shortest waves) to lowest energy (longest waves).

visual input is then relayed along the optic nerve to the brain for interpretation.

Heat is the kinetic energy associated with random motion of atoms, ions, or molecules. It is usually considered a "waste product" that accompanies all changes in energy form because heat is the only type of energy that is not available to do work. (An exception is the energy available from a heat gradient, such as occurs in a steam engine.) Heat is measured as the **temperature** of a substance.

 WHAT DID YOU LEARN?

2 Muscle contraction is an example of what form of energy?

3.1c Laws of Thermodynamics

LEARNING OBJECTIVES

4. State the first law and second law of thermodynamics.
5. Explain why energy conversion is always less than 100%.

Energy can be converted from one form to another. For example:

- When a candle is burned, chemical energy in the burning wax is converted to both light and heat.
- Light energy from the sun is converted by the retinal cells into electrical energy associated with a nerve impulse involved in sight.
- Chemical energy in the food we eat is first converted into another chemical form (ATP), which is then converted in our cells into mechanical energy used to power muscle contraction.

In these examples, energy is simply changing from one form to another. The study of energy transformations is called **thermodynamics** (ther′mō-dī-nam′iks; *thermo* = heat; *dynamis* = force).

Two laws describe energy transformations: the first and second laws of thermodynamics. The **first law of thermodynamics** states that energy can neither be created nor destroyed—it can only be transformed or converted from one form to another.

The **second law of thermodynamics** states that every time energy is transformed from one form to another, some of that energy is converted to heat. That means there is never 100% conversion of one form of usable energy to another. Energy conversions have a price, and it always appears as heat. Because heat is not available to do work, the usable amount of energy is decreased each time an energy conversion occurs. For example, the conversion of the chemical energy in gasoline to the mechanical energy (movement) of a car is approximately 25%. This means that approximately 75% of gasoline's chemical energy is converted to sound and heat.

Heat is produced when the chemical energy stored in the foods we eat is used to power our muscle contractions. One of the functions of muscle tissue is to produce heat that keeps the body warm (see section 10.1a). When the environmental temperature drops, and we begin to move around in the hope of generating enough heat to keep ourselves warm, we are applying the second law of thermodynamics.

Figure 3.3 summarizes the two major states of energy, the various forms of energy as they relate to the body, and the laws of energy.

 WHAT DID YOU LEARN?

 3 Energy can neither be created nor destroyed. However, according to the first and second laws of thermodynamics, what can happen to it, and what is always generated?

3.2 Chemical Reactions

Chemical energy is used in the energy-requiring processes of cells. To understand the central role of chemical energy in living cells, we need to know about chemical reactions and how they occur.

3.2a Chemical Equations

LEARNING OBJECTIVES

1. Explain what occurs in a chemical reaction.
2. Distinguish between reactants and products.

Millions of chemical reactions are occurring in living organisms at any given time. **Metabolism** is the collective term for all chemical reactions in living organisms. A **chemical reaction** occurs when chemical bonds in an existing molecular structure are broken and new ones formed to produce a different structure. When chemical structures are changed, a summary of their changes is written as a **chemical equation.** The components of a chemical equation are called reactants and products.

Reactants are the substrates, or substances, that are present prior to the start of the chemical reaction; they are usually written on the left side of the equation. **Products** are substances that are formed by the subsequent chemical reaction and they are generally written on the right side of the equation. For example, a generic chemical reaction is written

$$A + B \longrightarrow C$$

A and B are reactants in this reaction and C is the product. An arrow is used to indicate the reaction direction. A chemical reaction typically has the arrow drawn to the right, indicating a net change of reactants to products.

The number of elements on one side of the reaction, in a balanced equation, is equal to the number on the other side. For example:

$$Ca + 2 Cl \longrightarrow CaCl_2$$

which indicates that one calcium atom combines with two chlorine atoms to form calcium chloride.

 WHAT DID YOU LEARN?

 4 What are the differences between reactants and products in a chemical equation?

Figure 3.3 **Energy as it Relates to Human Body Function.**
(*a*) Potential and kinetic energy. (*b*) Forms of usable energy. (*c*) Laws of energy.

(a) Potential and Kinetic Energy | The Two States of Energy

Potential Energy: The energy of position

Na^+ ions have potential energy due to concentration gradient difference between the outside and inside of the cell.

Na^+ Na^+ Na^+ Na^+

Kinetic Energy: The energy of motion

Na^+ Na^+

Na^+

Na^+ ions exhibit kinetic energy as they move down the concentration gradient.

Na^+ Na^+ Na^+

A perched eagle has potential energy.

When the eagle flies, it converts its potential energy to kinetic energy.

(b) Forms of Usable Energy Available to Do Work

Energy of Position

Chemical Energy: Energy stored in chemical bonds of molecules

Glycogen

Potential energy in chemical bonds

Example: Glucose, a high energy molecule, can be stored as glycogen for later use.

Electrical Energy: Movement of charged particles

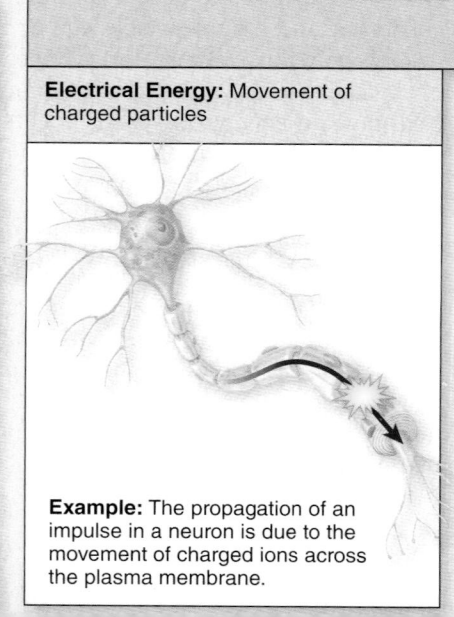

Example: The propagation of an impulse in a neuron is due to the movement of charged ions across the plasma membrane.

(c) Laws of Energy

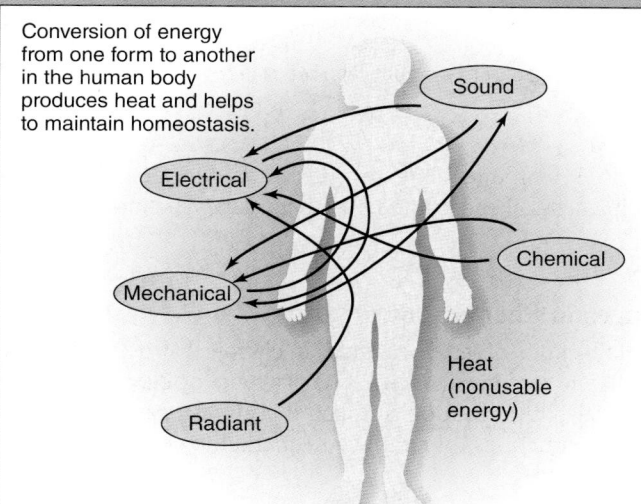

Conversion of energy from one form to another in the human body produces heat and helps to maintain homeostasis.

Sound

Electrical

Mechanical

Chemical

Radiant

Heat (nonusable energy)

First Law of Thermodynamics

Energy cannot be created or destroyed, it can only be converted from one form to another.

Second Law of Thermodynamics

Every time energy is transformed from one form to another, some of that energy is converted to heat.

Energy is constantly being converted from one form to another in order to perform the tasks that keep the human body alive and active.

(Heat radiating from forearm)

Energy of Motion

Mechanical Energy: Movement of a structure or a substance

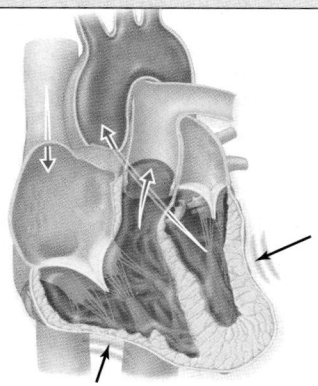

Example: The pumping action of the heart to circulate blood is a form of mechanical energy.

Sound Energy: Movement of compressed molecules through a medium initiated by a vibrating object

Example: Sound waves vibrating the tympanic membrane of the ear stimulate sensory receptors for hearing.

Radiant Energy: Movement of electromagnetic waves that travel in the universe and vary in wavelength and frequency

Example: Visible light, a form of radiant energy, is focused on the retina of the eye for vision.

LEARNING STRATEGY

- **Catabolism** involves complex molecules being broken down, or digested, into simpler molecules. We can remember catabolism by thinking of a "cat" eating from a "bowl," which leads to food molecules being digested.
- **Anabolism** is the reverse reaction, namely synthesis or the building of complex molecules from simple molecules. For example, some athletes illegally use anabolic steroids to stimulate synthesis of contractile proteins within muscle tissue.
- **Metabolism** is the collective term for all chemical reactions that occur in the human body; these include the processes of both catabolism and anabolism.

3.2b Classification of Chemical Reactions

LEARNING OBJECTIVES

3. Describe the three classifications of chemical reactions.
4. Distinguish between catabolism and anabolism.
5. Discuss the exchange that takes place in an oxidation-reduction reaction.
6. Explain ATP cycling.

Chemical reactions are classified based upon three different criteria that include: (1) changes in chemical structure, (2) changes in chemical energy, and (3) whether the reaction is irreversible or reversible.

Classification Based on Changes in Chemical Structure

The general categories of chemical reactions based on changes in chemical structure include decomposition, synthesis, and exchange reactions (figure 3.4). The first category is referred to as a **decomposition** (dē′kom-pō-zish′ŭn) **reaction** because the initial large molecule is digested or broken down into smaller structures. A simplified equation for a decomposition reaction is

$$AB \longrightarrow A + B$$

Decomposition reactions occur during the *hydrolysis reaction* (section 2.7a) of sucrose into glucose and fructose molecules in the digestive tract (figure 3.4a). All of the decomposition reactions in the body are collectively referred to as either **catabolism** (kă-tab′ō-lizm; *katabole* = a casting down) or *catabolic reactions*.

Decomposition reaction: A large molecule is broken down into smaller chemical structures; $AB \longrightarrow A + B$

(a)

Synthesis reaction: Two or more atoms, ions, or molecules are combined to form a larger chemical structure; $A + B \longrightarrow AB$

(b)

Exchange reaction: Atoms, molecules, ions, or electrons are exchanged between two chemical structures; $AB + C \longrightarrow A + BC$

(c)

Figure 3.4 Classification of Chemical Reactions. Chemical reactions can be classified according to the chemical changes that occur. These reactions include (a) decomposition, (b) synthesis, and (c) exchange reactions.

A **synthesis** (sin'thĕ-sis; *syn* = together, *thesis* = arranging) **reaction** occurs when two or more atoms, ions, or molecules are combined to form a larger chemical structure as existing bonds are broken and new bonds are formed. A simplified equation for a synthesis reaction is

$$A + B \longrightarrow AB$$

An example of a synthesis reaction is the *dehydration* synthesis reaction (section 2.7a) that occurs during the formation of a dipeptide from two amino acids (figure 3.4b). **Anabolism** (ă-nab'ō-lizm; *ana* = up) is the collective term for all synthesis reactions in the body. These are also called *anabolic reactions.*

The third category of reactions based on changes in chemical structure is the **exchange reaction,** in which atoms, molecules, ions, or electrons are exchanged between two chemical structures; such a reaction has both decomposition and synthesis components. This type of reaction is the most prevalent type in the human body. A simplified equation for an exchange reaction is

$$AB + C \longrightarrow A + BC$$

The production of adenosine triphosphate (ATP) in muscle tissue is an example of an exchange reaction:

$$\text{Creatine phosphate} + \text{Adenosine diphosphate (ADP)} \longrightarrow \text{Creatine} + \text{ATP}$$

The bond between phosphate and creatine is broken in this reaction. The creatine becomes a free molecule, while the phosphate is transferred and bonded to ADP to form ATP (figure 3.4c).

Oxidation-Reduction Reactions

An **oxidation-reduction reaction** (also termed a *redox reaction*) is a specific type of exchange reaction that involves the movement of electrons from one chemical structure to another. The term oxidation-reduction refers to

- **Oxidation,** which occurs as a molecule, atom, or ion loses an electron(s) and thus becomes **oxidized**
- **Reduction,** which occurs as a molecule, atom, or ion gains an electron(s) and thus becomes **reduced**

The term "reduced" is used because the chemical structure gains an electron, a *negatively* charged particle, so it can be thought of as "reduced" in charge. Oxidation and reduction reactions always occur together because one chemical structure loses the electron(s) and another gains the electron(s).

The electron transferred from one chemical structure to another may be moved alone, designated chemically as e⁻—or be accompanied by a hydrogen ion (H⁺), designated as H (i.e., an electron plus a hydrogen ion that together are shown as a hydrogen atom, H).

WHAT DO YOU THINK?

1 Electron transfer occurs when NAD⁺ becomes NADH. Is the NAD⁺ oxidized or reduced? Explain.

An example of an oxidation-reduction reaction in the cells involves the **nicotinamide adenine dinucleotide (NAD⁺)** molecule, which is a modified dinucleotide that is linked at the phosphates and contains nicotinamide. NAD is important in ATP synthesis. **Figure 3.5** shows an example in which an energy-rich molecule, such as glucose, is oxidized because it has given up

Figure 3.5 Different Forms of Nicotinamide Adenine Dinucleotide. Two hydrogen (H) atoms are donated from an energy-rich molecule (e.g., glucose) to the oxidized form of nicotinamide adenine dinucleotide (NAD⁺). NAD⁺ accepts one hydrogen atom (H) and one electron (e⁻). One H⁺ ion is released into the surrounding local environment. The energy-rich molecule (e.g., glucose) has released (lost) its electrons and is oxidized, and NAD⁺ has gained electrons and is reduced to become NADH. NADH is later oxidized when it releases the H⁺ and 2 electrons. **AP|R**

two hydrogen atoms, while NAD^+ has gained both a hydrogen ion (H^+) and two electrons (e^-) and is reduced. (Note that one H^+ is released into the surrounding local environment during this reaction.)

The movement of electrons can be harnessed to do work. Thus, the electrons in oxidation-reduction reactions represent energy transfer. Consequently, when we say that glucose is oxidized, we indicate that the glucose is losing its electrons and releasing its chemical energy. Other molecules are reduced and gain both electrons and energy (e.g., such as NAD^+ becoming NADH).

Classification Based on Changes in Chemical Energy

Chemical reactions are also classified by the relative amounts of chemical energy associated with the reactants and products. These two categories are based upon energy change and are termed exergonic reactions and endergonic reactions.

Exergonic (ek'sĕr-gon'ik; *exo* = outside; *ergon* = work) **reactions** involve reactants at the start of a reaction that have *more* energy within their chemical bonds than do the products that are formed (**figure 3.6a**). Exergonic means that energy "goes out," or is released during the course of breakdown reactions. Decomposition reactions, such as the decomposition of glucose to carbon dioxide and water, are normally exergonic reactions.

Endergonic (en'dĕr-gon'ik; *endo* = within) **reactions** involve reactants that have *less* energy within their chemical bonds than do the products. Endergonic means that energy must be "put in," or supplied, to proceed (figure 3.6b). Endergonic reactions yield products that have a net increase in potential energy as compared to what was present in the substrates. Synthesis reactions, such as the formation of a dipeptide from two amino acids, are endergonic reactions.

ATP Cycling **ATP cycling** is the continuous formation and breakdown of ATP (**figure 3.7**). This cycling involves ATP formation (an endergonic reaction) and ATP splitting (an exergonic reaction). ATP is formed when energy is released in exergonic reactions using glucose or other fuel molecules from the foods we eat. These molecules undergo oxidation, and energy stored within their chemical bonds is transferred to ADP and P_i (free phosphate) to form ATP. In turn, ATP is then oxidized, and the energy released is used for endergonic reactions, as well as other energy-requiring cellular processes. Thus, energy released in exergonic reactions in the body is coupled to end-

ergonic reactions that require energy input so that endergonic reactions can proceed. A cell cannot stockpile ATP, so typically only a few seconds worth of ATP is present. Instead, the formation of ATP must occur continuously through the processes of breakdown of glucose (and other fuel molecules) to provide energy for endergonic reactions.

Classification Based on Whether the Reaction Is Irreversible or Reversible

A third way of classifying chemical reactions is based on whether they are irreversible or reversible. An **irreversible reaction** involves reactants converted to product at a rate that yields a net loss of reactants and a net gain in product. Many reactions are irreversible, and are written with the arrow to the right:

$$A + B \longrightarrow AB \quad \text{or} \quad AB \longrightarrow A + B$$

A **reversible reaction** differs from an irreversible reaction because it does not proceed only to the right with reactants becoming products over time, but instead reactants become products at a rate equal to products becoming reactants. Consequently, there is no net change in concentration in either reactants or products, and the reaction is in a state of equilibrium. The relationship of the reactants and products in a reversible reaction is shown with arrows in both directions:

$$A + B \longleftrightarrow AB$$

A reversible reaction remains in equilibrium if left undisturbed. However, the equilibrium can be disturbed in a reversible reaction if a change in either the amount of reactant or the amount of product occurs. For example, either an increase in reactants or a decrease in products drives the equation to the right, which contributes to the formation of additional product until a new equilibrium is reached. In contrast, a decrease in reactants or an increase in product drives the equation to the left, which contributes to the formation of additional reactants until a new equilibrium is reached.

An important example of a reversible reaction in the human body occurs when carbon dioxide (CO_2) and water (H_2O) combine to form carbonic acid (H_2CO_3). The reaction is

$$CO_2 + H_2O \longleftrightarrow H_2CO_3$$

The newly formed carbonic acid is unstable, and it dissociates to yield both bicarbonate ion (HCO_3^-) and hydrogen ion (H^+). The equation for the complete chemical reaction is

$$CO_2 + H_2O \longleftrightarrow H_2CO_3 \longleftrightarrow H^+ + HCO_3^-$$

(a) Exergonic reaction

(b) Endergonic reaction

Figure 3.6 Exergonic and Endergonic Reactions. Chemical reactions are classified based on the change in chemical energy of the reactants and products. (*a*) The reactants have more energy than the products, and energy is released, during an exergonic reaction. (*b*) The reactants have less energy than the products, and energy must be supplied, in an endergonic reaction.

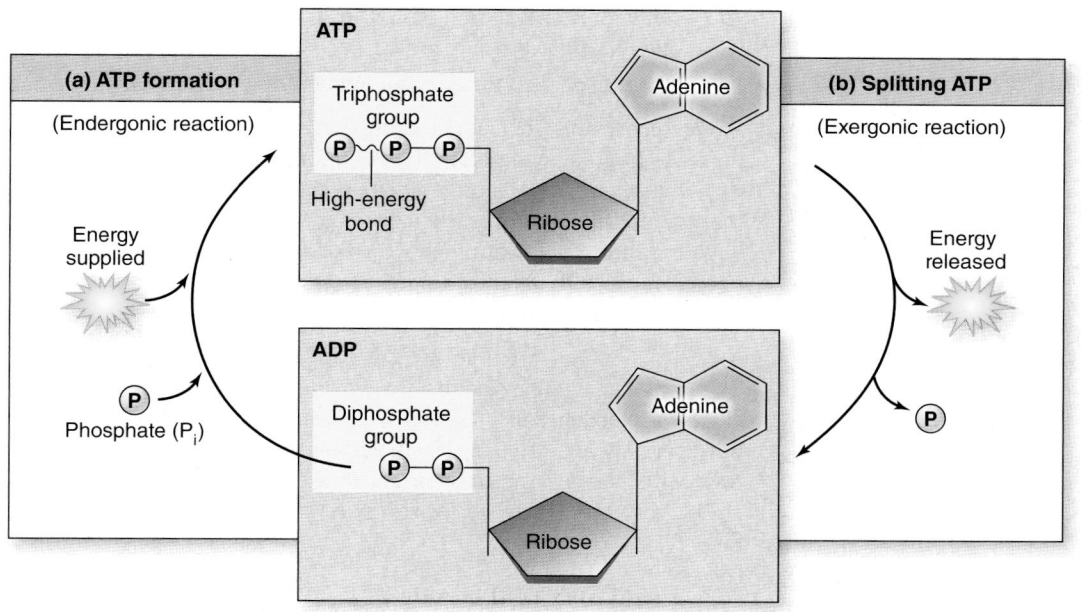

Figure 3.7 ATP Cycling. (*a*) The high-energy chemical bond of ATP is formed by a dehydration reaction between ADP and P_i. Energy is required and is supplied by the energy-releasing oxidation of fuel molecules. (*b*) The high-energy chemical bond of ATP is split by hydrolysis to form ADP and P_i.

This reversible reaction occurs in different locations within the human body and is important in several critical physiologic processes, including breathing regulation and maintaining pH balance. (See chapters 23 and 25.)

Table 3.1 summarizes the three major ways chemical reactions are classified.

WHAT DID YOU LEARN?

5 For a chemical reaction that involves simple chemical structures bonded together into a more complex molecule, choose the more accurate term in each pair that best describes this type of chemical reaction: (a) Synthesis or decomposition reaction; (b) Exergonic or endergonic reaction; (c) Collective term for this type of reaction (catabolism or anabolism).

6 What molecule is formed from exergonic reactions and used as the energy currency for endergonic reactions and other energy-requiring processes in the cell?

7 Explain what occurs when the equilibrium is disturbed in reversible reactions by changes in reactants and products.

3.2c Reaction Rates and Activation Energy

LEARNING OBJECTIVES

7. Define chemical reaction rate.
8. Explain activation energy.

Reaction rate is the measure of how quickly a chemical reaction takes place. A primary factor that determines the reaction rate is the energy

Table 3.1	Classification of Chemical Reactions	
Type of Chemical Reaction	**Definition**	**Example**
CHANGE IN CHEMICAL STRUCTURE		
Decomposition	Complex chemical structure broken down into simpler structures	Sucrose → glucose and fructose
Synthesis	Simple chemical structures bonded together into a more complex structure	Amino acids → dipeptide
Exchange	Atoms, molecules, ions, or electrons exchanged between two chemical structures	Creatine phosphate + ADP → Creatine + ATP
CHANGES IN CHEMICAL ENERGY		
Exergonic	Energy released	Glucose and oxygen → carbon dioxide and water
Endergonic	Energy required	Amino acids → dipeptide
NET DIRECTION OF REACTION		
Irreversible	Net change of reactants to products	Most chemical reactions A + B → AB, or AB → A + B
Reversible	Formation of products = formation of reactants	$H_2O + CO_2 \leftrightarrow H_2CO_3 \leftrightarrow HCO_3^- + H^+$

required to break the chemical bonds in a substrate so that new bonds can form the product. The energy required to break existing chemical bonds is called the **activation energy**, or E_a. A chemical reaction occurs when sufficient energy is supplied to overcome the E_a.

In the laboratory setting, merely heating a mixture of reactants often overcomes the E_a. An elevation in temperature increases the kinetic energy of the molecules, providing enough energy to break chemical bonds. However, this approach is not feasible in a living cell. The consequence of an increase in temperature within the cell would denature all of its proteins and cause its death (see section 2.8b). Cells have solved their E_a problem through the use of biologically active protein catalysts called enzymes, the topic of the next section.

WHAT DID YOU LEARN?

8 Explain the effect a fever would have on chemical reaction rates within the body. What is the risk to protein structure with a high fever?

3.3 Enzymes

Chemical reactions must proceed at a rate that is sufficient to sustain life. Enzymes are the chemical structures that facilitate the millions of chemical changes that occur in the human body every second, and their importance cannot be overstated.

3.3a Function of Enzymes

LEARNING OBJECTIVE

1. Describe the general function of enzymes.

Enzymes are biologically active **catalysts** that function to accelerate normal chemical activities by decreasing the activation energy (E_a) of cellular reactions. **Figure 3.8** shows the difference in E_a of an **uncatalyzed reaction** (chemical reaction without an enzyme) and **catalyzed reaction** (chemical reaction with an enzyme) of sucrose decomposition to yield glucose and fructose. Notice the following:

- The reaction is exergonic because the substrate sucrose has higher potential energy than the combined potential energy of the products glucose and fructose.

Figure 3.8 Activation Energy (E_a). The energy barrier that must be overcome for a reaction to proceed is the activation energy (E_a). Comparison of the E_a of an uncatalyzed reaction and a catalyzed reaction.

- Activation energy is required to initiate the reaction to occur even though it is exergonic.
- The presence of an enzyme lowers the required E_a.

More glucose and fructose are formed in a given period of time in the presence of an enzyme than would be formed without the enzyme.

Note that enzymes only facilitate chemical reactions to proceed that would already occur; their presence increases the rate of product formation by lowering the E_a. For example, let's compare the uncatalyzed and catalyzed rate of production for the reversible **carbonic acid reaction**:

$$CO_2 + H_2O \longleftrightarrow H_2CO_3 \longleftrightarrow H^+ + HCO_3^-$$

This reaction is catalyzed by the enzyme carbonic anhydrase. The chemical reaction still proceeds when carbonic anhydrase is absent, however only about 100 H_2CO_3 molecules are formed per hour. In contrast, when the enzyme carbonic anhydrase is present, up to 2.16 billion H_2CO_3 molecules may be formed per hour—a tremendously greater rate.

WHAT DID YOU LEARN?

9 What is the relationship of enzymes and activation energy?

3.3b Enzyme Structure and Location

LEARNING OBJECTIVES

2. Describe the key structural components of enzymes.

3. Identify places in the body where enzymes may be found.

Most enzymes are globular proteins (see section 2.8b) that range in size from relatively small proteins composed of about 60 amino acids to very large proteins of more than 2500 amino acids. The amino acids in the protein chain form a unique three-dimensional molecular structure with a region called the **active site.** The active site accommodates the substrate(s) of a reaction to temporarily form an **enzyme-substrate complex** (figure 3.9). The **specificity** in the shape of the active site permits only a single substrate, or type of substrate, to bind to the active site, and thus the enzyme is capable of catalyzing only one specific reaction.

Enzymes are produced by normal protein synthesis processes within cells (section 4.7). Once formed, the location of the enzyme varies. Enzymes may

- Remain within the cell; an example is DNA polymerase, which helps form new DNA.

Figure 3.9 Enzyme Structure. An enzyme is a globular protein with a depressed or grooved region that serves as the active site. AP|R

- Become embedded within the plasma membrane (the outer boundary of a cell); an example is lactase, which digests the milk sugar lactose and is found in plasma membranes of small intestine cells.
- Be secreted from the cell; an example is pancreatic amylase released from the pancreas into the small intestine to participate in the digestion of starch.

WHAT DID YOU LEARN?

10 What is the active site of an enzyme and how does it relate to a substrate?

3.3c Mechanism of Enzyme Action

LEARNING OBJECTIVES

4. Explain the steps by which an enzyme catalyzes a reaction.

5. Describe cofactors and their role in reactions.

Examples of enzymatic activity are diagrammed in **figure 3.10.** We show both an example of a decomposition reaction involving the enzyme lactase and a synthesis reaction involving the enzyme glycogen synthetase. In both cases, the enzyme facilitates the reaction as follows:

1 The substrate enters the active site of the enzyme, and the enzyme temporarily binds with the substrate to form an enzyme-substrate complex.

2 Entry of the substrate into the active site induces the conformation (structure) of the enzyme to change slightly, resulting in an even closer fit between substrate and enzyme. This response is referred to as the *induced-fit model* of enzyme function. The interaction is analogous to giving someone a hug.

3 Stress on chemical bonds in the substrate molecule is caused by the change in enzyme shape. Consequently, this stress lowers E_a, and the bonds in the substrates are more easily broken, permitting new chemical bonds to be formed.

4 The newly formed molecule, now called the product, is released from the enzyme. The enzyme is then free to repeat the process again and again with other substrates.

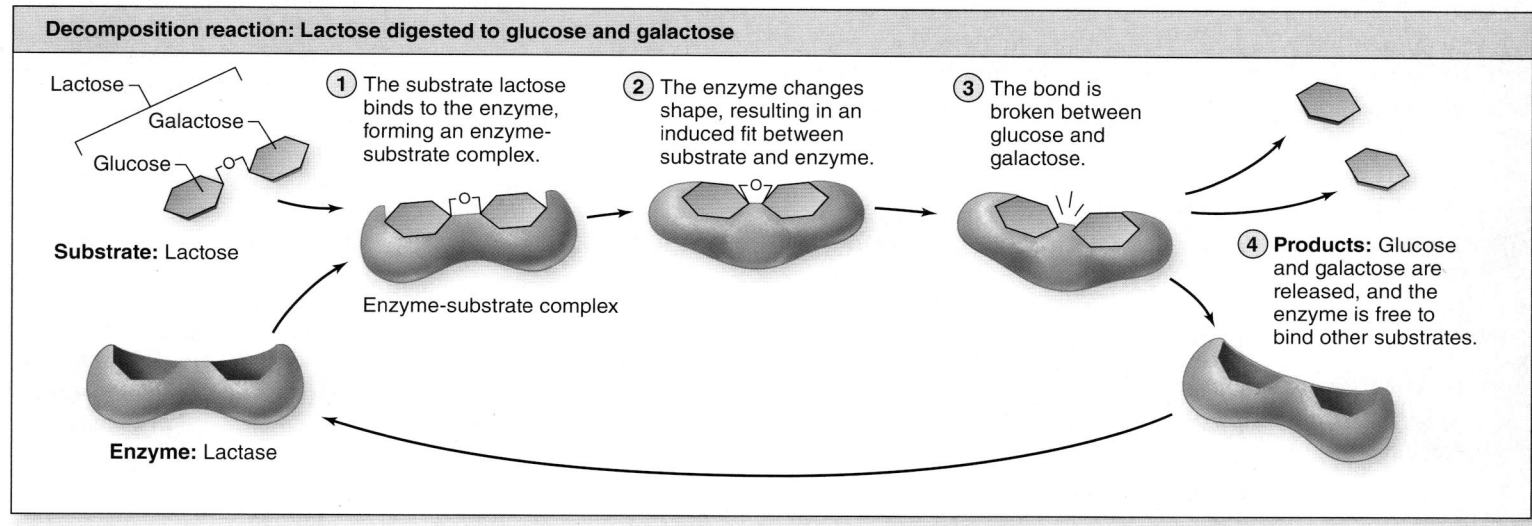

Decomposition reaction: Lactose digested to glucose and galactose

Lactose
Galactose
Glucose

Substrate: Lactose

Enzyme: Lactase

1 The substrate lactose binds to the enzyme, forming an enzyme-substrate complex.

Enzyme-substrate complex

2 The enzyme changes shape, resulting in an induced fit between substrate and enzyme.

3 The bond is broken between glucose and galactose.

4 Products: Glucose and galactose are released, and the enzyme is free to bind other substrates.

(a)

Synthesis reaction: Glucose molecules synthesized into a glycogen molecule

Glucose

Substrate: Glucose monomers

Enzyme: Glycogen synthetase

1 The glucose substrate binds to the enzyme, forming an enzyme-substrate complex.

2 The enzyme changes shape, resulting in an induced fit between substrate and enzyme.

3 Bonds are broken and a new bond is formed between the new glucose molecule and the growing glycogen molecule.

4 Product: Glycogen is released, and the enzyme is free to bind other substrates.

(b)

Figure 3.10 Mechanism of Action for Enzymes in Decomposition and Synthesis Reactions. (*a*) Enzymes may decompose larger complex molecules into simpler chemical structures, such as when lactose is broken down into glucose and galactose. (*b*) Enzymes may synthesize simple chemical structures into larger complex structures, such as when glucose molecules are bonded together to form glycogen.

Cofactors

Enzymes often require **cofactors** that are "helper" molecules or ions to ensure that a reaction occurs. A cofactor is a *nonprotein* structure that may be either an inorganic or organic substance (section 2.7a) associated with a particular enzyme or enzymatic reaction. Inorganic cofactors are attached to the enzyme and are required for their normal function. For example, zinc ion is bound to carbonic anhydrase enzyme; without zinc, carbonic anhydrase is unable to function. In addition, many vitamins (e.g., B_6 and B_{12}), derivatives of vitamins, or modified nucleotides such as NAD^+ may serve as organic cofactors. Organic cofactors are not attached to enzymes and have specific functions in assisting enzymes. For example, the NAD^+ coenzyme accepts hydrogen during chemical reactions to become NADH. Organic cofactors are more specifically referred to as **coenzymes** in some sources, and this term is also used in this text.

 WHAT DID YOU LEARN?

11 What is the mechanism of enzyme action, including the role of cofactors?

3.3d Classification and Naming of Enzymes

 LEARNING OBJECTIVES

6. Identify the six major classes of enzymes and the general functions of enzymes in each class.

7. Describe the naming conventions for enzymes.

There are thousands of different enzymes. To help make sense of the many different types of enzymes, biochemists organize them into six major functional classes, with subclasses within each category. **Table 3.2** briefly describes the six major classes of enzymes, including oxidoreductase, transferase, hydrolase, isomerase, ligase, and lyase.

Enzymes in the oxidoreductase class, for example, participate in oxidation-reduction reactions. **Dehydrogenase** (dē-hī'drō-jen-ās) enzymes are a subcategory of enzymes within the oxidoreductase class. These enzymes participate in oxidation-reduction reactions by moving hydrogen between molecules.

Another example of a class of enzymes is the transferase class. All enzymes in this class transfer atoms or molecules between chemical structures. **Kinase** (kī'nās) enzymes belong to this class because they specifically transfer a phosphate functional group from one molecule to another. You will learn about specific examples of both dehydrogenase and kinase enzymes later in this chapter.

 WHAT DO YOU THINK?

2 Given what you already know about isomers (section 2.3a), what can you predict that an enzyme in the isomerase class would do?

The name of a given enzyme is generally based upon the name of the substrate or product involved in the chemical reaction, sometimes the name of the subclass, and the suffix *-ase*, added to the final word of the name. Here are three examples:

- **Pyruvate dehydrogenase** is an enzyme that transfers a hydrogen (dehydrogenase subclass), specifically from a pyruvate molecule.
- **DNA polymerase** is central to the formation of the polymer DNA from deoxyribonucleotides.
- **Lactase** digests the disaccharide lactose (See Clinical View: Lactose Intolerance included in figure 3.14.)

Although the name of an enzyme generally contains an *-ase* suffix and the rest of the name reflects its function, there are exceptions. For example, pepsin, trypsin, and chymotrypsin (section 26.4b) are all protein-digesting enzymes with names that do not provide clear clues to these molecules' enzymatic nature or specific activity.

 WHAT DID YOU LEARN?

12 Explain how enzymes are generally named.

Table 3.2	Major Classes of Enzymes	
Enzyme Class	**Description**	**Examples**
Oxidoreductase	Transfers electrons from one substance to another	Dehydrogenase uses NAD^+ or a molecule other than oxygen as electron acceptor. Peroxidase uses hydrogen peroxide (H_2O_2) as electron acceptor.
Transferase	Transfers a functional group	Phosphorylase transfers a phosphate (PO_4^{3-}) to a different substance. Kinase transfers a phosphate (PO_4^{3-}) from ATP to a different substance.
Hydrolase	Splits a chemical bond using water	Phosphatase removes phosphate. Protease removes amino acids from proteins. Lipase splits lipids (e.g., triglyceride). Sucrase splits sucrose.
Isomerase	Converts one isomer to another	Mutase transfers atoms within a molecule.
Ligase	Bonds two molecules together	Synthetase bonds two molecules using ATP.
Lyase	Splits a chemical bond in the absence of water	Decarboxylase cleaves a molecule to release carbon dioxide.

3.3e Enzymes and Reaction Rates

LEARNING OBJECTIVES

8. Define how enzyme and substrate concentration affect reaction rates.
9. Explain the effect of temperature on enzymes.
10. Describe how pH changes affect enzymes.

Several conditions influence the reaction rates catalyzed by enzymes. The most significant factors are enzyme and substrate concentration, temperature, and pH.

Effect of Enzyme and Substrate Concentration

The rate of a chemical reaction may be accelerated by either an increase in enzyme concentration or an increase in substrate concentration. An increase in substrate concentration, however, increases the rate of reaction only up to the point of saturation of the enzyme (figure 3.11a). **Saturation** occurs when so much substrate is present that all enzyme molecules are actively engaged in the chemical reaction, resulting in no further (notable) increase in reaction rate.

Effect of Temperature

Enzymes are proteins, and their three-dimensional shape is dependent upon environmental variables, including temperature and pH. Each enzyme has a specific environment in which it can most effectively participate in a chemical reaction. Human enzymes function most efficiently at their **optimal temperature,** usually 37°C (98.6°F), which is the normal body temperature (figure 3.11b). Temperature increases enhance immune functions (e.g., increased phagocytosis).

More severe increases in temperature—meaning temperatures greater than 40°C (104°F) in humans—weaken the intramolecular bonds that hold an enzyme's protein structure in its three-dimensional shape. The protein subsequently denatures, permanently losing function. The greater the increase in temperature, the more likely this is to occur.

Effect of pH

Enzymes function most efficiently at their **optimal pH.** Optimal pH for most human enzymes is between pH 6 and 8, and changes in pH can affect the enzyme (figure 3.11c). An increase in H$^+$ (which means a decrease in pH) results in additional H$^+$ binding to the enzyme. In contrast, a decrease in H$^+$ (which means an increase in pH) results in the release of H$^+$ from an enzyme. In either case, the change in amount of H$^+$ attached to the enzyme disrupts the electrostatic interactions that hold the enzyme protein in its shape. A significant disruption results in denaturation of the enzyme. (Denaturation of proteins is described in detail in section 2.8b.)

Not all enzymes have an optimal pH between 6 and 8. The pH in the stomach, for example, is between 2 and 4; thus, the optimal pH for the stomach enzyme pepsin corresponds to this pH range.

WHAT DID YOU LEARN?

13. How do changes in substrate concentration, temperature, and pH affect the reaction rate of enzyme-catalyzed chemical reactions?

(a)

(b)

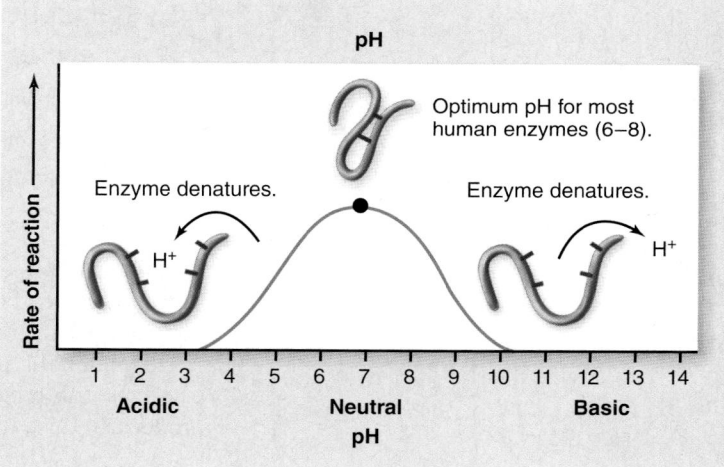

(c)

Figure 3.11 Environmental Conditions That Influence Reaction Rates of Enzymes. Reaction rates are influenced by changes in (a) the concentration of substrates, (b) temperature, and (c) pH. AP|R

3.3f Controlling Enzymes

✔ LEARNING OBJECTIVE

11. Describe how competitive and noncompetitive inhibitors control enzyme action.

An enzyme continues to facilitate the conversion of its substrate(s) to product as long as ample substrate is present and environmental conditions are close to normal. However, uncontrolled enzymes would result in depleted substrate levels and concentration of products that exceeds what is needed. Thus, enzymes must be temporarily "turned off" to prevent overproduction. Control of enzymes occurs through **inhibitors** that are substances that bind to an enzyme and turn it off, thus preventing it from catalyzing the reaction. Later, the release of the inhibitor from the enzyme allows it to function and continue catalyzing the reaction. This switching occurs in different ways, depending upon whether the inhibitor is competitive or noncompetitive.

A **competitive inhibitor** resembles the substrate and binds to the active site of the enzyme. Consequently, the substrate and the regulatory compound compete with each other for occupation of the enzyme's active site (**figure 3.12a**). The amount of substrate relative to the amount of competitive inhibitor determines the degree of inhibition. The greater the concentration of the substrate, the less likely the competitive inhibitor will occupy the enzyme's active site. In contrast, if substrate concentration decreases, the competitive inhibitor is more likely to occupy the enzyme's active site, and lower amounts of product are formed.

Noncompetitive inhibitors do not resemble the substrate. They inhibit an enzyme by binding to a site on the enzyme other than the active site, a site termed the **allosteric** (al′ō-ster′ik; *allo* = other, *stereo* = three-dimensionality) **site.** Binding of a noncompetitive inhibitor to the allosteric site induces a conformational change in the enzyme with an accompanying change in the shape of the enzyme's active site (figure 3.12b). Noncompetitive inhibitors are also called **allosteric inhibitors** because they bind to the allosteric site. This type of inhibition is not influenced by the concentration of substrate.

💡 WHAT DID YOU LEARN?

 How are enzymes regulated through competitive and noncompetitive inhibitors?

3.3g Metabolic Pathways and Multienzyme Complexes

✔ LEARNING OBJECTIVES

12. Distinguish between a metabolic pathway and a multienzyme complex.

13. Explain the role of negative feedback in enzyme regulation.

14. Identify and explain the processes involving phosphate that commonly are used to regulate enzymes.

Usually multiple enzymes are required to convert an initial substrate to a final product. Depending upon both the substrate and sequence of conversion, these multiple enzymes are arranged either in a metabolic pathway or as a multienzyme complex.

A **metabolic pathway** is formed by a series of enzymes (**figure 3.13**). Each enzyme catalyzes one progressive change to its specific substrate molecule and then releases the product. In turn, the product of one enzyme becomes the substrate of the next enzyme. For

Figure 3.12 Enzyme Inhibition. A substrate can be prevented from binding to an active site by (*a*) a competitive inhibitor that enters the active site, or (*b*) a noncompetitive inhibitor (allosteric inhibitor) that binds to a site other than the active site.

example, there are the numerous enzymes involved in the chemical breakdown of glucose to produce carbon dioxide and water during the production of ATP (as described later).

A **multienzyme complex** is a group of enzymes that are physically attached to each other through noncovalent bonds to form the complex. These attached enzymes work in a sequence of reactions. Pyruvate dehydrogenase, the multienzyme complex involved in breakdown of glucose, is an example as described later.

A multienzyme complex has two major advantages. First, the product from one chemical reaction is immediately bound to the next enzyme in the multienzyme complex. This makes it more likely that the needed product is formed and less likely that the substance will diffuse away and come into contact with an enzyme from a different biochemical pathway. Second, the enzymatic pathway can be regulated by controlling the single complex rather than multiple individual enzymes.

Metabolic pathways and multienzyme complexes must be regulated to prevent overproduction of an unneeded product and exhaustion of substrates that could be used elsewhere. This regulation occurs through the process of negative feedback. The product from a metabolic pathway acts as an allosteric inhibitor to turn off an enzyme early in the metabolic pathway, for example. As the product accumulates, it is more likely to become bound to the enzyme and inhibit the metabolic pathway, with progressively less and less product being formed. Over time, as the amount of product decreases, the inhibition is reduced, and activity of that enzymatic pathway increases once again. In this way, a steady state of product is produced.

One specific mechanism for regulating enzymes is by either phosphorylation or dephosphorylation of the enzyme. **Phosphorylation** (fos'fōr-i-lā'shŭn) is the addition of a phosphate group, whereas **dephosphorylation** is the removal of a phosphate group. Note that phosphorylation may turn on some enzymes but turn off other enzymes. Equally, dephosphorylation may cause opposite effects in activity by different types of enzymes. The enzymes that add phosphate are generally called **protein kinases,** whereas enzymes that remove the phosphates are called **phosphatases** (see figure 4.19). This concept is described in more detail in section 17.5b in discussion of the endocrine system.

Figure 3.14 summarizes some important concepts of enzymes, including their function, structure and location, mechanism of action, and other features.

WHAT DID YOU LEARN?

15 What is a metabolic pathway? Explain the role of negative feedback in enzyme regulation.

16 What two processes involve phosphate and are commonly used to regulate enzymes in a metabolic pathway or a multienzyme complex?

Figure 3.13 Metabolic Pathway. A metabolic pathway is composed of a series of enzymes to convert a specific substrate to the final product. The product of one enzyme is the substrate for the next enzyme in the pathway. Metabolic pathways can be regulated by negative feedback that involves a product that serves as an allosteric inhibitor binding to an enzyme early in the pathway.

Figure 3.14 **How Enzymes Work.** Characteristics of enzymes include (*a*) enzyme function; (*b*) structure and location; (*c*) naming of enzymes; (*d*) mechanism of action; (*e*) reaction rate; (*f*) metabolic pathway, multienzyme complex and regulation; and (*g*) controlling enzymes.

(a) Enzyme function

Enzymes decrease the activation energy (E$_a$) so reaction rate increases and more product is formed in a given time period.

(b) Structure and location

Most enzymes are globular proteins with a unique active site.

Enzymes can be located inside a cell, outside a cell, or embedded in a cell's plasma membrane.

(c) Naming of enzymes

The name of an enzyme typically includes the name of the substrate or product, or sometimes the name of the subclass involved in the chemical reaction with an -ase ending.

Example:

Lactose + *-ase* = Lactase

(d) Mechanism of action

Enzymes participate in either decomposition or synthesis reactions.

(e) Reaction rate

(Speed of a chemical reaction) is influenced by substrate or enzyme concentration, temperature, and pH.

Increasing the substrate concentration (to the point of enzyme saturation) increases the rate of reaction.

Increasing the temperature increases the rate of reaction up to the point of denaturation of the enzyme.

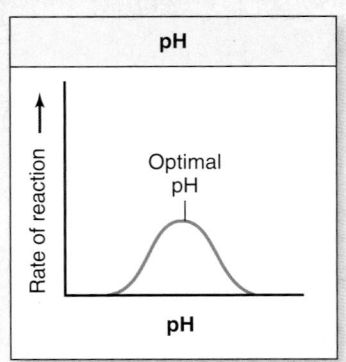

Enzymes are most effective at their optimal pH. Either an increase or decrease from the optimal pH decreases the rate of the reaction.

(f) Metabolic pathway and multienzyme complex

Metabolic pathway: Series of enzymes

Many metabolic pathways are regulated by negative feedback by a product.

Substrate

Product

Enzyme

Allosteric site

Negative feedback

Product regulates activity of the metabolic pathway

Multienzyme complex: Physically linked enzymes

The product of one enzyme becomes the substrate of a different enzyme in the complex.

Substrates

Active site

Enzymes

Products of each enzyme in the complex are less likely to diffuse away to participate in other chemical reactions.

(g) Controlling enzymes

Competitive inhibitor

Competitive inhibitors interfere with active site directly.

Substrate

Active site access blocked

Enzyme

Competitive inhibitor

Noncompetitive inhibitor

Allosteric inhibitors change shape of enzyme so the substrate cannot bind to the active site.

Substrate

Active site shape change

Enzyme

Allosteric inhibitor

INTEGRATE

CLINICAL VIEW
Lactose Intolerance

Lactose intolerance is caused by a deficiency in the enzyme lactase. This enzyme is required to break the bond in the disaccharide lactose (milk sugar) into glucose and galactose for its absorption from the digestive tract into the blood. Lactose intolerance is more common in older adults because they produce less lactase over time. Abdominal upset including nausea, diarrhea, bloating, and gas are the most common symptoms. Avoidance of foods containing milk, drinking milk with lactose removed (lactose-free milk), or the oral administration of products containing lactase enzymes are recommended to avoid symptoms of lactose intolerance.

Lactose

Glucose

Galactose

Lactase

Lactase embedded in plasma membrane of cells lining the small intestine

SELL BY

REDUCED FAT

MILK

INTEGRATE

CONCEPT CONNECTION

Cellular respiration typically requires an uninterrupted supply of O_2 and the continuous removal of CO_2. In chapter 23, we describe the systemic processes of respiration, which involve both the respiratory system and cardiovascular system. These systems function in both the delivery of O_2 from the atmosphere to the body's cells and the movement of CO_2 from the body's cells to the atmosphere. Individuals with either impaired respiratory function (e.g., emphysema) or cardiovascular disease (e.g., congestive heart failure) may experience difficulty in the delivery of O_2 to the body's cells. These individuals often experience "energy problems" and feel lethargic and tired. This decrease in energy results from the dependence of cellular respiration on O_2 delivery for maximum production of ATP as described in this chapter.

3.4 Cellular Respiration

Cellular respiration is a multistep metabolic pathway whereby organic molecules (e.g., glucose, fatty acids, amino acids) are disassembled in a controlled manner by a series of enzymes. During this disassembly, potential energy stored in the molecule's chemical bonds is released; the energy is then used to make new bonds between ADP and P_i to form ATP (see figure 3.7). It is important to note the following about the processes of cellular respiration:

- These processes are exergonic or energy-releasing.
- The organic molecule that has given up its energy has done so by releasing high-energy electrons; thus the molecule is said to be oxidized.
- The energy released is used to synthesize ATP, which is an endergonic or energy-requiring process.
- Oxygen is required for maximum ATP production.

Although different types of organic molecules may be chemically digested during the collective processes of cellular respiration, our discussion here focuses on the oxidation of glucose.

3.4a Overview of Glucose Oxidation

✓ LEARNING OBJECTIVES

1. Write the overall formula for glucose oxidation.
2. Name the two pathways that generate ATP.
3. List the four stages of glucose oxidation and where each stage occurs within a cell.

Glucose oxidation occurs within cells and is a step-by-step enzymatic breakdown of glucose with the accompanying release of energy to synthesize ATP. If oxygen is available, glucose is completely broken down and carbon dioxide and water are formed. Here we describe several significant features of glucose oxidation.

Overall Chemical Reaction Glucose has the chemical formula $C_6H_{12}O_6$. It is an energy-rich molecule because of its many C—C, C—H and C—O chemical bonds. When enzymes completely disassemble glucose, the net chemical reaction for the process is

$$C_6H_{12}O_6 + 6\ O_2 \longrightarrow 6\ CO_2 + 6\ H_2O$$

Pathways for ATP Production Glucose oxidation is an exergonic reaction. During the many enzymatic reaction steps that accomplish the breakdown of glucose, some of the energy of the broken bonds is captured to attach P_i to ADP to synthesize ATP: The energy transfer from bonds in the glucose molecule can be used either directly (least common way) or indirectly (most common way) to form ATP. The direct method of synthesizing ATP is called **substrate-level phosphorylation.** The indirect method—in which the energy is first released to coenzymes (i.e., NAD^+, FAD) that then transfer the energy to form ATP—is called **oxidative phosphorylation**.

Cellular Location The complete oxidation of glucose requires at least 20 different enzymes that are located in both the cell's cytosol and its mitochondria (**figure 3.15**). **Cytosol** is the semifluid contents of the cell. **Mitochondria** (sing., mitochondrion) are small organelles within the cell that are described later.

Four Stages of Cellular Respiration We separate the processes of glucose oxidation into four stages: glycolysis, intermediate stage, citric acid cycle, and the electron transport system. Glycolysis occurs in the cytosol and it is also called **anaerobic cellular respiration** because it can occur without oxygen. The other three stages occur in the mitochondria and are collectively referred to as **aerobic cellular respiration** because they require oxygen.

Figure 3.15 Cellular Structures Required for Cellular Respiration. Components of the cell associated with glucose oxidation include the cytosol, where the enzymes for anaerobic respiration (glycolysis) are located, and mitochondria where the enzymes for aerobic cellular respiration (intermediate stage, citric acid cycle, and electron transport system) are housed. AP|R

WHAT DID YOU LEARN?

17 Write the overall chemical reaction for glucose oxidation, and explain the general process of what is occurring.

18 What are the four stages of cellular respiration for glucose oxidation, and identify the cellular location in which each occurs?

3.4b Glycolysis: Anaerobic Cellular Respiration

LEARNING OBJECTIVE

4. Summarize the metabolic pathway of glycolysis, including the molecules formed in the transfer of energy from glucose.

Glycolysis (glī-kol'i-sis; *glykys* = sweet, *lysis* = loosening) does not require oxygen and thus is an anaerobic process. Ten enzymes within the cytosol of a cell participate in the metabolic pathway of glycolysis. Glucose is broken down in this pathway into two pyruvate molecules with an accompanying energy transfer to form a net production of 2 ATP molecules and 2 NADH molecules.

INTEGRATE

LEARNING STRATEGY

Keep in mind the following questions as you read through each of the first three stages of cellular respiration (the stages required for completely oxidizing [disassembling] glucose):

1. Does it occur in the cytosol or mitochondria of a cell?
2. Does it require oxygen (i.e., is it aerobic or anaerobic)?
3. What is the initial substrate and the final product?
4. Is energy released to produce ATP directly (substrate-level phosphorylation), or transferred to a coenzyme that serves as a "temporary holder" that will participate in oxidative phosphorylation, or both?

(a) Overview of glycolysis

Glycolysis
Location: Cytosol

ATP acts as an allosteric inhibitor to
"turn off" phosphofructokinase (PFK)
through negative feedback.

Steps 1–5:

① **Hexokinase**
Transfers phosphate
(Pᵢ) from ATP (traps
glucose in cell)

Glucose (6 C) → Glucose 6-P

② **Phosphoglucose Isomerase**
Converts glucose 6-P
to fructose 6-P isomer

Glucose 6-P → Fructose 6-P

③ **Phosphofructo-kinase (PFK)**
Transfers phosphate
(Pᵢ) from ATP

Fructose 6-P → Fructose 1,6-P

④ **Aldolase**
Splits the 6-carbon
molecule into two
3-carbon molecules

⑤ **Isomerase**
Converts
to isomer

Dihydroxyacetone phosphate

Glyceraldehyde 3-phosphate (G3P)

(b) Details of glycolysis

Figure 3.16 Metabolic Pathway of Glycolysis. Glycolyis is an anaerobic metabolic pathway that occurs in the cytosol. The pathway contains ten enzymes involved in the conversion of glucose to pyruvate. The fate of pyruvate is dependent on the availability of oxygen to the cell. (*a*) An overview of glycolysis. (*b*) The detailed pathway of glycolysis. AP|R

Steps of Glycolysis

The ten enzymatically regulated chemical reactions of glycolysis are shown in **(figure 3.16)**; both an overview figure and the detailed steps are included. Note that steps 1 through 5 occur once per glucose, and steps 6 through 10 occur *twice* per glucose because glucose is split into *two* three-carbon molecules.

(1–5) Steps 1 through 5 of glycolysis involve splitting glucose into two molecules of glyceraldehyde 3-phosphate (G3P) through the action of the first five enzymes. ATP is "invested" when kinase enzymes transfer Pᵢ from ATP to the breakdown products of glucose (steps 1 and 3). Thus, an investment of 2 ATP molecules occurs at these two steps.

(6–7) Steps 6 and 7 of glycolysis occur twice in oxidation of a glucose molecule. Step 6 involves transferring an unattached Pᵢ to the substrate (so this molecule now has two phosphates), and two hydrogen atoms are released to NAD⁺ to form an NADH (and H⁺). This transfer of hydrogen is catalyzed by a hydrogenase enzyme. In step 7, the original Pᵢ is transferred to ADP to form ATP through substrate-level phosphorylation by a kinase enzyme.

(8–10) Steps 8 through 10 of glycolysis also occur twice in oxidation of a glucose molecule. These steps involve converting the substrate from step 7 to an isomer (step 8)

Steps 6–7   Steps 8–10

Steps 6-10

Dehydrogenase
transfers free P_i

Forms NADH by
transferring e^- + H
to NAD^+

**Phosphoglycerate
kinase**

Transfer P_i to ADP
to form ATP

**Phosphoglycero-
mutase**

Rearrange molecule: Transfer
P_i from oxygen on carbon
3 to oxygen on carbon 2

Enolase

Removes H_2O

Pyruvate kinase

Transfers P_i to
ADP to form ATP

Fate of pyruvate
is dependent
on availability
of oxygen

Dehydrogenase
transfers free P_i

**Phosphoglycerate
kinase**

**Phosphoglycero-
mutase**

Enolase

Pyruvate kinase

and then the loss of a water molecule (step 9). The remaining P_i is transferred to ADP to form ATP through substrate-level phosphorylation by a kinase enzyme (step 10), forming the final product of pyruvate.

WHAT DO YOU THINK?

3 What is the net energy transfer during glycolysis?

Summary of Glycolysis

Glycolysis is a metabolic process that occurs in the cytosol without the requirement of oxygen. Glucose is the initial substrate and pyruvate is the final product. The net transfer of energy is used in the formation of 2 ATP and 2 NADH molecules.

- **Formation of ATP.** Two ATP molecules are invested early in glycolysis (steps 1 and 3). Four ATP molecules are formed during glycolysis (steps 7 and 10, which occur twice per the

original glucose molecule). Thus, there is a net of 2 ATP molecules formed during glycolysis (2 ATP invested, 4 ATP formed).

- **Formation of NADH.** Two NADH molecules are formed from glucose breakdown during glycolysis (step 6, which occurs twice per the original glucose molecule).

Regulation of Glycolysis

Glycolysis is regulated through negative feedback like many metabolic pathways. ATP acts as an allosteric inhibitor to "turn off" phosphofructokinase (PFK) (step 3).

As ATP levels increase in the cell cytosol, ATP binding inhibits PFK, and the glycolytic pathway is progressively shut down. In contrast, as ATP decreases, glycolysis increases. Phosphofructokinase is also regulated in a similar way by other substances that indicate the "energy status" of the cell, including NADH, citrate (an intermediate in the citric acid cycle), fatty acids, and other fuel molecules. Increased levels of these substances results in a decrease in the processes of glycolysis.

The Fate of Pyruvate

Pyruvate is the final product of glycolysis. What chemical changes are then made to pyruvate depend upon the availability of oxygen. If sufficient oxygen is available, pyruvate enters a mitochondrion to complete its aerobic breakdown yielding carbon dioxide and water (described next). In contrast, if sufficient oxygen is not available, pyruvate is converted to lactate (described in a later section).

WHAT DID YOU LEARN?

19 Describe glycolysis—where it occurs, if the process is aerobic or anaerobic, the net chemical reaction, and the net energy transfer.

20 What are the two general fates of pyruvate, and what is the criterion that determines its fate?

3.4c Aerobic Cellular Respiration: Intermediate Stage

LEARNING OBJECTIVES

5. Explain the enzymatic reaction involving pyruvate dehydrogenase in the intermediate stage.

6. Define decarboxylation.

The remaining stages of cellular respiration, including the intermediate stage, citric acid cycle, and the electron transport system are aerobic processes that occur within mitochondria.

Mitochondrion Structure

A mitochondrion is a double-membrane organelle, composed of an outer membrane and an inner membrane that has inward folds called **cristae (figure 3.17a).** The fluid-filled space between the two membranes is the **outer compartment.** The innermost space in a mitochondrion is called the **matrix.** Both the multienzyme complex of the intermediate stage and the enzymes of the citric acid cycle metabolic pathway reside in the matrix. The significant molecules that participate in the electron transport system are embedded in the cristae.

Intermediate Stage and Pyruvate Dehydrogenase

The **intermediate stage** (figure 3.17b) is the "link" between the multistep metabolic processes of glycolysis (first stage) with the multistep metabolic processes that occur in the citric acid cycle (third stage). The intermediate stage is catalyzed by a multi-enzyme complex called **pyruvate dehydrogenase.**

During the intermediate stage, pyruvate dehydrogenase brings together pyruvate and a molecule of coenzyme A (CoA) that is already present within the matrix to form acetyl CoA (a two-carbon molecule with CoA attached). Concurrently, a carboxyl group, consisting of one carbon atom and two oxygen atoms, is released from the pyruvate as CO_2. This process is termed **decarboxylation** (dē'kar-bok'si-lā'shŭn; de = away). Energy is released during decarboxylation as two hydrogen atoms (two electrons plus two hydrogen ions) are transferred to the coenzyme NAD^+ to form NADH (and H^+) during this process. The acetyl CoA then enters the third stage of glucose oxidation, termed the citric acid cycle.

Note that the intermediate stage must occur twice for the complete digestion of the original glucose molecule, because two pyruvate molecules were produced from each glucose that went through glycolysis. Thus, 2 NADH are produced from the original glucose molecule.

WHAT DID YOU LEARN?

21 Explain the enzymatic reaction involving pyruvate dehydrogenase in the intermediate stage—where it occurs, if the process is aerobic or anaerobic, the net chemical reaction, and the net energy transfer.

3.4d Aerobic Cellular Respiration: Citric Acid Cycle

LEARNING OBJECTIVE

7. Summarize the metabolic pathway of the citric acid cycle.

The **citric acid cycle** is a cyclic metabolic pathway that occurs through the activity of nine enzymes located within the matrix of mitochondria. During the citric acid cycle, the acetyl CoA produced in the intermediate stage is converted to two CO_2 molecules and a CoA molecule is released. Energy is transferred to form one ATP molecule, three NADH molecules, and 1 $FADH_2$ molecule during one "turn" of the citric acid cycle.

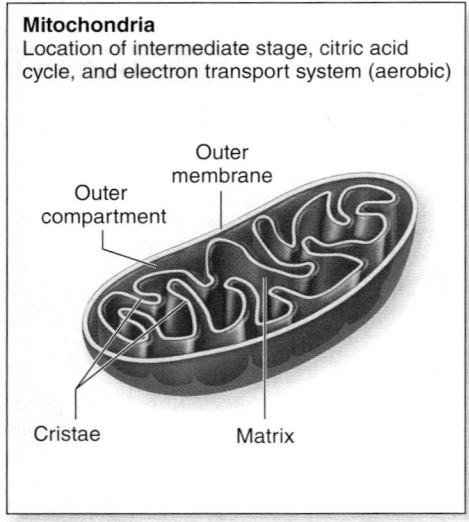

Mitochondria
Location of intermediate stage, citric acid cycle, and electron transport system (aerobic)

Outer compartment
Outer membrane
Cristae
Matrix

(a)

Cellular Respiration

Glycolysis
Intermediate stage
Citric acid cycle
Electron transport system

Intermediate stage
Location: Mitochondria

Pyruvate (3 C) + CoA $\xrightarrow[\text{dehydrogenase}]{\text{Pyruvate}}$ Acetyl CoA (2 C) + CO_2

NAD$^+$ → NADH

(b)

Figure 3.17 Aerobic Cellular Respiration: Intermediate Stage. (a) Mitochondria are the cellular organelles where aerobic cellular respiration occurs. (b) The intermediate stage involves a multienzyme complex called pyruvate dehydrogenase.

Steps of the Citric Acid Cycle

The nine enzymatic steps of the citric acid cycle are shown in (figure 3.18); both an overview figure and the detailed steps are included.

(1) Step 1 of the citric acid cycle uses the first enzyme to combine an acetyl CoA molecule produced in the intermediate stage with a molecule of **oxaloacetic acid (OAA)** (ok′să-lō-ă-sē′tik as′id) to form **citrate**. (Note that the addition of a hydrogen ion to citrate forms citric acid.) The production of citric acid in the first step of this cycle gives this enzymatic pathway its name.

(2–3) Steps 2 and 3 of the citric acid cycle form an isomer by removing a water molecule from citrate and then reattaching it to a different location on the molecule.

(4–5) Steps 4 and 5 of the citric acid cycle occur through two different hydrogenase enzymes that participate in

Cellular Respiration

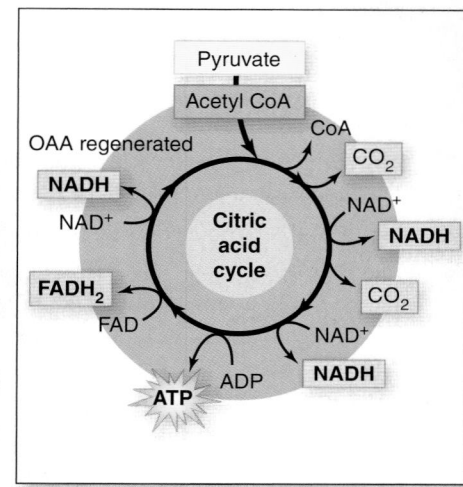

(a) Net chemical reaction of citric acid cycle

Citric acid cycle
Location: Mitochondria

① Acetyl CoA and OAA are bonded together to form citrate with release of CoA

(Aconitate is an intermediate molecule when H_2O is removed)

② Forms isomer by removing H_2O

③ Modifies molecule to a different isomer by attaching water at a different site on the molecule

④ Release CO_2 by decarboxylation Transfer 2 e⁻ + H to $NAD^+ \rightarrow NADH$

⑤ Release CO_2 by decarboxylation Transfer 2 e⁻ + H to $NAD^+ \rightarrow NADH$ Add CoA

⑥ Remove CoA and form ATP

⑦ Transfer 2 hydrogens to $FAD \rightarrow FADH_2$

⑧ Add H_2O

⑨ Transfer e⁻ + H to $NAD^+ \rightarrow NADH$

Citrate synthetase — Acetyl CoA — Oxaloacetate — Malate dehydrogenase — Malate — Fumerase — Fumarate — Succinic dehydrogenase — Succinate — Succinyl CoA synthetase — Succinyl CoA — α-ketoglutarate dehydrogenase — α-ketoglutarate — Isocitrate dehydrogenase — Isocitrate — Aconitase — Citrate

Begin again

Pyruvate

(b) Details of citric acid cycle

Figure 3.18 Aerobic Cellular Respiration: Citric Acid Cycle. The citric acid cycle is the metabolic pathway that occurs within the matrix of the mitochondria for the chemical breakdown of acetyl CoA. (a) An overview of the citric acid cycle. (b) The detailed pathway of the citric acid cycle. AP|R

93

the transfer of hydrogen to NAD$^+$ to form NADH. CoA is also attached during step 5.

(6) Step 6 of the citric acid cycle involves the removal of CoA and the formation of ATP through substrate level phosphorylation.

(7) Step 7 of the citric acid cycle occurs through the action of a dehydrogenase that transfers hydrogens to FAD to form FADH$_2$.

(8) Step 8 of the citric acid cycle is the removal of water.

(9) Step 9 of the citric acid cycle is catalyzed by a dehydrogenase that transfers hydrogen to NAD$^+$ to form NADH. Oxaloacetic acid is regenerated in this final step.

Summary of the Citric Acid Cycle

The citric acid cycle is a metabolic process that occurs in mitochondria and requires the presence of oxygen. Acetyl CoA is the initial substrate and two CO$_2$ molecules and one CoA molecule are the products. The net transfer of energy produced in this cycle is used to form 1 ATP molecule, 3 NADH molecules, and 1 FADH$_2$ molecule.

- **Formation of ATP.** One ATP molecule is formed during the citric acid cycle (step 6) through substrate level phosphorylation.
- **Formation of NADH.** Three NADH molecules are formed from acetyl CoA during the citric acid cycle (steps 4, 5, and 9).
- **Formation of FADH$_2$.** One FADH$_2$ molecule is formed from acetyl CoA during the citric acid cycle (step 7).

≋≋ **WHAT DO YOU THINK?**
4 Why is the enzymatic pathway of the citric acid cycle considered to be a "cycle"?

This enzymatic pathway is called a "cycle" because oxaloacetic acid is involved in the first step and is regenerated in the last step. Note that two "turns" of the citric acid cycle must also occur for the complete digestion of the original glucose molecule (one per each acetyl CoA generated from the original glucose molecule). Consequently, the number of high-energy molecules produced within the citric acid cycle from one glucose molecule is: 2 ATP molecules, 6 NADH molecules, and 2 FADH$_2$ molecules.

Regulation of the Citric Acid Cycle

Regulation of the citric acid cycle occurs primarily at the enzyme in the first step of the citric acid cycle (citrate synthetase). If cellular energy demands are high, levels of NADH, ATP, and pathway intermediates are low, and the activity of the cycle is increased. In contrast, an increase in these substances results in a decrease in the activity of the cycle. These physiologic adjustments help maintain homeostatic levels of ATP molecules.

Completion of Glucose Digestion

Following glycolyis and two "turns" through both the intermediate stage (which generates 2 CO$_2$ molecules) and the citric acid cycle (which produces 4 CO$_2$ molecules), glucose has been completely digested and the six carbon atoms of glucose (C$_6$H$_{12}$O$_6$) have been released as 6 CO$_2$ molecules.

Summary of the Chemical Breakdown of Glucose

Table 3.3 and figure 3.19 provide a summary of each of the first three stages of glucose oxidation that results in the chemical breakdown of glucose into carbon dioxide. The following critical aspects of this process include

- **Anaerobic cellular respiration.** Glycolysis occurs in the cytosol and is anaerobic. Energy is transferred to form 2 ATP molecules (net) and 2 NADH molecules. If sufficient oxygen is available, the pyruvate formed enters a mitochondrion and is further metabolized in the intermediate stage and the citric acid cycle.

- **Aerobic cellular respiration—the intermediate stage.** The intermediate stage occurs in a mitochondrion. It involves a multienzyme complex that converts pyruvate to acetyl CoA and 1 CO$_2$ molecule. Energy is transferred to form 1 NADH molecule. Remember, one NADH molecule is formed per pyruvate entering the intermediate stage. Recall that two pyruvates are produced from one glucose molecule. Thus, the intermediate stage must occur twice—so a total of 2 NADH molecules are formed from the original glucose molecule.

- **Aerobic cellular respiration—the citric acid cycle.** The citric acid cycle also occurs in a mitochondrion and completes the breakdown of glucose. Two CO$_2$ molecules are produced per turn of the cycle. Energy is transferred during this process to form 1 ATP, 3 NADH, and 1 FADH$_2$.

Table 3.3	Comparison of the First Three Stages of Glucose Breakdown		
Characteristics	**Glycolysis (Anaerobic Cellular Respiration)**	**Intermediate Stage (Aerobic Cellular Respiration)**	**Citric Acid Cycle (Aerobic Cellular Respiration)**
Where it occurs	Cytosol	Mitochondria	Mitochondria
Anaerobic or aerobic	Anaerobic	Aerobic	Aerobic
Substrate	Glucose	Pyruvate (2 pyruvates from each glucose)	Acetyl CoA (2 acetyl CoA from each glucose)
Product	2 pyruvate molecules	Acetyl CoA and 1 CO$_2$ per pyruvate	2 CO$_2$ per acetyl CoA
Pathway or complex	Metabolic pathway	Multienzyme complex	Metabolic pathway
Net energy molecules produced	2 ATP (net) and 2 NADH	1 NADH per pyruvate	1 ATP per acetyl CoA 3 NADH per acetyl CoA 1 FADH$_2$ per acetyl CoA
How lack of oxygen affects the stage	Lactic acid produced (to regenerate NAD$^+$ so glycolysis can continue)	Pathway inhibited by lack of oxygen	Pathway inhibited by lack of oxygen

Chemical Breakdown of Glucose

$$C_6H_{12}O_6 + 6\,O_2 \longrightarrow 6\,CO_2 + 6\,H_2O$$

Figure 3.19 Summary of Glucose Digestion. Three major stages of cellular respiration are required for the chemical breakdown of glucose: glycolysis, the intermediate stage, and the citric acid cycle.

Cytosol (anaerobic cellular respiration)

Glycolysis

10-enzyme metabolic pathway

Glucose (6 C)

2 ATP

2 ADP + 2 P$_i$

2 (G3P)

NAD$^+$ → NADH   NAD$^+$ → NADH

ADP + P$_i$ → ATP   ADP + P$_i$ → ATP

ADP + P$_i$ → ATP   ADP + P$_i$ → ATP

Intermediate stage

Pyruvate   Pyruvate (3 C)

Multienzyme complex

NAD$^+$ → NADH → CO$_2$

Acetyl-CoA (2 C)

Mitochondria (aerobic cellular respiration)

Citric acid cycle

9-enzyme metabolic pathway

OAA regenerated

NADH ← NAD$^+$

Citric acid cycle

CO$_2$

NAD$^+$ → NADH

FADH$_2$ ← FAD

CO$_2$

NAD$^+$

ADP → ATP → NADH

— Occurs twice per original glucose molecule

Remember, this reflects the energy transferred per each acetyl CoA entering the citric acid cycle. Two acetyl CoA molecules are produced from one glucose molecule. Thus, the citric acid cycle must occur twice—so a total of 2 ATP, 6 NADH, and 2 FADH$_2$ are formed from the original glucose molecule.

Thus, through glycolysis and two turns of the intermediate stage and citric acid cycle, the six carbons in the original glucose have been released as 6 CO$_2$ molecules and the energy has been transferred to form:

2 ATP	2 NADH	(glycolysis)
	2 NADH	(intermediate stage)
2 ATP	6 NADH	2 FADH$_2$ (citric acid cycle)

WHAT DID YOU LEARN?

22 Summarize the metabolic pathway of the citric acid cycle—where it occurs, if the process is aerobic or anaerobic, the net chemical reaction, and the net energy transfer.

23 What energy molecules are produced from the chemical breakdown of glucose during each of the three steps of cellular respiration?

3.4e Aerobic Cellular Respiration: The Electron Transport System

Given that the breakdown of glucose is completed by the end of the citric acid cycle, what is the function of the electron transport system, the final stage of cellular respiration? The **electron transport system** involves the transfer of electrons (energy) from the coenzymes NADH and FADH$_2$ that are produced during the first three stages of cellular respiration. The energy released from these coenzymes is used to form ATP. This is a critical stage in cellular respiration because most of the energy captured in glucose oxidation is initially transferred to form NADH from NAD$^+$, as well

as the smaller amounts of energy to form FADH$_2$ from FAD. These processes involve structures located in the inner membrane (or cristae) of mitochondria.

Structures of the Electron Transport System

Several significant types of molecules are embedded within the cristae of the mitochondria: electron carriers, H$^+$ pumps, and ATP synthetase enzymes **(figure 3.20a)**. Proteins in the cristae membrane serve as electron carriers to "catch" electrons and pass them from one to the other in a series. This series of the electron carriers is collectively called the **electron transport chain**. Each protein acts as a H$^+$ pump to transport H$^+$ from the matrix to the outer membrane compartment. This maintains a H$^+$ gradient between the outer compartment and the matrix within a mitochondrion, with more H$^+$ in the outer compartment than in the matrix. ATP synthetase then allows for the passage of H$^+$ from the outer com-

Cellular Respiration

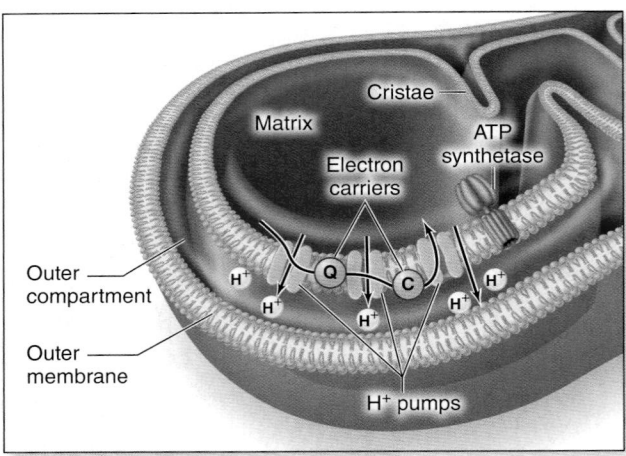

(a) Structures of the electron transport system

(b) Net chemical reaction of the electron transport system

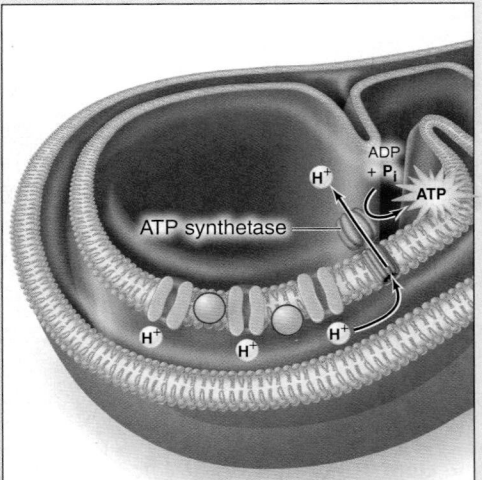

① Electrons are transferred from NADH and FADH$_2$ through a series of electron carriers within the cristae. O$_2$ is the final electron acceptor.

② Energy of electrons "falling" is used to move H$^+$ up its concentration gradient from the matrix to the outer compartment.

③ ATP synthetase harnesses the kinetic energy of the H$^+$ "falling" down its concentration gradient to bond ADP and P$_i$ to form ATP.

(c) Details of the electron transport system

Figure 3.20 Aerobic Cellular Respiration: The Electron Transport System. (*a*) Anatomic structures associated with the electron transport system are housed in the inner mitochondrial membrane and include a series of electron carriers, H$^+$ pumps, and the enzyme ATP synthetase. (*b*), (*c*) The process can be organized into three steps in which energy temporarily held by the coenzymes NADH and FADH$_2$ is used to form a bond between ADP and P$_i$, yielding ATP. **AP|R**

partment back into the matrix. During this process, the flow of H^+ down its concentration gradient is harnessed to bond P_i to ADP to form ATP.

Steps of the Electron Transport System

The processes of the electron transport system are organized into three major steps (figure 3.20b, c):

① **Electrons are transferred from coenzymes to O_2.** The coenzyme, either NADH or FADH₂, releases hydrogen (e⁻ and H^+) and it is oxidized. The released electrons are passed through a series of electron carriers in the electron transport system to O_2, which serves as the final electron acceptor. O_2 combines with 4 e⁻ + 4 H^+ to produce two molecules of H_2O. Thus, oxygen is a reactant in cellular respiration, and it becomes part of the water that is produced.

② **Proton gradient is established.** As electrons are "falling" and passed between electron carriers their potential energy is converted to kinetic energy. The kinetic energy is harnessed by H^+ pumps to move H^+ from the mitochondrial matrix into the outer compartment, establishing a proton gradient.

③ **Proton gradient is harnessed to form ATP.** H^+ moves down its concentration gradient as it is transported across the inner membrane by ATP synthetase. It moves from the outer compartment into the matrix. (Note that H^+ moves back into the area of the mitochondrion from which it was just pumped.) This process is analogous to water falling over a dam and turning a water wheel. The kinetic energy of the falling H^+ is harnessed by ATP synthetase to form a new bond between ADP and P_i, producing an ATP.

This process of forming ATP is referred to as **oxidative phosphorylation** because it involves oxygen as the final electron acceptor, and ATP is formed from the phosphorylation of ADP. This process is distinguished from substrate-level phosphorylation, which forms ATP from energy directly released from a substrate, as occurs in specific steps of glycolysis (see figure 3.16, steps 7 and 10) and the citric acid cycle (see figure 3.18, step 6).

WHAT DID YOU LEARN?

24 What is the importance of NADH and FADH₂ in energy transfer?

25 What are the three primary steps that take place in the electron transport system?

 LEARNING OBJECTIVE

10. Calculate the number of ATP molecules produced in both anaerobic and aerobic cellular respiration.

The number of ATP molecules generated when electrons are released from coenzymes is dependent upon the entry point of the electrons into the electron transport system (figure 3.20). The electrons from NADH enter at the top of the electron transport system and are passed through three H^+ pumps, which results in enough energy being released to generate 3 ATP molecules. In contrast, the electrons from FADH₂ enter at the second H^+ pump; this results in the generation of 2 ATP molecules. Consequently, each NADH generates 3 ATP and each FADH₂ generates 2 ATP.

WHAT DO YOU THINK?

5 Given that energy from each NADH produces 3 ATP molecules and each FADH₂ produces 2 ATP molecules, calculate the number of ATP molecules generated from glucose during cellular respiration.

We are able to calculate the specific number of ATP molecules produced in breakdown of a glucose molecule by knowing the following: (1) the specific number of energy molecules (i.e., ATP, NADH, and FADH₂) that are generated from glucose breakdown in each of the first three stages of cellular respiration, and (2) the specific number of ATP generated by the oxidation of each type of coenzyme in the electron transport system (NADH = 3 ATP molecules and FADH = 2 ATP molecules).

Below is a summary of the number of ATP molecules produced by substrate-level phosphorylation and the number of ATP produced by oxidative phosphorylation from glucose oxidation.

Stage/Total	Substrate Level Phosphorylation	Oxidative Phosphorylation
Glycolysis	2 ATP	2 NADH → 6 ATP
Intermediate Stage	—	2 NADH → 6 ATP
Citric Acid Cycle	2 ATP	6 NADH → 18 ATP
		2 FADH₂ → 4 ATP
Total Number of ATP/ Based on Method of Formation	**4 ATP**	**34 ATP**

The total ATP produced from one glucose molecule is 38 ATP. However—and this is very important for energy totals—the 2 NADH produced during glycolysis are made in the cytosol. Therefore, to "cash in" these glycolysis-produced NADH molecules, they must be shipped from the cytosol into the electron transport system of the mitochondria at a cost of 1 ATP per NADH. Consequently, the net value normally given for ATP generated from the oxidation of glucose is 36 ATP.

 **WHAT DID YOU LEARN?**

26 How many ATP molecules are generated through the anaerobic processes of glycolysis that occur in the cytosol (i.e., without participation of mitochondria)? How many ATP molecules are formed through the combined processes that occur in the cytosol and those that occur within mitochondria?

3.4g The Fate of Pyruvate with Insufficient Oxygen

11. Explain the fate of pyruvate when oxygen is in short supply.

12. Describe the impact on ATP production if there is insufficient oxygen.

We followed pyruvate in the previous discussion assuming that sufficient oxygen was present for oxidative phosphorylation to occur. If sufficient oxygen is not available we must consider the following:

1. Aerobic cellular activity decreases, including the activity of the electron transport chain. Electrons remain with the NADH and $FADH_2$ molecules and NADH and $FADH_2$ accumulate. This is accompanied by decreased levels of NAD^+ and FAD.
2. The cell becomes increasingly dependent on the anaerobic processes of glycolysis, a metabolic pathway that requires NAD^+ to continue.
3. Extended anaerobic conditions would ultimately result in the complete shutdown of glycolysis within the cell because of the lack of NAD^+.
4. NAD^+ must be regenerated if glycolysis is to continue.

Regenerating NAD^+ involves the transfer of hydrogen from NADH. Two electrons and hydrogen are transferred from NADH to pyruvate, which is converted to lactate (lactic acid). This enzymatic reaction is catalyzed by lactate dehydrogenase **(figure 3.21)**.

Although an effective means to permit glycolysis to continue, we must keep in mind that without the availability and use of mitochondria, only 2 ATP are produced per glucose. Compared to the 36 ATP produced with sufficient oxygen, there is significantly less ATP generated (2 ATP versus 36 ATP). This is an 18-fold difference! Remember the important association that low O_2 equals low energy. Individuals with decreased ability to deliver oxygen to cells (e.g., those with impaired respiratory or cardiovascular function) will have less available ATP required to meet the body's energy needs.

🔅 **WHAT DID YOU LEARN?**

27 Pyruvate is converted to what molecule if there is insufficient oxygen? Explain why this occurs.

3.4h Other Fuel Molecules That Are Oxidized in Cellular Respiration

13. Describe the entry point in the metabolic pathway of cellular respiration for both fatty acids and amino acids.

There are other fuel molecules, such as fatty acids and amino acids that may be oxidized to generate ATP. In general, the use of these fuel molecules increases during conditions of fasting or starvation. However, fatty acids are the preferred fuel molecule for muscle tissue at rest.

Recall from section 2.7b that triglyceride molecules are composed of glycerol and fatty acids. Triglycerides provide long-term energy reserves and are stored in adipose connective tissue; these reserves may be mobilized and oxidized as needed.

Fatty acids are enzymatically changed two carbon units at a time to form acetyl CoA. This process is called **beta-oxidation**. Acetyl CoA then enters the cell respiration metabolic pathway at the citric acid cycle. Because fatty acids enter this metabolic pathway in the mitochondria, they can only be oxidized aerobically. (Note that a by-product of fatty acid metabolism is the production of ketoacids, with significant amounts produced in individuals with uncontrolled diabetes mellitus; see Clinical View: Lactic Acidosis and Ketoacidosis in chapter 25.)

A different pathway is employed if protein is used for fuel. The point of entry of deaminated amino acids (amino acids with the amine group [-NH_2] removed) is dependent upon the specific type of amino acids. Different amino acids enter the metabolic pathway at glycolysis, the intermediate stage, or the citric acid cycle. The amine group is a waste product that is converted to urea and excreted by the kidneys. The point of entry for both fatty acids and amino acids is shown in figure 27.8.

🔅 **WHAT DID YOU LEARN?**

28 Why is oxygen required to burn fatty acids?

Figure 3.21 Conversion of Pyruvate to Lactate. Lactate dehydrogenase converts pyruvate to lactate to regenerate NAD^+ molecules.

INTEGRATE

CONCEPT CONNECTION

What happens to the increased levels of lactate produced by skeletal muscle tissue? Lactate is either absorbed by surrounding muscle tissue or transported by the blood to the liver. Muscle cells may use lactate immediately for ATP synthesis by converting it back to pyruvate or converting it to glucose and storing it as glycogen. Liver cells convert lactate into glucose. Glucose formed in the liver is either stored as glycogen in the liver or released back into the blood (for muscles to take up). This cycling of lactate from muscles to the liver, the conversion of lactate to glucose, and the subsequent transport of glucose from the liver to muscle is called the Cori cycle.

CHAPTER SUMMARY

- The concepts discussed are energy, chemical reactions, enzymes, metabolic pathways, and the production of ATP through cellular respiration.

3.1 Energy 71

- Energy is the capacity to do work.

3.1a States of Energy 71

- Energy exists in two states: energy based on position, called potential energy, and energy of motion, called kinetic energy.
- Energy can be converted from potential energy to kinetic energy (or vice versa). Examples are the movement of a substance down its concentration gradient, or the movement of electrons from a higher-energy state to a lower-energy state.

3.1b Forms of Energy 72

- Energy exists in different forms, including chemical, electrical, mechanical, sound, radiant, and heat.

3.1c Laws of Thermodynamics 73

- The first law of thermodynamics states that energy cannot be created or destroyed, only converted from one form to another.
- The second law of thermodynamics states that some energy is lost as heat with every energy conversion.

3.2 Chemical Reactions 73

- Chemical reactions are expressed in chemical equations and are classified using various criteria.

3.2a Chemical Equations 73

- Metabolism is the collective term for all chemical reactions that occur in the body.
- Reactants become products in a chemical reaction, and an arrow indicates the direction of change.

3.2b Classification of Chemical Reactions 76

- Chemical reactions can be classified using different criteria: change in chemical structure, change in chemical energy, and if the reaction is irreversible or reversible.

3.2c Reaction Rates and Activation Energy 79

- Reaction rate is the measure of how quickly the chemical reaction takes place and activation energy is the amount of energy required for the reaction to proceed.

3.3 Enzymes 80

- Enzymes facilitate chemical reactions.

3.3a Function of Enzymes 80

- Enzymes are biologically active catalysts that increase reaction rates by lowering activation energy (E_a).

3.3b Enzyme Structure and Location 80

- Generally, enzymes are globular proteins with an active site that bind a specific substrate. Enzymes can be located within cells, embedded in the plasma membrane, or present in fluid outside of cells.

3.3c Mechanism of Enzyme Action 81

- Enzymes are catalysts that participate in both decomposition and synthesis reactions.

3.3d Classification and Naming of Enzymes 82

- Enzymes are usually named based upon their function. Often their name contains the -*ase* suffix.

3.3e Enzymes and Reaction Rates 83

- The reaction rate is dependent upon the concentrations of both the enzyme and substrate, temperature, and pH.

3.3f Controlling Enzymes 84

- Enzymes can be controlled by either competitive inhibitors or noncompetitive inhibitors.

3.3g Metabolic Pathways and Multienzyme Complexes 84

- A metabolic pathway is a series of enzymes that subsequently converts a substrate to a final product. Metabolic pathways are regulated by negative feedback to maintain the needed amount of the final product.
- A multienzyme complex is a structure composed of enzymes physically linked to convert a substrate to a final product.
- Phosphorylation is the addition of a phosphate group, and dephosphorylation is the removal of a phosphate group. This is a common means of regulating enzymes.

3.4 Cellular Respiration 88

- Cellular respiration is the metabolic process for oxidizing organic molecules (e.g., glucose) to release energy to synthesize ATP.

3.4a Overview of Glucose Oxidation 88

- The net chemical reaction for glucose oxidation is $C_6H_{12}O_6 + 6\ O_2 \longrightarrow 6\ CO_2 + 6\ H_2O$.
- ATP is produced directly through substrate-level phosphorylation and indirectly by oxidative phosphorylation.
- Glucose oxidation occurs within a cell: glycolyis (or anaerobic cellular respiration) within the cytosol, and aerobic cellular respiration (the intermediate stage, the citric acid cycle, and the electron transport system) within mitochondria.

3.4b Glycolysis: Anaerobic Cellular Respiration 89

- Glycolysis is a metabolic pathway that uses ten enzymes and does not require oxygen (i.e., it is anaerobic). Glucose is converted to two pyruvate molecules, producing 2 net ATP and 2 NADH in this metabolic pathway.
- The fate of pyruvate is dependent upon the availability of oxygen.

(continued on next page)

3.4 Cellular Respiration *(continued)*

3.4c Aerobic Cellular Respiration: Intermediate Stage 92
- In the intermediate stage, pyruvate dehydrogenase converts pyruvate to acetyl CoA within a mitochondrion. It occurs as CO_2 is released from the pyruvate, and NADH is produced during this stage.
- The intermediate stage occurs twice per the original glucose.

3.4d Aerobic Cellular Respiration: Citric Acid Cycle 92
- The citric acid cycle completes the digestion of glucose. In the process 1 ATP molecule, 3 NADH molecules, and 1 $FADH_2$ molecule are generated per pyruvate, and two molecules of CO_2 waste are generated and released from the digestion of glucose.
- The citric acid cycle occurs twice per the original glucose.

3.4e Aerobic Cellular Respiration: The Electron Transport System 96
- The electron transport system involves several significant structures that are embedded in the cristae membrane of a mitochondrion including electron carriers, H^+ pumps, and the enzyme ATP synthetase.
- Electrons from NADH and $FADH_2$ are transferred to electron carriers in the electron transport system of a mitochondrion, and ultimately to O_2. The electrons, oxygen, and hydrogen ions form H_2O.
- A H^+ gradient is formed, and H^+ then flow down this gradient and the energy is harnessed by ATP synthetase to produce ATP through oxidative phosphorylation.

3.4f ATP Production 97
- Two ATP are produced in anaerobic cellular respiration, and thirty-six ATP are produced if glucose oxidation is complete; a process that is aerobic.

3.4g The Fate of Pyruvate with Insufficient Oxygen 98
- If insufficient oxygen is available, pyruvate will be converted by lactate dehydrogenase to lactate to regenerate NAD^+ so glycolysis can continue.

3.4h Other Fuel Molecules That Are Oxidized in Cellular Respiration 98
- The digestion of other fuel molecules, such as fatty acids and amino acids, can also be oxidized to generate ATP.

CHALLENGE YOURSELF

Do You Know the Basics?

____ 1. Energy in ATP is used to power skeletal muscle contraction. This is an example of what type of energy conversion?

    a. chemical energy to mechanical energy

    b. light energy to mechanical energy

    c. chemical energy to light energy

    d. electrical energy to chemical energy

____ 2. Oxidation-reduction can be best classified as a(n) _____ reaction.

    a. exchange   c. synthesis

    b. endergonic   d. reversible

____ 3. All of the following increase the reaction rate *except*

    a. an increase in temperature.

    b. an increase in pH.

    c. an increase in concentration of the substrate.

    d. an increase in concentration of the enzyme that catalyzes the reaction.

____ 4. ATP inhibits phosphofructokinase by binding to an allosteric site in glycolysis. ATP is functioning as a

    a. competitive inhibitor.   c. noncompetitive inhibitor.

    b. competitive activator.   d. noncompetitive activator.

____ 5. All of the following are accurate about enzymes *except*:

    a. Enzymes are typically globular proteins with an active site.

    b. Enzymes decrease activation energy.

    c. Enzymes can be used over and over to catalyze a substrate to a product.

    d. Enzymes are versatile and can catalyze different types of chemical reactions.

____ 6. Glucose is converted to pyruvate in which stage of cellular respiration?

    a. glycolysis   c. citric acid cycle

    b. intermediate stage   d. electron transport system

____ 7. NAD^+ and FAD^+ are examples of

    a. enzymes.

    b. high-energy organic molecules that are digested in cellular respiration.

    c. allosteric inhibitors.

    d. coenzymes.

____ 8. All stages of cellular respiration are decreased in conditions of insufficient oxygen *except*

    a. glycolysis.   c. the citric acid cycle.

    b. the intermediate stage.   d. the electron transport system.

____ 9. In anaerobic respiration, _____ ATP are formed, and if sufficient oxygen is present, _____ ATP are formed.

    a. 2, 2   c. 2, 36

    b. 36, 38   d. 10, 30

_____ 10. Oxidative phosphorylation involves
  a. electrons transported in the electron transport chain and accepted by O_2.
  b. ATP synthetase harnessing the energy in a proton gradient.
  c. coenzymes NADH and $FADH_2$ giving up their electrons.
  d. all of the above.

11. List and define the different forms of energy, and give one example each of their application in the human body.

12. Describe the different ways of classifying chemical reactions, and explain what category oxidation-reduction belongs to.

13. Explain ATP cycling.

14. Describe the structure and mechanism of enzymes.

15. Describe a metabolic pathway, and explain how it is controlled by negative feedback.

16. Summarize glycolysis, including where it occurs in a cell, if it requires oxygen, the substrate and final product, and the formation of energy containing molecules (i.e., ATP, NADH, $FADH_2$).

17. In general terms, explain the fate of pyruvate if there is (a) sufficient oxygen, and (b) insufficient oxygen.

18. Describe how oxygen becomes part of water during cellular respiration.

19. Identify the source of carbon in carbon dioxide.

20. Based on what you know about anaerobic and aerobic respiration, explain the advantage in terms of ATP production of a healthy respiratory and cardiovascular system.

Can You Apply What You've Learned?

1. Albinism (achromia) is a genetic condition in which an individual cannot synthesize melanin from tyrosine (an amino acid), a brown pigment of the hair, skin, and eyes. These individuals lack
  a. specific fatty acids.
  b. a protein that contains tyrosine.
  c. an enzyme that converts tyrosine to melanin.
  d. cofactors that convert tyrosine to melanin.

2. If an individual has impaired respiratory function, such as occurs with emphysema, you would expect all of the following *except*

  a. production of additional lactic acid.
  b. an impaired ability to make ATP.
  c. low energy levels and complaints of being tired.
  d. increased aerobic cellular respiration.

3. Another challenge to a patient with impaired respiratory function is the buildup of CO_2 in the blood. What would you predict given the following enzymatic reaction that occurs in the blood?
$$H_2O + CO_2 \longleftrightarrow H_2CO_3 \longleftrightarrow H^+ + HCO_3$$

  a. increased production of H_2O
  b. increased production of H^+ (with an accompanying decrease in pH)
  c. decreased production of H^+ (with an accompanying increase in pH)
  d. All of the above.

4. You would expect decreased production of ATP in all of the following individuals *except*

  a. an individual with impaired ability to transport oxygen in the blood, such as a person with anemia.
  b. an individual with severe asthma.
  c. an individual in congestive heart failure.
  d. an athlete.

5. Brown adipose tissue contains cells that allow H^+ to fall down the concentration gradient in the electron transport system without producing ATP. Instead, all of the kinetic energy is converted to heat. If scientists could increase the amount of brown adipose tissue in our bodies, then

  a. our body temperature would be cooler.
  b. these cells would be more efficient at producing ATP.
  c. we could eat more and not gain weight.
  d. we would be able to run faster.

Can You Synthesize What You've Learned?

1. Tiffany had returned to her college dorm and was having difficulty breathing. She knew she was having an asthma attack. What changes in her energy level are predicted?

2. Provide a general explanation to a patient on the advantages of aerobic fitness in terms of ATP production.

3. What occurs to the amount of product formed in a metabolic pathway if inhibition does not occur?

chapter 4
Biology of the Cell

Heart cells contract to pump blood out of the heart chambers; retinal cells of the eye detect light; phagocytic white blood cells engulf foreign substances (e.g., bacteria, viruses); and pancreatic cells synthesize and secrete the hormone insulin. All human body processes are ultimately dependent upon cells and their activities. For this reason, the cell is often referred to as the "functional unit of the body." Knowledge of cellular structure and function is critical for understanding the concepts of all later chapters. ➡

A cytologist examines cells under a microscope to detect abnormalities that may indicate cancer or other diseases. Cytologists prepare cell samples using specialized equipment and apply stains or other techniques to enhance specimens for detailed observation. Drawing upon an extensive knowledge of cell structure and function, they then analyze cell samples and provide their findings to a pathologist, who ultimately makes a diagnosis.

Anatomy & Physiology | REVEALED®
aprevealed.com

Module 2: Cells and Chemistry

Throughout this chapter, we present a broad discussion of a cell by describing how cells are studied and the general structural components and functions of cells. Subsequent chapters examine specialized cells and provide details of their unique functions.

4.1 Introduction to Cells

Our examination of cells begins with a description of how we study cells. We then describe the typical size and shape of cells and how some cells may vary from the typical cell. The section concludes with a discussion of common structural features and functions that all cells possess.

4.1a How Cells Are Studied

✓ LEARNING OBJECTIVE

1. Distinguish among types of microscopy using LM, TEM, and SEM.

The study of cells is called **cytology.** The small size of cells is the greatest obstacle to determining their nature. Cells were discovered after microscopes were invented because high-magnification microscopes are required to see the smallest human body cells. The dimensional unit often used to measure cell size is the micrometer (µm). One micrometer is equal to 1/10,000 of a centimeter (about 1/125,000 of an inch).

Microscopy is the use of a microscope to view small-scale structures, and it is a valuable asset in anatomic investigations. The most commonly used instruments are the light microscope, the transmission electron microscope, and the scanning electron microscope.

Microscopy specimen samples have no inherent contrast (difference between specimen and background) so structures cannot be seen clearly. To provide contrast, colored-dye stains are used with light microscopes, and heavy-metal stains are used with both transmission electron and scanning electron microscopes. **Figure 4.1** compares the images produced when each of these types of microscopes is used to examine the same specimen—in this case, cilia on the surface of epithelial tissue lining the respiratory tract.

The **light microscope (LM)** produces a two-dimensional image by passing visible light through the specimen. Glass lenses focus and magnify the image as it is projected toward the eye (figure 4.1a).

The **electron microscope (EM)** uses a beam of electrons to "illuminate" the specimen. Electron microscopes easily exceed the magnification obtained by light microscopy—but more importantly, they improve the resolution (ability to see details) by more than a thousand-fold over the light microscope. A **transmission electron microscope (TEM)** directs an electron beam through a thin-cut section of the specimen. The resultant two-dimensional image is focused onto a screen for viewing or onto photographic film to record the image. The TEM in figure 4.1b shows a close-up section of the cilia on the surface of the epithelial cells.

For detailed three-dimensional study of a specimen's surface, **scanning electron microscope (SEM)** analysis is the method of choice (figure 4.1c). Here, the electron beam is moved across the surface of the specimen, and reflected electrons generate a surface-topography image captured on a television screen.

💡 WHAT DID YOU LEARN?

❶ What is the advantage of using a TEM instead of an LM to study intracellular structure?

(a) Light microscopy

(b) Transmission electron microscopy

(c) Scanning electron microscopy

Figure 4.1 Microscopic Techniques for Cellular Studies. Different techniques are used to investigate cellular anatomy. (*a*) A light microscope (LM) shows hairlike structures, termed cilia, that project from cells lining the respiratory tract. (*b*) A transmission electron microscope (TEM) reveals the ultrastructure, and (*c*) a scanning electron microscope (SEM) shows the three-dimensional image of the cilia of the same type of cells.

4.1b Cell Size and Shape

✅ LEARNING OBJECTIVES

2. Describe the range in size of human cells.
3. Name some of the shapes cells may exhibit.

Cells are typically depicted as being of one size and either spherical or cubelike in shape, when in reality the structure of the approximately 75 trillion cells of the adult human shows great variety. Most cells are microscopic in size, but some are large enough to be seen with the naked eye **(figure 4.2)**. For example, red blood cells (erythrocytes) are relatively small with a diameter of about 7–8 μm, whereas a human oocyte has a diameter of about 120 μm. Cells also vary greatly in shape **(figure 4.3)**. Although some cells are spherical or cubelike, others may be columnlike, cylindrical, disc-shaped, or have an irregular form. Note that a relationship exists between the size and shape of a cell and its function in the body.

💡 WHAT DID YOU LEARN?

2 What is the range in size of a typical cell?

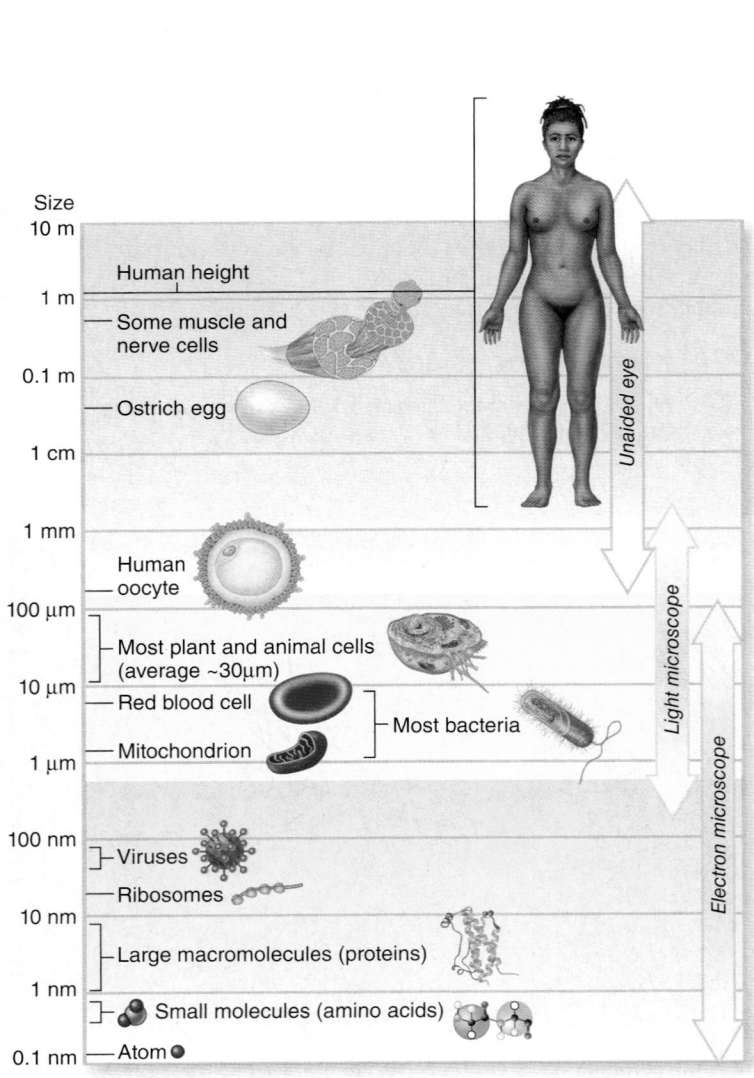

Figure 4.2 The Range of Cell Sizes. Most cells in the human body are between 1 micrometer (μm) and 100 μm in diameter.

Figure 4.3 The Variety of Cell Shapes. Cells throughout the body exhibit different shapes that support various functions.

4.1c Common Features and General Functions

LEARNING OBJECTIVES

4. Describe the three main structural features of a cell.
5. Identify the membrane-bound and non-membrane-bound organelles.
6. Distinguish between organelles and cell inclusions.
7. Explain the general functions that cells must perform.

Most cells are composed of characteristic parts that work together to allow each cell type in the body to perform certain common functions.

Overview of Cellular Components

The generalized cell shown in **figure 4.4** isn't an actual body cell, but rather a representation of a cell that combines features of different types of body cells. The common features include the following:

- **Plasma membrane.** The plasma (plaz´mă; *plasso* = to form) membrane forms the outer, limiting barrier separating the internal contents of the cell from the external environment. Modified extensions of the plasma membrane include cilia, a flagellum, and microvilli.
- **Nucleus.** The nucleus (nū´klē-ŭs; *nux* = the kernel) is the largest structure within the cell and is enclosed by a nuclear envelope. Much of the internal content of the nucleus is the genetic material, deoxyribonucleic acid (DNA). The fluid within the nucleus is called the nucleoplasm. Within the nucleus is a dark-staining body called the nucleolus.

Figure 4.4 The Structure of a Cell. This generalized cell illustrates most of the common features found in mature human cells, which include the plasma membrane, nucleus, and cytoplasm. Composing the cytoplasm is cytosol and organelles that are either membrane-bound or non-membrane-bound. Some cells also contain inclusions, which are temporary stores of specific molecules. AP|R

- **Cytoplasm.** Cytoplasm (sī′tō-plazm; *kytos* = cell, *plasma* = a thing formed) is a general term for all cellular contents located between the plasma membrane and the nucleus. The three primary components of the cytoplasm are the cytosol, organelles, and inclusions.

Cytoplasmic Components

The **cytosol** (sī′tō-sol; *sol* = soluble), also called the *intracellular fluid* (ICF) or *cytoplasmic matrix*, is the viscous, syruplike fluid of the cytoplasm. It has a high water content and contains many dissolved macromolecules that include carbohydrates, lipids, proteins, and small molecules such as glucose and amino acids. Cytosol also contains various types of ions that are used in cellular functions.

Organelles (or′gă-nel; *organon* = organ, *elle* = the diminutive suffix), meaning "little organs," are complex, organized structures within cells that have unique characteristic shapes and functions. Two categories of organelles are recognized: membrane-bound organelles and non-membrane-bound organelles. **Membrane-bound organelles,** or *membranous organelles,* are enclosed by a membrane similar to the plasma membrane. The membrane separates the organelle's contents from the cytosol so that the specific activities of the organelle can proceed without disruption from other cellular activities. Membrane-bound organelles include: the endoplasmic reticulum (rough and smooth), Golgi apparatus, lysosomes, peroxisomes, and mitochondria (figure 4.4). Vesicles are temporary membrane-bound structures formed from the endoplasmic reticulum, Golgi apparatus, and plasma membrane. The **non-membrane-bound organelles,** or *nonmembranous organelles,* are not enclosed within a membrane. These structures are generally composed of protein and include ribosomes (either fixed to a membrane or free within the cytosol), the cytoskeleton, the centrosome, and proteasomes. Each of these organelles is discussed in detail later in this chapter.

The cytosol of some cells temporarily store **inclusions,** a large and diverse group of molecules. Most inclusions are not bound by a membrane and are not considered organelles. Pigments (e.g., melanin, a stored pigment in some skin, hair, and eye cells) and nutrient stores (e.g., glycogen and triglycerides) are examples of cellular inclusions.

General Cell Functions

The following are general functions that cells must perform:

- **Maintain integrity and shape of a cell.** The integrity and shape of a cell is dependent on both the plasma membrane, which forms the external boundary of the cell and the internal contents, which function to support the cell.
- **Obtain nutrients and form chemical building blocks.** Each cell must get nutrients and other needed materials from its surrounding fluid. Cells form new chemical structures and harvest the energy necessary for survival through diverse metabolic processes.
- **Dispose of wastes.** Cells must dispose of the waste molecules they produce, so they do not accumulate and disrupt normal cellular activities.

In addition, some cells are capable of undergoing cell division to make more cells of the same type. These new cells help to maintain the tissue or organ to which they belong by providing cells for new growth and replacing cells that die. However, during development, many cells lose their ability to divide (described later).

 WHAT DID YOU LEARN?

3 What are the three main structural features of a cell?

4 What cellular structure is responsible for forming the boundary of a cell and maintaining its integrity?

4.2 Chemical Structure of the Plasma Membrane

The plasma membrane is not a rigid boundary, but rather is a fluid matrix composed of approximately an equal mixture, by weight, of lipids and proteins. It regulates the movement of most substances both into and out of a cell.

4.2a Lipid Components

LEARNING OBJECTIVE

1. List the lipid components of the plasma membrane, and explain the actions of each component.

The plasma membrane contains several different types of lipids including phospholipids, cholesterol, and glycolipids **(figure 4.5)**.

Most of the plasma membrane lipids are **phospholipids** (section 2.3c). Often these molecules are artistically portrayed in the membrane as a "balloon with two tails." The balloonlike "head" is polar and hydrophilic. In contrast, the two "tails" are nonpolar and hydrophobic. Phospholipid molecules readily associate to form two parallel sheets of molecules lying tail-to-tail, with the hydrophobic tails forming the internal environment of the membrane and their hydrophilic polar heads directed outward. This basic structure of the plasma membrane framework is called the **phospholipid bilayer.** The phospholipid bilayer ensures that cytosol remains inside the cell, and **interstitial fluid** (the fluid that surrounds cells) remains outside.

Cholesterol is scattered within the hydrophobic regions of the phospholipid bilayer. It strengthens the membrane and stabilizes it at temperature extremes.

Glycolipids are lipids with attached carbohydrate groups. They are located only on the outer phospholipid layer of the membrane, where they are exposed to the interstitial fluid. Together, the carbohydrate portion of the glycolipid molecules and the glycoprotein molecules (described in the next section) help to form the **glycocalyx** (glī′kō-kā′liks; *glykys* = sweet, *kalyx* = husk), a "coating of sugar" on the cell's surface. It is interesting to note that the pattern of sugars of the glycocalyx is unique to each individual except identical twins.

The lipid portion of the plasma membrane is insoluble in water, which ensures that the plasma membrane will not simply dissolve when it comes into contact with water. Rather, this boundary is an effective nonpolar physical barrier to most substances. Only small and nonpolar substances can readily penetrate (move through) this barrier without assistance.

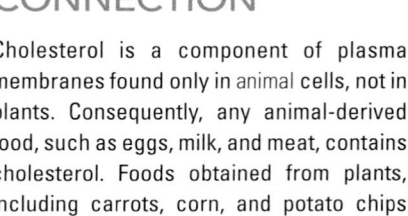

INTEGRATE

CONCEPT CONNECTION

Cholesterol is a component of plasma membranes found only in animal cells, not in plants. Consequently, any animal-derived food, such as eggs, milk, and meat, contains cholesterol. Foods obtained from plants, including carrots, corn, and potato chips cooked in vegetable oil, do not contain cholesterol.

WHAT DID YOU LEARN?

5 How do lipids maintain the basic physical barrier of the plasma membrane?

Phospholipid

Polar head of phospholipid molecule

Phospholipid bilayer

Nonpolar tails of phospholipid molecule

Glycolipid

Cholesterol

Carbohydrate

Interstitial fluid

Glycoprotein

Protein

Integral protein

Peripheral protein

Filaments of cytoskeleton

Cytosol

Functions of Plasma Membrane

1. **Physical barrier:** Establishes a flexible boundary, protects cellular contents, and supports cell structure. Phospholipid bilayer separates substances inside and outside the cell
2. **Selective permeability:** Regulates entry and exit of ions, nutrients, and waste molecules through the membrane
3. **Electrochemical gradients:** Establishes and maintains an electrical charge difference across the plasma membrane
4. **Communication:** Contains receptors that recognize and respond to molecular signals

(a) Plasma membrane

Cytosol

Phospholipid bilayer — Phospholipid bilayer

Cytosol

(b) Phospholipid bilayer

Figure 4.5 Structure and Functions of the Plasma Membrane. (*a*) The plasma membrane is a phospholipid bilayer, with cholesterol and proteins scattered throughout and associated with its surfaces. (*b*) The phospholipid bilayers of two adjacent cells is visible in a TEM. AP|R

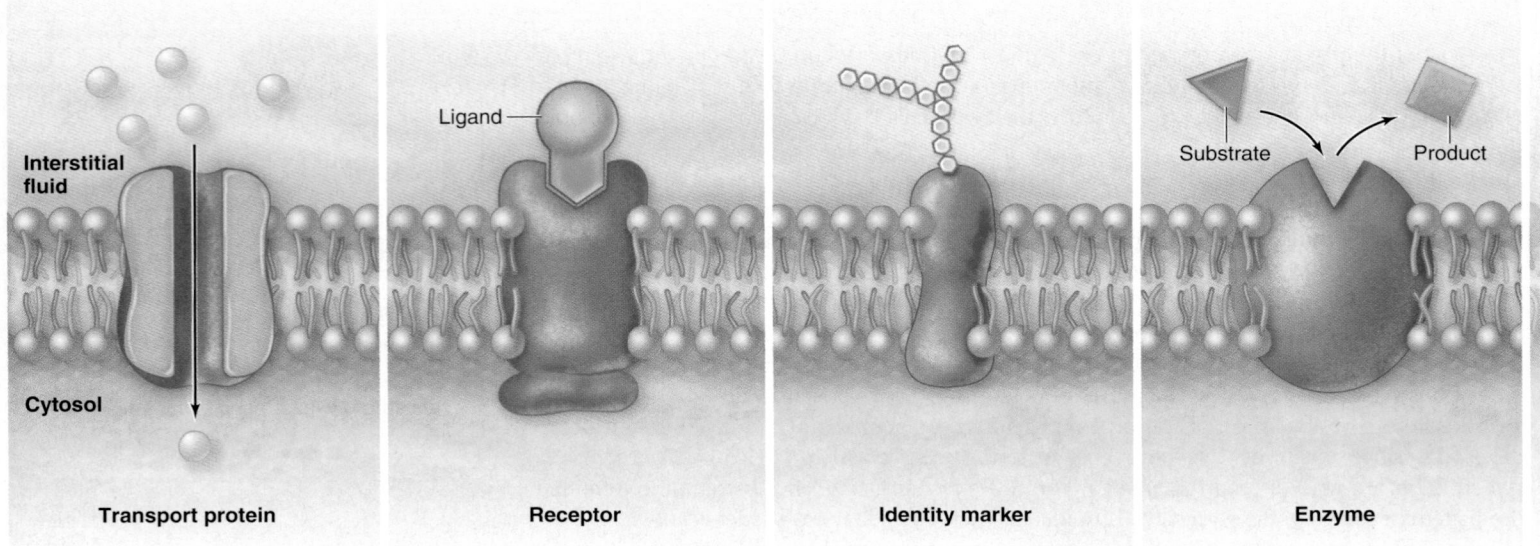

Interstitial fluid

Cytosol

Transport protein   Receptor   Identity marker   Enzyme

Ligand

Substrate   Product

Figure 4.6 Plasma Membrane Proteins. The major functional categories of plasma membrane proteins include the three types of transport proteins (channels, carriers, and pumps), cell surface receptors, identity markers, enzymes, anchoring sites for the cytoskeleton, and cell-adhesion proteins.

4.2b Membrane Proteins

LEARNING OBJECTIVES

2. Differentiate between the two types of membrane proteins based on their relative position in the plasma membrane.

3. Name the six major roles played by membrane proteins.

Although lipids form the main component of the plasma membrane, the proteins dispersed within the lipids make up about half of the plasma membrane by weight. Proteins can "float" and move about the fluid bilayer, much like a beach ball floating on the water surface in a swimming pool. Most of the membrane's specific functions are determined by its resident proteins.

Membrane proteins are classified as one of two structural types: integral or peripheral. **Integral proteins** are embedded within, and extend across, the phospholipid bilayer (figure 4.5). Hydrophobic regions within the integral proteins interact with the hydrophobic interior of the membrane. In contrast, the hydrophilic regions of the integral proteins are exposed to the aqueous environments on either side of the membrane. Many integral membrane proteins are **glycoproteins** that have carbohydrates exposed to the interstitial fluid. In contrast, **peripheral proteins** are not embedded within the lipid bilayer. They are attached loosely to either the external or internal surfaces of the membrane and are often "anchored" to the exposed parts of an integral protein.

Proteins and glycoproteins are also categorized functionally based upon the specific role they serve **(figure 4.6)**.

- **Transport proteins** provide a means of regulating the movement of substances across the plasma membrane. Different types of transport proteins include **channels, carriers,** and **pumps.**
- **Cell surface receptors** bind specific molecules that are called ligands. **Ligands** are molecules released from one cell that bind to receptors within the plasma membrane of another cell. Examples of ligands include neurotransmitters released from nerve cells and hormones released from endocrine cells.
- **Identity markers** are either proteins or glycoproteins that communicate to other cells that they belong to the body. Cells of the immune system use identity markers to

distinguish normal, healthy cells from foreign, damaged, or infected cells that are to be destroyed (see chapter 22).

- **Enzymes** may be attached to either the internal or external surface of a cell for catalyzing chemical reactions (section 3.3b).
- **Anchoring sites** are proteins that secure the cytoskeleton (the internal, protein support of a cell) to the plasma membrane.
- **Cell-adhesion proteins** are for cell-to-cell attachments. Proteins that form membrane junctions perform a number of functions including binding cells to one another.

WHAT DID YOU LEARN?

6. What type of plasma membrane protein provides the means for moving materials across the plasma membrane? What are its three subtypes?

4.3 Membrane Transport

One important function of the plasma membrane is to regulate the movement of materials into and out of a cell. A cell must acquire various substances from the interstitial fluid (e.g., nutrients, oxygen, ions), and must also eliminate wastes (e.g., carbon dioxide, ions) into the interstitial fluid.

Obtaining and eliminating substances across the plasma membrane occur through the processes of **membrane transport**. These processes are organized into two major categories based on the requirement for expending cellular energy. **Passive processes** do not require energy expenditure. Instead they simply depend upon the kinetic energy inherent within a substance as it moves down its concentration gradient (i.e., from where there is more of a substance to where there is less). Diffusion and osmosis are the two types of passive processes. Active processes differ because they require cells to expend energy. This involves either the movement of a substance up its concentration gradient (i.e., from where there is less of a substance to where there is more) or the release (or formation) of a membrane-bound vesicle. These energy-requiring processes are called active transport and vesicular transport, respectively.

Cytoskeleton protein

Anchoring site

Interstitial fluid

Cell-adhesion protein

4.3a Passive Processes: Diffusion

✓ LEARNING OBJECTIVES

1. Summarize the general concept of diffusion.
2. Distinguish between simple diffusion and facilitated diffusion that occur within cells.

Molecules and ions are in constant motion due to their kinetic energy. They randomly move about and when they strike obstacles such as other molecules and ions they bounce off, moving in a different direction. If a concentration gradient exists, the substance becomes more evenly distributed over time. This net movement of a substance from where it is more concentrated to where it is less concentrated is called **diffusion** (di-fū′zhun; *diffundo* = to pour in different directions). Diffusion, if unopposed, occurs until the substance reaches **equilbrium** (i.e., the molecules become evenly distributed throughout a given area(s)) **(figure 4.7)**.

The rate that substances diffuse is not constant, but is dependent on environmental conditions including

- **The "steepness" of its concentration gradient.** Steepness of a concentration gradient is a measure of the difference in concentration of a substance between two areas. A steeper concentration gradient causes a faster rate of diffusion.

Figure 4.7 Diffusion. When a drop of dye is placed into a beaker of water, the dye molecules diffuse into the water down the concentration gradient, spreading out until equilibrium has been reached. AP|R

- **Temperature.** Temperature reflects the kinetic energy (or random movement) of a substance. When the temperature is higher, there is a greater random movement of the molecules and ions composing a substance, resulting in a faster rate of diffusion.

Cellular Diffusion

Diffusion occurs across the plasma membrane, and is dependent upon concentration gradients that generally exist between the cytosol and interstitial fluid for different substances (e.g., O_2, CO_2, glucose, ions). Whether a substance diffuses unassisted through the plasma membrane or is facilitated by a plasma membrane protein determines if the substance moves by simple diffusion or facilitated diffusion.

Simple Diffusion   Solutes that are small and nonpolar move into or out of a cell down their concentration gradient by **simple diffusion**. These molecules do not require a transport protein. They simply pass between the phospholipid molecules that form the plasma membrane **(figure 4.8)**. Materials that move via simple diffusion include respiratory gases (O_2 and CO_2), small nonpolar fatty acids, ethanol, and urea (a nitrogenous waste produced from amino acids).

The plasma membrane cannot regulate simple diffusion—rather, the movement of these substances is dependent only upon the concentration gradient. The substance continues to move across the plasma membrane as long as a concentration gradient exists. Impaired respiratory and cardiovascular function can alter the concentration gradients of oxygen and carbon dioxide, resulting in decreased diffusion of these gases.

Facilitated Diffusion   Small solutes that are charged or polar are effectively blocked from entry into the cell by the nonpolar phospholipid bilayer. Their transport into the cell must be assisted by plasma membrane proteins in a process called **facilitated** (fa-sil′i-tā-ted) **diffusion**. Two types of facilitated diffusion—channel-mediated diffusion and carrier-mediated diffusion—are distinguished by the type of transport protein used to move the substance across the membrane.

Channel-mediated diffusion is the movement of small ions across the plasma membrane through water-filled protein chan-

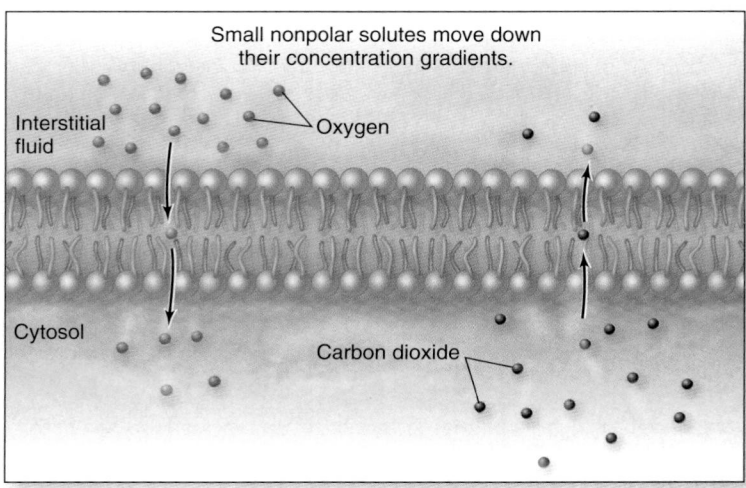

Small nonpolar solutes move down their concentration gradients.

Interstitial fluid

Oxygen

Cytosol

Carbon dioxide

Figure 4.8 Simple Diffusion of Solutes. Simple diffusion occurs when small, nonpolar substances pass between plasma membrane phospholipid molecules. A substance moves down its concentration gradient. Here, oxygen diffuses into a cell and carbon dioxide diffuses out of a cell.

nels **(figure 4.9a)**. Each channel is typically specific for one type of ion. The channel is either a **leak channel,** which is continuously open, or a **gated channel,** which is usually closed, and opens only in response to a stimulus (e.g., chemical, light, voltage change). For example, Na^+ leak channels allow Na^+ to pass through continuously. In contrast, chemically gated Na^+ channels open only to allow Na^+ to move through the channel in response to the presence of a particular chemical (e.g., neurotransmitter). Gated channels generally open for just a fraction of a second before they close. Channels and channel-mediated diffusion are important in the normal function of muscle and nerve cells (see chapters 10 and 12).

Carrier-mediated diffusion is the movement of small, polar molecules, such as simple sugars or amino acids. They are assisted across the plasma membrane by a **carrier protein.** Carrier proteins transport substances such as glucose. The binding of the substance induces the carrier protein to change shape and move it to the other side of the membrane. Like channels, a carrier moves a substance *down* its gradient. Figure 4.9b depicts how a carrier protein binds

the substance, changes shape, and then releases the substance on the other side of the membrane. A carrier that transports only one substance is called a **uniporter.** Glucose carriers are uniporters that normally prevent the loss of glucose in the urine (section 24.6c).

The number of channels and carriers in a plasma membrane determines the maximum rate at which a substance can be transported. The rate of facilitated diffusion is faster when there are a greater number of these transport proteins.

WHAT DID YOU LEARN?

7 How does O_2 diffuse into a cell and CO_2 diffuse out of a cell?

8 Compare and contrast how an ion is transported across the plasma membrane versus how a small, polar molecule is transported.

4.3b Passive Processes: Osmosis

LEARNING OBJECTIVES

3. Define osmosis.

4. Define osmotic pressure.

5. Describe the relationship of osmosis and tonicity.

Osmosis is unlike the other types of passive membrane transport, because it involves water movement and does not involve the movement of solutes. **Osmosis** (os-mō′sis; *osmos* = a thrusting) is the passive movement of water through a **selectively permeable** (or *semipermeable*) membrane. This movement occurs in response to a difference in relative concentration of water on either side of a membrane. Please refer to **figure 4.10** as you read through this section.

Plasma Membrane: A Selectively Permeable Membrane

The plasma membrane is a selectively permeable membrane that allows the passage of water, but its phospholipid bilayer prevents the movement of most solutes.

Water molecules cross the plasma membrane in one of two ways: They either "slip between" the molecules of the phospholipid bilayer (limited amounts) or they move through integral protein water channels called **aquaporins** (ak-kwă-pōr′in; *aqua* = water; *porus* = channel).

The phospholipid bilayer of the plasma membrane is impermeable to most solutes. In the context of osmosis, solutes are classified into two categories based upon whether their passage across the plasma membrane is prevented by the phospholipid bilayer. **Permeable** solutes (e.g., small and nonpolar solutes such as oxygen, carbon dioxide, and urea) pass through the bilayer, and **nonpermeable** solutes (e.g., charged, polar, or large solutes such as ions, glucose, and proteins) are prevented from crossing the bilayer.

(a) Channel-mediated diffusion

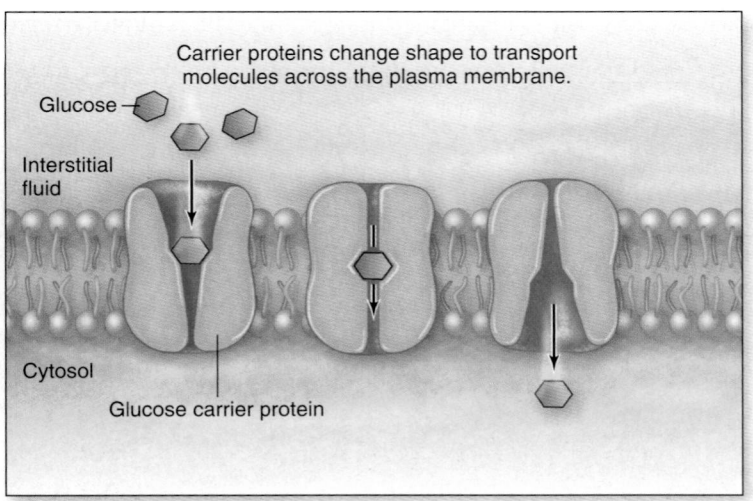

(b) Carrier-mediated diffusion

Figure 4.9 Facilitated Diffusion of Solutes. Facilitated diffusion occurs when ions or small polar molecules are transported either through or by plasma membrane proteins down their concentration gradient. (*a*) Channel-mediated diffusion: Ions (e.g., Na^+ and K^+) move through specific water-filled protein channels. (*b*) Carrier-mediated diffusion: Small polar molecules (e.g., glucose) are transported by protein carriers. AP|R

Concentration Gradients Across the Plasma Membrane

A difference in solute concentration can exist between the cytosol and the interstitial fluid because solutes are prevented from moving across the bilayer of the plasma membrane. Note that when a solute concentration exists, a water concentration also exists. A solution with a greater concentration of solutes contains a lower concentration of water. For example, a solution containing 3% solutes has a lower water concentration (97% water) than a solution with 1% solutes (99% water).

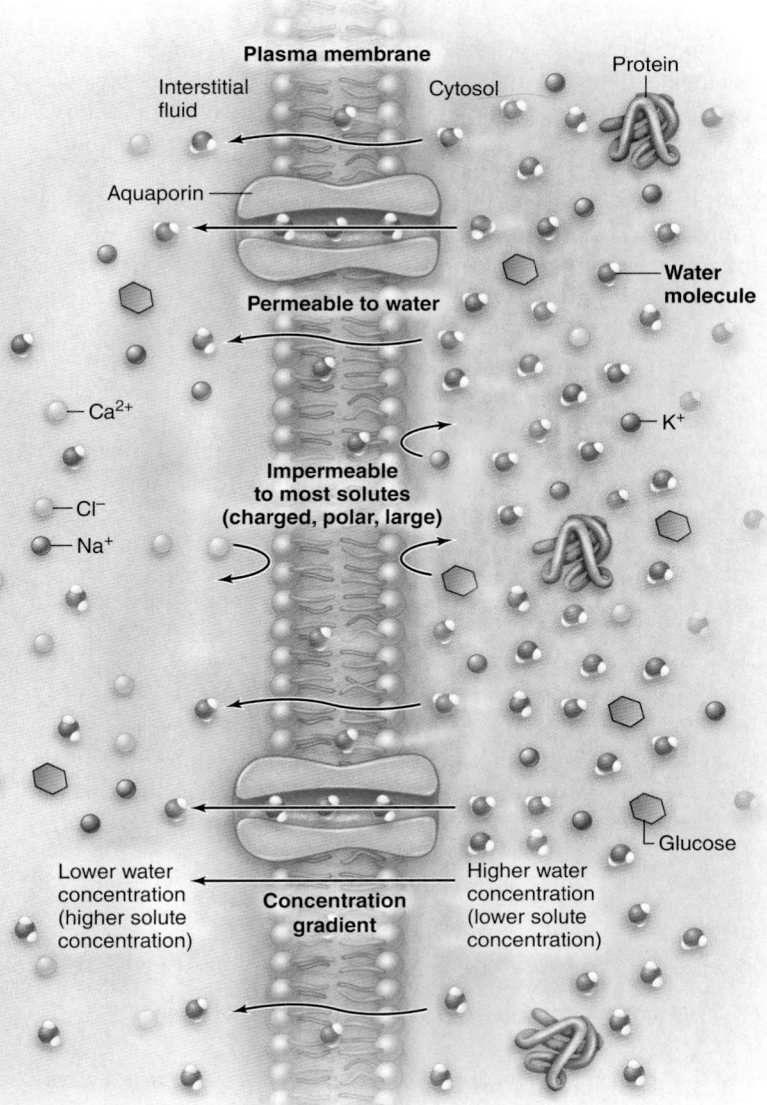

Plasma membrane

Interstitial fluid

Cytosol

Protein

Aquaporin

Permeable to water

Water molecule

—Ca²⁺

—Cl⁻

—Na⁺

Impermeable to most solutes (charged, polar, large)

K⁺

Glucose

Lower water concentration (higher solute concentration)

Concentration gradient

Higher water concentration (lower solute concentration)

Movement of Water Into or Out of a Cell by Osmosis

The net movement of water by osmosis is dependent upon the concentration gradient between the cytosol and the solution in which the cell is immersed. Water moves down its gradient from the solution containing 1% solutes (and 99% water) into the solution containing 3% solutes (and 97% water). Water continues to move until equilibrium is reached (the concentration of water in the cell and surrounding fluid are equal). Observe that water moves toward the solution with the lower water concentration (or stated another way, water moves toward the solution with the greater solute concentration).

Figure 4.10 shows water moving across the plasma membrane by osmosis from an area of high water concentration to an area of low water concentration.

Osmotic Pressure

Osmotic pressure is the pressure exerted by the movement of water across a semipermeable membrane due to a difference in solution concentration. The steeper the gradient, the greater the amount of water moved by osmosis and the higher the osmotic pressure.

Figure 4.11 helps us to visualize the movement of water by osmosis. Each U-shaped tube has two areas separated by a semipermeable membrane that allows the passage of water, but restricts the passage of solutes. Initially side A has more solutes and less water than side B. Water moves from side B into side A by osmosis (against the force of gravity) until the two fluids are equal in concentration.

Osmotic pressure can be measured indirectly. Imagine placing a stopper on side A in figure 4.11b and exerting force to return the fluid to its original level. The force exerted creates hydrostatic pressure within the U-shaped tube. (**Hydrostatic pressure** is the pressure exerted by a fluid on the inside wall of its container.) The osmotic pressure exerted in this setup is equal to the hydrostatic pressure produced to return the fluid to its original level.

Figure 4.10 Osmosis in Cells. Osmosis occurs in cells across the plasma membrane, which is permeable to water and impermeable to most solutes. Water always moves across the plasma membrane from an area of high water concentration to an area of low water concentration until equilibrium is reached. AP|R

WHAT DO YOU THINK?

1 Which setup would exhibit the greater osmotic pressure: a cell with a cytosol concentration of 0.9% immersed in (a) pure water, or (b) a 0.2% NaCl solution? Explain.

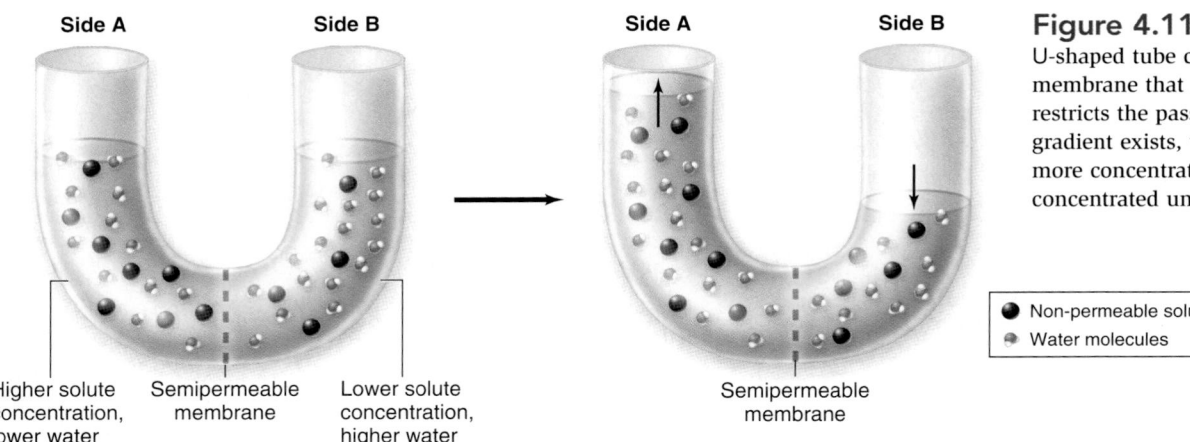

Side A   Side B   Side A   Side B

Higher solute concentration, lower water concentration

Semipermeable membrane

Lower solute concentration, higher water concentration

Semipermeable membrane

Figure 4.11 Osmotic Pressure. Each U-shaped tube contains a semipermeable membrane that allows the passage of water but restricts the passage of solutes. If a water gradient exists, water moves from where it is more concentrated to where it is less concentrated until equilibrium is reached.

● Non-permeable solutes (glucose, Na⁺, protein)
● Water molecules

Initial setup: Side A contains proportionately more solute and less water.

Final setup: Water moved by osmosis from side B down the water gradient to side A until the concentrations of side A and side B are equal.

Osmosis and Tonicity

When water crosses the plasma membrane of a cell by osmosis, the cell either gains or loses water with an accompanying change in the cell's volume and osmotic pressure. The ability of a solution to change the volume or pressure (or the "tone") of the cell by osmosis is called **tonicity.** Three terms are used to describe the relative concentration of solutions: isotonic, hypotonic, or hypertonic **(figure 4.12).**

In an **isotonic** (ī'sō-ton'ik; *iso* = equal; *tonus* = stretching) solution, both the cytosol and the solution have the same relative concentration of solutes. An example of a solution that is isotonic to erythrocytes (red blood cells) is normal physiologic saline with a concentration of 0.9% NaCl. Under these conditions, the relative amounts of water inside and outside the cell are equal, and no net movement of water occurs (figure 4.12a).

In a **hypotonic** (hī'pō-ton'ik; *hypo* = under) solution, the solution has a lower concentration of solutes, and there is a higher concentration of water than in the cytosol. Pure water contains no solutes, so it is the most extreme example of solution that is hypotonic to erythrocytes. Under these conditions, water moves down its concentration gradient from where there is more water (outside the cell) to where there is less water (inside the cell). The entry of water increases both the volume and pressure of the cell (figure 4.12b). **Lysis** (or rupture) of the cell can occur if the difference in concentration is large enough. **Hemolysis** (hē-mol'i-sis; *hem* = blood; *lysis* = destruction) is the specific term for rupturing red blood cells.

A **hypertonic** (hī'pĕr-ton'ik; *hyper* = above) solution has a higher concentration of solutes, and thus a lower concentration of water than does the cytosol. For example, a solution that contains 3% NaCl is hypertonic to red blood cells. In this case, water moves out of the cell into the surrounding fluid where the water concentration is lower. Thus, a decrease in cell volume and pressure occurs (figure 4.12c). If the difference in concentration is large, the cell shrinks, a process called **crenation** (krē-nā'shŭn; *crena* = notch).

WHAT DID YOU LEARN?

9 Define osmosis.

10 What occurs to the tonicity of a cell when it is placed in an isotonic, hypotonic, and hypertonic solution?

11 What general conclusion can you make concerning the movement of water? There is always a net movement of water by osmosis toward (a) an isotonic solution, (b) a hypotonic solution, or (c) a hypertonic solution.

Figure 4.12 Tonicity. Tonicity has an effect on water movement; it refers to the relative solute concentration strength of a solution. (*a*) In an isotonic solution (e.g., 0.9% NaCl), there is no net movement of water. The cell shape remains unchanged. (*b*) In a hypotonic solution (e.g., pure water), water moves into the cell. (*c*) In a hypertonic solution (e.g., 3% NaCl), water moves out of the cell. AP|R

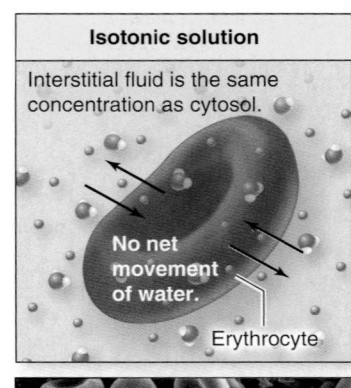

Isotonic solution

Interstitial fluid is the same concentration as cytosol.

No net movement of water.

Erythrocyte

Normal erythrocytes

(a)

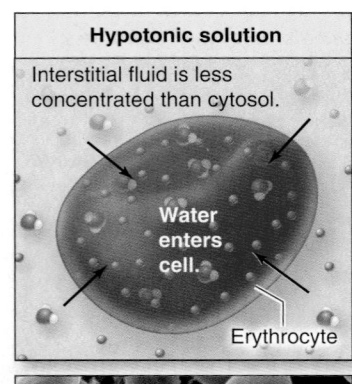

Hypotonic solution

Interstitial fluid is less concentrated than cytosol.

Water enters cell.

Erythrocyte

Erythrocytes nearing hemolysis

(b)

Hypertonic solution

Interstitial fluid is more concentrated than cytosol.

Water leaves cell.

Erythrocyte

Erythrocytes undergoing crenation

(c)

CONCEPT CONNECTION

Osmosis is important in several significant physiologic processes, including capillary exchange between the blood and body cells (chapter 20), formation of urine (chapter 24), and maintaining fluid balance (chapter 25).

4.3c Active Processes

LEARNING OBJECTIVES

6. Compare and contrast primary and secondary active transport.
7. Explain the difference between exocytosis and endocytosis.
8. Describe the endocytotic processes of phagocytosis, pinocytosis, and receptor-mediated endocytosis.

Active processes of membrane transport are those that require the expenditure of cellular energy from the breakdown of ATP. These processes occur only in living organisms. Active processes are organized into active transport and vesicular transport.

Active Transport

Active transport *opposes* the movement of solutes by diffusion and prevents the distribution of dissolved substances from reaching equilibrium. A solute is moved across a plasma membrane against a concentration gradient during active transport. Active transport processes are responsible for maintaining concentration gradients between a cell and interstitial fluid. The direct source of energy for active transport determines whether the movement is called primary active transport or secondary active transport.

Primary Active Transport   **Primary active transport** uses energy derived directly from the breakdown of ATP. This breakdown also provides the phosphate group that is added to the transport protein, resulting in a change in the protein's shape and the subsequent movement of a solute across the membrane. The addition of the phosphate to a protein is called *phosphorylation* (see section 3.3g).

Active transport proteins that move ions across the membrane are called **ion pumps.** Ion pumps are a major factor in a cell's ability to maintain its internal concentrations of ions. As an example, Ca^{2+} pumps embedded in the plasma membranes of erythrocytes move calcium out of the cell to prevent the cell from becoming rigid due to the accumulation of calcium (figure 4.13). Therefore, the erythrocyte remains flexible enough to move through capillaries (the smallest blood vessels). H^+ pumps are another type of transport protein that function in maintaining cellular pH.

The **sodium-potassium (Na^+/K^+) pump** is a special type of ion pump. It is specifically called an *exchange pump* because it moves one ion into a cell against its concentration gradient, while moving another type of ion out of the cell against its concentration gradient. (You may find it helpful to think of the Na^+/K^+ pump as a "dual pump" because it moves two different ions against their respective concentration gradients.) The plasma membrane preserves steep concentration gradient differences for these ions by continuously exporting Na^+ out of the cell and moving K^+ into the cell.

Figure 4.14 shows the steps in the process in which three Na^+ ions are pumped out of a cell for every two K^+ ions that are pumped into a cell. The cell must expend ATP to maintain the levels of these ions on each side of the membrane. The Na^+/K^+ pump is also called a *sodium-potassium ATPase* because the protein pump is an enzyme that splits ATP.

One significant function of Na^+/K^+ pumps is to maintain an **electrochemical gradient,** which is an electrical charge difference across the plasma membrane. The electrical charge difference is due to the unequal distribution of positively and negatively charged ions and molecules on either side of the plasma membrane. This electrical, or voltage, difference represents potential energy and for this reason is called the **membrane potential.** When a

Figure 4.13 Ca^{2+} Pump. A Ca^{2+} pump uses ATP to move calcium ions against the calcium gradient from the inside to the outside of the cell.

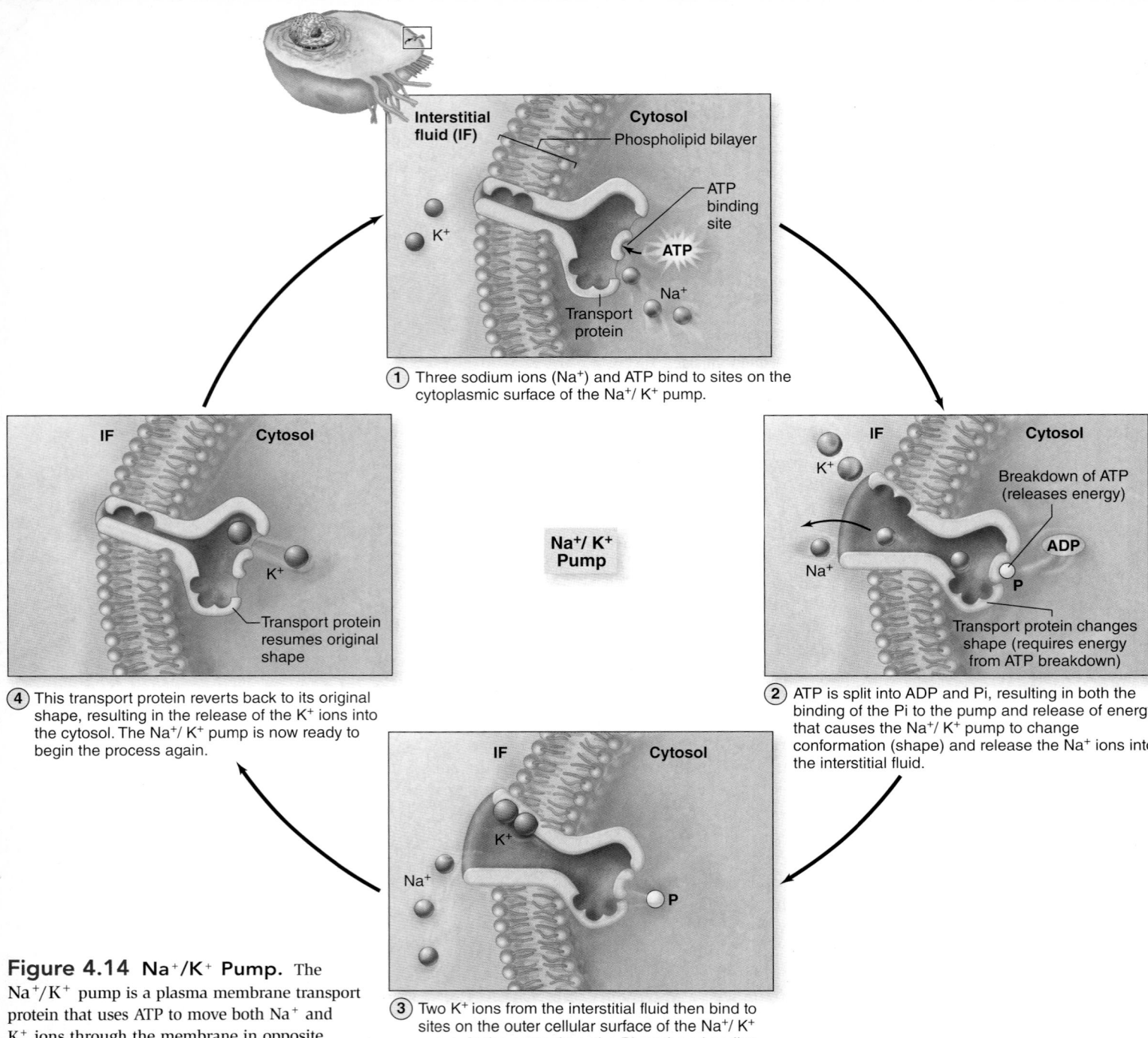

Interstitial fluid (IF) | **Cytosol**
Phospholipid bilayer
ATP binding site
ATP
Na^+
Transport protein
K^+

① Three sodium ions (Na^+) and ATP bind to sites on the cytoplasmic surface of the Na^+/K^+ pump.

IF | **Cytosol**
K^+
Breakdown of ATP (releases energy)
ADP
Na^+
P
Transport protein changes shape (requires energy from ATP breakdown)

② ATP is split into ADP and Pi, resulting in both the binding of the Pi to the pump and release of energy that causes the Na^+/K^+ pump to change conformation (shape) and release the Na^+ ions into the interstitial fluid.

Na^+/K^+ Pump

IF | **Cytosol**
K^+
Transport protein resumes original shape

④ This transport protein reverts back to its original shape, resulting in the release of the K^+ ions into the cytosol. The Na^+/K^+ pump is now ready to begin the process again.

IF | **Cytosol**
K^+
Na^+
P

③ Two K^+ ions from the interstitial fluid then bind to sites on the outer cellular surface of the Na^+/K^+ pump. At the same time, the Pi produced earlier by ATP hydrolysis is released into the cytosol.

Figure 4.14 Na^+/K^+ Pump. The Na^+/K^+ pump is a plasma membrane transport protein that uses ATP to move both Na^+ and K^+ ions through the membrane in opposite directions from their region of low concentration to their region of high concentration. **AP|R**

cell is at rest, this difference is more specifically called the **resting membrane potential (RMP)**. The central role of the Na^+/K^+ pump in maintaining membrane potentials is described in detail in section 12.7b.

Secondary Active Transport **Secondary active transport** is also called *coupled transport*. It moves a substance against its concentration gradient using energy provided by the movement of a second substance down its specific concentration gradient through a channel. Put another way, the kinetic energy of one substance moving down its concentration gradient provides the "power" to pump the other substance against its concentration gradient (much like water moving over a dam and turning a water wheel can generate electricity; see section 3.1a). The substance that moves down its concentration gradient often is Na^+. The two types of secondary active transport include

- **Symport.** If the two substances are moved in the same direction, these transport proteins are called **symporters** (or *cotransporters*), and the process is **symport secondary active transport**.

- **Antiport.** If the two substances are moved in opposite directions, then the transport proteins are called **antiporters** (or *countertransporters*) and the process is **antiport secondary active transport.**

Figure 4.15 compares the processes of transporting a substance by a symporter or an antiporter. In the symport example, glucose binds to the transport protein in the membrane (figure 4.15a). This binding helps alter the shape of the transport protein, and then both glucose and Na^+ are transported into the cell. The Na^+ moves down its concentration gradient into the cell and provides the energy to move glucose up its concentration gradient into the cell. Notice that both Na^+ and glucose are moved in the *same* direction. In contrast, an antiporter moves the two substances in the *opposite* direction (figure 4.15b). The H^+ is moved out of the cell as Na^+ is transported into the cell. The movement of Na^+ down its concentration gradient has provided the energy to move H^+ up its concentration gradient, but in the opposite direction of the Na^+ movement.

Secondary active transport mechanisms are ultimately dependent upon the primary active transport mechanisms of Na^+/K^+ pumps (described earlier). The activity of these pumps produce and sustain a distinct concentration gradient difference between sodium (Na^+) and potassium (K^+) ions on opposite sides of the plasma membrane. The enormous sodium ion gradient that results has potential energy that is harnessed in secondary active transport.

INTEGRATE

CONCEPT CONNECTION

The tubule cells in the kidney (chapter 24) provide an example of secondary active transport. Glucose molecules filtered from blood during the process of urine formation are pumped from the lumen of the kidney tubule back into the blood as sodium ions move into the lumen.

Vesicular Transport

Vesicular transport is also called *bulk transport*. It involves energy input to transport large materials across the plasma membrane by a **vesicle** (ves′i-kl; *vesica* = bladder), which is a membrane-bounded sac filled with materials. Vesicular transport is organized into processes of exocytosis and endocytosis. A vesicle fuses with the plasma membrane to release substances to the outside of the cell by exocytosis, whereas endocytosis involves the formation of a vesicle from the plasma membrane that encloses material to be moved into the cell from outside.

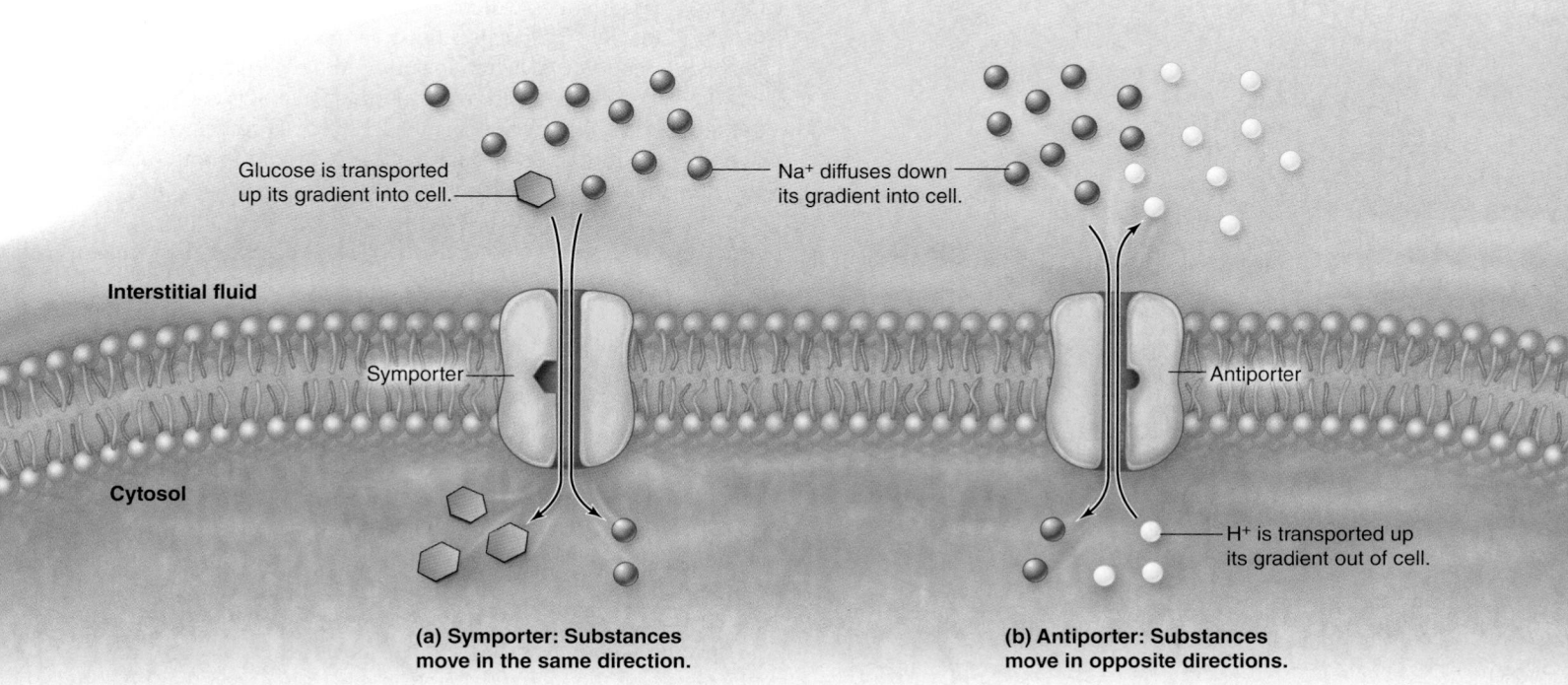

Figure 4.15 Secondary Active Transport. Secondary active transport moves one substance against its concentration gradient, and is powered by the movement of a second substance down its concentration gradient. (*a*) A symporter transports both substances in the same direction. (*b*) An antiporter transports the two substances in opposite directions.

Exocytosis   The means by which either large substances or large amounts of substances are secreted from the cell is called **exocytosis** (ek′sō-sī-tō′sis; *exo* = outside, *kytos* = cell, *osis* = condition of) (**figure 4.16**). Macromolecules, such as large proteins and poly-

① Vesicle nears plasma membrane

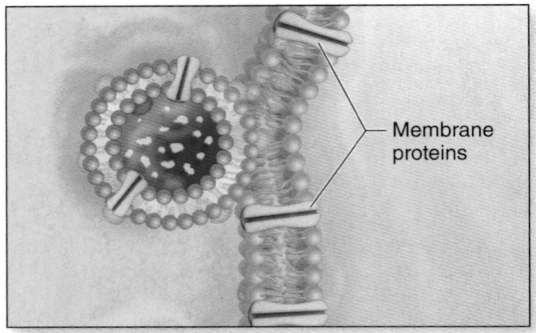

② Fusion of vesicle membrane with plasma membrane

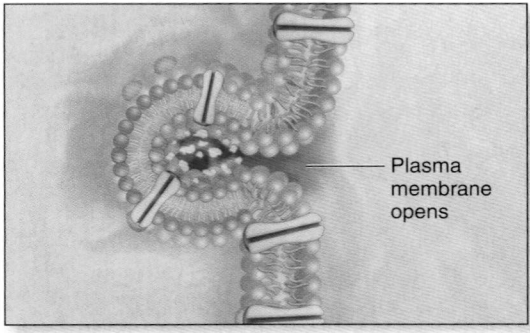

③ Plasma membrane opens to outside of cell

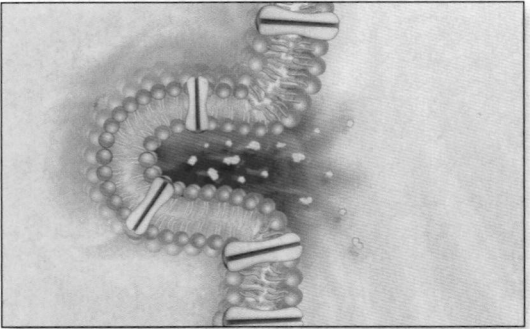

④ Release of vesicle components into the interstitial fluid and integration of vesicle membrane components into the plasma membrane

Figure 4.16 Exocytosis. In exocytosis, the cell secretes bulk volumes of materials from the cell into the interstitial fluid as a vesicle fuses with the plasma membrane.

saccharides, are too large to be moved across the membrane, even with the assistance of transport proteins. The material for secretion typically is packaged within intracellular transport vesicles. When the vesicle and plasma membrane come into contact, the lipid molecules of the vesicle and plasma membrane bilayers rearrange themselves so that the two membranes fuse. The fusion of these lipid bilayers requires the cell to expend energy in the form of ATP. Following fusion, the vesicle contents are released to the outside of the cell. An example of exocytosis is the release of neurotransmitter molecules from nerve cells.

Endocytosis   The cellular uptake of large substances or large amounts of substances from the external environment into the cell is called **endocytosis** (en′dō-sī-tō′sis; *endon* = within). Endocytosis is used for the uptake of nutrients and extracellular debris for digestion, retrieval of membrane regions added to the plasma membrane during exocytosis, and regulation of composition of membrane proteins to alter cellular processes (e.g., membrane transport and communication).

The steps of endocytosis are similar to the exocytosis steps, only in reverse. Endocytosis occurs when substances within the interstitial fluid are packaged into a vesicle that forms at the cell surface for internalization into the cell (**figure 4.17**). A small area of plasma membrane folds inward into the cytosol to form a pocket, or **invagination** (in-vaj′i-nā-zhun; *in* = in, *vagina* = a sheath). The pocket deepens as the process proceeds and then it pinches off when the lipid bilayer fuses. This fusion is the energy-expending step. The new intracellular vesicle now present contains material that was formerly outside the cell.

The three types of endocytosis include phagocytosis, pinocytosis, and receptor-mediated endocytosis. They are differentiated based upon the specific material being transported and the mechanism involved. These three types are compared in figure 4.17.

Phagocytosis (fag′ō-sī-tō′sis; *phago* = to eat) means "cellular eating." It is a nonspecific process that occurs when a cell engulfs or captures a large particle external to the cell by forming membrane extensions that are called **pseudopodia** (sū-dō-pō′dē-ă; *pseudes* = false; *pous* = foot) or *false feet*, to surround the particle (figure 4.17a). Once the particle is engulfed by the pseudopodia, it is enclosed within a membrane sac. When the sac is internalized, its contents are broken down chemically (digested) after it fuses with a lysosome (a cellular organelle containing digestive enzymes, described later). Only a few types of cells are able to perform phagocytosis. For example, it occurs regularly when a white blood cell engulfs and digests a microbe (e.g., bacterium).

Pinocytosis (pin′ō-sī-tō′sis or pī′nō-; *pineo* = to drink) is known as "cellular drinking." This process occurs when the cell internalizes droplets of interstitial fluid that contain dissolved solutes. Multiple, small vesicles are formed (figure 4.17b). This process is considered nonspecific because all solutes dissolved within the droplet are taken into the cell. Most cells perform this type of membrane transport. An example of pinocytosis occurs within cells of a capillary wall. Vesicles fill with a fluid droplet from the blood plasma. (The vesicle is transported to the other side of the cell, and the substances are then expelled outside the capillary wall by exocytosis.)

Receptor-mediated endocytosis is the movement of specific molecules from the interstitial environment into a cell that first bind to a receptor. Receptor-mediated endocytosis enables the cell to obtain bulk quantities of certain substances, even though those substances may not be very concentrated in the interstitial fluid.

This process begins when specific molecules in the interstitial fluid attach to their distinct integral membrane protein receptors in

(a) Phagocytosis

(b) Pinocytosis

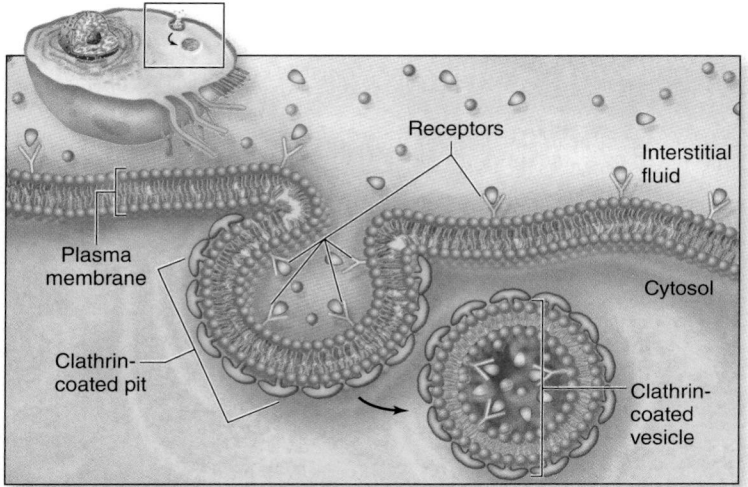

(c) Receptor-mediated endocytosis

Figure 4.17 Three Forms of Endocytosis. Endocytosis is the process whereby a vesicle is formed as the cell acquires materials from the interstitial fluid. (*a*) Phagocytosis occurs when membrane extensions called pseudopodia engulf a relatively large particle and internalize it into a vesicle. (*b*) Pinocytosis is the incorporation of numerous droplets of interstitial fluid into the cell in small vesicles. (*c*) Receptor-mediated endocytosis occurs when receptors in the plasma membrane for specific molecules bind to them, aggregate within the membrane, and then the specific molecules are internalized when the membrane invaginates, forming a vesicle.

the plasma membrane to form a ligand-receptor complex. Following the binding of the ligand, the ligand-receptor complexes move laterally in the plane of the plasma membrane and accumulate at special membrane regions that contain **clathrin** protein on the internal surface of the membrane. The clathrin-coated regions of the plasma membrane housing the ligand-receptor complex folds inward to form an invagination called a *clathrin-coated pit* (figure 4.17*c*). This invagination deepens, pinches off, and the lipid bilayer of the plasma membrane fuses to form a *clathrin-coated vesicle* that then moves into the cytosol. Following the formation of the clathrin-coated vesicles, the clathrin coat must be enzymatically removed before the vesicle may proceed to its intracellular destination. Again, it is the fusion of these lipid bilayers that requires the cell to expend energy in the form of ATP.

The transport of cholesterol from the blood to a cell is an example of receptor-mediated endocytosis. When cholesterol travels in the blood it is bound to protein molecules in structures called low-density lipoproteins (or LDLs). LDLs move from the blood into the interstitial fluid and then bind to LDL receptors in the cell's plasma membrane. LDLs are then internalized by the process of receptor-mediated endocytosis just described (see section 27.4c).

A summary of the various types of transport mechanisms is given in **figure 4.18**. These processes are also described in **table 4.1**.

INTEGRATE

CLINICAL VIEW

Familial Hypercholesteremia

Familial hypercholesteremia is an inherited genetic disorder that involves defective or absent cellular receptor proteins that bind LDLs, defects in the proteins of the LDLs, or other possible mutations. Defects in either the LDL receptor or the proteins of the LDLs interfere with the normal process of receptor-mediated endocytosis of cholesterol into cells. LDLs that contain cholesterol remain in the blood, resulting in greatly elevated levels of blood cholesterol. Consequently, cholesterol accumulates in the blood vessels, causing plaque buildup and narrowing of the blood vessels (atherosclerosis), especially those providing blood to the heart (coronary vessels). Individuals with this genetic defect are likely to experience blockage of the coronary arteries, resulting in a heart attack. The age of occurrence of a heart attack depends upon the severity of the protein defect. In severe cases, an individual may experience a heart attack during the teen years.

WHAT DID YOU LEARN?

12 What transport process involved in the movement of Na$^+$ down its gradient is used to power another substance up its gradient?

13 Engulfing of a bacterium by a white blood cell occurs by what type of cellular transport?

Figure 4.18 **Passive and Active Processes of Membrane Transport.**

Transport processes are separated into two major categories. (*a*) Passive processes, which do not require expenditure of cellular energy, include simple diffusion, facilitated diffusion (channel-mediated and carrier-mediated), and osmosis. (*b*) Active processes, which require cellular energy, include active transport (primary and secondary) and vesicular transport (exocytosis and various forms of endocytosis).

| **(a) Passive Processes** | Do not require expenditure of cellular energy; substance moves into or out of a cell down its concentration gradient. |

DIFFUSION: Movement of a solute from an area of higher concentration to an area of lower concentration.

Simple Diffusion: Small and nonpolar substances move between phospholipid molecules of the plasma membrane.

Oxygen

Carbon dioxide

Interstitial fluid   Cytosol

Facilitated Diffusion: Small, charged, or polar substances move assisted by a transport protein (channel or carrier).

Na⁺

Channel-Mediated: Ion (e.g., Na⁺) movement is facilitated by channels across the plasma membrane.

Channel

Carrier

Glucose

Carrier-Mediated: Small polar molecule movement (e.g., glucose) is facilitated by protein carriers across the plasma membrane.

Interstitial fluid   Cytosol

OSMOSIS: Movement of water across a selectively permeable membrane from an area of higher water concentration to an area of lower water concentration.

Interstitial fluid   Cytosol

Aquaporin

Solute

Water

Plasma membrane

(b) Active Processes | Require expenditure of cellular energy; substance moves up its concentration gradient or involves a vesicle.

ACTIVE TRANSPORT: Movement of a substance against its concentration gradient via a protein pump.

Primary Active Transport: Pumps are powered directly by splitting an ATP molecule.

Transport protein changes shape (requires energy from ATP breakdown)

ADP + P

ATP

Cytosol

Na⁺

Note: The two ion species are not simultaneously attached to the pump

K⁺

Interstitial fluid

Secondary Active Transport: Pumps are powered by energy harnessed as a second substance (usually Na⁺) moves through a channel down a concentration gradient.

Cytosol

Interstitial fluid

Glucose

Na⁺

Symport: Two substances are moved in the same direction.

Antiport: Two substances are moved in opposite directions.

H⁺

VESICULAR TRANSPORT: Movement of a substance across the plasma membrane via a vesicle.

Exocytosis: Movement of a substance out of a cell via a vesicle.

Vesicle

Plasma membrane opens

Cytosol

Interstitial fluid

Endocytosis: Movement of a substance into a cell via a vesicle. The three types of endocytosis include phagocytosis, pinocytosis, and receptor-mediated endocytosis.

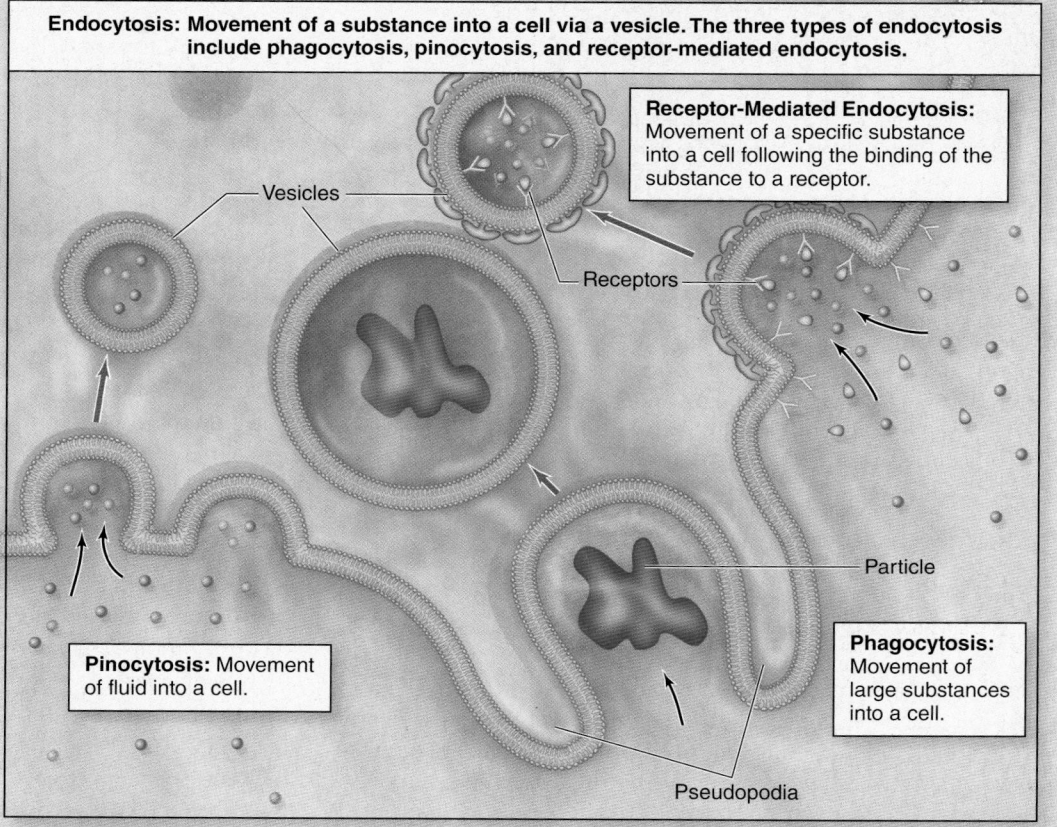

Receptor-Mediated Endocytosis: Movement of a specific substance into a cell following the binding of the substance to a receptor.

Vesicles

Receptors

Particle

Pinocytosis: Movement of fluid into a cell.

Phagocytosis: Movement of large substances into a cell.

Pseudopodia

Table 4.1 Transport Processes Across a Plasma Membrane

Process	Type of Movement	Example
PASSIVE PROCESSES	Movement of substances down a concentration gradient due to the kinetic energy of substance; no expenditure of cellular energy is required; continues until equilibrium is reached (if unopposed)	
Simple diffusion	Unassisted net movement of small, nonpolar substances down their concentration gradient across a selectively permeable membrane	Exchange of oxygen and carbon dioxide between blood and body tissues
Facilitated diffusion	Movement of ions and small, polar molecules down their concentration gradient; assisted across a selectively permeable membrane by a transport protein	
Channel-mediated	Movement of ion down its concentration gradient through a protein channel	Na^+ moves through Na^+ channel into cell
Carrier-mediated	Movement of small, polar molecule down its concentration gradient by a carrier protein	Transport of glucose into cells by glucose carrier
Osmosis	Diffusion of water across a selectively permeable membrane; direction is determined by relative solute concentrations; continues until equilibrium is reached	Solutes in blood in systemic capillaries "pulls" fluid from interstitial space back into the blood
ACTIVE PROCESSES	Movement of substances requires expenditure of cellular energy	
Active transport	Transport of ions or small molecules across the membrane against a concentration gradient by transmembrane protein pumps	
Primary	Movement of substance up its concentration gradient; powered directly by ATP	Ca^{2+} pumps transport Ca^{2+} out of the cell Na^+/K^+ pump moves Na^+ out of cell and K^+ into cell
Secondary	Movement of a substance up its concentration gradient is powered by harnessing the movement of a second substance (e.g., Na^+) down its concentration gradient	
Symport	Movement of substance up its concentration gradient in the same direction as Na^+	Na^+/glucose transport
Antiport	Movement of substance up its concentration gradient in the opposite direction from Na^+	Na^+/H^+ transport
Vesicular transport	Vesicle formed or lost as material is brought into a cell or released from a cell	
Exocytosis	Bulk movement of substance out of the cell by fusion of secretory vesicles with the plasma membrane	Release of neurotransmitter by nerve cells
Endocytosis	Bulk movement of substances into the cell by vesicles forming at the plasma membrane	
Phagocytosis	Type of endocytosis in which vesicles are formed as particulate materials external to the cell are engulfed by pseudopodia	White blood cell engulfing a bacterium
Pinocytosis	Type of endocytosis in which vesicles are formed as interstital fluid is taken up by the cell	Formation of small vesicles in capillary wall to move substances
Receptor-mediated endocytosis	Type of endocytosis in which plasma membrane receptors first bind specific substances; receptor and bound substance then taken up by the cell	Uptake of cholesterol into cells

4.4 Cell Communication

The plasma membrane plays a significant role in communication between cells in addition to serving as a boundary, functioning in transport, and establishing an RMP. Numerous structures in the membrane, including glycoproteins and glycolipids, facilitate both direct interaction with other cells and recognition and response to certain ligand signals external to the cell.

4.4a Direct Contact Between Cells

⟩✓⟨ LEARNING OBJECTIVE

1. Explain how cells communicate through direct contact.

Physical or direct contact between two cells is important in the normal functioning of some cells, especially those of the immune system. One of the primary functions of the immune system is to make contact with and destroy both unhealthy cells (e.g., infected cells, cancer cells) and foreign cells (e.g., bacterial cells, transplanted cells). Body cells communicate to our immune cells that they both belong to the body and are healthy through direct contact that involves the glycocalyx. Recall that the glycocalyx is the coating of carbohydrates on the external surface of a cell. These carbohydrates extend from the proteins and lipids of the plasma membrane. The pattern of sugars is unique to each individual except identical twins. The immune system is able to distinguish normal, healthy cells from unwanted cells by making direct contact with a cell to determine if it exhibits the same pattern of sugars of the glycocalyx as the body's cells. It is because unhealthy cells and foreign cells express a different pattern that they are subsequently destroyed.

Another example of direct contact between cells is the contact that occurs between sperm and an ovum (egg) during the process of fertilization. The sperm recognizes and binds to the egg by its unique glycocalyx.

Direct contact is also critical in the process of development and in cellular regrowth following injury. If you cut the skin of your finger, the cells in the upper layer of the skin (the epidermis) begin to divide (see section 6.4). Cell division continues to fill in the gap created by the injury. When the damaged tissue has been replaced, overgrowth of skin tissue is prevented by inhibition caused by cellular contact.

WHAT DID YOU LEARN?

14 What are some examples of how cells communicate through direct contact?

4.4b Ligand-Receptor Signaling

LEARNING OBJECTIVE

2. Describe the three general mechanisms of response to the binding of a ligand with a receptor.

Most communication between cells occurs through ligands. Recall ligands are molecules released from one cell that bind to receptors of another cell. The ligands can be neurotransmitters from nerve cells or hormones from endocrine cells. The cell that receives the information has a receptor that can bind the ligand. Binding initiates mechanisms for controlling the growth, reproduction, and cellular processes of individual cells.

There are three general types of receptors that bind ligands. They differ in their response to ligand binding as follows **(figure 4.19)**:

- **Channel-linked receptors** (or **chemically gated channels**) permit ion passage either into or out of a cell in response to neurotransmitter binding (figure 4.19*a*). Channel-linked receptors are required to initiate electrical changes in both muscle cells and nerve cells.
- **Enzymatic receptors** function as protein kinase enzymes and are activated to directly phosphorylate (add a phosphate to) other enzymes within the cell (figure 4.19*b*). Recall that enzymes can be either turned on or turned off through phosphorylation (see section 3.3f). This provides a mechanism for altering enzymatic activity within a cell in response to external signals.
- **G protein–coupled receptors** also involve protein kinase activation; note that these protein kinase enzymes are activated indirectly through the G protein that serves as an intermediate molecule. The general steps of activation are described in figure 4.19*c*, and a detailed discussion of G proteins is provided in section 17.5b.

WHAT DID YOU LEARN?

15 How do action of enzymatic receptors and G protein–coupled receptors differ?

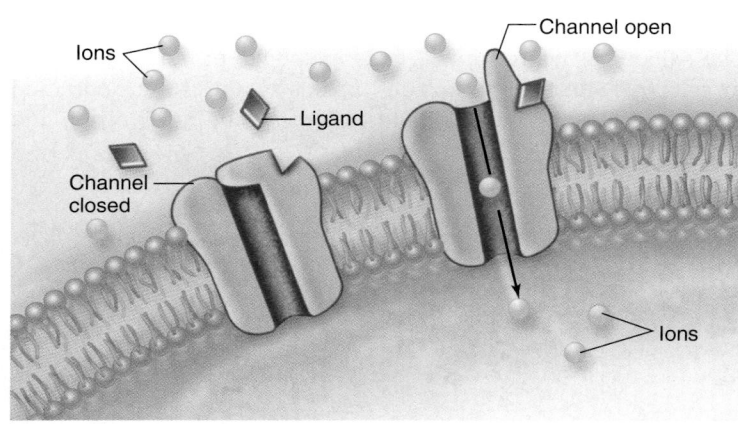

(a) Channel-linked receptors

(b) Enzymatic receptors

(c) G protein–coupled receptors

Figure 4.19 Membrane Receptors. Receptors bind ligands that will initiate a cellular change (*a*) Channel-linked receptors bind a neurotransmitter and open to allow a specific ion to move down its concentration gradient. (*b*) Enzymatic receptors (generally protein kinase enzymes) bind a ligand and are activated to phosphorylate other enzymes. (*c*) G protein–coupled receptors bind ligand and activate protein kinase enzymes indirectly through a G-protein, as described in steps 1–5.

4.5 Cellular Structures

The cellular structures described in this section include membrane-bound organelles, non-membrane-bound organelles, vesicles for transport, and structures that extend from the cell's surface. The structure and function of all of the cellular structures discussed in this chapter are summarized in **table 4.2**.

4.5a Membrane-Bound Organelles

✓ LEARNING OBJECTIVES

1. List the membrane-bound organelles of a typical human cell.
2. Describe the structure and main function(s) of each.

Membrane-bound organelles within the cytoplasm are surrounded by a membrane (similar in composition to the plasma membrane) that separates the organelle's contents from the cytosol so that the activities of the organelle may proceed in a relatively isolated and controlled environment. Each organelle differs in its shape, membrane composition, and associated enzymes. These differences account for the unique functions of each. Membrane-bound intracellular organelles include the endoplasmic reticulum, Golgi apparatus, lysosomes, peroxisomes, and mitochondria (see figure 4.4).

Endoplasmic Reticulum

The **endoplasmic reticulum** (en′dō-plas′mik; *endon* = within; re-tik′ū-lum; *rete* = net) **(ER)** is an extensive interconnected membrane network that varies in shape (e.g., parallel sheets, sacs or cisternae, tubules) and separates fluid within the membranous structure from the cytosol (**figure 4.20**). It typically extends from the nuclear envelope to the plasma membrane. The extensive ER membrane surface serves as a point of attachment for ribosomes and insertion of various types of enzymes. Endoplasmic reticulum with ribosomes attached is referred to as **rough ER,** whereas ER portions without ribosomes attached is referred to as **smooth ER.**

Rough ER   The ribosomes of rough ER produce proteins. These proteins are inserted into and moved through the membrane into the lumen of the ER as they are synthesized. Within the lumen of the ER, the original structure of the protein is changed by either the addition of other molecules (e.g., carbohydrates) or removal of part of what was originally synthesized; the modified proteins are packaged and stored. Transport from the ER occurs when small, enclosed membrane sacs pinch off from the ER containing what was the contents of the ER. These sacs are termed **transport vesicles** (figure 4.20). They shuttle proteins from the rough ER lumen to another organelle called the Golgi apparatus for further modification. The amount of rough ER is greater in cells producing large amounts of protein for secretion, such as a cell in the pancreas that releases enzymes for digestion. Peroxisomes (described shortly) are membrane-bound organelles that are also produced from the ER.

Smooth ER   The smooth ER is continuous with the rough ER. Smooth ER resembles multiple interconnected branches of tubules. The smooth ER carries out diverse metabolic processes that vary by cell type. Smooth ER functions include synthesis, transport, and storage of different types of lipids; carbohydrate metabolism; and

TEM 12,510×

Cisternae

Nucleus

Transport vesicle

Peroxisome

Rough ER

Ribosomes

Ribosomes

Rough ER

Smooth ER

Rough ER   Ribosomes

Functions of Endoplasmic Reticulum

1. **Synthesis:** Provides a place for chemical reactions
   a. Rough ER synthesizes proteins for secretion, incorporation into the plasma membrane, and as enzymes within lysosomes
   b. Smooth ER is the site of lipid synthesis and carbohydrate metabolism
2. **Transport:** Moves molecules through lumen from one part of the cell to another; sequestered away from the cytosol
3. **Packaging and storage:** Packages and stores newly synthesized molecules
4. **Detoxification:** Smooth ER detoxifies drugs, alcohol, and poisons
5. **Structure formation:** Segments of ER are pinched off to form transport vesicles and peroxisomes

Figure 4.20 The Endoplasmic Reticulum (ER). The rough ER is composed of cisternal membranes with ribosomes attached to their cytoplasmic surface. It is readily distinguishable from the even-surfaced, interconnected tubules of the smooth ER, which lacks associated ribosomes. However, the two are continuous. AP|R

Table 4.2	Components of the Cell		
Component	**Structure**	**Function**	**Appearance**
Plasma membrane	Phospholipid bilayer containing cholesterol and proteins (integral and peripheral) and some carbohydrates (externally); forms a selectively permeable boundary of the cell	Acts as a physical barrier to enclose cell contents; regulates material movement into and out of the cell; establishes and maintains an electrical charge difference across the plasma membrane; functions in cell communication	Plasma membrane
Cilia	Short, numerous membrane extensions supported by microtubules, which occur on exposed membrane surfaces of some cells	Move substances (e.g., mucus, and dissolved materials) over the cell surface	Cilia
Flagellum	Long, singular membrane extension supported by microtubules; present on sperm cells	Propels sperm	Flagellum
Microvilli	Numerous thin membrane folds projecting from the free cell surface; supported by microfilaments	Increase membrane surface area for greater absorption	Microvilli
Nucleus	Large structure enclosed within a double membrane; contains chromatin, nucleolus, and nucleoplasm	Houses the DNA that serves as the genetic material for directing protein synthesis	Nucleus
Nuclear envelope	Double membrane boundary between cytoplasm and nuclear contents; continuous with rough endoplasmic reticulum	Separates nucleus from cytoplasm	Nuclear pores, Nuclear envelope, Nucleolus, Chromatin
Nuclear pores	Openings through the nuclear envelope	Allow passage of materials between the cytoplasm and nucleoplasm, including ribonucleic acid (RNA), protein, ions, and small water-soluble molecules	
Nucleolus	Large, prominent structure within the nucleus	Functions in synthesis of ribosomes	
Cytoplasm	Contents of cells between the plasma membrane and nuclear envelope	Responsible for many cellular processes	Cytoplasm, Cytosol, Organelles, Inclusions
Cytosol	Viscous fluid medium containing various solutes (e.g., ions, proteins, carbohydrates, lipids)	Provides support for organelles; serves as the viscous fluid medium through which diffusion occurs	
Organelles	Membrane-bound and non-membrane-bound structures	Carry out specific metabolic activities of the cell	
Rough endoplasmic reticulum (rough ER)	Extensive interconnected membrane network that varies in shape (e.g., cisternae, tubules); ribosomes attached on cytoplasmic surface	Modifies, transports, and stores proteins produced by attached ribosomes; these proteins are secreted, become components of the plasma membrane, or serve as enzymes of lysosomes	
Smooth endoplasmic reticulum (smooth ER)	Extensive interconnected membrane network lacking ribosomes	Synthesizes, transports, and stores lipids (e.g., steroids); metabolizes carbohydrates; detoxifies drugs, alcohol, and poisons; forms vesicles and peroxisomes	

(continued on next page)

| Table 4.2 | Components of the Cell (*continued*) |

Component	Structure	Function	Appearance
Golgi apparatus	Series of several elongated, flattened saclike membranous structures	Modifies, packages, and sorts materials that arrive from the ER in transport vesicles; forms secretory vesicles and lysosomes	
Vesicles	Spherical-shaped membrane-bound sacs; contain various types of materials to be transported through the cell	Transport cellular material	
Lysosomes	Spherical-shaped membrane-bound organelles formed from the Golgi apparatus; contain digestive enzymes	Digest microbes or materials (e.g., ingested by the cell, worn-out cellular components, or the entire cell)	
Peroxisomes	Smaller, spherical-shaped membrane-bound organelles formed from the ER or through fission; contain oxidative enzymes	Detoxify specific harmful substances either produced by the cell or taken into the cell; engage in beta oxidation of fatty acids to acetyl CoA	
Mitochondria	Double membrane-bound organelles containing a circular strand of DNA (genes for producing mitochondrial proteins)	Synthesize most ATP during aerobic cellular respiration by digestion of fuel molecules (e.g., glucose) in the presence of oxygen	
Ribosomes	Organelles composed of both protein and ribosomal RNA (rRNA) that are organized into both a large and small subunit; may be bound to a membrane or free in cytosol	Engage in protein synthesis: Bound ribosomes produce proteins that are secreted, incorporated into plasma membrane, and within lysosomes; free ribosomes produce proteins used within the cell	Bound ribosomes / Free ribosomes
Cytoskeleton	Organized network of protein filaments and hollow tubules, including microfilaments, intermediate filaments, and microtubules	Maintains intracellular structural support and organization of cells; participates in cell division; facilitates movement	Cytoskeleton / Intermediate filament / Microtubule / Microfilament
Microfilaments	Actin protein monomers organized into two thin, intertwined protein filaments (actin filaments)	Maintain cell shape; support microvilli; separate two cells during cytokinesis (a process of cell division); facilitate change in cell shape; participates in muscle contraction	
Intermediate filaments	Various protein components	Provide structural support; stabilize junctions between cells	
Microtubules	Hollow cylinders composed of tubulin protein	Maintain cell shape and rigidity; organize and move organelles; support cilia and flagella; participate in vesicular transport; separate chromosomes during the process of cell division	
Centrosome	Amorphous region adjacent to nucleus; contains a pair of centrioles	Organizes microtubules; participates in mitotic spindle formation during cell division	Centriole / Centrosome
Proteasomes	Large, barrel-shaped protein complexes located in both the cytosol and nucleus	Degrade and digest damaged or unneeded proteins; ensure quality of exported proteins	
Inclusions	Aggregates of specific types of molecules (e.g., melanin protein, glycogen, or lipid)	Serve as temporary storage for these molecules	

detoxification of drugs, alcohol, and poisons. Abundant amounts of smooth ER occur within the cells of the testes (interstitial cells) to produce the steroid hormone testosterone, and in the cells of the liver to process digested nutrients and detoxify drugs and alcohol.

Golgi Apparatus

The **Golgi apparatus,** also called the *Golgi complex* or *Golgi body,* is typically composed of several (e.g., about four or five) elongated, flattened saclike membranous structures called *cisternae* **(figure 4.21)**. The Golgi apparatus exhibits a distinct polarity. The two poles are called the *cis*-face and *trans*-face. The **cis-face** is closer in proximity to the ER and the diameter of its flattened sac is larger compared to the **trans-face.** You may find it helpful to think of the Golgi

apparatus as a "warehouse" with the *cis*-face as the *receiving region* and the *trans*-face as the *shipping region.*

One of the primary functions of the Golgi apparatus is to modify, package, and sort proteins (and glycoproteins) that are made in the rough ER (figure 4.21*b*). Transport vesicles arrive from the ER and fuse with *cis*-face of the Golgi apparatus. Materials move between cisternae from the *cis*-face to the *trans*-face. Within the lumen of the Golgi apparatus, molecules are modified; this may involve removal of portions of a molecule, or additions to a molecule (e.g., addition of a carbohydrate or a phosphate group). At the *trans*-face, secretory vesicles form and carry the modified materials away for different fates. Some secretory vesicles become components of the plasma membrane and others release their contents from the cell into the interstitial fluid by exocytosis. Thus, the Golgi apparatus is especially extensive and active in cells

Functions of Golgi Apparatus

1. **Modification, packaging, and sorting** [Process summarized in (b)]
2. **Transport:** Moves materials from *cis*-face to *trans*-face
3. **Structure formation:** Segments of Golgi apparatus form secretory vesicles and lysosomes

(a)

Synthesis, Modification, and Shipping of Proteins

1. RER synthesizes protein that is released in a transport vesicle.

2. Vesicle from the RER moves to the Golgi apparatus.

3. Vesicle fuses with Golgi apparatus at the *cis*-face.

4. Proteins are modified as they move through Golgi apparatus (e.g., addition of carbohydrate).

5. Modified proteins are packaged and released within secretory vesicle from the *trans*-face.

6. Secretory vesicles (6a) merge with the plasma membrane to insert molecules into the plasma membrane (6b), or release contents by exocytosis (6c). They may also serve as lysosomes.

(b) Endomembrane System: Movement of materials through the Golgi apparatus

Figure 4.21 The Golgi Apparatus and Endomembrane System. Each Golgi apparatus is composed of several flattened membrane sacs (cisternae). The arrangement of these sacs exhibits both structural and functional polarity. (*a*) A TEM and a drawing provide different views of the Golgi apparatus. (*b*) The Golgi apparatus is part of the endomembrane system, which is a system of membranous structures of a cell that provide a means of transporting substances into, out of, and within a cell. **AP|R**

specialized for protein secretion. Lysosomes (described next) are also produced as secretions of the Golgi apparatus pinch off from the *trans*-face.

Lysosomes

Lysosomes (lī′sō-sōm; *soma* = body) are small, membranous sacs that contain digestive enzymes **(figure 4.22)**. They are formed by the Golgi apparatus. Lysosomes participate in digestion of unneeded or unwanted substances. Within a healthy cell, lysosomes digest the contents of endocytosed vesicles. For example, following phagocytosis of microorganisms by certain white blood cells, the vesicle fuses with a lysosome. Its digestive enzymes break down the large biomolecules composing the microorganism (e.g., proteins, fats, polysaccharides, and nucleic acids) into smaller molecules. Lysosomes also digest molecular structures of damaged organelles in a similar fashion; this process is specifically called **autophagy** (aw-tōf′ă-jē; *autos* = self, *phago* = to eat). Lysosomes are sometimes referred to as the "garbagemen" of the cell because of their "cleanup" activities.

When a cell is damaged or dies, enzymes from its lysosomes are eventually released into the cytosol, resulting in the rapid digestion of the molecular components of the cell itself. This process is called **autolysis** (aw-tol′i-sis; *lysis* = dissolution).

WHAT DO YOU THINK?

2 What would happen to a cell if it didn't contain any lysosomes (or if its lysosomes weren't functioning)? Would the cell be able to survive?

Peroxisomes

Peroxisomes (per-ok′si-sōm) are membrane-enclosed sacs that are usually smaller in diameter than lysosomes **(figure 4.23)**. Perixomes are formed by pinching off vesicles from the rough ER. Recent evidence shows that peroxisomes also replicate through fission (a process in which something splits into two components).

Peroxisomes contain various oxidative enzymes that serve two major functions: detoxification and beta oxidation. Detoxification

involves removal of hydrogen from a molecule with the accompanying production of hydrogen peroxide. Hydrogen peroxide is then used to oxidize other substances (e.g., alcohol, formaldehyde). The name "peroxisomes" is based on the production of hydrogen peroxide that occurs within these organelles.

Peroxisomes engage in the beta oxidation of fatty acids. This is a process that removes two hydrogen-carbon units at a time from the fatty acid chain. These units are then converted to acetyl CoA and may be taken up by the mitochondria within the cell, where they are oxidized to transfer energy to form ATP (section 3.4h).

Peroxisomes are most abundant in liver cells, where they are central to the detoxification of alcohol and other harmful substances.

Lysosomes

Lysosome

TEM 16,000x

Functions of Lysosomes

Digestion: Digest materials in vesicles that enter cell by endocytosis, remove damaged organelles and cellular components (autophagy), and break down cellular components following cellular death (autolysis)

Figure 4.22 Lysosomes. These organelles are membrane-bound organelles that house enzymes for intracellular digestion. Both a drawing and TEM are shown. **AP|R**

Peroxisome

Peroxisome

TEM 90,000x

Functions of Peroxisomes

1. **Detoxification:** Detoxify harmful substances using oxidative enzymes
2. **Beta oxidation:** Break down fatty acid molecules to acetyl CoA

Figure 4.23 Peroxisomes. A TEM and drawing show a peroxisome within a cell. Peroxisomes are small, membrane-bound organelles that contain oxidative enzymes that detoxify molecules and help break down fatty acids.

Endomembrane System

The **endomembrane system** is an extensive array of membrane-bound structures that includes the endoplasmic reticulum, Golgi apparatus, vesicles, lysosomes, and peroxisomes. The plasma membrane and nuclear envelope are also considered part of this membrane system. All of these structures are either directly attached to one another or are connected through vesicles that move between them. They are involved in various forms of metabolic processes that occur within a cell, and provide a means of transporting substances within the cell, as shown in figure 4.21b.

Mitochondria

Mitochondria (mī'tō-kon'drē-ă; sing., *mitochondrion,* mī-tō-kon'drē-on; *mitos* = thread, *chondros* = granule) were first described in chapter 3. They are oblong-shaped organelles with a double membrane and contain a small, unique circular fragment of DNA that has genes for producing mitochondrial proteins (**figure 4.24**). Mitochondria engage in aerobic cellular respiration to complete the digestion of glucose and other fuel molecules, such as fatty acids, for the transfer of energy to synthesize ATP molecules, the cell's energy currency. For this reason, mitochondria are called the "powerhouses" of the cell. Mitochondria numbers within cells increase (by fission) with greater demands for ATP production.

WHAT DID YOU LEARN?

16 Which two membrane-bound organelles function primarily in digestion inside the cell? Which one is involved in energy production?

17 Vesicles are "vehicles" for transporting material between organelles and the plasma membrane. Which of the following form vesicles during endocytosis? (a) endoplasmic reticulum, (b) Golgi apparatus, or (c) plasma membrane

4.5b Non-Membrane-Bound Organelles

LEARNING OBJECTIVES

3. List the non-membrane-bound organelles of a typical human cell.
4. Describe the structure and main function(s) of each.

Non-membrane-bound organelles are composed of either protein alone or protein and RNA. They include ribosomes, the cytoskeleton, centrosome, and proteasomes.

Ribosomes

Ribosomes are non-membrane-bound organelles containing protein and ribonucleic acid (RNA) that are arranged into both a large and small subunit. The large subunit has three hollow areas designated as the *E, P,* and *A sites* (**figure 4.25**). You can think of the ribosomal subunits as puzzle pieces that are made within the nucleolus and then moved into the cytosol where the pieces are put together into one complete puzzle (a ribosome).

Outer mitochondrial membrane

Matrix

Cristae

Inner mitochondrial membrane

TEM 80,000x

Function of Mitochondria

Energy harvesting: Digest organic molecules (e.g., glucose) to produce ATP by aerobic cellular respiration; called the "powerhouse" of the cell

Nucleus
Nucleolus

Bound ribosome

Free ribosome

E P A
Large subunit
+
Small subunit
=
E P A
Functional ribosome
(a)

Free ribosomes

Rough endoplasmic reticulum with bound ribosomes

TEM 12,510x

(b)

Functions of Ribosomes

Protein synthesis:
1. Bound ribosomes synthesize proteins destined to be incorporated into the plasma membrane, exported from the cell, or housed within lysosomes
2. Free ribosomes synthesize proteins for use within the cell

Figure 4.24 Mitochondria. A drawing and TEM show the parts of a mitochondrion. Mitochondria are the double-membrane-bound organelles within the cytoplasm that produce ATP for energy-requiring cellular processes.

Figure 4.25 Ribosomes. Ribosomes function in protein synthesis and are either bound to the endoplasmic reticulum or free within the cytosol. (*a*) Ribosomes consist of both small and large subunits. (*b*) A TEM shows both free and bound ribosomes in the cell cytosol. AP|R

Ribosomes are either bound or free. **Bound ribosomes** are attached to the external surface of the ER membrane to form rough ER. Recall that bound ribosomes are used to synthesize proteins destined for export out of the cell, to become an integral part of the plasma membrane, or to serve as enzymes within lysosomes. **Free ribosomes** are suspended within the cytosol. In general, all other proteins that function within the cell are synthesized by free ribosomes.

Cytoskeleton

The **cytoskeleton** has a central role in numerous cellular activities that include intracellular structural support and organization of organelles, cell division, and movement of materials. Formed by a framework of diverse fibrous proteins, the cytoskeleton extends throughout the interior of a cell and anchors to proteins in the plasma membrane. Three separate types of protein molecules form the cytoskeleton—microfilaments, intermediate filaments, and microtubules **(figure 4.26)**.

Microfilaments (mī-krō-fil'ă-ment; *micros* = small) are the smallest components of the cytoskeleton with a diameter of about 7 nanometers. They are composed of actin protein monomers that are organized into two thin, intertwined protein filaments (actin filaments) similar to two twisted pearl necklaces. They form an interlacing network on the cytoplasmic side of the plasma membrane. Microfilaments help maintain cell shape, form internal support of microvilli (described shortly), separate the two cells formed during cytokinesis (a process of cell division described later), facilitate cytoplasmic streaming (the movement of the cytoplasm associated with changing cell shape), and participate in muscle contraction. Individual globular actin proteins are added to one end of the microfilament for growth in a particular direction and removed from the other end for shortening.

Intermediate filaments are between 8 and 12 nanometers in diameter. They are more rigid than microfilaments, and they support

cells structurally and stabilize junctions between them. Their protein composition differs, depending upon the cells in which they occur. Keratin, a protein of the skin, hair, and nails, is an example of one type of intermediate filament; another type forms neurofilaments of nerve cells.

Microtubules (mī-krō-tū'būl; *tubus* = tube) are hollow cylinders that are approximately 25 nanometers in diameter. They are composed of long chains of a globular protein called *tubulin*. Microtubules are not permanent structures. They may be elongated or shortened as needed to complete their functions. Microtubules help maintain cell shape, organize and move organelles within a cell, form protein components of cilia and flagella, participate in cellular transport of vesicles, and separate chromosomes during cell division.

Centrosome

The **centrosome** is a structure typically in close proximity to the nucleus. It contains a pair of perpendicularly oriented cylindrical **centrioles** (sen'trē-ōl; *kentron* = a point, center) surrounded by protein that is amorphous (without a distinctive shape) **(figure 4.27)**. The primary function of a centrosome is organizing microtubules within the cytoskeleton. The centrosome is best known for its function in cellular division, during which microtubules form a mitotic spindle to facilitate chromosome movement, as described in a later section.

Proteasomes

Large, barrel-shaped protein complexes called **proteasomes** (prō'tē-ă-sōm) are major protein-digesting organelles located within both the cytosol and nucleus of cells **(figure 4.28)**. Proteasomes degrade cell proteins through an ATP-dependent pathway; these

Figure 4.26 **The Cytoskeleton.** Filamentous proteins form the cytoskeleton. They help give the cell its shape and coordinate cellular movements. The three cytoskeletal elements are microfilaments, intermediate filaments, and microtubules. AP|R

Mitochondrion

Microfilament

Intermediate filament

Microtubule

Centrosome

Functions of Cytoskeleton

1. **Structural support and organization of cell:** Maintains cell shape; protein support of microvilli, cilia, and flagella; stabilizes cell junctions; organizes organelles
2. **Cell division:** Separates chromosomes during cell division; splits cell into two daughter cells (cytokinesis)
3. **Movement:** Facilitates cytoplasmic streaming; involved in movement of vesicles within a cell; participates in muscle contraction

Figure 4.27 **Centrosome and Centrioles.** A TEM and a drawing show that a region of the cytoplasm called the centrosome contains a centriole pair immediately adjacent to the nucleus.

Functions of Centrosomes and Centrioles
1. **Organization:** Arranges microtubules (proteins of cytoskeleton) and supports their growth in nondividing cells
2. **Cell division:** Directs formation of mitotic spindle in dividing cells

Figure 4.28 **Proteasomes.** These organelles maintain order within the cell by digesting abnormal and unwanted cellular proteins. A sketch of a TEM and drawing are both shown.

Functions of Proteasomes
1. **Protein digestion:** Degrades proteins that are damaged, incorrectly folded, or those that are no longer needed
2. **Quality assurance:** Controls the quality of exported cell proteins

proteins include damaged proteins, incorrectly folded proteins, and normal proteins that nevertheless are no longer needed by the cell. The action of proteasomes also provides a means to control the quality of exported cell proteins. This latter function is especially critical during the regulation of cellular metabolism, cell division, and activities associated with cell signaling. When a protein is targeted for removal by proteasomes, it usually is marked for destruction by having a protein called ubiquitin bound to it. This is the first step in the ultimate degradation of the protein by proteasomes. You may find it helpful to think of proteasomes as "garbage disposals" for unwanted protein.

Recent research has shown that significant age-related alterations in proteasome structure and function may prevent or inhibit the normal removal of proteins from the cell.

INTEGRATE

CONCEPT CONNECTION

A specific example of proteasome action occurs when a virus or other infectious agent enters a cell. Proteins of the infectious agent are cleaved by a proteasome. These degraded peptide fragments of the infectious agent are considered "nonself" and are presented to specialized white blood cells, alerting the immune system that the body has been "invaded" (section 22.4c).

WHAT DID YOU LEARN?

18 Which non-membrane-bound organelle functions primarily in digestion within the cell?

4.5c Structures of the Cell's External Surface

LEARNING OBJECTIVES

5. Distinguish between cilia and flagella.

6. Describe the function of microvilli.

The structures that extend from the cell's surface include cilia, flagella, and microvilli. Cilia and flagella are extensions of the cell membrane involved in movement, whereas microvilli are structures that increase the surface area of the plasma membrane.

Cilia and Flagella

Cilia (sil′ē-ă; sing., sil′ē-ŭm; *cilium* = an eyelash) and **flagella** (flă-jel′ă; sing., *flagellum*, flă-jel′ŭm; a whip) are projections extending from the cell. They contain both cytoplasm and supportive microtubule proteins, and they are enclosed by the plasma membrane. Cilia are usually found in large numbers on the exposed surfaces of specific cells such as those that line portions of the respiratory passageways (see figure 4.1). These ciliated cells are associated with mucin-secreting cells. The beating of the cilia moves the mucus formed from mucin and any adherent substances along the cell

Figure 4.29 Microvilli. Microvilli are thin, microscopic projections. They extend from the surface of the plasma membrane and are supported by microfilaments. Microvilli function to increase the surface area of the plasma membrane. AP|R

surface toward the throat, where it may then be expelled from the respiratory system (section 23.1c).

Flagella are similar to cilia in basic structure—however, they are longer and usually appear alone. The function of a flagellum is to help propel an entire cell. In humans, the only example of a cell with a flagellum is sperm (see figure 28.18), which needs to move through the female reproductive tract to reach the ovum.

Microvilli

Microvilli are thin, microscopic membrane extensions from the surface of the plasma membrane. They are much smaller than cilia, much more densely packed together, and lack powered movement **(figure 4.29)**. Each microvillus is supported by microfilaments (actin proteins are cross-linked into a dense bundle that serves as its structural core). In essence, these projections form a

more extensive plasma membrane surface for molecules to travel across to facilitate more efficient membrane transport. Just as not all cells have cilia, not all cells have microvilli. Cells with microvilli occur, for example, throughout the small intestine, where increased surface area is needed to absorb digested nutrients.

WHAT DID YOU LEARN?

19 What are the structural and functional differences between cilia and microvilli?

4.5d Membrane Junctions

LEARNING OBJECTIVE

7. Compare and contrast the structure and function of the three major types of membrane junctions.

Cell membrane junctions connect, buttress, and support cells. Most of our cells are arranged into structural units called *tissues* (see chapter 5) that act together in a common function. To provide an orderly arrangement between some cells and coordinate their interactions, membrane junctions form between adjacent cells. There are three major types of junctions: tight junctions, desmosomes, and gap junctions **(figure 4.30)**.

Tight Junctions

A **tight junction**, also called a *zonula* (zō′nyū-lă) *occludens*, encircles certain types of cells (e.g., epithelial cells) near their exposed apical (upper) surface and completely attaches each cell to its neighbors. Plasma membrane proteins among neighboring cells fuse, so the apical surfaces of the cells are tightly connected everywhere around the cell. This connection seals off the intercellular space and prevents substances from passing between the epithelial cells. These junctions force all materials to move through, rather than between, the cells. For example, in the small intestine, tight junctions prevent corrosive digestive enzymes that are within the lumen of the intestine from moving between cells and damaging

Figure 4.30 Membrane Junctions. The lateral surface of some cells contain tight junctions that prevent leakage between cells, desmosomes to bind neighboring cells, and gap junctions that provide a small passageway for movement of small molecules between adjoining cells. A hemidesmosome is essentially one-half of a desmosome that anchors a cell to the underlying basement membrane.

internal body structures. These junctions also prevent leakage of urine through the urinary bladder wall.

Desmosomes

Desmosomes (dez'mō-sōm; *desmos* = a band, *soma* = body), also called *macula adherens* ("adhering spot"), are like snaps between adjacent cells. Each is a small region that holds cells together and provides resistance to mechanical stress at a single point. The neighboring cells are separated by a small space that is spanned by a fine web of protein filaments. These filaments anchor into a thickened protein plaque located at the internal surface of each cell. Intermediate filaments of the cytoskeleton penetrate the plaque and extend throughout the cell to provide support and strength. Each cell contributes half of the complete desmosome. The cells of tissues exposed to stress, such as the external layer of the skin (epidermis) and cardiac muscle, contain desmosomes. Hemidesmosomes ("half of a desmosome") anchor the basal (bottom) layer of cells of the epidermis to the underlying components.

Gap Junctions

Gap junctions are formed across the intercellular space between neighboring cells. This gap (about 2 nanometers in length) is bridged by six transmembrane proteins, called **connexons** (kon-neks'onz), that form tiny, fluid-filled tunnels or pores. Gap junctions provide a direct passageway for substances to travel between neighboring cells. Ions, glucose, amino acids, and other small solutes can pass directly from the cytoplasm of one cell into the neighboring cell through these channels. The flow of ions between cells allows spread of electrical activity in *cardiac muscle of the heart* and coordinates such cellular activities as the beating of cilia.

WHAT DID YOU LEARN?

20 Differentiate between a desmosome and a tight junction.

4.6 Structure of the Nucleus

The nucleus is the largest structure in the cell, typically averaging about 5 μm to 7 μm in diameter. It is often called the cell's control center (**figure 4.31**). A cell typically has one nucleus. However,

(a) Structure of nucleus

(b) Levels of organization

Functions of the Nucleus

1. **Cellular regulation:** Houses DNA molecules that serve as the genetic instructions for synthesis of proteins
2. **Production:** Produces ribosomal subunits in nucleolus and exports them into cytoplasm for assembly into ribosomes

(c) Functional unit: A gene

Figure 4.31 Nucleus, DNA and Chromatin Structure, and Genes. (*a*) A TEM and drawing show the structural characteristics of the nucleus within a cell. DNA is the genetic material housed within the cell nucleus. (*b*) DNA is a polymer of nucleotides in the shape of a double helix. Strands of DNA and histone proteins associate to form chromatin, which forms chromosomes when cell division occurs. (*c*) The functional unit of DNA is the gene, which is a sequence of DNA that directs the synthesis of a specific protein. AP|R erythrocytes contain no nucleus, and skeletal muscle cells have many nuclei. The shape of the nucleus generally mirrors the shape of a cell. For example, a cuboidal cell has a spherical nucleus in the center of the cell, whereas a thin, flattened cell has a nucleus elongated in the same direction as the cell. Some cells contain a uniquely shaped nucleus. For example, some white blood cells have a multilobed nucleus that may have two or more segments (see figures in table 18.6).

4.6a Nuclear Envelope and Nucleolus

LEARNING OBJECTIVES

1. Describe the nuclear envelope.
2. Explain the structure and function of a nucleolus.

The nucleus is enclosed within a double membrane that is called the **nuclear envelope** (or *nuclear membrane*). It separates the cytoplasm from the **nucleoplasm** (the fluid within the nucleus). This boundary controls the movement of materials between the nucleus and the surrounding cytoplasm. Each layer of the nuclear envelope is a phospholipid bilayer, similar in structure to the plasma membrane. Externally it is continuous with the rough ER in the cytoplasm. **Nuclear pores** are channel-like open passageways that penetrate fused regions within the double membrane throughout the entire nuclear envelope. They allow the passage of large particles both into the nucleus (e.g., proteins) and out of the nucleus (e.g., messenger RNA). Ions and water-soluble molecules also pass through nuclear pores.

The cell nucleus typically contains one dark-staining, usually spherical, body called a **nucleolus** (nū-klē-ō-lŭs) (figure 4.31*a*). (The plural term is **nucleoli** [nū-klē-ō-lī].) A nucleolus is not membrane-bound. It is composed of protein and RNA, and is responsible for producing the small and large subunits of ribosomes.

Not all cells contain a nucleolus. Its presence and relative number indicate the protein synthesis activity of a cell. For example, nerve cells contain more than one nucleolus because they produce many proteins. In contrast, sperm have no nucleoli because they produce no proteins.

WHAT DID YOU LEARN?

21 What is the function of nuclear pores within the nuclear envelope?

22 What is the function of the nucleolus?

4.6b DNA, Chromatin, and Chromosomes

LEARNING OBJECTIVE

3. Describe the relationship of DNA, chromatin, and genes.

The nucleus houses the nuclear DNA along with the nucleolus and nucleoplasm. Recall that DNA is a nucleic acid biomolecule composed of repeating monomers called **nucleotides** (section 2.7d). Each **deoxyribonucleotide** is composed of the five-carbon sugar deoxyribose, a phosphate, and one of four nitrogenous bases: adenine (A), cytosine (C), guanine (G), and thymine (T). Nucleotide monomers are linked through the phosphate groups by **phosphodiester bonds** to form a polymer strand. Each DNA molecule contains two complementary strands of nucleotides. They are bonded together by weak hydrogen bonds between the nucleotide bases to form a double helix structure (see figure 2.22). Note that the base adenine pairs only with the base thymine, whereas the base guanine pairs only with the base cytosine. This specific interaction between bases is called **complementary base pairing**: A to T, and C to G.

Think of the DNA as a spiral ladder, where the sugar and phosphate components of the nucleotide monomers form the vertical "struts" of the ladder (figure 4.31*b*). The horizontal "rungs" of the ladder are formed by pairs of nucleotide bases interconnected by weak hydrogen bonds to the complementary strand. The order of the bases in the nucleotides ultimately codes for specific proteins that the body needs.

DNA is an enormous macromolecule that houses most of the genetic material of the cell (a small amount is found within mitochondria). The amount of DNA in a human cell contains over 3 billion pairs of nucleotides. A human body cell nucleus has 46 separate double-stranded DNA molecules. During cell division, these molecules are identifiable microscopically as chromosomes. To help package the DNA within the nucleus, the long DNA double helix winds around a cluster of special nuclear proteins, called **histones,** forming a complex called a **nucleosome** (figure 4.31b). When a cell is not dividing, the DNA and its associated proteins are in the form of a finely filamented mass called **chromatin** (krō′matin; *chroma* = color), which resembles an unrolled spool of thread. The tightly coiled chromatin is what we see as **chromosomes** during cell division.

DNA is organized functionally into discrete units called **genes** (figure 4.31c). Genes are segmental units of nucleotides within DNA that provide the instructions for the synthesis of specific proteins. About 1–2% of the total amount of DNA composes genes. The average length of a gene is about 3000 nucleotide base pairs. Associated with each gene is a *promoter* region that is analogous to a "start" signal, and a *terminator* region that is analogous to a "stop" signal for the transcription, or copying, of a gene into an RNA molecule to direct the synthesis of a protein (described shortly).

 WHAT DID YOU LEARN?

23 Describe the structural relationship of DNA and chromatin, and the functional relationship of DNA and genes.

4.7 Function of the Nucleus and Ribosomes

We continue our discussion of cellular functions by describing protein synthesis, the central process upon which all other cellular activities ultimately depend. The DNA directs protein synthesis, which occurs at ribosomes in the cytoplasm. Consequently, two major events are involved: (1) **transcription,** which is the formation of a ribonucleic acid (RNA) copy of a gene from DNA in the nucleus; and (2) **translation,** which uses RNA for the synthesis of the protein by ribosomes in the cytoplasm. For both processes we first describe the required structures and then the mechanism involved.

4.7a Transcription: Synthesizing RNA

 LEARNING OBJECTIVES

1. List the required structures for transcription.
2. Explain the three steps of transcription.

Transcription occurs in the nucleus of the cell. This process occurs when a segment of DNA is "read" and copied to produce a newly formed strand of RNA.

Required Structures

DNA is the major structure required in transcription. This process is needed to form an RNA molecule that is complementary to the sequence of nucleotides in DNA. RNA (as described in section 2.7d) is a nucleic acid composed of repeating ribonucleotide monomers. Each of these nucleotides has a five-carbon sugar ribose, a phosphate, and one of four nitrogenous bases that include adenine (A), cytosine (C), guanine (G), and uracil (U). Unlike DNA, RNA is only a single strand of nucleotides (see figure 2.22).

Forming RNA during transcription requires both large numbers of RNA building blocks called **ribonucleotides** and the enzyme **RNA polymerase.** These structures are located within the nucleoplasm in the nucleus. RNA polymerase assembles the ribonucleotides by complementary base pairing ribonucleotides with DNA as follows:

Although other enzymes and many regulatory factors are involved in the process, we limit our discussion to the basic process of transcription that involves DNA, ribonucleotides, and the enzyme RNA polymerase.

Process of Transcription

Three functional types of RNA are produced during transcription: messenger RNA (mRNA), transfer RNA (tRNA), and ribosomal (rRNA). The general process of transcription includes three major events: *initiation, elongation,* and *termination.* Here we describe the process for the formation of mRNA **(figure 4.32)**.

Initiation   DNA is usually coiled into a double helix, so it first must be unwound in the region of the gene so its information is available for "reading" (copying). Specific enzymes help to partially unwind the DNA and make it accessible to RNA polymerase, the enzyme that catalyzes the synthesis of an **mRNA (messenger RNA)** molecule. After the partial unwinding of DNA, RNA polymerase attaches to the DNA strand and moves along its length until it comes in contact with the promoter region (the "start" region) associated with a gene.

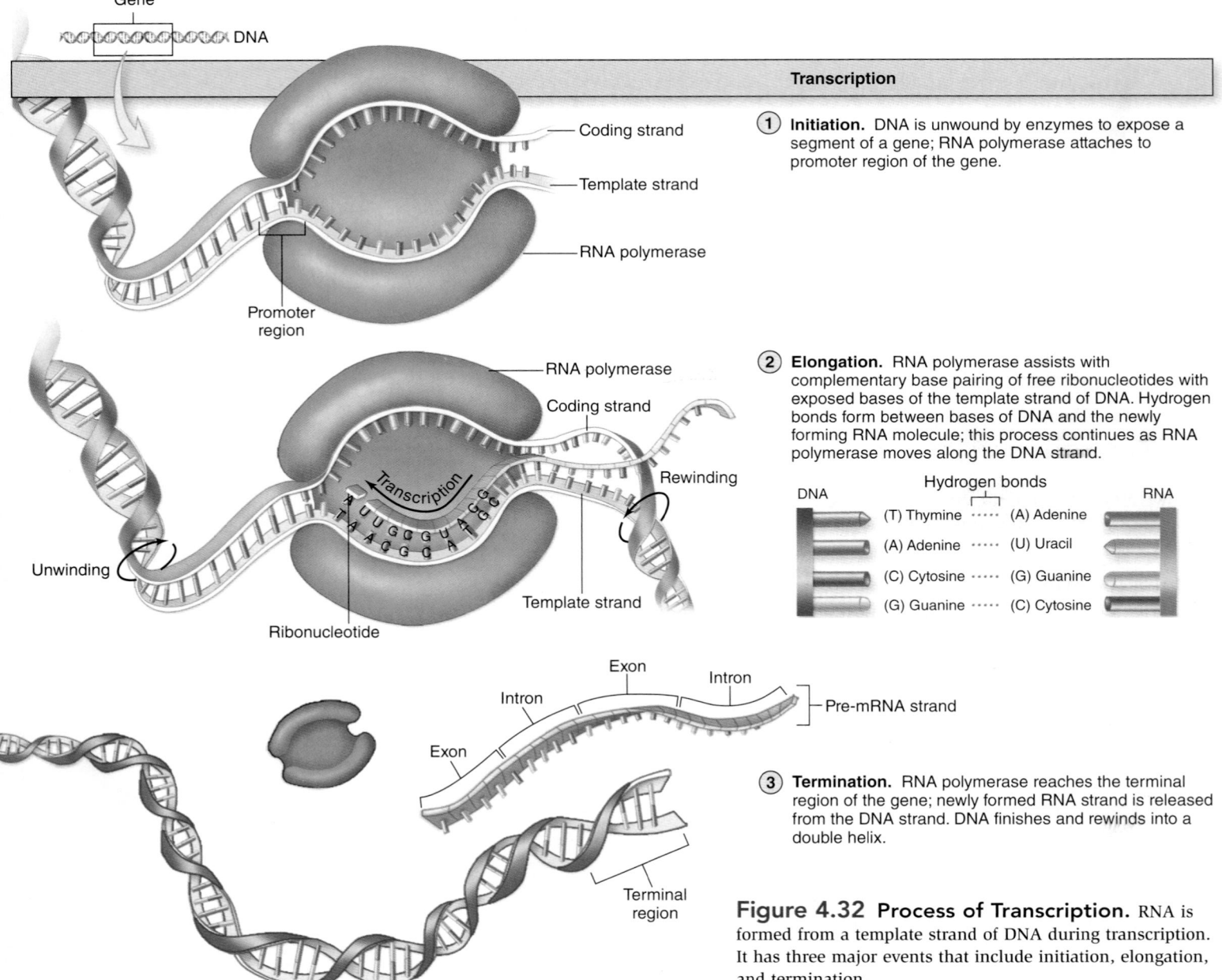

Figure 4.32 Process of Transcription. RNA is formed from a template strand of DNA during transcription. It has three major events that include initiation, elongation, and termination.

The gene is marked for transcription by a number of regulatory factors that reflect a requirement for the specific protein coded for by that gene. The promoter serves as the start point for gene transcription. When identification of the gene and binding of the appropriate factors occurs, the hydrogen bonds between the two strands of DNA break, thus allowing expansion or "bubbling out" in that region. That permits the nitrogenous bases in the region to be exposed. Because RNA is a single-stranded molecule, only one strand of DNA is copied. This DNA strand is referred to as the **template strand.** The other DNA strand is the **coding strand,** and is not copied.

Elongation   Free ribonucleotides are base-paired in a complementary way with the exposed bases in the DNA template strand during the elongation process. The enzyme RNA polymerase assists in this base pairing. Base pairing involves the formation of hydrogen bonds between a base of a ribonucleotide and its complementary base of the DNA strand. For example, if the base sequence of a DNA template strand is TTAGCTAGC, then the base sequence of the newly formed RNA strand will be AAUCGAUCG. (Recall that RNA contains uracil instead of thymine.) A phosphodiester bond is formed between each of the ribonucleotides to form the RNA polymer. RNA polymerase continues to move along the length of DNA until the entire gene has been transcribed. As a result, a new mRNA is formed from the "information" in the gene.

Termination   When the terminal region is reached at the end of the gene, RNA polymerase is released from the DNA as hydrogen bonds are broken between the DNA strand and newly formed mRNA strand. The newly formed mRNA is a "recipe" for synthesizing a specific protein (e.g., insulin). The DNA rewinds into a double helix. (This is included in steps in figure 4.32.)

Modifications to mRNA

Several significant changes are made to the newly formed mRNA before it leaves the nucleus. The initially synthesized strand of mRNA is more specifically called the **pre-mRNA** (or primary transcript). The changes result in the formation of a **mature mRNA,** which is then used as the recipe to make the protein.

Splicing   Pre-mRNA includes **introns,** which are noncoding regions. These introns are removed (most are degraded, but some have specialized functions in regulating gene expression). **Exons** are the coding regions of DNA and they are subsequently **spliced** together. This process is catalyzed by a ribonucleoprotein molecule complex (composed of RNA and protein) called a **spliceosome.** The pattern of splicing varies depending on several factors, including the organism's stage of development and the cell type. Thus, splicing provides a means of producing a larger number of proteins from the available DNA.

Other Changes   Further modifications to form the mature mRNA include capping and addition of a polyA tail. **Capping** involves the unique bonding of a ribonucleotide containing guanine to the lead end of the mRNA. This increases the stability of an mRNA strand helping to prevent its digestion by nucleic acid digesting enzymes (nucleases) that are present within the cytoplasm. The **polyA tail** addition involves removal of terminal segments of the mRNA and placing numerous adenine-containing ribonucleotides at the tail end of the mRNA. The addition of a polyA tail, like the splicing, provides a means of producing more than one mature mRNA transcript, because the segment that is removed and the addition of the polyA tail can be done at different sites. One function of the polyA tail is to serve as a measure of age of the mRNA. These nucleotides are subsequently removed over time, and the tail is shortened. When only a certain amount of the tail remains, nuclease enzymes will destroy the mRNA.

The newly formed mature mRNA exits the nucleus following its modification. It leaves through nuclear pores to enter the cytoplasm as it makes it way to a ribosome for translation (the second event of protein synthesis).

 WHAT DID YOU LEARN?

24 What are the three major structures required for transcription? Explain where and how transcription occurs.

INTEGRATE

LEARNING STRATEGY

You may find it helpful to think of the splicing of pre-mRNA like the splicing of film that occurs with producing a movie. Unwanted segments of the film are cut out, and the remaining segments are spliced together to produce the final version of the movie. Interestingly, the same pre-mRNA can be spliced in various ways to produce different mature mRNA (much like a film can be spliced in different ways to create a different story).

LEARNING STRATEGY

The required components of translation may be compared to a chef cooking up a masterpiece. The ribosome is the kitchen, the mRNA is the chef, the tRNAs are the chef's assistants, the amino acids are the ingredients, and the protein is the completed dish. The tRNA assistants bring the amino acid ingredients to the kitchen, as directed by the mRNA chef, to produce a protein masterpiece.

4.7b Translation: Synthesizing Protein

LEARNING OBJECTIVES

3. List the required structures for translation.

4. Name the three functional forms of RNA, explain what is meant by codon, and identify three types of codon sequences.

5. Describe the three steps of translation.

Translation is the synthesis of a new protein. The mRNA is threaded through a ribosome, and the information it contains is "read." The code in the nucleotide sequence of mRNA is translated, meaning that it is converted into the language of amino acids to produce newly formed strands of protein. Translation takes place at ribosomes within the cytoplasm.

Required Structures

Translation requires ribosomes (composed of rRNA and protein), mRNA, tRNA, and large numbers of free amino acids. Protein is the product formed.

Three functional types of RNA are required for protein synthesis **(figure 4.33)**. One functional type of RNA is embedded in the structure of ribosomes and is aptly called **ribosomal RNA (rRNA).** Three sites are associated with a ribosome: (1) The A (aminoacyl) site, which is the place where new amino acids are added, (2) the P (peptidyl) site that holds the newly forming polypeptide, and (3) the E (exit) site for the tRNA that is exiting the ribosome.

Mature mRNA is the molecule that was transcribed from a gene. It carries the "instructions" for synthesizing a protein. Messenger RNA is a linear sequence of nucleotides varying in length, depending upon the size of the protein to be made. The mRNA is read three nucleotide bases at a time. Each three-base unit is called a **codon.** A molecule of mRNA contains three categories of codons:

- A **start codon** that always contains the three bases AUG; this is the signal that indicates where protein synthesis begins.

- The consecutive codons following the start codon and before the stop codon serve to direct the assembly of amino acids into a newly synthesized protein.

- The **stop codon** follows the codons used to assemble the new protein, and it is always one of these three sequences of bases: UAA, UAG, or UGA. Collectively they serve as the point where the reading of mRNA ends.

The third type of RNA is **transfer RNA (tRNA).** It serves as an "adapter" to bring a specific amino acid to a specific mRNA codon. Transfer RNAs are typically composed of between 70 and 100 nucleotides: When shown in simplified form, it is shaped like a cloverleaf. A tRNA molecule has two significant regions. The first region is a sequence of three nucleotide bases called an **anticodon.** The anticodon in the tRNA base-pairs with its complementary codon in the mRNA. The second region is the amino acid acceptor end. Here a specific amino acid becomes attached to a tRNA. The attachment of a specific amino acid is based upon the tRNA's anticodon sequence, and it is catalyzed by a specific enzyme called **aminoacyl-tRNA synthetase** (not shown in figure 4.33). There are 20 aminoacyl-tRNA synthetase enzymes. Prior to translation, each amino acid is attached to the correct tRNA by its

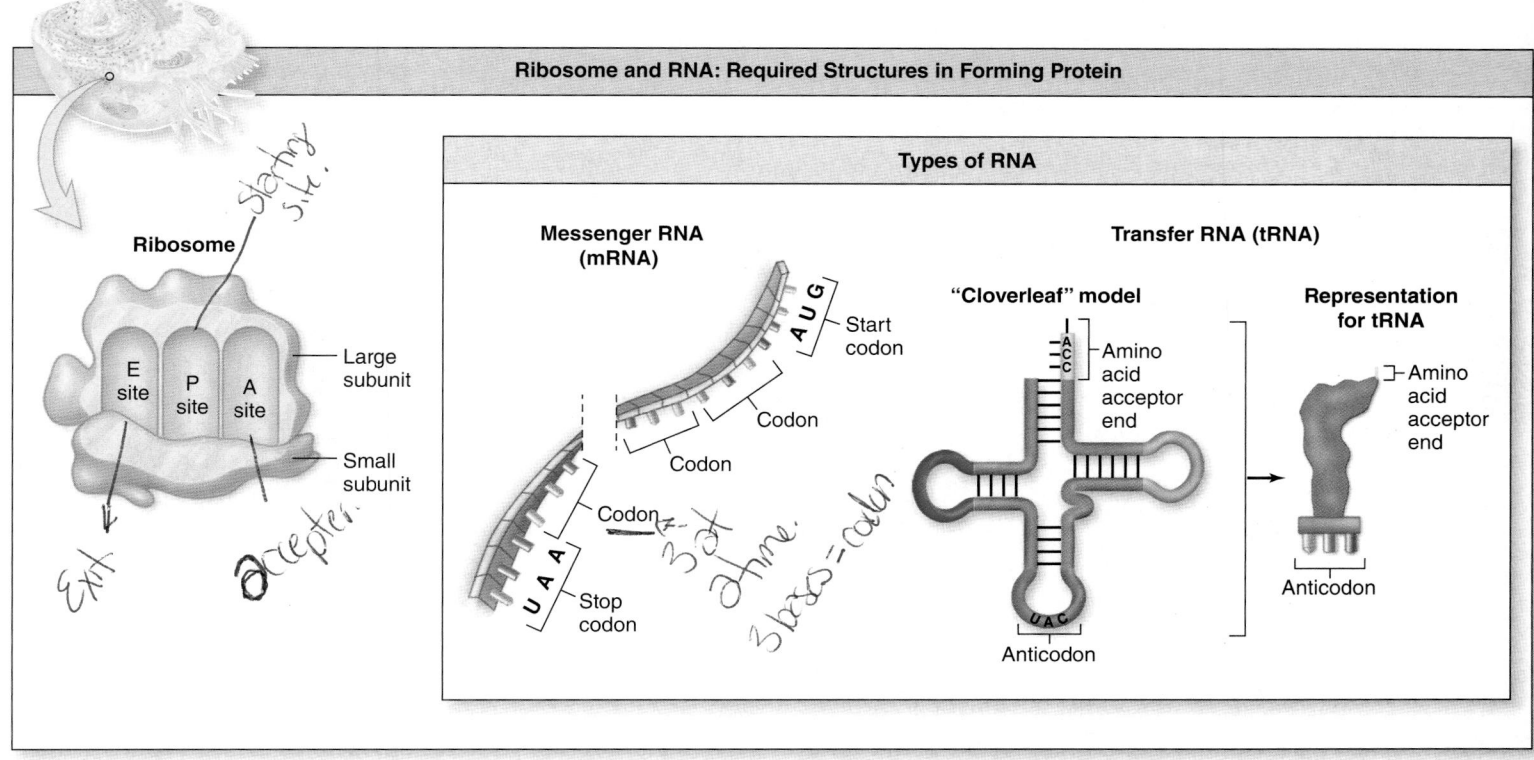

Ribosome and RNA: Required Structures in Forming Protein

Ribosome

- E site
- P site
- A site
- Large subunit
- Small subunit

Starting site.
Exit
acceptor

Types of RNA

Messenger RNA (mRNA)

A U G — Start codon
Codon
Codon
Codon
U A A — Stop codon

3 at a time.
3 bases = codon

Transfer RNA (tRNA)

"Cloverleaf" model

A C C — Amino acid acceptor end
U A C — Anticodon

Representation for tRNA

- Amino acid acceptor end
- Anticodon

(a)

Amino acids and Proteins: "Building Blocks" and "Finished Product"

Amino acid

- Amine
- Carboxylic acid

H—N—C—C—OH
         ‖
         O
R

Representation for amino acid

A strand of amino acids

Protein

(b)

Figure 4.33 Required Structures for Translation. The process of translation uses the information in the mRNA to direct protein synthesis. (*a*) Translation occurs at ribosomes and requires both messenger RNA and transfer RNA. (*b*) Amino acids are the building blocks used to produce the newly formed protein molecule.

own specific aminoacyl-tRNA synthetase. The tRNA is now called a *charged* tRNA after the binding of the amino acid has occurred.

Finally, individual amino acids are the building blocks for synthesizing the new protein. Recall that there are 20 different amino acids normally found in the proteins of living organisms (see figure 2.26). We discussed in chapter 2 that the properties of the R groups form the basis for organizing and grouping amino acids. Thus, to synthesize a new protein, which may contain hundreds to thousands of individual amino acids, the necessary amounts of the 20 different amino acids must be available in the cytosol in proximity to ribosomes.

Figure 4.34 Process of Translation. Protein is synthesized at ribosomes by translation of the mRNA. It is directed by mRNA and facilitated by tRNA. The three major events include initiation, elongation, and termination. **AP|R**

Process of Translation

Translation of the mRNA recipe into a functional protein also involves three major events, similar to those of transcription: *initiation, elongation,* and *termination* (**figure 4.34**).

Initiation A complex composed of a small subunit of a ribosome, a large subunit of a ribosome, the newly formed mRNA, and a tRNA is formed. The small subunit of a ribosome moves along the mRNA until it reaches the start codon (AUG). A charged tRNA that possesses the anticodon UAC then base-pairs to the start codon AUG in the mRNA. The amino acid methionine is bound to this tRNA. Methionine is always the first amino acid to be used in the synthesis of a protein, but later it may be removed as protein synthesis continues and the protein matures. The large subunit then joins with the small subunit of the ribosome. The start codon now occupies the P site of the ribosome.

Elongation Elongation involves the orderly delivery of all subsequent amino acids by specific tRNAs to form the protein, which thus elongates. A charged tRNA with a complementary anticodon base-pairs with the codon of the mRNA in the A site. A peptide bond is formed between the amino acid in the P site and the amino acid in the A site (as the bond of amino acid to tRNA in P site breaks). The ribosome then "shifts" (or moves) three nucleotide positions (the equivalent of a codon) "downstream" (beyond) the start codon on the mRNA. There is, of course, an accompanying change in position of the tRNAs. The tRNA that was in the A site is now in the P site, and the A site is again open. (The E site is the exit site from which the now-uncharged tRNA is released.) These processes repeat until the entire mRNA sequence has been translated. The product is a protein composed of a linear strand of amino acids.

Termination Translation is ended when a stop codon (UAA, UAG, or UGA) enters the A site. A release factor enters the A site at this point instead of a charged tRNA. When the ribosome hits the factor bound to the mRNA stop codon, the two subunits of the ribosome are separated from the mRNA and the newly synthesized protein is released.

Note that a single mRNA can be read by more than one ribosome simultaneously, and thus many copies of that protein can be made quickly. An mRNA with many ribosomes attached along its length is called a **polyribosome.**

WHAT DO YOU THINK?

3 What might be the potential consequences to protein structure and ability to function if DNA is mutated in a specific gene?

Figure 4.35 summarizes the process of transcription and translation. Transcription of DNA in the nucleus forms an RNA molecule from the template strand of DNA. Newly formed mRNA is then processed prior to exiting the nucleus through the nuclear pores. Translation of the mRNA into protein occurs at a ribosome located

INTEGRATE

CONCEPT CONNECTION

Chemical reactions are generally catalyzed by enzymes that are globular proteins (see section 3.3). Ribosomes are composed of both protein and rRNA. It is the rRNA of the ribosome—and not the protein—that catalyzes the synthesis of protein. For this reason, the rRNA of the ribosome is called a **ribozyme,** a catalytic RNA molecule. The protein of the ribosome in this case primarily serves a structural role to hold the rRNA molecules in the correct orientation.

A peptide bond is formed

Met — Glu

2b. Peptide bond is formed between the two amino acids.

Growing polypeptide strand

Met
Glu

Thr

U G U

2c. Ribosome shifts down one codon. Additional amino acids delivered by tRNA base-pair with mRNA until a stop codon is reached. (Steps a–c are repeated.)

Protein is released

Release factor

Stop codon (UAA, UAG, or UGA)

③ **Termination.** Release factor binds with stop codon of mRNA; newly formed protein strand is released.

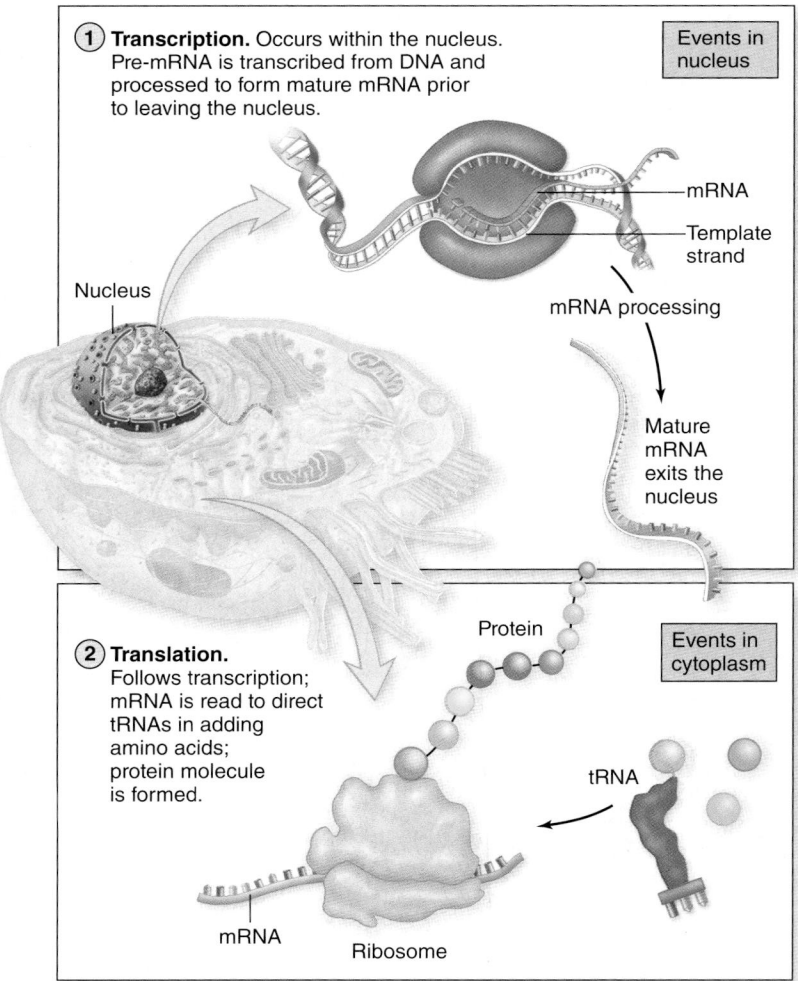

① **Transcription.** Occurs within the nucleus. Pre-mRNA is transcribed from DNA and processed to form mature mRNA prior to leaving the nucleus.

Events in nucleus

Nucleus

mRNA

Template strand

mRNA processing

Mature mRNA exits the nucleus

Protein

Events in cytoplasm

② **Translation.** Follows transcription; mRNA is read to direct tRNAs in adding amino acids; protein molecule is formed.

tRNA

mRNA

Ribosome

Figure 4.35 Steps Required for Protein Synthesis.

in the cytoplasm by bonding amino acids together, a process facilitated by numerous tRNAs.

WHAT DID YOU LEARN?

25 What is a codon and an anticodon?

26 How is mRNA attached to ribosomes and translated into the language of protein?

4.7c DNA as the Control Center of a Cell

LEARNING OBJECTIVE

6. Explain why DNA is considered the cell's control center.

Recall from chapter 2 that the human body is estimated to contain over 10,000 proteins. These proteins serve a vast array of different functions that include catalyzing reactions, defense, transport, support, movement, regulation, and storage. DNA is responsible for directing the synthesis of the proteins that carry out body functions.

Additionally, DNA is indirectly responsible for other metabolic changes that occur within a cell—including the synthesis of steroids and other lipids, and the enzymatic pathway of glucose oxidation—because DNA controls synthesis of the enzymes that are responsible for catalyzing both the decomposition and synthesis of chemical structures. All of these roles explain why DNA is considered a main component of the control center of the cell and sometimes is referred to as the "boss" of the cell.

WHAT DID YOU LEARN?

27 The genetic code of DNA is the specific instructions to make what biomolecule?

4.8 Cell Division

Cells divide in two ways, depending upon the cell type. **Mitosis** (mī-tō′sis; *mitos* = thread) is the cell division process that occurs in **somatic cells.** These are all of the cells in the body other than the sex cells that give rise to sperm or secondary oocytes. **Sex cells** undergo a cell division process called **meiosis.** This is discussed in detail in section 28.2. Here we define and describe somatic cell division.

Cell division occurs when one cell divides to produce two cells. It is essential to produce, replace, and maintain the trillions of cells that form a normally functioning human body. It is a necessary process for development, tissue growth, replacement of old or dying cells, and tissue repair required by loss of tissue from trauma or disease.

4.8a Cellular Structures

LEARNING OBJECTIVES

1. Explain the structure and function of centrioles in cell division.
2. Describe the structural difference between chromatin and chromosomes, and note when each is present in a cell.

Earlier we saw that a centrosome was a structure containing a pair of perpendicularly oriented cylindrical **centrioles** located in close proximity to the nucleus (see figure 4.27). The centrosome organizes the microtubules that facilitate movement of chromosomes during cell division.

The nucleus of human cells typically contains 46 separate DNA molecules, and we have learned that the genetic material is organized in a cell as either loosely coiled chromatin or tightly coiled chromosomes (see figure 4.31). Chromatin is the arrangement typically present in a cell because, in this loosely coiled form, DNA is able to direct the production of cellular proteins through the process of transcription. A **chromosome** (krō′mō-sōm; *chromo* = color, *soma* = body) is the most compact, organized level of genetic material. Chromosomes are present and visible in a cell only when it is dividing.

WHAT DID YOU LEARN?

28 How is chromatin distinguished from a chromosome?

4.8b The Cell Cycle

LEARNING OBJECTIVES

3. Summarize the phases of the cell cycle and the activities that occur in each phase.
4. Name and explain the four main stages of mitosis.
5. Explain the function of cytokinesis.

The **cell cycle** depicts the steps in the division of a somatic cell. It consists of all changes the cell undergoes in both structure and function between its formation and the time it divides into two identical cells called **daughter cells.** There are two major phases in the cell cycle: **interphase** and the **mitotic (M) phase**

Figure 4.36 The Cell Cycle. The cell cycle includes two basic phases: interphase and the mitotic (M) phase. Interphase is a growth period that is subdivided into G_1, S, and G_2. The mitotic phase includes mitosis, the process of nuclear division, and cytokinesis, the division of the cytoplasm. AP|R

(figure 4.36). The phases and events of the somatic cell cycle are described here and summarized in **table 4.3.**

Interphase

Most cells are in interphase during the greatest part of their lives. Interphase is the time between cell divisions during which the cell maintains itself and carries out normal metabolic activities. It is also the period of time the cell prepares for division (if it is going to divide). The DNA within the nucleus remains in the form of loosely coiled chromatin during interphase.

Interphase has three distinct phases: G_1, S, and G_2. The following activities occur in the G_1 **phase** (called the *first gap stage*) of the cell cycle: Cells grow and produce new organelles; however, they continue to carry out their specific metabolic activities. Structures needed for DNA replication are also formed during this phase including the duplication of the centrioles to produce two centriole pairs.

During the **S phase** (called *synthesis*) the 46 double helix strands of DNA (i.e., the 46 chromosomes) are replicated. They form duplicated chromosomes that appear as two identical **sister chromatids.** The two identical strands of each chromosome remain attached at the **centromere** (sen′trō-mēr; *kentron* = center, *meros* = part). Forming DNA requires large numbers of DNA building blocks called **deoxyribonucleotides** and the enzyme **DNA polymerase.** All of these components are located in the nucleoplasm within the nucleus.

The steps in DNA replication **(figure 4.37)** involve unwinding, breaking, assembly, and restoration.

① **Unwinding of DNA molecule.** The spiral, complementary DNA strands are unwound from each other by specific enzymes.

② **Breaking the parent strands apart.** The hydrogen bonds holding the complementary bases together in the DNA strands are broken. Once strands are separated, binding proteins (not shown) ensure that the strands remain separated.

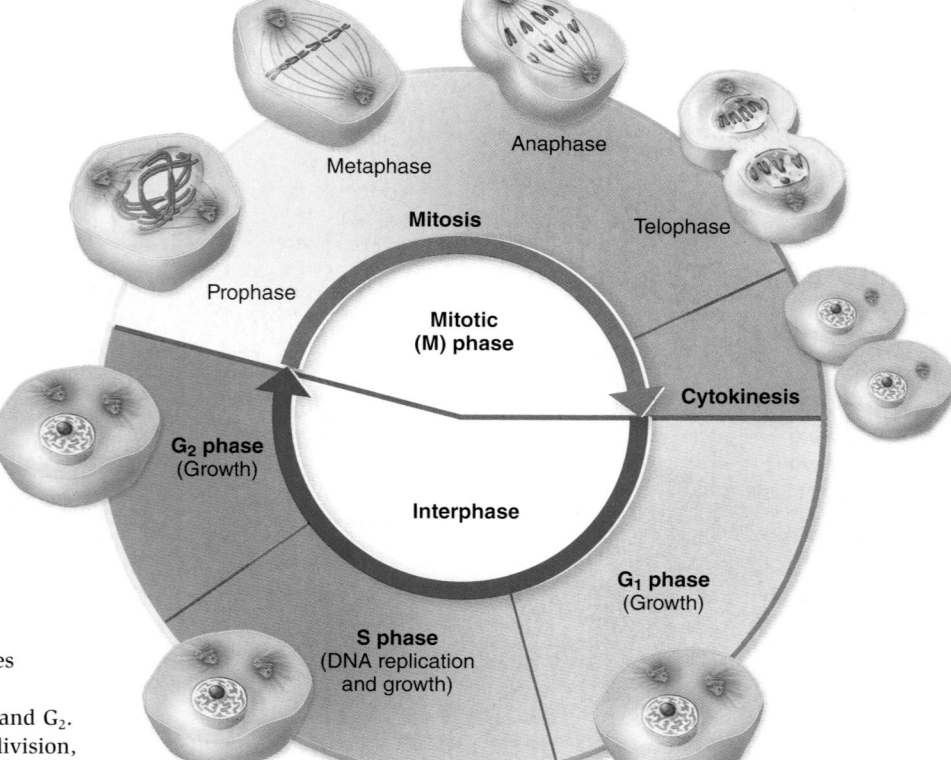

Metaphase · Anaphase · **Mitosis** · Telophase · Prophase · **Mitotic (M) phase** · Cytokinesis · G_2 phase (Growth) · Interphase · G_1 phase (Growth) · S phase (DNA replication and growth)

③ **Assembly of new DNA strands.** Both strands of DNA are read as templates by DNA polymerase enzymes that move along both parental strands and assemble new strands of DNA as complementary deoxyribonucleotides are paired. For example, if the base sequence of a small portion of a DNA strand is TTAGCTAGC, then the base sequence of the newly formed complementary DNA strand assembled by DNA polymerase would be AATCGATCG.

Complementary base pairs are held together by hydrogen bonds. The bond between nucleotides in the DNA polymer is a phosphodiester bond.

④ **Restoration of DNA double helix.** The DNA double strands are returned to their coiled, helix structure.

The process continues until the entire length of both strands of DNA are replicated.

Table 4.3	Somatic Cell Cycle Events
Phase	**Cellular Events**
INTERPHASE	A time of normal metabolic activities when the cell is not dividing; chromatin is not visible by light microscopy
G_1 phase	First gap phase: a growth phase during which protein synthesis and metabolic activity occur; new organelles are produced; centriole replication begins at end of this phase
S phase	Nuclear DNA is replicated
G_2 phase	Second gap phase: brief growth period for production of cell division enzymes; organelle replication continues; centriole replication finishes
MITOTIC (M) PHASE	Cell division produces two identical daughter cells from one mother cell
Mitosis	Division of the nucleus; continuous series of nuclear events that distribute two sets of chromosomes into two daughter nuclei; mitosis is divided into four phases—prophase, metaphase, anaphase, and telophase (see figure 4.38 for description of each phase of mitosis)
Cytokinesis	Usually begins before telophase ends; cleavage furrow formed from a contractile ring of microfilaments; cytoplasm divides, completing formation of two daughter cells

Figure 4.37 DNA Replication. The two helical strands of the double-stranded parent DNA molecule are separated and unwound to make both parental strands available as templates for construction of new DNA strands. AP|R

WHAT DO YOU THINK?

4 Describe the difference in DNA replication and transcription in terms of (a) the type of nucleic acid formed, and (b) the amount of DNA copied.

The last part of interphase, called the **G₂ phase** (or the *second gap phase*), is brief (see figure 4.36). During this phase, centriole replication is completed, organelle production continues, and enzymes needed for cell division are synthesized.

M Phase (Mitotic Phase)

Following interphase, cells enter the M (mitotic) phase. Two distinct events occur in this phase to produce two new cells: Mitosis, or division of the nucleus, begins first, with later processes overlapped by cytokinesis, which is the division of the cytoplasm. Four consecutive phases take place during mitosis: prophase, metaphase, anaphase, and telophase, which can be remembered with the acronym P-MAT. Each phase merges smoothly into the next in a nonstop process. The events of each stage are summarized in **figure 4.38**.

Prophase is the first stage of mitosis. Chromatin becomes supercoiled into the chromosomes that are more maneuverable and are less likely to become tangled during cell division. The DNA and protein within the chromatin coil, wrap, and twist, forming the chromosomes. Chromosomes are composed of the two sister chromatids that resemble relatively short, thick rods, and become noticeable with a light microscope during the prophase stage as dark-staining structures within the nucleus.

Figure 4.38 Interphase, Mitosis, and Cytokinesis. Drawings and micrographs depict what happens inside a cell during the stages of (*a*) interphase and (*b–e*) mitotic cell division. Cytokinesis overlaps with mitosis and generally begins during anaphase.

Interphase and Mitosis

(a) Interphase
Synthesis of cellular components needed for cell division, including synthesis of DNA.

(b) Prophase
Chromosomes appear due to coiling of chromatin.
Nucleolus breaks down.
Spindle fibers begin to form from centrioles.
Centrioles move toward opposing cell poles.
Nuclear envelope breaks down at the end of this stage.

The following events occur in addition to the supercoiling of chromatin into chromosomes. The nucleolus breaks down and disappears. Elongated microtubules called *spindle fibers* begin to grow from the centrioles. The two centriole pairs are pushed apart by the elongating microtubules; eventually, the centriole pairs come to lie at opposite poles (ends) of the cell. The end of prophase is marked by the dissolution of the nuclear envelope. This permits the chromosomes to move freely into and through the cytoplasm.

Metaphase is the second stage of mitosis, during which the chromosomes are aligned along the equatorial plate of the cell. This alignment occurs through the growth of spindle fibers from each centriole toward the chromosomes and some fibers attach to the centromere of each chromosome. The collection of spindle fibers extending from the centrioles to the chromosomes form an oval-structured array termed the *mitotic spindle*. This arrangement remains in place until the next phase begins.

Anaphase initiates as the spindle fibers cause the sister chromatids to be moved apart toward the cell's poles; its centromere leads the way, and its "arms" trail behind. Each chromatid is now a chromosome composed of one DNA double helix with its own centromere.

Telophase begins with the arrival of a group of new chromosomes at each cell pole. Essentially, the processes of prophase are reversed in telophase. The chromosomes begin to uncoil and return to the form of dispersed threads of chromatin, each new nucleus forms a nucleolus, the mitotic spindle breaks up and disappears, and a new nuclear envelope forms around each set of chromosomes. Telophase signals the end of nuclear division.

(c) Metaphase

Spindle fibers attach to the centromeres of the chromosomes extending from the centrioles.

Chromosomes are aligned at the equatorial plate of the cell by spindle fibers.

(d) Anaphase

Centromeres that held chromatid pairs together separate; each sister chromatid is now a chromosome with its own centromere.

Sister chromatids are separated and moved toward opposite ends of the cell.

Cytokinesis begins.

(e) Telophase

Chromosomes uncoil to form chromatin.

A nucleolus reforms within each nucleus.

Spindle fibers break up and disappear.

New nuclear envelope forms around each set of chromosomes.

Cytokinesis continues as cleavage furrow deepens.

INTEGRATE

CLINICAL VIEW
Tumors

Normally, many regulatory mechanisms signal a cell when it should divide and when to stop dividing. Tumors arise when cells either proceed through the cell cycle without a start signal or fail to respond to signals that normally stop cell division. The tumor may, due to its size, interfere with the function of the normal surrounding cells. A cancerous tumor is invasive, and cells may enter the blood or lymph and metastasize to other areas of the body and establish secondary tumors.

Cytokinesis **Cytokinesis** (sī′tō-ki-nē′sis; *kytos* = cell, *kinesis* = movement) is the other major event in the mitotic phase, and it is the division of the cytoplasm between the two newly forming cells. This phase may begin early and overlap with anaphase and telophase of mitosis. A contractile ring of microfilament proteins at the periphery of the cell equator pinches the mother cell into two separate cells in a manner analogous to the tightening of a belt. The resulting **cleavage furrow** that appears indicates where the cytoplasm is dividing. The two new daughter cells then enter the interphase of their life cycle.

WHAT DID YOU LEARN?

29 Describe the process of DNA replication that occurs during the S phase of interphase.

30 What are the events that occur during the mitotic phase (mitosis and cytokinesis)? Explain each.

4.9 Cell Aging and Death

LEARNING OBJECTIVES

1. Define apoptosis.
2. List the actions that occur in a cell during apoptosis.

Aging is a normal, continuous process that often exhibits obvious body signs. In contrast, changes within cells at the molecular level due to aging are neither obvious nor well understood. The reduced metabolic functions of normal cells often have wide-ranging effects throughout the body, including a reduced ability of cells to maintain homeostasis. These signs of aging reflect a lower number of normally functioning body cells, and may even suggest abnormal functions of some remaining cells.

Cells affected by aging may exhibit alteration in either the structure or number of specific organelles. For example, if mitochondrial function begins to fail, the cell's ability to synthesize ATP dimin-

ishes. Additionally, changes in the distribution and structure of the chromatin and chromosomes within the nucleus may occur. Often, both chromatin and chromosomes clump, shrink, or fragment as a result of repeated divisions.

Essentially, cells die by one of two mechanisms: (1) They are killed by harmful agents or mechanical damage; or (2) they are induced to commit suicide, a process of programmed cell death called **apoptosis** (ap′op-tō′sis; *apo* = off, *ptosis* = a falling).

Apoptosis occurs in orderly, well-defined continuous degradative steps to destroy and remove cellular components and eventually cell remnants. This biochemical mechanism is initiated by ligand-receptor signaling. Upon binding of ligand to a receptor, inactive, self-destructive enzymes within the cytoplasm are turned on and initiate the following actions:

- Nuclear changes (chromatin degradation)
- Destruction of DNA polymerase to prevent the synthesis of new DNA
- Digestion of the DNA into small fragments
- Shrinkage in volume
- Digestion of the cytoskeleton, thus destroying structural support for organelles and the nucleus—the cell appears to shrink and become rounded and the nuclear shape changes
- Abnormal development in both organelle and plasma membrane structure
- Condensation of the cytoplasm and destruction of organelles—specifically, the mitochondria to deprive the cell of ATP needed for work
- Initiation of other cell membrane signals to stimulate destruction of the cell externally by phagocytic cells
- Formation of small irregular blebs (bubbles) on the cell membrane surface.

Programmed cell death occurs both to promote proper development and to remove harmful cells. For example, the proper development of fingers and toes begins with the formation of a paddlelike structure at the distal end of the developing limb. Programmed cell death removes the cells and tissues between the fingers and toes developing within this paddle structure.

Programmed cell death sometimes destroys harmful cells, reducing potential health threats. Cells of our immune system promote programmed cell death in some virus-infected cells to reduce the further spread of infection. Cells that have damage to their DNA often appear to promote events leading to apoptosis, presumably to prevent these cells from causing developmental defects or becoming cancerous. Some cancer therapy treatments lead to apoptosis in certain types of cancer cells.

WHAT DID YOU LEARN?

31 What are the specific changes that occur to DNA during apoptosis?

4.1 Introduction to Cells   103

- Cells are the structural and functional units of the body.
- Cells vary in size and shape, but have certain common features and functions.

4.1a How Cells Are Studied   103

- Cells are microscopic and can be studied using a light microscope (LM), transmission electron microscope (TEM), and scanning electron microscope (SEM).

4.1b Cell Size and Shape   104

- Although some cells are round or cubelike, other cells are flat, cylindrical, oval, or quite irregular in shape.

4.1c Common Features and General Functions   105

- The three major structural components of a cell include the nucleus, plasma membrane, and cytoplasm (composed of cytosol, organelles, and perhaps cell inclusions).
- All cells must maintain their integrity and shape, obtain nutrients and chemical building blocks, dispose of wastes, and if possible, replace cells.

4.2 Chemical Structure of the Plasma Membrane   106

- The plasma membrane is a fluid matrix that has approximately an equal mixture of lipids and proteins by weight.

4.2a Lipid Components   106

- The plasma membrane is composed of a bilayer of phospholipids with embedded cholesterol molecules. Glycolipids are lipids with carbohydrates extending from the outer surface of the cell.

4.2b Membrane Proteins   108

- Plasma membrane proteins are integral proteins that extend through the plasma membrane, whereas peripheral proteins reside on either the internal or external surface of the plasma membrane.
- Functionally, the plasma membrane proteins include several types of transport proteins, receptors, identity markers, enzymes, attachment sites for the cytoskeleton, and cell-adhesion proteins.

4.3 Membrane Transport   108

- Substances are moved into and out of cells by processes of membrane transport, and are organized into passive processes and active processes. Active processes require cellular energy and passive processes do not.

4.3a Passive Processes: Diffusion   109

- Diffusion is the movement of a solute from an area where it is more concentrated to an area where it is less concentrated.
- The rate of diffusion is dependent upon the steepness of the concentration gradient and temperature.
- Simple diffusion is the unassisted movement of small nonpolar molecules through the phospholipid bilayer.
- Channel-mediated facilitated diffusion is the transport of ions through channels that are either always open (leak channels), or they open and close as a result of a stimulus (gated channels).
- Carrier-mediated facilitated diffusion is the transport of small polar molecules through a carrier that is induced to change shape to move the molecules across the plasma membrane.

4.3b Passive Processes: Osmosis   110

- Osmosis is the passive movement of water across a semipermeable membrane down a water concentration gradient.
- Osmotic pressure is the pressure exerted by the movement of water across a selectively permeable membrane due to a difference in solution concentration; the greater the difference, the greater the osmotic pressure.
- Isotonic, hypotonic, or hypertonic describe the relative concentration of solutions.

4.3c Active Processes   113

- Active processes require the expenditure of cellular energy and include both active transport and vesicular transport.
- The two types of active transport are primary active transport, which obtains its energy directly from ATP; and secondary active transport, which is "powered" by the movement of a second substance (usually sodium ion) down its gradient.
- A symporter moves the two substances in the same direction, while an antiporter moves the two substances in opposite directions during secondary active transport.
- Vesicular transport occurs through energy-requiring processes that involve a vesicle for transporting large materials or relatively large amounts of a substance across the plasma membrane.
- Exocytosis moves material out of a cell, and endocytosis moves substances into a cell.
- The three types of endocytosis are phagocytosis, pinocytosis, and receptor-mediated endocytosis.

4.4 Cell Communication   120

- Cell communication occurs either through direct contact or through binding of chemicals released from other cells.

4.4a Direct Contact Between Cells 120

- Direct contact is used as a means of cell communication by the cells of the immune system in protecting the body from potentially harmful substances. It is also used during development and cellular repair.

(continued on next page)

4.4 Cell Communication 120 *(continued)*	**4.4b Ligand-Receptor Signaling 121** • Three general types of receptors are distinguished by their different response to the binding of a ligand: they include channel-linked receptors, enzymatic receptors, and G protein–coupled receptors.
4.5 Cellular Structures 122	• Structures to be examined are membrane-bound and non-membrane-bound organelles, vesicles, and structures extending from the cell surface. **4.5a Membrane-Bound Organelles 122** • Membrane-bound organelles are surrounded by a membrane that separates the organelle's contents from the cytosol so that the specific activities of the organelle can proceed without being disrupted by other cellular activities. • The membrane-bound organelles include the endoplasmic reticulum, the Golgi apparatus, lysosomes, peroxisomes, and mitochondria. They are involved in various forms of metabolic processes, including synthesis and degradation processes that occur within a cell. **4.5b Non-Membrane-Bound Organelles 127** • Non-membrane-bound organelles are composed of either protein alone or protein and RNA; they include ribosomes, the cytoskeleton, centrosomes with centrioles, and proteasomes. **4.5c Structures of the Cell's External Surface 129** • Cilia are numerous hairlike structures for sweeping materials along the cell's outer surface; a flagellum, located only on sperm, moves the sperm through the female reproductive tract. • Microvilli are extensions of the plasma membrane that increase its surface area for more efficient membrane transport. **4.5d Membrane Junctions 130** • Tight junctions between adjacent cells prevent dissolved substances from passing through the interstitial space, forcing them to move through the cells' cytoplasm. • Desmosomes hold adjacent cells together at a single region and resist mechanical stress; each cell contributes half of the desmosome structure. • Gap junctions link adjacent cells via a group of six connexon proteins that form pores between the cells; they serve as a passageway for flow of substances.
4.6 Structure of the Nucleus 131	• The nucleus is a large, typically spherical structure within a cell. **4.6a Nuclear Envelope and Nucleolus 132** • The nuclear envelope is a double phospholipid bilayer that serves as the boundary between nucleoplasm and the cytoplasm. • A cell typically contains one nucleolus within its nucleus. It is a structure responsible for synthesizing the large and small subunits of ribosomes. **4.6b DNA, Chromatin, and Chromosomes 132** • DNA is wrapped around histone proteins and packaged as chromatin. • Chromatin is supercoiled into chromosomes only when a cell is proceeding through nuclear division (mitosis or meiosis). • DNA contains functional units called genes; a gene is a segment of DNA that carries instructions for making a protein, and it is transcribed into RNA for synthesizing a specific protein.
4.7 Function of the Nucleus and Ribosomes 133	• The nucleus and ribosomes are required to synthesize proteins, a process that involves transcription and translation. **4.7a Transcription: Synthesizing RNA 133** • RNA is formed from DNA through transcription, a process that occurs in the nucleus and requires DNA, free ribonucleotides, and the enzyme RNA polymerase. **4.7b Translation: Synthesizing Protein 136** • Translation occurs in the cytoplasm and requires ribosomes (composed of protein and rRNA), messenger (mRNA), transfer RNA (tRNA), and large numbers of free amino acids. **4.7c DNA as the Control Center of a Cell 139** • DNA is responsible for directing the synthesis of proteins.
4.8 Cell Division 140	• Mitosis is one of two types of cell division that occurs in cells. • Cell division involving mitosis produces two identical cells when one divides, and is a necessary process for development, tissue growth, replacement of old or dying cells, and tissue repair. **4.8a Cellular Structures 140** • The major structures required in cell replication are chromatin (chromosomes), centrioles, free deoxyribonucleotides, and the enzyme DNA polymerase. **4.8b The Cell Cycle 140** • The cell cycle consists of a series of changes the cell undergoes between its formation and the time it divides into two identical cells, called daughter cells. It is divided into two major phases: interphase and mitosis.
4.9 Cell Aging and Death 144	• Cellular changes associated with aging are neither obvious nor well understood. • Cell death occurs by harmful agents or mechanical damage, or through induction that leads to suicide, a process called apoptosis.

CHALLENGE YOURSELF

Do You Know the Basics?

_____ 1. All of the following general functions are carried out by all cells *except*

    a. obtaining nutrients and chemical building blocks.

    b. maintaining integrity of the plasma membrane.

    c. replacing cells through cell replication.

    d. disposing of wastes.

_____ 2. The molecule that is responsible for most functions of the plasma membrane is

    a. the phospholipid bilayer.

    b. cholesterol.

    c. glycolipid.

    d. protein.

_____ 3. All of the following are active processes, requiring cellular energy *except*

    a. primary active transport.

    b. carrier-mediated facilitated diffusion.

    c. endocytosis.

    d. exocytosis.

_____ 4. One substance flows down its concentration gradient, and the energy is harnessed to move another substance up its gradient in the same direction. This best describes

    a. primary active transport.

    b. endocytosis.

    c. symport secondary active transport.

    d. antiport secondary active transport.

_____ 5. All of the following are membrane-bound organelles *except*

    a. ribosomes.

    b. lysosomes.

    c. the Golgi apparatus.

    d. the endoplasmic reticulum.

_____ 6. This organelle is composed of extensive amounts of membrane. It synthesizes lipids, stores and transports proteins, and detoxifies harmful substances such as alcohol. This organelle is

    a. the smooth endoplasmic reticulum.

    b. a mitochondrion.

    c. a proteasome.

    d. a lysosome.

_____ 7. Which of the following organelles destroys malformed proteins, proteins that do not fold normally, and proteins that are no longer needed by a cell?

    a. centrioles

    b. peroxisomes

    c. proteasomes

    d. nucleolus

_____ 8. The process of forming RNA from DNA is called

    a. mitosis.

    b. DNA replication.

    c. translation.

    d. transcription.

_____ 9. During this stage of mitosis, the chromatin coils to form chromosomes, the nuclear membrane disappears, the nucleolus dissolves, spindle fibers are formed, and the centrioles migrate to the poles.

    a. prophase

    b. metaphase

    c. anaphase

    d. telophase

_____ 10. Erythrocytes do not have a nucleus. In what two cellular processes can they *not* engage?

    a. apoptosis and synthesis of lipid

    b. protein synthesis and cell division

    c. digestion of unwanted protein and cell division

    d. formation of vesicles and protein synthesis

11. Describe the general structure and function of the three major structures of a cell.

12. List and describe the functions of plasma membrane proteins.

13. Describe the passive processes of membrane transport including simple diffusion, facilitated diffusion, and osmosis.

14. Describe the active processes of membrane transport including primary active transport, secondary active transport, and the various forms of vesicular transport.

15. List the membrane-bound structures, and describe the structure and function of each.

16. Describe the three types of proteins that form the cytoskeleton, and explain the general function of each.

17. Compare and contrast the structure and function of cilia and microvilli.

18. Describe the processes of transcription and translation.

19. Explain how DNA either directly or indirectly controls the processes of a cell.

20. Explain the processes that occur in the different stages of the cell cycle, including DNA replication, mitosis, and cytokinesis.

Can You Apply What You've Learned?

1. Michael was born with Tay-Sachs disease. Which of the following organelles in Michael's cells lacks a specific enzyme that digests organic molecules?

    a. mitochondria

    b. lysosomes

    c. the Golgi apparatus

    d. centrioles

2. A young man in his 20s has a heart attack and is rushed to the hospital. Blood is drawn, and his cholesterol level is tested and found to be very high. The doctor tells him that he has a genetic condition in which he is unable to effectively remove LDL particles containing cholesterol from his blood and into his cells. Which cellular process is not functioning normally?

   a. channel-mediated facilitated diffusion
   b. receptor-mediated endocytosis
   c. exocytosis
   d. simple diffusion

3. Tumors involve a malfunction in this cellular process.

   a. transcription
   b. translation
   c. apoptosis
   d. mitosis

4. A rare genetic disease involves the inability of the cells to respond to testosterone. The cells are lacking

   a. enzymes for testosterone.
   b. protein carriers for testosterone.
   c. receptors for testosterone.
   d. all plasma membrane proteins.

5. The hormone insulin is a protein composed of repeating units of amino acids. It is produced through the process(es) of

   a. transcription and translation.
   b. DNA replication.
   c. mitosis.
   d. differentiation.

Can You Synthesize What You've Learned?

1. The liver produces a protein called albumin. The major function of albumin is to exert osmotic pressure to pull fluid back into the blood. Predict what happens to osmotic pressure in a patient who has cirrhosis of the liver and is not producing adequate levels of albumin.

2. In a patient with pneumonia (a respiratory condition that results in lower levels of oxygen in the blood), will diffusion of oxygen increase, decrease, or stay the same in comparison to normal? Explain.

3. Explain to a young man, with reduced numbers of receptors for LDL, why his cholesterol level is elevated.

chapter 5
Tissue Organization

The trillions of cells in the human body are organized into more complex units called tissues. **Tissues** are groups of similar cells and extracellular material that perform a common function, such as providing protection or facilitating body movement. The study of tissues is called **histology** (his-tol′ō-jē; *histos* = web). Tissues in the body are classified into four types: epithelial tissue, connective tissue, muscle tissue, and nervous tissue. These four tissue types vary in the structure of their cells, the ➡

The microscopic anatomy of cells and tissues is studied by a histologist. The histologist uses various microscopy techniques such as light microscopy (LM) and electron microscopy (EM). In the hospital setting, a histologist may prepare frozen tissue sections taken from patient biopsies for rapid analysis by a pathologist. A thorough understanding of the characteristics of the four basic tissue types is essential for this health care professional. Having an in-depth knowledge base of normal tissue structure ensures the histologist also can recognize possible tissue abnormalities, and thus possible evidence of disease or infection.

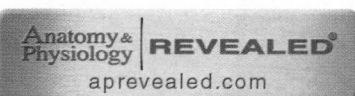

Module 3: Tissues

functions of these cells, and the composition of an extracellular matrix (mā′triks; *matrix* = womb). The extracellular matrix is produced by the cells and surrounds them. It is composed of varying amounts of water, protein fibers, and dissolved molecules (e.g., glucose, oxygen). Its consistency ranges from fluid to semisolid to solid. Epithelial, muscle, and nervous tissue typically have relatively little extracellular matrix between their cells. In contrast, connective tissue types contain varying amounts of extracellular matrix that differ in ratio of matrix components and consistency (fluid to solid) of the matrix.

5.1 Epithelial Tissue: Surfaces, Linings, and Secretory Functions

Epithelial (ep-i-thē′lē-ăl; *epi* = upon, *thelium* = nipple) **tissue** covers the body surfaces, lines the body cavities, and forms the majority of glands. An **epithelium** (pl., epithelia) is composed of one or more layers of closely packed cells, and it contains little to no extracellular matrix between these cells. Additionally, no blood vessels penetrate an epithelium.

5.1a Characteristics of Epithelial Tissue

LEARNING OBJECTIVE

1. Describe the common features of epithelial tissue.

All epithelia exhibit the following common characteristics, some of which are shown in **figure 5.1**:

- **Cellularity.** Epithelial tissue is composed almost entirely of tightly packed cells. A minimal amount of extracellular matrix separates the cells in an epithelium.

Apical surface — Epithelium

Lateral surface — Basement membrane

Basal surface

Connective tissue

Figure 5.1 Characteristics of Epithelia. An epithelium exhibits polarity, is composed mostly of cells, and the lateral surfaces of cells are connected by intercellular junctions (see figure 4.30). Epithelium attaches to underlying tissue via a basement membrane. AP|R

- **Polarity.** An epithelium has an **apical** (āp′i-kăl) **surface** (free, or superficial, surface), which is exposed either to the external environment or to some internal body space. The apical surface may have either microvilli or cilia. Recall from section 4.5c that microvilli are tiny projections on the apical surface of the cell that increase the surface area for secretion and absorption, whereas cilia are numerous, short, membrane-attached projections that move fluid, mucus, and materials over the cell surface. The lateral surfaces contain intercellular junctions. Additionally, each epithelium has a **basal** (bā′săl) **surface** (a fixed or deep surface), where the epithelium is attached to the underlying connective tissue.

- **Attachment to a basement membrane.** The epithelial layer is bound to a thin **basement membrane** at its basal surface. This is a complex structure produced by the collective efforts of the epithelium and underlying connective tissue. The basement membrane may be observed as a single layer internal to the epithelium using the light microscope—however, in reality it consists of three layers when viewed using an electron microscope: the *lamina lucida*, the *lamina densa*, and the *reticular lamina*. The two lamina closest to the epithelium contain collagen fibers as well as specific proteins and carbohydrates, some of which are secreted by the epithelial cells. Cells in the underlying connective tissue secrete the reticular lamina, which contains protein fibers and carbohydrates. Together, these basement membrane components strengthen the attachment and form a selective molecular barrier between the epithelium and the underlying connective tissue.

- **Avascularity.** All epithelial tissues lack blood vessels. Nutrients for epithelial cells are obtained either directly across the apical surface or by diffusion across the basal surface from the underlying connective tissue.

- **Extensive innervation.** Epithelia are richly innervated to detect changes in the environment at that body or organ region.

- **High regeneration capacity.** Because epithelial cells have an apical surface that is exposed to the environment, they are frequently damaged or lost by abrasion. However, both damaged and lost epithelial cells generally are replaced quickly because epithelia have a high regeneration capacity. In other words, the cells undergo mitosis frequently. The continual replacement occurs through the mitotic divisions of the deepest epithelial cells (called stem cells), which are adjacent to the basement membrane.

WHAT DID YOU LEARN?

1. Why does an epithelium need to be highly regenerative?

5.1b Functions of Epithelial Tissue

✅ LEARNING OBJECTIVE

2. Explain the four functions that may be served by epithelial tissues.

Epithelia have several functions, although no one epithelium performs all of them. These functions include the following:

- **Physical protection.** Epithelial tissues protect both external and internal surfaces from dehydration, abrasion, and destruction by physical, chemical, or biological agents.
- **Selective permeability.** All substances that enter or leave the body must pass through an epithelium, and thus epithelial cells act as "gatekeepers." An epithelium typically exhibits a range of permeability; it may be relatively impermeable to some substances, while promoting and assisting the passage of other molecules.
- **Secretions.** Some epithelial cells are specialized to produce secretions. Individual gland cells may be scattered among other cell types in an epithelium, or a large group of gland cells may form either an exocrine gland or an endocrine gland that produces specific secretions.
- **Sensations.** Epithelial tissues contain nerve endings to detect changes in the external environment at their surface. These sensory nerve endings—and those in the underlying connective tissue—continuously supply information to the nervous system concerning touch, pressure, temperature, and pain. Additionally, several organs contain a specialized epithelium, called a *neuroepithelium,* that houses specific cells responsible for the senses of sight, taste, smell, hearing, and equilibrium.

🤔 WHAT DO YOU THINK?

1. Why do you think epithelial tissue does not contain any blood vessels? Can you think of any epithelial function that could be compromised if blood vessels were running through the tissue?

💡 WHAT DID YOU LEARN?

2. Why does an epithelium need to be considered selectively permeable?

INTEGRATE
LEARNING STRATEGY ✍

To distinguish cilia from microvilli on an epithelium, recall that cilia appear under the light microscope like individual fine hairs extending from the apical surface of the epithelium, whereas microvilli appear collectively as a fuzzy, bright brush border at the apical surface of the epithelium.

5.1c Classification of Epithelial Tissue

✅ LEARNING OBJECTIVES

3. Name the classes of epithelia based on cell layers and cell shapes.
4. Give examples of each type of epithelium.

The body contains many different types of epithelia, and the classification of each type is indicated by a two-part name. The first part of the name refers to the *number* of epithelial cell layers, and the second part describes the *shape* of cells at the apical (superficial) surface of the epithelium.

Classification by Number of Cell Layers

Epithelia may be classified as either simple or stratified (**figure 5.2a**). A **simple epithelium** is one cell layer thick, and all of the epithelial cells are in direct contact with the basement membrane. A simple epithelium is found in areas where stress is minimal and where filtration, absorption, or secretion is the primary function. Examples of locations include the lining of the air sacs of the lung, the intestines, and blood vessels.

A **stratified epithelium** contains two or more layers of epithelial cells. Only the cells in the deepest (basal) layer are in direct contact with the basement membrane. A stratified epithelium resembles a brick wall, where the bricks in contact with the ground represent the basal layer and the bricks at the top of the wall represent the apical (superficial) layer. A stratified epithelium is found in areas likely to be subjected to abrasive activities or mechanical stresses, as multiple layers of cells are better able to resist the wear and tear (e.g., the skin, internal lining of the esophagus, and the internal lining of parts

Apical surface —
Basal surface —
Basement membrane
Simple epithelium

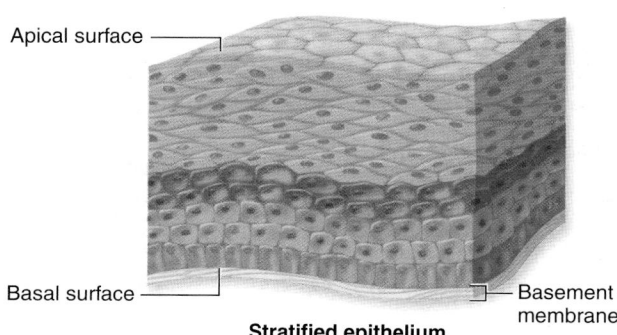

Apical surface —
Basal surface —
Basement membrane
Stratified epithelium

(a) Layer classifications

Nucleus — Basement membrane
Squamous cell

Nucleus — Basement membrane
Cuboidal cell

Nucleus — Basement membrane
Columnar cell

(b) Shape classifications

Figure 5.2 Classification of Epithelia. Two criteria are used to classify epithelia: the number of cell layers and the shape of the cell at the apical surface. (*a*) An epithelium is simple if it is one cell layer thick, and stratified if it has two or more layers of cells. (*b*) Epithelial cell shapes include squamous (thin, flattened cells), cuboidal (cells about as tall as they are wide), and columnar (cells taller than they are wide).

of the pharynx). Cells in the basal layer continuously regenerate as the cells in the apical layer are lost due to abrasion or stress.

A **pseudostratified** (sū′dō-strat′i-fīd; *pseudo* = false, *stratum* = layer) **epithelium** looks layered (stratified) because the cells' nuclei are distributed at different levels between the apical and basal surfaces. Although all of these epithelial cells are attached to the basement membrane, some of them do not reach its apical surface. For our purposes, we have classified pseudostratified epithelium as a type of simple epithelium, because all of the cells are attached to the basement membrane.

Classification by Cell Shape

Epithelia are also classified by the shape of the cell at the apical surface. In a simple epithelium, all of the cells display the same shape. Note that in a stratified epithelium, a difference in shape can be seen between cells at the basal layer and those in the apical layer. Figure 5.2b shows the three common cell shapes observed in epithelia: squamous, cuboidal, and columnar. (Note that the cells in this figure all appear hexagonal when viewed from their apical surface. Thus, these terms describe the cells' shapes when viewed laterally, or from the side.)

Squamous (skwā′mŭs; *squamosus* = scaly) **cells** are flat, wide, and somewhat irregular in shape. The cells are arranged like flattened floor tiles, and the nucleus is somewhat flattened. **Cuboidal** (kū-boy′dăl) **cells** are about as tall as they are wide. The cells do not resemble perfect cubes because their edges are somewhat rounded. The cell nucleus is spherical and located within the center of the cell. **Columnar** (kol-ŭm′năr) **cells** are slender and taller than they are wide. The cell nucleus is oval and usually oriented lengthwise and in the basal region of the cell. Another shape that occurs in epithelial cells is called **transitional**. These cells can readily change their shape, depending upon how stretched the epithelium becomes. They occur where the epithelium cycles between distended and relaxed states, such as in the lining of the bladder, which fills with urine and is later emptied. When transitional epithelium is in a relaxed state, the cells are polyhedral in shape, whereas when this epithelium is stretched, the surface cells become more flattened.

Using the classification system just described, epithelium can be broken down into the primary types shown in **table 5.1**.

Simple Squamous Epithelium

A **simple squamous epithelium** is the thinnest possible barrier, because it consists of a single layer of flattened cells (**table 5.2a**). When viewed "en face" (looking onto the surface), the irregularly shaped cells display a spherical to oval nucleus, and the cells are tightly bound together. Each squamous cell resembles a fried egg, with the nucleus of the cell representing the yolk. This epithelium is extremely delicate and highly specialized to allow rapid movement of molecules across its surface by diffusion, osmosis, or filtration. Simple squamous epithelium forms the lining of the air sacs (alveoli) of the lung, where this thin epithelium is well suited for the exchange of oxygen and carbon dioxide between the blood and the inhaled air. Simple squamous epithelium also is found lining the lumen (inside space) of blood vessel walls, where it allows for rapid exchange of nutrients and waste between the blood and the interstitial fluid surrounding the blood vessels. The simple squamous epithelium that lines the blood vessel and lymph vessel walls is termed **endothelium** (en-dō-thē′lē-ŭm; *endon* = within).

Mesothelium (mez-ō-thē′lē-ŭm; *mesos* = middle) is the name given to the simple squamous epithelium that forms the serous membranes of body cavities. Mesothelium gets its name from the embryonic primary germ layer called mesoderm, from which it is derived (see section 5.6a).

Simple Cuboidal Epithelium

A **simple cuboidal epithelium** contains uniformly shaped cells, and it is ideal for building small ducts and glands. This epithelium consists of a single layer of cells that are about as tall as they are wide (**table 5.2b**). A spherical nucleus is located in the center of the cell. A simple cuboidal epithelium functions primarily to absorb fluids and other materials across its apical surface, and

Table 5.1	Types of Epithelia
Type	**Structure**
SIMPLE EPITHELIUM One cell layer thick; all cells are tightly bound together and attach directly to the basement membrane	
Simple squamous	One layer of flattened cells
Simple cuboidal	One layer of cells about as tall as they are wide
Simple columnar	One layer of cells that are taller than they are wide; nonciliated form may contain microvilli while ciliated form contains cilia
Pseudostratified columnar	One layer of cells of varying heights; all cells attach to basement membrane; ciliated form contains cilia and goblet cells; nonciliated form lacks cilia and goblet cells
STRATIFIED EPITHELIUM Two or more cell layers thick; only the deepest layer directly attaches to the basement membrane	
Stratified squamous, keratinized	Many layers thick; cells in surface layers are dead, flat, and filled with the protein keratin
Stratified squamous, nonkeratinized	Many layers thick; no keratin in cells; surface layers are flat and kept moist, alive
Stratified cuboidal	Two or more layers of cells; apical layer of cells is cuboidal-shaped
Stratified columnar	Two or more layers of cells; apical layer of cells is columnar-shaped
Transitional	Multiple layers of polyhedral cells (when tissue is relaxed), or flattened cells (when tissue is distended); some cells may be binucleated

Table 5.2 Simple Epithelia

(a) SIMPLE SQUAMOUS EPITHELIUM AP|R

Simple squamous epithelial cell
Basement membrane

Structure
Single layer of thin, flat cells resembling irregular floor tiles; the single nucleus of each cell bulges at its center

Function
Rapid diffusion, filtration, and some secretion in serous membranes

Location
Air sacs in lungs (alveoli); lining of lumen of lymph vessels and blood vessels (endothelium); serous membranes of body cavities (mesothelium)

LM 200x

(b) SIMPLE CUBOIDAL EPITHELIUM AP|R

Simple cuboidal cell
Lumen of kidney tubule
Nucleus
Basement membrane

Structure
Single layer of cells about as tall as they are wide; spherical and centrally located nucleus

Function
Absorption and secretion

Location
Kidney tubules; ducts and secretory regions of most glands; surface of ovary; thyroid gland follicles

LM 1000x

(c) NONCILIATED SIMPLE COLUMNAR EPITHELIUM AP|R

Nonciliated simple columnar cell
Goblet cell
Microvilli (brush border)
Nucleus
Basement membrane

Structure
Single layer of cells taller than they are wide; oval-shaped nucleus oriented lengthwise in basal region of cell; apical regions of cell may have microvilli; may contain goblet cells that secrete mucin

Function
Absorption and secretion; secretion of mucin

Location
Lining of most of digestive tract

LM 400x

(d) CILIATED SIMPLE COLUMNAR EPITHELIUM AP|R

Cilia
Ciliated simple columnar cell
Basement membrane

Structure
Single layer of ciliated cells taller than they are wide; oval-shaped nucleus oriented lengthwise in basal region of cell; may contain goblet cells

Function
Secretion of mucin and movement of mucus along apical surface of epithelium by cilia; oocyte movement through uterine tube

Location
Larger bronchioles of respiratory tract and lining of uterine tubes

LM 100x

to secrete specific molecules. It forms the walls of kidney tubules, where it participates in the reabsorption of nutrients, ions, and water that are filtered out of the blood. It also forms the secretory regions of most glands and smaller ducts of exocrine glands, which secrete materials. Simple cuboidal epithelium covers the surface of the ovary and also forms the follicles of the thyroid gland.

Simple Columnar Epithelium

A **simple columnar epithelium** is composed of a single layer of cells that are taller than they are wide. The nucleus is oval, oriented lengthwise, and located in the basal region of the cell. This type of epithelium is ideal for both secretory and absorptive functions. Simple columnar epithelium has two forms: One type has no cilia, whereas the apical surface of the other type is covered with cilia.

Nonciliated simple columnar epithelium often contains microvilli and a scattering of unicellular glands called goblet cells (table 5.2c). Individual microvilli cannot be distinguished under the microscope; rather, the microvilli collectively appear as a bright, fuzzy structure known as a brush border. Goblet cells secrete mucin (mū′sin), which is a glycoprotein that when hydrated (mixed with water) forms mucus. Nonciliated simple columnar epithelium lines most of the digestive tract, from the stomach to the anal canal.

Ciliated simple columnar epithelium has cilia that project from the apical surfaces of the cells (table 5.2d). Mucus covers these apical surfaces and is moved along by the beating of the cilia. Goblet cells typically are interspersed throughout this epithelium. Ciliated columnar epithelium is present in the bronchioles (smaller air passageways) in the lung. It also lines the luminal (internal) surface of the uterine tubes, where it helps move an oocyte from the ovary to the uterus.

Pseudostratified Columnar Epithelium

A pseudostratified columnar epithelium is so named because upon first glance, it *appears* to consist of multiple layers of cells. Note that this epithelium is not really stratified, because all of its cells are in direct contact with the basement membrane. It may look stratified because the nuclei are scattered at different distances from the basal surface, but not all of the cells reach the apical surface in this epithelium (table 5.3). The columnar cells within this epithelium always reach the apical surface, and the shorter cells are stem cells that give rise to the columnar cells. Pseudostratified columnar epithelium consists of two forms: pseudostratified ciliated columnar epithelium, which contains cilia on its apical surface, and pseudostratified nonciliated columnar epithelium, which lacks cilia. Both types perform protective functions. The ciliated form houses goblet cells—like goblet cells in simple columnar epithelium, these cells secrete mucin, which hydrates to become the mucus that traps foreign particles and is moved by the beating cilia. This type is found in the larger air passageways of the respiratory system (e.g., the nasal cavity, part of the pharynx [throat], larynx [voice box], trachea, and bronchi). The nonciliated form is rare, lacks goblet cells and cilia, and occurs primarily in part of the male urethra and epididymis.

Stratified Squamous Epithelium

A stratified squamous epithelium is designed to protect against abrasion and friction. This tissue has multiple cell layers, and only the deepest layer of cells is in direct contact with the basement membrane. The cells in the basal layers have a cuboidal or polyhedral shape, whereas the apical cells display a flattened, squamous shape. Thus, stratified squamous epithelium is so named because of its multiple cell layers and the shape of the apical cells. This epithelium is adapted to protect underlying tissues from damage due to activities that cause abrasion and friction. Stem cells in the basal layer continuously divide, to produce a new stem cell and a committed cell that is gradually displaced toward the surface to replace those cells that have been lost. This type of epithelium exists in two forms: nonkeratinized and keratinized.

The cells in nonkeratinized stratified squamous epithelium remain alive all the way to the tissue's apical surface, and they are kept moist with secretions such as saliva or mucus. These cells lack keratin (ker′ă-tin; *keras* = horn), the tough, protective protein that is abundant in the keratinized form of this epithelium (described next). Because all of the cells are still alive, the flattened nuclei characteristic of squamous cells are visible throughout the tissue (table 5.4a). Nonkeratinized stratified squamous epithelium lines the oral cavity (mouth), part of the pharynx (throat), the esophagus, the vagina, and the anus.

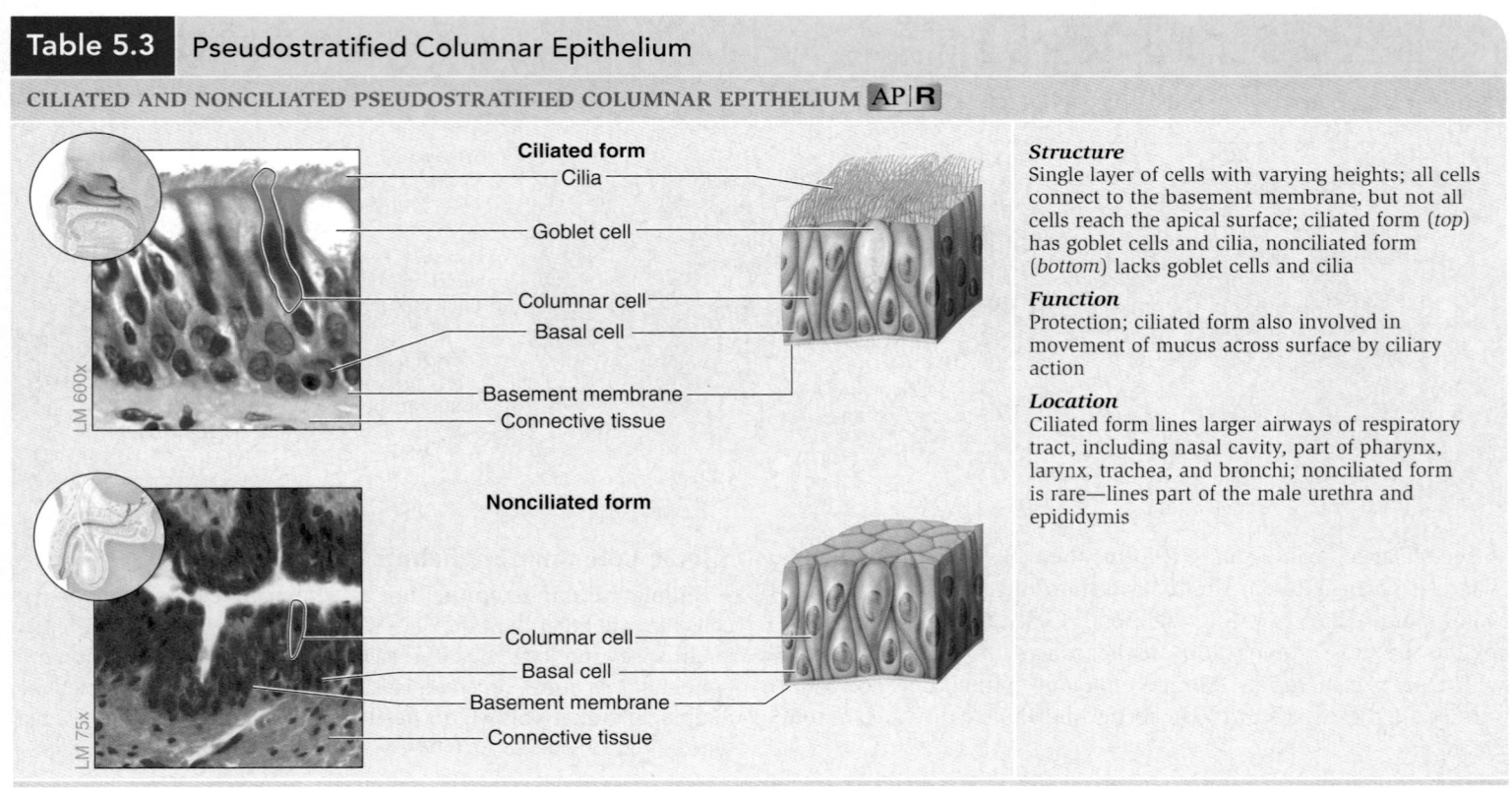

Table 5.3	Pseudostratified Columnar Epithelium

CILIATED AND NONCILIATED PSEUDOSTRATIFIED COLUMNAR EPITHELIUM AP|R

Ciliated form
- Cilia
- Goblet cell
- Columnar cell
- Basal cell
- Basement membrane
- Connective tissue

LM 600x

Nonciliated form
- Columnar cell
- Basal cell
- Basement membrane
- Connective tissue

LM 75x

Structure
Single layer of cells with varying heights; all cells connect to the basement membrane, but not all cells reach the apical surface; ciliated form (*top*) has goblet cells and cilia, nonciliated form (*bottom*) lacks goblet cells and cilia

Function
Protection; ciliated form also involved in movement of mucus across surface by ciliary action

Location
Ciliated form lines larger airways of respiratory tract, including nasal cavity, part of pharynx, larynx, trachea, and bronchi; nonciliated form is rare—lines part of the male urethra and epididymis

Table 5.4 Stratified Epithelia

(a) NONKERATINIZED STRATIFIED SQUAMOUS EPITHELIUM AP|R

- Squamous epithelial cell
- Basement membrane
- Connective tissue

LM 125x

Structure
Multiple cell layers; basal cells are cuboidal or polyhedral, while apical (superficial) cells are squamous; superficial cells are alive and kept moist

Function
Protection of underlying tissue

Location
Lining of oral cavity, part of pharynx, esophagus, lining of vagina, and anus

(b) KERATINIZED STRATIFIED SQUAMOUS EPITHELIUM AP|R

- Keratinized stratified squamous epithelial cells
- Living stratified squamous epithelial cells
- Basement membrane
- Connective tissue

LM 100x

Structure
Multiple cell layers; basal cells are cuboidal or polyhedral, whereas apical cells are squamous; apical cells are dead and filled with the protein keratin

Function
Protection of underlying tissue

Location
Epidermis of skin

(c) STRATIFIED CUBOIDAL EPITHELIUM AP|R

- Cuboidal cell
- Basement membrane
- Connective tissue

LM 100x

Structure
Two or more layers of cells; cells at the apical surface are about as tall as they are wide

Function
Protection and secretion

Location
Ducts of most exocrine glands and some regions of the male urethra

(d) STRATIFIED COLUMNAR EPITHELIUM AP|R

- Columnar cell
- Basement membrane
- Connective tissue

LM 500x

Structure
Two or more layers of cells; cells at the apical surface are taller than they are wide

Function
Protection and secretion

Location
Large ducts of salivary glands and in membranous part of male urethra

(e) TRANSITIONAL EPITHELIUM AP|R

Transitional epithelium (relaxed)

- Epithelial cell, polyhedral shape
- Binucleated cell
- Basement membrane

LM 180x

Transitional epithelium (distended)

- Flattened epithelial cell
- Binucleated cell
- Basement membrane
- Connective tissue

LM 100x

Structure
Epithelial appearance varies, depending upon whether tissue is stretched or relaxed; relaxed epithelium (top) has polyhedral, rounded cells at the apical surface, while distended epithelium (bottom) has flattened cells at the apical surface; some cells are binucleated

Function
Distension (stretching) and relaxation to accommodate urine volume changes in the urinary bladder, ureters, and part of urethra

Location
Lining of urinary bladder, ureters, and part of urethra

In **keratinized stratified squamous epithelium**, the superficial layers are composed of cells that are dead. These cells lack nuclei and all organelles when observed under the microscope, and instead are filled with the protein keratin (table 5.4*b*). New cells produced in the basal region of the epithelium migrate toward the apical surface of the tissue. During their migration, the cells fill with keratin they produce, which makes them very strong, but as a consequence the cells lose their organelles and nuclei, and die. Thus, the strength of keratin has a trade-off. The epidermis (outer layer) of the skin consists of keratinized stratified squamous epithelium.

Stratified Cuboidal Epithelium

A **stratified cuboidal epithelium** contains two or more layers of cells, and the superficial cells tend to be cuboidal in shape (table 5.4*c*). This tissue forms the walls of the ducts of most exocrine glands, such as the ducts of the sweat glands in the skin. Although the function of stratified cuboidal epithelium is mainly protective, it also serves to strengthen the walls of the gland ducts, and some sections of male urethra.

Stratified Columnar Epithelium

A **stratified columnar epithelium** is relatively rare in the body. It consists of two or more layers of cells, but only the cells at the apical surface are columnar in shape (table 5.4*d*). This type of epithelium protects and secretes. It is found in the large ducts of salivary glands and in the membranous segment of the male urethra.

Transitional Epithelium

A **transitional epithelium** is limited to the urinary tract (urinary bladder, ureters, and part of the urethra). It varies in appearance, depending upon whether it is in a relaxed state or a stretched state (table 5.4*e*). In a relaxed state, the basal cells appear cuboidal or polyhedral, and the apical cells are large and rounded. When transitional epithelium stretches, it thins and the apical cells flatten and become almost squamous in shape. One distinguishing feature of transitional epithelium is the presence of some **binucleated** (containing two nuclei) cells. By being able to stretch as the bladder fills, this epithelium ensures that toxic urine does not seep into the underlying tissues and structures of these organs.

INTEGRATE

CLINICAL VIEW
Stem Cells

Why all the interest in stem cells?

Stem cells are immature, undifferentiated cells. These cells are able to divide into two cells, the first of which is another stem cell, and the other a cell that could differentiate into a specialized, mature cell with a unique function. Stem cells have generated interest in the scientific and medical communities because of their potential for repair or replacement of damaged or dying tissue. Bone marrow replacement has been performed for years to replace white blood cells destroyed by chemotherapy. Researchers are exploring stem cell use as a treatment for Parkinson disease, Alzheimer disease, and spinal cord injuries. Individuals with debilitating muscle pathologies like muscular dystrophy may be able to grow new healthy muscle tissue with stem cells.

What are the two basic characteristics of stem cells?

All stem cells exhibit two characteristics: self-renewal and potency. **Self-renewal** refers to their ability to divide repeatedly to produce both new cells for maturation and new stem cells. **Potency** is the potential for differentiation: Different stem cells have varying ability to differentiate into almost any type of cell. Stem cells exhibit four levels of potency: totipotency, pluripotency, multipotency, and unipotency.

- **Totipotent** stem cells have a "total potential," meaning that they exhibit the ability to differentiate into any cell type within an organism. A totipotent cell is produced when a secondary oocyte is fertilized by a sperm, giving rise to a zygote. The first few cell divisions of the zygote result in equally totipotent cells. Thus, only embryonic (and not adult) stem cells have the potential to be totipotent.
- **Pluripotent** stem cells are derived from totipotent stem cells. These stem cells are formed from the embryoblast portion (inner cell mass) of the **blastocyst.** The blastocyst is a ball of cells that develops during the first week of development from the zygote. The embryoblast is the portion of the blastocyst that will eventually become an embryo and then a fetus. Pluripotent stem cells can form cells in any of the tissue layers of the embryo, but they cannot form structures such as the placenta. Again, only embryonic stem cells have the potential to be pluripotent.

- **Multipotent** stem cells are derived from pluripotent stem cells. They have the capability to differentiate into a restricted number of some cell types and not others. For example, stem cells in the bone marrow may be stimulated to mature and differentiate into different types of blood cells, but not into some other types of cells. Some adult stem cells have the potential to be multipotent.
- **Unipotent** stem cells have the ability to differentiate into a single type of cell, yet these cells still retain the ability to renew themselves. Epithelial stem cells (discussed previously) are examples of unipotent stem cells. Many adult stem cells are unipotent.

What are the differences between embryonic and adult stem cells?

Stem cells may be categorized as either **embryonic stem cells** or **adult stem cells.** Embryonic stem cells include those that have begun to divide in the zygote and the cells in the blastocyst. Embryonic stem cells exhibit the greatest degree of potency—and thus, the greatest potential to differentiate into multiple cell types. In contrast, adult stem cells are the immature cells found in postnatal (already born) organisms. Adult stem cells typically are multipotent or unipotent, and thus they exhibit less potency than embryonic stem cells.

How are stem cells harvested?

Most embryonic stem cells must be harvested from a structure no more differentiated than a blastocyst. Most of these blastocysts were donated by families undergoing in vitro fertilization who had stored more blastocysts than needed for a successful pregnancy. If these blastocysts were not used by the family and not donated for research, they typically would be

WHAT DO YOU THINK?

2 Which types of epithelia are well suited for protection and why?

Now that you have examined all the different types of epithelia, refer to **figure 5.3** to reexamine the relationship between epithelial type and function. Note in this figure that the simple epithelia are better designed for diffusion, absorption, and secretion functions, since these epithelia are thinner than stratified epithelium. Stratified epithelia are best suited for protective functions. Thus, when you examine organs with different epithelia, you will have a clue about the organ's function based on its epithelium.

WHAT DID YOU LEARN?

3 How does simple epithelium differ from stratified epithelium?

4 What epithelial tissue lines the air sacs of the lungs?

5 What epithelial tissue contains multiple layers of cells, and the most superficial cells are squamous, dead, and filled with the protein keratin?

---

destroyed. Note that opponents of embryonic stem cell research counter that these blastocysts could be implanted and lead to viable infants who could be adopted, and any medical benefit from embryonic stem cells does not justify using them in research. Opponents also maintain that adult stem cell research should be explored instead.

Adult stem cells may be extracted from the bone marrow or tissue of an individual. The main problem with adult stem cells is their limited potency, which suggests that their use for treatment in diseases is limited. Embryonic stem cells exhibit greater promise for treatment because of their greater potency.

Embryonic stem cells	**Adult Stem Cells**
Embryonic stem cells originate from the dividing cells of the zygote or embryoblast portion of the blastocyst. They may be totipotent or pluripotent.	Adult stem cells are the undifferentiated stem cells in the body after birth. They may be multipotent or unipotent.

Totipotent stem cells are those cells formed from the zygote, and can give rise to every differentiated cell in the organism and the placenta.	**Pluripotent** stem cells are derived from the embryoblast portion of the blastocyst. This type of stem cell has the capability to mature and specialize into a cell within any tissue in the body (except the placenta).	**Multipotent** stem cells (as in bone marrow) are capable of differentiating into a restricted number of some cell types and not others.	**Unipotent** stem cells (such as epithelial stem cells) have the ability to differentiate into a single type of cell.

Zygote

Morula

Embryoblast

Blastocyst

Red bone marrow

LM 25x

Red bone marrow cells

Epidermis of skin

Epithelial stem cell

Figure 5.3 The Relationship Between Epithelial Type and Function. (*a*) Simple epithelium is designed for the functions of absorption, secretion, and diffusion. In contrast, (*b*) stratified epithelium's many layers make it best suited for protection.

Mucus

Goblet cell

Epithelial cells

PSEUDOSTRATIFIED CILIATED COLUMNAR EPITHELIUM

Location: Ciliated form in most of upper respiratory tract, including the trachea

Function: Protection, secretion of mucus; cilia propels mucus along epithelial surface

(a) Simple Epithelia | Best suited for absorption, secretion, or diffusion

Blood capillary

Erythrocyte

Simple squamous epithelium of capillary wall

Simple squamous epithelium of alveolus wall

Alveolus

SIMPLE SQUAMOUS EPITHELIUM

Location: Alveolus walls in the lung and in capillary walls

Function: A single thin layer of cells allows for rapid diffusion of gases between an alveolus of the lung and a capillary

Microvilli

Simple columnar cell

Nutrients

Mucus

Goblet cell

Blood capillary

Lymphatic capillary

SIMPLE COLUMNAR EPITHELIUM

Location: Small intestine

Function: The microvilli and single layer of cells facilitates absorption of nutrients and the goblet cells secrete mucus

Convoluted tubule in the kidney

Simple cuboidal epithelial cells

Blood capillary

Exchange of filtrate

SIMPLE CUBOIDAL EPITHELIUM

Location: Convoluted tubules of the kidney

Function: A single layer of cuboidal cells functions in absorption and secretion of materials from filtrate in the kidney

(b) Stratified Epithelia | Best suited for physical protection

NONKERATINIZED STRATIFIED SQUAMOUS EPITHELIUM

Location: Lining of the oral cavity and esophagus

Function: The multiple layers of cells withstand abrasion from ingested materials

Nonkeratinized stratified squamous epithelial cells

Epidermis of the skin

Keratinized stratified squamous epithelial cells

KERATINIZED STRATIFIED SQUAMOUS EPITHELIUM

Location: Epidermis of the skin

Function: The strong multiple layers of keratinized cells protect underlying tissue from UV rays; offers stronger protection than nonkeratinized epithelium

Distended (stretched) transitional epithelial cells

Relaxed transitional epithelial cells

Binucleated cell

TRANSITIONAL EPITHELIUM

Location: Lining of the urinary bladder, ureters, and part of urethra

Function: The distensible multilayer tissue protects deeper tissue from urine, distends and relaxes to accommodate urine volume changes

5.1d Glands

LEARNING OBJECTIVES

5. Define glands.
6. Distinguish between endocrine and exocrine glands.
7. List exocrine gland types based on both anatomic form and physiologic method of secretion.

Glands are either individual cells or multicellular organs composed predominantly of epithelial tissue. They secrete substances either for use elsewhere in the body or for elimination from the body. Glandular secretions may include mucin, electrolytes, hormones, enzymes, and urea (a nitrogenous waste produced by the body).

Endocrine and Exocrine Glands

Endocrine (en′dō-krin; *endon* = within, *krino* = to separate) **glands** lack ducts and secrete their products, called *hormones,* directly into the interstitial fluid and blood. Hormones act as chemical messengers to influence cell activities elsewhere in the body. Endocrine glands are discussed in depth in chapter 17.

Exocrine (ek′sō-krin) **glands** typically originate from an invagination of epithelium that burrows into the deeper connective tissues. These glands usually maintain their connection with the epithelial surface by means of a **duct,** an epithelium-lined tube through which the gland sections are discharged onto the epithelial surface. Examples of exocrine glands include sweat glands, mammary glands, and salivary glands.

Exocrine glands may be unicellular (one-celled) or multicellular. **Unicellular exocrine glands** typically do not contain a duct, and they are located close to the surface of the epithelium in which they reside. The most common type of unicellular exocrine gland is the goblet cell, which is commonly found in both simple columnar epithelium and pseudostratified ciliated columnar epithelium (refer to tables 5.2c, *d* and 5.3 for examples). In contrast, **multicellular exocrine glands** contain numerous cells that work together to produce a secretion (**figure 5.4**). The gland consists of **acini** (as′i-nī; *acinus* = grape), which are the clusters of cells that produce the secretion, and one or more smaller **ducts,** which merge to form a larger duct that transports the secretion to the epithelial surface. Multicellular exocrine glands typically are surrounded by a fibrous capsule, and extensions of the capsule called *septa* partition the gland into **lobes.**

Classification of Exocrine Glands

Multicellular exocrine glands may be classified either by anatomic form or by method of secretion, which may be thought of as a physiologic classification.

Classification by Anatomic Form Exocrine glands may be classified anatomically based on the structure and complexity of their ducts. **Simple glands** have a single, unbranched duct; **compound glands** have branched ducts. In addition, glands may be classified according to the shape of their secretory portions. The gland is called **tubular** if the secretory portion and the duct are of uniform diameter. If the secretory portion forms an expanded sac, the gland is called **acinar.** Finally, a gland with both tubules and acini is called a **tubuloacinar gland. Figure 5.5** shows several types of exocrine glands based on their anatomic form.

Classification by Method of Secretion Glands may be classified physiologically by their method of secretion. The three basic

types of glands in this classification are merocrine glands, apocrine glands, and holocrine glands (**figure 5.6**).

Merocrine (mer′ō-krin; *meros* = share) **glands** package their secretions into secretory vesicles and release the secretions by exocytosis. The glandular cells remain intact and are not damaged in any way by producing the secretion. Examples of merocrine glands include lacrimal (tear) glands; salivary glands; some sweat glands, also known as *eccrine glands*; the exocrine glands of the pancreas; and the gastric glands of the stomach.

Apocrine (ap′ō-krin; *apo* = away from, off) **glands** produce their secretion in the following way: The apical membrane around a portion of the glandular cell cytoplasm with the secretory product pinches off and becomes the secretion. The glandular cells repair the damage and then continue to produce new secretions in the same manner. Examples include the mammary glands and some sweat glands in the axillary and pubic regions.

Holocrine (hōl′ō-krin; *holos* = whole) **glands** are formed from cells that accumulate a product; the entire cell then disintegrates. Thus, a holocrine secretion is a viscous mixture of both cell fragments and the product the cell produced prior to its disintegration. The ruptured, dead cells are continuously replaced by other epithelial cells undergoing mitosis. The oil-producing glands (sebaceous glands) in the skin are examples of holocrine glands.

WHAT DID YOU LEARN?

6 What are the two basic parts of a multicellular exocrine gland?

7 What are the differences between holocrine and merocrine glands?

Exocrine gland

Duct

Lobe

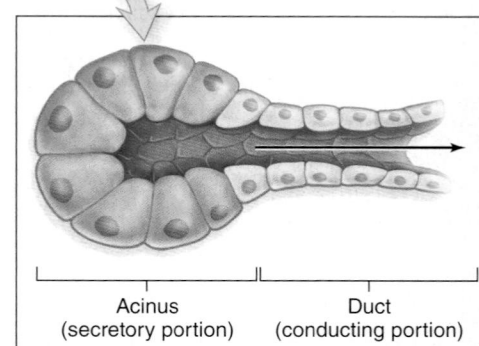

Figure 5.4 General Structure of Exocrine Glands. Exocrine glands contain secretory portions called acini, and conducting portions composed of many ducts that merge to form a larger duct that transports the secretion to the epithelial surface.

Acinus (secretory portion)

Duct (conducting portion)

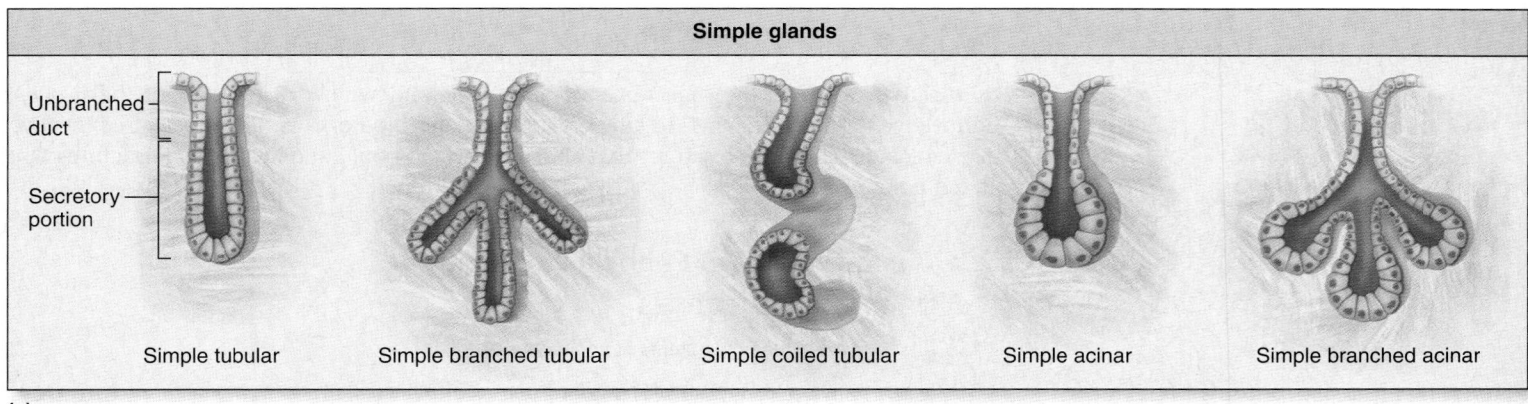

Simple glands

Unbranched duct

Secretory portion

| Simple tubular | Simple branched tubular | Simple coiled tubular | Simple acinar | Simple branched acinar |

(a)

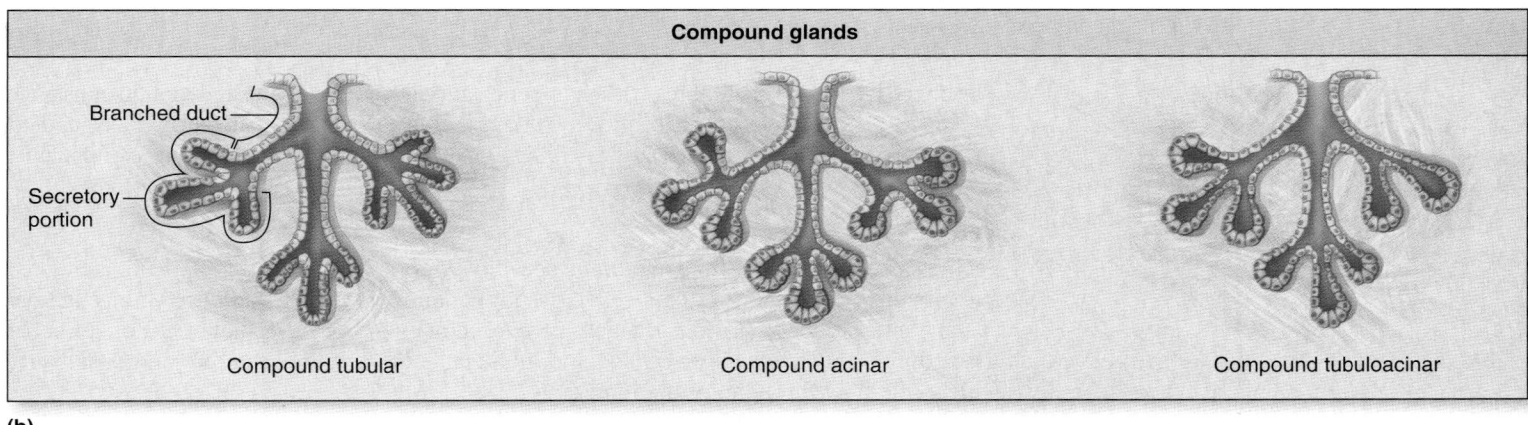

Compound glands

Branched duct

Secretory portion

| Compound tubular | Compound acinar | Compound tubuloacinar |

(b)

Figure 5.5 Structural Classification of Multicellular Exocrine Glands. Simple glands (*a*) have unbranched ducts, whereas compound glands (*b*) have ducts that branch. These glands also exhibit different forms: Tubular glands have secretory cells in a space with a uniform diameter, acinar glands have secretory cells arranged in sac-like acini, and tubuloacinar glands have secretory cells in both types of regions.

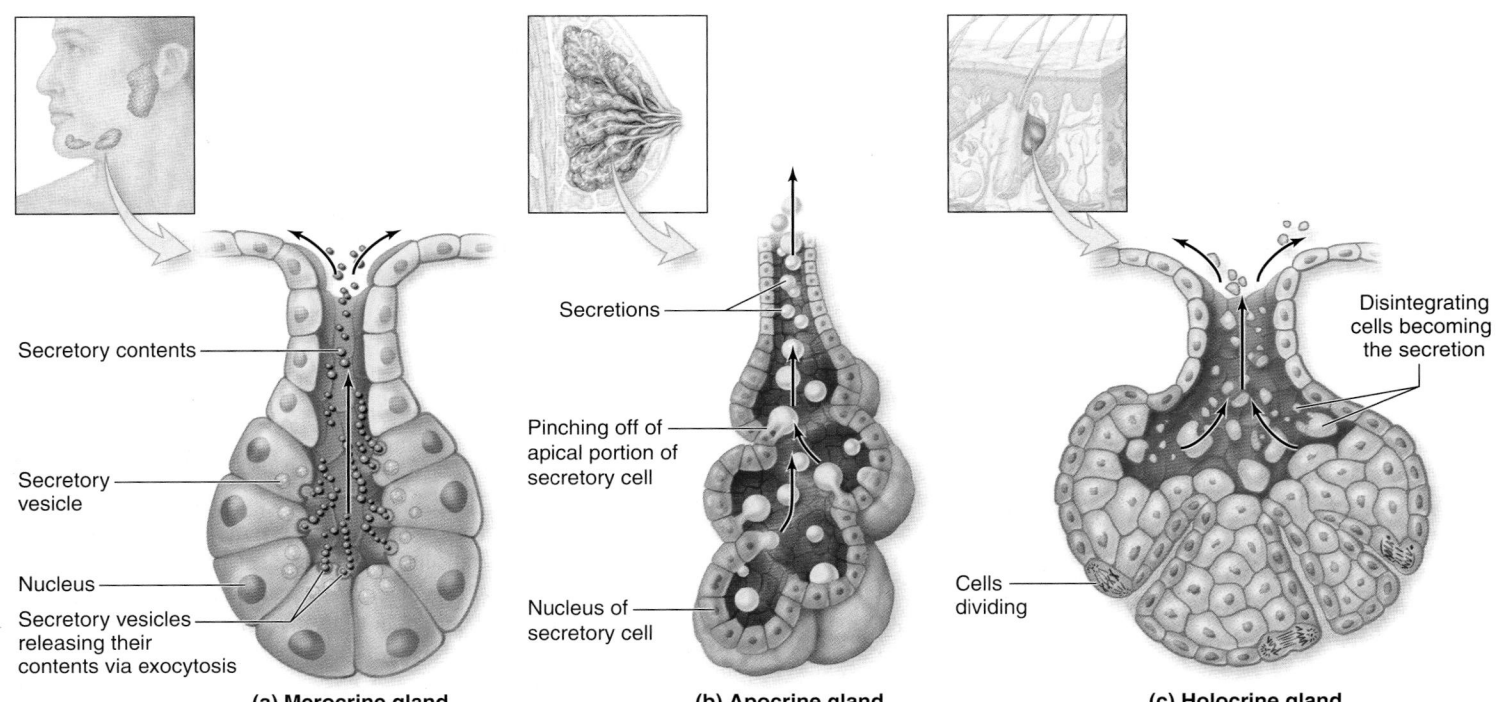

Secretory contents

Secretory vesicle

Nucleus

Secretory vesicles releasing their contents via exocytosis

(a) Merocrine gland

Secretions

Pinching off of apical portion of secretory cell

Nucleus of secretory cell

(b) Apocrine gland

Disintegrating cells becoming the secretion

Cells dividing

(c) Holocrine gland

Figure 5.6 Methods of Exocrine Gland Secretion. Exocrine glands use different processes to release their secretory product. (*a*) Merocrine glands secrete products by means of exocytosis at the apical surface of the secretory cells. (*b*) Apocrine gland secretion is produced by a pinching off of the apical surface of the cell. (*c*) Holocrine gland secretion is produced through the destruction of the entire secretory cell. Lost cells are replaced by cell division at the base of the gland.

5.2 Connective Tissue: Cells in a Supportive Matrix

Connective tissue is the most diverse, abundant, and widely distributed of the tissues. Connective tissue is designed to support, protect, and bind organs. Examples of connective tissue include tendons (structures that attach muscle to bone) and ligaments (structures that attach bone to bone), body fat, cartilage, bone, and blood.

5.2a Characteristics of Connective Tissue

✓ LEARNING OBJECTIVES

1. Describe the three components of connective tissue.
2. Give examples of resident cells and wandering cells in connective tissue proper.
3. Name three types of protein fibers found in connective tissue.
4. Identify three types of molecules that may be found in ground substance.

All connective tissues share three basic components: cells, protein fibers, and ground substance (figure 5.7). The diversity in connective tissue is due to both the differences in types and amounts of protein fibers, as well as the varying proportions of the connective tissue components.

Cells

Each class of connective tissue contains specific types of cells. For example, connective tissue proper (one category of connective tissue) contains fibroblasts, adipose connective tissue contains adipocytes, and cartilage is composed of chondrocytes. Unlike cells of epithelial tissue, most connective tissue cells are not in direct contact with each other and usually are widely scattered throughout the tissue.

Connective tissue proper contains two classes of cells: resident cells and wandering cells. **Resident cells** are stationary cells that are permanently housed within the connective tissue. They help support, maintain, and repair the extracellular matrix. Examples of resident cells include the following:

- **Fibroblasts** (fī′brō-blast; *fibra* = fiber, *blastos* = germ) are relatively flat cells with tapered ends and are the most abundant resident cells in connective tissue proper. They produce the fibers and ground substance components of the extracellular matrix.
- **Adipocytes** (ad′i-pō-sīt; *adip* = fat), also called *fat cells,* appear in small clusters within some types of connective tissue proper. If large clusters of these cells dominate an area, the connective tissue is called adipose connective tissue.
- **Mesenchymal cells** (me-seng′ki-mal) are a type of embryonic stem cell within connective tissue. If the tissue becomes damaged, these cells will divide. One cell that is produced replaces the mesenchymal stem cell, while the other cell becomes a committed cell that moves into the damaged area and differentiates into the type of connective tissue cell that is needed.
- **Fixed macrophages** are relatively large, irregular-shaped cells that are derived from a type of white blood cell called a monocyte. They are dispersed throughout the

---

INTEGRATE

CLINICAL VIEW
Scurvy

Collagen is an important protein that strengthens and supports almost all body tissues, especially connective tissue. Vitamin C (ascorbic acid) is essential for the production and maintenance of healthy collagen fibers. **Scurvy,** a disease caused by vitamin C deficiency, is marked by weakness, ulceration of gums resulting in tooth loss, hemorrhages, abnormal bone growth, and easily ruptured capillaries. Scurvy was prevalent among nineteenth-century sailors who, on long sea voyages, lacked vitamin C in their food. Sailors eventually learned that eating citrus fruits, such as limes and lemons, on their voyages prevented scurvy (this also explains why sailors received the nickname "limeys"). Today, collagen production disorders are treated by consuming foods high in vitamin C, such as citrus fruits, broccoli, cauliflower, peppers, spinach, and tomatoes, or by taking vitamin C supplements.

Blood vessel

Ground substance

Extracellular
matrix

Protein fibers

Elastic fiber

Collagen fiber

Reticular fiber

Resident cells

Mesenchymal cell

Macrophage

Adipocyte

Fibroblast

Figure 5.7 Connective Tissue Components and Organization. Connective tissue is composed of cells and an extracellular matrix of protein fibers and ground substance. AP|R

matrix, where they phagocytize (engulf) damaged cells or pathogens. When they encounter foreign materials, the cells also release chemicals that stimulate the immune system and lure numerous wandering cells to the tissue.

Wandering cells continuously move throughout the connective tissue proper and are components of the immune system. They also may help repair damaged extracellular matrix. These cells are primarily types of **leukocytes** (lū′kō-sīt; *leukos* = white), also known as *white blood cells*, and help the body mount an immune response. Examples of wandering cells and their specific functions in the immune response include the following:

- **Mast cells** are small, mobile cells that usually are found close to blood vessels; they secrete heparin to inhibit blood clotting and histamine to dilate blood vessels and increase blood flow.

- **Plasma cells** are formed when B-lymphocytes are activated by exposure to foreign materials. Plasma cells produce **antibodies,** which are proteins that immobilize a foreign material and prevent it from causing further damage.

- **Free macrophages** are mobile, phagocytic cells that wander through the connective tissue. They function like fixed macrophages, yet they are able to move throughout the tissue.

- **Other leukocytes** also migrate through the blood vessel walls into the connective tissue. These include neutrophils, a type of leukocyte that phagocytizes bacteria, and lymphocytes, a type of leukocyte which attacks and kills foreign materials.

Protein Fibers

The protein fibers in connective tissue usually strengthen and support the tissue. Three basic types of protein fibers may be found in connective tissue: collagen fibers, reticular fibers, and elastic fibers.

Collagen fibers are unbranched, 'cablelike' long fibers that are strong, flexible, and resistant to stretching. Collagen forms about 25% of the body's protein, and the fibers appear white in fresh tissue, so they often are called *white fibers.* In tissue sections stained with hematoxylin and eosin, they appear pink. Collagen fibers are numerous in structures such as tendons and ligaments.

INTEGRATE

CONCEPT CONNECTION

Proteoglycans and glycoproteins are similar in that both consist of proteins and carbohydrates. Most proteoglycans, however, have over 90% of their structure composed of carbohydrates, whereas glycoproteins have a more balanced ratio of protein to carbohydrates.

Reticular fibers are similar to collagen fibers but much thinner. They contain the same protein subunits found in collagen, but their subunits are combined in a different way, and they are coated with a glycoprotein. These fibers form a branching, interwoven framework that is tough but flexible. Reticular fibers are especially abundant in the **stroma** (connective tissue framework) of organs such as the lymph nodes, spleen, and liver.

Finally, **elastic fibers** contain the protein elastin. The fibers branch and rejoin, and appear wavy. Elastic fibers stretch and recoil easily to permit the skin, lungs, and arteries to return to their normal shape after being stretched. Fresh elastic fibers have a yellowish color and often are called *yellow fibers*. These fibers are visible only in tissue sections that have been stained with special stains, which make the elastic fibers appear black.

Ground Substance

Ground substance is a nonliving material produced by the connective tissue cells, and it is within this ground substance that the connective tissue cells and protein fibers reside. The ground substance may be viscous (as in blood), semisolid (as in cartilage), or solid (as in bone). Together, the ground substance and the protein fibers it houses form an **extracellular matrix.**

Ground substance contains different large molecules as well as varying amounts of water. **Glycosaminoglycans** (glī′kōs-am-i-nō-glī′kan; *glykys* = sweet, *glycan* = saccharide), or **GAGs,** are one type of large molecule in the ground substance. A GAG is a polysaccharide that is composed completely of carbohydrate building blocks, some of which have an attached amine group. GAGs are negatively charged and hydrophilic. The negative charges attract cations, such as sodium (Na^+), and as a result water follows the movement of the positive ion. Thus, GAGs are able to attract and absorb water. Different GAGs attract varying amounts of water, depending on their number of negative charges, so the fluidity of the ground substance varies as a result. Different types of GAGs include chondroitin sulfate, heparin sulfate, and hyaluronic acid.

When a GAG is linked to a protein, it forms an even larger molecule within the ground substance called a **proteoglycan.** Proteoglycans have over 90% of their structure composed of carbohydrates, in the form of GAGs. Most GAGs are an integral part of proteoglycans. The large structure of a proteoglycan is due primarily to the large number of negative charges in its GAGs, which then repel each other and cause the molecule to spread out and occupy more space. As we will see in this and future chapters, GAGs and proteoglycans perform numerous important functions in the body.

The ground substance includes other molecules like **adherent glycoproteins** (proteins with carbohydrates attached), which act like glue to bond connective tissue cells and fibers to the ground substance. Examples of adherent glycoproteins include fibronectin, fibrillin, and laminin.

WHAT DID YOU LEARN?

8 What are the basic functional differences between resident cells and wandering cells in connective tissue?

9 What are the function of GAGs in ground substance?

5.2b Functions of Connective Tissue

LEARNING OBJECTIVE

5. Describe the functions of connective tissue.

The many types of connective tissue collectively perform a wide variety of functions, including:

- **Physical protection.** Bones of the skull and the thoracic cage protect delicate organs such as the brain, heart, and lungs; adipose connective tissue packed both around the kidneys and posterior to the eyes help protect these organs.
- **Support and structural framework.** Bones serve as the framework for the adult body and provide a place for muscle attachment; cartilage keeps air tubes like the trachea and bronchi patent (open); and connective tissue proper forms supportive capsules around organs such as the kidney and spleen.
- **Binding of structures.** Ligaments bind bone to bone, tendons bind muscle to bone, and dense irregular connective tissue anchors the skin to the underlying muscle and bone.

- **Storage.** Adipose connective tissue is the major energy reserve in the body; bone is the primary reservoir for calcium and phosphorus.
- **Transport.** Blood carries nutrients, gases, and wastes between different regions of the body.
- **Immune protection.** Many connective tissues contain leukocytes that protect the body against disease and mount an immune response when necessary. Additionally, the viscous nature of the extracellular matrix restricts the movement and spread of disease-causing organisms.

 WHAT DID YOU LEARN?

 10 In what ways does connective tissue provide a structural framework?

5.2c Embryonic Connective Tissue

 LEARNING OBJECTIVE

6. Compare and contrast mesenchyme and mucous connective tissue.

Two types of embryonic connective tissue have been identified: mesenchyme and mucous connective tissue. **Mesenchyme** (mez′en-kīm; *enkyma* = infusion) is the first type of connective tissue to emerge in the developing embryo. It has star-shaped (stellate) or spindle-shaped mesenchymal cells dispersed within a gel-like ground substance that contains fine, immature protein fibers **(table 5.5a)**. In fact, ground substance makes up a larger proportion than mesenchymal cells in this type of tissue. Mesenchyme is the source of all other connective tissues. Adult connective tissues often house numerous mesenchymal (stem) cells that provide support in the repair of the tissue following damage or injury.

A second type of embryonic connective tissue is **mucous connective tissue,** also known as *Wharton's jelly* (table 5.5b). The immature protein fibers in this tissue are more numerous than those within mesenchyme. Mucous connective tissue is located within the umbilical cord only.

 WHAT DID YOU LEARN?

11 What is the composition of mesenchyme and what is its function?

Table 5.5	Embryonic Connective Tissue

(a) MESENCHYME

Immature protein fiber
Mesenchymal cells
Ground substance

Structure
Ground substance is a viscous fluid with some immature protein fibers; mesenchymal cells are stellate or spindle-shaped

Function
Common origin for all other connective tissue types

Location
Throughout the body of the embryo and fetus

(b) MUCOUS CONNECTIVE TISSUE

Immature protein fiber
Mesenchymal cell
Ground substance

Structure
Mesenchymal cells scattered within a viscous ground substance; immature protein fibers are more abundant here than in mesenchyme

Function
Support of structures in umbilical cord

Location
Umbilical cord of fetus

CLINICAL VIEW
Marfan Syndrome

Marfan syndrome is a rare genetic disease of connective tissue that causes skeletal, cardiovascular, and visual system abnormalities. It is caused by an abnormal gene on chromosome 15. Patients with Marfan syndrome tend to have (1) abnormally long fingers, toes, and upper and lower limbs; (2) malformation of the thoracic cage, vertebral column, or both as a result of excessive growth of ribs; and (3) easily dislocated joints, resulting from weak ligaments, tendons, and joint capsules. Cardiovascular system problems involve a weakness in the aorta and abnormal heart valves. Visual system abnormalities develop because the thin fibers that hold the lens of the eye in place are weak, allowing the lens to slip out of place. Patients usually exhibit symptoms of Marfan syndrome by age 10; those affected often die of cardiovascular-related problems before they reach 50 years of age.

Individual with Marfan syndrome.

5.2d Classification of Connective Tissue

✅ LEARNING OBJECTIVE

7. Distinguish the types of connective tissue and the locations where each type is found.

All connective tissue is ultimately derived from mesenchyme. Mesenchyme begins to differentiate in the developing fetus as it forms the connective tissues that ultimately are found in the adult body. The connective tissue types present after birth are classified into three broad categories: connective tissue proper, supporting connective tissue, and fluid connective tissue (figure 5.8).

Connective Tissue Proper

Connective tissue proper is divided into two broad categories: loose connective tissue and dense connective tissue. This classification is based upon the relative proportions of cells, fibers, and ground substance.

Loose Connective Tissue   **Loose connective tissue** contains relatively fewer cells and protein fibers than dense connective tissue. The protein fibers are sparse and irregularly arranged (hence, the name "loose connective tissue"), and there is abundant ground substance. Loose connective tissues act as the body's "packing material" by supporting and surrounding structures and organs. There are three types of loose connective tissue: areolar connective tissue, adipose connective tissue, and reticular connective tissue.

Areolar (ă-rē′ō-lăr) **connective tissue** has a loosely unconfined organization of collagen and some elastic fibers and has an abundant distribution of blood vessels (**table 5.6a**). This connective tissue type contains all of the fixed and wandering cells of connective tissue proper, although the predominant cell is the fibroblast. The ground substance is abundant and viscous. Areolar connective tissue is found nearly everywhere in the body. It is found in the papillary layer of the dermis (skin) and is a major component of the subcutaneous layer that is deep to the skin. It also surrounds organs, individual nerve and muscle cells, and blood vessels.

Figure 5.8 Connective Tissue Classification. Mesenchymal cells are the origin of all connective tissue cell types. The three classes of connective tissue are connective tissue proper, supporting connective tissue, and fluid connective tissue.

Table 5.6 Connective Tissue Proper: Loose Connective Tissue

(a) AREOLAR CONNECTIVE TISSUE AP|R

- Collagen fiber
- Elastic fiber
- Fibroblast
- Ground substance

LM 240x

Structure
Abundant, viscous ground substance; scattered fibroblasts; many blood vessels

Function
Protects tissues and organs; binds some epithelia to deeper tissue

Location
Papillary layer of the dermis (skin); subcutaneous layer (deep to skin); surrounds organs, nerves, and blood vessels

(b) ADIPOSE CONNECTIVE TISSUE AP|R

- Adipocyte nucleus
- Adipocyte

LM 200x

Structure
Closely packed adipocytes; nucleus pushed to edge of cell by large fat droplet

Function
Stores energy; insulates, cushions, and protects

Location
Subcutaneous layer; surrounds and covers some organs

(c) RETICULAR CONNECTIVE TISSUE AP|R

- Ground substance
- Reticular fibers
- Leukocyte

LM 280x

Structure
Viscous ground substance; scattered arrangement of reticular fibers, fibroblasts, and leukocytes

Function
Provides stroma (supportive framework) to lymphatic organs

Location
Spleen, lymph nodes, thymus, and bone marrow

Adipose connective tissue (commonly known as *fat*) is a loose connective tissue composed primarily of adipocytes (table 5.6b). Adipocytes are filled with lipid droplets, but on a histology slide, the lipid is extracted during tissue processing so all that is left is the plasma membrane of the adipocyte, with the nucleus pushed to the outside. This connective tissue type stores energy, acts as an insulator, and serves both as packing around structures as well as a cushion against shocks. It is located throughout the body in places such as the subcutaneous layer deep to the skin and surrounding various organs. Typically, the number of adipocytes remains relatively stable in an individual, and weight gain or loss is due to the adipocytes enlarging or shrinking in size, respectively.

Reticular connective tissue contains a meshwork of reticular fibers, fibroblasts, and leukocytes (table 5.6c). This tissue forms the stroma (structural framework) of many lymphatic organs, such as the spleen, thymus, lymph nodes, and bone marrow.

Dense Connective Tissue **Dense connective tissue** is composed primarily of protein fibers and has proportionately less ground substance than loose connective tissue. It also is known as *collagenous tissue* because collagen fibers usually are the dominant fiber type. There are three categories of dense connective tissue: dense regular connective tissue, dense irregular connective tissue, and elastic connective tissue.

Dense regular connective tissue contains collagen fibers that are packed tightly and align parallel to one another. The fibers resemble lasagna noodles stacked one on top of another **(table 5.7a)**. This tissue type is found in tendons (which attach muscle to bone) and ligaments (which attach bone to bone), where stress typically is applied in a single direction. Dense regular connective tissue has few blood vessels, and thus it takes a long time to heal following injury, since a rich blood supply is necessary for quick healing.

Dense irregular connective tissue contains bundles and clumps of collagen fibers that extend in all directions (table 5.7b). This tissue provides support and resistance to stress in multiple directions, and has an extensive blood supply. Dense irregular connective tissue is found in most of the dermis of the skin, the periosteum surrounding bone, and the perichondrium surrounding cartilage. It also forms capsules around some internal organs, such as the liver, kidneys, and spleen.

Elastic connective tissue has branching, densely packed elastic fibers (table 5.7c). It also has more fibroblasts than in loose connective tissue. The elastic fibers provide the ability for the tissue to stretch and recoil. This tissue is found in the walls of large arteries, the trachea, vocal cords, and the suspensory ligament of the penis.

 WHAT DO YOU THINK?

3 What type of connective tissue have you damaged when you sprain your ankle?

Supporting Connective Tissue

There are two types of supporting connective tissue: cartilage and bone. Both form a strong, durable framework that protects and supports the soft body tissue. The extracellular matrix contains many protein fibers and a ground substance that ranges from semisolid (cartilage) to solid (bone).

Cartilage Cartilage has a firm, semisolid extracellular matrix that contains variable amounts of collagen and elastic protein fibers. Mature cartilage cells are called **chondrocytes** (kon′drō-sīt; *chondros* = gristle, cartilage). These cells occupy small spaces called **lacunae** (lă-kū′nā; *lacus* = a hollow, a lake) within the extracellular matrix. Most cartilage is surrounded by a dense irregular connective tissue covering called the **perichondrium** (per-i-kon′drē-ŭm; *peri* = around). The perichondrium has two distinct layers: an outer fibrous layer and an inner cellular layer. Cartilage is stronger and more resil-

Table 5.7	Connective Tissue Proper: Dense Connective Tissue

(a) DENSE REGULAR CONNECTIVE TISSUE AP|R

Collagen fibers
Ground substance
Fibroblast nucleus
LM 250x

Structure
Densely packed, parallel arrays of collagen fibers; fibroblasts squeezed between layers of fibers; scarce ground substance; greatly reduced blood supply

Function
Attaches bone to bone (ligament) as well as muscle to bone (tendon); resists stress applied in one direction

Location
Tendons; ligaments

(b) DENSE IRREGULAR CONNECTIVE TISSUE AP|R

Fibroblast nucleus
Collagen fiber bundles
Ground substance
LM 200x

Structure
Collagen fibers randomly arranged and clumped together; fibroblasts in spaces among fibers; more ground substance than in dense regular connective tissue; extensive blood supply

Function
Withstands stresses applied in all directions; durable

Location
Most of dermis of skin; periosteum covering bone; perichondrium covering cartilage, some organ capsules

(c) ELASTIC CONNECTIVE TISSUE AP|R

Ground substance
Elastic fibers
LM 200x

Structure
Predominantly composed of elastic fibers; fibroblasts occupy some spaces between fibers

Function
Allows for stretching and recoil

Location
Walls of elastic arteries (such as the aorta), trachea, vocal cords; suspensory ligament of penis

ient than previously discussed connective tissue types, and it provides more flexibility than bone. It occurs in areas of the body that need support and must withstand deformation, such as the tip of the nose or the auricle (external part) of the ear.

Chondrocytes produce and secrete a chemical that prevents blood vessel growth and formation within the extracellular matrix. Thus, mature cartilage is avascular, and as a result the chondrocytes must exchange nutrients and waste products with blood vessels outside of the cartilage by diffusion.

Three major types of cartilage are found in the body: hyaline cartilage, fibrocartilage, and elastic cartilage. They exhibit both differences in density and dispersal of chondrocytes within the extracellular matrix.

Hyaline (hī′ă-lin; *hyalos* = glass) **cartilage** is the most common type of cartilage. It is named for its clear, glassy appearance under the microscope **(table 5.8a)**. Its chondrocytes are irregularly scattered: The collagen within the extracellular matrix is not readily observed by light microscopy. Hyaline cartilage is surrounded by a perichondrium. If this tissue type is stained with hematoxylin and eosin and examined under the microscope, the tissue resembles carbonated grape soda, where the lacunae represent the bubbles in the soda. Hyaline cartilage is found in many areas of the body, including the nose, trachea, larynx, costal cartilage (cartilage attached to ribs), and the articular ends of long bones. It also forms most of the fetal skeleton.

Fibrocartilage (fī′brō-kar′ti-lij; *fibro* = fiber) is a weight-bearing cartilage. It has numerous coarse, readily visible protein fibers that are arranged as irregular bundles between large chondrocytes (table 5.8b). There is only a sparse amount of ground substance. The densely interwoven collagen fibers contribute to the durability of this cartilage. There is no perichondrium. Fibrocartilage acts as a good shock absorber and resists compression. It is located in the intervertebral discs (circular supportive structures between adjacent vertebrae), pubic symphysis (between the anterior parts of the hip bones), and the menisci of the knee joint.

Elastic cartilage is the flexible, springy cartilage. It is so named because it contains numerous elastic fibers within its extracellular matrix (table 5.8c). The chondrocytes are closely packed and surrounded by a small amount of extracellular matrix. The elastic fibers are densely packed together and ensure that this tissue is both resilient and very flexible. Elastic cartilage is surrounded by a perichondrium. Elastic cartilage is similar to elastic

Table 5.8	Supporting Connective Tissue: Cartilage

(a) HYALINE CARTILAGE AP|R

LM 250x

Ground substance
Chondrocyte
Lacuna

Structure
Glassy-appearing matrix; sparsely arranged chondrocytes in lacunae; usually covered by perichondrium

Function
Forms most of fetal skeleton; provides support

Location
Tip of nose; trachea; most of larynx, costal cartilage; articular ends of long bones; most of fetal skeleton

(b) FIBROCARTILAGE AP|R

LM 250x

Collagen fibers
Lacuna
Chondrocyte
Ground substance

Structure
Readily visible, numerous parallel collagen fibers; large chondrocytes in lacunae; no perichondrium

Function
Resists compression; acts as shock absorber in some joints

Location
Intervertebral discs; pubic symphysis; menisci of knee joints

(c) ELASTIC CARTILAGE AP|R

LM 200x

Chondrocyte
Elastic fibers
Ground substance

Structure
Abundant elastic fibers that form weblike mesh; chondrocytes in lacunae; perichondrium present

Function
Maintains shape while permitting extensive flexibility

Location
External ear; epiglottis of larynx

LEARNING STRATEGY

Ask yourself the following questions to help distinguish the types of connective tissue proper under the microscope:

1. *Is the connective tissue loose or dense?* Loose connective tissue has fewer protein fibers and both more space and ground substance, while dense connective tissue has densely packed protein fibers.

2. *If the tissue is loose, what types of cells are there?* Areolar connective tissue primarily contains fibroblasts, whereas adipose connective tissue contains adipocytes. The presence of numerous leukocytes may indicate reticular connective tissue.

3. *If the tissue is dense, are the protein fibers oriented in different-sized clumps (which would indicate dense irregular connective tissue) or parallel (dense regular connective tissue)?* Elastic connective tissue may resemble dense regular connective tissue, but its fibers are not as neatly arranged.

connective tissue, in that both contain abundant amounts of elastic fibers. Note that elastic connective tissue has a fluid ground substance; elastic cartilage has a semisolid ground substance and contains chondrocytes.

Elastic cartilage is found in the external ear and the epiglottis (a structure that prevents swallowed materials from entering the trachea). You can see for yourself how flexible elastic cartilage is by performing this experiment: Fold your external ear over your finger, hold for 10 seconds, and release. Your ear springs back to its original shape because the elastic cartilage resists the deformational pressure you applied. (This also explains why our ears aren't permanently misshapen if we sleep on them in an unusual way!)

Bone   Bone connective tissue is also known as *osseous connective tissue* and makes up the mass of most of the structures referred to as "bones." Bone is more solid than cartilage and provides greater support, although it is not as flexible. Section 7.2e provides a detailed description of the histology of bone connective tissue.

The extracellular matrix of bone consists of organic components (collagen fibers and glycoproteins) and inorganic components composed of a mixture of calcium salts, primarily calcium phosphate. The bone cells are called **osteocytes** (os'tē-ō-sīt) and are housed within spaces in the extracellular matrix called **lacunae.** Almost all of the external bone surface, except for those surfaces that participate in joints, are covered by a dense irregular connective tissue called the **periosteum** (per-ē-os'tē-ŭm; *osteon* = bone), which is similar to the perichondrium of cartilage.

The two forms of bone tissue are compact bone and spongy (cancellous, trabecular) bone. **Compact bone** appears completely solid but is in fact perforated by a number of neurovascular canals (**table 5.9**). It has a uniform histologic pattern. Compact bone is formed from cylindrical structures called **osteons** (os'tē-on), which display concentric rings of bone connective tissue called lamellae. The lamellae encircle a central canal that houses blood vessels and nerves. **Spongy bone** is located within the interior of a bone, and it contains a latticework structure of bone connective tissue that is very strong, yet lightweight.

Bone serves a variety of functions. Bones provide levers for movement, and they support soft tissues as well as protect vital body organs. The hard extracellular matrix of bone stores important minerals, such as calcium and phosphorus. Finally, some spongy bone houses **hemopoietic** (hē'mō-poy-et'ik; *hemat* = blood) cells, which form a type of reticular connective tissue that makes blood cells (a process called hemopoiesis).

Fluid Connective Tissue

There are two types of fluid connective tissue: blood and lymph. **Blood** is a fluid connective tissue composed of **formed elements.** Formed elements include cells, both

Table 5.9 Supporting Connective Tissue: Bone

BONE AP|R

LM 200x

- Osteocyte in lacuna
- Concentric lamellae
- Osteon
- Central canal
- Canaliculi

Structure
Calcified extracellular matrix containing osteocytes trapped in lacunae; compact bone arranged in osteons (concentric lamellae arranged around a central canal); spongy bone (not shown) is a meshwork that has a different organization from compact bone

Function
Provides levers for body movement, supports soft structures, protects organs, stores calcium and phosphorus; spongy bone contains hemopoetic tissue and is the site for hemopoeisis

Location
Bones of the body

Table 5.10 Fluid Connective Tissue: Blood

BLOOD AP|R

LM 720x

- Erythrocytes (red blood cells)
- Neutrophil (white blood cell)
- Platelet
- Lymphocyte (white blood cell)
- Plasma

Structure
Contains formed elements (erythrocytes, leukocytes, and platelets); dissolved protein and a liquid ground substance called plasma

Function
Erythrocytes transport respiratory gases (oxygen and carbon dioxide); leukocytes help initiate and control the immune response; and platelets help with blood clotting. Dissolved protein fibers will coalesce and help with blood clotting when needed. Plasma transports nutrients, wastes, and hormones throughout the body.

Location
Primarily within blood vessels and in the heart; leukocytes also located in lymphatic structures and organs, and can migrate to infected or inflamed tissues of the body

erythrocytes (red blood cells) and leukocytes (white blood cells), and cellular fragments called platelets (table 5.10). The liquid ground substance is called **plasma,** and within it are dissolved proteins.

Blood has numerous functions. The erythrocytes transport respiratory gases (oxygen and carbon dioxide), while the leukocytes mount an immune response. Platelets and the protein fibers help clot the blood. Plasma transports nutrients, wastes, and hormones throughout the body. Blood is discussed in greater detail in chapter 18. **Lymph** is derived from blood plasma and ultimately is returned to the bloodstream. We discuss it in greater detail in chapter 21.

Figure 5.9 summarizes the relationships between connective tissue types and their functions.

WHAT DID YOU LEARN?

12 Compare loose connective tissue to dense connective tissue with respect to fiber density and distribution, and the amount of ground substance.

13 Describe the composition and location of fibrocartilage.

14 Why is blood considered a connective tissue?

INTEGRATE — CONCEPT OVERVIEW

Figure 5.9 The Relationship Between Connective Tissue Type and Function. (a) Connective tissue proper binds structures together, whereas (b) supporting connective tissue either provides a framework for or protects underlying soft tissues. (c) Fluid connective tissue is responsible for fluid, nutrient, gas, and waste transport.

(a) Connective Tissue Proper | Binds structures together

DENSE CONNECTIVE TISSUE

Location: Dense irregular connective tissue in the dermis of the skin, dense regular connective tissue in interosseous membrane (tendon between the arm bones), and elastic connective tissue in the aorta

Main function: Dense irregular connective tissue binds the epidermis to the underlying subcutaneous layer of the skin.

Dense regular connective tissue forms tendons that bind muscle to bone and ligaments that bind bone to bone.

Elastic connective tissue allows for stretching and recoil in some organs (e.g., aorta).

Elastic connective tissue

Dense irregular connective tissue

Dense regular connective tissue

Dermis (primarily dense irregular CT)

Subcutaneous layer (adipose and areolar CT)

LOOSE CONNECTIVE TISSUE

Location: Areolar and adipose connective tissue in subcutaneous layer of skin, reticular connective tissue in spleen

Main function: Supports and surrounds structures and organs

Areolar and adipose connective tissues form the subcutaneous layer, which binds the skin and muscle.

Other functions: Reticular connective tissue houses leukocytes, which offer protection.

Adipose connective tissue stores lipids, insulates and cushions

Reticular connective tissue

(b) Supporting Connective Tissue
Provides physical protection to underlying tissues or a structural framework for soft body tissues

Elastic cartilage

CARTILAGE

Location: Hyaline cartilage in the costal cartilage, fibrocartilage in the intervertebral discs, and elastic cartilage in the external ear

Main functions: Protection and structural support, with more flexibility than bone

Hyaline cartilage

Fibrocartilage

BONE

Location: Bones of the skeletal system

Main functions: Protection and structural support, more rigid and solid than cartilage; serves as a reservoir for calcium and phosphorus

(c) Fluid Connective Tissue
Transports nutrients, gases, and wastes

BLOOD

Location: Within blood vessels and the heart

Main function: Transport of substances through the body

5.3 Muscle Tissue: Movement

LEARNING OBJECTIVES

1. Describe the structure of skeletal, cardiac, and smooth muscle.

2. Compare the functions of each type of muscle and where each type is found.

Muscle tissue is composed of specialized cells that can contract when stimulated by the nervous system. When this tissue contracts, it produces movement, such as the voluntary motion of body parts, contraction of the heart, and propulsion of materials through the digestive and urinary tracts. The three types of muscle tissue are skeletal muscle, cardiac muscle, and smooth muscle. These tissues are described briefly here and discussed in greater detail in later chapters.

Skeletal muscle tissue, also known as *striated* or *voluntary muscle tissue,* is primarily responsible for movement of the skeleton (although this tissue also moves some nonskeletal structures, such as the skin of the face). It is composed of long cylindrical cells called

skeletal muscle fibers. These fibers typically are arranged in parallel bundles that run the length of the entire muscle. Such long fibers need more than one nucleus to control and carry out all cellular functions; thus, each skeletal muscle fiber is multinucleated, with nuclei located at the periphery of the fiber (**table 5.11a**). Under the light microscope, skeletal muscle fibers exhibit alternating light and dark bands, called **striations,** that reflect the overlapping pattern of parallel thick and thin contractile protein filaments. Additionally, skeletal muscle is considered **voluntary** because it usually does not contract unless stimulated by the somatic (voluntary) nervous system.

Cardiac muscle tissue is confined to the thick middle layer of the heart wall, called the myocardium; it is responsible for the contraction of the heart to pump blood. Cardiac muscle tissue contains visible striations, but unlike skeletal muscle, the cardiac muscle cells are short and often bifurcating (branching) (**table 5.11b**). Cardiac muscle cells contain one or two centrally located nuclei. In addition, the cells are connected by **intercalated** (in-ter'kă-lā-ted; *intercalates* = inserted between) **discs,** which are strong attachments between the cells composed of desmosomes

Table 5.11 | Muscle Tissue

(a) SKELETAL MUSCLE TISSUE [AP|R]

Labels: Nucleus, Striations, Skeletal muscle fiber
LM 500x

Structure and characteristics
Long, cylindrical, striated fibers (cells) arranged parallel and unbranched; fibers are multinucleated; fiber is under voluntary control

Function
Primarily responsible for moving skeleton and selected other components of the body

Location
Attaches to bones or sometimes to skin (e.g., facial muscles)

(b) CARDIAC MUSCLE TISSUE [AP|R]

Labels: Nucleus, Intercalated discs, Cardiac muscle cell
LM 500x

Structure and characteristics
Short, striated cells typically branching; cells contain one or two centrally located nuclei; intercalated discs between cells; under involuntary control

Function
Pumps blood through heart

Location
Heart wall (myocardium)

(c) SMOOTH MUSCLE TISSUE [AP|R]

Labels: Nucleus, Smooth muscle cells
LM 160x

Structure and characteristics
Nonstriated cells that are short and fusiform in shape; contain one centrally located nucleus; under involuntary control

Function
Moves and propels materials through internal organs

Location
Walls of hollow internal organs, such as intestines, stomach, airways, urinary bladder, uterus, and blood vessels

and gap junctions. Intercalated discs appear as dark, thick lines when viewed in the microscope. Intercalated discs strengthen the connection between cells and promote the rapid conduction of electrical activity through many cardiac muscle cells at once, allowing the cardiac muscle cells of a heart chamber to contract as a unit. Cardiac muscle cells are considered **involuntary** because they do not require nervous system activity to initiate a contraction; instead, specialized cardiac muscle cells (pacemaker cells) in the heart wall initiate the contraction.

Smooth muscle tissue, also called *visceral* or *involuntary muscle tissue,* is so named because it lacks the striations seen in other muscle tissue, and so this tissue appears smooth (table 5.11c). Smooth muscle cells are fusiform (spindle-shaped), which means they are thick in the middle and tapered at their ends. These cells are relatively short and contain one centrally located oval nucleus. Smooth muscle tissue is also called *visceral muscle tissue* because it is found in the walls of most viscera, such as the intestines, stomach, airways, urinary bladder, uterus, and blood vessels. The contraction of smooth muscle helps propel material movement through these organs. This tissue is considered involuntary because we do not have voluntary control over the muscle.

WHAT DO YOU THINK?

4 Why do you think smooth muscle lacks striations?

WHAT DID YOU LEARN?

15 Compare and contrast the structure of skeletal and cardiac muscle tissue.

5.4 Nervous Tissue: Information Transfer and Integration

LEARNING OBJECTIVES

1. Describe the structure of nervous tissue.
2. List the functions of nervous tissue.

Nervous tissue is located within the brain, spinal cord, and the nerves that traverse through the body. It consists of cells called **neurons** (nūr′onz) that receive, transmit, and process nerve impuls-

INTEGRATE

LEARNING STRATEGY

Ask the following questions to help distinguish the types of muscle tissue viewed in the microscope:

1. *What is the shape of the cell?* Skeletal muscle cells are long and cylindrical, cardiac muscle cells are short and bifurcated (branching), and smooth muscle cells are short and fusiform.

2. *How many nuclei are present, and are the nuclei centrally located or at the periphery of the cell?* Skeletal muscle has multiple nuclei that are located at the periphery of the cell. Cardiac muscle has one or two centrally located nuclei. Smooth muscle has a single centrally located nucleus.

3. *Do the cells have striations?* Skeletal and cardiac muscle have striations, but smooth muscle does not. Further, only cardiac muscle has intercalated discs between the cells.

es. It also contains a larger number of cells called **glial cells** (or *supporting cells*), which do not transmit nerve impulses but instead are responsible for the protection, nourishment, and support of the neurons **(table 5.12)**.

Each neuron has a prominent **cell body** that houses both the nucleus and other organelles. Extending from the cell body are branches called **nerve cell processes.** The shorter and more numerous processes are **dendrites** (den′drītes), that receive incoming signals and transmit the information to the cell body. The single long process extending from the cell body is the **axon** (ak′son), which carries outgoing signals to other cells. Because of the extensive lengths of some axons, neurons are usually the longest cells in the body; some are longer than 1 meter. We discuss nervous tissue in detail beginning in chapter 12.

WHAT DID YOU LEARN?

16 What is the difference between a neuron and a glial cell?

Table 5.12	Nervous Tissue

NERVOUS TISSUE AP|R

Cell body of neuron

Dendrite

Axon

Nucleus of glial cell

LM 1000x

Structure
Contains neurons, which have a cell body, dendrites, and an axon that extend from the cell body; also contains glial cells, which lack the processes seen in neurons

Function
Neurons receive, send, and process nerve impulses while glial cells help support, protect, and nourish neurons.

Location
Brain, spinal cord, and nerves

5.5 Integration of Tissues in Organs and Body Membranes

We have learned that a tissue is a group of similar cells that perform a common function. Organs and body membranes also perform certain specialized functions, and they consist of a collection of tissues that support their function.

5.5a Organs

LEARNING OBJECTIVES

1. Define an organ.
2. Explain the roles of different tissues in an organ.

An **organ** is a structure that is composed of two or more tissue types that work together to perform specific, complex functions. The key to organ structure is that the different tissue types must work in concert. For example, the stomach contains all four types of tissue. It is lined by an epithelium, has both areolar and dense connective tissue in its walls, contains three layers of smooth muscle in those walls, and possesses abundant nervous tissue **(figure 5.10)**.

All these tissues work together to perform the functions of the stomach. Epithelial tissue secretes substances for chemical digestion of ingested nutrients. Smooth muscle contracts and relaxes so that these materials may be mechanically mixed and broken down. Connective tissue houses the blood vessels and nerves that supply the stomach as well as providing shape and support. Nervous tissue is responsible for regulating contraction of muscle and the stimulation of secretion by the glandular cells.

WHAT DID YOU LEARN?

17. Describe why the stomach is considered an organ.

5.5b Body Membranes

LEARNING OBJECTIVES

3. Explain the structure and functions of mucous, serous, cutaneous, and synovial membranes.
4. Identify the locations of these membranes.

Epithelial and connective tissue together form structures called body membranes, which should not be confused with the plasma membranes of cells. **Body membranes** are formed from an epithelial layer that is bound to an underlying connective tissue. These membranes are designed to line body cavities, cover the viscera, or cover the body's external surface. There are four types of body membranes: mucous, serous, cutaneous, and synovial, shown in **figure 5.11**.

A **mucous membrane,** also called a **mucosa** (mū-kō'să), lines passageways and compartments that eventually open to the external environment; these include the digestive, respiratory, urinary, and reproductive tracts. Mucous membranes perform absorptive, protective, and secretory functions, or a combination of these functions. A mucous membrane is formed by an epithelium and an underlying connective tissue called the lamina propria. Often, this membrane is covered with a layer of mucus derived from goblet cells, multicellular glands, or both.

A **serous membrane** lines body cavities that typically do not open to the external environment. The membrane is composed

Tissue types

Epithelial tissue	Connective tissue
Muscular tissue	Nervous tissue

Stomach (organ)

Mucosa

Dense irregular connective tissue
Nerve plexus
Oblique layer
Smooth muscle (3 layers)
Nerve plexus between muscle layers
Circular layer
Areolar connective tissue
Serous membrane
Mesothelium, (simple squamous epithelium)
Longitudinal layer

Simple columnar epithelium
Areolar connective tissue
Gastric glands (formed from epithelium)
Nerve ending

Figure 5.10 Roles of Tissues in an Organ. Different tissue types work together to perform the functions of the stomach: epithelial, muscular, connective, and nervous.

Mucous membrane
- Mucosa of respiratory tract
- Mucosa of digestive tract

Serous membrane
- Parietal layer (of pleura)
- Serous cavity (between parietal and visceral layers)
- Visceral layer (of pleura)

Cutaneous membrane
- Skin

Synovial membrane
- Joint lined by synovial membrane

Figure 5.11 Body Membranes. Body membranes are formed from epithelial and connective tissue and are designed to line body cavities, cover the viscera, or cover the external surface of the body. The four types of body membranes are mucous, serous, cutaneous, and synovial.

of a simple squamous epithelium called mesothelium. Serous membranes produce a thin, watery **serous fluid,** or *transudate* (tran′sū-dāt; *trans* = across, *sudo* = to sweat), which is derived from blood plasma. Serous membranes are composed of two parts: a **parietal layer** that lines the inside of the body cavity and a **visceral layer** that covers the surface of the internal organs. Between these two layers is a **serous cavity,** which is a potential space into which the serous fluid is secreted. The serous fluid reduces the friction between their opposing surfaces. Examples of serous membranes include part of the pericardium (which is associated with the heart),

INTEGRATE

CONCEPT CONNECTION

Serous membranes reduce friction in a similar manner for many body systems. In the cardiovascular system, the serous fluid produced by the pericardium prevents similar friction from the movement of the beating heart. The serous fluid secreted by the pleura of the respiratory system prevents painful abrasion when the lungs are expanding with air and coming into contact with the internal thoracic wall. In the digestive system, the serous fluid secreted by the peritoneum prevents friction between the moving abdominal organs and the abdominal wall.

the pleura (associated with the lungs) and the peritoneum (associated with abdominal organs).

The largest body membrane is the **cutaneous** (kū-tā′nē-ŭs; *cutis* = skin) **membrane**, also known as the *skin,* which covers the external surface of the body. The cutaneous membrane is composed of a keratinized stratified squamous epithelium (called the epidermis) and an underlying layer of connective tissue (called the dermis). Its many functions include protecting internal organs and preventing water loss. This membrane is discussed in greater detail in chapter 6.

Some joints in the body are lined by a **synovial** (si-nō′vē-ăl) **membrane** that is composed of areolar connective tissue covered with a superficial layer of squamous epithelial cells that lack a basement membrane. The epithelial cells secrete a **synovial fluid** that reduces friction among the moving bone parts and distributes nutrients to the cartilage on the articular surfaces of bone.

WHAT DID YOU LEARN?

18 What are the differences between the parietal and visceral layers of the serous membrane?

5.6 Tissue Development and Aging

The process by which the many different tissues of the body are generated from a single cell, the fertilized egg, could take up an entire book. Here we describe the milestones of this complex process; you will learn more in chapter 29. In addition, we consider how tissues change over time and with different conditions. We conclude with a brief summary of how the aging process affects the body's tissues.

5.6a Tissue Development

LEARNING OBJECTIVES

1. Explain the stages of tissue development in the embryo.
2. Describe the three primary germ layers and the tissues to which they give rise.

To understand how all tissues form, some basic information about the human embryo is required. When an oocyte (egg) is fertilized by a sperm, it forms a diploid cell called a **zygote.** The zygote undergoes multiple cell divisions; eventually, a multicellular structure called a blastocyst is formed. The cells that form the embryo are collectively known as the **embryoblast.**

Embryoblast cells differentiate in the second and third weeks of development. By the third week of development, three **primary germ layers** are formed. All body tissues develop from these layers **(figure 5.12)**. The three primary germ layers are called ectoderm, mesoderm, and endoderm. When these three primary germ layers have formed, the growing structure may now be referred to as an **embryo.**

Ectoderm is initially located on the dorsal and external surfaces of the embryo. It is responsible for forming many externally placed tissues, such as the epidermis of the skin, hair, nails, and the exocrine glands of the skin. Thus, some but not all epithelial tissues are derived from ectoderm. Tooth enamel, the lens of the eye, and the adrenal medulla are derived from ectoderm, as is all nervous tissue such as the brain, spinal cord, and nerves.

Mesoderm is the middle primary germ layer. It forms all muscle tissue and the epithelial lining of vessels and serous membranes that line the body cavities. Mesoderm becomes mesenchyme, which then goes on to form all connective tissues in the body. The dermis of the skin, adrenal cortex, heart, spleen, kidneys and ureters, and internal reproductive structures are mesoderm-derived.

Endoderm becomes the innermost germ layer when the embryo undergoes shape changes. It forms the epithelial linings of the tympanic cavity (middle ear) and auditory tube, as well as the digestive, respiratory, reproductive, and urinary tracts. Endoderm also forms organs such as the thyroid gland, parathyroid glands, the thymus and portions of the palatine tonsils, as well as most of the liver, gallbladder, and pancreas.

WHAT DID YOU LEARN?

19 What are the three primary germ layers, and when do they form?

5.6b Tissue Modification

✓ LEARNING OBJECTIVE

3. Describe how tissues may change in form, size, or number of cells.

As we mature and place different stresses on our bodies, our tissues may undergo various changes as well. Sometimes a mature epithelium changes to a different form of mature epithelium, a phenomenon called **metaplasia** (met-ă-plā′zē-ă; *metaplasis* = transformation). Metaplasia may occur as an epithelium adapts to environmental conditions. For example, smokers typically experience metaplastic changes in the epithelium of the trachea (windpipe). The smoke and its by-products are the environmental stressors that change the normal pseudostratified ciliated columnar epithelium lining the trachea to a nonkeratinized stratified squamous epithelium. Another example occurs in some individuals with chronic acid reflux, also known as heartburn. Here, the nonkeratinized stratified squamous epithelium of the lower esophagus may transform to a simple columnar epithelium, like that seen in the stomach.

Figure 5.12 Primary Germ Layers and Their Derivatives. The primary germ layers (ectoderm, mesoderm, and endoderm) are formed during the third week of development and will give rise to all of the tissues in the body.

Fertilization → Zygote → Blastocyst → 3rd week **Embryoblast** (Ectoderm, Mesoderm, Endoderm)

Late week 4 **Embryo**
Ectoderm
Yolk sac
Mesoderm
Connecting stalk
Amniotic cavity
Endoderm

Ectoderm
Epidermis of skin and epidermal derivatives (hair, nails, sweat glands, mammary glands)
Nervous tissue and sense organs
Pituitary gland
Adrenal medulla
Enamel of teeth
Lens of eye

Mesoderm
Dermis of skin
Epithelial lining of blood vessels, lymph vessels, serous membranes
Muscle tissue
Connective tissue
Adrenal cortex
Heart
Kidneys and ureters
Internal reproductive organs
Spleen

Endoderm
Epithelial lining of respiratory tract, GI tract, tympanic cavity, auditory tube, urinary tract, reproductive tract
Liver (most of)
Gallbladder
Pancreas
Palatine tonsils (portion of)
Thyroid gland
Parathyroid glands
Thymus

CLINICAL VIEW
Gangrene

Gangrene is the necrosis (death) of the soft tissues of a body part due to a diminished or obstructed arterial blood supply to that region. The body parts most commonly affected are the limbs, fingers, or toes. Gangrene is a major complication of diabetics, who often suffer from diminished blood flow to their extremities as a consequence of their disease. Gangrene occurs in several different forms.

Intestinal gangrene usually follows an obstruction of the blood supply to the intestines. Without a sufficient blood supply, the tissue will undergo necrosis and gangrene. Untreated intestinal gangrene leads to death.

Dry gangrene is where the involved body part is desiccated, sharply demarcated, and shriveled, usually due to constricted blood vessels as a result of exposure to extreme cold. Dry gangrene can be a complication of frostbite or of a variety of cardiovascular diseases that restrict blood flow, primarily to the hands and feet.

Wet gangrene is caused by a bacterial infection of tissues that have lost their blood and oxygen supply. The cells in the dying tissue rupture and release fluid (hence the name "wet" gangrene). The wet environment allows bacteria to flourish, and they often produce a foul-smelling pus. The most common bacteria associated with wet gangrene include *Streptococcus, Staphylococcus, Enterobacter,* and *Klebsiella.* Wet gangrene must be treated quickly with antibiotics and removal of the necrotic tissue.

Gas gangrene most often affects muscle tissue, and the bacteria associated with gas gangrene typically are *Clostridium.* As the bacteria invade the necrotic tissue, a release of gases from the tissue produces gas bubbles. These bubbles make a crackling sound in the tissue, especially if the patient is moved. Symptoms of fever, pain, and edema (localized swelling) occur within 72 hours of the initial trauma to the region. The treatment for gas gangrene is similar to that of wet gangrene.

Dry gangrene of the foot.

Gas gangrene in a recently amputated limb.

Tissues may change in size, form, or number of cells. **Hypertrophy** refers to an increase in the size of the existing cells in a tissue, although the *number* of cells remains constant. **Hyperplasia** is an increase in the number of cells in a tissue. When tissue growth proceeds out of control, a tumor composed of abnormal tissue develops, and the condition is called **neoplasia** (nē-ō-plā′zē-ă; *neo* = new, *plasis* = molding). Shrinkage of tissue by a decrease in either cell number or cell size is called **atrophy** (at′rō-fē). Atrophy may result from normal aging (senile atrophy) or from failure to use an organ or tissue (disuse atrophy). If an individual becomes bedridden or must wear a cast for a broken bone, the affected muscles exhibit disuse atrophy as the skeletal muscle fibers become smaller. If the atrophy is not due to long-term problems, then typically physical therapy and a reuse of the tissues can minimize or reverse the atrophic changes.

Necrosis is the term for tissue death. Necrosis typically occurs due to tissue damage that is not reversible, and an inflammatory response (see section 22.3d) usually occurs in the tissue in response to the damage. Gangrene is an example of tissue necrosis, and is described in detail (see Clinical View: "Gangrene").

5.6c Aging of Tissues
✔ LEARNING OBJECTIVE

4. List some changes that occur in tissues with age.

All tissues change as a result of aging. Proper nutrition, good health, normal circulation, and relatively infrequent wounds promote continued normal tissue functioning past middle age. Thereafter, the support, maintenance, and replacement of cells and extracellular matrix become less efficient. Physical damage and physiologic changes can alter the structure and chemical composition of many tissues. For example, as individuals age, epithelia become thinner and connective tissues lose their pliability and resiliency. The amount of collagen in the body declines with age, so tissue repair takes longer. Bones become brittle, and muscle and nervous tissue begin to atrophy. Poor diet and circulation problems accelerate these tissue declines. Eventually, cumulative losses from relatively minor damage or injury may contribute to major health problems.

💡 WHAT DID YOU LEARN?

20 What is the difference between hypertrophy and hyperplasia?

💡 WHAT DID YOU LEARN?

21 How do epithelia and connective tissue change when they age?

CLINICAL VIEW
Tissue Transplant

Grafting is the process of surgically transplanting healthy tissue to replace diseased, damaged, or defective tissue. Tissue transplant may be characterized in four ways: an autograft, a syngenetic graft, an allograft, or a heterograft.

An **autograft** (aw'tō-graft; *autos* = self) is a tissue transplant from one site to a different site on the same individual. Autografts are often performed with skin, as healthy skin from one part of the body is grafted to another part of the body where the skin has been damaged by burns or chemicals. Since an autograft is a person's own body tissue, the body will not reject the tissue as foreign. However, autografts may not be feasible in certain situations, such as when the amount of skin damaged is so great that it would not be possible to transplant such a large portion of tissue.

A **syngenetic** (sin-jĕ-net'ik; *syn* = together) **graft**, also called an *isograft*, is a tissue transplant from one person to a genetically identical person (i.e., identical twins). It is unlikely the patient's body will reject the syngenetic graft because it came from a genetically identical individual. Very few of us, however, have an identical twin, so this type of graft is not possible for most people.

An **allograft** (al'ō-graft; *allos* = other) is a tissue transplant from one person to another person who is genetically different. Many tissue types have been used as allografts, including skin, muscle, bone, and cartilage. The term allograft also is used for the transplantation of organs or parts of organs, such as heart valves, kidneys, and the liver. Although most tissue allografts are successful, transplantation of entire organs is much more problematic. The patient and the organ donor must be as genetically similar as possible; traits such as blood type and other blood factors must match between patient and donor. The closer the match, the less likely the allograft will be rejected. The recipient of the transplanted organ(s) must take powerful immunosuppressant drugs, which help prevent the body from rejecting the organ. Unfortunately, these same drugs work by suppressing the entire immune system, making the transplant patient more susceptible to illness. Even with immunosuppressant drugs, rejection of the allograft commonly occurs.

A **xenograft** (zē'nō-graft; *xeno* = foreign), also called a *heterograft* (hĕ'ter-ō-graft; *heteros* = other), is a tissue transplant from an animal into a human being. For example, porcine (pig) and bovine (cattle) tissues have been used as replacements for heart valves, blood vessels, and bone. Rejection of these animal tissues usually occurs frequently and quickly, but a few of these transplants have worked for a short time.

CHAPTER SUMMARY

5.1 Epithelial Tissue: Surfaces, Linings, and Secretory Functions 150	• Tissues are classified into four general types: epithelial tissue, connective tissue, muscle tissue, and nervous tissue.
	• Epithelial tissue covers the surface of the body, lines body cavities, and forms secretory structures called glands.
	5.1a Characteristics of Epithelial Tissue 150
	• The characteristics of epithelia include: cellularity, polarity, attachment to a basement membrane, avascularity, rich innervation, and high regeneration ability.
	5.1b Functions of Epithelial Tissue 151
	• Epithelia provide physical protection, are selectively permeable, produce secretions, and contain nerve endings to detect sensations.
	5.1c Classification of Epithelial Tissue 151
	• Epithelia are classified by the number of cell layers and the shape of the surface (apical) cells.
	• A simple epithelium has only one layer of cells that is in direct contact with the basement membrane; a stratified epithelium has two or more layers of cells and only the deepest (basal) layer is in direct contact with the basement membrane.
	• Examples of cell shape include squamous (cells are flattened), cuboidal (cells are about as tall as they are wide), and columnar (cells are taller than they are wide).
	• Pseudostratified columnar epithelium appears stratified but is not; all cells are in contact with the basement membrane.
	• Transitional epithelium contains several layers of rounded cells, and the epithelium appearance changes between a relaxed and distended state.
	5.1d Glands 160
	• Endocrine glands secrete hormones into the blood, whereas exocrine glands secrete their products onto the epithelial surface.
	• Multicellular glands may be classified either by anatomic form (simple vs. compound and tubular vs. acinar) or physiologically by their method of secretion (merocrine, apocrine, or holocrine).
5.2 Connective Tissue: Cells in a Supportive Matrix 162	• Connective tissue supports, protects, and binds the body organs.
	5.2a Characteristics of Connective Tissue 162
	• Connective tissue contains cells, protein fibers, and a ground substance. The protein fibers and ground substance together form the extracellular matrix.

CHALLENGE YOURSELF

Do You Know the Basics?

_____ 1. Which tissue contains a calcified ground substance and is specialized for structural support?

    a. muscle tissue

    b. dense regular connective tissue

    c. areolar connective tissue

    d. bone connective tissue

_____ 2. Which of the following is *not* a characteristic of areolar connective tissue?

    a. predominant cell type is the fibroblast

    b. abundant ground substance

    c. densely packed protein fibers

    d. occurs in the subcutaneous layer of the skin

____ 3. _____ membranes line body cavities that typically open to the exterior, such as the nasal cavity.

  a. Mucous
  b. Serous
  c. Cutaneous
  d. Synovial

____ 4. Which of the following is a correct statement about a simple epithelium?

  a. All of the cells are in direct contact with the basement membrane.
  b. It is designed for protection against mechanical abrasion.
  c. It is formed from multiple layers of cells.
  d. It may contain the protein keratin.

____ 5. All of the following are characteristics of an epithelium *except*

  a. It is selectively permeable.
  b. It may form exocrine glands.
  c. Its cells are highly regenerative.
  d. It contains abundant blood vessels.

____ 6. Which connective tissue type is composed of cells called chondrocytes and may be surrounded by a covering called perichondrium?

  a. bone
  b. dense irregular
  c. cartilage
  d. areolar

____ 7. Which tissue type is formed from mesoderm?

  a. epidermis (outer layer) of skin
  b. nervous tissue
  c. smooth muscle tissue
  d. epithelial lining of the urinary bladder

____ 8. Which muscle type consists of long, cylindrical, striated fibers with multiple nuclei located at the periphery of the fiber?

  a. smooth muscle
  b. skeletal muscle
  c. cardiac muscle
  d. All of these are correct.

____ 9. Which epithelial tissue type lines the trachea (air tube)?

  a. simple columnar epithelium
  b. pseudostratified ciliated columnar epithelium
  c. simple squamous epithelium
  d. transitional epithelium

____ 10. A gland that releases its secretion by exocytosis into secretory vesicles is called a(an) _____ gland.

  a. merocrine
  b. apocrine
  c. holocrine
  d. All of these are correct.

11. What are some characteristics of all types of epithelium?

12. Describe the two main criteria by which epithelia are classified.

13. List the epithelia type that lines (a) the lumen of the stomach, (b) the oral cavity, (c) the urinary bladder, and (d) the air sacs (alveoli) of the lungs.

14. What are the types of exocrine glands, classified by method of secretion, and how does each method of secretion work?

15. Name the four types of body membranes, and cite a location of each type.

16. What characteristics are common to all connective tissues?

17. What are the main structural differences between dense regular and dense irregular connective tissue?

18. In what regions of the body would you expect to find hyaline cartilage, fibrocartilage, and elastic cartilage, and why would these types be located in these regions?

19. What are the similarities and differences between skeletal muscle, cardiac muscle, and smooth muscle?

20. What is the difference between neurons and glial cells in nervous tissue?

Can You Apply What You've Learned?

1. John is a 53-year-old construction worker who has come into your office complaining of a sore knee joint. You see a buildup of fluid close to the patella (kneecap) but deep to the skin and suspect the soreness is due to bursitis, an inflammation of membranes that surround some joints. Which type of body membrane is inflamed?

  a. cutaneous membrane
  b. serous membrane
  c. synovial membrane
  d. mucous membrane

2. Your optometrist shines a light in your eye and notices your pupil constricts (becomes smaller) in response to the light. She tells you the iris (the colored part of the eye) is a muscle that adjusts the size of the pupil automatically in response to the amount of light entering the eye. Based on this information, which type of muscle do you think forms the iris?

   a. skeletal
   b. cardiac
   c. smooth
   d. visual

Use the following paragraph to answer questions 3–5.

During a biology lab, Erin used a cotton swab to remove some tissue from the inner side of her cheek. She then placed the tissue on a slide to examine it under the microscope.

3. Why was the tissue able to be removed so easily without causing injury to the rest of Erin's cheek?

   a. The tissue contained abundant amounts of ground substance to keep the tissue puffy and relatively intact.
   b. The tissue contained multiple layers of cells, so removing a few cells wouldn't harm the rest of the tissue.
   c. The tissue contained lots of blood vessels, so blood filled any gaps left when the original cells were removed.
   d. The remaining cells were interconnected by intercalated discs, which formed a strong bond between the cells.

4. When Erin examined the cells under the microscope, what shape were the cells?

   a. squamous
   b. cuboidal
   c. columnar
   d. circular

5. If Erin removed a large chunk of this tissue from the same site, the shape and characteristics of the deepest cells would be

   a. the same shape as the original cells under the microscope.
   b. cuboidal.
   c. binucleated and circular.
   d. squamous.

Can You Synthesize What You've Learned?

1. During a microscopy exercise in the anatomy laboratory, a student makes the following observations about a tissue section: (a) The section contains some different types of scattered protein fibers—that is, they exhibit different widths, some are branched, some are long and unbranched. (b) The observed section has some "open spaces"—that is, places between both cells and the observed fibers that appear clear with no recognizable features. (c) Several connective tissue cell types are scattered throughout the section, but these cells are not grouped tightly together. What type of tissue is the student observing? Where might this tissue be found in the body?

2. Your father is suffering from a painful knee joint. He has been told that he either has the early stages of arthritis or some inherent joint problems. His friend recommends that he take a chemical supplement with his meals, called chondroitin sulfate, which has been shown to help some people with joint aches and pains. Specifically, this supplement may alleviate symptoms caused by degenerated cartilage on the surfaces on bones in joints. Based on your knowledge of connective tissues, do you think the chondroitin sulfate supplements could help your father's knee problems?

INTEGRATE

ONLINE STUDY TOOLS
www.mhhe.com/mckinleyap

Clinical Case Study: Did Abraham Lincoln suffer from Marfan's Syndrome?

Interactive Questions: This chapter's content is served up in a number of multimedia question formats for student study.

LearnSmart: Topics and terminology include characteristics and functions of epithelial tissue; characteristics and functions of connective tissue; embryonic connective tissue; movement of muscle tissue; information transfer and integration of nervous tissue; tissue

integration in organs and body membranes; tissue development and aging

Anatomy & Physiology Revealed: Topics include simple epithelia; pseudostratified columnar epithelia; stratified columnar epithelia; loose connective tissue types; dense connective tissue types; supporting connective tissue types; compact bone; fluid connective tissue: blood; muscle tissue types; nervous tissue

Animation: Pleural membranes

chapter 6

Integumentary System

The **integument** (in-teg'ū-ment; *integumentium* = a covering) is the skin that covers your body. Skin is also known as the **cutaneous** (kū-tā'nē-ŭs; *cutis* = skin) **membrane**. The **integumentary** (in-teg-ū-men'tă-rē) **system** consists of the skin and its derivatives: nails, hair, sweat glands, and sebaceous (oil) glands. We are most conscious of this highly visible body system because it characterizes our self-image and reflects our emotions. Our skin is a barrier to the outside world and is subjected to trauma, ➡

A dermatologist is a physician that cares for the integumentary system (e.g., skin, hair, nails, and exocrine glands) and treats its diseases. The skin is our interface with the world around us and provides clues about our health. The dermatologist must have a thorough understanding of the tissues that compose the skin and how the integumentary system repairs itself when exposed to trauma. Here, a dermatologist is inspecting a patient's skin for evidence of melanoma, which is a malignant cancer of melanocytes (one cell type found in the epidermis of the skin).

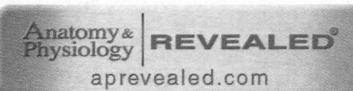

Anatomy & Physiology REVEALED®
aprevealed.com

Module 4: Integumentary System

harmful chemicals, pollutants, microbes, and damaging sunlight. It usually remains strong and pliable, is easily cleaned, is self-renewing, and is a visual indicator of our physiology and health. Changes in the color of the skin may reflect body disorders or anomalies; skin changes or lesions sometimes reflect systemic infections or disease. The scientific study and treatment of the integumentary system is called **dermatology** (der-mă-tol′ō-jē; *derma* = skin, *logos* = study). In this chapter, we examine the specific layers of the integument and the tissues that compose each layer. We also will see how the structure of the integument is related to its functions. We conclude by discussing integument repair and how the integumentary system ages.

6.1 Composition of the Integument

The integument is the body's largest organ and is composed of all tissue types that function in concert to protect internal body structures. Its surface is covered by an epithelium that protects underlying body layers. The connective tissue that underlies the epithelium provides strength and resilience to the skin. This connective tissue also contains smooth muscle associated with hair follicles (arrector pili) that alters hair position. Finally, nervous tissue detects and monitors sensory stimuli in the skin, which provide information about touch, pressure, temperature, and pain.

The integument accounts for 7% to 8% of the body weight and covers the entire body surface with an area that ranges between about 1.5 and 2.0 square meters (m^2). Its thickness ranges between 1.5 millimeters (mm) and 4 mm or more, depending on body location. The integument consists of two distinct layers: a layer of stratified squamous epithelium called the epidermis, and a deeper layer of primarily dense irregular connective tissue called the dermis (figure 6.1). Deep to the dermis is a layer of areolar and adipose connective tissue called the subcutaneous layer, or hypodermis. The subcutaneous layer is not part of the integumentary system; however, it is described in this chapter because it is closely involved with both the structure and function of the skin.

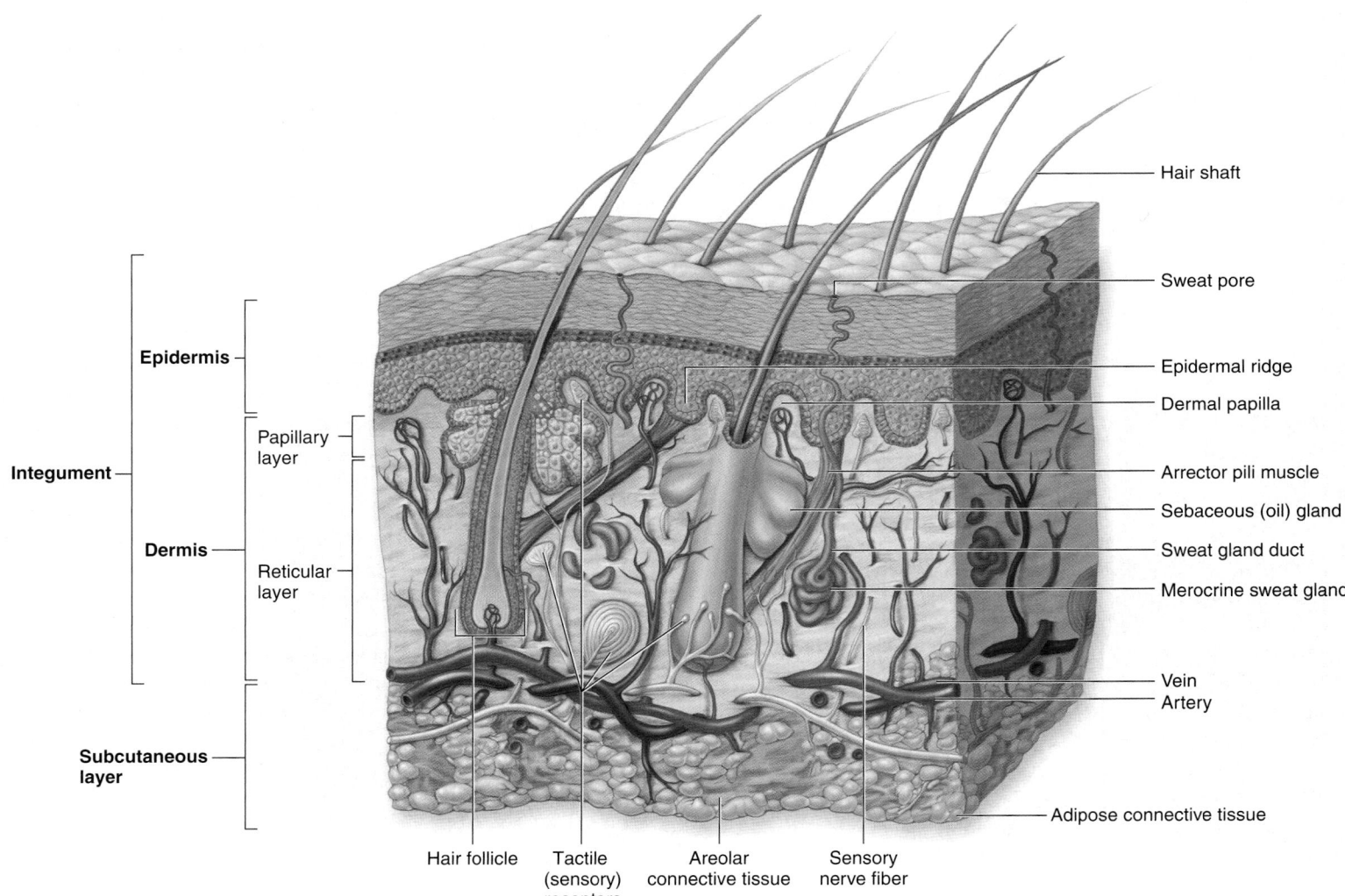

Figure 6.1 Layers of the Integument. A diagrammatic sectional view through the integument shows its relationship to the underlying subcutaneous layer. AP|R

6.1a Epidermis

LEARNING OBJECTIVES

1. Describe the five layers (strata) of the epidermis.
2. Differentiate between thick skin and thin skin.
3. Explain what causes differences in skin color.

The epithelium of the integument is called the **epidermis** (ep-i-derm'is; *epi* = on, *derma* = skin). It is a keratinized, stratified squamous epithelium.

Careful examination of the epidermis, from the basement membrane to its surface, reveals several specific layers, or strata. From deep to superficial, these layers are the stratum basale, stratum spinosum, stratum granulosum, stratum lucidum (found in thick skin only), and the stratum corneum **(figure 6.2)**. The first three strata listed are composed of living keratinocytes, whereas the most superficial two strata contain dead keratinocytes.

Stratum Basale

The deepest epidermal layer is the **stratum basale** (strat'ŭm bah-sā'lē), also known as the *stratum germinativum*, or *basal layer*. This single layer of cuboidal to low columnar cells is tightly attached to an underlying basement membrane that separates the epidermis from the connective tissue of the adjacent dermis. Three types of cells occupy the stratum basale (figure 6.2b):

1. **Keratinocytes** (ke-ra'ti-nō-sīt; *keras* = horn) are the most abundant cell type in the epidermis and are found throughout all epidermal strata. The stratum basale is dominated by large keratinocyte stem cells, which divide to generate new cells that replace dead keratinocytes shed from the surface. Their name is derived from their synthesis of **keratin,** a protein that strengthens the epidermis considerably.

2. **Melanocytes** (mel'ă-nō-sīt; *melano* = black) have long, branching processes and are scattered among the keratinocytes of the stratum basale. They produce and store the pigment **melanin** (mel'ă-nin) in response to ultraviolet light exposure. Their cytoplasmic processes transfer pigment granules, called **melanosomes,** into the keratinocytes within the basal layer and sometimes in more superficial layers. This pigment (which includes the colors black, brown, tan, or yellow-brown) accumulates around the nucleus of the keratinocyte and shields the nuclear DNA from ultraviolet radiation. The darker tones of the skin result from melanin produced by the melanocytes.

3. **Tactile cells,** also called *Merkel cells,* are few in number and found scattered among the cells within the stratum basale. Tactile cells are sensitive to touch and, when compressed, they release chemicals that stimulate sensory nerve endings, providing information about objects touching the skin.

Stratum Spinosum

Several layers of polygonal keratinocytes form the **stratum spinosum** (spī-nō'sŭm), or *spiny layer*. Each time a keratinocyte stem cell in the stratum basale divides, a daughter cell is pushed toward the external surface from the stratum basale, while the other cell remains as a stem cell in the stratum basale. Once this new cell enters the stratum spinosum, it begins to differentiate into a nondividing, highly specialized keratinocyte. Sometimes the deepest cells in this layer still undergo mitosis to help replace epidermal cells that exfoliate from the surface. The nondividing keratinocytes in the stratum spinosum attach to their neighbors by many intercellular junctions called desmosomes (described in section 4.5d).

The process of preparing epidermal tissue for observation on a microscope slide shrinks the cytoplasm of the cells in the stratum spinosum. Since the cytoskeletal elements and desmosomes remain intact, the shrunken stratum spinosum cells resemble miniature

Figure 6.2 Epidermal Strata. (*a*) Photomicrograph and (*b*) diagram compare the order and relationship of the epidermal strata in thick skin.
AP|R

porcupines that are attached to their neighbors. This spiny appearance accounts for the name of this layer.

In addition to the keratinocytes, the stratum spinosum also contains the fourth epidermal cell type called **epidermal dendritic** (*Langerhans*) **cells** (figure 6.2b). Epidermal dendritic cells are immune cells that help fight infection in the epidermis. These immune cells are often present in the stratum spinosum and stratum granulosum, but they are not identifiable in standard histologic preparations. Their phagocytic activity initiates an immune response to protect the body against pathogens that have penetrated the superficial epidermal layers as well as epidermal cancer cells. (See Chapter 22 for a detailed discussion of the immune system.)

Stratum Granulosum

The **stratum granulosum** (gran-ū-lō′sum), or *granular layer,* consists of three to five layers of keratinocytes superficial to the stratum spinosum. Within this stratum begins a process called **keratinization** (ker′ă-tin-i-zā′shŭn), where the keratinocytes fill up with the protein keratin, and in so doing, cause both the cell's nucleus and organelles to disintegrate and the cell starts to die. Keratinization is not complete until the cells reach the more superficial epidermal layers. A fully keratinized cell is dead (because it has neither a nucleus nor organelles), but it is structurally strong because of the keratin it contains.

Stratum Lucidum

The **stratum lucidum** (lū′sĭ-dum), or *clear layer,* is a thin, translucent region of about two to three cell layers that is superficial to the stratum granulosum. This stratum is found only in the thick skin within the palms of the hands and the soles of the feet. Cells occupying this layer appear pale and featureless and have indistinct boundaries. The keratinocytes within this layer are flattened and filled with the translucent protein called **eleidin** (ē-lē′ĭ-din), which is an intermediate product in the process of keratin maturation. This layer helps protect the skin from ultraviolet light.

Stratum Corneum

The **stratum corneum** (kōr′nē-ŭm; *corneus* = horny), or *hornlike layer,* is the most superficial layer of the epidermis. It is the stratum you see when you look at your skin. The stratum corneum consists of about 20 to 30 layers of dead, scaly, interlocking keratinized cells. The dead cells are **anucleate** (lacking a nucleus) and are tightly packed together.

A keratinized, or *cornified*, epithelium contains large amounts of keratin. After keratinocytes are formed from stem cells within the stratum basale, they change in structure and in their relationship to their neighbors as they progress through the different strata until they eventually reach the stratum corneum and are sloughed off its external surface. Major changes during keratinocyte migration include synthesis of keratin and the loss of the nucleus and organelles as described. What remains of these cells in the stratum corneum is essentially keratin protein enclosed in a thickened plasma membrane. Migration of the keratinocyte to the stratum corneum occurs during the first 2 weeks of the keratinocyte's life. The dead, keratinized cells usually remain for an additional 2 weeks in the exposed stratum corneum layer, providing a barrier before they are shed. Overall, individual keratinocytes are present in the integument for about 1 month following their formation.

The normally dry stratum corneum presents a thickened surface unsuitable for the growth of many microorganisms. Additionally, some secretions onto the surface of the epidermis from exocrine glands help prevent the growth of microorganisms on the epidermis, thus supporting its barrier function.

Variations in the Epidermis

The epidermis exhibits variations both between different body regions within one individual and differences between individuals. The epidermis varies in its thickness, coloration, and skin markings.

Thick Skin Versus Thin Skin   Over most of the body, the skin ranges in thickness between 1 mm and 2 mm. Skin is classified as either thick or thin based on the number of epidermal strata and the

---

Figure 6.3 Thick Skin and Thin Skin. The stratified squamous epithelium of the epidermis varies in thickness, depending upon the region of the body in which it is located. (*a*) Thick skin contains all five epidermal strata and covers the soles of the feet and the palms of the hands. (*b*) Thin skin covers most body surfaces; it contains only four epidermal strata and lacks a stratum lucidum. AP|R

relative thickness of the epidermis, rather than the thickness of the entire integument (**figure 6.3**).

Thick skin is found on the palms of the hands, the soles of the feet, and corresponding surfaces of fingers and toes. All five epidermal strata occur in the thick skin. The epidermis of thick skin ranges between 0.4 mm and 0.6 mm thick. It houses sweat glands but has no hair follicles or sebaceous (oil) glands.

Thin skin covers most of the body. It lacks a stratum lucidum, so it has only four specific layers in the epidermis. Thin skin contains the following structures: hair follicles, sebaceous glands, and sweat glands. The epidermis of thin skin ranges from 0.075 mm to 0.150 mm thick.

WHAT DO YOU THINK?

1 Why do you think thick skin lacks hair follicles and sebaceous glands? Think about the locations of where thick skin is found, and how that may interfere with the job of skin in that area.

Skin Color Normal skin color results from a combination of the colors of hemoglobin, melanin, and carotene. **Hemoglobin** (hē-mō-glō'bin; *haima* = blood) is an oxygen-binding protein present in red blood cells. It exhibits a bright red color upon binding oxygen, thus giving blood vessels in the dermis a reddish tint that is seen most easily in lightly pigmented individuals. If the blood vessels in the superficial layers vasodilate (in other words, the blood vessel diameter increases), such as during physical exertion, then the red tones are much more visible.

Melanin is a pigment produced and stored in melanocytes, and occurs in a variety of black, brown, tan, and yellow-brown shades as mentioned earlier. Recall that melanin is transferred in vesicles from melanocytes to keratinocytes in the stratum basale. Because keratinocytes are displaced toward the stratum corneum, melanocyte activity affects the color of the entire epidermis (**figure 6.4**).

Figure 6.4 Production of Melanin by Melanocytes. Melanin gives a yellow-brown to tan to brown or black color to the skin. (*a*) Vesicles in melanocytes transport the melanin pigment to the keratinocytes, where the pigment surrounds the nucleus. (*b*) Melanin is incorporated into the keratinocytes primarily of the stratum basale.

CLINICAL VIEW
UV Radiation, Sunscreens, and Sunless Tanners

The sun generates three forms of ultraviolet radiation: UVA (ultraviolet A), UVB (ultraviolet B), and UVC (ultraviolet C). The wavelength of UVA ranges between 320 and 400 nanometers (nm), that of UVB ranges between 290 and 320 nm, and UVC ranges between 100 and 280 nm. In contrast, visible light ranges begin at about 400 nm (the deepest violet). UVC rays are absorbed by the upper atmosphere and do not reach the earth's surface; UVA and UVB rays do reach the surface and can affect individuals' skin color. UVA light commonly is termed "tanning rays," whereas UVB often is called "burning rays." Many tanning salons claim to provide a safe tan because they use only UVA rays. However, UVA rays can cause burning as well as tanning, and they also inhibit the immune system. Both UVA and UVB rays are believed to cause skin cancer. Thus, there is no such thing as a healthy suntan.

Sunscreens are lotions that contain materials that absorb or block UVA and UVB rays. Sunscreens can help protect the skin, not only for light-skinned people but also for those with darker skin colors—but *only* if they are used correctly. First, sunscreen must be applied liberally over all exposed body surfaces, and reapplied after being in the water or perspiring. Second, a sunscreen must have a high enough **SPF (sun protection factor).** SPF is a number determined experimentally by exposing subjects to a light spectrum. The amount of light that induces redness in sunscreen-protected skin, divided by the amount of light that induces redness in unprotected skin, equals the SPF. For example, a sunscreen with an SPF of 15 will delay the onset of sunburn in a person who would otherwise burn in 10 minutes to 150 minutes. It is never safe, however, to assume that a sunscreen may protect you completely from the harmful rays of the sun.

Sunless tanners create a tanned, bronzed skin without UV light exposure. The most effective ones contain **dihydroxyacetone (DHA)** as their active ingredient. When applied to the epidermis, DHA interacts with the amino acids in the cells to produce a darkened, brownish color change. Because only the most superficial epidermal cells are affected, the color change is temporary and lasts about 5 to 7 days. Other sunless tanners on the market containing different chemicals do not appear to be as effective.

Sunless tanners contain no sunscreen and offer no protection against UV rays. Thus, individuals who use sunless tanners should also apply sunscreen to protect their skin.

The amount of melanin in the skin is determined by both heredity and light exposure. All people have about the same *number* of melanocytes. However, melanocyte *activity* and the *color* of the melanin produced by these cells varies among individuals and races, resulting in different skin color tones. Darker-skinned individuals have melanocytes that produce relatively more and darker melanin than lighter-skinned individuals. Further, these more active melanocytes tend to package melanin into cells in the more superficial epidermal layers, such as the stratum granulosum. Recall that exposure to ultraviolet light stimulates melanocytes to make more melanin.

Carotene (kar'ō-tēn) is a yellow-orange pigment that is acquired from various yellow-orange vegetables, such as carrots, corn, and squashes. Normally, it accumulates inside keratinocytes of the stratum corneum and in the subcutaneous fat. Within the body, carotene is converted into vitamin A, which plays an important role in normal vision. Vitamin A has also been thought to reduce potentially dangerous molecules called *free radicals* that form during normal metabolic activity in the body. Additionally, carotene may improve immune cell number and activity.

Skin Markings A **nevus** (nē-vŭs; pl., *nevi*), commonly called a *mole*, is a harmless localized overgrowth of melanin-forming cells. On rare occasions, a nevus may become malignant, typically as a consequence of excessive UV light exposure. Thus, nevi should be monitored for changes that may suggest malignancy. **Freckles** are yellowish or brown spots that represent localized areas of increased melanocyte activity, not an increase in melanocyte numbers. A freckle's degree of pigmentation varies and is dependent upon both sun exposure and heredity.

A **hemangioma** (he-man'jē-ō'mă) is an anomaly that results in skin discoloration due to blood vessels that proliferate to form a benign tumor. **Capillary hemangiomas,** or *strawberry-colored birthmarks,* appear in the skin as bright red to deep purple nodules that are usually present at birth and disappear in childhood. However, their development may occur in adults. **Cavernous hemangiomas,** also known as *port-wine stains,* involve larger dermal blood vessels and may last a lifetime.

The contours of the skin surface follow ridge patterns, varying from small conical pegs (in thin skin) to the complex arches and whorls called **friction ridges.** Friction ridges are found on the fingers (fingerprints), palms, soles, and toes **(figure 6.5)**. These ridges are formed from large folds and valleys of both dermis and epidermis. They help increase friction on contact, so that our hands can firmly

Arch

Whorl

Loop

Combination

Figure 6.5 Friction Ridges of Thick Skin. Friction ridges form fingerprints, palm prints, and toe prints. Shown here are four basic fingerprint patterns.

grasp items and our feet do not slip when we walk barefoot. Some researchers have suggested friction ridges also provide flexibility to the skin and allow it to deform without being damaged. When the sweat pores in the ridges secrete sweat, noticeable fingerprints may be left on touched surfaces. Each individual has a unique pattern of friction ridges, allowing matching of prints and identification of individuals.

WHAT DID YOU LEARN?

1 As you trim your roses, a thorn penetrates your palm through all epidermal strata. What are the layers of the epidermis penetrated, starting from the surface of the skin?

2 Briefly describe the process of keratinization. Where does it occur? Why is it important?

3 How does hemoglobin contribute to skin color?

4 What is the function of friction ridges?

6.1b Dermis

LEARNING OBJECTIVES

4. Characterize the two layers of the dermis.

5. Explain the significance of cleavage lines.

6. Describe how dermal blood vessels function in temperature regulation.

The **dermis** (der′mis) is deep to the epidermis and ranges in thickness from 0.5 mm to 3.0 mm. This layer of the integument is composed of connective tissue proper, and contains primarily collagen fibers, although both elastic and reticular fibers also are found within the dermis. Additionally, researchers recently have discovered motile cells in the dermis called dendritic cells. These cells are similar to the epidermal dendritic cells in that

they serve an immune function, yet they differ in that they are located in the dermis. Other components of the dermis are blood vessels, sweat glands, sebaceous glands, hair follicles, nail roots, sensory nerve endings, and arrector pili. Two major regions of the dermis can be distinguished: a superficial papillary layer and a deeper reticular layer (**figure 6.6**).

Papillary Layer of the Dermis

The **papillary** (pap′i-lār-ē) **layer** is the superficial region of the dermis that is found directly adjacent and internal to the epidermis. It is composed of areolar connective tissue, and it derives its name from the projections of the dermis called **dermal papillae** (der′măl pă-pil′ē; *papilla* = a nipple). The dermal papillae interdigitate with deep projections of the epidermis called **epidermal ridges.** Together, the epidermal ridges and dermal papillae increase the area of contact between the two layers and interlock them. Each dermal papilla contains the capillaries that supply nutrients to the cells of the epidermis. Additionally, dermal papillae contain sensory nerve endings that serve as tactile receptors (figure 6.1); these receptors continuously monitor touch on the surface of the epidermis. Tactile receptors are discussed in detail in section 16.2a.

Reticular Layer of the Dermis

The **reticular layer** forms the deeper, major portion of the dermis that extends from the papillary layer to the underlying subcutaneous layer. The reticular layer consists primarily of dense irregular connective tissue through which large bundles of collagen fibers project

Figure 6.6 Layers of the Dermis.
The dermis is composed of a papillary layer and a reticular layer. AP|R

Epidermis

Dermis

Papillary layer

Reticular layer

Subcutaneous layer

Epidermal ridges

Dermal papillae

Tactile (sensory) receptor

Artery

Vein

Areolar connective tissue

Adipose connective tissue

in all directions. These fibers are interwoven into a meshwork that surrounds structures in the dermis, such as the hair follicles, sebaceous glands and sweat glands, nerves, and blood vessels. The word *reticular* means "network" and refers to this meshwork of collagen fibers. Note that the reticular layer is different from reticular connective tissue, described in section 5.2d.

Lines of Cleavage, Stretch Marks, and Wrinkles

The majority of the collagen and elastic fibers in the skin are oriented in parallel bundles at specific body locations. The alignment of fiber bundles within the dermis is a result of the direction of applied stress during routine movement; therefore, the function of the bundles is to resist stress. **Lines of cleavage** (*tension lines*) in the skin identify the predominant orientation of collagen fiber bundles (**figure 6.7**). These are clinically and surgically significant because any procedure resulting in a cut at right angles to a cleavage line usually is pulled open as a result of the recoil resulting from cut elastic fibers. This often results in slow healing and increased scarring. In contrast, an incision made parallel to a cleavage line usually will remain closed. Therefore, surgical procedures should be planned to consider lines of cleavage, thus ensuring rapid healing and prevention of scarring.

Collagen fibers and elastic fibers together contribute to the observed physical characteristics of the skin. Whereas the collagen fibers impart tensile strength, elastic fibers allow some stretch and recoil in the dermis during normal movement activities. Stretching of the skin that may occur as a result of excessive weight gain or

pregnancy often exceeds the elastic capabilities of the skin. When the skin is stretched beyond its capacity, some collagen fibers are torn and result in stretch marks, called **striae** (strī′ē; *stria* = furrow). Both the flexibility and thickness of the dermis are diminished by effects of exposure to ultraviolet light and aging, causing either sagging or wrinkled skin.

Figure 6.7 Lines of Cleavage. Lines of cleavage partition the skin and indicate the predominant direction of underlying collagen fibers in the reticular layer of the dermis.

An incision perpendicular to cleavage lines may gape and delay healing.

An incision parallel to cleavage lines is more likely to heal quickly and not gape open.

Innervation and Blood Supply

The dermis of the skin has an extensive **innervation**, which refers to its distribution of nerve fibers. Sensory nerve fibers in the skin monitor stimuli in both the dermis and epidermis. Touch receptors (e.g., tactile corpuscles) detect stimuli such as pressure, vibration, and cold, and then initiate sensory input to the brain (see section 16.2). This rich innervation allows us to be very aware of our surroundings and to differentiate among the different kinds of sensory signals from receptors in the skin. In addition, motor nerve fibers extend to the skin to control both blood flow and gland secretions.

Recall that all epithelia, including the epidermis, are avascular. Therefore, blood vessels within the dermis must supply nutrients to the living cells in the epidermis as well as to the dermis. The largest of these blood vessels lie along the border between the reticular layer of the dermis and the subcutaneous layer. Smaller vessels branch into the dermis to supply the hair follicles, sweat glands, sensory receptors, and other structures housed there. The smallest arterial vessels connect to capillary loops within the dermal papillae.

Dermal blood vessels have an important role in body temperature and blood pressure regulation. **Vasoconstriction** (vā′sō; *vas* = a vessel) means that the diameters of the vessels narrow, so relatively less blood can travel through them. Since less blood can flow through these dermal blood vessels, relatively more blood must travel through blood vessels deeper under the skin. The net effect is a shunting of blood *away* from the periphery of the body and toward deeper structures. Vasoconstriction of dermal blood vessels occurs if the body is trying to conserve heat. This is why we look paler when we are exposed to cold temperatures.

Conversely, **vasodilation** of the dermal blood vessels means that the diameter of the vessels increases, so relatively more blood can travel through them. The dermal blood vessels vasodilate so

---

Table 6.1	Integument Layers and the Subcutaneous Layer AP|R		
Layer		**Specific Layer**	**Description**
INTEGUMENT: EPIDERMIS			
	Stratum corneum	Stratum corneum	Most superficial layer of epidermis; 20–30 layers of dead, flattened, anucleate, keratin-filled keratinocytes
	Stratum lucidum	Stratum lucidum	2–3 layers of anucleate, dead cells; seen only in thick skin (e.g., palms of hands, soles of feet)
	Stratum granulosum	Stratum granulosum	3–5 layers of keratinocytes with distinct granules in cytoplasm; keratinization begins in this layer
	Stratum spinosum	Stratum spinosum	Several layers of keratinocytes attached to neighbors by desmosomes; epidermal dendritic cells present
	Stratum basale	Stratum basale	Deepest, single layer of cuboidal to low columnar cells in contact with basement membrane; mitosis occurs here; contains keratinocytes, melanocytes, and tactile cells
INTEGUMENT: DERMIS			
	Papillary layer	Papillary layer	More superficial layer of dermis; composed of areolar connective tissue; forms dermal papillae
	Reticular layer	Reticular layer	Deeper layer of dermis; dense irregular connective tissue surrounding hair follicles, sebaceous glands and sweat glands, nerves, and blood vessels
SUBCUTANEOUS LAYER			
		No specific layers	Not considered part of the integument; deep to dermis; composed of areolar and adipose connective tissue

that more blood will travel close to the body surface and excess heat may be lost if the body is too warm. This additional blood flow through the dermis results in a more reddish/pinkish hue to the skin. Your face may become flushed when you exercise, for example, because your dermal blood vessels dilate in an attempt to release the excess heat.

 WHAT DID YOU LEARN?

5 Compare and contrast the papillary versus reticular layer of the dermis, with respect to their tissue type and the structures they contain.

6 What is indicated by the lines of cleavage in the skin, and why is this medically important?

7 Describe why your face becomes paler when you are outside on a cold day.

6.1c Subcutaneous Layer

LEARNING OBJECTIVE

7. List the functions of the subcutaneous layer.

Deep to the integument is the **subcutaneous** (sŭb-kū-tā′nē-ŭs; *sub* = beneath; *cutis* = skin) **layer,** also called the *hypodermis,* or *superficial fascia.* It is not considered a part of the integument. This layer consists of both areolar connective tissue and adipose connective tissue (see figure 6.1). In some locations of the body, adipose connective tissue predominates, thus the subcutaneous layer is called **subcutaneous fat.** The connective tissue fibers of the reticular layer of the dermis are extensively interwoven with those of the subcutaneous layer to stabilize the position of the skin and bind it to the underlying structures. The subcutaneous layer pads and protects the body, acts as an energy reservoir, and provides thermal insulation.

Drugs often are injected into the subcutaneous layer because its extensive vascular network promotes rapid absorption. Normally, the subcutaneous layer is thicker in women than in men, and its regional distribution also differs between the sexes. Adult males tend to accumulate subcutaneous fat primarily at the neck, upper arms, abdomen, lower back, and buttocks, while adult females accumulate adipose connective tissue primarily in the breasts, buttocks, hips, and thighs.

Table 6.1 reviews the layers of the integument and the subcutaneous layer.

 WHAT DID YOU LEARN?

8 What types of tissue form the subcutaneous layer?

6.2 Integumentary Structures Derived from Epidermis

The nails, hair, and exocrine glands of the skin all are derived from the epidermal epithelium. These structures also are known as **epidermal derivatives**, or appendages, of the integument. They formed during embryologic development as portions of the epidermis invaginated into the dermis. Both hair and nails are composed primarily of dead, keratinized epithelial cells, whereas the exocrine glands are composed of living epithelial cells.

6.2a Nails

LEARNING OBJECTIVES

1. Describe the function of nails.

2. List the main components of the nail.

Nails are scalelike modifications of the stratum corneum layer of the epidermis that form on the dorsal edges of the fingers and toes. They protect the distal tips of the digits and prevent damage or extensive distortion during jumping, kicking, or catching. Fingernails also assist us in grasping objects.

Each nail has a distal whitish **free edge,** a pinkish **nail body,** and a **nail root,** which is the proximal part embedded in the skin **(figure 6.8).** Together, these parts form the **nail plate.** The nail body covers a layer of epidermis that is called the **nail bed,** which contains only the deeper, living cell layers of the epidermis.

Most of the nail body appears pink because of the blood flowing in the underlying capillaries; the free edge of the nail appears white because there are no underlying capillaries. At the nail root and the proximal end of the nail body, the nail bed thickens to form the **nail matrix,** which is the actively growing part of the nail. The **lunula** (lū′nū-lă; *luna* = moon) is the whitish semilunar area of the proximal end of the nail body. It has a whitish appearance because a thickened stratum basale obscures the underlying blood vessels.

Along the lateral and proximal borders of the nail, folds of skin called **nail folds** overlap the nail. The **eponychium** (ep-ō-nik′ē-ŭm; *epi* = upon, *onyx* = nail), also known as the **cuticle** (kū′ti-kl), is a

Figure 6.8 Structure of a Fingernail. Nails are a hard derivative of the stratum corneum that protect sensitive fingertips. (*a*) Surface view of a fingernail. (*b*) Sagittal section showing the internal details of a fingernail. **AP|R**

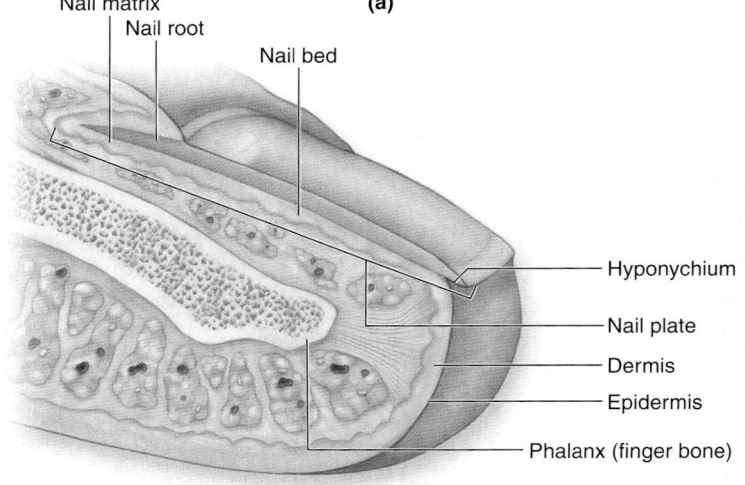

CLINICAL VIEW
Nail Disorders

Changes in the shape, structure, or appearance of the nails are clinically significant. A change may indicate the existence of a disease process affecting metabolism throughout the body. In fact, the state of a person's fingernails and toenails can be indicative of his or her overall health. Nails are subject to various disorders.

Brittle nails are prone to vertical splitting and separation of the nail plate layers at the free edge. Overexposure to water or to certain household chemicals can cause brittle nails. Keeping the nails moisturized and limiting exposure to water and chemicals can alleviate brittle nails.

An **ingrown nail** occurs when the edge of a nail digs into the skin around it. This painful condition is first characterized by pain and inflammation at the site. If left untreated, some ingrown toenails can cause infection. Ingrown nails may result from overly tight shoes and improper trimming of the nails.

Onychomycosis (on'i-kō-mī-kō'sis; *onych* = nail, *mykes* = fungus, *osis* = condition) is a fungal infection that occurs in nails constantly exposed to warmth and moisture. The fungus starts to grow under the nail and

eventually causes a yellowish discoloration, a thickened nail, and brittle, cracked edges. Fungal infections can result in permanent damage to the nail and a potential for spread of infection. Treatment involves taking oral fungal medications for long periods of time (a minimum of 6 to 12 weeks, and in some cases up to a year) to eradicate the fungal infection.

Yellow nail syndrome occurs when growth and thickening of the nail slows or stops completely. As the nail growth slows, the nails become yellowish or sometimes greenish. Yellow nail syndrome often, but not always, may be an outward sign of respiratory disease, such as chronic bronchitis.

Spoon nails, or *koilonychia* (koy-lō-nik'ēă; *koilos* = hollow, *onych* = nail), are a nail malformation where the outer surface of the nails are concave instead of convex. Spoon nails frequently are a sign of an iron deficiency. Treating the iron deficiency should alleviate the spoon nail condition.

Beau's lines run horizontally across the nail and indicate a temporary interference with nail growth at the time this portion of the nail was formed. Injury to the nail or severe illness can cause Beau's lines. They also may be seen in individuals suffering from chronic malnutrition.

Vertical ridging of the nails is common and usually does not indicate any serious medical problems. The condition occurs more frequently as we get older.

Onychomycosis

Yellow nail syndrome

Spoon nails

Beau's lines

narrow band of epidermis extending from the margin of the nail wall onto the nail body. The **hyponychium** (hi-pō-nik'ē-ŭm; *hypo* = below, *onyx* = nail) is a region of thickened stratum corneum over which the free nail edge projects.

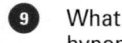 **WHAT DID YOU LEARN?**

9 What is the difference between the eponychium and the hyponychium of a fingernail?

6.2b Hair

 LEARNING OBJECTIVES

3. Describe the structure of a hair and a follicle.

4. List the functions of hair.

Hair is found almost everywhere on the body except the palms of the hands and palmar surface of the fingers, the sides and soles of the feet and toes, the lips, and portions of the external genitalia. The general structure of hair and its relationship to the integument is shown in **figure 6.9.**

Hair Type and Distribution

A single hair, or *pilus*, has the shape of a slender filament; it is composed of keratinized cells growing from hair follicles that extend

deep into the dermis, often projecting into the underlying subcutaneous layer. Differences in hair density are due primarily to differences in the texture and pigmentation of the hair.

We produce three kinds of hair during our lives: lanugo, vellus, and terminal hair. **Lanugo** (lă-nū'gō) is a fine, unpigmented, downy hair that first appears on the fetus in the last trimester of development. At birth, most of the lanugo has been replaced by similarly fine unpigmented or lightly pigmented hair called **vellus** (vel'ŭs; *vellus* = fleece). Vellus is the primary human hair and is found on the upper and lower limbs. **Terminal hair** is usually coarser, pigmented, and longer than vellus. It grows on the scalp, and it is also the hair of eyebrows and eyelashes. At puberty, terminal hair replaces vellus hair in the axillary and pubic regions, and it forms the beard on the faces of males.

Hair Structure and Follicles

Three zones can be recognized along the length of a hair: the hair bulb, root, and shaft. The **hair bulb** consists of epithelial cells and is a swelling at the base where the hair originates in the dermis. The epithelium at the base of the bulb surrounds a small **hair papilla,** which is composed of a small amount of connective tissue containing tiny blood vessels and nerves. The **root** is the portion of the hair deep to the skin surface. The **shaft** is that portion of the hair that extends beyond the skin surface. The hair bulb contains living epithelial cells, while the root and shaft consist of dead epithelial cells.

Figure 6.9 Hair. Hair is a derivative of the epithelium. (*a*) A hair grows from a follicle extending from the epidermis into the dermis. (*b*) Photomicrographs of a hair follicle. AP|R

Hair production involves a specialized type of keratinization that occurs within the **hair matrix,** a structure at the base of the hair bulb. Epithelial cells near the center of the hair matrix divide, producing new cells that are gradually pushed toward the surface. The **medulla,** not found in all hair types, is a remnant of the soft core of the matrix. It is composed of loosely arranged cells and air spaces, and contains flexible, soft keratin. Several layers of flattened cells closer to the outer surface of the developing hair form the relatively hard **cortex.** A single cell layer around the cortex forms the **cuticle,** which coats the hair.

The **hair follicle** (fol′i-kl) is an oblique tube that surrounds the hair root. It always extends into the dermis and sometimes into the subcutaneous layer. The cells of the follicle walls are organized into two principal concentric layers: an outer **connective tissue root sheath,** which originates from the dermis; and an inner **epithelial tissue root sheath,** which originates from the epidermis (figure 6.9*b*). Extending from the hair follicle to the dermal papillae are thin ribbons of smooth muscle that collectively are called the **arrector pili** (ă-rek′tŏr pī′lī). Stimulation of the arrector pili is usually a result of an emotional state, such as fear or rage, or as a response to exposure to cold temperatures. Upon stimulation, the arrector pili contracts, pulling on the hair follicle and elevating the hair, producing "goose bumps."

Functions of Hair

The millions of hairs distributed on the surface of the human body have important functions that include

- **Protection.** The hair on the head protects the scalp from sunburn and injury. Hair within the nostrils entraps particles before they travel deeper into the respiratory system, while hairs within the external ear canal protect the ear from insects and foreign particles. Eyelashes protect the eyes, and eyebrows help prevent sweat on the forehead from dripping into the eyes.

- **Heat retention.** Hair on the head prevents the loss of conducted heat from the scalp to the surrounding air. Individuals who have lost their scalp hair release much more heat through the scalp than those who have a full head of hair.

- **Sensory reception.** Hair has associated tactile receptors (hair root plexuses) that detect light touch (see section 16.2a).

- **Visual identification.** Hair characteristics are important in determining age and sex, and in identifying individuals. (Hair analysis also assists in determining animal species.)
- **Chemical signal dispersal.** Hairs help disperse *pheromones,* which are chemical signals involved in attracting members of the opposite sex and in sex recognition. Pheromones are secreted by specific sweat glands onto hairs in the axillary and pubic regions, as described shortly.

Hair Color

Hair color is a result of the synthesis of melanin in the matrix adjacent to the hair papillae. Variations in hair color reflect genetically determined differences in the structure of the melanin. Additionally, environmental and hormonal factors may influence the color of the hair. As people age, the production of pigment decreases, and thus hair becomes lighter in color. Gray hair results from the gradual reduction of melanin production within the hair follicle; white hair occurs due to a complete stoppage of melanin production.

Hair Growth and Replacement

A hair in the scalp normally grows about one-third of a millimeter per day for 2 to 5 years, and it may attain a length of about a meter. Normally, hair enters a dormant phase of about 3 to 4 months after its growth phase. A new hair begins to grow inside the follicle internal to the older hair. The older hair is pushed out and eventually falls from the follicle.

Hair growth rate and the duration of the hair growth cycle varies; however, the scalp normally loses between 10 and 100 hairs per day. Continuous losses that exceed 100 hairs per day often are an indication of a potential health problem. Sometimes hair loss may be temporary as a result of one or more of the following factors: exposure to drugs, dietary factors, radiation, high fever, or stress.

Thinning of the hair is called **alopecia** (al-ō-pē′shē-ă) and can occur in both sexes, usually as a result of aging. **Diffuse hair loss** is a condition where hair is shed from all parts of the scalp. Women primarily suffer from this condition, which may be due to hormones, medications, or iron deficiency. In males, the condition called **male pattern baldness** causes loss of hair from only some regions of the scalp rather than uniformly. It is caused by a combination of genetic and hormonal influences. The relevant gene has two alleles, one for uniform hair growth and one for baldness. The baldness allele is dominant in males and is expressed only in the presence of the high level of testosterone that is characteristic of men. In men who are either heterozygous or homozygous for the baldness allele, testosterone causes the terminal hair of the scalp to be replaced by thinner vellus, beginning on the top of the head and later, the sides. In females, the baldness allele is recessive.

WHAT DID YOU LEARN?

10 What are the three portions of a hair?

11 How does hair function in protection and heat retention?

6.2c Exocrine Glands of the Skin

LEARNING OBJECTIVES

5. Differentiate between the two types of sweat glands.

6. Describe the function of sebaceous glands.

7. Name two other modified integumentary glands.

The skin houses many types of exocrine glands. The two most common types of exocrine glands are **sweat** (*sudoriferous*) **glands** and **sebaceous glands;** these are shown in **figure 6.10.**

Sweat Glands

The two different groups of sweat glands in the skin are merocrine (*eccrine*) sweat glands and apocrine sweat glands. Both have a coiled, tubular secretory portion that is located in the reticular layer of the dermis, and a **sweat gland duct** that carries the secretion to the surface of the epidermis (in a merocrine gland) or into a hair follicle (in an apocrine gland). The opening of the sweat gland duct on the epidermal surface is an indented region called a **sweat pore.**

Both types of sweat glands contain myoepithelial cells. These specialized epithelial cells are sandwiched between the secretory gland cells and the underlying basement membrane. In response to sympathetic nervous system stimulation, myoepithelial cells contract to squeeze the gland, causing it to discharge its accumulated secretions.

WHAT DO YOU THINK?

2 The sympathetic nervous system is a part of the nervous system that can be activated when we are frightened or nervous. What would you expect to happen to sweat gland production and secretion when we are frightened or nervous?

Merocrine Sweat Glands **Merocrine** (*eccrine*) **sweat glands** (figure 6.10*b*) are the most numerous and widely distributed sweat glands. The adult integument contains between 3 and 4 million merocrine sweat glands. They are simple, coiled tubular glands that discharge their secretions directly onto the surface of the skin. The clear secretion they release by exocytosis (see section 5.1d) is called **sweat;** it consists of approximately 99% water and 1% other chemicals that include electrolytes (primarily sodium and chloride), metabolites (lactic acid), and waste products (urea and ammonia).

The major function of merocrine sweat glands is **thermoregulation,** which is the regulation of body temperature by evaporation of fluid from the skin (see section 1.5b). Merocrine sweat gland secretions provide a means for the loss of both water and electrolytes. The secretions also may help eliminate a number of ingested drugs. Finally, merocrine sweat gland secretions provide some protection from environmental hazards both by diluting harmful chemicals and by preventing the growth of microorganisms (antibacterial activity).

Apocrine Sweat Glands **Apocrine sweat glands** (figure 6.10*c*) are coiled, tubular glands that release their secretion into hair follicles in the axillae, around the nipples, in the pubic region, and in the anal region. Originally, these glands were called *apocrine* because their cells were thought to secrete their product by an apocrine mechanism (meaning that the apical portion of the cell's cytoplasm pinches off and, along with cellular components of the apical region, becomes the secretory product—see section 5.1d). Now, researchers have shown that both apocrine and merocrine sweat glands produce their secretion by exocytosis. However, the secretory portion of an apocrine gland has a much larger lumen than that of a merocrine gland, and the secretions they produce are different, so these glands continue to be called apocrine glands. The secretion they produce is viscous and cloudy, and it contains both proteins and lipids that are acted upon by bacteria to produce a distinct, noticeable odor. (Underarm deodorant is designed to mask the odor while a deodorant with antiperspirant also helps prevent the formation of sweat.) These sweat glands become active and produce secretions beginning around puberty.

Sebaceous Glands

Sebaceous glands are holocrine glands that produce an oily, waxy secretion called **sebum** (sē′bŭm; *sebum* = tallow) that is usually dis-

Sweat pore

Sweat gland duct

Hair follicle

Sebaceous gland

Merocrine sweat gland

Arrector pili muscle

Apocrine sweat gland

(a)

Merocrine sweat gland duct

(b) Merocrine sweat gland

Apocrine sweat gland duct

(c) Apocrine sweat gland

Hair follicle

Sebaceous glands

(d) Sebaceous glands

Figure 6.10 Exocrine Glands of the Skin. (*a*) The integument contains sweat glands and sebaceous glands. (*b*) Merocrine sweat glands have a duct with a narrow lumen that opens onto the skin surface through a pore. (*c*) Apocrine sweat glands exhibit a duct with a larger lumen to convey secretion products into a hair follicle. (*d*) The cells of sebaceous glands are destroyed during the release of their oily secretion into the hair follicle. **AP|R**

charged into a hair follicle and onto the hair itself. Sebum acts as a lubricant to keep the skin and hair from becoming dry, brittle, and cracked. Sebum also has some bactericidal (bacteria-killing) properties. Several sebaceous glands may open onto a single follicle.

The secretion of sebum is stimulated by hormones, especially androgens (male sex hormones). Sebaceous glands are relatively inactive during childhood; however, they are activated during puberty in both sexes, when the production of sex hormones increases (see section 28.1b).

Other Integumentary Glands

Some specialized glands of the integument are restricted to specific locations. Two important examples are the ceruminous glands and the mammary glands.

Ceruminous (sĕ-rū′mi-nŭs) **glands** are modified apocrine sweat glands located only in the external acoustic meatus (ear canal), where their secretion forms a waterproof earwax called **cerumen** (sĕ-rū′men). Both cerumen and the tiny hairs in the meatus help trap foreign particles or small insects and keeps them from reaching the eardrum. Cerumen also helps lubricate the external acoustic meatus and eardrum.

The **mammary glands** of the breasts are modified apocrine sweat glands. Both males and females have mammary glands, but

these glands only become functional in pregnant and lactating females, when they produce milk, a secretion that nourishes offspring. The development of the glands and its secretions are controlled by a complex interaction between gonadal and pituitary hormones, discussed in section 28.3.

WHAT DID YOU LEARN?

12 How do apocrine sweat glands differ from merocrine sweat glands in terms of their location, secretions, and function?

13 What do sebaceous glands secrete, and where is this material secreted?

6.3 Functions of the Integument: Protection and More

The integument is more than just a wrapping around the body. It serves many varied functions. Here we've subdivided these functions into those performed primarily by the epidermis and those performed primarily by the dermis.

6.3a Epidermis Functions

LEARNING OBJECTIVES

1. Name ways in which the epidermis protects the body and prevents water loss.

2. Describe the epidermis' involvement in calcium and phosphorus utilization.

3. Describe the integument's role in secretion and absorption.

4. Identify the immune cells that reside in the integument, and describe their actions.

The epidermis serves a protective function, helps prevent water loss, and is involved with metabolic regulation. The epidermis and the dermis together secrete and absorb materials, and both play a role in immunity. We explore these functions in detail.

Protection

The epidermis acts as a physical barrier that protects the entire body from physical injury and trauma. It offers protection against harmful chemicals, toxins, microbes, and excessive heat or cold. The skin also protects deeper tissues from solar radiation, especially UV rays. When exposed to the sun, the melanocytes become more active and produce more melanin, thus giving the skin a tanned look. Even when you get a sunburn, the deeper tissues (muscles and internal organs) remain unaffected.

Prevention of Water Loss

The epidermis is water resistant and helps prevent unnecessary water loss. (If the skin were *not* water resistant, then each time you took a bath you would swell up like a sponge as the skin absorbed water!) Water cannot easily exit the skin, unless it is specifically secreted by the sweat glands. The skin also prevents the water within the body cells and in the interstitial fluid (fluid in the spaces between the cells) from "leaking out." When the skin is severely burned, one of the main dangers is dehydration, because without the protective skin barrier, water can escape from body tissues.

Although the epidermis is water resistant, it is not entirely waterproof. Some interstitial fluids slowly penetrate through the epidermis to the surface, where they evaporate into the surrounding air, a process called transpiration (see section 25.2). Transpiration is the release of water vapor from sweat glands when we are *not* sweating.

Metabolic Regulation

Vitamin D₃, also called **cholecalciferol** (kō′lē-kal-sif′er-ol), is synthesized from a steroid precursor by the keratinocytes when they are exposed to ultraviolet radiation. Vitamin D₃ is then released into the blood and transported to the liver where it is converted to another intermediate molecule (calcidiol), and then transported to the kidney where it is converted to **calcitriol** (kal-si-trī′ol). Calcitriol is the active form of vitamin D and is considered a hormone (see section 7.6a). It increases absorption of calcium and phosphate from the

---

INTEGRATE

CLINICAL VIEW
Acne and Acne Treatments

Acne (ak′nē) is the term used to describe plugged sebaceous ducts. Acne typically becomes abundant beginning at puberty, because increases in hormone levels stimulate sebaceous gland secretion, making the pores more prone to blockage. Acne is prevalent during the teenage years, although any age group may experience acne.

The types of acne lesions include

- **Comedo** (kom′ē-dō). A sebaceous gland plugged with sebum. An open comedo is called a **blackhead,** because the plugged material has a dark, blackish appearance. A closed comedo is called a **whitehead,** because the top surface is whitish in color.

- **Papule** (pap′ūl) and **pustule** (pŭs′tyūl). Both are dome-shaped lesions. Papules typically are fluid-filled, form red elevations on the skin and do not contain pus. Papules may become pustules,

which are filled with a mixture of white blood cells, dead skin cells, and bacteria (called pus).

- **Nodule** (nod′ūl). Similar to a pustule, but extending into the deeper skin layers and usually rupturing the hair follicle wall. Nodules can be prone to scarring.

- **Cyst.** A large, fluid-filled nodule that can become severely inflamed and painful and can lead to scarring of the skin.

Many medicinal treatments are available for acne, depending upon the type and severity. The effectiveness of the following medications varies from individual to individual. These treatments include benzoyl peroxide, salicylic (sal-i-sil′ik) acid, topical and oral antibiotics, topical vitamin A-like compounds (e.g., retinoids such as tretinoin [Retin-A]), and systemic retinoids such as isotretinoin (e.g., Accutane).

Other treatments include light chemical skin peels and comedo extraction by a dermatologist. Untreated acne, if severe, can lead to scarring, as can picking at the acne lesions.

Blackhead
(open comedo)

Whitehead
(closed comedo)

Pustule

Nodule

Cyst

small intestine into the blood. Thus, the synthesis of vitamin D_3 is important in regulating the levels of calcium and phosphate in the blood. As little as 10 to 15 minutes of direct sunlight a day provides your body with its daily vitamin D.

The skin also is involved in other forms of metabolic regulation. It is able to convert some compounds to slightly different forms that may be used by the skin. For example, when topical corticosteroids (e.g., hydrocortisone) are applied to the skin, the corticosteroid medication enters the keratinocytes, where the cells convert and use the medication to stop the inflammation and itching. In addition, UV rays stimulate the melanocytes to produce melanin, giving the skin a more tanned look.

WHAT DO YOU THINK?

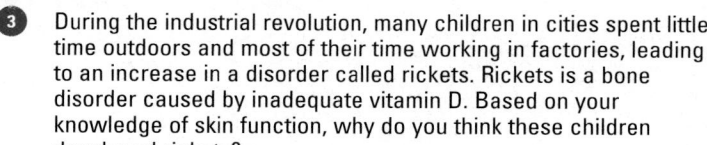

3 During the industrial revolution, many children in cities spent little time outdoors and most of their time working in factories, leading to an increase in a disorder called rickets. Rickets is a bone disorder caused by inadequate vitamin D. Based on your knowledge of skin function, why do you think these children developed rickets?

Secretion and Absorption

Skin exhibits a secretory function when it discharges substances from the body during sweating. Sweating occurs when the body needs to cool itself off. Notice that sweat sometimes feels "gritty" because of the waste products being secreted onto the skin surface. These substances include water, salts, and *urea,* a nitrogen waste product of body cells. The amount of urea, salts, and water secreted can be adjusted by the skin, and in so doing, the skin alters electrolyte levels in the body (see chapter 25). Thus, the skin also plays a role in electrolyte homeostasis. Sebum, excreted by sebaceous glands, lubricates the skin surface and hair.

The skin can absorb certain chemicals and drugs, such as estrogen from a birth control patch or nicotine from a nicotine patch. Thus, the skin is referred to as being **selectively permeable** because some materials are able to pass through it, while others are effectively blocked. In a process called **transdermal administration,** drugs that are soluble either in oils or lipid-soluble carriers may be administered transdermally by an adhesive patch that keeps the drug in contact with the skin surface. Drugs administered in this way slowly penetrate the epidermis and can be absorbed into the blood vessels of the dermis. Transdermal patches are especially useful because they release a continual, slow absorption of the drug into the blood over a relatively long period of time. The barrier to drug diffusion through the epidermis requires that the concentration of the drug in the patch be relatively high.

Immune Function

Earlier we described a small population of immune cells within the stratum spinosum called epidermal dendritic cells. These cells play an important role in initiating an immune response against pathogens that have penetrated the skin. These cells also mount an attack against epidermal cancer cells. In addition, the dermis also contains its own population of dendritic cells, which also serve an immune function.

WHAT DID YOU LEARN?

14 How does the skin produce vitamin D?

15 Is the skin entirely waterproof? Explain.

16 Describe how the skin's selective permeability is useful for the administration of transdermal drugs.

6.3b Dermis Functions

 LEARNING OBJECTIVES

5. List some of the shared functions between the dermis and epidermis.

6. Explain how skin helps cool the body or retain warmth.

7. List the five sensations detected by the skin's sensory receptors.

The dermis shares some of its functions with the epidermis. For example, both the dermis and the epidermis secrete and absorb various substances. The dermis also contains a population of dendritic cells that serve an immune function.

Temperature Regulation

We previously discussed temperature regulation in section 1.5. Body temperature can be influenced by the vast capillary networks and sweat glands in the dermis. When the body is too warm and needs to dissipate heat, the blood vessels in the dermis vasodilate, allowing for more blood flow and helping to release heat. In addition, sweat glands release fluid onto the skin surface, and the body cools off due to evaporation of the sweat.

Conversely, when the body is cold and needs to conserve heat, the blood vessels in the dermis vasoconstrict, so more blood is shunted to deeper body tissues, conserving the warmth from the blood. Note how on a cold day your face may be paler than normal. When you come in from the cold, your face may become flushed as your body adjusts to the warmer temperature.

Sensory Reception

The skin contains numerous sensory receptors. These receptors are located primarily in the dermis (some are in the epidermis) and detect heat, cold, touch, pressure, and vibration. Because the skin is responsible for perceiving many stimuli, it needs different sensory receptor types to detect, distinguish, and interpret these stimuli.

Figure 6.11 illustrates how the anatomy of the integument is designed to help with these various functions.

WHAT DID YOU LEARN?

17 What are some ways the skin can dissipate excess heat?

INTEGRATE

CONCEPT CONNECTION

The integumentary system protects virtually all body systems and provides the first line of defense against pathogens and toxins trying to enter the body.

- The integument prevents fluid loss, and thus helps the cardiovascular system maintain blood volume.
- When muscular exertion generates heat, the integumentary system helps release excess heat via sweating and vasodilation.
- The integument provides abundant sensory information to the nervous system.
- The integument can synthesize the vitamin D that is required for calcium homeostasis.
- Dendritic cells work with the rest of the immune system in initiating an immune response.
- Hairs in the nasal cavity help the respiratory system filter inspired air.
- The integumentary system and the urinary system both excrete nitrogenous waste products.

Figure 6.11 How Integument Form Influences Its Functions.
(a) The epidermis is composed of multiple layers of keratinized epithelial cells that make it well suited for protection and prevention of water loss. It also participates in secretion and absorption, metabolic regulation, and immunity. (b) The dermis is composed of well-vascularized connective tissue that participates in temperature regulation, secretion, absorption and sensory reception.

Epidermis

Dermis

Subcutaneous layer

Keratinized stratified squamous epithelium

Areolar connective tissue

Dense irregular connective tissue

(b) Dermis Functions

TEMPERATURE REGULATION

Dilating blood vessels in the dermis release heat; constricting vessels conserve heat.

Sweat glands release fluid onto the skin surface, and the body cools off by evaporation of the sweat.

Sensory receptors

Sensory nerve fiber

SECRETION AND ABSORPTION

Sweat glands secrete sodium, water, and urea onto the epidermal surface, and in so doing help maintain electrolyte homeostasis.

Sebaceous glands secrete sebum, which lubricates the skin and also helps make the integument water resistant.

Sweat gland

Sebaceous gland

Sensory receptors

SENSORY RECEPTION

A variety of sensory receptors structures detect and relay pain, heat, cold, touch, pressure, and vibration. (Note: There also are some sensory receptors in the epidermis.)

(a) Epidermis Functions

Stratum corneum

Stratum spinosum

Stratum basale

Melanocyte

Epidermal dendritic cell

PROTECTION

Toxins, microbes, UV light

Epidermal strata provide layers of protection against harmful chemicals, toxins, microbes, and excessive heat or cold. Skin also protects deeper tissues from UV radiation as melanocytes are stimulated to produce more melanin.

METABOLIC REGULATION

Upon exposure to UV rays, keratinocytes produce vitamin D_3 and melanocytes are stimulated to produce more melanin, giving the skin a more tanned look.

Sunlight

PREVENTION OF WATER LOSS

The epidermis is water resistant and keeps water from easily exiting the skin.

SECRETION AND ABSORPTION

Materials (e.g., sebum, sodium, water, urea) secreted by dermal structures are released onto the epidermal surface. The skin is selectively permeable because some materials (e.g., certain drugs, like nicotine and estrogen patches) may be absorbed while others are blocked.

Transdermal nicotine patch

IMMUNE FUNCTION

Pathogen

Epidermal dendritic cells engulf and destroy pathogens, alert the immune system to the presence of pathogens, and initiate an immune response. (Note: The dermis contains its own dendritic cells.)

6.4 Repair and Regeneration of the Integumentary System

LEARNING OBJECTIVES

1. Distinguish between regeneration and fibrosis.
2. Describe the process of wound healing.

The components of the integumentary system exhibit a tremendous ability to respond to stressors, trauma, and damage. Repetitive mechanical stresses applied to the integument stimulate mitotic activity in the stem cells of the stratum basale, resulting in a thickening of the epidermis and an improved ability to withstand stress. For example, walking about without shoes causes the soles of the feet to thicken, thus providing more protection for the underlying tissues.

Damaged tissues are normally repaired in one of two ways. The replacement of damaged or dead cells with the same cell type is called **regeneration.** This restores organ function. When regeneration is not possible because part of the organ is too severely damaged or its cells lack the capacity to divide, the body fills in the gap with scar tissue. This process, known as **fibrosis,** effectively binds the damaged parts back together. The replacement scar tissue is produced by fibroblasts and is composed primarily of collagen fibers. Some structural restoration occurs; however, functional activities are not restored. Fibrosis is the repair response in tissues subjected to severe injuries or burns.

Both regeneration and fibrosis may occur in the healing of damage to the skin. **Figure 6.12** illustrates stages in wound healing of the skin.

(1) Cut blood vessels initiate bleeding into the wound. The blood brings clotting proteins, numerous leukocytes (white blood cells), and antibodies.

(2) A blood clot forms, temporarily patching the edges of the wound together and acting as a barrier to prevent the entry of pathogens into the body. Internal to the clot, macrophages and neutrophils (two types of leukocytes, see section 18.3d) clean the wound of cellular debris.

(3) The cut blood vessels regenerate and grow in the wound. A soft mass deep in the wound becomes **granulation** (gran'ū-lā-shŭn) **tissue,** which is a vascular connective tissue that initially forms in a healing wound. Macrophages within the wound begin to remove the clotted blood. Fibroblasts produce new collagen fibers in the region.

(4) Epithelial regeneration of the epidermis occurs due to division of epithelial cells at the edge of the wound. These new epithelial cells migrate over the wound, creeping internally to the now superficial remains of the clot (the scab). The connective tissue is replaced by fibrosis.

INTEGRATE

CLINICAL VIEW

Psoriasis

Psoriasis (sō-rī'-ă-sis) is a chronic autoimmune skin disease that has periods of flare-ups and remissions throughout a person's lifetime. A type of leukocyte called a T-lymphocyte mistakenly attacks the keratinocytes, causing rapid overgrowth and overproduction of new skin cells. The normal sloughing-off cycle of keratinocytes is thrown out of balance, and the proliferation of cells develops into patches of typically whitish, scaly skin (called *plaques*) that form on the epidermal surface. The plaques are not contagious, but for the affected individual they may cause severe itching, pain, and skin cracking and bleeding. Any part of the skin may be affected, but common areas of involvement include the scalp, the limbs, and the buttocks. Treatments for psoriasis include topical corticosteroids, ultraviolet light therapy, and certain oral medications (e.g., methotrexate) that may interfere with the production of skin cells.

Multiple whitish plaques on the forearm of a person with psoriasis.

Wound

Epidermis

Dermis

Leukocyte

(1) Cut blood vessels bleed into the wound.

Blood clot

Macrophages

Fibroblast

Neutrophils

(2) Blood clot forms, and leukocytes clean wound.

Blood clot

Granulation tissue

Macrophages

Regrowth of blood vessel

Fibroblast

(3) Blood vessels regrow, and granulation tissue forms.

Scab

Regenerated epidermis

Scar tissue (fibrosis)

Fibroblast

(4) Epithelium regenerates, and connective tissue fibrosis occurs.

Figure 6.12 Stages in Wound Healing. Cut blood vessels in tissue initiate the process of wound healing.

The skin repair and regeneration process is not rapid. The wider and deeper the surface affected, the longer it takes for skin to be repaired. Additionally, the area under repair usually is more susceptible to complications due to fluid loss and infection. As the severity of the damage increases, the repair and regeneration ability of the integument is strained and its return to its original condition becomes much less likely. Some integumentary system components that are not repaired following severe damage to the integument include hair follicles, exocrine glands, nerves, and the arrector pili muscle cells.

 WHAT DID YOU LEARN?

18 What is granulation tissue, and when does it appear during wound healing of the skin?

CLINICAL VIEW
Burns

Burns are a major cause of accidental death and are usually caused by heat, radiation, harmful chemicals, sunlight, or electrical shock. The immediate threat to life results primarily from fluid loss, infection, and the effects of burned, dead tissue.

Burns are classified by depth of tissue involvement. First- and second-degree burns are called *partial-thickness burns;* third-degree burns are called *full-thickness burns.*

How are first-, second-, and third-degree burns distinguished?

First-degree burns involve only the epidermis and are characterized by redness, pain, and slight edema. An example is a mild sunburn. Treatment involves immersing the burned area in cool water or applying cool, wet compresses, possibly followed by covering the burn with sterile, nonadhesive bandages. The healing time averages about 3 to 5 days, and typically there is no scarring.

Second-degree burns involve the epidermis and part of the dermis. The skin appears red, tan, or white. The skin also is blistered and painful. Examples include very severe sunburns (where the skin also blisters) or scalding from hot liquids or chemicals. The treatment is similar to that for first-degree burns, and care must be taken not to break the blisters, which would increase risk of infection. Applying ointments to the blisters is not recommended, because the ointments can retain heat in the burned area. In addition, burned limbs should be elevated to prevent swelling. Healing times are approximately 2 to 4 weeks, and slight scarring may occur.

Third-degree burns involve the epidermis, dermis, and subcutaneous layer, which often are destroyed. Third-degree burns typically are caused by contact with corrosive chemicals or fire, or prolonged contact with extremely hot water. Dehydration is a major concern with a third-degree burn, because the entire portion of skin has been lost, and water cannot be retained in the area. Third-degree burn victims must be aggressively treated for dehydration, or they may die. In addition, patients typically are given antibiotics because risk of infection is very great. The treatment may vary slightly, depending upon what caused the burn. Most third-degree burns require hospitalization. Skin grafting typically is needed for patients with third-degree burns, since the entire dermis and its vasculature are destroyed and regeneration is limited. A **skin graft** is a piece of skin transplanted from one part of the body to another to cover a destroyed area. Skin grafts help prevent infection and dehydration in the affected area, and they also help minimize abnormal connective tissue fibrosis and disfigurement.

How is the overall severity of a burn injury determined?

The severity of a burn injury is measured not only by the degree of the burn, but also by the age of the patient, the general size of the burn, and the location of the burn. For example, a burn on the face may require more extensive treatment than a similar burn on an extremity. The **rule of nines** is used to

First-degree burn

Second-degree burn

Third-degree burn

6.5 Development and Aging of the Integumentary System

The integumentary system structures are derived from both ectoderm and mesoderm germ layers (see section 5.6a). The ectoderm is the origin of the epidermis, whereas the mesoderm is the origin of the dermis.

6.5a Integument and Integumentary Derivatives Development

LEARNING OBJECTIVES

1. Describe how integument develops from two germ layers.
2. Explain the developmental origins of nails, hair, and glands.

By the end of the seventh week of development, the ectoderm forms a layer of squamous epithelium that flattens and then becomes both a covering layer called the **periderm,** and an underlying basal layer. The basal layer will form the stratum basale and all other epidermal layers. By the twenty-first week, the stratum corneum and friction ridges form. During the fetal period, the periderm is eventually sloughed off. The sloughed-off cells mix with sebum secreted by the sebaceous glands, producing a waterproof protective coating called the **vernix caseosa** that coats the skin of the fetus.

The dermis is derived from mesoderm. During the embryonic period, this mesoderm becomes **mesenchyme.** The mesenchymal cells begin to form the components of the dermis at about eleven weeks.

Fingernails and toenails start to form in the tenth week of development. The fingernails reach the tips of the fingers by 32 weeks, whereas the toenails become fully formed by about 36 weeks.

estimate surface area of a burn. Simply put, most major body areas approximately account for some factor of 9% of the total body surface area. In adults, the anterior and posterior parts of the head and neck count 9% of the total body surface area, each upper limb counts 9%, each lower limb and gluteal region counts 18%, the anterior trunk counts 18%, the posterior trunk counts 18%, and the perineum is 1%. Estimating surface area of a burn is critical for determining appropriate fluid replacement. The greater the surface area of the burn, the greater the volume of fluids that are lost, and these fluids must be replaced, either orally or intravenously.

Burns are considered very severe or critical if one of the following criteria is met:

1. Over 25% of the body has second-degree burns.
2. Over 10% of the body has third-degree burns.
3. Third-degree burns are present on the hands, feet, face, or perineum.

What treatments are used for burn injuries?

In general, acute treatment involves managing fluid loss, relieving swelling, pain management, removing dead tissue and foreign material from the wound (debridement), controlling infection, and increasing caloric intake.

Swelling also may occur as the blood capillaries become more permeable ("leaky"), and fluid may collect in localized tissues, which exacerbates the overall fluid loss in the circulation. In severe cases, a procedure called an **escharotomy** (es-kă-rot′ō-mē) is performed, where an incision is made in the dermis to lessen the constriction caused by the swelling.

Pain medications may be given to alleviate any discomfort from the burn and resulting swelling. Antibiotics and other medications may be given to help limit and prevent infection.

Finally, individuals with severe burns become hypermetabolic as the body attempts to heal, and so their demand for nutrition greatly increases. The burn patient must be given additional caloric intake, sometimes as much as two to three times their normal caloric intake, to meet the demands. Typically, this supplementary nutrition is given through feeding tubes, IVs, or both.

Rule of nines method to determine the extent of burn in adults and infants.

Hair follicles begin to appear between 9 and 12 weeks of development as pockets of cells, called **hair buds,** invade the dermis from the overlying stratum basale of the epidermis. These hairs do not become easily recognizable in the fetus until about the twentieth week. Finally, sweat and sebaceous glands develop from the stratum basale of the epidermis and first appear at about 20 weeks on the palms and soles and later in other regions.

WHAT DID YOU LEARN?

19 What two primary germ layers form the integument?

6.5b Aging of the Integument

LEARNING OBJECTIVES

3. Explain changes to the skin with age.
4. List factors that contribute to skin aging.

Although some adolescents develop acne when they enter puberty, most skin problems do not become obvious until an individual reaches middle age. Then, the skin repair processes take longer to complete because of a reduced number and activity of stem cells. Skin repair and regeneration activities that took 3 weeks in a healthy young person often take twice that time for a person in the seventh decade of life. Additionally, the reduced stem cell activity in the epidermis results in a thinner skin that is less likely to protect against abrasive, mechanical trauma.

Collagen fibers in the dermis decrease in number and organization, and elastic fibers lose elasticity. Years of particular facial expressions (squinting, smiling) produce crease lines in the integument. As a result, the skin forms wrinkles and becomes less resilient. In addition, the skin's immune responsiveness is diminished by a decrease in the number and efficiency of epidermal dendritic cells. Also, hair follicles either produce thinner hairs or stop production entirely.

CLINICAL VIEW
Botox and Wrinkles

Many individuals have explored ways to diminish the appearance of age-related wrinkles. One popular treatment for wrinkles caused by repeated facial muscle expression is Botox. This medicine is derived from the toxin produced by the bacterium *Clostridium botulinum*. Although large doses of this toxin may be deadly, small therapeutic doses temporarily block nerve impulses to the facial expression muscles, thereby decreasing or eliminating the wrinkles they produce.

The procedure is done in a doctor's office, where the doctor injects Botox in the specific facial muscles responsible for the wrinkles, such as frown lines and crows' feet. The effect is temporary, and an individual must repeat the procedure after about four months, as the muscles regain their function.

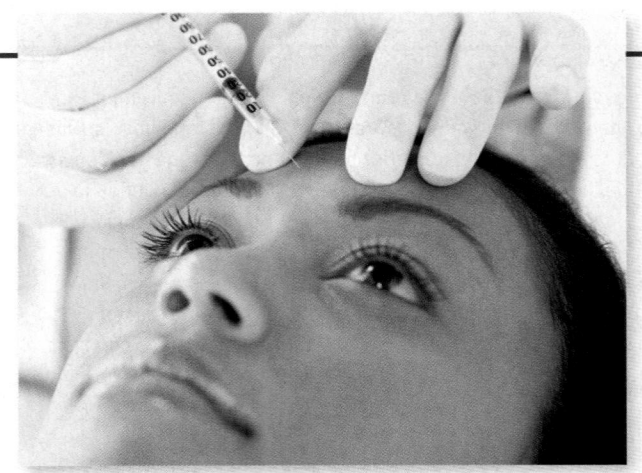

Botox is relatively safe, but some individuals may experience adverse effects, and overuse of Botox can produce a face that appears frozen and devoid of much facial expression.

Chronic overexposure to UV rays can damage the DNA in epidermal cells and accelerate aging, and it is the predominant factor in the development of nearly all skin cancers. Skin cancer is the most common type of cancer. It occurs most frequently on the head and neck regions, followed by other regions commonly exposed to the sun. Fair-skinned individuals, especially those who had severe sunburns as children, are most at risk for skin cancer.

Skin cancer can arise in anyone of any age. Individuals should use sunscreen regularly and avoid prolonged exposure to the sun.

An individual should regularly and thoroughly inspect his or her skin for any changes, such as an increase in the number or size of moles, or appearance of new skin lesions. In addition, a person should be examined routinely by a dermatologist. **Table 6.2** compares and describes the three main types of skin cancer.

WHAT DID YOU LEARN?

20 How do UV rays contribute to skin aging?

Table 6.2	Skin Cancer
Appearance	**Type/Description**
	Basal cell carcinoma Most common type of skin cancer Least dangerous type as it seldom metastasizes Originates in stratum basale First appears as small, shiny elevation Elevation enlarges, develops central depression with "pearly" edge Usually occurs on face Treated by surgical removal of lesion
	Squamous cell carcinoma Arises from keratinocytes of stratum spinosum Lesions usually appear on scalp, ears, lower lip, or dorsum of hand Early lesions are raised, reddened, scaly Later lesions form concave ulcers with elevated edges May metastasize to other parts of the body Treated by early detection and surgical removal of lesion
	Malignant melanoma Most deadly type of skin cancer due to aggressive growth and metastasis Arises from melanocytes, usually in a preexisting mole Individuals at increased risk include those who have had severe sunburns, especially as children Characterized by change in mole diameter, color, shape of border, and asymmetry Survival rate improved by early detection and surgical removal of lesion Advanced cases (metastasis of disease) difficult to cure and are treated with chemotherapy, interferon therapy, and radiation therapy

- The integumentary system includes both the skin (integument) and its derivatives (nails, hair, sweat glands, and sebaceous glands).

6.1 Composition of the Integument 185

- The integument has a superficial epidermis (composed of keratinized stratified squamous epithelium) and a deeper dermis (that is primarily dense irregular connective tissue).
- Deep to the integument is the subcutaneous layer, which helps adhere the integument to underlying structures.

6.1a Epidermis 186

- Cell types in the epidermis include keratinocytes (the most abundant cell type), melanocytes (produce melanin), epidermal dendritic cells (initiate an immune response), and tactile cells (sensitive to touch).
- The epidermis is organized into specific layers called strata. From deepest to most superficial, they are the stratum basale (deepest layer, with actively dividing keratinocytes), stratum spinosum, stratum granulosum, stratum lucidum, and stratum corneum (many layers of dead keratinocytes).
- Keratinization is the process by which keratinocytes fill up with the protein keratin, and as a result the cell dies. Keratinization begins in the stratum granulosum.
- Thick skin (palms of hands, soles of feet) has five epidermal strata, whereas thin skin (on the rest of the body) has four.
- Skin color is a result of hemoglobin in the blood vessels of the dermis, melanin pigment, and carotene pigment.

6.1b Dermis 190

- The dermis has a superficial papillary layer and a deep reticular layer.
- The papillary layer is primarily areolar connective tissue. Its dermal papillae interlock with the epidermal ridges of the epidermis.
- The reticular layer is composed of dense irregular connective tissue, and contains the hair follicles and the secretory portions of glands.
- The dermis contains abundant innervation and a rich blood supply. Vasodilation of these blood vessels causes increased circulation to the skin and a loss of excess heat through the blood, whereas vasoconstriction results in decreased circulation to the skin and a conservation of heat from the blood.

6.1c Subcutaneous Layer 193

- The subcutaneous layer protects body parts, acts as an energy reservoir, and provides thermal insulation.

6.2 Integumentary Structures Derived from Epidermis 193

- Nails, hair and the exocrine glands of the skin are all derived from the epidermis, and are known as epidermal derivatives.

6.2a Nails 193

- Nails are formed from the stratum corneum layer of the epidermis; they protect the digits and aid in grasping objects.

6.2b Hair 194

- Hair consists of a bulb (a swelling where the hair originates in the dermis), a root (the portion of the hair deep to the skin surface), and the shaft (the portion of the hair that extends beyond the skin surface).
- Arrector pili muscles can contract to elevate the hair.
- Among the functions of hair are protection, heat retention, sensory reception, visual identification, and chemical signal (pheromone) dispersal.

6.2c Exocrine Glands of the Skin 196

- Merocrine sweat glands produce a watery secretion called sweat.
- Apocrine sweat glands produce a viscous secretion that, when acted upon by bacteria, produces a noticeable odor.
- Sebaceous glands discharge sebum onto hair follicles by holocrine secretion.
- Ceruminous glands produce cerumen (earwax) to lubricate the external acoustic meatus and eardrum.
- Mammary glands are modified apocrine sweat glands to produce breast milk.

6.3 Functions of the Integument: Protection and More 197

- The integument has numerous functions including protection, prevention of water loss, temperature regulation, metabolic regulation, immune function, sensory reception, and secretion.

6.3a Epidermis Functions 198

- The epidermis is selectively permeable; it can act as a physical barrier to some compounds yet let other materials (e.g., certain drugs) in easily.
- The epidermis is water resistant, contains immune cells that detect pathogens, and serves an absorptive and secretory function.

6.3b Dermis Functions 199

- The integument can conserve heat by constricting blood vessels in the dermis, and it can release excess heat by sweating and by dilating blood vessels in the dermis.
- The dermis works with the integument to secrete and absorb materials. It also serves a sensory reception function.

(continued on next page)

6.4 Repair and Regeneration of the Integumentary System 202	• Regeneration refers to the replacement of damaged or dead cells. Fibrosis is the replacement of damaged tissues with scar tissue. • The wider and deeper the surface affected, the longer it takes for the skin to be repaired.
6.5 Development and Aging of the Integumentary System 204	• The epidermis and epidermal derivates are derived from ectoderm, and the dermis is derived from mesoderm. **6.5a Integument and Integumentary Derivatives Development 204** • The integument begins to form during the embryonic period. • Nails start to form in the tenth week of development, hair follicles first appear between 9 and 12 weeks of development, and exocrine glands first appear during the fetal period. **6.5b Aging of the Integument 205** • As an individual ages, the skin repair processes take longer, wrinkles appear, the epidermis becomes thinner (due to reduced stem cell activity), and skin cancers may become more likely.

CHALLENGE YOURSELF

Do You Know the Basics?

____ 1. Which statement is false about sebaceous glands?

    a. They release their secretion onto a hair follicle.

    b. They release their product by apocrine secretion.

    c. They are located in the dermis.

    d. The product they secrete acts as a lubricant and waterproofer.

____ 2. The layer of the epidermis in which cells begin the process of keratinization is the

    a. stratum corneum.   c. stratum lucidum.

    b. stratum basale.   d. stratum granulosum.

____ 3. The sweat glands that communicate with skin surfaces throughout the body, producing a secretion that is primarily water, are

    a. apocrine glands.   c. sebaceous glands.

    b. merocrine glands.   d. All of these are correct.

____ 4. Which of the following is *not* a function of the integument?

    a. acts as a physical barrier

    b. stores calcium in the dermis

    c. regulates temperature through vasoconstriction and dilation of dermal blood vessels

    d. participates in immune defense

____ 5. What layer listed here contains areolar connective tissue and dermal papillae?

    a. papillary layer of dermis

    b. subcutaneous layer

    c. reticular layer of dermis

    d. epidermis

____ 6. Melanin is

    a. an orange-yellow pigment that strengthens the epidermis.

    b. a pigment that accumulates inside keratinocytes.

    c. a protein fiber that is found in the dermis.

    d. a pigment that gives the characteristic color to hemoglobin.

____ 7. A _____ degree burn typically involves the epidermis and part of the dermis. The subcutaneous layer is not affected.

    a. first-   c. third-

    b. second-   d. fourth-

____ 8. The cells in a hair follicle that are responsible for forming hair are the

    a. hair papilla cells.   c. medullary cells.

    b. matrix cells.   d. cortex cells.

____ 9. Which epidermal cell type is responsible for detecting touch sensations?

    a. keratinocyte   c. tactile cell

    b. melanocyte   d. epidermal dendritic cell

____ 10. At what stage of wound healing does granulation tissue first form?

    a. after scar tissue forms along the wound

    b. before the blood completely clots

    c. before leukocytes enter the site and clean the wound

    d. after a blood clot forms and prior to scar tissue forming

11. Describe the composition of the layers of the epidermis.

12. List the four main cell types in the epidermis, their function, and the layer(s) of the integument in which they reside.

13. Describe the tissue type and structure of the two specific layers of the dermis.

14. Compare the structure and composition of the following nail parts: nail body, nail bed, eponychium, and lunula.

15. What are the three types of hair?

16. Where are ceruminous glands located, and what do they secrete?

17. Describe how the skin is involved in vitamin D production.

18. Discuss the steps involved in wound repair of the integument.

19. What embryonic tissues form the integument?

20. What are some effects of aging on the integument?

Can You Apply What You've Learned?

1. Alexander is a 15-year-old boy with extensive acne on his nose, forehead, and cheeks. He reached puberty at age 14, at which point his acne became more abundant in these areas. What is the anatomic basis for his acne?

   a. His merocrine sweat glands have begun producing abundant amounts of sweat.
   b. His sebaceous gland ducts have become blocked.
   c. His sebaceous glands are not producing enough sebum to lubricate his skin.
   d. His apocrine sweat glands are producing a secretion that has a marked odor.

2. During anatomy lab, Susan scratched her arm and noticed that some skin cells had sloughed off. She decided to prepare a slide of these cells and examine them under a microscope. What characteristics do you expect the cells to have?

   a. polygonal cells with prominent nuclei
   b. cuboidal cells, some of which were undergoing mitosis
   c. flattened anucleate cells
   d. oval cells surrounded by abundant collagen

3. While running to class, Jennifer slipped and skinned her knee. The wound appeared superficial, yet there was extensive bleeding. Based on this information, and her knowledge of the composition of the integument, she determined that the wound penetrated

   a. the stratum corneum layer of the epidermis only.
   b. all layers of the epidermis but not the dermis.
   c. all layers of the epidermis and part of the dermis.
   d. all layers of the epidermis, dermis, and the subcutaneous layer.

Can You Synthesize What You've Learned?

1. When you are outside on a cold day, your skin is much paler than normal. Later, when you enter a warm room, your face becomes flushed. What are the reasons for the change in color of your face?

2. Teri is a 14-year-old with a bad case of acne and blackheads. Explain the probable cause(s) of Teri's skin condition.

3. As a young man, John would spend every summer afternoon at the pool for many years. As he approached the age of 50, his skin was quite wrinkled, and he discovered some suspicious growths on his face. He visited a dermatologist who removed these growths. What were the growths, and what probably caused them?

INTEGRATE

ONLINE STUDY TOOLS
www.mhhe.com/mckinleyap

Clinical Case Study: A Case of Malignant Melanoma in a Young Woman

Interactive Questions: This chapter's content is served up in a number of multimedia question formats for student study.

LearnSmart: Topics and terminology include composition of the integument; integumentary structures derived from the epidermis;

functions of the epidermis; repair and regeneration of the integumentary system; development and aging of the integumentary system

Anatomy & Physiology Revealed: Topics include thick skin and subcutaneous tissue; thick and thin skin magnifications of dermis and epidermis; fingernail structure; hair follicle structure; sebaceous glands

chapter 7

Skeletal System: Bone Structure and Function

Mention of the skeletal system conjures up images of dry, supposedly lifeless bones in various sizes and shapes. But the **skeleton** (skel'ĕ-ton; *skeletos* = dried) is much more than a supporting framework for the soft tissues of the body. The skeletal system is composed of dynamic living tissues; it interacts with all of the other organ systems and continually rebuilds and remodels itself. ➡️

Radiographers and radiology technicians use an array of medical imaging techniques (such as radiography, CT and MRI) to create images that view details of internal body structures. These imaging techniques tend to be noninvasive and are ideal for diagnosis of internal pathology and trauma. All radiographers must be able to accurately identify skeletal structures and distinguish them from associated muscles and soft tissues. In addition, the radiographer must be able to tell the difference between a broken bone and a growing bone, because both may appear similar in radiographs to the layperson.

aprevealed.com

Module 5: Skeletal System

We begin this chapter with a brief description of the skeletal system and a detailed discussion of bone anatomy, the primary organ of this system. Then we examine several important concepts of bone physiology including cartilage growth; bone formation and growth; bone remodeling; the relationship of bone, hormones, and the regulation of blood calcium; and the effects of aging on the skeletal system. Our chapter concludes with a discussion of bone fracture and repair.

7.1 Introduction to the Skeletal System

LEARNING OBJECTIVES

1. Compare and contrast compact and spongy bone.
2. Identify the types and locations of cartilage within the skeletal system.

Figure 7.1 Distribution of Cartilage in the Adult and Juvenile Skeletons. Two types of cartilage are found in the adult and juvenile skeletons: hyaline cartilage and fibrocartilage.

Our skeletal system includes the bones of the skeleton as well as cartilage, ligaments, and other connective tissues that stabilize or connect the bones.

Bones of the skeleton are the primary organs of the skeletal system. They form the rigid framework of the body and perform other functions described shortly. Two types of bone connective tissue are present in most of the bones of the body: compact bone and spongy bone. **Compact bone** (also called *dense* or *cortical* bone) is a relatively dense connective bone tissue that appears white, smooth, and solid. It makes up approximately 80% of the total bone mass. **Spongy bone** (also called *cancellous* or *trabecular* bone) is located internal to compact bone, appears porous, and makes up approximately 20% of the total bone mass. The interior cavity of bone contains a connective tissue that is either red bone marrow or yellow bone marrow.

Cartilage is a semi-rigid connective tissue that is more flexible than bone. Recall from section 5.2d that there are three subtypes of cartilage, two of which are found in the adult and juvenile skeletons (**figure 7.1**).

- **Hyaline cartilage** attaches ribs to the sternum (costal cartilage), covers the ends of some bones (articular cartilage), and is the cartilage within growth plates (epiphyseal plates). Hyaline cartilage also provides a model for the formation of most of the bones in the body.
- **Fibrocartilage** is a weight-bearing cartilage that withstands compression. It forms the intervertebral discs, the pubic symphysis (cartilage between bones of the pelvis), and cartilage pads of the knee joints (menisci).

The role of **ligaments** (dense regular connective tissue that anchors bone to bone), **tendons** (dense regular connective tissue that anchors muscle to bone), and other connective tissue structures associated with the skeletal system are described in chapter 9.

WHAT DID YOU LEARN?

1. Describe the composition of compact bone and spongy bone.
2. In what three locations of the body do you find fibrocartilage?

7.2 Bone: The Major Organ of the Skeletal System

Our bones—such as the bone of the thigh (femur) or bone of the upper arm (humerus)—are organs. Here we describe the general functions, classification based upon shape, gross anatomy, and histology of bone.

7.2a General Functions

LEARNING OBJECTIVE

1. Describe the general functions of bone.

Bones perform several basic functions: support and protection, movement, hemopoiesis, and storage of mineral and energy reserves.

Support and Protection

Bones provide structural support and serve as a framework for the entire body. Bones also protect many delicate tissues and organs from injury and trauma. The rib cage protects the heart and lungs; the cranial bones enclose and protect the brain; the vertebrae enclose the spinal cord; and the pelvis cradles urinary and reproductive organs, as well as the terminal end of the gastrointestinal tract.

Movement

Bones serve as attachment sites for skeletal muscles, other soft tissues, and some organs. Muscles attached to the bones of the skeleton contract and exert a pull on the skeleton that then functions as a system of levers. The bones of the skeleton can alter the direction and magnitude of the forces generated by the skeletal muscles. Potential movements range from powerful contractions needed for running and jumping to delicate and precise movements required to remove a splinter from the finger.

Hemopoiesis

Hemopoiesis (hē'mō-poy-ē'sis; *haima* = blood, *poiesi* = making) is the process of blood cell production. It occurs in red bone marrow connective tissue that contains stem cells that form blood cells and platelets. (The process of hemopoiesis is described in greater detail in section 18.3a.)

Storage of Mineral and Energy Reserves

Most of the body's reserves of the minerals calcium and phosphate are stored within and then released from bone. Calcium is an essential mineral for such body functions as muscle contraction, blood clotting, and nerve signal transmission. Phosphate is required for ATP utilization and is an important component of the plasma membrane.

When calcium or phosphate is needed by the body, some bone connective tissue is broken down, and the minerals are released into the blood. In addition, potential energy in the form of lipids is stored in yellow bone marrow in the shafts of some adult bones.

WHAT DID YOU LEARN?

3 What two minerals are stored in bone, and what are their functions in the body?

INTEGRATE

CONCEPT CONNECTION

Both the muscular system and the nervous system need calcium to properly function. Luckily, the skeletal system typically houses a sufficient supply of calcium that may be "tapped" by both of these systems when blood calcium levels are low.

7.2b Classification of Bones

LEARNING OBJECTIVE

2. Describe the four major classes of bones as determined by shape.

Bones appear in various shapes and sizes, depending on their function. The four classes of bone as determined by shape are long bones, short bones, flat bones, and irregular bones **(figure 7.2)**.

Long bones are greater in length than width. These bones have an elongated, cylindrical shaft (diaphysis). This is the most common bone shape. Long bones are found in the upper limbs (namely, the arm, forearm, palm, and fingers) and lower limbs (thigh, leg, sole of the foot, and toes). Long bones vary in size. The small bones in the fingers and toes are long bones, as are the larger tibia and fibula of the lower limb.

Short bones have a length nearly equal to their width. Examples of short bones include the carpals (wrist bones) and tarsals (bones in the foot). *Sesamoid bones,* which are small, sesame seed-shaped bones along the tendons of some muscles, are also classified as short bones. The patella (kneecap) is the largest sesamoid bone.

Flat bones are so named because they have flat, thin surfaces that may be slightly curved. They provide extensive surfaces for muscle attachment and protect underlying soft tissues. Flat bones

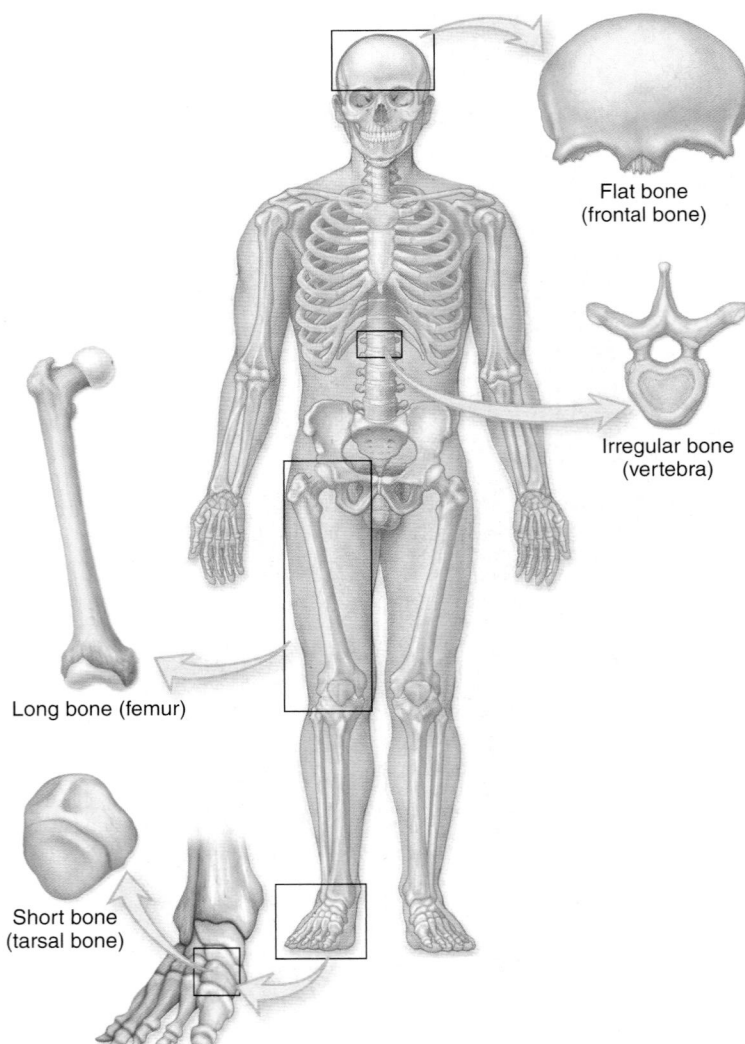

Flat bone
(frontal bone)

Irregular bone
(vertebra)

Long bone (femur)

Short bone
(tarsal bone)

Figure 7.2 Classification of Bone by Shape. *Four different classes of bone are recognized according to shape: long, short, flat, and irregular.*

form the roof of the skull, the scapulae (shoulder blades), the sternum (breastbone), and the ribs.

Irregular bones have elaborate, sometimes complex shapes and do not fit into any of the preceding categories. The vertebrae; ossa coxae (hip bones); and several bones in the skull, such as the ethmoid, sphenoid, and sutural bones, are examples of irregular bones.

WHAT DID YOU LEARN?

4 What are several examples of flat bones in the body?

7.2c Gross Anatomy of Bones

LEARNING OBJECTIVES

3. Explain the structural components of a long bone.
4. Compare the gross anatomy of other bones to that of a long bone.
5. Explain the general function of blood vessels and nerves that serve a bone.

Our discussion continues with details of the gross anatomy of a long bone. We compare it to other classes of bones, and discuss the vascularization and innervation of bone.

Gross Anatomy of a Long Bone

Long bones are the most common bone shape in the body and thus serve as a useful model of bone structure **(figure 7.3a)**.

Regions of a Long Bone   One of the principal gross features of a long bone is its shaft, which is called the **diaphysis** (dī-af'i-sis; pl., *diaphyses,* dī-af'i-sēz; growing between). The elongated, usually cylindrical, diaphysis provides for the leverage and major weight support of a long bone. Extending inward from the compact bone of the diaphysis are spicules (think spike-like structures) of spongy bone. The hollow, cylindrical space within the diaphysis is called the **medullary** (*marrow*) **cavity.** In children, this cavity contains red bone marrow, which later is replaced by yellow bone marrow in adults.

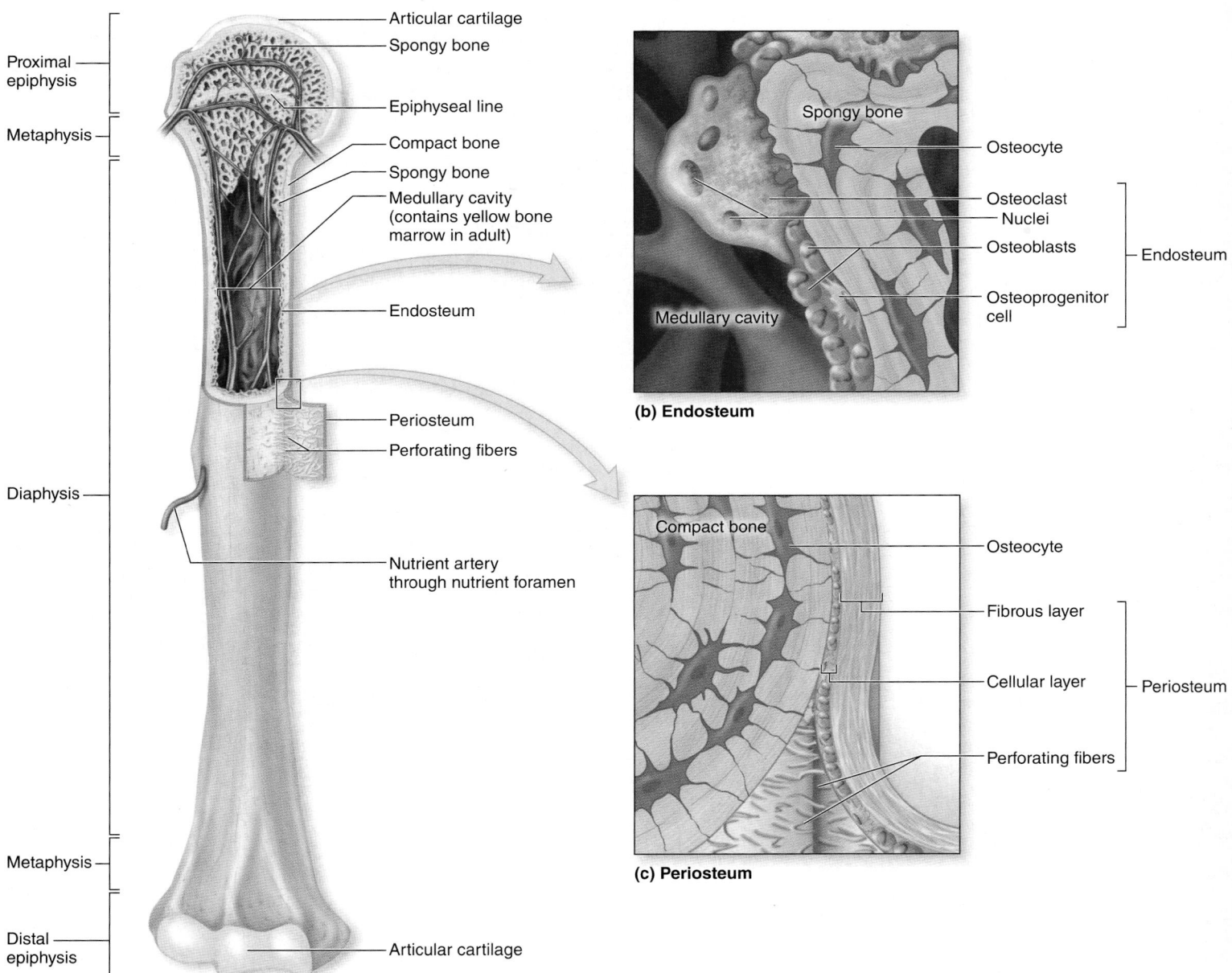

(a) Humerus, anterior view

(b) Endosteum

(c) Periosteum

Figure 7.3 Gross Anatomy of a Long Bone. Long bones support soft tissues in the limbs. (*a*) A typical long bone, such as the humerus, contains both compact and spongy bone. (*b*) The endosteum lines the internal surface of the bone along the edge of the medullary cavity. (*c*) The periosteum lines the external surface of the bone shaft. AP|R

An expanded knobby region called the **epiphysis** (e-pif'i-sis; pl., *epiphyses,* e-pif'i-sēz; *epi* = upon, *physis* = growth) is at each end of a long bone. A **proximal epiphysis** is the end of the bone closest to the body trunk, and a **distal epiphysis** is the end farthest from the trunk. An epiphysis is composed of an outer thin layer of compact bone and an inner, more extensive region of spongy bone. Spongy bone within the epiphysis resists stress that is applied from many directions. Covering the joint surface of an epiphysis is a thin layer of hyaline cartilage called the **articular cartilage.** This cartilage helps reduce friction and absorb shock in moveable joints.

The **metaphysis** (mĕ-taf'i-sis) is the region in a mature bone sandwiched between the diaphysis and the epiphysis. This region contains the **epiphyseal** (ep-i-fiz'ē-ăl), or *growth,* **plate** in a growing bone. It is a thin layer of hyaline cartilage that provides for the continued lengthwise growth of the bone. The remnant of the epiphyseal plate in adults is a thin, defined area of compact bone called the **epiphyseal line.**

Coverings and Linings of Bone A tough sheath called **periosteum** (per-ē-os'tē-ŭm; *peri* = around, *osteon* = bone) covers the outer surface of the bone except for the areas covered by articular cartilage (figure 7.3*a, c*). The periosteum consists of two layers. The outer fibrous layer of dense irregular connective tissue protects the bone from surrounding structures, anchors blood vessels and nerves to the surface of the bone, and serves as an attachment site for ligaments and tendons. The inner cellular layer includes osteoprogenitor cells, osteoblasts, and osteoclasts. The function of these cells is described shortly. The periosteum is anchored to the bone by numerous collagen fibers called **perforating fibers,** or *Sharpey's fibers,* which run perpendicular to the diaphysis.

The **endosteum** (en-dos'tē-ŭm; *endo* = within) is an incomplete layer of cells that covers all internal surfaces of the bone within the medullary cavity (figure 7.3*a, b*). The endosteum, like the periosteum, contains osteoprogenitor cells, osteoblasts, and osteoclasts.

Gross Anatomy of Other Bone Classes

Short, flat, and irregular bones differ in their gross anatomic structure from long bones. The external surface generally is composed of compact bone, the interior is composed entirely of spongy bone, and there is no medullary cavity. **Figure 7.4** shows the compact and

Figure 7.4 Flat Bones Within the Skull. These bones are composed of two layers of compact bone, with a region of spongy bone (diploë) sandwiched between them. Both layers of compact bone are covered by periosteum.

spongy bone arrangement in the skull bone. Observe the roughly parallel compact bone with a layer of internally placed spongy bone. In a flat bone of the skull, the spongy bone is also called **diploë** (dip′lō-ē; *diplous* = double).

Blood Supply and Innervation of Bone

Bone is highly vascularized (meaning it is supplied by many blood vessels), especially in regions containing spongy bone (see figure 7.3*a*). Blood vessels enter bones from the periosteum. Typically, only one nutrient artery enters and one nutrient vein exits the bone via a small opening or hole in the bone called a **nutrient foramen.** Blood vessels supply nutrients and oxygen required by cells and remove waste products from bone cells.

Nerves that supply bones accompany blood vessels through the nutrient foramen and innervate the bone as well as its periosteum, endosteum, and marrow cavity. These are mainly sensory nerves that signal injuries of the skeleton.

WHAT DID YOU LEARN?

5 How do the diaphysis and epiphysis of a bone differ in structure?

6 What is the function of a nutrient foramen in bone?

7.2d Bone Marrow

LEARNING OBJECTIVE

6. Compare and contrast the structure and location of the two types of bone marrow.

Bone marrow is the soft connective tissue of bone that includes red bone marrow and yellow bone marrow **(figure 7.5)**. **Red bone marrow** (myeloid tissue) is hemopoietic (blood cell forming) and contains reticular connective tissue, immature blood cells, and fat.

The locations of red bone marrow differ between children and adults. In children, red bone marrow is located in the spongy bone of most of the bones of the body as well as the medullary cavity of long bones. Much of the red bone marrow degenerates and turns into a fatty substance called **yellow bone marrow** as children mature into adults. As a result, adults have red bone marrow only in selected portions of the axial skeleton, such as the flat bones of the skull, the vertebrae, the ribs, the sternum, and the ossa coxae. Adults also have red bone marrow in the proximal epiphyses of each humerus and femur.

Note that severe anemia—a condition in which erythrocyte (red blood cell) numbers are lower than normal, resulting in insufficient oxygen reaching the cells of the body—may trigger conversion of yellow bone marrow back to red bone marrow, a change that facilitates the production of additional erythrocytes.

Red bone marrow

Yellow bone marrow

(b) Head of femur, sectioned

(a) Red bone marrow in the adult

Figure 7.5 Red and Yellow Bone Marrow. (*a*) Distribution of red bone marrow in the adult skeleton. (*b*) Sectional view of a femoral head, comparing red and yellow bone marrow.

WHAT DID YOU LEARN?

7 Where is red bone marrow found in the adult skeleton?

7.2e Microscopic Anatomy: Bone Connective Tissue

LEARNING OBJECTIVES

7. Name the four types of bone cells and their functions.
8. Describe the composition of bone's matrix.
9. Explain bone matrix formation and resorption.
10. Compare the structure of compact bone and spongy bone.

The primary component of bone is **bone connective tissue,** also called *osseous* (os'ē-ŭs; *os* = bone) *connective tissue.* Bone is composed of both cells and extracellular matrix, like all connective tissue. We now describe the cells and matrix that compose bone connective tissue, how the matrix is formed and resorbed, and then the two microscopic arrangements (compact bone and spongy bone).

Cells of Bone

Four types of cells are found in bone connective tissue: osteoprogenitor cells, osteoblasts, osteocytes, and osteoclasts **(figure 7.6)**.

Osteoprogenitor cells develop into osteoblasts.

Osteoblast (forms bone matrix)

Some osteoblasts differentiate into osteocytes.

Osteocyte (maintains bone matrix)

(a) Bone cells

Fusing bone marrow cell

Nuclei

Lysosomes

Ruffled border

Endosteum

Osteoclast

Resorption lacuna

(b) Osteoclast

LM 400x

Osteocytes

Osteoblasts

Osteoclast

(c) Bone tissue

Figure 7.6 Types of Cells in Bone Connective Tissue. Four different types of cells are found in bone connective tissue. (*a*) Osteoprogenitor cells develop into osteoblasts, many of which differentiate to become osteocytes. (*b*) Some bone marrow cells fuse to form osteoclasts. (*c*) A photomicrograph shows osteoblasts, osteocytes, and an osteoclast. AP|R

Osteoprogenitor (os′tē-ō-prō-jen′i-ter) **cells** are stem cells derived from mesenchyme (see section 5.2c). When they divide through the process of mitosis, another stem cell is produced along with a "committed cell" that matures to become an osteoblast. As previously described, these stem cells are located in both the periosteum and the endosteum.

Osteoblasts (*blast* = germ) are formed from osteoprogenitor stem cells. Often, osteoblasts are positioned side by side on bone surfaces. Active osteoblasts exhibit a somewhat cuboidal shape and have abundant rough endoplasmic reticulum and Golgi apparati, reflecting the activity of these cells. Osteoblasts perform the important function of synthesizing and secreting the initial semisolid organic form of bone matrix called **osteoid** (os′tē-oyd; *eidos* = resemblance). Osteoid later calcifies as a result of salt crystal deposition. As a consequence of this mineral deposition on osteoid, osteoblasts become entrapped within the matrix they produce and secrete, and thereafter they differentiate into osteocytes.

Osteocytes (*cyt* = cell) are mature bone cells derived from osteoblasts that have lost their bone-forming ability when enveloped by calcified osteoid. Connections between the original neighboring osteoblasts are maintained as they become osteocytes. Osteocytes maintain the bone matrix and detect mechanical stress on a bone. If stress is detected, osteoblasts are signaled, and it may result in the deposition of new bone matrix at the surface.

Osteoclasts (os′-tē-ō-klast; *klastos* = broken) are large, multinuclear, phagocytic cells. They are derived from fused bone marrow cells similar to those that produce monocytes (described in section 18.3c). These cells exhibit a ruffled border where they contact the bone, which increases their surface area exposure to the bone. An osteoclast is often located within or adjacent to a depression or pit on the bone surface called a **resorption lacuna** (*Howship's lacuna*). Osteoclasts are involved in breaking down bone in an important process called bone resorption (described shortly).

Composition of the Bone Matrix

The matrix of bone connective tissue has both organic and inorganic components. The organic component is osteoid, which is produced by osteoblasts. Osteoid is composed of both collagen protein plus a semisolid ground substance of proteoglycans (including chondroitin sulfate) and glycoproteins that suspends and supports the collagen fibers. These organic components give bone tensile strength by resisting stretching and twisting, and contribute to its overall flexibility.

The inorganic portion of the bone matrix is made up of salt crystals that are primarily calcium phosphate, $Ca_3(PO_4)_2$. Calcium phosphate and calcium hydroxide interact to form crystals of **hydroxyapatite** (hī-drok′sē-ap-a-tīt), which is $Ca_{10}(PO_4)_6(OH)_2$. The crystals also incorporate other salts (e.g., calcium carbonate) and ions (e.g., sodium, magnesium, sulfate, and fluoride) during the process of calcification. These crystals deposit around the long axis of collagen fibers in the extracellular matrix. The crystals harden the matrix and account for the rigidity or relative inflexibility of bone that provide its compressional strength.

The correct proportion of organic and inorganic substances in the matrix of bone allows it to function optimally. A loss of protein, or the presence of abnormal protein, results in brittle bones; insufficient calcium results in soft bones.

Bone Matrix: Its Formation and Resorption

Bone formation begins when osteoblasts secrete the initial semisolid organic form of bone matrix called osteoid. **Calcification** (kal′si-fi-kā′shŭn), or *mineralization*, subsequently occurs to osteoid formation when hydroxyapatite crystals deposit in the bone matrix. Calcification occurs when the concentration of calcium ions and phosphate ions reach critical levels and precipitate out of solution, thus forming the hydroxyapatite crystals that deposit in and around the collagen fibers. The entire process of bone formation requires a number of substances, including vitamin D (which enhances calcium absorption from the gastrointestinal tract) and vitamin C (which is required for collagen formation), as well as calcium and phosphate for calcification.

Bone resorption is a process whereby bone matrix is destroyed by substances released from osteoclasts into the extracellular space adjacent to the bone. Proteolytic enzymes released from lysosomes within the osteoclasts chemically digest the organic components (collagen fibers and proteoglycans) of the matrix, while hydrochloric acid (HCl) dissolves the mineral parts (calcium and phosphate) of the bone matrix. The liberated calcium and phosphate ions enter the blood. Bone resorption may occur when blood calcium levels are low (described in detail later in this chapter).

CLINICAL VIEW
Osteitis Deformans

Osteitis deformans (*Paget disease of bone*) results from a disruption in the balance between osteoclast and osteoblast function. It is characterized by excessive bone resorption (excessive osteoclast activity) followed by excessive bone deposition (excessive osteoblast activity). In osteitis deformans, the osteoclasts are five times larger than normal and may contain 20 or more nuclei (compared to about 3 to 5 nuclei in normal osteoclasts). As a result, these larger osteoclasts resorb bone at a higher rate. In response to this excessive bone resorption, the osteoblasts deposit additional bone, but this new bone is poorly formed and unstable, making it more susceptible to deformation and fractures. The bones most commonly affected include the pelvis, skull, vertebrae, femur (thigh bone), and tibia (leg bone). Initial symptoms include bone deformity and pain. Eventually, the lower limb bones may be bowed, and the skull often becomes thicker and enlarged.

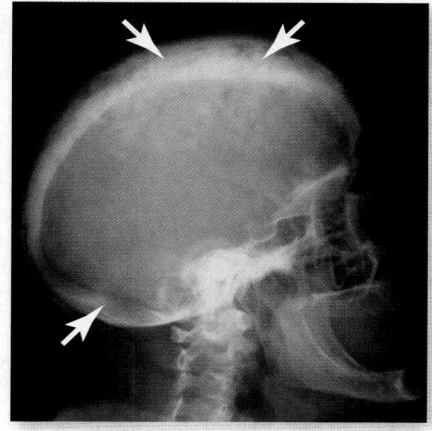

Lateral x-ray of a skull with osteitis deformans. White arrows indicate areas of excessive bone deposition.

INTEGRATE

LEARNING STRATEGY

Think of bone matrix like concrete poured among rebar (interlinking grid of steel bars) to form a basement floor. The collagen fibers are the rebar, and the ground substance with hydroxyapatite is the concrete. Without the rebar, the concrete crumbles; and without the concrete, the bars bend.

Comparison of Compact and Spongy Bone Microscopic Anatomy

Compact bone and spongy bone have unique and differing microscopic architecture (figure 7.7).

Compact Bone Microscopic Anatomy
Compact bone is composed of small cylindrical structures called **osteons,** or *Haversian systems.* An osteon is the basic functional and structural unit of mature compact bone (figure 7.7a, b). Osteons are oriented parallel

Figure 7.7 Components of Bone. (a) An expanded section of the humerus shows the arrangement of osteons within (b) the compact bone and (c) the arrangement of trabeculae within spongy bone. AP|R

LEARNING STRATEGY

The analogy of an archery target can help you remember the components of an osteon:

- The entire *target* represents the *osteon*.
- The *bull's-eye* of the target is the *central canal*.
- The *rings* of the target are the *concentric lamellae*.

(a) Compact bone

Lacuna (with osteocyte) — Osteon — Central canal — Concentric lamellae — Canaliculi — LM 75x

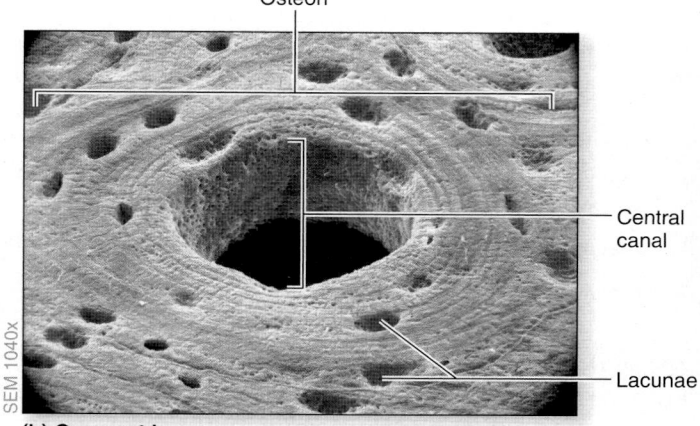

(b) Compact bone

Osteon — Central canal — Lacunae — SEM 1040x

(c) Spongy bone

Trabeculae of spongy bone — Red bone marrow — LM 25x

Figure 7.8 Microscopic Anatomy of Bone. (*a*) Light micrograph and (*b*) SEM of osteons in a cross section of compact bone. (*c*) Light micrograph of spongy bone. AP|R

to the diaphysis of the long bone. When an osteon is viewed in cross section, it has the appearance of a bull's-eye target. An osteon has several components:

- **The central** (*Haversian*) **canal** is a cylindrical channel that lies in the center of the osteon and runs parallel to it. Traveling within the central canal are the blood vessels and nerves that supply the bone.

- **Concentric lamellae** (lă-mel′-ē; sing., *lamella,* lă-mel′ă; *lamina* = plate, leaf) are rings of bone connective tissue that surround the central canal and form the bulk of the osteon. The numbers of concentric lamellae vary among osteons. Each lamella contains collagen fibers oriented at an angle in one direction; adjacent lamellae contain collagen fibers oriented at an angle that is 90 degrees different from both the previous and next lamellae. This alternating pattern of collagen fiber direction gives bone part of its strength and resilience.

- **Osteocytes** are mature bone cells found in small spaces (see next) between adjacent concentric lamellae. These cells maintain the bone matrix.

- **Lacunae** are the small spaces that house an osteocyte.

- **Canaliculi** (kan-ă-lik′ū-lī; sing., *canaliculus,* kan-ă-lik′ū-lŭs; *canalis* = canal) are tiny, interconnecting channels within the bone connective tissue that extend from each lacuna, travel through the lamellae, and connect to other lacunae and the central canal. Canaliculi house osteocyte cytoplasmic projections that permit intercellular contact and communication. Nutrients, minerals, gases, and wastes can travel through the cytoplasmic extensions within these passageways between the blood vessels of the central canal and the osteocytes.

Figure 7.8 shows cross sections of osteons as observed through a light microscope and a scanning electron microscope. Several other structures occur in compact bone but are not part of the osteon proper, including the following (see figure 7.7*a*):

- **Perforating** (*Volkmann*) **canals** resemble central canals in that they also contain blood vessels and nerves. However, perforating canals run perpendicular to the central canals and help connect multiple central canals within different osteons, thus creating a vascular and innervation connection among the multiple osteons.

- **Circumferential lamellae** are rings of bone immediately internal to the periosteum of the bone (**external circumferential lamellae**) or internal to the endosteum (**internal circumferential lamellae**). Both external and internal circumferential lamellae run the entire circumference of the bone itself (hence, their name).

- **Interstitial lamellae** (*interstitial systems*) are either the components of compact bone that are between osteons or are the leftover parts of osteons that have been partially resorbed—thus they often look like a "bite" has been taken out of them. The interstitial lamellae are incomplete and typically have no central canal.

Spongy Bone Microscopic Anatomy   Unlike compact bone, spongy bone contains no osteons (figures 7.7*c*, 7.8*c*) Rather its structure is an open lattice of narrow rods and plates of bone, called **trabeculae** (tră-bek′ū-lē; sing., *trabecula*, tră-bek′ū-lă; *trabs* = a beam). Bone marrow (when present) fills in between the trabeculae. When a segment of spongy bone is examined microscopically, you can see **parallel lamellae** composed of bone matrix. Between adjacent lamellae are osteocytes resting in lacunae, with numerous canaliculi radiating from the lacunae. Nutrients reach the osteocytes by diffusion through cytoplasmic processes within the canaliculi that open onto the surfaces of the trabeculae.

Note that the trabeculae often form a meshwork of crisscrossing bars and plates of small bone pieces. This structure provides great resistance to stresses applied in many directions by distributing the stress throughout the entire framework. As an analogy, visualize the jungle gym climbing apparatus on a children's playground. It is capable of supporting the weight of numerous children whether they are distributed throughout its structure or all localized in one area. This is accomplished because stresses and forces are distributed throughout the structure.

WHAT DID YOU LEARN?

8   What are the functions of the osteoprogenitor cell, osteoblast, osteocyte, and osteoclast?

9   What organic and inorganic substances compose bone matrix?

10   What are the major components of an osteon?

7.2f Microscopic Anatomy: Hyaline Cartilage Connective Tissue

LEARNING OBJECTIVE

11.   Analyze the structure of hyaline cartilage and the cells in its matrix.

Hyaline cartilage contains a population of cells scattered throughout a glassy-appearing matrix of protein fibers (primarily collagen) embedded within a gel-like ground substance. This ground substance is similar to that of bone in that it includes proteoglycans, such as chondroitin sulfate, but it differs from bone because its inorganic salts do not include calcium. This makes hyaline cartilage both resilient and flexible. Additionally, cartilage also contains a high percentage of water (60% to 70% by weight). The high water content makes it highly compressible, allowing hyaline cartilage to function as a good shock absorber.

Chondroblasts (kon′drō-blast; *chondros* = grit or gristle) are derived from mesenchymal cells and they produce the cartilage matrix. Once chondroblasts become encased within the matrix they have produced and secreted, the cells are called **chondrocytes** (kon′drō-sīt; *cyte* = cell) and occupy small spaces called **lacunae.** These mature cartilage cells maintain the matrix. Hyaline cartilage—except the articular cartilage—is covered by a dense irregular connective tissue sheet called the **perichondrium** that helps maintain its shape. Mature cartilage is avascular (not penetrated by blood vessels) and contains no nerves. Nutrients and oxygen are supplied to the cartilage by diffusion from blood vessels in the perichondrium. Several important differences between bone connective tissue and hyaline cartilage connective tissue are summarized in **table 7.1.**

WHAT DID YOU LEARN?

11   What are the primary ways that hyaline cartilage tissue differs from bone tissue?

	Table 7.1	Comparison of Bone Connective Tissue and Hyaline Cartilage Connective Tissue

Characteristics	Bone Connective Tissue	Hyaline Cartilage Connective Tissue
Cells that form matrix	Osteoblasts	Chondroblasts
Mature cells	Osteocytes	Chondrocytes
Calcium present in matrix	Yes	No
Blood supply in mature tissue	Extensive	Avascular

7.3 Cartilage Growth

LEARNING OBJECTIVE

1.   Compare interstitial and appositional growth of cartilage.

We focus on the process of cartilage growth before discussing bone growth because certain types of bone formation and bone growth are dependent upon the growth of hyaline cartilage.

Cartilage development and growth begins during embryologic development. Cartilage can grow both in length through the process of interstitial growth, or can grow in width by appositional growth **(figure 7.9).**

Interstitial (in-ter-stish′ăl) **growth** occurs within the internal regions of cartilage through the following series of four steps (figure 7.9*a*):

(1)   Chondrocytes housed within lacunae are stimulated to undergo mitotic cell division.

(2)   Following cell division, two cells occupy a single lacuna; they are now called chondroblasts.

(3)   As chondroblasts begin to synthesize and secrete new cartilage matrix, they are pushed apart. These cells now reside in their own lacuna and are called chondrocytes.

(4)   The cartilage continues to grow in the internal regions as chondrocytes continue to produce more matrix.

Appositional (ap-ō-zish′ŭn-ăl) **growth** is an increase in width along the cartilage's outside edge, or periphery. The following three steps occur in this process (figure 7.9*b*):

(1)   Undifferentiated stem cells at the internal edge of the perichondrium begin to divide. (Note the perichondrium contains mesenchymal cells as well as these stem cells.)

(2)   New undifferentiated stem cells and committed cells that differentiate into chondroblasts are formed. These chondroblasts are located at the periphery of the old cartilage, where they begin to produce and secrete new cartilage matrix.

(3)   The chondroblasts, as a result of matrix formation, push apart and become chondrocytes, with each occupying its own lacuna. The cartilage continues to grow at the periphery as chondrocytes continue to produce more matrix.

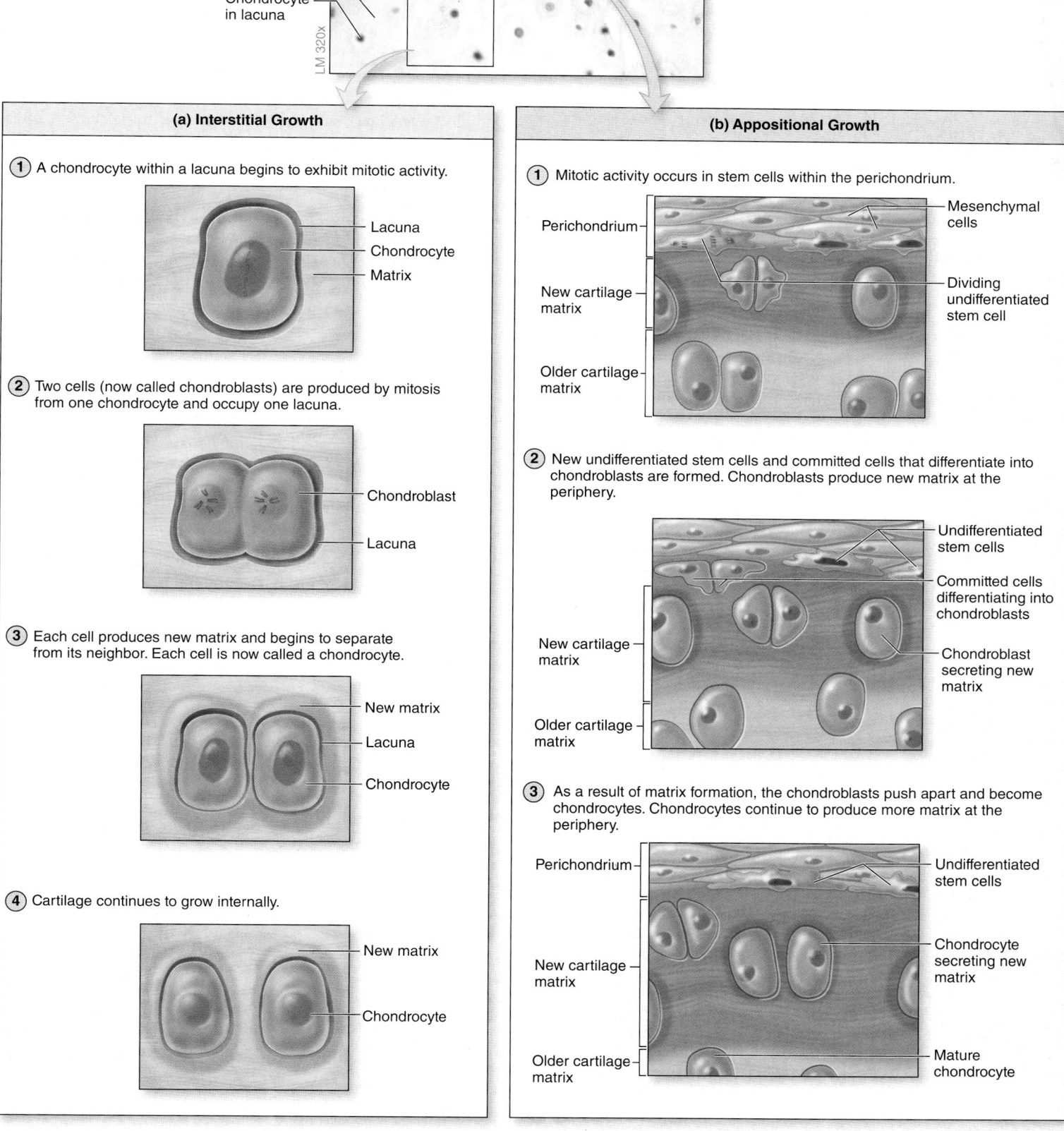

Figure 7.9 Formation and Growth of Cartilage. Cartilage grows either (a) from within by interstitial growth or (b) at its periphery or edge by appositional growth. AP|R

The content within the figure includes:

Top micrograph labels: Matrix, Chondrocyte in lacuna, Hyaline cartilage, Perichondrium, LM 320x

(a) Interstitial Growth

1. A chondrocyte within a lacuna begins to exhibit mitotic activity.
   Labels: Lacuna, Chondrocyte, Matrix

2. Two cells (now called chondroblasts) are produced by mitosis from one chondrocyte and occupy one lacuna.
   Labels: Chondroblast, Lacuna

3. Each cell produces new matrix and begins to separate from its neighbor. Each cell is now called a chondrocyte.
   Labels: New matrix, Lacuna, Chondrocyte

4. Cartilage continues to grow internally.
   Labels: New matrix, Chondrocyte

(b) Appositional Growth

1. Mitotic activity occurs in stem cells within the perichondrium.
   Labels: Perichondrium, New cartilage matrix, Older cartilage matrix, Mesenchymal cells, Dividing undifferentiated stem cell

2. New undifferentiated stem cells and committed cells that differentiate into chondroblasts are formed. Chondroblasts produce new matrix at the periphery.
   Labels: New cartilage matrix, Older cartilage matrix, Undifferentiated stem cells, Committed cells differentiating into chondroblasts, Chondroblast secreting new matrix

3. As a result of matrix formation, the chondroblasts push apart and become chondrocytes. Chondrocytes continue to produce more matrix at the periphery.
   Labels: Perichondrium, New cartilage matrix, Older cartilage matrix, Undifferentiated stem cells, Chondrocyte secreting new matrix, Mature chondrocyte

During early embryonic development, both interstitial and appositional cartilage growth occur simultaneously. Note that interstitial growth declines rapidly as the cartilage matures because the cartilage becomes semirigid, and it is no longer able to expand. Further growth can occur only at the periphery of the tissue, so later growth is primarily appositional. Once the cartilage is fully mature, new cartilage growth typically stops. Thereafter, cartilage growth usually occurs only after injury to the cartilage, yet this growth is limited due to the lack of blood vessels in the tissue.

 WHAT DID YOU LEARN?

12 Where do interstitial and appositional growth of cartilage occur?

7.4 Bone Formation

Ossification (os'i-fi-kā'shŭn; *facio* = to make), or **osteogenesis** (os'tē-ō-jen'ĕ-sis; *genesis* = beginning), refers to the formation and development of bone connective tissue. Ossification begins in the embryo and continues as the skeleton grows during childhood and adolescence. By the eighth through twelfth weeks of embryonic development, the skeleton begins forming from either thickened condensations of mesenchyme (intramembranous ossification) or a hyaline cartilage model of bone (endochondral ossification).

7.4a Intramembranous Ossification

LEARNING OBJECTIVES

1. Identify bones that are produced by intramembranous ossification.
2. Explain the four main steps in intramembranous ossification.

Intramembranous (in'tră-mem'brā-nŭs) **ossification** literally means "bone growth within a membrane." It is so named because the thin layer of mesenchyme in these areas is sometimes referred to as a membrane. Intramembranous ossification also is called *dermal ossification* because the mesenchyme that is the source of these bones is in the area of the future dermis. Recall from section 5.2 that mesenchyme is an embryonic connective tissue that has mesenchymal cells and abundant ground substance.

Intramembranous ossification produces the flat bones of the skull, some of the facial bones (zygomatic bone, maxilla), the mandible (lower jaw), and the central part of the clavicle (collarbone). It begins when mesenchyme becomes thickened and condensed with a dense supply of blood capillaries, and it continues in several steps (figure 7.10):

1. **Ossification centers form within thickened regions of mesenchyme beginning at the eighth week of development.** Some cells in the thickened, condensed mesenchyme divide, and the committed cells that are formed then differentiate into osteoprogenitor cells. Some osteoprogenitor cells become osteoblasts and begin to secrete osteoid. Multiple ossification centers develop within the thickened mesenchyme as the number of osteoblasts increases.

2. **Osteoid undergoes calcification.** Osteoid formation is quickly followed by calcification, as calcium salts are deposited onto the osteoid and then they crystallize (solidify). When calcification entraps osteoblasts within lacunae in the matrix, the entrapped cells become osteocytes.

3. **Woven bone and its surrounding periosteum form.** Initially, the newly formed bone connective tissue is

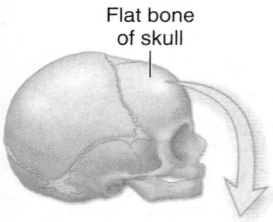

Flat bone of skull

Figure 7.10 Intramembranous Ossification. A flat bone in the skull forms from mesenchymal cells in a series of continuous steps.

1 Ossification centers form within thickened regions of mesenchyme.

Osteoid

Osteoblast

Ossification center

Collagen fiber

Mesenchymal cell

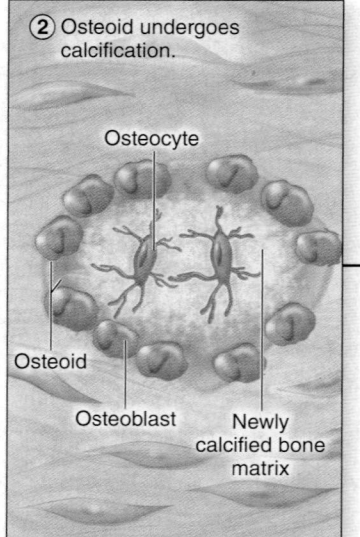

2 Osteoid undergoes calcification.

Osteocyte

Osteoid

Osteoblast

Newly calcified bone matrix

3 Woven bone and surrounding periosteum form.

Blood vessel

Trabecula of woven bone

Mesenchyme condensing to form the periosteum

4 Lamellar bone replaces woven bone, as compact and spongy bone form.

Compact bone

Spongy bone

Lamellar bone

Periosteum

LEARNING STRATEGY

Endochondral bone growth is a complex process. Before trying to remember every detail, first learn these basics:

1. A hyaline cartilage model of bone forms.
2. Bone first replaces hyaline cartilage in the diaphysis.
3. Next, bone replaces hyaline cartilage in the epiphyses.
4. Eventually, bone replaces hyaline cartilage everywhere, except the epiphyseal plates and articular cartilage.
5. By a person's late 20s, all epiphyseal plates have ossified, and lengthwise bone growth is complete.

immature and not well organized, a type called **woven bone,** or *primary bone*. Eventually woven bone is replaced by **lamellar bone,** or *secondary bone* (see next). The mesenchyme that still surrounds the woven bone begins to

thicken and eventually organizes to form the periosteum. Mesenchymal cells grow and develop to produce additional osteoblasts. Newly formed blood vessels also branch throughout this region. The calcified trabeculae and intertrabecular spaces are composed of spongy bone.

(4) **Lamellar bone replaces woven bone, as compact bone and spongy bone form.** Lamellar bone replaces the trabeculae of woven bone. On the internal and external surfaces, spaces between the trabeculae are filled and the bone becomes compact bone. Internally, the trabeculae are modified slightly and produce spongy bone. The typical structure of a flat cranial bone is composed of two external layers of compact bone with a layer of spongy bone in between.

WHAT DID YOU LEARN?

13 When does intramembranous ossification begin? What bones are formed from this method?

CLINICAL VIEW

Forensic Anthropology: Determining Age at Death

When the epiphyseal plates ossify, they fuse to the rest of the bone in an orderly manner, and the timing of such fusion is well known. If an epiphyseal plate has not yet ossified, the diaphysis and epiphysis are still two separate pieces of bone. Thus, a skeleton that displays separate epiphyses and diaphyses (as opposed to whole fused bones) is that of a juvenile rather than an adult. Forensic anthropologists use this anatomic information to help determine the age of skeletal remains.

(Left) *Partial union—a femur with partially fused epiphyses.*
(Right) *Open—no fusion between the epiphyses and the diaphysis.*

Fusion of an epiphyseal plate is progressive, and is usually scored as follows:
- **Open** (no bony fusion or union between the epiphysis and the other bone end)
- **Partial union** (some fusion between the epiphysis and the rest of the bone, but a distinct line of separation may be seen)
- **Complete union** (all visible aspects of the epiphysis are united to the rest of the bone)

When determining the age at death from skeletal remains, the skeleton will be older than the oldest complete union and younger than the youngest open center. For example, if one epiphyseal plate that typically fuses at age 17 is completely united, but another plate that typically fuses at age 19 is open, the skeleton is that of a person between the ages of 17 and 19.

Current standards for estimating age based upon epiphyseal plate fusion have primarily used male skeletal remains. Female epiphyseal plates tend to fuse approximately 1 to 2 years earlier than those of males, so this fact needs to be considered when estimating the age of a female skeleton. Further, population differences may exist with some epiphyseal plate unions. With these caveats in mind, the following table lists standards for selected epiphyseal plate unions.

Bone	Male Age at Complete Epiphyseal Union
Humerus, lateral epicondyle	11–16 (female: 9–13)
Humerus, medial epicondyle	11–16 (female: 10–15)
Humerus, head	14.5–23.5
Proximal radius	14–19
Distal radius	17–22
Distal fibula and tibia	14.5–19.5
Proximal tibia	15–22
Femur, head	14.5–21.5
Distal femur	14.5–21.5
Clavicle	19–30

8–12 weeks

Perichondrium

Hyaline cartilage

① Fetal hyaline cartilage model develops.

Ten-week fetus, special staining highlights the cartilaginous models of the bones. Arrow points to the humerus.

Fetal period

Deteriorating cartilage matrix

Epiphyseal blood vessels

Periosteum

Periosteal bone collar

Primary ossification center

Blood vessel of periosteal bud

Hyaline cartilage

② Cartilage calcifies, and a periosteal bone collar forms around diaphysis.

③ Primary ossification center forms in the diaphysis.

Sixteen-week fetus, showing diaphyses of developing bones.

Newborn to child

Epiphyseal blood vessel

Developing compact bone

Medullary cavity

Calcified cartilage

Secondary ossification centers

④ Secondary ossification centers form in epiphyses.

Skeleton of a neonate.

INTEGRATE CONCEPT OVERVIEW

Figure 7.11 **The Process of Endochondral Ossification.**
Endochondral ossification of a long bone occurs in progressive stages. Bone growth is complete when each epiphyseal plate has ossified and the epiphyseal line has formed. Depending upon the bone, epiphyseal plate ossification occurs between the ages of 10 and 25 years.

7.4b Endochondral Ossification

✓ LEARNING OBJECTIVES

3. Explain the steps in endochondral ossification of a long bone.
4. Differentiate between intramembranous ossification and endochondral ossification.

Endochondral (en-dō-kon′drāl; *endo* = within, *chondral* = cartilage) **ossification** begins with a hyaline cartilage model and produces most bones of the skeleton, including those of the upper and lower limbs, the pelvis, the vertebrae, and the ends of the clavicle.

Long bone development in the limb is a good example of this process, which takes place in the following six steps (**figure 7.11**):

① **The fetal hyaline cartilage model develops.** During the eighth to twelfth week of development, chondroblasts secrete cartilage matrix and a hyaline cartilage model forms. Chondrocytes are trapped within lacunae, and a perichondrium surrounds the cartilage.

② **Cartilage calcifies, and a periosteal bone collar forms.** Within the center of the cartilage model (future diaphysis), chondrocytes start to hypertrophy (enlarge) and

Child

Articular cartilage
Spongy bone
Epiphyseal plate
Periosteum
Compact bone
Medullary cavity
Epiphyseal plate
Articular cartilage

(5) Bone replaces cartilage, except the articular cartilage and epiphyseal plates.

Humerus from a 5-year-old child. Note the unfused epiphyses and diaphyses.

Late teens to adult

Articular cartilage
Epiphyseal line (remnant of epiphyseal plate)
Spongy bone
Medullary cavity
Compact bone
Periosteum
Spongy bone
Articular cartilage
Epiphyseal line

(6) Epiphyseal plates ossify and form epiphyseal lines.

X-ray of an adult humerus.

resorb (eat away) some of the surrounding cartilage matrix, producing larger holes in the matrix. As these chondrocytes enlarge, the cartilage matrix begins to calcify. Chondrocytes in this region die and disintegrate because nutrients cannot diffuse to them through this calcified matrix. The result is a calcified cartilage shaft with large holes where living chondrocytes had been.

As the cartilage in the shaft is calcifying, blood vessels grow toward the cartilage and start to penetrate the perichondrium around the shaft. Stem cells within the perichondrium divide to form osteoblasts. The osteoblasts

develop as this supporting connective tissue becomes highly vascularized, and the perichondrium becomes a periosteum. The osteoblasts within the internal layer of the periosteum start secreting a layer of osteoid around the calcified cartilage shaft. The osteoid hardens and forms a periosteal bone collar around this shaft.

(3) **The primary ossification center forms in the diaphysis.** A growth of capillaries and osteoblasts, called a **periosteal bud,** extends from the periosteum into the core of the cartilage shaft, invading the spaces left by the chondrocytes.

The remains of the calcified cartilage serve as a template on which osteoblasts begin to produce osteoid. This region is called the **primary ossification center** because it is the first major center of bone formation. Bone development extends in both directions toward the epiphyses from the primary ossification center. Healthy bone connective tissue quickly displaces the calcified, degenerating cartilage in the shaft. Most, but not all, primary ossification centers have formed by the twelfth week of development.

4. **Secondary ossification centers form in the epiphyses.** The same basic process that formed the primary ossification center occurs later in the epiphyses. Beginning around the time of birth, the hyaline cartilage in the center of each epiphysis calcifies and begins to degenerate. Epiphyseal blood vessels and osteoprogenitor cells enter each epiphysis. **Secondary ossification centers** form as bone displaces calcified cartilage. Note that not all secondary ossification centers form at birth; some form later in childhood. As the secondary ossification centers form, osteoclasts resorb some bone matrix within the diaphysis, creating a hollow medullary cavity.

5. **Bone replaces almost all cartilage, except the articular cartilage and epiphyseal cartilage.** By late bone development, almost all of the hyaline cartilage is displaced by bone. Hyaline cartilage only remains as articular cartilage on the articular surface of each epiphysis and at the epiphyseal plates.

6. **Lengthwise growth continues until the epiphyseal plates ossify and form epiphyseal lines.** Lengthwise bone growth continues into puberty until the epiphyseal plate is converted to the epiphyseal line, indicating that the bone has reached its adult length. Depending upon the bone, most epiphyseal plates ossify to become epiphyseal lines between the ages of 10 and 25. (The last epiphyseal plates to ossify are those of the clavicle in the late 20s.)

WHAT DO YOU THINK?

1. Why does endochondral bone formation involve so many complex steps? Instead of having the hyaline cartilage model followed by the separate formation of the diaphysis and epiphyses, why can't bone simply be completely formed in the fetus?

WHAT DID YOU LEARN?

14. Briefly describe the process by which a long bone forms by endochondral ossification.

7.5 Bone Growth and Bone Remodeling

Bone growth and bone remodeling both begin during embryologic development. We examine both processes here and the major hormones that regulate them.

7.5a Bone Growth

LEARNING OBJECTIVES

1. Compare and contrast the five zones of the epiphyseal plate, and describe how growth in length occurs there.

2. Describe the steps of appositional growth.

As with cartilage growth, a long bone's growth in length is called interstitial growth, and its growth in diameter or thickness is called appositional growth.

Interstitial Growth

Interstitial growth is dependent upon growth of cartilage within the epiphyseal plate. The epiphyseal plate exhibits five distinct micro-

Zone 1: Zone of resting cartilage

Zone 2: Zone of proliferating cartilage

Zone 3: Zone of hypertrophic cartilage

Zone 4: Zone of calcified cartilage

Zone 5: Zone of ossification

LM 70x

(a) Epiphyseal plate

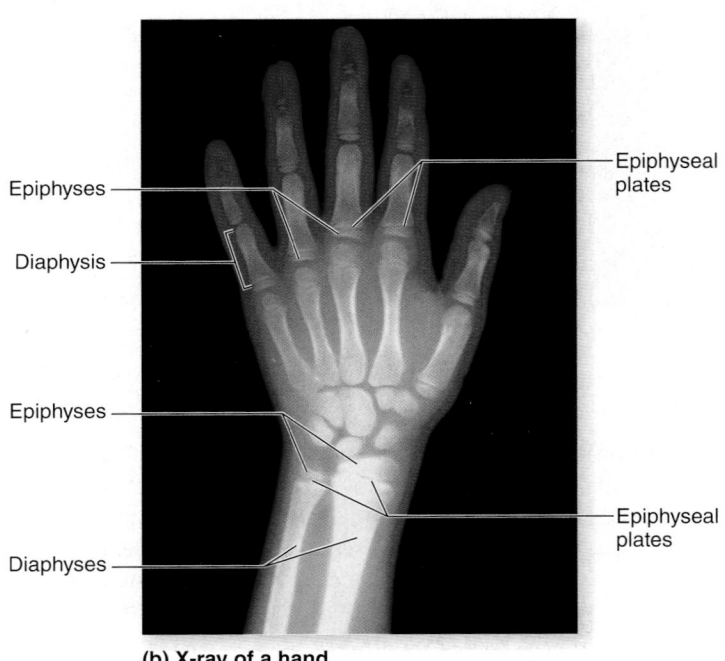

Epiphyses

Diaphysis

Epiphyses

Diaphyses

Epiphyseal plates

Epiphyseal plates

(b) X-ray of a hand

Figure 7.12 Epiphyseal Plate. (*a*) In a growing long bone, the epiphyseal plate, located at the boundary between the diaphysis and the epiphysis, exhibits five distinct but continuous zones. Zones 1–4 are cartilage, and zone 5 is bone. (*b*) An x-ray of a child's hand shows the cartilaginous epiphyseal plate as a dark line between the epiphysis and the diaphysis of a long bone. AP|R scopic zones that are continuous from the first zone nearest the epiphysis to the last zone nearest the diaphysis (figure 7.12):

1. **Zone of resting cartilage.** This zone is farthest from the medullary cavity of the diaphysis and nearest the epiphysis. It is composed of small chondrocytes distributed throughout the cartilage matrix. It resembles mature and healthy hyaline cartilage. This region secures the epiphysis to the epiphyseal plate.
2. **Zone of proliferating cartilage.** Chondrocytes in this zone undergo rapid mitotic cell division, enlarge slightly, and become aligned like a stack of coins into longitudinal columns of flattened lacunae. These columns are parallel to the diaphysis.
3. **Zone of hypertrophic cartilage.** Chondrocytes cease dividing and begin to hypertrophy (enlarge in size) in this zone. The walls of the lacunae become thin because the chondrocytes resorb matrix as they hypertrophy.
4. **Zone of calcified cartilage.** This zone usually is composed of 2 to 3 layers of chondrocytes. Minerals are deposited in the matrix between the columns of lacunae; this calcification destroys the chondrocytes and makes the matrix appear opaque.
5. **Zone of ossification.** The walls break down between lacunae in the columns, forming longitudinal channels. These spaces are invaded by capillaries and osteoprogenitor cells from the medullary cavity. New matrix of bone is deposited on the remaining calcified cartilage matrix.

Growth in bone length occurs specifically within zone 2 as chondrocytes undergo mitotic cell division, and in zone 3 as chondrocytes hypertrophy. These activities combine to push the zone of resting cartilage toward the epiphysis. Note that it is the flexible matrix of hyaline cartilage, and not the hard, calcified matrix of bone, that permits this growth. Once growth in length has occurred, new bone connective tissue is then produced at the same rate in zone 5. Thus, growth in length is due to growth in hyaline cartilage connective tissue that is later replaced with bone. This process is similar to the endochondral ossification process that occurs during bone development.

The epiphyseal plate maintains its thickness during childhood as it is pushed away from the center of the shaft. At maturity, the rate of epiphyseal cartilage production slows, and the rate of osteoblast activity accelerates. As a result, the epiphyseal plate continues to narrow until it ultimately disappears, and interstitial growth completely stops. Eventually, the only remnant of each epiphyseal plate is an internal thin line of compact bone called an **epiphyseal line.**

The loss of the hyaline cartilage and the appearance of the remnant epiphyseal line signals the end of interstitial growth.

 WHAT DO YOU THINK?

 2 How could a physician determine whether a person had reached full height by examining x-rays of the patient's bones?

Appositional Growth

Appositional growth occurs within the periosteum (figure 7.13). In this process, osteoblasts in the inner cellular layer of the periosteum produce and deposit bone matrix within layers parallel to the surface, called external circumferential lamellae. These lamellae are analogous to tree rings: As they increase in number, the structure increases in diameter. Thus, the bone becomes wider as new bone is laid down at its periphery. As this new bone is being laid down, osteoclasts along the medullary cavity resorb bone matrix, creating an expanding medullary cavity. The combined effects of bone growth at the periphery and bone resorption within the medullary cavity transform an infant bone into a larger version called an adult bone.

 WHAT DID YOU LEARN?

 15 How does a bone grow in width?

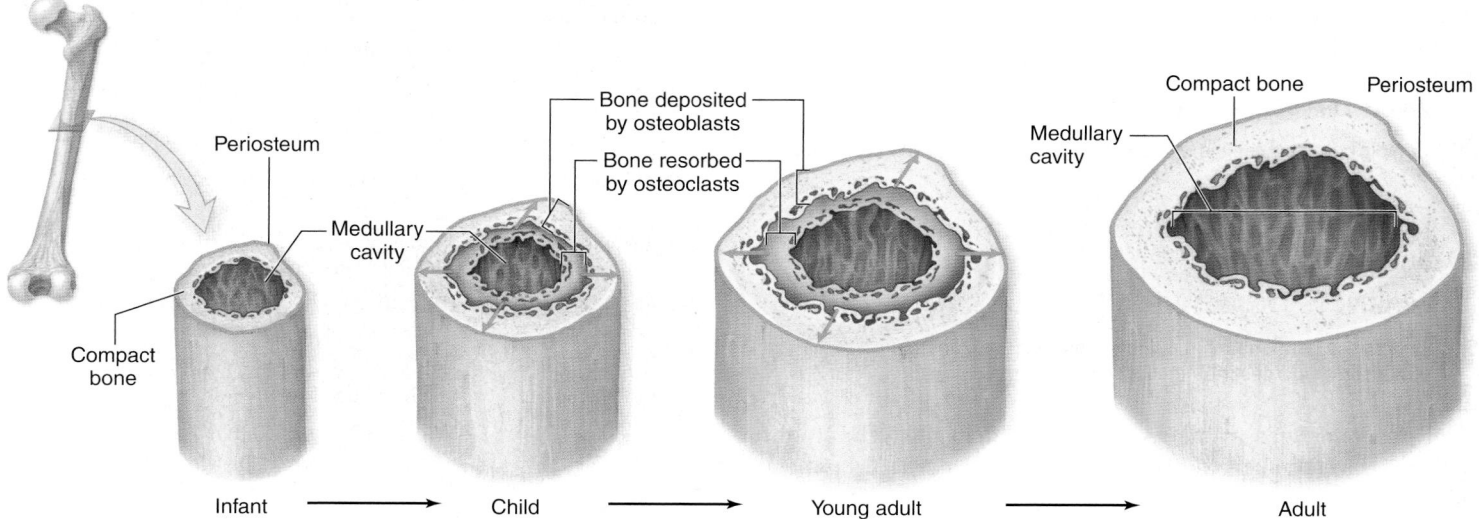

Figure 7.13 Appositional Bone Growth. A bone increases in diameter as new bone is added to the surface. At the same time, some bone may be removed from the inner surface to enlarge the medullary cavity. **AP|R**

Infant — Child — Young adult — Adult

Periosteum
Medullary cavity
Compact bone
Bone deposited by osteoblasts
Bone resorbed by osteoclasts
Medullary cavity
Compact bone
Periosteum

7.5b Bone Remodeling

3. Define bone remodeling, and give examples of how it varies in different bones and different portions of the same bone.
4. Explain the effect of mechanical stress on bone remodeling.

Even when adult bone size has been reached, the bone continues to renew and reshape itself throughout a person's lifetime. This constant, dynamic process of continual addition of new bone tissue (bone deposition) and removal of old bone tissue (bone resorption) is a process called **bone remodeling.** This ongoing process occurs at both the periosteal and endosteal surfaces of a bone.

It is estimated that about 20% of the adult human skeleton is replaced yearly. However, bone remodeling does not occur at the same rate everywhere in the skeleton. For example, the compact bone in our skeleton is replaced at a slower rate than the spongy bone. The distal part of the femur (thigh bone) is replaced every 4 to 6 months, whereas the diaphysis of this bone may not be completely replaced during an individual's lifetime.

Clearly, bone remodeling is dependent upon the coordinated activities of osteoblasts, osteocytes, and osteoclasts. The relative activities of these cells is influenced by two primary factors: hormones (described in the next section) and mechanical stress to the bone.

Mechanical stress occurs in the form of weight-bearing movement and exercise, and it is required for normal bone remodeling. Stress is detected by osteocytes and communicated to osteoblasts. Osteoblasts increase synthesis of osteoid, and this is followed by deposition of mineral salts. Bone strength increases over a period of time in response to mechanical stress.

Mechanical stresses that significantly affect bone result from skeletal muscle contraction and gravitational forces. Typically, the bones of athletes become noticeably thicker as a result of repetitive and stressful exercise. Weight-bearing activities, such as weight lifting, walking, or running help build and retain bone mass. Research has shown that regular weight-bearing exercise can increase total bone mass in adolescents and young adults prior to its inevitable reduction later in life. In fact, recent studies suggest that even 70- and 80-year-olds who perform moderate weight training can increase their bone mass.

In contrast, removal or significant decrease of mechanical stress weakens bone through both reduction of collagen formation and demineralization. When a person has a fractured bone and wears a cast or is bedridden, the strength of the unstressed bone decreases in the immobilized limb. While in space, astronauts must exercise so that the lack of gravity won't cause their bones to lose mass.

WHAT DID YOU LEARN?

16 What is bone remodeling, where does it occur, and when does it occur?

7.5c Hormones That Influence Bone Growth and Bone Remodeling

LEARNING OBJECTIVE

5. Identify the hormones that influence bone growth and bone remodeling, and describe their effects.

Hormones are defined as molecules released from one cell into the blood, and travel throughout the body to affect other cells. A hormone binds to cellular receptors of specific cells to initiate cellular change. (The details of hormones are described in chapter 17.) Certain hormones influence bone composition and growth patterns by altering the rates of chondrocyte, osteoblast, and osteoclast activity (table 7.2).

INTEGRATE
CLINICAL VIEW
Why are Males Typically Taller than Females?

Two processes determine why males typically are taller than females. First, the growth spurt in females is triggered primarily by estrogen, and in males it is caused primarily by testosterone. Ironically, estrogen is a more powerful growth stimulant than testosterone. The growth plate closes more quickly in response to estrogen, which consequently provides a smaller window of time for accelerated growth. Second, females enter puberty about 2 to 3 years earlier than males, so females have fewer years of childhood growth prior to puberty than do males.

Growth hormone is also called **insulin-like growth factor,** and is produced by the anterior pituitary gland (see section 17.9a). It affects bone growth by stimulating the liver to form another hormone called **somatomedin** (sō′mă-tō-mē′din). Both growth hormone and somatomedin directly stimulate growth of cartilage in the epiphyseal plate.

Thyroid hormone is secreted by the thyroid gland and stimulates bone growth by influencing the basal metabolic rate of bone cells (see section 17.9b). If maintained in proper balance, growth hormone and thyroid hormone regulate and maintain normal activity at the epiphyseal plates until puberty. Hypothyroidism that results from low thyroid hormone levels leads to impaired skeletal growth and other problems in children.

Sex hormones (**estrogen** and **testosterone**), which begin to be secreted in relatively large amounts at puberty (see section 28.1b), dramatically accelerate bone growth. Sex hormones increase the rate of both cartilage growth and bone formation within the epiphyseal plate. This results in increased length of long bones and increased height. Ironically, the appearance of high levels of sex hormones at puberty also signals the beginning of the end for growth at the epiphyseal plate. This happens because the rate of bone formation occurs at a faster rate than the rate of cartilage growth. Bone growth eventually overcomes the region of cartilage, replacing all cartilage with bone.

Table 7.2	Effects of Hormones on Bone Maintenance and Growth
Hormone	**Effect on Bone**
Growth hormone	Stimulates liver to produce the hormone somatomedin, which causes cartilage proliferation at epiphyseal plate and resulting bone elongation
Thyroid hormone	Stimulates bone growth by stimulating metabolic rate of osteoblasts
Calcitonin	Promotes calcium deposition in bone and inhibits osteoclast activity
Parathyroid hormone	Increases blood calcium levels by encouraging bone resorption by osteoclasts
Sex hormones (estrogen and testosterone)	Stimulate osteoblasts; promote epiphyseal plate growth and closure
Glucocorticoids	Increase bone loss and, in children, impair bone growth when there are chronically high levels of glucocorticoids (e.g., cortisol, cortisone)
Serotonin	Inhibits osteoprogenitor cells from differentiating into osteoblasts when there are chronically high levels of serotonin

CONCEPT CONNECTION

Many hormones in the endocrine system (see chapter 17) are responsible for normal growth and homeostasis of bone tissue. Growth hormone, thyroid hormone, calcitonin, and sex hormones help promote bone growth, while parathyroid hormone, glucocorticoids, and serotonin may either inhibit bone growth or increase bone resorption. Disorders of the endocrine system, as a result, often are manifested in part by skeletal system disorders.

WHAT DO YOU THINK?

3 Given what you know about the effects of testosterone, explain why there is a risk of stunted growth to a young boy (pre-puberty) taking anabolic steroids (substances that have similar effects to testosterone).

Glucocorticoids are a group of steroid hormones that are released from the adrenal cortex and regulate blood glucose levels. Cortisol is the primary glucocorticoid. High amounts of cortisol increase bone loss and, in children, impairs growth at the epiphyseal plate. It is because of this relationship that a child's growth is monitored if receiving high doses of glucocorticoids as an anti-inflammatory, such as a treatment for children with severe asthma.

Serotonin (ser-ō-tō′nin) is a chemical-signaling molecule that is called a neurotransmitter for the nervous system, but it also acts like a hormone in other body systems. Researchers have discovered that most bone cells have serotonin receptors, and specifically that when levels of circulating serotonin are too high, osteoprogenitor cells are prevented from differentiating into osteoblasts. Thus, serotonin appears to play a role in the rate and regulation of normal bone remodeling since it affects osteoblast differentiation. Further research is ongoing to see if abnormally high levels of serotonin are linked to low bone density disorders.

Three additional hormones—parathyroid hormone, calcitriol, and calcitonin—participate in regulating bone remodeling and are discussed in detail in the next section.

WHAT DID YOU LEARN?

17 What are the effects of growth hormone and thyroid hormone on bone growth and bone mass?

7.6 Regulating Blood Calcium Levels

Regulating calcium concentration in blood is essential because calcium is required for numerous physiologic processes such as initiation of muscle contraction; exocytosis of molecules from cells, including nerve cells (neurons); stimulation of the heart by pacemaker cells; and blood clotting. Maintaining blood calcium concentration in a normal range, between 8.9 and 10.1 milligrams per deciliter (mg/dL), is essential for life. The two primary hormones that regulate blood calcium are calcitriol (an active form of vitamin D) and parathyroid hormone. The thyroid gland also produces calcitonin, a third calcium-regulating hormone, but it seems to play a less significant role. We describe blood calcium regulation here because of the role of the skeleton in storage of calcium.

7.6a Activation of Vitamin D to Calcitriol

LEARNING OBJECTIVE

1. Explain the activation of vitamin D to calcitriol.

To effectively describe the actions of calcitriol and parathyroid hormone we first describe the enzymatic pathway of activating vitamin D to calcitriol. The three steps are as follows **(figure 7.14)**:

1 Ultraviolet light converts the precursor molecule (7-dehydrocholesterol, a modified cholesterol molecule) circulating in the blood to vitamin D_3 (cholecalciferol). Vitamin D_3 also is absorbed from the small intestine into the blood from the diet (the major source of vitamin D_3 for most individuals is milk).

2 Vitamin D_3 circulates throughout the blood. As it passes through the blood vessels of the liver, it is converted by liver enzymes to calcidiol by the addition of a hydroxyl group (—OH). Both steps 1 and 2 occur continuously with limited regulation.

Ultraviolet light   or   Dietary intake (e.g., milk)

Precursor molecule (7-dehydrocholesterol)

HO

Vitamin D_3 (cholecalciferol)

Calcidiol

Calcitriol

1 The precursor molecule is converted to Vitamin D_3 (cholecalciferol).

2 Vitamin D_3 is converted to calcidiol in the liver (when an —OH group is added).

3 Calcidiol is converted to calcitriol in the kidney (when another —OH group is added).

Figure 7.14 Calcitriol Production. Calcitriol is produced as follows: When keratinocytes are exposed to UV rays, a precursor molecule (7-dehydrocholesterol) in keratinocytes is transformed to vitamin D_3 (cholecalciferol). Humans also may obtain vitamin D_3 from dietary sources, such as milk. The liver then synthesizes calcidiol from the vitamin D_3. Finally, the kidneys will convert calcidiol to calcitriol.

Calcidiol circulates in the blood: As it passes through blood vessels of the kidney, it is converted to calcitriol by kidney enzymes (when another —OH group is added). Calcitriol is the active form of Vitamin D_3. The presence of parathyroid hormone increases the rate of this final enzymatic step in the kidney. Thus, greater amounts of calcitriol are formed when PTH is present.

Vitamin D in its active form of calcitriol hormone has the unique function of stimulating absorption of calcium ions (Ca^{2+}) from the small intestine into the blood.

WHAT DO YOU THINK?

4. Why is milk typically supplemented with vitamin D?

WHAT DID YOU LEARN?

18. What organs are involved in activating vitamin D_3 to calcitriol?

7.6b Parathyroid Hormone and Calcitriol

LEARNING OBJECTIVES

2. Discuss the release of parathyroid hormone.
3. Explain how parathyroid hormone and calcitriol function together to regulate blood calcium levels.

Parathyroid hormone (PTH) is secreted and released by the parathyroid glands (see section 17.2a) in response to reduced blood calcium levels **(figure 7.15)**. Calcidiol formation is occurring continuously. The final enzymatic step converting calcidiol to calcitriol in the kidney occurs more readily in the presence of PTH.

PTH and calcitriol interact with selected major organs as follows:

- **Bone connective tissue of the skeleton.** PTH and calcitriol act synergistically (their combined effect is greater than the sum of their individual effects) to increase the release of calcium from the bone into the blood. Specifically, these hormones increase osteoclast activity, so the osteoclasts resorb bone matrix, resulting in calcium release from the bone into the blood.
- **Kidneys.** PTH and calcitriol act synergistically to stimulate the kidney to excrete less calcium in the urine (and thus retain more calcium in the blood). This occurs specifically by increasing calcium reabsorption in the tubules in the kidney (see section 24.6).
- **Small intestine.** A function unique to calcitriol is to increase absorption of calcium from the small intestine into the blood.

The removal of calcium from bone, the decrease in loss of calcium from the kidney, and increase in calcium absorption from the gastrointestinal tract result in elevating blood calcium and returning it to within the normal homeostatic range. Subsequently, the release of additional PTH is inhibited.

Notice that this homeostatic system involving PTH and calcitriol is regulated by negative feedback. A decrease in blood plasma calcium concentration stimulates PTH release, and both PTH release and calcitriol formation trigger an increase in blood calcium. This increase in blood calcium inhibits further release of PTH.

WHAT DID YOU LEARN?

19. When are parathyroid hormone and calcitriol secreted, and what organs respond to them?

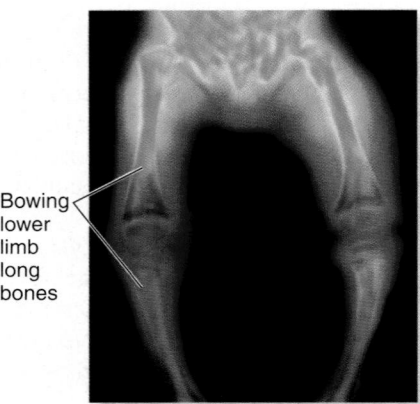
7.6c Calcitonin

LEARNING OBJECTIVE

4. Discuss the homeostatic system involving the hormone calcitonin and its effect on blood calcium levels.

Calcitonin (kal-si-tō'nin; *calx* = lime, *tonos* = stretching) is another hormone that aids in regulating blood calcium levels—however, it has a less significant role than either PTH or calcitriol. Calcitonin is released from the thyroid gland (specifically, from its parafollicular cells) in response to high blood calcium levels; it is also secreted in response to stress from exercise.

Figure 7.15 Effects of Parathyroid Hormone and Calcitriol on Blood Calcium Levels. Blood calcium levels are closely regulated by a negative feedback mechanism that involves the parathyroid gland, calcitriol, and various effectors (bone, kidneys, and intestine). A low blood calcium level is the initial stimulus for the parathyroid glands to release parathyroid hormone. Together, PTH and calcitriol target various effectors to ultimately instigate a rise in blood calcium levels and return to homeostasis.

The entire function of calcitonin is still unclear. However, the following organs contain receptors for and respond to calcitonin to decrease blood calcium levels:

- **Bone connective tissue of the skeleton.** Calcitonin primarily inhibits osteoclast activity. Thus, relatively less calcium is released from the bone into the blood.
- **Kidneys.** Calcitonin stimulates the kidneys to increase the loss of calcium in the urine, thereby reducing blood calcium levels.

The following limitations are observed with calcitonin:

- Calcitonin seems to have the greatest effect under conditions where there is the greatest turnover of bone, such as in growing children.

- If high doses of calcitonin are administered, blood calcium levels decrease only temporarily. Thus, therapeutic injections of calcitonin cannot provide long-term decrease in blood calcium.
- Blood calcium regulation does not appear to be affected by either the absence of calcitonin (e.g., if parafollicular cells are removed from the body), or abnormally high levels of calcitonin, such as occurs with rare tumors of the parafollicular cells that produce calcitonin.

WHAT DID YOU LEARN?

20 How does calcitonin work on the kidneys and bone connective tissue to regulate blood calcium levels?

CLINICAL VIEW
Osteoporosis

Osteoporosis, meaning "porous bones," is a disease that results in decreased bone mass and leads to weakened bones that are prone to fracture. The occurrence of osteoporosis is greatest among the elderly, especially Caucasian women, and the severity is closely linked to both age and onset of menopause. Smoking is also a risk factor for osteoporosis. Postmenopausal women are at risk because (1) women have less bone mass than men, (2) women begin losing bone mass earlier and faster in life (sometimes around 35 years of age), and (3) postmenopausal women no longer produce significant amounts of estrogen, which appears to help protect against osteoporosis by stimulating bone growth. As a result of osteoporosis, the incidence of fractures increases, most frequently in the wrist, hip, and vertebral column.

The best treatment for osteoporosis seems to be prevention. Young adults should maintain good nutrition and physical activity to ensure adequate bone density, thus allowing for the normal, age-related loss later in life. Calcium supplements with vitamin D help maintain bone health, but by themselves will not stimulate new bone growth. Medical treatments involve two strategies: (1) slowing the rate of bone loss and (2) attempting to stimulate new bone growth.

Medications called *bisphosphonates* (e.g., Fosamax, Actonel, Boniva), currently are prescribed to slow the progression of osteoporosis. These drugs work by interfering with osteoclast function and thus retarding the removal of bone during remodeling. Unfortunately, these drugs have also been implicated in increased risk of osteonecrosis (bone death) of the jaw and some other bone growth abnormalities, so patients are recommended not to take the drugs for longer than 5 years at a time. Thus, these medications may not be the cure-all individuals had hoped, and that regulating bone growth is much more complex than researchers currently understand.

(a) Normal bone

(b) Osteoporotic bone

7.7 Effects of Aging

LEARNING OBJECTIVE

1. Describe how age influences bone structure.

Aging affects bone connective tissue in two ways. First, the tensile strength of bone decreases due to a reduced rate of protein synthesis by osteoblasts. Consequently, the relative amount of inorganic minerals in the bone matrix increases (due to decreased matrix protein), and the bones of the skeleton become brittle and susceptible to fracture.

Second, bone loses calcium and other minerals (demineralization). The bones of the skeleton become thinner and weaker, resulting in insufficient ossification, a condition called **osteopenia** (os'tē-ō-pēn'ē-ă; *penia* = poverty). Aging causes all people to become slightly osteopenic. This reduction in bone mass may begin as early as 35–40 years of age, when osteoblast activity declines, while osteoclast activity continues at previous levels. Different parts of the skeleton are affected unequally. Vertebrae, jaw bones, and epiphyses lose large amounts of mass, resulting in reduced height, loss of teeth, and fragile limbs.

Every decade, women lose roughly more of their skeletal mass than do men. A significant percentage of older women and a smaller proportion of older men suffer from **osteoporosis** (os'tē-ō-pō-rō'sis; *poros* = pore; *osis* = condition), a condition characterized by reduction in bone mass sufficient to compromise normal function (see Clinical View: "Osteoporosis").

In addition, vitamin D and numerous hormones including growth hormone, estrogen, and testosterone decrease with age. This decrease in hormone levels contributes to reduction in bone mass.

WHAT DID YOU LEARN?

21 Explain why women are more likely to develop osteoporosis than men.

7.8 Bone Fracture and Repair

LEARNING OBJECTIVE

1. Explain the four steps by which fractures heal.

Bone has great mineral strength, but it may break as a result of unusual stress or a sudden impact. Breaks in bones are called **fractures** and are classified in several ways. A **stress fracture** is a thin break caused by increased physical activity in which the bone experiences repetitive loads (e.g., as seen in some runners). A **pathologic fracture** usually occurs in bone that has been weakened by disease. In a **simple fracture,** the broken bone does not penetrate the skin, whereas in a **compound fracture,** one or both ends of the broken bone pierce the overlying skin. **Figure 7.16** shows the different classifications of fractures.

The healing of a simple fracture takes about 2 to 3 months, whereas a compound fracture takes longer to heal. Fractures heal much more quickly in young children (average healing time, 3 weeks) and become slower to heal as we age. In the elderly, the normal thinning and weakening of bone increases the incidence of fractures, and some complicated fractures require surgical intervention to heal properly. Bone fracture repair can be described as a series of four steps **(figure 7.17):**

 A fracture hematoma forms. A bone fracture tears blood vessels inside the bone and within the periosteum, causing

Figure 7.16 Classification of Bone Fractures.

Classification of Bone Fractures	
Fracture	**Description**
Avulsion	Complete severing of a body part (typically a toe or finger)
Colles	Fracture of the distal end of the lateral forearm bone (radius); produces a "dinner fork" deformity
Comminuted	Bone is splintered into several small pieces between the main parts
Complete	Bone is broken into two or more pieces
Compound (open)	Broken ends of the bone protrude through the skin
Compression	Bone is squashed (may occur in a vertebra during a fall)
Depressed	Broken part of the bone forms a concavity (as in skull fracture)
Displaced	Fractured bone parts are out of anatomic alignment
Epiphyseal	Epiphysis is separated from the diaphysis at the epiphyseal plate
Greenstick	Partial fracture; one side of bone breaks—the other side is bent
Hairline	Fine crack in which sections of bone remain aligned (common in skull)
Impacted	One fragment of bone is firmly driven into the other
Incomplete	Partial fracture extends only partway across the bone
Linear	Fracture is parallel to the long axis of the bone
Oblique	Diagonal fracture is at an angle
Pathologic	Weakening of a bone caused by disease process (e.g., cancer)
Pott	Fracture is at the distal ends of the tibia and fibula
Simple (closed)	Bone does not break through the skin
Spiral	Fracture spirals around axis of long bone; results from twisting stress
Stress	Thin fractures due to repeated, stressful impact such as running (These fractures often are difficult to see on x-rays, and a bone scan may be necessary to accurately identify their presence.)
Transverse	Fracture is at right angles to the long axis of the bone

bleeding. This bleeding results in a **fracture hematoma** that forms from the clotted blood.

2. **A fibrocartilaginous (soft) callus forms.** Regenerated blood capillaries infiltrate the fracture hematoma due to an increase in osteoblasts in both the periosteum and endosteum near the fracture site. First, the fracture hematoma is reorganized into an actively growing connective tissue called a *procallus*. Fibroblasts within the procallus produce collagen fibers that help connect the broken ends of the bones. Chondroblasts

in the newly growing connective tissue form a dense regular connective tissue associated with the cartilage. Eventually, the procallus becomes a **fibrocartilaginous (soft) callus** (kal'ŭs; hard skin). The fibrocartilaginous callus stage lasts at least 3 weeks.

3. **A hard (bony) callus forms.** Within a week after the injury, osteoprogenitor cells in areas adjacent to the fibrocartilaginous callus become osteoblasts and produce trabeculae of primary bone. The fibrocartilaginous callus

could take years.

(1) A fracture hematoma forms. (2) A fibrocartilaginous (soft) callus forms. (3) A hard (bony) callus forms. (4) The bone is remodeled.

Figure 7.17 Fracture Repair. The repair of a bone fracture occurs in a series of steps.

CLINICAL VIEW
Bone Scans

Bone scans are tests that can detect bone pathologies. The patient often is injected intravenously with a small amount of a radioactive tracer compound that is absorbed by bone. A scanning camera then detects and measures the radiation emitted from the bone. The images produced show normal bone tissue with an even distribution of gray coloring (although note in the adjacent figure the axial skeleton typically appears uniformly darker than the appendicular skeleton). An abnormal bone scan may have focal darker areas called "hot spots," or lighter areas called "cold spots." Hot spots typically indicate increased metabolism or greater turnover of the bone tissue, as may be experienced by a stress fracture or cancer metastasis to bone. Cold spots indicate less metabolic activity of bone tissue, as may occur with avascular necrosis (death due to lack of blood supply) of a bone. AP|R

Normal bone scan.

Hot spots

Abnormal bone scan; "hot spots" in both tibiae indicative of stress fractures.

is then replaced by this bone, which forms a **hard (bony) callus.** The trabeculae of the hard callus continue to grow and thicken for several months.

④ **The bone is remodeled.** Remodeling is the final phase of fracture repair. The hard callus persists for at least 3 to 4 months, as osteoclasts remove excess bony material from both exterior and interior surfaces. Compact bone replaces primary bone. The fracture usually leaves a slight

thickening of the bone (as detected by x-ray); however, in some instances healing occurs with no persistent obvious thickening.

WHAT DID YOU LEARN?

㉒ What are the four basic steps in fracture repair?

㉓ Explain the risk of bearing weight on a bone when the fibrocartilage callus is forming.

CHAPTER SUMMARY

	• The skeletal system is composed of dynamic living tissue.
7.1 Introduction to the Skeletal System 211	• Bones, cartilage, ligaments, and other connective tissue that stabilize or connect bones compose the skeletal system.
7.2 Bone: The Major Organ of the Skeletal System 211	• Bones are organs that contain all tissue types, the most abundant being bone (osseous) connective tissue.

7.2a General Functions 212
- The functions of bone include support and protection, movement, hemopoiesis, and storage of minerals and energy reserves.

7.2b Classification of Bones 212
- Bones are classified by shape as long, short, flat, or irregular.
- Long bones have a greater length than width; short bones have a nearly equal length and width; flat bones exhibit thin, flat surfaces; and irregular bones have elaborate, complex shapes.

7.2c Gross Anatomy of Bones 213
- A long bone contains the following regions: diaphysis, epiphysis, metaphysis, articular cartilage, medullary cavity.
- A long bone is covered externally by the periosteum and lined internally by the endosteum.
- Other types of bones (all bones except long bones) generally are composed of compact bone enclosing spongy bone, and the bone covered externally by the periosteum.
- All bones contain a rich blood supply and innervation.

CHALLENGE YOURSELF

Do You Know the Basics?

____ 1. The skeletal system is composed of all of the following *except*

    a. bones.

    b. ligaments.

    c. cartilage.

    d. tendons.

____ 2. All of the following are functions of cartilage *except*

    a. cartilage serves as a site for hemopoiesis.

    b. cartilage provides support for soft tissue.

    c. cartilage forms the initial model in endochondral ossification.

    d. cartilage provides a smooth gliding surface at the end of bones in freely movable joints.

____ 3. A bone is considered an organ because it is composed of two or more tissues. Which of the following are tissues of the bone?

    a. dense irregular connective tissue of the periosteum

    b. hyaline cartilage connective tissue of the epiphyseal plate and articular cartilage

    c. bone connective tissue that is the supportive framework of the body

    d. All of the above are tissues of bone.

____ 4. The femur is an example of a

    a. short bone.

    b. flat bone.

    c. long bone.

    d. irregular bone.

____ 5. The immature cells that produce osteoid are called

    a. osteocytes.

    b. osteoblasts.

    c. osteoclasts.

    d. osteons.

____ 6. A small space within compact bone housing an osteocyte is termed a

    a. lamella.

    b. lacuna.

    c. canaliculus.

    d. medullary cavity.

____ 7. The specific tissue that engages in hemopoiesis is

    a. yellow marrow.

    b. hyaline cartilage connective tissue.

    c. red bone marrow.

    d. compact bone.

____ 8. All of the following accurately describe the hyaline cartilage *except*

    a. the matrix of hyaline cartilage contains calcium.

    b. hyaline cartilage is avascular.

    c. hyaline cartilage lacks nerves.

    d. hyaline cartilage is a flexible, semirigid connective tissue.

____ 9. Endochondral ossification begins with a _____ model of bone.

    a. dense regular connective tissue

    b. hyaline cartilage

    c. fibrocartilage

    d. elastic cartilage

____ 10. An epiphyseal line appears when

    a. epiphyseal plate growth has ended.

    b. epiphyseal plate growth is just beginning.

    c. growth in bone diameter is just beginning.

    d. the bone is fractured at that location.

11. Describe the structure of a typical long bone.

12. Describe the general function of both osteoblast and osteoclast activity.

13. Describe the microscopic anatomy of compact bone.

14. Why is spongy bone able to withstand stress in an area such as the expanded end of a long bone?

15. Compare and contrast interstitial growth versus appositional growth of cartilage.

16. List the steps involved in endochondral ossification.

17. Which of the five zones in the epiphyseal plate cartilage are specifically responsible for bone growth in length? Explain.

18. Discuss the effect of exercise on bone mass.

19. Describe how parathyroid hormone regulates blood plasma calcium concentration.

20. What are the steps in fracture repair?

Can You Apply What You've Learned?

1. Jorge is donating bone marrow to a friend of his who has leukemia (a type of blood cell cancer). Jorge is 30 years old, so the doctor knows she must insert the needle in

    a. the diaphysis of the femur.

    b. the hip bone.

    c. the distal epiphysis of the tibia.

    d. the diaphysis of the humerus.

2. You are given the following assignment. Obtain two small chicken or turkey bones. Bake one bone in the oven at a high temperature for approximately 30 minutes. Place the other in vinegar (acidic pH) for several days. Which of the following would most accurately reflect what occurred?

   a. Proteins in the bone matrix have denatured in the bone that is baked, and the vinegar has denatured the proteins in the soaked bone, so both bones are flexible.
   b. Proteins in the bone matrix are lost from the baked bone, and the bone becomes flexible. The soaked bone loses calcium and results in a brittle bone.
   c. Proteins in matrix have denatured from high temperature, and the bone is brittle; calcium has been removed from the bone soaked in vinegar and it has become flexible.
   d. Proteins are lost in the baked bone matrix, and this bone becomes flexible. Calcium loss from the bone soaked in vinegar results in a flexible bone.

3. Your dog is chewing on an adult cow long bone and breaks it open. He pulls out some fleshy material within the diaphysis of the bone. You know that this fleshy material

   a. produced red blood cells for the adult cow.
   b. contains fat.
   c. was formed from osteoblasts.
   d. is abnormal and is not normally found in bone.

4. To identify the approximate age of skeletal remains of a body found in the forest, the forensic anthropologists are most interested in which of the following?

   a. whether the epiphyses have fused to the diaphyses
   b. number of bones in the skeleton
   c. length of the long bones in the legs
   d. presence or absence of articular cartilage

5. In your anatomy and physiology laboratory, you look at prepared slides of developing bone. In the epiphyseal plate region, you note the chondrocytes are slightly enlarged and stacked in a longitudinal array. What epiphyseal plate zone is in your field of view?

   a. zone of rest
   b. zone of proliferation
   c. zone of hypertrophy
   d. zone of calcification

Can You Synthesize What You've Learned?

1. The traditional surgical procedure to treat advanced thyroid gland tumors is to remove the affected organ. Some concerns with the results of this surgery were raised regarding the parathyroid glands, which are small attachments on the posterior side of the thyroid gland. Why should the surgeon be concerned about the removal of these glands? A new procedure has been developed to sequester some parathyroid gland tissue into a plastic mesh holder and implant this small holder back into the body. Why is this implant an advantage to the patient?

2. A fireman fell from a ladder while fighting a fire and severely fractured the thigh and leg bones in his right leg. He was hospitalized for several weeks, then he was wheelchair-bound for several months while his leg bones healed. Upon removal of the cast, it was apparent that his right thigh and leg bones were thin and weak. What factors contributed to this thinning and weakening of the bones, and what should the fireman do to improve the strength of these bones?

3. Elise is 14 and lives in an apartment in the city. She does not like outdoor activities, so she spends most of her spare time watching TV, playing video games, drinking soft drinks, and talking to friends on the phone. One afternoon, Elise tries to run down the stairs while talking on the phone, and falls, breaking her leg. Although she appears healthy, her leg takes longer to heal than expected. What might cause the longer healing time?

chapter 8

Skeletal System: Axial and Appendicular Skeleton

The bones of the skeleton form an internal framework to support soft tissues, protect vital organs, bear the body's weight, and help us move. An adult skeleton typically has 206 named bones, although this number varies in some individuals. Bones differ in size, shape, and weight, and this diversity is related directly to the skeleton's many functions.

For criminologists, pathologists, and anthropologists, bones can tell an intricate anatomic story. The skeleton can provide information about an individual. In this

Chiropractors are health care professionals who focus on the musculoskeletal system. These individuals palpate bony surface landmarks to pinpoint their manual therapy of both the bones and the overlying muscle and connective tissue. By manipulating the spine and other bony regions, chiropractors may adjust various muscle imbalances and may improve the functioning of the nerves that may be impinged by the spine. Here, a chiropractor is palpating the spinous and transverse processes of the patients back in order to perform a spinal adjustment.

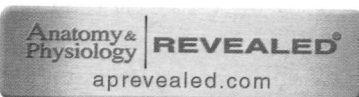

Anatomy & Physiology REVEALED
aprevealed.com

Module 5: Skeletal System

chapter, not only will you learn the names of and features on the individual bones, we also provide an overview of how you can determine age at death from the skeletal remains, as well as how you can tell the difference in sex between certain bones of the skeleton. You can practice determining age at death and determining sex using the bones in your anatomy lab. This will permit you to learn some of the variations seen in bone morphology so you can start to unlock the mysteries of the bones in front of you in the lab.

8.1 Components of the Skeleton

The names for characteristic markings on bones are discussed in this section. We then examine the two subdivisions of the skeleton: the axial skeleton and the appendicular skeleton.

8.1a Bone Markings

✓ LEARNING OBJECTIVE

1. Become familiar with terminology for common bone markings.

Distinctive **bone markings** are the surface features that characterize each bone in the body. Projections from the bone surface mark the point where muscles, tendons, and ligaments attach. Sites of articulation between adjacent bones tend to be smooth areas. Depressions, grooves, and openings through bones indicate sites where blood vessels and nerves travel.

Anatomists use specific terms to describe these characteristics (figure 8.1).

Knowing the names of bone markings will help you learn about specific bones described in this chapter. For example, when trying to

General Structure	Anatomic Term	Description
Articulating surfaces	Condyle	Large, smooth, rounded articulating oval structure
	Facet	Small, flat, shallow articulating surface
	Head	Prominent, rounded epiphysis
	Trochlea	Smooth, grooved, pulley-like articular process
Depressions	Alveolus (pl., *alveoli*)	Deep pit or socket in the maxillae or mandible
	Fossa (pl., *fossae*)	Flattened or shallow depression
	Sulcus	Narrow groove
Projections for tendon and ligament attachment	Crest	Narrow, prominent, ridgelike projection
	Epicondyle	Projection adjacent to a condyle
	Line	Low ridge
	Process	Any marked bony prominence
	Ramus (pl., *rami*)	Angular extension of a bone relative to the rest of the structure
	Spine	Pointed, slender process
	Trochanter	Massive, rough projection found only on the femur
	Tubercle	Small, round projection
	Tuberosity	Large, rough projection
Openings and spaces	Canal	Passageway through a bone
	Fissure	Narrow, slitlike opening through a bone
	Foramen (pl., *foramina*)	Rounded passageway through a bone
	Meatus	Passageway through a bone
	Sinus	Cavity or hollow space in a bone

Facet
Crest
Fossa
Spine
Line
Foramen
Ramus

Pelvis

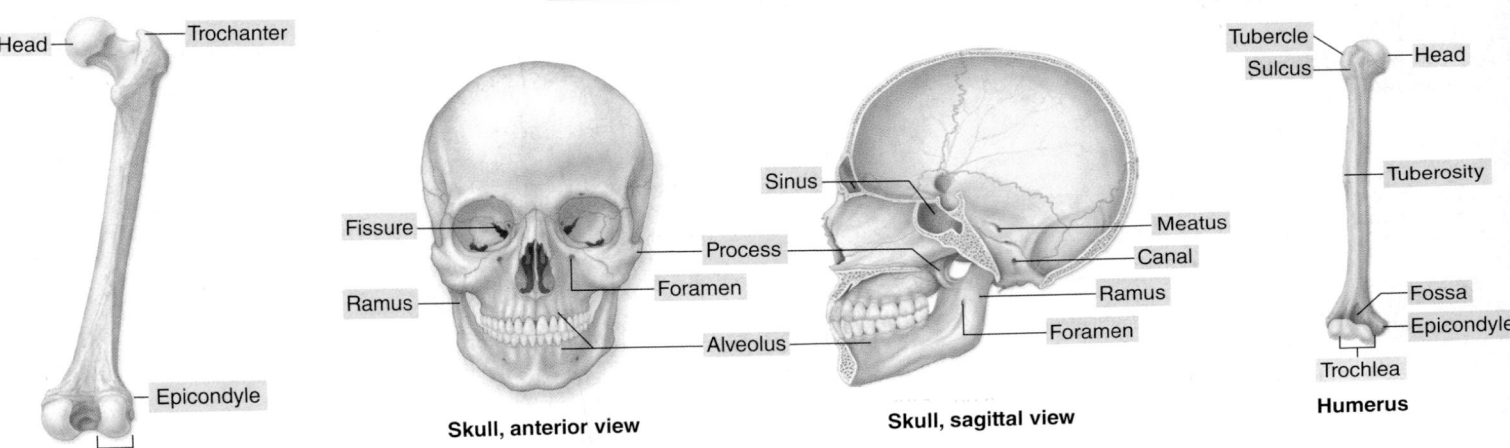

Head — Trochanter

Epicondyle

Condyle

Femur

Fissure
Ramus
Process
Foramen
Alveolus

Skull, anterior view

Sinus
Meatus
Canal
Ramus
Foramen

Skull, sagittal view

Tubercle
Sulcus — Head
Tuberosity
Fossa
Epicondyle
Trochlea

Humerus

Figure 8.1 Bone Markings. Specific anatomic terms describe the characteristic features on bones.

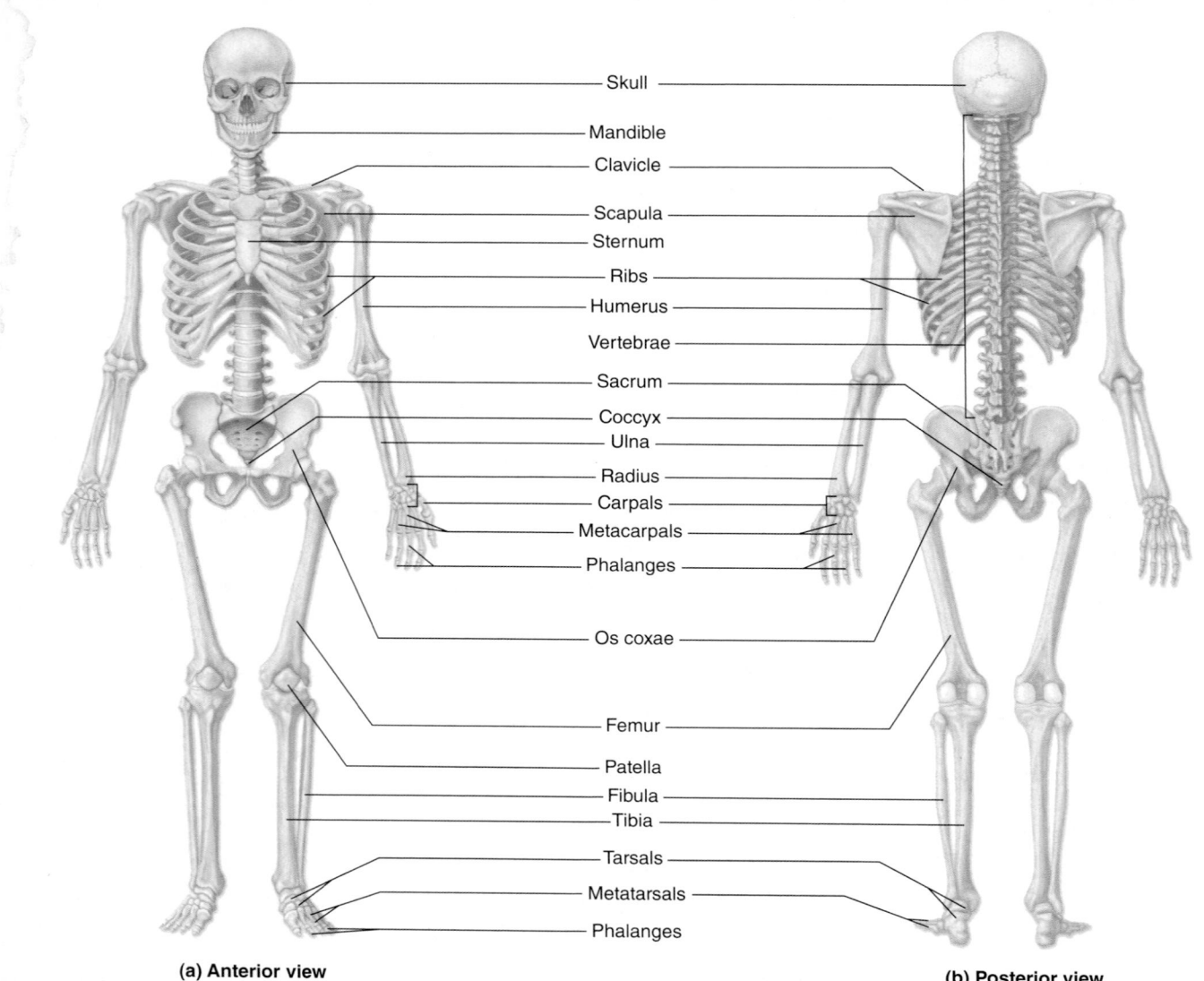

Skull
Mandible
Clavicle
Scapula
Sternum
Ribs
Humerus
Vertebrae
Sacrum
Coccyx
Ulna
Radius
Carpals
Metacarpals
Phalanges
Os coxae
Femur
Patella
Fibula
Tibia
Tarsals
Metatarsals
Phalanges

(a) Anterior view

(b) Posterior view

Bones of the Axial Skeleton (80)				
Skull (22)	Cranial bones (8) Frontal bone (1), parietal bones (2), temporal bones (2), occipital bone (1), sphenoid bone (1), ethmoid bone (1)	**Vertebral column (26)**	Cervical vertebrae (7)	
			Thoracic vertebrae (12)	
	Facial bones (14) Zygomatic bones (2), lacrimal bones (2), nasal bones (2), vomer (1), inferior nasal conchae (2), palatine bones (2), maxillae (2), mandible (1)		Lumbar vertebrae (5)	
			Sacrum (1)	
			Coccyx (1)	
Associated bones of the skull (7)	Auditory ossicles (6) Malleus (2), incus (2), stapes (2) Hyoid bone (1)	**Thoracic cage (25)**	Sternum (1)	
			Ribs (24)	
Bones of the Appendicular Skeleton (63 bones per each side of the body, 126 bones total)				
Pectoral girdle (4 bones total)	Clavicle (2)	**Pelvic girdle (2 bones total)**	Os coxae (2)	
	Scapula (2)			
Upper limbs (30 bones per each upper limb, 60 bones total)	Humerus (2)	**Lower limbs (30 bones per each lower limb, 60 bones total)**	Femur (2)	
	Radius (2)		Patella (2)	
	Ulna (2)		Tibia (2)	
	Carpals (16)		Fibula (2)	
	Metacarpals (10)		Tarsals (14)	
	Phalanges (28)		Metatarsals (10)	
			Phalanges (28)	

Figure 8.2 Axial and Appendicular Skeleton. (*a*) Anterior and (*b*) posterior views compare the axial and appendicular components of the skeleton. The axial skeleton is colored blue and the appendicular skeleton is colored tan.

240 Chapter Eight Skeletal System: Axial and Appendicular Skeleton locate the foramen magnum of the skull, you have an advantage if you know that foramen means "hole" or "passageway."

 WHAT DID YOU LEARN?

1 What is the difference between a foramen and a fissure?

8.1b Axial and Appendicular Skeleton

 LEARNING OBJECTIVE

2. Compare and contrast the functions and composition of the axial and appendicular skeletons.

INTEGRATE

LEARNING STRATEGY

Many bones of the body have the same names as the body regions where they are found. Before you begin learning the bones of the skeleton, it may help you to review table 1.2 (Anatomic Directional Terms) and table 1.3 (Human Body Regions).

The skeletal system is organized into two divisions: the axial skeleton and the appendicular skeleton **(figure 8.2)**.

The **axial skeleton** is so named because it is composed of the bones along the central axis of the body that are commonly divided into three regions—the skull, the vertebral column, and the thoracic cage. The main function of the axial skeleton is to create a framework that supports and protects the organs. Additionally, the spongy bone of most of the axial skeleton contains hemopoietic tissue that is responsible for blood cell formation (see section 18.3b).

The **appendicular skeleton** includes the bones of the upper and lower limbs, and the girdles of bones that attach the upper and lower limbs to the axial skeleton. The pectoral girdle consists of bones that hold the upper limbs in place, while the pelvic girdle consists of bones that hold the lower limbs in place.

 WHAT DID YOU LEARN?

2 What is the general function of the axial skeleton, and what bones are considered part of the axial skeleton?

8.2 Bones and Features of the Skull

We begin our examination of the skeleton by discussing its most complex structure, the skull. The skull is comprised of 22 bones. Here we describe the anatomy and landmarks of the skull, the sutures (fibrous joints) that connect the bones of the cranium, and the specialized features of the orbital and nasal complexes and paranasal sinuses.

8.2a General Anatomy of the Skull

 LEARNING OBJECTIVE

1. Distinguish between the cranial and the facial bones.

The **skull** is composed of both cranial and facial bones. **Cranial bones** form the rounded **cranium** (krā′nē-um; *kranion* = skull), which completely surrounds and encloses the brain.[1] The cranium consists of a roof and a base. The roof of the cranium, called the **calvaria** (kal-vā′rē-ă), or *skullcap,* is composed of part of the frontal bone, the parietal bones, and part of the occipital bone. The **base** of the cranium is composed of portions of the ethmoid, sphenoid, occipital, and temporal bones. Some skulls in the anatomy lab have had their calvariae cut away, making the distinction between the calvaria and base easier to distinguish.

Facial bones form the face. They also protect the entrances to the digestive and respiratory systems. Touch your cheeks, your jaws, and the bridge of your nose; these bones are facial bones. The facial bones give shape and individuality to the face, form part of the orbit and nasal cavities, support the teeth, and provide for the attachment of muscles involved in

---

[1] Osteologists (scientists who study bones) define the cranium as the entire skull minus the mandible. In this text, we use the term *cranium* to denote the bones of the braincase only.

facial expression and mastication (chewing). There are 14 facial bones, including the paired zygomatic bones, lacrimal bones, nasal bones, inferior nasal conchae, palatine bones, maxillae, and the unpaired vomer and mandible.

The skull contains several prominent cavities (**figure 8.3**). The largest is the **cranial cavity** (or *endocranium*) that encloses, protects, and supports the brain. (Volume of an adult cranial cavity ranges from approximately 1300 to 1500 cubic centimeters.) The skull also forms and has several smaller cavities, including the orbits (eye sockets), the oral cavity, the nasal cavity, and the paranasal sinuses.

 WHAT DID YOU LEARN?

3 What bones form the skull? Which of these bones are cranial bones? Which of these bones are facial bones?

8.2b Views of the Skull and Landmark Features

 LEARNING OBJECTIVES

2. Identify the locations of cranial and facial bones in various views of the skull.

3. Learn key bone markings and features of each of the bones of the cranium.

4. Compare and contrast the locations and contents of three cranial fossae.

To best understand the complex nature of the skull, we first examine the skull as a whole and learn which bones are best seen from a particular view. Note that only some major features will be mentioned in this section. Later in the chapter, we examine the individual skull bones in detail.

WHAT DO YOU THINK?

1 What is the benefit of the skull's being made of multiple smaller bones, rather than one big bone?

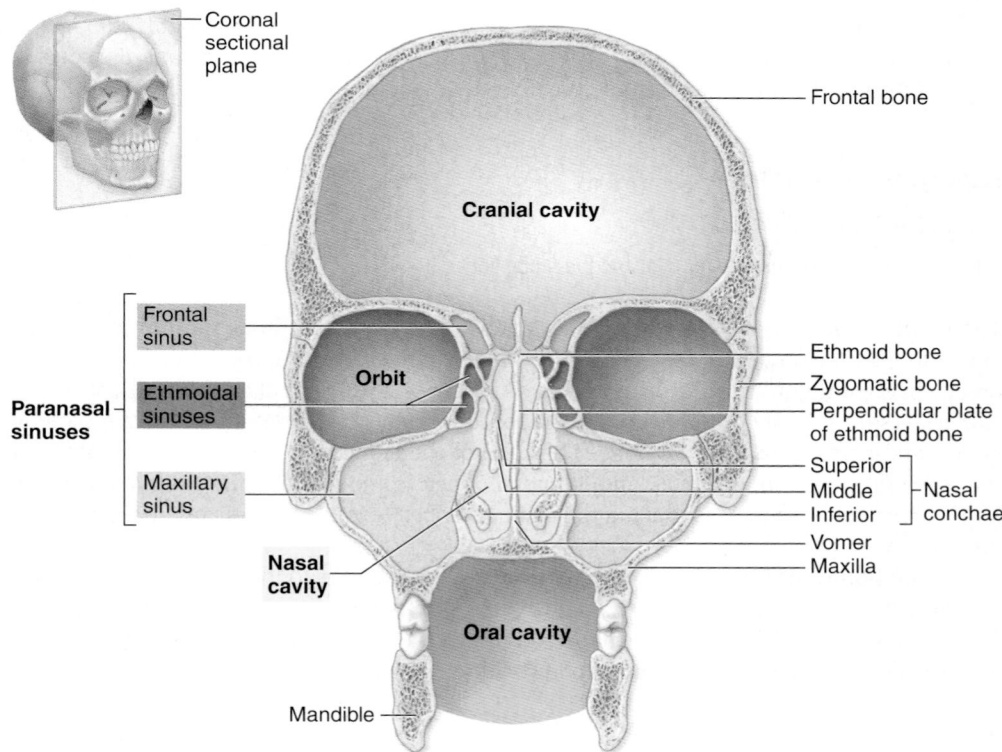

Figure 8.3 Major Cavities of the Skull. A coronal section diagram highlights the cranial cavity, orbits, paranasal sinuses, nasal cavity, and oral cavity.

A cursory glance at the skull reveals numerous bone markings, such as canals, fissures, and foramina that serve as passageways for blood vessels and nerves. The major foramina of the cranial and facial bones are summarized in **table 8.1**. Refer to this table as we examine the skull from various directions. (This table also will be important when we study nerves in section 13.9 and section 14.5 and blood vessels in chapter 20.)

Table 8.1	Passageways Within the Skull	
Passageway	**Location**	**Primary Structures That Pass Through**
CRANIAL BONES		
Carotid canal	Petrous part of temporal bone	Internal carotid artery
Cribriform foramina	Cribriform plate of ethmoid bone	Olfactory nerves (CN I)
Foramen lacerum	Between petrous part of temporal bone, sphenoid bone, and occipital bone	None
Foramen magnum	Occipital bone	Vertebral arteries; spinal cord; accessory nerves (CN XI)
Foramen ovale	Greater wing of sphenoid bone	Mandibular branch of trigeminal nerve (CN V_3)
Foramen rotundum	Greater wing of sphenoid bone	Maxillary branch of trigeminal nerve (CN V_2)
Foramen spinosum	Greater wing of sphenoid bone	Middle meningeal vessels
Hypoglossal canal	Anteromedial to occipital condyle of occipital bone	Hypoglossal nerve (CN XII)
Inferior orbital fissure	Junction of maxilla, sphenoid, and zygomatic bones	Infraorbital nerve (branch of CN V_2)
Jugular foramen	Between temporal bone and occipital bone (posterior to carotid canal)	Internal jugular vein; glossopharyngeal nerve (CN IX); vagus nerve (CN X); accessory nerve (CN XI)
Mastoid foramen	Posterior to mastoid process of temporal bone	Mastoid emissary veins
Optic canal	Posteromedial part of orbit in lesser wing of sphenoid bone	Optic nerve (CN II)
Stylomastoid foramen	Between mastoid and styloid processes of temporal bone	Facial nerve (CN VII)
Superior orbital fissure	Posterior part of orbit between greater and lesser wings of sphenoid bone	Ophthalmic veins; oculomotor nerve (CN III); trochlear nerve (CN IV); ophthalmic branch of trigeminal nerve (CN V_1); abducens nerve (CN VI)
Supraorbital foramen	Supraorbital margin of orbit in frontal bone	Supraorbital artery; supraorbital nerve (branch of CN V_1)
FACIAL BONES		
Greater and lesser palatine foramina	Palatine bone	Palatine vessels; greater and lesser palatine nerves (branches of CN V_2)
Incisive foramen	Posterior to incisor teeth in hard palate of the maxilla	Nasopalatine nerve (branch of CN V_2)
Infraorbital foramen	Inferior to orbit in maxilla	Infraorbital artery; infraorbital nerve (branch of CN V_2)
Lacrimal groove	Lacrimal bone	Nasolacrimal duct
Mandibular foramen	Medial surface of ramus of mandible	Inferior alveolar blood vessels; inferior alveolar nerve (branch of CN V_3)
Mental foramen	Inferior to second premolar on anterolateral surface of mandible	Mental blood vessels; mental nerve (branch of CN V_3)

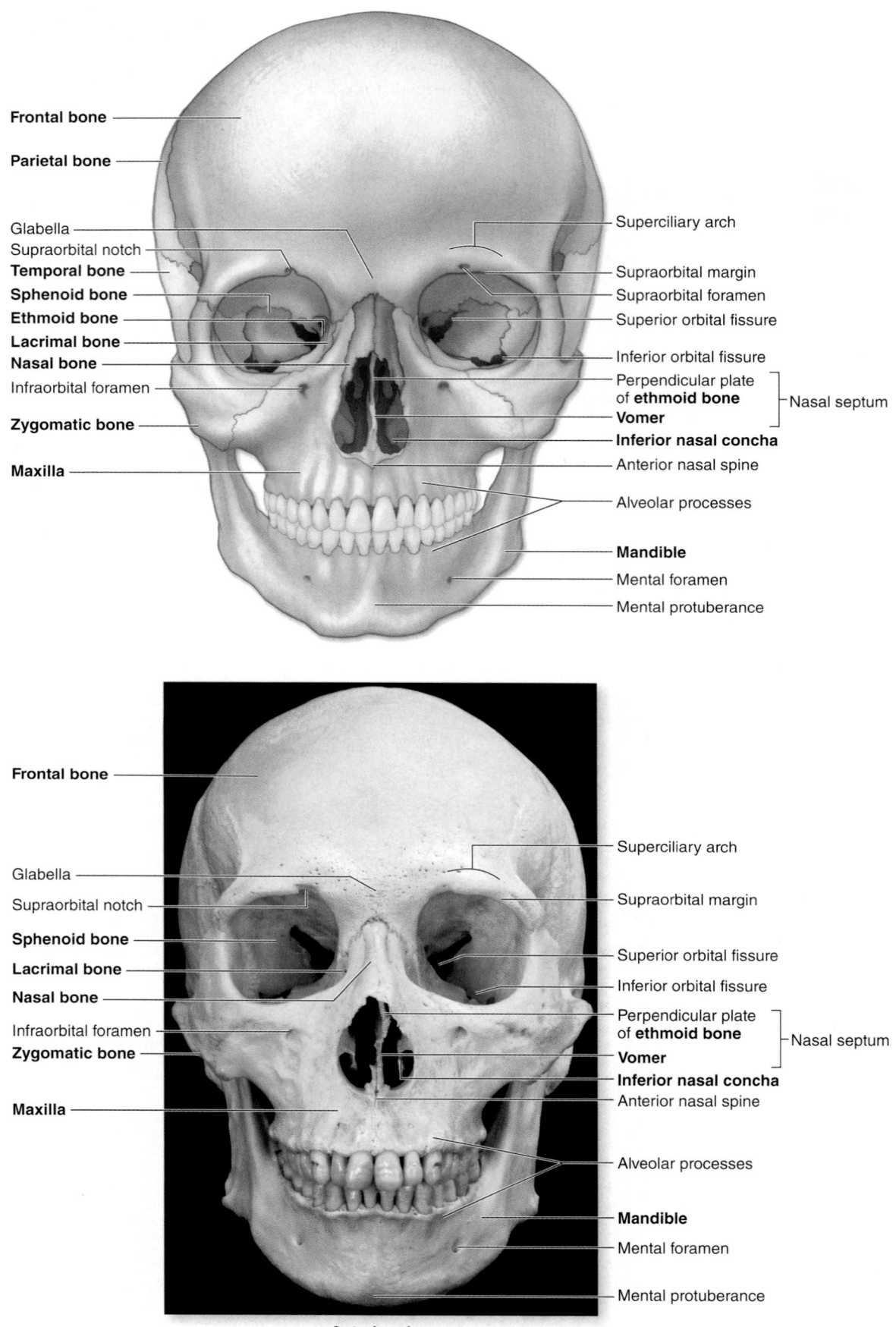

Frontal bone

Parietal bone

Glabella
Supraorbital notch
Temporal bone
Sphenoid bone
Ethmoid bone
Lacrimal bone
Nasal bone
Infraorbital foramen

Zygomatic bone

Maxilla

Superciliary arch

Supraorbital margin
Supraorbital foramen
Superior orbital fissure

Inferior orbital fissure

Perpendicular plate
of **ethmoid bone**
Vomer
Inferior nasal concha
Anterior nasal spine
⎱ Nasal septum

Alveolar processes

Mandible
Mental foramen
Mental protuberance

Frontal bone

Glabella

Supraorbital notch

Sphenoid bone

Lacrimal bone

Nasal bone

Infraorbital foramen
Zygomatic bone

Maxilla

Superciliary arch

Supraorbital margin

Superior orbital fissure

Inferior orbital fissure

Perpendicular plate
of **ethmoid bone**
Vomer
Inferior nasal concha
Anterior nasal spine
⎱ Nasal septum

Alveolar processes

Mandible

Mental foramen

Mental protuberance

Anterior view

Figure 8.4 Anterior View of the Skull. The frontal bone, nasal bones, maxillae, and mandible are prominent in this view. **AP|R**

Anterior View

An anterior view **(figure 8.4)** shows several major bones of the skull. The **frontal bone** forms the forehead. The left and right **orbits** are formed from a complex articulation of multiple skull bones. There are two large openings within each orbit called the **superior orbital fissure** and the **inferior orbital fissure.** Superior to the orbits on the anterior surface of the frontal bone are the **superciliary** (soo-per-sil′ē-ār-ē; *super* = above; *cilium* = eyelid) **arches,** otherwise known as the brow ridges. Male skulls tend to have larger and more pronounced superciliary arches than do female skulls. The left and right **nasal bones** form the bony bridge of the nose. Superior to the nasal bones and between the orbits is a landmark area called the **glabella** (glă-bel′ă; *glabellus* = smooth).

The left and right **maxillae** (mak-sil′ē; sing., *maxilla*, mak-sil-ă; jawbone), also called *maxillary bones,* fuse in the midline to form most of the upper jaw and the lateral boundaries of the nasal cavity. The maxillae also help form a portion of both the floor of each orbit and the roof of the oral cavity. Inferior to each orbit in the maxilla is an **infraorbital foramen,** which conducts blood vessels and nerves to the face.

The lower jaw is formed by the **mandible.** The prominent "chin" of the mandible is called the **mental protuberance.** The oral margins of the maxillae and mandible each have **alveolar** (al-vē′ō-lăr) **processes** that contain the teeth.

The nasal cavity is also seen in an anterior view. Its inferior border is marked by a prominent **anterior nasal spine.** The thin ridge of bone that divides the nasal cavity into left and right halves is called the **nasal septum.** Along the inferolateral walls of the nasal cavity are two scroll-shaped bones called the **inferior nasal conchae** (kon′kē; sing., *concha,* kon′kă; shell).

Superior View

The superior view of the skull in **figure 8.5a** primarily shows four of the cranial bones: the frontal bone, both **parietal** (pă-rī′ĕ-tăl; *paries* = wall) **bones,** and the **occipital** (ok-sip′i-tăl; *occiput* = back of head) **bone.** The articulation between the frontal and parietal bones is the coronal suture, so named because it runs along a coronal plane. The sagittal suture connects the left and right parietal bones along the midline of the skull.

Along the posterior one-third of the sagittal suture is either a single **parietal foramen** or paired **parietal foramina,** which serve as the passage of small veins between the brain and the scalp. The lateral surface of each parietal bone exhibits a rounded, smooth area called the **parietal eminence.** The superior part of the lambdoid suture represents the articulation of the occipital bone with both parietal bones.

Posterior View

The posterior view of the skull in figure 8.5b shows a portion of the occipital, parietal, and temporal bones, as well as the lambdoid suture between the occipital and parietal bones. Within the lambdoid suture there may be one or more sutural (Wormian) bones. The **external occipital protuberance** (prō-too′ber-ans) is a prominence on the posterior aspect of the skull. Palpate the back of your head; males tend to have a prominent, pointed external occipital protuberance, whereas females have a more subtle, rounded protuberance. Intersecting the external occipital protuberance are two horizontal ridges, the **superior** and **inferior nuchal** (noo′kăl) **lines** (see figure 8.7).

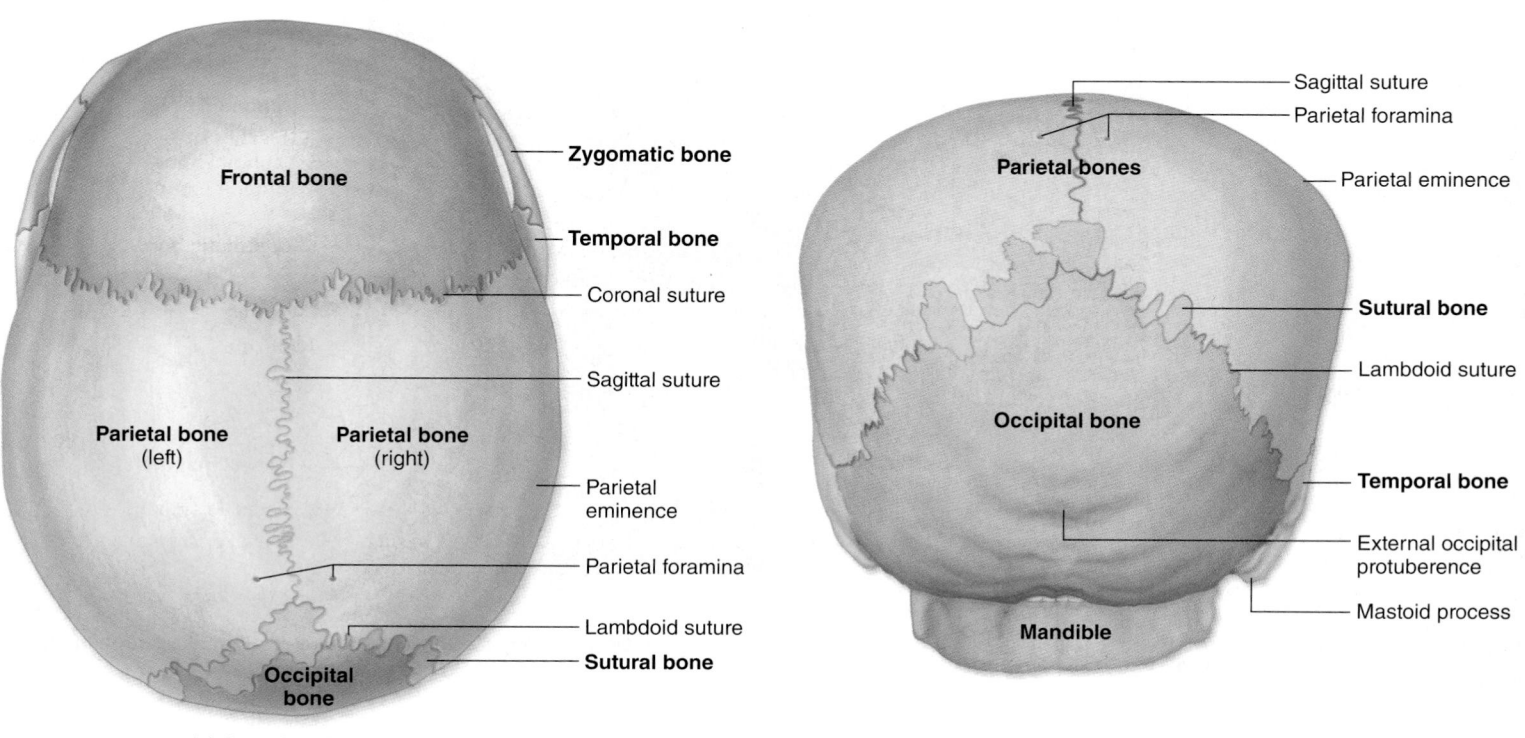

(a) Superior view

(b) Posterior view

Figure 8.5 Superior and Posterior Views of the Skull. (*a*) The superior aspect of the skull shows the major sutures and the flat bones of the skull. (*b*) The posterior view is dominated by the occipital and parietal bones.

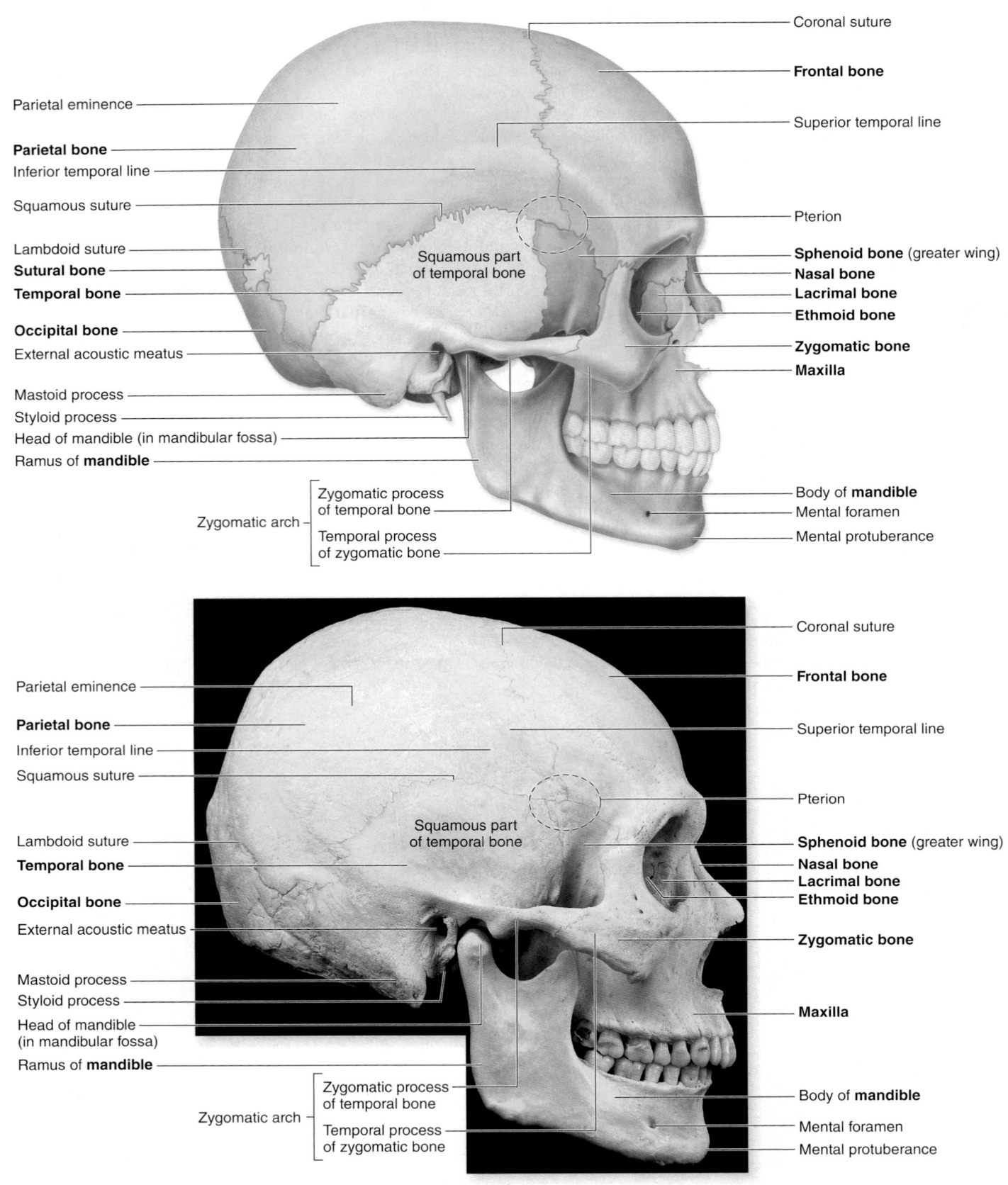

Figure 8.6 Lateral View of the Skull. The parietal, temporal, zygomatic, frontal, and occipital bones, as well as the maxilla and mandible, are prominent in this view. AP|R

Lateral View

A lateral view of the skull (**figure 8.6**) shows one parietal bone, **temporal bone,** and **zygomatic** (zī′gō-mat′ik; *zygoma* = a joining, a yoke) **bone.** This view also shows part of the maxilla, mandible, frontal bone, and occipital bone. The **superior** and **inferior temporal lines** arc across the surface of the parietal and frontal bones and mark the attachment site of the temporalis muscle (see section 11.3c). The small **lacrimal** (lak'ri-măl; *lacrima* = a tear) **bone** articulates with the maxilla anteriorly and with the ethmoid bone posteriorly. A portion of the **sphenoid** (sfē'noyd; wedge-shaped) **bone** articulates with the frontal, parietal, and temporal bones. This region is called the **pterion** (tĕ'rē-on; *ptéron* = wing) and is circled on figure 8.6. Pterion includes the H-shaped set of sutures of these four articulating bones.

The **temporal process** of the **zygomatic bone** and the **zygomatic process** of the **temporal bone** fuse to form the **zygomatic arch.** Put your fingers along the bony prominences ("apples") of your cheeks and move your fingers posteriorly toward your ears; you are feeling the zygomatic arch. The zygomatic arch terminates superior to the point where the mandible articulates with the **mandibular** (man-dib'ū-lăr) **fossa** of the temporal bone. This articulation is called the **temporomandibular joint (TMJ)** and is described further in section 9.7a. By putting your finger anterior to your external ear opening and then opening and closing your jaw, you can feel that joint moving.

The squamous part of the temporal bone lies directly inferior to the squamous suture. Immediately posterolateral to the mandibular fossa is the tympanic (tim-pan'ik; *tympanon* = drum) part of the temporal bone. This is a small, bony ring surrounding the external ear opening called the **external acoustic meatus** (mē-ā'tŭs; a passage), or *external auditory canal.* Inferior and posterior to this meatus is the **mastoid** (mas'toyd; *masto* = breast; *eidos* = resemblance) **process,** the bump you feel behind your external ear opening.

Sagittal Sectional View

Cutting the skull along a sagittal sectional plane reveals bones that form the endocranium and the nasal cavity (**figure 8.7a**). The cranial cavity is formed from a complex articulation of the frontal, parietal, temporal, occipital, **ethmoid** (eth'moyd; *ethmos* = sieve), and sphenoid bones.

Vessel impressions may be visible on the internal surface of the skull. The **frontal sinus** (a space in the frontal bone) and the **sphenoidal sinus** (open space in the sphenoid bone) are visible in a sagittal view.

A sagittal sectional view also shows the bones that form the nasal septum more clearly. The **perpendicular plate** of the **ethmoid** forms the posterosuperior portion of the nasal septum, whereas the **vomer** (vō'mer; plowshare) forms the posteroinferior portion. (The anterior part of the nasal septum is cartilaginous.) The ethmoid bone serves as the division between the anterior floor of the cranial cavity and the roof of the nasal cavity. The **palatine process** of the maxillae and the **palatine** (pal'a-tin) **bones** form the hard palate (figure 8.7b), which acts as both the floor of the nasal cavity and a portion of the roof of the mouth. Move your tongue along the roof of your mouth; you are palpating the maxillae anteriorly and palatine bones posteriorly.

Inferior (Basal) View

In an inferior (basal) view, the most anterior structure is the hard palate (figure 8.7b). On the posterior aspect of either side of the palate are the **medial** and **lateral pterygoid** (ter'i-goyd; *pteryx* = winglike) **plates** of the sphenoid bone. Both plates form a **pterygoid process.** Medially adjacent to these structures are the internal openings of the nasal cavity, called the **choanae** (kō'an-ă; funnel).

Between the mandibular fossa and the pterygoid processes are several paired foramina and canals. Typically, these openings provide passage for specific blood vessels and nerves. For example, the **jugular** (jŭg'ū-lar; *jugulum* = throat) **foramen** is an opening between the temporal and occipital bones that provides passageway for the internal jugular vein and several nerves. The *foramen lacerum* (anteromedial to the carotid canal) extends between the occipital and temporal bones. This opening is covered by cartilage in a living individual. The entrance to the **carotid** (ka-rot'id; *karoo* = to put to sleep) **canal** is anteromedial to the jugular foramen; the internal carotid artery passes through this canal.

The **styloid** (stī'loyd; *stylos* = pillar, post) **process** is a thin, pointed projection of bone located anteromedial to the mastoid process. It serves as an attachment site for several hyoid and tongue muscles. The **stylomastoid foramen** lies between the mastoid process and the styloid process. The facial nerve (CN VII) extends through the stylomastoid foramen to innervate the facial muscles.

The largest foramen of all is the **foramen magnum,** literally meaning "big hole." Through this opening, the spinal cord enters the cranial cavity and is continuous superiorly with the brainstem. On either side of the foramen magnum are the rounded **occipital condyles,** which articulate with the first cervical vertebra of the vertebral column. At the anteromedial edge of each condyle is a **hypoglossal canal** through which the hypoglossal nerve (CN XII) extends to supply tongue muscles.

Frontal bone

Coronal suture

Sphenoid bone

Sphenoidal sinus

Frontal sinus

Ethmoid bone — Crista galli

Perpendicular plate

Nasal bone

Vomer

Palatine bone

Maxilla

Mandible

Vessel impressions

Parietal bone

Temporal bone

Occipital bone

Squamous suture

Sella turcica

Lambdoid suture

Internal acoustic meatus

Hypoglossal canal

Pterygoid processes

Styloid process

Mandibular foramen

(a) Sagittal section

Incisive foramen

Hard palate — Palatine process of **maxilla**

Palatine bone

Palatine foramina

Choana

Vomer

Sphenoid bone

Foramen ovale

Foramen spinosum

Foramen lacerum

Stylomastoid foramen

Jugular foramen

Carotid canal

Mastoid foramen

Inferior nuchal line

Superior nuchal line

Temporal process of **zygomatic bone** — Zygomatic arch

Zygomatic process of temporal bone

Lateral pterygoid plate — Pterygoid processes

Medial pterygoid plate

Styloid process

Mandibular fossa

Basilar part of occipital bone

Temporal bone

Mastoid process

Occipital condyle

Hypoglossal canal

Foramen magnum

Occipital bone

External occipital crest

Lambdoid suture

External occipital protuberance

(b) Inferior view

Figure 8.7 Sagittal Section and Inferior View of the Skull. (*a*) Features such as the perpendicular plate of the ethmoid bone, the vomer, and the frontal and sphenoidal sinuses, as well as the internal relationships of the skull bones, are best seen in sagittal section. (*b*) The hard palate, sphenoid bone, parts of the temporal bone, and the occipital bone with its foramen magnum may be seen in the inferior view. AP|R

Internal View of Cranial Base

When the top of the skull is cut and removed, the internal view of the cranial base (figure 8.8) is revealed. Here we see the frontal bone surrounding the delicate **cribriform** (krib'ri-fōrm; *cribrum* = sieve; *forma* = form) **plate** of the ethmoid bone. The plate has numerous perforations called the **cribriform foramina,** which provide passageways for the olfactory nerves (CN I) into the superior portion of the nasal cavity. The anteromedial part of the cribriform plate exhibits a midsagittal elevation called the **crista galli** (kris'tă = crest; gal'lē = of a rooster), to which the cranial dural septa of the brain attach (see section 13.2a).

The relatively large sphenoid is located posterior to the frontal bone. It is often referred to as a "bridging bone" because it unites the cranial and facial bones. The lateral expansions of the sphenoid bone are called the **greater wings** and the **lesser wings** of the **sphenoid.** The pituitary gland is suspended inferior to the base of the brain within the bony depression on the sphenoid called the **sella turcica** (sel'ă = saddle; tur'si-ka = Turkish). Anterior to the sella turcica are the **optic canals** through which the optic nerves (CN II) extend from the eyes in the orbits to the brain.

The lateral regions of the cranial base are formed by the **petrous** (pet'rŭs; *petra* = a rock) **part** of each temporal bone, whereas the posterior region is formed by the occipital bone. The **internal acoustic meatus** (also called the *internal auditory canal*) opens in the more medial portion of the temporal bone and contains the proximal part of the facial nerve (CN VII) and the vestibulocochlear nerve (CN VIII).

An internal landmark of the occipital bone is the **internal occipital protuberance.** The **internal occipital crest** extends from the protuberance to the posterior border of the foramen magnum. Large grooves within the cranium are formed from impressions from the venous sinuses that lie within them (see section 13.2a).

Each bone of the cranium has specific surface features, and each specific bone is shown and summarized in **table 8.2**. The facial bones are summarized in **table 8.3**.

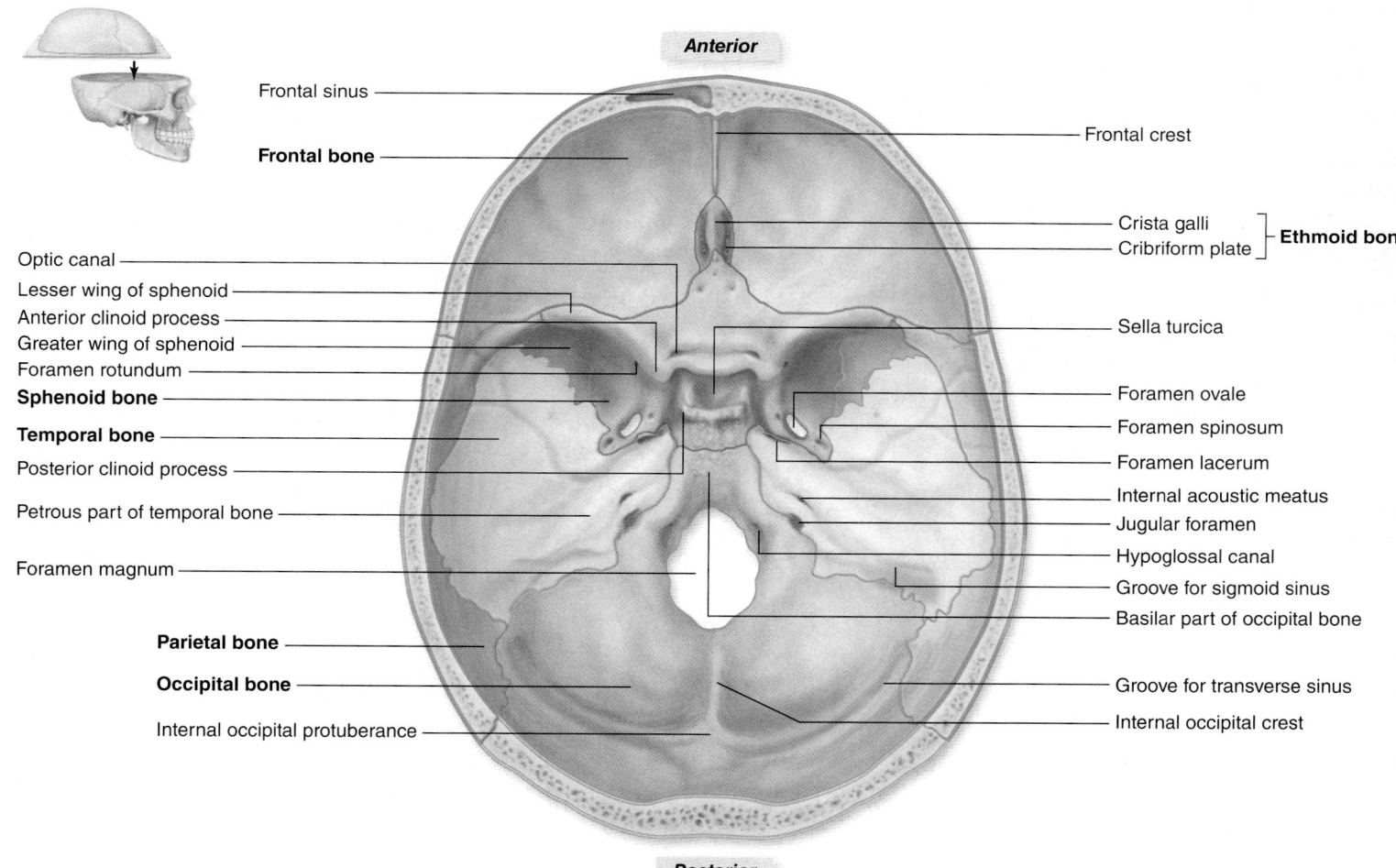

Figure 8.8 Internal View of the Cranial Base. In this transverse section, the internal portions of the frontal, ethmoid, sphenoid, temporal, and occipital bones are prominent. AP|R

Table 8.2	Cranial Bones and Selected Features[1]

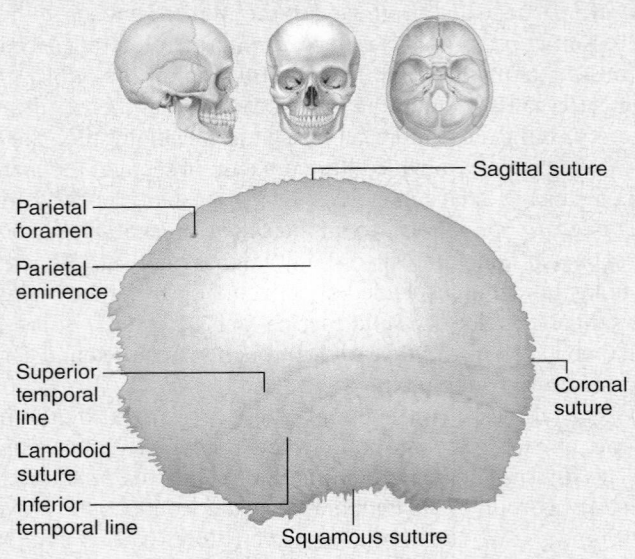

(a) Frontal Bone AP|R		**(b) Parietal Bones** AP|R	
Associated Passageways	Supraorbital notch or foramen	*Associated Passageways*	Parietal foramen
Description and Boundaries of Bone	Forms the superior and anterior parts of the skull; part of anterior cranial fossa and orbit	*Description and Boundaries of Bone*	Each forms most of lateral and superior walls of the skull
Selected Features and Their Functions	**Frontal crest:** Attachment site for meninges to help stabilize brain within the skull **Frontal sinuses:** Lighten bone, moisten inhaled air, and give resonance to voice **Orbital part:** Forms roof of orbit **Squamous part:** Attachment of scalp muscles **Supraorbital margin:** Forms protective superior border of orbit	*Selected Features and Their Functions*	**Inferior and superior temporal lines:** Attachment sites for temporalis muscle **Parietal eminence:** Forms rounded prominence on each side of the skull

1. Note: Not all features may be shown in this table; please refer to figures 8.4–8.8 in this chapter.

Squamous suture

External acoustic meatus

Squamous part

Zygomatic process

Articular tubercle

Mandibular fossa

Mastoid process

Tympanic part

Styloid process

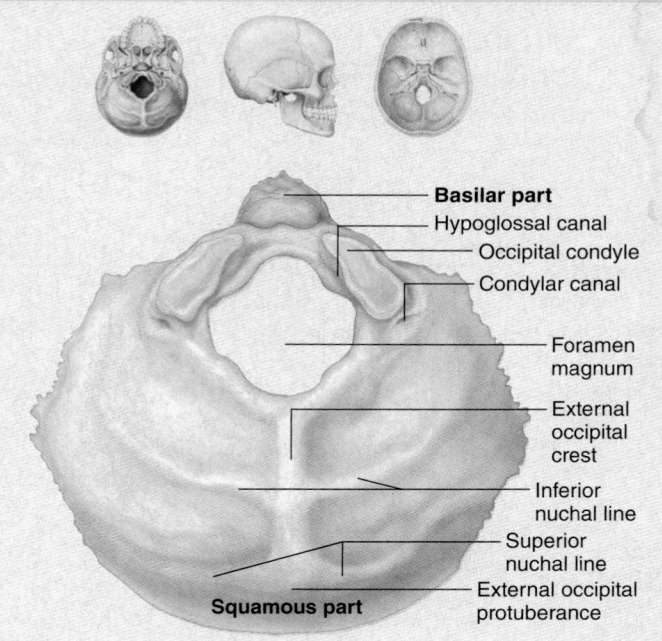

Basilar part

Hypoglossal canal

Occipital condyle

Condylar canal

Foramen magnum

External occipital crest

Inferior nuchal line

Superior nuchal line

External occipital protuberance

Squamous part

(c) Temporal Bones AP|R		(d) Occipital Bone AP|R	
Associated Passageways	Stylomastoid foramen Internal acoustic meatus Carotid canal Mastoid foramen External acoustic meatus	*Associated Passageways*	Foramen magnum Hypoglossal canal Jugular foramen (with temporal bone) Condylar canal
Description and Boundaries of Bone	Each forms inferolateral wall of the skull; forms part of middle cranial fossa. Three parts are included below.	*Description and Boundaries of Bone*	Forms posteroinferior part of the skull, including most of posterior cranial fossa; forms part of base of the skull
Selected Features and Their Functions	**Petrous part:** Protects sensory structures in inner ear **Squamous part:** Attachment site of some jaw muscles **Tympanic part:** Houses external acoustic meatus **Mastoid process:** Attachment site of some neck muscles to extend or rotate head **Styloid process:** Attachment site for hyoid bone ligaments and muscles **Zygomatic process:** Articulates with zygomatic bone to form zygomatic arch **Mandibular fossa:** Articulates with mandible **Articular tubercle:** Limits displacement of head of mandible within mandibular fossa	*Selected Features and Their Functions*	**External occipital crest:** Attachment site for ligaments **External occipital protuberance:** Attachment site for neck ligaments and muscles **Inferior** and **superior nuchal lines:** Attachment sites for neck ligaments and muscles **Occipital condyles:** Articulate with first cervical vertebra

(continued on next page)

Table 8.2   Cranial Bones and Selected Features (continued)

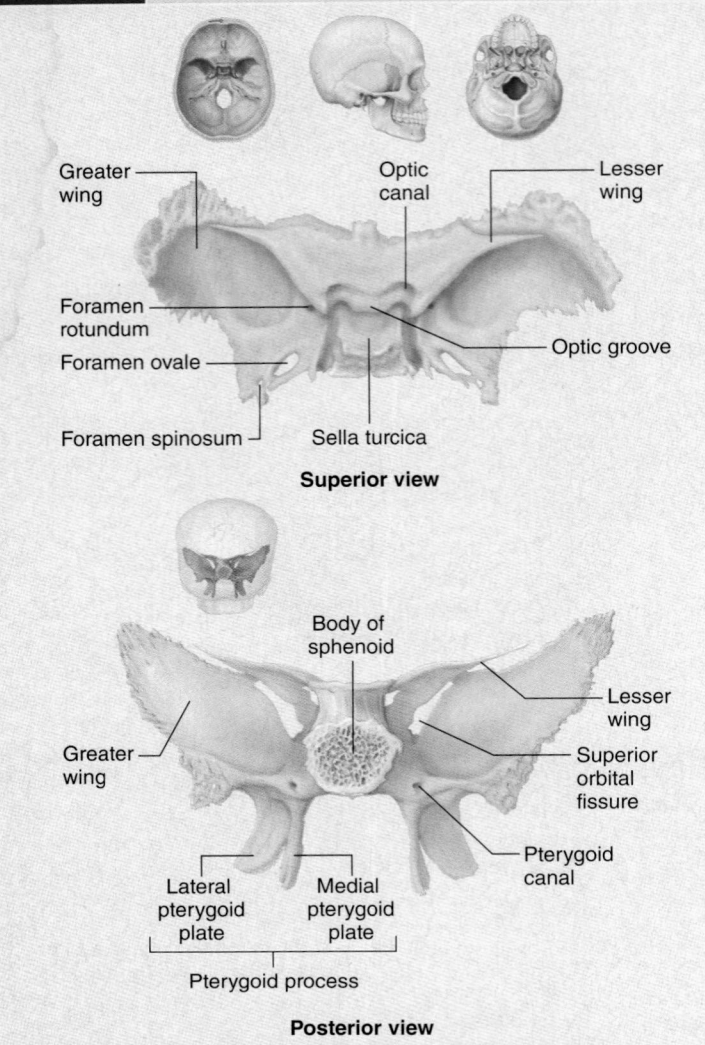

Superior view

Greater wing · Optic canal · Lesser wing · Foramen rotundum · Foramen ovale · Optic groove · Foramen spinosum · Sella turcica

Posterior view

Body of sphenoid · Lesser wing · Superior orbital fissure · Greater wing · Pterygoid canal · Lateral pterygoid plate · Medial pterygoid plate · Pterygoid process

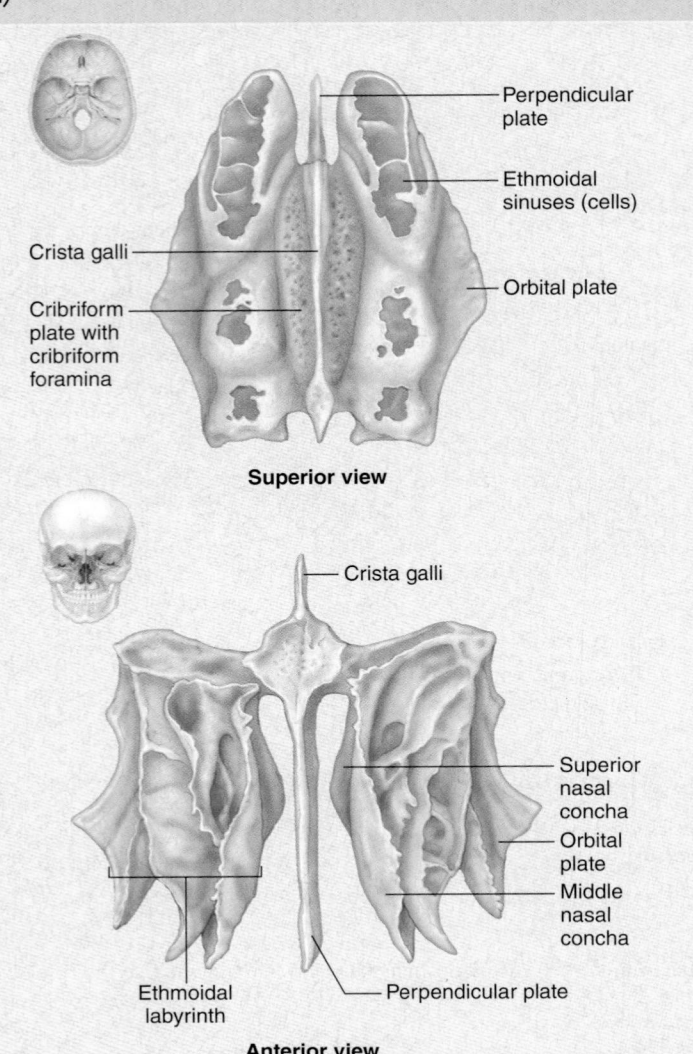

Superior view

Perpendicular plate · Ethmoidal sinuses (cells) · Crista galli · Orbital plate · Cribriform plate with cribriform foramina

Anterior view

Crista galli · Superior nasal concha · Orbital plate · Middle nasal concha · Perpendicular plate · Ethmoidal labyrinth

(e) Sphenoid Bone AP|R		(f) Ethmoid Bone AP|R	
Associated Passageways	Foramen lacerum (with temporal and occipital bones) Foramen ovale Foramen rotundum Foramen spinosum Optic canal Pterygoid canal Superior orbital fissure	*Associated Passageways*	Cribriform foramina
Description and Boundaries of Bone	Forms part of the base of the skull; posterior part of orbit; part of anterior and middle cranial fossae	*Description and Boundaries of Bone*	Forms part of anterior cranial fossa; part of nasal septum, roof and lateral walls of nasal cavity; part of medial wall of orbit
Selected Features and Their Functions	**Body:** Houses sphenoidal sinuses **Sella turcica:** Houses pituitary gland **Optic groove:** Depression on body between the optic canals **Medial** and **lateral pterygoid plates:** Attachment sites for chewing muscles **Lesser wings:** Form part of anterior cranial fossa; contain optic canals **Greater wings:** Form part of middle cranial fossa, lateral surface of skull, and orbits **Sphenoidal sinuses:** Lighten bone, moisten inhaled air, and give resonance to voice	*Selected Features and Their Functions*	**Cribriform plate:** Contains cribriform foramina for passageway of olfactory nerves (CN I) **Crista galli:** Attachment site for cranial dural septa to help stabilize brain within the skull **Ethmoidal labyrinths:** Contain ethmoidal sinuses and nasal conchae **Ethmoidal sinuses (cells):** Lighten bone, moisten inhaled air, and give resonance to voice **Nasal conchae (superior** and **middle):** Increase airflow turbulence through nasal cavity so air can be adequately moistened and cleaned by nasal mucosa **Orbital plate:** Forms part of medial wall of orbit **Perpendicular plate:** Forms superior part of nasal septum

Table 8.3   Facial Bones and Selected Features[1]

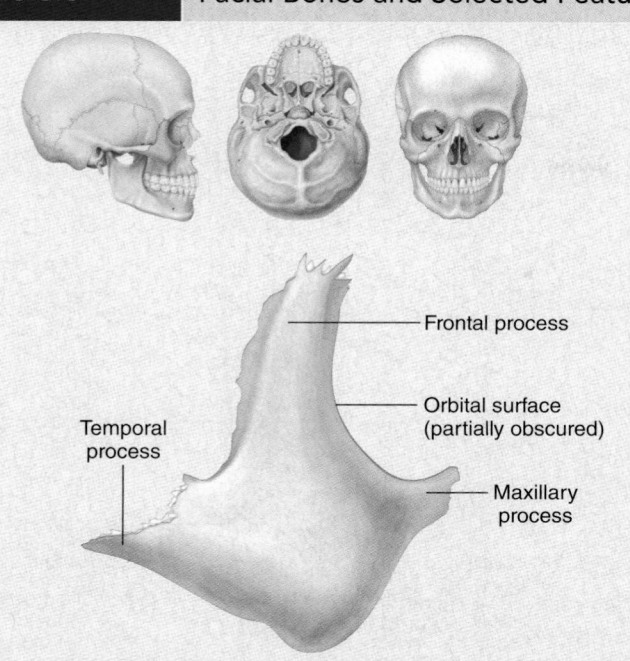

Frontal process

Orbital surface
(partially obscured)

Temporal
process

Maxillary
process

Lateral view

Lateral

Medial

Lacrimal
bone

Lacrimal
groove

Right lacrimal bone, anterior view

(a) Zygomatic Bone

Associated Passageways	none
Description and Boundaries of Bone	Each forms a cheek and lateral part of the orbit
Selected Features and Their Functions	**Frontal process:** Articulates with frontal bone **Temporal process:** Articulates with temporal bone to form zygomatic arch **Maxillary process:** Articulates with maxilla

(b) Lacrimal Bone

Associated Passageways	Lacrimal groove (see also figure 8.6)
Description and Boundaries of Bone	Each forms part of the medial wall of the orbit
Selected Features and Their Functions	**Lacrimal groove:** Contains nasolacrimal duct

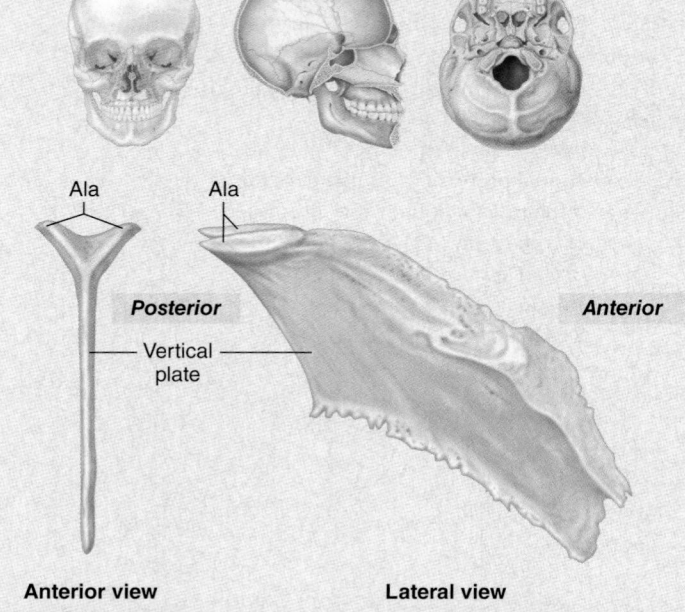

Ala   Ala

Posterior   **Anterior**

Vertical
plate

Anterior view   **Lateral view**

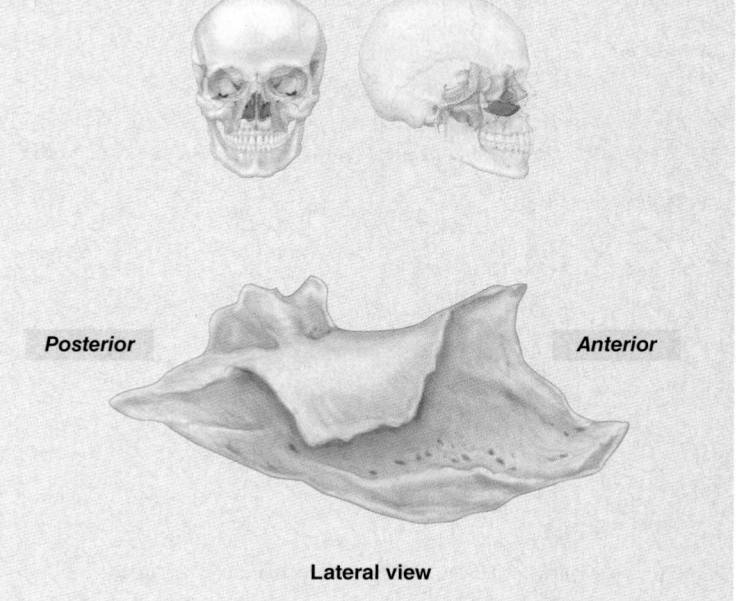

Posterior   **Anterior**

Lateral view

(c) Vomer

Associated passageways	none
Description and Boundaries of Bone	Forms inferior and posterior part of nasal septum
Selected Features and Their Functions	**Ala:** Articulates with sphenoid bone **Vertical plate:** Articulates with perpendicular plate of ethmoid bone

(d) Inferior Nasal Concha

Associated Passageways	none
Description and Boundaries of Bone	Curved bone that projects medially from lateral walls of the nasal cavity
Selected Features and Their Functions	Increase airflow turbulence in nasal cavity

1. Nasal bones are not in the table and are shown on figures 8.4 and 8.6.

(continued on next page)

Table 8.3   Facial Bones and Selected Features *(continued)*

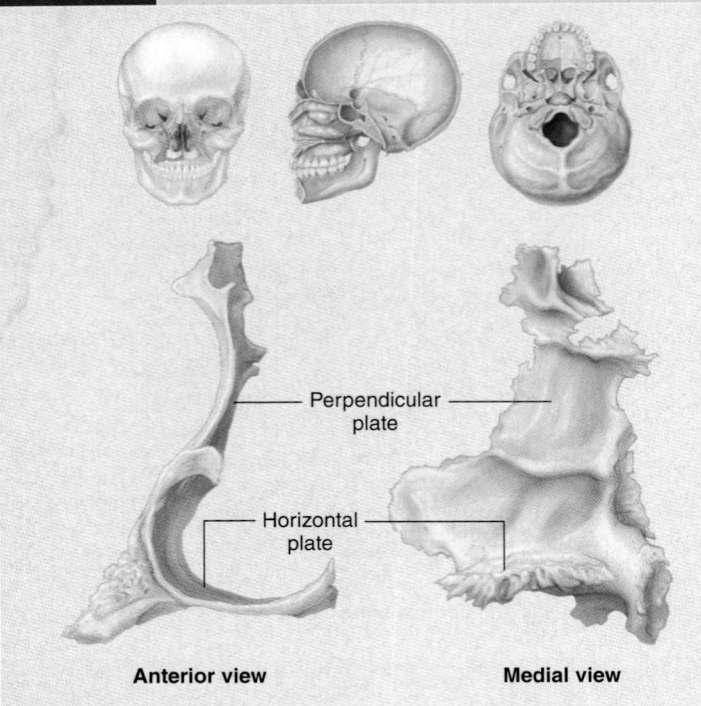

Anterior view   **Medial view**

Perpendicular plate

Horizontal plate

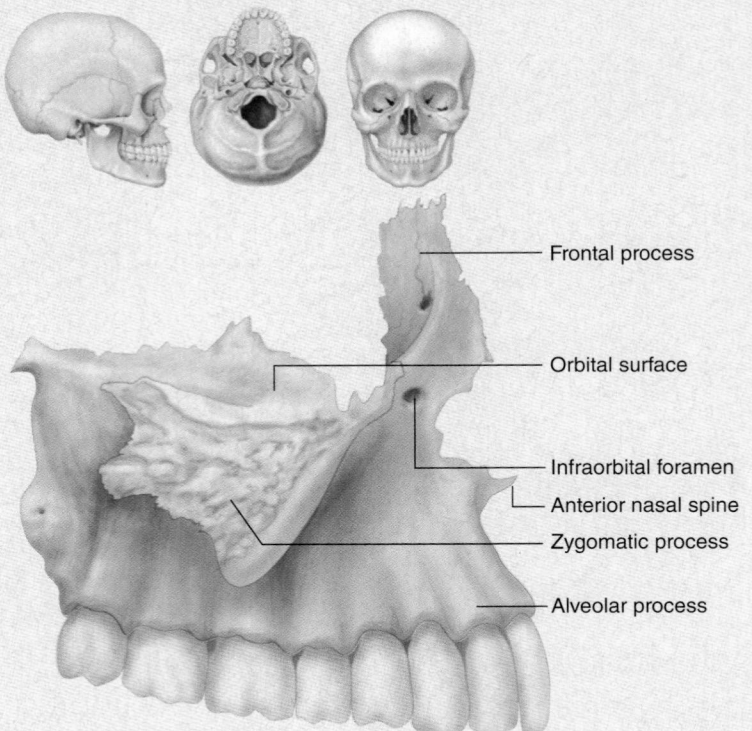

Frontal process

Orbital surface

Infraorbital foramen

Anterior nasal spine

Zygomatic process

Alveolar process

Right maxilla, lateral view

(e) Palatine Bone		(f) Maxilla AP R	
Associated Passageways	Greater and lesser palatine foramina	*Associated Passageways*	Incisive foramen Infraorbital foramen
Description and Boundaries of Bone	Each forms posterior part of hard palate; also forms small part of nasal cavity and orbit wall	*Description and Boundaries of Bone*	Each forms anterior portion of face; upper jaw and parts of hard palate, inferior parts of orbits, and part of the walls of nasal cavity
Selected Features and Their Functions[2]	**Horizontal plate:** Forms posterior part of hard palate **Perpendicular plate:** Forms part of nasal cavity and orbit	*Selected Features and Their Functions[2]*	**Anterior nasal spine:** Anterior projection formed by union of left and right maxillae **Alveolar process:** Houses the teeth **Frontal process:** Forms part of lateral aspect of the nasal bridge **Infraorbital margin:** Forms inferolateral border of orbit **Maxillary sinus:** Lightens bone **Orbital surface:** Forms part of orbit **Palatine process:** Forms most of bony palate **Zygomatic process:** Articulates with zygomatic bone

2. Note: Not all features listed in the table may be shown in above art; please refer to the other images in this chapter.

Lateral view

Cleft lip

Cleft palate

(g) Mandible AP R	
Associated Passageways	Mandibular foramen Mental foramen
Description and Boundaries of Bone	Forms the lower jaw
Selected Features and Their Functions[2]	**Alveolar process:** Houses the teeth **Angle of the mandible:** Junction between the body and ramus **Body:** Horizontal portion of mandible **Condylar** (kon'di-lăr) **process:** Posterior projection off ramus; contains head of mandible **Coronoid** (kōr'ŏ-noyd; *korone* = a crow) **process:** Anterior projection off ramus **Head of mandible:** Articulates with temporal bone **Mandibular notch:** U-shaped depression between coronoid and condylar processes **Mental protuberance:** Forms the chin **Mylohyoid** (mī'lō-hī-oyd) **line:** Attachment site for mylohyoid muscle **Ramus** (rā'mŭs): Vertical portion of mandible

2. Note: Not all features listed in the table may be shown in above art; please refer to the other images in this chapter.

INTEGRATE

CLINICAL VIEW
Cleft Lip and Palate

A **cleft lip** is the incomplete fusion of upper jaw components of the developing embryo, resulting in a split upper lip extending from the mouth to the side of one nostril. Cleft lip appears in 1 per 1000 births and tends to be more common in males. The etiology of cleft lip is multifactorial, in that both genetic and environmental factors (such as cigarette smoking or alcohol ingestion during pregnancy) appear to contribute to the condition.

Another anomaly that can develop is **cleft palate,** a congenital fissure in the midline of the palate. A cleft palate results when the left and right maxillary and palatine bones fuse incompletely or do not fuse at all. In the more severe cases, children have swallowing and feeding problems because food can easily travel from the oral cavity into the nasal cavity. Cleft palate occurs in about 1 per 2500 births and tends to be more common in females. Like cleft lip, the etiology of cleft palate is multifactorial. Cleft palate sometimes occurs in conjunction with cleft lip.

Figure 8.9 Internal Bones of the Skull. Several bones of the skull, such as the ethmoid and sphenoid, are primarily located deep to other bones. This figure illustrates the positioning of these internal bones, relative to the externally placed skull bones.

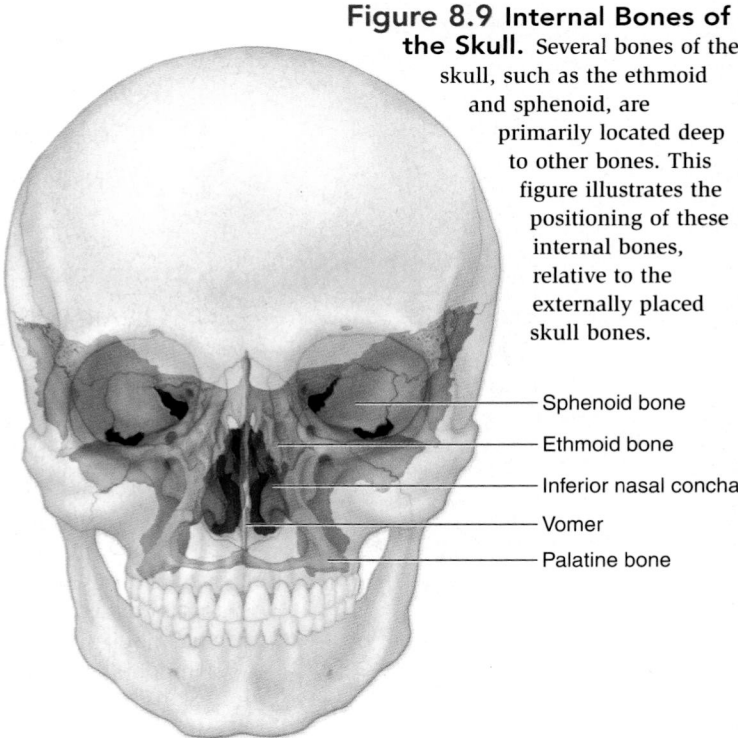

Sphenoid bone
Ethmoid bone
Inferior nasal concha
Vomer
Palatine bone

Articulations of selected cranial and facial bones that are obscured by more superficial bones are shown in **figure 8.9**.

Frontal lobe of cerebrum	Anterior cranial fossa	Cribriform plate

Frontal lobe of cerebrum

Temporal lobe of cerebrum

Cerebellum

Posterior cranial fossa

Middle cranial fossa

Anterior cranial fossa

Anterior cranial fossa

Middle cranial fossa

Posterior cranial fossa

Cribriform plate

Lesser wing of sphenoid

Sella turcica

Foramen ovale

Petrous part of temporal bone

Jugular foramen

Foramen magnum

(a) Lateral view   **(b) Superior view**

Figure 8.10 Cranial Fossae. (*a*) Lateral and (*b*) superior views show the three levels of depression in the cranium (anterior, middle, and posterior) that parallel the contours of the ventral surface of the brain.

Cranial Fossae   The contoured floor of the cranial cavity exhibits three curved depressions called the **cranial fossae (figure 8.10)**.

The **anterior cranial fossa** is the shallowest of the three depressions. It is formed by the frontal bone, the ethmoid bone, and the lesser wings of the sphenoid bone. The anterior cranial fossa houses the frontal lobes of the brain (see section 13.3b).

The **middle cranial fossa** is inferior and posterior to the anterior cranial fossa. It ranges from the posterior edge of the lesser wings of the sphenoid bone (anteriorly) to the anterior region of the petrous part of the temporal bone (posteriorly). It houses the temporal lobes of the brain and the pituitary gland.

The **posterior cranial fossa** is the most inferior cranial fossa and extends from the posterior region of the petrous part of the temporal bones to the occipital bone. This fossa supports the cerebellum and part of the brainstem (see sections 13.5 and 13.6).

WHAT DID YOU LEARN?

4   What bones may be prominently seen in an anterior view of the skull?

5   What bones form the middle cranial fossa, and which part of the brain resides in this fossa?

8.2c Sutures

LEARNING OBJECTIVE

5.   Describe the locations of the sutures between the cranial bones.

Sutures (soo′choor; *sutura* = a seam) are immovable joints that form the boundaries between the cranial bones (see figures 8.5–8.7). Dense regular connective tissue connects cranial bones firmly together at a suture. The sutures often have intricate interlocking forms, like puzzle pieces.

Numerous sutures are present in the skull, each with a specific name. Many of the smaller sutures are named for the bones or features they interconnect. For example, the occipitomastoid suture connects the occipital bone with the portion of the temporal bone that houses the mastoid process. Here we discuss only the largest sutures: the coronal, lambdoid, sagittal, and squamous sutures:

- The **coronal** (kō-rō′nal; *coron* = crown) **suture** extends laterally across the superior surface of the skull along a coronal plane. It represents the articulation between the anterior frontal bone and the more posterior parietal bones.
- The **lambdoid** (lam′doyd) **suture** extends like an arc across the posterior surface of the skull, articulating with the parietal bones and the occipital bone. It is named for the Greek letter "lambda," which its shape resembles.
- The **sagittal** (saj′i-tăl; *sagitta* = arrow) **suture** extends between the coronal and lambdoid sutures along the midsagittal plane. It articulates the right and left parietal bones.
- A **squamous** (skwā′mus) **suture** (or *squamosal suture*) on each side of the skull articulates the temporal bone and the parietal bone of that side. The squamous part of the temporal bone typically "overlaps" the parietal bone.

One common variation in sutures is the presence of **sutural bones** (*Wormian bones*) (see figure 8.5*b*). Sutural bones may range in size from a tiny pebble to a quarter, but they can be much larger. Sutural bones represent independent bone ossification centers and are most common and numerous in the lambdoid suture.

In adulthood, the sutures typically are obliterated (closed) as the adjoining bones fuse. This fusion starts internally and is followed by fusion on the skull's external surface. Although the timing of suture closure can be highly variable, the coronal suture typically is the first to fuse, usually in the late 20s to early 30s, followed by the sagittal suture (usually in the 30s or later) and then the lambdoid suture (usually in the 40s). The squamous suture usually does not fuse until late adulthood (60 + years), or it may not fuse at all. Osteologists can estimate the approximate age at death of an individual skull by examining the extent of suture closure in the skull.

WHAT DID YOU LEARN?

6 What bones articulate at the lambdoid suture? When does this suture typically fuse?

CLINICAL VIEW
Craniosynostosis and Plagiocephaly

Sagittal synostosis

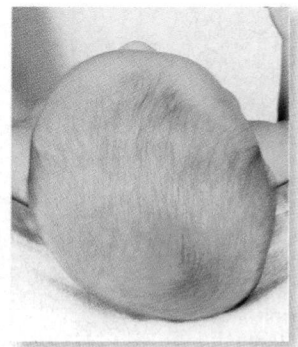

Coronal synostosis

When cranial growth has stopped in adulthood, the sutures gradually fuse and are obliterated. **Craniosynostosis** (krā′nē-ō-sin′os-tō′sis) refers to the premature fusion or closing of one or more of these cranial sutures, and may be due to multiple causes. If this premature fusion occurs early in life or *in utero,* skull shape is dramatically affected. If not surgically treated, a craniosynostotic individual typically grows up with an unusual craniofacial shape. For example, if the sagittal suture fuses prematurely (a condition called **sagittal synostosis**), the skull cannot grow and expand laterally as the brain grows, and compensatory skull growth occurs in an anterior-posterior fashion. A child with sagittal synostosis develops a very elongated, narrow skull shape, a condition called **scaphocephaly,** or *dolichocephaly*. **Coronal synostosis** refers to premature fusion of the coronal suture, which causes the skull to be abnormally short and wide.

Plagiocephaly is the term used to describe an asymmetric head shape, where one part of the skull (usually the frontal or occipital region) has an oblique flattening. Plagiocephaly may be caused by unilateral coronal cranio-synostosis or asymmetric lambdoid synostosis. It also is commonly caused by normal deformational factors, such as sleeping on the same side of the head. Incidence of plagiocephaly has risen in the United States since the 1990s, primarily due to the National Institute of Child Health and Human Development Back to Sleep Campaign, which encourages parents to place children on their backs to sleep (instead of on their stomachs) so as to reduce the incidence of SIDS. Mild forms of plagiocephaly may be corrected by wearing a corrective helmet; more severe forms may necessitate surgery.

Plagiocephaly

Roof of orbit

Lesser wing of sphenoid bone — Orbital part of frontal bone

Zygomatic process of frontal bone
Greater wing of sphenoid bone — **Lateral wall**
Orbital surface of zygomatic bone

Optic canal
Superior orbital fissure

Medial wall
Frontal process of maxilla
Lacrimal bone
Orbital plate of ethmoid bone

Inferior orbital fissure

Orbital process of palatine bone — Orbital surface of maxilla — Zygomatic bone

Floor of orbit

Figure 8.11 Left Orbit. Several bones compose the orbit of the eye and collectively form the orbital complex. AP|R

8.2d Orbital and Nasal Complexes, Paranasal Sinuses

LEARNING OBJECTIVES

6. List the bones that form the orbital and nasal complexes.

7. Describe the location and function of the paranasal sinuses.

The bony cavities called orbits enclose and protect the eyes and the muscles that move them. The **orbital complex** consists of multiple bones that form each orbit. The borders of the orbital complex are shown and listed in **figure 8.11**.

The **nasal complex** is composed of bones and cartilage that enclose the nasal cavity and the paranasal sinuses. Most of these bones are best seen in sagittal section, as shown in **figure 8.12**.

Frontal bone

Crista galli of **ethmoid bone**
Cribriform plate of **ethmoid bone**

Frontal sinus
Nasal bone
Superior nasal concha
Middle nasal concha
Lacrimal bone
Inferior nasal concha
Maxilla
Palatine process of maxilla

Sella turcica
Sphenoidal sinus
Perpendicular plate of **palatine bone**
Sphenoid bone
Horizontal plate of **palatine bone**

(a) Sagittal section, lateral wall of nasal complex

Ethmoidal sinus
Right orbit

Brain
Frontal sinus
Superior nasal concha
Middle nasal concha
Maxillary sinus
Inferior nasal concha

(b) Coronal section

Figure 8.12 Nasal Complex. Multiple skull bones form the intricate nasal complex. (*a*) A sagittal section shows the right side of the nasal complex. (*b*) Cadaver photo of coronal section through the head shows the nasal complex.

(a) Anterior view

(b) Lateral view

Figure 8.13 Paranasal Sinuses. The paranasal sinuses are air-filled chambers within the frontal, ethmoid, and sphenoid bones and the maxillae. They are shown in (*a*) anterior and (*b*) lateral views. They are lined with a mucous membrane and act as extensions of the nasal cavity.

The auditory ossicles and the hyoid bone are bones of the axial skeleton associated with the skull. **Auditory ossicles** (os'i-kl) are three tiny ear bones housed within the petrous part of each temporal bone. These bones—the **malleus** (mal'ē-us), the **incus** (ink'kus), and the **stapes** (stā'pēz)—are discussed in depth in section 16.5a.

The **hyoid bone** is a slender, curved bone located inferior to the skull between the mandible and the larynx (voice box) **(figure 8.14)**. It does not articulate with any other bone in the skeleton. The hyoid has a medial **body** and two paired hornlike processes, the **greater cornua** (kōr'noo-ă; sing., *cornu*, kōr'noo = horn) and the **lesser cornua**. The cornua and body serve as attachment sites for tongue and larynx (voice box) muscles and ligaments.

WHAT DID YOU LEARN?

9 What are the names of auditory ossicles and in which specific bone are they found?

We have already described the ethmoidal, frontal, maxillary, and sphenoidal sinuses in connection with the bones where they are found. As a group, these air-filled chambers that open into the nasal cavities are called the **paranasal sinuses** (sī'nŭs; cavity, hollow) **(figure 8.13)**. The sinuses have a mucous membrane lining that helps to humidify and warm inhaled air. Additionally, the sinus spaces cause the skull bones in which they rest to be lighter, and also provide resonance to the voice.

WHAT DID YOU LEARN?

7 What bones form the floor of the orbit?

8 In which four bones are the paranasal sinuses located?

8.3 Bones Associated with the Skull

LEARNING OBJECTIVES

1. Locate and identify the auditory ossicles.
2. Describe the structure and function of the hyoid bone.

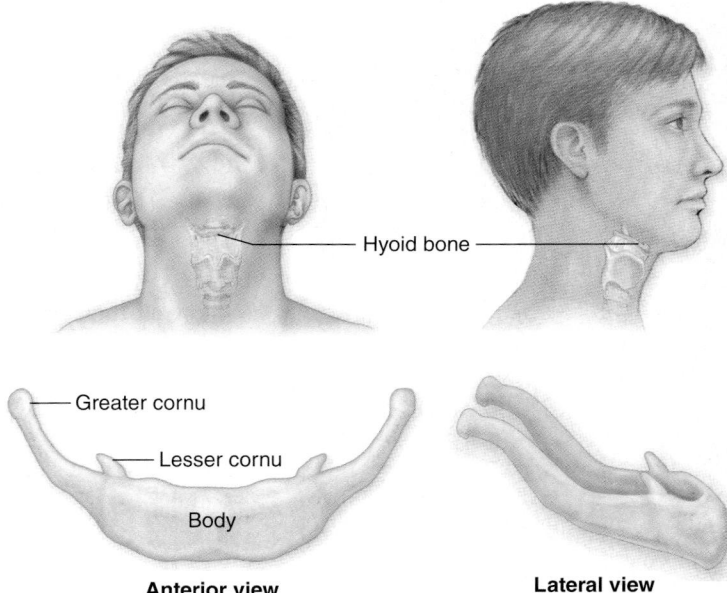

Anterior view

Lateral view

Figure 8.14 Hyoid Bone. The hyoid bone is inferior to the mandible and is not in direct contact with any other bone.

8.4 Sex and Age Determination from Analysis of the Skull

The skull can provide insight about the sex and age of an individual. We first describe some diagnostic features of the skull used to determine the sex of an individual. Then we compare how the skull changes through the fetal period, childhood, early adulthood, and old age.

8.4a Sex Differences in the Skull

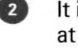 **LEARNING OBJECTIVE**

1. Identify the similarities and differences between male and female skulls.

Human female and male skulls display some obvious differences in general shape and size, a phenomenon known as **sexual dimorphism.** Typical "female" features tend to be gracile (delicate, small), while "male" features tend to be more robust (larger, sturdier, bulkier). **Table 8.4** summarizes the general sex differences seen in the skull.

However, caution is required when a skull and other skeletal remains are used to determine an individual's sex. Both skeletons and skeletal features vary in their general size and robusticity among populations. For example, some male Asian skeletal remains may be less robust than those of a female Native American. Further, it often is difficult or impossible to determine the sex of infant and juvenile remains, because skull characteristics appear femalelike until well after puberty.

The most accurate method of determining sex is to look at multiple skeletal features and make a judgment based on the majority of features present. For example, if a skull displays two femalelike characteristics and four malelike characteristics, the skull will likely be classified as male. If your anatomy lab uses real skulls, use table 8.4 to try to determine the sex of the skull you are studying.

 WHAT DO YOU THINK?

2 It is difficult to determine the sex of a young child's skull because both male and female skulls at this stage of development appear femalelike. What factors do you think cause those features to change in males by adulthood?

 WHAT DID YOU LEARN?

10 What are some features that differ between female and male skulls?

8.4b Aging of the Skull

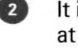 **LEARNING OBJECTIVES**

2. Compare the structure of fetal, child, and adult skulls.

3. List the fontanelles and the ages at which they close.

The shape and structure of cranial elements differ between infants and adults, causing variations in their proportions and size. The most significant growth in the skull occurs before age 5, when the brain is still growing and exerting pressure against the developing skull bones' internal surface. Brain growth is 90–95% complete by age 5, at which time cranial bone growth is close to completion, and the cranial sutures are almost fully developed. Note that early in life the skull grows at a much faster rate than does the rest of the body. Thus, a young child's cranium is relatively larger compared to the rest of its body than that of an adult.

Table 8.4	Sex Differences in the Skull	
View	**Female**	**Male**
Anterior View		
Lateral View		

Anterior View — Female: Thin, sharp supraorbital margin; Superciliary arch not prominent; More triangular mental protuberance.

Anterior View — Male: More blunt supraorbital margin; More prominent superciliary arch; Squarish chin.

Lateral View — Female: Rounded frontal bone; Smooth external occipital protuberance; Obtuse mandibular angle.

Lateral View — Male: Sloping frontal bone; Prominent external occipital protuberance; Flared, less obtuse angle.

Skull Feature	**Female Skull Characteristic**	**Male Skull Characteristic**
General size and appearance	More gracile (delicate and small)	More robust (big and bulky), more prominent muscle markings
Nuchal lines and external occipital protuberance	External surface of occipital bone is relatively smooth, with no major bony projections; external occipital protuberance is rounded	Well-demarcated nuchal lines and a prominent bump or "hook" for external occipital protuberance
Mastoid process	Relatively small	Large, may project inferior to external acoustic meatus
Squamous part of frontal bone	Usually more vertically oriented and rounded than males	Exhibits a sloping angle
Supraorbital margin	Thin, sharp border	Thick, rounded, blunt border
Superciliary arches	Little or no prominence	More prominent and bulky
Mandible (general features)	Smaller and lighter	Larger, heavier, more robust
Mental protuberance	More pointed and triangular-shaped, less forward projection	Squarish, more forward projection
Mandibular angle	Typically greater than 125 degrees	Typically less obtuse and less than 125 degrees (closer to 90 degrees); angle edges may flare outward

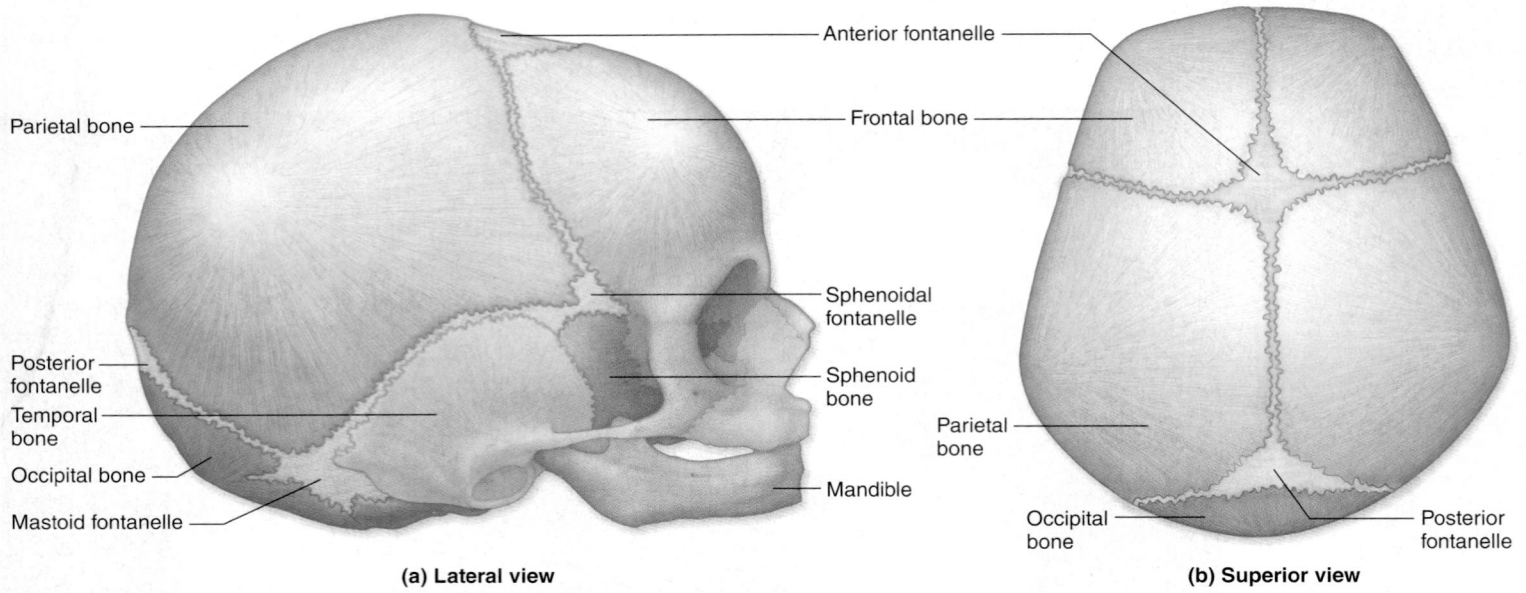

Figure 8.15 Fetal Skull. (*a*) Lateral and (*b*) superior views show the flat bones in an infant skull, which are separated by fontanelles. These allow for the distortion of the skull during birth and the growth of the brain after birth.

A neonatal (infant) cranium is shown in lateral and superior views in **figure 8.15**. The infant's cranial bones are not yet large enough to surround the brain completely, so some cranial bones are interconnected by flexible areas of dense regular connective tissue membrane in regions called **fontanelles** (fon′tă-nel = little spring; sometimes spelled *fontanels*). Fontanelles are sometimes referred to as the "soft spots" on a baby's head. The fontanelles enable some flexion in the bony plates within the skull during birth, thus allowing the child's head to pass through the birth canal in order to ease the baby's passage (see section 29.6d). Newborns frequently have a "cone-shaped" head due to this temporary deformation, but the cranial bones usually return to their normal position by a few days after birth. Some fontanelles, such as the small **mastoid** and **sphenoidal fontanelles,** close relatively quickly after birth. However others are present until many months after birth, when skull bone growth finally starts to keep pace with brain growth. The **posterior fontanelle** normally closes around 9 months of age; the larger **anterior fontanelle** doesn't close until about 15 months of age.

The skull undergoes many more changes as we age. The maxillary sinus becomes more prominent after age 5, and by age 10 the frontal sinus is becoming well formed. Later, the cranial sutures start to fuse and ossify. As a person ages, the teeth start to wear down from use, a process called *dental attrition.* Finally, if an individual loses some or all of his or her teeth, the alveolar processes of the maxillae and mandible regress and eventually disappear.

 WHAT DID YOU LEARN?

11 What are the two largest fontanelles, and when do they disappear?

8.5 Bones of the Vertebral Column

The adult **vertebral column** is composed of 26 bones, including 24 individual **vertebrae** (ver′tĕ-brā; sing., *vertebra,* ver′tĕ-bră) and the fused vertebrae that form both the sacrum and the coccyx. Each vertebra (except the first and the last) articulates with one superior vertebra and one inferior vertebra. Here we consider the vertebral column's general function and regions, the curves of the spine, anatomy of a generalized vertebra, and anatomic details of the components of the five regions of the vertebral column.

8.5a Types of Vertebrae

 LEARNING OBJECTIVES

1. Describe the functions of the vertebral column.
2. List the five types of vertebrae.

The vertebral column provides vertical support for the body and supports the weight of the head. It helps maintain an upright body position. Most important, it houses and protects the delicate spinal cord.

The vertebral column is partitioned into five divisions or regions **(figure 8.16)**. Vertebrae are identified by using a capital letter to denote their region, followed by a numerical subscript that indicates their sequence going from a superior to an inferior location:

- Seven **cervical** (ser′vĭ-kal; *cervix* = neck) **vertebrae** (designated C_1–C_7) form the bones of the neck (cervical region). The first cervical vertebra (C_1) articulates superiorly with the occipital condyles of the skull. The seventh cervical vertebra articulates inferiorly with the first thoracic vertebra.

- Twelve **thoracic vertebrae** (designated T_1–T_{12}) form the superior region of the back (thoracic region). Each thoracic vertebra articulates laterally with one or two pairs of ribs. The twelfth thoracic vertebra articulates inferiorly with the first lumbar vertebra.

- Five **lumbar vertebrae** (designated L_1–L_5) form the inferior concave region ("small") of the back (lumbar region). The fifth lumbar vertebra articulates inferiorly with the first sacral vertebra.

- The **sacrum** (sā′krŭm) is formed from five sacral vertebrae (designated S_1–S_5) that fuse into a single bony structure by the mid to late 20s. The sacrum articulates with L_5 superiorly, the first coccygeal vertebra inferiorly, and laterally with the two ossa coxae (hip bones).

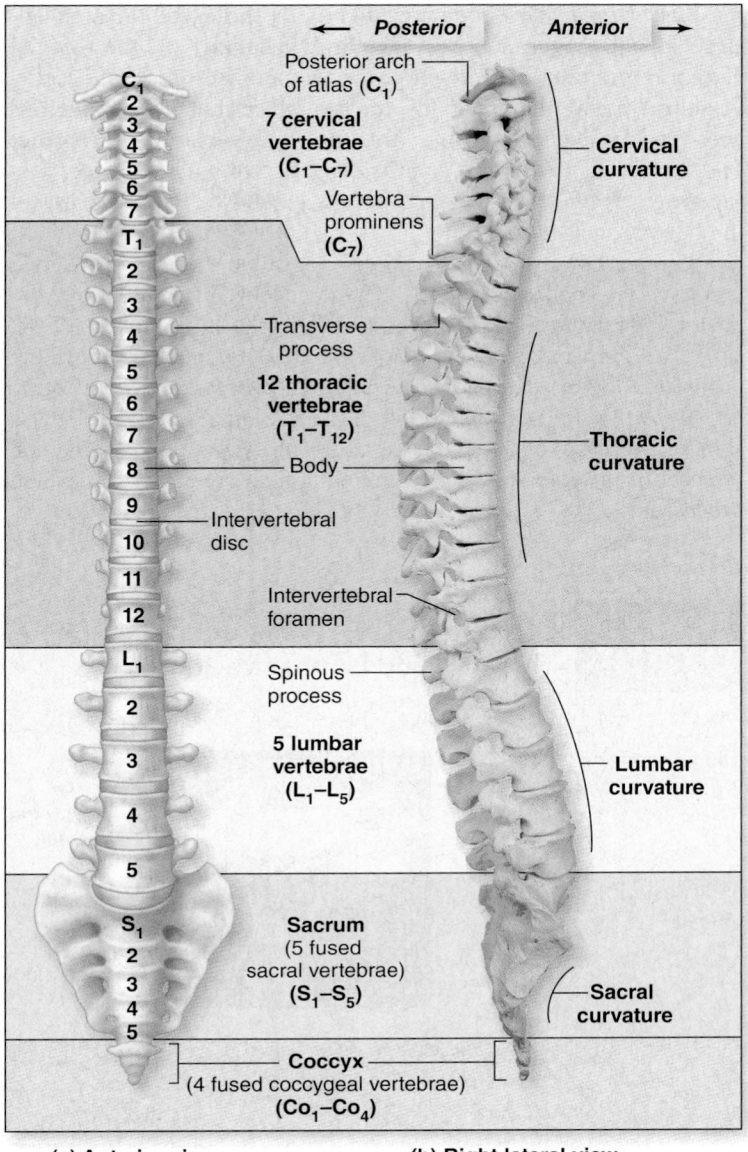

C1
2
3
4
5
6
7

Posterior arch
of atlas (C1)

**7 cervical
vertebrae
(C1–C7)**

Vertebra
prominens
(C7)

Posterior ← → Anterior

Cervical
curvature

T1
2
3
4
5
6
7
8
9
10
11
12

Transverse
process

**12 thoracic
vertebrae
(T1–T12)**

Body

Intervertebral
disc

Intervertebral
foramen

Thoracic
curvature

L1
2
3
4
5

Spinous
process

**5 lumbar
vertebrae
(L1–L5)**

Lumbar
curvature

S1
2
3
4
5

Sacrum
(5 fused
sacral vertebrae)
(S1–S5)

Sacral
curvature

Coccyx
(4 fused coccygeal vertebrae)
(Co1–Co4)

(a) Anterior view   **(b) Right lateral view**

Figure 8.16 Vertebral Column. (*a*) Anterior and (*b*) right lateral views show the types of vertebrae and curvatures in the vertebral column. AP|R

- The **coccyx** (kok'siks) is commonly called the "tailbone" and is formed from four **coccygeal vertebrae** (designated Co1–Co4) that start to unite during puberty. The first coccygeal vertebra (Co1) articulates with the inferior end of the sacrum. In much later years, the coccyx also may fuse to the sacrum.

WHAT DID YOU LEARN?

12 Which vertebrae are located in the 'small' of the back, and how many of these vertebrae are there?

8.5b Spinal Curvatures

LEARNING OBJECTIVES

3. Name the four spinal curvatures of an adult vertebral column.

4. Explain the sequence of curvature development.

The vertebral column has some flexibility because it is not straight and rigid. When viewed from a lateral perspective, the adult vertebral column has four **spinal curvatures:** the **cervical, thoracic,**

CLINICAL VIEW
Spinal Curvature Abnormalities

There are three main spinal curvature deformities: kyphosis, lordosis, and scoliosis.

Kyphosis (kī-fō'sis) is an exaggerated thoracic curvature that is directed posteriorly, producing a "hunchback" look. Kyphosis often results from osteoporosis, but also may occur due to a vertebral compression fracture, osteomalacia (a disease in which adult bones become demineralized), abnormal vertebral growth, or chronic contractions in muscles that insert on the vertebrae.

Lordosis (lōr-dō'sis) is an exaggerated lumbar curvature, often called *swayback,* that is observed as a protrusion of the abdomen and buttocks. Lordosis may have the same causes as kyphosis, or it may result from the added abdominal weight associated with pregnancy or obesity.

Scoliosis (skō-lē-ō'sis) is the most common spinal curvature deformity. It is an abnormal lateral curvature that sometimes results during development when both the vertebral arch and body fail to form, or form incompletely, on one side of a vertebra. It can also be caused by unilateral muscular paralysis, or spasm, in the back. Mild cases of scoliosis may be treated in adolescence by wearing a back brace, whereas more severe cases may require surgical intervention.

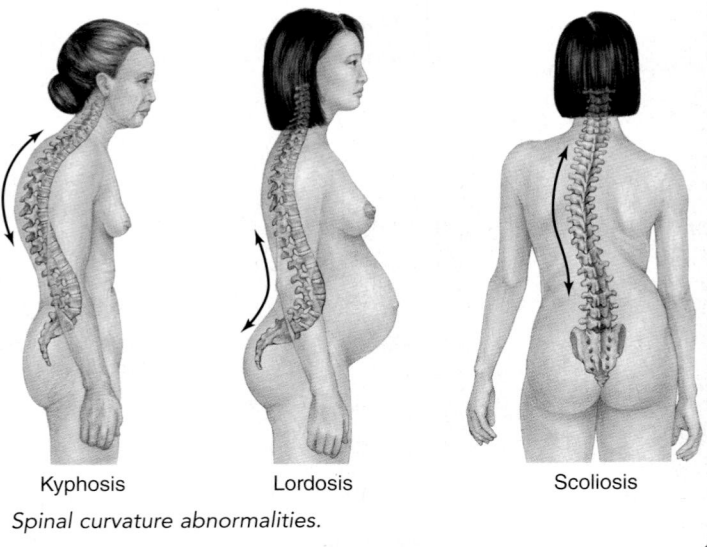

Kyphosis   Lordosis   Scoliosis

Spinal curvature abnormalities.

lumbar, and **sacral curvatures.** This arrangement better supports the weight of the body when standing than could a straight spine.

The spinal curvatures appear sequentially during fetal, newborn, and child developmental stages. The **primary curves** are the thoracic and sacral curvatures. In the newborn, only primary curves are present, and the vertebral column is C-shaped.

The **secondary curves** are called the cervical and lumbar curvatures, and they appear after birth. These curvatures arch anteriorly and are also known as *compensation curves* because they help shift the trunk weight over the legs. The cervical curvature appears when the child is first able to hold up its head without support (usually around 3–4 months of age). The lumbar curvature appears when the child is learning to stand and walk (typically by the first year of life). These curvatures become accentuated as the child becomes more adept at walking.

WHAT DID YOU LEARN?

13 What are the secondary curves, and when do they appear? What is their general function?

8.5c Vertebral Anatomy

LEARNING OBJECTIVES

5. Identify the parts of a typical vertebra.

6. Compare and contrast the different types of vertebrae.

All vertebrae share some common structural features (**figure 8.17**). The anterior region of each vertebra is a thick, cylindrical **body,** or *centrum,* which is the weight-bearing structure of each vertebra. Posterior to the vertebral body is the **vertebral arch,** also called

the *neural arch.* The body together with the vertebral arch enclose an opening called the **vertebral foramen.** All the stacked vertebral foramina collectively form a superior-to-inferior directed **vertebral canal** that contains the spinal cord. Lateral openings between adjacent vertebrae are the **intervertebral foramina.** The intervertebral foramina provide a horizontally directed passageway through which spinal nerves extend to various parts of the body (see section 14.5).

The vertebral arch is composed of two pedicles and two laminae. The **pedicles** (ped'ĭ-kl; *pes* = foot) originate from the posterolateral margins of the body, while the **laminae** (lam'i-nē; sing., *lamina,* lam'i-nă = layer) extend posteromedially from the posterior edge of each pedicle. A **spinous process** projects posteriorly from the junction of the left and right laminae. Most of these spinous processes can be palpated along the skin of the back. Lateral projections on both sides of the vertebral arch are called **transverse processes.**

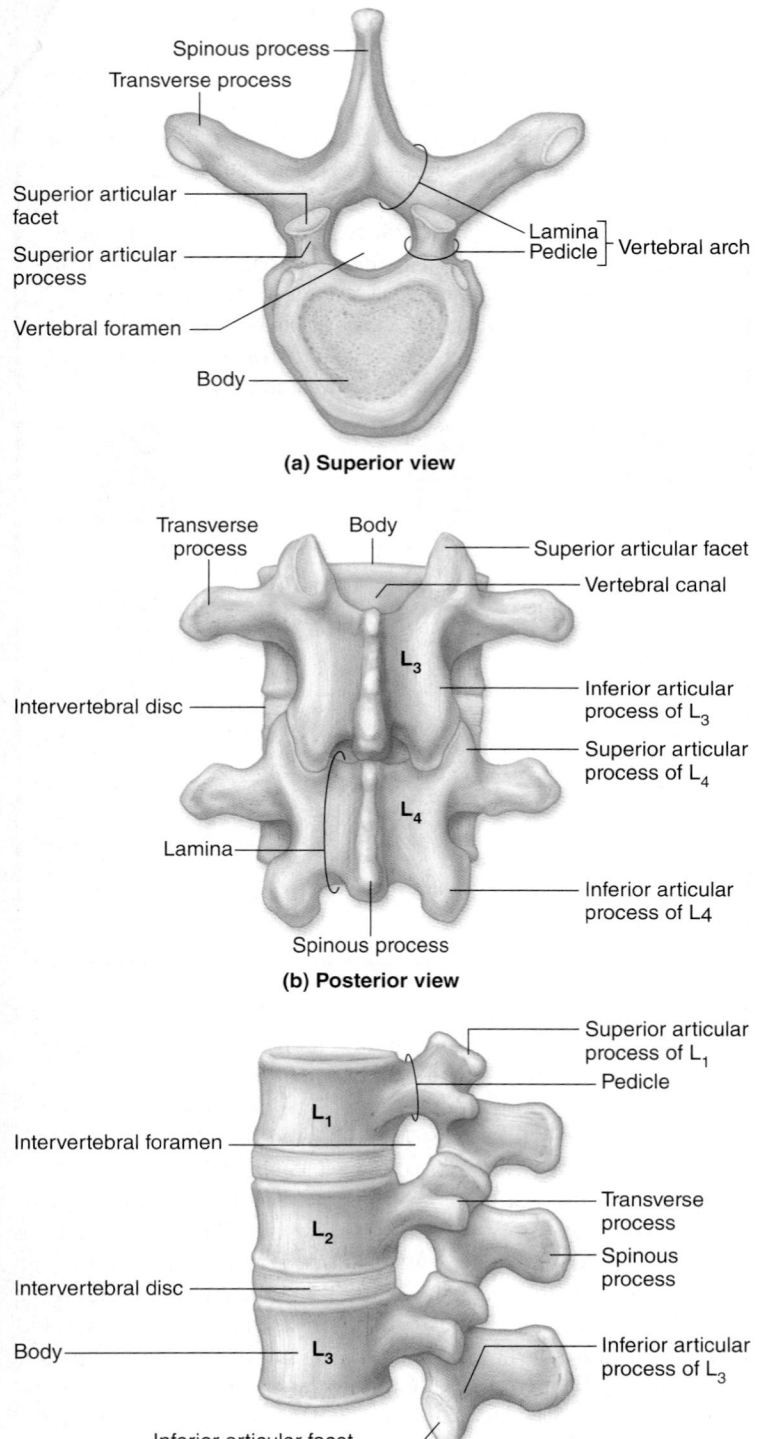

Figure 8.17 Vertebral Anatomy. (*a*) Superior view of a thoracic vertebra. (*b*) Articulation between lumbar vertebrae, posterior view. (*c*) Articulation between lumbar vertebrae, lateral view. AP|R

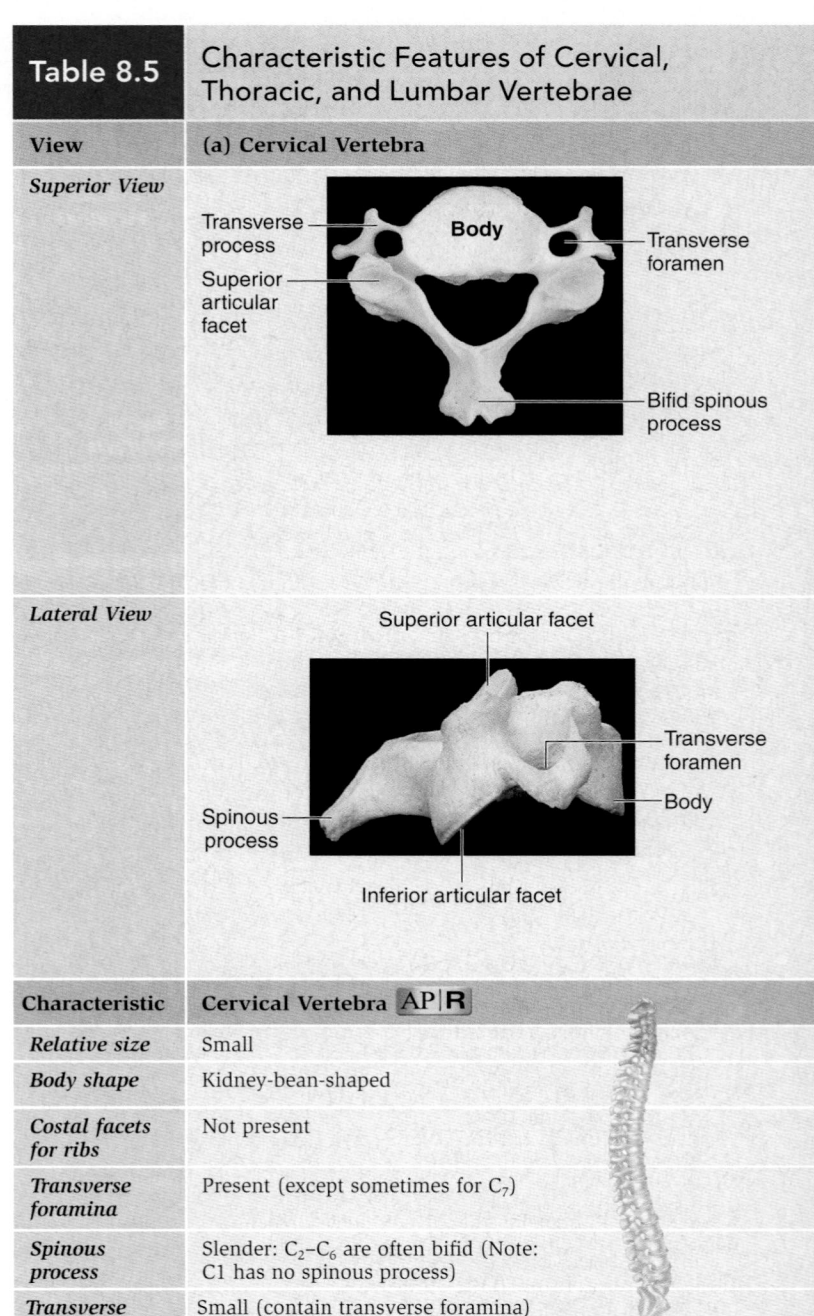

Table 8.5	Characteristic Features of Cervical, Thoracic, and Lumbar Vertebrae
View	**(a) Cervical Vertebra**
Superior View	
Lateral View	

Characteristic	Cervical Vertebra AP|R
Relative size	Small
Body shape	Kidney-bean-shaped
Costal facets for ribs	Not present
Transverse foramina	Present (except sometimes for C₇)
Spinous process	Slender: C₂–C₆ are often bifid (Note: C1 has no spinous process)
Transverse processes	Small (contain transverse foramina)

Each vertebra has **superior** and **inferior articular processes** that originate at the junction between the pedicles and laminae. Each articular process has a smooth surface called an **articular facet** (fas′et, fǎ-set′). The facets on the inferior articular processes of each vertebra articulate with the facets on the superior articular processes of the vertebra immediately inferior to it.

The stack of vertebral bodies is stabilized and interconnected by ligaments. Adjacent vertebral bodies are separated by pads of fibrocartilage, called the **intervertebral** (in-ter-ver′te-brǎl) **discs.** Intervertebral discs are composed of an outer ring of fibrocartilage, called the **anulus fibrosus** (an′ū-lǔs fī-brō′sus), and an inner gelatinous circular region, called the **nucleus pulposus** (shown in Clinical View: Herniated Discs). Intervertebral discs make up approximately one-quarter of the entire vertebral column length. They act as shock absorbers between the vertebral bodies and also permit the vertebral column to bend. For example, when you bend your torso anteriorly, the intervertebral discs are compressed at the bending (anterior) surface and pushed out at the opposite (posterior) surface.

Over the course of a day, as body weight and gravity act on the vertebral column, the intervertebral discs become compressed and flattened. But while a person is lying horizontally during sleep, the intervertebral discs are able to expand and spring back to their original shape.

In general, the vertebrae are smallest near the skull. They become gradually larger moving inferiorly through the body trunk as weight-bearing increases. Although vertebrae are divided into regions, there are no anatomically discrete "cutoffs" between the regions. For example, the most inferior cervical vertebra has some structural similarities to the most superior thoracic vertebra, since the two vertebrae are adjacent to one another. Likewise, the most inferior thoracic vertebra may look similar to the first lumbar vertebra. **Table 8.5** compares the characteristics of the cervical, thoracic, and lumbar vertebrae and lists unique features of each regional group of vertebrae.

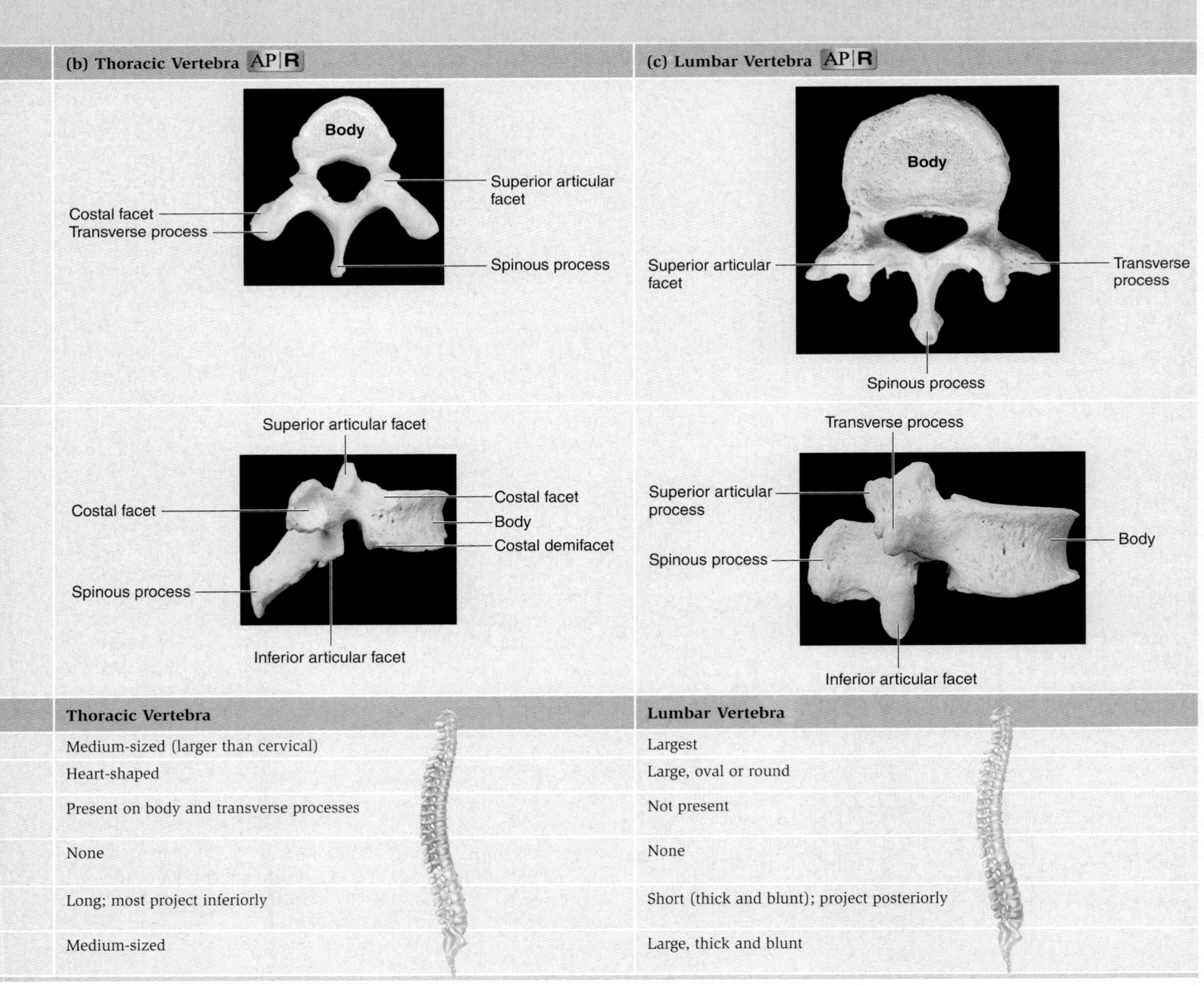

Thoracic Vertebra	Lumbar Vertebra
Medium-sized (larger than cervical)	Largest
Heart-shaped	Large, oval or round
Present on body and transverse processes	Not present
None	None
Long; most project inferiorly	Short (thick and blunt); project posteriorly
Medium-sized	Large, thick and blunt

CLINICAL VIEW
Herniated Discs

A **herniated** (her′nē-ā-ted) **disc** occurs when the gelatinous nucleus pulposus protrudes into or through the anulus fibrosus. This herniation produces a bulging of the disc contents posterolaterally into the vertebral canal and pinches the spinal cord and/or nerves of the spinal cord. The cervical and lumbar intervertebral discs are the most common discs to be injured, because the vertebral column has more mobility in these regions, and the lumbar region bears increased weight. Cervical herniated discs can cause neck pain and pain down the upper limb, whereas lumbar herniated discs frequently cause low back pain. If a herniated lumbar disc starts to pinch nerve roots, the patient may feel pain down the entire lower limb, a condition known as **sciatica.**

Treatment options include "wait-and-see" if the disc heals on its own, nonsteroidal anti-inflammatory drugs (NSAIDS) such as ibuprofen, steroidal drugs, and physical therapy. Surgical treatments include **microdiscectomy,** a microsurgical technique whereby the portion of the herniated disc is removed, or **discectomy,** a more invasive technique in which the laminae of the nearby vertebrae and the back muscles are incised before removing the herniated portions of the disc.

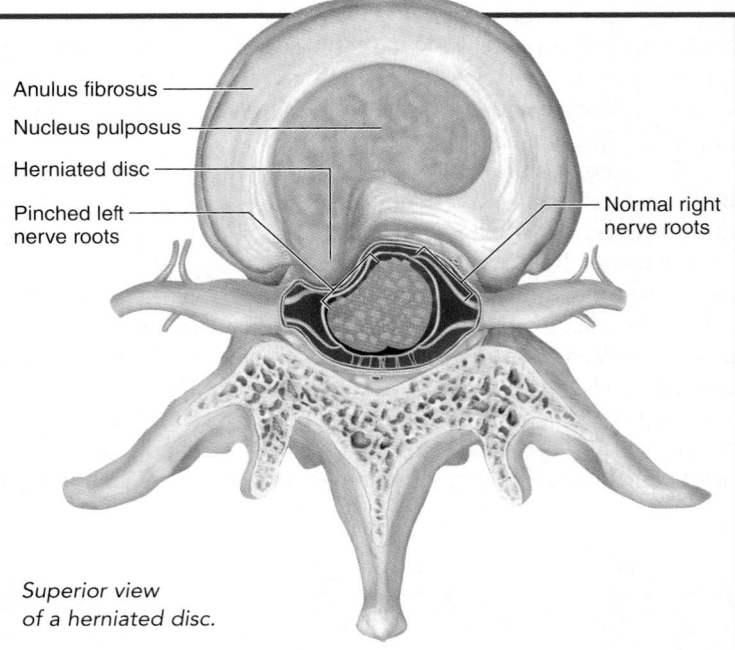

Anulus fibrosus
Nucleus pulposus
Herniated disc
Pinched left nerve roots
Normal right nerve roots

Superior view of a herniated disc.

Cervical Vertebrae

The cervical vertebrae are the most superiorly placed vertebrae. They typically have kidney-bean shaped bodies and extend inferiorly from the occipital bone of the skull through the neck to the thorax. Since cervical vertebrae support only the weight of the head, their vertebral bodies are relatively small and light. Most cervical vertebrae are distinguished from other vertebrae by the presence of **transverse foramina** in their transverse processes that house the vertebral artery and vein (sometimes C_7 does not have these foramina). Table 8.5 summarizes the key features of the typical cervical vertebra (C_3–C_6); the other cervical vertebrae are described below.

Atlas (C₁) The first cervical vertebra, called the **atlas** (at′las), supports the head through its articulation with the occipital condyles of the occipital bone **(figure 8.18a)**. This vertebra is named for the Greek mythological figure Atlas, who carried the world on his shoulders. The articulation between the occipital condyles and the atlas, called the atlanto-occipital joint, permits us to nod our heads "yes." The atlas is readily distinguished from the other vertebrae because it lacks both a body and a spinous process. Instead,

the atlas has lateral masses that are connected by semicircular **anterior** and **posterior arches,** each containing slight protuberances, the **anterior** and **posterior tubercles** (too′ber-kl). The atlas has depressed, oval **superior** and **inferior articular facets** that articulate with the occipital condyles and the axis, respectively. Finally, the atlas has an **articular facet for dens** on its anterior arch (see next).

Axis (C₂) The body of the atlas separates from the atlas and fuses during development to the body of the second cervical vertebra, called the **axis** (ak′sis) (figure 8.18b). This fusion produces the most distinctive feature of the axis, the prominent **dens,** or *odontoid* (ō-don′toyd; *odont* = tooth) *process*. The dens acts as a pivot for the lateral rotation of both the atlas and the skull. This articulation between the atlas and axis, called the atlantoaxial joint, permits us to shake our heads "no" (figure 8.18c).

Vertebra Prominens (C₇) The seventh cervical vertebra represents a transition from cervical to the thoracic vertebral region (see figure 8.16). The spinous process of both C_7 and all the thoracic vertebrae are nonbifid (forked)—however, this process in C_7 is much longer than it is within the other cervical vertebrae. It is easily palpated through the skin between the shoulder blades and inferior to the neck. Thus, C_7 also is called the **vertebra prominens** (prom′ĭ-nens; prominent).

Thoracic Vertebrae

There are 12 thoracic vertebrae, and each articulates with the ribs (table 8.5). Thoracic vertebrae typically have heart-shaped bodies and are distinguished from all other types of vertebrae by the presence of **costal facets** or **costal demifacets** (semicircular facets) on the lateral side of the body and on the sides of the transverse processes. The head of the rib articulates with the costal facet or

CONCEPT CONNECTION

Healthy, normal vertebrae are vital for the proper functioning of our nervous system. If intervertebral discs herniate, they may pinch on the spinal cord or portions of spinal nerves and cause pain or numbness. Severe abnormal spinal curvatures may similarly impinge on the spinal cord. Finally, malformed intervertebral foramina may pinch on exiting spinal nerves (section 14.5), resulting in pain from that nerve.

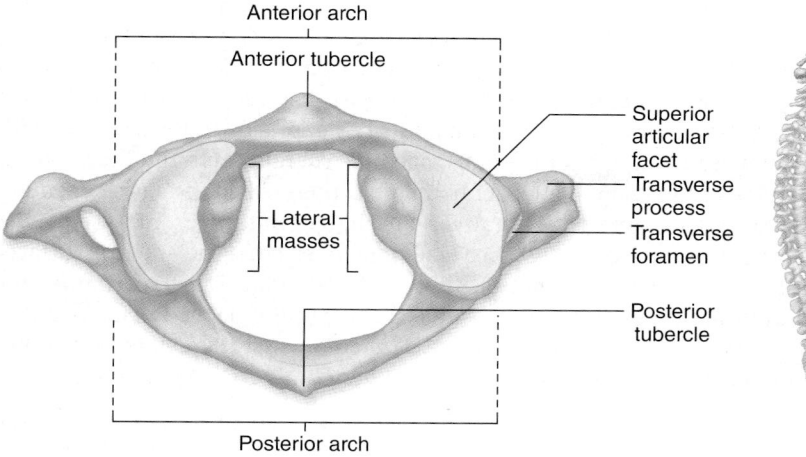

Anterior arch
Anterior tubercle
Superior articular facet
Transverse process
Lateral masses
Transverse foramen
Posterior tubercle
Posterior arch

(a) Atlas (C₁), superior view

Figure 8.18 Cervical Vertebrae C₁ and C₂. The atlas (C₁) and the axis (C₂) differ in structure from a typical cervical vertebra. (*a*) A superior view of the atlas shows the atlas lacks a body and a spinous process. (*b*) Posterosuperior view of the axis clearly illustrates the dens. (*c*) The articulation of the atlas and axis, called the atlantoaxial joint, allows partial rotation of the atlas. **AP R**

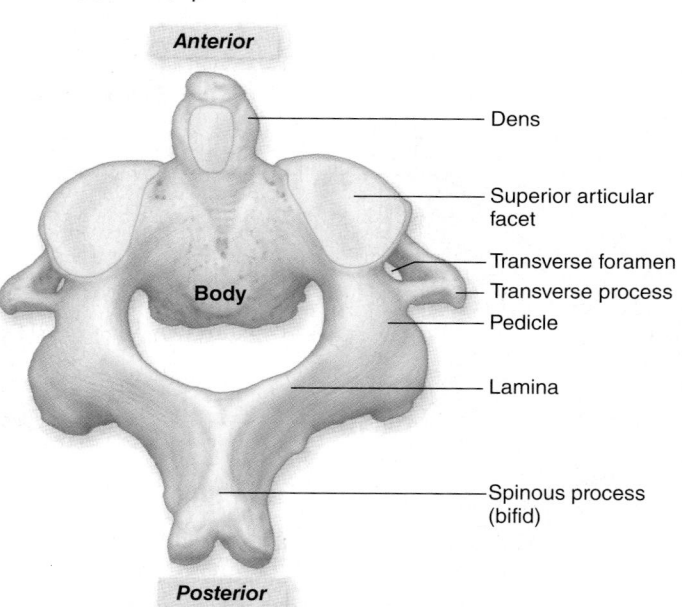

Anterior
Dens
Superior articular facet
Transverse foramen
Transverse process
Body
Pedicle
Lamina
Spinous process (bifid)
Posterior

(b) Axis (C₂), posterosuperior view

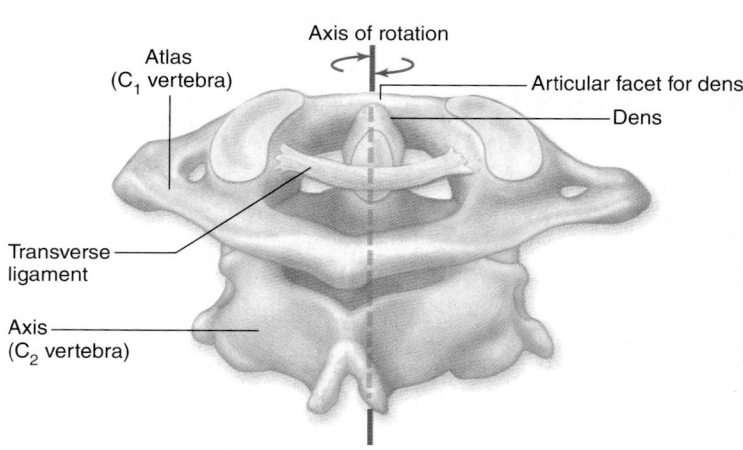

Axis of rotation
Atlas (C₁ vertebra)
Articular facet for dens
Dens
Transverse ligament
Axis (C₂ vertebra)

(c) Atlas and axis, posterosuperior view

demifacet on the body of the thoracic vertebra. The tubercle of the rib articulates with the costal facets on the transverse processes of the vertebra.

The thoracic vertebrae vary slightly with respect to their transverse costal facets. Vertebrae T_1–T_{10} have transverse costal facets on their transverse processes; T_{11} and T_{12} lack these transverse costal facets because the eleventh and twelfth ribs do not have tubercles (and thus do not articulate with the transverse processes). The costal facets on the bodies of the thoracic vertebrae also display variations. Some vertebrae may have a single whole facet; others may have two demifacets.

Lumbar Vertebrae

The largest vertebrae are the lumbar vertebrae. A typical lumbar vertebra body is thicker than that of all the other vertebrae, and its body is oval (table 8.5). The lumbar vertebrae are distinguished by the features they lack—that is, lumbar vertebrae have neither transverse foramina nor costal facets.

The lumbar vertebrae bear most of the weight of the body. The thick spinous processes provide extensive surface area for the attachment of inferior back muscles that reinforce or adjust the lumbar curvature.

 WHAT DO YOU THINK?

3 You are given a vertebra to identify. It has transverse foramina and a bifid spinous process. Is this a cervical, thoracic, or lumbar vertebra?

Sacrum

The sacrum is an anteriorly curved, somewhat triangular bone that forms the posterior wall of the pelvic cavity **(figure 8.19)**. The **apex** of the sacrum is a narrow, pointed portion of the bone that projects inferiorly, whereas the bone's broad superior surface forms the **base.** The lateral sacral curvature is more pronounced in males than in females.

The sacrum is composed of five fused sacral vertebrae. These vertebrae start to fuse shortly after puberty and are usually completely fused between ages 20 and 30. The horizontal lines of fusion that remain are called **transverse ridges.** Superiorly, the sacrum articulates with L₅ via a pair of **superior articular processes.** The vertebral canal becomes much narrower and continues through the sacrum on its posterior side as the **sacral canal.** The sacral canal terminates in an inferior opening called the **sacral hiatus** (hī-ā′tŭs; *hio* = to yawn). On either side of the sacral hiatus are bony projections called the **sacral cornua.**

The anterosuperior edge of the first sacral vertebra bulges anteriorly into the pelvic cavity and is called the **promontory.** Four transverse ridge lines cross the anterior surface of the sacrum, marking the lines of fusion of the sacral vertebrae. The paired **anterior** and **posterior sacral foramina** permit the passage of nerves to the pelvic organs and the gluteal region, respectively. A dorsal ridge, termed the **median sacral crest,** is formed by the fusion of the spinous processes of individual sacral vertebrae. On each lateral surface

Figure 8.19 Sacrum and Coccyx. The sacrum is formed by the fusion of five sacral vertebrae, and the coccyx is formed by the fusion of four coccygeal vertebrae. (*a*) The promontory of the sacrum is clearly seen in anterior view, while (*b*) a posterior view shows the median sacral crest and sacral hiatus. APR

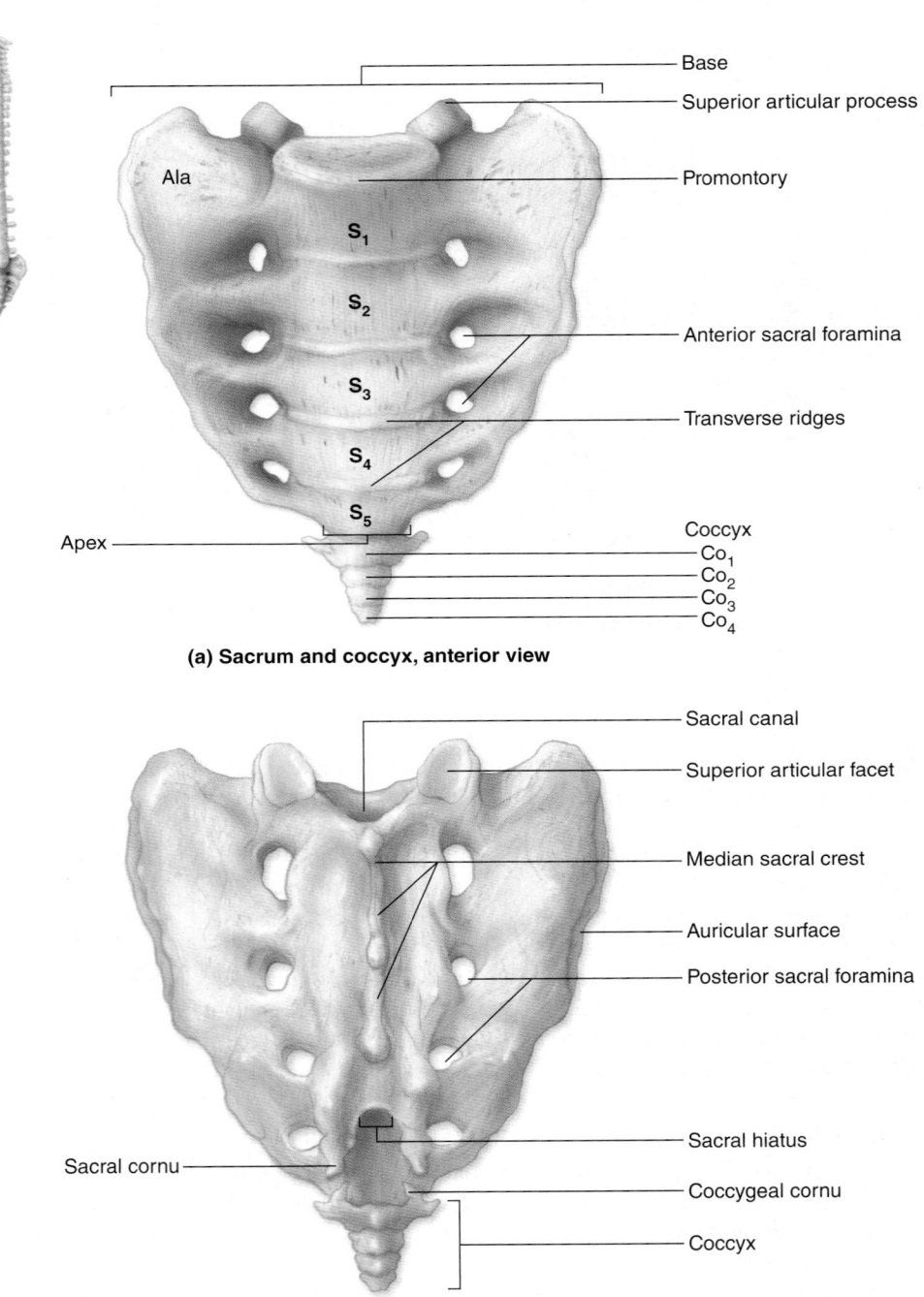

(a) Sacrum and coccyx, anterior view

(b) Sacrum and coccyx, posterior view

of the sacrum is the **ala** (meaning "wing"). On the lateral surface of the ala is the **auricular surface,** which marks the site of articulation with the os coxae of the pelvic girdle, forming the strong, stable **sacroiliac** (sā-krō-il'ē-ak) **joint.**

Coccyx

Four small coccygeal vertebrae fuse to form the **coccyx.** These individual vertebrae begin to fuse by about age 25. The coccyx is an attachment site for several ligaments and some muscles. The first and second coccygeal vertebrae have unfused vertebral arches and transverse processes. The prominent laminae of the first coccygeal vertebrae are known as the **coccygeal cornua,** which curve to meet the sacral cornua. In males, the coccyx tends to project anteriorly, but in females it tends to project more inferiorly. In very elderly individuals, the coccyx may fuse with the sacrum.

 WHAT DID YOU LEARN?

14 Compare the locations and functions of the transverse foramina, intervertebral foramina, and the vertebral foramen.

15 How do the atlas and axis differ from other cervical vertebrae?

8.6 Bones of the Thoracic Cage

The bony framework of the chest is called the **thoracic cage** and consists of the thoracic vertebrae posteriorly, the ribs laterally, and the sternum anteriorly **(figure 8.20)**. The thoracic cage acts as a protective enclosure around the thoracic organs and also provides attachment points for many muscles.

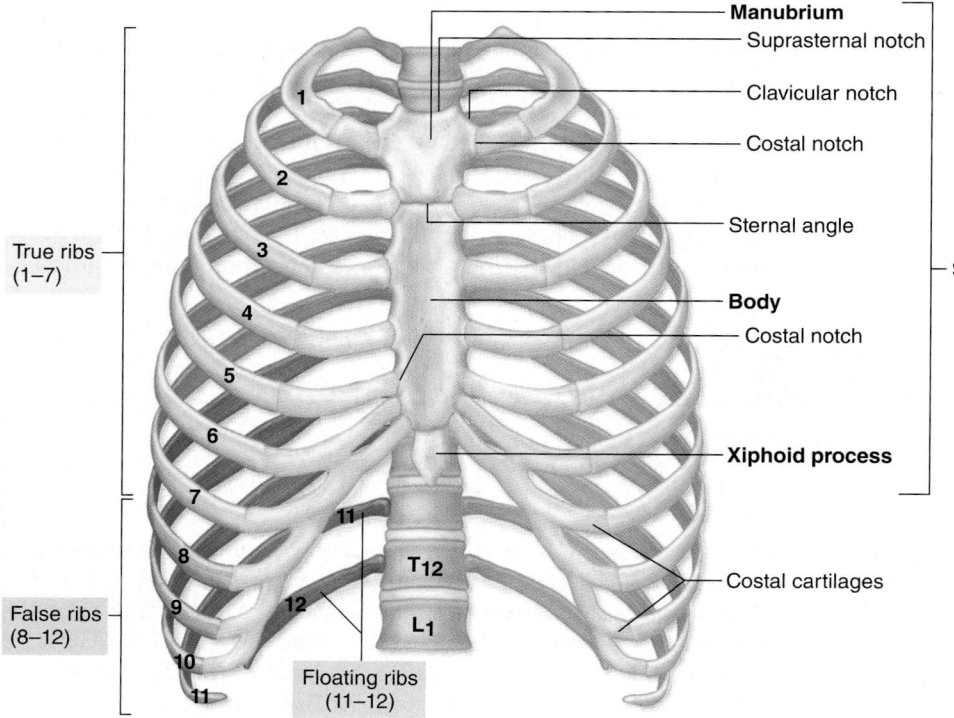

Figure 8.20 Thoracic Cage. The thoracic cage is composed of the thoracic vertebrae, ribs, and sternum. It protects and encloses the organs in the thoracic cavity. AP|R

8.6a Sternum

✔ LEARNING OBJECTIVE

1. Identify the three main components of the sternum and their features.

The **sternum** (ster′nŭm; *sternon* = the chest), also referred to as the "breastbone," is a flat bone that forms in the anterior midline of the thoracic wall. Its shape has been likened to that of a sword. The sternum is composed of three parts: the manubrium, the body, and the xiphoid process.

The **manubrium** (mă-noo′brē-ŭm) is the widest and most superior portion of the sternum (the "handle" of the bony sword). Two **clavicular notches** articulate the sternum with the left and right clavicles. The shallow superior indentation between the clavicular notches is called the **suprasternal** (or *jugular*) **notch.** A single pair of **costal notches** represent articulations for the first ribs' costal cartilages.

The **body** is the longest part of the sternum and forms its bulk (the "blade" of the bony sword). Individual costal cartilages from ribs 2–7 are attached to the body at indented articular costal notches. The body and the manubrium articulate at the **sternal angle,** a horizontal ridge that may be palpated under the skin. The sternal angle is an important landmark in that the costal cartilages of the second ribs attach there; thus, it may be used to count the ribs.

The **xiphoid** (zi′foyd; *xiphos* = sword) **process** represents the very tip of the "sword blade." This small, inferiorly pointed cartilaginous projection often doesn't ossify until after age 40.

💡 WHAT DID YOU LEARN?

16 What sternal structures form the sternal angle, and what is its clinical significance?

8.6b Ribs

✔ LEARNING OBJECTIVES

2. Describe the features found on all ribs.

3. Differentiate between true ribs and false ribs.

The ribs are elongated, curved, flattened bones that originate on or between the thoracic vertebrae and end in the anterior wall of the thorax **(figure 8.21a)**. Both males and females have 12 pairs of ribs. Ribs 1–7 are called **true ribs.** True ribs connect individually to the sternum by separate cartilaginous extensions called **costal** (kos′tal; *costa* = rib) **cartilages** (figure 8.20). The smallest true rib is the first.

Ribs 8–12 are called **false ribs** because their costal cartilages do not attach directly to the sternum. The costal cartilages of ribs 8–10 fuse to the costal cartilage of rib 7 and thus indirectly articulate with the sternum. The last two pairs of false ribs (ribs 11 and 12) are called **floating ribs** because they have no connection with the sternum.

The vertebral end of a typical rib articulates with the vertebral column at the **head** (figure 8.21). The articular surface of the head is divided into **superior** and **inferior articular facets** by an interarticular **crest.** The surfaces of these facets articulate with the costal demifacets or facets on the bodies of the thoracic vertebrae. The **neck** of the rib lies between the head and the tubercle. The **tubercle** of the rib has an articular facet for the costal facet on the transverse process of the thoracic vertebra. Figure 8.21*b, c* illustrates how most of the ribs articulate with the thoracic vertebrae.

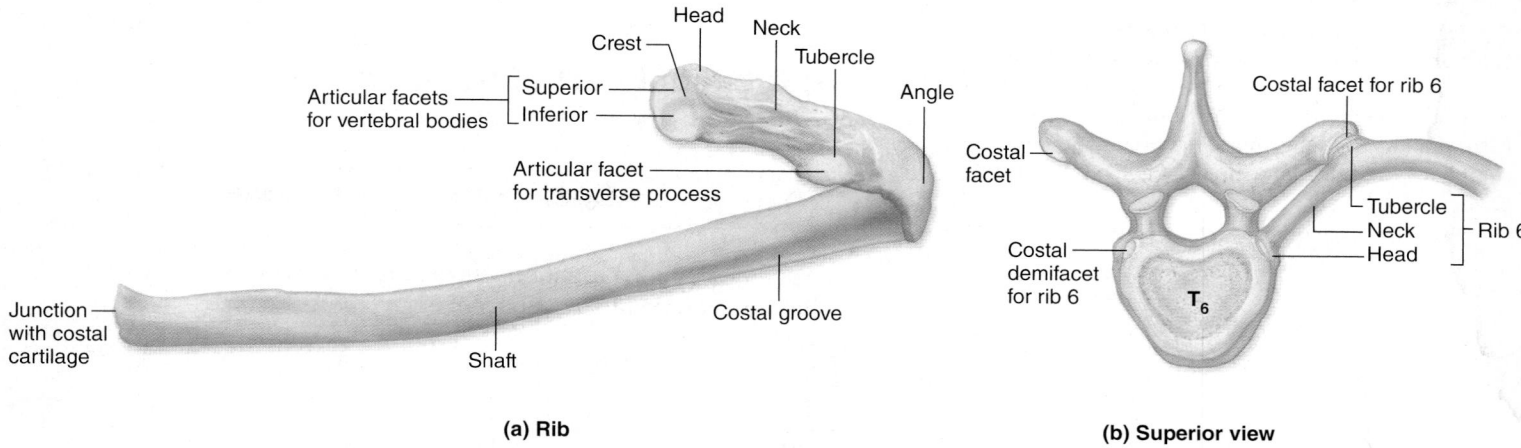

(a) Rib

(b) Superior view

(c) Lateral view

Figure 8.21 Rib Anatomy and Articulation with Thoracic Vertebrae. Paired ribs attach to thoracic vertebrae posteriorly and extend anteroinferiorly to the anterior chest wall. (*a*) Features of ribs 2–10. (*b*) Superior and (*c*) lateral views show the articulation of a rib with two vertebrae.

The **angle** (*border*) of the rib indicates the site where the tubular **shaft** begins to curve anteriorly toward the sternum. A prominent **costal groove** along its inferior internal border marks the path of nerves (see section 14.5c) and blood vessels to the thoracic wall.

 WHAT DID YOU LEARN?

17 Where specifically do the head and tubercle of a rib each articulate?

8.7 The Upper and Lower Limbs: A Comparison

LEARNING OBJECTIVES

1. Identify skeletal features common to the upper and lower limbs.
2. Describe the functional reasons for differences between the upper and lower limb skeletons.

Humans evolved from quadrupeds, which are animals that move on four feet. Quadruped limbs are very similar because all of the limbs are designed to support the body weight and move the animal. However, as our ancestors evolved into modern human beings, we became bipedal creatures. Only our lower limbs normally support our body weight and are responsible for propelling our bodies when we walk or run. In contrast, our upper limbs have been freed from these functions and are able to do other things, such as grasping objects and utilizing tools with our hands.

Our upper and lower limb skeletons share some common features based on this evolutionary history, and they exhibit some differences based on the primary functions of each limb. **Figure 8.22** summarizes the similarities. The *proximal part* of both upper and lower limbs are supported by a "girdle" of bones; the pectoral girdle (clavicles and scapulae) holds

Figure 8.22 Similarities Between the Upper Limb and Lower Limb Skeletons. (*a*) The proximal part of each limb has a girdle that holds the limb in place. (*b*) The distal part of each limb contains two long bones, followed by multiple short bones and then numerous long bones in the hand and foot.

(a) Proximal part of the limb

A "girdle" supports each limb.

Each girdle has a rounded, cuplike depression (socket) in which the head of the proximal part of each limb bone fits.

Pectoral girdle = left and right clavicles and scapulae

Upper Limb

Pelvic girdle = left and right ossa coxae

Lower Limb

The proximal part of the limb contains a single bone with a rounded head.

The rounded heads of the humerus and femur fit within their respective girdles, and allow for a wide range of movement at the shoulder and hip joints.

Head

Humerus

Femur

Shaft

Upper Limb   **Lower Limb**

The distal part of each limb contains two bones connected by an interosseous membrane.

The interosseous membrane keeps the bones a fixed distance apart and allows these bones to pivot about one another. (Note: pivoting is much more limited in the lower limb.)

The styloid processes of the radius and ulna are structurally similar to the malleoli of the tibia and fibula.

Ulna

Radius

Interosseous membrane

Tibia

Fibula

Styloid process

Lateral malleolus

Medial malleolus

Upper Limb

Lower Limb

(b) Distal part of the limb

The hands and the feet have similar arrangements of bones.

Both the hand and the foot have 5 metacarpals or metatarsals respectively, and 14 phalanges. Note the thumb and the big toe are the most robust of the digits, yet they each have only 2 phalanges.

Phalanges of digits

Phalanges of digits

Metatarsals

Metacarpals

Carpals

Tarsals

Upper Limb

Lower Limb

The multiple carpal and tarsal bones allow for a wide range of movement at either the wrist or the ankle joints.

the upper limbs in place, while the pelvic girdle (both ossa coxae) articulates with the lower limb. The *proximal part* of each limb has one large bone; the humerus in the upper limb and the femur in the lower limb. The *distal part* of each limb contains two bones; these bones are able to pivot slightly about one another. Both the wrist and the proximal foot contain multiple bones (carpal and tarsal bones, respectively) that allow for a range of movement. Finally, the feet and hands are very similar in that both contain either 5 metacarpals (palm of hand) or 5 metatarsals (arch of foot), and each contains a total of 14 phalanges (bones of the fingers/toes).

The structural differences between the upper and lower limb skeletons arise from the functional differences. Understanding these general differences between upper and lower limbs will make the study of their individual bones easier. Since the lower limb is weight bearing and is used for locomotion, some mobility at specific joints has been sacrificed for greater stability. The upper limb is not weight bearing, so both arm and forearm bones are relatively smaller and lighter than the similar respective lower limb bones. Additionally, the upper limb joints are relatively more mobile than the respective lower limb joints, so we may utilize the upper limbs for a wide range of activities. Unfortunately, more mobile joints are less stable, and that is why some of the upper limb joints (such as the shoulder joints) are the most frequently injured.

WHAT DID YOU LEARN?

18 What are some of the functional differences between the upper and lower limbs?

8.8 The Pectoral Girdle and Its Functions

The **pectoral** (pek'tŏ-răl; *pectus* = breastbone) **girdle** articulates with the trunk and supports the upper limbs. A pectoral girdle consists of the clavicles and the scapulae.

8.8a Clavicle

LEARNING OBJECTIVE

1. Identify and locate the clavicle and its landmarks.

The **clavicle** (klav'i-kl; *clavis* = key), commonly known as the *collarbone*, is an elongated S-shaped bone that extends between the manubrium of the sternum and the acromion of the scapula **(figure 8.23)**. Its **sternal end** (medial end) is roughly pyramidal in shape and articulates with the manubrium of the sternum, forming the sternoclavicular joint. The **acromial end** (lateral end) of the clavicle is broad and flattened. The acromial end articulates with the acromion of the scapula, forming the acromioclavicular joint. You can palpate your own clavicle by first locating the superior aspect of your sternum and then moving your hand laterally. The curved bone you feel under your skin, and close to the neck opening of your shirt is your clavicle.

The superior surface of the clavicle is relatively smooth and the inferior surface is marked by grooves and ridges for muscle attachment. On the inferior surface, near the acromial end, is a rough tuberosity called the **conoid** (kō'noyd; *konoeides* = cone-shaped) **tubercle.** The inferiorly located prominence at the sternal end of the clavicle is called the **costal tuberosity.**

WHAT DID YOU LEARN?

19 How do the sternal end and acromial end of the clavicle differ?

8.8b Scapula

LEARNING OBJECTIVE

2. Describe the landmarks and features of the scapula.

The **scapula** (skap'ū-lă) is a broad, flat, triangular bone that forms the *shoulder blade* **(figure 8.24)**. You can palpate your scapula by putting your hand on your superolateral back region and moving

(a) Right clavicle, superior view

(b) Right clavicle, inferior view

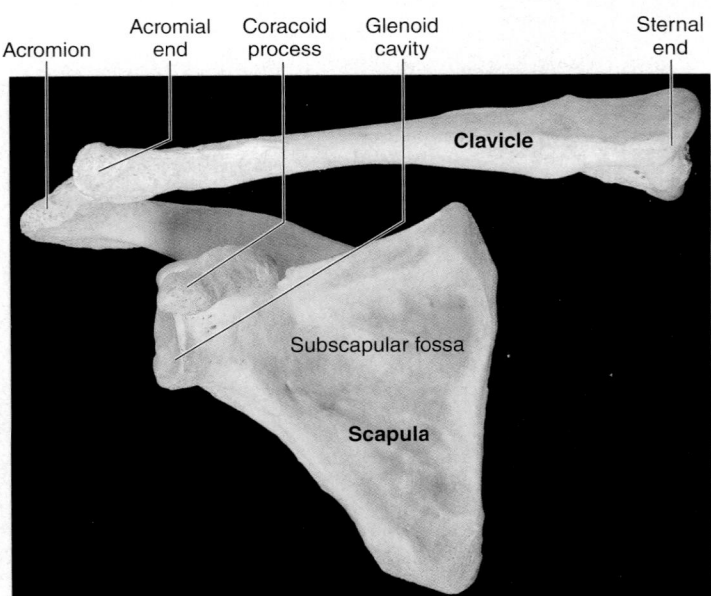

(c) Right scapula and clavicle articulation, anterior view

Figure 8.23 Clavicle. The S-shaped clavicle represents the only direct connection between the pectoral girdle and the axial skeleton. (*a*) Superior and (*b*) inferior views of the right clavicle. (*c*) Anterior view of an articulated right clavicle and scapula. AP|R

Acromion Coracoid process
          Suprascapular notch
             Superior border
                Superior angle

Lateral angle

Glenoid cavity

Subscapular fossa

Medial border

Lateral border

Inferior angle

(a) Right scapula, anterior view

Coracoid process Acromion
Suprascapular notch
Superior border

Superior angle

Supraspinous
fossa
                              Lateral angle
Spine

                              Glenoid cavity

Infraspinous
fossa
                              Lateral border

Medial border

Inferior angle

(b) Right scapula, posterior view

Figure 8.24 Scapula. The right scapula is known as the "shoulder blade" and is shown in (*a*) anterior and (*b*) posterior views. **AP|R**

your upper limb; the bone you feel moving is the scapula. The **spine** of the scapula is a ridge of bone on the posterior aspect of the scapula. It is easily palpated under the skin. The spine is continuous with a larger, posterior process called the **acromion** (a-krō′mē-on; *akron* = tip; *omos* = shoulder), which forms the bony tip of the shoulder. Palpate your upper shoulder; the prominent bump you feel is the acromion. The **coracoid** (kōr′ă-koyd) **process** is the smaller, more anterior projection that is a site for muscle attachment.

The triangular shape of the scapula forms three sides, or borders. The **superior border** is the horizontal edge of the scapula superior to the spine of the scapula; the **medial border** (also called the *vertebral border*) is the edge of the scapula closest to the vertebrae; and the **lateral border** (also called the *axillary border*) is closest to the axilla (armpit). A **suprascapular notch** (which in some individuals is a **suprascapular foramen**) in the superior border provides passage for the suprascapular nerve and blood vessels.

Between these borders are the superior, inferior, and lateral angles. The **superior angle** is located between the superior and medial borders; the **inferior angle** is located between the medial and lateral borders. The **lateral angle** is primarily made up of the cup-shaped, shallow **glenoid** (glē′noyd; resembling a socket) **cavity,** or *glenoid fossa*, which articulates with the humerus, the bone of the arm.

The broad, relatively smooth, anterior surface of the scapula is called the **subscapular** (sŭb-skap′ū-lăr; *sub* = under) **fossa** (fos′ă; pl., *fossae,* fos′ē). A large muscle called the subscapularis overlies this fossa. The spine subdivides the posterior surface of the scapula into two shallow fossae. The depression superior to the spine is the

supraspinous (soopră-spī′nŭs; *supra* = above) **fossa;** inferior to the spine is a broad, extensive surface called the **infraspinous fossa.** The supraspinatus and infraspinatus muscles, respectively, occupy these fossae (see section 11.8a).

 WHAT DID YOU LEARN?

20 What fossae are located on the scapula, and what is located in each fossa?

8.9 Bones of the Upper Limb

The upper limb consists of the brachium (arm), antebrachium (forearm), and hand. The complex structure of the hand in particular gives humans capabilities beyond those of most other vertebrates.

Each upper limb contains a total of 30 bones:

- 1 humerus, located in the brachium region
- 1 radius and 1 ulna, located in the antebrachium region
- 8 carpal bones, which form the wrist
- 5 metacarpal bones, which form the palm of the hand
- 14 phalanges, which form the fingers

8.9a Humerus

LEARNING OBJECTIVES

1. Describe the articulations of the humerus.

2. List landmarks and features of the humerus.

The **humerus** (hū′mer-ŭs) is the longest and largest upper limb bone (figure 8.25). Its proximal end has a hemispherical **head** that articulates with the glenoid cavity of the scapula. The prominent **greater tubercle** is positioned lateral to the head and helps form the rounded contour of the shoulder. The **lesser tubercle** is smaller and located more medial to the head. Between the two tubercles is the **intertubercular sulcus** (or *bicipital sulcus*, or *bicipital groove*), a depression that contains the tendon of the long head of the biceps brachii muscle (see section 11.8c).

Between the tubercles and the head of the humerus is the **anatomical neck,** an almost indistinct groove that marks the location of the former epiphyseal plate. The **surgical neck** is a narrowing of the bone immediately distal to the tubercles, at the transition from the head to the shaft. This feature is called the "surgical" neck because it is a common fracture site.

The **shaft** of the humerus has a roughened area, termed the **deltoid** (del′toyd; *deltoides* = like the Greek letter Δ) **tuberosity** (too′ber-os′i-tē), which extends along its lateral surface for about half the length of the humerus. The deltoid muscle of the shoulder attaches to this roughened surface (see section 11.8b). The **radial groove** (or *spiral groove*) is located adjacent to the deltoid tuberosity and is where the radial nerve (see section 14.5e) and some blood vessels travel.

Together, the bones of the humerus, radius, and ulna form the elbow joint (figure 8.25c). The **medial** and **lateral epicondyles** (ep-i-kon′dīl; *epi* = upon; *kondylos* = a knuckle) are bony side projections on the distal humerus that provide surfaces for muscle attachment. Palpate the sides of your elbow; the bumps you feel are the medial and lateral epicondyles. Traveling posterior to the medial epicondyle is the ulnar nerve (see section 14.5e). (You actually are hitting this nerve when you hit your "funny bone.")

The distal end of the humerus has two smooth, curved surfaces for articulation with the bones of the forearm. The rounded **capitulum** (kă-pit′ū-lŭm; *caput* = head) is located laterally and articulates with the head of the radius. The pulley-shaped **trochlea** (trok′lē-ă; *trochileia* = a pulley) is located medially and articulates with the trochlear notch of the ulna. Additionally, the distal end of the humerus exhibits three depressions, two on its anterior surface and one on its posterior surface. The anterolaterally placed **radial fossa** accommodates the head of the radius; the anteromedially placed **coronoid** (kōr′ŏ-noyd; *korone* = a crown; *eidos* = resembling) **fossa**

Figure 8.25 Humerus and Elbow Joint. The right humerus is shown in (*a*) anterior and (*b*) posterior views. (*c*) Anterior view of the elbow joint. **AP|R**

(a) Right humerus, anterior view

(b) Right humerus, posterior view

(c) Right elbow joint, anterior view

accommodates the coronoid process of the ulna. The posterior depression, called the **olecranon** (ō-lek'ră-non; *olene* = ulna; *kranion* = head) **fossa,** accommodates the olecranon of the ulna when the elbow is extended (straight).

💡 WHAT DID YOU LEARN?

21 What is the difference between the anatomical and surgical neck of the humerus?

22 What features on the humerus articulate with the radius and ulna?

8.9b Radius and Ulna

✅ LEARNING OBJECTIVES

3. Compare and contrast the features of the radius and the ulna.

4. Explain how the radius, ulna, and humerus articulate.

5. Differentiate between supination and pronation of the forearm.

The radius and ulna form the forearm (**figure 8.26**). In anatomic position, these bones are parallel, and the **radius** (rā'dē-ŭs; spoke of

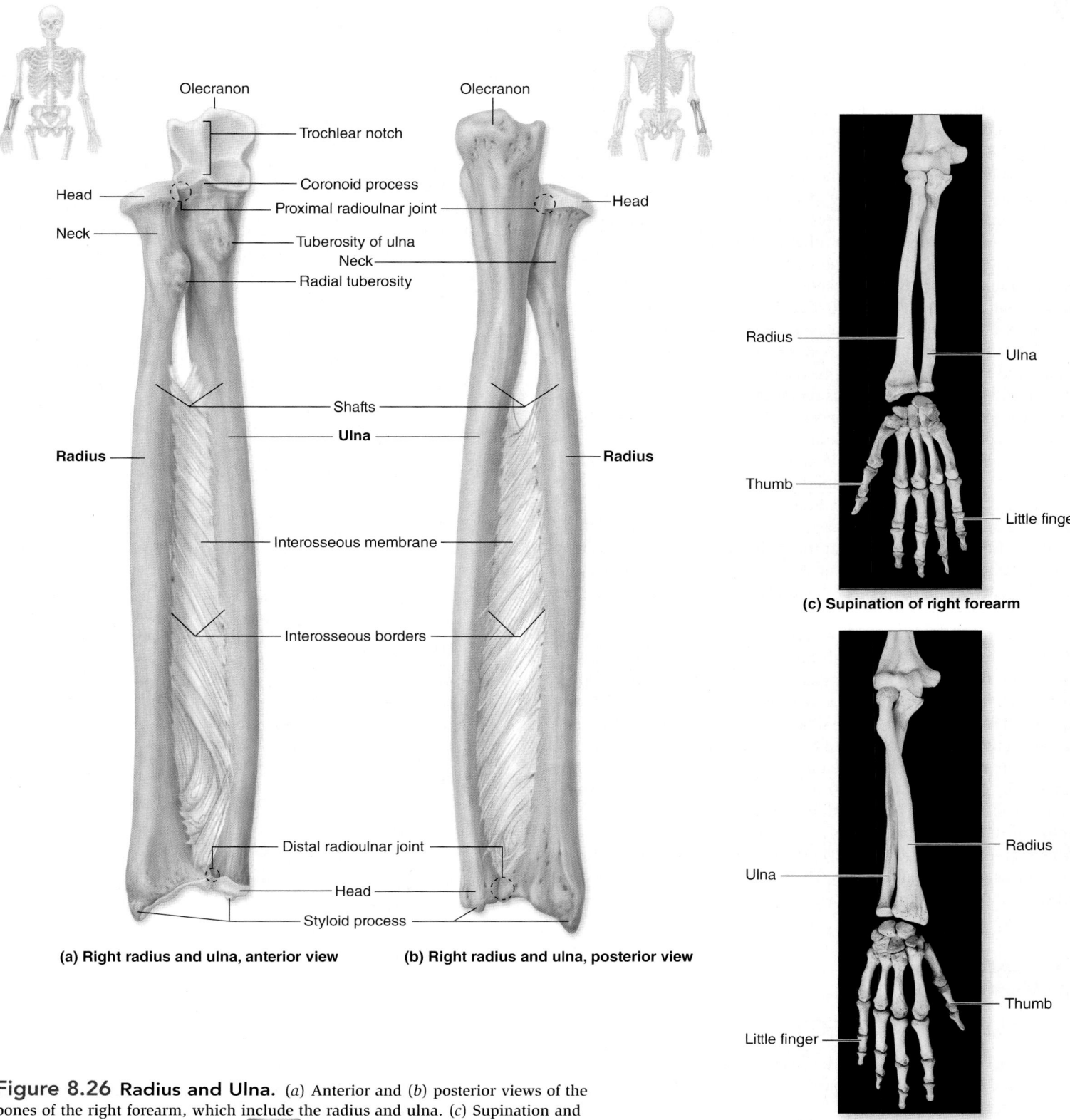

(a) **Right radius and ulna, anterior view**

(b) **Right radius and ulna, posterior view**

(c) **Supination of right forearm**

(d) **Pronation of right forearm**

Figure 8.26 Radius and Ulna. (*a*) Anterior and (*b*) posterior views of the bones of the right forearm, which include the radius and ulna. (*c*) Supination and (*d*) pronation of the right forearm. AP|R a wheel, ray) is located more laterally. The proximal end of the radius has a distinctive disc-shaped **head** that articulates with the capitulum of the humerus. A narrow **neck** extends from the radial head to the **radial tuberosity** (or *bicipital tuberosity*). The radial tuberosity is an attachment site for the biceps brachii muscle.

The **shaft** of the radius curves slightly and leads to a wider distal end where there is a laterally placed **styloid** (stī′loyd) **process.** This bony projection can be palpated on the lateral side of the wrist, just proximal to the thumb. On the distal medial surface of the radius is an **ulnar notch,** which articulates with the medial surface of the distal end of the ulna.

The **ulna** (ŭl′nă; *olene* = elbow) is the longer, medially placed bone of the forearm. At the proximal end of the ulna, a C-shaped **trochlear notch** interlocks with the trochlea of the humerus. The posterosuperior aspect of the trochlear notch has a prominent projection called the **olecranon.** The olecranon articulates with the olecranon fossa of the humerus and forms the posterior "bump" of the elbow. The inferior lip of the trochlear notch, called the **coronoid process,** articulates with the humerus at the coronoid fossa. Lateral to the coronoid process, a smooth, curved radial notch accommodates the head of the radius and helps form the proximal radioulnar joint. Also at the proximal end of this bone is the **tuberosity of ulna.** At the distal end of the ulna, the shaft narrows and terminates in a knoblike **head** that has a posteromedial **styloid process.** The styloid process of the ulna may be palpated on the medial ("little finger") side of the wrist.

Both the radius and the ulna exhibit **interosseous borders,** which face each other; the ulna's interosseous border faces laterally, while the radius' interosseous border faces medially. These interosseous borders are connected by an **interosseous membrane** (*interosseous ligament*), composed of dense regular connective tissue. This membrane helps keep the radius and ulna a fixed distance apart from one another and provides a pivot of rotation for the forearm. The bony joints that move during this rotation are the proximal and distal radioulnar joints.

In anatomic position, the palm of the hand is facing anteriorly, and the bones of the forearm are said to be in **supination** (soo′pi-nā′shŭn) (figure 8.26c). Note that the radius and the ulna are parallel with one another. If you view your own supinated forearm, the radius is on the lateral (thumb) side of the forearm, while the ulna is on the medial (little finger) side.

Pronation (prō-nā′shŭn) of the forearm requires that the radius cross over the ulna and that both bones pivot along the interosseous membrane (figure 8.26d). When the forearm is pronated, the palm of the hand is facing posteriorly. When you pronate your forearm, the head of the radius is still along the lateral side of the elbow, but the distal end of the radius has crossed over and become a more medial structure.

When an individual has the upper limbs extended and forearms supinated, note that the bones of the forearm may angle laterally from the elbow joint. This positioning is referred to as the **carrying angle** of the elbow, and this angle positions the bones of the forearms such that the forearms will clear the hips during walking as the forearms swing. Females have wider carrying angles than males, presumably because they have wider hips than males.

INTEGRATE

LEARNING STRATEGY

No matter what the position of the forearm (pronated or supinated), the distal end of the radius is always near the thumb, and the distal end of the ulna is near the little finger.

WHAT DID YOU LEARN?

23 What are some bony features that the radius and ulna share?

24 Describe how the radius and ulna are positioned when the forearm is pronated.

8.9c Carpals, Metacarpals, and Phalanges

LEARNING OBJECTIVES

6. Locate and identify the carpals and metacarpals.

7. Describe the phalanges and their relative locations.

The bones that form the wrist and hand are the carpals, metacarpals, and phalanges **(figure 8.27).** The **carpals** (kar′păl; *karpus* = wrist) are small, short bones that form the wrist. They are arranged in two rows (a proximal row and a distal row) of four bones each and allow for the multiple movements possible at the wrist.

The *proximal row* of carpal bones, listed from lateral to medial, are the **scaphoid** (skaf′oyd; *skaphe* = boat), **lunate** (loo′nāt; *luna* = moon), **triquetrum** (trī-kwē′trŭm; *triquetrus* = three-cornered), and **pisiform** (pis′i-fōrm; *pisum* = pea; *forma* = appearance).

The *distal row* of the carpal bones, listed from lateral to medial, are the **trapezium** (trap-ē′zē-ŭm; *trapeza* = table), **trapezoid** (trap′ĕ-zoyd), **capitate** (kap′itāt), and **hamate** (ha′māt; *hamus* = hook).

Bones in the palm of the hand are called **metacarpals** (met′ă-kar′păl; *meta* = beyond). Five metacarpal bones articulate with the distal carpal bones and support the palm. Roman numerals I–V denote the metacarpal bones, with metacarpal I located at the base of the thumb, and metacarpal V at the base of the little finger.

A total of 14 bones are present in the digits; these are called **phalanges** (fă-lan′jēz; sing., *phalanx*, fā′langks; line of soldiers). Three phalanges are found in each of the second through fifth fingers, but only two phalanges are present within the thumb, also known as the **pollex**

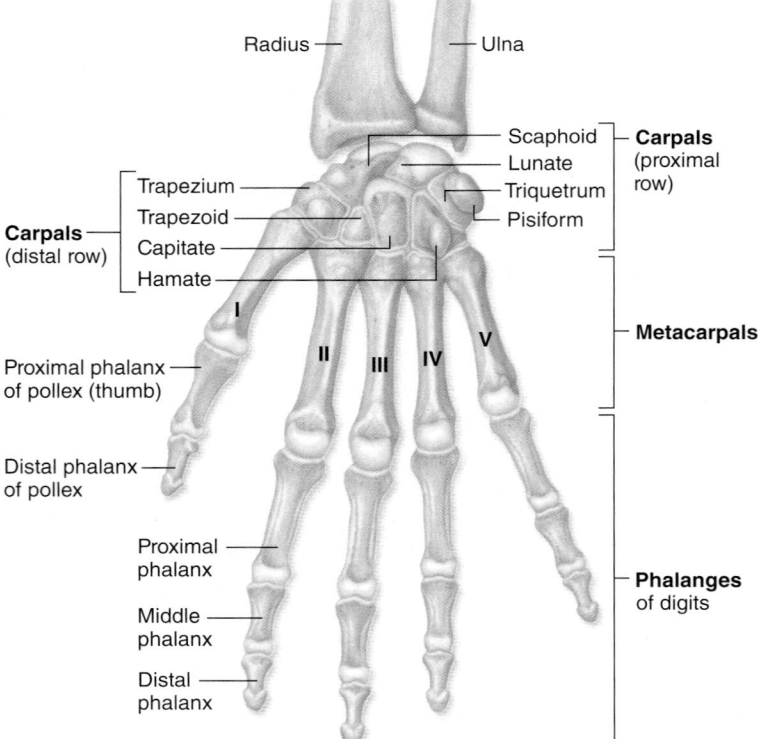

Right wrist and hand, anterior view

Figure 8.27 Bones of the Carpals, Metacarpals, and Phalanges. The carpal bones form the wrist, and the metacarpals and phalanges form the hand. Anterior (palmar) view of the right wrist and hand. **AP|R**

(pol'eks; thumb). The **proximal phalanx** articulates with the head of a metacarpal, while the **distal phalanx** is the bone in the very tip of the finger. The **middle phalanx** of each finger lies between the proximal and distal phalanges; however, a middle phalanx is not present in the thumb.

WHAT DID YOU LEARN?

25 List the eight carpal bones. Which of these bones may be prone to developing avascular necrosis if fractured?

8.10 The Pelvic Girdle and Its Functions

The adult **pelvis** (pel'vis; pl., *pelves,* pel'vēz; basin) is composed of four bones: the sacrum, the coccyx, and the right and left **ossa coxae** (os'ă cox'ē; sing., *os coxae;* hip bone) **(figure 8.28)**. The pelvis protects and supports the viscera in the inferior part of the ventral body cavity.

The term **pelvic girdle** refers to both the left and right ossa coxae only. The pelvic girdle articulates with the trunk and provides an attachment point for each lower limb. When a person is standing upright, the pelvis is angled (or 'tipped') slightly anteriorly.

(a) Anterior view

(b) Pelvis radiograph, anterior view

Figure 8.28 Pelvis. The complete pelvis consists of (*a*) the two ossa coxae, the sacrum, and the coccyx. (*b*) A radiograph shows an anterior view of the articulation between the pelvis and the femur. AP|R

8.10a Os Coxae

 LEARNING OBJECTIVES

1. Name the three bones that make up each os coxae.
2. Describe how the ossa coxae articulate with the femora and sacrum.
3. Describe landmarks and features of an os coxae.

The os coxae is commonly referred to as the *hip bone* (and sometimes as the *coxal bone* or the *innominate bone*). Each os coxae is formed from three separate bones: the ilium, ischium, and pubis **(figure 8.29)**. These three bones fuse between the ages of 13 and 15 years to form the single os coxae.

Each os coxae articulates posteriorly with the sacrum at the sacroiliac joint. The femur articulates with a deep, curved depression on the lateral surface of the os coxae called the **acetabulum** (as-ĕ-tab′ū-lŭm; shallow cup). The acetabulum contains a smooth curved surface, called the **lunate surface,** which is C-shaped and articulates with the femoral head. The ilium, ischium, and pubis all contribute a portion to the acetabulum—thus, it represents a region where these bones have fused.

WHAT DO YOU THINK?

4 Compare and contrast the glenoid cavity of the scapula with the acetabulum of the os coxae. Which girdle maintains stronger, more tightly fitting bony connections with its respective limb—the pectoral girdle or the pelvic girdle? Why?

The largest of the three coxal bones is the **ilium** (il′ē-ŭm; groin, flank), which forms the superior region of the os coxae and part of the acetabular surface. The wide, fan-shaped portion of the ilium is called the **ala** (ā′lă; wing). The ala terminates inferiorly at a ridge called the **arcuate** (ar′kū-āt; *arcuatus* = bowed) **line** on the medial surface of the ilium. On the medial side of the ala is a depression termed the **iliac fossa.** On the lateral surface of the ilium, the **anterior, posterior,** and **inferior gluteal** (gloo′tē-ăl; *gloutos* = buttock) **lines** are attachment sites for the gluteal muscles of the buttock (see section 11.9a). The posterome-dial side of the ilium exhibits a large, roughened area called the **auricular** (aw-rik′ū-lăr; *auris* = ear) **surface,** where the ilium articulates with the sacrum.

The superiormost ridge of the ilium is the **iliac crest.** Palpate the posterosuperior edges of your hips; the ridge of bone you feel on each side is the iliac crest. The iliac crest arises anteriorly from a projection called the **anterior superior iliac spine** and extends posteriorly to the **posterior superior iliac spine.** Located inferiorly to the ala of the ilium are the **anterior inferior iliac spine** and the **posterior inferior iliac spine.** The posterior inferior iliac spine is adjacent to a prominent **greater sciatic notch** (sī-at′ik; *sciaticus* = hip joint), through which the sciatic nerve travels to the lower limb (see section 14.5g).

The ilium fuses with the **ischium** (is′kē-ŭm; *ischion* = hip) near the superior and posterior margins of the acetabulum. Posterior to the acetabulum, the prominent triangular **ischial** (is′kē-ăl) **spine** projects medially. The bulky bone superior to the ischial spine is called the ischial **body.** The **lesser sciatic notch** is a semicircular depression inferior to the ischial spine. The posterolateral border of the ischium is a roughened projection called the **ischial tuberosity.** The ischial tuberosities also are called the *sitz bones* by some health professionals and fitness instructors because they support the weight of the body when seated. If you palpate your buttocks while in a sitting position, you can feel the large ischial tuberosities. An elongated **ramus** (rā′mŭs; pl., *rami,* rā′mē) of the ischium extends from the ischial tuberosity toward its anterior fusion with the pubis.

The **pubis** (pew′bŭs) fuses with the ilium and ischium at the acetabulum. The ischial ramus fuses anteriorly with the **inferior pubic ramus** to form the **ischiopubic ramus** (see figure 8.28). The **superior pubic ramus** originates at the anterior margin of the acetabulum. The **obturator** (ob′too-rā-tōr; *obturo* = to occlude) **foramen** is a space in the os coxae that is encircled by both pubic and ischial rami. A roughened ridge, called the **pubic crest,** is located on the anterosuperior surface of the superior pubic ramus, and it ends at the **pubic tubercle.** A roughened area on the anteromedial surface of the pubis, called the **symphysial surface** or *pubic symphysis* (sim′fĭ-sis; growing together), denotes the site of articulation between the pubic bones. On the medial surface of the pubis, the **pectineal** (pek-tin′ē-ăl) **line** originates and extends diagonally across the pubis to merge with the arcuate line.

WHAT DID YOU LEARN?

 26 What three bones fuse to form the os coxae?

 **27** Where are the ischial tuberosities located, what is an alternative name for them, and what is their function?

Ilium

Posterior   Anterior

Ischium   Pubis

Iliac crest

Ala

Anterior gluteal line

Posterior gluteal line

Posterior superior iliac spine

Anterior superior iliac spine

Inferior gluteal line

Posterior inferior iliac spine

Greater sciatic notch

Anterior inferior iliac spine

Lunate surface

Acetabulum

Body of ischium

Ischial spine

Lesser sciatic notch

Ischial tuberosity

Superior pubic ramus

Pubic crest

Pubic tubercle

Inferior pubic ramus

Obturator foramen

Ramus of ischium

(a) Right os coxae, lateral view

Ilium

Anterior   Posterior

Pubis   Ischium

Iliac crest

Iliac fossa

Anterior superior iliac spine

Posterior superior iliac spine

Auricular surface

Anterior inferior iliac spine

Arcuate line

Posterior inferior iliac spine

Greater sciatic notch

Pectineal line

Superior pubic ramus

Pubic tubercle

Ischial spine

Lesser sciatic notch

Body of ischium

Symphysial surface

Obturator foramen

Inferior pubic ramus

Ischial tuberosity

Ramus of ischium

(b) Right os coxae, medial view

Figure 8.29 Os Coxae. Each os coxae is formed by the fusion of three bones: an ilium, an ischium, and a pubis. Diagrams show the features of these bones in (*a*) lateral and (*b*) medial views. AP|R

8.10b True and False Pelves

✓ LEARNING OBJECTIVES

4. Differentiate between the true and false pelves.
5. Compare and contrast the pelvic inlet and pelvic outlet.

The **pelvic brim** is a continuous oval ridge that extends from the pubic crest, pectineal line, and arcuate line to the rounded inferior edges of the sacral ala and promontory. This pelvic brim helps subdivide the entire pelvis into a true pelvis and a false pelvis **(figure 8.30)**. The **true pelvis** lies *inferior* to the pelvic brim. It encloses the pelvic cavity and forms a deep bowl that contains the pelvic organs. The **false pelvis** lies *superior* to the pelvic brim. It is enclosed by the alae of the ilia. It forms the inferior region of the abdominal cavity and houses the inferior abdominal organs.

The pelvis also has a superior and an inferior opening, and each has clinical significance. The **pelvic inlet,** also known as the *superior pelvic aperture,* is the superiorly positioned space enclosed by the pelvic brim. In other words, the pelvic brim is the bony oval *ridge* of bone, whereas the pelvic inlet is the *space* surrounded by the pelvic brim. The pelvic inlet is the opening at the boundary between the true pelvis and the false pelvis.

The **pelvic outlet,** also known as the *inferior pelvic aperture,* is the inferiorly placed opening bounded by the coccyx, the ischial tuberosities, and the inferior border of the symphysial surface. In males, the ischial spines commonly project into the pelvic outlet, thereby narrowing the diameter of this outlet. In contrast, female ischial spines less frequently project into the pelvic outlet (so the birth canal will not be obstructred by these bony prominences). The pelvic outlet is covered with muscles and skin, and it forms the body region called the **perineum** (per'i-nē'ŭm). The width and size of the pelvic outlet is especially important in females, because the opening must be wide enough to accommodate the fetal head during childbirth (see section 29.6).

💡 WHAT DID YOU LEARN?

28 How is the pelvic inlet distinguished from the pelvic outlet?

8.10c Sex Differences in the Pelvis

✓ LEARNING OBJECTIVE

6. Compare and contrast the anatomy of male and female pelves.

Although it is possible to determine the sex of a skeleton by examining the skull, the most reliable indicator of sex is the pelvis, primarily the ossa coxae. The ossa coxae are the most sexually dimorphic bones of the body due to the demands of pregnancy and childbirth in females. For example, the female pelvis is shallower and wider

(a) Pelvis, medial view

False pelvis

Sacral promontory

True pelvis

Coccyx

Pelvic inlet (space enclosed by pelvic brim)

Pelvic outlet

False pelvis   **True pelvis**

(b) Anterolateral views

Sacral promontory

Coccyx

Ischial spine

Pubic symphysis

Pelvic inlet (space enclosed by pelvic brim)

Pelvic outlet

Ischial spine

Pubic symphysis

Male   **Female**

(c) Pelvis, Anterosuperior views

Figure 8.30 Features of the Pelvis. The pelvic brim is the oval bony ridge that subdivides the pelvis into a true pelvis and a false pelvis. The pelvic inlet is the space enclosed by the pelvic brim, whereas the pelvic outlet is the inferior opening in the true pelvis. (*a*) Medial and (*b*) anterolateral views of the true and false pelves. (*c*) Anterosuperior view of male and female pelves, demonstrating the sex differences between the pelvic inlet and outlet.

than the pelvis of a male in order to accommodate the infant's head as it passes through the birth canal.

Some of these differences are obvious, such as that males have narrower hips than females do. But we can find many other differences by examining the shapes and orientations of the pelvic bones. For example, the female ilium flares more laterally, while the male ilium projects more superiorly, which is why males typically have narrower hips. Because the female pelvis is wider, the acetabulum projects more laterally, and the greater sciatic notch is much wider as well. In contrast, the male acetabulum projects more anteriorly, and the male greater sciatic notch is much narrower, deeper and U-shaped. Females tend to have a **preauricular sulcus,** which is a depression/groove between the greater sciatic notch and the sacroiliac articulation. Males tend not to have this sulcus. The sacrum tends to be shorter and wider in females.

The body of the pubis in females is much longer and almost rectangular in shape, compared to the shorter, triangular-shaped male pubic body. The **subpubic angle** (or *pubic arch*) is the angle formed when the left and right pubic bones are aligned at their symphysial surfaces. Since females have much longer pubic bones, the corresponding subpubic angle is much wider and more convex, usually much greater than 100 degrees. The male subpubic angle is much narrower and typically does not extend past 90 degrees.

Several significant differences between the female and male pelves are shown and listed in **table 8.6**.

INTEGRATE

CONCEPT CONNECTION

The skeletal system and female reproductive system (section 28.3) are linked by the fact that the shape of the bony pelvis has a direct relation on whether a female will have a difficult labor and delivery.

Table 8.6	Sex Differences Between the Female and Male Pelvis	
View	**Female**	**Male**
Medial View	Wider and more flared ilium; Preauricular sulcus; Wide greater sciatic notch	Narrower and more vertical ilium; Narrow greater sciatic notch
Anterior View	Wider and more flared ilia; Rectangular pubic body; Triangular obturator foramen; Wide subpubic angle	Narrower and more vertical ilia; Triangular pubic body; Large, oval obturator foramen; Narrow subpubic angle
Feature	**Female Characteristic**	**Male Characteristic**
General appearance	Less massive; gracile processes, less prominent muscle markings	More massive; more robust processes, more muscle markings
General width	Ilia are wider, more flared	Ilia are narrower and more vertically oriented, less flared
Pelvic inlet	Spacious, wide and oval	Heart shaped
Greater sciatic notch	Wide and shallow	Narrow and U-shaped, deep
Obturator foramen	Smaller and triangular	Larger and oval
Subpubic angle	Broader, more convex, usually greater than 100 degrees	Narrow, V-shaped, usually less than 90 degrees
Body of pubis	Longer, more rectangular	Short, triangular
Preauricular sulcus	Usually present	Usually absent
Sacrum	Shorter and wider; flatter sacral curvature	Narrower and longer; more curved (greater sacral curvature)
Ischial Spine	Rarely projects into pelvic outlet	Frequently rotated inward, projects into pelvic outlet

29 How do male and female pelves differ with respect to the shape of the pubis, subpubic angle, greater sciatic notch, and overall shape of the pelvis?

8.10d Age Differences in the Ossa Coxae

LEARNING OBJECTIVE

7. Describe changes to the ossa coxae as a person ages.

The ossa coxae are an excellent indicator of both sex and age, and they also can provide a reliable estimate of age at death. These estimates are given in age ranges (as opposed to precise numbers) because some variation may occur in how an os coxae exhibits the age-related changes.

Osteologists have noted age-related changes to the auricular surface of the ilium. The auricular surface of a young adult typically has some billowing texture to it (e.g., appears to have "hills and valleys"), and the surface is fine-grained. As the auricular surface ages, the billowing flattens out and the surface becomes more coarse and granular. In much older individuals, the surface may develop some bony lipping (evidence of osteoarthritic changes) and the surface becomes even more rough and irregular.

Osteologists also have documented that the symphysial surface of the pubis undergoes uniform, age-related changes as well. In fact, the symphysial surface has become one of the most reliable indicators for estimating age at death. In a young adult (age range from 15–24), the symphysial surface is billowed, and no well-formed rim is found around the surface. As the person ages, this billowing becomes more flattened, and a bony rim begins to form around the circumference of the symphysial surface. This rim is completed about ages 35–50 for most individuals. Once the rim is complete, the symphysial surface becomes depressed and concave and may become pitted in much older individuals. The rim or border may start to break down, and bony lipping (arthritis) develops along the edges of the symphysial surface. These last stages typically occur after age 50.

 WHAT DID YOU LEARN?

30 What are some differences in the symphysial surface between a young adult and an older (50-plus) adult?

8.11 Bones of the Lower Limb

The lower limb comprises the thigh, leg, and foot. The structure of the foot enables it to support the body during bipedal walking and running.

The arrangement and numbers of bones in the lower limb are similar to those of the upper limb. Each lower limb contains a total of 30 bones:

- 1 femur, located in the femoral region
- 1 patella (kneecap), located in the patellar region
- 1 tibia and 1 fibula, located in the crural region
- 7 tarsal bones, which form the bones of the ankle and proximal foot
- 5 metatarsal bones, which form the arched part of the foot
- 14 phalanges, which form the toes

8.11a Femur and Patella

LEARNING OBJECTIVES

1. Describe the articulations of the femur.

2. Identify key landmarks and features of the femur.

3. Describe the location and function of the patella.

The **femur** (fē′mŭr; thigh) is the longest bone in the body as well as the strongest and heaviest (**figure 8.31**). The nearly spherical **head** of the femur articulates with the os coxae at

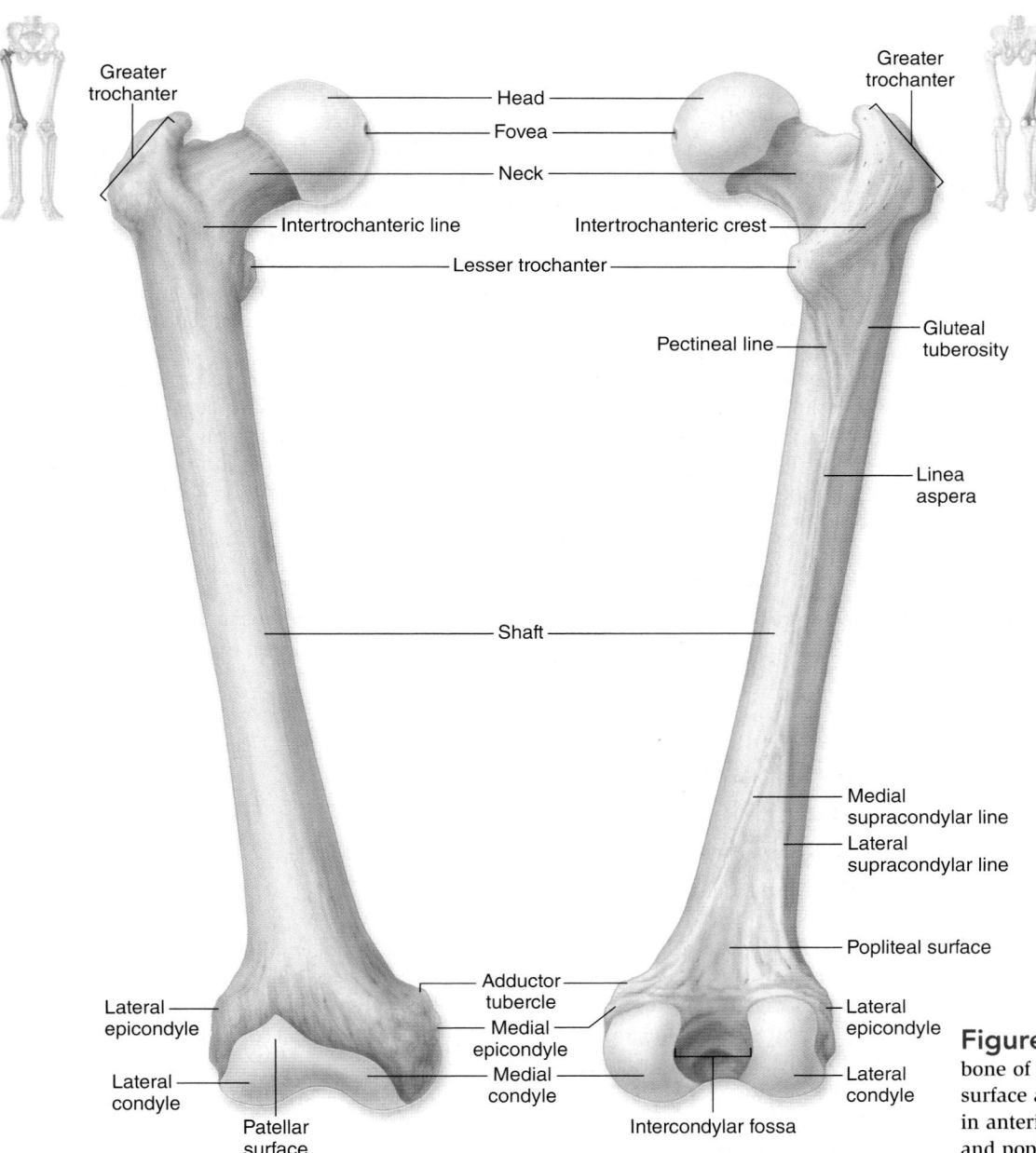

Greater trochanter — Head — Greater trochanter

Fovea

Neck

Intertrochanteric line — Intertrochanteric crest

Lesser trochanter

Pectineal line — Gluteal tuberosity

Linea aspera

Shaft

Medial supracondylar line
Lateral supracondylar line

Popliteal surface

Lateral epicondyle — Adductor tubercle — Lateral epicondyle

Medial epicondyle

Lateral condyle — Medial condyle — Lateral condyle

Patellar surface

Intercondylar fossa

(a) Right femur, anterior view   **(b) Right femur, posterior view**

Figure 8.31 Femur. The femur is the bone of the femoral region. (*a*) The patellar surface and intertrochanteric line are best seen in anterior view, while (*b*) the lesser trochanter and popliteal surface are best seen in posterior view. **AP|R**

the acetabulum. There is a tiny depression within the head of the femur, called the **fovea** (fō'vē-ă; a pit), or *fovea capitis* (kăp'i-tĭs). Here a tiny ligament connects the head of the femur to the acetabulum. Distal to the head, an elongated, constricted **neck** joins the **shaft** of the femur at an angle. This results in a medial angling of the femur, which brings the knees closer to the midline.

The **greater trochanter** (trō-kan'ter; a runner) projects laterally from the junction of the neck and shaft. A **lesser trochanter** is located on the femur's posteromedial surface. These are rough processes that serve as insertion sites for powerful gluteal and thigh muscles. The greater and lesser trochanters are connected on the posterior surface of the femur by a thick oblique ridge of bone called the **intertrochanteric** (in'ter-trō-kan-tār'ik) **crest.** Anteriorly, a raised **intertrochanteric line** travels between the two trochanters and marks the distal edge of the hip joint capsule. Inferior to the intertrochanteric crest, the **pectineal line** marks the attachment of the pectineus muscle; the **gluteal tuberosity** marks the attachment of the gluteus maximus muscle (see section 11.9a).

The gluteal tuberosity and pectineal line merge into an elevated, midline ridge called the **linea aspera** (lin'ē-ă ass'pĕ-ră), where many thigh muscles attach. Distally, the linea aspera branches into **medial** and **lateral supracondylar lines.** A flattened triangular area, called

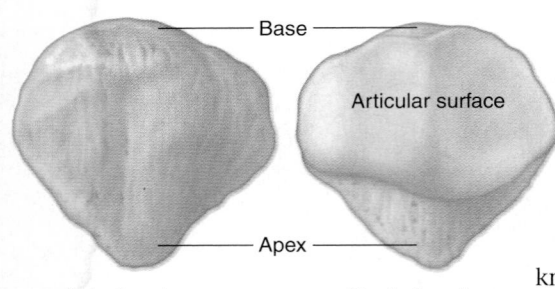

Base
Articular surface
Apex

Anterior view   Posterior view

Figure 8.32 Patella. The patella is a sesamoid bone located within the tendon of the quadriceps femoris muscle. These views show the right patella. **AP|R**

the **popliteal** (pop-lit′ē-ăl; *poples* = ham of knee) **surface,** is bordered by these ridges. The medial supracondylar ridge terminates in the **adductor tubercle.** This is a rough, raised projection that is the site of attachment for the adductor magnus muscle (see section 11.9).

On the distal, inferior surface of the femur there are two smooth, oval articulating surfaces called the **medial** and **lateral condyles.** Superior to each condyle are projections called the **medial epicondyle** and **lateral epicondyle,** respectively. When you flex your knee, you can palpate these epicondyles in the thigh on the sides of your knee joint. The medial and lateral supracondylar lines terminate at these epicondyles. On the distal posterior surface of the femur, a deep **intercondylar fossa** separates the two condyles. A smooth medial depression on the anterior surface, called the **patellar surface,** is the place where the patella articulates with the femur.

The **patella** (pa-tel′ă; *patina* = shallow disk), or *kneecap,* is a large, roughly triangular sesamoid bone housed within the tendon of the quadriceps femoris muscle **(figure 8.32).** The patella allows the tendon to glide more smoothly, and it protects the knee joint. The superior **base** of the patella is broad, while its inferior **apex** is pointed. The posterior aspect of the patella has an **articular surface** that articulates with the patellar surface of the femur.

WHAT DID YOU LEARN?

31 What are the locations and functions of the greater and lesser trochanter?

32 Where does the patella articulate with the femur?

8.11b Tibia and Fibula

LEARNING OBJECTIVES

4. Describe the features of the tibia and fibula.

5. Explain how the function of the tibia differs from that of the fibula.

6. Describe how the tibia and fibula articulate.

The skeleton of the leg (crural region) has two parallel bones, the thick, strong tibia and a slender fibula **(figure 8.33).** Like the radius and ulna, these two bones are connected by an interosseous membrane that extends between their **interosseous borders.** The interosseous membrane stabilizes the relative positions of the tibia and fibula, and additionally provides a pivot of minimal rotation for the two bones.

The **tibia** (tib′ē-ă; large shinbone) is the medially placed bone and the only weight-bearing bone of the crural region. Its broad, superior head has two relatively flat surfaces, the **medial** and **lateral condyles,** which articulate with the medial and lateral condyles of the femur, respectively. Separating the condyles of the tibia is a prominent ridge called the **intercondylar eminence** (em′i-nens). On the proximal posterolateral side of the tibia is a **fibular articular surface,** where the head of the fibula articulates to form the **superior** (or *proximal*) **tibiofibular joint.**

The rough anterior surface of the tibia near the proximal condyles is the **tibial tuberosity,** which can be palpated just inferior to the patella and marks the attachment site for the patellar ligament. The **anterior border** (or *margin*), often referred to as the *shin,* is a prominent ridge that extends distally along the anterior tibial surface from the tibial tuberosity.

The tibia narrows distally, but at its medial border it forms a large, prominent process called the **medial malleolus** (ma-lē′ō-lŭs; *malleus* = hammer). Palpate the medial side of your ankle; the bump you feel is your medial malleolus. There is a **fibular notch** on the distal posterolateral side of the tibia where the fibula articulates and forms the **inferior** (or *distal*) **tibiofibular joint.** On the inferior distal surface of the tibia is the smooth **inferior articular surface** for the talus, one of the tarsal bones.

The **fibula** (fib′ū-lă; buckle, clasp) is the long, thin, laterally placed bone of the leg. The fibula does not bear any weight, but several muscles originate from it. The rounded, knoblike **head** of the fibula is slightly inferior and posterior to the lateral condyle of the tibia. Distal to the fibular head is the **neck** of the fibula, followed by its **shaft.** The fibula's distal tip, called the **lateral malleolus,** extends laterally to the ankle joint, where it provides lateral stability. Palpate the lateral side of your ankle; the bump you feel is your lateral malleolus.

Figure 8.33 Tibia and Fibula. The tibia and fibula are the bones of the crural (leg) region. Diagram and photo show the right tibia and fibula in (a) an anterior view and (b) a posterior view. APR

🌿 **WHAT DO YOU THINK?**

⑤ The medial and lateral malleoli of the leg are similar to what bony features of the forearm?

💡 **WHAT DID YOU LEARN?**

㉝ What are some bony features shared by the tibia and fibula?

㉞ What is the primary function of the tibia?

CLINICAL VIEW
Pathologies of the Foot

A **bunion** (bŭn′yŭn; *buigne* = bump) is a localized swelling at the first meta-tarsophalangeal joint. This bump causes that toe to point toward the second toe instead of in a purely anterior direction. Bunions are usually caused by wearing shoes that fit too tightly, and are among the most common foot problems.

Pes cavus (pes că′vus), or *clawfoot*, is characterized by excessively high longitudinal arches. The joints between the metatarsals and proximal phalanges are often overly extended, and the joints between the different phalanges are bent so that they appear clawed.

Talipes equinovarus (tal′i-pēz ē-kwī-nō-vā′rŭs) is usually referred to as *congenital clubfoot*. This foot deformity typically occurs when there isn't enough room in the womb. In this condition, the feet are permanently inverted (the soles of the feet are twisted medially), and the ankles are plantar flexed (the soles of the feet are twisted more posteriorly), as if the patient were trying to stand on tiptoe.

Pes planus (pla′nus), commonly known as *flat feet*, is where the medial longitudinal arch is flattened so that the entire sole touches the ground. Pes planus is often caused by excessive weight, postural abnormalities, or weakened supporting tissue. Individuals who spend most of their day standing may have slightly fallen arches by the end of the day, but with proper rest their arches can return to normal shape.

A **metatarsal stress fracture** usually results when repetitive pressure or stress on the foot causes a small crack to develop in the outer surface of the bone. Runners are especially prone to this injury because they put repetitive stress on their feet.

Bunion

Pes cavus

Talipes equinovarus (congenital clubfoot)

Pes planus

Metatarsal stress fractures

8.11c Tarsals, Metatarsals, and Phalanges

LEARNING OBJECTIVES

7. Locate and identify the tarsals and metatarsals.
8. Describe the phalanges and their relative locations.

The bones that form the ankle and foot are the tarsals, metatarsals, and phalanges **(figure 8.34)**. The seven **tarsals** (tar′săl; *tarsus* = flat surface) of the ankle and proximal foot are similar to the eight carpal bones of the wrist in some respects, although their shapes and arrangement are different from those of their carpal bone counterparts.

The talus, calcaneus, and navicular bone are considered the *proximal row* of tarsal bones. The superiormost and second largest tarsal bone is the **talus** (tă′lŭs; ankle bone), which articulates with the tibia. The **calcaneus** (kal-kā′nē-ŭs) is the largest tarsal bone and forms the heel. Its posterior end is a rough, knob-shaped projection that is the point of attachment for the calcaneal (Achilles) tendon extending from the strong posterior leg muscles (see section 11.9c). The **navicular** (nă-vik′ū-lăr; *navis* = ship) **bone** is on the medial side of the ankle.

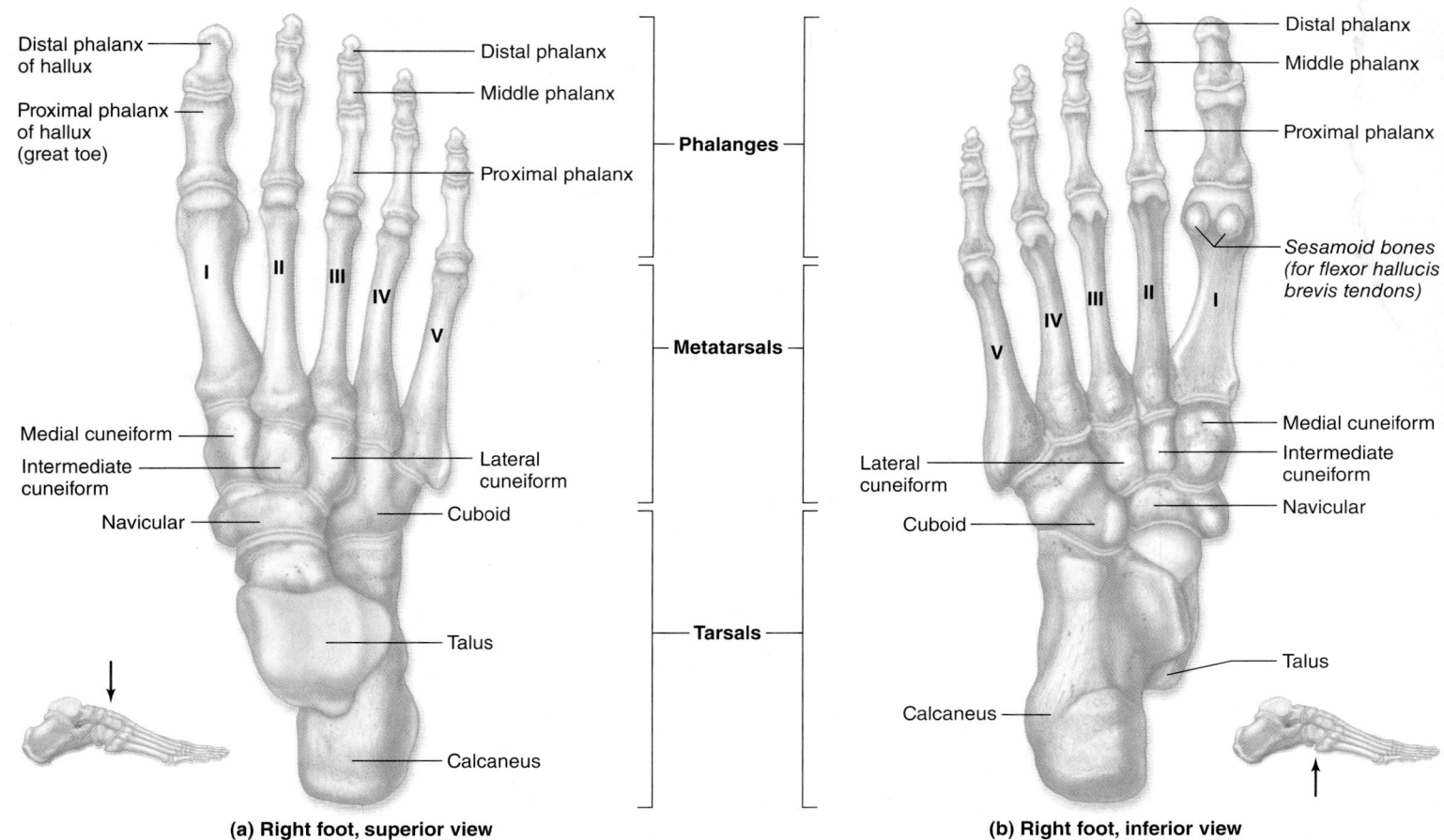

Figure 8.34 Bones of the Tarsals, Metatarsals, and Phalanges. Tarsal bones form the ankle and proximal foot, metatarsals form the arched sole of the foot, and phalanges form the toes. Diagrams show (*a*) superior and (*b*) inferior views of the right foot. **AP|R**

The *distal row* of four tarsal bones includes the cuneiforms and the cuboid bone. The **medial cuneiform** (kū'nē-i-fōrm; *cuneus* = wedge), **intermediate cuneiform,** and **lateral cuneiform bones** are wedge-shaped bones that articulate with and are positioned anterior to the navicular bone. The laterally placed **cuboid** (kū'boyd; *kybos* = cube) **bone** articulates at its medial surface with the lateral cuneiform and at its posterior surface with the calcaneus.

The **metatarsals** (met'ă-tar'săl) of the foot are five long bones similar in arrangement and name to the metacarpal bones of the hand. They form the arched sole of the foot and are identified with Roman numerals I–V, proceeding medially to laterally. The metatarsals articulate proximally either with the cuneiform bones or the cuboid bone. Distally, each metatarsal bone articulates with a proximal phalanx. At the head of the first metatarsal are two tiny sesamoid bones, which insert on the tendons of the flexor hallucis brevis muscle and help these tendons move more freely (see section 11.9d).

The bones of the toes (like the bones of the fingers and thumb) are called **phalanges.** The toes contain a total of 14 phalanges. The great toe is the **hallux** (hal'ŭks; *hallex* = great toe), and it has only two phalanges (proximal and distal); each of the other four toes has three phalanges (proximal, middle, and distal).

WHAT DID YOU LEARN?

35 What are the seven tarsal bones?

8.11d Arches of the Foot

LEARNING OBJECTIVE

9. Describe the three arches of the foot and their functions.

Normally, the sole of the foot is arched, which helps it support the weight of the body and ensures that the blood vessels and nerves on the sole of the foot are not pinched when we are standing. The three arches of the foot are the medial longitudinal, lateral longitudinal, and transverse arches (figure 8.35).

The **medial longitudinal arch** (*arcus* = bow) is the highest of the three arches and extends from the heel to the great toe. It is formed from the calcaneus, talus, navicular, and cuneiform bones, and metatarsals I–III. The medial longitudinal arch prevents the medial side of the foot from touching the ground and gives our footprint its characteristic shape (see figure 8.35d).

The **lateral longitudinal arch** is not as high as the medial arch, so the lateral part of the foot *does* contribute to a footprint. This arch extends between the little toe and the heel, and it is formed from the calcaneus and cuboid bones, and metatarsals IV and V.

The **transverse arch** runs perpendicular to the longitudinal arches. It is formed from the distal row of tarsals and the bases of all five metatarsals.

The shape of the foot arches is maintained primarily by the foot bones themselves. These bones are shaped so that they can interlock and support their weight in an arch, much like the wedge-shaped blocks of an arched bridge can support the bridge without other mechanical supports. Secondarily, strong ligaments that attach to the bones and contracting muscles pull on the tendons, thereby helping to maintain the arches' shapes.

WHAT DID YOU LEARN?

36 Why is it preferable to have an arched (versus a flat) foot?

(a) **Right foot, medial view**

(b) **Right foot, lateral view**

(c) **Right foot, distal row of tarsals and metatarsals**

(d) **Footprint of right foot**

Figure 8.35 Arches of the Foot. The foot's two longitudinal arches and one transverse arch allow for better weight support. (*a*) Medial longitudinal arch. (*b*) Lateral longitudinal arch. (*c*) Transverse arch as seen in cross-sectional view. (*d*) A footprint illustrates the placement of the longitudinal arches.

8.12 Development of the Skeleton

LEARNING OBJECTIVES

1. Describe how the limb buds form.

2. Compare and contrast upper and lower limb bud development.

As mentioned in section 7.4, bone forms by either intramembranous ossification or endochondral ossification. Many of the bones of the skull are formed from intramembranous ossification, while almost all of the remaining bones of the skeleton form through endochondral ossification. (The exception is the clavicle, which is formed from a central membranous ossification center; its ends are formed from endochondral ossification centers.)

The appendicular skeleton begins to develop during the fourth week, when **limb buds** appear as small ridges along the lateral sides of the embryo. The upper limb buds appear early in the fourth week (approximately day 26), while the lower limb buds appear a few days later (day 28) **(figure 8.36)**. Lower limb development lags behind upper limb development by about 2 to 4 days. The upper and lower limbs form proximodistally, meaning that the more proximal parts of the limbs form first (in weeks 4–5), while the more distal parts differentiate later.

Early limb buds are composed of lateral plate mesoderm and covered by a layer of ectoderm. The musculature of the limbs forms from somitic mesoderm that migrates to the developing limbs during the fifth week of development.

At the apex of each limb bud, part of the ectoderm forms an elevated thickening called the **apical ectodermal** (ek-tō-der′măl) **ridge.** By mechanisms not completely understood, this ridge "signals" the underlying tissue to form the various components of the limb.

Initially, the limb buds are cylindrical. The distal portion of the upper limb bud forms a rounded, paddle-shaped **hand plate** by the early fifth week. It later becomes both the palm and fingers. In the lower limb bud, a corresponding **foot plate** forms during the sixth week. These plates develop longitudinal thickenings called **digital rays,** which eventually form the digits. The digital rays in the hand plate appear in the late sixth week, and the foot digital rays appear during the early seventh week. The digital rays initially are connected by intermediately placed tissue, which later undergoes programmed cell death (apoptosis; see section 4.9). Thus, as this intermediate tissue dies, notching occurs between the digital rays, and separate digits are formed. This process occurs in the seventh week and is complete by the eighth week for both the fingers and the toes.

WHAT DID YOU LEARN?

37 How does a rounded hand plate (or foot plate) evolve into separate fingers (or toes)?

Figure 8.36 Development of the Appendicular Skeleton. The upper and lower limbs develop between weeks 4 and 8. Upper limb development precedes corresponding lower limb development by 2 to 4 days.

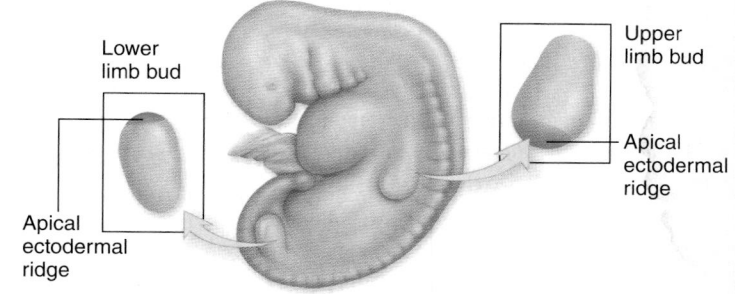

Week 4: Upper and lower limb buds form.

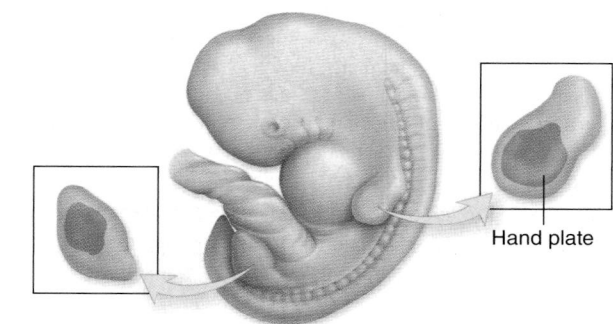

Week 5: Hand plate forms.

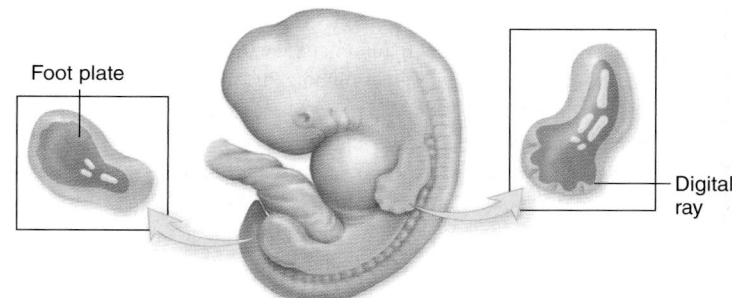

Week 6: Digital rays appear in hand plate. Foot plate forms.

Week 7: Notching develops between digital rays of hand plate. Digital rays appear in foot plate.

Week 8: Separate fingers and toes formed.

CLINICAL VIEW
Limb Malformations

Limb and finger malformations may occur due to genetic or environmental influences. Some limb and finger malformations include the following:

- **Polydactyly** (pol-ĕ-dak'ti-lē; *poly* = many; *daktylos* = finger) is the condition of having extra digits. Polydactyly tends to run in families and appears to have a genetic component.

- **Ectrodactyly** (ek-trō-dak'ti-lē; *ectro* = congenital absence of a part) is the absence of a digit. Like polydactyly, ectrodactyly runs in families.

- **Syndactyly** (sin-dak'ti-lē; *syn* = together) refers to "webbing" or abnormal fusion of the digits. It occurs when the intermediate tissue between the digital rays fails to undergo normal programmed cell death. In mild cases, some extra tissue is found between the digits, while more severe cases may have two or more digits that are completely fused.

- **Amelia** (ă-mē'lē-ă; *a* = without; *melos* = a limb) refers to the complete absence of a limb, whereas **meromelia** (mer-ō-mē'lē-ă; *mero* = part) refers to the partial absence of a limb.

- **Phocomelia** (fō-kō-mē'lē-ă; *phoke* = a seal) refers to a short, poorly formed limb that resembles the flipper of a seal.

All of these conditions may be caused by genetic factors, but most often they result from environmental influences, such as medications or drugs ingested by the pregnant mother. A notable instance of limb malformation involved the drug **thalidomide,** which was first marketed in Europe in 1954 as a nonbarbiturate sleep aid. Physicians later discovered that the drug also helped quell nausea, and so some prescribed it for their pregnant patients who were experiencing morning sickness.

In the late 1950s and early 1960s, the incidence of limb malformations in Europe and Canada skyrocketed (thalidomide was not approved for use in the United States). Researchers later found that thalidomide binds to particular regions of chromosomal DNA, effectively "locking up" specific genes and preventing their expression. Among the genes most affected in the fetus were those responsible for blood vessel growth. In the absence of an adequate vascular network, limb bud formation is disrupted. Researchers and clinicians discovered that if a pregnant female took thalidomide during weeks 4–8 of embryonic development (the time when the limbs are at their critical stage of development), limb formation was severely disrupted.

Thalidomide was taken off the market in the 1960s, but recently it has made a comeback because it has been shown to be an excellent anti-inflammatory agent, and has proved especially effective in reducing the more devastating effects of leprosy. Thalidomide also is being used as a treatment of multiple myeloma (a type of cancer of bone marrow cells), treating the symptoms of AIDS, and treating lupus (an autoimmune disease). Thalidomide is the classic example of how teratogens can affect the delicate cycle of embryonic development, and why females of childbearing age should be sure they aren't pregnant before taking any medication.

Shortened flipperlike upper limb

Radiograph of a child with phocomelia.

CHAPTER SUMMARY

8.1 Components of the Skeleton 239	• The adult skeleton is typically composed of 206 bones; skeletal features can be used to determine height, age at death, sex, and general health.
	8.1a Bone Markings 239
	• Specific anatomic terms are used to describe various features on bones.
	8.1b Axial and Appendicular Skeleton 241
	• The axial skeleton includes the skull, vertebral column, and thoracic cage.
	• The appendicular skeleton includes the pectoral and pelvic girdles, the bones of the upper limb, and the bones of the lower limb.
8.2 Bones and Features of the Skull 241	**8.2a General Anatomy of the Skull** 241
	• Cranial bones enclose the cranial cavity; facial bones support the entrances to the digestive and respiratory systems.
	8.2b Views of the Skull and Landmark Features 242
	• Specific bones, foramina, processes, and bone landmarks of the skull are seen in multiple views of the skull.
	• The cranial bones include the frontal bone, paired parietal bones, occipital bone, paired temporal bones, sphenoid bone, and ethmoid bone.
	• The facial bones include the paired zygomatic bones, lacrimal bones, nasal bones, inferior nasal conchae, palatine bones, maxillae, a single vomer bone, and a single mandible.
	• The anterior, middle, and posterior cranial fossae are located within the cranial cavity and house specific regions of the brain.

(continued on next page)

8.10 The Pelvic Girdle and Its Functions 279	• The pelvic girdle consists of two ossa coxae, while the pelvis is composed of the ossa coxae, sacrum, and the coccyx.
	8.10a Os Coxae 280
	• Each os coxae forms through the fusion of an ilium, an ischium, and a pubis. The acetabulum of the os coxae articulates with the head of the femur.
	8.10b True and False Pelves 282
	• The pelvic brim is an oval ridge of bone that divides the pelvis into a true pelvis and a false pelvis.
	8.10c Sex Differences in the Pelvis 282
	• The ossa coxae are the most sexually dimorphic bones of the body.
	• The female pelvis is wider, has a broader greater sciatic notch, and a more rectangular-shaped pubis than the male pelvis.
	8.10d Age Differences in the Ossa Coxae 284
	• As a person ages, the symphysial surface transforms from a billowed surface to more oval and flattened.
8.11 Bones of the Lower Limb 284	• Each lower limb is composed of the femur, patella, tibia, fibula, 7 tarsals, 5 metatarsals, and 14 phalanges.
	8.11a Femur and Patella 284
	• The femur has a rounded head and an elongated neck.
	• The medial and lateral condyles of the femur articulate with the condyles on the tibia.
	• The patella is the kneecap and inserts within the quadriceps femoris tendon.
	8.11b Tibia and Fibula 286
	• The tibia is the medially located thick and strong bone of the leg, and its medial malleolus forms the medial bump of the ankle.
	• The fibula is the laterally located slender bone, and its lateral malleolus forms the lateral bump of the ankle.
	8.11c Tarsals, Metatarsals, and Phalanges 288
	• The tarsal bones form the proximal foot, the 5 metatarsals form the bones of the arch of the foot, and the 14 phalanges form the bones of the toes.
	8.11d Arches of the Foot 289
	• The three arches of the foot support the body's weight and ensure plantar structures do not get compressed when we are standing.
8.12 Development of the Skeleton 291	• The appendicular skeleton forms from limb buds beginning in the fourth week. Development of the limbs is mostly complete by week 8.

CHALLENGE YOURSELF

Do You Know the Basics?

____ 1. The bony portion of the nasal septum is formed by the
   a. perpendicular plate of the ethmoid bone and vomer.
   b. perpendicular plate of the ethmoid bone only.
   c. nasal bones and perpendicular plate of the ethmoid bone.
   d. vomer and sphenoid bones.

____ 2. The mandible articulates with the _____ bone(s).
   a. occipital
   b. frontal
   c. temporal
   d. parietal

____ 3. The frontal and parietal bones articulate at the _____ suture.
   a. coronal
   b. sagittal
   c. lambdoid
   d. squamosal

____ 4. The compression of an infant's skull bones at birth is facilitated by spaces between unfused cranial bones called
   a. ossification centers.
   b. fontanelles.
   c. foramina.
   d. fossae.

____ 5. Most _____ vertebrae have a heart-shaped body and a long spinous process that is angled inferiorly.
   a. cervical
   b. thoracic
   c. lumbar
   d. sacral

____ 6. The female pelvis typically has which of the following characteristics?
   a. narrow, U-shaped greater sciatic notch
   b. wide subpubic angle, greater than 100 degrees
   c. short, triangular pubic body
   d. smaller, heart-shaped pelvic inlet

_____ 7. The posterior surface depression at the distal end of the humerus is the

    a. intercondylar fossa.

    b. coronoid fossa.

    c. glenoid fossa.

    d. olecranon fossa.

_____ 8. The spine of the scapula separates which two fossae?

    a. supraspinous, subscapular

    b. subscapular, infraspinous

    c. infraspinous, supraspinous

    d. supraspinous, glenoid

_____ 9. The femur articulates with the tibia at the

    a. linea aspera.

    b. medial and lateral condyles.

    c. head of the femur.

    d. greater trochanter of the femur.

_____ 10. When sitting upright, you are resting on your

    a. pubic bones.

    b. ischial tuberosities.

    c. sacroiliac joints.

    d. iliac crest.

11. What are sutures, and how do they affect skull shape and growth?

12. List the seven bones that form the orbit and discuss their arrangement.

13. What are the functions of the paranasal sinuses?

14. Identify the first two cervical vertebrae, and describe the unique functions these vertebrae perform in spinal mobility.

15. Describe similarities and differences among true, false, and floating ribs.

16. Compare the anatomic and functional features of the pectoral and pelvic girdles.

17. What is the difference between the anatomical neck and the surgical neck of the humerus?

18. Distinguish between the true and false pelves. What bony landmark separates the two?

19. Discuss the functions of the arches of the foot.

20. Discuss the development of the limbs. What primary germ layers form the limb bud? List the major events during each week of limb development.

Can You Apply What You've Learned?

Use the following paragraph to answer questions 1–5.

You are called to a crime scene reported in the woods. A hiker found a skeleton underneath some leaves—and as the osteologist of the team, it is up to you to identify the bones, as well as determine the age and sex of the skeleton. You begin examining the skeleton.

1. The first bone you identify is long and rather large. It has a rounded head, an elongated neck, and smooth condyles on its distal surface. There also are large bony projections near the neck of this bone. Based on these features, you determine that the bone in question is a

    a. humerus.

    b. radius.

    c. femur.

    d. tibia.

2. As you examine the rest of the skeleton, you notice an S-shaped bone that appears to have been fractured prior to death. This bone likely was fractured due to a fall on the outstretched hand. What bone is it?

    a. clavicle

    b. metacarpal

    c. rib

    d. phalanx

3. You pick up the skull and begin examining it. The mastoid process is rather small, and the external occipital protuberance is not well defined. The orbital rims are rather sharp, and the mental protuberance is pointed (instead of squared-off). All of these features lead you to the following conclusion:

    a. The skeleton has been buried for a long time.

    b. The skull is from a female.

    c. The skull is from a male.

    d. The skull is from a young child.

4. Based on the answer you gave to question 3, what feature(s) would you expect to see in the pelvis?

    a. narrow pelvic inlet

    b. elongated, rectangular pubic bones

    c. narrow, U-shaped sciatic notch

    d. 90-degree subpubic arch

    e. You would expect to see all of these features.

5. The police officers also want to know if you can determine the age at death of the skeleton. You determine that all long bone epiphyses have fused to their diaphyses, and all permanent teeth are erupted. The cranial sutures are still open, and the symphysial surface is flattened, but there is no complete rim around the symphysis. Based on these features, a likely age range for the skeleton would be

    a. younger than 10 years.

    b. 10–20 years.

    c. 20–35 years.

    d. 35–50 years.

    e. older than 50 years.

Can You Synthesize What You've Learned?

1. Paul viewed his newborn daughter through the nursery window at the hospital and was distressed because the infant's skull was badly misshapen. A nurse told him not to worry—the shape of the infant's head would return to normal in a few days. What caused the misshapen skull, and what anatomic feature of the neonatal skull allows it to return to a more rounded shape?

2. A female in her first trimester of pregnancy sees her physician. She suffers from lupus and has read that the drug thalidomide has shown remarkable promise in treating the symptoms. Should the physician prescribe this drug for her at this time? Why or why not?

3. Forensic anthropologists are investigating portions of a human pelvis found in a cave. How can they tell the sex, relative age, and some physical characteristics of the individual based on the pelvis only?

INTEGRATE

ONLINE STUDY TOOLS
www.mhhe.com/mckinleyap

Clinical Case Study: A Historical Case of Spinal Involvement with Tuberculosis

Interactive Questions: This chapter's content is served up in a number of multimedia question formats for student study.

LearnSmart: Topics and terminology include skull bones and features; sex and age determination from skull analysis; bones of the vertebral column; bones of the thoracic cage; upper and lower limbs; pectoral girdle; pelvic girdle; development of the skeleton

Anatomy & Physiology Revealed: Topics include skull and skull bones; vertebral column; thoracic, cervical, and lumbar vertebrae; sacrum; thoracic cage; bones of the arm and hand; bones of the pelvis; bones of the leg, ankle, and foot

Animation: The skull

chapter 9

Skeletal System: Articulations

A sports medicine physician can diagnose musculoskeletal injuries, especially those involving the articulations (joints) we discuss in this chapter. This physician must be aware of the normal range of movement at each joint, the muscular and ligamentous structures that support the joint, and how injury may impact mobility and ultimate healing of the joint. Here, a sports medicine physician is examining and taping a soccer player's ankle after an injury on the field.

Our skeleton protects vital organs and supports soft tissues. Its marrow cavity is the source of new blood cells. When it interacts with the muscular system, the skeleton helps the body move. Bones are too rigid to bend—but they meet at joints that anatomists call articulations. In this chapter, we examine how bones articulate and permit some freedom of movement, depending on both the shapes and supporting structures of the different joints.

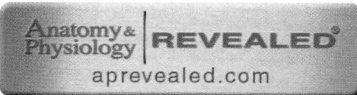

Anatomy & Physiology | REVEALED®
aprevealed.com

Module 5: Skeletal System

9.1 Classification of Joints

1. Define a joint.
2. Compare the structural and the functional classification of joints.
3. Explain the inverse relationship between mobility and stability within a joint.

A **joint,** or **articulation** (ar-tik-ū-lā′shŭn), is the place of contact between bones, between bone and cartilage, or between bones and teeth. Bones are said to **articulate** with each other at a joint. The scientific study of joints is called **arthrology** (ar-throl′ō-jē; *arthron* = joint; *logos* = study).

Joints are classified by both their structural characteristics and the movements they allow **(table 9.1)**. Joints are categorized structurally on the basis of the type of connective tissue that binds the articulating surfaces of the bones and whether a space occurs between the articulating bones:

- A **fibrous** (fī′brŭs) **joint** has no joint cavity and occurs where bones are held together by dense regular (fibrous) connective tissue.
- A **cartilaginous** (kar-ti-laj′i-nŭs) **joint** has no joint cavity and occurs where bones are joined by cartilage.
- A **synovial** (si-nō′vē-ăl) **joint** has a fluid-filled joint cavity that separates the articulating surfaces of the bones. The

articulating surfaces are enclosed within a connective tissue capsule, and the bones are attached to each other by various ligaments.

Joints are classified functionally based on the extent of movement they permit.

- A **synarthrosis** (sin′ar-thrō′sis; pl., *synarthroses,* sin′ar-thrō′sēz; *syn* = joined, together) is an immobile joint. Two types of fibrous joints and one type of cartilaginous joint are synarthroses.
- An **amphiarthrosis** (am′fi-ar-thrō′sis; pl., *amphiarthroses,* am′fi-ar-thrō′sēz; *amphi* = around) is a slightly mobile joint. One type of fibrous joint and one type of cartilaginous joint are amphiarthroses.
- A **diarthrosis** (dī-ar-thrō′sis; pl., *diarthroses,* dī-ar-thrō′sēz; *di* = two) is a freely mobile joint. All synovial joints are diarthroses.

The motion permitted at a joint ranges from no movement, such as where some skull bones interlock at a suture, to extensive movement like that seen at the shoulder, where the humerus articulates with the scapula. The structure of each joint determines both its mobility and its stability. There is an inverse relationship between mobility and stability in articulations. When the mobility of a joint increases, its stability decreases. In contrast, if a joint is immobile, it has maximum stability. **Figure 9.1** illustrates the "tradeoff" between mobility and stability for various joints. It allows you to view and compare the structural versus functional classification of some common joints.

Table 9.1	Joint Classifications				
Structural Classification	**Structural Characteristics**	**Structural Categories**		**Example(s)**	**Functional Classification**
Fibrous (see figure 9.2)	Dense regular connective tissue holds together the ends of bones and bone parts; no joint cavity	**Gomphosis:** Periodontal membranes hold tooth to bony jaw		Tooth to jaw	Synarthrosis (immobile)
		Suture: Dense regular connective tissue connects skull bones		Lambdoid suture (connects occipital and parietal bones)	Synarthrosis (immobile)
		Syndesmosis: Dense regular connective tissue fibers (interosseous membrane) between bones		Articulation between radius and ulna, and between tibia and fibula	Amphiarthrosis (slightly mobile)
Cartilaginous (see figure 9.3)	Pad of cartilage is wedged between the ends of bones; no joint cavity	**Synchondrosis:** Hyaline cartilage between bones		Epiphyseal plates in growing bones; costochondral joints	Synarthrosis (immobile)
		Symphysis: Fibrocartilage pad between bones		Pubic symphysis; intervertebral disc articulations	Amphiarthrosis (slightly mobile)
Synovial (see figure 9.6)	Ends of bones covered with articular cartilage; joint cavity separates the articulating bones; joint enclosed by an articular capsule, lined by a synovial membrane; contains synovial fluid	*Uniaxial* **Plane joint:** Flattened or slightly curved faces slide across one another **Hinge joint:** Convex feature of one bone fits into concave depression of another bone **Pivot joint:** Bone with a rounded surface fits into a ring formed by a ligament and another bone		**Plane joint:** Intercarpal joints, intertarsal joints **Hinge joint:** Elbow joint, knee joint, IP (interphalangeal) joints **Pivot joint:** Atlantoaxial joint	Diarthrosis (freely mobile)
		Biaxial **Condylar joint:** Oval articular surface on one bone closely interfaces with a depressed oval surface on another bone **Saddle joint:** Saddle-shaped articular surface on one bone closely interfaces with a saddle-shaped surface on another bone		**Condylar joint:** MP (metacarpophalangeal or metatarsophalangeal) joints **Saddle joint:** Articulation between carpal and first metacarpal bone	Diarthrosis (freely mobile)
		Multiaxial (Triaxial) **Ball-and-socket joint:** Round head of one bone rests within cup-shaped depression in another bone		**Ball-and-socket joint:** Glenohumeral (shoulder) joint, hip joint	Diarthrosis (freely mobile)

Figure 9.1 **The Relationship Between Mobility and Stability in Joints.** The more mobile a joint is, the less stable it is, and vice versa.

In every joint, there is a tradeoff between mobility and stability.

Stable (yet limited mobility)
The more stable a joint, the less mobile it is.

Immobile — — Most stable

Suture

Slightly mobile — — Stable

Interosseous membrane

Intervertebral joints

Knee joint

Most mobile — — Most unstable

Glenohumeral joint (shoulder)

Mobile (yet more unstable)
The more mobile a joint, the less stable it is.

Fibrous Joints

Their primary function is to hold two bones together. They are immobile or slightly mobile. Examples: **Sutures** and **interosseous membrane**

Cartilaginous Joints

Their primary function is to resist compression and tension stress and act as resilient shock absorbers. They are immobile or slightly mobile. Example: **Intervertebral joints**

Synovial Joints

Their primary function is movement, so they are all freely mobile. Examples: **Glenohumeral joint** (shoulder), and **knee joint**

LEARNING STRATEGY

You can logically figure out the names of most joints by putting together the names of the bones that form them. For example, the *glenohumeral* joint is where the glenoid cavity of the scapula meets the head of the humerus, and the *sternoclavicular* joint is where the manubrium of the sternum articulates with the sternal end of the clavicle.

The following detailed discussion of articulations is based on their structural classification, with functional categories included as appropriate.

WHAT DID YOU LEARN?

1 What is the relationship between mobility and stability in a joint?

2 Are all fibrous joints also synarthroses? Explain why or why not.

9.2 Fibrous Joints

Articulating bones in fibrous joints are connected by dense regular connective tissue. Fibrous joints have no joint cavity; thus, they lack a space between the articulating bones. Most fibrous joints are immobile or at most only slightly mobile; their primary function is to hold together two bones. Examples include the articulations of the teeth in their sockets, sutures between skull bones, and the articulations between either the radius and ulna or the tibia and fibula. In this section we look at the three most common types of fibrous joints: gomphoses, sutures, and syndesmoses (**figure 9.2**).

9.2a Gomphoses

LEARNING OBJECTIVE

1. Explain the location and characteristics of gomphoses.

A **gomphosis** (gom-fō′sis; pl., *gomphoses*, -sēz; *gomphos* = bolt; *osis* = condition) resembles a "peg in a socket." The only gomphoses in the human body are the articulations of the roots of individual teeth with the sockets of the mandible and the maxillae. A tooth is held firmly in place by fibrous **periodontal** (per′ē-ō-don′tăl; *peri* = around; *odous* = tooth) **membranes.** This joint is functionally classified as a synarthrosis.

The reasons orthodontic braces can be painful and take so long to correctly position the teeth are directly related to the architecture of the gomphosis. The orthodontist's job is to reposition these normally immobile joints through the use of clamps, bands, rings, and braces. In response to these mechanical stressors, osteoblasts and osteoclasts work together to modify the alveolar process, resulting in the remodeling of the joints and the slow repositioning of the teeth.

WHAT DID YOU LEARN?

3 Where are gomphoses located, and what type of movement do they allow?

9.2b Sutures

LEARNING OBJECTIVE

2. Describe the location and functions of sutures.

Sutures (sū′chŭr; *sutura* = a seam) are immobile fibrous joints (synarthroses) that are found only between certain bones of the skull. Sutures have distinct, interlocking, usually irregular edges that both

(a) Gomphosis

(b) Suture

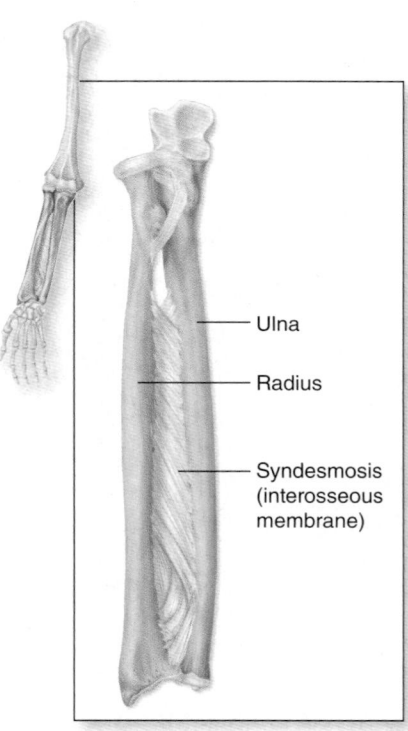

(c) Syndesmosis

Figure 9.2 Fibrous Joints. Dense regular connective tissue binds the articulating bones in fibrous joints to prevent or restrict movement. (*a*) A gomphosis is the immobile joint between a tooth and the jaw. (*b*) A suture is an immobile joint between bones of the skull. (*c*) A syndesmosis permits slight mobility between the radius and the ulna. AP|R increase their strength and decrease the number of fractures at these articulations. In addition to joining bones, sutures permit the skull to grow as the brain increases in size during childhood. In an older adult, the dense regular connective tissue in the suture becomes ossified, fusing the skull bones together. When the bones have completely fused across the suture line, these obliterated sutures become **synostoses** (sin-os-tō'sēz; sing., -sis; *syn* = together; *osteon* = bone).

 WHAT DID YOU LEARN?

 ❹ What is the composition of a suture, and where in the body it is found?

9.2c Syndesmoses

 LEARNING OBJECTIVE

3. List the locations of syndesmoses and describe their function.

Syndesmoses (sin'dez-mō'sēz; sing., *syndesmosis*; *syndesmos* = a fastening) are fibrous joints in which articulating bones are joined by long strands of dense regular connective tissue only. Because syndesmoses allow for slight mobility, they are classified as amphiarthroses. Syndesmoses are found both between the radius and ulna and between the tibia and fibula. The shafts of the two articulating bones are bound by a broad ligamentous sheet called an **interosseous membrane** (or *interosseous ligament*). The interosseous membrane provides a pivot where the radius and ulna (or the tibia and fibula) can move against one another.

 WHAT DID YOU LEARN?

 ❺ What type of movement is allowed at a syndesmosis?

9.3 Cartilaginous Joints

Cartilaginous joints have cartilage between the articulating bones. Like fibrous joints, cartilaginous joints also lack a joint cavity. They may be either immobile or slightly mobile. The cartilage found between the articulating bones is either hyaline cartilage or fibrocartilage. The two types of cartilaginous joints are synchondroses and symphyses (**figure 9.3**).

9.3a Synchondroses

 LEARNING OBJECTIVE

1. Describe the locations and functions of synchondroses.

An articulation in which bones are joined by hyaline cartilage is called a **synchondrosis** (sin'kon-drō'sis; pl., *synchondroses*, -sēz; *chondros* = cartilage). Functionally, all synchondroses are immobile and thus are classified as synarthroses.

 WHAT DO YOU THINK?

❶ Why is a synchondrosis also a synarthrosis? Why would you want a synchondrosis to be immobile?

The hyaline cartilage of epiphyseal plates in children forms synchondroses that bind the epiphyses and diaphysis of long bones (figure 9.3a). When the hyaline cartilage stops growing, bone replaces the cartilage and a synchondrosis no longer exists (see section 7.4b).

The spheno-occipital synchondrosis is found between the body of the sphenoid and the basilar part of the occipital bone. This synchondrosis fuses between 18 and 25 years of age, making it a useful tool for assessing the age of the skull (see section 8.4b).

Other examples of synchondroses are formed from costal cartilage. The **costochondral** (kos-tō-kon'drăl; *costa* = rib) **joint,** the

---

(a)

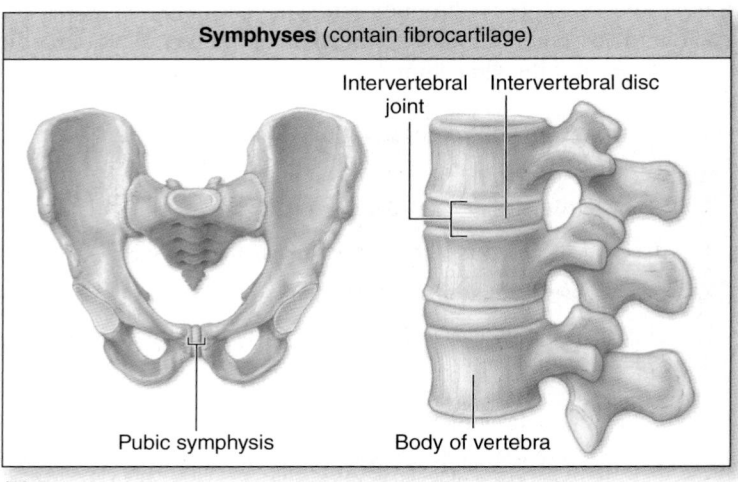

(b)

Figure 9.3 Cartilaginous Joints. Articulating bones are joined by cartilage in cartilaginous joints. (*a*) Synchondroses are immobile joints that occur in an epiphyseal plate in a long bone, between each rib and its respective costal cartilage, and in the joint between the first rib and the sternum. (*b*) Symphyses are slightly mobile and occur in the pubic symphysis and the intervertebral joints. AP|R joint between each bony rib and its respective costal cartilage, is a synchondrosis. Finally, the attachment of the first rib to the sternum by costal cartilage (called the *first sternocostal joint*) is another synchondrosis. Here, the first rib and its costal cartilage (it is hyaline cartilage) are united firmly to the manubrium of the sternum to provide stability to the rib cage. (Note that the sternocostal joints between the sternum and the costal cartilage of ribs 2–7 are synovial joints and not synchondroses.)

WHAT DID YOU LEARN?

6 What is the composition of a synchondrosis, and where in the body is it found?

9.3b Symphyses

LEARNING OBJECTIVE

2. Name the locations of symphyses and their functions in these locations.

A **symphysis** (sim'fi-sis; pl., *symphyses,* -sēz; growing together) has a pad of fibrocartilage between the articulating bones (figure 9.3*b*). The fibrocartilage resists both compression and tension stresses and acts as a resilient shock absorber. All symphyses are amphiarthroses—thus they allow slight mobility.

One example of a symphysis is the pubic symphysis, which is located between the right and left pubic bones. In pregnant females, the pubic symphysis becomes more mobile to allow the pelvis to change shape slightly as the fetus passes through the birth canal.

Other examples of symphyses are the intervertebral joints, where the bodies of adjacent vertebrae are both separated and united by intervertebral discs. Individual intervertebral discs allow only slight movements between the adjacent vertebrae; however, the collective movements of all the intervertebral discs afford the spine considerable flexibility.

WHAT DID YOU LEARN?

7 Into what functional category is a symphysis placed? Why is it in this category?

9.4 Synovial Joints

Synovial joints are freely mobile articulations. Most of the commonly known joints in the body are synovial joints, including the glenohumeral (shoulder) joint, the temporomandibular joint, the elbow joint, and the knee joint.

9.4a Distinguishing Features and Anatomy of Synovial Joints

LEARNING OBJECTIVES

1. Describe the characteristics common to all synovial joints.
2. List the basic features of a synovial joint.
3. Explain the composition and function of synovial fluid in a typical synovial joint.

Unlike the joints previously discussed, the bones in a synovial joint are separated by a space called a joint cavity. Functionally, all synovial joints are classified as diarthroses, since all are freely mobile. Often, the terms *diarthrosis* and *synovial joint* are equated. All synovial joints include several basic features: an articular capsule, a joint cavity, synovial fluid, articular cartilage, ligaments, nerves, and blood vessels **(figure 9.4)**.

Each synovial joint is composed of a double-layered capsule called the **articular** (ar-tik'ū-lăr) **capsule,** or *joint capsule.* Its outer layer is called the **fibrous layer,** and the inner layer is a **synovial membrane** (or *synovium*). The fibrous layer is formed from dense connective tissue. It strengthens the joint to prevent the bones from being pulled apart. The synovial membrane is composed primarily of areolar connective tissue; it covers all the internal joint surfaces not covered by cartilage and lines the articular capsule, and helps produce synovial fluid (described shortly).

All articulating bone surfaces in a synovial joint are covered by a thin layer of hyaline cartilage called **articular cartilage.** This cartilage has numerous functions: It reduces friction in the joint during movement, acts as a spongy cushion to absorb compression placed on the joint, and prevents damage to the articulating ends of the bones. This special hyaline cartilage lacks a perichondrium. Mature cartilage is avascular, so it does not have blood vessels to bring nutrients to and remove waste products from the cartilage. The repetitious compression and expansion that occurs during exercise is vital to maintaining healthy articular cartilage because this action enhances its nutrition and waste removal.

Only synovial joints house a **joint cavity** (or *articular cavity*), a space that permits separation of the articulating bones. The articular cartilage and synovial fluid (described next) within the joint cavity together reduce friction as bones move at a synovial joint.

Lining the joint cavity is the synovial membrane, which secretes **synovial fluid.** Synovial fluid, which is a viscous, oily substance located within a synovial joint, is both the secretions produced from the synovial membrane cells and filtrate formed from blood plasma. Synovial fluid has three functions:

1. Synovial fluid lubricates the articular cartilage on the surface of articulating bones (in the same way that oil in a car engine lubricates the moving engine parts).
2. Synovial fluid nourishes the articular cartilage's chondrocytes. The relatively small volume of synovial fluid must be

Periosteum
Yellow bone marrow
Fibrous layer
Synovial membrane — **Articular capsule**
Joint cavity (containing synovial fluid)
Articular cartilage
Ligament

Typical synovial joint

Figure 9.4 Synovial Joints. All synovial joints are diarthroses, and they permit a wide range of motion. **AP|R**

circulated continually to provide nutrients to and remove wastes from these cells. Whenever movement occurs at a synovial joint, the combined compression and re-expansion of the articular cartilage circulates the synovial fluid into and out of the cartilage matrix.

3. Synovial fluid acts as a shock absorber, distributing stresses and force evenly across the articular surfaces when the pressure in the joint suddenly increases.

Ligaments (lig′ă-ment; *ligamentum* = a band) are composed of dense regular connective tissue, and they connect one bone to another bone. Ligaments function to stabilize, strengthen, and reinforce most synovial joints. **Extrinsic ligaments** are outside of, and physically separate from, the joint capsule, whereas **intrinsic ligaments** represent thickenings of the articular capsule itself. Intrinsic ligaments include *extracapsular ligaments* outside the joint capsule and *intracapsular ligaments* within the joint capsule.

All synovial joints have numerous **sensory nerves** and **blood vessels** that innervate and supply the articular capsule and associated ligaments. The sensory nerves detect painful stimuli in the joint and report on the amount of movement and stretch within the joint. By monitoring stretching at a joint, the nervous system can detect changes in our posture and adjust body movements.

Tendons (ten′dŏn; *tendo* = extend) are like ligaments and are composed of dense regular connective tissue but they are not part of the synovial joint itself. Whereas a ligament binds bone to bone, a tendon attaches a muscle to a bone. When a muscle contracts, the tendon from that muscle moves the bone to which it is attached, thus creating movement at the joint. Tendons help stabilize joints because they pass across or around a joint to provide mechanical support, and sometimes they limit the range or amount of movement permitted at a joint.

Synovial joints usually have bursae and fat pads as accessory structures in addition to the main components just described. A **bursa** (ber′să; pl., *bursae*, ber′sē; a purse) is a fibrous, saclike struc-

ture that contains synovial fluid and is lined internally by a synovial membrane (**figure 9.5a**). Bursae are associated with most synovial joints and also where bones, ligaments, muscles, skin, or tendons overlie each other and rub together. Bursae may be either connected to the joint cavity or completely separate from it. They are designed to alleviate the friction resulting from the various body movements, such as where a tendon or ligament rubs against bone. An elongated bursa called a **tendon sheath** wraps around a tendon where there may be excessive friction. Tendon sheaths are especially common in the confined spaces of the wrist and ankle (figure 9.5b).

Fat pads are often distributed along the periphery of a synovial joint. They act as packing material and provide some protection for the joint. Often fat pads fill the spaces that form when bones move and the joint cavity changes shape (figure 9.5a).

Femur

Bursa deep to gastrocnemius muscle

Articular capsule

Articular cartilage

Meniscus

Joint cavity filled with synovial fluid

Tibia

Suprapatellar bursa

Synovial membrane

Patella

Prepatellar bursa

Fat pad

Infrapatellar bursae

Patellar ligament

(a) Bursae of the knee joint, sagittal section

Tendon sheath (opened)

Tendon of flexor digitorum profundus

Tendon of flexor digitorum superficialis

Tendon sheath around flexor pollicis longus tendon

Tendon of flexor carpi radialis

Tendon of flexor pollicis longus

Digital tendon sheaths

Common flexor tendon sheath

Tendons of flexor digitorum superficialis and flexor digitorum profundus

(b) Tendon sheaths of wrist and hand, anterior view

Figure 9.5 Bursae and Tendon Sheaths. Synovial fluid–filled structures called bursae and tendon sheaths reduce friction where ligaments, muscles, tendons, and bones rub together. (*a*) The knee joint contains a number of bursae (blue and purple). (*b*) The wrist and hand contain numerous tendon sheaths (blue).

WHAT DID YOU LEARN?

8 What are the basic characteristics of all types of synovial joints?

9 What is the purpose of synovial fluid in the joint?

9.4b Classification of Synovial Joints

✓ LEARNING OBJECTIVES

4. Explain the movement of a joint with respect to the three perpendicular axes of space.

5. Compare and contrast the six types of synovial joints.

Synovial joints are classified by the shapes of their articulating surfaces and the types of movement they allow. Movement of a bone at a synovial joint is best described with respect to three intersecting perpendicular planes or axes:

- A joint is said to be **uniaxial** (yū-nē-ak′sē-ăl; *unus* = one) if the bone moves in just one plane or axis.
- A joint is **biaxial** (bī-ak′sē-ăl; *bi* = double) if the bone moves in two planes or axes.
- A joint is **multiaxial** (or **triaxial** (trī-ak′sē-ăl; *tri* = three) if the bone moves in multiple planes or axes.

All synovial joints are diarthroses, as mentioned, but some are more mobile than others. From least mobile to most freely mobile, the six specific types of synovial joints are plane joints, hinge joints, pivot joints, condylar joints, saddle joints, and ball-and-socket joints. These joints and examples of where they are found in the body are shown in **figure 9.6**.

🔆 WHAT DO YOU THINK?

2 If a ball-and-socket joint is more mobile than a gliding joint, which of these two joints is the more stable?

A **plane** (*planus* = flat) **joint,** also called a *planar* or *gliding joint,* is the simplest synovial articulation and the least mobile type of diarthrosis. Anatomists have debated how to describe the movement of this joint with respect to perpendicular planes. We describe this type of synovial joint as a uniaxial joint because it usually allows only limited side-to-side movements in a single plane, and because there is no rotational or angular movement with this joint. The articular surfaces of the bones are flat, or planar. Examples of plane joints include the intercarpal and intertarsal joints (the joints between the carpal bones and tarsal bones, respectively).

A **hinge joint** is formed by the convex surface of one articulating bone fitting into a concave depression on the other bone in the joint. Movement is confined to a single axis, like the movement observed at the hinge of a door, so a hinge joint is considered a uniaxial joint. An example is the elbow joint. The trochlear notch of the ulna fits directly into the trochlea of the humerus, so the forearm can be moved only anteriorly toward the arm or posteriorly away from the arm. Other hinge joints occur in the knee and the finger (interphalangeal [IP]) joints.

A **pivot joint** is a uniaxial joint in which one articulating bone with a rounded surface fits into a ring formed by a ligament and another bone. The first bone rotates on its longitudinal axis relative to the second bone. An example is the proximal radioulnar joint, where the rounded head of the radius pivots along the ulna and permits the radius to rotate. Another example is the atlantoaxial joint between the first two cervical vertebrae. The rounded dens of the axis fits snugly against an articular facet on

the anterior arch of the atlas. This joint pivots when you shake your head "no."

Condylar (kon′di-lar) **joints,** also called *condyloid* or *ellipsoid joints,* are biaxial joints with an oval, convex surface on one bone that articulates with a concave articular surface on the second bone of the joint. Biaxial joints can move in two axes, such as back-and-forth and side-to-side. Examples of condylar joints are the metacarpophalangeal (met′ă-kar′pō-fă-lan′jē-ăl) (MP) joints of fingers 2 through 5. The MP joints are commonly referred to as "knuckles." Examine your hand and look at the movements along the MP joints; you can flex and extend the fingers at this joint, which is one axis of movement. You also can move your fingers apart from one another and move them closer together, which is the second axis of movement.

A **saddle joint** is so named because the articular surfaces of the bones have convex and concave regions that resemble the shape of a saddle. This biaxial joint allows a greater range of movement than either a condylar or hinge joint. The carpometacarpal joint of the thumb (between the trapezium and the first metacarpal) is an example of a saddle joint. This joint permits the thumb to move toward the other fingers so that we can grasp objects.

Ball-and-socket joints are multiaxial joints in which the spherical articulating head of one bone fits into the rounded, cuplike socket of a second bone. Examples of these joints are the coxal (hip) and glenohumeral (shoulder) joints. The multiaxial nature of these joints permits movement in three planes. Move your arm at your shoulder, and observe the wide range of movements that can be produced. The ball-and-socket joint is considered the most freely mobile type of synovial joint.

🔆 WHAT DID YOU LEARN?

10 What types of movements do each of the six kinds of joints allow?

9.5 Synovial Joints and Levers

When analyzing synovial joint movement and muscle contraction, anatomists often compare the movement to the mechanics of a lever; this practice of applying mechanical principles to biology is known as **biomechanics.**

9.5a Terminology of Levers

✓ LEARNING OBJECTIVES

1. Define a lever.

2. Discriminate between the effort arm and the resistance arm in a lever.

A **lever** (lev′er, lē′ver; to lift) is an elongated, rigid object that rotates around a fixed point called the **fulcrum** (ful′krum). A seesaw is a familiar example of a lever. Levers have the ability to alter or change the speed and distance of movement produced by a force, the direction of an applied force, and the force strength.

Movement occurs when an **effort** applied to one point on the lever exceeds a **resistance** located at some other point. The part of a lever from the fulcrum to the point of effort is called the **effort arm,** and the lever part from the fulcrum to the point of resistance is the **resistance arm.** In the body, a long bone acts as a lever, a joint serves as the fulcrum, and the effort is generated by a muscle attached to the bone.

🔆 WHAT DID YOU LEARN?

11 What is the difference between the effort arm and the resistance arm in a lever?

Figure 9.6 Synovial Joints. The six types of synovial joints and their locations in the body are shown.

Hinge joint
(uniaxial)

Carpal bones

Trapezium

First metacarpal bone

Phalanges

Triquetrum

Hamate bone

MP joint ("knuckle")

IP joints

Metacarpal bone

Proximal phalanx

Plane joint
(uniaxial)

Humerus

Radius

Ulna

Saddle joint
(biaxial)

Condylar joint
(biaxial)

Ball-and-socket joint
(multiaxial)

Ilium

Head of femur

Dens of axis

Atlas

Axis

Uniaxial joint
Biaxial joint
Multiaxial joint

Pivot joint
(uniaxial)

9.5b Type of Levers

✓ **LEARNING OBJECTIVE**

3. Compare and contrast the three types of levers in the human body.

Three classes of levers are found in the human body: first-class, second-class, and third-class **(figure 9.7)**.

First-Class Levers

A **first-class lever** has a fulcrum in the middle, between the effort (force) and the resistance. An example of a first-class lever is a pair of scissors. The effort is applied to the handle of the scissors while the resistance is at the cutting end of the scissors. The fulcrum (pivot for movement) is along the middle of the scissors, between the handle and the cutting ends. In the body, an example of a first-class lever is the atlanto-occipital joint of the neck, where the muscles on the posterior side of the neck pull inferiorly on the nuchal lines of the skull and oppose the tendency of the head to tip anteriorly.

Second-Class Levers

The resistance in a **second-class lever** is between the fulcrum and the applied effort. A common example of this type of lever is lifting the handles of a wheelbarrow, allowing it to pivot on its wheel at the opposite end and lift a load in the middle. The load weight is the resistance, and the upward lift on the handle is the effort. A small force can balance a larger weight in this type of lever, because the effort is always farther from the fulcrum than the resistance. Second-class levers are rare in the body, but one example occurs when the

foot is depressed (plantar flexed) so that a person can stand on tiptoe. The contraction of the calf muscle causes a pull superiorly by the calcaneal tendon attached to the heel (calcaneus).

Third-Class Levers

A **third-class lever** is observed when the effort is applied between the resistance and the fulcrum, as when picking up a small object with a pair of forceps. Third-class levers are the most common levers in the body. A third-class lever is found at the elbow where the fulcrum is the joint between the humerus and ulna, the effort is applied by the biceps brachii muscle, and the resistance is provided by any

(a)

(b)

(c)

Figure 9.7 Classes of Levers. (*a*) In a first-class lever, the fulcrum is located between the resistance and effort, such as with a pair of scissors or the trapezius muscle (in the neck). (*b*) In a second-class lever, the resistance is between the fulcrum and effort, such as with a wheelbarrow or the calf muscles. (*c*) The most common type of lever is the third-class lever, where effort is applied between the resistance and the fulcrum, such as with forceps (tweezers) or the arm muscles.

weight in the hand or by the weight of the forearm itself. The mandible acts as a third-class lever when you bite with your incisors on a piece of food. The temporomandibular joint is the fulcrum, and the temporalis muscle exerts the effort, while the resistance is the item of food being bitten.

 WHAT DID YOU LEARN?

12 How does the position of the fulcrum, resistance, and effort vary in first-class, second-class, and third-class levers?

9.6 The Movements of Synovial Joints

Four types of motion occur at synovial joints: gliding, angular, rotational, and special movements (motions that occur only at specific joints) (table 9.2).

9.6a Gliding Motion

 LEARNING OBJECTIVE

1. Describe gliding motion, and name joints in which it occurs.

Gliding is a simple movement in which two opposing surfaces slide slightly back-and-forth or side-to-side with respect to one another. In a gliding motion, the angle between the bones does not change, and only limited movement is possible in any direction. Gliding motion typically occurs along plane joints, such as between the carpals or the tarsals.

 WHAT DID YOU LEARN?

13 What joints typically use gliding motion?

9.6b Angular Motion

LEARNING OBJECTIVES

2. Describe angular motion.
3. Name the specific types of angular motion.
4. Give examples of joints that exhibit angular motion.

Angular motion either increases or decreases the angle between two bones. These movements may occur at many of the synovial joints. They include the following specific types: flexion and extension, hyperextension, lateral flexion, abduction and adduction, and circumduction.

Table 9.2	Movements at Synovial Joints	
Movement	**Description**	**Opposing Movement**[1]
GLIDING MOTION	Two opposing articular surfaces slide past each other in almost any direction; the amount of movement is slight	
ANGULAR MOTION	The angle between articulating bones increases or decreases	
Flexion	The angle between articulating bones decreases	Extension
Extension	The angle between articulating bones increases	Flexion
Hyperextension	Extension movement continues past the anatomic position	Flexion
Lateral flexion	The vertebral column moves (bends) in a lateral direction along a coronal plane	None
Abduction	Movement of a bone away from the midline	Adduction
Adduction	Movement of a bone toward the midline	Abduction
Circumduction	A continuous movement that combines flexion, abduction, extension, and adduction in succession; the distal end of the limb or digit moves in a circle	None
ROTATIONAL MOTION	A bone pivots around its own longitudinal axis	
Pronation	Rotation of the forearm where the palm is turned posteriorly	Supination
Supination	Rotation of the forearm in which the palm is turned anteriorly	Pronation
SPECIAL MOVEMENTS	Types of movement that do not fit in the previous categories	
Depression	Movement of a body part inferiorly	Elevation
Elevation	Movement of a body part superiorly	Depression
Dorsiflexion	Ankle joint movement where the dorsum (superior surface) of the foot is brought toward the anterior surface of the leg	Plantar flexion
Plantar flexion	Ankle joint movement where the sole of the foot is brought toward the posterior surface of the leg	Dorsiflexion
Inversion	Twisting motion of the foot that turns the sole medially or inward	Eversion
Eversion	Twisting motion of the foot that turns the sole laterally or outward	Inversion
Protraction	Anterior movement of a body part from anatomic position	Retraction
Retraction	Posterior movement of a body part from anatomic position	Protraction
Opposition	Special movement of the thumb across the palm toward the fingers to permit grasping and holding of an object	Reposition

1. Some movements (e.g., circumduction) do not have an opposing movement.

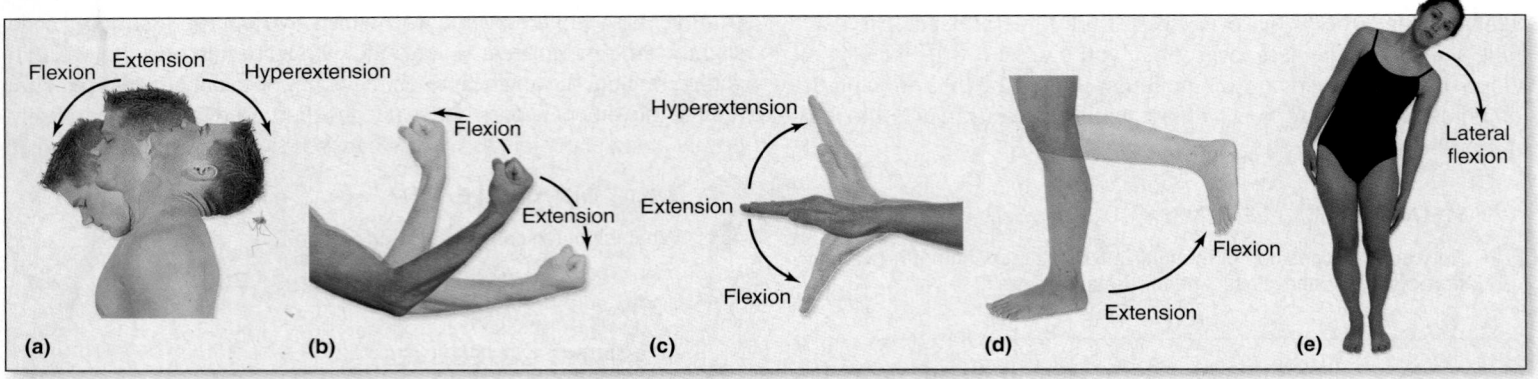

Figure 9.8 Flexion, Extension, Hyperextension, and Lateral Flexion. Flexion decreases the joint angle in an anterior-posterior (AP) plane, while extension increases the joint angle in the AP plane. Hyperextension is extension of a joint beyond 180 degrees. Lateral flexion decreases a joint angle, but in a coronal plane. Examples of joints that allow some of these movements are (*a*) the atlanto-occipital joint, (*b*) the elbow joint, (*c*) the radiocarpal joint, (*d*) the knee joint, and (*e*) the intervertebral joints.

Flexion (flek′shŭn; *flecto* = to bend) is movement in an anterior-posterior (AP) plane of the body that *decreases* the angle between the bones. Bones are brought closer together as the angle between them decreases. Examples are the bending of the fingers toward the palm to make a fist, the bending of the forearm toward the arm at the elbow, flexion at the shoulder when the arm is raised anteriorly, and flexion of the neck when the head is bent anteriorly and you look down at your feet.

The opposite of flexion is **extension** (eks-ten′shŭn; *extensio* = a stretching out), which is movement in an anterior-posterior plane that *increases* the angle between the articulating bones. Extension is a straightening action that occurs in an anterior-posterior (AP) plane. Straightening the arm and forearm until the upper limb projects directly away from the anterior side of your body, or straightening the fingers after making a clenched fist, are examples of extension.

When a joint is extended more than 180 degrees, the movement is termed **hyperextension** (hī′per-eks-ten′shŭn; *hyper* = above normal). For example, if you extend your arm and hand with the palm facing inferiorly, and then raise the back of your hand as if admiring a new ring on your finger, the wrist is hyperextended. If you glance up at the ceiling while standing, your neck is hyperextended. Flexion, extension, and hyperextension of various body parts are illustrated in **figure 9.8a–d**.

Lateral flexion occurs when the trunk of the body moves in a coronal plane laterally away from the body. This type of movement occurs primarily between the vertebrae in the cervical and lumbar regions of the vertebral column (figure 9.8e).

WHAT DO YOU THINK?

3 When sitting upright in a chair, are your hip and knee joints flexed or extended?

Abduction (ab-dŭk′shŭn) means to "move away," and it is a lateral movement of a body part *away from* the body midline. Abduction occurs when either the arm or the thigh is moved laterally away from the body midline. Abduction of either the fingers or the toes means that you spread them apart, away from the longest digit that acts as the midline.

Figure 9.9 Abduction and Adduction. Abduction moves a body part away from the trunk in a lateral direction, while adduction moves the body part toward the trunk. Some examples occur at (*a*) the glenohumeral joint, (*b*) the radiocarpal joint, (*c*) the hip joint, and (*d*) the metacarpophalangeal (MP) joints.

Figure 9.10 Circumduction. Circumduction is a complex movement that involves flexion, abduction, extension, and adduction in succession. Examples of joints that allow this movement are (*a*) the glenohumeral joint and (*b*) the hip joint.

Abducting the wrist (also known as *radial* deviation) involves pointing the hand and fingers laterally, away from the body. The opposite of abduction is **adduction** (ad-dŭk′shŭn), meaning to "move toward." This is the medial movement of a body part *toward* the body midline. Adduction occurs when the raised arm or thigh is brought back toward the body midline, or in the case of the digits, toward the midline of the hand. Adducting the wrist (also known as *ulnar* deviation) involves pointing the hand and fingers medially, toward the body. Abduction and adduction of various body parts are shown in **figure 9.9**.

Circumduction (ser-kŭm-dŭk′shŭn; *circum* = around; *duco* = to draw) is a sequence of movements in which the proximal end of an appendage remains relatively stationary while the distal end makes a circular motion **(figure 9.10)**. The resulting movement makes an imaginary cone shape. This is demonstrated when you draw a circle on the blackboard. The shoulder remains stationary while your hand moves. The tip of the imaginary cone is the stationary shoulder, while the rounded "base" of the cone is the circle made by the hand. Circumduction is a complex movement that occurs as a result of a continuous sequence of flexion, abduction, extension, and adduction.

WHAT DID YOU LEARN?

14 How do flexion and extension differ? What movements are involved in circumduction?

9.6c Rotational Motion

LEARNING OBJECTIVE

5. Explain rotational motion, and name joints in which it occurs.

Rotation is a pivoting motion in which a bone turns on its own longitudinal axis **(figure 9.11)**. Rotational movement occurs at the atlantoaxial joint, which pivots when you

Figure 9.11 Rotational Movements. Rotation allows a bone to pivot on its longitudinal axis. Examples of joints that allow this movement are (*a*) the atlantoaxial joint, (*b*) the glenohumeral joint, and (*c*) the hip joint. (*d*) Pronation and supination occur at the forearm.

rotate your head to gesture "no." Some limb rotations are described as either away from the median plane or toward it. For example, **lateral rotation** (or *external* rotation) turns the anterior surface of the femur or humerus laterally, while **medial rotation** (or *internal* rotation) turns the anterior surface of the femur or humerus medially.

Pronation (prō-nā'shŭn) is the medial rotation of the forearm so that the palm of the hand is directed posteriorly or inferiorly. The radius and ulna are crossed to form an X (see section 8.9b). **Supination** (sū'pi-nā'shŭn) occurs when the forearm rotates laterally so that the palm faces anteriorly or superiorly. In the anatomic position, the forearm is supinated. Figure 9.11d illustrates pronation and supination.

(a)

WHAT DID YOU LEARN?

15 What is pronation, and where in the body may this type of movement be performed?

9.6d Special Movements

LEARNING OBJECTIVE

6. Explain what is meant by special movements, and give examples of joints at which they occur.

Some movements occur only at specific joints and do not readily fit into any of the functional categories previously discussed. These special movements include depression and elevation, dorsiflexion and plantar flexion, eversion and inversion, protraction and retraction, and opposition.

Depression (dē-presh'ŭn; *de* = away, down; *presso* = to press) is the inferior movement of a part of the body. Examples of depression include the movement of the mandible while opening the mouth to chew food and the movement of your shoulders in an inferior direction. **Elevation** (el-ē-vā'shŭn) is the superior movement of a body part. Examples of elevation include the superior movement of the mandible while closing the mouth and the movement of the shoulders in a superior direction (shrugging your shoulders). **Figure 9.12a** illustrates depression and elevation at the glenohumeral joints.

Dorsiflexion and plantar flexion are limited to the ankle joint (see figure 9.12b). **Dorsiflexion** (dōr-si-flek'shŭn) occurs when the talocrural (ankle) joint is bent such that the dorsum (superior surface) of the foot and the toes moves toward the leg. This movement occurs when you dig in your heels, and it prevents your toes from scraping the ground when you take a step. **Plantar flexion** (plan'tăr; *planta* = sole of foot) is a movement of the foot at the talocrural joint so that the toes point inferiorly. When a ballerina is standing on her tiptoes, her ankle joint is in full plantar flexion.

Inversion and eversion are movements that occur at the intertarsal joints of the foot only (see figure 9.12c). The sole of the foot turns medially during **inversion** (in-ver'zhŭn), whereas during **eversion** (ē-ver'zhŭn) the sole of the foot turns to face laterally. (*Note:* Some orthopedists and runners use the terms pronation and supination when describing foot movements as well, instead of using inversion and eversion. Simply put, inversion is foot supination, whereas eversion is foot pronation.)

Protraction (prō-trak'shŭn) is the anterior movement of a body part from anatomic position, as when jutting your jaw anteriorly at the temporomandibular joint or hunching the shoulders anteriorly by crossing the arms. In the latter case, the clavicles move anteriorly due to movement at both the acromioclavicular and sternoclavicular joints. **Retraction** (rē-trak'shŭn) is the posteriorly directed movement of a body part from the anatomic position. Figure 9.12d illustrates protraction and retraction at the temporomandibular joint.

At the carpometacarpal joint, the thumb moves toward the palmar tips of the fingers as it crosses the palm of the hand. This movement is called **opposition** (op'pō-si'shŭn) (figure 9.12e). It enables the hand to grasp objects and is the most distinctive digital movement in humans. The opposite movement is called **reposition.**

WHAT DID YOU LEARN?

16 What is the difference between inversion and eversion, and which joints allow these movements?

Table 9.3	Axial Skeleton Joints

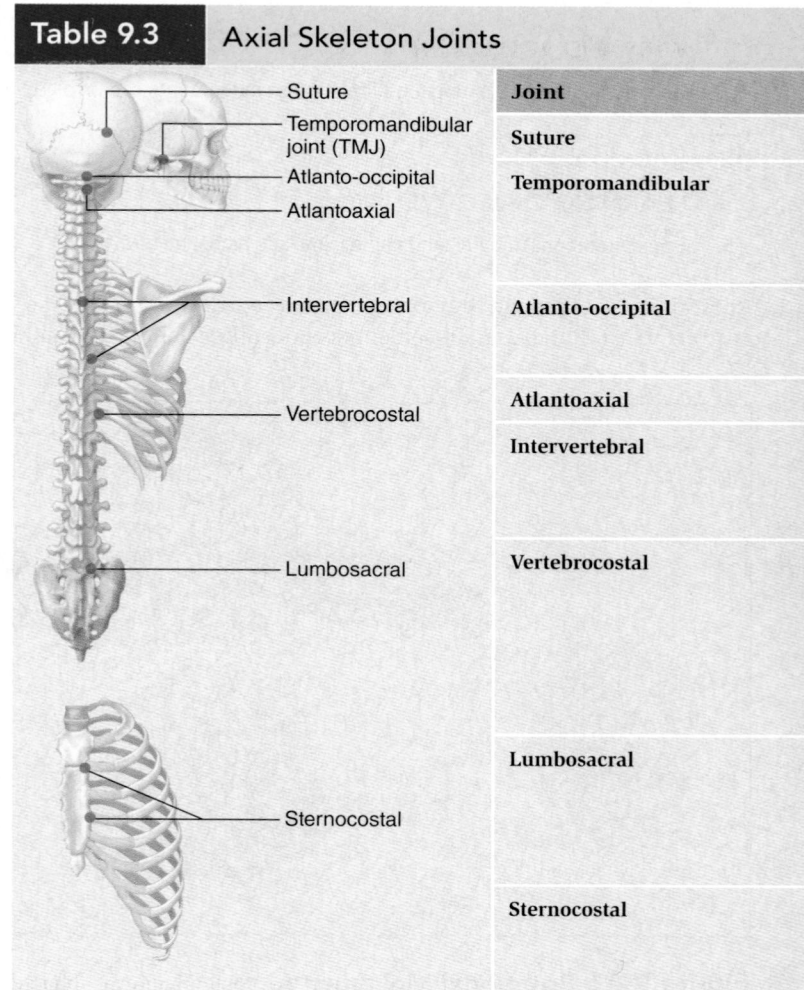

	Joint
Suture	Suture
Temporomandibular joint (TMJ)	Temporomandibular
Atlanto-occipital	Atlanto-occipital
Atlantoaxial	Atlantoaxial
Intervertebral	Intervertebral
Vertebrocostal	Vertebrocostal
Lumbosacral	Lumbosacral
Sternocostal	Sternocostal

Figure 9.12 Special Movements Allowed at Synovial Joints. (a) Depression and elevation at the glenohumeral joint. (b) Dorsiflexion and plantar flexion at the talocrural joint. (c) Inversion and eversion at the intertarsal joints. (d) Protraction and retraction at the temporomandibular joint. (e) Opposition at the carpometacarpal joints.

9.7 Features and Anatomy of Selected Joints

Both the axial skeleton and appendicular skeleton exhibit many more joints than are individually discussed here. Table 9.3 summarizes the main features of major joints of the axial skeleton. Table 9.4 lists the features of the major joints of the pectoral girdle and upper limbs, and Table 9.5 summarizes features of major joints of the pelvic girdle and lower limbs.

The structure and function of the more commonly known articulations of the axial and appendicular skeletons are examined in this section. These are the temporomandibular joint of the skull; the shoulder joint and elbow joint; and the hip joint, knee joint, and talocrural (ankle) joint.

Articulation Components	Structural Classification	Functional Classification	Description of Movement
Adjacent skull bones	Fibrous joint	Synarthrosis	None allowed
Head of mandible and mandibular fossa of temporal bone Head of mandible and articular tubercle of temporal bone	Synovial (hinge, plane) joints	Diarthrosis	Depression, elevation, lateral displacement, protraction, retraction, slight rotation
Superior articular facets of atlas and occipital condyles of occipital bone	Synovial (condylar) joint	Diarthrosis	Extension and flexion of the head; slight lateral flexion of head to sides
Anterior arch of atlas and dens of axis	Synovial (pivot) joint	Diarthrosis	Head rotation
Vertebral bodies of adjacent vertebrae Superior and inferior articular processes of adjacent vertebrae	Cartilaginous joint (symphysis) between vertebral bodies; synovial (plane) joint between articular processes	Amphiarthrosis between vertebral bodies; diarthrosis between articular processes	Extension, flexion, lateral flexion of vertebral column
Facets of heads of ribs and bodies of adjacent thoracic vertebrae and intervertebral discs between adjacent vertebrae Articular part of tubercles of ribs and facets of transverse processes of thoracic vertebra	Synovial (plane) joint	Diarthrosis	Some slight gliding
Body of the fifth lumbar vertebra and the base of the sacrum Inferior articular facets of fifth lumbar vertebra and superior articular facets of first sacral vertebra	Cartilaginous joint (symphysis) between lumbar body and base of sacrum; synovial (plane) joint between articular processes	Amphiarthrosis between lumbar body and base of sacrum; diarthrosis between articular processes	Extension, flexion, lateral flexion of vertebral column
Sternum and first seven pairs of ribs	Cartilaginous joint (synchondrosis) between sternum and first ribs; synovial (plane) joint between sternum and ribs 2–7	Synarthrosis between sternum and first ribs; diarthrosis between sternum and ribs 2–7	No movement between sternum and first ribs; some gliding movement permitted between sternum and ribs 2–7

Table 9.4 **Pectoral Girdle and Upper Limb Joints**

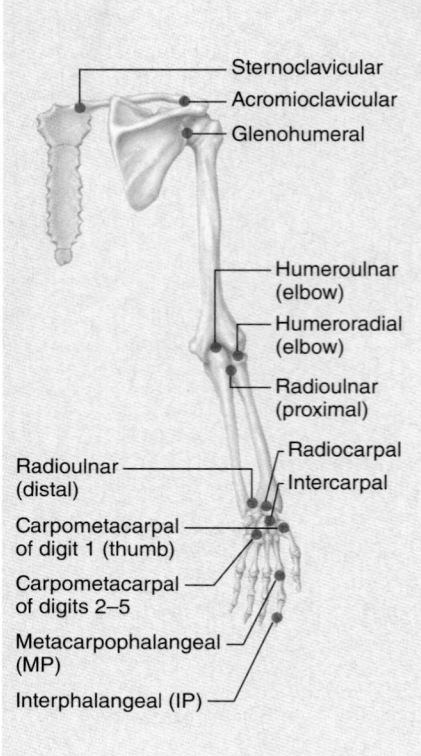

Joint	Articulation Components	Structural Classification	Functional Classification	Description of Movement
Sternoclavicular	Sternal end of clavicle, manubrium of sternum, and first costal cartilage	Synovial (saddle)	Diarthrosis	Elevation, depression, circumduction
Acromioclavicular	Acromial end of clavicle and acromion of scapula	Synovial (plane)	Diarthrosis	Gliding of scapula on clavicle
Glenohumeral	Glenoid cavity of scapula and head of humerus	Synovial (ball-and-socket)	Diarthrosis	Abduction, adduction, circumduction, extension, flexion, lateral rotation, and medial rotation of arm
Elbow	**Humeroulnar joint:** Trochlea of humerus and trochlear notch of ulna **Humeroradial joint:** Capitulum of humerus and head of radius	Synovial (hinge)	Diarthrosis	Extension and flexion of forearm
Radioulnar	**Proximal joint:** Head of radius and radial notch of ulna **Distal joint:** Distal end of ulna and ulnar notch of radius	Synovial (pivot)	Diarthrosis	Rotation of radius with respect to ulna
Radiocarpal	Distal end of radius; lunate, scaphoid, and triquetrum	Synovial (condylar)	Diarthrosis	Abduction, adduction, circumduction, extension and flexion of wrist
Intercarpal	Adjacent bones in proximal row of carpal bones Adjacent bones in distal row of carpal bones Adjacent bones between proximal and distal rows (midcarpal joints)	Synovial (plane)	Diarthrosis	Gliding
Carpometacarpal	**Thumb:** Trapezium and first metacarpal **Other digits:** Carpals and metacarpals II–V	Synovial (saddle) at thumb; synovial (plane) at other digits	Diarthrosis	Abduction, adduction, circumduction, extension, flexion, and opposition at thumb; gliding at other digits
Metacarpophalangeal (MP joints, "knuckles")	Heads of metacarpals and bases of proximal phalanges	Synovial (condylar)	Diarthrosis	Abduction, adduction, circumduction, extension and flexion of phalanges
Interphalangeal (IP joints)	Heads of proximal and middle phalanges with bases of middle and distal phalanges, respectively	Synovial (hinge)	Diarthrosis	Extension and flexion of phalanges

| Table 9.5 | Pelvic Girdle and Lower Limb Joints |

Joint	Articulation Components	Structural Classification	Functional Classification	Description of Movement
Sacroiliac	Auricular surfaces of sacrum and ilium	Synovial (plane)	Diarthrosis	Slight gliding; more movement during pregnancy and childbirth
Hip (coxal)	Head of the femur and acetabulum of os coxae	Synovial (ball-and-socket)	Diarthrosis	Abduction, adduction, circumduction, extension, flexion, medial and lateral rotation of thigh
Pubic symphysis	Two pubic bones	Cartilaginous (symphysis)	Amphiarthrosis	Very slight gliding; more movement during childbirth
Knee	**Patellofemoral joint:** Patella and patellar surface of femur **Tibiofemoral joint:** Medial condyle of femur, medial meniscus, and medial condyle of tibia	Both synovial (hinge) and synovial (plane) at patellofemoral joint; synovial (hinge) at tibiofemoral joint[1]	Diarthrosis	Extension, flexion, lateral rotation of leg in flexed position, slight medial rotation
Tibiofibular	**Superior joint:** Head of fibula and lateral condyle of tibia **Inferior joint:** Distal end of fibula and fibular notch of tibia	**Superior joint:** Synovial (plane) **Inferior joint:** Fibrous (syndesmosis)	Amphiarthrosis	Slight rotation of fibula during dorsiflexion of foot
Talocrural	Distal end of tibia and medial malleolus with talus Lateral malleolus of fibula and talus	Synovial (hinge)	Diarthrosis	Dorsiflexion and plantar flexion
Intertarsal	Between the tarsal bones	Synovial (plane)	Diarthrosis	Eversion and inversion of foot
Tarsometatarsal	Three cuneiforms and cuboid (tarsals) and bases of five metatarsals	Synovial (plane)	Diarthrosis	Slight gliding
Metatarso-phalangeal (MP joints)	Heads of metatarsals and bases of proximal phalanges	Synovial (condylar)	Diarthrosis	Abduction, adduction, circumduction, extension and flexion of phalanges
Interphalangeal (IP joints)	Heads of proximal and middle phalanges with bases of middle and distal phalanges, respectively	Synovial (hinge)	Diarthrosis	Extension and flexion of phalanges

Diagram labels (top to bottom): Sacroiliac, Hip, Pubic symphysis, Patellofemoral (knee), Tibiofemoral (knee), Tibiofibular (superior), Tibiofibular (inferior), Talocrural, Intertarsal, Tarsometatarsal, Metatarsophalangeal (MP), Interphalangeal (IP)

1. Although anatomists classify the tibiofemoral joint as a hinge joint, some kinesiologists and exercise scientists prefer to classify the tibiofemoral joint as a modified condylar joint.

9.7a Temporomandibular Joint

LEARNING OBJECTIVES

1. Describe the features of the temporomandibular joint (TMJ).
2. List the movements of the TMJ.

The **temporomandibular** (tem′pŏ-rō-man-dib′ū-lăr) **joint (TMJ)** is the articulation formed at the point where the head of the mandible articulates with the temporal bone; specifically, articular tubercle anteriorly and the mandibular fossa posteriorly. This small, complex articulation is the only mobile joint between bones in the skull (**figure 9.13**; table 9.3).

The temporomandibular joint has several unique anatomic features. A loose **articular capsule** surrounds the joint and promotes an extensive range of motion. It contains an **articular disc** that is a thick pad of fibrocartilage separating the articulating bones and extending horizontally to divide the synovial cavity into two separate chambers. As a result, the temporomandibular joint is really two synovial joints—one between the temporal bone and the articular disc, and a second between the articular disc and the mandible.

Several ligaments support this joint. The **sphenomandibular ligament** (an extracapsular ligament) is a thin band that extends anteriorly and inferiorly from the sphenoid to the medial surface of the mandibular ramus. The **temporomandibular ligament** (or *lateral ligament*) is composed of two short bands that extend inferiorly and posteriorly from the articular tubercle to the mandible.

The temporomandibular joint exhibits hinge, gliding, and some pivot joint movements. It functions like a hinge during jaw depression and elevation while chewing. It glides slightly forward during protraction of the jaw for biting, and glides slightly from side to side to grind food between the teeth during chewing.

WHAT DID YOU LEARN?

17 What movements are allowed at the temporomandibular joint?

Hinge joint   Gliding joint

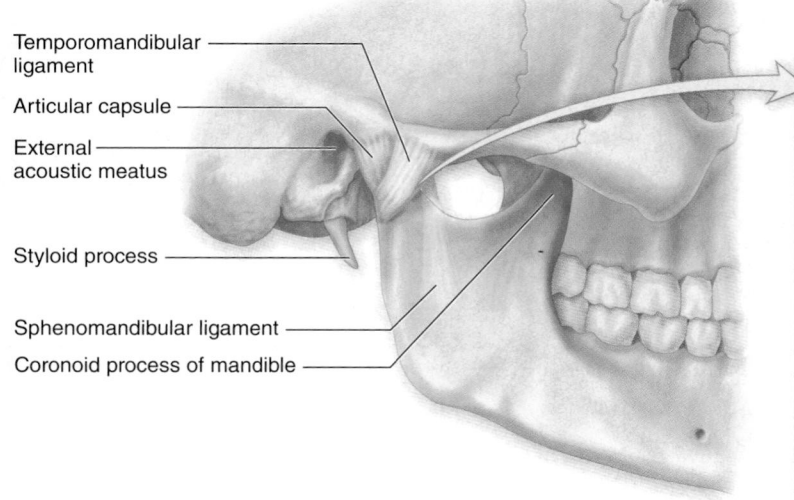

Temporomandibular ligament

Articular capsule

External acoustic meatus

Styloid process

Sphenomandibular ligament

Coronoid process of mandible

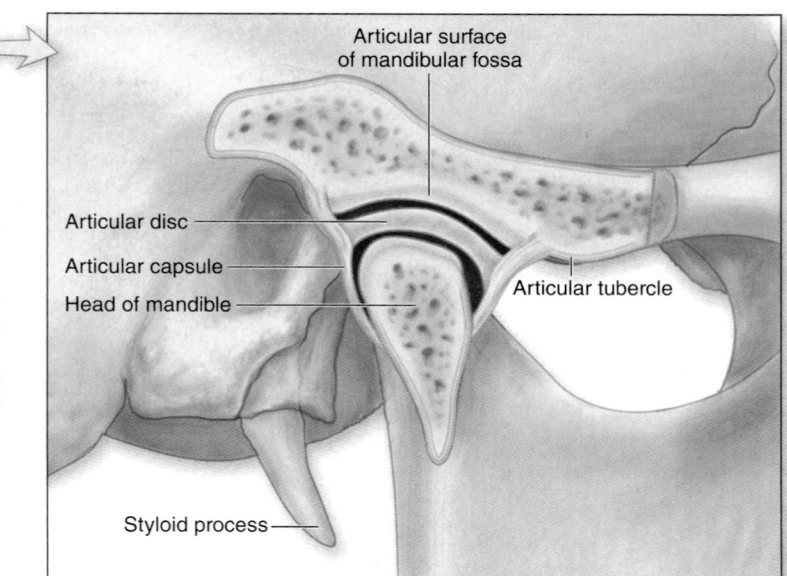

Articular surface of mandibular fossa

Articular disc

Articular capsule

Head of mandible

Articular tubercle

Styloid process

Figure 9.13 Temporomandibular Joint. The articulation between the head of the mandible and the mandibular fossa of the temporal bone exhibits a wide range of movements. AP|R

9.7b Shoulder Joint

LEARNING OBJECTIVES

3. Describe the three individual joints that make up the shoulder articulation.
4. Explain why the glenohumeral joint is relatively unstable.

The joints associated with movement at the shoulder include the sternoclavicular joint, the acromioclavicular joint, and the glenohumeral joint (see table 9.4).

Sternoclavicular Joint

The **sternoclavicular** (ster′nō-kla-vik′ū-lăr) **joint** is a saddle joint formed by the articulation between the manubrium of the sternum and the sternal end of the clavicle (**figure 9.14**). An **articular disc** partitions the sternoclavicular joint into two parts and forms two separate synovial cavities. As a result, a wide range of movement is possible, including elevation, depression, and circumduction.

Support and stability are provided to this articulation by the fibers of the articular capsule and by multiple extracapsular ligaments, such as the sternoclavicular and costoclavicular ligaments. This design makes the sternoclavicular joint very stable. If you fall on an outstretched hand so that force is applied to the joint, the clavicle will fracture before this joint dislocates.

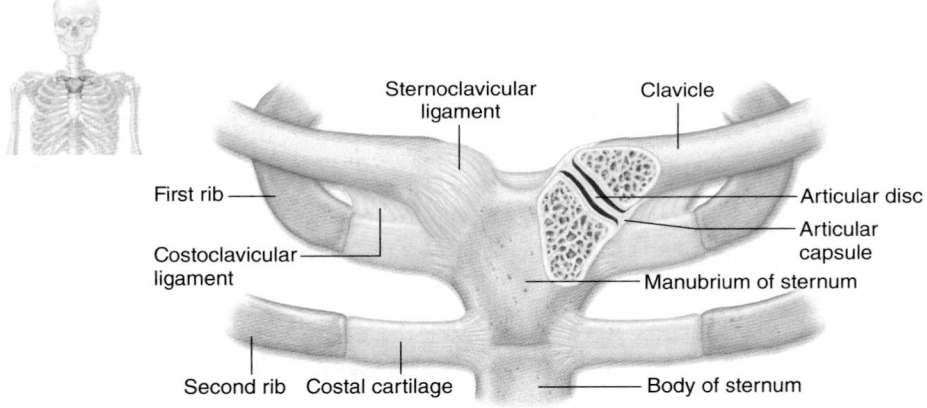

(a) Anterior view with upper limbs in anatomic position

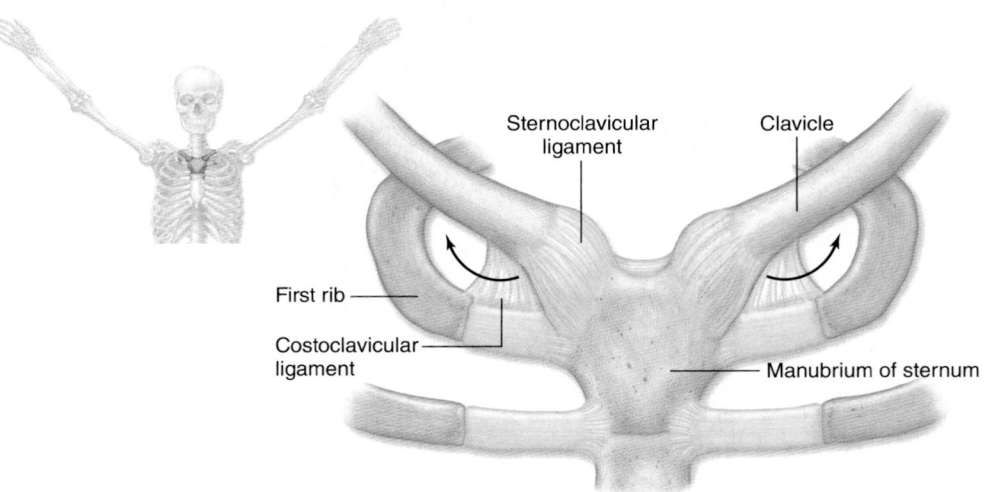

(b) Anterior view with upper limbs raised

Figure 9.14 Sternoclavicular Joint. The sternoclavicular joint helps stabilize movements of the entire shoulder. The positioning of the joint is compared (*a*) with the upper limbs by the sides of the body and (*b*) with the upper limbs raised.

Acromioclavicular Joint

The **acromioclavicular** (ă-krō'mē-ō-kla-vik'ū-lăr) **joint** is a plane joint between the acromion and the lateral end of the clavicle (figure 9.15). A fibrocartilaginous articular disc lies within the joint cavity between these two bones. This joint works with both the sternoclavicular joint and the glenohumeral joint to give the upper limb a full range of movement.

Several ligaments provide great stability to this joint. The fibrous joint capsule is strengthened superiorly by an **acromioclavicular ligament.** In addition, a very strong **coracoclavicular** (kōr'ă-kō-kla-vik'ū-lăr) **ligament** binds the clavicle to the coracoid process of the scapula. If this ligament is torn (as occurs in severe shoulder separations; see Clinical View: "Shoulder Separation"), the acromion and clavicle no longer align properly.

Glenohumeral (Shoulder) Joint

The **glenohumeral** (glē'nō-hū'mer-ăl) **joint** is commonly referred to as the shoulder joint. It is a ball-and-socket joint formed by the articulation of the head of the humerus and the glenoid cavity of the scapula (figure 9.15). It permits the greatest range of motion of any joint in the body, and so it is also both the most unstable joint in the body and the one most frequently dislocated.

The fibrocartilaginous **glenoid labrum** encircles and covers the surface of the glenoid cavity. A relatively loose articular capsule attaches to the surgical neck of the humerus. The glenohumeral joint has several major ligaments. The **coracoacromial** (kōr'ă-kō-ă-krō' mē-ăl) **ligament** extends across the space between the coracoid process and the acromion. The large **coracohumeral** (kōr'ă-kō-hū'mer-ăl) **ligament** is a thickening of the superior part of the joint capsule. It extends from the coracoid process to the humeral head.

INTEGRATE

CLINICAL VIEW
Dislocation of the Glenohumeral Joint

Since the glenohumeral joint is very mobile and relatively unstable, dislocations are common. Glenohumeral dislocations usually occur when a fully abducted humerus is struck hard—for example, when a quarterback is hit as he is about to release a football, or when a person falls on an outstretched hand.

The following sequence of events occurs in a glenohumeral dislocation: The initial blow pushes the head of the humerus into the inferior part of the capsule and tears it as the humerus dislocates. Once the humeral head is no longer held in place by the capsule, the chest muscles pull superiorly and medially on the humeral head, causing it to lie just inferior to the coracoid process. The result is that the shoulder appears flattened and "squared-off," because the humeral head is now anterior and inferior to the glenohumeral joint capsule.

Some glenohumeral dislocations can be repaired by popping the humerus back into the glenoid cavity, but this should be attempted only by trained personnel. More severe dislocations may need surgical repair.

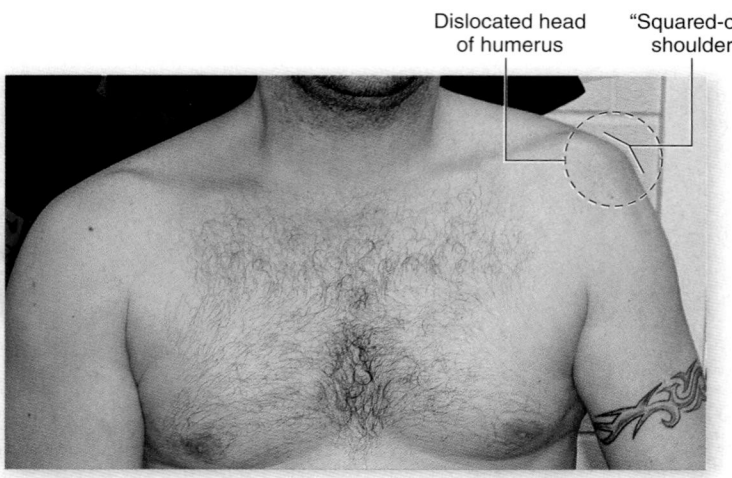

Dislocated glenohumeral joint.

Dislocated head of humerus · "Squared-off" shoulder

Clavicle

Glenoid cavity

Displaced head of humerus

Radiograph of a glenohumeral joint dislocation.

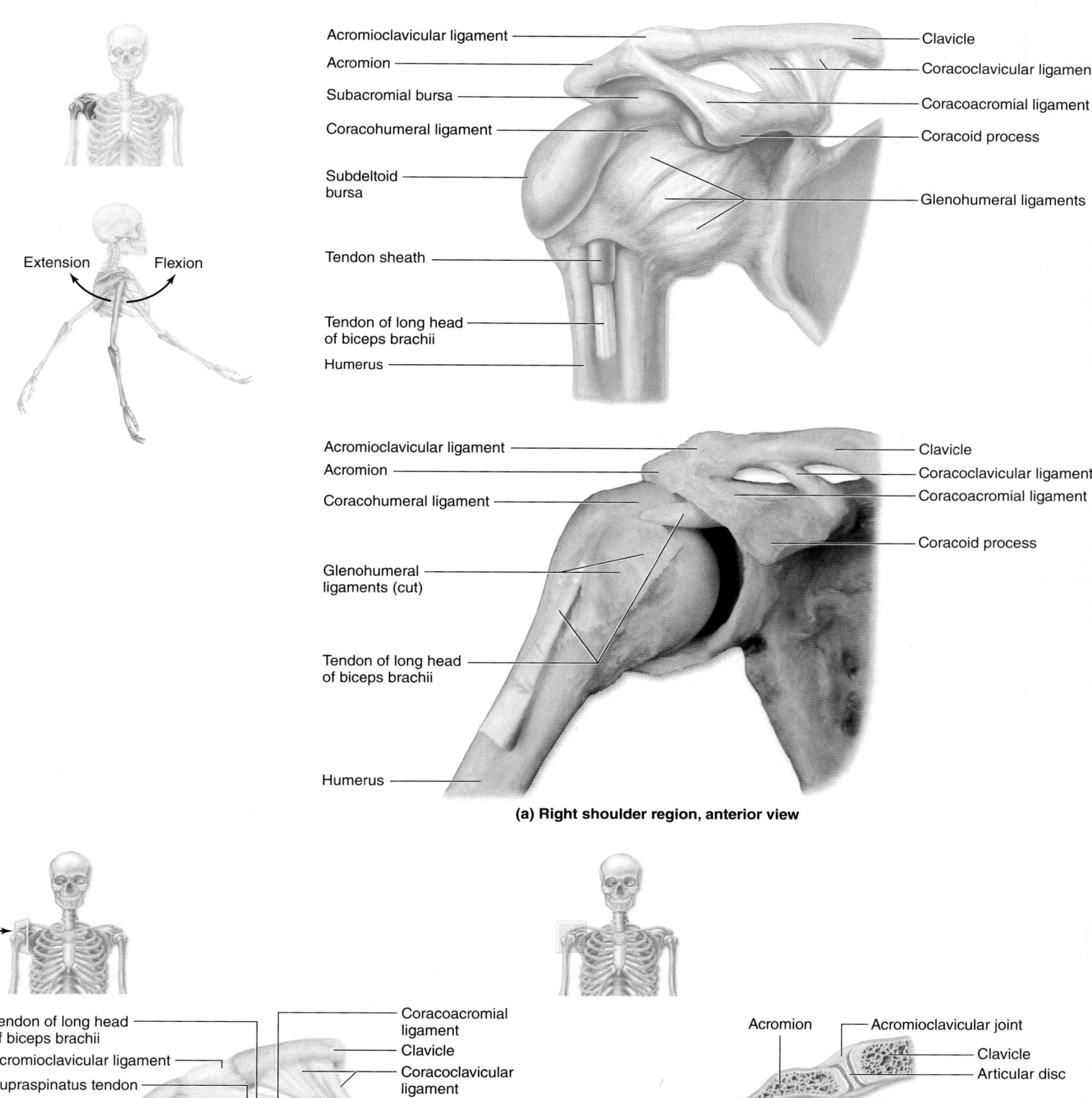

Extension   Flexion

Acromioclavicular ligament — Clavicle
Acromion — Coracoclavicular ligament
Subacromial bursa — Coracoacromial ligament
Coracohumeral ligament — Coracoid process
Subdeltoid bursa — Glenohumeral ligaments
Tendon sheath
Tendon of long head of biceps brachii
Humerus

Acromioclavicular ligament — Clavicle
Acromion — Coracoclavicular ligament
Coracohumeral ligament — Coracoacromial ligament
— Coracoid process
Glenohumeral ligaments (cut)
Tendon of long head of biceps brachii
Humerus

(a) Right shoulder region, anterior view

Tendon of long head of biceps brachii — Coracoacromial ligament
Acromioclavicular ligament — Clavicle
Supraspinatus tendon — Coracoclavicular ligament
Acromion — Coracoid process
Infraspinatus tendon
Bursa
Teres minor muscle — Subscapularis muscle
Glenoid cavity — Bursa
Glenoid labrum — Glenohumeral ligaments
Articular capsule
Scapula

(b) Right shoulder, lateral view

Acromion — Acromioclavicular joint
— Clavicle
— Articular disc
Tendon of long head of biceps brachii — Supraspinatus tendon
Bursa — Synovial membrane
Deltoid muscle — Glenoid cavity of scapula
Humerus — Glenoid labrum
— Articular capsule

(c) Right shoulder, coronal section

Figure 9.15 Acromioclavicular and Glenohumeral Joints. (a) Anterior diagrammatic view and cadaver photo of both joints on the right side of the body. (b) Right lateral view and (c) right coronal section show the articulating bones and supporting structures at the shoulder.

317

INTEGRATE

CONCEPT CONNECTION

The shoulder joint illustrates the interrelatedness of the skeletal system and muscular system. The stability of the glenohumeral joint primarily comes from the musculature, as opposed to the skeletal elements. Injury to this musculature will affect the workings of this joint.

The term **subluxation** refers to an incomplete dislocation, in which the contact between the bony joint surfaces is altered, but they are still in partial contact. In subluxation of the head of the radius, the head is pulled out of the anular ligament. The layman's terms for this injury include *pulled elbow, nursemaid's elbow,* or *slipped elbow.* This injury occurs commonly and almost exclusively in children (typically those younger than age 5), because a child's anular ligament is thin and the head of the radius is not fully formed. After age 5, both the ligament and the radial head are more fully formed so the risk of this type of injury lessens dramatically. However, it may occur if an individual pulls suddenly on a child's pronated forearm.

Luckily, treatment is simple: The pediatrician applies posteriorly placed pressure to the head of the radius while slowly supinating and extending the child's forearm. This movement literally screws the radial head back into the anular ligament. In most cases, this manual treatment brings immediate relief.

The **glenohumeral ligaments** are three thickenings of the anterior portion of the articular capsule. These ligaments are often indistinct or absent and provide only minimal support. In addition, the tendon of the long head of biceps brachii travels within the articular capsule and helps stabilize the humeral head in the joint.

Ligaments of the glenohumeral joint strengthen the joint only minimally. Most of the joint's strength is due to the **rotator cuff** muscles surrounding it (see section 11.8b). The rotator cuff muscles (infraspinatus, subscapularis, supraspinatus, and teres minor) work as a group to hold the head of the humerus in the glenoid cavity. The tendons of these muscles encircle the joint (except for its inferior portion) and fuse with the articular capsule. Because the inferior portion of the joint lacks support from rotator cuff muscles, this area is weak and is the most likely site of injury.

Bursae help decrease friction at the specific places on the shoulder where both tendons and large muscles extend across the joint capsule. The shoulder has a relatively large number of bursae.

WHAT DID YOU LEARN?

18 Why is the shoulder joint considered the most mobile and at the same time the most unstable joint in the human body?

9.7c Elbow Joint

LEARNING OBJECTIVES

5. Describe the elbow joint and its motion.

6. Explain why the elbow joint is relatively stable.

The **elbow joint** is a hinge joint composed of two articulations: (1) the humeroulnar joint, where the trochlear notch of the ulna articulates with the trochlea of the humerus; and (2) the humeroradial joint, where the capitulum of the humerus articulates with the head of the radius. Both joints are enclosed within a single articular capsule (**figure 9.16**; see table 9.4).

The elbow is an extremely stable joint for several reasons. First, the articular capsule is fairly thick, and thus effectively protects the articulations. Second, the bony surfaces of the humerus and ulna interlock very well, and thus provide a solid bony support. Finally, multiple strong supporting ligaments help reinforce the articular capsule. Because of the tradeoff between stability and mobility, the elbow joint is very stable but is not as mobile as some other joints, such as the glenohumeral joint.

The elbow joint has two main supporting ligaments. The **radial collateral ligament** (or *lateral collateral ligament*) is responsible for stabilizing the joint at its lateral surface; it extends around the head of the radius between the anular ligament and the lateral epicondyle of the humerus. The **ulnar collateral ligament** (or *medial collateral ligament*) stabilizes the medial side of the joint and extends from the medial epicondyle of the humerus both to the coronoid process of the ulna and to the olecranon. In addition, an **anular** (an'ū-lăr; *anulus* = ring) **ligament** surrounds the neck of the radius and binds the proximal head of the radius to the ulna. The anular ligament helps hold the head of the radius in place.

Despite the support from the capsule and ligaments, the elbow joint is subject to damage from severe impacts or unusual stresses. For example, if you fall on an outstretched hand and the elbow joint is partially flexed, the posterior stress on the ulna combined with contractions of muscles that extend the elbow may break the ulna at the center of the trochlear notch. Sometimes dislocations result from stresses to the elbow. This is particularly true when growth is still occurring at the epiphyseal plate, so children and teenagers may be prone to humeral epicondyle dislocations or fractures.

WHAT DID YOU LEARN?

19 What is the function of the anular ligament in the elbow joint, and what injury may occur to this ligament and joint in young children?

Flexion

Extension

Humerus

Lateral epicondyle

Articular capsule

Radial collateral ligament

Anular ligament

Tendon of biceps brachii (cut)

Radius

Ulna

Medial epicondyle

Ulnar collateral ligament

(a) Right elbow, anterior view

Humerus

Lateral epicondyle

Radial collateral ligament

Articular capsule

Anular ligament

Tendon of biceps brachii (cut)

Radius

Ulna

(b) Right elbow, lateral view

Tendon of biceps brachii (cut)

Radius

Anular ligament

Articular capsule

Humerus

Medial epicondyle

Ulnar collateral ligament

Ulna

(c) Right elbow, medial view

Trochlea

Articular capsule

Coronoid process

Radius

Ulna

Humerus

Articular cartilage

Olecranon

Trochlear notch

(d) Right elbow, medial sagittal section

Figure 9.16 Elbow Joint. The elbow joint is a hinge joint. The right elbow is shown here in (*a*) anterior view, (*b*) lateral view, (*c*) medial view, and (*d*) sagittal section. AP|R

9.7d Hip Joint

LEARNING OBJECTIVES

7. Describe the hip joint and its motions.

8. Explain why the hip joint is more stable than the glenohumeral joint.

The **hip joint,** also known as the *coxal joint,* is the articulation between the head of the femur and the relatively deep, concave acetabulum of the os coxae (**figure 9.17**; table 9.5). A fibrocartilaginous **acetabular labrum** further deepens this socket. The hip joint's more extensive bony architecture is therefore much stronger and more stable than that of the glenohumeral joint. Conversely, the hip joint's increased stability means that it is less mobile than the glenohumeral joint. The hip joint must be more stable (and thus less mobile) because it supports the body weight.

The hip joint is secured by a strong articular capsule, several ligaments, and a number of powerful muscles. The articular capsule extends from the acetabulum to the trochanters of the femur, enclosing both the femoral head and neck. This arrangement prevents the head from moving away from the acetabulum. The ligamentous fibers of the articular capsule reflect around the neck of the femur. These reflected fibers, called **retinacular** (ret-i-nak′ū-lăr) **fibers,** provide additional stability to the capsule. Traveling through the retinacular fibers are retinacular arteries (branches of the deep femoral artery), which supply almost all of the blood to the head and neck of the femur.

The articular capsule is reinforced by three spiraling intracapsular ligaments: The **iliofemoral** (il′ē-ō-fem′ŏ-răl) **ligament** is a Y-shaped ligament that provides strong reinforcement for the anterior region of the articular capsule. The **ischiofemoral** (is-kē-ō-fem′ŏ-răl) **ligament** is a spiral-shaped, posteriorly located ligament. The **pubofemoral** (pū′bō-fem′ŏ-răl) **ligament** is a triangular thickening of the capsule's inferior region. All of these spiraling ligaments become taut when the hip joint is extended, so the hip joint is most stable in the extended position. Try this experiment: Flex your hip joint, and try to move the femur; you may notice a great deal of mobility. Now extend your hip joint (stand up), and try to move the femur. Because those ligaments are taut, you don't have as much mobility in the joint as you did when the hip joint was flexed.

Another tiny ligament, the **ligament of head of femur,** also called the *ligamentum teres,* originates along the acetabulum. Its attachment point is the fovea of the head of the femur. This ligament does not provide strength to the joint; rather, it typically contains a small artery that supplies the head of the femur.

The combination of a deep bony socket, a strong articular capsule, supporting ligaments, and muscular padding gives the hip joint its stability. Movements possible at the hip joint include flexion, extension, abduction, adduction, rotation, and circumduction.

 WHAT DID YOU LEARN?

20 How do the glenohumeral and hip joints compare with respect to their mobility and stability?

INTEGRATE

CLINICAL VIEW
Fracture of the Femoral Neck

Fracture of the femoral neck is often incorrectly referred to as a "fractured hip," because the os coxae isn't broken: The break is in the femoral neck. With this injury, the pull of the lower limb muscles causes the leg to rotate laterally and appear shorter by several inches. Fractures of the femoral neck are of two types: intertrochanteric and subcapital.

Intertrochanteric fractures of the femoral neck occur distally to or outside the hip joint capsule—in other words, these fractures are *extracapsular.* The fracture line runs between the greater and lesser trochanters. This type of injury typically occurs in younger and middle-aged individuals. It usually occurs in response to trauma.

Subcapital (or *intracapsular*) **fractures** of the femoral neck occur within the hip articular capsule, very close to the head of the femur itself. This type of fracture usually occurs in elderly people whose bones have been weakened by osteoporosis and thus are more susceptible to fracture.

Subcapital fractures result in a tearing of the retinacular arteries that supply the head and neck of the femur. The ligament of the head of the femur may be torn as well. As a result, the head and neck of the femur lose their blood supply and may develop **avascular necrosis,** which is death of the bone due to lack of blood. Frequently, hip replacement surgery is needed, whereby a metal femoral head and neck replace the dying bone. This surgery is not without risk, however, and many elderly individuals do not survive because of surgical complications.

Extension **Flexion**

Abduction
Adduction

Iliofemoral
ligament

Greater
trochanter

Pubofemoral
ligament

Lesser
trochanter

(a) Right hip, anterior view

Iliofemoral ligament
Ischiofemoral ligament

Greater
trochanter

Lesser
trochanter

Ischial tuberosity

(b) Right hip, posterior view

Acetabular labrum
Articular capsule

Acetabulum

Greater
trochanter
of femur

Ligament of
head of femur

Retinacular
fibers

Ischium

(c) Right hip, coronal section

Acetabular labrum
Ligament of
head of femur

Head of femur

Articular
capsule (cut)

(d) Right hip, anterior view, internal aspect of joint

Figure 9.17 Hip Joint. The hip joint is formed by the head of the femur and the acetabulum of the os coxae. The right hip joint is shown in (a) anterior view, (b) posterior view, and (c) coronal section. (d) Cadaver photo of the coxal joint, with the articular capsule cut to show internal structures. **AP|R**

9.7e Knee Joint

The **knee joint** is the largest and most complex diarthrosis of the body (**figure 9.18**; table 9.5; see also figure 9.5). It is primarily a hinge joint, but when the knee is flexed, it is also capable of slight rotation and lateral gliding. Structurally, the knee is composed of two separate articulations: (1) The **tibiofemoral** (tib-ē-ō-fem′ŏ-răl) **joint** is between the condyles of the femur and the condyles of the tibia, and (2) the **patellofemoral joint** is between the patella and the patellar surface of the femur.

The knee joint has an articular capsule that encloses only the medial, lateral, and posterior regions of the knee joint. The articular capsule does not cover the anterior surface of the knee joint; rather, the quadriceps femoris muscle tendon passes over the knee joint's anterior surface. The patella is embedded within this tendon, and the **patellar ligament** extends beyond the patella and continues to where it attaches on the tibial tuberosity of the tibia. Thus, there is no single unified capsule in the knee, nor is there a common joint cavity. Posteriorly the capsule is strengthened by several popliteal ligaments.

On either side of the knee joint are two collateral ligaments that become taut on extension and provide additional stability to the joint. The **fibular collateral ligament** (*lateral collateral ligament*) reinforces the lateral surface of the joint. This ligament extends from the femur to the fibula and prevents hyperadduction of the leg at the knee. (In other words, it prevents the leg from moving too far medially relative to the thigh). The **tibial collateral ligament** (*medial collateral ligament*) reinforces the medial surface of the knee joint. This ligament runs from the femur to the tibia and prevents hyperabduction of the leg at the knee. (In other words, it prevents the leg from moving too far laterally relative to the thigh.) This ligament is attached to the medial meniscus of the knee joint as well, so an injury to the tibial collateral ligament usually affects the medial meniscus.

Deep to the articular capsule and within the knee joint itself are a pair of C-shaped fibrocartilage pads positioned on the condyles of the tibia. These pads are called the **medial meniscus** and the **lateral meniscus.** They partially stabilize the joint medially and laterally, act as cushions between articular surfaces, and continuously change shape to conform to the articulating surfaces as the femur moves.

Two **cruciate** (kroo′shē-āt) **ligaments** are deep to the articular capsule of the knee joint. They limit the anterior and posterior movement of the femur on the tibia. These ligaments cross each other in the form of an **X**, hence the name "cruciate" (which means "cross"). The **anterior cruciate ligament (ACL)** extends from the posterior femur to the anterior side of the tibia. When the knee is extended, the ACL is pulled tight and prevents hyperextension. The ACL prevents the tibia from moving too far anteriorly on the femur. The **posterior cruciate ligament (PCL)** runs from the anteroinferior femur to the posterior side of the tibia. The PCL becomes taut on flexion, and so it prevents hyperflexion of the knee joint. The PCL also prevents posterior displacement of the tibia on the femur.

Humans are bipedal animals, meaning that we walk on two feet. An important aspect of bipedal locomotion is the ability to "lock" the knees in the extended position and stand erect without tiring the leg muscles. At full extension, the tibia rotates laterally so as to tighten the anterior cruciate ligament and squeeze the menisci between the tibia and femur. Muscular contraction by the popliteus muscle unlocks and flexes the knee joint. (This ability should be distinguished from being unable to bend or straighten the knee because of injury or disease, which is sometimes also called locking.)

  WHAT DID YOU LEARN?

21 What are the functions of each of the intracapsular ligaments of the knee joint?

Figure 9.18 Knee Joint. This joint is the most complex diarthrosis of the body. (*a*) Anterior superficial, (*b*) posterior superficial, (*c*) anterior deep, and (*d*) posterior deep views reveal the complex interrelationships of the parts of the right knee. AP|R

Flexion

Extension

(a) **Right knee, anterior superficial view**

Quadriceps femoris muscle

Quadriceps femoris tendon

Tibial collateral ligament

Patellar ligament

Tibia

Fibula

Fibular collateral ligament

Patella within quadriceps tendon

(b) **Right knee, posterior superficial view**

Femur

Gastrocnemius muscle heads (cut)

Articular capsule

Oblique popliteal ligament

Tibial collateral ligament

Popliteus muscle (cut)

Fibular collateral ligament

Arcuate popliteal ligament

Fibula

Tibia

(c) **Right knee, anterior deep view**

Articular cartilage

Lateral condyle

Lateral meniscus

Fibular collateral ligament

Fibula

Posterior cruciate ligament

Medial condyle

Medial meniscus

Anterior cruciate ligament

Tibial collateral ligament

Tibia

(d) **Right knee, posterior deep view**

Femur

Anterior cruciate ligament

Lateral condyle

Fibular collateral ligament

Lateral meniscus

Posterior cruciate ligament

Medial condyle

Medial meniscus

Tibial collateral ligament

Tibia

Fibula

CLINICAL VIEW
Knee Ligament and Cartilage Injuries

Although the knee is capable of bearing much weight and has numerous strong supporting ligaments, it is highly vulnerable to injury, especially among athletes. Because the knee is reinforced by tendons and ligaments only, ligamentous injuries to the knee are very common.

The tibial collateral ligament is frequently injured when the leg is forcibly abducted at the knee, such as when a person's knee is hit on the lateral side. Because the tibial collateral ligament is attached to the medial meniscus, the medial meniscus may be injured as well.

Injury to the fibular collateral ligament can occur if the medial side of the knee is struck, resulting in hyperadduction of the leg at the knee. This type of injury is fairly rare, in part because the fibular collateral ligament is very strong and also because medial blows to the knee are not common.

The anterior cruciate ligament (ACL) can be injured when the leg is hyperextended—for example, if a runner's foot hits a hole. Because the ACL is rather weak compared to the other knee ligaments, it is especially prone to injury. To test for ACL injury, a physician gently tugs anteriorly on the tibia. In this so-called **anterior drawer test**, too much forward movement indicates an ACL tear.

Posterior cruciate ligament (PCL) injury may occur if the leg is hyperflexed or if the tibia is driven posteriorly on the femur. PCL injury occurs rarely, because this ligament is rather strong. To test for PCL injury, a physician gently pushes posteriorly on the tibia. In this **posterior drawer test**, too much posterior movement indicates a PCL tear.

The menisci also may be prone to injury. Tears in the meniscus may occur due to blows to the knee or due to general overuse of the joint. Since the menisci are composed of fibrocartilage, they cannot regenerate and often must be surgically treated.

The **unhappy triad** of injuries refers to a triple injury of the tibial collateral ligament, medial meniscus, and anterior cruciate ligament. This is the most common type of football injury. It occurs when a player is illegally "clipped" by a lateral blow to the knee, and the leg is forcibly abducted and laterally rotated. If the blow is severe enough, the tibial collateral ligament tears,

followed by tearing of the medial meniscus, since these two structures are connected. The force that tears the tibial collateral ligament and the medial meniscus is thus transferred to the ACL. Since the ACL is relatively weak, it tears as well.

The treatment of ligamentous knee injuries depends upon the severity and type of injury. Conservative treatment involves immobilizing the knee for a period of time to rest the joint. Surgical treatment can include repairing the torn ligaments or replacing the ligaments with a graft from another tendon or ligament (such as the quadriceps tendon). Many knee surgeries now may be performed with arthroscopy. **Arthroscopy** is a type of conservative surgical treatment where a small incision is made in the knee and then an **arthroscope** (an instrument with a camera and light source) is inserted in the knee, allowing the surgeon to clearly see the surgical area without having to make large incisions.

Lateral blow to knee

Torn anterior cruciate ligament

Torn tibial collateral ligament

Torn medial meniscus

9.7f Talocrural (Ankle) Joint

LEARNING OBJECTIVE

11. Describe the talocrural joint and its motion.

The **talocrural (ankle) joint** is a highly modified hinge joint that permits both dorsiflexion and plantar flexion. It includes two articulations within one joint capsule. One articulation is between the distal end of the tibia and the talus; the other is between the distal end of the fibula and the lateral aspect of the talus (figure 9.19; table 9.5). The medial and lateral malleoli of the tibia and fibula, respectively, form extensive medial and lateral margins and prevent the talus from sliding side-to-side.

The talocrural joint includes several distinctive anatomic features. Its articular capsule covers the distal surfaces of the tibia, the medial malleolus, the lateral malleolus, and the

Plantar flexion

Dorsiflexion

Fibula — — Tibia

Posterior tibiofibular ligament

Anterior tibiofibular ligament

Talus

Lateral ligament

Calcaneus

Metatarsal V

(a) Right foot, lateral view

Tibia

Deltoid ligament

Navicular bone

Talus

Metatarsal I

Calcaneus

(b) Right foot, medial view

Figure 9.19 Talocrural Joint. (*a*) Lateral and (*b*) medial views of the right foot show that the talocrural joint contains articulations among the tibia, fibula, and talus. This joint permits dorsiflexion and plantar flexion only. AP|R

talus. A multipart **deltoid ligament** (or *medial ligament*) binds the tibia to the foot on the medial side. This ligament prevents overeversion of the foot. It is incredibly strong and rarely tears; in fact, it will pull off the medial malleolus before it ever ruptures! A much thinner multipart **lateral ligament** binds the fibula to the foot on the lateral side. This ligament prevents overinversion of the foot. It is not as strong as the deltoid ligament, and is prone to sprains and tears. Two **tibiofibular** (tib-ē-ō-fib′ū-lar) **ligaments** (**anterior** and **posterior**) bind the tibia to the fibula.

WHAT DID YOU LEARN?

22 What bones articulate at the talocrural joint, and what movements are permitted at this joint?

9.8 Development and Aging of the Joints

LEARNING OBJECTIVES

1. Explain how the three major types of joints form in the embryo and fetus.
2. Describe some of the common age-related changes in joints.

Joints start to form by the sixth week of development and progressively differentiate during the fetal period. In the area of future fibrous joints, the mesenchyme around the developing bone differentiates into dense regular connective tissue, whereas in cartilaginous joints, it differentiates into either fibrocartilage or hyaline cartilage.

The development of the synovial joints is more complex. The most *laterally* placed mesenchyme forms the articular capsule and supporting ligaments of the joint. Just medial to this region, the mesenchyme forms the synovial membrane, which then starts secreting synovial fluid into the joint cavity. The *centrally* located mesenchyme may be reabsorbed or can form menisci or articular discs, depending on the type of synovial joint.

Prior to the closure of the epiphyseal plates, some injuries to a young person may result in subluxation or fracture of an epiphysis, with potential adverse effects on the future development and health of the joint. Some adverse effects include the bone not reaching its potential full length, or the individual may develop arthritic-like changes in the joint.

INTEGRATE

CLINICAL VIEW
Arthritis

Arthritis (ar-thrī'tis) is a group of inflammatory or degenerative diseases of joints that occur in various forms. Each form presents the same symptoms: swelling of the joint, pain, and stiffness. It is the most prevalent crippling disease in the United States. Some common forms of arthritis are gouty arthritis, osteoarthritis, and rheumatoid arthritis.

Gouty arthritis is typically seen in middle-aged and older individuals, and is more common in males. Often called *gout*, this disease occurs as a result of an increased level of uric acid (a normal cellular waste product) in the blood. This abnormal level causes urate crystals to accumulate in the blood, synovial fluid, and synovial membranes. The body's inflammatory response to the urate crystals results in joint pain. Gout usually begins with an attack on a single joint (often in the great toe), and later progresses to other joints. Eventually, gouty arthritis may immobilize joints by causing fusion between the articular surfaces of the bones.

Osteoarthritis (OA) is the most common type of arthritis. This chronic degenerative joint condition also is termed *wear-and-tear arthritis* because repeated use of a joint gradually wears down the articular cartilage, much like the repeated use of a pencil eraser wears down the eraser. If the cartilage is worn down enough, osteoarthritis results. Eventually, bone rubs against bone, causing abrasions on the bony surfaces. Without the protective articular cartilage, movements at the joints become stiff and painful. The joints most affected by osteoarthritis are those of the fingers, knuckles, hips, knees, and shoulders. Osteoarthritis is typically seen in older individuals, although more and more athletes are experiencing arthritis at an earlier age due to the repetitive stresses placed on their joints.

Rheumatoid (roo'mă-toyd) **arthritis (RA)** is typically seen in younger and middle-aged adults, and it is much more prevalent in women. The common age at onset is approximately 40–50 years of age. Symptoms include pain and swelling of the joints, muscle weakness, osteoporosis, and assorted problems with both the heart and the blood vessels. Rheumatoid arthritis is an *autoimmune disorder* in which the body's immune system targets its own tissues for attack. Rheumatoid arthritis starts with synovial membrane inflammation. Fluid and white blood cells leak from small blood vessels into the joint cavity, causing an increase in synovial fluid volume. As a consequence, the joint swells, and the inflamed synovial membrane thickens; eventually, the articular cartilage and, often, the underlying bone become eroded. Scar tissue eventually forms and ossifies, and bone ends fuse together (a process called **ankylosis**), immobilizing the joint. Two types of medications often are prescribed to treat RA. The faster-acting first-line medications include NSAIDs and corticosteroids and are used to relieve joint pain. The slower, but longer-acting second-line medications, such as methotrexate and hydroxychloroquine, help put the disease into remission and slow down the destruction of the joints.

A photograph and radiograph of hands with rheumatoid arthritis.

Arthritis is a rheumatic disease that involves damage to articular cartilage (see Clinical View: "Arthritis"). The primary problem that develops in an aging joint is osteoarthritis, also known as degenerative arthritis. The cause of the damage may vary, but it usually results from cumulative wear and tear at the joint surface.

Just as the strength of a bone is maintained by continual application of stress, the health of joints is directly related to moderate exercise. Exercise compresses the articular cartilages, causing synovial fluid to be squeezed out of the cartilage and then pulled back inside the cartilage matrix. This flow of fluid gives the chondrocytes within the cartilage the nourishment required to maintain their health. Exercise also strengthens the muscles that support and stabilize the joint. However, extreme exercise should be avoided, because it aggravates potential joint problems and may worsen osteoarthritis.

 WHAT DID YOU LEARN?

23 What are some ways that joints change as a person ages?

CHAPTER SUMMARY

	• Articulations are the joints where bones interact. Joints differ in structure, function, and the amount of movement they allow.
9.1 Classification of Joints 298	• The three structural categories of joints are fibrous, cartilaginous, and synovial.
	• The three functional categories of joints are synarthroses (immobile joints), amphiarthroses (slightly mobile joints), and diarthroses (freely mobile joints).
9.2 Fibrous Joints 300	• Fibrous joints interconnect articulating bones by dense regular connective tissue.
	• Fibrous joints have no joint cavity and are immobile or only slightly mobile.
	9.2a Gomphoses 300
	• A gomphosis is a synarthrosis between the tooth and either the mandible or the maxillae.
	9.2b Sutures 300
	• A suture is a synarthrosis that tightly binds the bones of the skull. Fused sutures are called synostoses.
	9.2c Syndesmoses 301
	• A syndesmosis is an amphiarthrosis, and the bones are connected by interosseous membranes.
9.3 Cartilaginous Joints 301	• Cartilaginous joints lack a joint space; the cartilage may be either hyaline cartilage or fibrocartilage.
	9.3a Synchondroses 301
	• A synchondrosis is a synarthrosis where hyaline cartilage is wedged between the articulating bones.
	9.3b Symphyses 302
	• A symphysis is an amphiarthrosis, where a disc of fibrocartilage is wedged between the articulating bones.
9.4 Synovial Joints 302	• All synovial joints are diarthroses.
	9.4a Distinguishing Features and Anatomy of Synovial Joints 302
	• Synovial joints contain an articular capsule, a joint cavity, synovial fluid, articular cartilage, ligaments, nerves, and blood vessels.
	9.4b Classification of Synovial Joints 304
	• The six types of synovial joints are plane, hinge, pivot, condylar, saddle, and ball-and-socket.
9.5 Synovial Joints and Levers 304	• Biomechanics is the practice of applying mechanical principles to biology.
	9.5a Terminology of Levers 304
	• Synovial joints may be compared to levers, which have a fixed point (fulcrum) around which movement occurs when effort applied to one point exceeds resistance at another point.

(continued on next page)

| 9.5 Synovial Joints and Levers 304 (continued) | **9.5b Types of Levers 306**
- A first-class lever has a fulcrum between the effort and resistance.
- A second-class lever has the resistance placed between the fulcrum and the effort.
- A third-class lever, the most common type of lever in the human body, has the effort applied between the resistance and the fulcrum. |
|---|---|
| 9.6 The Movements of Synovial Joints 307 | - Motions that occur at synovial joints include gliding, angular, rotational, and special.
9.6a Gliding Motion 307
- Gliding is a simple movement where two opposing surfaces slide back-and-forth or side-to-side against one another.
9.6b Angular Motion 307
- Angular movements include flexion, extension, hyperextension, lateral flexion, abduction, adduction, and circumduction.
9.6c Rotational Motion 309
- Rotational movements involve a pivoting motion. Lateral rotation, medial rotation, pronation, and supination are examples of rotational movements.
9.6d Special Movements 310
- Special movements include depression and elevation, dorsiflexion and plantar flexion, inversion and eversion, protraction and retraction, and opposition. |
| 9.7 Features and Anatomy of Selected Joints 311 | - In each articulation, unique features of the articulating bones support the intended movements.
9.7a Temporomandibular Joint 314
- The temporomandibular joint is an articulation between the head of the mandible and the mandibular fossa of the temporal bone.
9.7b Shoulder Joint 315
- The sternoclavicular joint and acromioclavicular joint support movement of the shoulder.
- The glenohumeral joint is a ball-and-socket joint between the glenoid cavity of the scapula and the head of the humerus.
9.7c Elbow Joint 318
- The elbow is a hinge joint among the humerus, radius, and ulna.
9.7d Hip Joint 320
- The hip joint is a ball-and-socket joint between the head of the femur and the acetabulum of the os coxae.
9.7e Knee Joint 322
- The knee joint is primarily a hinge joint but is capable of slight rotation and gliding.
9.7f Talocrural (Ankle) Joint 324
- The talocrural joint is a hinge joint that permits dorsiflexion and plantar flexion. |
| 9.8 Development and Aging of the Joints 326 | - Joints begin to form during week 6 of development.
- Osteoarthritis is a common joint problem that occurs with aging. |

CHALLENGE YOURSELF

Do You Know the Basics?

____ 1. The greatest range of mobility of any joint in the body is found in the

 a. knee joint.
 b. hip joint.
 c. glenohumeral joint.
 d. elbow joint.

____ 2. A movement of the foot that turns the sole outward or laterally is called

 a. dorsiflexion.
 b. inversion.
 c. eversion.
 d. plantar flexion.

_____ 3. A _____ is formed when two bones previously connected by a suture fuse.

    a. gomphosis

    b. synostosis

    c. symphysis

    d. syndesmosis

_____ 4. The ligament that helps to maintain the alignment of the condyles between the femur and tibia and to limit the anterior movement of the tibia on the femur is the

    a. tibial collateral ligament.

    b. posterior cruciate ligament.

    c. anterior cruciate ligament.

    d. fibular collateral ligament.

_____ 5. The glenohumeral joint is primarily stabilized by the

    a. coracohumeral ligament.

    b. glenohumeral ligaments.

    c. rotator cuff muscles that move the humerus.

    d. scapula.

_____ 6. In this type of lever, the effort is located between the resistance and the fulcrum. An example would be your knee joint.

    a. first-class

    b. second-class

    c. third-class

    d. None of these are correct.

_____ 7. A metacarpophalangeal (MP) joint, which has oval articulating surfaces and permits movement in two planes, is what type of synovial joint?

    a. condylar

    b. plane

    c. hinge

    d. saddle

_____ 8. All of the following ligaments provide stability to the hip joint except the

    a. ischiofemoral ligament.

    b. pubofemoral ligament.

    c. iliofemoral ligament.

    d. ligament of the head of the femur.

_____ 9. Which of the following is a function of synovial fluid?

    a. lubricates the joint

    b. provides nutrients for bone

    c. absorbs shock within the joint

    d. All of these are correct.

_____ 10. Plantar flexion and dorsiflexion are movements permitted at the _____ joint.

    a. hip

    b. knee

    c. sternoclavicular

    d. talocrural

11. Discuss the factors that influence both the stability and mobility of a joint. What is the relationship between a joint's mobility and its stability?

12. Describe the structural differences between fibrous joints and cartilaginous joints.

13. List and describe all joints that are functionally classified as synarthroses.

14. Compare a hinge joint and a pivot joint with respect to structure, function, and location within the body.

15. Compare and contrast first-, second-, and third-class levers.

16. Describe and compare the movements of abduction, adduction, pronation, and supination.

17. Describe the basic anatomy of the glenohumeral joint.

18. What are the main supporting ligaments of the elbow joint?

19. Compare the functions of the tibial and the fibular collateral ligaments in the knee joint. Which of the two is injured more frequently and why?

20. Explain the primary age-related change that can occur in a joint and what symptoms it may cause.

Can You Apply What You've Learned?

Use the following paragraph to answer questions 1–3.

A mother and her 4-year-old son were visiting a toy store, and the child did not want to leave. As the child threw a temper tantrum and resisted his mother, the mother pulled on the boy's arm to lead him out of the store. Immediately after the pull, the boy cried out in pain and displayed a prominent bump on the lateral side of the elbow. The mother drove the boy to the doctor in a panic. The doctor examined the boy's elbow and determined the boy had a subluxated head of the radius.

1. Which ligament failed to keep the head of the radius in place when the mother pulled on the boy's elbow?

    a. anular ligament

    b. ulnar collateral ligament

    c. radial collateral ligament

    d. coronoid ligament

2. The doctor mentions this type of injury is common in children younger than 5 years of age. What is one reason for this?

   a. The olecranon of the ulna does not fit in properly with the olecranon fossa of the radius.

   b. The head of the radius is not fully formed.

   c. The medial and lateral epicondyle epiphyseal plates have not yet fused to the rest of the humerus.

   d. The articular capsule of the elbow joint is weak in its anterior surface.

3. What bony feature caused the prominent "bump" on the lateral side of the elbow?

   a. lateral epicondyle of the humerus

   b. coronoid process of the ulna

   c. head of the radius

   d. radial collateral ligament

4. While Robert was running, he stepped into a pothole and he twisted his right ankle. A swelling appeared along the lateral side of this ankle. Which ligament was injured, and what movement resulted in the injury?

   a. deltoid ligament, caused by overeversion of the foot

   b. lateral ligament, caused by overeversion of the foot

   c. deltoid ligament, caused by overinversion of the foot

   d. lateral ligament, caused by overinversion of the foot

5. Most knee ligaments become taut upon extension of the joint, except for one. Which knee ligament becomes taut upon *flexion* of the joint, and prevents hyperflexion of the joint?

   a. anterior cruciate ligament

   b. posterior cruciate ligament

   c. patellar ligament

   d. tibial collateral ligament

Can You Synthesize What You've Learned?

1. During soccer practice, Erin tripped over the outstretched leg of a teammate and fell directly onto her shoulder. She was taken to the hospital in excruciating pain. Examination revealed that the head of the humerus had moved inferiorly and anteriorly into the axilla. What happened to Erin in this injury?

2. While Lucas and Omar were watching a football game, a player was penalized for "clipping," meaning that he had hit an opposing player on the lateral knee, causing hyperabduction at the knee joint. Lucas asked Omar what the big deal was about clipping. What joint is most at risk, and what kind of injuries can occur if a player gets clipped?

3. Jackie visits her physician because she is experiencing pain by her right ear. The doctor checks her ears and sees no sign of infection. She asks Jackie to open and close her mouth while she palpates the portions of her face adjacent to her ears. Why is the doctor having Jackie move her mouth, when she is experiencing ear pain? How may the two be related? What do you think the doctor will discover when Jackie opens and closes her mouth?

chapter 10

Muscle Tissue

When we hear the word "muscle," most of us think of the muscles that move the skeleton. Over 700 skeletal muscles have been named, and together they form the **muscular system.** Skeletal muscles, however, are not the only places where muscle tissue is found. Muscle tissue is distributed almost everywhere in the body and is responsible for the movement of materials within and throughout the body. This vital tissue propels the food we eat along the gastrointestinal tract, expels ➡

Athletic trainers are allied health care professionals that assess and diagnose injuries, develop safe and effective strength and physical fitness enhancement programs, and are interested in educating others in the prevention and treatment of athletic injuries. They work with athletes, coaches, and other health care professionals under the direction of a physician.

The majority have earned a master's degree or higher and are board certified. Their educational background includes human anatomy and physiology, biomechanics, methods in physical training, rehabilitation of musculoskeletal injuries, first aid, and nutrition.

Anatomy & Physiology | REVEALED®
aprevealed.com

Module 6: Muscular System

the waste products we produce, changes the amount of air that enters the lungs, and pumps blood to body tissues.

The three types of muscle tissue—skeletal muscle, cardiac muscle, and smooth muscle—were first introduced and compared in section 5.3. Here we describe the details of skeletal muscle anatomy and physiology. The chapter finishes with a brief description of cardiac muscle and a general discussion about smooth muscle. The naming of individual skeletal muscles of the muscular system is covered in chapter 11.

10.1 Introduction to Skeletal Muscle

Skeletal muscle typically composes 40–50% of the weight of an adult. It is primarily attached to the skeleton but is also found at the openings of the gastrointestinal and urinary tracts. We begin our discussion on skeletal muscle by describing both the general functions of skeletal muscle organs and characteristics of skeletal muscle tissue.

10.1a Functions of Skeletal Muscle

 LEARNING OBJECTIVE

1. Explain the five general functions of skeletal muscle.

The hundreds of skeletal muscles within the body perform the following functions:

- **Body movement.** Contraction of muscles attached to bones of the skeleton move the body. The integrated functioning of muscles, bones, and joints can produce both highly coordinated movements such as running and relatively simple, localized movements such as underlining a word in a book.
- **Maintenance of posture.** Contraction of specific skeletal muscles stabilizes joints and helps maintain the body's posture, such as holding the head and trunk erect. These postural muscles contract continuously when you are awake to keep you from collapsing.
- **Protection and support.** Some skeletal muscle is arranged in layers along the walls of the abdominal cavity and the floor of the pelvic cavity. These layers of muscle protect the internal organs and support their normal position within the abdominopelvic cavity.
- **Storage and movement of materials.** Circular muscle bands, called **sphincters** (sfingk'ter; *sphincter* = a band) contract and relax to regulate passage of material. These skeletal muscle sphincters at the **orifices** (or'i-fis; *orificium* = opening) of the gastrointestinal and urinary tracts allow you to voluntarily control the expulsion of feces and urine, respectively.
- **Heat production.** Energy is required for muscle tissue contraction, and heat is always produced by this energy use (the second law of thermodynamics; see section 3.1c). Thus, muscles are like small furnaces that continuously generate heat and function to help maintain your normal body temperature. You shiver when you are cold because

involuntary muscle contraction gives off heat. Likewise, you sweat during exercise to release the additional heat produced by your working muscles (see sections 1.5 and 6.3).

 WHAT DID YOU LEARN?

1 What are the five major functions of skeletal muscle?

10.1b Characteristics of Skeletal Muscle Tissue

 LEARNING OBJECTIVE

2. Describe the five characteristics of skeletal muscle tissue.

Skeletal muscle tissue is composed of muscle cells that exhibit these characteristics—excitability, conductivity, contractility, elasticity, and extensibility:

- **Excitability** is the ability of skeletal muscle cells to respond to stimulation by the nervous system. Neurons (section 5.4) release molecules called neurotransmitters that bind to receptors of a muscle cell.
- **Conductivity** involves an electrical change that travels along the plasma membrane of the skeletal muscle cell. The electrical change is initiated in response to binding of neurotransmitter molecules. This electrical activity is similar to what occurs in nervous tissue.
- **Contractility** is exhibited when contractile proteins within skeletal muscle cells slide past one another, causing skeletal muscle cells to shorten. Tension is generated within muscle cells to pull on bones of the skeleton or move specific body parts.
- **Elasticity** is due to specialized protein fibers within skeletal muscle cells that act like compressed coils when a muscle contracts. When skeletal muscle contraction has ended, the tension in these proteins is released, and the muscle returns to its original length.
- **Extensibility** is the lengthening of a muscle cell. For example, when you flex your elbow joint, you are contracting the biceps brachii on the anterior side of your arm, while the triceps brachii on the posterior side is extended with the motion. The reverse is true when you straighten your elbow joint.

 WHAT DID YOU LEARN?

2 Explain the skeletal muscle characteristics of contractility, elasticity, and extensibility. How do these differ?

10.2 Anatomy of Skeletal Muscle

A single muscle, such as the rectus femoris muscle on the anterior thigh, may be composed of thousands of muscle cells that are typically as long as the entire muscle. Because of their potentially extraordinary length, skeletal muscle cells are often referred to as **muscle fibers** (or *myofibers*). Here we describe the gross anatomy of skeletal muscle, the microscopic anatomy of individual skeletal muscle fibers, and innervation of skeletal muscle fibers.

10.2a Gross Anatomy of Skeletal Muscle

✅ LEARNING OBJECTIVES

1. Identify and describe the three connective tissue layers associated with a muscle.
2. Describe the structure and function of a tendon and an aponeurosis.
3. Explain the function of blood vessels and nerves serving a muscle.

A skeletal muscle is an organ composed of skeletal muscle fibers, connective tissue sheets, blood vessels, and nerves. The organization of a muscle is shown in **figure 10.1**. Notice that within the muscle many muscle fibers are organized into bundles called **fascicles** (fas′i-kl; *fascis* = bundle).

Connective Tissue Components

Three layers of connective tissue occur within muscles: the epimysium, the perimysium, and the endomysium. These layers provide protection, sites for distribution of blood vessels and nerves, and a means of attachment to the skeleton or other structures within the body.

- The **epimysium** (ep-i-mis′ē-ŭm; *epi* = upon; *mys* = muscle) is a layer of dense irregular connective tissue that surrounds the whole skeletal muscle.
- The **perimysium** (per-i-mis′ē-ŭm; *peri* = around) surrounds the fascicles. The dense irregular connective tissue sheath of the perimysium contains extensive arrays of blood vessels and nerves that branch to supply muscle fibers within each individual fascicle.
- The **endomysium** (en′dō-mis′ē-ŭm; *endon* = within) is the innermost connective tissue layer. It is a delicate, areolar connective tissue layer that surrounds and electrically insulates each muscle fiber. It contains reticular protein fibers to help bind together neighboring muscle fibers and to support capillaries near these fibers.

A **tendon** is a thick, cordlike structure composed of dense regular connective tissue. It is formed by the three connective tissue layers as they merge and extend past the muscle fibers. Tendons attach the muscle to bone, skin, or another muscle. Sometimes, the connective tissue layers instead form a thin, flattened sheet of dense irregular tissue, termed an **aponeurosis** (ap′ō-nū-rō′sis; *apo* = from, *neuron* = sinew) (see figures 11.5 and 11.16).

Deep fascia (fash′ē-ă; band or filler), also called *visceral* or *muscular fascia,* is an additional expansive sheet of dense irregular connective tissue that is external to the epimysium. Deep fascia separates individual muscles; binds together muscles with similar functions; contains nerves, blood vessels, and lymph vessels; and serves to fill spaces between muscles. The deep fascia is internal or deep to a layer called the **superficial fascia** (or *subcutaneous layer;* see section 6.1c).

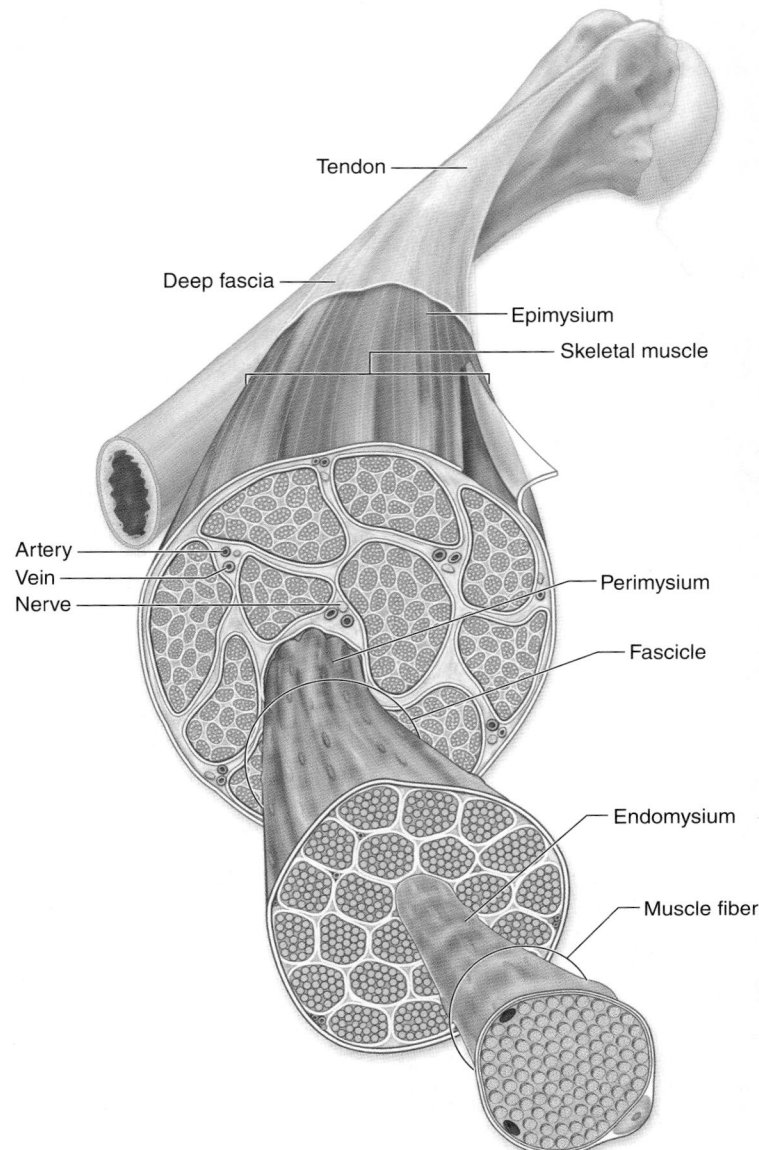

Figure 10.1 Structural Organization of Skeletal Muscle. A skeletal muscle consists of multiple fascicles (bundles of muscle fibers) ensheathed in a tough outer connective tissue membrane called the epimysium. Each fascicle is wrapped in a connective tissue layer called the perimysium. Within fascicles, each muscle fiber is surrounded by a delicate connective tissue layer termed endomysium. **AP|R**

The superficial fascia is composed of areolar connective tissue and adipose connective tissue that separates muscle from skin.

Blood Vessels and Nerves

Skeletal muscle is **vascularized** (vas′kyū-lăr-īzd; *vas* = vessel) by an extensive network of blood vessels. The blood vessels deliver both oxygen and nutrients to the muscle fibers. They also remove waste products produced by the muscle fibers.

Skeletal muscle is **innervated** (in′ĕr-vāt′ed; *nervus* = nerve) by or functionally connected to and controlled by motor neurons. **Motor neurons** extend from the brain and spinal cord to skeletal muscle fibers. Each motor neuron has a long extension called an **axon** (nerve fiber) that branches extensively at its terminal end. The axon extends through all three connective tissue layers to almost, but not quite, make contact with an individual muscle fiber (i.e., there is a very small gap between the motor neuron and muscle fiber). The junction between the axon and the muscle fiber itself is called a neuromuscular junction, which is discussed later in this chapter. Skeletal muscle is classified as **voluntary muscle** because the muscle fibers can be consciously controlled by the nervous system.

WHAT DID YOU LEARN?

3 Identify the location and function of these connective tissue structures associated with muscle: endomysium, perimysium, epimysium, deep fascia, and superficial fascia.

10.2b Microscopic Anatomy of Skeletal Muscle

LEARNING OBJECTIVES

4. Explain how a skeletal muscle fiber becomes multinucleated.
5. Describe the sarcolemma, T-tubules, and sarcoplasmic reticulum of a skeletal muscle fiber.
6. Distinguish between thick and thin filaments.
7. Explain the organization of myofibrils, myofilaments, and sarcomeres.
8. List and describe the structures associated with energy production within skeletal muscle fibers.

Skeletal muscle fibers are the cells comprising a muscle. **Sarcoplasm** (sar′kō-plazm; *sark* = flesh), which is the cytoplasm of muscle fibers, contains the typical cellular structures such as the Golgi apparatus, ribosomes, and vesicles (see section 4.5). Here we describe the specialized cellular structures of a skeletal muscle fiber including the details of its contractile proteins.

A Multinucleated Cell

A skeletal muscle fiber is typically between 10 and 500 micrometers (μm) in diameter, and as previously noted extends the length of the entire muscle, ranging from about 100 μm to 30 centimeters. To reach this length, groups of embryonic cells termed **myoblasts** (mī′ō-blast; *blastos* = germ) fuse to form single skeletal muscle fibers during development **(figure 10.2)**. During this fusion process, each myoblast nucleus contributes to the eventual total number of nuclei in the fiber. Consequently, skeletal muscle fibers are **multinucleated cells** (i.e., they have numerous nuclei).

Some myoblasts do not fuse with muscle fibers during development and instead remain in adult skeletal muscle tissue as **satellite cells.** If a skeletal muscle is injured, some satellite cells may be stimulated to differentiate and assist to a limited extent in its repair and regeneration.

WHAT DO YOU THINK?

1 What is a benefit of having multiple nuclei in an elongated skeletal muscle fiber?

Myoblasts

Myoblasts fuse to form a skeletal muscle fiber.

Muscle fiber

Satellite cell

Muscle fiber

Nuclei

Satellite cell

Figure 10.2 Development of Skeletal Muscle. Embryonic muscle cells called myoblasts fuse to form a single skeletal muscle fiber. After development, both muscle fibers and satellite cells are present. Satellite cells are myoblasts that do not go on to form the skeletal muscle fiber. Instead, satellite cells remain with postnatal skeletal muscle tissue and assist in repair of muscles.

Sarolemma and T-tubules

The plasma membrane of a skeletal muscle fiber is called the **sarcolemma** (sar′kō-lem′ă; *lemma* = husk) **(figure 10.3)**. Deep invaginations of the sarcolemma, called **T-tubules** or **transverse** (trans-vers′; *trans* = across, *versus* = to turn) **tubules,** extend into the skeletal muscle fibers as a network of narrow membranous tubules.

Located along the length of both the sarcolemma and T-tubules are sodium-potassium (Na^+/K^+) pumps (figure 10.3b). The activity of these pumps creates concentration gradients for both sodium ions (Na^+) and potassium ions (K^+) by pumping three Na^+ out of a skeletal muscle fiber for every two K^+ pumped in (see section 4.3c). As a result, Na^+ has a higher concentration outside the muscle fiber, and K^+ concentration is greater inside the muscle fiber. Additionally, a resting membrane potential (RMP) is maintained by Na^+/K^+ pumps due to the unequal distribution of ions. The inside of the cell is relatively negative (−95 millivolts [mV]) in comparison to the outside. (RMPs are described in detail in section 12.7.) The RMP is responsible for the excitability of skeletal muscle fibers (much like the difference of charges across a barrier accounts for how a battery functions).

Also located along the length of the sarcolemma and T-tubules are both voltage-gated Na$^+$ channels and voltage-gated K$^+$ channels (see section 4.3a). Conductivity (or propagation) of an electrical change along the sarcolemma of a muscle fiber is due to these specialized channels. The details of the physiologic role of these channels are described later in the chapter.

Sarcoplasmic Reticulum

The **sarcoplasmic reticulum** (sar-kō'-plaz'mik re-tik'ū-lŭm; *rete* = a net) is an internal membrane complex that is similar to the smooth endoplasmic reticulum of other cells (figure 10.3a). Segments of sarcoplasmic reticulum surround bundles of contractile proteins called myofibrils (described shortly). The sarcoplasmic reticulum fits around the myofibril like a sleeve of membrane netting. At either end of individual sections of the sarcoplasmic reticulum are blind sacs called **terminal cisternae** (sis-ter'nē; sing., sis-ter'nă; *cista* = a box), which are much like the

(a) Skeletal muscle fiber

(b) Sarcolemma and T-tubules

(c) Sarcoplasmic reticulum

Figure 10.3 Structure and Organization of a Skeletal Muscle Fiber. (*a*) A muscle fiber is composed predominantly of myofibrils. Each myofibril extends the length of the muscle fiber and is enclosed within portions of the sarcoplasmic reticulum. (*b*) The sarcolemma, which is the plasma membrane of a muscle cell, contains Na$^+$/K$^+$ pumps, voltage-gated Na$^+$ channels, and voltage-gated K$^+$ channels. These participate in muscle excitability and conductivity. (*c*) The sarcoplasmic reticulum membrane contains both Ca^{2+} pumps and voltage-gated Ca^{2+} channels. Muscle contraction is initiated with the release of Ca^{2+} from the sarcoplasmic reticulum. AP|R hem of a sleeve; they serve as the reservoirs for calcium ions (Ca^{2+}). Terminal cisternae are immediately adjacent to each T-tubule. Together, two terminal cisternae and a centrally placed T-tubule interact to form a structure called a **triad** that functions during muscle contraction.

Two types of transport proteins are embedded within the membrane of the sarcoplasmic reticulum (figure 10.3c): Ca^{2+} pumps and voltage-gated Ca^{2+} channels. Calcium pumps move Ca^{2+} into the sarcoplasmic reticulum where it is stored bound to specialized proteins called **calmodulin** (kal-mod'ū-lin) and **calsequestrin** (kal'sē-kwes'trin). Calcium voltage-gated channels open to release Ca^{2+} from the **sarcoplasmic reticulum** into the sarcoplasm. Release of Ca^{2+} from the sarcoplasmic reticulum causes muscle contraction, as described later in detail.

Muscle Fibers and Myofibrils

Approximately 80% of the volume of a muscle fiber is composed of long, cylindrical structures termed **myofibrils** (mī'ō-fī'bril) (figure 10.3a). A skeletal muscle fiber contains hundreds to thousands of myofibrils. Each myofibril is about 1 to 2 micrometers in diameter and extends the length of the entire skeletal muscle fiber.

Each myofibril contains bundles of muscle protein filaments called **myofilaments** (mī'ō-fil'ă-ment; *filum* = thread). A myofilament is not as long as a myofibril; rather it takes *many* successive units of myofilaments to extend the entire length of the myofibril. Myofibril bundles contain two types of myofilaments: thick filaments and thin filaments.

Thick Filaments   **Thick filaments** (or *thick myofilaments*) have a diameter of about 11 nanometers. They are assembled from bundles of 200 to 500 **myosin** protein molecules **(figure 10.4a)**. Each myosin protein consists of two strands; each strand has a globular head and an elongated tail. The head contains a binding site for actin of the thin filaments. The head also has the site where adenosine triphosphate (ATP) attaches and is split into adenosine diphos-

phate (ADP) and phosphate (P_i) by the enzyme ATPase to provide the energy for muscle contraction. The tails of two strands of a myosin molecule are intertwined. The myosin molecules are oriented so that the long tails point toward the center of the thick filaments and the heads point toward the edges of the thick filaments.

Thin Filaments   **Thin filaments** (or *thin myofilaments*) are approximately 5 to 6 nanometers in diameter, which is about half of the diameter of thick filaments. Thin filaments are primarily composed of two strands of **actin** protein that are twisted around each other to form a helical shape (figure 10.4b). In each strand of actin, many small, spherical molecules (G, or globular, actin) are connected to form a fibrous strand (F, or filamentous, actin). F-actin resembles two beaded necklaces that are twisted and intertwined together, with G-actin as the individual beads. Each globular G-actin molecule has a significant feature called a **myosin binding site.** The myosin head attaches to the myosin binding site of actin during muscle contraction.

Tropomyosin and troponin are regulatory proteins associated with thin filaments. Together they are called the troponin-tropomyosin complex. **Tropomyosin** (trō-pō-mī'ō-sin) is a short, thin, twisted filament that is a "stringlike" protein. Consecutive tropomyosin molecules cover small bands of the actin strands, including the myosin binding sites in a noncontracting muscle. **Troponin** (trō'pō-nin) is a globular or "ball-like" protein attached to tropomyosin. Troponin is the binding site for Ca^{2+}.

Organization of a Sarcomere

Myofilaments within myofibrils are arranged in repeating microscopic cylindrical units (2 micrometers in length) called **sarcomeres** (sar'kō-mēr; *meros* = part). **Figure 10.5a** shows several repeating sarcomeres in a section of a myofibril within a muscle fiber. The number of sarcomeres will vary with the length of the myofibril within the muscle fiber. Each sarcomere is composed of overlapping thick filaments and thin filaments.

Figure 10.4 Molecular Structure of Thick and Thin Filaments.
Myofilaments, which include thick filaments and thin filaments, are the contractile proteins bundled within myofibrils. (*a*) A thick filament consists of 200 to 500 myosin protein molecules. (*b*) A thin filament is composed of actin, tropomyosin, and troponin proteins.
AP|R

(a) Thick filament

(b) Thin filament

A two-dimensional view of a cylindrical sarcomere is shown in figure 10.5b. Here we see that each sarcomere is delineated at both ends by Z discs. **Z discs** (also called *Z lines*) are composed of specialized proteins that are positioned perpendicular to the myofilaments and serve as anchors for the thin filaments. Although the Z disc appears as a flat disc when the myofibril is viewed from its "end," only the edge of the disc is visible in a side view, and it sometimes looks like a zigzagged line.

The thick filaments and thin filaments overlap within a sarcomere, forming the following regions:

- **I bands** extend from both directions of a Z disc and are bisected by the Z disc. These end regions contain only thin filaments; this region appears light when viewed with a microscope. At maximal muscle contraction, the thin filaments are pulled past the thick filaments, causing the I band to disappear.

- The **A band** is the central region of a sarcomere that contains the entire thick filament. Thin filaments partially overlap the thick filament on each end of an A band. The A band appears dark when viewed with a microscope.

- The **H zone** (also called the *H band*) is the most central portion of the A band in a resting sarcomere. This region does not have thin filament overlap; only thick filaments are present. During maximal muscle contraction, this zone disappears when the thin filaments are pulled past thick filaments.

- The **M line** is a thin transverse protein meshwork structure in the center of the H zone. It serves as an attachment site for the thick filaments and keeps the thick filaments aligned during contraction and relaxation events.

The overlapping myofilaments form unique patterns of alternating light and dark regions within a skeletal muscle fiber. When a longitudinal section of skeletal muscle tissue is viewed in a microscope, it appears **striated** (striped) (see figure 10.12). This striated appearance is due to both the size and density differences between thin filaments and thick filaments.

Figure 10.5c shows cross sections through various regions in a sarcomere. It presents the relative sizes, arrangements, and organization of thick and thin filaments at different locations within the sarcomere. Notice in a cross section of an A band the arrangement

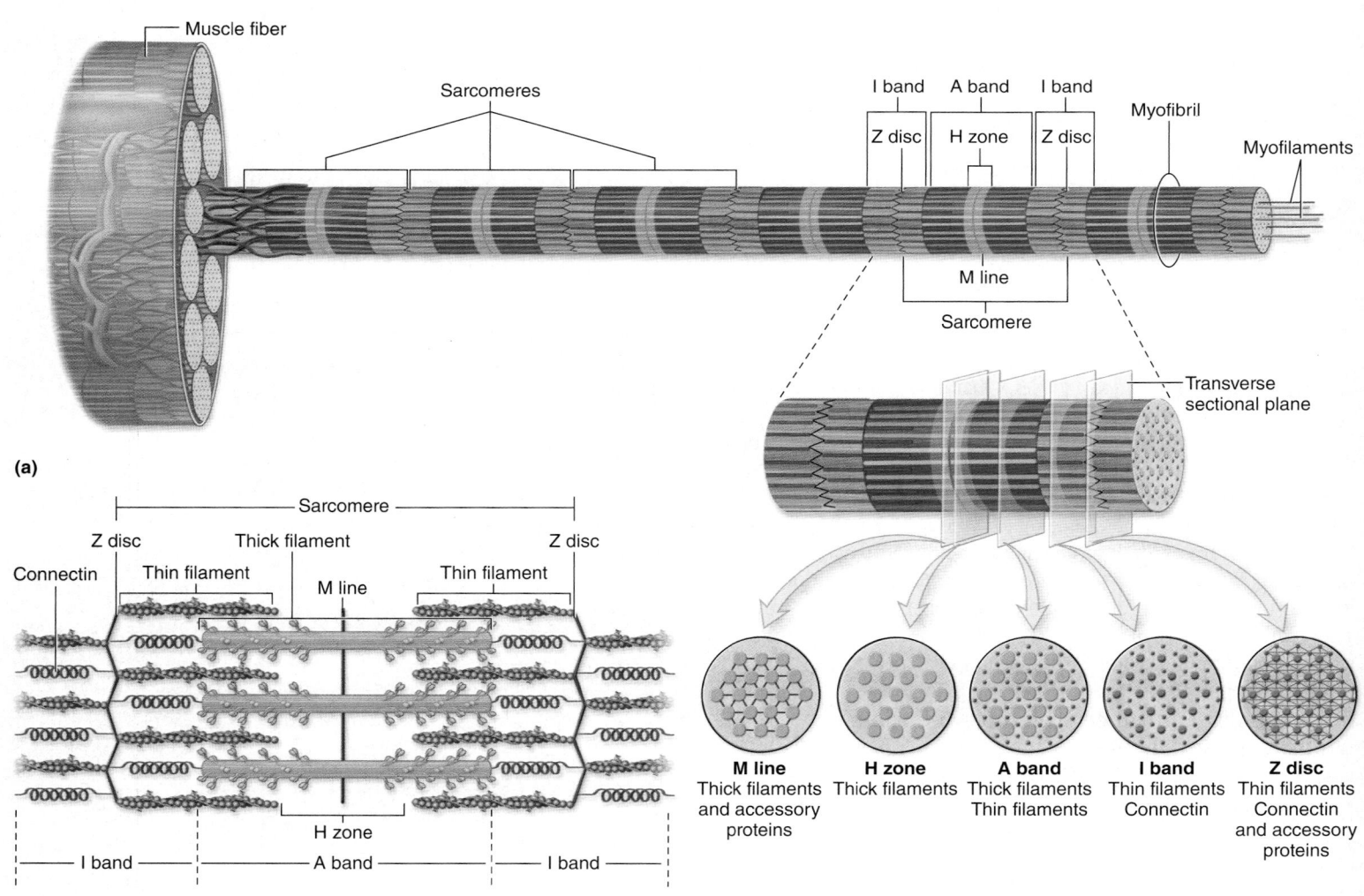

Figure 10.5 Structure of a Sarcomere. (*a*) Numerous sarcomeres extend the length of a myofibril. (*b*) Longitudinal section of a sarcomere. (*c*) Cross sections of different regions of a sarcomere. AP|R

INTEGRATE

LEARNING STRATEGY

To help remember what shortens (and what stays the same length) during skeletal muscle contraction, try this experiment: Interweave your fingers together with the fingertips overlapping—they represent the length of the thick and thin filaments. Your thumbs (pointing upward) represent the Z discs. The distance between your thumbs is the sarcomere. Now slide your fingers toward each other. Your fingers (the thick and thin filaments) remain the same length. The distance between your thumbs (the sarcomere) shortens. This illustrates that the filaments do *not* change length—only the *distance* between the Z discs is affected.

of thick filaments relative to thin filaments: Each thin filament has three thick filaments around it that form a triangle at its periphery, and each thick filament is sandwiched by six thin filaments.

WHAT DO YOU THINK?

2 If a muscle is contracted, what happens to the following: (a) width of the A band, (b) width of the H zone, (c) relationship of the Z discs, and (d) width of the I band?

Other Structural and Functional Proteins   There are other proteins that have structural and functional roles within muscle fibers. These include connectin, nebulin, and dystrophin (only connectin is shown in figure 10.5).

Connectin (kon-nek′tin), also called *titin*, is a "cablelike" protein that extends from the Z discs to the M line through the core of each thick filament (see figure 10.5*b*). It stabilizes the position of the thick filament and maintains thick filament alignment within a sarcomere. Additionally, portions of the connectin molecules are coiled and "springlike" so that during contraction they are compressed to produce passive tension. During relaxation this passive tension is released as the sarcomere is returned to its normal resting length. Thus, connectin contributes to muscle fiber elasticity.

Nebulin (neb′yū-lin) appears to be an actin-binding protein that is part of the I band of the sarcomere. Studies indicate that the length of nebulin is proportional to the length of the thin filament—thus, it has been proposed to act as a "ruler," that is responsible for the thin filament length during sarcomere assembly. Recent experiments suggest that the orderly structure of the sarcomere is totally disrupted without the presence of nebulin.

Dystrophin (dis-trō′fin) is part of a protein complex that anchors myofibrils that are adjacent to the sarcolemma to proteins in the sarcolemma. These proteins of the sarcolemma also extend to the connective tissue of the endomysium. Thus, dystrophin links internal myofilament proteins of a muscle fiber to external proteins. The genetic disorder of *muscular dystrophy* is caused by abnormal structure, or amounts, of dystrophin protein.

Mitochondria and Other Structures Associated with Energy Production

Skeletal muscle fibers have a great demand for energy and contain several components that facilitate the production of ATP. Skeletal muscle fibers have abundant mitochondria for aerobic cellular respiration (see section 3.4); a typical skeletal muscle fiber contains approximately 300 mitochondria. The fibers also contain glycogen stores (granules called glycosomes) for use as an immediate fuel molecule. **Myoglobin** (mī-ō-glō′bin) is a molecule unique to muscle tissue. Myoglobin is a reddish, globular protein that is somewhat

similar to hemoglobin. It binds oxygen when the muscle is at rest and releases it for use during muscular contraction. This additional source of oxygen provides the means to enhance aerobic cellular respiration and the production of ATP. Skeletal muscle fibers also contain another type of molecule unique to muscle tissue called creatine phosphate. Creatine phosphate provides muscle fibers with a means of supplying ATP anaerobically (creatine phosphate is described later in the chapter).

(a)

(b)

Figure 10.6 A Motor Unit. (*a*) A motor unit is a motor neuron and all of the skeletal muscle fibers it innervates. Different colors distinguish the two motor units in this figure. (*b*) Light micrograph of a motor neuron and skeletal muscle fibers in a motor unit. AP|R

WHAT DID YOU LEARN?

4 Draw and label a diagram of a sarcomere.

5 Place the following gross anatomic and microscopic anatomic structures in order from largest to smallest: fascicle, myofibril, myofilament, muscle, and muscle fiber.

10.2c Innervation of Skeletal Muscle Fibers

LEARNING OBJECTIVES

9. Define a motor unit, and describe its distribution in a muscle and why it varies in size.

10. Describe the three components of a neuromuscular junction.

The anatomic relationship of skeletal muscle fibers and motor neurons that control them is described in this section.

Motor Unit

Recall that motor neurons are nerve cells that transmit nerve signals from the brain or spinal cord to control skeletal muscle activity. The axon of each motor neuron splits to form many individual branches to innervate numerous skeletal muscle fibers. A single motor neuron and the muscle fibers it controls is called a **motor unit (figure 10.6)**.

The number of skeletal muscle fibers a single motor neuron innervates—and thus the size of the motor unit—varies and can range from small motor units that have less than five muscle fibers to large motor units that have several thousand muscle fibers. The size of the motor unit determines the degree of control. There is an

inverse relationship between the size of a motor unit and the degree of control. For example, motor neurons innervating eye muscles are small because greater control is essential in the muscles that move the eye. In contrast, a single motor neuron controls several thousand individual skeletal muscle fibers in the power-generating muscles in our lower limbs, where less precise control is required.

The skeletal muscle fibers of a motor unit are not clustered within one area of a muscle, but rather are dispersed throughout most of a muscle. Normally, the stimulation of a motor unit does not produce a strong contraction in a localized area within the muscle, but a weak contraction over a wide area.

Neuromuscular Junctions

Each skeletal muscle fiber has one neuromuscular junction. A **neuromuscular** (nūr-ō-mŭs′kū-lăr) **junction** is the specific location, usually in the mid-region of the muscle fiber where it is innervated by a motor neuron **(figure 10.7a)**. The neuromuscular junction has the following parts: synaptic knob, motor end plate, and synaptic cleft.

Synaptic Knob The **synaptic** (si-nap′tik) **knob** of a motor neuron is an expanded tip of an axon. Where the axon nears the sarcolemma of a muscle fiber, the synaptic knob enlarges and flattens to cover a relatively large surface area of the sarcolemma. The synaptic knob cytosol houses numerous **synaptic vesicles** (small membrane sacs) filled with molecules of the neurotransmitter **acetylcholine** (a-sē′til-kō′lēn) **(ACh).**

Several points can be made about synaptic knobs (figure 10.7b). First, Ca^{2+} pumps are embedded within the plasma membrane of

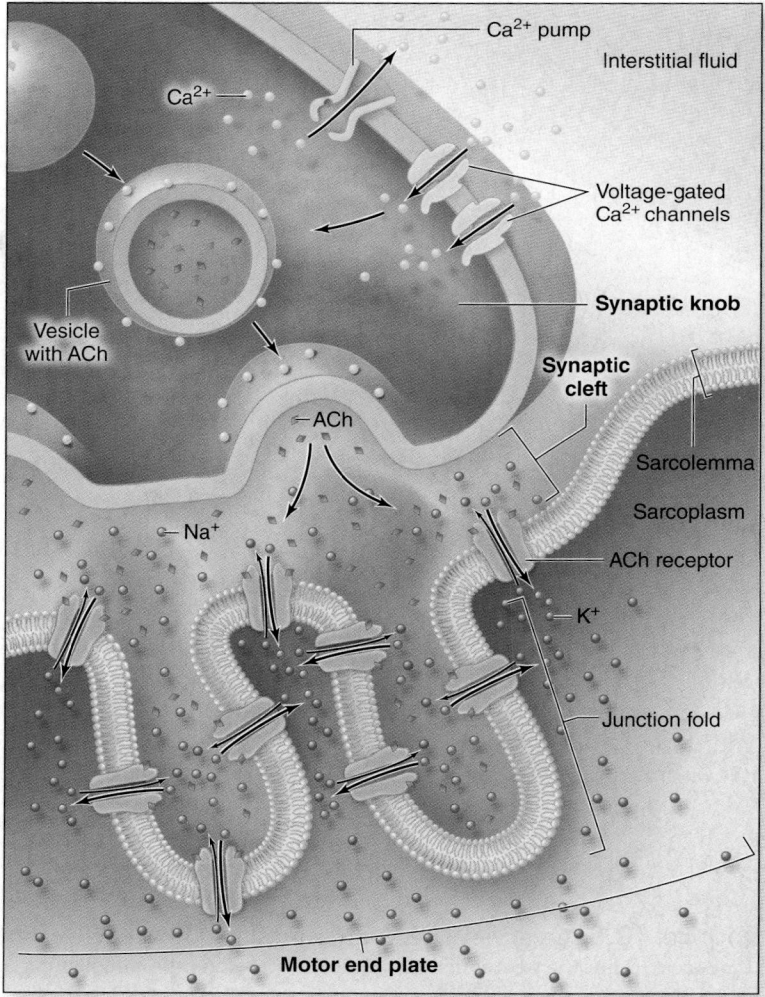

Figure 10.7 Structure and Organization of a Neuromuscular Junction. The synaptic knob of an axon meets a skeletal muscle fiber to form a neuromuscular junction. (*a*) Three primary components are within a neuromuscular junction and include a synaptic knob, motor end plate, and synaptic cleft. (*b*) Synaptic knobs house synaptic vesicles containing the neurotransmitter acetylcholine (ACh). Embedded in the plasma membrane of the synaptic knob are Ca^{2+} pumps and voltage-gated Ca^{2+} channels. The motor end plate contains ACh receptors, which are chemically gated ion channels. AP|R

the synaptic knob. Prior to the arrival of the nerve signal at the synaptic knob, Ca^{2+} pumps within the axonal membrane have established a Ca^{2+} concentration gradient, with more Ca^{2+} outside the neuron than inside it. Second, voltage-gated Ca^{2+} channels are also embedded in the membrane of the synaptic knob. Opening of these channels allows Ca^{2+} to flow down its concentration gradient from the interstitial fluid into the synaptic knob. Third, vesicles are normally repelled from the membrane of the synaptic knob.

Motor End Plate

The **motor end plate** is a specialized region of the sarcolemma of a muscle fiber. It has numerous folds and indentations (junction folds) to increase the membrane surface area covered by the synaptic knob. The motor end plate has vast numbers of **ACh receptors.** These plasma membrane protein channels are chemically gated ion channels (section 4.3a). Binding of ACh opens these channels, allowing Na^+ entry into the muscle fiber and K^+ to exit. ACh receptors are like doors; ACh is the only "key" to open these receptor doors.

Synaptic Cleft

The **synaptic cleft** is an extremely narrow (20 nanometers), fluid-filled space separating the synaptic knob and the motor end plate. The enzyme **acetylcholinesterase** (a-sē'til-kō'lēn-es'ter-ās)

(AChE) resides within the synaptic cleft and quickly breaks down ACh molecules following their release into the synaptic cleft.

WHAT DID YOU LEARN?

6 What is a motor unit, and why does it vary in size?

7 Diagram and label the anatomic structures of a neuromuscular junction.

10.3 Physiology of Skeletal Muscle Contraction

A contracting skeletal muscle fiber decreases in length as thick and thin protein filaments within sarcomeres interact to cause sarcomeres to shorten. Ultimately, **tension** is exerted on the portions of the skeleton where the muscle is attached to cause movement in the body.

The anatomic structures and associated physiologic processes of skeletal muscle contraction include the events that occur at: (1) neuromuscular junction; (2) sarcolemma, T-tubules, and sarcoplasmic reticulum; and (3) sarcomeres. An overview of these processes is included in **figure 10.8.**

① NEUROMUSCULAR JUNCTION: EXCITATION OF A SKELETAL MUSCLE FIBER

Release of neurotransmitter acetycholine (ACh) from synaptic vesicles and subsequent binding of ACh to ACh receptors.

② SARCOLEMMA, T-TUBULES, AND SARCOPLASMIC RETICULUM: EXCITATION-CONTRACTION COUPLING

ACh binding triggers propagation of an action potential along the sarcolemma and T-tubules to the sarcoplasmic reticulum, which is stimulated to release Ca^{2+}.

③ SARCOMERE: CROSSBRIDGE CYCLING

Ca^{2+} binding to troponin triggers sliding of thin filaments past thick filaments of sarcomeres; sarcomeres shorten, causing muscle contraction.

Neuromuscular junction
Synaptic vesicle (contains ACh)
Action potential
Muscle fiber
ACh
ACh receptor
T-tubule
Terminal cisterna of SR
Sarcoplasmic reticulum
Ca^{2+}
Sarcolemma
Sarcomere
Ca^{2+}
Ca^{2+}
Thin filament   Thick filament

Figure 10.8 Overview of Events in Skeletal Muscle Contraction. Skeletal muscle contraction involves the physiologic events that occur (1) at the neuromuscular junction, (2) along the sarcolemma and T-tubules to the sarcoplasmic reticulum of a skeletal muscle fiber, and (3) within a sarcomere. AP|R

10.3a Neuromuscular Junction: Excitation of a Skeletal Muscle Fiber

LEARNING OBJECTIVE

1. Explain the events that lead to release of the neurotransmitter ACh from a motor neuron.

The first physiologic event of skeletal muscle contraction is muscle fiber *excitation* by a motor neuron—an event that occurs at the neuromuscular junction and results in release of ACh and its subsequent binding to ACh receptors.

Calcium Entry at Synaptic Knob

A nerve signal is propagated down a motor axon. (You will learn more about nerve signals in section 12.8c.) The nerve signal triggers the opening of voltage-gated Ca^{2+} channels within the synaptic knob. Calcium moves down its concentration gradient from the interstitial fluid through the open channels into the synaptic knob. Calcium binds with membrane proteins (synaptotagmin) exposed on the external surface of synaptic vesicles.

Release of ACh from Synaptic Knob

The binding of Ca^{2+} to synaptic vesicles triggers the merging of synaptic vesicles with the synaptic knob plasma membrane resulting in exocytosis of ACh into the synaptic cleft. Approximately 300 vesicles are released per nerve signal.

Binding of ACh at Motor End Plate

ACh diffuses across the fluid-filled synaptic cleft to bind with ACh receptors within the motor end plate. This causes excitation of a muscle fiber. These events are summarized in **figure 10.9**.

WHAT DID YOU LEARN?

8. What triggers the binding of synaptic vesicles to the synaptic knob membrane to cause exocytosis of ACh?

(1) NEUROMUSCULAR JUNCTION: EXCITATION OF A SKELETAL MUSCLE FIBER

Nerve signal

Voltage-gated Ca^{2+} channel

Synaptic knob — (1a)

— Ca^{2+}

Synaptic vesicles (contain ACh)

Ca^{2+}

Synaptic vesicle

ACh

Interstitial fluid

(1b)

Synaptic cleft —

(1c)

ACh

ACh receptor —

Motor end plate

(1a) Ca^{2+} entry at synaptic knob

A nerve signal is propagated down a motor axon and triggers the entry of Ca^{2+} into the synaptic knob.

Ca^{2+} binds to proteins in synaptic vesicle membrane.

(1b) Release of ACh from synaptic knob

Calcium binding triggers synaptic vesicles to merge with the synaptic knob plasma membrane and ACh is exocytosed into the synaptic cleft.

(1c) Binding of ACh to ACh receptor at motor end plate

ACh diffuses across the fluid-filled synaptic cleft in the motor end plate to bind with ACh receptors.

Figure 10.9 Neuromuscular Junction: Excitation of a Skeletal Muscle Fiber. A skeletal muscle fiber is excited by the release of neurotransmitter from a motor neuron synaptic knob. AP|R

Interstitial fluid

Voltage-gated Na$^+$ channel ②b

Voltage-gated K$^+$ channel

Sarcolemma

EPP

Na$^+$

Synaptic cleft

②a

Na$^+$

ACh receptor

ACh

K$^+$

Sarcoplasm

Motor end plate

K$^+$

②b Initiation and propagation of an action potential along sarcolemma and T-tubules

An action potential is propagated along the sarcolemma and T-tubules.

First, voltage-gated Na$^+$ channels open, and Na$^+$ moves in to cause depolarization.

Second, voltage-gated K$^+$ channels open, and K$^+$ moves out to cause repolarization.

②a Development of an end-plate potential (EPP) at the motor end plate

Binding of ACh to ACh receptors in the motor end plate triggers the opening of these chemically gated ion channels. Na$^+$ rapidly diffuses into and K$^+$ slowly diffuses out of the muscle fiber.

The result is a reversal in the electrical charge difference across the membrane of a muscle fiber at the motor end plate, which is called an **end-plate potential (EPP)**. (The inside which was negative is now positive.)

Figure 10.10 Skeletal Muscle Fiber: Excitation-Contraction Coupling. Skeletal muscle fiber excitation by a motor neuron is coupled to the contraction of myofilaments within the muscle fiber.

10.3b Sarcolemma, T-tubules, and Sarcoplasmic Reticulum: Excitation-Contraction Coupling

LEARNING OBJECTIVE

2. Describe the steps in excitation-contraction coupling.

The second physiologic event of muscle contraction is excitation-contraction coupling—an event that involves the sarcolemma, T-tubules, and sarcoplasmic reticulum. This event "couples" or links the events of skeletal muscle stimulation at the neuromuscular junction (first step) to the events of contraction caused by sliding myofilaments within the sarcomeres of skeletal muscle fiber (third step). Three events occur during excitation-contraction coupling: development of an end-plate potential at the motor end plate, initiation and propagation of an action potential along the sarcolemma and T-tubules, and release of Ca^{2+} from the sarcoplasmic reticulum.

Development of an End-Plate Potential at the Motor End Plate

ACh binds to ACh receptors in the motor end plate of a skeletal muscle fiber (as described previously). The ACh receptors, which are chemically gated ion channels, are stimulated to open. The opening of these channels allows both Na$^+$ to rapidly diffuse into the skeletal muscle fiber and K$^+$ to slowly diffuse out of the skeletal muscle fiber. More Na$^+$ diffuses in then K$^+$ diffuses out, and

there is a net gain of positive charge on the inside of the skeletal muscle fiber. The net gain in positive charge is large enough to cause a reversal in the electrical charge difference across the membrane at the motor end plate of the skeletal muscle fiber (i.e., the inside, which was relatively negative, is now relatively positive). This reversal in polarity is called an **end plate potential (EPP)**. The EPP is both transient (short-lived) and localized at the motor end plate. Because it is transient the skeletal muscle fiber can be stimulated again almost immediately.

Initiation and Propagation of Action Potential Along the Sarcolemma and T-tubules

The EPP triggers an action potential that is propagated along the sarcolemma and T-tubules of the skeletal muscle fiber. An **action potential** involves two events: depolarization that causes the inside of the sarcolemma of the skeletal muscle fiber to become positive due to the influx of Na$^+$; and repolarization, which is the returning of the inside of the sarcolemma to its relatively negative resting membrane potential due to the outward flow of K$^+$.

The electrical change of the EPP in the motor end plate stimulates the opening of voltage-gated Na$^+$ channels in the adjacent area of the sarcolemma. The opening of voltage-gated Na$^+$ channels allows Na$^+$ to rapidly move across the sarcolemma down its

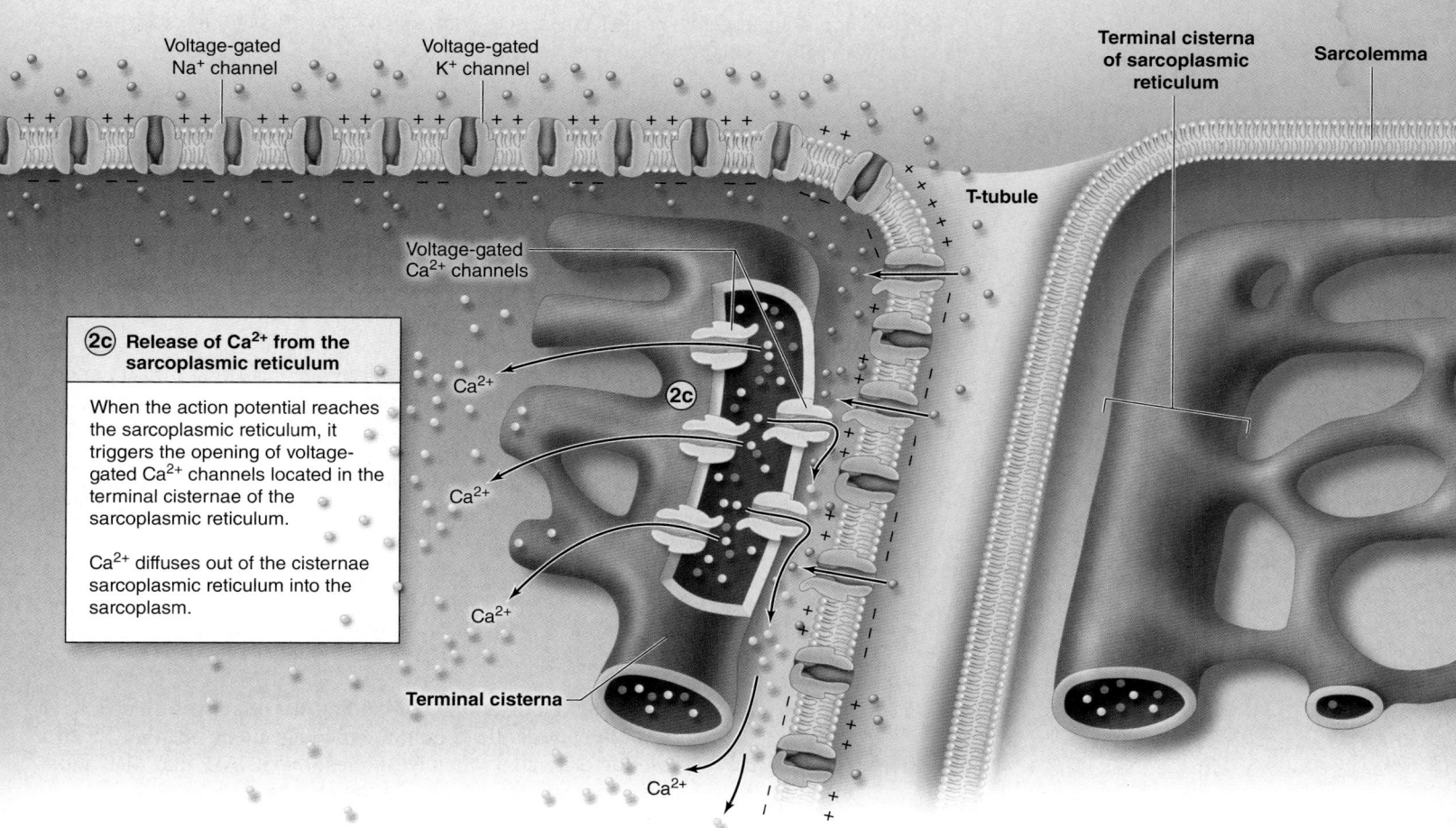

Voltage-gated Na⁺ channel

Voltage-gated K⁺ channel

Terminal cisterna of sarcoplasmic reticulum

Sarcolemma

T-tubule

Voltage-gated Ca²⁺ channels

2c **Release of Ca²⁺ from the sarcoplasmic reticulum**

When the action potential reaches the sarcoplasmic reticulum, it triggers the opening of voltage-gated Ca²⁺ channels located in the terminal cisternae of the sarcoplasmic reticulum.

Ca²⁺ diffuses out of the cisternae sarcoplasmic reticulum into the sarcoplasm.

Ca^{2+}

Terminal cisterna

---

concentration gradient into the muscle fiber. Sufficient Na⁺ enters to cause a reversal of the membrane potential of the sarcolemma. The inside, which was relatively negative, becomes relatively positive. This reversal in polarity at the sarcolemma is referred to as **depolarization.**

The propagation of depolarization along the length of the sarcolemma and T-tubules involves the sequential opening of voltage-gated Na⁺ channels. The inflow of Na⁺ at the initial portion of the sarcolemma causes adjacent regions of the sarcolemma to experience electrical changes that initiates voltage-gated Na⁺ channels in these areas to open. Sodium flows in to cause depolarization in this region of the sarcolemma. Adjacent depolarization is repeated rapidly down the sarcolemma and T-tubules. The propagation of an action potential along the sarcolemma and T-tubule is similar to the falling of a series of stacked dominoes—once started, it does not stop until it reaches the end.

Voltage-gated K⁺ channels located along the sarcolemma and T-tubules open immediately following the opening of the voltage-gated Na⁺ channels. The opening of voltage-gated K⁺ channels allows K⁺ to move across the sarcolemma down its concentration gradient and out of the skeletal muscle fiber. Sufficient K⁺ exits so that the membrane potential at the sarcolemma and T-tubules reverses and the negative resting membrane potential (−95 millivolts) is reestablished. This process is referred to as **repolarization.**

The opening of voltage-gated K⁺ channels also occurs sequentially, and repolarization is propagated along the sarcolemma and T-tubules.

Repolarization allows the muscle fiber to propagate a new action potential when stimulated again by a motor neuron. The period of time between depolarization and repolarization is called the **refractory period**. The refractory period is significant because during this brief period of time the muscle cannot be restimulated.

Release of Calcium from the Sarcoplasmic Reticulum

When the action potential reaches the sarcoplasmic reticulum it triggers the opening of voltage-gated Ca²⁺ channels that are located in the terminal cisternae of the sarcoplasmic reticulum. The opening of voltage-gated Ca²⁺ channels allows Ca²⁺ to diffuse out of the cisternae of the sarcoplasmic reticulum into the sarcoplasm. Calcium now "mingles" with the thick filaments and thin filaments of myofibrils. These events are summarized in **figure 10.10.**

WHAT DID YOU LEARN?

9 What two events are linked in the physiologic process called excitation-contraction coupling?

10 Provide a description of the events of excitation-contraction coupling.

10.3c Sarcomere: Crossbridge Cycling

LEARNING OBJECTIVE

3. Summarize the changes that occur within a sarcomere during contraction.

The third physiologic event in skeletal muscle contraction involves binding of Ca^{2+} and crossbridge cycling. This results in muscle contraction.

Calcium Binding

Calcium released from the sarcoplasmic reticulum binds to a subunit of globular troponin, a component of thin filaments. This induces a conformational change in troponin. Recall that troponin is attached to tropomyosin, forming the troponin-tropomyosin complex. When troponin changes shape, the entire troponin-tropomyosin complex is moved and the myosin binding sites of actin are exposed. Crossbridge cycling is initiated.

Crossbridge Cycling

Four steps are then repeated in crossbridge cycling: (1) crossbridge formation (attaching of myosin head to actin), (2) power stroke (pulling thin filament by movement of myosin head), (3) release of myosin head from actin, and (4) resetting of myosin head.

Crossbridge formation   Myosin heads, which are in the "cocked," or ready, position attach to exposed myosin binding sites of actin. Binding of each myosin head results in formation of a **crossbridge** between the thick and thin filament.

Power stroke   After forming a crossbridge, the myosin head swivels (or ratchets) in what is called a **power stroke**. The swiveling of a myosin head pulls the thin filament a small distance past the thick filament toward the center of the sarcomere. ADP and P_i are released during this process, and the ATP binding site becomes available again.

Release of Myosin Head   ATP then binds to the ATP binding site of a myosin head, which causes the release of the myosin head from the binding site on actin.

Reset Myosin Head   ATPase (an enzyme on the myosin head) splits ATP into ADP and Pi, providing the energy to reset the myosin head in the cocked position.

If Ca^{2+} is still present, and the myosin binding sites are still exposed, then these four steps involving the myosin heads continue: attach, pull, release, and reset. It is the repetitive action of these steps that results in sarcomere shortening, and a sarcomere moves from its relaxed state into a contracted state. These events are summarized in **figure 10.11**.

INTEGRATE

CLINICAL VIEW

Muscular Paralysis and Neurotoxins

Muscular paralysis may occur if either nervous system function at the neuromuscular junction or excitation-contraction coupling is impaired. Two such conditions are tetanus and botulism.

Tetanus is a form of spastic paralysis caused by a toxin produced by the bacterium *Clostridium tetani*. The toxin blocks the release of glycine (an inhibitory neurotransmitter in the spinal cord), resulting in overstimulation of the muscles and excessive muscle contractions. Penetrating wounds contaminated with soil and vegetable matter are especially prone to developing *C. tetani* infection. This condition is potentially life-threatening, and so we routinely are vaccinated against it.

Botulism (bot'ū-lizm), a potentially fatal muscular paralysis, is caused by a toxin produced by a related bacterium, *Clostridium botulinum*. The toxin prevents the release of acetylcholine (ACh) at synaptic knobs and leads to muscular paralysis. Like *C. tetani*, *C. botulinum* is common in the environment and also produces its toxin only under anaerobic conditions. Most cases of botulism poisoning result from ingesting the toxin in canned foods that were not processed at temperatures high enough to kill the botulism spores. Similarly, ingestion of unpasteurized honey by infants in the first year of life can introduce *C. botulinum* spores into the gastrointestinal tract.

The Food and Drug Administration (FDA) approved the use of botulinum toxin type A (Botox) for temporary diminishing of wrinkles. For example, to remove frown lines between the eyebrows, small doses of the purified toxin are injected into the contracted muscles causing the frown lines. The toxin temporarily paralyzes or weakens the injected muscle by blocking the release of ACh. Botox is reportedly effective for up to 120 days, and the FDA recommends that injections be administered no more than once every 3 months.

③ SARCOMERE: CROSSBRIDGE CYCLING

Relaxed sarcomere
(prior to Ca²⁺ release)

3a Ca²⁺ binding
Ca^{2+} binds to troponin in muscle thin filaments, causing a conformational change in troponin. Troponin changes shape and the entire troponin-tropomyosin complex is moved—thus, tropomyosin no longer covers the myosin binding site on actin.

Ca²⁺
Myosin binding sites exposed
Troponin
Thin filament — Tropomyosin
Actin
Thick filament
Myosin

3e Reset myosin head ("reset")
ATP is split into ADP and P_i by myosin ATPase. This provides the energy to reset the myosin head.

Thin filament
Myosin head
P_i ADP

Crossbridge cycling:
Multiple repetitions of attach, pull, release, and reset lead to fully contracted sarcomere.

3b Crossbridge formation ("attach")
Myosin heads, which are in the "cocked" position, bind to the exposed myosin binding site on actin forming a **crossbridge** between myosin and actin.

Actin
Thin filament
Crossbridge
P_i ADP
Myosin head

3d Release of myosin head ("release")
ATP binds to the ATP binding site on the myosin head, which causes the release of the myosin head from the binding site on actin.

Thin filament
ATP
Myosin head

3c Power stroke ("pull")
The myosin head swivels toward the center of the sarcomere, pulling along the attached thin filament. This motion is called a power stroke. ADP and P_i are released during this process.

Thin filament
Myosin head
ADP
P_i

Figure 10.11 Sarcomere: Skeletal Muscle Contraction. Contractile proteins slide past each other toward the center of the sarcomere, and the sarcomere shortens. AP|R

A sarcomere in both a relaxed and contracted skeletal muscle is shown in **figure 10.12**. The following changes to the sarcomere occur in the contracted muscle: The H zone disappears, the I band narrows in width and may disappear, and the Z discs in one sarcomere move closer together. However, the thin and thick filaments do not shorten. A description of the repetitive movement of thin filaments sliding past thick filaments is called the **sliding filament theory**. The three major events of skeletal muscle contraction are summarized in **figure 10.13**.

WHAT DO YOU THINK?

3 Calcium is released from the sarcoplasmic reticulum following death. Without available ATP, rigor mortis (stiffening of the body) occurs. Explain why, if ATP is unavailable, muscles remain in a contracted state.

WHAT DID YOU LEARN?

11 What is the function of Ca^{2+} in skeletal muscle contraction?

12 Describe the four processes that repeat in crossbridge cycling to cause sarcomere shortening.

13 What causes the release of the myosin head from actin? What resets the myosin head?

(a) Relaxed skeletal muscle

(b) Fully contracted skeletal muscle

Figure 10.12 Sarcomere Shortening. Illustrations and corresponding electron micrographs demonstrate sarcomere shortening during skeletal muscle contraction. (*a*) In a relaxed skeletal muscle, the A band, I band, and H zone are all visible. (*b*) In a fully contracted muscle, the sarcomere shortens, the Z discs move closer together, the I band narrows and may disappear, and the H zone disappears.

CLINICAL VIEW
Rigor Mortis

Within a few hours after the heart stops beating, ATP levels in skeletal muscle fibers have been completely exhausted. The sarcoplasmic reticulum loses its ability to return Ca^{2+} from the sarcoplasm and move it back into the sarcoplasmic reticulum. As a result, the Ca^{2+} already present in the sarcoplasm, as well as the Ca^{2+} that continues to leak out of the sarcoplasmic reticulum, trigger a sustained contraction in the fibers. Remember that ATP is needed to detach the myosin head of the thick filament from the myosin binding site of actin on the thin filaments. Because no ATP is available, the crossbridges between thick and thin filaments cannot detach. All skeletal muscles lock into a contracted position and the body of the deceased individual becomes rigid. This physiologic state, termed **rigor mortis** (rig'er mōr'tis), continues for about 15 to 24 hours. Rigor mortis then disappears because lysosomal enzymes are released within the muscle fibers, causing autolysis (self-destruction and breakdown) of the myofibrils.

Forensic pathologists often use the development and resolution of rigor mortis to establish an approximate time of death. Because a number of factors affect the rate of development and resolution of rigor mortis, environmental conditions need to be taken into consideration. For example, a warmer body will develop and resolve rigor mortis much more quickly than a body of normal temperature. The following chart provides rough guidelines for estimating the death interval, assuming that body temperature and ambient (surrounding environment) temperature are within normal range.

Death Interval	Body Temperature	Stiffness
Dead less than 3 hours	Warm	No stiffness
Dead 3–8 hours	Warm, but cooling	Developing stiffness
Dead 8–24 hours	Ambient temperature	Stiff, but resolving
Dead 24–36 hours	Ambient temperature	No stiffness

10.3d Skeletal Muscle Relaxation

✓ LEARNING OBJECTIVES

4. Discuss what happens to each of the following to allow for skeletal muscle relaxation: ACh, action potential, Ca^{2+} concentration in sarcoplasm, and troponin-tropomyosin complex.

5. Explain the relationship of skeletal muscle elasticity and muscle relaxation.

Skeletal muscle relaxation involves returning all muscle fiber components to their resting state when stimulation from the motor neuron ceases. The first event in muscle relaxation is the termination of the nerve signal in the motor neuron. This prevents further release of ACh. Acetylcholinesterase in the synaptic cleft continually hydrolyzes ACh to dissociate it from its receptor on the motor end plate and terminate its stimulation of the skeletal muscle fiber. The ACh receptor closes, and both the end plate potential at the motor end plate and the action potential along the sarcolemma and T-tubules ceases.

Voltage-gated Ca^{2+} channels in the sarcoplasmic reticulum close. The Ca^{2+} already released from the sarcoplasmic reticulum is continuously returned into the terminal cisternae by Ca^{2+} pumps. After cessation of skeletal muscle fiber stimulation, the remaining Ca^{2+} in the sarcoplasm is transported back into storage within the sarcoplasmic reticulum.

Troponin returns to its original shape when Ca^{2+} is removed, and simultaneously the tropomyosin moves over the myosin binding sites on actin. This prevents myosin-actin crossbridge formation. Through the natural elasticity of the muscle fiber, the muscle returns to its original relaxed position, a process facilitated by the release of passive tension that developed in connectin proteins that were compressed during contraction.

💡 WHAT DID YOU LEARN?

14 How do acetylcholinesterase and Ca^{2+} pumps function in the relaxation of a muscle?

① Neuromuscular Junction

Excitation of a muscle fiber

1a A nerve signal triggers voltage-gated Ca^{2+} channels to open—Ca^{2+} enters synaptic knob and binds to synaptic vesicles.

1b ACh is released by exocytosis into synaptic cleft.

1c ACh binds to ACh receptor.

2a ACh binding causes Na^+ to rapidly enter the skeletal muscle fiber and K^+ to slowly exit the skeletal muscle fiber, which triggers an end-plate potential (EPP).

2b The EPP initiates an action potential along sarcolemma and T-tubules.

3e Reset: ATP split and myosin head is reset.

3d Release: ATP binds to myosin head releasing myosin head from actin.

Nerve signal

Axon

Synaptic knob

Voltage-gated Ca^{2+} channel

EPP

EPP

Ca^{2+}

ACh

Synaptic vesicle

ACh

Synaptic cleft

ACh receptor

K^+

Na^+

Motor end plate

ADP
P_i

ATP

INTEGRATE CONCEPT OVERVIEW

Figure 10.13 Skeletal Muscle Contraction. A summary of skeletal muscle contraction, which includes the events at (1) the neuromuscular junction, (2) the sarcolemma, T-tubules, and sarcoplasmic reticulum, and (3) sarcomeres.

② Sarcolemma, T-tubules, and Sarcoplasmic Reticulum

Excitation-contraction coupling

Action potential

Na⁺ channel

Na⁺

K⁺ →

K⁺ channel

Sarcolemma

T-tubule

2c Action potential triggers Ca^{2+} release from sarcoplasmic reticulum (SR) cisternae.

Sarcoplasmic reticulum

Ca^{2+}

Ca^{2+}

Thin filament

Thick filament

③ Sarcomere

Crossbridge cycling (cycle repeats and sarcomere shortens)

3a Ca^{2+} binds to troponin and myosin binding sites on actin are exposed.

Troponin — Ca^{2+}

Myosin binding site

Terminal cisterna

Ca^{2+}

3b **Attach:** Crossbridge formation between myosin and actin.

Actin

Crossbridge

ADP
Pᵢ

Myosin head

Crossbridge formation

Myosin head

3c **Pull:** Power stroke motion of myosin head pulls thin filament past it.

Power stroke

ADP
Pᵢ

Contracting Sarcomere

10.4 Skeletal Muscle Metabolism

We discussed how cells form ATP through the process of cellular respiration in section 3.4. Here those concepts are integrated to describe specifically how a muscle fiber meets its very-high-energy needs—and also how its various means of supplying ATP are used to classify skeletal muscle fiber into three primary types.

10.4a Supplying Energy for Skeletal Muscle Contraction

LEARNING OBJECTIVES

1. Describe immediate, short-term, and long-term means that muscle fibers use to supply ATP for muscle contraction.
2. Explain how the means of supplying ATP is related to intensity and duration of exercise.

A skeletal muscle fiber has three major means for generating ATP. These are differentiated based upon the relative amount of time required to generate ATP and are appropriately called the immediate, short-term, and long-term means for supplying ATP.

Immediate Supply of ATP: The Phosphagen System

The immediate supply of ATP is generated by the **phosphagen system,** which uses molecules that contain a high-energy phosphate. The phosphagen system is not dependent upon the presence of oxygen—that is, the processes of this system are anaerobic. This system represents both the available ATP and the immediate means of forming ATP from other phosphate-containing molecules. See **figure 10.14** as you read through this section.

ATP that is already present within the skeletal muscle fiber is hydrolyzed by **ATPase** into ADP and P_i. This usually provides only enough energy for about 5 to 6 seconds of maximal exertion (figure 10.14*a*).

An additional few seconds of energy in muscle is generated when the enzyme **myokinase** transfers a phosphate from one adenosine diphosphate (ADP) to another ADP, yielding ATP and adenosine monophosphate (AMP) (figure 10.14*b*).

One means of supplying ATP that occurs only in muscle tissue involves **creatine phosphate.** ATP is generated when the enzyme **creatine kinase** transfers P_i from creatine phosphate to ADP, yielding creatine and ATP. This provides an additional 10 to 15 seconds of energy. During times of rest, as small amounts of ATP accumulate, the pathway described in figure 10.14*c* is reversed. Creatine kinase

transfers P_i from ATP to creatine, yielding creatine phosphate and ADP.

WHAT DO YOU THINK?

④ When skeletal muscle tissue is damaged, creatine kinase is released. What relationship do you think exists between creatine kinase levels in the blood and the extent of muscle tissue damage?

Short-Term Supply of ATP: Anaerobic Cellular Respiration

Recall from section 3.4 that the metabolic processes for generating ATP involve both anaerobic and aerobic metabolic pathways. The short-term supply for ATP is provided by **anaerobic cellular respiration** (glycolysis), a process that occurs in the cytosol and does not require oxygen **(figure 10.15*a*)**. Glucose is made available either directly from glycogen stores in the muscle fiber or delivered by the blood; through many enzymatic steps glucose is broken down to two pyruvate molecules. The net energy released during glycolysis is 2 ATP molecules per glucose molecule.

Pyruvate normally enters the mitochondria to be oxidized through metabolic pathways of aerobic cellular respiration. This process requires oxygen. If insufficient oxygen is delivered to the muscle tissue, increasing amounts of pyruvate are converted to lactic acid. Lactic acid can either be removed directly by the muscle where it is produced or enter the blood. Lactic acid that enters the blood can then either be taken up by the heart to be used as fuel to generate ATP or is taken up by the liver to produce glucose by gluconeogenesis (see section 17.7).

(a)   (b)   (c)

Figure 10.14 The Phosphagen System. Immediate sources of ATP are available for muscle cells from (*a*) small amounts of stored ATP within the muscle fiber, (*b*) the transfer of phosphate (P_i) from one ADP to another ADP that is catalyzed by myokinase enzyme, and (*c*) the transfer of P_i from creatine phosphate (CP) to ADP that is catalyzed by creatine kinase (CK) enzyme.

Figure 10.15 Metabolic Processes for Generating ATP. (*a*) Short-term anaerobic pathway for ATP production within the cytosol. (*b*) Long-term aerobic pathway for ATP generation within mitochondria.

Labels in figure:
- Glycolysis
- Glucose
- NADH
- 2 ATP
- 2 pyruvate
- Insufficient oxygen
- Cytosol
- Lactic acid
- Oxygen
- Outer mitochondrial membrane
- Mitochondrion
- Pyruvate
- NADH
- Acetyl CoA
- CO_2
- Outer membrane compartment
- Inner mitochondrial membrane
- Mitochondrial matrix
- NADH
- CO_2
- Citric acid cycle
- FADH$_2$
- 2 ATP
- e⁻
- H⁺ O$_2$ H$_2$O
- 32 ATP
- e⁻ Electron e⁻ transport chain
- ATP synthetase (oxidative phosphorylation)
- H⁺

(a) **Short-term energy supply** (anaerobic cellular respiration)

(b) **Long-term energy supply** (aerobic cellular respiration)

Long-Term Supply of ATP: Aerobic Cellular Respiration

The long-term supply of ATP is provided by **aerobic cellular respiration** that occurs within mitochondria. The nutrient source for aerobic production of ATP is the pyruvate made available following anaerobic cellular respiration. Aerobic cellular respiration requires the presence of oxygen that is both delivered by the blood and provided by myoglobin (described earlier in the chapter).

Pyruvate enters a mitochondrion, where it is oxidized completely to carbon dioxide (CO_2) through the metabolic pathways of the intermediate stage and citric acid cycle (see section 3.4). The oxidation of pyruvate results in the transfer of chemical bond energy to coenzymes, NADH and FADH$_2$. The energy transferred to NADH and FADH$_2$ is then used to generate ATP in the electron transport system by a process called *oxidative phosphorylation*. The total amount of energy produced through oxidative phosphorylation is 34 ATP molecules.

ATP is also generated in aerobic cellular respiration from triglycerides, structures composed of glycerol and three fatty acids (see section 2.7b). The amount of ATP generated is dependent upon the length of the fatty acid chain. The longer the chain, the more ATP produced. Fatty acids are the preferential fuel molecule for generating ATP in most skeletal muscle tissue. However, one of the major drawbacks to the use of fatty acids is that oxygen must be present. Thus, sufficient oxygen must be delivered continuously during sustained exercise for skeletal muscle tissue to use fatty acids to generate energy.

Energy Supply and Varying Intensity of Exercise

The use of immediate, short-term, and long-term sources for supplying ATP is dependent upon both the intensity and duration of an activity. To illustrate the use of energy, we describe the primary means of supplying ATP for runners at a track meet in which individuals run different distances (**figure 10.16**).

When an individual participates in a 50-meter sprint, an event that may take 5 to 6 seconds, ATP is supplied primarily by the phosphagen system. In a longer sprint of 400 meters, an event that may take 50 to 60 seconds, ATP is supplied initially by the

50 meters: 5–6 seconds

400 meters: 50–60 seconds

1500 meters: 5–6 minutes

Phosphagen system = immediate energy source
Anaerobic cellular respiration = short-term energy source
Aerobic cellular respiration = long-term energy source

1500-meter track

Figure 10.16 Utilization of Immediate, Short-Term, and Long-Term Energy Sources. The intensity and duration of an activity are important factors in energy utilization. For short sprints, the phosphagen system is primarily used, whereas for longer runs, anaerobic cellular respiration is used initially but will be replaced by aerobic cellular respiration.

phosphagen system and then primarily by anaerobic cellular respiration. Finally, in a 1500-meter run, an event that may take 5 to 6 minutes, ATP is supplied by all three means, but primarily by aerobic processes after about the first minute. Keep in mind, however, that there is overlap between the three different energy sources.

Intense exercise that is sustained longer than approximately 1 minute is dependent upon the body's ability to deliver sufficient oxygen through the cardiovascular and respiratory systems. One consequence of participating in aerobic exercise (defined as a sustained exercise of moderate intensity that involves raising the heart rate above the baseline) is that it produces changes within both the respiratory and cardiovascular system that enhances oxygen delivery, thus allowing an individual to exercise both at greater levels of intensity and for longer periods of time.

 WHAT DID YOU LEARN?

15 Additional ATP is made immediately available in muscle tissue through which unique phosphate-containing molecule?

16 What are the various means for making ATP available in a 1500-meter race?

10.4b Oxygen Debt

LEARNING OBJECTIVE

3. Define oxygen debt, and explain why it occurs.

There are limitations to how much oxygen can be supplied to skeletal muscle in a given time period. When an individual participates in exercise during which the demand for oxygen exceeds the availability of oxygen, an oxygen debt is incurred. **Oxygen debt** is the amount of additional oxygen that must be inhaled following exercise to restore pre-exercise conditions. This additional oxygen is required primarily to

- replace oxygen on hemoglobin molecules in the blood and myoglobin molecules in muscle,
- replenish glycogen stored in muscle fibers,
- replenish ATP and creatine phosphate in the phosphagen system, and
- convert lactic acid back to glucose, a process that occurs when lactic acid is delivered by the blood to the liver.

The next time you see someone breathing hard following exercise, you will realize that they are "paying off" their oxygen debt, helping to return the body to its state prior to exercise, and as just described, much of that oxygen is used by muscle tissue to once again meet its energy needs.

 WHAT DID YOU LEARN?

17 What is oxygen debt, and how is the additional oxygen used following intense exercise?

10.5 Skeletal Muscle Fiber Types

Skeletal muscle fiber types are organized into three primary categories. Here we discuss the criteria used to classify them, and then describe the three primary muscle fiber types.

10.5a Criteria for Classification of Muscle Fiber Types

LEARNING OBJECTIVE

1. Explain the two primary criteria used to classify skeletal muscle fiber types.

Skeletal muscle fibers that compose a muscle are differentiated into three categories based upon two criteria: (1) the type of contraction generated, and (2) the primary means used for supplying ATP.

Type of Contraction Generated

Skeletal muscle fibers differ in the power, speed, and duration of the muscle contraction generated. **Power** is related to the diameter of a muscle fiber; large muscle fibers are more densely packed with myofibrils and produce a more powerful contraction.

Speed has traditionally been described based upon whether the skeletal muscle fiber contains the relatively slow or fast genetic variant of myosin ATPase, the enzyme that splits ATP. Those with a fast variant are called **fast-twitch fibers,** and those with the slow variant are called **slow-twitch fibers.** However, recent evidence shows that fast-twitch fibers also have both a fast rate of action potential conduction along the sarcolemma and are quick in their Ca^{2+} release and reuptake by the sarcoplasmic reticulum in comparison to slow-twitch fibers. Thus, these fibers initiate a contraction more quickly following stimulation than a slow-twitch fiber (0.01 milliseconds [msec] versus at least 0.02 msec), and produce a contraction of shorter **duration** (7.5 msec versus 100 msec).

Fast-twitch fibers typically have all three characteristics: They produce a strong contraction, initiate a contraction more quickly following stimulation, and produce a contraction of shorter duration. These characteristics account for why fast-twitch fibers exhibit both power and speed in comparison to slow-twitch fibers.

Means for Supplying ATP

The second criterion to differentiate skeletal muscle fibers is whether the primary means the muscle uses to supply ATP is either aerobic cellular respiration or anaerobic cellular respiration. **Oxidative fibers** use aerobic cellular respiration and have several features that support these processes, including an extensive capillary network, large numbers of mitochondria, and a large supply of the red pigment myoglobin. (The presence of myoglobin gives these fibers a red appearance, and fibers with myoglobin are sometimes called **red fibers.**) The higher levels of ATP generated provide energy for oxidative fibers to continue contracting for extended periods of time without tiring or fatiguing—thus, these fibers are also called **fatigue-resistant.**

In contrast, **glycolytic fibers** use anaerobic cellular respiration. Generally, they have fewer structures needed for aerobic cellular respiration—thus, they have sparse capillary networks, few mitochondria, and small amounts of myoglobin. (The lack of myoglobin is why these fibers have a white appearance and are sometimes called **white fibers.**) However, they do have large glycogen reserves for supplying glucose for anaerobic cellular respiration, which is useful for when oxygen stores are low. The small amounts of ATP generated through glycolysis limit the exercise duration these muscles can sustain. Glycolytic fibers generally tire easily after a short time of sustained muscular activity—thus, these fibers are also called **fatigable.**

 WHAT DID YOU LEARN?

18 Explain how a fast-twitch fiber differs from a slow-twitch fiber, and how an oxidative fiber differs from a glycolytic fiber.

10.5b Classification of Muscle Fiber Types

LEARNING OBJECTIVE

2. Compare and contrast the three muscle fiber types.

Physiologists use both the type of contraction generated and type of energy used to supply ATP to differentiate skeletal muscle fibers into three subtypes (**table 10.1**):

Table 10.1	**Structural and Functional Characteristics of Different Types of Skeletal Muscle Fibers**		

Fiber Characteristics	Slow Oxidative (SO) Fibers (Type I Fibers)	Fast Oxidative (FO) Fibers (Type IIa Fibers)	Fast Glycolytic (FG) Fibers (Type IIb Fibers)
ATP Use	Slow	Fast	Fast
Capacity to Make ATP	High, aerobic	Moderate, aerobic	Limited, anaerobic
Concentration of Capillaries	Extensive	Moderately extensive	Sparse
Color of Fibers	Red	Lighter red	White (pale)
Contraction Velocity	Slow	Fast	Fast
Resistance to Fatigue	Highest	High	Low
Fiber Diameter	Smallest	Intermediate	Largest
Number of Mitochondria	Many	Many	Few
Amount of Myoglobin	Large	Medium	Small
Primary Fiber Function	Endurance (e.g., maintaining posture, marathon running)	Medium duration, moderate movement (e.g., walking, biking)	Short duration, intense movement (e.g., sprinting, lifting weights)
Muscles with a large abundance	Trunk and calf muscles	Leg muscles	Upper limb muscles

- **Slow oxidative (SO) fibers,** also called *type I,* typically have half the diameter of other skeletal muscle fibers and contain slow ATPase. These cells produce contractions that are slower and less powerful. However, they can contract over long periods of time without fatigue because ATP is supplied primarily through aerobic cellular respiration. These fibers appear dark red because of the presence of large amounts of myoglobin.

- **Fast oxidative (FO) fibers,** also called *intermediate fibers,* or *type IIa,* are the least numerous of the skeletal muscle fiber types. They are intermediate in size and contain fast ATPase. They produce a fast, powerful contraction with ATP provided primarily through aerobic respiration. However, the vascular supply to fast oxidative fibers is less extensive than the network of capillaries serving SO fibers—thus, the delivery rate of nutrients and oxygen is lower. These fibers also contain myoglobin, but less than the amount found in SO fibers. Consequently, these fibers can be distinguished from SO fibers on a microscopic image because they appear a lighter red than SO fibers.

- **Fast glycolytic (FG) fibers,** also called *fast anaerobic fibers,* or *type IIb,* are the most prevalent skeletal muscle fiber type. They are largest in diameter, contain fast ATPase, and provide both power and speed. However, they can contract for only short bursts because ATP is provided primarily through anaerobic cellular respiration. These fibers appear white because of the relative lack of myoglobin.

10.5c Distribution of Muscle Fiber Types

LEARNING OBJECTIVE

3. Describe the distribution of muscle fiber types in a muscle and how this relates to function.

A mixture of muscle fiber types in a typical skeletal muscle is shown in **figure 10.17**. Although most muscles contain a mixture of all three fiber types, the relative percentage of the muscle fiber types varies between different skeletal muscles of the body and reflects the function of the muscle. For example, the muscles of the eye and hand require swift but brief contractions and so they contain a high percentage of FG fibers. In contrast, SO fibers dominate many postural back and calf muscles, which contract almost continually to help us maintain an upright posture.

Variations are also present between individuals, and this is seen most dramatically in high-caliber athletes. Top distance runners have

Figure 10.17 Comparison of Fiber Types in Skeletal Muscle. A cross section of a skeletal muscle using a specific staining technique demonstrates the types of fibers in the muscle. The fibers are distinguished by their shade of color. Fast glycolytic (FG) fibers are the lightest; slow oxidative (SO) fibers are the darkest; and fast oxidative (FO) fibers are less dark than the SO fibers.

higher proportions of SO fibers in their leg muscles, and top athletes that participate in brief periods of intense activity, such as sprinting or weight lifting, have a higher percentage of FG fibers. These variations in the proportion of the muscle fiber types are determined primarily by a person's genes and less so by the type of training. A proportion of FG fibers may develop the appearance and functional capabilities of FO fibers with physical conditioning if the muscle is used repeatedly for endurance events. Whether this shift actually represents a change of muscle fiber type—or is simply a temporary alteration to the muscle that reverts back when the training ceases—remains controversial.

 WHAT DID YOU LEARN?

20 Which muscle fiber type primarily composes muscles that maintain posture?

10.6 Measurement of Skeletal Muscle Tension

Muscle tension is the force generated when a skeletal muscle is stimulated to contract. Muscle tension produced in a contracting muscle is measured in several classic laboratory experiments. One variation of these experiments uses the specimen of a gastrocnemius (calf) muscle with an attached sciatic nerve that is excised from a frog. The gastrocnemius muscle is then anchored to an apparatus that produces a myogram, a graphic recording of changes in muscle tension when it is stimulated. Here we describe the generation and graphic recording of (1) a muscle twitch; (2) motor unit recruitment; and (3) treppe, wave summation, incomplete tetany, and tetany.

10.6a Muscle Twitch

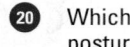 **LEARNING OBJECTIVE**

1. Describe what occurs in a muscle during a single twitch, and relate each event to a graph of a twitch.

Electrodes that either are in direct contact with the muscle or the sciatic nerve are used to apply single, brief episodes of stimulation to the muscle. The voltage is increased in increments until the muscle responds, producing a twitch. A **twitch** is defined as a single, brief contraction period and then relaxation period of a skeletal muscle in response to a single stimulation **(figure 10.18)**. The minimum voltage needed to stimulate the muscle to generate a twitch is the **threshold.** The voltage below the threshold is called a *subthreshold stimulus.*

There is a delay called a **latent period** (*lag period*) that occurs in a twitch after the stimulus is applied and before the contraction of the muscle fiber begins. There is no change in fiber length during the latent period. This delay can be accounted for by the time necessary for the occurrence of all of the events in excitation-contraction coupling, Ca^{2+} release from the sarcoplasmic reticulum into the cytosol, and the beginning of tension generation within the muscle fiber. The **contraction period** begins as repetitive power strokes pull the thin filaments past the thick filaments, shortening the sarcomeres; muscle tension increases during muscle contraction. The **relaxation period** begins with release of crossbridges resulting from return of Ca^{2+} back into the sarcoplasmic reticulum; muscle tension decreases during muscle relaxation. Notice that the contraction phase has a shorter duration than the relaxation phase because contraction is an active process that forms crossbridges and generates the power stroke, whereas relaxation is a passive process that depends upon the elasticity of connectin within muscle tissue to return to its original length.

 WHAT DO YOU THINK?

5 Based on skeletal muscle fiber type distribution described earlier, would you predict that the duration of a muscle twitch in an extrinsic eye muscle is shorter or longer than it is in the gastrocnemius muscle? Explain.

 WHAT DID YOU LEARN?

21 What events are occurring in a muscle that produce the different components of a muscle twitch (latent period, contraction, and relaxation)?

10.6b Changes in Stimulus Intensity: Motor Unit Recruitment

LEARNING OBJECTIVE

2. Explain the events that occur in motor unit recruitment as the intensity of stimulation is increased.

The gastrocnemius muscle is stimulated repeatedly in a set of experiments to demonstrate motor unit recruitment, and each stimulation event is at a greater voltage. The frequency of stimulation remains the same, and the time between stimulation events is sufficient for the muscle to contract and relax before it is stimulated again. Because motor units vary in their sensitivity to stimulation, each increase in voltage causes a greater number of motor units to contract **(figure 10.19)**. Consequently, the tension generated with each muscle contraction increases until the point of maximum contraction is reached when all motor units have been stimulated. This increase in muscle tension that occurs with an

Figure 10.18 Muscle Twitch. A single brief stimulation of a muscle results in a single contraction event called a twitch. The latent period is the elapsed time between stimulation of the muscle fiber and the generation of contractile force. The contraction period is the time during which there is an increase in muscle tension. The relaxation period is the time when there is a decrease in muscle tension.

Figure 10.19 Skeletal Muscle Response to Change in Stimulus Intensity. Increasing the intensity of stimulation increases the number of motor units involved, resulting in recruitment, or multiple motor unit summation.

increase in stimulus intensity is called **recruitment,** or **multiple motor unit summation.**

Recruitment helps to account for how our muscles can exhibit both the all-or-none law and exert varying degrees of force. The **all-or-none law** states that if a muscle fiber contracts in response to stimulation, it will contract completely (all)—and if the stimulus is not sufficient, it will not contract (none). This means that the muscle fiber contracts maximally or not at all.

The difference in the force and precision of muscle movement is varied primarily by changing the number of motor units that are activated. If a reduced number of motor units are activated, then fewer muscle fibers contract and less force is exerted. In contrast, if a greater number of motor units are activated, more muscle fibers contract and a greater force is exerted. This permits us to control the contraction of the muscles of our arm to exert the force needed to lift a pencil or to lift a suitcase.

 WHAT DID YOU LEARN?

22 What is recruitment? Explain its importance in the body.

10.6c Changes in Stimulus Frequency: Treppe, Wave Summation, Incomplete Tetany, and Tetany

LEARNING OBJECTIVE

3. Distinguish between treppe, wave summation, incomplete tetany, and tetany that occur with an increase in frequency of stimulation.

A different set of experiments subjects the muscle to increasing frequency of stimulation, while the voltage remains the same. Treppe and different degrees of additive contraction activities may be seen. Note that the three graphs in **figure 10.20** have a different frequency of stimulation; each subsequent graph shows a greater frequency than the previous graph.

The stimulation frequency of a skeletal muscle may occur at a relatively slow rate (less than 10 stimuli per second) (figure 10.20a). At this rate, each muscle twitch shows that the muscle is contracting and completely relaxing before the next stimulation event. The muscle tension produced in each muscle twitch is the same.

The frequency of stimulation is increased (between 10 and 20 stimuli per second), as shown in figure 10.20b. Again, the rate of frequency allows time for muscle contraction and complete relaxation. However, the generated muscle tension is greater. This increase is not due to an increase in voltage because voltage remains the same. Rather, the increase in muscle tension may be produced because there is insufficient time to remove all of the Ca^{2+} from the sarcoplasm and return it back into the sarcoplasmic reticulum. Consequently, more crossbridges may form upon subsequent stimulation, causing a stronger contraction. The heat generated by muscle contraction also results in more efficient molecular interactions or functions, such as the activity of the enzyme ATPase. The result is a stepwise increase in strength of contraction termed **treppe** (trĕp′e; from German *treppe* = staircase), or sometimes referred to as the "warming-up" effect.

Stimulation can occur so rapidly (20 to 40 stimuli per second) that relaxation of the muscle does not occur before the next stimulation event (figure 10.20c). The restimulated muscle displays a summation of contractile forces as the effect of each new wave is added to the previous wave. This effect is often called either

Figure 10.20 Skeletal Muscle Response to Change in Stimulus Frequency. (*a*) A twitch always produces the same amount of muscle tension because of a slow rate of stimulation. (*b*) Treppe is an increase in muscle tension that occurs when not all Ca^{2+} is returned to the sarcoplasmic reticulum prior to the next stimulus and muscle temperature increases. Stimulation is occurring at the same frequency and voltage. (*c*) Wave summation, incomplete tetany, and tetany are observed when the muscle is stimulated at varying frequencies that prevent different degrees of relaxation.

(a) Twitch

(b) Treppe

(c) Wave summation, incomplete tetany, and tetany

wave summation because contraction waves are added together or "summed," or **temporal summation** because it depends upon increasing frequency of stimulation over time.

Further increases in stimulation frequency allow less time for relaxation between contraction cycles, and now **incomplete tetany** (the tension tracing continues to increase and the distance between waves decreases) is noted. Stimulation frequency is further increased (40 to 50 stimuli per second) until ultimately the contractions of the muscle fiber "fuse" and form a continuous, smooth contraction that lacks any relaxation. This continuous contraction is called **tetany** (the tension tracing is a smooth line). If stimulation continues, the muscle reaches **fatigue**—a decrease in muscle tension occurs from repetitive stimulation (muscle fatigue is described in a later section). Changes in muscle stimulation frequency by the nervous system primarily allow skeletal muscle contraction to exert a coordinated action that gradually increases in force.

Nervous stimulation of muscles in the human body usually does not exceed 25 stimuli per second. Therefore, muscle tetany is seen only in laboratory experiments. Sustained contractions in the body occur when you are holding something you do not want to drop because the nervous system stimulates different motor units within the same muscle in an overlapping pattern, so the muscle tension can be maintained for a longer period.

 WHAT DID YOU LEARN?

23 What happens during wave summation? Explain its importance in the body.

10.7 Factors Affecting Skeletal Muscle Tension Within the Body

The discussion of muscle tension continues with a description of several factors that influence the action of muscles within the human body, including resting tension in the muscle, the relationship between muscle tension and resistance, how contraction force generated is dependent upon myofilament overlap, and the factors that influence muscle fatigue.

10.7a Muscle Tone

 LEARNING OBJECTIVE

1. Describe muscle tone, and explain its significance.

Muscles do not completely relax even when at rest. **Muscle tone** is the resting tension in a muscle generated by involuntary nervous stimulation of the muscle. Limited numbers of motor units within a muscle are usually stimulated randomly at any given time to maintain a constant tension; the specific motor units being stimulated during rest change continuously so motor units do not become fatigued.

This random contraction of small numbers of motor units causes the muscle to develop tension, called **resting muscle tone.** These random contractions do not generate enough tension to cause movement. The resting muscle tone establishes constant

tension on the muscle's tendon, thus stabilizing the position of the bones and joints. Note that muscle tone decreases during deep sleep (sleep associated with rapid eye movement, or REM, sleep).

 WHAT DID YOU LEARN?

24 What is the function of skeletal muscle tone?

10.7b Isometric Contractions and Isotonic Contractions

 LEARNING OBJECTIVE

2. Distinguish between isometric and isotonic contractions, and give examples of both.

Two primary factors must be considered when describing the consequences of consciously initiating muscle contraction: (1) force generated by the muscle, and (2) resistance (load) that must be overcome. When muscle tension is insufficient to overcome the resistance (i.e., force generated is less than the load), there is no movement of the muscle. This type of muscle contraction is called an **isometric** (ī-sō-met′rik; iso = same, metron = measure) **contraction.** Thus, the muscle contracts and muscle tension increases, but muscle length stays the same. Some examples of isometric contractions include pushing on a wall (a posture for stretching one's leg muscles), holding a very heavy weight in the gym while your arm does not move, attempting to move a shovel load of snow that is too heavy, or holding a baby in one position **(figure 10.21a)**.

When muscle tension is greater than the resistance (load) (i.e., force generated is greater than the load), there is movement of the muscle. This type of muscle contraction is called an **isotonic** (ī-sō-ton′ik; tonos = tension) **contraction** and results in movement of body structures. The tone in the muscle remains the same as the length of muscle changes. Examples of an isotonic contraction include walking, lifting a baby, or swinging a tennis racket. Isotonic contractions are differentiated into two subclasses based on whether the muscle is shortening or lengthening as it contracts (figure 10.21b). The shortening of muscle length is a **concentric contraction**. It may occur in the biceps

Muscle tension is less than resistance.

Muscle tension is greater than resistance.

Concentric: Muscle shortens

Eccentric: Muscle lengthens

Isometric contraction	**Isotonic contraction**
Muscle tension is less than the resistance. Although tension is generated, the muscle does not shorten, and no movement occurs.	Muscle tension is greater than the resistance. The muscle shortens (concentric) or lengthens (eccentric), and movement occurs.

(a)

(b)

Figure 10.21 Isometric Versus Isotonic Contraction.

CLINICAL VIEW

Isometric Contraction and Increase in Blood Pressure

An increase in blood pressure is generally associated with sustained isometric contractions of skeletal muscles. Thus, individuals who already have high blood pressure may experience an additional spike in pressure during intensive exercise placing them at an increased risk of having a heart attack. This is something for those at risk of having a heart attack to consider before shoveling snow, because both the sustained isometric contractions and the general peripheral vasoconstriction (that results from being in the cold) can raise blood pressure to unhealthy levels.

A skeletal muscle fiber stimulated when it is at a normal resting length generates a maximum contractile force because there is optimal overlap of thick and thin filaments. In contrast, a muscle that is either already contracted, or one that is overly stretched, produces a weaker contraction when stimulated. Weaker contractions in muscles that are already contracted occur because the thick filaments are close to the Z discs, and sliding filaments are limited in their movement. Weaker contractions occur in muscles that are overly stretched because there is minimal thick and thin filament overlap for cross-bridge formation. So, for example, you may be able to lift a heavier dumbbell when your elbow is partially flexed than when your elbow is fully extended, because there is minimal overlap of thick and thin filaments during the full extension.

 WHAT DID YOU LEARN?

26 Describe the relative force of contraction that can be developed in your back muscles when you bend at the knees to lift an object and when you bend at the waist to lift an object, based on the length-tension relationship. Explain the significance.

brachii (muscle of the anterior arm) when lifting a baby. In contrast, lengthening of muscle is an **eccentric contraction**. This occurs, for example, in the biceps brachii when placing a baby into a crib.

 WHAT DID YOU LEARN?

25 When you flex your biceps brachii while doing "biceps curls," what is the type of movement?

10.7c Length-Tension Relationship

 LEARNING OBJECTIVE

3. Explain the length-tension relationship in skeletal muscle contraction.

One factor that influences the amount of tension a muscle can generate when stimulated is the amount of overlap of thick and thin filaments when the muscle begins its contraction. This principle is termed the **length-tension relationship.** A muscle generates different amounts of tension dependent upon its length at the time of stimulation. The graphical presentation of the length-tension relationship is called the **length-tension curve (figure 10.22)**.

10.7d Muscle Fatigue

LEARNING OBJECTIVE

4. Define muscle fatigue, and explain some of its causes.

Muscle fatigue is the reduced ability or inability of the muscle to produce muscle tension. The primary cause of muscle fatigue during excessive or sustained exercise (e.g., running a marathon) is caused by a decrease in glycogen stores. However, there are many other causes of muscle fatigue. These are organized by the specific physiologic event of muscle contraction that is affected.

- **Excitation at the neuromuscular junction.** Muscle fatigue may be caused either by insufficient free Ca^{2+} at the neuromuscular junction to enter the synaptic knob or by a decreased number of synaptic vesicles to release neurotransmitter. Both limit the ability of motor neurons to stimulate a muscle.

- **Excitation-contraction coupling.** Muscle fatigue may be due to a change in ion concentration (e.g., Na^+, K^+) that interferes with the ability of the muscle fiber to conduct an action potential along the sarcolemma. This interferes with stimulating release of Ca^{2+} from the sarcoplasmic reticulum.

Figure 10.22 Length-Tension Curve.
The tension generated by a muscle is graphically related to its precontraction resting length. (*a*) If the muscle is already contracted at the time of stimulation, it does not have the ability to shorten much more, and it exhibits a weak contraction. (*b*) Muscle at its normal resting length is generally capable of exhibiting the strongest contraction because of optimal overlap of myofilaments. (*c*) If the muscle is very stretched when stimulated, relatively little contraction may occur because myofilaments have minimal overlap.

CLINICAL VIEW
Muscle Pain Associated with Exercise

Accumulation of lactic acid produced from anaerobic cellular respiration is commonly (but, incorrectly) thought to cause muscle pain as a result of exercise. Studies have shown, however, that muscle pain is due in part to some minor tearing of the skeletal muscle fibers, which results in a buildup of fluid and inflammation.

- **Crossbridge cycling.** Muscle fatigue may result from increased phosphate ion (P_i) concentration. Elevated P_i concentration in the muscle sarcoplasm interferes with P_i release from the myosin head during crossbridge cycling, and this slows the rate of cycling. Muscle fatigue also may occur when lower amounts of Ca^{2+} are available for release from the sarcoplasmic reticulum (part of which is due to its binding with the excess P_i). Lower Ca^{2+} levels results in less Ca^{2+} binding to troponin, producing a weaker muscle contraction. Thus, both an increase in P_i concentration and lower Ca^{2+} levels result in a weaker force generated during muscle contraction.

Lack of ATP is not currently thought to be a primary cause of muscle fatigue. This is because ATP levels are generally maintained through aerobic cellular respiration in mitochondria during sustained exercise. It remains to be determined if ATP may still be a factor because of its location in the cell—that is, within the mitochondria and not in proximity to myofilaments.

WHAT DID YOU LEARN?

 27   How can muscle fatigue result from changes in each of the three primary events of skeletal muscle contraction?

CONCEPT CONNECTION

Mental fatigue, or "central fatigue," may result from the accumulation of tryptophan (an amino acid) in the blood as amino acids are released from cells and transported in the blood to the liver for additional production of glucose through gluconeogenesis (synthesis of glucose from noncarbohydrate sources; see section 17.7). Tryptophan crosses the blood-brain barrier and is converted to serotonin, a neurotransmitter that causes sleepiness. This partly explains why we may feel physically and mentally tired after a heavy workout.

10.8 Effects of Exercise and Aging on Skeletal Muscle

Skeletal muscle is affected by the process of exercise and aging. Here we describe the effects on our skeletal muscle of both a sustained exercise program and a lack of exercise, along with the changes that occur as we age.

10.8a Effects of Exercise

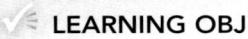 **LEARNING OBJECTIVE**

1.   Compare and contrast the changes in skeletal muscle that occur as a result of an exercise program or from the lack of exercise.

Changes in Muscle from a Sustained Exercise Program

Exercise that involves repetitive stimulation of skeletal muscle fibers primarily results in an increase in their size. This is called **hypertrophy** (hī-pĕr′trō-fē; *hyper* = above or over, *trophe* = nourishment) (see section 5.6b). Hypertrophy results in more mitochondria, larger glycogen reserves, and an increased ability to produce ATP. Additionally, each muscle fiber develops more myofibrils that contain a larger number of myofilaments. These are changes associated with a sustained exercise program. An athlete who competes as a bodybuilder or weight lifter exhibits obvious hypertrophied muscular development; however, healthy muscle can be maintained without going to such an extreme. Recent evidence suggests that some (limited) increase in the *number* of muscle fibers also may occur, a process called **hyperplasia.**

Changes in Muscle from Lack of Exercise

Lack of exercise or muscle use results primarily in decreasing the muscle fiber size, a process called **atrophy** (at′rō-fē; *a* = without). This causes a decrease in muscle fiber size, tone, and power, and the muscle becomes flaccid. Even a temporary reduction in muscle use can lead to muscular atrophy. Comparing limb muscles before and after a cast that has been worn for a fracture reveals the loss of muscle tone and size for the casted limb. Individuals who suffer damage to the nervous system or are paralyzed by spinal injuries gradually lose muscle tone and size in the areas affected. Although muscle atrophy is initially reversible, dead or dying muscle fibers are not replaced. When extreme atrophy occurs, the loss of gross muscle function is permanent because muscle is replaced with connective tissue. For these reasons, physical therapy is required for patients who suffer temporary loss of mobility.

WHAT DID YOU LEARN?

28   What anatomic changes occur in a skeletal muscle fiber when it undergoes hypertrophy?

10.8b Effects of Aging

LEARNING OBJECTIVE

2.   Summarize the effects of aging on skeletal muscle.

A slow, progressive loss of skeletal muscle mass typically begins in a person's mid-30s as a direct result of decreased activity. The size and power of skeletal muscles also decrease. Often, the lost muscle mass is replaced by either adipose or fibrous connective tissue. There is a loss both in fiber number and fiber diameter. A decrease

Anabolic (an-ă-bol'ik) **steroids** are synthetic substances that mimic the actions of natural testosterone. (Recall from section 3.2b that the term "anabolism" refers to the synthesis of complex molecules (e.g., protein) from simple molecules (e.g., amino acids). To date, over 100 compounds have been developed with anabolic properties, but they all require a prescription for legal use in the United States. Anabolic steroids have only a few accepted medical uses—among them, the treatment of delayed puberty, certain types of impotence, and the wasting condition associated with HIV infection and other diseases. Because anabolic steroids stimulate the manufacture of muscle proteins, these compounds have become popular with some athletes as performance enhancers.

Relatively large doses of anabolic steroids are needed to stimulate excessive muscle development that results in extra strength and speed. But this enhanced muscle power and speed comes at a price. Medical professionals have reported many devastating side effects associated with extended anabolic steroid use, including increased risk of heart disease and stroke, kidney damage, liver tumors, testicular atrophy

and a reduced sperm count, abnormal breast development in males, acne, high blood pressure, aggressive behavior, and personality aberrations. Because anabolic steroids mimic the effects of testosterone, female athletes who use them often experience menstrual irregularities, growth of facial hair, and in extreme circumstances atrophy of the uterus and mammary glands; sterility has even been reported. Adding to these problems is the route of administration. Because many of these steroid preparations must be injected, the improper use or sharing of needles raises the possibility of transferring pathogens that cause disease (e.g., AIDS or hepatitis). For all of these reasons, the use of anabolic steroids as performance enhancers has been widely banned.

in fiber diameter is due to a reduction in both the size and number of myofibrils and the number of myofilaments. Oxygen storage capacity decreases because there is less myoglobin, glycogen reserves are reduced, and a decreased ability to produce ATP also occurs with aging. Overall, muscle strength and endurance are impaired, and the individual has a tendency to fatigue more quickly. Decreased cardiovascular performance often accompanies aging; thus, the circulatory supply to active muscles is much slower in elderly people as they begin to exercise.

Muscle tissue has a reduced capacity to recover from disease or injury as a person grows older. The number of satellite cells in skeletal muscle steadily decreases, and scar tissue often forms due to diminished repair capabilities. Finally, the elasticity of skeletal muscle also decreases. Muscle mass is often replaced by dense regular (fibrous) connective tissue, a process called **fibrosis** (fī-brō'sis). The increasing amounts of this connective tissue decrease the flexibility of muscle; an increase in collagen fibers can restrict movement and circulation.

All of us will eventually experience a decline in muscular performance, regardless of our lifestyle or exercise patterns. But we can improve our chances of being in good shape later in life by striving for physical fitness throughout life.

WHAT DID YOU LEARN?

29 What changes in skeletal muscle accompany aging?

10.9 Cardiac Muscle Tissue

LEARNING OBJECTIVE

1. List and describe the similarities and differences between skeletal muscle and cardiac muscle.

In addition to skeletal muscle, two other types of muscle are found in the body: cardiac muscle and smooth muscle (see section 5.3). Here we briefly review the characteristics of cardiac muscle (for a detailed description of cardiac muscle, see section 19.3e).

Cardiac muscle cells are individual muscle cells arranged in thick bundles within the heart wall (**figure 10.23**). Cardiac muscle cells branch and are both shorter and thicker than skeletal muscle fibers. (They typically have a diameter of about 15 μm and range in length from 50 to 100 μm.) Individual cells are joined to adjacent muscle cells at junctions termed intercalated discs. **Intercalated** (in-ter'kă-lā'ted) **discs** are unique to cardiac muscle; they are composed of desmosomes and gap junctions (see section 4.5d). These cells have only one or two nuclei. Cardiac muscle cells are striated because, like skeletal muscle fibers, cardiac muscle cells also contain sarcomeres. Cardiac muscle cells contain a large number of mitochondria, and use aerobic respiration almost exclusively to generate the ATP required for their unceasing work.

Cardiac muscle cells are stimulated by a specialized **autorhythmic** pacemaker. This feature is responsible for the repetitious, rhythmic heartbeat. The autonomic nervous

Figure 10.23 Cardiac Muscle. Cardiac muscle is found only in the heart walls. Cardiac muscle cells branch and are connected by intercalated discs. AP|R

system (discussed in depth in chapter 15) controls the rate and force of contraction of cardiac muscle.

 30 What are three anatomic or physiologic differences between skeletal muscle and cardiac muscle?

10.10 Smooth Muscle Tissue

Smooth muscle tissue is located throughout the body typically composing approximately 2% of the weight of an adult. Here we describe the general features of smooth muscle, including locations, microscopic anatomy, mechanism of contraction, how it is controlled, and its functional categories.

10.10a Location of Smooth Muscle

✓ **LEARNING OBJECTIVE**

1. Identify organs of various body systems where smooth muscle is located.

Smooth muscle tissue is found in the walls of organs of many different body systems. Smooth muscle function is determined by its location. For example (**figure 10.24**):

- Cardiovascular system: Blood vessels regulate blood pressure and the distribution of blood flow.
- Respiratory system: Bronchioles (air passageways) control the amount of air that enters and exits the air sacs (alveoli) of the lungs.
- Digestive system: The stomach, small intestine, and large intestine mix and propel ingested material as it is moved along the gastrointestinal tract.
- Urinary system: Ureters propel urine from the kidney to the urinary bladder.
- Female reproductive system: The uterus helps expel the baby during delivery.

These are but a few examples of smooth muscle distribution in our bodies. Smooth muscle also composes other specialized structures, including the iris of the eye to control the amount of light entering the eye, the ciliary body of the eye for focusing on an object (see section 16.4b), and the arrector pili muscles that produce "goose bumps" (see section 6.2b).

Smooth muscle resembles both skeletal muscle and cardiac muscle because it has cells that can increase in size (hypertrophy). Both skeletal muscle and cardiac muscle, however, have limited ability to increase in number through mitosis (hyperplasia), whereas smooth muscle retains this ability. The smooth muscle in the wall of the uterus exemplifies this characteristic as it increases in thickness during pregnancy from a combination of both hypertrophy and hyperplasia (see section 29.5c). There is a significant advantage for any tissue that retains mitotic ability because following an injury the damaged tissue is replaced with the original tissue (not scar tissue) (see section 4.8). Thus, as you consider the various locations of smooth muscle in the body, keep in mind that if smooth muscle is damaged, it is typically replaced with new smooth muscle tissue and has the potential to continue functioning as it did before.

 WHAT DID YOU LEARN?

31 Where is smooth muscle located in the human body?

10.10b Microscopic Anatomy

✓ **LEARNING OBJECTIVE**

2. Compare the microscopic anatomy of smooth muscle to skeletal muscle.

Smooth muscle cells are small and fusiform shaped (widest in the middle and tapered on the ends) with a centrally located nucleus (**figure 10.25**). They typically have a diameter of 5 to 10 micrometers and a length of 50 to 200 micrometers. Thus, their diameter is up to ten times smaller and their length thousands of times shorter than a skeletal muscle fiber. An endomysium wraps around

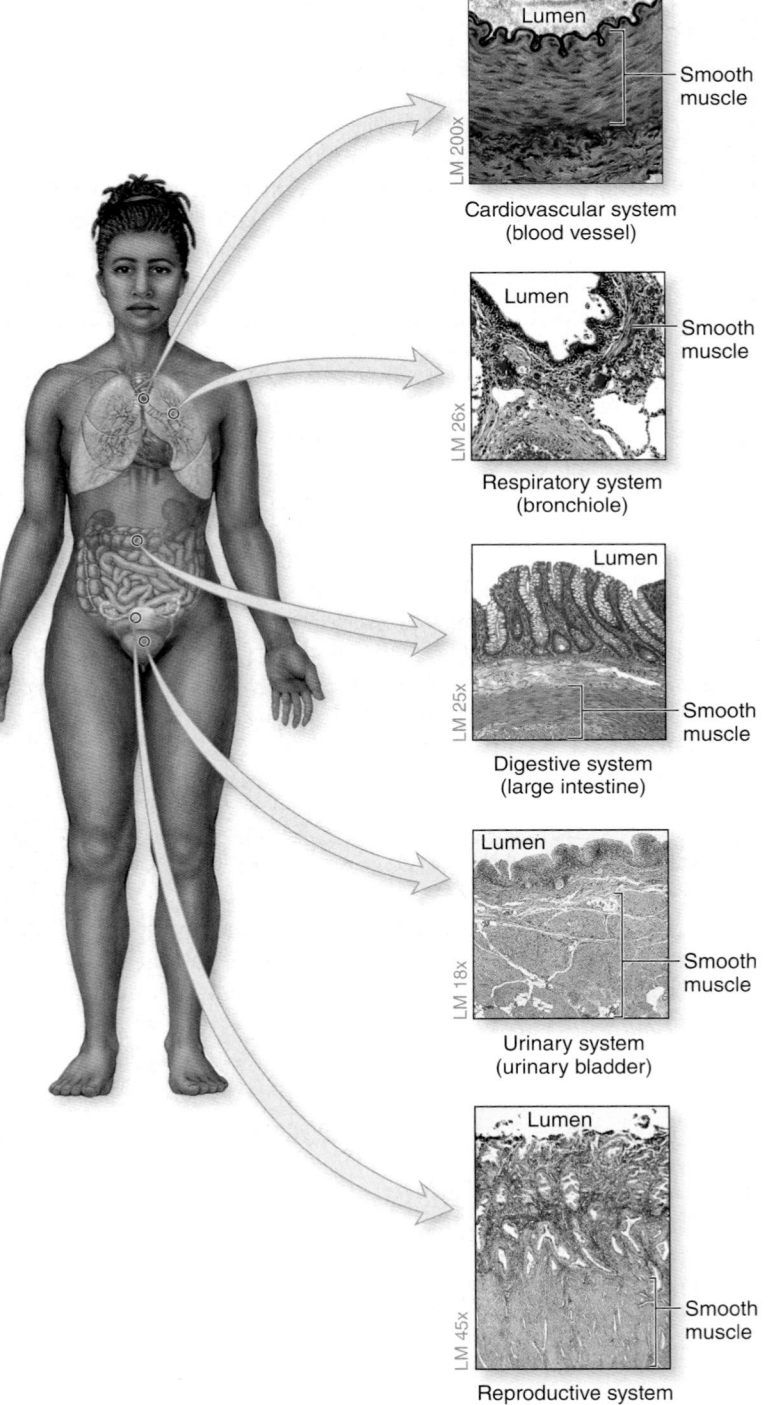

Figure 10.24 Location of Smooth Muscle. Smooth muscle tissue is located throughout the human body, including the walls of most viscera.

each smooth muscle cell. The small tapered ends of the cells overlap the larger middle area of adjacent cells to provide for close packing of cells.

The sarcolemma contains various types of Ca^{2+} channels (e.g., voltage-gated, chemically gated, modality gated) that allow these cells to respond to different types of stimuli. Transverse tubules are absent in smooth muscle cells. Instead, the sarcolemma surface area is increased by "flasklike" invaginations called *caveolae* (kav′ē-ŏ-lē; pl. *caveola;* sing., small pocket). The sarcoplasmic reticulum is sparse and located close to the sarcolemma with some tubules in contact with it. The source of Ca^{2+} comes from either outside the cell or from the sarcoplasmic reticulum.

Arrangement of Anchoring Proteins and Contractile Proteins of Smooth Muscle

Smooth muscle contains a unique arrangement of anchoring protein structures that includes the cytoskeleton, dense bodies, and dense plaques. The cytoskeletal network is composed of an extensive array of **intermediate filaments** (see section 4.5b). The intermediate filaments are linked with **dense bodies** at points where they interact within the sarcoplasm of the smooth muscle cell, whereas intermediate filaments are linked by **dense plaques** at points where they attach on the inner surface of the sarcolemma. Thus, intermediate filaments extend across the cell with dense bodies as "spot welds" that anchor intermediate filaments to each other and dense plaques that anchor the intermediate filaments to the plasma membrane.

The contractile proteins in smooth muscle are arranged between dense bodies and dense plaques rather than in sarcomeres as they are in both skeletal and cardiac muscle. The Z discs that anchor the sarcomere on either end in skeletal muscle fibers are also absent. Lack of sarcomeres and Z discs contributes to the absence of striations, giving these muscle cells their "smooth" appearance.

The contractile proteins are oriented at oblique angles to the longitudinal axis of the smooth muscle cell and appear to spiral. Consequently, contraction (as described in the next section) results in a twisting of the smooth muscle, which is similar to a corkscrew (figure 10.25c).

Comparison of Myofilaments of Smooth Muscle and Skeletal Muscle

Thick filaments in smooth muscle have myosin heads along their entire length, rather than only at the ends as in skeletal muscle. The more numerous heads can form additional crossbridges with actin to produce a powerful muscle contraction. Additionally, these myosin heads have modifications that allow them to "latch on" to the actin of thin filaments and remain attached without using additional ATP. This mechanism is called the **latchbridge mechanism.**

Smooth muscle thin filaments are composed of actin and tropomyosin, but they do not contain troponin molecules that bind Ca^{2+} like in skeletal muscle fibers. Instead, two other proteins are required for initiation of smooth muscle contraction: (1) calmodulin, a protein that binds Ca^{2+} to form a **Ca^{2+}-calmodulin complex;** and (2) **myosin light-chain kinase (MLCK),** an enzyme that is activated by the Ca^{2+}-calmodulin complex to phosphorylate the smooth muscle myosin head. The phosphorylation of the smooth muscle myosin head causes activation of its ATPase activity.

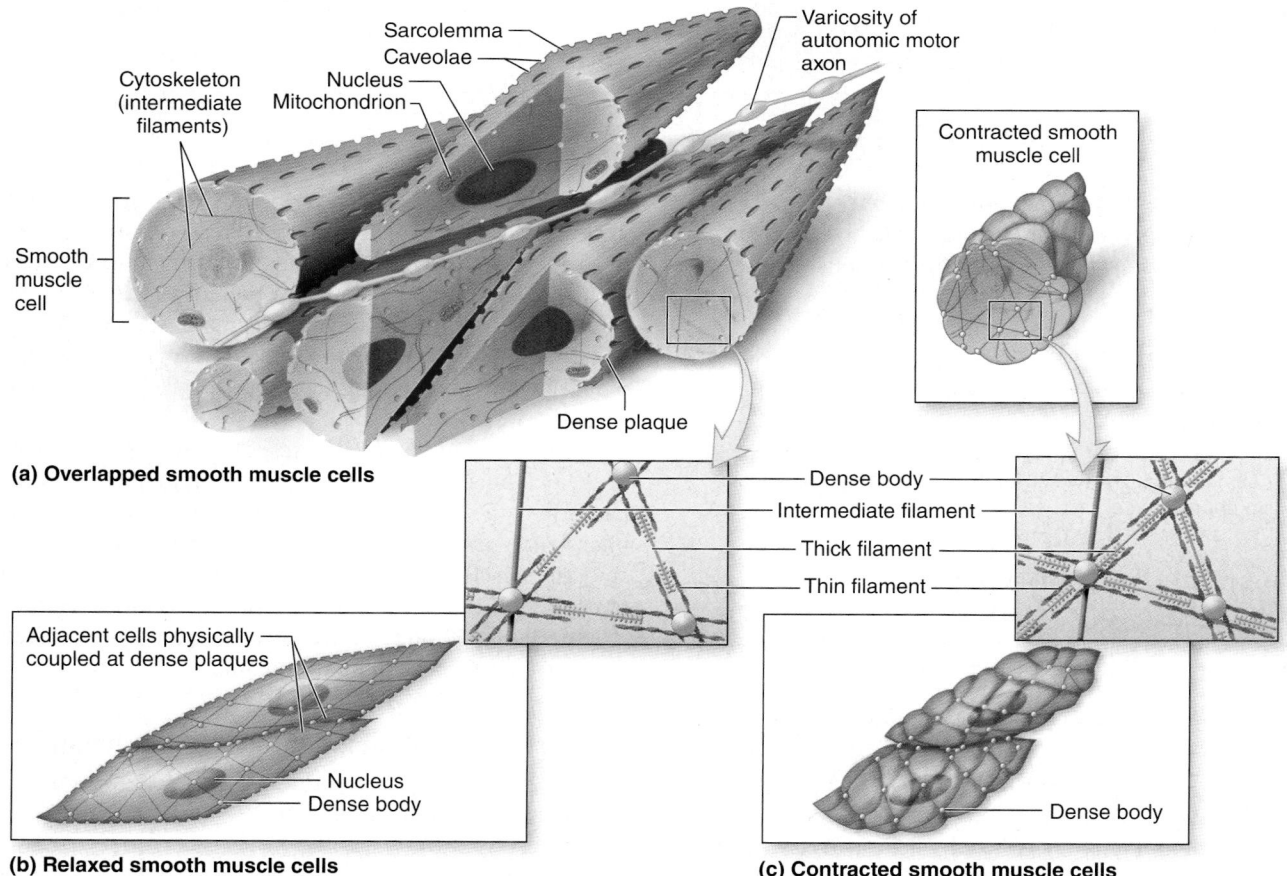

Figure 10.25 Microscopic Anatomy of Smooth Muscle. (*a*) Smooth muscle cells are fusiform cells that overlap to provide close packing of cells. (*b*) Relaxed smooth muscle cells are elongated in the fusiform shape. (*c*) Contracted smooth muscle cells are compact due to the tension exerted by the contractile proteins on the intermediate filaments that pull on both dense bodies within the sarcoplasm and dense plaques within the plasma membrane. AP|R

Figure 10.26 Smooth Muscle Contraction

(1) Opening of voltage-gated Ca²⁺ channels

Stimuli (e.g., action potential, stretch of the muscle) triggers opening of voltage-gated Ca²⁺ channels. Ca²⁺ enters the sarcoplasm, primarily from the interstitial fluid.

(2) Binding of Ca²⁺ to calmodulin

Ca²⁺ binds to calmodulin to form a Ca²⁺-calmodulin complex.

(3) Activation of myosin light-chain kinase (MLCK)

Ca²⁺-calmodulin complex activates MLCK, a phosphorylating enzyme.

(4) Activation of myosin head

Activated MLCK phosphorylates (adds phosphate to) myosin head, activating myosin—a relatively slow process.

(5) Crossbridge formation, power stroke, reattachment

Activated myosin heads bind to thin filaments to form crossbridges. Myosin ATPase hydrolyzes ATP, providing the energy for the power stroke. This process is repeated, the force generated is transferred to the anchoring filaments, and the smooth muscle cell shortens.

Labels in figure: Ca²⁺ · Caveolae · Voltage-gated Ca²⁺ channel · Calmodulin · Ca²⁺-calmodulin complex · Inactive MLCK · Activated MLCK · ATP · ADP · P_i · Interstitial fluid · Cytosol

Figure 10.26 Smooth Muscle Contraction. Detailed steps for smooth muscle contraction.

A third protein called **myosin light-chain phosphatase** is an enzyme that dephosphorylates the myosin head, resulting in the inactivation of the ATPase activity. This inactivation is required for relaxation of smooth muscle.

WHAT DID YOU LEARN?

32 How are anchoring filaments and contractile proteins in smooth muscle cells arranged?

33 What is the specific role of the following structures within smooth muscle cells: calmodulin, myosin light-chain kinase, and myosin light-chain phosphatase?

10.10c Smooth Muscle Contraction

LEARNING OBJECTIVE

3. Explain the sequence of steps in smooth muscle contraction.

Smooth muscle contraction resembles skeletal muscle contraction in that it (1) is initiated by Ca²⁺, (2) involves the sliding of thin filaments past thick filaments, and (3) requires ATP. There are significant differences, however, as shown in **figure 10.26**.

In response to stimulation, Ca²⁺ enters the sarcoplasm from both the interstitial fluid and sarcoplasmic reticulum. It binds to calmodulin to form a Ca²⁺-calmodulin complex that then binds to MLCK, resulting in its activation. The activated kinase (MLCK) phosphorylates the myosin head to both activate the myosin ATPase activity of the myosin head and to allow the myosin head to bind to

actin forming a crossbridge. Myosin ATPase hydrolyzes ATP to produce the power stroke. The myosin head releases and reattaches to the actin repetitively, causing the thin filament to slide past the thick filament. This sliding results in a pull on the attached dense bodies anchored to the intermediate filaments of the cytoskeleton and the dense plaques attached to the sarcolemma. The anchoring filaments move inward and the entire smooth muscle cell shortens (figure 10.25c).

Relaxation of smooth muscle is more complex than relaxation of skeletal muscle. It requires, in addition to both cessation of stimulation and the removal of Ca²⁺ from the sarcoplasm, the dephosphorylation of myosin by myosin light-chain phosphatase. Note that smooth muscle may remain in the contracted state following the removal of Ca²⁺ and dephosphorylation of the myosin head due to the special latchbridge mechanism described previously that keeps the myosin attached to the thin filament.

Characteristics of Smooth Muscle Contraction

Smooth muscle contraction exhibits three characteristics that allow it to effectively fulfill its functions.

Initiation and Duration of Contraction Smooth muscle contraction is usually slow to develop with maximum tension at about 500 milliseconds after stimulation. The relatively long latent period is due primarily to both the requirement for phosphorylating the myosin head by MLCK enzymes and variations in the speed of

ATPase activity. The duration of contraction typically extends over a 1- to 2-second period due to the slowness of Ca^{2+} pumps in removing Ca^{2+} from the sarcoplasm, the requirement for dephosphorylation of the myosin head by phosphatase, and the possibility of myosin locking to actin (latchbridge mechanism). Contraction of smooth muscle does not generally require a rapid onset, but it does require the ability to remain in the contracted state for extended periods of time. This characteristic is important because smooth muscle must maintain continuous tone (tonic contraction) in visceral walls, such as the gastrointestinal tract and blood vessels.

Fatigue-Resistant   The energy requirements for smooth muscle contraction are relatively low in comparison to skeletal muscle, and ATP is generally supplied through aerobic cellular respiration. The latchbridge mechanism provides the means of maintaining muscle contraction without use of additional ATP. Consequently, smooth muscle may contract for extended periods of time without becoming fatigued—obviously a necessary requirement for maintaining the tonic contractions just described.

Length-Tension Curve   Smooth muscle exhibits a broader length-tension curve than skeletal muscle. Recall that the force of muscle contraction generated by skeletal muscle is dependent upon its muscle length at the time of stimulation. It shows maximum force at its optimal resting length, but a decreased force of contraction if it is either shortened or lengthened (see figure 10.22). These limitations are due to the Z discs that prevent additional shortening and lack of myosin heads in the center of thick filaments, respectively. Smooth muscle has neither of these limitations—thus, it can contract forcefully when compressed to approximately half its resting length or stretched to twice its resting length. Consider, for example, that the storage of urine in the urinary bladder results in stretching of the urinary bladder wall. The greater the amount of urine, the greater the amount of stretch of the smooth muscle in the urinary bladder wall. The ability of smooth muscle to contract forcefully at varying degrees of stretch allows us to easily empty our bladder regardless of the amount of urine it is holding.

 WHAT DID YOU LEARN?

34 What are the steps of smooth muscle contraction?

35 What unique characteristics of smooth muscle allow it to fulfill its functions? Explain.

10.10d Controlling Smooth Muscle

LEARNING OBJECTIVE

4.   Briefly explain the different means of controlling smooth muscle.

We cannot voluntarily control the contraction of the smooth muscle in the wall of the digestive tract, as we find when our stomach "growls" at an inappropriate time. Smooth muscle is controlled by the autonomic nervous system (components of the nervous system that control cardiac muscle, smooth muscle, and glands involuntarily). The response of smooth muscle to stimulation by the nervous system—that is, whether it contracts or relaxes—is dependent upon the specific neurotransmitter that is released. Smooth muscle within the walls of bronchioles, for example, contracts in response to the release of ACh, and relaxes in response to norepinephrine.

   Smooth muscle also contracts in response to being stretched. Its response, however, is not continuous if the

stretch is prolonged. Instead, the smooth muscle exhibits what is called the **stress-relaxation response.** This occurs when smooth muscle is "stressed" by being stretched. It responds by contracting, but after a given period of time, it relaxes. For example, swallowed materials entering the stomach cause its wall to stretch, and the smooth muscle in the wall initially contracts. After a period of time it relaxes, allowing additional food to more easily enter the stomach.

   Smooth muscle is also stimulated to contract by various hormones, a decrease in pH, low oxygen concentration, increased carbon dioxide levels, certain drugs, and pacemaker cells. For example, the hormone oxytocin causes contraction of smooth muscle in the uterus to expel the baby at childbirth. A pacemaker (similar to the pacemaker in the heart) stimulates smooth muscle in the walls of the stomach and small intestine to contract rhythmically to mix and propel the contents through the lumen of these organs.

WHAT DID YOU LEARN?

36 What are the various forms of stimulation for controlling smooth muscle?

37 Explain the stress-relaxation response of smooth muscle.

10.10e Functional Categories

LEARNING OBJECTIVES

5.   Explain the primary functional difference between multiunit and single-unit smooth muscle.

6.   Compare the location and regulation of both multiunit and single-unit smooth muscle.

Smooth muscle is classified into two broad groups based upon whether the smooth muscle fibers are either stimulated to contract independently or as one unit. Multiunit smooth muscle cells receive stimulation to contract individually, whereas single-unit smooth muscle cells are stimulated to contract in unison (syncytium) (**figure 10.27**).

Figure 10.27 Multiunit and Single-Unit Smooth Muscle. (*a*) Smooth muscle fibers of multiunit smooth muscle are stimulated to contract independently. Anatomic arrangement is in motor units similar to skeletal muscle fibers, except the motor neuron is part of the autonomic nervous system. (*b*) Single-unit smooth muscle cells are stimlated to contract as a group. This is facilitated by both numerous varicosites of autonomic motor neurons that stimulate smooth muscle and gap junctions located between cells that spread the stimulation.

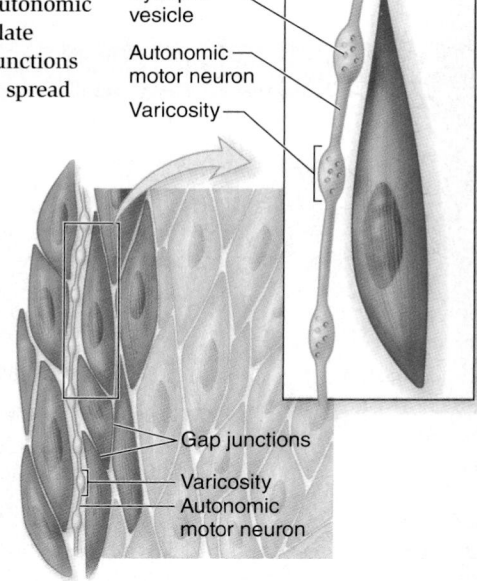

Synaptic vesicle

Autonomic motor neuron

Varicosity

Autonomic motor neuron

Synapses

Gap junctions

Varicosity
Autonomic motor neuron

(a) Multiunit smooth muscle   **(b) Single-unit smooth muscle**

Multiunit smooth muscle is found within the eye in both the iris and ciliary muscles, composing the arrector pili muscles in the skin, the wall of larger air passageways within the respiratory system, and the walls of larger arteries. Smooth muscle cells in these body structures are arranged into motor units, and they have a neuromuscular junction. These two features are similar to skeletal muscle, except that the motor neuron here is a component of the autonomic nervous system. The degree of contraction of this smooth muscle is dependent upon the number of motor units activated, thus facilitating increasing degrees of tension as more motor units are stimulated.

Most smooth muscle belongs to the category of **single-unit smooth muscle.** The smooth muscle cells of single unit smooth muscle typically form two or three sheets. These sheets of smooth muscle are within the walls of the digestive, urinary, and reproductive tracts, as well as smaller portions of the respiratory tract, and most blood vessels. These large sheets of smooth muscle are functionally linked by gap junctions between cells. The smooth muscle cells of single-unit smooth muscle are also called **visceral smooth muscle** because they are found in the walls of most viscera (organs).

Nerve stimulation of single-unit smooth muscle occurs through numerous swellings of the autonomic motor neurons that pass in close proximity to several smooth muscle cells; these swellings are called **varicosities** (figure 10.27b). Synaptic vesicles within the varicosities contain one type of neurotransmitter (e.g., ACh or norepinephrine). Receptors in smooth muscle cells are scattered diffusely across the sarcolemma of these cells. This contrasts to their distribution in skeletal muscle cells, where receptors are clustered in a motor end plate. This scattered and loose arrangement of receptors in single-unit smooth muscle is called a *diffuse junction.* Neurotransmitter released from varicosities stimulates numerous smooth muscle cells simultaneously. This occurs much like the extensions of a sprayer releasing water onto a lawn or garden. The stimulation subsequently is spread from cell to cell via gap junctions, and smooth muscle cells contract synchronously as one unit.

As a review of the key points we have covered in this chapter, **Table 10.2** compares the properties of skeletal, cardiac, and smooth muscle.

Table 10.2	Muscle Tissue Types: *General Comparisons*	
Muscle Tissue	**Location of Muscle**	**Connective Tissue Components**
Skeletal Muscle	Attached to bones (usually via tendons) or to subcutaneous layer	Epimysium, perimysium, endomysium
Cardiac Muscle	Only in heart wall	Endomysium only
Smooth Muscle	Walls of hollow organs (e.g., intestines, blood vessels); in iris and cilary body of eye, and arrector pili in the integument	Endomysium only

 WHAT DID YOU LEARN?

38 Explain why smooth muscle of the eye is multiunit smooth muscle and the smooth muscle in the wall of digestive organs is single-unit smooth muscle.

CHAPTER SUMMARY

	• Muscle tissue moves the skeleton and materials within and throughout the body.
10.1 Introduction to Skeletal Muscle 332	• Muscles have a number of functions and exhibit certain properties.
	10.1a Functions of Skeletal Muscle 332 • Skeletal muscles produce body movement, maintain posture, protect and support body structures, store and move materials, and produce heat to help maintain body temperature.
	10.1b Characteristics of Skeletal Muscle Tissue 332 • Muscle exhibits excitability, conductivity, contractility, elasticity, and extensibility.
10.2 Anatomy of Skeletal Muscle 333	• Individual skeletal muscles extend the entire length of a muscle and are called muscle fibers.
	10.2a Gross Anatomy of Skeletal Muscle 333 • Muscles are ensheathed by three connective tissue layers: an outer epimysium, a middle perimysium, and an inner endomysium.
	• Tendons or aponeuroses are extensions of these three layers of connective tissue that attach muscle ends to other structures.
	• Skeletal muscle is highly vascularized, and it is innervated by motor neurons that exert voluntary control of the muscle.

Appearance and Shape of Cell	Regeneration Capacity	Calcium Source	Contractile Unit and Ca^{2+} Binding	Stimulation	Response and Primary Energy Source
Long cylindrical fibers; with multiple peripheral nuclei; striated; T-tubules *Diameter:* Large (10–500 µm) *Length:* Long (100 µm–30 cm)	Limited	Well-developed sarcoplasmic reticulum	Sarcomere; Ca^{2+} binds to troponin	Nervous control is voluntary (by somatic nervous system); excitatory	Slow oxidative (SO): Slow; aerobic production of ATP Fast oxidative (FO): Rapid and powerful; aerobic production of ATP Fast glycolytic (FG): Rapid and powerful; anaerobic production of ATP
Medium-sized branching cells with 1 or 2 centrally located nuclei; striated; T tubules; intercalated discs *Diameter:* Large (about 15 µm diameter) *Length:* Short (50–100 µm)	Limited	Sarcoplasmic reticulum not as well developed as in skeletal muscle; most from interstitial fluid	Sarcomere; Ca^{2+} binds to troponin	Autorhythmic due to pacemaker within heart; spread by gap junctions; nervous control is involuntary (autonomic nervous system); excitatory or inhibitory	Slow: Aerobic production of ATP
Small, overlapping fusiform cells with a single centrally located nucleus; nonstriated; caveolae *Diameter:* Small (5–10 µm) *Length:* Short (50–200 µm)	Extensive	Sarcoplasmic reticulum not well developed; most from interstitial fluid	No sarcomeres; Calcium binds calmodulin, not troponin	Multiunit smooth muscle: regulated by autonomic nervous system; excitatory or inhibitory; no gap junctions Single-unit smooth muscle: autonomic nervous stimulation is through varicosities spread by gap junctions; other stimuli (e.g., stretch, pH)	Very slow and long duration: Aerobic production of ATP

(continued on next page)

10.3 Physiology of Skeletal Muscle Contraction (continued)

10.3b Sarcolemma, T-tubules, and Sarcoplasmic Reticulum: Excitation-Contraction Coupling   342
- Excitation-contraction coupling links excitation of the muscle by the motor neuron to muscle contraction through the sarcolemma, T-tubules, and sarcoplasmic reticulum.

10.3c Sarcomere: Crossbridge Cycling   344
- Crossbridge cycling is initiated by the release of Ca^{2+} from the sarcoplasmic reticulum. This allows myosin heads to bind to actin to pull thin filaments past thick filaments. This process is the sliding filament theory.

10.3d Skeletal Muscle Relaxation   347
- Muscle returns to the resting state when stimulation ceases through the natural elasticity of the muscle fiber.

10.4 Skeletal Muscle Metabolism   350
- Muscle tissue exhibits a high metabolic demand for energy.

10.4a Supplying Energy for Skeletal Muscle Contraction   350
- The three major means to supply energy to a muscle are immediate (phosphagen system), short term (anaerobic cellular respiration), and long term (aerobic cellular respiration).
- The duration and intensity of activity determines the primary means of supplying adenosine triphosphate (ATP).

10.4b Oxygen Debt   352
- Oxygen debt is the additional oxygen that must be taken in after exercise to restore pre-exercise conditions.

10.5 Skeletal Muscle Fiber Types   352
- Two criteria are used to classify muscle fiber types into three categories.

10.5a Criteria for Classification of Muscle Fiber Types   352
- The criteria for classifying muscle fiber types include the type of contraction generated (power, speed, duration) and the primary means of supplying ATP (anaerobic and aerobic cellular respiration).

10.5b Classification of Muscle Fiber Types   352
- The three subtypes of skeletal muscle fibers are slow oxidative (SO) fibers, fast oxidative (FO) fibers, and fast glycolytic (FG) fibers.

10.5c Distribution of Muscle Fiber Types   353
- Muscles typically contain all muscle fiber types; however, the relative percentage will vary between different skeletal muscles of the body and between individuals for certain muscles, such as the muscles of the leg.

10.6 Measurement of Skeletal Muscle Tension   354
- Muscle tension is the force generated when a muscle is stimulated to contract.

10.6a Muscle Twitch   354
- A muscle twitch is a single, brief contraction and then relaxation of a skeletal muscle fiber in response to stimulation.

10.6b Changes in Stimulus Intensity: Motor Unit Recruitment   354
- Increasing stimulus intensity results in recruitment of additional motor units to produce progressively more muscle tension.

10.6c Changes in Stimulus Frequency: Treppe, Wave Summation, Incomplete Tetany, and Tetany   355
- Increasing the stimulus frequency produces four observable changes in the graphic records of muscle tension: treppe, wave summation, incomplete tetany, and complete tetany.

10.7 Factors Affecting Skeletal Muscle Tension Within the Body   356
- Four factors are associated with muscle tension in the human body: muscle tone, isometric and isotonic contractions, length-tension relationship, and muscle fatigue.

10.7a Muscle Tone   356
- Muscle tone is the resting tension in a muscle to stabilize joints.

10.7b Isometric Contractions and Isotonic Contractions   356
- Isometric contractions result in the production of tension that does not exceed resistance; there is no muscle shortening.
- Isotonic contractions produce tension that exceeds the resistance; fibers change length. In concentric isotonic contractions, muscle fibers shorten, and in eccentric isotonic contractions, muscle fibers lengthen.

10.7c Length-Tension Relationship   357
- Muscle tension is influenced by the degree of overlap of myofilaments at stimulation; this is described as the length-tension relationship.

10.7d Muscle Fatigue   357
- Fatigue is the reduced ability, or inability, of the muscle to produce a contractile force.

10.8 Effects of Exercise and Aging on Skeletal Muscle   358
- Skeletal muscle is affected by exercise and aging.

10.8a Effects of Exercise   358
- A muscle hypertrophies in response to a sustained exercise program and atrophies due to lack of exercise. Prolonged atrophy can lead to permanent loss of muscle.

10.8b Effects of Aging   358
- The general response of muscle tissue to aging is progressive atrophy and fibrosis that is accelerated by lack of exercise.

10.9 Cardiac Muscle Tissue   359
- Cardiac muscle is composed of striated, branching cells located in the wall of the heart. The rhythm of contraction is controlled by a pacemaker and altered involuntarily by the autonomic nervous system.

CHALLENGE YOURSELF

Do You Know the Basics?

_____ 1. The unit of muscle structure that is composed of bundles of myofibrils, enclosed within a sarcolemma, and surrounded by a connective tissue covering called endomysium is a

    a. myofibril.

    b. fascicle.

    c. myofilament.

    d. muscle fiber.

_____ 2. The plasma membrane of a skeletal muscle fiber is called the

    a. sarcoplasmic reticulum.

    b. sarcolemma.

    c. sarcoplasm.

    d. sarcomysium.

_____ 3. In a skeletal muscle fiber, Ca^{2+} is stored within

    a. ACh receptors.

    b. the motor end plate.

    c. the sarcoplasmic reticulum.

    d. the sarcolemma and T-tubules.

_____ 4. The bundle of dense regular connective tissue that attaches a skeletal muscle to bone is called a(n)

    a. tendon.

    b. ligament.

    c. endomysium.

    d. fascicle

_____ 5. In excitation-contraction coupling, the transverse tubules function to

    a. conduct an action potential into the sarcoplasmic reticulum.

    b. uptake and store excess Na^+ and K^+ from the sarcoplasm.

    c. keep the thin and thick myofilaments separated.

    d. provide structural support for sarcomeres.

_____ 6. During muscle contraction, the I band

    a. hides the H zone.

    b. shortens or narrows.

    c. overlaps the Z line.

    d. always remains the same length.

_____ 7. During a concentric contraction of a muscle fiber, myofibrils

    a. lengthen.

    b. remain unchanged.

    c. increase in diameter.

    d. shorten.

_____ 8. What event causes troponin to regain its original shape in muscle relaxation?

    a. stimulation of ACh receptors

    b. diffusion of Na^+ back into transverse tubules

    c. return of Ca^{2+} into the sarcoplasmic reticulum

    d. breaking the bond with tropomyosin

_____ 9. A storage form of energy unique to muscle tissue is

    a. ADP.

    b. lactic acid.

    c. creatine phosphate.

    d. fatty acid.

_____ 10. Which of the following changes in skeletal muscles is associated with aging?

    a. Muscle fibers increase in diameter.

    b. Muscles become more elastic.

    c. Muscle fibers increase their glycogen reserves.

    d. The number of satellite cells in muscle decreases.

11. Explain the structural relationship between a sarcomere, myofibril, myofilament, and a muscle fiber.

12. Diagram and label a sarcomere including a thick filament, thin filament, A band, H zone, I band, Z disc, and M line.

13. Explain why the ratio of motor neurons to muscle fibers is greater in muscles that control eye movement than in postural muscles of the leg.

14. Put the following skeletal muscle contraction events in the order that they occur:

    a. The myosin head pivots toward the center of the sarcomere.
    b. Calcium ions are released from the sarcoplasmic reticulum and bind to troponin.
    c. An action potential is propagated along the sarcolemma and transverse tubules.
    d. Myosin binds to actin, forming crossbridges.
    e. Myosin heads bind ATP molecules and detach from actin.
    f. Tropomyosin molecules are moved off active sites on actin.
    g. ATPase splits ATP, providing the energy to reset the myosin head.

15. Compare and contrast the features of the phosphagen system versus the anaerobic means for supplying energy needed by a contracting muscle.

16. Explain why athletes who excel at short sprints probably have fewer slow-twitch fibers in their leg muscles.

17. Explain why skeletal muscle generates the most force when it is at its resting length at the time of stimulation based on the length-tension relationship.

18. Describe the characteristics of smooth muscle that allow it to contract for extended periods of time and not fatigue.

19. Describe the response of smooth muscle to sustained stretch.

20. Identify the location of both multiunit smooth muscle and single-unit smooth muscle, and explain the difference in how each is regulated.

Can You Apply What You've Learned?

1. A bacterial toxin is known to block the release of ACh at the motor end plate of skeletal muscle. Consequently,
   a. the skeletal muscle contracts with increasing force.
   b. the skeletal muscle contracts with increasing frequency.
   c. the ability to stimulate the muscle is impaired.
   d. other neurotransmitters would stimulate the muscle.

2. One of the primary reasons that one individual is faster in a 50-meter sprint than another is due to
   a. a greater number of muscle fibers of smaller diameter.
   b. more oxidative fibers in the leg muscles.
   c. an enhanced ability to deliver oxygen to the muscles.
   d. a greater percentage of fast-twitch fibers in the leg muscles.

3. Which electrolyte imbalance is least likely to impair muscle contraction because it is not required in muscle contraction?
   a. F^- c. K^+
   b. Na^+ d. Ca^{2+}

4. Rigor mortis occurs following death because
   a. tropomyosin remains over the myosin binding sites of actin.
   b. myosin heads attach to actin and are not released due to lack of ATP.
   c. the myosin becomes misshapen.
   d. all of the Ca^{2+} remains within the sarcoplasmic reticulum.

5. An athelete participates in aerobic exercise three times a week. One of the changes is an increased ability to deliver oxygen to her skeletal muscles. Over time she notices that she can continue the exercise with greater intensity and duration. The reason for this change is that there is a(n):
   a. greater response from the phosphagen system.
   b. greater production of ATP from anaerobic cellular respiration and less from aerobic cellular respiration.
   c. greater production of ATP from aerobic cellular respiration.
   d. increased production of lactic acid.

Can You Synthesize What You've Learned?

1. A friend of yours is interested in both human anatomy and physiology and runs on the track team. He wants to know how ATP is supplied to his muscles when he runs a 400-meter race compared to when he runs a mile.

2. Savannah has been regularly lifting weights at the gym and notices that her muscles seem more toned. She is curious and asked you to explain what changes have occurred to cause this.

3. Paul broke his left radius playing football, and the doctor placed his forearm in a cast for 6 weeks. When the cast was removed, his left forearm was noticeably thinner and less well developed than his right forearm. How can you explain the noticeable decrease in muscle mass in the left forearm?

Muscular System: Axial and Appendicular Muscles

The partitioning of the skeletal system into axial and appendicular divisions provides a useful guideline for subdividing the muscular system. **Axial muscles** have both their origins and insertions on parts of the axial skeleton. Axial muscles support and move the head and vertebral column, function in nonverbal communication by affecting facial features, move the mandible during chewing, assist in food processing and swallowing, aid breathing, and support and protect the abdominal and pelvic organs. The ➤

Physical therapists help injured individuals achieve greater mobility and improvement of their quality of life. Orthopedic physical therapists (a specialty of physical therapy) treat musculoskeletal disorders and help patients regain mobility after orthopedic surgery. An understanding of skeletal muscle function and which muscles work synergistically and antagonistically is essential for orthopedic physical therapists. These health care professionals utilize this knowledge to develop treatment plans for the patient, such as the patient above (who is recovering from a wrist injury).

Anatomy & Physiology | REVEALED®
aprevealed.com

Module 6: Muscular System

appendicular muscles control the movements of the upper and lower limbs, and stabilize and control the movements of the pectoral and pelvic girdles. These muscles are organized into groups based upon their location in the body or the part of the skeleton they move. Some muscles of both divisions are shown in **figure 11.1**.

The muscles in this chapter have been organized in groups according to their location in the body. For each group, tables provide descriptions of the muscles as well as information about their action, origin, insertion, and innervation. (Note: The word *innervation* refers to the nerve(s) that supplies a muscle and stimulates it to contract. For further information about the nerves listed in the tables, see sections 13.9 and 14.5.)

(a) Anterior view

Figure 11.8 Muscles of Mastication. (*a*) Superficial and (*b*) deep lateral views of the muscles of mastication (shown in bold), which move the mandible.

AP|R

(a) Superficial lateral view   (b) Deep lateral view

11.3c Muscles of the Oral Cavity and Pharynx

LEARNING OBJECTIVES

5. Describe how each of the four muscles of mastication affects mandibular movement.

6. Describe the actions of the intrinsic muscles and the four paired extrinsic muscles of the tongue.

7. Explain what function the three primary muscles of the pharynx accomplish.

The muscles of the oral cavity and pharynx include muscles that help us chew, move the tongue, and swallow.

Muscles of Mastication

The term **mastication** (mas-ti-kā′shŭn) refers to the process of chewing. These muscles move the mandible at the temporomandibular joint (TMJ). There are four paired muscles of mastication: the temporalis, the masseter, and the lateral and medial pterygoids (figure 11.8). The muscles of mastication are innervated by the mandibular division of CN V (trigeminal).

The **temporalis** (or *temporal* muscle) is a broad, fan-shaped muscle that extends from the temporal lines of the skull and inserts on the coronoid process of the mandible. It elevates and retracts (pulls posteriorly) the mandible. You can palpate the temporalis by placing your fingers along your temple (lateral skull at same level of orbits) as you open and close your jaw. The muscle you feel contracting is the temporalis.

The **masseter** elevates and protracts (pulls anteriorly) the mandible. It is the most powerful and important of the masticatory muscles. This short, thick muscle is superficial to the temporalis. You can feel the movement of the masseter by palpating near the angle of the mandible as you open and close your mouth.

The **lateral** and **medial pterygoid** muscles arise from the pterygoid processes of the sphenoid bone and insert on the mandible. Both pterygoids protract the mandible and move it from side to side during chewing. These movements maximize the efficiency of the teeth while chewing or grinding foods of various consistencies. The medial pterygoid also elevates the mandible.

Table 11.3 summarizes the characteristics of the muscles of mastication.

Table 11.3	Muscles of Mastication		
Muscle	**Action**	**Origin/Insertion**	**Innervation (see section 13.9)**
Temporalis (tem-pŏ-rā′lis) *tempora* = pertaining to temporal bone	Elevates and retracts mandible	O: Superior and inferior temporal lines I: Coronoid process of mandible	CN V$_3$ (trigeminal nerve, mandibular division)
Masseter (ma′se-ter) *maseter* = chewer	Elevates and protracts mandible; prime mover of mandible elevation	O: Zygomatic arch I: Coronoid process, lateral surface and angle of mandible	CN V$_3$ (trigeminal nerve, mandibular division)
Medial pterygoid (ter′i-goyd) *pterygoid* = winglike	Elevates and protracts mandible; produces side-to-side movement of mandible	O: Maxilla, palatine, and medial surface of lateral pterygoid plate I: Medial surface of mandibular ramus	CN V$_3$ (trigeminal nerve, mandibular division)
Lateral pterygoid	Protracts mandible; produces side-to-side movement of mandible	O: Greater wing of sphenoid and lateral surface of lateral pterygoid plate I: Condylar process of mandible	CN V$_3$ (trigeminal nerve, mandibular division)

Table 11.9 — Muscles of Respiration

Muscle	Action	Origin/Insertion	Innervation (see sections 14.5c, d)
Serratus posterior superior (sĕr-ā′tŭs) *serratus* = a saw	Elevates ribs during forced inspiration	O: Spinous processes of C_7–T_3 vertebrae I: Lateral borders of ribs 2–5	Thoracic spinal nerves
Serratus posterior inferior	Depresses ribs during forced expiration	O: Spinous processes of T_{11}–L_3 vertebrae I: Inferior borders of ribs 8–12	Thoracic spinal nerves
Scalene muscles (see also table 11.7)	Elevate 1st and 2nd ribs during forced inspiration when neck is fixed	O: Transverse processes of cervical vertebrae I: Superior surface of 1st and 2nd ribs	Cervical spinal nerves
External intercostals (in′ter-kos′talz) *inter* = between *cost* = rib	Elevate ribs during quiet and forced inspiration	O: Inferior border of superior rib I: Superior border of inferior rib	Thoracic spinal nerves
Internal intercostals	Depresses ribs during forced expiration	O: Superior border of inferior rib I: Inferior border to superior rib	Thoracic spinal nerves
Transversus thoracis (trans-ver′sŭs thō-ra′sis)	Depresses ribs during forced expiration	O: Posterior surface of xiphoid process and inferior region of sternum I: Costal cartilages 2–6	Thoracic spinal nerves
Diaphragm (dī′ă-fram) *dia* = across *phragm* = partition	Contraction causes flattening of diaphragm (moves inferiorly) during inspiration and thus expands thoracic cavity; increases pressure in abdominopelvic cavity	O: Inferior internal surface of ribs 7–12; xiphoid process of sternum and costal cartilages of inferior 6 ribs; lumbar vertebrae I: Central tendon	Phrenic nerves (C_3–C_5)

The **external intercostals** extend inferomedially from the superior rib to the adjacent inferior rib. The external intercostals assist in expanding the thoracic cavity by elevating the ribs during inspiration. This movement is like lifting a bucket handle—that is, as the bucket handle (rib) is elevated, its distance from the center of the bucket (thorax) increases. Thus, contraction of the external intercostals increases the transverse dimensions of the thoracic cavity. The **internal intercostals** lie deep to the external intercostals, and their muscle fibers are at right angles to the external intercostals. The internal intercostals depress the ribs only during forced expiration; normal, quiet expiration takes no active muscular effort. A small **transversus thoracis** extends across the inner surface of the thoracic cage and attaches to ribs 2–6. It helps depress the ribs during forced expiration.

Finally, the **diaphragm** is an internally placed, dome-shaped muscle that forms a partition between the thoracic and abdominal cavities. (The term *diaphragm* refers to a muscle or group of muscles that covers or partitions an opening.) The diaphragm is the most important muscle associated with breathing. The muscle fibers of the diaphragm converge from its margins toward a fibrous

central tendon. During inspiration, the diaphragm contracts and the central tendon is pulled inferiorly toward the abdominal cavity, thereby increasing the vertical dimensions of the thoracic cavity.

Table 11.9 summarizes the characteristics of the muscles of respiration. Further details about muscles of respiration are found in section 23.5b.

WHAT DO YOU THINK?

2. After you've eaten a very large meal, it is sometimes difficult to take a big, deep breath. Why is it more difficult to breathe deeply with a full GI tract?

WHAT DID YOU LEARN?

14. Compare the actions of the external intercostals and the internal intercostals.

15. How is the diaphragm involved in respiration?

11.6 Muscles of the Abdominal Wall

LEARNING OBJECTIVES

1. List the four pairs of abdominal muscles.
2. Compare the actions of the rectus abdominis muscle with the oblique muscles and transversus abdominis.

The anterolateral wall of the abdomen is reinforced by four pairs of muscles that collectively compress and hold the abdominal organs in place: the external oblique, internal oblique, transversus abdominis, and rectus abdominis (**figure 11.16**). These muscles also work together to flex and stabilize the vertebral column.

INTEGRATE

CONCEPT CONNECTION

When the diaphragm contracts, it compresses the abdominal cavity, thus increasing intra-abdominal pressure. Increased intra-abdominal pressure is necessary for urination (section 24.7c), defecation (section 26.3d), and childbirth (section 29.6). Beyond respiration, diaphragm movements are also important in helping return venous blood to the heart from the inferior half of the body (section 20.4a).

Figure 11.1 Body Musculature. (*a*) Anterior view shows superficial muscles on the right side of the body and some deeper muscles on the left side. (*b*) Posterior view shows superficial muscles on the left side of the body and some deeper muscles on the right side. Labels for the axial muscles are in bold; not all muscles shown in the figure are identified.

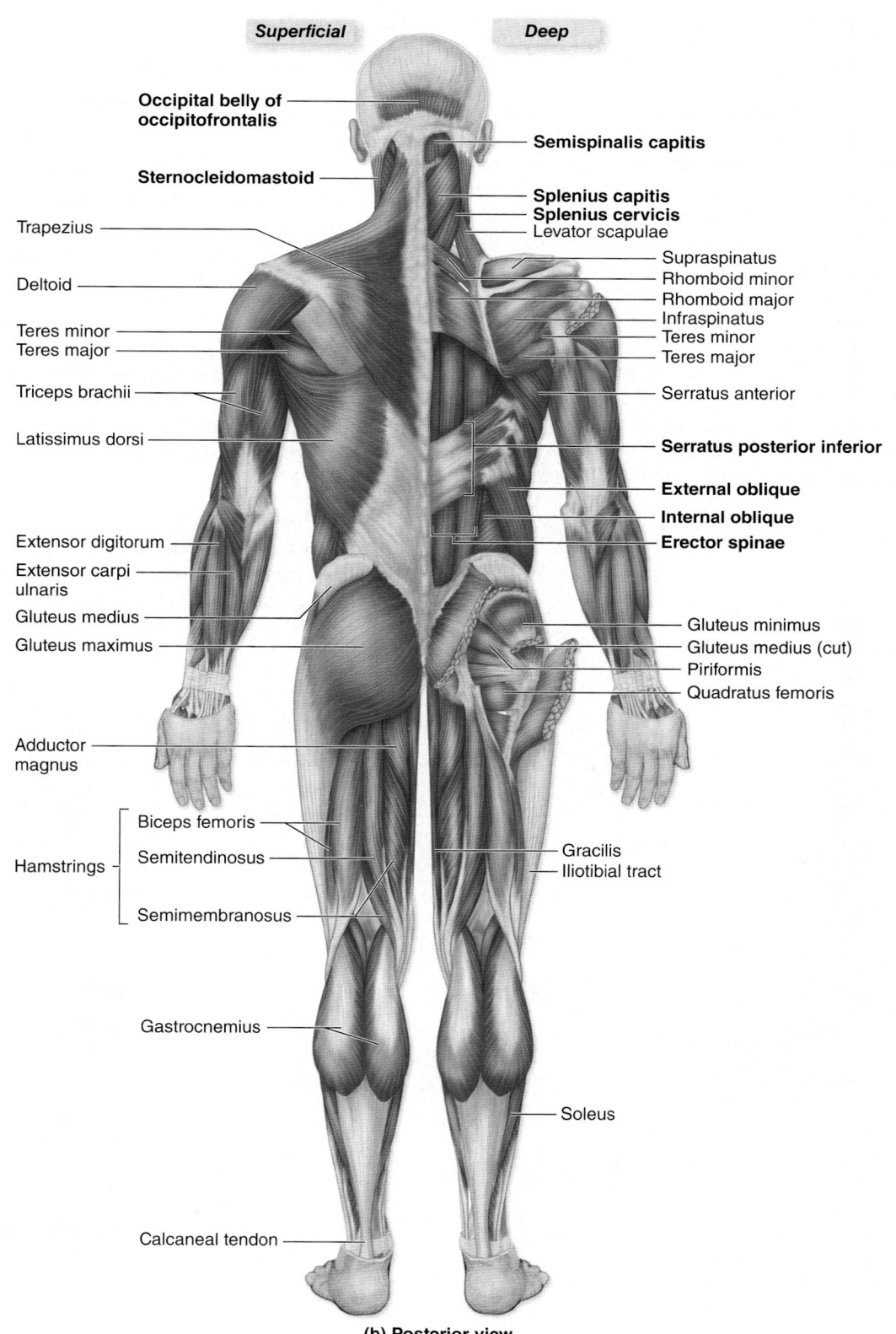

Superficial   *Deep*

Occipital belly of occipitofrontalis

Semispinalis capitis

Sternocleidomastoid

Splenius capitis
Splenius cervicis
Levator scapulae

Trapezius

Supraspinatus
Rhomboid minor
Rhomboid major
Infraspinatus
Teres minor
Teres major

Deltoid

Teres minor
Teres major

Triceps brachii

Serratus anterior

Latissimus dorsi

Serratus posterior inferior

External oblique

Internal oblique
Erector spinae

Extensor digitorum

Extensor carpi ulnaris

Gluteus medius

Gluteus maximus

Gluteus minimus
Gluteus medius (cut)
Piriformis
Quadratus femoris

Adductor magnus

Biceps femoris

Gracilis
Iliotibial tract

Hamstrings — Semitendinosus

Semimembranosus

Gastrocnemius

Soleus

Calcaneal tendon

(b) Posterior view

11.1 Skeletal Muscle Composition and Actions

In section 10.2, we examined the macroscopic and microscopic anatomy of skeletal muscle. Here we compare the origin versus the insertion of a skeletal muscle, the organizational patterns exhibited by skeletal muscle fibers, and the general actions of skeletal muscles.

11.1a Origin and Insertion

✅ LEARNING OBJECTIVE

1. Compare and contrast the origin and the insertion of a skeletal muscle.

Many skeletal muscles extend between bones and cross at least one moveable joint. Upon contraction, one bone moves while the other bone usually remains fixed. The less moveable attachment of a muscle is called its **origin** (ōr′i-jin; *origo* = source). The more moveable attachment of the muscle is its **insertion** (in-ser′shŭn; *inserto* = to plant in) **(figure 11.2)**. Usually, the insertion is pulled toward the origin. In the limbs, the origin typically lies proximal to the insertion. For example, the biceps brachii muscle originates on the scapula and inserts on the radius. The contraction of this muscle pulls the forearm toward the shoulder.

Sometimes, neither the origin nor the insertion can be determined easily either by movement or position. In this case, other criteria are used. For example, if a muscle extends between a broad aponeurosis and a narrow tendon, the aponeurosis is considered the origin, and the tendon is attached to the insertion. If there are sev-eral tendons at one end of the muscle and just one tendon at the other end, each of the multiple tendons is considered an origin, and the single tendon at the other end of the bone is considered the insertion.

WHAT DID YOU LEARN?

❶ What is the difference between the origin and insertion of a skeletal muscle?

11.1b Organizational Patterns of Skeletal Muscle Fibers

✅ LEARNING OBJECTIVE

2. Describe and differentiate between the organizational patterns in muscle fascicles.

As mentioned in section 10.2a, bundles of muscle fibers, termed fascicles, lie parallel to each other within each muscle. However, the organization of fascicles in different muscles often varies. There are four different patterns of fascicle arrangement: circular, parallel, convergent, and pennate **(figure 11.3)**.

Circular Muscles

A **circular muscle** has concentrically arranged fibers around an opening or recess. A circular muscle is also called a *sphincter*, and its contraction decreases the passageway diameter. An example is the orbicularis oris muscle that encircles the opening of the mouth.

Parallel Muscles

The fascicles in a **parallel muscle** run parallel to its long axis. Sometimes these muscles are cylindrical with an expanded central region. In this case, parallel muscles have a central body, called the

Figure 11.2 Muscle Origin and Insertion. The origin is the less mobile point of attachment of the muscle, whereas the insertion is more mobile, as shown in this view of the biceps brachii muscle.

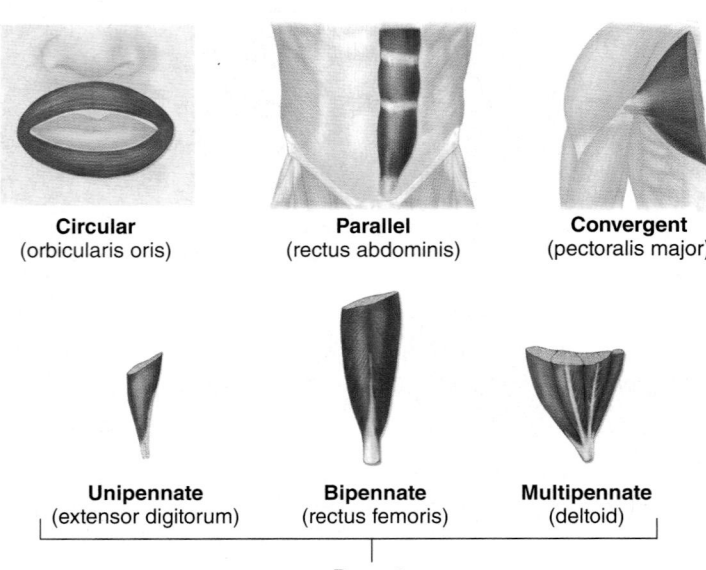

Figure 11.3 Organization of Muscle Fibers. Muscle fascicles may be organized into one of four basic patterns: circular, parallel, convergent, or pennate.

CLINICAL VIEW
Intramuscular Injections

An **intramuscular injection** is one way that a medication may be administered. Since skeletal muscle has a rich blood supply, the medication may be inserted into the muscle with a syringe. The medication enters the cardiovascular system through the muscle's blood vessels and from there is transmitted throughout the body. This method of medication delivery allows a large amount of medication to be delivered at once without significant discomfort, and it ensures the delivery is slower and more uniform than if the medication was taken orally or intravenously. Further, some medications may be better absorbed via the muscle than orally, and some large doses of medications may not be tolerated when taken orally.

Examples of medications that are taken intramuscularly include most vaccines, some fertility and contraceptive medications, and large doses of selected antibiotics (such as penicillin). Common intramuscular injection sites include the deltoid, gluteal, and quadriceps muscles.

belly, or *gaster*. This muscle shortens when it contracts, and its body increases in diameter. Parallel muscles have high endurance but are not strong. Examples of parallel muscle include the rectus abdominis (an anterior abdominal muscle) or the biceps brachii of the arm.

Convergent Muscles

A **convergent** (kon-ver'jent) **muscle** has widespread muscle fibers over a broad area that converge on a common attachment site. This attachment site may be a single tendon, a tendinous sheet, or a slender band of collagen fibers known as a **raphe** (rā'fē; *rhaphe* = seam). These muscle fibers are often triangular in shape, resembling a broad fan with a tendon at the tip. A convergent muscle is versatile—that is, the direction of its pull can be modified merely by activating a specific, single group of muscle fibers at any one time. However, when the fibers in a convergent muscle all contract at once, they do not pull as hard on the tendon as a parallel muscle of the same size because the muscle fibers on opposite sides of the tendon are not working together; rather, they are pulling in different directions. An example of a convergent muscle is the pectoralis major of the chest.

Pennate Muscles

Pennate (pen'āt; *penna* = feather) **muscles** are so named because the fascicles exhibit the same angle with respect to their tendon—that is, they resemble a large feather. Pennate muscles have one or more tendons extending through their body, and the fascicles are arranged at an oblique angle to the tendon. Because pennate muscle fibers pull at an angle to the tendon, this type of muscle does not move its tendons as far as parallel muscles move their tendons. However, the contraction of a pennate muscle generates more tension than does a parallel muscle of the same size, and thus it is stronger.

There are three types of pennate muscles:

- In a **unipennate muscle,** all of the muscle fibers are on the same side of the tendon. The extensor digitorum, a long muscle that extends the fingers, is a unipennate muscle.
- A **bipennate muscle,** the most common type, has muscle fibers on both sides of the tendon. The interosseous muscles on both the palmar and dorsal sides of the metacarpals are composed of bipennate muscles that help adduct and abduct the digits.
- A **multipennate muscle** has branches of the tendon within the muscle. The triangular deltoid that covers the superior surface of the shoulder joint is a multipennate muscle.

 WHAT DID YOU LEARN?

 Which muscle is stronger—a pennate muscle or a parallel muscle?

11.1c Actions of Skeletal Muscles

LEARNING OBJECTIVE

3. Differentiate between agonists, antagonists, and synergists.

Skeletal muscles generally do not work in isolation; rather, they work together to produce movements. Muscles are grouped according to their primary actions into three types: agonists, antagonists, and synergists.

An **agonist** (ag'on-ist; *agon* = a contest), also called a *prime mover,* is a muscle that contracts to produce a particular movement, such as extending the forearm. The triceps brachii of the forearm is an agonist that causes extension.

An **antagonist** (an-tag'ō-nist; *anti* = against) is a muscle whose actions oppose those of the agonist. For example, if the agonist produces extension, the antagonist produces flexion. The contraction of the agonist stretches the antagonist, and vice versa. As this movement occurs, the stretched muscle usually does not relax completely. Instead, the tension within the muscle being stretched is adjusted to control the speed of the movement and ensure that it is smooth. When the triceps brachii acts as an agonist to extend the forearm, the biceps brachii muscle on the anterior side of the humerus acts as an antagonist to stabilize the movement and to produce the opposing action, which is flexion of the forearm.

A **synergist** (sin'er-jist; *ergo* = work) is a muscle that assists the agonist in performing its action. The contraction of a synergist usually either contributes to tension exerted close to the insertion of the muscle or stabilizes the point of origin. Usually, synergists are most useful at the start of a movement when the agonist is stretched and cannot exert much power. Examples of synergistic muscles are the biceps brachii and the brachialis muscles of the arm. Both muscles work synergistically (together) to flex the elbow joint. Synergists may also assist an agonist by preventing movement at a joint and thereby stabilizing the origin of the agonist. In this case, these synergistic muscles are called *fixators.*

 WHAT DID YOU LEARN?

 What is the difference between an agonist and a synergist?

11.2 Skeletal Muscle Naming

LEARNING OBJECTIVES

1. List the seven aspects of muscles that may contribute to their names.

2. Give examples of muscles whose names contain an indication of action, specific body region, or shape or size.

In section 1.4, you learned some of the anatomic terminology used to describe the body; in chapter 8, you saw how anatomic terms are applied to the bones of the skeleton. Naming of skeletal muscles follows similar conventions, and usually muscle names provide clues to their identification. As **figure 11.4** shows, skeletal muscles are named according to the following criteria:

- **Muscle action.** Names that indicate the primary function or movement of the muscle include *flexor, extensor,* and *pronator.* These are such common actions that the names almost always contain other clues to the appearance or location of the muscle. For example, the flexor digitorum longus muscle is a long muscle responsible for flexing the digits.

- **Specific body regions.** The rectus femoris is on the thigh (*femur*), and the tibialis anterior is on the *anterior* surface of the *tibia.* Muscles that are close to the body surface often are termed *superficialis* (sū'per-fish-ē-ā'lis) or *externus* (eks-ter'nŭs). In contrast, deeper placed muscles may have names such as *profundus* (prō-fŭn'dŭs; deep) or *internus.*

- **Muscle attachments.** Many muscle names identify their origins, insertions, or other prominent attachments. In these cases, the first part of the name indicates the origin and the second part the insertion. For example, the sternocleidomastoid has origins on the *sternum* and the *clavicle* (*cleido*) and an insertion on the *mastoid* process of the temporal bone.

- **Orientation of muscle fibers.** The rectus abdominis muscle is named for its lengthwise-running muscle fibers; *rectus* means "straight." Similarly, names such as *oblique* or *obliquus* (ob-lī'kwŭs) indicate muscles with fibers extending at an angle to the longitudinal axis of the body. The internal and external oblique muscles are abdominal muscles that have angled muscle fibers.

- **Muscle shape.** Examples of shape in muscle names include *deltoid* (shaped like a triangle), *orbicularis* (circular muscle fibers), *rhomboid* (shaped like a rhombus), and *trapezius* (shaped like a trapezoid). Short muscles may be called *brevis* (brev'is); long muscles are called *longus* (lon'gŭs) or *longissimus* (lon-jĭs'ĭ-mŭs; longest). *Teres* (ter'ēz) muscles are both long and round.

- **Muscle size.** Large muscles may be called *magnus* (big), *major* (bigger), or *maximus* (biggest). Small muscles may be called *minor* (smaller) or *minimus* (smallest). Examples of muscles named by size include the buttocks muscles: gluteus maximus, gluteus medius, and gluteus minimus.

- **Muscle heads/tendons of origin.** Some muscles are named after specific features; for example, how many tendons of origin or how many muscle bellies or heads each contains. A *biceps* muscle has two tendons of origin, a *triceps* muscle has three heads or tendons, and a *quadriceps* muscle has four heads or tendons.

WHAT DID YOU LEARN?

4 What are some words used in muscle names that refer to muscle shape?

5 The gluteus maximus muscle gets its name from which categories for naming muscles?

INTEGRATE

LEARNING STRATEGY

The following suggestions may help you learn the muscles:

- Muscles may be organized into groups. Learning the muscles in groups is easiest.

- When studying a particular muscle, try to palpate it on yourself, and look in a mirror so you can better visualize the muscle's location. Contract the muscle to sense its action.

- Repeat the name of a muscle aloud to become familiar with it.

- Associate visual images from models, cadavers, a photographic atlas, or dissected animals with muscle names.

- Locate the origins and insertions of muscles on an articulated skeleton to understand how they produce their actions.

- Learn the derivation of each muscle name.

Muscle action	Example
Adductor (adducts body part)	Adductor magnus
Abductor (abducts body part)	Abductor pollicis longus
Flexor (flexes a joint)	Flexor carpi radialis
Extensor (extends a joint)	Extensor hallucis longus
Specific body regions	**Example**
Oris (mouth)	Orbicularis oris
Cervicis (neck)	Semispinalis cervicis
Brachial (arm)	Biceps brachii
Carpi (wrist)	Flexor carpi ulnaris
Pollicis (thumb)	Opponens pollicis
Gluteal (buttocks)	Gluteus medius
Femoris (thigh)	Quadratus femoris
Hallucis (great toe)	Extensor hallucis longus
Anterior (toward the front of the body)	Tibialis anterior
Posterior or dorsal/dorsi (toward the back of the body)	Tibialis posterior Latissimus dorsi
Superior (closer to the head)	Serratus posterior superior
Inferior (closer to the feet)	Serratus posterior inferior
Superficialis (superficial)	Flexor digitorum superficialis
Profundus (deep)	Flexor digitorum profundus
Muscle attachments	**Example**
Sternum and clavicle (cleido)	Sternocleidomastoid
Between the ribs	Intercostal
Subscapular fossa	Subscapularis
Fibula	Fibularis longus
Zygomatic bone	Zygomaticus major
Orientation of muscle fibers	**Example**
Rectus (straight)	Rectus abdominis
Oblique (angled)	External oblique
Orbicularis (circular)	Orbicularis oculi
Muscle shape	**Example**
Deltoid (triangular)	Deltoid
Quadratus (rectangular)	Pronator quadratus
Trapezius (trapezoidal)	Trapezius
Longus (long)	Abductor pollicis longus
Brevis (short)	Abductor pollicis brevis
Muscle size	**Example**
Major (larger of two muscles)	Pectoralis major
Minor (smaller of two muscles)	Pectoralis minor
Maximus (largest)	Gluteus maximus
Medius (medium sized)	Gluteus medius
Minimus (smallest)	Gluteus minimus
Muscle heads / tendons of origin	**Example**
Biceps (two heads)	Biceps femoris
Triceps (three heads)	Triceps brachii
Quadriceps (four heads)	Quadriceps femoris

Figure 11.4 Muscle Naming. Muscles are named according to a variety of features.

11.3 Muscles of the Head and Neck

The muscles of the head and neck are separated into several specific groups. Almost all of these muscles (except for a few muscles of the anterior neck) originate on either the bones of the skull or the hyoid bone.

11.3a Muscles of Facial Expression

LEARNING OBJECTIVES

1. Name the muscles that move the forehead, the skin around the eyes and the nose, and describe their actions.

2. List the muscles that move the mouth and cheeks and their actions.

The muscles of facial expression originate in the superficial fascia or on the skull bones (figure 11.5). These muscles insert into the superficial fascia of the skin, so when they contract, they pull on the skin, causing it to move. Most of these muscles are innervated by the seventh cranial nerve (CN VII), the facial nerve (see section 13.9).

The **epicranius** is composed of the **occipitofrontalis muscle** and a broad **epicranial aponeurosis,** also called the *galea aponeurotica.* The **frontal belly** of the occipitofrontalis is superficial to the frontal bone on the forehead. When this muscle contracts, it raises the eyebrows and wrinkles the skin of the forehead. The **occipital belly** of the occipitofrontalis covers the posterior aspect of the skull. When this muscle contracts, it retracts the scalp slightly.

Deep to the frontal belly of the occipitofrontalis is the **corrugator supercilii.** This muscle draws the eyebrows together and creates vertical wrinkle lines around the nose. The **orbicularis oculi** consists of circular muscle fibers that surround the eye's orbit. When this muscle contracts, the eyelid closes, as when you wink, blink, or squint. The **levator palpebrae superioris** elevates the upper eyelid when you open your eyes.

Several muscles of facial expression are associated with the nose. The **nasalis** elevates the corners of the nostrils. When you "flare" your nostrils, you are using the nasalis muscles. If you wrinkle your nose in distaste after smelling a foul odor, you have

used your **procerus** muscle. This muscle is continuous with the frontal belly of the occipitofrontalis muscle and runs over the bridge of the nose, where it produces transverse wrinkles when it contracts.

The mouth is the most expressive part of the face. The **orbicularis oris** consists of muscle fibers that encircle the opening of the mouth. When this muscle contracts, you close your mouth. In addition, when you "pucker up" for a kiss, you are using this muscle. The **depressor labii inferioris** does what its name suggests—it pulls the lower lip inferiorly. The **depressor anguli oris** is considered the "frown" muscle, because it pulls the corners of the mouth inferiorly. (Note, however, that it takes more muscles than just this one to produce a frown.)

In contrast, some muscles of the mouth elevate part or all of the upper lips. The **levator labii superioris** pulls the upper lip superiorly, as if a person is sneering or snarling. The **levator anguli oris** pulls the corners of the mouth superiorly and laterally. The **zygomaticus major** and **zygomaticus minor** work with the levator anguli oris muscles. You use all of these muscles when you smile. The **risorius** pulls the corner of the lips laterally; you use this muscle if you make a closed-mouth smile.

The **mentalis** attaches to the lower lip, and when it contracts, it protrudes the lower lip (as when a person "pouts"). The **platysma** tenses the skin of the neck and pulls the lower lip inferiorly. If you

INTEGRATE

CLINICAL VIEW

Idiopathic Facial Nerve Paralysis (Bell Palsy)

Unilateral paralysis of the muscles of facial expression is termed **facial nerve (CN VII) paralysis.** If the cause of the condition is unknown, doctors refer to it as **idiopathic** (id′e̅-o̅-path′ik; *idios* = one's own; *pathos* = suffering) **facial nerve paralysis,** or *Bell palsy.* CN VII paralysis has sometimes been associated with herpes simplex 1 viral infection. Facial nerve paralysis is also associated with exposure to cold temperatures, and is commonly seen in individuals who sleep with one side of their head facing an open window. Whatever the underlying cause, the nerve becomes inflamed and compressed within the narrow stylomastoid foramen, through which the facial nerve travels. The muscles on the same side of the face are paralyzed as a result.

Treatment of facial nerve paralysis usually means alleviating the symptoms. Doctors often use prednisone (a type of steroid) to reduce the

Facial nerve (CN VII) paralysis on the left side of the face. Note the drooping left side of the mouth (arrow) and the lack of contraction by the left orbicularis oris when the woman tries to smile.

inflammation and swelling of the nerve. If herpes simplex infection is suspected, an antiviral medication known as acyclovir (Zovirax) is also given. Like its underlying cause, recovery from idiopathic facial nerve paralysis is equally mysterious. Over 50% of all patients experience a complete, spontaneous recovery within 30 days of their first symptoms. Recovery may take longer for some, whereas other patients may never recover.

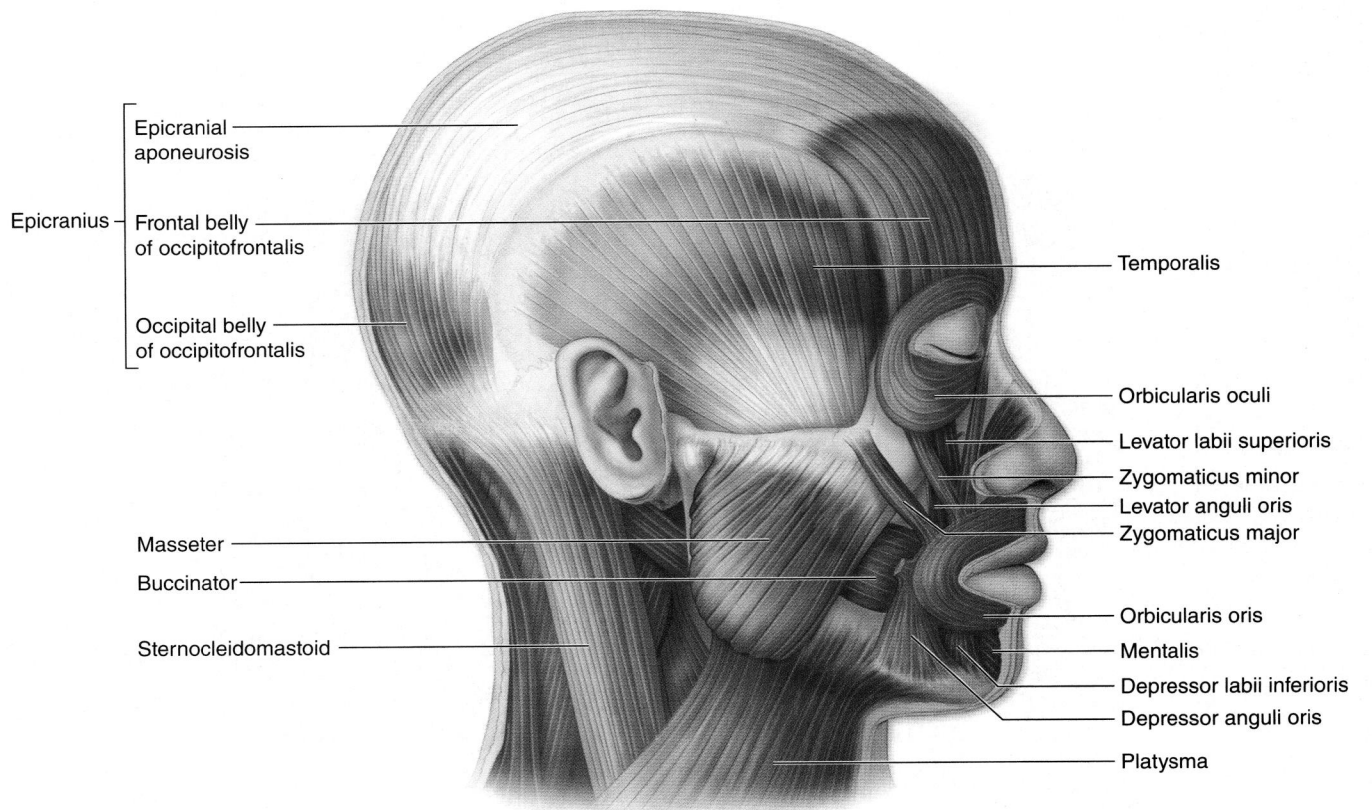

Epicranius {
Epicranial aponeurosis

Frontal belly of occipitofrontalis
}

Procerus

Orbicularis oculi

Levator labii superioris
Zygomaticus minor
Zygomaticus major

Risorius

Depressor anguli oris

Depressor labii inferioris

Platysma

Corrugator supercilii

Levator palpebrae superioris

Nasalis

Levator anguli oris (cut)
Masseter
Buccinator

Orbicularis oris

Mentalis

Sternocleidomastoid

(a) Anterior view

Epicranius {
Epicranial aponeurosis

Frontal belly of occipitofrontalis

Occipital belly of occipitofrontalis
}

Masseter

Buccinator

Sternocleidomastoid

Temporalis

Orbicularis oculi

Levator labii superioris
Zygomaticus minor
Levator anguli oris
Zygomaticus major

Orbicularis oris

Mentalis

Depressor labii inferioris

Depressor anguli oris

Platysma

(b) Lateral view

Figure 11.5 Muscles of Facial Expression. AP|R

stand in front of a mirror and tense the skin of your neck, you can see these thin muscles bulging out.

The **buccinator** compresses the cheek against the teeth when we chew (and is the reason our cheeks don't "bulge out" like a squirrel's when we eat). Infants use the buccinator when they suckle at the breast. Some trumpet players (such as Dizzy Gillespie) have stretched out their buccinator muscles, allowing their cheeks to be "puffy" with air when they play the trumpet.

Table 11.1 summarizes the attachments and movements of the muscles of facial expression. **Figure 11.6** illustrates how these muscles produce some of the more characteristic expressions.

WHAT DID YOU LEARN?

6 What muscles of facial expression must contract for you to smile?

7 The corners of the mouth are pulled inferiorly into a frown position by the contraction of what muscle?

Table 11.1	Muscles of Facial Expression		
Region/Muscle	**Action**	**Origin/Insertion**	**Innervation (see section 13.9)**
SCALP			
Epicranius (ep′ī-krā′nē-us; *epi* = over; *cran* = skull): Composed of an epicranial aponeurosis and the two bellies of the occipitofrontalis muscle			
Frontal belly of occipitofrontalis (ok-sip′i-tō-fron-tā′lis) *front* = forehead	Moves scalp, eyebrows; wrinkles skin of forehead	O: Frontal bone I: Epicranial aponeurosis	CN VII (facial nerve)
Occipital belly of occipitofrontalis *occipito* = base of skull	Retracts scalp	O: Superior nuchal line I: Epicranial aponeurosis	CN VII (facial nerve)
NOSE			
Nasalis (nā′ză-lis)	Compresses bridge and depresses tip of nose; elevates corners of nostrils	O: Maxillae and alar cartilage of nose I: Dorsum of nose	CN VII (facial nerve)
Procerus (prō-sē′rŭs) *procerus* = long	Moves and wrinkles nose	O: Nasal bone and lateral nasal cartilage I: Aponeurosis at bridge of nose and skin of forehead	CN VII (facial nerve)
MOUTH			
Buccinator (buk′sĭ-nā′tŏr) *bucco* = cheek	Compresses cheek, holds food between teeth during chewing	O: Alveolar processes of mandible and maxillae I: Orbicularis oris	CN VII (facial nerve)
Depressor anguli oris (dē-pres′ŏr ang′yū-lī ŏr′is) *depressor* = depresses *angul* = angle *or* = mouth	Draws corners of mouth inferiorly and laterally ("frown" muscle)	O: Body of mandible I: Skin at inferior corner (angle) of mouth	CN VII (facial nerve)
Depressor labii inferioris (lā′bē-ī in-fēr′ē-ōr-is) *labi* = lip *infer* = below	Draws lower lip inferiorly	O: Body of mandible lateral to midline I: Skin at inferior lip	CN VII (facial nerve)
Levator anguli oris (lē-vā′tor, le-vā′ter) *leva* = raise	Draws corners of mouth superiorly and laterally ("smile" muscle)	O: Lateral maxilla I: Skin at superior corner (angle) of mouth	CN VII (facial nerve)
Levator labii superioris (sū-pēr′ē-ōr-is)	Opens lips; raises and furrows the upper lip ("Elvis" lip snarl)	O: Zygomatic bone; maxilla I: Skin and muscle of superior lip	CN VII (facial nerve)

Table 11.1	Muscles of Facial Expression (continued)		
Region/Muscle	**Action**	**Origin/Insertion**	**Innervation (see section 13.9)**
Mentalis (men-tă′lis) *ment* = chin	Protrudes lower lip ("pout"); wrinkles chin	O: Central mandible I: Skin of chin	CN VII (facial nerve)
Orbicularis oris (ōr-bik′ū-lă′ris) *orb* = circular	Compresses and purses lips ("kiss" muscle)	O: Maxilla and mandible; blend with fibers from other facial muscles I: Encircling mouth; skin and muscles at angles to mouth	CN VII (facial nerve)
Risorius (ri-sōr′ē-ūs) *risor* = laughter	Draws corner of lip laterally; tenses lips	O: Deep fascia associated with masseter muscle I: Skin at angle of mouth	CN VII (facial nerve)
Zygomaticus major (zī′gō-mat′i-kūs) *zygomatic* = cheekbone *major* = greater	Elevates corner of the mouth ("smile" muscle)	O: Zygomatic bone I: Skin at superolateral edge of mouth	CN VII (facial nerve)
Zygomaticus minor *minor* = lesser	Elevates corner of the mouth ("smile" muscle)	O: Zygomatic bone I: Skin of superior lip	CN VII (facial nerve)
EYE			
Corrugator supercilii (kōr′ū-gā-ter sū′per′sil′ē-ī) *corrugo* = to wrinkle *cilium* = eyelid	Pulls eyebrows inferiorly and medially; creates vertical wrinkles above nose	O: Medial end of superciliary arch I: Skin superior to supraorbital margin and superciliary arch	CN VII (facial nerve)
Levator palpebrae superioris (pal-pē′brā) *palpebra* = eyelid	Elevates superior eyelid	O: Lesser wing of sphenoid bone I: Superior tarsal plate and skin of superior eyelid	CN III (oculomotor nerve)
Orbicularis oculi (ok′ū-lī) *ocul* = eye	Closes eye; produces winking, blinking, squinting ("blink" muscle)	O: Medial wall or margin of the orbit I: Skin surrounding eyelids	CN VII (facial nerve)
NECK			
Platysma (plă-tiz′mă) *platy* = flat	Pulls lower lip inferiorly; tenses skin of neck	O: Fascia of deltoid and pectoralis major muscles and acromion of scapula I: Skin of cheek and mandible	CN VII (facial nerve)

Depressor anguli oris (frown)

Orbicularis oculi (blink/close eyes)

Zygomaticus major (smile)

Orbicularis oris (close mouth/kiss)

Frontal belly of occipitofrontalis (wrinkle forehead, raise eyebrows)

Platysma (tense skin of neck)

Figure 11.6 Surface Anatomy of Some Muscles of Facial Expression.
These muscles permit complex expressions that often are used as a means of communication.

11.3b Extrinsic Eye Muscles

✓ LEARNING OBJECTIVES

3. Become familiar with the six extrinsic muscles of the eye, and describe how each affects eye movement.

4. Name the three cranial nerves that innervate the extrinsic eye muscles, and identify which muscles they act upon.

The **extrinsic eye muscles,** often called *extraocular muscles,* move the eyes. They are termed extrinsic because they insert onto the outer surface of the eye, called the sclera. There are six extrinsic eye muscles: the four rectus muscles (medial, lateral, inferior, and superior) and the two oblique muscles (inferior and superior) **(figure 11.7).**

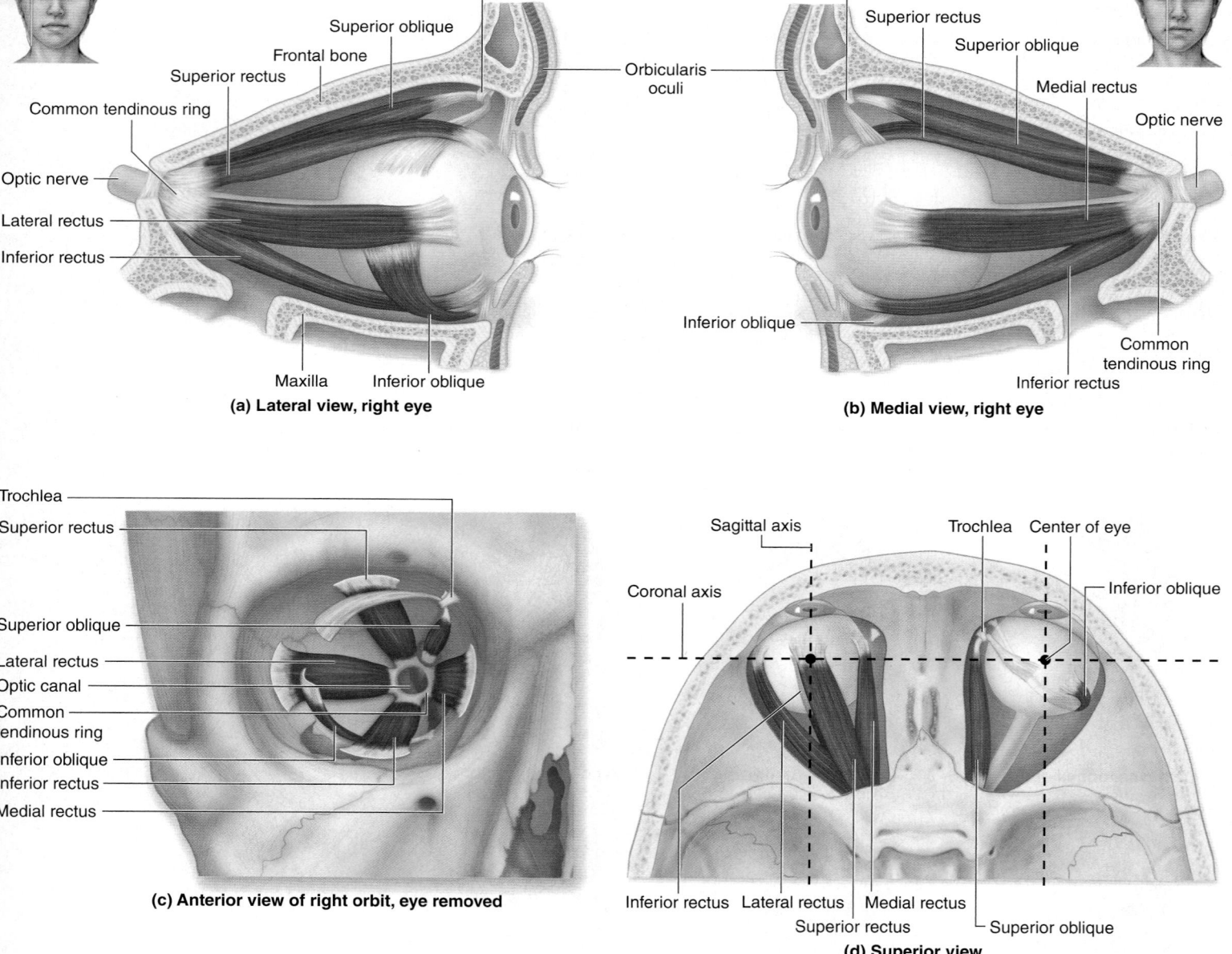

Figure 11.7 Extrinsic Muscles of the Eye. The extrinsic eye muscles control movements of the eye. (*a*) The insertions for most of the extrinsic eye muscles are noticeable in a lateral view of the right eye. (*b*) The medial rectus muscle appears prominently in a medial view of the right eye. (*c*) Most eye muscles originate from a common tendinous ring, shown here in an anterior view of the right orbit. (*d*) A superior view of the left and right orbits illustrates the insertion differences between the rectus and oblique muscles and how these insertion differences affect their movement of the eye. **AP|R**

The rectus eye muscles originate from a **common tendinous ring** in the orbit. These muscles attach to the *anterior* part of the eye, and are named according to which side of the eye they are located (medial, lateral, inferior, or superior).

The **medial rectus** attaches to the anteromedial surface of the eye and pulls the eye medially (adducts the eye). It is innervated by CN III (oculomotor nerve). The **lateral rectus** attaches to the anterolateral surface of the eye and pulls the eye laterally (abducts the eye). This muscle is innervated by CN VI (abducens). (Notice that this nerve's name tells you what muscle it innervates—the muscle that abducts the eye.) The **inferior rectus** attaches to the anteroinferior part of the eye. The inferior rectus pulls the eye inferiorly (as when you look down) and medially (as when you look at your nose). The **superior rectus** is located superiorly and attaches to the anterosuperior part of the sclera. The superior rectus pulls the eye superiorly (as when you look up) and medially (as when you look at your nose). The inferior and superior rectus muscles are innervated by CN III. Figure 11.7*d* illustrates that the superior and inferior rectus muscles do not pull directly parallel to the long axis of the eye; that is why both muscles also move the eye slightly in the medial direction.

The oblique eye muscles originate from within the orbit and insert on the *posterolateral* part of the sclera of the eye. The **inferior oblique** elevates the eye and turns the eye laterally. Since this muscle attaches to the inferior *posterior* part of the eye, contracting this muscle pulls the posterior part of the eye inferiorly (but *elevates* the *anterior* part of the eye). This muscle is innervated by CN III. The **superior oblique** depresses the eye and turns the eye laterally. This muscle passes through a pulleylike loop, called the **trochlea,** in the anteromedial orbit. This muscle attaches to the superior *posterior* part of the eye, so contracting this muscle pulls the posterior part of the eye superiorly (but *depresses* the *anterior* surface of the eye). This muscle is innervated by CN IV (trochlear). (Notice that this nerve's name is derived from the trochlea that holds the superior oblique in place.)

Table 11.2 compares the extrinsic muscles of the eye. Refer to section 13.9 to review the cranial nerves mentioned in this section.

WHAT DID YOU LEARN?

8 Which extrinsic eye muscles abduct the eye (move the eye laterally)?

Table 11.2	Extrinsic Eye Muscles		
Group/Muscle	**Action**	**Origin/Insertion**	**Innervation (see section 13.9)**
RECTUS MUSCLES			
Medial rectus (mē′dē-ăl rek′tus) *rectus = straight*	Moves eye medially (adducts eye)	O: Common tendinous ring I: Anteromedial surface of eye	CN III (oculomotor nerve)
Lateral rectus (lat′er-ăl)	Moves eye laterally (abducts eye)	O: Common tendinous ring I: Anterolateral surface of eye	CN VI (abducens nerve)
Inferior rectus	Moves eye inferiorly (depresses eye) and medially (adducts eye)	O: Common tendinous ring I: Anteroinferior surface of eye	CN III (oculomotor nerve)
Superior rectus	Moves eye superiorly (elevates eye) and medially (adducts eye)	O: Common tendinous ring I: Anterosuperior surface of eye	CN III (oculomotor nerve)
OBLIQUE MUSCLES			
Inferior oblique (ob-lēk′) *obliquus = slanting*	Moves eye superiorly (elevates eye) and laterally (abducts eye)	O: Anterior orbital surface of maxilla I: Posteroinferior, lateral surface of eye	CN III (oculomotor nerve)
Superior oblique	Moves eye inferiorly (depresses eye) and laterally (abducts eye)	O: Sphenoid bone I: Posterosuperior, lateral surface of eye	CN IV (trochlear nerve)

Figure 11.8 Muscles of Mastication. (*a*) Superficial and (*b*) deep lateral views of the muscles of mastication (shown in bold), which move the mandible.

Temporalis

Masseter
Buccinator
Orbicularis oris

(a) Superficial lateral view

Temporalis (cut)

Lateral pterygoid

Medial pterygoid

Buccinator
Orbicularis oris

(b) Deep lateral view

11.3c Muscles of the Oral Cavity and Pharynx

✓ LEARNING OBJECTIVES

5. Describe how each of the four muscles of mastication affects mandibular movement.

6. Describe the actions of the intrinsic muscles and the four paired extrinsic muscles of the tongue.

7. Explain what function the three primary muscles of the pharynx accomplish.

The muscles of the oral cavity and pharynx include muscles that help us chew, move the tongue, and swallow.

Muscles of Mastication

The term **mastication** (mas-ti-kā′shŭn) refers to the process of chewing. These muscles move the mandible at the temporomandibular joint (TMJ). There are four paired muscles of mastication: the temporalis, the masseter, and the lateral and medial pterygoids (figure 11.8). The muscles of mastication are innervated by the mandibular division of CN V (trigeminal).

The **temporalis** (or *temporal* muscle) is a broad, fan-shaped muscle that extends from the temporal lines of the skull and inserts on the coronoid process of the mandible. It elevates and retracts (pulls posteriorly) the mandible. You can palpate the temporalis by placing your fingers along your temple (lateral skull at same level of orbits) as you open and close your jaw. The muscle you feel contracting is the temporalis.

The **masseter** elevates and protracts (pulls anteriorly) the mandible. It is the most powerful and important of the masticatory muscles. This short, thick muscle is superficial to the temporalis. You can feel the movement of the masseter by palpating near the angle of the mandible as you open and close your mouth.

The **lateral** and **medial pterygoid** muscles arise from the pterygoid processes of the sphenoid bone and insert on the mandible. Both pterygoids protract the mandible and move it from side to side during chewing. These movements maximize the efficiency of the teeth while chewing or grinding foods of various consistencies. The medial pterygoid also elevates the mandible.

Table 11.3 summarizes the characteristics of the muscles of mastication.

Table 11.3	Muscles of Mastication		
Muscle	**Action**	**Origin/Insertion**	**Innervation (see section 13.9)**
Temporalis (tem-pŏ-rā′lis) *tempora* = pertaining to temporal bone	Elevates and retracts mandible	O: Superior and inferior temporal lines I: Coronoid process of mandible	CN V₃ (trigeminal nerve, mandibular division)
Masseter (ma′se-ter) *maseter* = chewer	Elevates and protracts mandible; prime mover of mandible elevation	O: Zygomatic arch I: Coronoid process, lateral surface and angle of mandible	CN V₃ (trigeminal nerve, mandibular division)
Medial pterygoid (ter′i-goyd) *pterygoid* = winglike	Elevates and protracts mandible; produces side-to-side movement of mandible	O: Maxilla, palatine, and medial surface of lateral pterygoid plate I: Medial surface of mandibular ramus	CN V₃ (trigeminal nerve, mandibular division)
Lateral pterygoid	Protracts mandible; produces side-to-side movement of mandible	O: Greater wing of sphenoid and lateral surface of lateral pterygoid plate I: Condylar process of mandible	CN V₃ (trigeminal nerve, mandibular division)

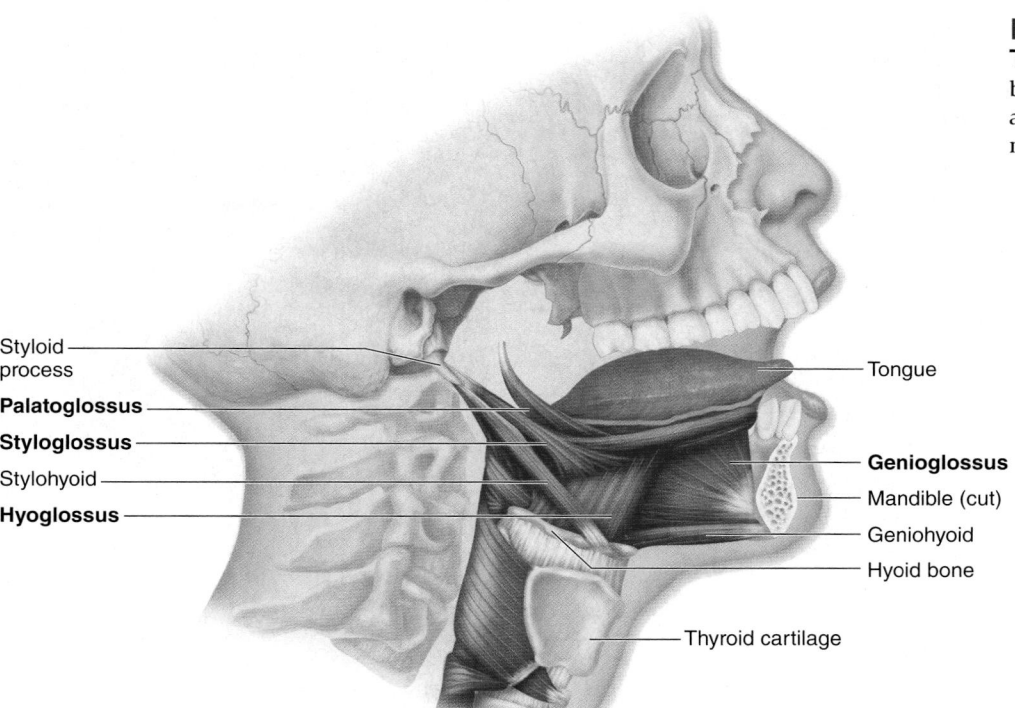

Figure 11.9 Muscles That Move the Tongue. Extrinsic tongue muscles (shown in bold) originate on structures other than the tongue and insert onto it to allow gross tongue movement.

Styloid process
Palatoglossus
Styloglossus
Stylohyoid
Hyoglossus
Tongue
Genioglossus
Mandible (cut)
Geniohyoid
Hyoid bone
Thyroid cartilage

Right lateral view

Muscles That Move the Tongue

The tongue is an agile, highly mobile organ. It consists of **intrinsic muscles** that curl, squeeze, and fold the tongue during chewing and speaking. Thus, the tongue itself is a big muscle.

The **extrinsic muscles** of the tongue have their origin on other head and neck structures and insert on the tongue. The extrinsic muscles end in the suffix –*glossus,* meaning "tongue" **(figure 11.9)**. These extrinsic tongue muscles are used in various combinations to accomplish the precise, complex, and delicate tongue movements required for proper speech and manipulating food within the mouth. Most of these muscles are innervated by CN XII, the hypoglossal nerve.

The left and right **genioglossus** muscles originate on the mandible and protract the tongue. You use these muscles when you stick out your tongue. The left and right **styloglossus** muscles originate on the styloid processes of the temporal bone. These muscles elevate and retract the tongue (pull the tongue posteriorly, back into the mouth). The left and right **hyoglossus** muscles originate on the hyoid bone and insert on the sides of the tongue. These muscles depress and retract the tongue. The left and right **palatoglossus** muscles originate on the soft palate and elevate the posterior portion of the tongue.

Table 11.4 summarizes the characteristics of the muscles that move the tongue.

Table 11.4	Muscles That Move the Tongue		
Muscle	**Action**	**Origin/Insertion**	**Innervation (see section 13.9)**
Genioglossus (jē′nī-ō-glos′ŭs) *geni* = chin *glossus* = tongue	Protracts tongue	O: Mental spines of mandible I: Inferior region of tongue; hyoid bone	CN XII (hypoglossal nerve)
Styloglossus (stī′lō-glos′ŭs) *stylo* = pertaining to styloid process of temporal bone	Elevates and retracts tongue	O: Styloid process of temporal bone I: Side and inferior aspect of tongue	CN XII (hypoglossal nerve)
Hyoglossus (hī′ō-glos′ŭs) *hyo* = pertaining to hyoid bone	Depresses and retracts tongue	O: Hyoid bone I: Inferolateral side of tongue	CN XII (hypoglossal nerve)
Palatoglossus (pal-ă-tō-glos′ŭs) *palato* = palate	Elevates posterior part of tongue	O: Anterior surface of soft palate I: Side and posterior aspect of tongue	CN X (vagus nerve) via pharyngeal plexus of nerves

Figure 11.10 Pharyngeal Constrictors, Palate Muscles, and Laryngeal Elevators.
A right lateral view reveals some of the muscles that constrict the pharynx when swallowing, move the palate, and elevate the larynx (palatopharyngeus and salpingopharyngeus not shown). **AP|R**

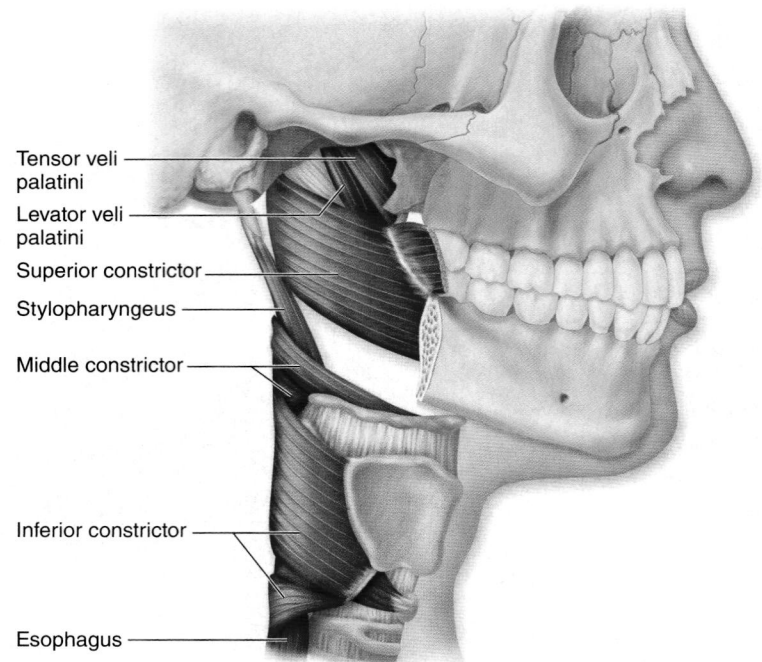

Tensor veli palatini

Levator veli palatini

Superior constrictor

Stylopharyngeus

Middle constrictor

Inferior constrictor

Esophagus

Right lateral view

Table 11.5	Muscles of the Pharynx		
Region/Muscle	**Action**	**Origin/Insertion**	**Innervation (see section 13.9)**
PALATE MUSCLES			
Levator veli palatini (vel′ī pal′ă-tē′nī) *velum* = veil	Elevates soft palate when swallowing	O: Petrous part of temporal bone I: Soft palate	CN X (vagus nerve)
Tensor veli palatini (ten′sōr) *tensus* = to stretch	Tenses soft palate and opens auditory tube when swallowing or yawning	O: Sphenoid bone; region around auditory tube I: Soft palate	CN V₃ (trigeminal nerve, mandibular division)
PHARYNGEAL CONSTRICTORS			
Superior constrictor (kon-strik′ter, -tōr) *constringo* = to draw together	Constricts pharynx in sequence to force bolus into esophagus; superior is innermost	O: Pterygoid process of sphenoid bone; medial surface of mandible I: Posterior median raphe (muscle fiber union from both sides)	CN X (vagus nerve) via branches of pharyngeal plexus
Middle constrictor	Constricts pharynx in sequence	O: Hyoid bone I: Posterior median raphe	CN X (vagus nerve) via branches of pharyngeal plexus
Inferior constrictor	Constricts pharynx in sequence; inferior is outermost	O: Thyroid and cricoid cartilage I: Posterior median raphe	CN X (vagus nerve) via branches of pharyngeal plexus
LARYNGEAL (VOICE BOX) ELEVATORS			
Palatopharyngeus (pal′ă-tō-fă-rin′jē′ŭs) *pharynx* = pharynx	Elevates pharynx and larynx	O: Soft palate I: Side of pharynx and thyroid cartilage of larynx	CN X (vagus nerve) via branches of pharyngeal plexus
Salpingopharyngeus (sal-ping′gō-fă-rin′jē-ŭs) *salpinx* = trumpet	Elevates pharynx and larynx	O: Auditory tube I: Blends with palatopharyngeus on lateral wall of pharynx	CN X (vagus nerve) via branches of pharyngeal plexus
Stylopharyngeus (stī′lō-fă-rin′jē-ŭs)	Elevates pharynx and larynx	O: Styloid process of temporal bone I: Side of pharynx and thyroid cartilage of larynx	CN IX (glossopharyngeal nerve) via branches of pharyngeal plexus

Pharynx Muscles

The **pharynx,** commonly known as the *throat*, is a funnel-shaped tube that lies posterior to both the oral and nasal cavities. Several muscles help form or attach to this tube and aid in swallowing **(figure 11.10)**. Most pharyngeal muscles are innervated by CN X (vagus nerve).

The primary pharynx muscles are the **pharyngeal constrictors** (**superior, middle,** and **inferior**). When a bolus of food enters the pharynx, these muscles contract sequentially to initiate swallowing and force the bolus inferiorly into the esophagus. Other pharyngeal muscles help elevate or tense the palate when swallowing. These muscles are summarized in **table 11.5**.

WHAT DID YOU LEARN?

9 What movements do the medial and lateral pterygoid muscles perform?

10 What is the general function of the extrinsic muscles of the tongue?

11.3d Muscles of the Anterior Neck: The Hyoid Muscles

LEARNING OBJECTIVE

8. Contrast the actions of the four suprahyoid muscles and the four infrahyoid muscles.

The muscles of the anterior neck are divided into the suprahyoid muscles, which are superior to the hyoid bone, and the infrahyoid muscles, which are inferior to the hyoid bone **(figure 11.11)**.

The **suprahyoid muscles** are associated with the floor of the mouth. In general, these muscles act as a group to elevate the hyoid bone during swallowing or speaking. Some of

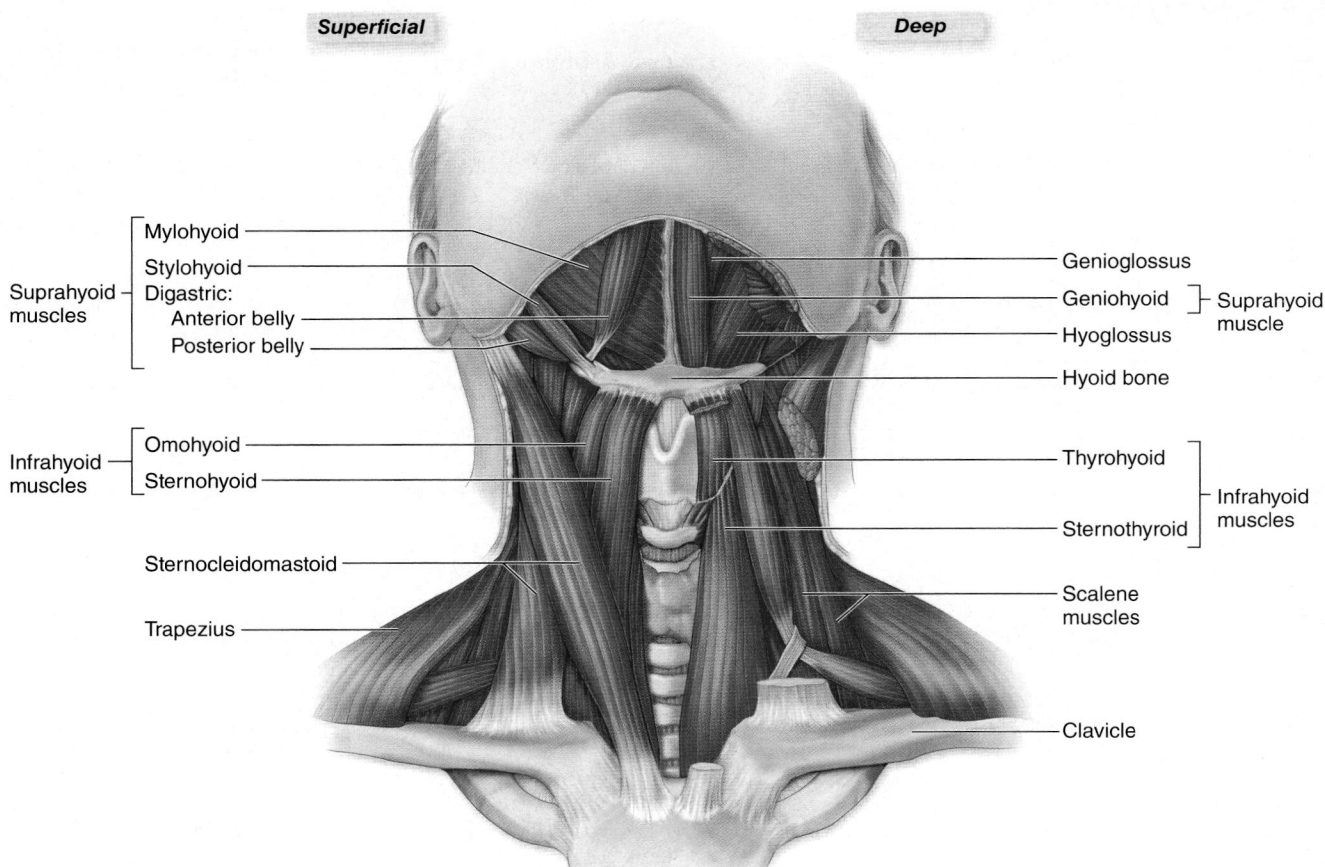

Anterior view

Figure 11.11 Muscles of the Anterior Neck. The anterior neck muscles move the hyoid bone and thyroid cartilage. Superficial muscles are shown on the right side of the body, and deeper muscles are shown on the left side of the body. AP|R these muscles perform additional functions: The **digastric** has two bellies, anterior and posterior. The anterior belly extends from the mental protuberance to the hyoid, and the posterior belly continues from the hyoid to the mastoid part of the temporal bone. The two bellies are united by an intermediate tendon that is held in position by a fibrous loop. In addition to elevating the hyoid bone, the digastric muscle can also depress the mandible. The **geniohyoid** attaches to the mental spines of the mandible and the hyoid bone. This muscle elevates the hyoid bone. The broad, flat **mylohyoid** provides a muscular floor to the mouth. When this muscle contracts, it both elevates the hyoid bone and raises the floor of the mouth. The muscle fibers of the left and right mylohyoid are aligned in a V shape. The **stylohyoid** connects the styloid process of the skull and the hyoid bone. Upon contraction, it elevates the hyoid bone, causing the floor of the oral cavity to elongate during swallowing.

As swallowing is completed, the **infrahyoid muscles** contract to influence the position of the hyoid bone and the larynx. In general, these muscles either depress the hyoid bone or depress the thyroid cartilage of the larynx. The **omohyoid** contains two thin muscle bellies anchored in place by a fascia "sling." This muscle is lateral to the sternohyoid and extends from the superior border of the scapula to insert on the hyoid, where it depresses the hyoid bone. The **sternohyoid** extends from the sternum to the hyoid bone, where it depresses the hyoid bone. The **sternothyroid** is deep to the sternohyoid. It extends from the sternum to the thyroid cartilage of the larynx. It depresses the thyroid cartilage to return it to its original position after swallowing. The **thyrohyoid** extends from the thyroid cartilage of the larynx to the hyoid bone. It depresses the hyoid bone and elevates the thyroid cartilage to close off the larynx during swallowing. In addition, the omohyoid, sternohyoid, and thyrohyoid help anchor the hyoid so the digastric can depress the mandible.

Table 11.6 summarizes the characteristics of these muscles.

 WHAT DO YOU THINK?

1 Since muscles frequently are named for their attachment sites, what do you think the prefix -*omo* in "omohyoid" means?

Table 11.6	Muscles of the Anterior Neck		
Region/Muscle	**Action**	**Origin/Insertion**	**Innervation (see sections 13.9 and 14.5d)**
SUPRAHYOID MUSCLES			
Digastric (dī-gas′trik) *di* = two *gaster* = belly	Depresses mandible; elevates hyoid bone	O: Anterior belly: Mandible near mental protuberance; posterior belly, mastoid process I: Hyoid bone via fascia sling	Anterior belly: CN V₃ (trigeminal nerve, mandibular division) Posterior belly: CN VII (facial nerve)
Geniohyoid (jĕ-nī-ō-hī′-oyd)	Elevates hyoid bone	O: Mental spines of mandible I: Hyoid bone	First cervical spinal nerve (C1) via CN XII (hypoglossal nerve)
Mylohyoid (mī′lō-hī′oyd) *myle* = molar	Elevates hyoid bone; elevates floor of mouth	O: Mylohyoid line of mandible I: Hyoid bone	CN V₃ (trigeminal nerve, mandibular division)
Stylohyoid (stī-lō-hī′oyd)	Elevates hyoid bone	O: Styloid process of temporal bone I: Hyoid bone	CN VII (facial nerve)
INFRAHYOID MUSCLES			
Omohyoid (ō-mō-hī′oyd) *omo* = shoulder	Depresses hyoid bone; fixes hyoid during opening of mouth	O: Superior border of scapula I: Hyoid bone	Cervical spinal nerves C1–C3 through ansa cervicalis (from cervical plexus)
Sternohyoid (ster′nō-hī′oyd) *sterno* = sternum	Depresses hyoid bone	O: Manubrium of sternum and medial end of clavicle I: Hyoid bone	Cervical spinal nerves C1–C3 through ansa cervicalis (from cervical plexus)
Sternothyroid (ster′nō-thī′royd) *thyro* = thyroid cartilage	Depresses thyroid cartilage of larynx	O: Posterior surface of manubrium of sternum I: Thyroid cartilage of larynx	Cervical spinal nerves C1–C3 through ansa cervicalis (from cervical plexus)
Thyrohyoid (thī-rō-hī′oyd)	Depresses hyoid bone and elevates thyroid cartilage of larynx	O: Thyroid cartilage of larynx I: Hyoid bone	First cervical spinal nerve C1 via CN XII (hypoglossal nerve)

WHAT DID YOU LEARN?

11 List the four suprahyoid muscles, and describe a common function for them.

11.3e Muscles That Move the Head and Neck

✔ LEARNING OBJECTIVE

9. Compare and contrast the actions of the anterolateral neck muscles and the posterior neck muscles.

Muscles that move the head and neck originate on the vertebral column, the thoracic cage, and the pectoral girdle, and insert on bones of the cranium (**figure 11.12**; see also figure 11.11).

Anterolateral Neck Muscles

The anterolateral neck muscles all flex the head and/or neck. The main muscles in this group are the sternocleidomastoid and the three scalenes.

The **sternocleidomastoid** is a thick, cordlike muscle that extends from the sternum and clavicle to the mastoid process posterior to the ear. Contraction of both sternocleidomastoid muscles (called **bilateral contraction**) flexes the neck. Contraction of just one sternocleidomastoid muscle (called **unilateral contraction**) results in lateral flexion of the head to its own side, accompanied by rotation of the head to the opposite side. Thus, if the left sternocleidomastoid muscle contracts, it rotates the head to the right side of the body. The three **scalene muscles** (**anterior, middle,** and **posterior**) work with the sternocleidomastoid to flex the neck. In addition, the scalene muscles elevate the first and second ribs during forced inhalation (see section 23.5b).

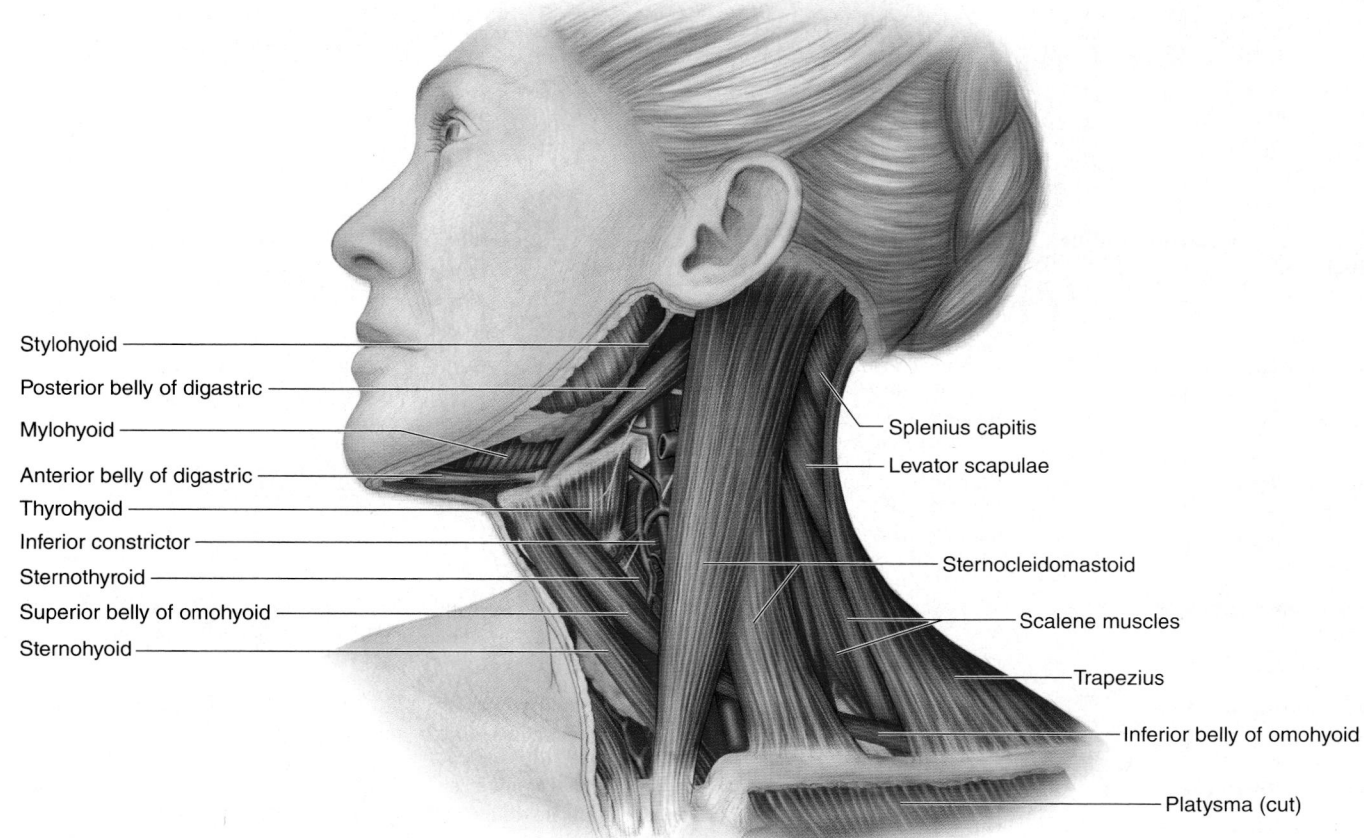

Stylohyoid
Posterior belly of digastric
Mylohyoid
Anterior belly of digastric
Thyrohyoid
Inferior constrictor
Sternothyroid
Superior belly of omohyoid
Sternohyoid

Splenius capitis
Levator scapulae
Sternocleidomastoid
Scalene muscles
Trapezius
Inferior belly of omohyoid
Platysma (cut)

Anterolateral view

Figure 11.12 Muscles That Move the Head and Neck. Anterolateral muscles collectively flex the neck, whereas posterior neck muscles extend the head and/or neck. AP|R

Figure 11.13 Posterior Neck
Muscles. An illustration shows the deep and deeper muscles that extend and rotate the head and neck. AP|R

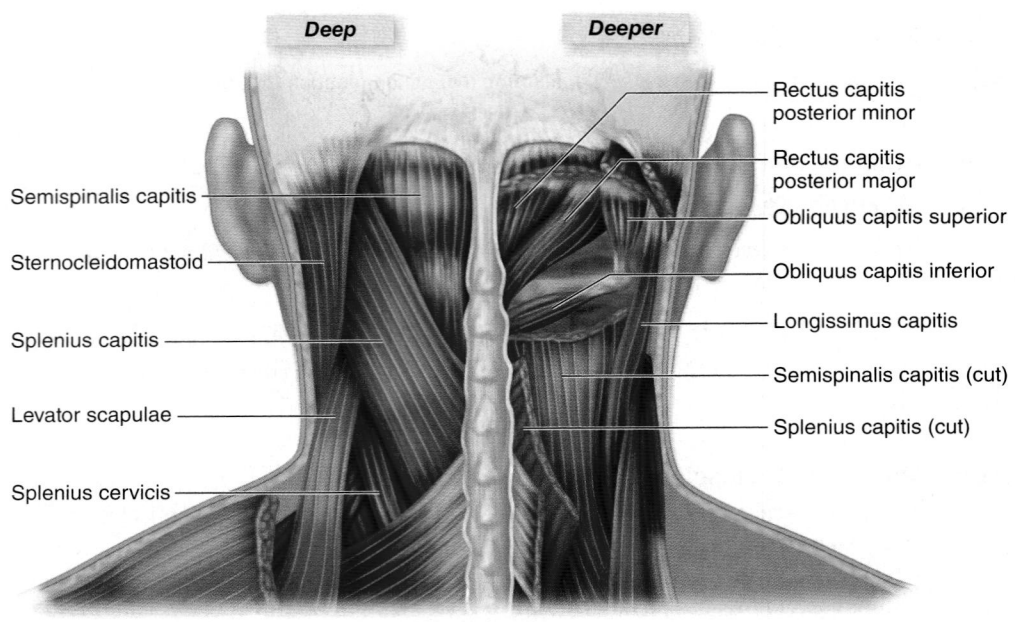

Deep

Deeper

Semispinalis capitis

Sternocleidomastoid

Splenius capitis

Levator scapulae

Splenius cervicis

Rectus capitis posterior minor

Rectus capitis posterior major

Obliquus capitis superior

Obliquus capitis inferior

Longissimus capitis

Semispinalis capitis (cut)

Splenius capitis (cut)

Posterior view

Posterior Neck Muscles

Many of the posterior neck muscles work together to extend the head and/or neck (**figure 11.13**). The trapezius attaches to the skull and helps extend the head, neck, or both, but its primary function is to help move the pectoral girdle.

When the left and right **splenius capitis, splenius cervicis, semispinalis capitis,** and **longissimus capitis** muscles bilaterally

contract, they extend the neck. Unilateral contraction turns the head and neck to the same side.

A group of muscles called the suboccipital muscles includes the obliquus capitis superior, obliquus capitis inferior, rectus capitis posterior major, and rectus capitis posterior minor. The oblique muscles turn the head to the same side, whereas the rectus muscles extend the head and neck.

Table 11.7 — Muscles That Move the Head and Neck

Muscle	Action	Origin/Insertion	Innervation (see sections 13.9 and 14.5c, d)
Sternocleidomastoid (ster′nō-klī′dō-măs-toyd) *sterno* = sternum *cleido* = clavicle *masto* = mastoid process	Unilateral action[1]: Lateral flexion, rotation of head to opposite side Bilateral action[2]: Flexes neck	O: Manubrium and sternal end of clavicle I: Mastoid process	CN XI (accessory nerve)
Scalene muscles (anterior, middle, posterior) (see also table 11.9) (skā′lēnz) *scalene* = uneven	Flex neck (when 1st rib is fixed); elevate 1st and 2nd ribs during forced inspiration when neck is fixed	O: Transverse processes of cervical vertebrae I: Superior surface of 1st and 2nd ribs	Cervical spinal nerves
Splenius capitis and **cervicis** (splē′nē-ŭs ka-pī-tis) (ser′vi′sis) *splenion* = bandage	Unilateral action: Turns head to same side Bilateral action: Extends head/neck	O: Ligamentum nuchae I: Occipital bone and mastoid process of temporal bone	Cervical spinal nerves
Longissimus capitis (lon-gis′i-mŭs) *longissimus* = longest *caput* = head	Unilateral action: Turns head to same side Bilateral action: Extends head/neck	O: Transverse process of T_1–T_4 and articular processes of C_4–C_7 vertebrae I: Mastoid process	Cervical and thoracic spinal nerves
Obliquus capitis superior (ob-lī′kwŭs) *obliquus* = slanting	Turns head to same side	O: Transverse process of atlas I: Inferior nuchal line of occipital bone	Suboccipital nerve (posterior ramus of C1 spinal nerve)
Obliquus capitis inferior	Turns head to same side	O: Spinous process of axis I: Transverse process of atlas	Suboccipital nerve (posterior ramus of C1 spinal nerve)
Rectus capitis posterior major	Extends head/neck	O: Spinous process of axis I: Inferior nuchal line of occipital bone	Suboccipital nerve (posterior ramus of C1 spinal nerve)
Rectus capitis posterior minor	Extends head/neck	O: Posterior tubercle of atlas I: Inferior nuchal line of occipital bone	Suboccipital nerve (posterior ramus of C1 spinal nerve)

1. *Unilateral action* means only one muscle (either the left or right muscle) is contracting.
2. *Bilateral action* means both the left and right muscles are contracting together.

CLINICAL VIEW
Congenital Muscular Torticollis

Photo of 7-year-old boy with CMT.

Congenital muscular torticollis (CMT), often known as *wryneck,* is a condition where a newborn presents with a shortened and tightened sternocleidomastoid muscle that may persist into childhood. It is thought to be a result of trauma resulting from either a difficult birth or prenatal position of the fetus. The trauma causes a hematoma and fibrosing of the muscle tissue. Pediatricians also have seen an increase in acquired muscular torticollis among newborns who are kept in infant seats for extended periods of time outside of the car. Children with CMT often tilt their heads to the affected side and their chins to the unaffected side. Because the child typically favors a particular head position when sleeping, plagiocephaly (flattening of the head) often accompanies CMT.

CMT treatment typically involves stretching the affected muscle several times a day, changing sleeping positions, and making the child use the affected side more frequently. A newer approach to treatment of CMT is the use of botulinum toxin type A (Botox), which impairs contraction of the affected muscle), combined with stretching.

Table 11.7 summarizes the characteristics of the muscles of the head and neck.

 WHAT DID YOU LEARN?

12 Which neck muscles extend the neck? Which neck muscles flex the neck?

11.4 Muscles of the Vertebral Column

 LEARNING OBJECTIVES

1. Name and describe the three groups of erector spinae muscles.
2. Describe the actions of the transversospinalis and quadratus lumborum muscles.

The muscles of the vertebral column are very complex; they have multiple origins and insertions, and they exhibit extensive overlap **(figure 11.14).** All of these muscles are covered by the most superficial back muscles, which actually move the upper limb.

Note that the neck is actually the cervical portion of the vertebral column. Thus, the posterior muscles discussed previously in connection with neck extension (splenius cervicis, splenius capitis, longissimus capitis, semispinalis capitis) extend the *cervical* region of the vertebral column.

The **erector spinae** are used to maintain posture and to help an individual stand erect. When the left and right erector spinae muscles contract together, they extend the vertebral column. If the erector spinae muscles on only one side contract, the vertebral column flexes laterally toward that same side.

Deep   **Deeper**

Longissimus capitis

Splenius capitis

Serratus posterior superior

External intercostals

Splenius cervicis

Erector spinae —
- Iliocostalis group
- Longissimus group
- Spinalis group

Serratus posterior inferior

Internal oblique

External oblique (cut)

Semispinalis capitis

Semispinalis cervicis

Semispinalis thoracis — **Transversospinalis**

Multifidus

Quadratus lumborum

Posterior view

Figure 11.14 Deep Muscles of the Vertebral Column. These deep muscles extend, modify, and/or stabilize the positions of the vertebral column, neck, and ribs. Major groups of deep muscles are in bold. **AP|R**

The erector spinae muscles are organized into three groups. The muscles are named based upon the body region with which they are associated.

- The **iliocostalis group** is the most laterally placed of the three erector spinae components. It is composed of three parts: cervical, thoracic, and lumbar.
- The **longissimus group** is medial to the iliocostalis group. The fibers of the longissimus muscle group insert on the transverse processes of the vertebrae. The longissimus group is composed of three parts: capitis, cervical, and thoracic.
- The **spinalis group** is the most medially placed of the erector spinae muscles. The spinalis muscle fibers insert on the spinous processes of the vertebrae. The spinalis group is composed of cervical and thoracic parts.

Deep to the erector spinae, a group of muscles collectively called the **transversospinalis muscles** connect and stabilize the vertebrae. This group includes several specific muscles, which are listed in the accompanying table.

A final pair of muscles helps move the vertebral column. The **quadratus lumborum muscles** are located primarily in the lumbar region. When the left and right quadratus lumborum muscles bilaterally contract, they extend the vertebral column. When either the left or right quadratus lumborum muscle unilaterally contracts, it laterally flexes the vertebral column.

Table 11.8 summarizes the characteristics of the muscles of the vertebral column.

WHAT DID YOU LEARN?

13 Which muscles form the erector spinae, and what are the general actions of the erector spinae?

Table 11.8	Muscles of the Vertebral Column		
Group/Muscle	**Action**	**Origin/Insertion**	**Innervation (see sections 14.5c, d, and f)**
ERECTOR SPINAE			
Iliocostalis group (il-ē-ō-kos-tă′lis) *ilio* = ilium *cost* = rib	Bilateral action: Extends neck and vertebral column; maintains posture Unilateral action: Laterally flexes vertebral column	O: Tendon from posterior part of iliac crest, posterior sacrum, and lumbar spinous processes I: Angles of ribs; transverse processes of cervical vertebrae	Cervical, thoracic, and lumbar spinal nerves
Longissimus group (lon-gis′i-mŭs)	Bilateral action: Extends neck and vertebral column; maintains posture Unilateral action: Rotates head and laterally flexes vertebral column	O: Tendon from posterior part of iliac crest, posterior sacrum, and lumbar spinous processes I: Mastoid process of temporal bone and transverse processes of cervical and thoracic vertebrae	Cervical and thoracic spinal nerves
Spinalis group (spī-nā′lis) *spin* = spine	Bilateral action: Extends neck and vertebral column; maintains posture Unilateral action: Laterally flexes vertebral column	O: Lumbar spinous processes (thoracic part) and C_7 spinous process (cervical part) I: Spinous process of axis and thoracic vertebrae	Cervical and thoracic spinal nerves
TRANSVERSOSPINALIS GROUP			
Multifidus (mul-tif′i-dŭs) *multus* = much *findo* = to cleave	Bilateral action: Extends vertebral column Unilateral action: Rotates vertebral column toward opposite side	O: Sacrum and transverse processes of each vertebra I: Spinous processes of vertebrae located 2–4 segments superior to origin	Cervical, thoracic, and lumbar spinal nerves
Rotatores (rō-tā′tōrz)	Bilateral action: Extends vertebral column Unilateral action: Rotates vertebral column toward opposite side	O: Transverse processes of each vertebra I: Spinous process of immediately superior vertebra	Cervical, thoracic, and lumbar spinal nerves
Semispinalis group (sem′ē-spī-nā′lis)	Bilateral action: Extends vertebral column and neck Unilateral action: Laterally flexes vertebral column and neck	O: Transverse processes of C_4–T_{12} vertebrae I: Occipital bone and spinous processes of cervical and thoracic vertebrae	Cervical and thoracic spinal nerves
SPINAL EXTENSORS AND LATERAL FLEXORS			
Quadratus lumborum (kwah-drā′tūs lŭm-bōr′ŭm) *quad* = four-sided	Bilateral action: Extends vertebral column Unilateral action: Laterally flexes vertebral column	O: Iliac crest and iliolumbar ligament I: 12th rib; transverse processes of lumbar vertebrae	Thoracic and lumbar spinal nerves

11.5 Muscles of Respiration

LEARNING OBJECTIVES

1. List the posterior and anterior thoracic muscle groups involved in respiration, and describe their actions.

2. Describe the role of the diaphragm in breathing and in raising intra-abdominal pressure.

The process of respiration involves inspiration and expiration. During **inspiration,** several muscles contract to increase the dimensions of the thoracic cavity to allow the lungs to fill with air. During **expiration,** some respiratory muscles contract and others relax, collectively decreasing the dimensions of the thoracic cavity and forcing air out of the lungs.

The muscles of respiration are on the posterior and anterior surfaces of the thorax. These muscles are covered by more superficial muscles (such as the pectoral muscles, trapezius, and latissimus dorsi) that move the upper limb.

Two posterior thorax muscles assist with respiration. The **serratus posterior superior** attaches to ribs 2–5 (see figure 11.14) and elevates these ribs during forced inspiration, thereby increasing the lateral dimensions of the thoracic cavity. The **serratus posterior inferior** attaches to ribs 8–12 and depresses those ribs during forced expiration.

Several groups of anterior thorax muscles change the dimensions of the thorax during respiration **(figure 11.15)**. The scalene muscles (discussed previously with other neck muscles) help elevate the first and second ribs during forced inspiration, thereby increasing the dimensions of the thoracic cavity.

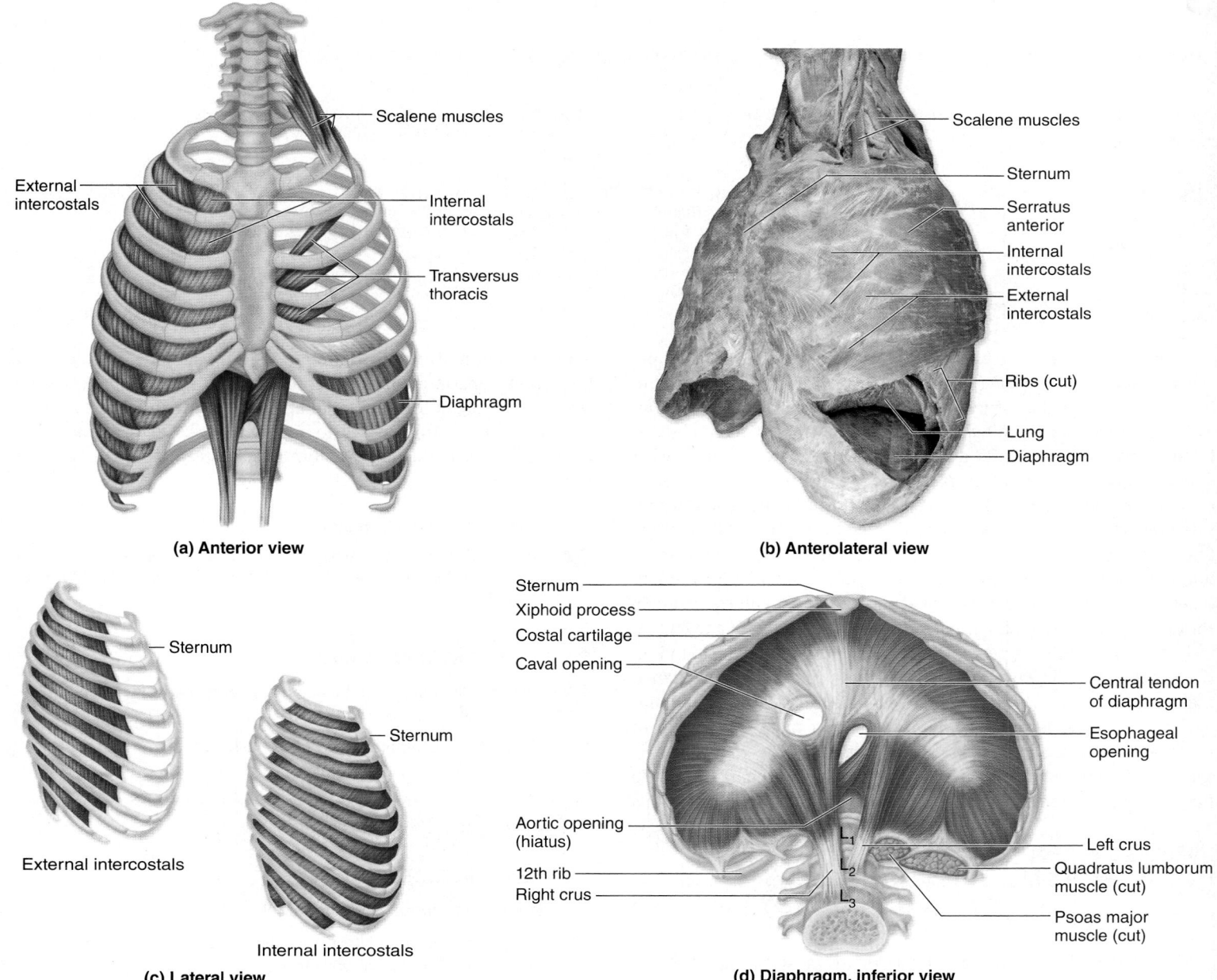

(a) Anterior view

(b) Anterolateral view

(c) Lateral view

(d) Diaphragm, inferior view

Figure 11.15 Muscles of Respiration. These skeletal muscles contract rhythmically to alter the size of the thoracic cavity and facilitate respiration. (*a*) Anterior view. (*b*) A cadaver photo provides an anterolateral view, with the inferior ribs cut to expose the thoracic cavity and the superior surface of the diaphragm. (*c*) Lateral views demonstrate fiber directions of the external and internal intercostals. (*d*) Inferior view of the diaphragm.

AP|R

Table 11.9   Muscles of Respiration

Muscle	Action	Origin/Insertion	Innervation (see sections 14.5c, d)
Serratus posterior superior (sĕr-ā′tŭs) *serratus* = a saw	Elevates ribs during forced inspiration	O: Spinous processes of C_7–T_3 vertebrae I: Lateral borders of ribs 2–5	Thoracic spinal nerves
Serratus posterior inferior	Depresses ribs during forced expiration	O: Spinous processes of T_{11}–L_3 vertebrae I: Inferior borders of ribs 8–12	Thoracic spinal nerves
Scalene muscles (see also table 11.7)	Elevate 1st and 2nd ribs during forced inspiration when neck is fixed	O: Transverse processes of cervical vertebrae I: Superior surface of 1st and 2nd ribs	Cervical spinal nerves
External intercostals (in′ter-kos′talz) *inter* = between *cost* = rib	Elevate ribs during quiet and forced inspiration	O: Inferior border of superior rib I: Superior border of inferior rib	Thoracic spinal nerves
Internal intercostals	Depresses ribs during forced expiration	O: Superior border of inferior rib I: Inferior border to superior rib	Thoracic spinal nerves
Transversus thoracis (trans-ver′sŭs thō-ra′sis)	Depresses ribs during forced expiration	O: Posterior surface of xiphoid process and inferior region of sternum I: Costal cartilages 2–6	Thoracic spinal nerves
Diaphragm (dī′ă-fram) *dia* = across *phragm* = partition	Contraction causes flattening of diaphragm (moves inferiorly) during inspiration and thus expands thoracic cavity; increases pressure in abdominopelvic cavity	O: Inferior internal surface of ribs 7–12; xiphoid process of sternum and costal cartilages of inferior 6 ribs; lumbar vertebrae I: Central tendon	Phrenic nerves (C_3–C_5)

The **external intercostals** extend inferomedially from the superior rib to the adjacent inferior rib. The external intercostals assist in expanding the thoracic cavity by elevating the ribs during inspiration. This movement is like lifting a bucket handle—that is, as the bucket handle (rib) is elevated, its distance from the center of the bucket (thorax) increases. Thus, contraction of the external intercostals increases the transverse dimensions of the thoracic cavity. The **internal intercostals** lie deep to the external intercostals, and their muscle fibers are at right angles to the external intercostals. The internal intercostals depress the ribs only during forced expiration; normal, quiet expiration takes no active muscular effort. A small **transversus thoracis** extends across the inner surface of the thoracic cage and attaches to ribs 2–6. It helps depress the ribs during forced expiration.

Finally, the **diaphragm** is an internally placed, dome-shaped muscle that forms a partition between the thoracic and abdominal cavities. (The term *diaphragm* refers to a muscle or group of muscles that covers or partitions an opening.) The diaphragm is the most important muscle associated with breathing. The muscle fibers of the diaphragm converge from its margins toward a fibrous

central tendon. During inspiration, the diaphragm contracts and the central tendon is pulled inferiorly toward the abdominal cavity, thereby increasing the vertical dimensions of the thoracic cavity.

Table 11.9 summarizes the characteristics of the muscles of respiration. Further details about muscles of respiration are found in section 23.5b.

 WHAT DO YOU THINK?

 ❷ After you've eaten a very large meal, it is sometimes difficult to take a big, deep breath. Why is it more difficult to breathe deeply with a full GI tract?

 WHAT DID YOU LEARN?

 ⓮ Compare the actions of the external intercostals and the internal intercostals.

⓯ How is the diaphragm involved in respiration?

11.6 Muscles of the Abdominal Wall

LEARNING OBJECTIVES

1. List the four pairs of abdominal muscles.
2. Compare the actions of the rectus abdominis muscle with the oblique muscles and transversus abdominis.

The anterolateral wall of the abdomen is reinforced by four pairs of muscles that collectively compress and hold the abdominal organs in place: the external oblique, internal oblique, transversus abdominis, and rectus abdominis **(figure 11.16)**. These muscles also work together to flex and stabilize the vertebral column.

 INTEGRATE

CONCEPT CONNECTION

When the diaphragm contracts, it compresses the abdominal cavity, thus increasing intra-abdominal pressure. Increased intra-abdominal pressure is necessary for urination (section 24.7c), defecation (section 26.3d), and childbirth (section 29.6). Beyond respiration, diaphragm movements are also important in helping return venous blood to the heart from the inferior half of the body (section 20.4a).

(a) Anterior view

Superficial

Deep

Pectoralis major

Pectoralis minor

Serratus anterior

Tendinous intersections

Rectus sheath

Rectus abdominis

Umbilicus

Transversus abdominis

Linea alba

Internal oblique (cut)

External oblique (cut)

Aponeurosis of external oblique

Inguinal ligament

External oblique

Internal oblique and rectus abdominis

(b) Anterolateral view

Tendinous intersections

External intercostal

Internal intercostal

Rectus sheath

Rectus abdominis

Umbilicus

Linea alba

Transversus abdominis

Internal oblique (cut)

Aponeurosis of external oblique

External oblique (cut)

Inguinal ligament

Inguinal ligament

Transversus abdominis

(c)

Figure 11.16 Muscles of the Abdominal Wall. The abdominal muscles compress abdominal contents and flex the vertebral column. (*a*) An illustration depicts the anterior view of some superficial and deep muscles. (*b*) A cadaver photo provides an anterolateral view of the muscles of the abdominal wall. (*c*) Diagrams show some individual abdominal muscles, ranging from superficial to deep. AP|R

LEARNING STRATEGY

The fibers of the external intercostals and external oblique muscles run in the same direction—inferomedially. This is the same direction that you put your hands in your pockets.

The fibers of the internal intercostals and internal oblique muscles run perpendicular (in the opposite direction) to the external muscles—superomedially.

The muscle fibers of the superficial **external oblique** are directed inferomedially. The external oblique is muscular along the lateral abdominal wall and forms an aponeurosis as it projects anteriorly. Inferiorly, the aponeurosis of the external oblique forms a strong, cordlike **inguinal ligament** that extends from the anterior superior iliac spine to the pubic tubercle. Immediately deep to the external oblique is the **internal oblique.** Its muscle fibers project superomedially, which is at right angles to the external oblique. Like the external oblique, this muscle forms an aponeurosis as it projects anteriorly. The deepest muscle is the **transversus abdominis,** whose fibers project transversely across the abdomen

INTEGRATE

CLINICAL VIEW

Hernias

The condition in which a portion of the viscera, particularly the intestine, protrudes through a weakened point of the muscular wall of the abdominopelvic cavity is called a **hernia** (her'nē-ă; rupture). A significant medical problem may develop if the herniated portion of the intestine swells, becoming trapped. Blood flow to the trapped segment may diminish, causing that portion of the intestine to die. This condition, called a *strangulated intestinal hernia,* is very painful and can be life-threatening if not treated promptly.

How do inguinal hernias form, and why are males more prone to get them?

Two common types of hernias are inguinal hernias and femoral hernias. An **inguinal hernia** is the most common type of hernia. The inguinal region is one of the weakest areas of the abdominal wall. Within this region is a canal (inguinal canal) that allows the passage of the spermatic cord in males, and a smaller structure called the *round ligament* in females. The inguinal canal, or the **superficial inguinal ring** associated with it, is often the site of a rupture or separation of the abdominal wall. Males are more likely to develop inguinal hernias than females because their inguinal canals and superficial inguinal rings are larger to allow room for the spermatic cord. Rising pressure in the abdominal cavity, as might develop while straining to lift a heavy object, provides the force to push a segment of the small intestine into the canal. There are two types of inguinal hernia:

- In a **direct inguinal hernia,** the loop of small intestine protrudes directly through the superficial inguinal ring, but not through the entire length of the inguinal canal, and creates a bulge in the lower anterior abdominal wall. This type of hernia is typically seen in middle-aged males with poorly developed abdominal muscles and protruding abdomens.

- In an **indirect inguinal hernia,** the herniation travels through the entire inguinal canal and may even extend all the way into the scrotum, since the path of the herniation follows the path of the spermatic cord. This type of hernia tends to occur in younger males or male children who have a congenital anomaly called *patent process vaginalis,* in which the embryonic path taken by the testis into the scrotum fails to regress.

How do physicians test for an inguinal hernia?

First, the physician must find the superficial inguinal ring by locating both the inguinal ligament (found inferior to the ring) and the pubic tubercle (just inferior and medial to the ring). The physician inserts a finger in the depression formed by the superficial inguinal ring and asks the patient to turn his head and cough, because the act of coughing increases intra-abdominal pressure and would encourage a portion of intestine to poke through the ring if there was a problem. While the patient coughs, the physician palpates the superficial inguinal ring to make sure no intestine is protruding through the ring.

How do femoral hernias compare to inguinal hernias?

A **femoral hernia** occurs in the upper thigh, just inferior to the inguinal ligament, originating in a region called the femoral triangle. The medial part of the femoral triangle is relatively weak and prone to stress injury, thus allowing a loop of small intestine to protrude. Women more commonly develop femoral hernias because of the greater width of their femoral triangle, which equates to the wider hip span of the female anatomy.

Anterior superior iliac spine

Inguinal ligament

Superficial inguinal ring

Pubic tubercle

Herniated intestine

Testing for a potential inguinal hernia on the right side. Note the herniated intestine protruding through the left superficial inguinal ring.

Table 11.10 Muscles of the Abdominal Wall

Muscle	Action	Origin/Insertion	Innervation (see sections 14.5c, f)
External oblique (ob-lēk)	Unilateral action[1]: Laterally flexes vertebral column; rotation of vertebral column Bilateral action[2]: Flexes vertebral column and compresses abdominal wall	O: External and inferior borders of the inferior 8 ribs I: Linea alba by a broad aponeurosis; some to iliac crest	Spinal nerves T8–T12, L1
Internal oblique	Unilateral action: Laterally flexes vertebral column; rotation of vertebral column Bilateral action: Flexes vertebral column and compresses abdominal wall	O: Lumbar fascia, inguinal ligament, and iliac crest I: Linea alba, pubic crest, inferior rib surfaces (last 4 ribs); costal cartilages of ribs 8–10	Spinal nerves T8–T12, L1
Transversus abdominis (ab-dom'i-nis) *transverse* = across	Unilateral action: Laterally flexes vertebral column Bilateral action: Flexes vertebral column and compresses abdominal wall	O: Iliac crest, cartilages of inferior 6 ribs; lumbar fascia; inguinal ligament I: Linea alba and pubic crest	Spinal nerves T8–T12, L1
Rectus abdominis	Flexes vertebral column and compresses abdominal wall	O: Superior surface of pubis near pubic symphysis I: Xiphoid process of sternum; inferior surfaces of ribs 5–7	Spinal nerves T7–T12

1. *Unilateral action* means only one muscle (either the left or right muscle) is contracting.

2. *Bilateral action* means both the left and right muscles are contracting together.

and has an aponeurosis as it projects anteriorly. When these three sets of muscles unilaterally contract, they laterally flex the vertebral column. These muscles also rotate the vertebral colum.

The **rectus abdominis** is a long, straplike muscle that extends vertically the entire length of the anteromedial abdominal wall between the sternum and the pubic symphysis. It is partitioned into four segments by three fibrous **tendinous intersections,** which form the traditional "six-pack" of a muscular, toned abdominal wall. The rectus abdominis is enclosed within a fibrous sleeve called the **rectus sheath,** which is formed from the aponeuroses of the external oblique, internal oblique, and transversus abdominis muscles. The left and right rectus sheaths are connected by a vertical fibrous strip termed the **linea alba.**

Table 11.10 summarizes the characteristics of the muscles of the abdominal wall.

You have probably noticed that multiple muscles may work together to perform a common function. For example, several neck muscles and back muscles work together to extend the vertebral column. Learning muscles in groups according to common function helps most students assimilate the anatomy information. **Table 11.11** summarizes the actions of various axial muscles and groups them according to common function. Note that a muscle that has multiple functions is listed in more than one group.

 WHAT DID YOU LEARN?

16 What are the main actions of the abdominal muscles?

Table 11.11 Muscle Actions on the Axial Skeleton

Extend the Head, Neck, and/or Vertebral Column	Flex the Head, Neck, and/or Vertebral Column	Laterally Flex the Vertebral Column	Rotate the Head and/or Neck to One Side	Elevate the Ribs	Depress the Ribs
Splenius muscles[2]	Sternocleidomastoid[2]	Quadratus lumborum[1]	Sternocleidomastoid[1]	Serratus posterior superior	Serratus posterior inferior
Erector spinae[2] (iliocostalis, longissimus, spinalis)	Scalene muscles[2]	External oblique[1]	Splenius muscles[1]	External intercostals	Internal intercostals
Quadratus lumborum[2]	External oblique[2]	Internal oblique[1]	Longissimus capitis[1]	Scalene muscles (1st and 2nd ribs only)	Transversus thoracis
Transversospinalis group[2]	Internal oblique[2]	Transversus abdominis[1]	Obliquus capitis inferior[1]		
Rectus capitis posterior major and minor[2]	Transversus abdominis[2] Rectus abdominis[2]		Obliquus capitis superior[1]		

1. Unilateral action of muscles

2. Bilateral action

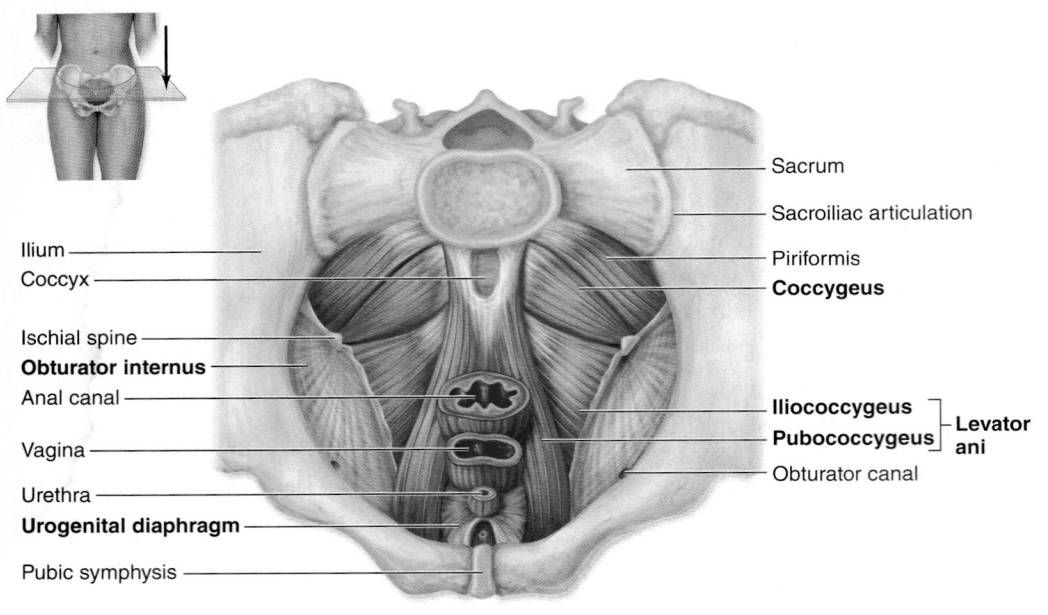

Figure 11.17 Muscles of the Pelvic Floor. The pelvic cavity floor is composed of muscle layers that form the urogenital and anal triangles, extend across the pelvic outlet, and support the organs in the pelvic cavity (puborectalis not shown). (*a*) Superior view of the female pelvic cavity. Inferior views show (*b*) male and (*c*) female perineal regions. Muscles of the pelvic floor are in bold.

Sacrum
Sacroiliac articulation
Piriformis
Coccygeus

Ilium
Coccyx

Ischial spine
Obturator internus
Anal canal

Vagina

Urethra
Urogenital diaphragm

Pubic symphysis

Iliococcygeus
Pubococcygeus } Levator ani
Obturator canal

(a) Female, superior view

Raphe
Bulbospongiosus
Ischiocavernosus
Superficial transverse perineal muscle

Urogenital triangle

Perineal body

Anal triangle

Levator ani
Gluteus maximus

Superficial

Pubic symphysis
Pubic ramus
External urethral sphincter
Urethra
Deep transverse perineal muscle

Anus
External anal sphincter

Deep

(b) Male, inferior view

Urethra
Vagina
Bulbospongiosus
Ischiocavernosus
Superficial transverse perineal muscle

Urogenital triangle

Perineal body

Anal triangle

Levator ani
Gluteus maximus

Superficial

Pubic symphysis
Pubic ramus
External urethral sphincter
Urethra
Vagina
Deep transverse perineal muscle

Anus
External anal sphincter

Deep

(c) Female, inferior view

11.7 Muscles of the Pelvic Floor

LEARNING OBJECTIVES

1. Describe the functions of the pelvic floor muscles.
2. Identify the boundaries of the perineum.

The floor of the pelvic cavity is formed by three layers of muscles and associated fasciae, collectively known as the **pelvic diaphragm.** The pelvic diaphragm extends from the ischium and pubis of the ossa coxae across the pelvic outlet to the sacrum and coccyx. These muscles collectively form the pelvic floor and support the pelvic viscera (**figure 11.17**).

The diamond-shaped region between the lower appendages is called the **perineum.** The perineum has four significant bony landmarks: the pubic symphysis anteriorly, the coccyx posteriorly, and both ischial tuberosities laterally. A transverse line drawn between the ischial tuberosities partitions the perineum into an anterior **urogenital triangle** that contains the external genitalia

and urethra, and a posterior **anal triangle** that contains the anus (figure 11.17b, c).

Table 11.12 describes the specific muscles of the pelvic floor and perineum, and summarizes their characteristics.

WHAT DID YOU LEARN?

17 What are the functions of the pelvic floor muscles?

Table 11.12	Muscles of the Pelvic Floor		
Group/Muscle	**Action**	**Origin/Insertion**	**Innervation (see section 14.5g)**
ANAL TRIANGLE			
Coccygeus (kok'si'jē-ŭs) *coccy* = coccyx	Forms pelvic floor and supports pelvic viscera	O: Ischial spine I: Lateral and inferior borders of sacrum	Spinal nerves S4–S5
External anal sphincter (ā'năl sfingk'ter) *anal* = referring to anus *sphin* = squeeze	Closes anal opening; must relax to defecate	O: Perineal body I: Encircles anal opening	Pudendal nerve (S2–S4)
Levator ani (lē-vā'tor, le-vā-ter ā'nī; *levator* = raises; *ani* = anus): Group of muscles that form the anterior and lateral parts of the pelvic diaphragm			
Iliococcygeus (il'ē-ō-kok-si'jē-ŭs)	Forms pelvic floor and supports pelvic viscera	O: Pubis and ischial spine I: Coccyx and median raphe	Pudendal nerve (S2–S4)
Pubococcygeus (pū-bō-kok-si'jē-ŭs)	Forms pelvic floor and supports pelvic viscera	O: Pubis and ischial spine I: Coccyx and median raphe	Pudendal nerve (S2–S4)
Puborectalis (pū-bō-rek'tăl-is) *rectal* = rectum	Supports anorectal junction; must relax to defecate	O: Pubis and ischial spine I: Coccyx and median raphe	Pudendal nerve (S2–S4)
UROGENITAL TRIANGLE			
Superficial layer			
Bulbospongiosus (female) (bul'bō-spŭn'jē-ō'sŭs) *bulbon* = bulb *spongio* = sponge	Narrows vaginal opening; compresses and stiffens clitoris	O: Sheath of collagen fibers at base of clitoris I: Perineal body	Pudendal nerve (S2–S4)
Bulbospongiosus (male)	Ejects urine or semen; compresses base of penis; stiffens penis	O: Sheath of collagen fibers at base of penis I: Median raphe and perineal body	Pudendal nerve (S2–S4)
Ischiocavernosus (ish'ē-ō-kav'er-nō-sŭs) *caverna* = hollow chamber	Assists with erection of penis or clitoris	O: Ischial tuberosities and ischial ramus I: Pubic symphysis	Pudendal nerve (S2–S4)
Superficial transverse perineal muscle (per'i-nē'ăl)	Supports pelvic organs	O: Ramus of ischium I: Perineal body	Pudendal nerve (S2–S4)
Deep layer (urogenital diaphragm)			
Deep transverse perineal muscle	Supports pelvic organs	O: Ischial ramus I: Median raphe of urogenital diaphragm	Pudendal nerve (S2–S4)
External urethral sphincter (ū-rē'thrăl)	Constricts urethra so as to voluntarily inhibit urination	O: Rami of ischium and pubis I: Median raphe of urogenital diaphragm	Pudendal nerve (S2–S4)

Superficial **Deep**

Trapezius

Deltoid (cut)
Subclavius

Deltoid

Subscapularis

Pectoralis major

Pectoralis minor
Pectoralis major (cut)
Deltoid (cut)

Teres major
Serratus anterior

Latissimus dorsi

Latissimus dorsi

Biceps brachii { Long head
Short head

Coracobrachialis

Long head } Biceps brachii
Short head

Anterior view

Figure 11.18 Anterior Muscles Associated with the Proximal Upper Limb. This anterior view compares some components of both the axial and appendicular musculature. Only those muscles that move the upper limb are labeled. Superficial muscles are shown on the right side of the body, and deep muscles are shown on the left side. AP|R

Superficial **Deep**

Trapezius

Levator scapulae

Rhomboid minor
Rhomboid major
Supraspinatus

Deltoid

Infraspinatus
Teres minor

Teres minor
Teres major

Teres major

Serratus anterior

Latissimus dorsi

Serratus posterior inferior

External oblique

Posterior view

Figure 11.19 Posterior Muscles Associated with the Proximal Upper Limb. This posterior view compares some components of both the axial and appendicular musculature. Only those muscles that move the upper limb are labeled. Superficial muscles are shown on the left, and deep muscles are shown on the right. AP|R

11.8 Muscles of the Pectoral Girdle and Upper Limb

Muscles that move the pectoral girdle and upper limbs are organized into specific groups:

- Muscles that move the pectoral girdle
- Muscles that move the glenohumeral joint/arm
- Arm and forearm muscles that move the elbow joint/forearm
- Forearm muscles that move the wrist joint, hand, and fingers
- Intrinsic muscles of the hand

Some of these muscles are superficial, and others are deep (**figures 11.18** and **11.19**).

11.8a Muscles That Move the Pectoral Girdle

✔ LEARNING OBJECTIVE

1. Compare and contrast how the anterior and posterior thoracic muscles move the pectoral girdle.

The muscles of the pectoral girdle originate on the axial skeleton and insert on the scapula and clavicle. These muscles both stabilize the scapula and move it to increase the arm's angle of movements. Some of the superficial muscles of the thorax are grouped together according to the scapular movement they direct: elevation, depression, protraction, or retraction (**figure 11.20**).

(a) Retraction and protraction of scapula

Figure 11.20 Actions of Some Thoracic Muscles on the Scapula.
Individual muscles may contribute to different, multiple actions. (*a*) The scapula can be retracted or protracted. When you are standing upright and have good posture, your scapulae are retracted. Conversely, poor posture demonstrates scapular protraction. (*b*) Muscles that elevate and depress the scapula. (*c*) Muscles that rotate the scapula.

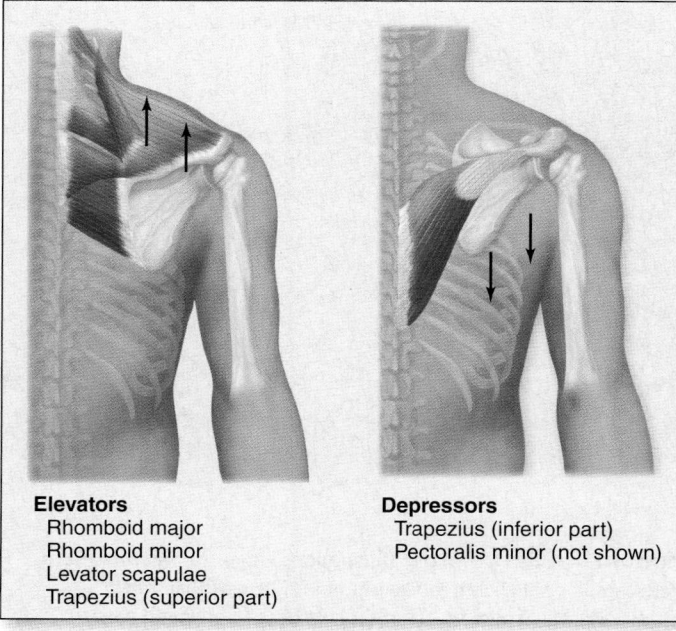

(b) Elevation and depression of scapula

(c) Superior and inferior rotation of scapula

The muscles that move the pectoral girdle are classified according to their location in the thorax as either anterior or posterior thoracic muscles. The anterior thoracic muscles are the pectoralis minor, serratus anterior, and subclavius (shown in **figure 11.21a**).

The **pectoralis minor** is deep to the pectoralis major. This muscle helps depress and protract (pull anteriorly) the scapula. When your shoulders are hunched forward, the pectoralis minor muscle is contracting. The **serratus anterior** is a large, flat,

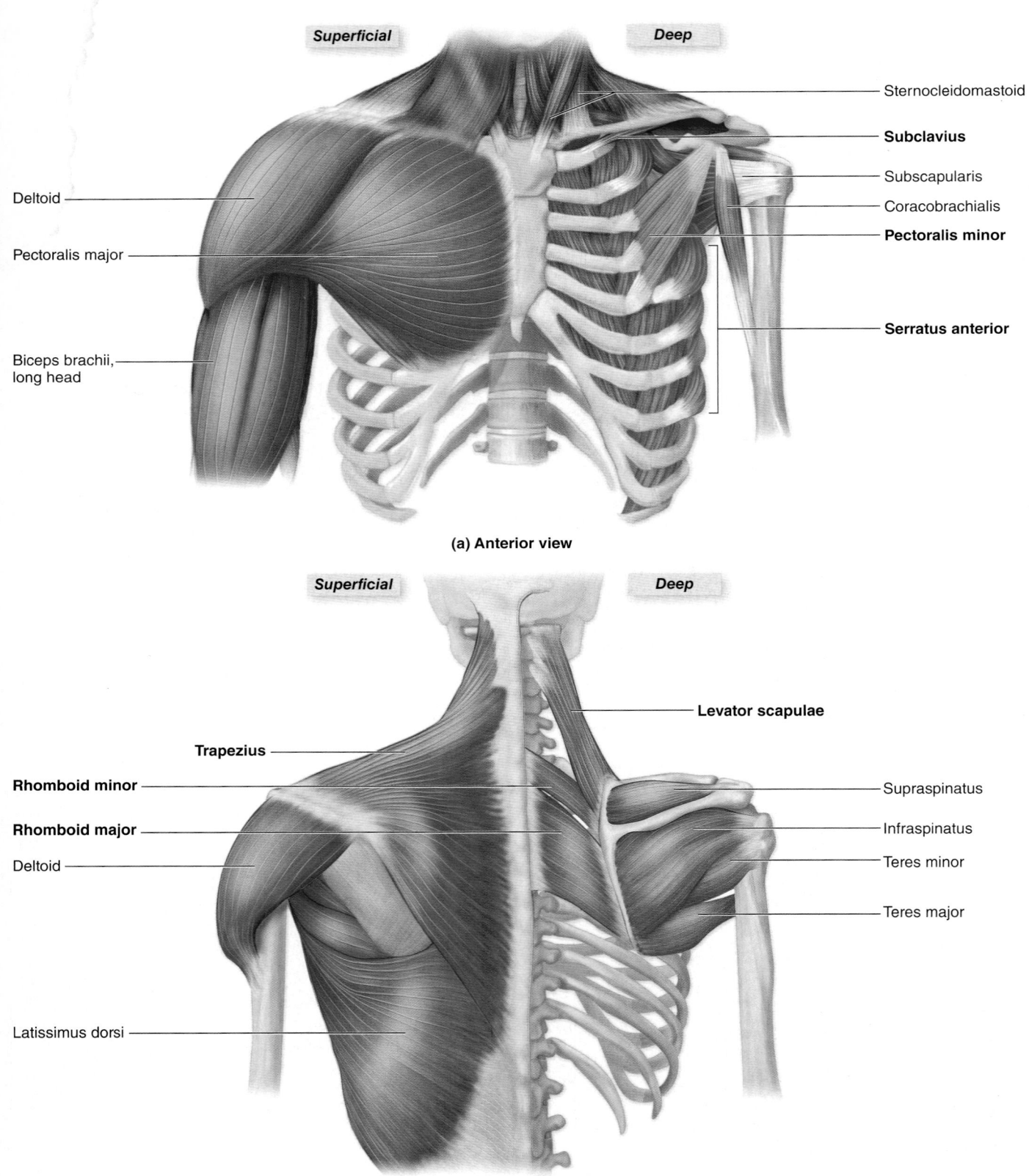

Superficial　　　　　*Deep*

Sternocleidomastoid

Subclavius

Subscapularis

Coracobrachialis

Pectoralis minor

Serratus anterior

Deltoid

Pectoralis major

Biceps brachii, long head

(a) Anterior view

Superficial　　　　　*Deep*

Levator scapulae

Trapezius

Rhomboid minor

Rhomboid major

Deltoid

Supraspinatus

Infraspinatus

Teres minor

Teres major

Latissimus dorsi

(b) Posterior view

Figure 11.21 Muscles That Move the Pectoral Girdle and the Glenohumeral Joint/Arm. Illustrations show (*a*) anterior and (*b*) posterior views of the muscles whose primary function is to move the pectoral girdle (scapula or clavicle), labeled in bold. Muscles that attach to the pectoral girdle but primarily move the arm are labeled but not in bold. Superficial muscles are shown on the right side of the body, and deep muscles on the left. AP|R

LEARNING STRATEGY

When studying appendicular muscle function, remember these two basic rules:

1. If a muscle or its tendons crosses over or spans a joint, then the muscle must move that joint. For example, the biceps brachii crosses the elbow joint and therefore must move it.

2. Conversely, if a muscle or its tendons does not cross over or span a joint, it cannot move that joint. For example, the deltoid is found in the shoulder, and no part of it crosses the elbow joint. Therefore, the deltoid does not move the elbow joint.

fan-shaped muscle positioned between the ribs and the scapula. Its name is derived from the saw-toothed (serrated) appearance of its origins on the ribs. This muscle is the agonist (prime mover) in scapula protraction, and helps stabilize the scapula against the posterior side of the rib cage. It also is a powerful superior rotator of the scapula by moving the glenoid cavity superiorly, as occurs

when you abduct the upper limb. The **subclavius** extends from the clavicle to the first rib, and its main action is to stabilize and depress the clavicle.

The posterior thoracic muscles are the levator scapulae, rhomboid major, rhomboid minor, and trapezius (shown in figure 11.21b). The **levator scapulae** originates from multiple heads on the transverse processes of the cervical vertebrae and inserts on the superior angle of the scapula. As its name implies, its primary action is to elevate the scapula. It can also inferiorly rotate the scapula so that the glenoid cavity points inferiorly.

Both the **rhomboid major** and **rhomboid minor** are located deep to the trapezius. These rhomboid muscles are parallel bands that run inferolaterally from the vertebrae to the scapula. They help elevate and retract (adduct) the scapula, as when you are standing up straight. The rhomboid muscles also inferiorly rotate the scapula.

The **trapezius** is a large, diamond-shaped muscle that extends from the skull and vertebral column to the pectoral girdle laterally. The trapezius can elevate, depress, retract, or rotate the scapula, depending upon which fibers of the muscle are contracting.

Table 11.13 summarizes the characteristics of the thoracic muscles that move the pectoral girdle.

 WHAT DID YOU LEARN?

 List the posterior thoracic muscles that move the pectoral girdle, and describe their common action(s).

Table 11.13	Thoracic Muscles That Move the Pectoral Girdle		
Group	**Actions**	**Origin/Insertion**	**Innervation (see sections 13.9 and 14.5d, e)**
ANTERIOR MUSCLES			
Pectoralis minor (pek'tō-ra'lis mī'ner) *pectus* = chest	Protracts and depresses scapula	O: Ribs 3–5 I: Coracoid process of scapula	Medial pectoral nerve (C8–T1)
Serratus anterior (ser-ā'tŭs an-tēr'ē-ōr) *serratus* = saw	Agonist in scapula protraction; superiorly rotates scapula (so glenoid cavity moves superiorly); stabilizes scapula	O: Ribs 1–8, anterior and superior margins I: Medial border of scapula; anterior surface	Long thoracic nerve (C5–C7)
Subclavius (sŭb-klā'vē-ŭs) *sub* = under *clav* = clavicle	Depresses and stabilizes clavicle	O: Rib 1 I: Inferior surface of clavicle	Nerve to subclavius (C5–C6)
POSTERIOR MUSCLES			
Levator scapulae (lē-vā'tor, le-vā'ter skap'ū-lē) *levator* = raises	Elevates scapula; inferiorly rotates scapula (pulls glenoid cavity inferiorly)	O: Transverse processes of C_1–C_4 I: Superior part of medial border of scapula	Cervical nerves (C3–C4) and dorsal scapular nerve (C5)
Rhomboid major (rom-bōid' mā'jŏr) *rhomboid* = diamond shaped	Elevates and retracts (adducts) scapula; inferiorly rotates scapula	O: Spinous processes of T_2–T_5 I: Medial border of scapula from spine to inferior angle	Dorsal scapular nerve (C5)
Rhomboid minor (rom-bōid mī'ner)	Elevates and retracts (adducts) scapula; inferiorly rotates scapula	O: Spinous processes of C_7–T_1 I: Medial border of scapula superior to spine	Dorsal scapular nerve (C5)
Trapezius (tra-pē'zē-ŭs) *trapezion* = irregular four-sided figure	Superior fibers: Elevate and superiorly rotate scapula Middle fibers: Retract scapula Inferior fibers: Depress scapula	O: Superior nuchal line of occipital bone; ligamentum nuchae; spinous processes of C_7–T_{12} I: Clavicle; acromion process and spine of scapula	Accessory nerve (CN XI)

11.8b Muscles That Move the Glenohumeral Joint/Arm

LEARNING OBJECTIVES

2. List the muscles that extend, flex, adduct, and abduct the glenohumeral joint.

3. Compare the actions of the four scapular muscles of the rotator cuff.

The phrases "moving the glenohumeral joint" and "moving the arm or humerus" mean the same thing. A movement such as flexion of the arm requires movement at the glenohumeral joint. Throughout this text, we refer to both the joint where the movement is occurring and the body region that is being moved to minimize any confusion.

The glenohumeral joint is crossed by 11 muscles that insert on the arm (humerus) or forearm (radius and/or ulna) (figure 11.21). The **latissimus dorsi** is a broad, triangular muscle located on the inferior part of the back. Often, it is referred to as the "swimmer's muscle," because its actions are required for many swimming strokes. It is the prime arm extensor and also adducts and medially rotates the arm. The **pectoralis major** is a large, thick, fan-shaped muscle that covers the superior part of the thorax. It is the principal flexor of the arm and also adducts and medially rotates the arm.

The latissimus dorsi and pectoralis major muscles are the primary attachments of the arm to the trunk, and they are the prime movers of the glenohumeral joint. These muscles are antagonists with respect to arm flexion and arm extension. However, these same two muscles work together (synergistically) when performing other movements, such as adducting and medially rotating the humerus.

The triceps brachii and biceps brachii, discussed in detail with the muscles that move the elbow joint, also participate in the glenohumeral joint. Specifically, the long head of the

triceps brachii originates on the infraglenoid tubercle, spans the glenohumeral joint, and helps extend and adduct the arm. The long head of the biceps brachii originates on the supraglenoid tubercle of the scapula and assists in flexing the arm.

The seven remaining muscles that move the humerus at the glenohumeral joint are termed the scapular muscles, because they originate on the scapula. They include the deltoid, coracobrachialis, teres major, and the four muscles of the rotator cuff.

The **deltoid** is a thick, powerful muscle that functions as a prime abductor of the arm and forms the rounded contour of the shoulder. Note that the fibers of the deltoid originate from three different points, and these different fiber groups all perform different functions: (1) The anterior fibers flex and medially rotate the arm. (2) The lateral fibers abduct the arm; in fact, the deltoid is the prime abductor of the arm. (3) The posterior fibers extend and laterally rotate the arm. The **coracobrachialis** is a synergist to the pectoralis major in flexing and adducting the arm. The **teres major** works synergistically with the latissimus dorsi by extending, adducting, and medially rotating the arm.

Among the scapular muscles, four **rotator cuff muscles** (subscapularis, supraspinatus, infraspinatus, and teres minor) provide the strength and stability of the glenohumeral joint (**figure 11.22**). These muscles attach the scapula to the humerus (see also figure 9.15).

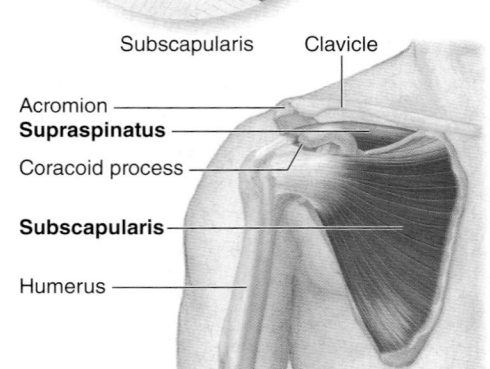

Figure 11.22 Rotator Cuff Muscles. The rotator cuff muscles reinforce the glenohumeral joint and secure the head of the humerus in the glenoid cavity. (*a*) The subscapularis is best seen in anterior view and medially rotates the humerus (as in winding up for a pitch). (*b*) The supraspinatus abducts the humerus (as in executing the pitch), while the infraspinatus and teres minor laterally rotate the humerus (as in completing the pitch and slowing down the pitching arm). These three muscles are located along the posterior aspect of the scapula. AP|R

Subscapularis   Clavicle
Acromion
Supraspinatus
Coracoid process
Subscapularis
Humerus

(a) Anterior view

Supraspinatus

Supraspinatus
Infraspinatus
Teres minor

(b) Posterior view

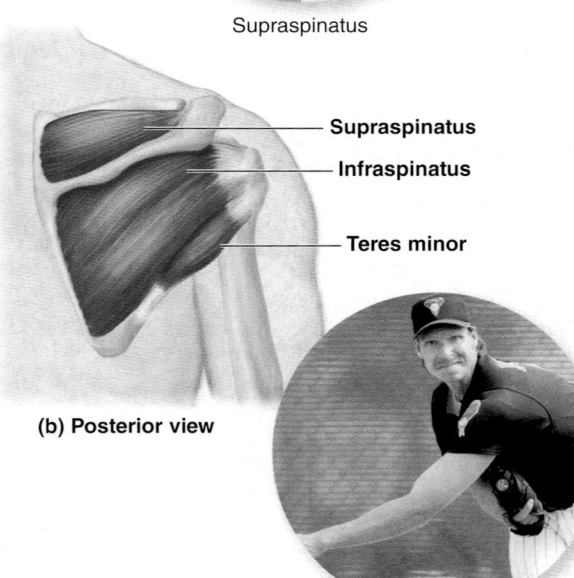

Infraspinatus and teres minor

The specific movements of each muscle are best learned when relating their actions to pitching a ball:

- The **subscapularis** is used when you wind up for a pitch. It medially rotates the arm.
- The **supraspinatus** is used when you start to execute the pitch, by fully abducting the arm.

- The **infraspinatus** and **teres minor** help slow down the pitching arm upon completion of the pitch. These two muscles adduct and laterally rotate the arm.

Table 11.14 summarizes the characteristics of the muscles that move the glenohumeral joint and arm.

Table 11.14	Muscles That Move the Glenohumeral Joint/Arm		
Group/Muscle	**Action**	**Origin/Insertion**	**Innervation (see section 14.5e)**
MUSCLES ORIGINATING ON AXIAL SKELETON			
Latissimus dorsi (lă-tis'i-mŭs dōr'sī) *latissimus* = widest *dorsi* = back	Agonist of arm extension; also adducts and medially rotates arm ("swimmer's muscle")	O: Spinous processes of T_7–T_{12}; ribs 8–12; iliac crest; thoracolumbar fascia I: Intertubercular groove of humerus	Thoracodorsal nerve (C6–C8)
Pectoralis major (pek'tō-răl'is mā'jŏr)	Agonist of arm flexion; also adducts and medially rotates arm	O: Medial clavicle; costal cartilages of ribs 2-6; body of sternum I: Lateral part of intertubercular groove of humerus	Lateral pectoral (C5–C7) and medial pectoral (C8–T1) nerves
MUSCLES ORIGINATING ON SCAPULA			
Deltoid (del'toyd) *delta* = triangular	Anterior fibers: Flex and medially rotate arm Middle fibers: Prime mover of arm abduction Posterior fibers: Extend and laterally rotate arm	O: Acromial end of clavicle; acromion and spine of scapula I: Deltoid tuberosity of humerus	Axillary nerve (C5–C6)
Coracobrachialis (kōr'ă-kō-brā-kē-a'lis) *coraco* = coracoid *brachi* = arm	Adducts and flexes arm	O: Coracoid process of scapula I: Middle medial shaft of humerus	Musculocutaneous nerve (C5–C6 nerve fibers)
Teres major (ter'ēz mā-jŏr) *teres* = round	Extends, adducts, and medially rotates arm	O: Inferior lateral border and inferior angle of scapula I: Lesser tubercle and intertubercular groove of humerus	Lower subscapular nerve (C5–C6)
Triceps brachii (long head) (trī'seps brā'kē-ī) *triceps* = three heads *brachi* = arm	Extends and adducts arm	O: Infraglenoid tubercle of scapula I: Olecranon of ulna	Radial nerve (C5–C7 nerve fibers)
Biceps brachii (long head) (bī'seps) *biceps* = two heads	Flexes arm	O: Supraglenoid tubercle of scapula I: Radial tuberosity and bicipital aponeurosis	Musculocutaneous nerve (C5–C6 nerve fibers)
Rotator cuff muscles (rō-tā'ter, tōr kŭf; *rotatio* = to revolve): Collectively, these four muscles stabilize the glenohumeral joint			
Subscapularis (sŭb-skap-ū-lār'ris)	Medially rotates arm	O: Subscapular fossa of scapula I: Lesser tubercle of humerus	Upper and lower subscapular nerves (C5–C6)
Supraspinatus (sū-prā-spī-nā'tŭs) *supra* = above, over *spin* = spine	Abducts arm	O: Supraspinous fossa of scapula I: Greater tubercle of humerus	Suprascapular nerve (C5–C6)
Infraspinatus (in-fră-spī-nā'tŭs) *infra* = below	Adducts and laterally rotates arm	O: Infraspinous fossa or scapula I: Greater tubercle of humerus	Suprascapular nerve (C5–C6)
Teres minor (ter'ēz mī'ner)	Adducts and laterally rotates arm	O: Upper dorsal lateral border of scapula (superior to teres major origin) I: Greater tubercle of humerus	Axillary nerve (C5–C6)

CLINICAL VIEW
Rotator Cuff Injuries

A **rotator cuff injury** is the result of trauma or disease that affects any portion of the rotator cuff musculature or tendons. Extensive and repetitive use of the rotator cuff muscles can cause tearing of muscle fibers or rupture of tendon attachments. The rotator cuff muscles also may be injured upon a fall on the shoulder or by trying to lift an object that is too heavy. The supraspinatus muscle is most commonly involved, likely because the tendon may become impinged (pinched) inferior to the acromion during use of the muscle. The risk of rotator cuff injuries increases with age due to years of use, reduced blood flow to the muscles and tendons as we age, and the increased likelihood of developing bone spurs in the shoulder that impinge on the tendons.

Common symptoms of a rotator cuff injury include swelling and tenderness in the area of the shoulder, as well as pain with specific shoulder movements, especially abduction. The pain may range from moderate to severe. This syndrome is especially common in baseball players because the repetitive shoulder movements while pitching and throwing the ball can impinge the supraspinatus tendon against the acromion. Painters also may experience rotator cuff injuries due to the repetitive overhead upper limb movements involved with their work. Diagnosis may be confimed with both a physical (that asks about a patient history and performs range of movement activities to the affected upper limb) and imaging studies, such as MRI or ultrasound.

Treatment is dependent on the severity of the injury. Initially, the pain may be controlled with icing, NSAIDS, or with corticosteroid shots to the affected region. Physical therapy is used to restore the shoulder's range of motion and strengthen affected muscles. Severe rotator cuff injuries that have not been helped with nonsurgical therapies typically require surgical repair, which may include removal of bone spurs as well as repair of the torn tendon. This surgery may be done **arthroscopically** (where a small camera called an **arthroscope** is inserted through a small incision into the joint to guide the physician's use of small surgical instruments), or a more invasive open repair surgery may be required. Physical therapy is required after surgery to restore range of motion.

The muscles that move the arm at the glenohumeral joint are grouped in **table 11.15** according to different types of actions. Note that a muscle that has multiple functions is listed in more than one group. For example, the deltoid may abduct, extend, or flex the humerus, depending on whether its middle, posterior, or anterior fibers are contracting. Pectoralis major and coracobrachialis both adduct and flex the humerus, so they are listed in both the adduction and flexion columns. We recommend that you copy the columns multiple times and then test your knowledge by trying to write out all of the muscles in a group without looking at your notes.

Table 11.15	Summary of Muscle Actions at the Glenohumeral Joint/Arm				
Abduction	**Adduction**	**Extension**	**Flexion**	**Lateral Rotation**	**Medial Rotation**
Deltoid (middle fibers)*	**Latissimus dorsi**	**Latissimus dorsi**	**Pectoralis major**	**Infraspinatus**	**Subscapularis**
Supraspinatus	**Pectoralis major**	**Deltoid (posterior fibers)**	**Deltoid (anterior fibers)**	**Teres minor**	Deltoid (anterior fibers)
	Coracobrachialis	Teres major	Coracobrachialis	Deltoid (posterior fibers)	Latissimus dorsi
	Teres major	Long head of triceps brachii	(Long head of biceps brachii)		Pectoralis major
	Teres minor				Teres major
	Infraspinatus				

*Boldface indicates an agonist; others are synergists. Parentheses around an entire muscle name, such as the long head of the biceps brachii under Flexion, indicate only a slight effect.

19 In general, posterior thoracic muscles perform what common action on the arm?

20 Identify the rotator cuff muscles, and describe their actions.

11.8c Arm and Forearm Muscles That Move the Elbow Joint/Forearm

LEARNING OBJECTIVES

4. Name the muscles in the arm's anterior and posterior compartments, and contrast their common functions.

5. Describe the muscles that pronate and supinate the forearm.

When you move the elbow joint, you move the bones of the forearm. Thus, the phrase "flexing the elbow joint" is synonymous with "flexing the forearm."

The muscles in the limbs are organized into **compartments,** which are surrounded by deep fascia. Each compartment houses functionally related skeletal muscles, as well as their associated nerves and blood vessels. In general, muscles in the same compartment tend to perform similar functions. **Figure 11.23** provides a visual overview of how the muscles are organized into compartments. Note how muscles in opposite compartments tend to be antagonists. For example, the anterior forearm muscles are primarily flexors and pronators, whereas the posterior forearm muscles are primarily extensors and supinators. Likewise, in the lower limb, knee extensors are in the anterior compartment of the thigh, whereas knee flexors are in the posterior compartment of the thigh. Hip adductors are in the medial compartment of the thigh, whereas a hip abductor is in the lateral compartment of the thigh. These compartments may help you to learn the muscles in common functional groups. If you know what compartment a muscle is in, you likely can figure out what action that muscle performs, and vice versa.

The muscles of the arm may be subdivided into an anterior compartment and a posterior compartment. The **anterior compartment** primarily contains elbow flexors, so it is also known as the *flexor compartment*. Muscles in this compartment are supplied by the deep brachial artery and are innervated by the musculocutaneous nerve. Muscles in this compartment include the coracobrachialis (note that this muscle is an arm flexor and not an elbow flexor), biceps brachii, brachialis, and brachioradialis muscles. Put your hand on your anterior arm, and then flex your elbow. Note how these muscles bulge as they contract, affirming that these anterior compartment arm muscles flex the elbow.

The **posterior compartment** contains elbow extensors, so this compartment is also called the *extensor compartment*. These muscles are innervated by the radial nerve and receive their blood supply from the deep brachial artery. The primary muscle in this compartment is the triceps brachii. Put your hand on your posterior arm, and then extend your elbow. You can feel your muscles contracting as you perform this action, affirming that posterior arm muscles extend the elbow. Perform these activities each time we discuss muscles in a particular limb compartment, so you can see and feel for yourself how these muscles move.

Muscles of the Arm's Anterior Compartment

On the anterior side of the humerus are the principal flexors of the forearm: the biceps brachii and brachialis (**figure 11.24**). The **biceps brachii** is a large, two-headed muscle on the anterior surface of the humerus. This muscle flexes the elbow joint, and it is a powerful supinator of the forearm when the elbow is flexed. (An example of this supination movement occurs when you tighten a screw with your right hand.) The tendon of the long head of the biceps brachii crosses the shoulder joint, and so this muscle helps flex the humerus as well (albeit weakly).

The **brachialis** is deep to the biceps brachii on the anterior surface of the humerus. It is the most powerful flexor of the forearm at the elbow. The **brachioradialis** is another prominent muscle on the anterolateral surface of the forearm. It is a synergist in elbow flexion, effective primarily when the prime movers of forearm flexion have already partially flexed the elbow.

Figure 11.23 **Muscle Compartmentalization.**

(*a, b*) In the upper limb, the arm and forearm both may be divided into anterior "flexor" compartments and posterior "extensor" compartments. (*c, d*) The thigh may be split into four compartments, whereas the leg is split into three compartments. Each compartment contains muscles that tend to perform similar movements.

(b)

(a)

(a) Left arm

Anterior upper limb muscles are flexors.

Anterior

Biceps brachii

Brachialis

Medial

Lateral

Humerus

Triceps brachii { Medial head
Lateral head
Long head

Posterior upper limb muscles are extensors.

Posterior

Muscle Compartments

Anterior
Posterior
Medial
Lateral

(b) Left forearm

Anterior forearm muscles are flexors.

Anterior

Palmaris longus
Flexor carpi radialis
Flexor digitorum superficialis
Flexor carpi ulnaris
Flexor digitorum profundus
Flexor pollicis longus

Brachioradialis

Extensor carpi radialis longus

Extensor carpi radialis brevis

Radius

Medial

Lateral

Ulna

Abductor pollicis longus
Extensor pollicis longus
Extensor digitorum
Extensor digiti minimi
Extensor carpi ulnaris

Posterior

Posterior forearm muscles are extensors.

(c) Right thigh

Lateral thigh and some gluteal muscles abduct the thigh.

Anterior thigh muscles flex the hip and/or extend the leg/knee.

Anterior

Iliotibial tract

Femur

Vastus lateralis
Rectus femoris
Vastus medialis
Vastus intermedius

Quadriceps femoris

Sartorius

Lateral

Biceps femoris, short head
Biceps femoris, long head
Semitendinosus
Semimembranosus

Hamstrings

Medial

Adductor longus
Adductor brevis
Adductor magnus
Gracilis

Posterior thigh muscles extend the thigh and/or flex the leg/knee.

Posterior

Medial thigh muscles adduct the thigh.

(d) Right leg

Anterior leg muscles dorsiflex the foot and/or extend the toes.

Anterior

Tibialis anterior
Extensor digitorum longus
Extensor hallucis longus
Fibularis longus
Fibularis brevis

Tibia

Fibula

Tibialis posterior
Flexor digitorum longus

Lateral

Medial

Flexor hallucis longus
Soleus
Plantaris tendon
Gastrocnemius (medial head)
Gastrocnemius (lateral head)

Lateral leg muscles plantar flex and evert the foot.

Posterior

Posterior leg muscles flex the leg, plantar flex the foot, and/or flex the toes.

(c)

(d)

407

(a) Anterior view

- Deltoid
- Pectoralis major
- Coracobrachialis
- **Biceps brachii, long head**
- **Biceps brachii, short head**
- **Triceps brachii**
- **Brachialis**
- **Brachioradialis**
- Bicipital aponeurosis

Superficial

- Coracoid process
- Biceps brachii, long head
- Biceps brachii, short head
- Biceps brachii tendon
- Radial tuberosity

Deep

- Coracobrachialis
- Brachialis
- Coronoid process of ulna

(b) Anterior muscles

Figure 11.24 Anterior Muscles That Move the Elbow Joint/Forearm. (*a*) The right arm and shoulder show the muscles that produce movements at the elbow joint, labeled in bold. (*b*) Superficial and deep anterior arm muscles. AP|R

(a) Posterior view

- Supraspinatus
- Infraspinatus
- Teres minor
- Teres major
- Lateral head
- Long head
- Medial head — **Triceps brachii**
- **Anconeus**
- Latissimus dorsi

Superficial

- Infraglenoid tubercle
- Long head
- Lateral head
- Medial head — **Triceps brachii**
- Triceps brachii tendon
- Anconeus

Deep

- Triceps brachii, medial head
- Triceps brachii tendon (cut)
- Olecranon of ulna

(b) Posterior muscles

Figure 11.25 Posterior Muscles That Move the Elbow Joint/Forearm. (*a*) The right arm and shoulder show the muscles that produce movements at the elbow joint, labeled in bold. (*b*) Superficial and deep posterior arm muscles.

Muscles of the Arm's Posterior Compartment

The posterior compartment of the arm contains two muscles that extend the forearm at the elbow: the triceps brachii and the anconeus (**figure 11.25**). The **triceps brachii** is the large, three-headed muscle on the posterior surface of the arm. The long head of the triceps brachii also crosses the glenohumeral joint, where it helps extend the humerus. All three parts of this muscle merge to form a common insertion on the olecranon of the ulna. A weak elbow extensor is the small **anconeus** that crosses the posterolateral region of the elbow.

WHAT DO YOU THINK?

3 The brachialis is on the anterior surface of the arm. Without looking at the muscle tables, determine whether this muscle flexes or extends the elbow joint. How did you reach your conclusion?

Muscles of the Forearm That Act on the Elbow Joint

Some forearm muscles pronate or supinate the forearm (**figure 11.26**). As their names imply, both the **pronator teres** and **pronator quadratus** rotate the radius across the surface of the ulna to pronate the forearm. These muscles are located in the anterior compartment of the forearm. They are antagonistic to the **supinator** in the posterior compartment of the forearm. The supinator works synergistically with the biceps brachii to supinate the forearm.

CLINICAL VIEW
Lateral Epicondylitis ("Tennis Elbow")

Lateral epicondylitis (ep'i-kon-di-lī'tis), or *tennis elbow,* is a painful condition resulting from trauma or overuse of the common extensor tendon of the posterior forearm muscles. The pain arises from the lateral epicondyle of the humerus, the attachment site of the common extensor tendon. Lateral epicondylitis most often results from the repeated forceful contraction of the forearm extensors, as when pulling a heavy object from an overhead shelf, shoveling snow, or hitting a backhand shot in tennis.

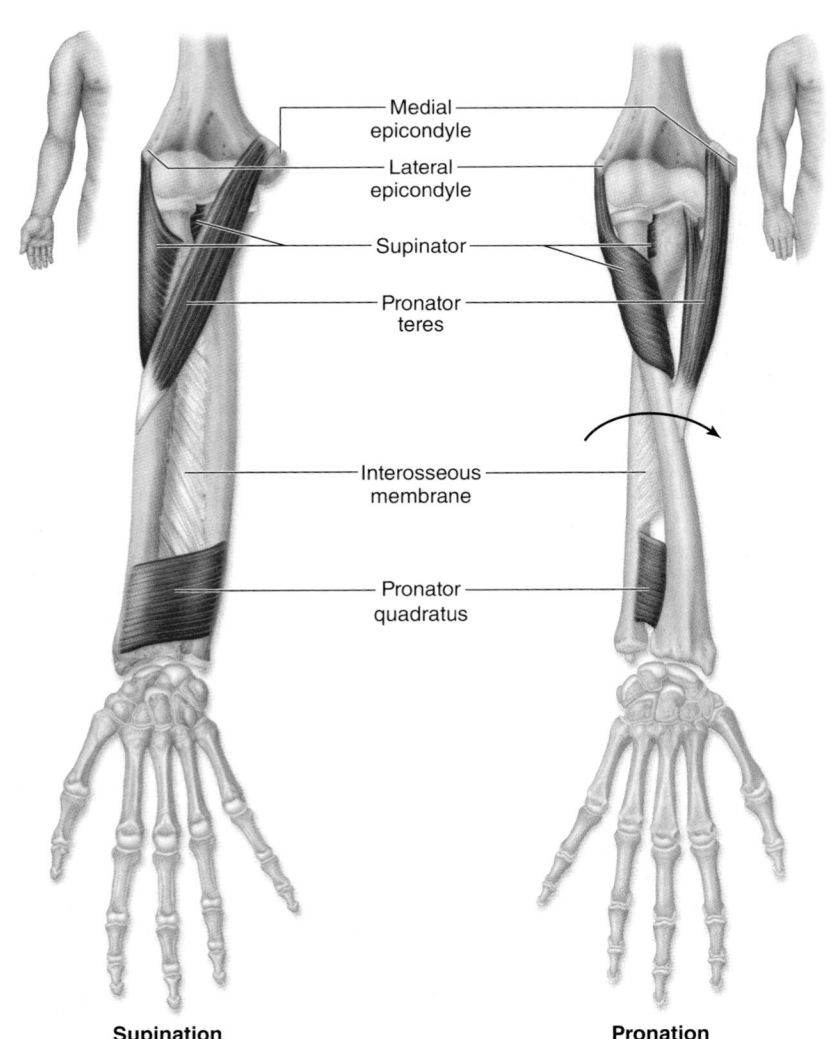

Supination   **Pronation**

Figure 11.26 Forearm Muscles That Supinate and Pronate. A view of the right upper limb shows the supinator muscle supinates the forearm, whereas pronator teres and pronator quadratus pronate the forearm. (The biceps brachii, an arm muscle not shown here, also supinates the forearm.)
AP|R

Table 11.16 — Muscles That Move the Forearm

Muscle	Action	Origin/Insertion	Innervation (see section 14.5e)
FLEXORS (ANTERIOR ARM)			
Biceps brachii (bī′seps brā′kē-ī)	Flexes forearm, powerful supinator of forearm Long head also flexes arm	O: Long head: Supraglenoid tubercle of scapula Short head: Coracoid process of scapula I: Radial tuberosity and bicipital aponeurosis	Musculocutaneous nerve (C5–C6 nerve fibers)
Brachialis (brā′kē-al′is)	Primary flexor of forearm	O: Distal anterior surface of humerus I: Tuberosity and coronoid process of ulna	Musculocutaneous nerve (C5–C6 nerve fibers)
Brachioradialis (brā′kē-ō-rā′dē-al′is)	Flexes forearm	O: Lateral supracondylar ridge of humerus I: Styloid process of radius	Radial nerve (C6–C7 nerve fibers)
EXTENSORS (POSTERIOR ARM)			
Triceps brachii (trī′seps) Long head Lateral head Medial head	Primary extensor of forearm Long head of triceps also extends and adducts arm	O: Long head: Infraglenoid tubercle of scapula Lateral head: Posterior humerus above radial groove Short head: Posterior humerus below radial groove I: Olecranon of ulna	Radial nerve (C5–C7 nerve fibers)
Anconeus (ang-kō′nē-ŭs) *ankon* = elbow	Extends forearm	O: Lateral epicondyle of humerus I: Olecranon of ulna	Radial nerve (C6–C8 nerve fibers)
PRONATORS (ANTERIOR FOREARM MUSCLES)			
Pronator quadratus (prō-nā-ter, prō-nā-tōr kwah-drā′tŭs)	Pronates forearm	O: Distal ¼ of ulna I: Distal ¼ of radius	Median nerve (C8–T1 nerve fibers)
Pronator teres (ter′ēz)	Pronates forearm	O: Medial epicondyle of humerus and coronoid process of ulna I: Lateral surface of radius	Median nerve (C6–C7 nerve fibers)
SUPINATOR (POSTERIOR FOREARM MUSCLE)			
Supinator (sū′pi-nā-tōr)	Supinates forearm	O: Lateral epicondyle of humerus and ulna distal to radial notch I: Anterolateral surface of radius distal to radial tuberosity	Radial nerve (C6–C8 nerve fibers)

Table 11.17 — Summary of Muscle Actions at the Elbow Joint/Forearm

Extension	Flexion	Pronation	Supination
Triceps brachii*	Brachialis	Pronator teres	Biceps brachii
(Anconeus)	Biceps brachii	Pronator quadratus	Supinator
	Brachioradialis		

*Boldface indicates an agonist; others are synergists. Parentheses around an entire muscle name indicate only a slight effect.

Table 11.16 summarizes the characteristics of the muscles that move the forearm, and table 11.17 groups them according to common function. By learning these muscles as groups, you can gain a better understanding of how they work together to perform specific functions.

WHAT DID YOU LEARN?

21 What are the muscles in the anterior compartment of the arm, and what common action(s) do they perform?

22 What muscles pronate or supinate the forearm?

11.8d Forearm Muscles That Move the Wrist Joint, Hand, and Fingers

LEARNING OBJECTIVES

6. Describe the muscles of the anterior compartment and their actions, and identify the layer in which each resides.

7. Explain the actions of the muscles of the posterior compartment, and identify the layer in which each resides.

Most muscles in the forearm move the hand at the wrist, the fingers, or both. These muscles are called extrinsic muscles of the wrist and hand, because the muscles originate on the forearm, not the wrist or hand. Palpate your own forearm; it is bigger near the elbow because the bellies of these forearm muscles form the bulk of this region, whereas distally at the wrist, only long tendons of these muscles are present.

Deep fascia partitions the forearm muscles into an anterior (flexor) compartment and a posterior (extensor) compartment (figure 11.27). Most of the **anterior compartment** muscles originate on the medial epicondyle of the humerus via a common flexor tendon. Muscles in the anterior compartment of the forearm generally tend to flex the wrist, the metacarpophalangeal (MP) joints.

(a) Right anterior forearm, superficial view

Medial epicondyle
Common flexor tendon
Pronator teres
Flexor carpi radialis

Brachioradialis

Palmaris longus
Flexor carpi ulnaris

Flexor retinaculum

Palmar aponeurosis

Medial epicondyle
Common flexor tendon

Pronator teres

Flexor carpi radialis
Palmaris longus

Brachioradialis

Flexor carpi ulnaris

Flexor retinaculum

Palmar aponeurosis

(b) Right anterior forearm, intermediate view

Radius
Ulna

Flexor digitorum superficialis

Flexor digitorum superficialis tendons

Flexor digitorum profundus tendons

(c) Right anterior forearm, deep view

Supinator

Flexor digitorum profundus

Flexor pollicis longus

Pronator quadratus

Flexor digitorum profundus tendons

Figure 11.27 Anterior Forearm Muscles. The anterior forearm muscles pronate the forearm or flex the wrist and fingers. They may be subdivided into superficial, intermediate, and deep layers. (*a*) Illustration and cadaver photo show the superficial muscles of the right anterior forearm. (*b*) Intermediate and (*c*) deep muscles of the right anterior forearm. AP|R

Some of these also flex the interphalangeal (IP) joints of the fingers. Most of the **posterior compartment** muscles originate on the lateral epicondyle of the humerus via a common extensor tendon. Muscles in the posterior compartment of the forearm tend to extend the wrist. Some also extend the MP joints and the IP joints.

Retinacula of the Forearm

At the wrist, the deep fascia of the forearm forms thickened, fibrous bands termed retinacula (ret-i-nak'ū-la; *retineo* = to hold back). The retinacula help hold the tendons close to the bone and prevent the tendons from "bowstringing" outward. The palmar (anterior) surface of the carpal bones is covered by the **flexor retinaculum** (figure 11.27*a*). Flexor tendons of the digits and the median nerve pass through the tight space between the bones and the flexor retinaculum, which is called the **carpal tunnel.** The **extensor retinaculum** is superficial to the dorsal surface of the carpal bones. Extensor tendons of the wrist and digits pass between the bones and the extensor retinaculum.

Muscles of the Forearm's Anterior Compartment

The muscles of the **anterior compartment** of the forearm may be subdivided into a superficial layer, an intermediate layer, and a deep layer. The muscles of the superficial and intermediate layers originate from the common flexor tendon that attaches to the medial epicondyle of the humerus. The deep layer of muscles originates directly on the bones of the forearm.

Note that not all anterior forearm muscles cause flexion. Both the pronator teres and the pronator quadratus, discussed previously, are located in the anterior compartment of the forearm but their primary function is pronation. Likewise, the supinator muscle is in the posterior compartment of the forearm, yet its primary function is supination.

The **superficial layer** of anterior forearm muscles is arranged from the lateral to the medial surface of the forearm in the following order: pronator teres (described previously), flexor carpi radialis, palmaris longus, and flexor carpi ulnaris. The **flexor carpi radialis** tendon is prominent on the lateral side of the forearm. This muscle flexes the wrist and abducts the hand at the wrist. The **palmaris longus** is absent in some individuals. This narrow, superficial muscle on the anterior surface of the forearm weakly assists in wrist flexion. The **flexor carpi ulnaris** flexes the wrist and adducts the hand at the wrist.

You can determine the positioning of the three superficial muscles of the anterior forearm and the pronator teres muscle on your own body by performing the exercise shown in **figure 11.28.** Wrap your thumb around the medial epicondyle of the other arm, so your thumb is positioned behind the elbow. Align your little finger along the medial border of your forearm. The natural placement of your four fingers overlies the placement of superficial layer muscles.

The **intermediate layer** in the anterior compartment of the forearm contains a single muscle (see figure 11.27*b*). The **flexor digitorum superficialis** splits into four tendons that each insert on

(Left hand covers medial epicondyle)

Figure 11.28 Positioning of the Superficial Anterior Forearm Muscles. By positioning the left hand at the medial epicondyle of the right humerus, fingers 2–5 lay in the approximate position of the superficial muscles of the anterior forearm.

the middle phalanges of fingers 2–5. This muscle crosses over the wrist, MP joints, and PIP (proximal interphalangeal) joints of fingers 2–5; thus, it flexes all of these joints. Since the flexor digitorum superficialis does not cross over the DIP (distal interphalangeal) joints of these fingers, it cannot move the DIP joints.

The **deep layer** of the forearm anterior compartment muscles includes the flexor pollicis longus (lateral side), the flexor digitorum profundus (medial side), and the pronator quadratus (deep) (see figure 11.27*c*). The **flexor pollicis longus** attaches to the distal phalanx of the thumb and flexes the MP and IP joints of the thumb. In addition, because this muscle crosses the wrist joint, it can weakly flex the wrist. The **flexor digitorum profundus** lies deep to the flexor digitorum superficialis. This muscle splits into four tendons that insert on the distal phalanges of fingers 2–5. The flexor digitorum profundus flexes the wrist, MP joints, PIP joints, and DIP joints of fingers 2–5.

Muscles of the Forearm's Posterior Compartment

Muscles of the **posterior compartment** of the forearm are primarily wrist and finger extensors. An exception is the supinator, which helps supinate the forearm. The posterior compartment muscles may be subdivided into a superficial layer and a deep layer.

The **superficial layer** of posterior forearm muscles originates from a common extensor tendon on the lateral epicondyle of the humerus (**figure 11.29***a*). These muscles are positioned laterally to medially as follows: The **extensor carpi radialis longus** is medial to the brachioradialis. It extends the wrist and abducts the hand at the wrist. The **extensor carpi radialis brevis** works synergistically with the extensor carpi radialis longus. The **extensor digitorum** splits into four tendons that insert on the distal phalanges of fingers 2–5. It extends the wrist, MP joints, PIP joints, and DIP joints of fingers 2–5. The **extensor digiti minimi** attaches to the distal phalanx of the pinky (finger 5). It works with the extensor digitorum to extend the little finger. On the medial surface of the posterior forearm, the **extensor carpi ulnaris** inserts on the fifth metacarpal bone, where it acts to extend the wrist and adduct the hand.

The **deep layer** muscles originate directly on the bones of the posterior forearm and insert on the wrist or hand (figure 11.29*b*). These muscles weakly extend the wrist and do the following other functions: (1) The **abductor pollicis longus** abducts the thumb. (2) The **extensor pollicis brevis** attaches to the proximal phalanx of the thumb and helps extend the MP joint of the thumb. (3) The **extensor pollicis longus** inserts on the distal phalanx of the thumb, so it extends the MP and IP joints of the thumb. (4) The **extensor indicis** extends the MP, PIP, and DIP joints of the index finger (finger 2).

INTEGRATE

CONCEPT CONNECTION

Because the median nerve (section 14.5e) passes deep to the flexor retinaculum, this nerve may be pinched within the carpal tunnel. Thus, the musculoskeletal anatomy is related to the proper functioning of selected components of the nervous system.

Brachioradialis

Extensor carpi radialis longus

Extensor carpi radialis brevis

Extensor digitorum

Abductor pollicis longus

Extensor pollicis brevis

Anconeus

Flexor carpi ulnaris

Extensor carpi ulnaris

Extensor digiti minimi

Extensor retinaculum

Extensor digitorum tendons

Anconeus

Brachioradialis

Extensor carpi radialis longus

Extensor carpi radialis brevis

Extensor digitorum

Extensor carpi ulnaris

Abductor pollicis longus

Extensor digiti minimi

Extensor pollicis brevis

Extensor retinaculum

Extensor digitorum tendons

(a) Right posterior forearm, superficial views

Olecranon process of ulna

Supinator

Abductor pollicis longus

Extensor pollicis longus

Extensor indicis

Extensor pollicis brevis

Dorsal interossei

(b) Right posterior forearm, deep view

Figure 11.29 Posterior Forearm Muscles. The posterior forearm muscles supinate the forearm or extend the wrist or fingers. They may be subdivided into (*a*) superficial and (*b*) deep layers, as shown in these views of the right forearm.

CLINICAL VIEW
Carpal Tunnel Syndrome

The space between the carpal bones and the flexor retinaculum is the **carpal tunnel.** Numerous finger flexor tendons extend through this tunnel as well as the median nerve, which innervates the skin on the lateral palmar region of the hand and the muscles that move the thumb. Any compression of either the median nerve or the tendons in the tunnel results in carpal tunnel syndrome. The syndrome is characterized by pain and **paresthesia** (par-es-thē′zē-ă; *aisthesis* = sensation), which is the feeling of "pins and needles." Sometimes, more extensive sensory loss as well as motor loss occurs in the muscles of the hand supplied by the median nerve.

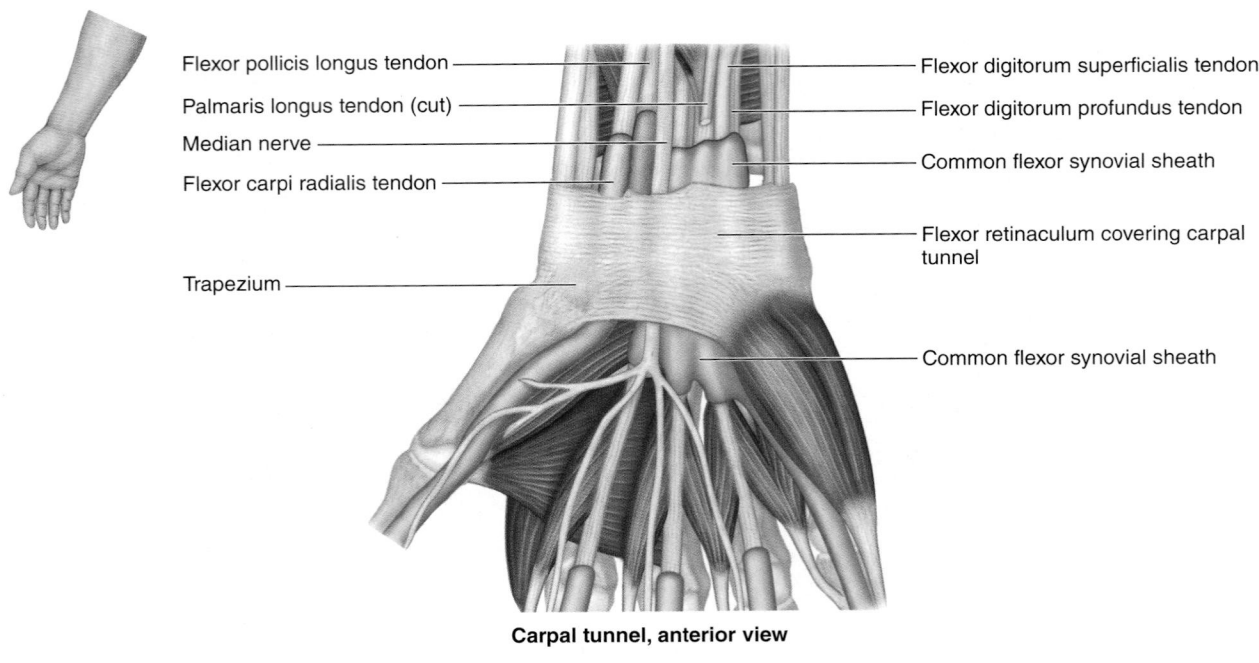

Flexor pollicis longus tendon

Palmaris longus tendon (cut)

Median nerve

Flexor carpi radialis tendon

Trapezium

Flexor digitorum superficialis tendon

Flexor digitorum profundus tendon

Common flexor synovial sheath

Flexor retinaculum covering carpal tunnel

Common flexor synovial sheath

Carpal tunnel, anterior view

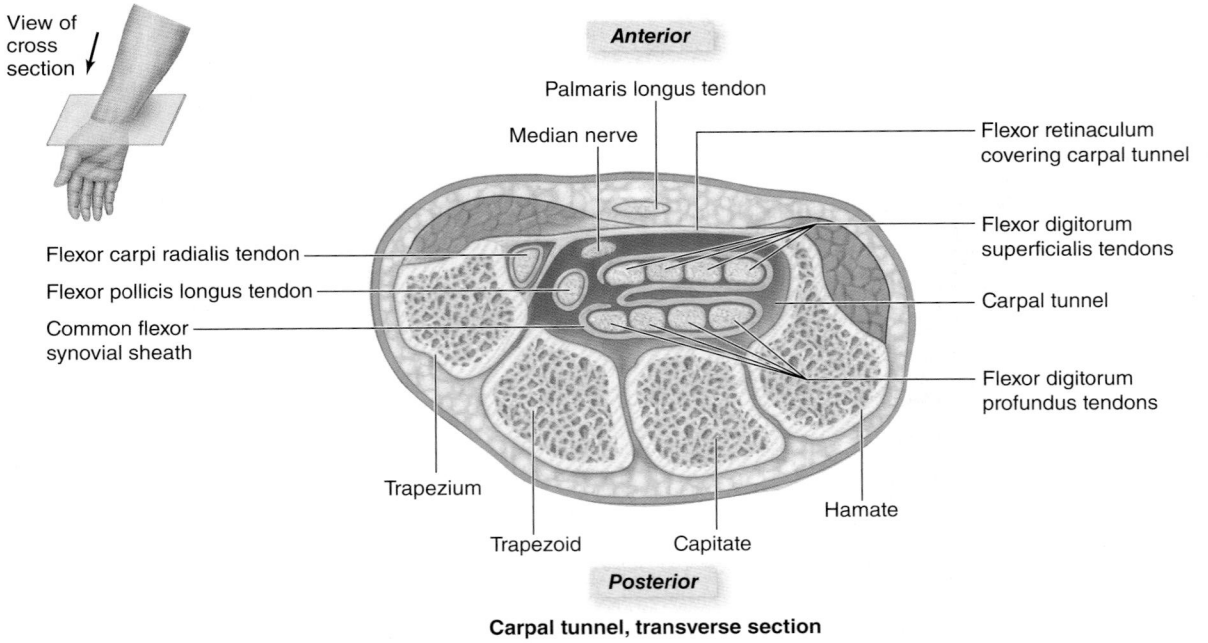

View of cross section

Anterior

Palmaris longus tendon

Median nerve

Flexor retinaculum covering carpal tunnel

Flexor digitorum superficialis tendons

Carpal tunnel

Flexor digitorum profundus tendons

Flexor carpi radialis tendon

Flexor pollicis longus tendon

Common flexor synovial sheath

Trapezium

Trapezoid

Capitate

Hamate

Posterior

Carpal tunnel, transverse section

Table 11.18 summarizes the characteristics of the muscles that move the wrist joint, hand, and fingers.

WHAT DID YOU LEARN?

23 What are the common actions of muscles in the anterior compartment of the forearm?

24 What muscles in the posterior compartment move the thumb?

Table 11.18	Forearm Muscles That Move the Wrist Joint, Hand, and Digits		
Group/Muscle	Action	Origin/Insertion	Innervation (see section 14.5e)
ANTERIOR MUSCLES: SUPERFICIAL			
Pronator teres (previously described in table 11.16)			
Flexor carpi radialis (flek'ser kar'pī rā-dē-alis) *carpi* = wrist	Flexes wrist and abducts hand	O: Medial epicondyle of humerus I: Base of metacarpals II and III	Median nerve (C6–C7 nerve fibers)
Palmaris longus (pawl-mar'is) *palma* = palm *longus* = long	Weak wrist flexor	O: Medial epicondyle of humerus I: Flexor retinaculum and palmar aponeurosis	Median nerve (C6–C7 nerve fibers)
Flexor carpi ulnaris (ŭl-nā'ris) *ulnar* = ulna	Flexes wrist and adducts hand	O: Medial epicondyle of humerus; olecranon and posterior surface of ulna I: Pisiform and hamate bones; base of metacarpal V	Ulnar nerve (C8–T1)
ANTERIOR MUSCLES: INTERMEDIATE			
Flexor digitorum superficialis (dij'i-tōr'ŭm sū'per-fish-ē-ā'lis) *digit* = finger, toe *superficial* = close to surface	Flexes wrist; 2nd–5th MP joints and PIP joints	O: Medial epicondyle of humerus, coronoid process of ulna I: Middle phalanges of fingers 2–5	Median nerve (C6–C7 nerve fibers)
ANTERIOR MUSCLES: DEEP			
Flexor pollicis longus (pol'i-sis) *pollex* = thumb	Flexes MP joint of thumb, IP joint of thumb; weakly flexes wrist	O: Anterior shaft of radius; interosseous membrane I: Distal phalanx of thumb	Median nerve (C6–C7 nerve fibers)
Flexor digitorum profundus (prō-fŭn'dŭs) *profound* = deep	Flexes wrist; 2nd–5th MP joints, PIP joints, and DIP joints	O: Anteromedial surface of ulna; interosseous membrane I: Distal phalanges of fingers 2–5	Lateral ½ of muscle innervated by median nerve (C6–C8 nerve fibers), medial ½ of muscle innervated by ulnar nerve (C8 nerve fibers)
Pronator quadratus (previously described in table 11.16)			
POSTERIOR MUSCLES: SUPERFICIAL			
Extensor carpi radialis longus (eks-ten'ser)	Extends wrist, abducts hand	O: Lateral supracondylar ridge of humerus I: Base of metacarpal II	Radial nerve (C6–C7 nerve fibers)
Extensor carpi radialis brevis (brev'is) *brevis* = short	Extends wrist, abducts hand	O: Lateral epicondyle of humerus I: Base of metacarpal III	Radial nerve (C6–C7 nerve fibers)
Extensor digitorum	Extends wrist; extends 2nd–5th MP joints, PIP joints and DIP joints	O: Lateral epicondyle of humerus I: Distal and middle phalanges of fingers 2–5	Radial nerve (C6–C8 nerve fibers)
Extensor digiti minimi *digitus minimus* = little finger	Extends MP and PIP joints of finger 5; extends wrist weakly	O: Lateral epicondyle of humerus I: Proximal phalanx of finger 5	Radial nerve (C6–C8 nerve fibers)
Extensor carpi ulnaris	Extends wrist, adducts hand	O: Lateral epicondyle of humerus; posterior border of ulna I: Base of metacarpal V	Radial nerve (C6–C8 nerve fibers)

(continued on next page)

Table 11.18	Forearm Muscles That Move the Wrist Joint, Hand, and Digits (continued)		
Group/Muscle	Action	Origin/Insertion	Innervation (see section 14.5e)
POSTERIOR MUSCLES: DEEP			
Abductor pollicis longus (ab-dŭk′ter, tōr)	Abducts thumb; extends wrist (weakly)	O: Proximal dorsal surfaces of radius and ulna; interosseous membrane I: Lateral edge of metacarpal I	Radial nerve (C6–C8 nerve fibers)
Extensor pollicis brevis	Extends MP joint of thumb; extends wrist (weakly)	O: Posterior surface of radius; interosseous membrane I: Proximal phalanx of thumb	Radial nerve (C6–C8 nerve fibers)
Extensor pollicis longus	Extends MP and IP joints of thumb, extends wrist (weakly)	O: Posterior surface of ulna; interosseous membrane I: Distal phalanx of thumb	Radial nerve (C6–C8 nerve fibers)
Extensor indicis *index* = forefinger	Extends MP PIP and DIP joints of finger 2; extends wrist (weakly)	O: Posterior surface of ulna; interosseous membrane I: Tendon of extensor digitorum	Radial nerve (C6–C8 nerve fibers)
Supinator (previously described in table 11.16)			

11.8e Intrinsic Muscles of the Hand

✓ LEARNING OBJECTIVE

8. Compare the actions of the three groups of intrinsic muscles of the hand.

The intrinsic muscles of the hand are small muscles that both originate and insert on the hand; they are housed entirely within the palm **(figure 11.30)**. These muscles are divided into three groups: The **thenar** (thē′nar) **group** forms the thick, fleshy mass (thenar eminence) at the base of the thumb; the **hypothenar group** forms a smaller fleshy mass (hypothenar eminence) at the base of the little finger; and the **midpalmar group** occupies the space between the first two groups.

The thenar and hypothenar groups contain smaller muscles:

- Small flexors (**flexor pollicis brevis** in the thenar group and **flexor digiti minimi brevis** in the hypothenar group) flex the thumb and the little finger, respectively.
- Abductors (**abductor pollicis brevis** in the thenar group and **abductor digiti minimi** in the hypothenar group) abduct the thumb and little finger, respectively.

- Opponens muscles (**opponens pollicis** in the thenar group and **opponens digiti minimi** in the hypothenar group) assist in the opposition of the thumb and little finger, respectively.

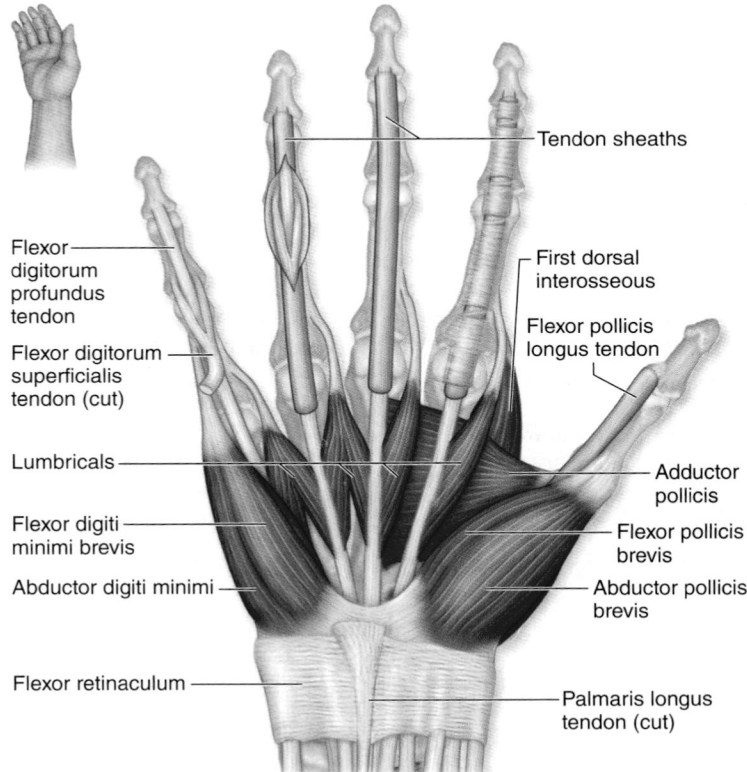

Flexor digitorum profundus tendon
Flexor digitorum superficialis tendon (cut)
Lumbricals
Flexor digiti minimi brevis
Abductor digiti minimi
Flexor retinaculum
Tendon sheaths
First dorsal interosseous
Flexor pollicis longus tendon
Adductor pollicis
Flexor pollicis brevis
Abductor pollicis brevis
Palmaris longus tendon (cut)

(a) Right hand, superficial palmar view

Figure 11.30 Intrinsic Muscles of the Hand. These muscles allow the fine, controlled movements necessary for such activities as writing, typing, and playing a guitar. (*a*) Palmar (anterior) views of the superficial muscles of the right hand. (*b*) Palmar view of the deep muscles. (*c*) Posterior (dorsal) view of the superficial muscles. **AP|R**

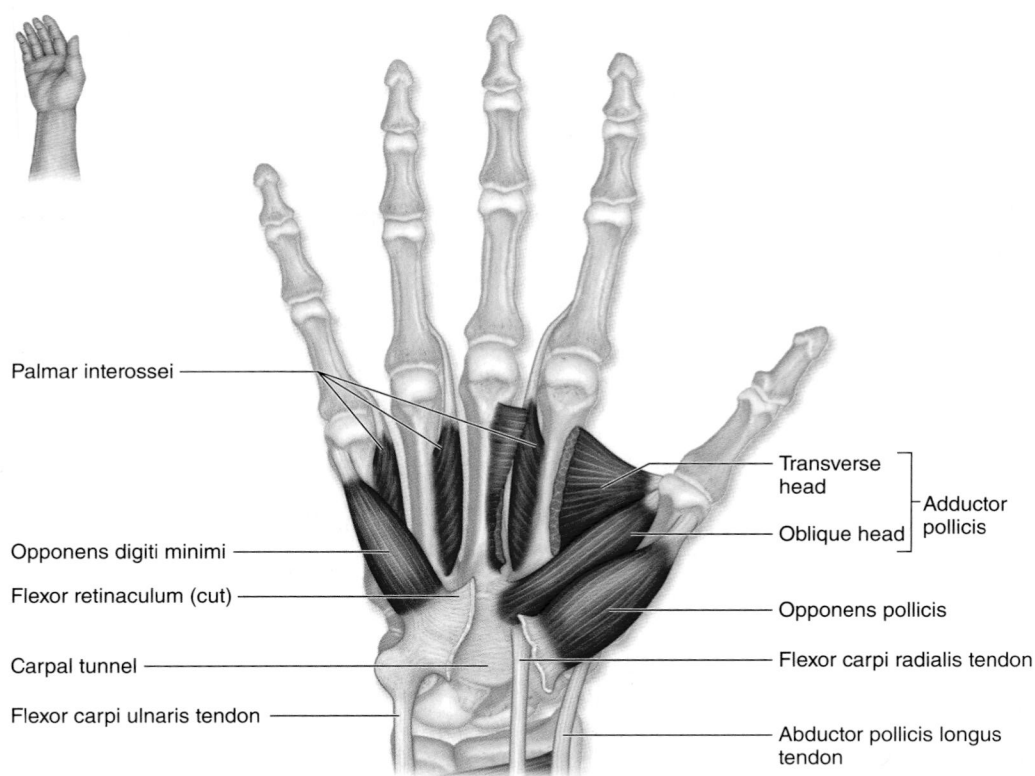

Palmar interossei

Opponens digiti minimi

Flexor retinaculum (cut)

Carpal tunnel

Flexor carpi ulnaris tendon

Transverse head ⎤
⎦ Adductor pollicis
Oblique head

Opponens pollicis

Flexor carpi radialis tendon

Abductor pollicis longus tendon

(b) Right hand, deep palmar view

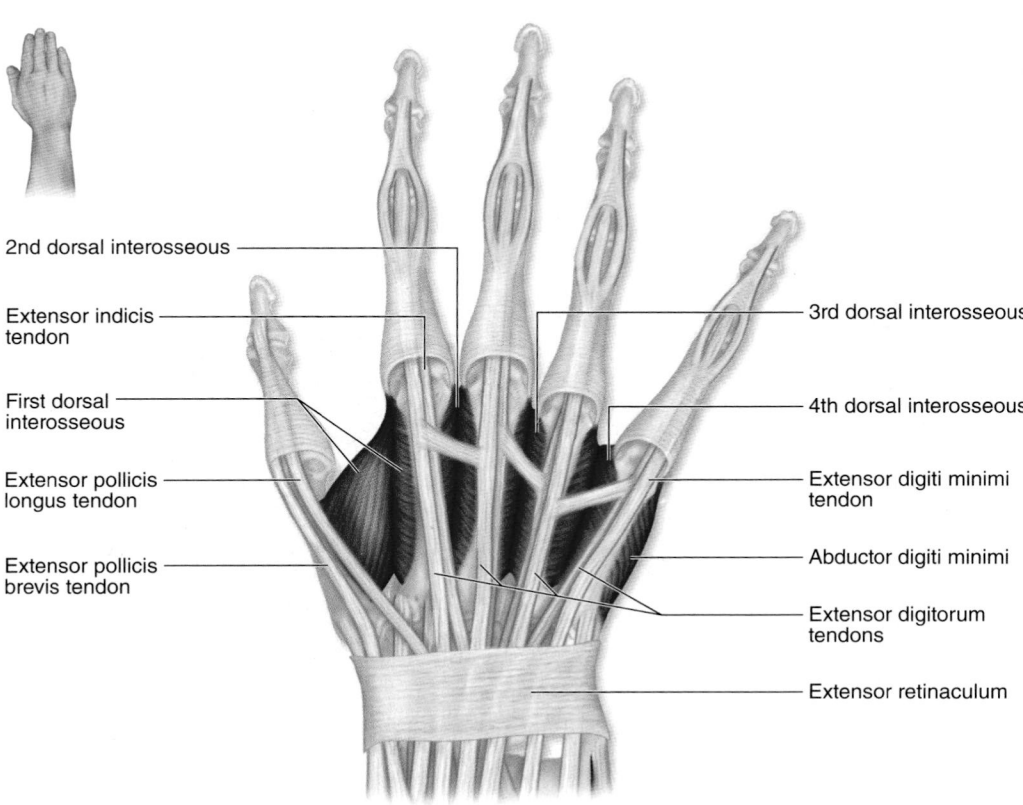

2nd dorsal interosseous

Extensor indicis tendon

First dorsal interosseous

Extensor pollicis longus tendon

Extensor pollicis brevis tendon

3rd dorsal interosseous

4th dorsal interosseous

Extensor digiti minimi tendon

Abductor digiti minimi

Extensor digitorum tendons

Extensor retinaculum

(c) Right hand, posterior view

The midpalmar group contains the following muscles: lumbricals, dorsal interossei, palmar interossei, and adductor pollicis. The **lumbrical muscles** are four worm-shaped muscles. These muscles flex the MP joints and at the same time extend the PIP and DIP joints of fingers 2–5. The **dorsal interossei** are four deep bipennate muscles located between the metacarpals. They flex the MP joints and at the same time extend the PIP and DIP joints of fingers 2–5. In addition, the dorsal interossei abduct fingers 2–5. The **palmar interossei** are three small muscles that adduct the fingers. In addition, these muscles work with the lumbricals and dorsal interossei to flex the MP joints and at the same time extend the PIP and DIP joints of fingers 2–5. The **adductor pollicis** is sometimes incorrectly classified as a palmar interosseous muscle. As its name suggests, this muscle adducts the thumb.

The muscles that control the specific movements of the fingers, hand, and wrist, are summarized in **table 11.19** and grouped according to common muscle actions in **table 11.20**.

 WHAT DID YOU LEARN?

25 Identify the intrinsic muscles of the hand that abduct the fingers.

Table 11.19	Intrinsic Muscles of the Hand		
Group/Muscle	**Action**	**Origin/Insertion**	**Innervation (see section 14.5e)**
THENAR GROUP			
Flexor pollicis brevis	Flexes thumb	O: Flexor retinaculum; trapezium I: Proximal phalanx of thumb	Median nerve (C8–T1 nerve fibers)
Abductor pollicis brevis	Abducts thumb	O: Flexor retinaculum, scaphoid, trapezium I: Lateral side of proximal phalanx of thumb	Median nerve (C8–T1 nerve fibers)
Opponens pollicis (ō-pō′nens) *opponens* = to place against	Opposition of thumb	O: Flexor retinaculum and trapezium I: Lateral side of metacarpal I	Median nerve (C8–T1 nerve fibers)
HYPOTHENAR GROUP			
Flexor digiti minimi brevis	Flexes finger 5	O: Hamate bone, flexor retinaculum I: Proximal phalanx of finger 5	Ulnar nerve (C8–T1)
Abductor digiti minimi	Abducts finger 5	O: Pisiform bone, tendon of flexor carpi ulnaris I: Proximal phalanx of finger 5	Ulnar nerve (C8–T1)
Opponens digiti minimi	Opposition of finger 5	O: Hamate bone, flexor retinaculum I: Metacarpal bone V	Ulnar nerve (C8–T1)
MIDPALMAR GROUP			
Lumbricals (lŭm′bri-kălz) *lumbricus* = earthworm	Flexes 2nd–5th MP joints and extends the 2nd–5th PIP and DIP joints	O: Tendons of flexor digitorum profundus I: Dorsal tendons on fingers 2–5	Median nerve (lateral two lumbricals 1, 2) and ulnar nerve (medial two lumbricals 3, 4)
Dorsal interossei (dōr′săl in′ter-os′ē-ī) *interossei* = between bones	Abducts fingers 2–5; flexes MP joints 2–5 and extends the PIP and DIP joints	O: Adjacent, opposing faces of metacarpals I: Dorsal tendons on fingers 2–5	Ulnar nerve (C8–T1)
Palmar interossei	Adducts fingers 2–5; flexes MP joints 2–5 and extends the PIP and DIP joints	O: Metacarpal bones II, IV, V I: Sides of proximal phalanges bases for fingers 2, 4, and 5	Ulnar nerve (C8–T1)
Adductor pollicis	Adducts thumb	O: Oblique head: Capitate bone, bases of metacarpals II, III Transverse head: Metacarpal III I: Medial side of proximal phalanx of thumb	Ulnar nerve (C8–T1)

Table 11.20	Summary of Muscle Actions at the Wrist and Hand		
Hand Abduction	**Hand Adduction**	**Wrist Extension**	**Wrist Flexion**
Flexor carpi radialis	Extensor carpi ulnaris	Extensor digitorum	Flexor carpi radialis
Extensor carpi radialis brevis	Flexor carpi ulnaris	Extensor carpi radialis brevis	Flexor carpi ulnaris
Extensor carpi radialis longus		Extensor carpi radialis longus	Flexor digitorum superficialis
		Extensor carpi ulnaris	Flexor digitorum profundus
		(Extensor indicis)	(Palmaris longus)
		(Extensor pollicis longus)	(Flexor pollicis longus)
		(Extensor pollicis brevis)	
		(Abductor pollicis longus)	
Finger Abduction	**Finger Adduction**	**IP Joint Extension**	**IP Joint Flexion**
Dorsal interossei	Palmar interossei	Extensor digitorum	Flexor digitorum profundus
Abductor pollicis longus	Adductor pollicis	Extensor indicis	Flexor digitorum superficialis
Abductor pollicis brevis		Extensor pollicis brevis	Flexor pollicis longus
Abductor digiti minimi		Extensor pollicis longus	Flexor pollicis brevis
		Extensor digiti minimi	Flexor digiti minimi
		Lumbricals	
		Dorsal interossei	
		Palmar interossei	

Parentheses around a muscle name indicate only a slight effect.

11.9 Muscles of the Pelvic Girdle and Lower Limb

The most powerful and largest muscles in the body are those of the lower limb. These muscles are designed to support the weight of the body and move the lower limbs during locomotion. Like the upper limb, the lower limb muscles also are organized in compartments (see figure 11.23).

As with the muscles of the pectoral girdle and upper limb, the pelvic girdle and lower limb muscles can be organized into groups:

- Muscles that move the hip joint/thigh
- Thigh muscles that move the knee joint/leg
- Muscles of the leg that move the ankle, foot, and toes
- Intrinsic muscles of the foot

INTEGRATE

CLINICAL VIEW
Shin Splints and Compartment Syndrome

Shin splints, also called *shin splint syndrome,* refers specifically to soreness or pain somewhere along the length of the tibia, usually on the inferior portion. Shin splints often occur in runners or joggers who are either new to the sport or poorly conditioned. Some healthcare professionals consider shin splints a type of compartment syndrome of the anterior compartment of the leg.

Generally, **compartment syndrome** is a condition in which the blood vessels within a limb compartment become compressed as a result of inflammation and swelling secondary to muscle strain, contusion, or overuse. For example, compartment syndrome can occur in an individual who suddenly embarks on an intensive exercise regimen. More severe

compartment syndrome can occur due to trauma to the limb compartment, such as a bone fracture or rupture of a blood vessel. A snake bite (where venom is injected into the bite location) also may cause swelling and resulting compartment syndrome. Any limb compartment may be affected, but the leg tends to be most prone to compartment syndrome.

Since the deep fascia is tight and cannot stretch, swelling from muscles or any accumulating fluid or blood increases pressure in the compartment. Both the circulatory supply and the nerves of the compartment become compressed and compromised. If the blood flow is not restored, this situation can lead to death of nerves within 2 hours and death of skeletal muscle within 6 hours. Mild cases of compartment syndrome may be treated by immobilizing and resting the affected limb. In more severe cases, the fascia may have to be incised (cut) to relieve the pressure and decompress the affected compartment.

11.9a Muscles that Move the Hip Joint/Thigh

1. Compare and contrast the functions of the muscles in the anterior, medial, lateral, and posterior compartments of the thigh.

2. Describe the actions of the three gluteal muscles.

Note that in the subsequent discussion the phrases "moving the thigh" and "moving the hip joint" mean the same thing. The **fascia lata,** the deep fascia of the thigh, encircles the thigh muscles like a supportive stocking and tightly binds them. The fascia lata partitions the thigh muscles into compartments, each with its own blood and nerve supply. The *anterior compartment* muscles either extend the knee or flex the thigh; these are discussed in the next section. The muscles of the *medial compartment* adduct the thigh. The single muscle in the *lateral compartment* abducts the thigh. Most muscles of the *posterior compartment* act as both flexors of the knee and extensors of the thigh. Some of these muscles also abduct the thigh. We discuss the muscles that move the thigh first.

Multiple muscles insert on the anterior thigh and flex the hip joint **(figure 11.31a)**: The **psoas major** and the **iliacus** have different origins (they originate on the lumbar vertebrae and ilium, respectively), but they share the common insertion at the lesser trochanter of the femur. Collectively, the two muscles merge and insert on the femur as the **iliopsoas.** Together, these muscles work synergistically to flex the thigh. The rectus femoris and a long, thin muscle called the sartorius flex the thigh. Both are examined later in this chapter in connection with the thigh muscles that move the leg.

Six muscles are located in the **medial compartment** of the thigh. Most of these muscles adduct the thigh, and some of them perform additional functions. The **adductor longus, adductor brevis, gracilis,** and **pectineus** also flex the thigh. A fifth muscle, the **adductor magnus,** also extends and laterally rotates the thigh. The **obturator externus** does not adduct the thigh, but it laterally rotates the thigh.

On the lateral thigh is a single muscle called the **tensor fasciae latae** (figure 11.31b). It attaches to a lateral thickening of the fascia lata, called the **iliotibial tract** (or *iliotibial band*), which extends from the iliac crest to the lateral condyle of the tibia. The tensor fasciae latae abducts and medially rotates the thigh.

The posterior muscles that move the thigh include three gluteal muscles and the "hamstring" muscle group (which are described in a later section). The **gluteus maximus** is the largest and heaviest of the three gluteal muscles; it is the chief extensor of the thigh and it laterally rotates the thigh. Deep to the gluteus maximus are the **gluteus medius** and **gluteus minimus,** which abduct and medially rotate the thigh (figure 11.31c).

Deep to the gluteal muscles are a group of muscles that collectively laterally rotate the thigh/hip joint, as when the legs are crossed with one ankle resting on the knee. These muscles are organized from superior to inferior within the posterior thigh as the **piriformis, superior gemellus, obturator internus, inferior gemellus,** and **quadratus femoris.**

Finally, the posterior thigh contains a group of muscles that are collectively referred to as the **hamstrings** because a ham is strung up by these muscles while being smoked. The hamstring muscles are the biceps femoris, semimembranosus, and semitendinosus. These muscles share a common origin on the ischial tuberosity of the os coxae, and insert on the leg. Thus, these muscles move both the thigh and the knee. Their primary thigh movement is extension. These muscles are discussed again in the next section on movement at the leg.

Table 11.21 summarizes the characteristics of the muscles that move the hip joint and thigh, and table 11.22 groups these muscles according to their common actions on the thigh.

 WHAT DID YOU LEARN?

26 List the compartments of the thigh, and describe the common action of the muscles in each.

Figure 11.31 Muscles That Act on the Hip and Thigh. (*a*) Anterior, (*b*) lateral, and (*c*) deep posterior views of the right thigh. Most muscles that act on the thigh (femur) originate from the os coxae. (Obturator externus not shown.) AP|R

Psoas minor

Psoas major

Iliacus

Iliopsoas

Pectineus

Adductor brevis

Adductor longus

Gracilis

Adductor magnus

(a) Right thigh, anterior view

Gluteus medius

Gluteus maximus

Vastus lateralis

Iliotibial tract

Biceps femoris, long head

Semimembranosus

Biceps femoris, short head

Gastrocnemius

Iliac crest

Tensor fasciae latae

Sartorius

Rectus femoris

Patella

(b) Right thigh, lateral view

Sacrum

Gluteus maximus (cut)

Piriformis

Superior gemellus

Obturator internus

Inferior gemellus

Ischial tuberosity

Gracilis

Biceps femoris, long head

Adductor magnus

Semitendinosus

Iliac crest

Gluteus medius (cut)

Gluteus minimus

Gluteus medius (cut)

Gluteus maximus (cut)

Quadratus femoris

Iliotibial tract

(c) Right thigh, deep posterior view

Table 11.21	Muscles That Move the Hip Joint/Thigh		
Group/Muscle	Action	Origin/Insertion	Innervation (see sections 14.5f, g)
ANTERIOR THIGH COMPARTMENT (THIGH FLEXORS)			
Psoas major (sō′as) *psoa* = loin muscle	Flexes thigh	O: Transverse processes and bodies of T_{12}–L_5 vertebrae I: Lesser trochanter of femur with iliacus	Branches of lumbar plexus (L2–L3)
Iliacus (il-ī′ă′kŭs) *iliac* = ilium	Flexes thigh	O: Iliac fossa I: Lesser trochanter of femur with psoas major	Femoral nerve (L2–L3 nerve fibers)
Sartorius (sar-tōr′ē-ŭs) *sartor* = tailor	Flexes thigh and laterally rotates thigh; flexes leg and medially rotates leg	O: Anterior superior iliac spine I: Tibial tuberosity, medial side	Femoral nerve (L2–L3 nerve fibers)
Rectus femoris (fem′ō-ris) *femoris* = femur	Flexes thigh; extends leg	O: Anterior inferior iliac spine I: Quadriceps tendon to patella and then patellar ligament to tibial tuberosity	Femoral nerve (L2–L4)
MEDIAL THIGH COMPARTMENT (THIGH ADDUCTORS)			
Adductor longus (a-dŭk′ter, tōr)	Adducts thigh; flexes thigh	O: Pubis near pubic symphysis I: Linea aspera of femur	Obturator nerve (L2–L4)
Adductor brevis	Adducts thigh; flexes thigh	O: Inferior ramus and body of pubis I: Upper third of linea aspera of femur	Obturator nerve (L2–L3 nerve fibers)
Gracilis (gras′i-lis) *gracilis* = slender	Adducts and flexes thigh; flexes leg	O: Inferior ramus and body of pubis I: Upper medial surface of tibia	Obturator nerve (L2–L4)
Pectineus (pek′ti-nē-ŭs) *pectin* = comb	Flexes thigh; adducts thigh	O: Pectineal line of pubis I: Pectineal line of femur	Femoral nerve (L2–L4) or obturator nerve (L2–L4)
Adductor magnus (mag′nŭs) *magnus* = large	Adducts thigh; adductor part of muscle flexes thigh; hamstring part of muscle extends and laterally rotates thigh	O: Inferior ramus of pubis and ischial tuberosity I: Hamstring part: Linea aspera of femur Adductor part: Adductor tubercle of femur	Adductor part: Obturator nerve (L2–L4) Hamstring part: Tibial division of sciatic nerve (L2–L4 nerve fibers)
Obturator externus (ob′tū-rā-tōr eks-ter′nŭs) *obturator* = any structure that occludes an opening *externus* = outside	Laterally rotates thigh	O: Margins of obturator foramen and obturator membrane I: Trochanteric fossa of posterior femur	Obturator nerve (L3–L4 nerve fibers)
LATERAL THIGH COMPARTMENT (THIGH ABDUCTOR)			
Tensor fasciae latae (ten′sōr fash′ă lā′tē) *tensor* = to make tense *fascia* = band *lata* = wide	Abducts thigh; medially rotates thigh	O: Iliac crest and lateral surface of anterior superior iliac spine I: Iliotibial band	Superior gluteal nerve (L4–S1)
GLUTEAL GROUP			
Gluteus maximus (glū-tē′ŭs mak′si-mŭs) *glutos* = buttock *maximus* = largest	Extends thigh; laterally rotates thigh	O: Iliac crest, sacrum, coccyx I: Iliotibial tract of fascia lata; linea aspera and gluteal tuberosity of femur	Inferior gluteal nerve (L5–S2)

Table 11.21

Group/Muscle	Action	Origin/Insertion	Innervation (see section 14.5g)
Gluteus medius (mē′dē-ŭs) *medius* = middle	Abducts thigh; medially rotates thigh	O: Posterior iliac crest; lateral surface between posterior and anterior gluteal lines I: Greater trochanter of femur	Superior gluteal nerve (L4–S1)
Gluteus minimus (min-i-mŭs) *minimus* = smallest	Abducts thigh; medially rotates thigh	O: Lateral surface of ilium between inferior and anterior gluteal lines I: Greater trochanter of femur	Superior gluteal nerve (L4–S1)

DEEP MUSCLES OF THE GLUTEAL REGION (LATERAL THIGH ROTATORS)

Group/Muscle	Action	Origin/Insertion	Innervation (see section 14.5g)
Piriformis (pir′i-fōr′mis) *pirum* = pear *forma* = form	Laterally rotates thigh	O: Anterolateral surface of sacrum I: Greater trochanter	Nerve to piriformis (S1–S2)
Superior gemellus (jē-mel′ŭs) *gemin* = twin, double	Laterally rotates thigh	O: Ischial spine and tuberosity I: Greater trochanter	Nerve to obturator internus (L5–S1)
Obturator internus (in-ter′nŭs) *internus* = inside	Laterally rotates thigh	O: Posterior surface of obturator membrane; margins of obturator foramen I: Greater trochanter	Nerve to obturator internus (L5–S1)
Inferior gemellus	Laterally rotates thigh	O: Ischial tuberosity I: Obturator internus tendon	Nerve to quadratus femoris (L5–S1)
Quadratus femoris	Laterally rotates thigh	O: Lateral border of ischial tuberosity I: Intertrochanteric crest of femur	Nerve to quadratus femoris (L5–S1)

HAMSTRING GROUP

Group/Muscle	Action	Origin/Insertion	Innervation (see section 14.5g)
Biceps femoris Long head Short head	Extends thigh (long head only); flexes leg (both long head and short head); laterally rotates leg	O: Long head: Ischial tuberosity Short head: Linea aspera of femur I: Head of fibula	Long head: Tibial division of sciatic nerve (L4-S1 nerve fibers) Short head: Common fibular division of sciatic nerve (L5–S1 nerve fibers)
Semimembranosus (sem′ē-mem-brǎ-nō-sǔs) *semi* = half *membranosus* = membrane	Extends thigh and flexes leg; medially rotates leg	O: Ischial tuberosity I: Posterior surface of medial condyle of tibia	Tibial division of sciatic nerve (L4–S1 nerve fibers)
Semitendinosus (sem′ē-ten-di-nō′sǔs) *tendinosus* = tendon	Extends thigh and flexes leg; medially rotates leg	O: Ischial tuberosity I: Proximal medial surface of tibia	Tibial division of sciatic nerve (L4–S1 nerve fibers)

Table 11.22   Summary of Muscle Actions at the Hip Joint/Thigh

Abduction	Adduction	Extension	Flexion	Lateral Rotation	Medial Rotation
Gluteus medius	Adductor brevis, longus, magnus	**Gluteus maximus***	**Iliopsoas**	Adductor magnus (hamstring part)	Gluteus medius
Gluteus minimus	Gracilis	Adductor magnus (hamstring part)	Adductor brevis, longus, magnus (adductor part)	Gluteus maximus	Gluteus minimus
Tensor fasciae latae	Pectineus	Biceps femoris (long head)	Pectineus	Sartorius	Tensor fasciae latae
		Semimembranosus	Sartorius	Obturator externus	
		Semitendinosus	Rectus femoris	Obturator internus	
			Gracilis	Piriformis	
				Superior gemellus	
				Inferior gemellus	
				Quadratus femoris	

*Boldface indicates an agonist; others are synergists.

11.9b Thigh Muscles That Move the Knee Joint/Leg

✓ LEARNING OBJECTIVES

3. List muscles of the thigh's anterior compartment that move the knee joint.

4. Describe the muscles of the thigh that flex the knee joint.

The muscles that act on the knee form most of the mass of the thigh. They include muscles of the anterior compartment and posterior compartment of the thigh as well as certain muscles already described in the preceding section.

Muscles of the Thigh's Anterior Compartment

The **anterior (extensor) compartment** of the thigh is composed of the large **quadriceps femoris,** the prime mover of knee extension (figure 11.32). The quadriceps femoris is a composite muscle with four heads: the **rectus femoris, vastus lateralis, vastus medialis,** and **vastus intermedius.** All four muscles converge on a single **quadriceps tendon,** which extends to the patella and then continues inferiorly as the **patellar ligament** and inserts on the tibial tuberosity.

Also within the anterior compartment is the **sartorius,** which acts on both the hip and knee joints, flexing and laterally rotating the thigh while flexing and medially rotating the leg. This muscle is the longest in the body and is termed the "tailor's muscle" because it helps us sit cross-legged, as tailors used to do.

Muscles of the Thigh's Medial Compartment

The **gracilis** muscle (in the medial compartment of the thigh) not only adducts the thigh, as described earlier, but also flexes the leg, since it spans the knee joint.

Muscles of the Thigh's Posterior Compartment

The **posterior (flexor) compartment** of the thigh contains the three hamstring muscles discussed previously (figure 11.33). These muscles also flex the leg. The **biceps femoris** is a two-headed muscle that inserts on the lateral side of the leg. This muscle also can laterally rotate the leg when the leg is flexed. The **semimembranosus** and **semitendinosus** insert on the medial side of the leg. The semimembranosus and semitendinosus also medially rotate the leg when the leg is flexed.

Finally, several leg muscles span the knee joint and work to flex the leg. These muscles (gastrocnemius, plantaris, and popliteus) are discussed in the next section, as we examine muscles of the leg.

Table 11.23 summarizes the characteristics of the thigh muscles that move the knee joint and leg.

☀ WHAT DID YOU LEARN?

27 List the thigh muscles that flex the knee joint.

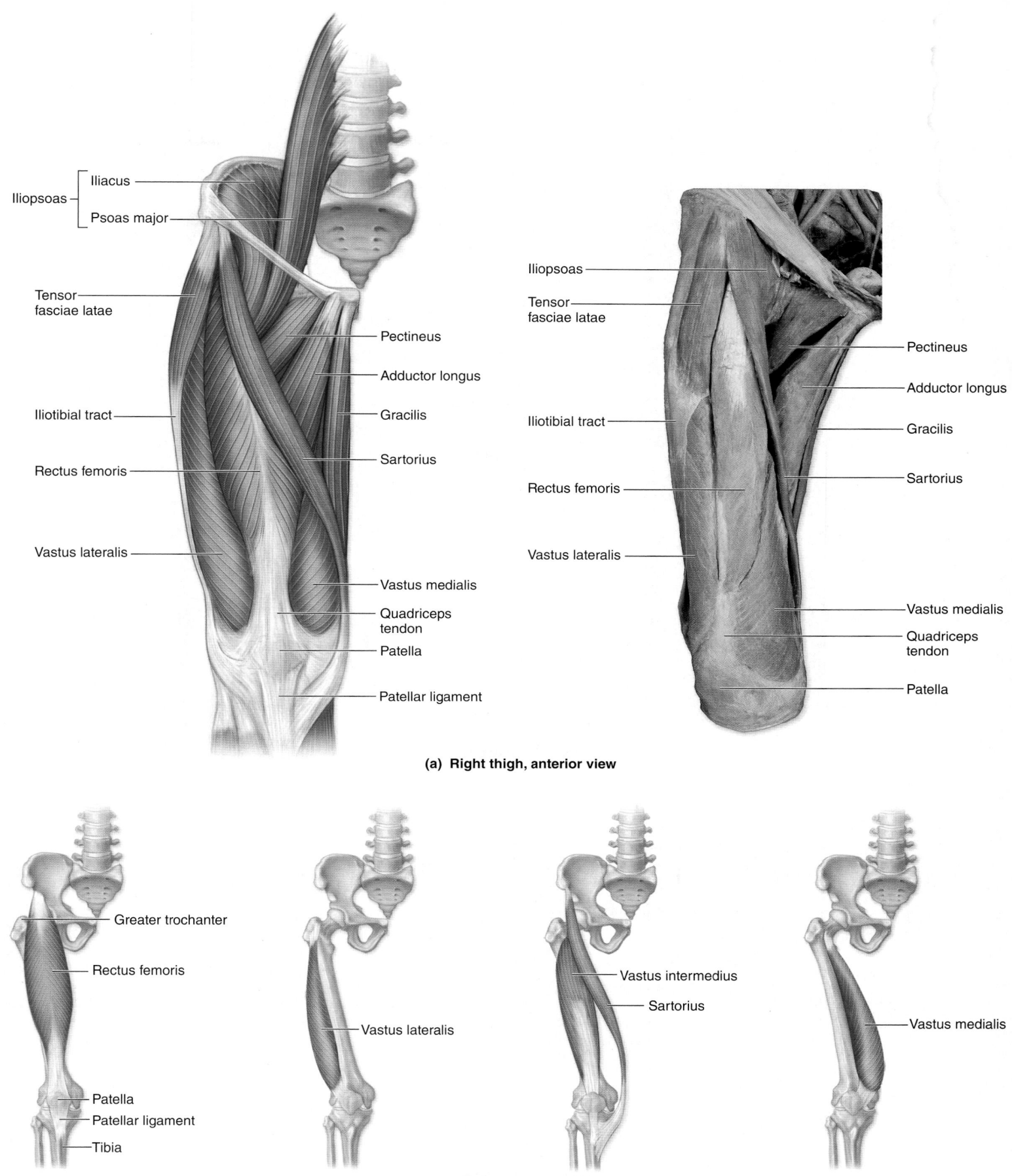

(a) Right thigh, anterior view

Iliopsoas
- Iliacus
- Psoas major

Tensor fasciae latae

Iliotibial tract

Rectus femoris

Vastus lateralis

Pectineus

Adductor longus

Gracilis

Sartorius

Vastus medialis

Quadriceps tendon

Patella

Patellar ligament

Iliopsoas

Tensor fasciae latae

Iliotibial tract

Rectus femoris

Vastus lateralis

Pectineus

Adductor longus

Gracilis

Sartorius

Vastus medialis

Quadriceps tendon

Patella

(b) Anterior thigh muscles

Greater trochanter

Rectus femoris

Patella

Patellar ligament

Tibia

Vastus lateralis

Vastus intermedius

Sartorius

Vastus medialis

Figure 11.32 Muscles of the Anterior Thigh. Muscles of the anterior thigh flex the thigh and extend the leg. (*a*) Illustration and cadaver photo show an anterior view of the right thigh. (*b*) Individual muscles of the right anterior thigh. AP|R

Iliac crest

Gluteus medius

Gluteus maximus

Adductor magnus

Gracilis

Iliotibial tract

Hamstrings
Semimembranosus

Semitendinosus

Biceps femoris,
long head

Biceps femoris,
short head

(a) Right thigh, posterior view

Ischial tuberosity

Linea aspera

Semitendinosus

**Biceps femoris,
long head**

Semimembranosus

Biceps femoris,
short head

**Adductor
magnus**

Head of fibula

(b) Thigh extensors

Figure 11.33 Muscles of the Gluteal Region and Posterior Thigh. Muscles of the posterior thigh extend the thigh and flex the leg.
(*a*) Illustration and cadaver photo show the gluteal and posterior muscles of the right thigh. (*b*) Individual muscles that extend the thigh are shown in
bold (note the short head of biceps femoris does not participate in thigh extension). AP|R

Table 11.23	Thigh Muscles That Move the Knee Joint/Leg		
Group/Muscle	Action	Origin/Insertion	Innervation (see section 14.5f)
LEG EXTENSORS (ANTERIOR THIGH MUSCLES)			
Quadriceps femoris			
Rectus femoris (rek'tūs fem'ō-ris)	Extends leg; flexes thigh	O: Anterior inferior iliac spine I: Quadriceps tendon to patella and then patellar ligament to tibial tuberosity	Femoral nerve (L2–L4)
Vastus intermedius (vas'tūs in-ter-mē'dē-ŭs) *vastus* = great *intermedius* = intermediate	Extends leg	O: Anterolateral surface of femur I: Quadriceps tendon to patella and then patellar ligament to tibial tuberosity	Femoral nerve (L2–L4)
Vastus lateralis (lat-er-ă'lis)	Extends leg	O: Greater trochanter and linea aspera I: Quadriceps tendon to patella and then patellar ligament to tibial tuberosity	Femoral nerve (L2–L4)
Vastus medialis (mē-dē-ă'lis)	Extends leg	O: Intertrochanteric line and linea aspera of femur I: Quadriceps tendon to patella and then patellar ligament to tibial tuberosity	Femoral nerve (L2–L4)
LEG FLEXORS			
Sartorius	Flexes thigh and rotates thigh laterally; flexes leg and rotates leg medially	See table 11.21	See table 11.21
Gracilis	Flexes and adducts thigh; flexes leg	See table 11.21	See table 11.21
Hamstrings (biceps femoris, semimembranosus, semitendinosus)	Extend thigh and flex leg; rotate leg laterally	See table 11.21	See table 11.21

11.9c Leg Muscles That Move the Ankle, Foot, and Toes

LEARNING OBJECTIVES

5. Compare and contrast the muscles of the three compartments of the leg and their actions.

6. Distinguish between the muscles of the superficial layer and deep layer of the leg's posterior compartment.

The muscles that move the ankle, foot, and toes are housed within the leg and are called the **crural muscles.** Some of these muscles also help flex the leg. The deep fascia partitions the leg musculature into three compartments (anterior, lateral, and posterior), each with its own nerve and blood supply, and muscles in the same compartment tend to share common functions (see figure 11.23).

INTEGRATE

CONCEPT CONNECTION

You will learn in section 20.4a that venous circulation of the lower limbs is reliant upon the muscular system. Specifically, the regular contraction and relaxation of the leg muscles works as a skeletal muscle "pump" to propel venous blood from the lower limb back to the torso. When the lower limbs are immobile for long periods of time (e.g., during long plane rides or when a person is bedridden), the skeletal muscle pump is inactive, and the risk of developing a blood clot in the lower limb veins increases.

Muscles of the Leg's Anterior Compartment

Anterior compartment leg muscles dorsiflex the foot, extend the toes, or both **(figure 11.34)**. The **extensor digitorum longus** dorsiflexes the foot and extends toes 2–5. The **extensor hallucis longus** sends a tendon to the dorsum of the great toe (hallux), and so it dorsiflexes the foot and extends the great toe. The **fibularis tertius** *(peroneus tertius)* dorsiflexes and weakly everts the foot. The **tibialis anterior** is the primary dorsiflexor of the foot. This muscle attaches to the medial plantar side of the foot, so it also inverts the foot. Analogous to tendons of the wrist, tendons of the muscles within the anterior compartment are held tightly against the ankle by multiple deep fascia thickenings, collectively referred to as **extensor retinaculum.**

Muscles of the Leg's Lateral Compartment

The **lateral compartment** leg muscles contain two synergistic muscles that are very powerful evertors of the foot and weak plantar flexors **(figure 11.35)**. The long, flat **fibularis longus** *(peroneus brevis)* inserts on the plantar side of the foot. The **fibularis brevis** *(peroneus brevis)* lies deep to the fibularis longus, and its tendon inserts onto the base of the fifth metatarsal.

Muscles of the Leg's Posterior Compartment

The **posterior compartment** of the leg is composed of seven muscles that are separated into superficial and deep groups **(figure 11.36)**. The superficial muscles and most of the deep muscles plantar flex the foot at the ankle.

The **superficial layer** of the posterior compartment contains the gastrocnemius, soleus, and plantaris. The **gastrocnemius** has two thick muscle bellies that form the prominence on the posterior part of the leg often referred to as the "calf." This muscle spans both the knee and the ankle joints; it flexes the leg and plantar flexes the foot. The **soleus** is a broad, flat muscle deep to the gastrocnemius *(solea* = sandal). This muscle plantar flexes the foot. The gastrocnemius and soleus are collectively known as the **triceps surae,** and together they are the most powerful plantar flexors of all of the leg muscles. These two muscles share a common tendon of insertion, the **calcaneal tendon** *(Achilles tendon)*. The **plantaris** is a small muscle that is absent in some individuals. It is a weak leg flexor and plantar flexor of the foot.

The **deep layer** of the posterior compartment contains four muscles. The **flexor digitorum longus** attaches to the distal phalanges of toes 2–5, plantar flexes the foot, and flexes the MP, PIP, and DIP joints of toes 2–5. The **flexor hallucis longus** plantar flexes the foot and flexes the great toe. The **tibialis posterior** is the deepest of the posterior compartment muscles. It plantar flexes and inverts the foot. The **popliteus** flexes the leg and medially rotates the tibia slightly to "unlock" the fully extended knee joint. This muscle originates and inserts in the popliteal region, so it only moves the knee, not the foot.

Table 11.24 summarizes the characteristics of the muscles that move the leg. **Table 11.25** groups muscles according to their action on the leg. Note that many thigh and leg muscles are involved with leg flexion.

WHAT DID YOU LEARN?

28 What are the common actions of each of the compartments of the leg?

Figure 11.34 Muscles of the Anterior Leg. The anterior muscles of the leg dorsiflex the foot and extend the toes. (*a*) An illustration shows an anterior view of the right leg. (*b*) Individual muscles of the right anterior leg.

Fibularis longus

Gastrocnemius

Tibia

Tibialis anterior

Fibularis brevis

Extensor digitorum longus

Extensor hallucis longus

Extensor retinaculum

Fibularis tertius tendon

Extensor digitorum brevis

Extensor hallucis longus tendon

Extensor digitorum longus tendons

Extensor hallucis brevis

(a) Right leg, anterior view

Tibialis anterior

Extensor digitorum longus

Fibularis tertius

Fibularis tertius tendon

Extensor hallucis longus

(b) Anterior leg muscles

Patella

Head of fibula

Gastrocnemius

Tibialis anterior

Soleus

Fibularis longus

Extensor digitorum longus

Fibularis brevis

Extensor hallucis longus

Fibularis tertius

Extensor hallucis brevis

Extensor digitorum brevis

Extensor hallucis longus tendon

Fibularis tertius tendon

Extensor digitorum longus tendons

5th metatarsal

Gastrocnemius

Soleus

Fibularis longus

Fibularis brevis

Fibularis tertius

Extensor digitorum brevis

Fibular retinaculum

Fibularis tertius tendon

Patella

Head of fibula

Tibialis anterior

Extensor digitorum longus

Extensor hallucis longus

Extensor retinaculum

Extensor hallucis brevis

Extensor hallucis longus tendon

Extensor digitorum longus tendons

5th metatarsal

(a) Right leg, lateral view

Fibularis longus

Fibularis longus tendon

Fibularis brevis

5th metatarsal

(b) Lateral leg muscles

Figure 11.35 Muscles of the Lateral Leg.

(*a*) Illustration and cadaver photo show a lateral view of the right leg. (*b*) The fibularis longus and the fibularis brevis evert and plantar flex the foot. **AP|R**

(a) Right leg, superficial posterior view

Plantaris

Gastrocnemius
Lateral head
Medial head

Soleus

Flexor hallucis
longus tendon

Flexor retinaculum

Medial malleolus

Calcaneus

Calcaneal
tendon

Fibular
retinaculum

Lateral
malleolus

(b) Deep posterior view

Plantaris (cut)

Gastrocnemius
(cut)

Popliteus

Tibialis
posterior

Fibularis
longus

Flexor
digitorum
longus

Flexor
hallucis
longus

Fibularis
brevis

Calcaneal
tendon (cut)

(c) Deep posterior leg muscles

Tibia

Tibialis
posterior

Interosseous
membrane

Tarsal and
metatarsal
bones

Flexor digitorum
longus

Distal
phalanges of
toes 2–5

Popliteus

Fibula

Flexor
hallucis
longus

Distal
phalanx
of hallux

Figure 11.36 Muscles of the Posterior Leg. The posterior muscles of the leg plantar flex the foot and flex the toes. (*a*) Superficial and (*b*) deep views of the posterior right leg. (*c*) Selected individual muscles of the deep posterior compartment.

Table 11.24

Table 11.24 — Leg Muscles

Group/Muscle	Action	Origin/Insertion	Innervation (see section 14.5g)
ANTERIOR COMPARTMENT (DORSIFLEXORS AND TOE EXTENSORS)			
Extensor digitorum longus	Extends toes 2–5; dorsiflexes foot	O: Lateral condyle of tibia; anterior surface of fibula; interosseous membrane I: Distal phalanges of toes 2–5	Deep fibular nerve (L4–S1)
Extensor hallucis longus (hal′ĭ-sis) *hallux* = great toe	Extends great toe (1); dorsiflexes foot	O: Anterior surface of fibula; interosseous membrane I: Distal phalanx of great toe (1)	Deep fibular nerve (L4–S1)
Fibularis tertius (fib-ū-lar′is ter′shē-ŭs) *fibularis* = fibula *tertius* = third	Dorsiflexes and weak evertor of foot	O: Anterior distal surface of fibula; interosseous membrane I: Base of metatarsal V	Deep fibular nerve (L5–S1 fibers)
Tibialis anterior (tib-ē-a′lis) *tibial* = tibia	Dorsiflexes foot; inverts foot	O: Lateral condyle and proximal shaft of tibia; interosseous membrane I: Metatarsal I and first (medial) cuneiform	Deep fibular nerve (L4–S1)
LATERAL COMPARTMENT (EVERTORS AND PLANTAR FLEXORS)			
Fibularis longus	Everts foot; weak plantar flexor	O: Head and upper ⅔ of shaft fibula; lateral condyle of tibia I: Base of metatarsal I; medial cuneiform	Superficial fibular nerve (L5–S2)
Fibularis brevis	Everts foot; weak plantar flexor	O: Midlateral shaft of fibula I: Base of metatarsal V	Superficial fibular nerve (L5–S2)
POSTERIOR COMPARTMENT (PLANTAR FLEXORS, FLEXORS OF THE LEG AND TOES)			
Superficial layer			
Triceps surae (sŭr′ē)			
Gastrocnemius (gas-trok-nē′mē-ŭs) *gaster* = belly *kneme* = leg	Flexes leg; plantar flexes foot	O: Superior and posterior surfaces of lateral and medial condyles of femur I: Calcaneus (via calcaneal tendon)	Tibial nerve (L4–S1 nerve fibers)
Soleus (sō-lē′ŭs) *solea* = sandal	Plantar flexes foot	O: Head and proximal shaft of fibula; medial border of tibia I: Calcaneus (via calcaneal tendon)	Tibial nerve (L4–S1 nerve fibers)
Plantaris (plan-tār′is) *planta* = sole of foot	Weak leg flexor and plantar flexor	O: Lateral supracondylar ridge of femur I: Posterior region of calcaneus	Tibial nerve (L4–S1 nerve fibers)
Deep layer			
Flexor digitorum longus	Plantar flexes foot; flexes MP, PIP and DIP joints of toes 2–5	O: Posteromedial surface of tibia I: Distal phalanges of toes 2–5	Tibial nerve (L5–S1 nerve fibers)
Flexor hallucis longus	Plantar flexes foot; flexes MP and IP joints of great toe (1)	O: Posterior lower ⅔ of fibula I: Distal phalanx of great toe (1)	Tibial nerve (L5–S1 nerve fibers)
Tibialis posterior	Plantar flexes foot; inverts foot	O: Fibula, tibia, and interosseous membrane I: Metatarsals II–IV; navicular bone; cuboid bone; all cuneiforms	Tibial nerve (L5–S1 nerve fibers)
Popliteus (pop-li-tē′ŭs) *poplit* = back of knee	Flexes leg; medially rotates tibia to unlock the knee	O: Lateral condyle of femur I: Posterior, proximal surface of tibia	Tibial nerve (L4–L5 nerve fibers)

Table 11.25 — Summary of Muscle Actions at the Knee Joint/Leg

Extension	Flexion
Quadriceps femoris:	Sartorius
Rectus femoris	Gracilis
Vastus lateralis	Adductor longus, brevis, magnus
Vastus intermedius	Biceps femoris
Vastus medialis	Semimembranosus
	Gastrocnemius
	Popliteus
	(Plantaris)

Parentheses around an entire muscle name indicate only a slight effect.

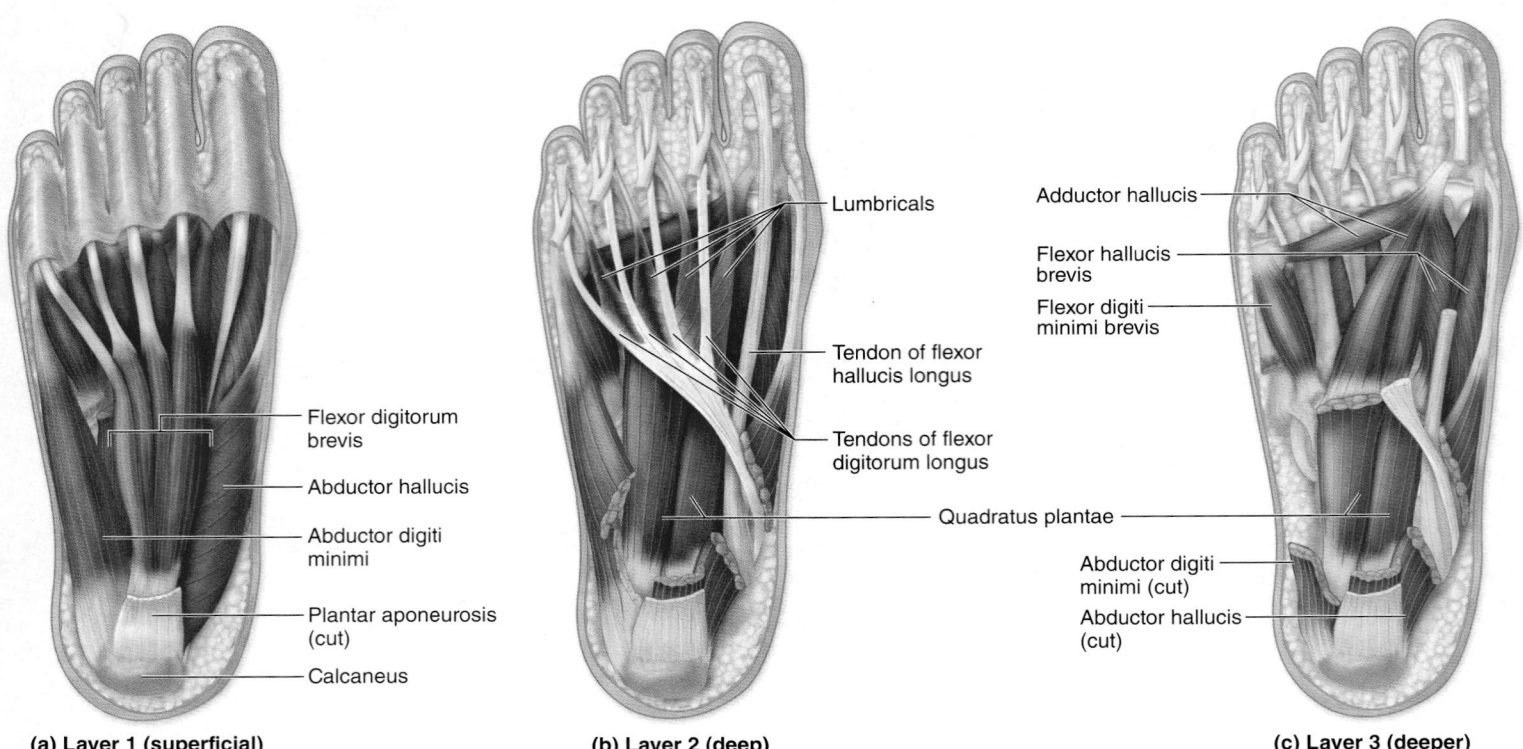

(a) Layer 1 (superficial)

Flexor digitorum brevis
Abductor hallucis
Abductor digiti minimi
Plantar aponeurosis (cut)
Calcaneus

(b) Layer 2 (deep)

Lumbricals
Tendon of flexor hallucis longus
Tendons of flexor digitorum longus
Quadratus plantae

(c) Layer 3 (deeper)

Adductor hallucis
Flexor hallucis brevis
Flexor digiti minimi brevis
Abductor digiti minimi (cut)
Abductor hallucis (cut)

Figure 11.37 Plantar Intrinsic Muscles of the Foot.
These muscles move the toes. (*a*) Superficial, (*b*) deep, and (*c*) deeper layers of the intrinsic muscles of the right foot. (*d*) Plantar and (*e*) dorsal views of the deepest layers. AP|R

(d) Layer 4 (deepest), plantar view

Plantar interossei

(e) Layer 4 (deepest), dorsal view

Dorsal interossei

11.9d Intrinsic Muscles of the Foot

LEARNING OBJECTIVE

7. Identify the muscles of each group and their actions.

The intrinsic muscles of the foot both originate and insert within the foot. They support the arches and move the toes to aid locomotion. Most of these muscles are comparable to the intrinsic muscles of the hand, meaning that they have similar names and locations. However, the intrinsic muscles of the foot rarely perform all the precise movements their names suggest.

The intrinsic foot muscles form a dorsal group and a plantar group. The dorsal group contains only two muscles: the extensor hallucis brevis and the extensor digitorum brevis (see figure 11.34). The **extensor hallucis brevis** extends the MP joint of the great toe. The **extensor digitorum brevis** extends the MP and PIP joints of toes 2–4.

WHAT DO YOU THINK?

4 The extensor digitorum brevis only goes to toes 2–4, so how is it possible to extend your little toe (toe 5)?

The plantar surface of the foot is supported by the **plantar aponeurosis** formed from the deep fascia of the foot. This aponeurosis extends between the phalanges of the toes and the calcaneus. It also encloses the plantar muscles of the foot. The plantar muscles are grouped into four layers (**figure 11.37**) and are described in detail in **table 11.26**.

Table 11.27 groups the leg and intrinsic foot muscles according to their common actions on the foot.

WHAT DID YOU LEARN?

29 Identify the intrinsic muscles of the foot that extend the toes.

INTEGRATE

CLINICAL VIEW
Plantar Fasciitis

Plantar fasciitis (fas-ē-ī′tis) is an inflammation of the plantar aponeurosis. Factors associated with plantar fasciitis include overexertion that stresses the fascia, weight-bearing activities (lifting heavy objects, jogging, or walking), excessive body weight, improperly fitting shoes, and poor biomechanics (e.g., wearing high-heeled shoes or having flat feet). Because plantar fasciitis can occur due to repetitively pounding the feet on the ground, this condition has become a common cause of heel pain in runners.

Table 11.26	Intrinsic Muscles of the Foot		
Group/Muscle	**Action**	**Origin/Insertion**	**Inversion (see section 14.5g)**
DORSAL SURFACE (TOE EXTENSORS)			
Extensor hallucis brevis	Extends MP joint of great toe (1)	O: Calcaneus and inferior extensor retinaculum I: Proximal phalanx of great toe (1)	Deep fibular nerve (S1–S2 nerve fibers)
Extensor digitorum brevis	Extends MP and PIP joints of toes 2–4	O: Calcaneus and inferior extensor retinaculum I: Middle phalanges of toes 2–4	Deep fibular nerve (S1–S2 nerve fibers)
PLANTAR SURFACE (TOE FLEXORS, ABDUCTORS, ADDUCTORS)			
Layer 1 (superficial)			
Flexor digitorum brevis	Flexes MP and PIP joints of toes 2–5	O: Calcaneus I: Middle phalanges of toes 2–5	Medial plantar nerve (S2–S3)
Abductor hallucis	Abducts great toe (1)	O: Calcaneus I: Medial side of proximal phalanx of great toe (1)	Medial plantar nerve (S2–S3)
Abductor digiti minimi	Abducts toe 5	O: Calcaneus (inferior surface tuberosity) I: Lateral side of proximal phalanx of toe 5	Lateral plantar nerve (S2–S3)
Layer 2 (deep)			
Quadratus plantae (plan'tē) *planta* = sole of foot	Pulls on flexor digitorum longus tendons to flex toes 2–5	O: Calcaneus, long plantar ligament I: Tendons of flexor digitorum longus	Lateral plantar nerve (S2–S3)
Lumbricals *lumbric* = earthworm	Flexes MP joints and extends PIP and DIP joints of toes 2–5	O: Tendons of flexor digitorum longus I: Tendons of extensor digitorum longus	Medial plantar nerve (1st lumbrical); lateral plantar nerve (2nd through 4th lumbricals)
Layer 3 (deeper)			
Adductor hallucis	Adducts great toe (1)	O: Transverse head: Capsules of MP joints III–V ; Oblique head: Bases of metatarsals II–IV I: Lateral side of proximal phalanx of great toe (1)	Lateral plantar nerve (S2–S3)
Flexor hallucis brevis	Flexes MP joint of great toe (1)	O: Cuboid and lateral cuneiform bones I: Proximal phalanx of great toe (1)	Medial plantar nerve (S2–S3)
Flexor digiti minimi brevis	Flexes MP joint of toe 5	O: Metatarsal V I: Proximal phalanx of toe 5	Lateral plantar nerve (S2–S3)
Layer 4 (deepest)			
Dorsal interossei	Abducts toes	O: Adjacent sides of metatarsals I: Sides of proximal phalanges of toes 2–4	Lateral plantar nerve (S2–S3)
Plantar interossei	Adducts toes	O: Sides of metatarsals III–V I: Medial side of proximal phalanges of toes 3–5	Lateral plantar nerve (S2–S3)

Table 11.27	Summary of Leg and Foot Muscle Actions at the Foot and Toes						
FOOT				**TOES**			
Dorsiflexion	**Plantar Flexion**	**Eversion**	**Innervation**	**Extension**	**Flexion**	**Abduction**	**Adduction**
Tibialis anterior*	**Gastrocnemius**	**Fibularis longus**	**Tibialis posterior**	Extensor digitorum longus	Flexor digitorum longus	Abductor hallucis	Adductor hallucis
Extensor digitorum longus	**Soleus**	**Fibularis brevis**	**Tibialis anterior**	Extensor hallucis longus	Flexor hallucis longus	Abductor digiti minimi	Plantar interossei
(Extensor hallucis longus)	Flexor digitorum longus	(Fibularis tertius)		Extensor digitorum brevis	Flexor digitorum brevis	Dorsal interossei	
(Fibularis tertius)	Flexor hallucis longus			Extensor hallucis brevis	Flexor hallucis brevis		
	Tibialis posterior				Flexor digiti minimi brevis		
	(Fibularis longus)						
	(Fibularis brevis)						

*Boldface indicates an agonist; others are synergists. Parentheses around an entire muscle name indicate only a slight effect.

- Axial muscles attach to components of the axial skeleton, whereas appendicular muscles stabilize or move components of the appendicular skeleton.

11.1 Skeletal Muscle Composition and Actions 372

- Skeletal muscle typically has origins and insertions, and the fascicles are organized in one of four basic patterns.

11.1a Origin and Insertion 372

- The origin is the less movable attachment of a muscle, whereas the insertion is the more movable attachment.

11.1b Organizational Patterns of Skeletal Muscle Fibers 372

- Muscle fibers may be arranged in circular, parallel, convergent, or pennate patterns.

11.1c Actions of Skeletal Muscles 373

- An agonist is a prime mover, whereas an antagonist opposes the agonist.
- A synergist assists an agonist.

11.2 Skeletal Muscle Naming 374

- Muscles receive their name according to muscle action, body region, muscle attachment, direction of the muscle fibers, shape, size, and muscle heads/origins.

11.3 Muscles of the Head and Neck 376

- Muscles of the head and neck are separated into groups based upon their specific activities.

11.3a Muscles of Facial Expression 376

- The muscles of facial expression arise from the skull and often attach to the skin.

11.3b Extrinsic Eye Muscles 380

- The six extrinsic eye muscles attach to the external surface of the eye and control the eye's movement.

11.3c Muscles of the Oral Cavity and Pharynx 382

- The muscles of mastication elevate and move the mandible during chewing.
- Intrinsic tongue muscles form the tongue itself, whereas extrinsic tongue muscles move the tongue during food manipulation, swallowing, and speech.
- Pharynx muscles function during swallowing.

11.3d Muscles of the Anterior Neck: The Hyoid Muscles 385

- The suprahyoid muscles elevate the hyoid bone, whereas the infrahyoid muscles depress the hyoid bone, move the thyroid cartilage during swallowing or speaking, or both.

11.3e Muscles That Move the Head and Neck 387

- Anterolateral neck muscles flex the head and neck, whereas posterior neck muscles extend the head and neck.

11.4 Muscles of the Vertebral Column 389

- The erector spinae muscles and other deep back muscles extend the vertebral column.

11.5 Muscles of Respiration 391

- The intercostal muscles, transversus thoracis, and diaphragm change the shape of the thoracic cavity when we breathe.

11.6 Muscles of the Abdominal Wall 392

- The abdominal wall muscles compress the abdomen, hold the abdominal organs in place, and flex the vertebral column.

11.7 Muscles of the Pelvic Floor 397

- The muscles of the pelvic floor support the pelvic organs and form a muscular wall that covers the inferior pelvic opening.

11.8 Muscles of the Pectoral Girdle and Upper Limb 399

- Five groups of muscles are associated with pectoral girdle and upper limb movement: muscles that move (1) the pectoral girdle; (2) the glenohumeral joint/arm; (3) the elbow joint/forearm; (4) the wrist joint, hand, and fingers; and (5) the intrinsic muscles of the hand.

11.8a Muscles That Move the Pectoral Girdle 399

- Anterior thoracic muscles tend to depress the scapula or clavicle, protract the scapula or clavicle, or both. The posterior thoracic muscles, in comparison, elevate the scapula, retract the scapula, or both.

11.8b Muscles That Move the Glenohumeral Joint/Arm 402

- The pectoralis major flexes the arm, and the latissimus dorsi and teres major extend it, whereas all adduct and medially rotate the arm.
- The deltoid flexes, extends, and abducts the arm.
- The rotator cuff muscles provide strength and stability to the glenohumeral joint.

11.8c Arm and Forearm Muscles That Move the Elbow Joint/Forearm 405

- The principal flexors are on the anterior side of the arm, and the principal extensors are on the posterior side of the arm.
- The pronator teres and pronator quadratus pronate the forearm, whereas the supinator and biceps brachii supinate the forearm.

11.8d Forearm Muscles That Move the Wrist Joint, Hand, and Fingers 410

- Anterior forearm muscles flex the wrist and finger joints, whereas posterior forearm muscles extend the wrist and joints of the fingers.
- The tendons of the anterior and posterior forearm muscles are held in place by bands of dense regular connective tissue called retinacula.

CHALLENGE YOURSELF

Do You Know the Basics?

_____ 1. Which statement is true about an agonist?

    a. It opposes the function of the prime mover.

    b. It is the primary muscle that produces a movement.

    c. It functions primarily to stabilize a joint.

    d. Its muscle fibers are always circular in structure.

_____ 2. When the left and right _____ contract, they flex the head and neck.

    a. sternocleidomastoid

    b. longissimus group

    c. splenius

    d. rectus abdominis

_____ 3. When this large muscle contracts, the vertical dimensions of the thoracic cavity increase.

    a. external intercostal

    b. internal intercostal

    c. diaphragm

    d. transversus thoracis

_____ 4. This muscle depresses and adducts the eye.

    a. inferior rectus

    b. inferior oblique

    c. lateral rectus

    d. superior oblique

_____ 5. Each of these muscles can laterally flex the vertebral column _except_ the

    a. external oblique.   c. spinalis.

    b. transversus abdominis.   d. internal oblique.

_____ 6. The dorsal interossei muscles in the hand

    a. adduct fingers 2–5.

    b. abduct fingers 2–5.

    c. flex the PIP and DIP joints.

    d. extend the MP joints.

_____ 7. Muscles in the anterior compartment of the leg

    a. evert the foot.

    b. dorsiflex the foot and extend the toes.

    c. plantar flex the foot.

    d. flex the toes.

_____ 8. All of the following muscles flex the forearm _except_ the

    a. brachialis.

    b. biceps brachii.

    c. brachioradialis.

    d. anconeus.

_____ 9. Which muscles originate on the ischial tuberosity and extend the thigh plus flex the leg?

    a. adductor   c. hamstring

    b. fibularis   d. quadriceps

_____ 10. The _____ plantar flexes the foot.

    a. iliopsoas

    b. gastrocnemius

    c. fibularis tertius

    d. vastus intermedius

11. What are some of the ways that muscles are named?

12. Which muscles of facial expression do you use to (a) smile, (b) close your eyes, and (c) close your mouth?

13. Distinguish between suprahyoid and infrahyoid muscles, and describe the functions of each group.

14. What is the effect of contracting the abdominal oblique muscles?

15. What movements are possible at the glenohumeral joint, and which muscles are the prime movers for each of these movements?

16. Identify the compartments of the arm (brachium), the muscles in each compartment, and their function.

17. Compare and contrast the flexor digitorum superficialis and the flexor digitorum profundus; where does each insert, how are their tendons interrelated, and what muscle actions do they perform?

18. What muscles are responsible for thigh extension? Which of these is the prime mover of thigh extension?

19. What leg muscles allow a ballet dancer to rise up and balance on her toes?

20. Which muscles are responsible for foot inversion?

Can You Apply What You've Learned?

1. A 50-year-old woman was concerned about the appearance of "crow's-feet" by her eyes. She was told by her physician that these wrinkles were caused by years of squinting and blinking using which muscle?

   a. frontal belly of occipitofrontalis

   b. orbicularis oculi

   c. risorius

   d. orbicularis oris

2. Eliza complained of double vision and went to see her optometrist. The optometrist tested the function of various eye muscles and discovered that Eliza could not move her right eye medially. Which muscle may be injured?

   a. superior oblique   c. medial rectus

   b. lateral rectus   d. inferior oblique

3. After an intensive workout, George felt especially sore in his posterior arm regions. What repetitive workout activity most likely caused the soreness?

   a. flexing the humerus   c. pronating the forearm

   b. flexing the forearm   d. extending the forearm

4. While Carly was playing soccer, she was kicked in the anterior thigh by an opposing teammate. Due to this injury, what muscle function may have been difficult to perform?

   a. extending the knee   c. extending the thigh

   b. flexing the knee   d. dorsiflexing the foot

5. Joshua broke his fibula and had to wear a cast for 6 weeks. The muscles attaching to this bone atrophied during this time. What muscle function was Joshua unable to perform as a result?

   a. plantar flexing the foot   c. everting the foot

   b. flexing the knee   d. dorsiflexing the foot

Can You Synthesize What You've Learned?

1. Albon is a 45-year-old male who characterizes himself as a "couch potato." He exercises infrequently and has a rounded abdomen ("beer belly"). While helping a friend move some heavy furniture, he felt a sharp pain deep within his abdominopelvic cavity. An emergency room resident told Albon that he had suffered an inguinal hernia. What is this injury, how did it occur, and how might Albon's poorly developed abdominal musculature have contributed to it?

2. While training on the balance beam, Pat slipped during her landing from a back flip and fell, straddling the beam. Although only slightly sore from the fall, she became concerned when she suddenly lost the ability to completely control her urination. What might have happened to Pat's pelvic floor structures during the fall?

3. After falling while skateboarding, Karen had surgery on her elbow. During her recovery, she must visit the physical therapist to improve muscle function around the elbow. Develop a series of exercises that may improve all of Karen's elbow movements, and determine which muscles are being helped by each exercise.

4. Why is it more difficult for Eric to lift a heavy weight when his forearm is pronated than when it is in the supine position?

INTEGRATE

ONLINE STUDY TOOLS
www.mhhe.com/mckinleyap

Clinical Case Study: A Young Boy Who is Losing His Ability to Walk

Interactive Questions: This chapter's content is served up in a number of multimedia question formats for student study.

LearnSmart: Topics and terminology include skeletal muscle composition and actions; skeletal muscle naming; muscles of the head and neck; muscles of the vertebral column; muscles of

respiration; muscles of the abdominal wall; muscles of the pelvic floor; muscles of the pectoral girdle and upper and lower limbs

Anatomy & Physiology Revealed: Topics include dissection of the head and neck, orbit, back, thorax, abdomen, shoulder, forearm, arm, wrist, hand, hip, thigh, and foot; muscle actions of pectoralis major, Latissimus Dorsi, flexor digitorum superficialis, and gastrocnemius

chapter 12

Nervous System: Nervous Tissue

Throughout the day, your body perceives and responds to multiple sensations. You smell spring flowers, feel the touch of a hand on your shoulder, and are visually aware of your environment. You control multiple muscle movements to walk, talk to the person sitting next to you, and hold this textbook. Other muscle movements occur without your voluntary input: Your heart beats, your stomach churns to digest your breakfast, and you jump at the sound of a honking horn. All of these sensations ➡

An electroencephalograph (EEG) technician monitors a patient's brain waves by attaching electrodes to the scalp. Results from an EEG help aid in the diagnoses of impaired brain function resulting from sleep disturbance, epilepsy, and infectious disease. They also help measure progress in the treatment of stroke and brain trauma. An essential function performed by EEG technicians is the definitive confirmation that a patient may have ceased brain functional activities. These professional duties are performed in neurological clinics and research facilities as well as hospitals and physicians offices.

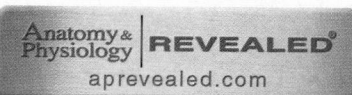

Module 7: Nervous System

and muscle movements are interpreted and controlled by your **nervous system.**

Here we introduce the study of the nervous system by first describing its general functions and overall organization and then discussing the components of nervous tissue, which is the primary tissue of the nervous system. The next several chapters investigate different aspects of the nervous system, including the structure and function of the brain and cranial nerves (see chapter 13), spinal cord and spinal nerves (see chapter 14), organization and function of the autonomic nervous system (see chapter 15), and the senses (see chapter 16).

12.1 Introduction to the Nervous System

The nervous system is composed of the brain, spinal cord, nerves, and ganglia. Here we examine the general functions of the nervous system and how it is organized both structurally and functionally.

12.1a General Functions of the Nervous System

LEARNING OBJECTIVE

1. Describe the three general functions of the nervous system.

The nervous system serves as the body's primary communication and control system. It provides a rapid means of integrating and regulating body functions through electrical activity transmitted along specialized nervous system cells called neurons to accomplish the following:

- **Collect information.** Receptors are specialized nervous system structures that monitor changes in both the internal and external environment called **stimuli** (sing., *stimulus*). For example, receptors in the skin detect stimuli associated with touch—this sensory input then is relayed along nerves to the spinal cord and brain.
- **Process and evaluate information.** After processing sensory input, the brain and spinal cord determine what response, if any, is required.
- **Initiate response to information.** The brain and spinal cord initiate a response as motor output via nerves to **effectors.** Effectors include all three types of muscle tissue and glands. The result, or effect, may be either muscle contraction (or relaxation) or a change in gland secretion.

WHAT DID YOU LEARN?

1 What is the function of receptors? What are the different types of effectors controlled by the nervous system?

12.1b Organization of the Nervous System

LEARNING OBJECTIVES

2. Identify the structural components included in both the CNS and the PNS.
3. Explain the functional organization of the nervous system.

Anatomists and physiologists have devised various ways to organize the structural and functional components of the nervous sys-

tem. However, always keep in mind that such artificial divisions are merely intended to simplify discussion—there is only one nervous system.

Structural Organization: Central Versus Peripheral Nervous System

The nervous system consists of two anatomic divisions: the central nervous system and the peripheral nervous system (figure 12.1*a*). The **central nervous system (CNS)** includes the brain and spinal cord. The brain is protected and enclosed within the skull, while the spinal cord is housed and protected within the vertebral canal.

The **peripheral** (pĕ-rif′ĕr-ăl) **nervous system (PNS)** includes **nerves,** which are bundles of neuron processes (axons) and **ganglia** (gang′glē-ă; sing., *ganglion;* swelling) that are clusters of neuron cell bodies located along nerves.

Functional Organization: Sensory Versus Motor Nervous System

The nervous system has two functional divisions: the sensory nervous system and the motor nervous system (figure 12.1*b*). Both the sensory nervous system and the motor nervous system have CNS and PNS components.

Sensory Nervous System The **sensory nervous system** or *afferent* (af′er-ent; *afferns* = to bring to) *nervous system* is responsible for receiving sensory information *from* receptors that detect stimuli and transmitting this information *to* the CNS.

The sensory nervous system may be further subdivided based on whether we are consciously aware of the stimuli that is detected. The two components are the somatic sensory and the visceral sensory. The **somatic** (sō-mat′ik; soma = body) **sensory** components may detect stimuli that we consciously perceive. Receptors of the somatic sensory nervous system include the eyes, nose, tongue, ears, skin, and proprioceptors (receptors in joints and muscles that detect body position).

In comparison, the **visceral** (vis′ĕr-ăl; *viscus* = internal organ) **sensory** components detect stimuli that we typically do not consciously perceive. Receptors of the visceral sensory nervous system include structures located within blood vessels and internal organs (e.g., heart, stomach, kidneys). Visceral receptors detect chemical composition of the blood or stretch of an organ wall, for example. The various types of receptors are described in detail in chapter 16.

Structural organization

Central nervous system (CNS)	Brain
	Spinal cord
Peripheral nervous system (PNS)	Nerves
	Ganglia

Functional organization

Sensory nervous system detects stimuli and transmits information from receptors to the CNS

Motor nervous system initiates and transmits information from the CNS to effectors

Somatic sensory
Sensory input that is consciously perceived from receptors (e.g., eyes, skin, ears)

Visceral sensory
Sensory input that is not consciously perceived from blood vessels and internal organs (e.g., heart)

Somatic motor
Motor output that is consciously or voluntarily controlled; effector is skeletal muscle

Autonomic motor
Motor output that is not consciously or is involuntarily controlled; effectors are cardiac muscle, smooth muscle, and glands

Figure 12.1 Organization of the Nervous System. The nervous system is organized into both structural and functional categories. (*a*) Structural divisions include the central nervous system (CNS), which includes the brain and spinal cord, and the peripheral nervous system (PNS), which is composed of nerves and ganglia. (*b*) Functionally, the nervous system consists of sensory (afferent) and motor (efferent) divisions, both of which are further divided into somatic and visceral (autonomic) components. AP|R

Motor Nervous System The **motor nervous system** or *efferent* (ef′er-ent; *efferens* = to bring out) *nervous system* is responsible for initiating and transmitting motor output *from* the CNS *to* effectors. This system controls muscle tissue and glands.

The motor nervous system, like the sensory nervous system, is subdivided into somatic and visceral parts. Here the distinction is based on whether the effector stimulated can be controlled consciously (voluntarily). The **somatic motor** component initiates and transmits motor output from the CNS to voluntary skeletal muscles. For example, you exert voluntary control over your leg muscles as you press on the accelerator of your car.

The **autonomic** (aw-tō-nom′ik; *auto* = self, *nomos* = law) **motor** (or *visceral motor*) component innervates and regulates cardiac muscle, smooth muscle, and glands without our conscious control. We can neither voluntarily make our heart stop beating nor prevent our stomachs from growling. The autonomic motor component has two further subdivisions—sympathetic and parasympathetic—which are described in chapter 15.

WHAT DID YOU LEARN?

 What are the two primary functional divisions of the nervous system? How do they differ?

12.2 Nervous Tissue: Neurons

Nervous tissue is the primary tissue of the nervous system and is composed of two distinct cell types: neurons and glial cells (first introduced in section 5.4). Neurons are excitable cells that initiate and transmit electrical signals and glial cells are nonexcitable cells that primarily support and protect the neurons. We describe neurons here and glial cells in detail in a later section.

12.2a General Characteristics of Neurons

LEARNING OBJECTIVE

1. Describe five distinguishing features common to all neurons.

The basic structural unit of the nervous system is the **neuron** (nū′ron). These cells have several special characteristics including

- **Excitability.** This is a responsiveness to stimulation. The type of stimulation that a neuron responds to is dependent upon its location. For example, neurons in the skin respond to pressure changes associated with touch. Most neurons usually respond only to binding of secreted molecules called neurotransmitters that are released from other neurons.

- **Conductivity.** These are electrical changes that are quickly propagated along the plasma membrane of neurons following stimulation. We will see later that conductivity can be local and short-lived (graded potentials) or self-propagating (action potentials).

- **Secretion.** Neurons release neurotransmitters in response to conductive activity. A given neuron typically releases only one type of neurotransmitter, and the neurotransmitter may have either an excitatory or an inhibitory effect on its target organ (other neurons or effectors).

- **Extreme longevity.** Most neurons formed during fetal development are still functional in very elderly individuals.
- **Amitotic.** During fetal development of neurons, mitotic activity is lost in most neurons, except those in the olfactory epithelium of the nose and in certain areas of the brain.

Prevailing medical wisdom for years has maintained that the number of neurons in your brain shortly after birth is your supply for a lifetime. Recent studies, however, have shown that this is not always the case. Researchers investigating the brain's hippocampus (a region involved in memory processing; see section 13.7a) have found that this region of the brain contains a population of neural stem cells. These stem cells were once thought to give rise only to new glial cells in adults, but it is now clear that under special circumstances they can mature into neurons. The new neurons appear able to incorporate themselves, at least to some degree, into the brain circuitry. Researchers have learned that the surrounding glial cells provide the chemical signals that direct a stem cell down the path of nerve cell maturation.

WHAT DID YOU LEARN?

3 Explain the neuron characteristics of excitability, conductivity, and secretion.

12.2b Neuron Structure

LEARNING OBJECTIVES

2. Describe the three basic anatomic features common to most neurons.

3. Identify and describe the structures unique to neurons.

Neurons come in many shapes and sizes, but they typically share certain basic structural features that include a cell body, dendrites, and an axon **(figure 12.2)**.

The **cell body** is also called the *soma,* and it is enclosed by a plasma membrane and contains cytoplasm surrounding a nucleus. Cell bodies serve as the neuron's control center. They also conduct electrical signals to the axon. This electrical signal is either initiated within the cell body or received from the dendrites.

The cytoplasm within the cell body is called the **perikaryon** (per'i-kar'ē-on; *peri* = around, *karyon* = kernel), although some anatomists use that term to describe the whole cell body. The nucleus accommodates a prominent nucleolus, where ribosomes are formed (see section 4.6a). Free and bound ribosomes together go by two names: (1) **chromatophilic** (krō-mă-tō-fil'ik; *chromo* = color, *phileo* = to love) **substance,** because they stain darkly with basic dyes; or (2) *Nissl bodies,* because they were first described by the German microscopist Franz Nissl. Cytologists consider that the gray color of gray matter seen in gross dissections of the brain and spinal cord is due to the chromatophilic substance, along with the absence of myelin, a glistening coat of insulating material (described later).

Dendrites (den'drīt; *dendrites* = relating to a tree) tend to be relatively short, small processes that branch off the cell body. Some neurons have only one dendrite; others have many. Dendrites conduct electrical signals toward the cell body; in essence, they receive input and then transfer it to the cell body for processing. The greater the number of dendrites, the more input a neuron may receive.

The **axon** (ak'son) is sometimes called a *nerve fiber.* It is typically a longer process emanating from the cell body to make contact with other neurons, muscle cells, or gland cells. The first part of the axon is a triangular region where the axon emanates from the cell body; it is called the **axon hillock** (hil'lok). The cytoplasm within an axon is called **axoplasm,** and the plasma membrane of an axon is called an **axolemma.** Unlike the cell body, the axon is devoid of chromatophilic substance. This distinctive difference allows the cell body to be distinguished from the axon when nervous tissue is viewed under a microscope.

Axons give rise to a few side branches called **axon collaterals.** Most axons and their collaterals branch extensively at their distal end into an array of fine terminal extensions called **telodendria** (tel-ō-den'drē-a; sing., *telodendrion; telos* = end), or *axon terminals.* The extreme tips of these fine extensions are slightly expanded regions called **synaptic** (si-nap'tik) **knobs,** also called *synaptic bulbs, end bulbs,* or *terminal boutons.* Within the synaptic knobs are numerous **synaptic vesicles** containing neurotransmitter. A synaptic knob meets at a functional junction called a synapse (described shortly).

Cytoskeleton

The **cytoskeleton** in a neuron is composed of microfilaments, intermediate filaments, and microtubules (see section 4.5b). The intermediate filaments, called **neurofilaments**

(a)

Dendrites

Perikaryon

Nucleolus

Nucleus

Cell body

Chromatophilic substance

Axon hillock

Axoplasm

Axolemma

Neurofibrils

Axon (beneath myelin sheath)

Axon collateral

Neurolemmocyte

Neurofibril node

Myelin sheath

Telodendria

Synaptic knobs

Synaptic vesicles containing neurotransmitter

Synaptic cleft

Postsynaptic neuron (or effector)

Synapse

(b)

LM 100x

Dendrite

Chromatophilic substance

Nucleus

Cell body

Axon hillock

Nucleus of glial cell

Axon

Figure 12.2 Structures in a Typical Neuron. (*a*) Anatomic structures of a neuron. The flow of electrical activity is from dendrites, through the cell body to the axon, until it reaches the synaptic knob, which houses neurotransmitter in synaptic vesicles. (*b*) Photomicrograph of a large motor neuron. AP|R (nūr-ō-fil'ă-ment; *filamentum* = thread), aggregate to form bundles called **neurofibrils** (nūr-ō-fī'bril; *fibrilla* = fiber). Neurofibrils extend as a complex network through the neuron, where their tensile strength provides support.

WHAT DID YOU LEARN?

4 What are the functions of these neuron structures: dendrites, axon, synaptic vesicles, and neurofibrils?

12.2c Neuron Transport

LEARNING OBJECTIVE

4. Distinguish between fast axonal transport and slow axonal transport, and give examples of the different substances moved by each.

Axons are generally dependent upon the cell body to provide them with newly synthesized materials and to break down or recycle their used materials. To accomplish this, substances are moved in both directions through an axon. **Anterograde transport** is the movement of materials from the cell body to synaptic knobs, and **retrograde transport** is the movement of materials from synaptic knobs to the cell body. The transport processes are classified as either fast axonal transport or slow axonal transport, depending upon the relative speed of movement.

Fast Axonal Transport

Fast axonal transport occurs at approximately 400 millimeters per day. The mechanism involves movement along microtubules. You may find it helpful to think of this process as similar to a substance being pulled along a train track. The power for this movement comes from specialized motor proteins (e.g., kinesin, dynein) that split ATP to supply the energy needed.

Substances can be moved in either direction (anterograde or retrograde). Substances formed in the cell body are moved by anterograde transport toward the synaptic knobs and include vesicles, organelles, and glycoproteins required at the synapse. Used vesicles to be broken down and recycled, and potentially harmful agents, are moved via retrograde transport from the synaptic knob to the cell body. Interestingly, new evidence supports the idea that some of these vesicles are transporting hormonelike molecules for the purposes of communication between neurons. This represents a means of neurons communicating information in a retrograde fashion from synaptic knobs to the cell body. Research continues in this area.

Slow Axonal Transport

Slow axonal transport occurs at approximately 0.1 to 3 millimeters per day. This type of movement results from the flow of the axoplasm, and is also called *axoplasmic flow*. The substances are only moved from the cell body towards the synaptic knob. These substances include enzymes, cytoskeletal components, and new axoplasm for regenerating axons.

WHAT DID YOU LEARN?

5 Which type of axonal transport is both anterograde and retrograde? Give examples of substances transported by this method.

12.2d Classification of Neurons

LEARNING OBJECTIVES

5. Name and describe the four structural categories of neurons.

6. Identify the three functional categories of neurons and where each is primarily located.

Neurons vary in morphology and location. Similar to the components of the entire nervous system, they are classified according to either their structure or their function.

Structural Classification

Neurons are classified structurally according to the number of neuron processes emanating directly from the cell body. Thus, they may be classified as multipolar, bipolar, unipolar, or anaxonic neurons **(table 12.1)**.

Table 12.1	Structural Classification of Neurons	
Neuron Type	**Structure**	**Description**
Multipolar Neuron	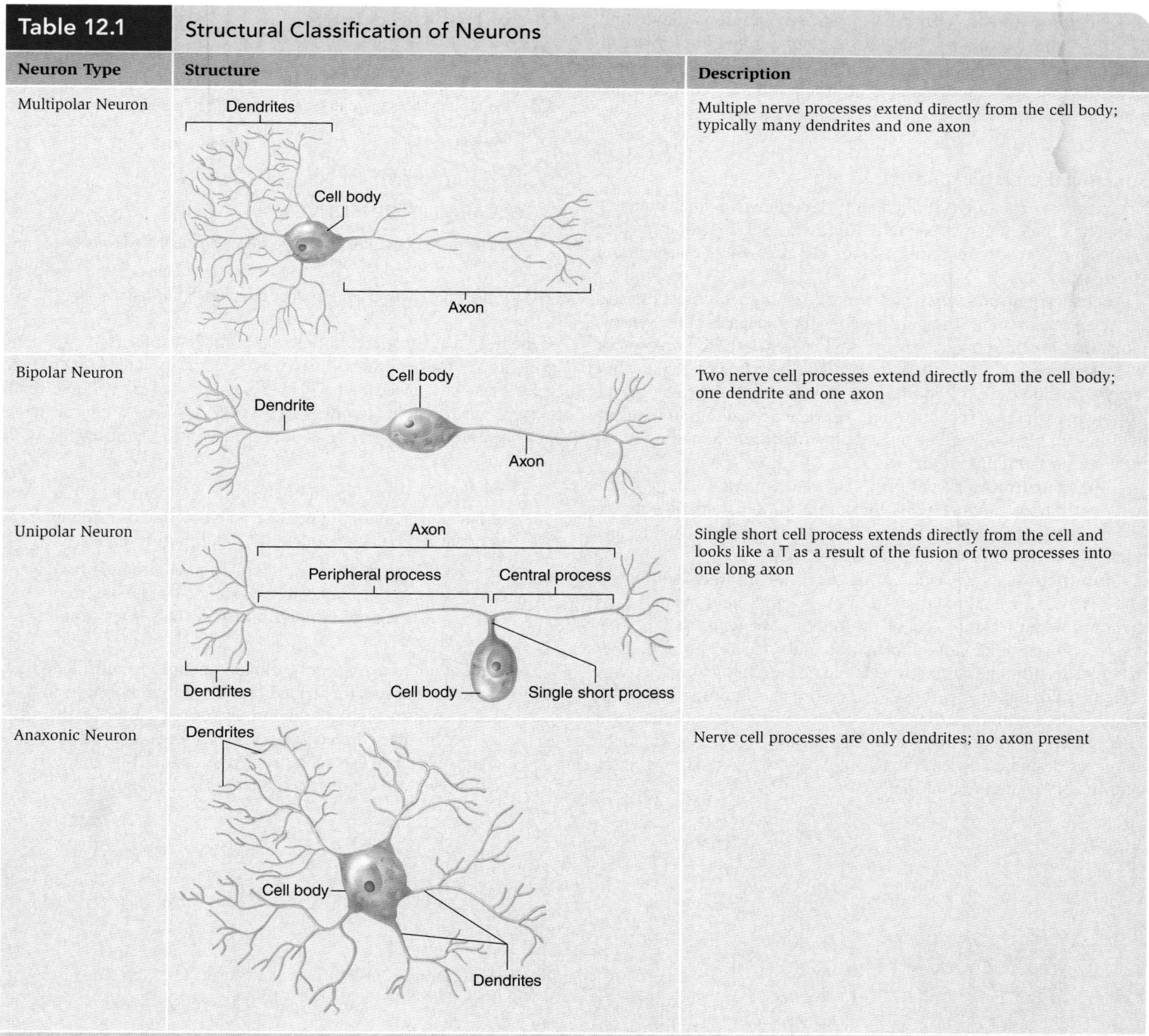	Multiple nerve processes extend directly from the cell body; typically many dendrites and one axon
Bipolar Neuron		Two nerve cell processes extend directly from the cell body; one dendrite and one axon
Unipolar Neuron		Single short cell process extends directly from the cell and looks like a T as a result of the fusion of two processes into one long axon
Anaxonic Neuron		Nerve cell processes are only dendrites; no axon present

Multipolar neurons are the most common type of neuron. These neurons have many dendrites and a single axon that extends from the cell body.

Bipolar neurons have two processes that extend from the cell body—one dendrite and one axon. The location of these neurons is relatively limited in humans (e.g., the retina of the eye and the olfactory mucosa in the nasal cavity).

Unipolar neurons have a single, short neuron process that emerges from the cell body and branches like a T. These neurons are also called **pseudounipolar** (sū′dō-yū-ni-pō-lăr; *pseudo* = false, *uni* = one) because they start out as bipolar neurons during development, but their two processes fuse into a single process. The naming of the branched processes in unipolar neurons has been a source of confusion with regard to the common definitions of dendrites and axons. It seems most appropriate to call the short, multiple-branched receptive endings dendrites. The other portion is called the axon because these processes, like other axons, generate and conduct action potentials (described later). These axons are composed of the combined **peripheral process** (from dendrites to the cell body) and **central process** (from the cell body into the CNS).

Anaxonic (an-aks'on; *an* = without) **neurons** have only dendrites and no axons. They are different from other types of neurons because they produce local electrical changes called graded potentials (described later), but they do not produce action potentials.

Functional Classification

Neurons are classified functionally according to the direction the action potential travels relative to the CNS. The three categories are sensory neurons, motor neurons, and interneurons (**figure 12.3**).

Sensory neurons (*afferent neurons*) are the neurons of the sensory nervous system. They are responsible for conducting sensory input from both somatic sensory and visceral sensory receptors. Most sensory neurons are unipolar. The cell bodies usually are located outside the CNS and housed within structures called posterior root ganglia (see section 14.5a). However, a few somatic sensory neurons are bipolar, such as those in the olfactory epithelium of the nose and in the retina of the eye.

Motor neurons (*efferent neurons*) are the neurons of the motor nervous system, conducting motor output to both somatic effectors and visceral effectors. All motor neurons are multipolar. The cell bodies of most motor neurons lie in the CNS.

Interneurons (*association neurons*) lie entirely within the CNS. They receive stimulation from many other neurons and carry out the integrative function of the nervous system—that is, they receive, process, and store information and "decide" how the body responds to stimuli. Interneurons facilitate communication between sensory and motor neurons. Interneurons outnumber all other neurons; it is estimated that 99% of our neurons are interneurons. The number of interneurons activated during processing or storing increases dramatically with the complexity of the response. Interneurons are generally multipolar.

WHAT DID YOU LEARN?

6 How are the different processes that extend from a cell body used to structurally classify neurons?

7 Where are interneurons located, and what is their function?

12.2e Relationship of Neurons and Nerves

LEARNING OBJECTIVES

7. Describe the structure of a nerve, including the three layers of connective tissue wrappings.

8. Explain how nerves are classified structurally and functionally.

A **nerve** is a cablelike bundle of parallel axons that are components of the peripheral nervous system. A single axon typically must be viewed using a microscope, whereas a nerve tends to be a macroscopic structure. **Figure 12.4** shows a typical nerve. Like a muscle, a nerve has three successive connective tissue wrappings:

- The **epineurium** (ep-i-nū'rē-ŭm; *epi* = upon) is a thick layer of dense irregular connective tissue that encloses the entire nerve and provides both support and protection.

- The **perineurium** (per-i-nū'rē-ŭm; *peri* = around) is a layer of dense irregular connective tissue that wraps fascicles (fas'i-kl), which are bundles of axons. This layer supports blood vessels.

- An individual axon in a myelinated neuron is surrounded by neurolemmocytes (described later) and then wrapped in the **endoneurium** (en-dō-nū'rē-ŭm; *endon* = within), a delicate layer of areolar connective tissue that separates and electrically insulates each axon. Also within this connective tissue layer are capillaries that supply each axon.

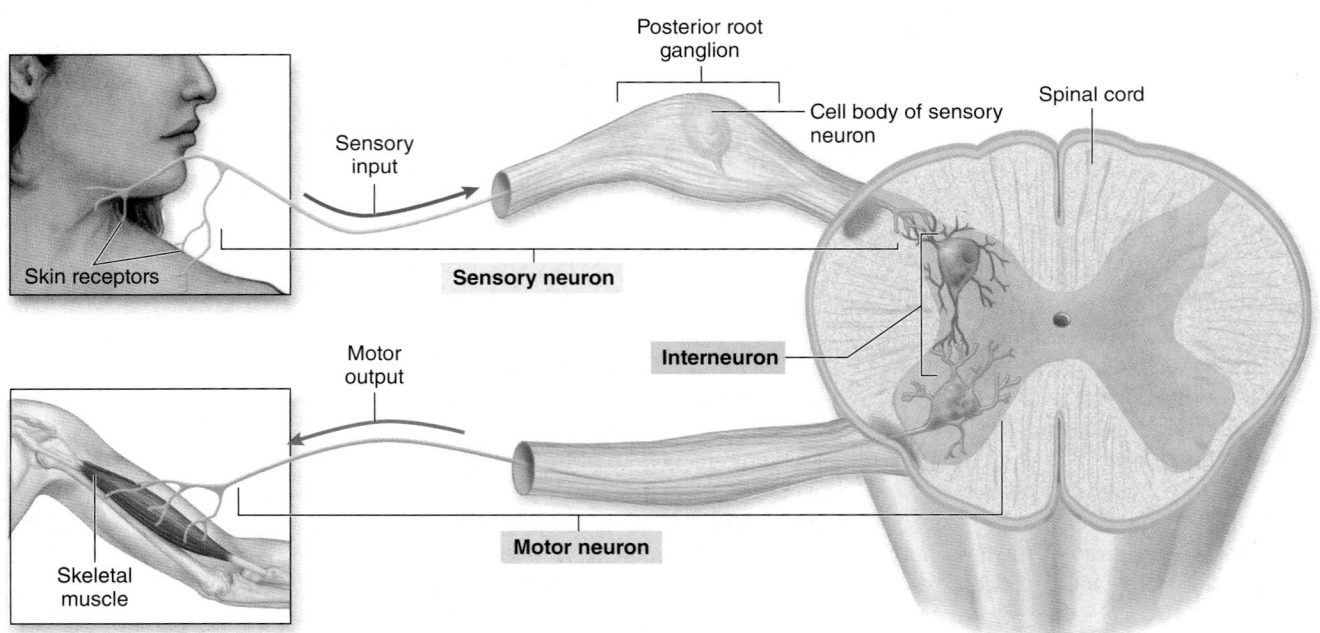

Figure 12.3 Functional Classification of Neurons. Sensory neurons transmit sensory input to the central nervous system. Interneurons process information within the CNS. Motor neurons transmit motor output from the CNS to effectors (muscle or gland). Notice that the most common structural type is drawn for each functional class: a unipolar sensory neuron, a multipolar interneuron, and a multipolar motor neuron. AP|R

Figure 12.4 **Structure of a Nerve and Ganglion.** (*a*) A nerve is ensheathed with a tough connective tissue layer called the epineurium. Each fascicle (bundle of axons) is wrapped within a tough connective tissue layer called the perineurium. An axon is surrounded by a delicate connective tissue layer called the endoneurium. In myelinated axons, neurolemmocytes are between the axon and endoneurium. (*b*) Inset of an electron micrograph showing the partial structure of a nerve, including connective tissue coverings within a nerve. (*c*) A ganglion is a collection of cell bodies along the length of a nerve.

Labels in figure (a):
- Epineurium
- Nerve
- Perineurium
- Fascicle
- Endoneurium
- Axon
- Neurolemmocyte
- Blood vessels

Labels in figure (b):
- Blood vessels
- Endoneurium
- Neurolemmocyte
- Axon
- Perineurium
- Fascicle
- SEM 450x

Labels in figure (c):
- Ganglion
- Nerve
- Cell bodies
- Axons
- Epineurium
- Blood vessels
- Axons

Classification of Nerves

Structural classification of nerves is based upon the CNS component from which the nerve extends: **Cranial nerves** extend from the brain (discussed in detail in section 13.9), and **spinal nerves** extend from the spinal cord (discussed in detail in section 14.5).

The functional classification of nerves is based upon the functional type of neuron (sensory neuron or motor neuron) a nerve contains. **Sensory nerves** contain only sensory neurons that relay information to the CNS, and **motor nerves** contain primarily motor neurons that relay information from the CNS. In contrast, **mixed nerves** contain both sensory and motor neurons. Most named nerves are mixed nerves. However, note that in mixed nerves individual sensory or motor neurons still transmit only one type of information.

WHAT DID YOU LEARN?

8 What are the three connective tissue wrappings in a nerve, and what specific structure does each ensheathe?

12.3 Synapses

LEARNING OBJECTIVES

1. Define a synapse.
2. Describe the essential structural and functional differences between a chemical synapse and an electrical synapse.

A **synapse** (sin′aps; *syn* = together, *hapto* = to clasp) is the specific location where a neuron is functionally connected to either another neuron or an effector. There are two types of synapses in the human body: chemical synapses and electrical synapses. Most synapses within the nervous system are chemical synapses.

A **chemical synapse** is composed of a **presynaptic** (prē-si-nap′tik; *pre* = before) **neuron,** which is the signal producer, and a **postsynaptic** (pōst-si-nap′tik; *post* = after) **neuron,** which is the signal receiver or target. The synapse may be between the axon of the presynaptic neuron and any portion of the surface of a postsynaptic neuron (dendrite, cell body, or axon), except those regions that are covered by a myelin sheath (described shortly). Most commonly a synapse is with a dendrite of the postsynaptic neuron. The synaptic knob of the presynaptic neuron almost, but does not quite make contact with the postsynaptic neuron (see inset, figure 12.2). The two neurons are separated by an extremely narrow fluid-filled gap (20 nanometers) called the **synaptic cleft.**

Transmission between a presynaptic and postsynaptic neuron occurs when **neurotransmitter** (nū′rō-trans′mit-ĕr) molecules stored in synaptic vesicles are released from the synaptic knob of a presynaptic neuron into the synaptic cleft. Some of the neurotransmitter diffuses across the cleft to bind to receptors within the postsynaptic plasma membrane to initiate another electrical signal. There is a **synaptic delay** associated with neurotransmitter release at chemical synapses. The delay is the time between the neurotransmitter release from the presynaptic cell, its diffusion across the synaptic cleft, and neurotransmitter binding to recep-

tors in the postsynaptic plasma membrane. This delay is usually between 0.3 to 0.5 milliseconds. Note that one postsynaptic neuron may be, and often is, stimulated by more than one presynaptic neuron simultaneously.

A second, and much less common, type of synapse is an electrical synapse. An **electrical synapse** is composed of a presynaptic neuron and a postsynaptic neuron physically bound together. Gap junctions (section 4.5d) are present in the plasma membranes of both neurons and facilitate the flow of ions between the cells. The cells act as though they share a common plasma membrane. Thus, the electrical signal passes between the cells with essentially no synaptic delay. Electrical synapses are located within limited regions of the brain and the eyes.

 WHAT DID YOU LEARN?

9 What is a chemical synapse within the nervous system, and how does it function?

Table 12.2	Glial Cells AP|R		
Cell Type	**Appearance**		**Functions**
CENTRAL NERVOUS SYSTEM			
Astrocyte	Neuron / Perivascular feet / **Astrocyte** / Capillary	Large cell with numerous cell processes; in contact with neurons and capillaries; most common type of glial cell	Helps form the blood-brain barrier Regulates tissue fluid composition Provides structural support and organization to the central nervous system (CNS) Assists with neuronal development Replicates to occupy space of dying neurons
Ependymal Cell	Central canal of spinal cord / **Ependymal cells** / Spinal cord	Simple cuboidal or columnar epithelial cells that line cavities in brain and spinal cord; cilia on apical surface	Lines ventricles of brain and central canal of spinal cord Assists in production and circulation of cerebrospinal fluid (CSF)
Microglial Cell	**Microglial cell** / Neuron	Small cell with slender branches from cell body; least common type of glial cell	Defends against infectious agents and engulfs debris from dead or dying neurons

12.4 Nervous Tissue: Glial Cells

Glial cells are the other distinct cell type within nervous tissue. These nonexcitable cells serve primarily to support and protect the neurons.

12.4a General Characteristics of Glial Cells

LEARNING OBJECTIVE

1. List the distinguishing features of glial cells.

Glial (glī'ăl) **cells** are sometimes referred to as *neuroglia* (nū-rog'lē-a; *glia* = glue). They are found within both the CNS and the PNS. Glial cells are both smaller than neurons and capable of mitosis. Glial cells do not transmit nerve signals, but they do assist neurons with their functions. The glial cells cooperate to physically protect and help nourish neurons as well as provide an organized, supporting scaffolding for all the nervous tissue. During development, glial cells form the framework that guides young, migrating neurons to their final destinations. Recent evidence has shown that glial cells are critical for the normal function at neural synapses, both maintaining the anatomic structure of synapses and modifying transmission that occurs there.

Glial cells far outnumber neurons. The nervous tissue of a young adult may contain 35 to 100 billion neurons and 100 billion to 1 trillion glial cells. Collectively, glial cells account for roughly half the volume of the nervous system. These cells are described next and summarized in **table 12.2**.

WHAT DID YOU LEARN?

10 If a person has a brain tumor, is it more likely to have developed from neurons or from glial cells? Why?

Table 12.2	Glial Cells (continued)		
Cell Type	**Appearance**		**Functions**
Oligodendrocyte		Rounded, bulbous cell with slender cytoplasmic extensions; extensions wrap around CNS axons	Myelinates and insulates CNS axons Allows faster action potential conduction along axons in the CNS
PERIPHERAL NERVOUS SYSTEM			
Satellite Cell		Flattened cell; groups of these cells cluster around neuronal cell bodies in a ganglion	Protects and regulates nutrient and waste exchange for cell bodies in ganglia
Neurolemmocyte		Flattened cell wrapped around a portion of an axon in the peripheral nervous system (PNS)	Myelinates and insulates PNS axons Allows for faster action potential conduction along an axon in the PNS

Oligodendrocyte appearance labels: Oligodendrocyte, Nucleus, Myelin sheath, Axons

Satellite Cell appearance labels: Posterior root ganglion, Satellite cells, Axon, Cell body of sensory neuron, Posterior root

Neurolemmocyte appearance labels: Neurofibril nodes, Axon, Nucleus, Myelin sheath, Neurilemma, Neurolemmocyte

12.4b Types of Glial Cells

Glial Cells of the CNS

Four types of glial cells are found in the central nervous system. These different cells are called astrocytes, ependymal cells, microglia, and oligodendrocytes (**figure 12.5a**). They can be distinguished based upon size, intracellular organization, and the presence of specific cytoplasmic processes.

Astrocytes (as'trō-sīt; *astron* = star) exhibit a starlike shape due to projections from their surface. These numerous cell processes touch both capillary walls and neurons. Astrocytes are the most abundant glial cell in the CNS and constitute over 90% of the nervous tissue in some areas of the brain. Astrocytes nurture, protect, support, and guide neurons, as follows:

- **Help form the blood-brain barrier.** The ends of astrocyte processes are called **perivascular feet:** They both cover and wrap around capillaries in the brain. The perivascular feet and the brain capillaries together contribute to a **blood-brain barrier (BBB).** The BBB strictly controls movement of substances from exiting the blood and entering the nervous tissue in the brain. The BBB protects the delicate neurons of the brain from toxins, but at the same time allows needed nutrients to pass through (see section 13.2d).

(a) CNS glial cells

(b) PNS glial cells

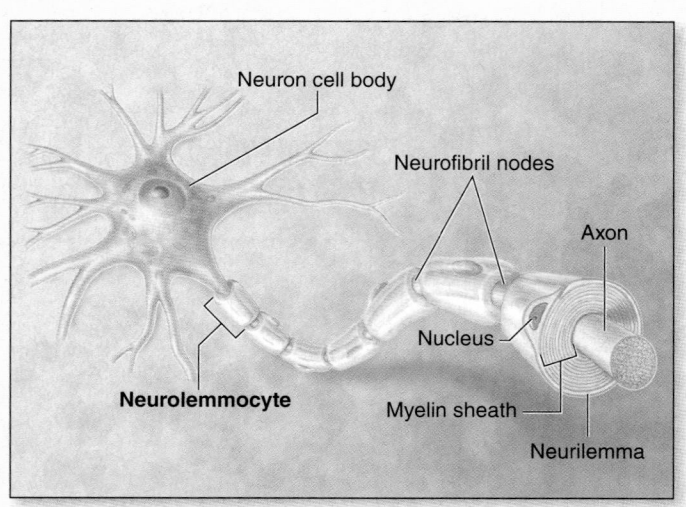

Figure 12.5 Cellular Organization of Nervous Tissue. (*a*) The four types of glial cells found in the CNS, and (*b*) the two types of glial cells found in the PNS are shown in relationship to a neuron.

CLINICAL VIEW
Tumors of the Central Nervous System

Neoplasms resulting from unregulated cell growth, commonly known as **tumors,** sometimes occur in the central nervous system (CNS). A tumor that originates within the organ where it is found is called a primary tumor. Because most mature neurons cannot undergo mitosis, primary CNS tumors typically originate in supporting tissues within the brain or spinal cord that have retained the capacity to undergo mitosis: the meninges (protective membranes of the CNS) or the glial cells. Glial cell tumors, termed **gliomas,** may be either relatively benign and slow-growing or malignant (capable of metastasizing or spreading to distant sites).

An MRI shows a glioma (arrow).

- **Regulate tissue fluid composition.** Astrocytes help regulate the chemical composition of the interstitial fluid (fluid around cells) within the brain by controlling movement of ions and molecules between the blood and the interstitial fluid. For example, astrocytes regulate potassium ion concentration by absorbing these ions and then dispersing them to regulate and sustain a constant potassium ion concentration that is critical to electrical activity of neurons.
- **Form a structural network.** The cytoskeleton in astrocytes strengthens and organizes nervous tissue in the CNS by forming a framework to support neurons.
- **Assist neuronal development.** Astrocytes help direct the development of neurons in the fetal brain by secreting chemicals that regulate the formation of connections between neurons.
- **Occupy the space of dying neurons.** When neurons are damaged and die, the space they formerly occupied is often filled by cells produced by astrocyte division, a process termed *astrocytosis.*

Ependymal (e-pen'di-măl) **cells** are ciliated simple cuboidal or simple columnar epithelial cells that line the internal cavities of the brain (ventricles) and the spinal cord (central canal). These cells have slender processes that branch extensively to make contact with other glial cells in the surrounding nervous tissue.

Ependymal cells and nearby blood capillaries together form a network called the *choroid* (ko'royd) *plexus.* The choroid plexus helps produce cerebrospinal fluid (CSF), a clear liquid that bathes the external surfaces of the CNS and fills its internal cavities. The cilia of ependymal cells help circulate the CSF. (see section 13.2c)

Microglia (mī-krog'lē-ă; *micros* = small) are typically small cells that have slender branches extending from the main portion of the cell. They represent the smallest percentage of CNS glial cells with some estimates of their prevalence as low as 5%. They are classified as phagocytic cells of the immune system (see section 22.2). Microglial cells wander through the CNS and replicate in response to an infection. They protect against microorganisms and other potentially harmful substances by engulfing infectious agents and removing debris from dead or damaged nervous tissue.

Oligodendrocytes (ol'i-gō-den'drō-sīt; *oligos* = few) are large cells with a bulbous body and slender cytoplasmic extensions or processes. The processes of oligodendrocytes ensheath portions of axons of many different neurons. Each process repeatedly wraps around an axon like electrical tape wrapped around a wire. This wrapping is called the *myelin sheath,* which we discuss shortly. The protective covering around the axon insulates it and prevents the passage of ions through the axonal membrane. This allows for faster action potential propagation within the CNS.

Glial Cells of the PNS

Two types of glial cells are found in the PNS. They are called satellite cells and neurolemmocytes (figure 12.5*b* and table 12.2).

Satellite cells are flattened cells arranged around neuronal cell bodies in a ganglion. (Recall that a ganglion is a collection of neuron cell bodies located outside the CNS.) For example, satellite cells surround the cell bodies of sensory neurons located in a posterior root ganglion (section 14.5a). Satellite cells physically separate cell bodies in a ganglion from their surrounding interstitial fluid. They regulate the continuous exchange of nutrients and waste products between neurons and their environment.

Neurolemmocytes (nūr-ō-lem'ō-sīt) are also called *Schwann cells.* These flattened cells ensheath PNS axons to form a myelin sheath. This allows for faster action potential propagation within the PNS. The process of forming the myelin sheath by both neurolemmocytes and oligodendrocytes is described next.

💡 WHAT DID YOU LEARN?

11 If a person suffers from meningitis (an inflammation of the coverings around the brain), which type of glial cell usually replicates in response to the infection?

12 Which specific type of glial cells ensheaths axons in the PNS?

12.4c Myelination

☑ LEARNING OBJECTIVES

3. Define myelination, and describe the composition and function of a myelin sheath.

4. Distinguish between the myelination process carried out by neurolemmocytes and by oligodendrocytes.

Myelination is the process by which part of an axon is wrapped with **myelin** (mī'e-lin; *myel* = medulla). Myelin is the insulating covering around the axon that consists of repeating concentric layers of plasma membrane of glial cells. Myelination is completed by neurolemmocytes in the PNS and by oligodendrocytes in the CNS. Myelin mainly consists of the membranes of these glial cells and contains a large proportion of lipids and a lesser amount of proteins. The high lipid content of the myelin gives an axon a distinct, glossy-white appearance and serves to effectively insulate an axon.

Figure 12.6 illustrates the process of myelinating a PNS axon. The neurolemmocyte starts to encircle a 1-millimeter portion of an axon. As the neurolemmocyte continues to wrap around the axon, the cytoplasm and nucleus of the neurolemmocyte are squeezed to the periphery of the axon (the outside edge). The overlapping inner layers of the plasma membrane form the **myelin sheath.** The periphery of the neurolemmocyte contains the cytoplasm and nucleus and is called the **neurilemma** (nūr-i-lem'ă; *lemma* = husk). This process is similar to what would happen if you were to take a balloon with a small amount of water in it and wrap it numerous times around a pencil. The balloon is wrapped over and over around a section of your pencil and the part of the balloon containing water is pushed to the outside. The wrapped layers of balloon represent the myelin sheath, and the external portion of the balloon with the water represents the neurilemma.

A neurolemmocyte in the PNS can myelinate only a 1-millimeter portion of a single axon. Thus, if an axon is longer than 1 millimeter (and most PNS axons are), it takes many neurolemmocytes to myelinate the entire axon. **Figure 12.7a** shows an axon that has seven neurolemmocytes wrapped around it. The axons in many of the nerves in the body have hundreds or thousands of neurolemmocytes along their entire length. The gaps between the neurolemmocytes are called **neurofibril nodes,** or *nodes of Ranvier.*

An oligodendrocyte in the CNS, in comparison, can myelinate a 1-millimeter portion of *many* axons at the same time and not just

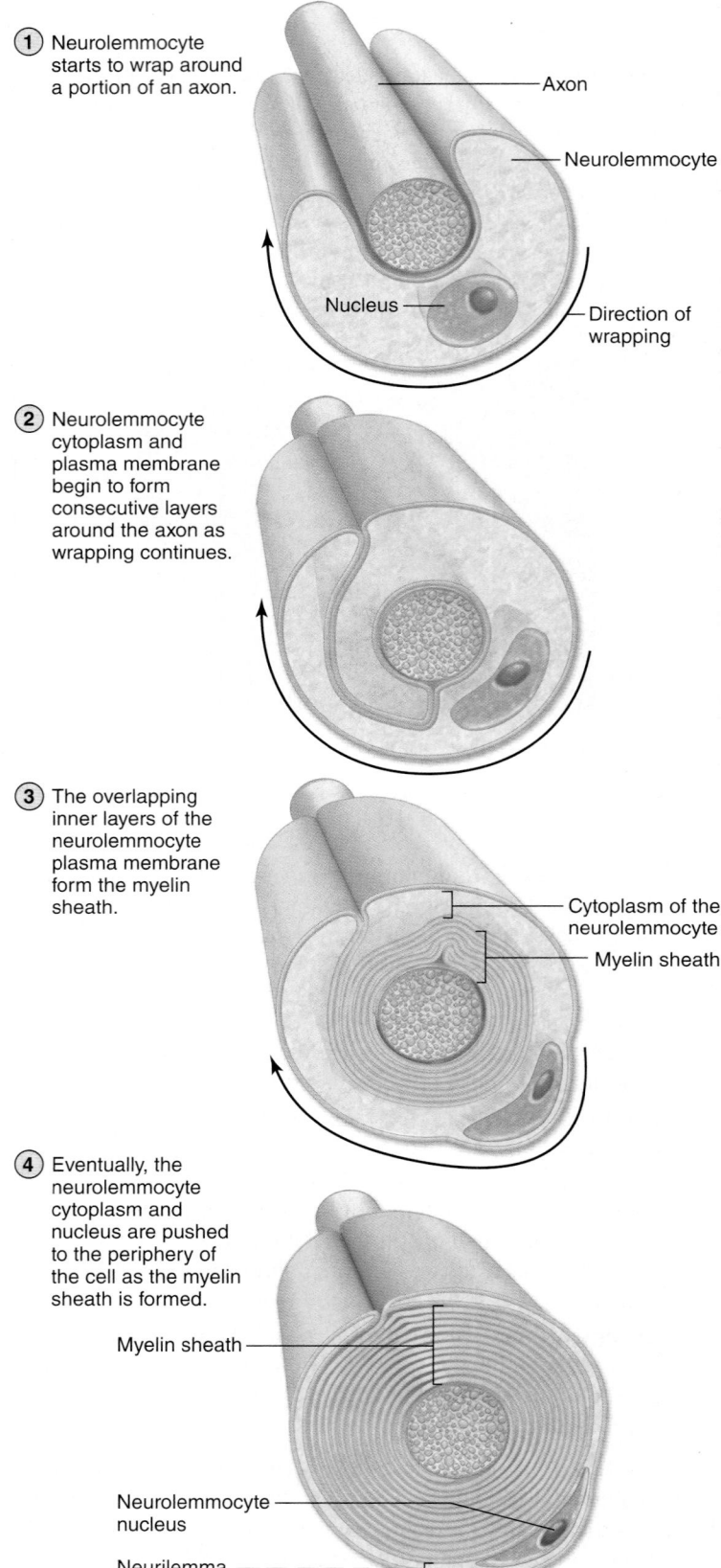

① Neurolemmocyte starts to wrap around a portion of an axon.

Axon

Neurolemmocyte

Nucleus

Direction of wrapping

② Neurolemmocyte cytoplasm and plasma membrane begin to form consecutive layers around the axon as wrapping continues.

③ The overlapping inner layers of the neurolemmocyte plasma membrane form the myelin sheath.

Cytoplasm of the neurolemmocyte

Myelin sheath

④ Eventually, the neurolemmocyte cytoplasm and nucleus are pushed to the periphery of the cell as the myelin sheath is formed.

Myelin sheath

Neurolemmocyte nucleus

Neurilemma

Figure 12.6 Myelination of PNS Axons. A myelin sheath surrounds most axons. In the PNS, neurolemmocytes form both a myelin sheath and neurilemma in a series of sequential stages. AP|R

PNS

- Neurolemmocytes
- Neuron cell body
- Neurofibril node
- Neurilemma
- Axon
- Myelin sheath

(a) Myelination by neurolemmocytes

CNS

- Oligodendrocytes
- Neurofibril node
- Axons
- Myelin sheath

(b) Myelination by oligodendrocytes

Figure 12.7 Myelin Sheaths in the PNS and CNS. (*a*) In the PNS, the neurolemmocyte ensheathes only one small part of a single axon to form both a myelin sheath and a neurilemma. (*b*) In the CNS, an oligodendrocyte wraps around a small part of multiple axons, forming a myelin sheath (but no neurilemma is formed).

one. Figure 12.7*b* shows oligodendrocytes myelinating portions of three different axons. The cytoplasmic extensions of the oligodendrocyte wrap repeatedly around a portion of each axon where plasma membrane layers form the myelin sheath. Note that no neurilemma is formed as the CNS neurons are myelinated. Neurofibril nodes are also located between adjacent oligodendrocyte "wraps." You may find it helpful to imagine that an oligodendrocyte is like a latex glove with fluid added to it. Each finger of the glove is wrapped numerous times around the axon of different neurons, and the fluid is pushed into the hand of the glove.

Not all axons are myelinated. **Unmyelinated axons** in the PNS **(figure 12.8)** are also associated with neurolemmocytes. However, no myelin sheath covers them. Thus, the axon merely rests in a depressed portion of the neurolemmocyte, but its plasma membrane does not form repeated layers around the axon. In the CNS, unmyelinated axons are not associated with oligodendrocytes.

WHAT DID YOU LEARN?

13 What is the function of the myelin sheath? How does myelination of axons occur in the PNS?

Unmyelinated axons

(1) Neurolemmocyte starts to envelop multiple axons.

- Neurolemmocyte
- Axons

(2) The unmyelinated axons are enveloped by the neurolemmocyte, but there are *no* myelin sheath wraps around each axon.

- Neurolemmocyte nucleus
- Unmyelinated axon
- Neurolemmocyte

(a)

- Unmyelinated axons
- Myelin sheath
- Myelinated axon
- Neurilemma

TEM 60,000x

(b)

Figure 12.8 Unmyelinated Axons. (*a*) Unmyelinated axons are surrounded by a neurolemmocyte but are not wrapped in a myelin sheath. (*b*) An electron micrograph shows a myelinated axon and several unmyelinated axons.

12.5 Axon Regeneration

LEARNING OBJECTIVES

1. Identify factors that influence regeneration of PNS axons, and explain why axon regeneration in the CNS is limited.

2. Describe the events of Wallerian degeneration and axon regrowth.

PNS axons are vulnerable to cuts, crushing injuries, and other types of trauma. However, a damaged axon can regenerate if the cell body remains intact and a critical amount of neurilemma remains. The success of PNS axon regeneration depends upon two primary factors: (1) the amount of damage, and (2) the distance between the site of the damaged axon and the structure it innervates. The possibility of repair is decreased with an increase in either of these two factors.

Neurolemmocytes play an active role in regeneration. This process is illustrated in **figure 12.9** and follows these stages:

1. The axon is severed by some type of trauma.

2. The portion proximal to the trauma seals off by membrane fusion and swells. The swelling is a result of axoplasmic flow (slow transport) from the neuron cell body through the axon. At the same time, the axon severed from the cell body and the myelin sheath surrounding the axon breaks down—a process called **Wallerian** (waw-lē′rē-ăn) **degeneration.** Macrophages (phagocytic cells) remove the debris. However, the neurilemma in the distal region survives.

3. The neurilemma in conjunction with the remaining endoneurium forms a regeneration tube.

4. The axon regenerates and remyelination occurs. The regeneration tube guides the axon sprout as it begins to grow rapidly through the regeneration tube at a rate of about 2 to 5 millimeters per day. This occurs under the influence of nerve growth factors released by the neurolemmocytes.

5. Innervation is restored as the axon reestablishes contact with its original structure. The structure is either a receptor for sensory neurons or an effector for motor neurons.

Potential regeneration of damaged neurons within the CNS is very limited for several reasons. First, oligodendrocytes do not release a nerve growth factor, and in fact they actively inhibit axon growth by producing and secreting several growth-inhibitory molecules. Second, the large number of axons crowded within the CNS tends to complicate regrowth activities. Finally, both astrocytes and connective tissue coverings may form some scar tissue that obstructs axon regrowth.

WHAT DID YOU LEARN?

14. What two primary factors determine the effectiveness of PNS axon regeneration?

15. How does the process of nerve regeneration occur in the PNS?

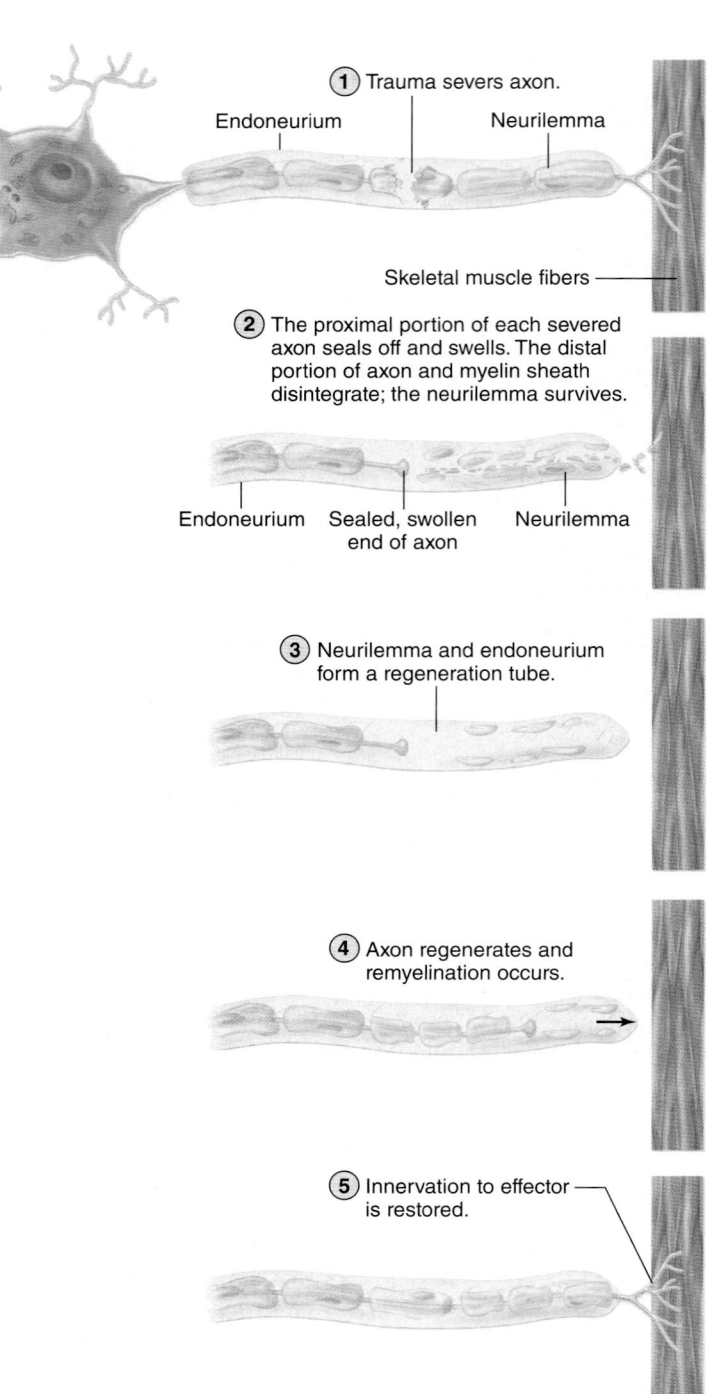

1. Trauma severs axon.
   Endoneurium   Neurilemma
   Skeletal muscle fibers

2. The proximal portion of each severed axon seals off and swells. The distal portion of axon and myelin sheath disintegrate; the neurilemma survives.
   Endoneurium   Sealed, swollen end of axon   Neurilemma

3. Neurilemma and endoneurium form a regeneration tube.

4. Axon regenerates and remyelination occurs.

5. Innervation to effector is restored.

Figure 12.9 Regeneration of PNS Axons. Following injury to a peripheral nerve, the severed axon may be repaired and grow out to reinnervate the receptor or effector (in this case, a skeletal muscle fiber).

12.6 Ultrastructure of Neurons

The ability of the nervous system to integrate and regulate body functions is ultimately dependent upon the transmission of electrical activity (i.e., graded potentials and action potentials) by neurons. Here we discuss the ultrastructure of neurons that makes transmitting electrical activity possible. Included are descriptions of the various types of pumps and channels in a neuron's plasma membrane, and the relative concentration of various substances between the inside and outside of these cells.

12.6a Pumps and Channels

Neurons contain transport proteins for moving substances across the plasma membrane. These include both pumps and various types of channels (figure 12.10). Transport proteins were first discussed in section 4.3 and are reviewed here.

Pumps move substances up (against) a concentration gradient, a process that requires energy (figure 12.10a). The plasma membrane of neurons contains both sodium-potassium (Na^+/K^+) pumps and calcium (Ca^{2+}) pumps.

Channels provide the means to move a substance down (with) a concentration gradient. Neurons contain the following major types of channels:

- **Leak (*passive*) channels.** These channels are always open, allowing continuous diffusion of a specific type of ion from a region of high concentration to a region of low concentration (figure 12.10b). Examples of leak channels are sodium ion (Na^+) leak channels and potassium ion (K^+) leak channels.

- **Chemically gated channels.** These channels are normally closed. They open in response to binding of a neurotransmitter. When open, they allow a specific type of ion (or ions) to diffuse across the plasma membrane (figure 12.10c). Examples of chemically gated channels include chemically gated K^+ channels and chemically gated chloride ion (Cl^-) channels.

(a) Sodium-potassium (Na^+/K^+) pump

(b) Leak (passive) channels

(c) Chemically gated channels

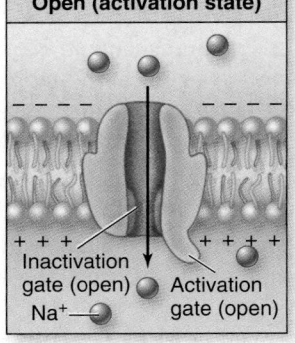

(d) Voltage-gated channels (three different states)

Figure 12.10 Membrane Pumps and Channels. (*a*) An Na^+/K^+ pump is a membrane transport protein that uses energy to transport both Na^+ and K^+ ions through the membrane. (*b*) Passive ion channels are always open and permit the movement of one specific type of ion through the channel by diffusion. (*c*) Chemically gated channels are closed unless they are exposed to specific chemicals in the environment. (*d*) A voltage-gated channel opens to permit ion movement when a specific transmembrane voltage is reached. The voltage-sensitive Na^+ channels exhibit three different stages: resting, activation, and inactivation.

- **Voltage-gated channels.** These channels are also normally closed, but they open in response to changes in electrical charge (potential) across the plasma membrane. When open, they allow a specific type of ion to diffuse across the membrane (figure 12.10d). Examples of voltage-gated channels include voltage-gated Na^+ channels, voltage-gated K^+ channels, and voltage-gated Ca^{2+} channels. Most gated channels have one gate that is in either one of two states: closed or open. Voltage-gated Na^+ channels are unique in that they have two gates (an *activation gate* and an *inactivation gate*) and thus exhibit three states as described next.

Three States of Voltage-Gated Na^+ channels

1. **Resting state.** Although the inactivation gate is open, the activation gate is closed, and entry of Na^+ is prevented (figure 12.10d).
2. **Activation state.** Both the inactivation gate (which remains open) and the activation gate are open (activation gate opens in response to a voltage change); Na^+ moves into the cell through the open channel.
3. **Inactivation state.** Although the activation gate is open, the inactivation gate is *temporarily* closed (for several milliseconds) following activation of the Na^+ channel—during this time, it cannot be stimulated to reopen, and entry of Na^+ is prevented. (The resting state of voltage-gated Na^+ channels is reestablished as the inactivation gate opens and the activation closes.)

Distribution of Pumps and Channels

Some pumps and channels are located throughout the entire neuron plasma membrane, whereas others are primarily located only in specific segments of a neuron's plasma membrane. Here we discuss the distribution of the types of pumps and channels within the neuron plasma membrane (figure 12.11). Note that the distribution of channels and pumps shown has been simplified for the purposes of this discussion and reflects their primary location in a typical multipolar neuron.

Entire Plasma Membrane of a Neuron Na^+ leak channels, K^+ leak channels, and Na^+/K^+ pumps are located throughout the entire neuron plasma membrane. These are important in establishing and maintaining the resting membrane potential of neurons (described shortly). Note that a neuron's plasma membrane contains more K^+ leak channels than Na^+ leak channels, and it is easier for K^+ to move through a K^+ leak channel than for Na^+ to move through a Na^+ leak channel.

Plasma Membrane of Functional Segments in a Neuron A typical neuron is functionally organized into four segments: receptive segment, initial segment, conductive segment, and transmissive segment. Each region differs in the primary types of channels and pumps located within its plasma membrane:

- The **receptive segment** includes both dendrites and the cell body, which are the regions of the neuron that receive stimuli to excite the neuron. Chemically gated channels (cation channels, K^+ channels, and Cl^- channels) are located in this segment; no significant numbers of voltage-gated channels are present. (Note that cation channels allow the passage of both Na^+ into the cell and K^+ out of the neuron. However, more Na^+ moves into the neuron than K^+ moves out.)
- The **initial segment** is composed of the *axon hillock*. This segment contains both voltage-gated Na^+ channels and voltage-gated K^+ channels.
- The **conductive segment** is equivalent to the length of the axon and its branches called telodendria. Like the axon hillock, it also contains both voltage-gated Na^+ channels and voltage-gated K^+ channels.
- The **transmissive segment** includes the synaptic knobs and contains voltage-gated Ca^{2+} channels and Ca^{2+} pumps.

WHAT DID YOU LEARN?

16 What is the difference between a chemically gated channel and a voltage-gated channel in terms of how they function?

17 Which functional segment of a neuron contains chemically gated channels? Which functional segments contains voltage-gated channels?

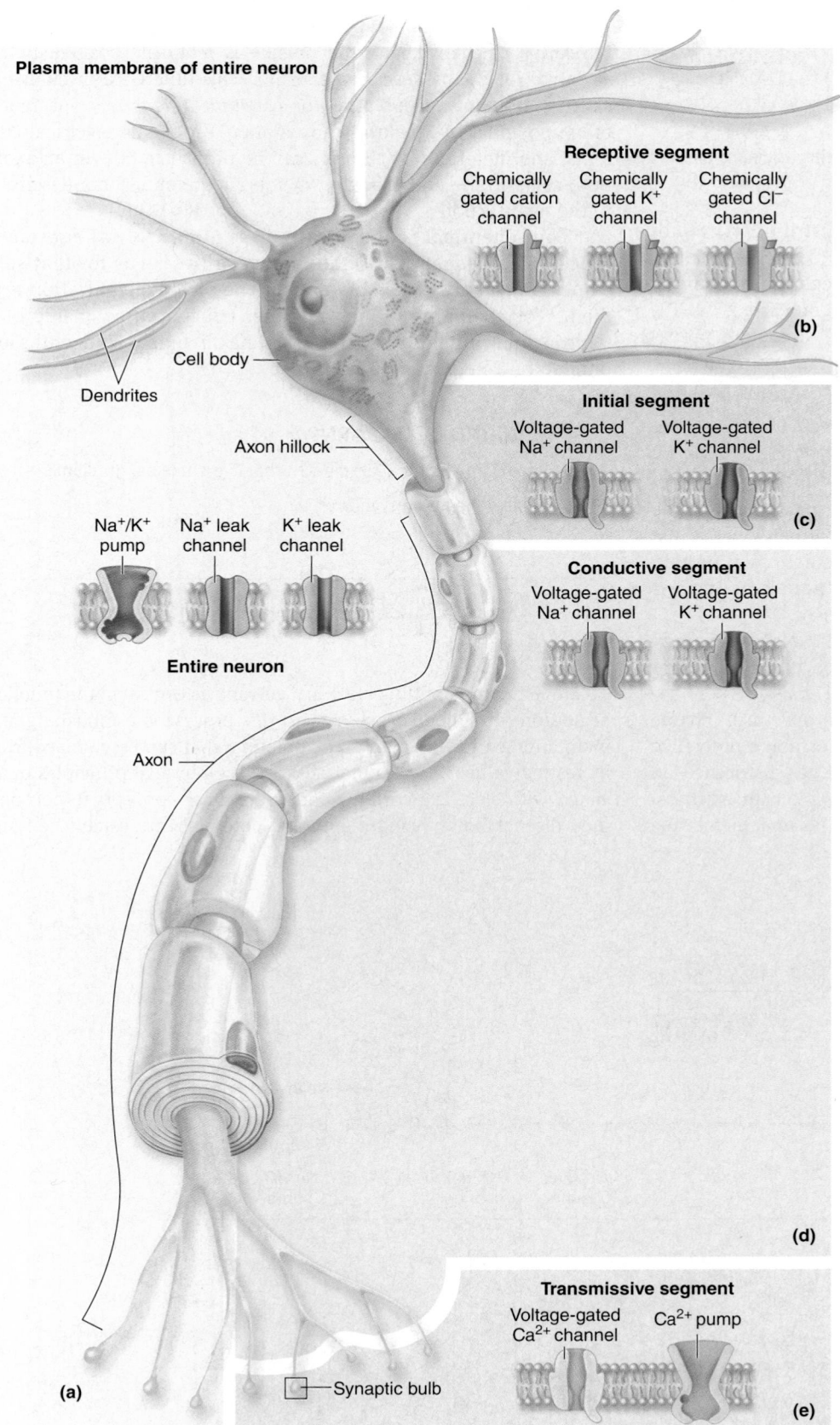

Figure 12.11 Distribution of Pumps and Channels in the Plasma Membrane of a Neuron. (*a*) Na$^+$/K$^+$ pumps, Na$^+$ leak channels, and K$^+$ leak channels are found throughout the entire plasma membrane of a neuron. Additional types of channels and pumps are present only in specific functional segments of the neuron. Channels present in the (*b*) receptive segment, (*c*) the initial segment, (*d*) the conductive segment, and (*e*) the transmissive segment are shown. Note that this represents a simplified depiction of the distribution of channels and pumps in a multipolar neuron plasma membrane. AP|R

12.6b Distribution of Substances and Membrane Potentials

LEARNING OBJECTIVE

3. Describe the distribution of substances between the inside and the outside of a neuron.

Neuron function is also dependent upon the distribution of substances contained within the cytosol of a neuron and the interstitial fluid (IF) outside of a neuron. Negatively charged phosphate ions as components of organic molecules (e.g., ATP), negatively charged protein molecules, and K^+ are more prevalent within a neuron's cytosol than in the IF. In contrast, Na^+ and Cl^- are in higher concentration in the IF than within the cytosol (figure 12.12).

Movement of Substances and Membrane Potentials

Ions, including Na^+, K^+, and Cl^-, are able to pass through the plasma membrane by transport proteins, which were just described. Both phosphate-containing molecules and protein molecules, however, are generally restricted from crossing the plasma membrane and remain within the cytosol.

The net movement of a given ion (e.g., K^+, Na^+) is dependent upon its **electrochemical gradient,** which is the combination of the electrical gradient and its chemical gradient.

An **electrical gradient** is a difference in electrical charge between two areas. All cells, including neurons, exhibit a difference in the total number of positive and negative charges distributed on each side of the plasma membrane and thus exhibit an electrical gradient *at the membrane.* The inside of the plasma membrane is *relatively* negative, and the outside is *relatively* positive (what accounts for this is described shortly). This difference in charge is called a **membrane potential** (or *potential difference*). The membrane potential of a neuron can be altered to create electrical currents, and the electrical currents can be propagated down an axon. Both establishing and changing membrane potentials are described in the next section.

The **chemical concentration gradient** of a substance reflects an unequal distribution between two areas for that substance. Each substance has its own chemical concentration gradient. For example, K^+ has a higher concentration inside of a neuron than outside, whereas Na^+ has a higher concentration outside of a neuron than within.

WHAT DID YOU LEARN?

18 What is an electrical gradient? What is a chemical gradient?

19 Define a membrane potential.

12.7 Introduction to Neuron Physiology

Creating and transmitting electrical currents is central to the function of neuron physiology. Necessary to this process is establishing and maintaining a resting membrane potential that can be changed from its resting value. Here we first describe the physical principles associated with electrical currents and relate these concepts to neurons, then discuss how resting membrane potentials are established and

Figure 12.12 Establishing and Maintaining the Resting Membrane Potential (RMP). A neuron at rest has a negative resting membrane potential (−70 mV). This results as K^+ diffuses out of a neuron and Na^+ diffuses in. Na^+/K^+ pumps move three Na^+ ions out of the neuron for every two K^+ ions transported in, primarily to maintain the concentration gradients of both K^+ and Na^+.

maintained and how the membrane potential can be changed from its resting value. We integrate these concepts in the next section to describe the physiologic events in a neuron—from the time its dendrites and cell body are stimulated until neurotransmitter is released from its synaptic knobs.

12.7a Neurons and Ohm's Law

✔ LEARNING OBJECTIVE

1. Integrate the concepts of voltage, current, and resistance with neuron structure and function.

Recall from section 3.1 that electrical energy is the movement of charged particles, and that all usable forms of energy are available to do work. Neuron activity is dependent upon electrical energy, specifically electrical currents. Three important and relevant characteristics are associated with electrical currents: voltage, current, and resistance.

- **Voltage** is the measure of the *amount of difference* in electrical charge. The unit of measurement is volts (V), or millivolts (mV); 1 V = 1000 mV. The larger the difference in charge, the higher the voltage. You may have noticed that batteries are available in different sizes (e.g., a small [1.5 V] or a large battery [12 V]). The voltage is an indication of the relative potential energy stored in the battery.

- **Current** is the *movement of charged particles* across the barrier that separates this charge difference. The greater the movement of charged particles, the greater the current. Movement of charged particles (or current) can be harnessed to do work (e.g., a current of electrons occurs between the positive and negative terminals in a battery when placed in a flashlight and the flashlight is turned on).

- **Resistance** is the *opposition to the movement of charged particles*. This is the barrier between the charged areas. The larger the resistance, the lower the current.

The relationship of voltage, current, and resistance is expressed by **Ohm's law:**

$$\text{Current} = \frac{\text{Voltage}}{\text{Resistance}}$$

This expression shows that current is directly related to voltage and inversely related to resistance. Thus, a greater current is possible with a larger voltage difference and a lower resistance.

Let us relate the general concepts of electrical currents to neurons. In neurons:

- Charged particles are ions (not like in a battery or with electricity, which involves the flow of electrons).
- There is a difference in charge distribution at the plasma membrane. This difference, as noted previously, is called its membrane potential.
- The plasma membrane phospholipid bilayer offers resistance because it generally does not allow the passage of charged particles.
- Resistance is altered across the plasma membrane through ion channels that open and close. Resistance is decreased when ion channels are open and increased when ion channels are closed.
- Current is generated when either positively charged ions or negatively charged ions diffuse across the plasma membrane through open channels.

 WHAT DID YOU LEARN?

20 What is the role of ions, the phospholipid bilayer, and plasma membrane channels in neurons relative to the concepts of current, voltage, and resistance?

12.7b Resting Membrane Potentials

✔ LEARNING OBJECTIVES

2. Define resting membrane potential, and state its typical value for neurons.

3. Describe how the resting membrane potential is established and maintained in neurons.

Recall that the relative difference in charge across a plasma membrane is the membrane potential; the membrane potential in a resting, excitable cell (e.g., neurons and muscle cells) is more specifically called a **resting membrane potential (RMP).**

A voltmeter is used to measure the voltage difference across the plasma membrane. This is done by placing one microelectrode into the neuron and the other microelectrode outside the neuron into the interstitial fluid (see figure 12.12). The RMP of a neuron has a negative value, which is typically –70 millivolts (mV), but can range between –40 mV and –90 mV. The value is negative because the voltage of the cytosol is *relatively* negative compared to the voltage measured in the IF—that is, more positive ions reside outside a neuron than inside a neuron when it is at rest.

INTEGRATE

LEARNING STRATEGY

To understand the concept of "relatively negative," consider the following simple arrangement: There are 100 positive charges (+) outside of a membrane and 30 positive charges (+) inside—thus, the inside is less positive, or it is *relatively* negative to the outside.

Establishing and Maintaining Resting Membrane Potentials

An RMP is chiefly a consequence of plasma membrane permeability to ions. It is primarily established by leak channels (K^+ and Na^+) and maintained by the activity of Na^+/K^+ pumps located in the plasma membrane.

The Role of K^+ Potassium diffusion is the most important factor in establishing the specific value of the resting membrane potential. K^+ movement is dependent upon its electrochemical gradient. Potassium ions exit the neuron moving down their relatively steep chemical concentration gradient moving into the IF. The loss of K^+ leaves relatively more negatively charged structures (e.g., phosphate and proteins) inside the cell. These structures remain within the cell because they are too large to cross the plasma membrane.

The movement of K^+ to the outside of a cell is, however, opposed by the electrical gradient. The positive charge on the outside of the cell repels the movement of K^+, and the negative charge on the inside of the cell attracts K^+. Thus, K^+ movement is facilitated by its chemical concentration gradient but opposed by the electrical gradient. As additional K^+ diffuses out of the neuron, the inside becomes more negative. Consequently, the pull to keep K^+ in the cell is greater. At some point, the force of the chemical gradient allowing K^+ out of a cell becomes equal to the electrical gradient that opposes this movement. Thus, K^+ movement has reached equilibrium. If only K^+ leak channels were present in neurons, the loss of the K^+ would result in an RMP with a value of −90 mV.

The Role of Na^+ The typical neuron RMP is −70 mV. The difference between −90 mV established by K^+ movement only and the RMP of −70 mV is primarily the result of Na^+ movement into a neuron. The Na^+ enters the cell through Na^+ leak channels. It moves down its chemical concentration gradient, and it is also "pulled" into the cell by the electrical gradient. Both forces facilitate the movement of Na^+ into a neuron. However, limited numbers of Na^+ leak channels prevent as much Na^+ movement into the neuron as K^+ out (i.e., there is greater resistance to Na^+ diffusion than K^+ diffusion).

The Role of Na^+/K^+ Pumps The Na^+/K^+ pumps play a relatively small role in establishing a membrane potential (approximately −3 mV of the total −70 mV difference). Their contribution is due to the pumping of more Na^+ from the cell than K^+ pumped into the cell. Recall from section 4.3c that three Na^+ are pumped out of the cell for every two K^+ transported into the cell—a ratio of 3:2, and an ATP molecule is split with each exchange of Na^+ and K^+ (figure 12.12). A great deal of energy is required to power the vast number of Na^+/K^+ pumps in a neuron's plasma membrane—approximately two-thirds of a neuron's energy expenditure!

Maintaining a Membrane Potential

The Na^+/K^+ pumps have a more significant role in maintaining the gradients of both K^+ and Na^+ following the diffusion of these ions as part of the neuron's generation of an electrical current, as described later. Each type of ion is pumped back up its concentration gradient by Na^+/K^+ pumps.

WHAT DID YOU LEARN?

21 What is the primary function of Na^+/K^+ pumps in maintaining the resting membrane potential?

12.7c Changing the Resting Membrane Potential

LEARNING OBJECTIVES

4. Explain depolarization and hyperpolarization.
5. Compare and contrast graded potentials and action potentials.

A membrane potential is a necessary condition for a neuron to be excited and to transmit electrical activity. Here we introduce the concepts of how a resting membrane potential is changed through depolarization and hyperpolarization and how the electrical change

(a) Resting membrane potential

(b) Depolarization: Na^+ flows in

(c) Hyperpolarization: K^+ flows out or Cl^- flows in

Figure 12.13 Changing the Resting Membrane Potential. (*a*) The resting membrane potential of neurons is −70 millivolts (mV). (*b*) Depolarization occurs when the membrane potential decreases below −70 mV (e.g., −60 mV) due to the opening of cation channels (either chemically gated or voltage-gated), and (*c*) hyperpolarization occurs when the membrane potential increases above −70 mV (e.g., −80 mV) due to the opening of either K^+ channels (either chemically gated or voltage-gated) or chemically gated Cl^- channels.

is either a local current (graded potential) or is propagated potentially a long distance as an action potential.

WHAT DO YOU THINK?

1 Will opening Na⁺ channels cause the membrane potential to become more positive or more negative? Explain.

Depolarization and Hyperpolarization

When neurons are stimulated, chemically gated channels or voltage-gated channels open, causing a change in ion flow across the membrane that alters the resting membrane potential. This results in depolarization or hyperpolarization of the neuron, depending upon both the type of ion that moves and the direction of its movement (figure 12.13).

Depolarization (dē-pō′lăr-i-zā-shŭn) occurs when the inside of a cell becomes more positive (less negative) than the resting membrane potential (e.g., from –70 mV to –60 mV). Depolarization occurs in neurons when gated channels (either cation channels or voltage-gated Na⁺ channels) open, allowing positively charged Na⁺ to move into the neuron (figure 12.13b). Thus, the entry of these positively charged ions (Na⁺) causes the inside of the neuron to become more positive (or less negative).

Hyperpolarization (hī′pĕr-pō′lăr-i-zā-shŭn) occurs when the inside of a cell becomes more negative (e.g., from –70 mV to –80 mV). Hyperpolarization results in neurons from either the opening of gated K⁺ channels, allowing positively charged K⁺ to move out of the neuron, or the opening of gated Cl⁻ channels, permitting negatively charged Cl⁻ to move into the cell (figure 12.13c). Either the loss of a positively charged ion (K⁺) or the gain of a negatively charged ion (Cl⁻) causes the inside of the neuron to become more negative.

Graded Potentials Versus Action Potentials

Voltage changes occur as either a local, graded potential or a propagated action potential. These two types of potentials are described here and summarized in table 12.3.

Graded potentials (local potentials) occur in the receptive segment of a neuron (dendrites and cell bodies) and are due to the opening of *chemically gated* channels. The chemically gated channels open temporarily allowing passage of a relatively small amount of a specific type of ion across the plasma membrane. A **local current** is established as ions then move along parallel to the plasma membrane. The more

channels that open, the larger the current. This flow of ions along the plasma membrane experiences resistance. Consider that when cation channels open, and Na⁺ enters a cell and moves along the inside of the plasma membrane, Na⁺ experiences resistance by the contents of the cytosol. Consequently, the local current of Na⁺ becomes weaker and eventually ceases. Graded potentials have these characteristics:

- The voltage change may result in the inside of the neuron becoming more positive (depolarization) or becoming more negative (hyperpolarization), depending upon the type of channel that opens.
- The degree of change is dependent upon the magnitude of the stimulus; thus, it is graded. A larger stimulus opens more chemically gated channels, and more ions flow across the plasma membrane than occurs during a weaker stimulus.
- A graded potential decreases in intensity (loses charge) with distance traveled along the membrane of the neuron. This is primarily due to the resistance experienced by the movement of the ion.
- A graded potential is short-lived (1 millisecond to a few milliseconds). It lasts only as long as the channels are open and until the local ion current ceases.

An **action potential** is generated within the initial segment and propagated along an axon of the neuron. (Recall from section 10.3b that propagation of action potentials occurs also along the sarcolemma of muscle cells.) An action potential is due to the opening of *voltage-gated* channels in response to a voltage change. The minimum voltage change to open voltage-gated channels is called the **threshold value.** Any voltage below this is not sufficient to open these channels and is called a **subthreshold value;** the channels remain closed. If a threshold value is reached, the channels open and remain open long enough so that the membrane potential is reversed. Consider that when voltage-gated Na⁺ channels open, sufficient Na⁺ enters the neuron to make the inside relatively positive. This local current of Na⁺ flows to adjacent areas along the plasma membrane and voltage-gated Na⁺ channels in these areas then open. This successive opening of voltage-gated Na⁺ channels continues down the axon, with each channel allowing the passage of enough Na⁺ to reverse the membrane potential.

The sequential opening of voltage-gated Na⁺ channels is followed by the sequential opening of voltage-gated K⁺ channels, and the subsequent movement of K⁺ out of the neuron to return the plasma membrane to its resting membrane potential Thus, an action potential

- involves a temporary reversal of polarity across the plasma membrane, when the inside of the axon becomes relatively positive and the outside of the axon becomes relatively negative. This is followed by a return to the RMP (the inside is once again relatively negative);
- is self-propagated (transmitted) and maintains its intensity (charge difference) as it moves along to the synaptic knob because of the successive opening of voltage-gated channels; and
- obeys what is referred to as the "all or none law." If the threshold is reached, an action potential is sent (all); if the threshold is not reached, an action potential is not sent (none). Note that all action potentials have the same intensity under the same conditions.

Table 12.3	Graded Potential Versus Action Potential	
Characteristics	**Graded Potential**	**Action Potential**
*Neuron segment**	Dendrites and cell body	Axon
Channels	Chemically gated channels	Voltage-gated channels
Direction of voltage change	Positive or negative	Positive then negative
Amount of voltage change	Relatively small change	Relatively large change that causes temporary reversal of polarity
Degree of voltage change	Dependent on magnitude of the stimulus	Generally does not vary
Duration	1 msec to a few msec	Travels length of axon
Change in intensity	Decreases with distance	Same intensity (because voltage-gated channels continue to open in sequence)

*The regions listed reflect the most common location for that type of potential.

WHAT DID YOU LEARN?

22 How does depolarization and hyperpolarization occur in a neuron?

23 How does a graded potential differ from an action potential in terms of the types of channels involved and where it occurs in a neuron?

12.8 Physiologic Events in the Neuron Segments

Here we discuss the physiologic events that occur in the functional neuron segments from the time of initial stimulation at the dendrites and cell body until release of a neurotransmitter from a synaptic knob. An overview of the events that occur in the receptive, initial, conductive, and transmissive segments is provided in figure 12.14.

12.8a Receptive Segment

LEARNING OBJECTIVES

1. Define a postsynaptic potential.

2. Compare and contrast the action of excitatory and inhibitory neurotransmitters in developing postsynaptic potentials (graded potentials) in the receptive segment.

3. Graph and explain an excitatory postsynaptic potential (EPSP) and an inhibitory postsynaptic potential (IPSP).

Figure 12.14 Overview of Events in Each Neuron Segment. The specific segments are illustrated on a multipolar neuron. AP|R

Initial segment	Conductive segment	Transmissive segment
Summation of graded potentials; initiation of action potential	Propagation of action potential	Action potential causes release of neurotransmitter

Receptive segment
Binding of neurotransmitter released from presynaptic neuron; production of graded potentials

Propagation of action potential

Neurotransmitter

We begin our discussion with **figure 12.15**, which shows the arrangement of several presynaptic neurons in close proximity to one postsynaptic neuron. Between each presynaptic and postsynaptic neuron is a synaptic cleft that is the fluid-filled space between them. Each presynaptic neuron releases neurotransmitter that binds with receptors (chemically gated channels) in the receptive segment—dendrites and cell body—of a postsynaptic neuron. The gated channels of the receptive segment open when the neurotransmitter binds. Specific ions then cross the membrane, initiating a graded potential in the postsynaptic neuron. This local potential is a small voltage change in the resting membrane potential.

Graded potentials that occur in postsynaptic neurons are specifically called **postsynaptic potentials.** Numerous postsynaptic potentials are typically generated because a postsynaptic neuron can bind many neurotransmitter molecules simultaneously. The type of graded potential formed—that is, whether depolarization or hyperpolarization occurs—depends upon whether the neurotransmitter released from the presynaptic neuron is an excitatory neurotransmitter or an inhibitory neurotransmitter.

INTEGRATE

CONCEPT CONNECTION

Sensory neurons are unique in that the receptive segments of their neurons contain modality gated channels (not chemically gated channels). Modality gated channels open in response to a stimulus other than a chemical or a voltage change. For example, sensory neurons in the eye contain modality gated channels that are stimulated by light (section 16.4c), and sensory neurons of the skin (section 16.2a) contain modality gated channels that are stimulated by mechanical pressure, such as when someone touches your arm to get your attention. The specific term for the graded potentials associated with sensory neurons is either *receptor potential* or *generator potential.*

Generation of EPSPs

The release of *excitatory neurotransmitter* from a presynaptic neuron causes the following events to occur (figure 12.15a):

1. Excitatory neurotransmitter crosses the synaptic cleft and binds specifically to a receptor that is a chemically gated cation channel, causing it to open.

2. More Na^+ moves down its concentration gradient into the neuron than K^+ moves out.

3. The inside becomes slightly more positive, or less negative, by gaining these positively charged ions. This temporary, less negative state, is called an **excitatory postsynaptic potential (EPSP).** (See graph in figure 12.15a.)

4. The local current of Na^+ becomes weaker as it moves along the neuron plasma membrane toward the axon hillock and decreases in intensity with the distance traveled.

The degree of change in the RMP is dependent upon the amount of neurotransmitter bound per unit of time. As more excitatory neurotransmitter is released by presynaptic neurons, then more cation channels open in the receptive segment of the postsynaptic neuron, and there is a greater change in the positive direction in this region: –70 mV toward –65 mV toward –60 mV. Thousands of cation channels need to be stimulated to open to initiate opening of voltage-gated channels in the axon hillock (described shortly).

Generation of IPSPs

Inhibitory neurotransmitter released from a presynaptic neuron causes the following actions (figure 12.15b):

1. Inhibitory neurotransmitter crosses the synaptic cleft and binds specifically either to a chemically gated K^+ channel or a chemically gated Cl^- channel, depending upon the neurotransmitter and channels present.

2. If the neurotransmitter binds to a receptor that is a chemically gated K^+ channel, this channel opens and K^+ moves out of the neuron down its concentration gradient, causing a loss of positively charged ions. In contrast, if

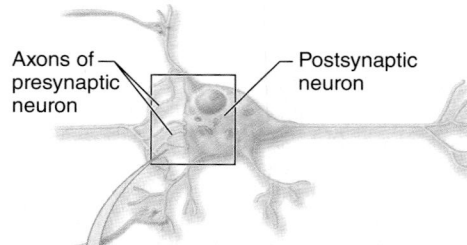

Axons of presynaptic neuron

Postsynaptic neuron

Release of excitatory neurotransmitter and generation of EPSP

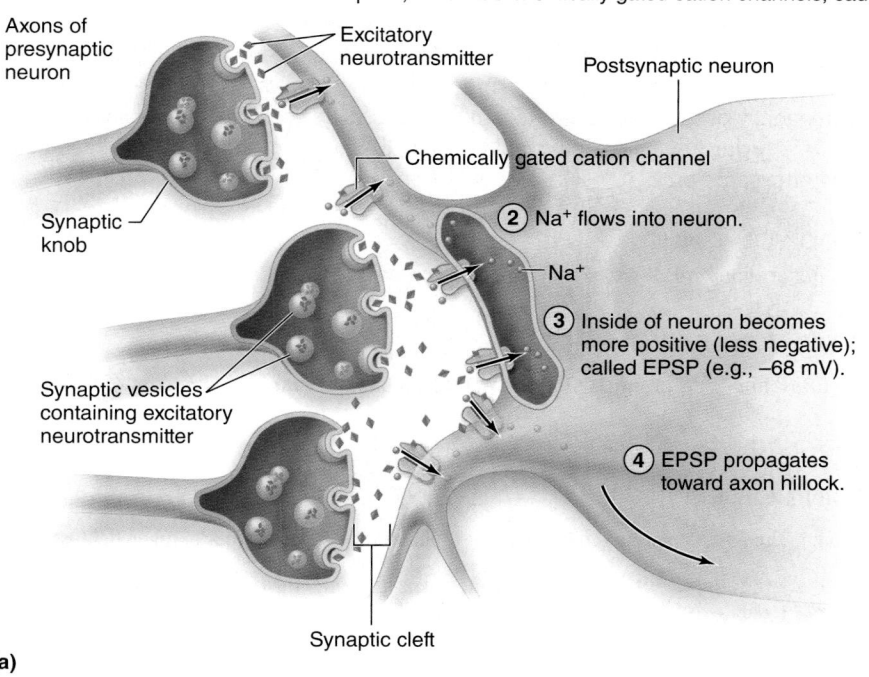

① Excitatory neurotransmitter released from presynaptic neuron binds to receptors, which are chemically gated cation channels, causing them to open.

Axons of presynaptic neuron

Excitatory neurotransmitter

Postsynaptic neuron

Synaptic knob

Chemically gated cation channel

② Na⁺ flows into neuron.

Na⁺

Synaptic vesicles containing excitatory neurotransmitter

③ Inside of neuron becomes more positive (less negative); called EPSP (e.g., –68 mV).

④ EPSP propagates toward axon hillock.

Synaptic cleft

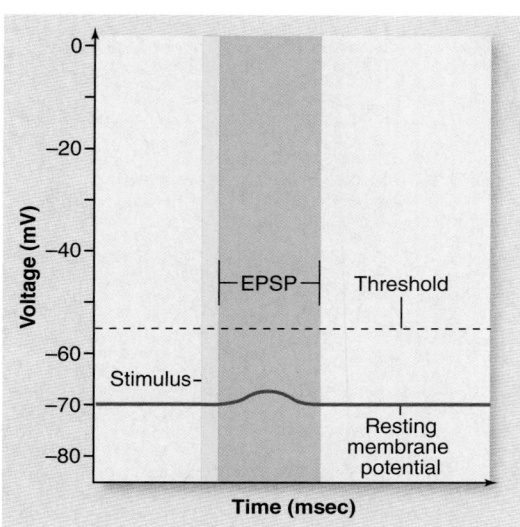

EPSP
Threshold
Stimulus-
Resting membrane potential

(a)

Release of inhibitory neurotransmitter and generation of IPSP

① Inhibitory neurotransmitter binds to either chemically gated K⁺ channels or chemically gated Cl⁻ channels, causing them to open.

Axons of presynaptic neuron

Inhibitory neurotransmitter

Postsynaptic neuron

Chemically gated K⁺ channel

Chemically gated Cl⁻ channel

Synaptic vesicles containing inhibitory neurotransmitter

K⁺

② Either K⁺ flows out of, or Cl⁻ flows into, the neuron, depending on the type of channel stimulated.

Cl⁻

③ Inside of neuron becomes more negative; called IPSP (e.g., –72 mV).

Cl⁻

④ IPSP propagates toward axon hillock.

Threshold
Stimulus-
Resting membrane potential
IPSP

(b)

Figure 12.15 Postsynaptic Potentials in the Receptive Segment. Neurotransmitter released from presynaptic neurons crosses the synaptic cleft and initiates a graded (postsynaptic) potential. (*a*) Binding of an excitatory neurotransmitter causes an excitatory postsynaptic potential (EPSP). (*b*) Binding of an inhibitory neurotransmitter causes an inhibitory postsynaptic potential (IPSP).

the neurotransmitter binds to a receptor that is a chemically gated Cl⁻ channel, opening of this channel allows Cl⁻ to flow down its concentration gradient to move into the neuron, causing the gain of negatively charged ions. The amount of neurotransmitter determines the number of channels that open.

③ The inside of the cell becomes slightly *more negative* if either chemically gated K⁺ channels open and K⁺ exits, or chemically gated Cl⁻ channels open and Cl⁻ enters. This temporary, more negative, state is called an **inhibitory postsynaptic potential (IPSP).** (See graph in figure 12.15*b*.)

④ The local current of ions becomes weaker as it moves along the neuron plasma membrane toward the axon hillock and decreases in intensity with the distance traveled.

Often excitatory neurotransmitter and inhibitory neurotransmitter is released from the numerous presynaptic neurons simultaneously. Thus, different channels are activated at the same time **(figure 12.16)**. Additionally, a single presynaptic neuron can stimulate channels by increasing its frequency of releasing neurotransmitter, and thus function to establish numerous graded potentials very quickly. The result could be many EPSPs, many IPSPs, or both, generated at approximately the same time.

WHAT DO YOU THINK?

② Does the generation of IPSPs make it more likely or less likely that a nerve signal will be sent?

WHAT DID YOU LEARN?

㉔ How are EPSP and IPSP graded potentials established in the receptive segment of a neuron?

12.8b Initial Segment

LEARNING OBJECTIVE

4. Define summation, and describe the two types of summation that can occur in the initial segment.

EPSPs and IPSPs graded potentials are local currents of ions that move along the plasma membrane toward the initial segment (axon hillock). Graded postsynaptic potentials are added together in the initial segment; this process is called **summation.** The initial segment, by adding postsynaptic potentials, determines if a threshold membrane potential is reached. The **threshold membrane potential** is –55 mV (although the specific value does vary somewhat between different types of neurons). This is a change of + 15 mV from the RMP. When this threshold is reached, it initiates the opening of voltage-gated channels and the generation of an action potential that will travel along the axon.

A single EPSP is incapable of causing the postsynaptic neuron to reach threshold. Additionally, IPSPs negate the effect of EPSPs. The occurrence of both EPSPs and IPSPs together creates a "tug-of-war" as to whether the threshold is reached. Thus, numerous EPSPs

Figure 12.16 Several Presynaptic Neurons with a Postsynaptic Neuron. A diagram and photograph of numerous axons of presynaptic neurons with the receptive segment of a postsynaptic neuron. This anatomic arrangement permits release of neurotransmitters from many presynaptic neurons and the subsequent, and simultaneous generation of both EPSPs and IPSPs in the postsynaptic neuron. AP|R (typically thousands, as noted) must be generated and arrive at the initial segment simultaneously, or nearly at the same time, if the threshold is to be reached.

Threshold can be reached through two types of summation called spatial summation and temporal summation, which may act in concert to produce an effect.

- **Spatial summation** occurs when multiple presynaptic neurons release neurotransmitter at various locations onto the receptive segment, thus generating EPSPs, IPSPs, or both **(figure 12.17a)**. If sufficient numbers of EPSPs are generated so that the threshold is reached, then an action potential is initiated.
- **Temporal summation** occurs when a single presynaptic neuron releases excitatory neurotransmitter to stimulate the postsynaptic neuron at the same location repeatedly in a very short period of time (figure 12.17b). If the resulting EPSPs reach the axon hillock within a small window of time, they will be added together. (An EPSP typically lasts for approximately 15 milliseconds.) An action potential is initiated if threshold is reached.

The **all or none law** (section 10.3b) applies to action potentials propagated along plasma membrane of neurons. If the threshold is reached, an action potential is propagated along the axon without decreasing in intensity. If only a subthreshold value is reached, it is not propagated. Additionally, values greater than the threshold result in the same intensity of response as the threshold. The initial segment is sometimes called the *trigger zone* because what occurs there is similar to what happens with a gun. Sufficient pressure is applied to the trigger of a gun and the bullet is fired from the chamber, or insufficient pressure is placed on the trigger and the gun is not fired. Likewise, the bullet travels at the same velocity regardless of whether the pressure placed on the trigger is greater than needed.

WHAT DID YOU LEARN?

25 What is the significance of the threshold membrane potential in the initial segment of a neuron?

Figure 12.17 Initial Segment: Summation at the Axon Hillock. Summation is the integration of the effects of postsynaptic potentials arriving in the axon hillock and includes (*a*) spatial summation, which involves postsynaptic potentials stimulated by numerous presynaptic neurons (P1-P5); and (*b*) temporal summation, which involves postsynaptic potentials formed by rapid stimulation by one presynaptic neuron (P2). Note that negating efffects of IPSPs are not shown.

12.8c Conductive Segment

☑ LEARNING OBJECTIVES

5. Describe the initiation and propagation of depolarization and repolarization, which constitutes a nerve signal.

6. Graph and explain the electrical changes that occur in an axon.

7. Define refractory period, and explain the difference between the absolute refractory period and relative refractory period associated with transmitting an action potential.

The conductive segment is equivalent to the total length of the axon. As mentioned earlier, the initial and conductive segments contain both voltage-gated Na⁺ channels and voltage-gated K⁺ channels. The main activity of axons is action potential propagation. An action potential is initiated along the axon when the threshold is reached in the initial segment. An action potential involves two processes: depolarization, which causes the inside of the axon to become positive due to influx of Na⁺; and repolarization, which is the returning of a neuron to its resting potential due to outward flow of K⁺ (figure 12.18). The propagation of an action potential is called a **nerve signal** or *nerve impulse* (figure 12.18a).

Depolarization and Its Propagation

Depolarization involves a positive change in membrane potential via voltage-gated Na⁺ channels in the plasma membrane of the axon (figure 12.18b). These channels are normally closed. The process begins when voltage-gated Na⁺ channels in the initial segment are triggered to open (changing from the resting state to the activation state) when the threshold of approximately –55 mV is reached. The opening of voltage-gated Na⁺ channels allows rapid Na⁺ entry. The voltage-gated Na⁺ channels are opened for only a very short duration and then close, changing from the activation state to the temporary inactivation state. Enough Na⁺ enters to quickly make the inside of the axon positive (+ 30 mV; although

---

INTEGRATE

CLINICAL VIEW
Effects of Neurotoxins

A **toxin** is a harmful substance synthesized by an organism. Usually, toxins are proteins, and their effect is to cause disease or cell death when they interact with protein receptors present in plasma membranes. This interaction may cause a wide range of effects that vary from minor annoyance to death. Certain toxins are classified as **neurotoxins** because they change the normal activity of neurons.

Specifically, a neurotoxin interacts with receptor proteins in neuron plasma membranes. Neurotoxins act by disrupting the activity of voltage-dependent channels, meaning that they prevent the neurons from firing action potentials or prevent them from repolarization after firing. In either case, nervous system function is disrupted. Examples of neurotoxins include (1) Na⁺ channel effectors, such as tetrodotoxin (found in some fish, amphibians, and even some worms); and (2) K⁺ channel effectors, such as agitoxin from scorpions.

(a)

(b)

(c)

Figure 12.18 Propagation of Action Potentials. (*a*) An action potential is propagated along the length of an axon. The propagation of an action potential is called a nerve signal. (*b*) Depolarization and its propagation involves the sequential opening of voltage-gated Na⁺ channels along the axon. Sufficient Na⁺ enters the axon to reverse its polarity. (*c*) Repolarization and its propagation involves the sequential opening of voltage-gated K⁺ channels along the axon that immediately follows the events of depolarization. Sufficient K⁺ exits the axon to return the axon to its resting membrane potential. **AP|R**

the exact value can vary from 0 mV to +50 mV) and depolarization occurs. This movement of Na^+ is extremely small, representing a change of approximately 0.01% in the Na^+ concentration, but is sufficient because depolarization only occurs at the plasma membrane.

The **propagation of depolarization** involves the sequential opening of voltage-gated Na^+ channels along the length of the axon. The flow of Na^+ into the cell causes adjacent regions of the axon's plasma membrane downstream from the cell body to also reach threshold, triggering the opening of voltage-gated Na^+ channels in these areas. Adjacent depolarization is repeated rapidly down the plasma membrane of the axon toward the synaptic knob. The reason action potentials do not stimulate previous regions of the axon is because the voltage-gated Na^+ channels in these previous regions are temporarily in the inactivated state.

The propagation of depolarization is analogous to the tipping of a row of dominoes. Once the first domino is initiated to fall, each domino falls in sequence until the last domino is reached.

Local anesthetics, such as lidocaine, inhibit the action of voltage-gated Na^+ channels, effectively blocking the nerve signal. Pain associated with local medical procedures—for example, administering stitches or filling a tooth cavity—that is normally detected and conducted along an axon of sensory neurons from the body is effectively blocked from reaching the CNS. Even applying ice to a painful area can help reduce pain sensation by slowing the transmission of sensory action potentials initiated by painful stimuli.

Repolarization and Its Propagation

Repolarization involves returning a neuron to its RMP through voltage-gated K^+ channels located in the plasma membrane of the axon (figure 12.18c). Voltage-gated K^+ channels are normally closed, but threshold also stimulates them to open. These channels are relatively slow to open and are not completely open until about the point that depolarization has ended. Enough K^+ exits to quickly make the inside of the axon negative and return the neuron to its RMP (-70 mV). Note that repolarization triggers the voltage-gated Na^+ channels to change from the inactivated state to the resting state, allowing voltage-gated Na^+ channels to reopen again to send a new nerve signal.

The **propagation of repolarization** occurs as voltage-gated K^+ channels in adjacent regions open sequentially along the length of the axon. Consider that propagation of repolarization is similar to the resetting up of a row of dominoes so that the process can happen again.

Hyperpolarization and Return to Resting Membrane Potential

The voltage-gated K^+ channels typically remain open longer than the time needed to reestablish the resting membrane potential (-70 mV). The inside of the neuron during this brief time is more negative than the RMP, or hyperpolarized. The RMP is then reestablished by Na^+/K^+ pumps following the closing of voltage-gated K^+ channels. The electrical changes associated with an action potential, sometimes called a *spike potential*, are shown and described in **figure 12.19**.

Refractory Period

A **refractory period** is the brief time period after an action potential has been initiated during which an axon is either incapable of generating another action potential or a greater than normal amount of stimulation is required to generate another action potential. The excitable plasma membrane recovers at this time and becomes ready to respond to another stimulus. The refractory

① The unstimulated axon has a resting membrane potential of –70 mV.

② Graded potentials reach axon hillock and are added together.

③ **Depolarization** occurs when the threshold (–55 mV) is reached; voltage-gated Na^+ channels open and Na^+ enters rapidly, reversing the polarity from negative to positive (–55 mV → +30 mV).

④ **Repolarization** occurs due to closure of voltage-gated Na^+ channels (inactivation state) and opening of voltage-gated K^+ channels. K^+ moves out of the cell into the IF and polarity is reversed from positive to negative (+30 mV → –70 mV).

⑤ **Hyperpolarization** occurs when voltage-gated K^+ channels stay open longer than the time needed to reach the resting membrane potential; during this time the membrane potential is less than the resting membrane potential of –70 mV.

⑥ Voltage-gated K^+ channels are closed, and the plasma membrane has returned to resting conditions by activity of Na^+/K^+ pumps.

Figure 12.19 Events of an Action Potential. A tracing of the membrane voltage changes (mV) associated with an action potential initiated in the axon hillock. Changes occur in just a few milliseconds, and result from the opening and closing of voltage-gated Na^+ channels and voltage-gated K^+ channels in the membrane of the axon, and are sometimes referred to as a *spike potential,* reflecting the shape of the recorded potential.

period has two phases: the absolute refractory period and the relative refractory period (figure 12.20).

The **absolute refractory period** is the time (about 1 millisecond) after an action potential onset when no amount of stimulus, no matter how strong, can initiate a second action potential. During this time, the voltage-gated Na^+ channels are first opened, and then the voltage-gated Na^+ channels are closed in the inactivated state. They generally remain in the inactivated state until the membrane potential has almost returned to the resting membrane potential through repolarization. Consequently, no voltage difference across the plasma membrane of an axon during this time can open the voltage-gated Na^+ channels for the next action potential. The absolute refractory period ensures that the action potential moves along the axon in only one direction toward the synaptic knobs.

The **relative refractory period** occurs immediately after the absolute refractory period. Another action potential may now be initiated in an axon only if the stimulation of the membrane is greater than the initial stimulus. At this time, voltage-gated Na^+ channels have returned to their resting state, but the neuron is hyperpolarized due to the slightly extended time that voltage-gated K^+ channels remain open during repolarization.

WHAT DID YOU LEARN?

26 How does depolarization and repolarization occur in the conductive segment of a neuron?

12.8d Transmissive Segment

LEARNING OBJECTIVES

8. Describe events that occur when the propagated action potential reaches the transmissive segment.

9. Explain the role of Ca^{2+} in neurotransmitter release.

Recall that the transmissive segment is the synaptic knob. The main activity that occurs at the transmissive segment is the release of neurotransmitter from synaptic vesicles (figure 12.21). Prior to the arrival of the action potential, Ca^{2+} pumps embedded in the plasma membrane of a synaptic knob (not shown in figure) establish a calcium concentration gradient by pumping Ca^{2+} out to the IF. Consequently, there is more calcium outside of the synaptic knob than inside it.

When the propagated action potential (or nerve signal) reaches the synaptic knob at the end of the axon, voltage-gated Ca^{2+} channels are triggered to open. Calcium ions move from the IF into the synaptic knob down their concentration gradient. Calcium ions bind to proteins of synaptic vesicles, which triggers a series of events, resulting in fusion of synaptic

Figure 12.20 Refractory Periods. The absolute refractory period is from the point of depolarization until repolarization is almost complete. During this time, it is not possible to initiate another action potential, no matter how strong the stimulus. The relative refractory period is the time immediately following the absolute refractory period, during which a stronger than normal stimulus is required to initiate another action potential because the neuron is hyperpolarized.

returns or exchanges will not be permitted (i) after 14 days or without receipt or (ii) for product not carried by Barnes & Noble or Barnes & Noble.com.

Policy on receipt may appear in two sections.

Return Policy

With a sales receipt or Barnes & Noble.com packing slip, a full refund in the original form of payment will be issued from any Barnes & Noble Booksellers store for returns of undamaged NOOKs, new and unread books, and unopened and undamaged music CDs, DVDs, toys/games and audio books made within 14 days of purchase from a Barnes & Noble Booksellers store or Barnes & Noble.com with the below exceptions:

A store credit for the purchase price will be issued (i) for purchases made by check less than 7 days prior to the date of return, (ii) when a gift receipt is presented within 60 days of purchase, (iii) for textbooks, (iv) when the original tender is PayPal, or (v) for products purchased at Barnes & Noble College bookstores that are listed for sale in the Barnes & Noble Booksellers inventory management system.

Opened music CDs/DVDs/audio books may not be returned, and can be exchanged only for the same title and only if defective. NOOKs purchased from other retailers or sellers are returnable only to the retailer or seller from which they are purchased, pursuant to such retailer's or seller's return policy. Magazines, newspapers, eBooks, digital downloads, and used books are not returnable or exchangeable. Defective NOOKs may be exchanged at the store in accordance with the applicable warranty.

Returns or exchanges will not be permitted (i) after 14 days or without receipt or (ii) for product not carried by Barnes & Noble or Barnes & Noble.com.

Policy on receipt may appear in two sections.

Return Policy

With a sales receipt or Barnes & Noble.com packing slip, a full refund in the original form of payment will be issued from any Barnes & Noble Booksellers store for returns of undamaged NOOKs, new and unread books, and unopened and undamaged music CDs, DVDs, toys/games and audio books made within 14 days of purchase from a Barnes & Noble Booksellers store or Barnes & Noble.com with the below exceptions:

A store credit for the purchase price will be issued (i) for purchases made by check less than 7 days prior to the date of return, (ii) when a gift receipt is presented within 60 days of purchase, (iii) for textbooks, (iv) when the original tender is PayPal, or (v) for products purchased at Barnes & Noble College bookstores that are listed for

Something New in the Barnes & Noble Cafe...

Try our new savory menu items:

Sandwiches, Pizzas and gluten-free Chicken Tenders. And presenting Sugar Rush inspired pastries!

Try one of our sandwiches, like our
Philly Cheesesteak or Farmer's Wrap,
experience our take on the classic
Cheese Pizza, or get your greens in
with our Veggie Pizza.
Then treat yourself with a Sugar Rush
inspired Gooey Chocolate Caramel Tart,
a Chocolate Oatmeal Chunker,
or a Spicy Malted Chipotle Brownie.

YOU MAY ALSO LIKE...

Anatomy Flash Cards
    by Kurt Albertine Ph.D.

Netter's Anatomy Flash Cards: with...
    by John T. Hansen

Patho Phlash!: Pathophysiology Flash Cards
    by Valerie I. Leek

CURRENT Medical Diagnosis and Treatment...
    by Gene Quinn

Merriam-Webster's Medical Dictionary
    by Merriam-Webster Inc. Staff

pursuant to such retailer's or seller's return policy. Magazines, newspapers, eBooks, digital downloads, and used books are not returnable or exchangeable. Defective NOOKs may be exchanged at the store in accordance with the applicable warranty.

Returns or exchanges will not be permitted (i) after 14 days or without receipt or (ii) for product not carried by Barnes & Noble or Barnes & Noble.com.

Policy on receipt may appear in two sections.

Return Policy

With a sales receipt or Barnes & Noble.com packing slip, a full refund in the original form of payment will be issued from any Barnes & Noble Booksellers store for returns of undamaged NOOKs, new and unread books, and unopened and undamaged music CDs, DVDs, toys/games and audio books made within 14 days of purchase from a Barnes & Noble Booksellers store or Barnes & Noble.com with the below exceptions:

A store credit for the purchase price will be issued (i) for purchases made by check less than 7 days prior to the date of return, (ii) when a gift receipt is presented within 60 days of purchase, (iii) for textbooks, (iv) when the original tender is PayPal, or (v) for products purchased at Barnes & Noble College bookstores that are listed for sale in the Barnes & Noble Booksellers inventory management system.

Opened music CDs/DVDs/audio books may not be returned, and can be exchanged only for the same title and only if defective. NOOKs purchased from other retailers or sellers are returnable only to the retailer or seller from which they are purchased, pursuant to such retailer's or seller's return policy. Magazines, newspapers, eBooks, digital downloads, and used books are not returnable or exchangeable. Defective NOOKs may be exchanged at the store in accordance with the applicable warranty.

Barnes & Noble Booksellers #2880
5155 Route 30
Greensburg, PA 15601
724-832-0622

STR:2880 REG:006 TRN:9744 CSHR:Karen D

Mosby's Medical Terminology Flash Cards
  9780323222587   T1
  (1 @ 40.95)   40.95

Subtotal   40.95
Sales Tax T1 (6.000%)   2.46
TOTAL   43.41
VISA DEBIT   43.41
  Card#: XXXXXXXXXXXX2119

A MEMBER WOULD HAVE SAVED   4.10

Thanks for shopping at
Barnes & Noble

101.36A   06/30/2015 02:29PM

CUSTOMER COPY

Neuromuscular junction

Voltage-gated Ca²⁺ channel

Synaptic cleft

Receptor

Ca²⁺

2 Voltage-gated Ca²⁺ channels open and Ca²⁺ enters the synaptic knob and binds with proteins of synaptic vesicles.

1 Action potential reaches synaptic knob.

3 Synaptic vesicles merge with synaptic knob plasma membrane and neurotransmitter is released by exocytosis.

Neurotransmitter

4 Neurotransmitter crosses synaptic cleft and attaches to receptors on a muscle, as shown. (Or to receptors of a neuron or gland.)

Synaptic knob

Synaptic vesicle (contains neurotransmitter)

Synaptic cleft

Synaptic vesicles

Muscle cell

Synaptic knob

(a)

(b)

vesicles with the neuron plasma membrane. Neurotransmitter is subsequently released into the synaptic cleft by exocytosis. Approximately 300 vesicles are released per action potential. Note that exocytosis of neurotransmitter is facilitated by numerous proteins (e.g., synaptotagmin, SNARE proteins), and research continues in this area to determine the exact functional role of each of these proteins.

The neurotransmitter then diffuses across the cleft between the synaptic knob and the cell to be stimulated. There it binds to specific cellular protein receptors of another neuron or an effector organ (muscle or gland).

The physiologic processes of a neuron in the four major functional segments—the receptive segment, initial segment, conductive segment, and transmissive segment—are summarized in **figure 12.22**.

WHAT DID YOU LEARN?

27 What is the sequence of events from the arrival of an action potential at the synaptic knob until the release of neurotransmitter into the synaptic cleft?

Figure 12.22   Events of Neuron Physiology.
Neuron physiology involves specific events that occur in the four functional segments of a neuron: (1) receptive segment, (2) initial segment, (3) conductive segment, and (4) transmissive segment.

Action potential along presynaptic neuron axon

Dendrites

Presynaptic neuron

Graded potentials of postsynaptic neuron

② Initial segment

Axon hillock

Postsynaptic neuron

Cell body

① Receptive segment

② **INITIAL SEGMENT: "Trigger Zone"**

Summation of EPSPs and IPSPs (not shown), includes both spatial summation of multiple presynaptic neurons and temporal summation of one presynaptic neuron quickly stimulating; determines if threshold (−55 mV) is reached.

Spatial summation

+30
0
−55
−70
mV
Action potential
Threshold
P1 P2 P3 P4 P5
Time (msec)

Temporal summation

+30
0
−55
−70
mV
Action potential
Threshold
P2
Time (msec)

Myelin sheath

Axon

③ Conductive segment

Action potential

Na⁺

K⁺

Diffusion of Na⁺ through axoplasm

Depolarization

Repolarization

① **RECEPTIVE SEGMENT: Establishing Graded Potentials: EPSPs and IPSPs**

EPSP

Chemically gated cation channel

Na⁺

Excitatory neurotransmitter

Chemically gated K⁺ channel

K⁺

Chemically gated Cl⁻ channel

Cl⁻

Inhibitory neurotransmitter

IPSP

Excitatory neurotransmitter is released from presynaptic neuron; it binds with chemically gated cation channels; more Na⁺ enters neuron than K⁺ exits and inside becomes more positive, which is an excitatory postsynaptic potential (EPSP).

mV
EPSP
Time (msec)

Inhibitory neurotransmitter is released from presynaptic neuron, which binds with either chemically gated K⁺ channels, and K⁺ exits neuron or to chemically gated Cl⁻ channels, and Cl⁻ enters neuron. In either case, the inside becomes more negative, which is an inhibitory postsynaptic potential (IPSP).

mV
IPSP
Time (msec)

3 CONDUCTIVE SEGMENT: Propagation of Action Potential

Repolarization

Voltage-gated K$^+$ channel

Depolarization

Action potential — Voltage-gated Na$^+$ channel

Na$^+$

K$^+$

Repolarization and its propagation:
Sequential opening of voltage-gated K$^+$ channels that immediately follows depolarization to reestablish RMP. K$^+$ moves out of axon.

Depolarization and its propagation:
Sequential opening of voltage-gated Na$^+$ channels in response to reaching threshold. Na$^+$ moves into axon.

Depolarization Repolarization

+30

Na$^+$ in

K$^+$ out

mV

−55

Threshold

−70

RMP

Hyperpolarization

Time (msec)

Telodendria

4 Transmissive segment

Action potential

Synaptic knob

4 TRANSMISSIVE SEGMENT: Release of Neurotransmitter

Arrival of an action potential at the synaptic knob triggers the opening of voltage-gated Ca^{2+} channels. Ca^{2+} enters the synaptic knob, causing the subsequent release of neurotransmitter from synaptic vesicles by exocytosis.

Ca^{2+}

Voltage-gated Ca^{2+} channel

Neurotransmitter

Synaptic vesicle

Neurotransmitter binds with receptors of either another neuron or an effector (muscle or gland).

12.9 Velocity of a Nerve Signal

Propagation of a nerve signal along an axon plasma membrane varies in its velocity and is influenced primarily by two factors: the diameter of an axon and the myelination of an axon.

- **Diameter of the axon.** In general, the larger the diameter of the axon, the faster the velocity of the nerve signal. This is because there is less resistance to the movement of ions in the larger axon, allowing these axons to reach threshold more rapidly than smaller axons.
- **Myelination of the axon.** Myelination of the axon was described earlier and is the more important factor influencing nerve signal velocity. Propagation of an action potential occurs more rapidly in myelinated axons than in unmyelinated axons.

12.9a Propagation

LEARNING OBJECTIVE

1. Compare and contrast continuous conduction and saltatory conduction in the mechanism and velocity of transmission of an action potential.

Continuous conduction occurs in unmyelinated axons and involves the sequential opening of voltage-gated Na^+ channels and voltage-gated K^+ channels located within the axon plasma membrane. When previously describing the process of action potential conduction, we describe it as it would occur in unmyelinated axons (see figure 12.18).

Saltatory conduction (*saltare* = to jump) occurs in myelinated axons. Here, action potentials do not occur in regions that are myelinated—rather they are propagated only at neurofibril nodes. This is due to anatomic differences in the two types of regions of a myelinated axon. Myelinated regions of an axon contain limited numbers of voltage-gated Na^+ channels and voltage-gated K^+ channels, and myelin is a great insulator that prevents ion movement even if additional channels are present. In contrast, neurofibril nodes have a relatively large number of both voltage-gated Na^+ channels and voltage-gated K^+ channels and of course lack myelin insulation. Ions are relatively free to flow into and out of the axon in these regions when the channels are open. A nerve signal is transmitted along a myelinated axon, as follows (**figure 12.23**):

- **Neurofibril node.** An action potential occurs at neurofibril nodes. Depolarization is due to opening of voltage-gated Na^+ channels; Na^+ diffuses into the axon. (This is followed by repolarization as voltage-gated K^+ channels open, and K^+ diffuses out.)

- **Myelinated regions.** The Na^+ diffuses through axoplasm of the axon under the axolemma (which is insulated by myelin). Two critical aspects should be noted regarding this Na^+ diffusion: (1) It is relatively fast, faster than the events at the neurofibril nodes, and (2) as Na^+ diffuses through the axoplasm it experiences resistance and the local current becomes weaker with distance.

- **Neurofibril node.** The arrival of the relatively weak Na^+ current is sufficient to cause the opening of voltage-gated Na^+ channels at the next neurofibril node, producing a new action potential. This results in the establishing of a new action potential as Na^+ enters the neuron and a new local current is established.

This process repeats as the nerve signal continues down the length of an axon until it reaches the synaptic knobs. The transmission of a nerve signal along an axon is called *saltatory conduction* because the action potential occurs only at neurofibril nodes; thus, it seems to "jump" from node to node.

Transmission of a nerve signal in a myelinated axon is much faster (120 meters per second) than in an unmyelinated axon (2 meters per second), because an action potential is generated only at the neurofibril nodes of myelinated axon rather than along the entire length of unmyelinated axon. Saltatory conduction also is more efficient because less energy is required by Na^+/K^+ pumps to maintain the RMP.

WHAT DID YOU LEARN?

 How does conduction of an action potential in an unmyelinated axon and myelinated axon differ?

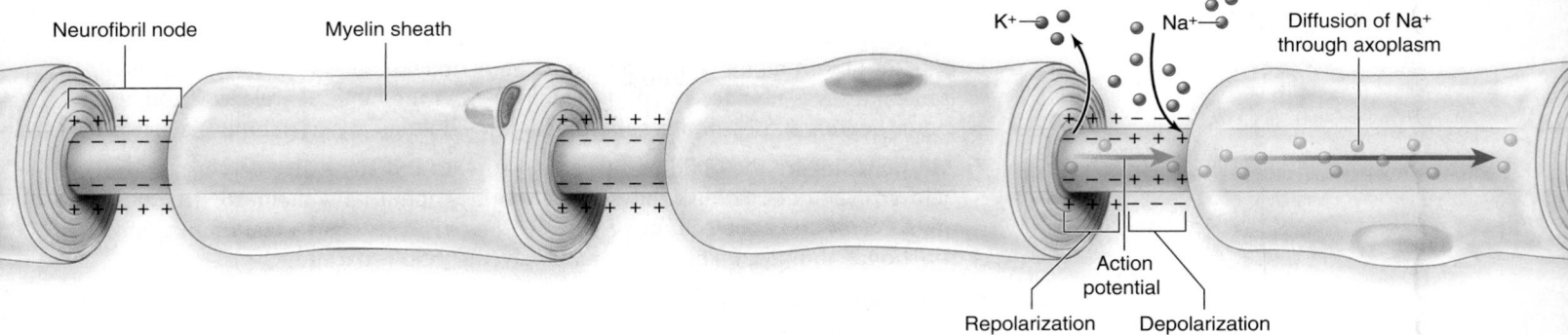

Neurofibril node   Myelin sheath   K+   Na+   Diffusion of Na+ through axoplasm

Action potential

Repolarization   Depolarization

Figure 12.23 Saltatory Conduction. A new action potential is initated at each neurofibril node. Thus, the action potential appears to jump between adjacent neurofibril nodes. AP|R

12.9b Nerve Fiber Classification

 LEARNING OBJECTIVE

2. Identify the criteria used to distinguish the groups of nerve fibers.

A nerve fiber is an axon and its myelin sheath. Nerve fibers are classified into three major groups called A, B, and C, based on their conduction velocity. Group A has a conduction velocity that may be as fast as 150 meters per second; these fibers have both a large diameter and are myelinated. Most somatic sensory neurons that extend from receptors to the CNS, and all somatic motor neurons that extend from the CNS to skeletal muscles, are included in this group. Group B conducts at approximately 15 meters per second, and group C conducts at 1 meter per second; group B and group C fibers are generally small in diameter, unmyelinated, or both. Sensory and motor visceral (autonomic) neurons, as well as small somatic sensory neurons that extend from the receptors of the skin to the CNS, are included in groups B and C.

WHAT DID YOU LEARN?

29 What are the general characteristics of group A nerve fibers, and what functions do they normally serve?

12.10 Neurotransmitters and Neuromodulation

Neurotransmitters are released at the synaptic cleft and their action is modified by neuromodulation. We first describe the different types of neurotransmitters and the different means of their removal from the synaptic cleft. We then discuss how the action of neurotransmitters can be altered through neuromodulation.

12.10a Neurotransmitters

LEARNING OBJECTIVES

1. Identify the four classes of neurotransmitters, and give examples of their actions.

2. Explain the two ways in which neurotransmitters are removed from the synaptic cleft.

Neurotransmitters are various small organic molecules that are released from neurons. Following their release, they are quickly removed from the synaptic cleft.

Classes of Neurotransmitters

There are approximately 100 known neurotransmitters, which can be classified into major groups (table 12.4):

- **Acetylcholine (ACh)** is an excitatory or inhibitory neurotransmitter; it is released in both the central nervous system and the peripheral nervous system. This neurotransmitter was first described in section 10.2c as the molecule released from a motor neuron at a neuromuscular junction to stimulate a skeletal muscle cell.

- **Amino acids** are the building blocks of proteins and some also serve as neurotransmitters. Some controversy continues about how chemical structures that are so plentiful in the cell for protein synthesis can serve this communication function. Examples include glutamate, glycine, and aspartate.

- **Monoamines** are derived from certain amino acids by the removal of a carboxyl group (—COOH) and the addition of another functional group (e.g., an amine group). The functional group added determines whether the molecule belongs to the more specific subgroup called catecholamines (norepinephrine, epinephrine, and dopamine).

- **Neuropeptides** are chains of amino acids that range in length from 2 to 40 amino acids. Examples of neuropeptides include enkephalins and somatostatin.

Removal of Neurotransmitters from the Synaptic Cleft

To prevent ongoing and unwanted stimulation of a neuron or effector organ by a neurotransmitter, the association between the neurotransmitter and its receptor is temporary. It is necessary that the neurotransmitter molecule is eliminated after each stimulation event. Its removal can occur by (1) *degradation,* in which the neurotransmitter is chemically inactivated in the synaptic cleft (e.g., the enzyme acetylcholinesterase [AChE] resides in the neuromuscular junction and rapidly breaks down molecules of ACh that are released from the synaptic knob; see section 10.3d); and (2) *reuptake,* in which the neurotransmitter is reabsorbed by a neurotransmitter transport protein in the membrane of the presynaptic neuron. These neurotransmitters are "recycled" by the presynaptic neuron once packaged into another synaptic vesicle for reuse.

Certain prescription medications were developed based on their ability to influence the amount of neurotransmitter in a synaptic cleft (e.g., selective serotoinin reuptake inhibitors [SSRIs] block the reuptake of serotonin and are used in the treatment of depression; see section 1.6).

 WHAT DID YOU LEARN?

30 What are the four primary classes of neurotransmitters?

12.10b Neuromodulation

 LEARNING OBJECTIVE

3. Define neuromodulation, including facilitation and inhibition.

Neuromodulation is the release of chemicals (other than neurotransmitters) from cells that locally regulate or alter the response of neurons to neurotransmitters. The substances released are called **neuromodulators.** Thus, neuromodulators become participants in the "decision making" that occurs during the transmission of information.

Neuromodulation generally results in either facilitation or inhibition. **Facilitation** occurs when there is greater response from a postsynaptic neuron because of the release of neuromodulators. Facilitation may result from either an increased amount of neurotransmitter in the synaptic cleft (greater release, or slower breakdown or reuptake) or an increased number of receptors on postsynaptic neurons. **Inhibition** occurs when there is less response from a postsynaptic neuron because of the release of neuromodulators. This results from either a decreased amount of neurotransmitter in the synaptic cleft (decreased release, or faster breakdown or reuptake) or decreased number of receptors on postsynaptic neurons.

WHAT DID YOU LEARN?

31 What is the general function of neuromodulators?

Table 12.4 Neurotransmitters

Neurotransmitter	Description/Action
ACETYLCHOLINE (ACh)	
	It has a chemical structure significantly different from other neurotransmitters and for this reason is placed in its own structural category; active in both the central nervous system (CNS) and peripheral nervous system (PNS); in the PNS it is released into the neuromuscular junction to stimulate skeletal muscle contraction, inhibits cardiac muscle, either inhibits or excites smooth muscle and glands
AMINO ACIDS	
	Molecules with both carboxyl (—COOH) and amine (—NH$_2$) groups and various R groups; building blocks of proteins; act as signaling molecules in the nervous system
Glutamate	Excites activity in nervous system to promote cognitive function in the brain (learning and memory); most common neurotransmitter in the brain
Aspartate	Excites activity primarily in descending motor pathways through the spinal cord to skeletal muscle
Serine	Activates specific receptors in diverse areas in the brain
Gamma-aminobutyric acid (GABA)	Modified amino acid that is synthesized from glutamate; primary inhibitory neurotransmitter in the brain; also influences muscle tone
Glycine	Inhibits activity between neurons in the brain, spinal cord, and eye
MONOAMINES	
	Molecules synthesized from an amino acid by removal of the carboxyl group and retaining the single amine group; also called biogenic amines
Histamine	Neurotransmitter of the CNS; plays a role in sleep and memory
Serotonin	Has various functions in the brain related to sleep, appetite, cognition (learning, memory), and mood
Catecholamines	A very distinct group of monoamines so named for a specific chemical structural similarity; originally described as hormones (chemicals produced by a gland in one part of the body that affect cells in other parts of the body)
Dopamine	Produces inhibitory activity in the brain; important roles in cognition (learning, memory), motivation, behavior, and mood
Norepinephrine (noradrenaline)	Neurotransmitter of peripheral autonomic nervous system (sympathetic division) and various regions of the CNS
Epinephrine (adrenaline)	Has various effects in the thalamus, hypothalamus, and spinal cord
NEUROPEPTIDES	
	Small molecules made of chains of amino acids; act as signals to assist in and modulate communication between neurons and other cells
Enkephalin	Helps regulate response to something that is perceived to be noxious or potentially painful
Neuropeptide Y	Involved in memory regulation and energy balance (increased food intake and decreased physical activity)
Somatostatin	Inhibits activities of neurons in specific brain areas
Substance P	Assists with pain information transmission into the brain
Cholecystokinin	Stimulates neurons in the brain to help mediate satiation (fullness) and repress hunger
Beta-endorphin	Prevents release of pain signals from neurons and fosters a feeling of well-being
Neurotensin	Helps control and moderate the effects of dopamine
OTHERS	
Adenosine	Part of a nucleotide (a building block of nucleic acid); has an inhibitory effect on neurons in the brain and spinal cord
Nitric oxide	Involved in learning and memory; relaxation of muscle in the digestive tract; relaxation of smooth muscle in blood vessels

12.11 Neural Integration and Neuronal Pools of the CNS

LEARNING OBJECTIVE

1. Identify the four different types of neuronal pools, and explain how they function.

The nervous system coordinates and integrates neuronal activity in part because billions of interneurons within the nervous system are grouped in complex patterns called **neuronal pools,** or *neuronal circuits* or *pathways*. Neuronal pools are identified based upon function into four types of circuits: converging, diverging, reverberating, and parallel-after-discharge **(figure 12.24)**. A pool may be localized, with its neurons confined to one specific location, or its neurons may be distributed in several different regions of the CNS. However, all neuronal pools are restricted in their number of input sources and output destinations.

The **converging circuit** involves input that come together (converge) at a single postsynaptic neuron (figure 12.24*a*). This neuron receives input from several presynaptic neurons. For example, multiple sensory neurons synapse on the neurons in the salivary nucleus in the brainstem, causing the salivary nucleus to alter activity of salivary glands to produce saliva at mealtime. The various inputs originate from more than one stimulus: smelling food, seeing dinnertime on the clock, hearing food preparation activities, or seeing pictures of food in a magazine. These multiple inputs lead to a single output: the production of saliva.

A **diverging circuit** spreads information from one presynaptic neuron to several postsynaptic neurons, or from one pool to multiple pools (figure 12.24*b*). The neurons in the brain control the movements of skeletal muscles in the legs during walking and also stimulate the muscles in the back to maintain posture and balance while walking. In this case, a single or a few inputs lead to multiple outputs.

Reverberating circuits utilize feedback to produce a repeated, cyclical stimulation of the circuit: This is termed *reverberation* (figure 12.24*c*). Once activated, a reverberating circuit may continue to function until the cycle is broken by either inhibitory stimuli or synaptic fatigue. **Synaptic fatigue** occurs when repeated stimuli cause exhaustion of neurotransmitter production in a presynaptic cell. The repetitious nature of a reverberating circuit ensures that we continue breathing while we are asleep.

In a **parallel-after-discharge circuit,** input is transmitted simultaneously along several neuron pathways to a common postsynaptic cell (figure 12.24*d*). Note that neuron pathways in a parallel-after-discharge circuit vary in the number of neurons within the pathway and thus the number of synapses within the pathway. Recall that neuron to

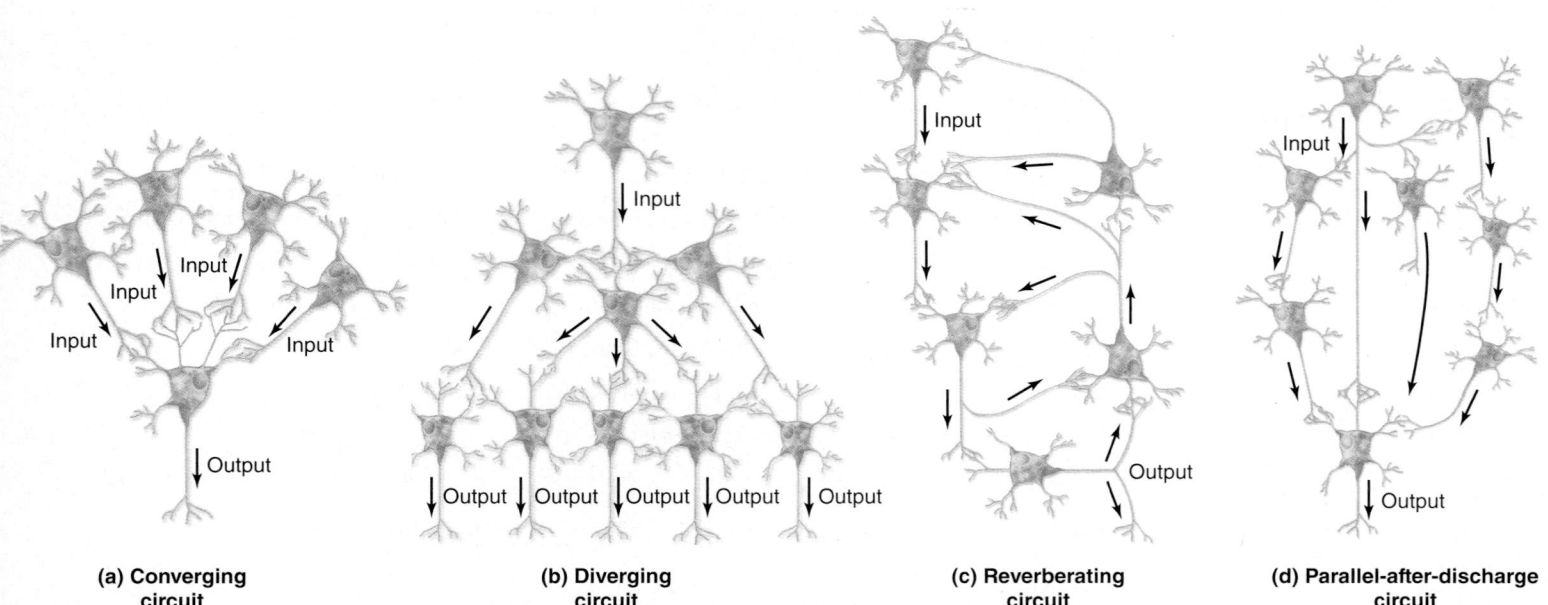

(a) Converging circuit

(b) Diverging circuit

(c) Reverberating circuit

(d) Parallel-after-discharge circuit

Figure 12.24 Neuronal Pools. Neuronal pools are groups of neurons arranged in specific patterns (circuits) through which input is conducted and distributed. Four types of neuronal pools are recognized.

neuron communication at a synapse involves a synaptic delay (the time delay for the events at a synapse). Consequently, the greater the number of neurons in the pathway, the greater the number of synapses and the greater the amount of time required to transmit the information. This results in the information arriving from the point of stimulus input to the common postsynaptic cell at varying times. You might find it helpful to think of the arrival of information from each group of neurons to the common postsynaptic cell as an "echo" of the original stimulus input. This type of circuit is believed to be involved in higher-order thinking; for example, it reinforces the repetitive neural activity needed for performing precise mathematical calculations.

 WHAT DID YOU LEARN?

32 How are neurons arranged in a converging circuit?

33 What are the differences between a reverberating circuit and a parallel-after-discharge circuit?

CHAPTER SUMMARY

	• The nervous system interprets and controls all sensory input from receptors and motor output to effectors.
12.1 Introduction to the Nervous System 438	• The nervous system is composed of the brain, spinal cord, nerves, and ganglia.
	12.1a General Functions of the Nervous System 438
	• The nervous system collects information through receptors and sensory input, processes and evaluates information, and responds through motor output.
	12.1b Organization of the Nervous System 438
	• The nervous system is organized structurally into the central nervous system (CNS) and the peripheral nervous system (PNS).
	• The nervous system is organized functionally into a sensory component and a motor component.
12.2 Nervous Tissue: Neurons 439	• Nervous tissue is composed of excitable neurons that initiate and transmit action potentials, and glial cells that support and protect them.
	12.2a General Characteristics of Neurons 439
	• General characteristics of neurons include excitability, conductivity, secretion, and longevity; in addition, they are typically amitotic.
	12.2b Neuron Structure 440
	• A generalized neuron has a cell body. Processes called dendrites, which are usually numerous and short, and a single and often long axon project from the cell body.
	12.2c Neuron Transport 442
	• Neurons transport substances between the cell body and synaptic knobs by fast axonal transport and slow axonal transport.
	12.2d Classification of Neurons 442
	• Neurons are classified structurally as multipolar, bipolar, unipolar, and anaxonic by the number of processes attached to the cell body.
	• The three functional categories of neurons are sensory neurons, motor neurons, and interneurons.
	12.2e Relationship of Neurons and Nerves 444
	• A nerve is a collection of axons that are wrapped in connective tissue.
	• Each axon is wrapped with an endoneurium, fascicles of axons are ensheathed with a perineurium, and the entire nerve is enclosed with an epineurium.
12.3 Synapses 445	• The location of the junction of a neuron with either another neuron or effector is a synapse.
	• Synapses are either chemical synapses or electrical synapses.
12.4 Nervous Tissue: Glial Cells 447	• Glial cells are the other distinct cell type of nervous tissue.
	12.4a General Characteristics of Glial Cells 447
	• Glial cells are nonexcitable cells that primarily support and protect the neurons.
	12.4b Types of Glial Cells 448
	• Four types of glial cells within the central nervous system include astrocytes, ependymal cells, microglia, and oligodendrocytes.
	• Two types of glials cells within the peripheral nervous system include satellite cells and neurolemmocytes.
	12.4c Myelination 449
	• Myelination is the process by which part of an axon is wrapped with myelin.
	• Neurolemmocytes myelinate axons in the PNS, and oligodendrocytes myelinate axons in the CNS.

(continued on next page)

12.5 Axon Regeneration 452	• Regeneration of damaged neurons is limited to PNS axons. • A PNS axon can regrow if the cell body is intact and a critical amount of neurilemma remains.
12.6 Ultrastructure of Neurons 452	• Establishing and changing a resting membrane potential is dependent upon various types of pumps and channels within a neuron's plasma membrane. **12.6a Pumps and Channels** 453 • Pumps and channels are membrane proteins that facilitate movement of ions across the neuron plasma membrane. Some are in the plasma membrane of the entire neuron, and some are primarily in specific functional neuron segments. **12.6b Distribution of Substances and Membrane Potentials** 456 • There is an unequal distribution of substances on either side of a neuron's plasma membrane. • A membrane potential is the electrical difference on either side of the plasma membrane.
12.7 Introduction to Neuron Physiology 456	• Neuron physiology involves the initiation and transmission of electrical currents. **12.7a Neurons and Ohm's Law** 457 • Ohm's law (current = voltage/resistance) has application in the principles of neuron physiology. **12.7b Resting Membrane Potentials** 457 • The resting membrane potential is the voltage difference across the membrane when the neuron is at rest, and it generally has a value of −70 mV. • Resting membrane potential is established by K^+ leak channels and Na^+ leak channels, and is maintained by Na^+/K^+ pumps. **12.7c Changing the Resting Membrane Potential** 458 • Depolarization is the entry of Na^+ that cause the inside of the neuron to become more positive than the resting membrane potential, and hyperpolarization is either the exit of K^+ or the entrance of Cl^- that cause the inside of the neuron to be more negative than the resting membrane potential. • Graded potentials are local potentials generated in dendrites and the cell body, and action potentials are self-propagating electrical changes generated along the axon.
12.8 Physiologic Events in the Neuron Segments 460	• Physiological events in neuron segments begin with stimulation of dendrites to the release of neurotransmitter from synaptic knobs. **12.8a Receptive Segment** 460 • The receptive segment includes the dendrites and cell body. This segment involves the formation and propagation of graded potentials: both excitatory postsynaptic potentials (EPSPs) and inhibitory postsynaptic potentials (IPSPs). **12.8b Initial Segment** 462 • The initial segment (axon hillock) adds together EPSPs and IPSPs to determine whether the threshold value (−55 mV) is reached. **12.8c Conductive Segment** 464 • The conductive segment is involved in the propagation of an action potential (nerve signal), a process that involves depolarization and repolarization. Saltatory conduction occurs if the axon is myelinated. **12.8d Transmissive Segment** 466 • The transmissive segment involves release of neurotransmitter from synaptic vesicles.
12.9 Velocity of a Nerve Signal 470	• Velocity of a nerve signal is primarily determined by the diameter of an axon and whether it is myelinated. **12.9a Propagation** 470 • A nerve signal is propagated along the axon by continuous conduction in unmyelinated axons and by saltatory conduction in myelinated axons; saltatory conduction occurs at a much faster rate than continuous conduction. **12.9b Nerve Fiber Classification** 471 • Nerve fibers, which are axons and their myelin sheath, are classified into three groups based on the velocity of the nerve signal conduction.
12.10 Neurotransmitters and Neuromodulation 471	• Neurotransmitters are released at synaptic clefts and their action is modified by neuromodulation. **12.10a Neurotransmitters** 471 • Neurotransmitters are small organic molecules released from synaptic knobs to regulate postsynaptic neurons, or effectors (muscles and glands). • Major classes of neurotransmitters include acetylcholine, amino acids, monoamines, and neuropeptides. **12.10b Neuromodulation** 472 • Neuromodulation is the release of chemicals other than neurotransmitters that either increase the responsiveness to a neurotransmitter (facilitation) or decrease the responsiveness to a neurotransmitter (inhibition).
12.11 Neural Integration and Neuronal Pools of the CNS 474	• Interneurons are organized into neuronal pools, which are groups of interconnected neurons with specific functions and are classified as converging, diverging, reverberating, and parallel-after-discharge.

Do You Know the Basics?

____ 1. The cell body of a neuron does all of the following *except*

    a. release neurotransmitter into the synaptic cleft.

    b. produce synaptic vesicles containing neurotransmitter that are subsequently transported to the synaptic knob.

    c. conduct graded potentials to the axon hillock.

    d. receive graded potentials from dendrites.

____ 2. Neurons that have only two processes attached to the cell body are called

    a. unipolar.   c. multipolar.

    b. bipolar.   d. efferent.

____ 3. Which neurons are located only within the CNS?

    a. afferent neurons   c. sensory neurons

    b. glial cells   d. interneurons

____ 4. EPSPs are caused by the movement of

    a. Na^+ out of the cell.

    b. Na^+ into the cell.

    c. K^+ into the cell.

    d. both Na^+ and K^+ into the cell.

____ 5. The glial cells that help produce and circulate cerebrospinal fluid in the CNS are

    a. satellite cells.

    b. microglia.

    c. ependymal cells.

    d. astrocytes.

____ 6. Which of the following is a part of the PNS?

    a. microglia

    b. spinal cord

    c. brain

    d. neurolemmocyte

____ 7. An action potential is generated when threshold is reached, at which time

    a. voltage-gated K^+ channels close.

    b. voltage-gated Na^+ channels open.

    c. chemically gated Na^+ channels open.

    d. Ca^{2+} enters the cell.

____ 8. Which type of neuronal pool utilizes nerve impulse feedback to repeatedly stimulate the circuit?

    a. converging circuit

    b. diverging circuit

    c. reverberating circuit

    d. parallel-after-discharge circuit

____ 9. At an electrical synapse, presynaptic and postsynaptic membranes interface through

    a. neurofibril nodes.

    b. gap junctions.

    c. telodendria.

    d. neurotransmitters.

____ 10. The two primary factors that influence the speed of an action potential propagation are axon diameter and

    a. myelination.

    b. the type of associated glial cell(s).

    c. concentration of K^+ in the cell.

    d. the length of the axon.

11. What are the four structural types of neurons? How do they compare to the three functional types of neurons?

12. Identify the principal glial cell types, and briefly discuss the function of each type.

13. How does myelination differ between the CNS and the PNS?

14. Describe the procedure by which a PNS axon may repair itself (axon regeneration).

15. Describe how the resting membrane potential is maintained in a neuron.

16. Compare and contrast graded potentials and action potentials.

17. Explain summation of EPSPs and IPSPs and the relationship to the initation of an action potential.

18. Graph and explain the events associated with an action potential.

19. Explain the mechanism for the release of neurotransmitter from the synaptic knob.

20. List and briefly describe the major types of neurotransmitters.

Can You Apply What You've Learned?

1. Andrew was brought to the doctor's office after he was bitten by a stray dog. The concern was that the dog might be infected with the rabies virus. The rabies virus infects neurons by using which method that normally transports materials from the synaptic knob to the cell body?

    a. anterograde transport

    b. fast axonal transport

    c. slow axonal transport

    d. All of these are correct.

2. An elderly neighbor was diagnosed with an astrocytoma tumor in the brain. This cancer affects what types of cell?

   a. ependymal cells
   b. microglia
   c. astrocytes
   d. satellite cells

3. Cynthia has received her lab results and is told that her blood calcium levels are abnormal. The event in neuron transmission that would most likely be affected would be

   a. summation of graded potentials in the axon hillock.
   b. production of graded potentials in the dendrites and cell body.
   c. release of neurotransmitter from the synaptic knob.
   d. propagation of an action potential in the axon.

4. Heidi's physician prescribed a medication that is known to block the reuptake of serotonin neurotransmitter from the synaptic cleft. This medication affects what segment in neuron transmission?

   a. initial segment
   b. conductive segment
   c. transmissive segment
   d. receptive segment

5. Sarah wants to call her new friend Julie and needs to write down her phone number but cannot find a pen. She continues to repeat the number over and over. This is most likely occurring in what type of neuronal pool?

   a. reverberating circuit
   b. divergent circuit
   c. convergent circuit
   d. parallel-after-discharge circuit

Can You Synthesize What You've Learned?

1. Over a period of 6 to 9 months, Marianne began to experience vision problems as well as weakness and loss of fine control of the skeletal muscles in her leg. Blood tests revealed the presence of antibodies (immune system proteins) that attack myelin. Beyond the presence of the antibodies, what was the cause of Marianne's vision and muscular difficulties?

2. Surgeons were able to reattach Irving's amputated limb, sewing both the nerves and the blood vessels back together. After the surgery, which proceeded very well, the limb regained its blood supply almost immediately, but the limb remained motionless and Irving had no feeling in it for several months. Why did it take longer to reestablish innervation than circulation?

3. Certain types of neurotoxins prevent depolarization of the axon. What specific type of channel is impaired?

chapter 13

Nervous System: Brain and Cranial Nerves

Approximately 4 to 6 million years ago, when the earliest humans were evolving, brain size was a mere 440 cubic centimeters (cc), not much larger than that of a chimpanzee. As humans evolved, brain size increased steadily and reached an average volume of 1200 cc to 1500 cc and an average weight of 1.35 to 1.4 kilograms. Additionally, the texture of the brain's outer surface (its hemispheres) has changed. The volume of our skull limits the size of the brain, so the tissue forming the brain's outer surface folded on itself so ➡

A medical imaging technologist is trained to utilize a variety of imaging techniques, such as magnetic resonance imaging (MRI), computed tomography (CT) and sonography. The technologist must be able to correctly interpret the physician's instructions, operate the imaging machinery, and communicate with the patient during the procedure. The image above shows a CT technician positioning a patient for a cranial CT scan. This technician must understand relevant brain anatomy and be able to interpret the sectional images produced of the brain.

Module 7: Nervous System

that more neurons could fit into the space within the skull. Although modern humans display variability in brain size, it isn't the *size* of the brain that determines intelligence, but the number of active synapses among neurons.

Our discussion in this chapter focuses first on the brain's four major regions: the cerebrum, the diencephalon, the brainstem, and the cerebellum. Then the cranial nerves, which originate within centers of the brain, are described.

13.1 Brain Development and Organization

The essentials of embryonic brain development help clarify how the structures of the adult brain are named and related. Anatomists distinguish the adult brain divisions and they have long noted the different tissue areas of gray matter and white matter in the brain.

13.1a Overview of Brain Anatomy

LEARNING OBJECTIVE

1. Describe the general anatomic features of the brain.

The brain and the attached spinal cord compose the central nervous system (CNS). The brain is associated with 12 pairs of cranial nerves that are considered part of the peripheral nervous system (PNS).

The brain is composed of four major regions: the cerebrum, diencephalon, brainstem, and cerebellum. **Figure 13.1** shows the major parts of the adult brain from several views. The cerebrum is divided into two halves, called the left and right cerebral hemispheres. Each hemisphere may be further subdivided into five functional areas called lobes.

The outer surface of an adult brain exhibits folds called **gyri** (jī'rī; sing., *gyrus; gyros* = circle) and shallow depressions between those folds called **sulci** (sŭl'kŭs; sing., *sulcus;* furrow, ditch), or deeper grooves called **fissures** (fish'ŭr).

Two directional terms are often used to describe relative positions of brain anatomy. Anterior is synonymous with **rostral** (meaning "toward the nose"), and posterior is synonymous with **caudal** (meaning "toward the tail").

WHAT DID YOU LEARN?

1 What are the four major regions of the brain?

13.1b Development of Brain Divisions

LEARNING OBJECTIVES

2. Describe the process of neurulation.
3. Provide the scientific names for the embryonic forebrain, midbrain, and hindbrain.
4. Name the five secondary brain vesicles, and describe their embryonic origins.

Before we can understand how the divisions of the brain form, we first must explore how the nervous system is derived from ectoderm. This process is called neurulation, and is described next.

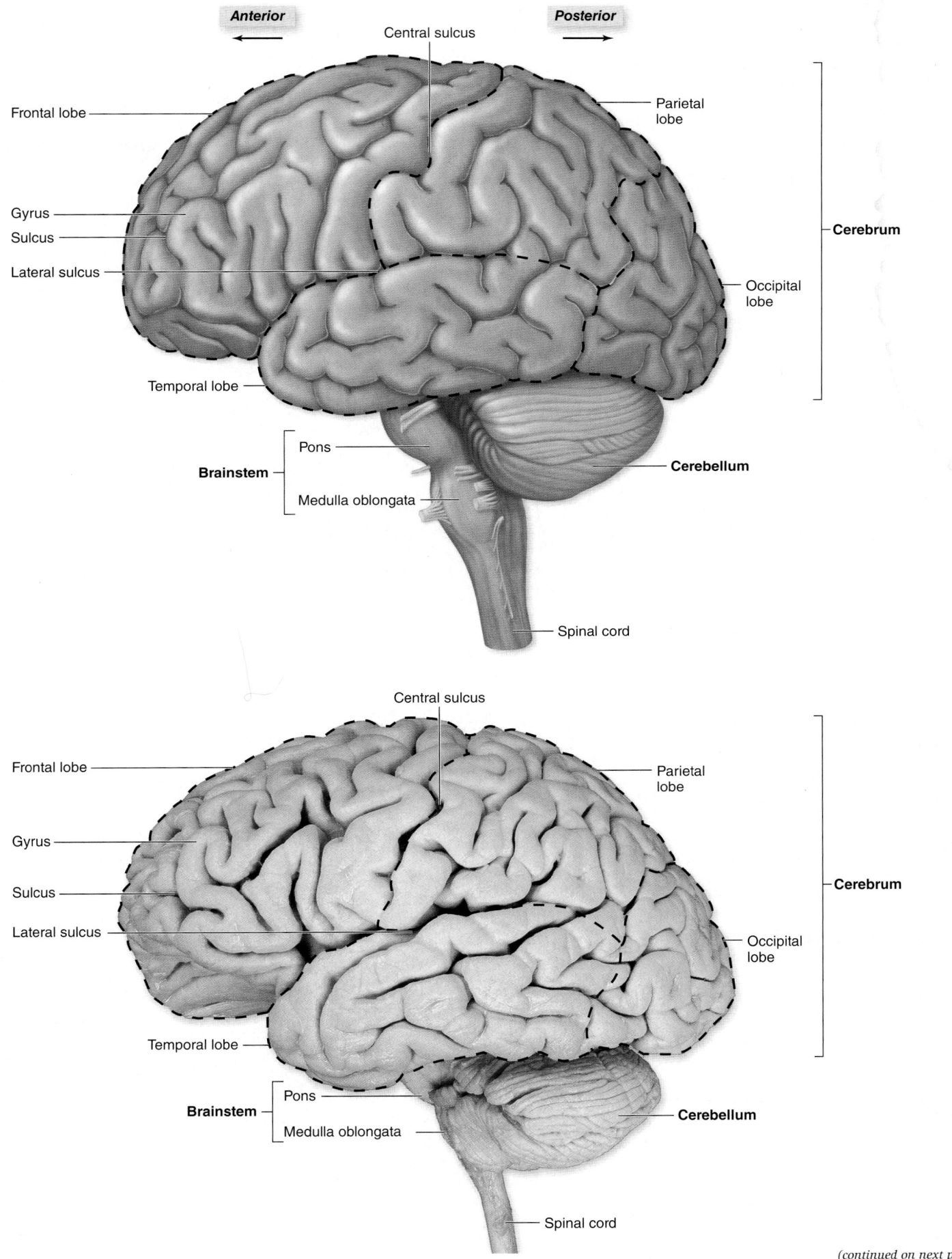

(a) Left lateral view

(continued on next page)

Figure 13.1 The Human Brain. The brain is a complex organ that is formed from several subdivisions. (*a*) An illustration and cadaver photo of a left lateral view show the cerebrum, cerebellum, and portions of the brainstem (in bold) in left lateral view; the diencephalon is not visible. AP|R

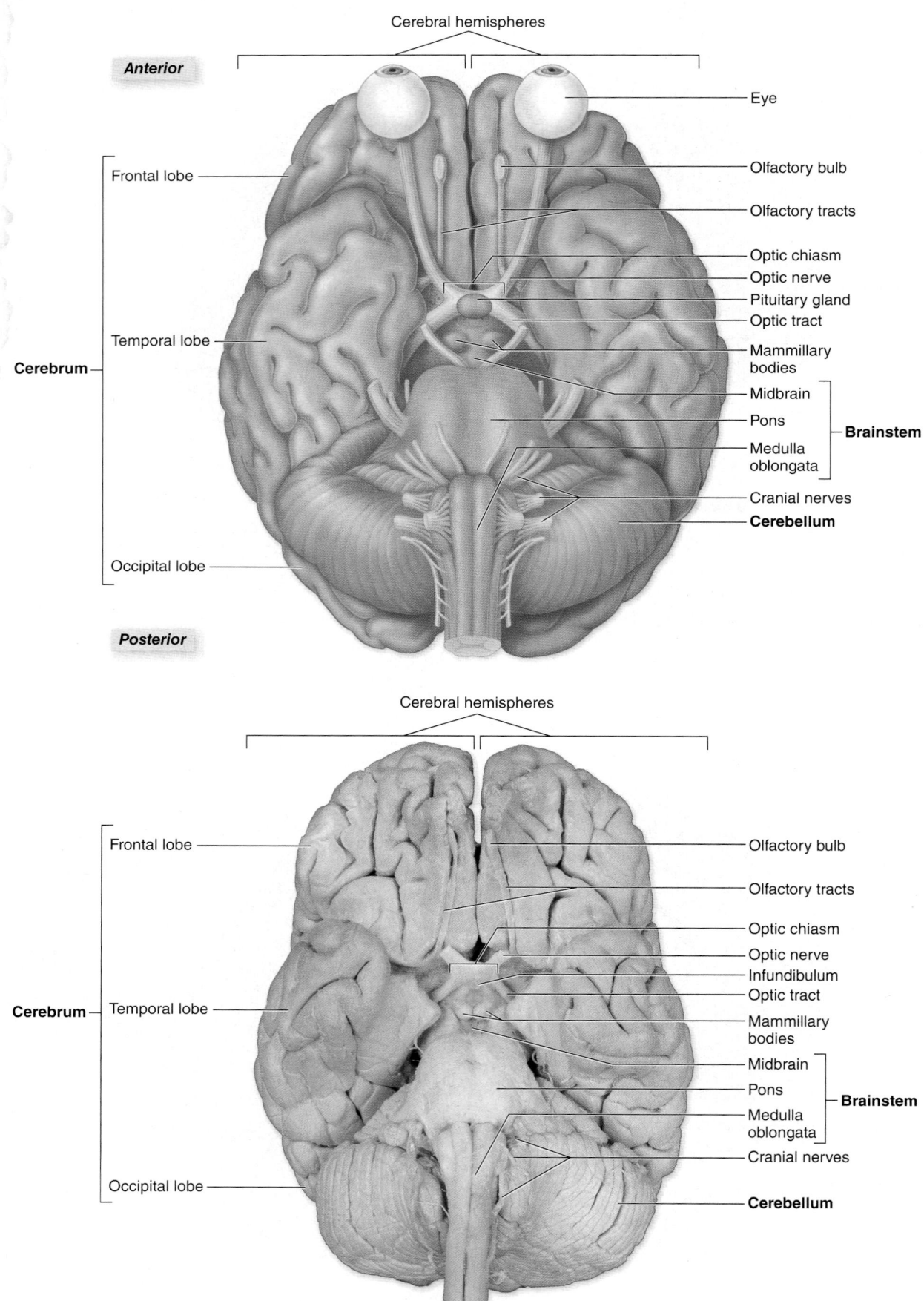

Anterior

Cerebral hemispheres

Eye

Frontal lobe

Olfactory bulb

Olfactory tracts

Optic chiasm

Optic nerve

Pituitary gland

Optic tract

Temporal lobe

Mammillary bodies

Cerebrum

Midbrain

Pons — **Brainstem**

Medulla oblongata

Cranial nerves

Cerebellum

Occipital lobe

Posterior

Cerebral hemispheres

Frontal lobe

Olfactory bulb

Olfactory tracts

Optic chiasm

Optic nerve

Infundibulum

Optic tract

Cerebrum Temporal lobe

Mammillary bodies

Midbrain

Pons — **Brainstem**

Medulla oblongata

Cranial nerves

Occipital lobe

Cerebellum

(b) Inferior view

Figure 13.1 The Human Brain (continued). (b) An illustration and cadaver photo best illustrate the cranial nerves arising from the base of the brain in inferior view. The major regions of the brain are in bold. AP|R

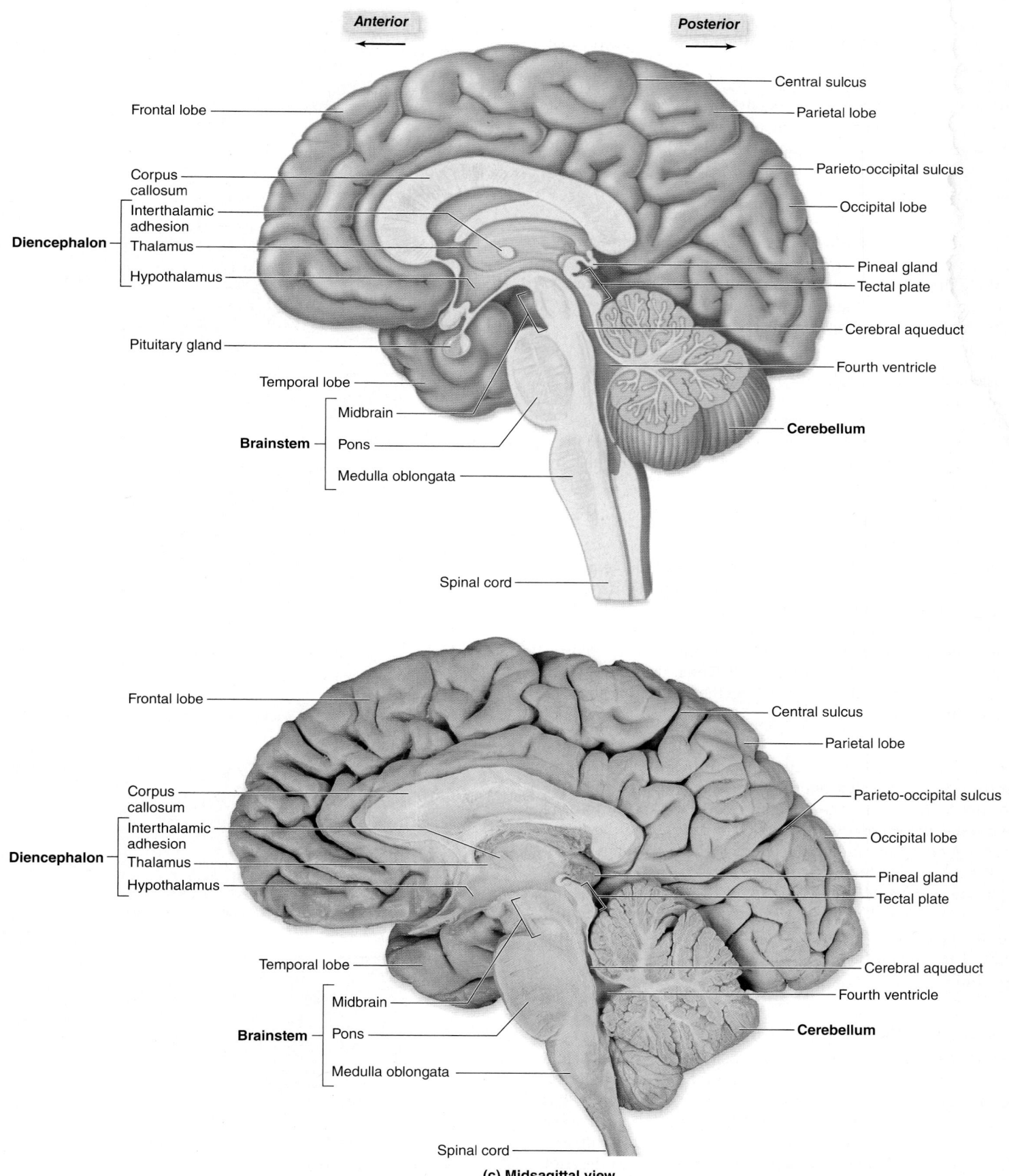

Anterior ←   → **Posterior**

Central sulcus

Frontal lobe

Parietal lobe

Corpus callosum

Parieto-occipital sulcus

Interthalamic adhesion

Occipital lobe

Diencephalon

Thalamus

Hypothalamus

Pineal gland

Tectal plate

Pituitary gland

Cerebral aqueduct

Fourth ventricle

Temporal lobe

Brainstem

Midbrain

Pons

Medulla oblongata

Cerebellum

Spinal cord

Frontal lobe

Central sulcus

Parietal lobe

Corpus callosum

Parieto-occipital sulcus

Interthalamic adhesion

Occipital lobe

Diencephalon

Thalamus

Hypothalamus

Pineal gland

Tectal plate

Temporal lobe

Cerebral aqueduct

Fourth ventricle

Brainstem

Midbrain

Pons

Cerebellum

Medulla oblongata

Spinal cord

(c) Midsagittal view

Figure 13.1 The Human Brain (continued). (*c*) Internal structures such as the thalamus and hypothalamus are best seen in midsagittal view in an illustration and cadaver photo. The major regions of the brain are in bold. AP|R

Neurulation

Nervous tissue development begins in the embryo during the third week of development when a portion of the ectoderm that overlies the notochord thickens (see section 5.6a). This thickened ectoderm is called the **neural plate,** and the cells of the plate collectively are called the **neuroectoderm.** The neural plate is induced by the notochord to form a neural tube, in a process called **neurulation** (noor-oo-lā′shŭn), to form nervous tissue structures. The process of neurulation is shown in **figure 13.2** and explained here:

1. The neural plate develops a central longitudinal indentation called the **neural groove.** As this is occurring, cells along the lateral margins of the neural plate proliferate, becoming the thickened **neural folds.** The tips of the neural folds form **neural crest cells** (or simply, the *neural crest*).

2. The neural folds elevate and approach one another as the neural groove continues to deepen. The neural crest cells are now at the very highest point of the neural groove. When viewed from a superior angle, the neural folds resemble the sides of a hot dog roll, with the neural groove represented by the opening in the roll.

3. The neural crest cells begin to pinch off from the neural folds and form other structures.

4. By the end of the third week, the neural folds have met and fused at the midline as the neural groove starts to form a **neural tube,** which has an internal space called the **neural canal.** The neural tube initially fuses at its midline, and later the neural folds slightly superior and inferior to this midline fuse as well. Thus, the neural tube forms as the neural folds "zip" together both superiorly and inferiorly.

For a short time, the neural tube is open at both its ends. These openings, called **neuropores** (noor′ō-pōr), close during the end of the fourth week. The opening closest to the future head is the **cranial neuropore,** while the opening closest to the future buttocks region is the **caudal neuropore.** If these openings do not close, the developing human will have a neural tube defect (see Clinical View: "Neural Tube Defects"). The developing neural tube forms the central nervous system. In particular, the cranial part of the neural tube expands to form the brain, while the caudal part of the neural tube expands to form the spinal cord (see section 14.7).

Development of the Brain

The brain develops from the cranial (rostral) part of the neural tube in the human embryo. The neural tube undergoes disproportionate growth rates in different regions. This growth has formed three **primary brain vesicles** by the late fourth week of development, which eventually give rise to all the different regions of the adult brain. The names of these vesicles describe their relative positions in the developing head: The forebrain is called the **prosencephalon** (pros-en-sef′ă-lon; *proso* = forward, *enkephalos* = brain); the midbrain is called the **mesencephalon** (mez-en-sef′ă-lon; *mes* = middle); and the hindbrain is called the

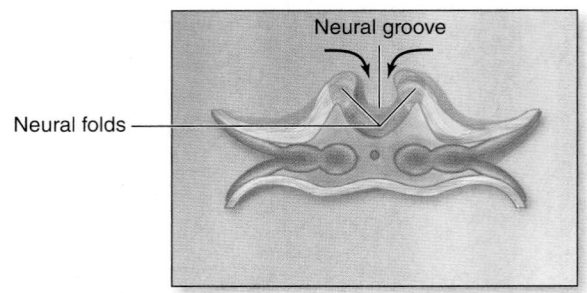

(1) Neural folds and neural groove form from the neural plate.

(2) Neural folds elevate and approach one another.

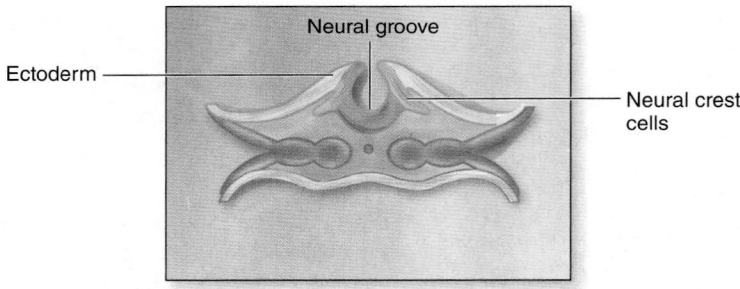

(3) Neural crest cells begin to "pinch off" from the neural folds and form other structures.

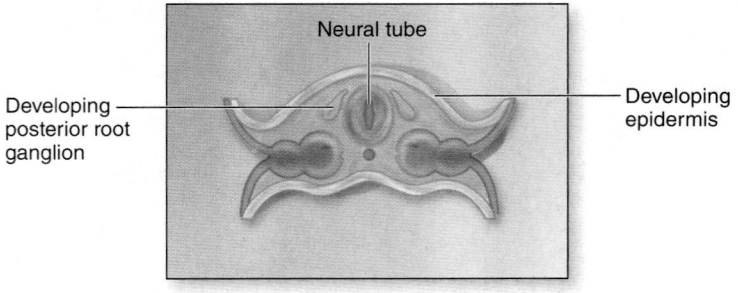

(4) Neural folds fuse to form the neural tube.

Figure 13.2 Nervous System Development. The process of neurulation begins in the third week, and the neural tube finishes closing by the end of week 4.

CLINICAL VIEW
Neural Tube Defects

Neural tube defects (NTD) are serious developmental deformities of the brain, spinal cord, and meninges. The two basic categories of NTDs are anencephaly and spina bifida. Both conditions result from localized failure of the developing neural tube to close.

Anencephaly (an'en-sef-ă-lē; *an* = without, *enkephalos* = brain) is substantial or complete absence of a brain as well as the bones making up the cranium. Infants with anencephaly rarely live longer than a few hours following birth. Fortunately, neural tube defects of this magnitude are rare, and are easily detected with prenatal ultrasound, thus alerting the parents to the condition.

Spina bifida (spī'nă bǐf'ǐ-dă; *spina* = spine, *bifidus* = cleft in two parts) occurs more frequently than anencephaly. This defect results when the

caudal portion of the neural tube, often in the lumbar or sacral region, fails to close. Two forms of spina bifida occur: the more severe spina bifida cystica and the less severe spina bifida occulta. In *spina bifida cystica*, almost no vertebral arch forms, so the posterior aspect of the spinal cord in this region is left unprotected (*figures a and b*). Typically, there is a large cystic structure in the back, filled with cerebrospinal fluid (CSF) and covered by a thin layer of skin or in some cases only by meninges (protective membranes around the spinal cord). Surgery is generally done promptly to close the defect, reduce the risk of infection, and preserve existing spinal cord function. Paralysis of the lower limbs is often part of the spina bifida syndrome. But even with these problems, most children with spina bifida cystica live well into adulthood.

Spina bifida occulta is less serious, but much more common than the cystica form. This condition is characterized by a partial defect of the vertebral arch, typically involving the vertebral lamina and spinous process (see *figure c*). The bony defect is small, and the spinal cord or meninges does not protrude. Often there is a tuft of hair in the region of the bony defect, which may alert the physician of the location of the possible defect. Most people with this condition are otherwise asymptomatic, and it is generally detected incidentally during an x-ray for an unrelated reason. Estimates of the incidence of spina bifida occulta range as high as 17% of the population in some x-ray studies.

Although the risk of neural tube defects cannot be eliminated, it can be greatly reduced. Researchers have discovered that increased intake of vitamin B_{12} and the B vitamin **folic acid (folate)** by pregnant women is correlated with a decreased incidence of neural tube defects. Both vitamin B_{12} and folic acid are critical to DNA formation and are necessary for cellular division and tissue differentiation. Thus, pregnant women are encouraged to take prenatal vitamins containing high levels of these two vitamins, and the food industry has begun fortifying many breads and grains with folate as well. In addition, all women of childbearing age are encouraged to have sufficient levels of folic acid in their diet, because these women may not realize they are pregnant until after week 4, when the neural tube formation is complete.

A newborn with anencephaly.

(a) **Spina bifida cystica**

(b) **Child with spina bifida cystica**

(c) **Spina bifida occulta**

Spina bifida is a neural tube disorder that occurs in two forms: (a, b) spina bifida cystica; (c) spina bifida occulta.

rhombencephalon (rom-ben-sef'ă-lon; *rhombo* = rhomboid) for its rhomboidal shape. (**figure 13.3a**).

By the fifth week of development, the three primary vesicles further develop into a total of five secondary brain vesicles (figure 13.3b):

- The **telencephalon** (tel-en-sef'ă-lon; *tel* = head end) arises from the prosencephalon and eventually forms the cerebrum.
- The **diencephalon** (dī-en-sef'ă-lon; *dia* = through) also derives from the prosencephalon, and it eventually forms the thalamus, hypothalamus, and epithalamus.
- The **mesencephalon** is the only primary vesicle that does not form a new secondary vesicle. It becomes the midbrain.
- The **metencephalon** (met-en-sef'ă-lon; *meta* = after) arises from the rhombencephalon and eventually forms the pons and cerebellum.
- The **myelencephalon** (mī-el-en-sef'ă-lon; *myelos* = medulla) also derives from the rhombencephalon, and it eventually forms the medulla oblongata.

Table 13.1 summarizes the embryonic brain structures and their corresponding structures in the adult brain. It also lists the adult derivatives from the neural canal (the space within the neural tube).

The telencephalon grows rapidly and envelops the diencephalon during the embryonic and fetal periods. As the future brain develops, its surface folds especially in the telencephalon, leading to the formation of the adult sulci and gyri. The bends and creases that occur within the developing brain help to determine the boundaries of the brain's cavities. Collectively, these bends, creases, and folds in the telencephalon surface are necessary in order to fit the massive amount of developing brain tissue within the confines of the cranial

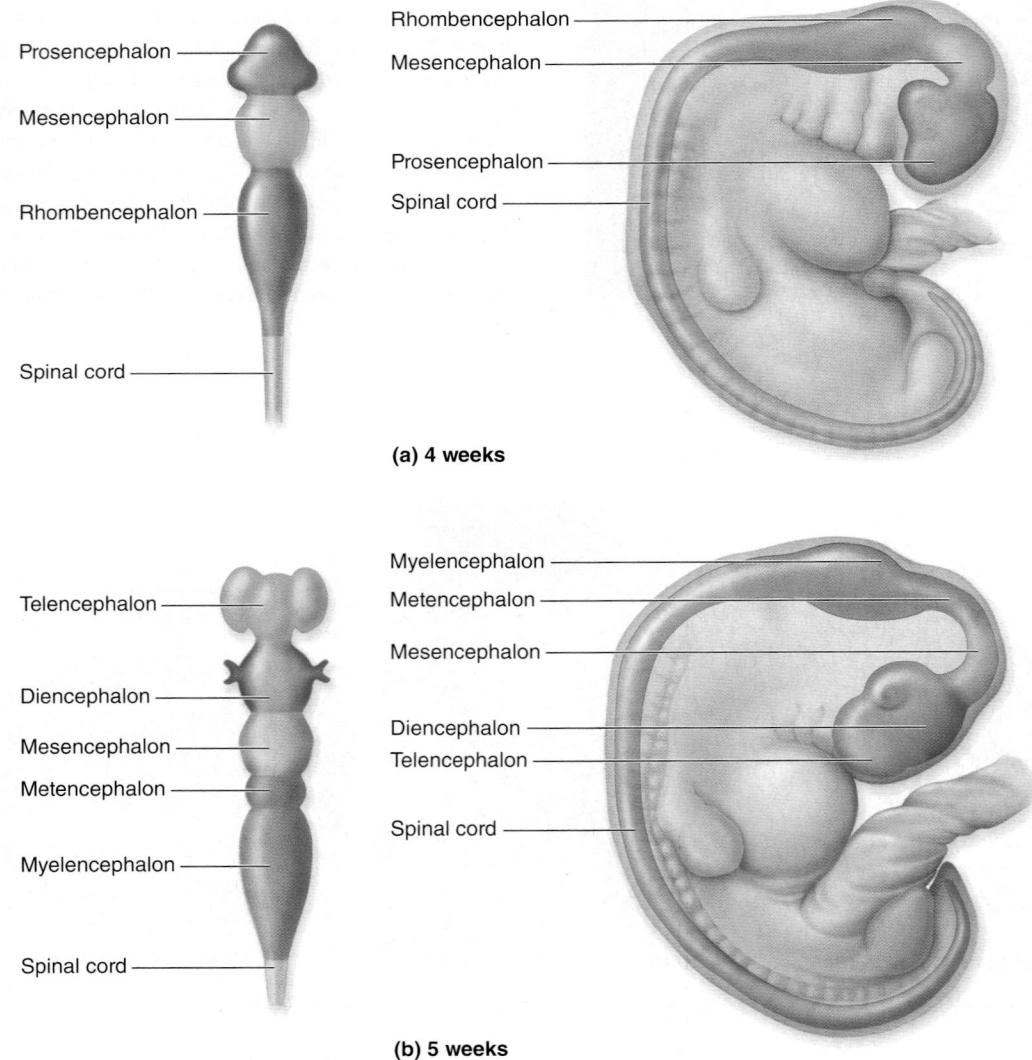

(a) 4 weeks

(b) 5 weeks

Figure 13.3 Structural Changes in the Developing Brain. (*a*) As early as 4 weeks, the growing brain is curled because of space restrictions in the developing head. (*b*) At 5 weeks, the secondary brain vesicles appear.

Figure 13.3 Structural Changes in the Developing Brain (continued). (*c*) By 13 weeks, the telencephalon grows rapidly and envelops the diencephalon. (*d*) Some major sulci and gyri are present by 26 weeks. (*e*) The features of an adult brain are present at birth. AP|R

Table 13.1 — Major Brain Structures: Embryonic Through Adult

EMBRYONIC DEVELOPMENT → ADULT STRUCTURE

Neural Tube	Primary Brain Vesicles	Secondary Brain Vesicles (Future Adult Brain Regions)[1]	Neural Canal Derivative[2]	Structures Within Brain Regions
Anterior		Telencephalon	Lateral ventricles	Cerebrum
	Prosencephalon (forebrain)	Diencephalon	Third ventricle	Epithalamus / Thalamus / Hypothalamus
	Mesencephalon (midbrain)	Mesencephalon (midbrain)	Cerebral aqueduct	Midbrain
	Rhombencephalon (hindbrain)	Metencephalon	Fourth ventricle (superior part)	Pons, cerebellum
		Myelencephalon	Fourth ventricle (inferior part); part of central canal	Medulla oblongata
Posterior	Neural canal	Neural canal		

1. The embryonic secondary vesicles form the adult brain regions—thus, they share the same names.
2. The neural canal in each specific brain region will form its own named space.

---

cavity. Most of the gyri and sulci develop late in the fetal period, so that by the time the fetus is born, its brain closely resembles that of an adult even though its functional development takes much longer (figure 13.3c–e).

WHAT DID YOU LEARN?

2 How does the neural plate form a neural tube?

3 Identify the five secondary vesicles, and list the adult brain structures they form.

13.1c Gray Matter and White Matter Distribution

LEARNING OBJECTIVE

5. Compare and contrast the distribution of gray and white matter throughout the brain divisions.

Two distinct tissue areas are recognized within the brain and spinal cord: gray matter and white matter. The **gray matter** primarily derives its color from the motor neuron and interneuron cell bodies and their associated capillary beds, as well as the neuronal dendrites and some unmyelinated axons. The **white matter** derives its color from the myelin on the abundant myelinated axons.

For example, an outer, superficial region of gray matter in the cerebrum forms during brain development from migrating peripheral neurons. These external sheets of gray matter, called the **cerebral cortex** (se-rē′bral kor′teks; bark), cover the surface of the cerebrum. The white matter lies deep to the gray matter of the cortex. However, within the masses of white matter, the brain also contains discrete internal clusters of gray matter called **cerebral nuclei.** These are oval, spherical, or sometimes irregularly shaped clusters of neuron cell bodies. **Figure 13.4** shows the distribution of gray matter and white matter in various regions of the CNS. **Table 13.2** is a glossary of nervous system structures.

Table 13.2 — Glossary of Nervous System Structures

Structure	Description
Ganglion	Cluster of neuron cell bodies in the peripheral nervous system (PNS)
Center	Group of central nervous system (CNS) neuron cell bodies with a common function
Nucleus	Center that displays discrete anatomic boundaries
Nerve	Bundle of axons extending through the PNS
Nerve plexus	Network of nerves
Tract	CNS axon bundle in which the axons have a similar function and share a common origin and destination
Funiculus	Group of tracts in a specific area of the spinal cord
Pathway	Centers and tracts that connect the CNS with body organs and systems

(a) Coronal section of cerebrum and diencephalon

Gray matter
Cortex

Cerebral nuclei

White matter
Inner white matter
Corpus callosum
Internal capsule

Lateral ventricle

(a)

Cerebrum
Cerebellum
Medulla oblongata

(b)
(c)

Spinal cord

(d)

Cortex (gray matter)   Inner gray matter

Cerebellum

Inner gray matter
Fourth ventricle
Brainstem
Outer white matter

(b) Cerebellum and brainstem

Fourth ventricle
Inner gray matter   Outer white matter

(c) Medulla oblongata

Central canal
Outer white matter
Inner gray matter

(d) Spinal cord

Figure 13.4 Gray and White Matter in the CNS. The gray matter represents regions containing neuron cell bodies, dendrites, and unmyelinated axons, whereas the white matter derives its color from myelinated axons. The distribution of gray and white matter is compared in (a) the cerebrum and diencephalon, (b) the cerebellum and brainstem, (c) the medulla oblongata (which is the inferior portion of the brainstem), and (d) the spinal cord. AP|R

 WHAT DID YOU LEARN?

4 Where is gray matter located within the cerebrum and spinal cord?

13.2 Protection and Support of the Brain

The brain is both protected and isolated by multiple structures. The bony cranium provides rigid support, while protective connective tissue membranes called meninges surround and partition portions of the brain. Cerebrospinal fluid (CSF) acts as a cushioning fluid between specific layers of meninges. Finally, the brain has a unique blood-brain barrier to prevent entry of harmful materials into the brain from the blood.

13.2a Cranial Meninges

✓ **LEARNING OBJECTIVES**

1. Compare and contrast the structure and locations of the three meninges, and list the spaces found between the meninges.
2. Describe the four cranial dural septa, and give their locations.

The **cranial meninges** (mĕ-nin′jes, mē′nin-jēz; sing., *meninx*, men′ingks; membrane) are three connective tissue layers that separate and support the soft tissue of the brain from the bones of the cranium, enclose and protect some of the blood vessels that supply the brain, and help contain and circulate cerebrospinal fluid. From deep (closest to the brain) to superficial (farthest from the brain), the cranial meninges are the pia mater, the arachnoid mater, and the dura mater **(figure 13.5)**.

Pia Mater

The **pia mater** (pī′a mā′ter, pē′ă mah′ter; *pia* = tender; *mater* = mother) is the innermost of the cranial meninges. It is a thin layer of delicate areolar connective tissue that tightly adheres to the brain and follows every contour of the brain surface.

Arachnoid Mater

The **arachnoid** (ă-rak′noyd) **mater**, also called the *arachnoid membrane*, lies external to the pia mater. The term *arachnoid* means "resembling a spider web," and this meninx is so named because it is partially composed of a delicate web of collagen and elastic fibers, termed the **arachnoid trabeculae.** Immediately deep to the arachnoid mater is the **subarachnoid space,** which contains cerebrospinal fluid (to be discussed in the next section). The arachnoid trabeculae extend through this space from the arachnoid to the underlying pia mater. Both the arachnoid trabeculae and cerebrospinal fluid support cerebral arteries and veins within the subarachnoid space. Between the arachnoid mater and the overlying dura mater is a potential space, the **subdural space.** The subdural space becomes an actual space if blood or fluid accumulates there, a condition called a subdural hematoma (see Clinical View: "Epidural and Subdural Hematomas").

Dura Mater

The **dura mater** (dū′ră; *dura* = tough) is an external, tough, dense irregular connective tissue layer composed of two fibrous layers. As its Latin name indicates, it is the strongest of the meninges. Within the cranium, the dura mater is composed of two layers. The **meningeal** (mĕ-nin′jē-ăl, men′in-jē′ăl) **layer** is immediately superficial to the arachnoid. The **periosteal** (per-ē-os′tē-ăl) **layer,** the more superficial layer, forms the periosteum on the internal

Arachnoid granulation
Arachnoid villus
Dural venous sinus (superior sagittal sinus)

Skin of scalp
Periosteum
Bone of skull
Periosteal layer ⎤ **Dura mater**
Meningeal layer ⎦
Subdural space (potential space)
Arachnoid mater
Subarachnoid space
Arachnoid trabeculae
Pia mater
Cerebral cortex
White matter

Falx cerebri

Figure 13.5 Cranial Meninges. A coronal section of the superior portion of the head depicts the organization of the three meningeal layers: the dura mater, the arachnoid mater, and the pia mater. In the midline, folds of the inner meningeal layer of the dura mater form the falx cerebri, which partitions the two cerebral hemispheres. The inner meningeal layer and the outer periosteal layer sometimes separate to form the dural venous sinuses, such as the superior sagittal sinus (shown here), which drain blood away from the brain.

surface of the cranial bones. The meningeal layer is usually fused to the periosteal layer, except in specific areas where these two layers separate to form large, blood-filled spaces called **dural venous sinuses.** (A sinus is a modified vein.) Dural venous sinuses are typically triangular in cross section, and unlike most other veins, they do not have valves to regulate venous blood flow. The dural venous sinuses drain blood from the brain, and most of the specific sinuses are shown in **figure 13.6**.

The dura mater and the bones of the skull may be separated by a potential **epidural** (ep-i-dū'răl) **space,** which contains the arteries and veins that nourish the meninges and bones of the cranium. Like the subdural space, the epidural space may become a real space if blood or fluid accumulates within it.

Cranial Dural Septa

The meningeal layer of the dura mater extends as flat partitions into the cranial cavity at four locations. Collectively, these double layers of dura mater are called **cranial dural septa** (sing., *septum* = wall). These membranous partitions separate specific parts of the brain and provide additional stabilization and support to the brain. There are four cranial dural septa: the falx cerebri, tentorium cerebelli, falx cerebelli, and diaphragma sellae (figure 13.6). The **falx cerebri** (falks sē-rē'bri; *falx* = sickle, *cerebro* = brain) is the largest of the four dural septa. This large, sickle-shaped vertical fold of dura mater is located in the midsagittal plane and projects into the longitudinal fissure between the left and right cerebral hemispheres. Anteriorly, its inferior portion attaches to the crista galli of the ethmoid bone; posteriorly, its inferior portion attaches to the internal occipital crest (see section 8.2). Running within the margins of either end of this dural septa are two dural venous sinuses: the **superior sagittal sinus** and the **inferior sagittal sinus.**

The **tentorium cerebelli** (ten-tō'rē-ŭm ser-e-bel'ī) is a horizontally oriented fold of dura mater that separates both the occipital and temporal lobes of the cerebrum from the cerebellum. It is named for the fact that it forms a dural "tent" over the cerebellum. The **transverse sinuses** run within its posterior border, whereas the **straight sinus** is found along its midsagittal plane. The anterior surface of the tentorium cerebelli has a gap or opening, called the

tentorial notch (or *tentorial incisure*), to allow for the passage of the brainstem.

Extending into the midsagittal line inferior to the tentorium cerebelli is the **falx cerebelli,** a sickle-shaped vertical partition that divides the left and right cerebellar hemispheres. A tiny **occipital sinus** (another dural venous sinus) runs in its posterior vertical border.

The **diaphragma sellae** (dī-ă-frag'mă sel'ē; *sella* = saddle) is the smallest of the dural septa. It forms a "roof" over the sella turcica of the sphenoid bone. A small opening within it allows for the passage of a thin stalk, called the infundibulum, that attaches the pituitary gland to the base of the hypothalamus (described later).

WHAT DO YOU THINK?

1 Which meningeal layer provides the most support and physical protection to the brain? Why?

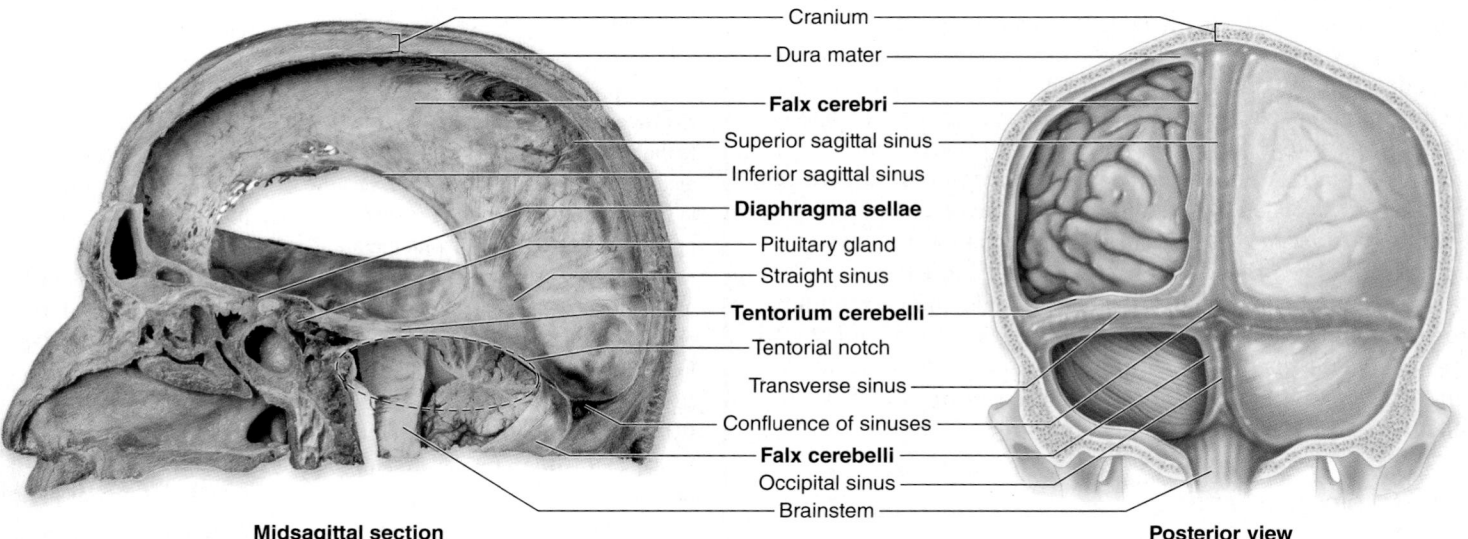

Cranium
Dura mater
Falx cerebri
Superior sagittal sinus
Inferior sagittal sinus
Diaphragma sellae
Pituitary gland
Straight sinus
Tentorium cerebelli
Tentorial notch
Transverse sinus
Confluence of sinuses
Falx cerebelli
Occipital sinus
Brainstem

Midsagittal section

Posterior view

Figure 13.6 Cranial Dural Septa. A midsagittal section and posterior view of the skull show the orientation of the falx cerebri, falx cerebelli, tentorium cerebelli, and diaphragma sellae.

CLINICAL VIEW
Meningitis

Meningitis is the inflammation of the meninges, and typically it is caused by viral or bacterial infection. Early symptoms may include fever, severe headache, vomiting, and a stiff neck (because pain from the meninges may be referred to the posterior neck). Bacterial meningitis typically produces more severe symptoms and may result in brain damage and death if left untreated. Both viral and bacterial meningitis are contagious and may be spread through respiratory droplets or oral secretions, so it is a disease that may spread rapidly through college dormitories or military barracks (where individuals live in close quarters). Thus, most teenagers are recommended to get the bacterial meningitis vaccine (which protects them against the most common bacterial strains that cause meningitis) prior to attending college.

 WHAT DID YOU LEARN?

5 From superficial (furthest away from the spinal cord) to deepest (closest to the spinal cord), name the meninges and the spaces between the meninges.

6 Where is the falx cerebri located, and what is its role?

13.2b Brain Ventricles
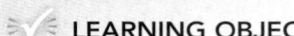 **LEARNING OBJECTIVE**

3. Describe the anatomy and location of the ventricles.

Ventricles (ven'tri-kl; little cavity) are cavities or expansions within the brain that are derived from the neural canal (the lumen of the embryonic neural tube). All of the ventricles are lined with ependymal cells (see section 12.3d) and contain cerebrospinal fluid. The ventricles share some communications with one another as well as with the central canal of the spinal cord (**figure 13.7**).

There are four ventricles within the brain: Two **lateral ventricles** are in the cerebrum, separated by a thin medial partition called the **septum pellucidum** (pe-lū'si-dum; *pellucid* = transparent) (figure 13.4). Within the diencephalon is a smaller, thinner ventricle called the **third ventricle** (figure 13.7). Each lateral ventricle communicates with the third ventricle through an opening called the **interventricular foramen** (formerly called the *foramen of Munro*). A narrow canal called the **cerebral aqueduct** (ak'we-dŭkt) (also called the *mesencephalic aqueduct* and formerly called the *aqueduct of Sylvius*) passes through the midbrain and connects the third ventricle with the sickle-shaped **fourth ventricle.** The fourth ventricle is located between the pons and cerebellum. It opens to the subarachnoid space via a single *median aperture* and paired *lateral apertures*. The fourth ventricle narrows at its inferior end before it merges with the slender **central canal** in the spinal cord.

 WHAT DID YOU LEARN?

7 Where is the fourth ventricle located, and how does it connect with the subarachnoid space?

13.2c Cerebrospinal Fluid
 LEARNING OBJECTIVES

4. Explain the three functions of cerebrospinal fluid.
5. Trace the circulation of cerebrospinal fluid, beginning with its origin and ending with its removal.

Cerebrospinal (sĕ-rē'brō-spī-nǎl) **fluid (CSF)** is a clear, colorless liquid that circulates in the ventricles and subarachnoid space. CSF bathes the exposed surfaces of the central nervous system and completely surrounds it. CSF performs several important functions:

- **Buoyancy.** The brain floats within the CSF, thereby reducing its apparent weight by more than 95%; this prevents the brain from being crushed under its own weight. Without CSF to support it, parts of the heavy brain would sink through the foramen magnum.

- **Protection.** CSF provides a liquid cushion to protect delicate neural structures from sudden movements. When you try to walk quickly in a swimming pool, your movements are slowed as the water acts as a "movement buffer." CSF likewise helps slow movements of the brain if the skull or body moves suddenly and forcefully.

- **Environmental stability.** CSF transports nutrients and chemical messengers to the brain and removes waste products from the brain. Additionally, CSF protects nervous tissue from chemical fluctuations that would disrupt neuron function. The waste products and excess CSF are eventually transported into the venous circulation.

CSF Formation

Cerebrospinal fluid is formed by the **choroid plexus** (ko'royd plek'sŭs; *chorioeides* = membrane, *plexus* = a braid), a region of specialized tissue in each ventricle. The choroid plexus is composed of a layer of **ependymal** (ep-en'di-mǎl; *ependyma* = an upper garment) **cells** and the blood capillaries that lie within the pia mater (**figure 13.8**).

CLINICAL VIEW
Hydrocephalus

Hydrocephalus (hī-drō-sef'a-lŭs; *hydro* = water, *kephale* = head) refers to the pathologic condition of excessive CSF, which often leads to brain distortion. Most cases of hydrocephalus result from either an obstruction in CSF flow that restricts its reabsorption into the venous bloodstream or some intrinsic problem with the arachnoid villi themselves.

If hydrocephalus develops in a young child, the head becomes enlarged and neurologic damage may result. If hydrocephalus develops after the cranial sutures have closed, the brain may be compressed within the fixed cranium as the ventricles expand, resulting in permanent brain damage. Hydrocephalus may be treated surgically by implanting shunts (tubes) that drain excess CSF to other body regions. The fluid is then absorbed into the blood.

Infant with hydrocephalus.

Posterior **Anterior**

Third ventricle

Interventricular foramen

Lateral ventricles

Cerebral aqueduct

Fourth ventricle

Lateral aperture

Median aperture

Central canal of spinal cord

(a) Lateral view

Cerebrum

Lateral ventricle

Interventricular foramen

Third ventricle

Cerebral aqueduct

Fourth ventricle

Central canal of spinal cord

(b) Anterior view

Figure 13.7 Ventricles of the Brain. The ventricles are formed from the embryonic neural canal. They contain cerebrospinal fluid (CSF), which transports chemical messengers, nutrients, and waste products. (*a*) Lateral and (*b*) anterior views show the positioning and relationships of the ventricles. AP|R

Figure 13.8 Choroid Plexus. The choroid plexus helps produce cerebrospinal fluid. (*a*) A coronal brain section shows the choroid plexus in lateral ventricles. (*b*) The choroid plexus is composed of ependymal cells and capillaries within the pia mater.

Longitudinal fissure

Choroid plexus in lateral ventricles

Corpus callosum

Ependymal cells

Capillary

Pia mater

Section of choroid plexus

Cavity of ventricle

CSF forms and enters the ventricle

(a) Coronal section of the brain, close-up

(b) Choroid plexus

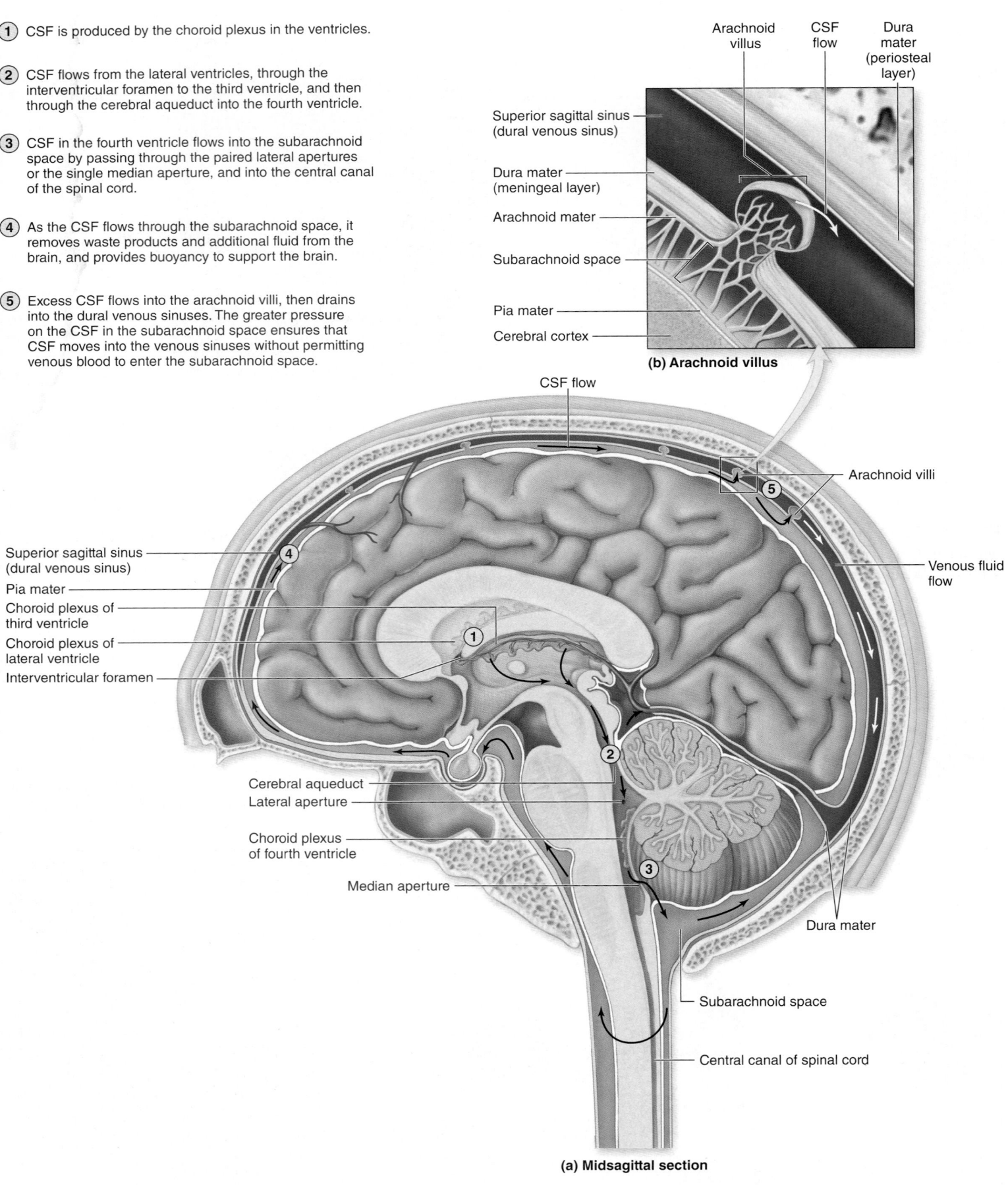

① CSF is produced by the choroid plexus in the ventricles.

② CSF flows from the lateral ventricles, through the interventricular foramen to the third ventricle, and then through the cerebral aqueduct into the fourth ventricle.

③ CSF in the fourth ventricle flows into the subarachnoid space by passing through the paired lateral apertures or the single median aperture, and into the central canal of the spinal cord.

④ As the CSF flows through the subarachnoid space, it removes waste products and additional fluid from the brain, and provides buoyancy to support the brain.

⑤ Excess CSF flows into the arachnoid villi, then drains into the dural venous sinuses. The greater pressure on the CSF in the subarachnoid space ensures that CSF moves into the venous sinuses without permitting venous blood to enter the subarachnoid space.

Arachnoid villus

CSF flow

Dura mater (periosteal layer)

Superior sagittal sinus (dural venous sinus)

Dura mater (meningeal layer)

Arachnoid mater

Subarachnoid space

Pia mater

Cerebral cortex

(b) Arachnoid villus

CSF flow

Arachnoid villi

Superior sagittal sinus (dural venous sinus)

Pia mater

Choroid plexus of third ventricle

Choroid plexus of lateral ventricle

Interventricular foramen

Venous fluid flow

Cerebral aqueduct

Lateral aperture

Choroid plexus of fourth ventricle

Median aperture

Dura mater

Subarachnoid space

Central canal of spinal cord

(a) Midsagittal section

Figure 13.9 Production and Circulation of Cerebrospinal Fluid. (*a*) A midsagittal section identifies the sites where cerebrospinal fluid (CSF) is formed and the pathway of its circulation toward the arachnoid villi. (*b*) CSF flows from the arachnoid villi into the dural venous sinuses. AP|R

CSF is produced by secretion of a fluid from the ependymal cells that originates from the blood plasma. CSF is somewhat similar to blood plasma, although certain ion concentrations differ between the two types of fluid. Once CSF enters the subarachnoid space, it receives some additional fluid filtered from the blood into the brain during capillary exchange.

CSF Circulation

The brain produces CSF at a rate of about 500 milliliters (mL) per day. The CSF circulates through the ventricles and then enters the subarachnoid space, where the total volume of CSF at any given moment ranges between 100 mL and 160 mL. Excess CSF is continuously removed from the subarachnoid space so that the fluid does not accumulate and compress or damage the nervous tissue.

Fingerlike extensions of the arachnoid mater project through the dura mater into the dural venous sinuses to form **arachnoid villi** (vil'ī; *villi* = shaggy hair). A collection of arachnoid villi forms an **arachnoid granulation.** Excess CSF moves across the arachnoid villi to return to the blood within the dural venous sinuses. **Figure 13.9** describes in detail and shows the process of CSF production, circulation, and removal. As a result, the arachnoid villi extending into the dural venous sinuses provide a conduit for a one-way flow of excess CSF to be returned to the blood within the dural venous sinuses.

WHAT DID YOU LEARN?

8 What are the three main functions of cerebrospinal fluid?

9 Where is CSF first produced, where does it circulate, and how does excess CSF get removed from the blood?

13.2d Blood-Brain Barrier

LEARNING OBJECTIVES

6. Describe the components that form the blood-brain barrier.

7. Explain how the blood-brain barrier protects the brain.

Nervous tissue is protected from the general circulation by the **blood-brain barrier (BBB),** which strictly regulates which substances can and cannot enter the interstitial fluid of the brain. The blood-brain barrier helps prevent exposure of neurons in the brain to drugs, waste products in the blood, and variations in levels of normal substances (e.g., ions, hormones) that could adversely affect brain function.

The **perivascular feet** of **astrocytes** were shown in section 12.4b to cover, wrap around, and completely envelop most capillaries in the brain. Both the capillary endothelial cells and the astrocyte perivascular feet contribute to the blood-brain barrier **(figure 13.10).** The continuous basement membrane of the endothelial cells also is a significant barrier. Tight junctions between adjacent endothelial cells reduce capillary permeability and prevent materials from diffusing across the capillary wall. The astrocytes act as "gatekeepers" to control which materials pass to the neurons after leaving the capillaries.

Even so, the barrier is not absolute. Lipid-soluble compounds, such as nicotine, alcohol, and some anesthetics, can diffuse across the endothelial plasma membranes (and thus past this barrier) and into the interstitial fluid of the CNS to reach the brain neurons. In addition, drugs such as cocaine and methamphetamine can damage this barrier.

The blood-brain barrier is markedly reduced or missing in three distinct locations in the CNS: the choroid plexus, hypothalamus, and pineal gland. The capillaries of the choroid plexus must be permeable to produce CSF, and the hypothalamus and pineal gland produce certain hormones that must have ready access to the bloodstream.

WHAT DID YOU LEARN?

10 How does the blood-brain barrier protect nervous tissue?

Astrocyte
Nucleus
Perivascular feet

Erythrocyte inside capillary

Capillary
Continuous basement membrane
Tight junction between endothelial cells
Nucleus of endothelial cell

(a)

Capillary
Basement membrane
Endothelial cells

Lipid-soluble substances freely pass through the blood-brain barrier.

Lipid

Perivascular feet of **astrocyte**

Glucose

Astrocytes selectively allow certain substances to cross the blood-brain barrier.

(b)

Erythrocyte

Figure 13.10 Blood-Brain Barrier. The perivascular feet of the astrocytes and the tight endothelial junctions of the capillaries work together to prevent harmful materials in the blood from reaching the brain. (*a*) Here we show just a few perivascular feet of astrocytes, so that their structure may be appreciated. (*b*) The astrocytes regulate the movement of most substances, but lipid-soluble substances can pass through the barrier regardless.

13.3 Cerebrum

The **cerebrum** is the location of conscious thought processes and the origin of all complex intellectual functions. It is readily identified as the two large hemispheres on the superior aspect of the brain (see figure 13.1). The functional activities in your cerebrum enable you to read and comprehend the words in this textbook, turn its pages, form and remember ideas, and talk about your ideas with your peers. It is the center of your intelligence, reasoning, sensory perception, thought, memory, and judgment, as well as your voluntary motor, visual, and auditory activities.

13.3a Cerebral Hemispheres

✓ LEARNING OBJECTIVES

1. Discriminate between the left and right cerebral hemispheres with respect to their general functions.
2. Identify the role of the corpus callosum.

The cerebrum is composed of two halves, called the left and right **cerebral hemispheres** (hem′i-sfēr; *hemi* = half, *sphaira* = ball) **(figure 13.11)**. These paired cerebral hemispheres are separated by a narrow, deep cleft called the **longitudinal fissure** that extends along the midsagittal plane. The cerebral hemispheres are separate from one another, except at a few locations where bundles of axons called **tracts** form white matter regions that allow for communication between them. The largest of these white matter tracts, the **corpus callosum** (kōr′pŭs kal-lō′sŭm; *corpus* = body, *callosum* = hard) connects the hemispheres (see a midsagittal section of the corpus callosum in figure 13.1c). The corpus callosum provides the main method of communication between these hemispheres.

Three points should be kept in mind with respect to the cerebral hemispheres:

- It is difficult to assign a precise function to a specific region of the cerebral cortex in most cases. Considerable overlap and indistinct boundaries permit a single region of the cortex to exhibit several different functions. Additionally, some aspects of cortical function, such as memory or consciousness, cannot easily be assigned to any single region.
- As a general rule, both cerebral hemispheres receive their sensory information from, and project motor commands to, the opposite side of the body. The right cerebral hemisphere controls the left side of the body, and vice versa.
- The two hemispheres appear as anatomic mirror images, but they display some functional differences, termed *cerebral lateralization*. For example, the regions of the

brain that are responsible for controlling speech and understanding verbalization are frequently located in the left cerebral hemisphere. These types of differences primarily affect higher-order functions, which are addressed later in this chapter.

❓ WHAT DO YOU THINK?

2 One past treatment for severe epilepsy was to cut the corpus callosum, thus confining epileptic seizures to just one cerebral hemisphere. How would cutting the corpus callosum affect communication between the left and right hemispheres?

💡 WHAT DID YOU LEARN?

11 What is the general function of each cerebral hemisphere?

12 What is the function of the corpus callosum?

13.3b Lobes of the Cerebrum

✓ LEARNING OBJECTIVE

3. Explain the physical boundaries, important features, and functions of each cerebral lobe.

Each cerebral hemisphere is divided into five anatomically distinct lobes. Four of these lobes are visible on the external surface and are named for the overlying cranial bones: the frontal, parietal,

Figure 13.11 Cerebral Hemispheres. A superior view shows the cerebral hemispheres, where our conscious activities, memories, behaviors, plans, and ideas are initiated and controlled. **AP|R**

temporal, and occipital lobes **(figure 13.12a)**. The fifth lobe, called the insula, is not visible at the surface of the hemispheres. Each lobe exhibits specific cortical regions and association areas.

The **frontal lobe** lies deep to the frontal bone and forms the anterior part of the cerebral hemisphere. The frontal lobe ends posteriorly at a deep groove called the **central sulcus** that marks the boundary with the parietal lobe. The inferior border of the frontal lobe is marked by the **lateral sulcus,** a deep groove that separates the frontal and parietal lobes from the temporal lobe. An important anatomic feature of the frontal lobe is the **precentral gyrus,** which is the mass of nervous tissue immediately anterior to the central sulcus. The frontal lobe is primarily concerned with voluntary motor functions, concentration, verbal communication, decision making, planning, and personality.

The **parietal lobe** lies deep to the parietal bone and forms the superoposterior part of each cerebral hemisphere. It terminates anteriorly at the central sulcus, posteriorly at a relatively indistinct **parieto-occipital sulcus,** and laterally at the lateral sulcus. An important anatomic feature of this lobe is the **postcentral gyrus,** which is the mass of nervous tissue immediately posterior to the central sulcus. The parietal lobe is involved with general sensory functions, such as evaluating the shape and texture of objects being touched.

The **temporal lobe** lies internal to the temporal bone and inferior to the lateral sulcus. This lobe is involved with hearing and smell.

The **occipital lobe** lies internal to the occipital bone and forms the posterior region of each hemisphere. This lobe is responsible for processing incoming visual information and storing visual memories.

The **insula** (in'sū-lă; *insula* = island) is a small lobe deep to the lateral sulcus. It can be observed by laterally reflecting (pulling aside) the temporal lobe. The insula's lack of accessibility has prevented aggressive studies of its function, but it is apparently involved in memory and the interpretation of taste.

Table 13.3 summarizes the lobes of the cerebrum and their subdivisions.

 WHAT DID YOU LEARN?

 13 List the five cerebral lobes and the main functions of each.

13.3c Functional Areas of the Cerebrum

LEARNING OBJECTIVES

4. Locate and list the functions of the three motor areas.
5. Differentiate among the five sensory areas.
6. Compare and contrast the actions of the five association areas and two functional brain regions.

Research has shown that specific structural areas of the cerebral cortex have distinct motor and sensory functions. In contrast, some higher mental functions, such as language and memory, are dispersed over large areas. Three categories of functional areas are recognized: **motor areas** that control voluntary motor functions; **sensory areas** that provide conscious awareness of sensation; and **association areas** that primarily integrate and store information. Although many structural areas have been identified, much still remains unknown or not well understood about the brain.

Motor Areas

The cortical areas that control motor functions are housed within the frontal lobes. The **primary motor cortex,** also called the *somatic motor area,* is located within the precentral gyrus of the frontal lobe (see figure 13.12). Neurons in this area control voluntary skeletal muscle activity. The axons of these neurons project contralaterally (to the opposite side) either within the brainstem or spinal cord. Thus, the left primary motor cortex controls the right-side voluntary muscles, and vice versa.

Table 13.3	Cerebral Lobes	
Lobe	**Cortices and Association Areas Within Lobe**	**Primary Functions of Lobe**
Frontal	Primary motor cortex (located within precentral gyrus) Premotor cortex Motor speech area (Broca area)—usually found only on the left frontal lobe Frontal eye fields	Higher intellectual functions (concentration, decision making, planning); personality; verbal communication; voluntary motor control of skeletal muscles
Parietal	Primary somatosensory cortex (located within postcentral gyrus) Somatosensory association area Part of Wernicke area Part of gnostic area	Sensory interpretation of textures and shapes; understanding speech and formulating words to express thoughts and emotions
Temporal	Primary auditory cortex Primary olfactory cortex Auditory association area Part of Wernicke area Part of gnostic area	Interpretation and storage of auditory and olfactory sensations; understanding speech
Occipital	Primary visual cortex Visual association areas	Conscious perception of visual stimuli; integration of eye-focusing movements; correlation of visual images with previous visual experiences
Insula	Primary gustatory cortex	Interpretation of taste; memory

Figure 13.12 **Anatomic and Functional Areas of the Cerebrum.** Each cerebral hemisphere is partitioned into five structural and functional areas called lobes. Within each lobe are specific cortical regions and association areas.

(a) Lobes of the Brain and Their Functional Areas

Frontal lobe (retracted)
- Primary motor cortex (in precentral gyrus)
- Premotor cortex
- Frontal eye field
- Motor speech area (Broca area)

Insula
- Primary gustatory cortex

Central sulcus

Parietal lobe
- Primary somatosensory cortex (in postcentral gyrus)
- Somatosensory association area

Parieto-occipital sulcus

Wernicke area

Gnostic area

Occipital lobe
- Primary visual cortex
- Visual association area

Lateral sulcus

Temporal lobe (retracted)
- Primary auditory cortex
- Auditory association area
- Primary olfactory cortex

(b) Motor Areas

Primary motor cortex

Control voluntary skeletal muscle activity

Premotor cortex

Plan and coordinate learned, skilled motor activities

Motor speech area

Regulate skeletal muscle movements involved with speech

(c) Sensory and Association Areas

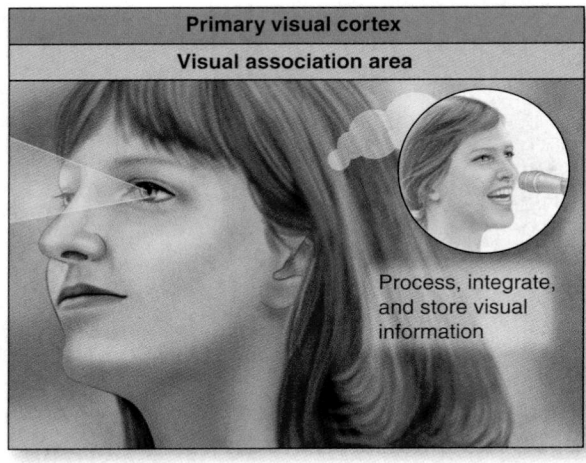

Primary visual cortex

Visual association area

Process, integrate, and store visual information

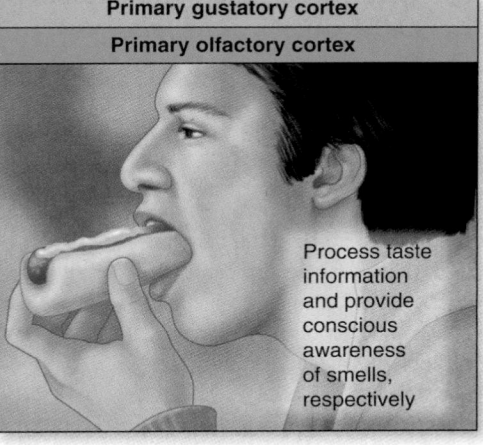

Primary gustatory cortex

Primary olfactory cortex

Process taste information and provide conscious awareness of smells, respectively

Primary auditory cortex

Auditory association area

Process, interpret sounds, and store auditory memories

Primary somatosensory cortex

Somatosensory association area

Receive and interpret somatic information from receptors

(d) Functional Brain Regions

Wernicke area

This multi-association area helps understand spoken or written language.

Gnostic area

Integrates all information being processed in adjacent lobes to provide a comprehensive understanding of a current activity

CLINICAL VIEW
Brodmann Areas

Korbinian Brodmann studied the comparative anatomy of the mammalian brain cortex in the early 1900s and was among the first to correlate physiologic activities with previously determined anatomic locations of the brain. Brodmann produced a map that shows the specific areas of the cerebral cortex where certain functions occur. Brodmann developed a numbering system that correlates with his map and shows that similar cognitive functions are usually sequential. For example, areas 3, 1, and 2 represent the primary somatosensory cortex; area 17 overlaps the primary visual cortex; and areas 44 and 45 form the motor speech area. Recent technological improvements allow neuroscientists to more precisely pinpoint the location of physiologic activities in the cortex, but the Brodmann Areas map is still useful for historical perspective and early views of the brain.

Modern rendition of Korbinian Brodmann's map of the brain, showing selected Brodmann areas.

The distribution of the primary motor cortex innervation to various body parts can be diagrammed as a **motor homunculus** (hō-mŭngk'ū-lŭs; "little man") on the precentral gyrus **(figure 13.13a)**. The bizarre, distorted proportions of the homunculus body reflect the amount of cortex dedicated to the motor activity of each body part. For example, the hands are represented by a much larger area of cortex than the trunk, because the hand muscles perform much more detailed, precise movements than do the trunk muscles. From a functional perspective, more motor activity is devoted to the human hand than in other animals because our hands are adapted for the precise, fine motor movements needed to manipulate the environment, and many motor units are devoted to muscles that move the hand and fingers.

The **motor speech area** (*Broca area*) is located in most individuals within the inferolateral portion of the left frontal lobe (see figure 13.12). This region is responsible for regulating the patterns of breathing and controlling the muscular movements necessary for vocalization.

Primary motor cortex (within precentral gyrus)

Primary somatosensory cortex (within postcentral gyrus)

← *Lateral*   *Medial* →

(a) Primary motor cortex (somatic motor area)

← *Medial*   *Lateral* →

(b) Primary somatosensory cortex

Figure 13.13 Primary Motor and Somatosensory Cortices. Body maps called the motor homunculus and the sensory homunculus illustrate the topography of (*a*) the primary motor cortex and (*b*) the primary somatosensory cortex in coronal section. The figure of the body (homunculus) depicts the nerve distributions; the size and location of each body region indicates relative innervation. **AP|R**

CLINICAL VIEW
The Case of Phineas Gage

The curious and tragic story of Phineas Gage has served to better the understanding of the brain and its higher-order functions. In 1848, while Mr. Gage was using an iron rod to tamp down blasting powder, the gunpowder exploded. The 13-pound, 3½-foot rod was shot through Gage's head, just below his left eye. He survived the accident and eventually regained his strength, but his personality was completely changed. Before the accident, he was described as capable, well-balanced, and shrewd; after his injury, he became irreverent, fitful, and grossly profane.

Computerized reconstructions of Mr. Gage's skull showing the sites of the injury have allowed researchers to determine fairly accurately what parts of

Computer reconstructions of Phineas Gage's skull injury.

his brain were damaged. Based in part on this case, medical science has learned that the frontal lobes are important to the proper functioning of our personalities and intimately linked to the basic elements of decision making.

The **frontal eye field** is on the superior surface of the middle frontal gyrus. It is immediately anterior to the premotor cortex in the frontal lobe. This cortical area controls and regulates the eye movements needed for reading and coordinating binocular vision. Some investigators include the frontal eye fields within the premotor area, as described shortly.

Sensory Areas

The cortical areas within the parietal, temporal, and occipital lobes are involved with conscious awareness of sensation. Each of the major senses has a distinct cortical area.

The **primary somatosensory cortex** is housed within the postcentral gyrus of the parietal lobes. Neurons within this cortex receive general somatic sensory information from proprioceptors as well as touch, pressure, pain, and temperature receptors. We typically are conscious of the sensations received by this cortex. A **sensory homunculus** may be traced on the postcentral gyrus surface, similar to the motor homunculus just described (figure 13.13*b*). The surface area of somatosensory cortex devoted to a body region indicates the amount of sensory information collected within that region. Thus, the lips, fingers, and genital region occupy larger portions of the homunculus, while the trunk of the body has proportionately fewer receptors, so its homunculus region is smaller.

Sensory information for sight, sound, taste, and smell arrives at cortical regions other than the parietal lobe (see figure 13.12). The **primary visual cortex** is located within the occipital lobe, where it receives and processes incoming visual information. The **primary auditory cortex** is located within the temporal lobe, where it receives and processes auditory information. The **primary olfactory** (ol-fak'to-rē; *olfactus* = smell) **cortex,** located within the temporal lobe, provides conscious awareness of smells. Finally, the **primary gustatory** (gŭs'tă-tōr-ē; *gustatio* = taste) **cortex** is in the insula and is involved in processing taste information.

Association Areas

The primary motor and sensory cortical regions are connected to adjacent **association areas** that either process and interpret incoming data or coordinate a motor response (see figure 13.12). Association areas integrate new sensory inputs with memories of past experiences. The following descriptions are of the main association areas.

The **premotor cortex** is called the *somatic motor association area,* and it is located within the frontal lobe immediately anterior to the precentral gyrus. It is primarily responsible for coordinating learned, skilled motor activities, such as moving the eyes in a coordinated fashion when reading a book or playing the piano. An individual who has sustained trauma to this area would still be able to understand written letters and words, but would have difficulty reading because his or her eyes couldn't follow the lines on a printed page. As mentioned earlier, some researchers consider the frontal eye field as part of this cortex.

The **somatosensory association area** is located within the parietal lobe and lies immediately posterior to the primary somatosensory cortex. It integrates sensory information and interprets sensations to determine the texture, temperature, pressure, and shape of objects. The somatosensory association area allows us to identify known objects without seeing them or when our eyes are closed. For example, even when our eyes are closed, we can tell the difference between the coarse feel of a handful of dirt, the smooth and round shape of a marble, and the thin, flat, rounded surface of a coin, because those interpretations of the textures and shapes have already been stored in the somatosensory association area.

The **visual association area** is located within the occipital lobe and it surrounds the primary visual area. It enables us to process visual information by analyzing color, movement, and form, and to use this information to identify the things we see. For example, when we look at a face, the primary visual cortex receives bits of visual information, but the visual association area is responsible for integrating all of this information into a recognizable picture of a face.

The **auditory association area** is located within the temporal lobe, posteroinferior to the primary auditory cortex. Within this association area, the cortical neurons interpret the characteristics of sound and store memories of sounds heard in the past. The next time a song is playing over and over in your head, you will know that this auditory association area is responsible.

A **functional brain region** acts like a multi-association area between lobes for integrating information from individual association areas. One functional brain region is the **Wernicke area**, which is typically located only within the left hemisphere. The Wernicke area is involved in recognizing, understanding, and comprehending spoken or written language. As you may expect, the Wernicke area and the motor speech area must work together for fluent communication to occur.

Another functional brain region that is called the **gnostic** (nos'tik) **area** (or *common integrative area*) is composed of regions of the parietal, occipital, and temporal lobes. This region integrates all somatosensory, visual, and auditory information being processed by the association areas within these lobes. Thus it provides comprehensive understanding of a current activity. For example, suppose you awaken from a daytime nap: The hands on the clock indicate that it is 12:30, you smell food cooking, and you hear your friends talking about being hungry. The gnostic area then interprets this information to mean it is lunchtime.

Figure 13.12 and table 13.3 summarize how the anatomic and functional areas of the cerebrum are distributed.

WHAT DID YOU LEARN?

14 Where are each of the motor areas located, and what are their functions?

15 What are the five association areas in the cerebrum?

16 In general, what is the purpose of the association areas?

13.3d Central White Matter

LEARNING OBJECTIVE

7. Identify the three main tracts of the central white matter.

The **central white matter** lies deep to the gray matter of the cerebral cortex. It is composed primarily of myelinated axons. Most of these axons are grouped into bundles called **tracts,** which are classified as association tracts, commissural tracts, or projection tracts (**figure 13.14**).

Association tracts connect different regions of the cerebral cortex within the same hemisphere. Short association tracts are composed of **arcuate** (ar′kū-āt; *arcuatus* = bowed) **fibers;** they connect neighboring gyri within the same lobe. An example of an association tract that is composed of arcuate fibers would be the tract that connects the premotor or motor association area with the primary motor cortex,

both of which are in the frontal lobe. The longer association tracts, called the **longitudinal fasciculi** (fă-sik′-ū-lī; *fascis* = bundle), connect gyri in different lobes of the same hemisphere. An example of a longitudinal fasciculus would be the tract that connects the Wernicke area to the motor speech area.

Commissural (kom-i-sūr′ăl) **tracts** extend between the cerebral hemispheres through axonal bridges called commissures. The prominent commissural tracts that link the left and right cerebral hemispheres include the large, C-shaped **corpus callosum** and the smaller **anterior** and **posterior commissure** (see figure 13.17).

Projection tracts link the cerebral cortex to both the inferior brain regions and the spinal cord (figure 13.14). Examples of projection tracts are the corticospinal tracts that carry motor signals from the cerebrum to the brainstem and spinal cord. The packed group of axons in these tracts passing in between the cerebral nuclei and the thalamus is called the **internal capsule** (see figure 13.4).

(a) Sagittal view

Arcuate fibers
Longitudinal fasciculi
Corpus callosum
Parietal lobe
Occipital lobe
Frontal lobe
Anterior commissure
Temporal lobe

Arcuate fibers
Longitudinal fasciculi
Commissural tracts
Projection tracts

Longitudinal fissure
Cortex
Cerebral nuclei
Lateral sulcus
Projection tracts
Decussation in pyramids

Commissural tracts (in corpus callosum)
Lateral ventricle
Thalamus
Third ventricle
Pons
Medulla oblongata

(b) Coronal section

Figure 13.14 Cerebral White Matter Tracts. White matter tracts are composed primarily of myelinated axons. Three major groups of axons are recognized based on their distribution. (*a*) A sagittal view shows arcuate fibers and longitudinal fasciculi association tracts, which extend between gyri within one cerebral hemisphere. (*b*) A coronal view shows how commissural tracts extend between cerebral hemispheres, while projection tracts extend between the hemispheres and the brainstem. AP|R

Table 13.4 summarizes the characteristics of the three white matter tracts of the cerebrum.

WHAT DID YOU LEARN?

17 What portions of the brain are linked by the association, commissural, and projection tracts?

13.3e Cerebral Lateralization

LEARNING OBJECTIVES

8. Explain the phenomenon of cerebral lateralization.
9. Identify the functions of left and right hemispheres in most individuals.

Anatomically, the left and right cerebral hemispheres appear identical, but careful examination reveals a number of differences. Humans tend to have shape asymmetries of the frontal and occipital lobes of the brain, called **petalias** (pe'tal-ē-ă). Right-handed individuals tend to have right frontal petalias, meaning that the right frontal lobe projects farther than the left frontal lobe, and left occipital petalias, meaning that the left occipital lobe projects farther than the right occipital lobe. Conversely, left-handed individuals tend to have the reverse pattern (left frontal and right occipital petalias). The hemispheres also differ with respect to some of their functions. Each hemisphere tends to be specialized for certain tasks, a phenomenon called **cerebral lateralization** (lat'er-al-ī-zā'shŭn). Higher-order centers in both hemispheres tend to have different but complementary functions **(figure 13.15)**.

Table 13.4	White Matter Tracts in the Cerebrum	
Tracts	**Distribution of Axons**	**Examples**
Association tracts	Connect separate cortical areas within the same hemisphere	Arcuate fibers, longitudinal fasciculi
Arcuate fibers	Connect neighboring gyri within a single cerebral lobe	Tracts connecting primary motor cortex (frontal lobe) to motor association area (frontal lobe)
Longitudinal fasciculi	Connect gyri between different cerebral lobes of the same hemisphere	Tracts connecting Wernicke area (parietal/temporal lobes) and motor speech area (frontal lobe)
Commissural tracts	Connect left and right cerebral hemispheres	Corpus callosum, anterior commissure, posterior commissure
Projection tracts	Connect cerebral cortex to the diencephalon, brainstem, cerebellum, and spinal cord	Corticospinal tracts (motor axons traveling from cerebral cortex to spinal cord; sensory axons traveling from spinal cord to cerebrum)

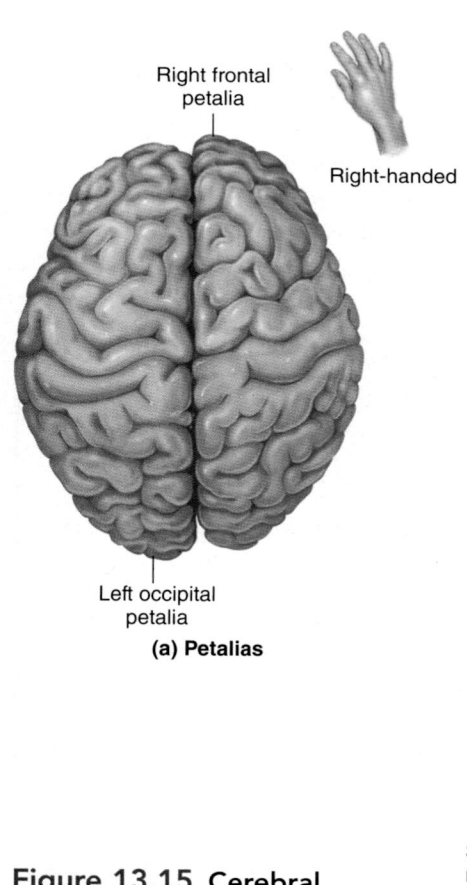

Right frontal petalia

Right-handed

Left occipital petalia

(a) Petalias

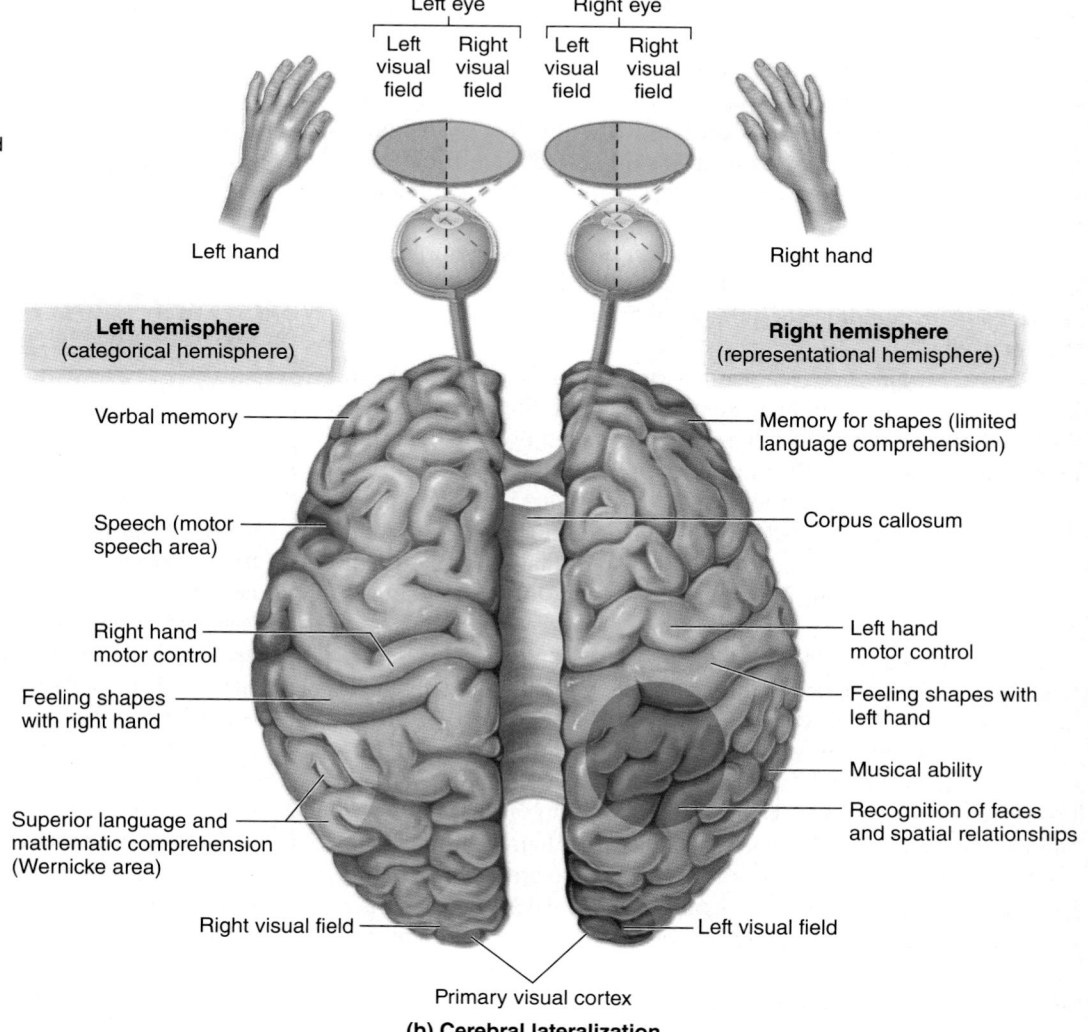

Left eye — Right eye

Left visual field | Right visual field | Left visual field | Right visual field

Left hand — Right hand

Left hemisphere (categorical hemisphere)

Right hemisphere (representational hemisphere)

Verbal memory — Memory for shapes (limited language comprehension)

Speech (motor speech area) — Corpus callosum

Right hand motor control — Left hand motor control

Feeling shapes with right hand — Feeling shapes with left hand

— Musical ability

— Recognition of faces and spatial relationships

Superior language and mathematic comprehension (Wernicke area)

Right visual field — Left visual field

Primary visual cortex

(b) Cerebral lateralization

Figure 13.15 Cerebral Lateralization. (*a*) Most individuals exhibit asymmetries, called petalias, in their frontal and occipital lobes. (*b*) The cerebral hemispheres exhibit functional differences as a result of some specialization.

INTEGRATE

CLINICAL VIEW
Hemispherectomies and Cerebral Lateralization

Epilepsy is a disorder in which neurons transmit action potentials too frequently and rapidly, causing seizures that detrimentally affect motor and sensory function. Most seizures may be controlled by medications, but if medications are ineffective then surgery may be deemed necessary. Surgical removal of the brain part that is the source of the seizures often eliminates the seizures. In the most severe cases, a drastic form of therapy for the epilepsy is a cerebral **hemispherectomy** (hem′ē-sfēr-ek′tō-mē) in which the side of the brain responsible for the seizure activity is surgically removed.

Although brain function does not return to complete normalcy following a hemispherectomy, the remaining hemisphere amazingly takes over some of the functions of the missing hemisphere. The younger the individual, the better the chances of functional recovery.

In most people, the left hemisphere is the **categorical hemisphere.** It usually contains the Wernicke area and the motor speech area. It is specialized for language abilities, and is also important in performing sequential and analytical reasoning tasks, such as those required in science and mathematics. This hemisphere appears to direct or partition information into smaller fragments for analysis. The term *categorical hemisphere* reflects this hemisphere's function in categorization and symbolization.

The other hemisphere (the right in most people) is called the **representational hemisphere,** because it is concerned with visuospatial relationships and analyses. It is the seat of imagination and insight, musical and artistic skill, perception of patterns and spatial relationships, and comparison of sights, sounds, smells, and tastes.

Both cerebral hemispheres remain in constant communication through commissures, especially through the corpus callosum, which contains hundreds of millions of axons that project between the hemispheres.

Lateralization of the cerebral hemispheres develops early in life (prior to 5–6 years of age). In a young child, the functions of a damaged or removed hemisphere are often taken over by the other hemisphere before lateralization is complete. Some aspects of lateralization differ between the sexes. Women have a thicker posterior part of the corpus callosum due to additional commissural axons in this region. Adult males exhibit more lateralization than females and suffer more functional loss when one hemisphere is damaged.

Cerebral lateralization is highly correlated with handedness. Right-handed individuals tend to have a slightly different lateralization pattern than those who are left-handed. In about 95% of the population, the left hemisphere is the categorical hemisphere, thus correlating with the 90% incidence of right-handed individuals in the population. However, the correlation is not nearly as strict among left-handed people, who may have either hemisphere as their categorical hemisphere. Interestingly, a thicker corpus callosum in left-handers suggests that more signals may be relayed between their hemispheres. Finally, the left hemisphere is the speech-dominant hemisphere; it controls speech in almost all right-handed people as well as in many left-handed ones.

WHAT DID YOU LEARN?

18 What is cerebral lateralization?

19 What are the primary functions of the left cerebral hemisphere? Of the right cerebral hemisphere?

13.3f Cerebral Nuclei

LEARNING OBJECTIVE

10. Identify the four cerebral nuclei, and explain their functions.

The **cerebral nuclei** (also called the *basal nuclei*) are paired, irregular masses of gray matter buried deep within the central white matter in the basal region of the cerebral hemispheres inferior to the floor of the lateral ventricle (**figure 13.16**; see also figure 13.4). (These masses of gray matter also are sometimes incorrectly called the basal ganglia. However, the term *ganglion* [sing.] is best restricted to clusters of neuron cell bodies *outside* the CNS, whereas a *nucleus* is a collection of cell bodies *within* the CNS.) In general, the cerebral nuclei help regulate motor output initiated by the cerebral cortex, and seem to help inhibit unwanted movements. Diseases that affect the cerebral nuclei (such as Huntington disease—see Clinical View: "Brain Disorders") often are associated with jerky, involuntary movements.

Cerebral nuclei have multiple components, and each component has its own specific functions related to the overall function of the cerebral nuclei. These components include

- The C-shaped **caudate** (kaw′dāt; *cauda* = tail) **nucleus** has an enlarged head and a slender, arching tail that parallels the swinging curve of the lateral ventricle. When a person begins to walk, the neurons in this nucleus stimulate the appropriate muscles to produce the pattern and rhythm of arm and leg movements associated with walking.

- The **amygdaloid** (ā-mig′dă-loyd; *amygdala* = almond) **body** (often just called the *amygdala*) is an expanded region at the

INTEGRATE

CLINICAL VIEW
Cerebrovascular Accident

A **cerebrovascular accident (CVA,** or **stroke)** is caused by reduced blood supply to a part of the brain due to either a blocked arterial blood vessel or hemorrhage from a blood vessel. The consequences of a CVA depend upon the location and duration of vessel blockage or hemorrhage. If impaired blood flow lasts longer than about 10 minutes, brain tissue may die. Symptoms of a CVA include loss or blurring of vision, weakness or slight numbness, headache, dizziness, and walking difficulties. Each side of the brain controls the opposite side of the body, so a CVA on the left side of the brain presents with symptoms on the right side of the body, and vice versa. The risk for a CVA increases with age, and is also influenced by family history, race, and gender.

A brief episode of lost sensation or motor ability or "tingling" in the limbs is called a **transient ischemic attack (TIA)** or *mini-stroke*. It results from a temporary plug in a blood vessel that dissolves in a matter of minutes. However, TIAs can indicate increased risk for a more serious vessel blockage in the future.

Cortex
Corpus callosum
Lateral ventricle
Septum pellucidum
Thalamus
Internal capsule
Lateral sulcus
Insula
Third ventricle
Optic tract
Hypothalamus

Cerebral nuclei

Caudate nucleus
Putamen ⎤
Globus pallidus ⎦ Lentiform nucleus ⎤ Corpus striatum
Claustrum
Amygdaloid body

Coronal section

Figure 13.16 Cerebral Nuclei. The cerebral nuclei are paired gray matter masses surrounded by white matter deep within the cerebrum. AP|R

tail of the caudate nucleus. It participates in the expression of emotions, control of behavioral activities, and development of moods (see the limbic system later in this chapter).

- The **lentiform** (len'ti-fōrm; *lenticula* = lentil, *forma* = shape) **nucleus** is a compact, rounded mass, made up of both the **putamen** (pū-tā'men; shell) and **globus pallidus** (glō'bŭs pal'i-dŭs; *globus* = ball, *pallidus* = pale), two masses of gray matter positioned between the bulging external surface of the insula and the lateral wall of the diencephalon. The putamen functions in controlling muscular movement at the subconscious level, while the globus pallidus both excites and inhibits the activities of the thalamus to control and adjust muscle tone.

- The **claustrum** (klaws'trŭm; barrier) is a thin sliver of gray matter formed by a layer of neurons located immediately internal to the cortex of the insula and derived from that cortex. It processes visual information at a subconscious level.

The term **corpus striatum** (strī-ā'tŭm; striped) describes the striated or striped appearance of the internal capsule as it passes among the caudate nucleus and the lentiform nucleus.

 WHAT DID YOU LEARN?

20 What is the general function of the cerebral nuclei, and what are the anatomic components that make up the nuclei?

13.4 Diencephalon

The **diencephalon** is a part of the prosencephalon sandwiched between the inferior regions of the cerebral hemispheres. This region is often referred to as the "in-between brain." The components of the diencephalon include the epithalamus, the thalamus, and the hypothalamus (**figure 13.17**). The diencephalon provides the relay

and switching centers for some sensory and motor pathways, and for control of visceral activities.

13.4a Epithalamus

 LEARNING OBJECTIVES

1. List components located in the epithalamus, and describe their functions.
2. Explain how circadian rhythm is regulated.

The **epithalamus** (ep'i-thal'ă-mŭs) partially forms the posterior roof of the diencephalon and covers the third ventricle. The posterior portion of the epithalamus houses the pineal gland and the habenular nuclei.

The **pineal** (pin'ē-ăl; *pineus* = pineconelike) **gland,** or *pineal body*, is an endocrine gland. It secretes the hormone **melatonin,** which appears to help regulate day-night cycles known as the body's **circadian rhythm.** (Some companies are marketing the sale of melatonin in pill form as a cure for jet lag and insomnia, although this cure has yet to be proven) (see section 17.2a).

The **habenular** (hă-ben'ū-lăr; *habena* = strap) **nuclei** help relay signals from the limbic system to the midbrain and are involved in visceral and emotional responses to odors.

 WHAT DID YOU LEARN?

21 What is the location and function of the pineal gland?

13.4b Thalamus

LEARNING OBJECTIVE

3. Discuss the action of the thalamus on sensory information.

The **thalamus** (thal'ă-mŭs; *thalamus* = bed) is identified as the paired oval masses of gray matter that lie on either side of the third

Corpus callosum

Septum pellucidum

Interthalamic adhesion

Anterior commissure

Hypothalamus

Frontal lobe

Mammillary body

Optic chiasm

Pituitary gland

Diencephalon

Fornix

Choroid plexus in third ventricle

Thalamus

Habenular nucleus ⎤
                 ⎥ **Epithalamus**
Pineal gland ⎦

Posterior commissure

Tectal plate

Cerebral aqueduct

Infundibulum

Cerebellum

Fourth ventricle

Midsagittal section

Figure 13.17 Diencephalon. The diencephalon encloses the third ventricle and connects the cerebral hemispheres to the brainstem. The right portion of the diencephalon is outlined and shown here in midsagittal section. The diencephalon and its major subdivisions are listed in bold. AP|R

ventricle **(figure 13.18)**, where they form the superolateral walls of the third ventricle. When viewed in midsagittal section, the thalamus is located between the anterior commissure and the pineal gland. The **interthalamic adhesion** (or *intermediate mass*) is a small, midline mass of gray matter that connects the right and left thalamic bodies.

Each part of the thalamus is a gray matter mass composed of about a dozen major **thalamic nuclei** that are organized into groups; axons from these nuclei project to particular regions of the cerebral cortex. Sensory impulses from all the conscious senses except olfaction converge on the thalamus and synapse in at least one of its nuclei. The major functions of each group of nuclei are detailed in **table 13.5**.

The thalamus is the principal and final relay point for incoming sensory information that is processed and then projected to the primary somatosensory cortex. Only a relatively small portion of the sensory information that arrives at the thalamus is forwarded to the cerebrum because the thalamus acts as an information filter. For example, the thalamus is responsible for filtering out

Medial group

Interthalamic adhesion

Lateral group

Pulvinar nucleus ⎤
                 ⎥ **Posterior group**
Lateral geniculate ⎦
nucleus

Anterior group

(a) Location of thalamus within brain

Ventral anterior nucleus   Ventral lateral nucleus   Ventral posterior nucleus

Ventral group

(b) Thalamus, superolateral view

Figure 13.18 Thalamus. (*a*) Lateral view of a transparent brain identifies the approximate location of the thalamus. (*b*) The thalamus is composed of clusters of nuclei organized into groups, as shown in this enlarged view. Not all nuclei may be seen from this angle. AP|R

Table 13.5	Functions Controlled by Thalamic Nuclei		
Nuclei Group	**Functions**		
Anterior group	Changes motor cortex excitability and modifies mood		
Lateral group	Controls sensory flow to parietal lobes and emotional information to cingulate gyrus (of the limbic system)		
Medial group	Sends signals about conscious awareness of emotional states to frontal lobes		
Posterior group			
Lateral geniculate nuclei	Relay visual information from optic tracts to visual cortex and midbrain		
Medial geniculate nuclei	Relay auditory information from inner ear to auditory cortex		
Pulvinar nuclei	Integrate and relay sensory information for projection to association areas of cerebral cortex		
Ventral group			
Ventral anterior nuclei	Relay somatic motor information from cerebral nuclei and cerebellum to primary motor cortex and premotor cortex of frontal lobe		
Ventral lateral nuclei	Same as ventral anterior nuclei		
Ventral posterior nuclei	Relay sensory information to primary somatosensory cortex of parietal lobe		

the sounds and sights in a busy dorm cafeteria when you are trying to study. The thalamus also "clues in" the cerebrum about where this sensory information came from. For example, the thalamus lets the cerebrum know that sensory information it receives came from the eye, indicating that the information is visual.

 WHAT DO YOU THINK?

3 If there were no thalamus, how would this affect the cerebrum's interpretation of sensory stimuli?

 WHAT DID YOU LEARN?

22 What is the general function of the thalamus?

INTEGRATE

CLINICAL VIEW
Brain Disorders

Brain disorders may be expressed either by a malfunction in sensory gathering or motor expression, or by some combination of both activities. Some disturbances of the brain include headache, cerebral palsy, encephalitis, Huntington disease, and Parkinson disease.

Headache typically is due either to dilated blood vessels in the skull or muscle contraction (such as may occur when an individual develops eyestrain from staring at a computer screen too long). **Migraine headaches** are severe, recurring headaches that often affect only one side of the head. Headaches are not a brain disorder, but they sometimes accompany other diseases or brain disorders.

Cerebral palsy (pawl'zē) is actually a group of neuromuscular disorders that usually result from damage to an infant's brain before, during, or immediately after birth. Three forms of cerebral palsy involve impairment of skeletal motor activity to some degree: *athetoid*, characterized by slow, involuntary, writhing hand movements; *ataxic*, marked by lack of muscular coordination; and *spastic*, exhibiting increased muscular tone. Mental retardation and speech difficulties sometimes accompany this disorder.

Encephalitis (en-sef-ă-lī'tis; *enkephalos* = brain, *itis* = inflammation) is an acute inflammatory disease of the brain, most often due to viral infection. Symptoms include drowsiness, fever, headache, neck pain, coma, and paralysis. Death may occur.

Huntington disease is an autosomal dominant hereditary disease that affects the cerebral nuclei. It causes rapid, jerky, involuntary movements that usually start unilaterally in the face, but over months and years progress to the arms and legs. Progressive intellectual deterioration also occurs, including personality changes, memory loss, and irritability. The disease has an onset age of 35–40, and is fatal within 10 to 20 years.

Parkinson disease is a slow-progressing neurologic condition that affects muscle movement and balance. Parkinson patients exhibit stiff posture, an expressionless face, slow voluntary movements, a resting tremor (especially in the hands), and a shuffling gait. The disease is caused by a deficiency of the neurotransmitter dopamine, which results from decreased dopamine production of degenerating neurons in the substantia nigra (nuclei in the midbrain). Dopamine deficiency prevents brain cells from performing their usual inhibitory functions within the basal nuclei. By the time symptoms develop, the person has lost 80–90% of the cells responsible for producing dopamine. Current treatments include medications that enhance the amount of dopamine in the remaining cells of the substantia nigra, and medications (e.g., rasagiline) to treat the symptoms.

Boxer Muhammad Ali and actor Michael J. Fox are two famous individuals with Parkinson disease.

13.4c Hypothalamus

LEARNING OBJECTIVE

4. Describe seven functions of the hypothalamus.

The **hypothalamus** (hī′pō-thal′ă-mŭs; *hypo* = under) is the antero-inferior region of the diencephalon. A thin, stalklike **infundibulum** (in-fŭn-dib′ū-lŭm; funnel) extends inferiorly from the hypothalamus to attach to the pituitary gland **(figure 13.19)**.

The hypothalamus has numerous functions that are controlled by specific nuclei as listed in **table 13.6**. Functions of the hypothalamus include

- **Master control of the autonomic nervous system.** The hypothalamus is a major autonomic integration center. In essence, it is the "president" of the corporation known as the autonomic nervous system (described in detail in chapter 15). It projects descending axons to autonomic nuclei in the inferior brainstem that influence heart rate, blood pressure, digestive activities, and respiration.

- **Master control of the endocrine system.** The hypothalamus is also "president" of another corporation—the endocrine system—overseeing most but not all of that system's functions. The hypothalamus secretes hormones that control secretory activities in the anterior pituitary gland, and it produces both antidiuretic hormone and oxytocin. Its function in the endocrine system is described in detail in section 17.8.

- **Regulation of body temperature.** The body's thermostat is located within the hypothalamus. Neurons in the preoptic area detect altered blood temperatures and signal other hypothalamic nuclei, which control the mechanisms that heat or cool the body (see sections 1.5b, 6.3b and 27.6b).

- **Control of emotional behavior.** The hypothalamus is located at the center of the limbic system, the part of the brain that controls emotional responses, such as pleasure, aggression, fear, rage, contentment, and the sex drive.

Table 13.6	Functions Controlled by Selected Hypothalamic Nuclei
Nucleus or Hypothalamic Region	**Function**
Anterior nucleus	"Thirst center" (stimulates fluid intake); autonomic control center
Arcuate nucleus	Regulates appetite, release of gonadotropin-releasing hormone, release of growth hormone–releasing hormone, and release of prolactin-inhibiting hormone
Mammillary body	Directs sensations related to olfaction; controls swallowing
Paraventricular nucleus	Produces oxytocin and antidiuretic hormone (ADH)
Preoptic area	"Thermostat" (regulates body temperature)
Suprachiasmatic nucleus	Regulates sleep-wake (circadian) rhythm
Supraoptic nucleus	Produces oxytocin and ADH
Ventromedial nucleus	"Satiety center" (produces hunger and satiety sensations)

- **Control of food intake.** Neurons within the ventromedial nucleus monitor levels of nutrients such as glucose and amino acids in the blood and produce sensations of hunger.

- **Control of water intake.** Specific neurons within the anterior nucleus of the hypothalamus continuously monitor the concentration of dissolved substances in the blood to regulate the sensation of thirst (see section 25.2). When the hypothalamus detects dehydration from the blood, our feelings of thirst are stimulated.

- **Regulation of sleep-wake (circadian) rhythms.** The suprachiasmatic nucleus directs the pineal gland to secrete melatonin at certain times of the day. Thus, both work to regulate circadian rhythms.

WHAT DID YOU LEARN?

23 How does the hypothalamus control our feelings of hunger and thirst?

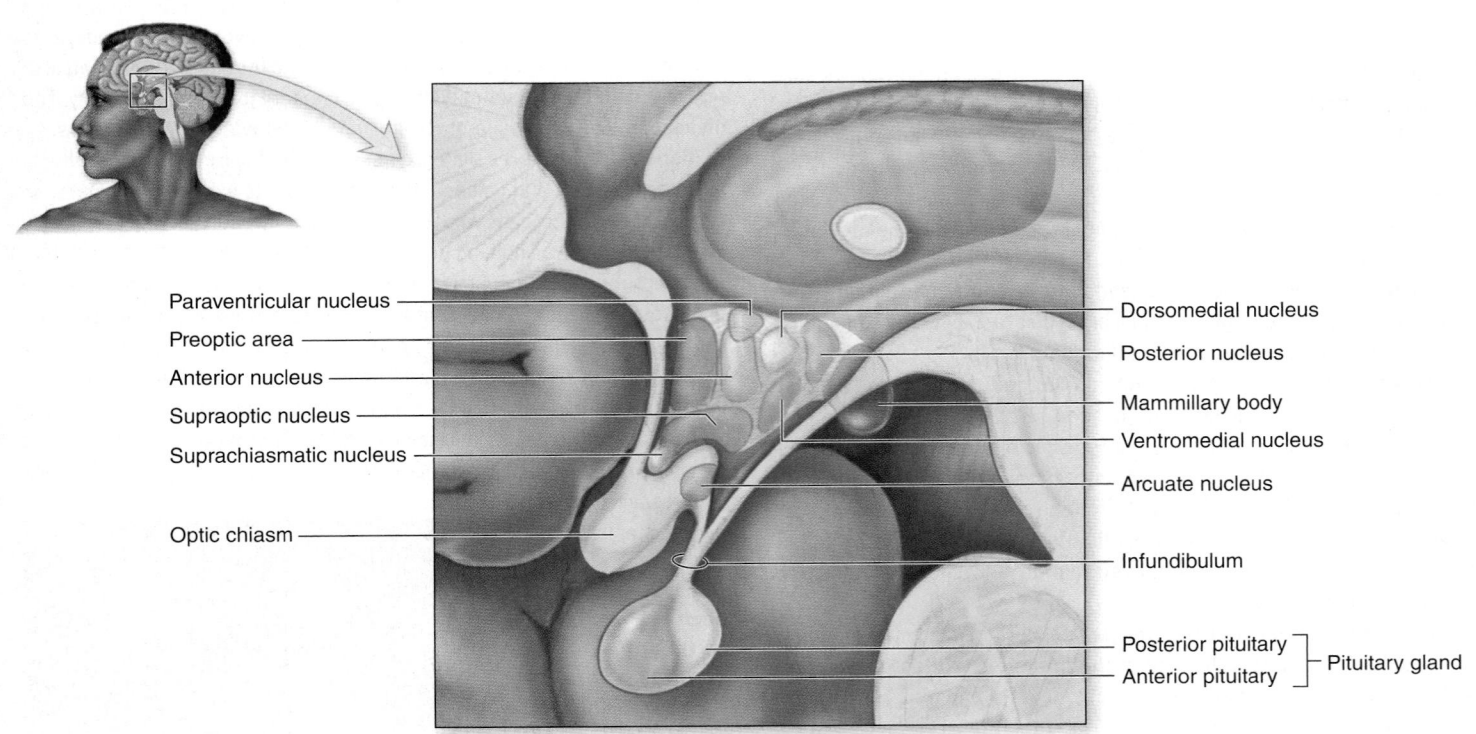

Paraventricular nucleus
Preoptic area
Anterior nucleus
Supraoptic nucleus
Suprachiasmatic nucleus
Optic chiasm

Dorsomedial nucleus
Posterior nucleus
Mammillary body
Ventromedial nucleus
Arcuate nucleus
Infundibulum
Posterior pituitary
Anterior pituitary
Pituitary gland

Sagittal section of hypothalamus

Figure 13.19 Hypothalamus. The hypothalamus is located anteroinferior to the thalamus and is organized into multiple nuclei.

13.5 Brainstem

The **brainstem** connects the cerebrum, dienephalon and cerebellum to the spinal cord. Three regions form the brainstem. From superior to inferior, these include: the midbrain, the pons, and the medulla oblongata **(figure 13.20)**.

The brainstem is a bidirectional passageway for all tracts extending between the major regions of the brain and the spinal cord. It also contains many autonomic centers and reflex centers required for our survival, and it houses nuclei of many of the cranial nerves.

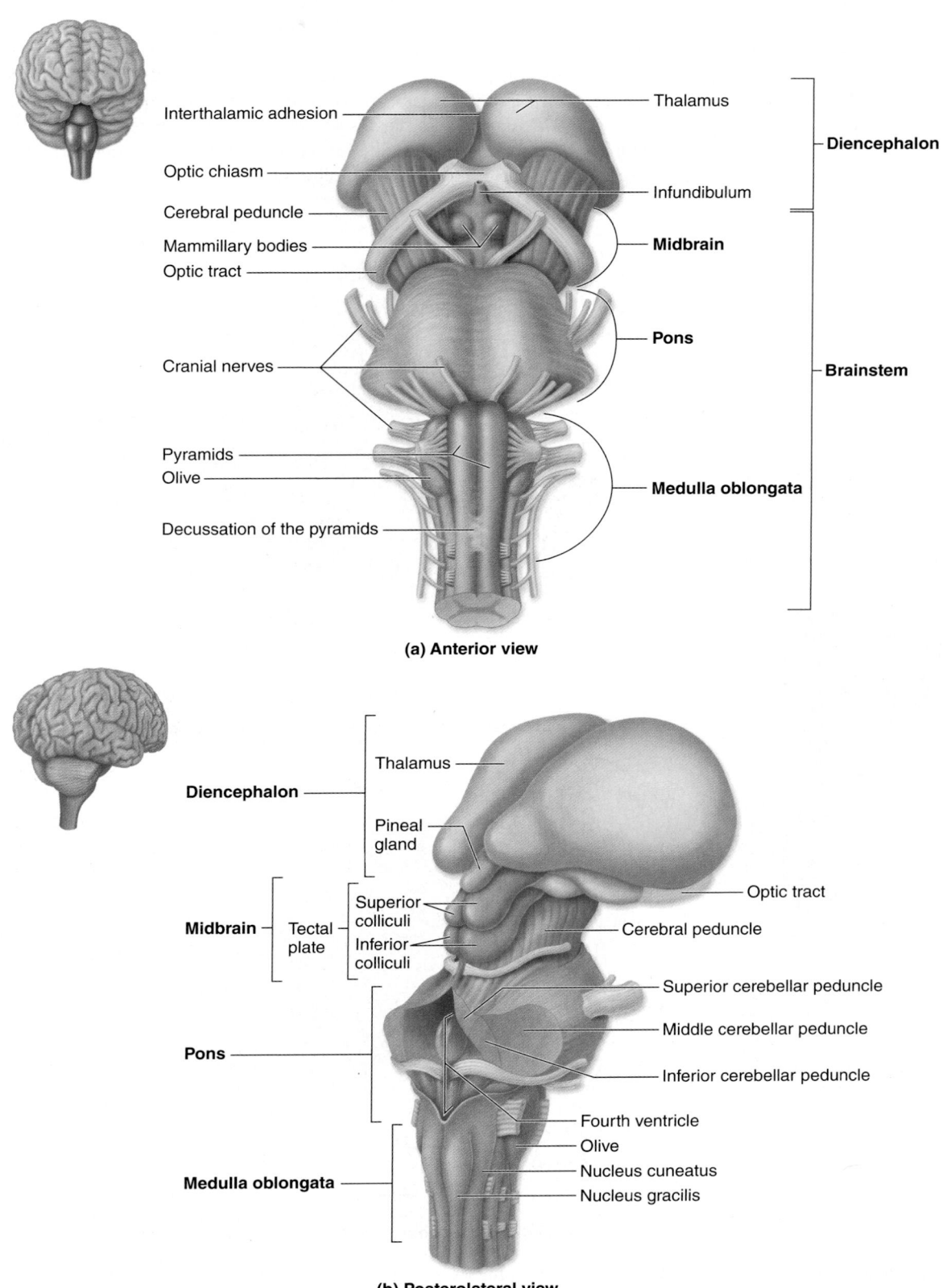

(a) Anterior view

(b) Posterolateral view

Figure 13.20 Brainstem. (*a*) Anterior and (*b*) posterolateral views show the locations of the midbrain, pons, and medulla oblongata within the brainstem. The diencephalon is located superior to the brainstem. **AP|R**

13.5a Midbrain

LEARNING OBJECTIVES

1. List the major features of the midbrain.

2. Identify the locations and functions of structures that are visible in a cross-sectional view of the midbrain.

3. Explain the involuntary actions produced by the superior and inferior colliculi of the tectal plate.

The **midbrain,** or *mesencephalon,* is the superior portion of the brainstem. The midbrain contains several major components, several of which are visible externally in figure 13.20. **Figure 13.21** shows cross sections of the midbrain and allows us to view its internal structures. These structures are discussed based on their position from anterior to posterior.

Cerebral peduncles (pĕ′dŭng-kl; *pedunculus* = little foot) are motor tracts located on the anterolateral surfaces of the midbrain. Descending axon bundles of the pyramidal system (corticospinal tracts) project through the cerebral peduncles and carry voluntary motor commands from the primary motor cortex of each cerebral hemisphere. Additionally, the midbrain is the final destination of the **superior cerebellar peduncles** connecting the cerebellum to the midbrain (figure 13.20).

The **substantia nigra** (sŭb-stan′shē-ă nī′gră; *substantia* = substance, *niger* = black) consists of bilaterally symmetrical nuclei within the midbrain (figure 13.21). Its name derives from its almost black appearance that is due to melanin pigmentation. The substantia nigra is squeezed between the cerebral peduncles and the tegmentum. The substantia nigra houses clusters of neurons that produce the neurotransmitter dopamine, which affects brain processes to control

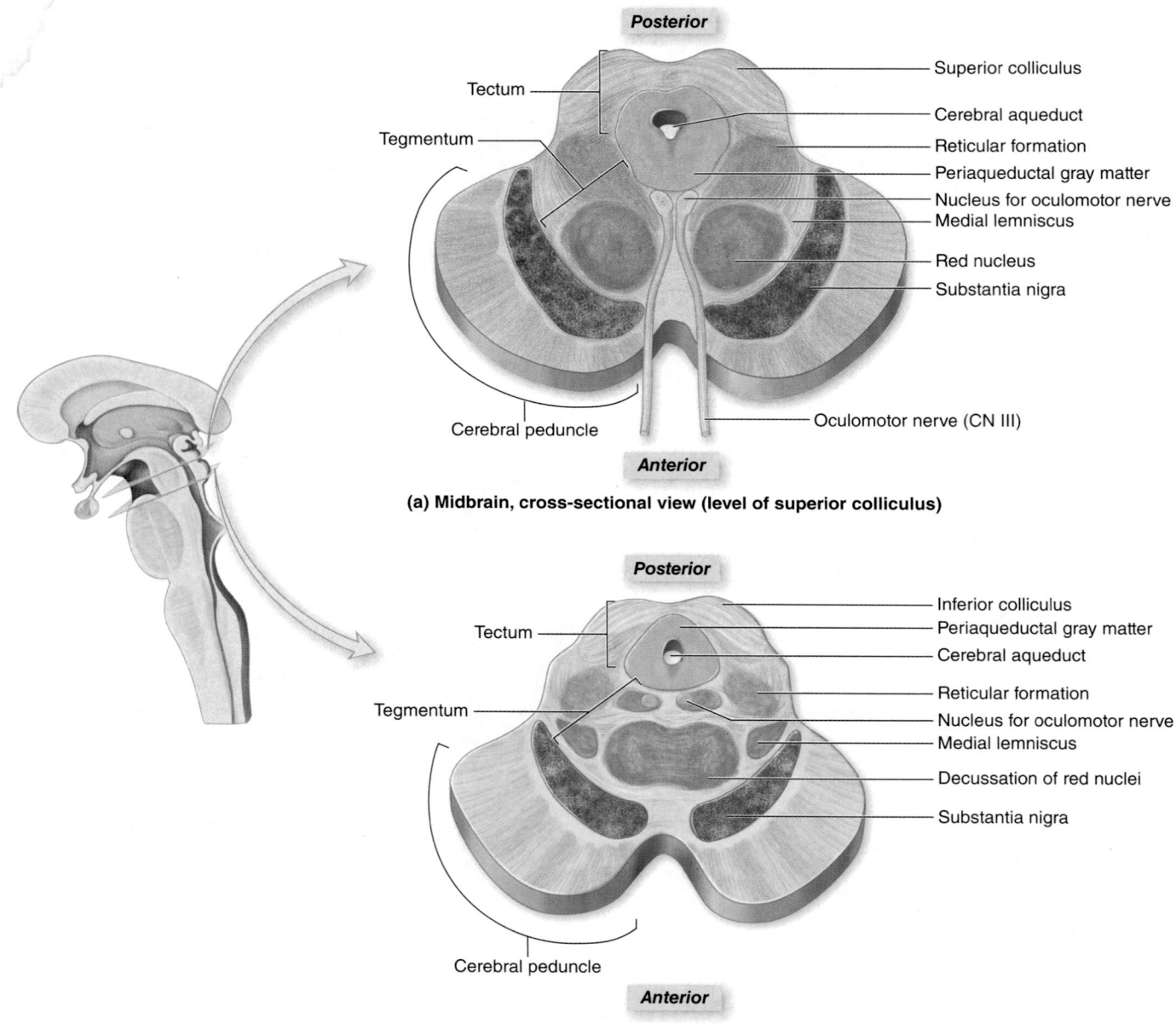

(a) Midbrain, cross-sectional view (level of superior colliculus)

(b) Midbrain, cross-sectional view (level of inferior colliculus)

Figure 13.21 Midbrain. Components of the midbrain at (*a*) the level of the superior colliculus and (*b*) the level of the inferior colliculus are shown in cross-sectional view. The nuclei for CN IV are not shown. AP|R movement, emotional response, and ability to experience pleasure and pain. These neurons are dark-hued due to the melanin they contain. Degeneration of these cells in the substantia nigra is a pathology that underlies Parkinson disease (see Clinical View: "Brain Disorders").

The **tegmentum** (teg-men′tŭm; covering structure) is sandwiched between the bilaterally symmetrical nuclei of the substantia nigra and the periaqueductal gray matter (described in the next paragraph). The tegmentum contains the pigmented **red nuclei** and the reticular formation. The reddish color of the nuclei is due to both blood vessel density and iron pigmentation in the neuronal cell bodies. The tegmentum integrates information from the cerebrum and cerebellum and issues involuntary motor commands to the erector spinae muscles of the back to help maintain posture while standing, bending at the waist, or walking.

Extending through the midbrain is the **cerebral aqueduct** connecting the third and fourth ventricles; it is surrounded by a region called the **periaqueductal gray matter.** The nuclei of two cranial nerves that control some eye movements are housed within the midbrain: the oculomotor nerve (CN III) and the trochlear nerve (CN IV) (these nerves are described in detail later in this chapter).

The **tectum** (tek′tŭm; = roof) is the posterior region of the midbrain dorsal to the cerebral aqueduct. It contains two pairs of sensory nuclei, the superior and inferior colliculi, which are collectively called the **tectal plate** (*quadrigeminal* [kwah′dri-jem′i-năl] *plate*, or *corpora quadrigemina*). These nuclei are relay stations in the processing pathway of visual and auditory sensations. The **superior colliculi** (ko-lik′yū-lī; sing., *colliculus* = mound) are the superior nuclei. They are called *visual reflex*

centers because they help visually track moving objects and control reflexes such as turning the eyes and head in response to a visual stimulus. For example, the superior colliculi are at work when you think you see a large animal running at you and turn suddenly toward the image. The paired **inferior colliculi** are the *auditory reflex centers*, meaning that they control reflexive turning of the head and eyes in the direction of a sound, such as a sudden loud bang.

WHAT DID YOU LEARN?

24 What is the function of the substantia nigra, and what disease may affect its proper working?

25 What parts of the midbrain contain paired visual and auditory sensory nuclei?

13.5b Pons

LEARNING OBJECTIVES

4. Identify the respiratory center located in the pons.

5. Identify the actions of the superior olivary complex.

The **pons** (ponz; bridge) is a bulging region on the anterior part of the brainstem that forms from part of the metencephalon (**figure 13.22**; see also figure 13.20). Sensory and motor tracts are located within and extend through it to connect to the brain and spinal cord. Additionally, the **middle cerebellar peduncles** are transverse axons that connect the pons to the cerebellum.

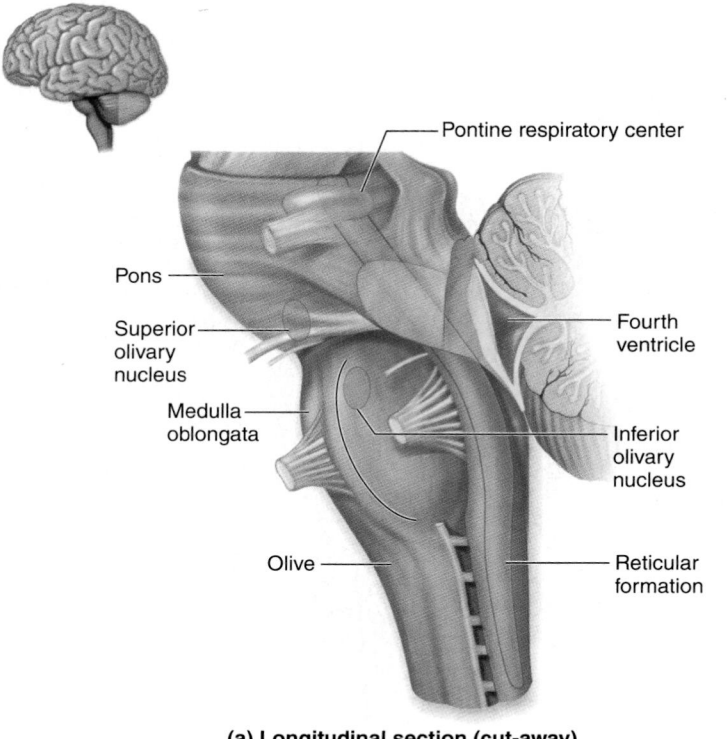

(a) Longitudinal section (cut-away)

Pontine respiratory center
Pons
Superior olivary nucleus
Medulla oblongata
Olive
Fourth ventricle
Inferior olivary nucleus
Reticular formation

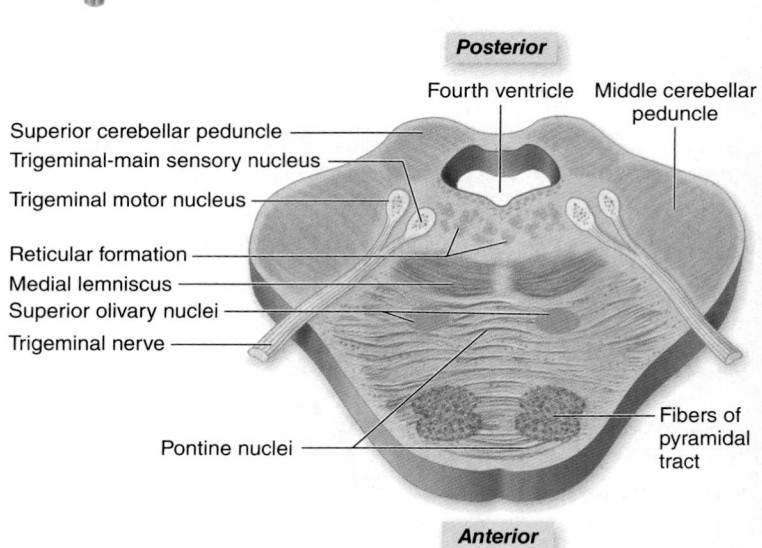

(b) Pons, cross-sectional view

Posterior

Fourth ventricle   Middle cerebellar peduncle
Superior cerebellar peduncle
Trigeminal-main sensory nucleus
Trigeminal motor nucleus
Reticular formation
Medial lemniscus
Superior olivary nuclei
Trigeminal nerve
Pontine nuclei
Fibers of pyramidal tract

Anterior

Figure 13.22 Pons. The pons is a bulge on the ventral side of the hindbrain that contains nerve tracts, nuclei, and part of the reticular formation. (*a*) A partially cut-away longitudinal section identifies the pontine respiratory center and the superior olivary nucleus. (*b*) A cross section through the pons shows the pontine nuclei, fiber tracts, and some cranial nerve nuclei.

The pons houses autonomic nuclei in the **pontine respiratory center** (previously called the *pneumotaxic* [nū-mō-tăk′sik] *center*). This vital center, along with the medullary respiratory center within the medulla oblongata, regulates the skeletal muscles of breathing.

Nuclei called the **superior olivary complex** are located in the inferior pons. This complex receives auditory input and is involved in the pathway for sound localization.

The pons also houses sensory and motor **cranial nerve nuclei** for the trigeminal (CN V), abducens (CN VI), and facial (CN VII) cranial nerves. Some of the nuclei for the vestibulocochlear cranial nerve (CN VIII) also are located there.

 WHAT DID YOU LEARN?

26 What is the name and the general function of the autonomic respiratory center in the pons?

13.5c Medulla Oblongata

 LEARNING OBJECTIVES

6. Describe the main features of the medulla oblongata.
7. List the autonomic centers of the medulla and the actions they control.

The **medulla oblongata** (me-dūl′ă ob-long-gah′tă; *medulla* = marrow or middle; *oblongus* = rather long) is often simply called the **medulla** and is formed from the myelencephalon. It is the most caudal (inferior) part of the brainstem and is continuous with the spinal cord inferiorly. The caudal portion of the medulla has a flattened, rounded shape and narrow central canal. As the central canal extends rostrally toward the pons, it enlarges and becomes the fourth ventricle. All communication between the brain and spinal cord involves tracts that ascend or descend through the medulla oblongata (**figure 13.23**; see also figures 13.20 and 13.22).

Several external landmarks are readily visible on the medulla oblongata. The anterior surface exhibits two longitudinal ridges called the **pyramids** (pir′ă-mid), which house the motor projection tracts called the corticospinal (pyramidal) tracts. In the caudal region of the medulla, most of these axons cross to the opposite side of the brain at a point called the **decussation** (dē-kŭ-sā′shŭn; *decussate* = to cross in the form of an X) **of the pyramids.** As a result of the crossover, each cerebral hemisphere controls the voluntary movements of the opposite side of the body. Immediately lateral to each pyramid is a distinct bulge, called the **olive**, which contains a large fold of gray matter called the **inferior olivary nucleus.** The inferior olivary nuclei relay ascending sensory impulses, especially proprioceptive information, to the cerebellum. Additionally, paired **inferior cerebellar peduncles** are tracts that connect the medulla oblongata to the cerebellum.

The medulla oblongata contains several autonomic nuclei that group together to form centers that regulate functions vital for life. The most important autonomic centers in the medulla oblongata and their functions include

- The **cardiac center,** which regulates both the heart's rate and its strength of contraction (see section 19.5b).

(a) Medulla oblongata, cross-sectional view

Posterior
Fourth ventricle
Nuclei of vestibulocochlear nerve (CN VIII)
Nucleus of hypoglossal nerve (CN XII)
Vagus nerve (CN X)
Medial lemniscus
Olive
Pyramid
Hypoglossal nerve (CN XII)
Spinal nerve C1

Nucleus of vagus nerve (CN X)
Inferior olivary nucleus
Decussation of pyramids
Lateral corticospinal tract axons
Anterior corticospinal tract axons
Spinal cord
Anterior

(b) Medulla oblongata, lateral view

Inferior olivary nucleus
Cardiac and vasomotor centers
Pyramid
Anterior

Ventral respiratory group
Dorsal respiratory group
Respiratory center
Nucleus cuneatus
Nucleus gracilis
Posterior
Reticular formation

Figure 13.23 Medulla Oblongata. The medulla oblongata connects the brain to the spinal cord. (*a*) A cross section illustrates important internal structures and decussations of the pyramids. (*b*) The medulla contains several nuclei that are involved in the regulation of heart rate, respiratory rate, and receiving and sending sensory information about limb movement. AP|R

- The **vasomotor center,** which controls blood pressure by regulating the contraction and relaxation of smooth muscle in the walls of the smallest arteries (the *arterioles*) to alter these vessels' diameter. Blood pressure increases when vessel walls constrict and lowers when vessel walls dilate (see section 20.4).
- The **medullary respiratory center,** which regulates the respiratory rate. It is composed of a ventral respiratory group and a dorsal respiratory group. These groups are influenced by the pontine respiratory center (see section 23.5c).
- Other nuclei in the medulla, which are involved in coughing, sneezing, salivation, swallowing, gagging, and vomiting.

WHAT DO YOU THINK?

4 Based on your understanding of the medulla oblongata's functions, would you expect severe injury to the medulla oblongata to cause death or merely be disabling? Why?

Finally, the medulla oblongata contains cranial nerve nuclei that are associated with the vestibulocochlear (CN VIII), glossopharyngeal (CN IX), vagus (CN X), accessory (CN XI), and hypoglossal (CN XII) cranial nerves. The medulla oblongata also contains the **nucleus cuneatus** (kū-nē-ā′tŭs; wedge) and the **nucleus gracilis** (gras-i′lis; slender), which relay somatic sensory information to the thalamus. Bands of myelinated axons composing a **medial lemniscus** exit these nuclei and decussate in the inferior region of the medulla oblongata. The medial lemniscus projects through the brainstem (where it is found posterior to the substantia nigra) to the ventral posterior nucleus of the thalamus.

WHAT DID YOU LEARN?

27 Where are the pyramids located and what is their function?

28 What are the three main autonomic centers located in the medulla?

13.6 Cerebellum

The **cerebellum** (ser-e-bel′ŭm; = little brain) is the second largest part of the brain, and it develops from the metencephalon. It produces fine control over muscular actions and stores memories of movement patterns, such as the playing of scales on a piano.

13.6a Structural Components of the Cerebellum

LEARNING OBJECTIVES

1. Name the parts and landmarks of the cerebellum.
2. Identify the three tracts through which the brainstem is linked to the cerebellum.

The cerebellum has a complex, highly convoluted surface covered by a layer of cerebellar cortex. The folds of the cerebellar cortex are called **folia** (fō′lē-ă; *folium* = leaf) (**figure 13.24**). The cerebellum is composed of left and right **cerebellar hemispheres.** Each hemisphere consists of two lobes, the **anterior lobe** and the **posterior lobe,** which are separated by the **primary fissure.**

A narrow band of cortex known as the **vermis** (ver′mis; worm) lies along the midline between the left and right cerebellar lobes. The vermis receives sensory input reporting torso position and balance.

The cerebellum is partitioned internally into three regions: an outer gray matter layer of cortex called the **cerebellar cortex,** an internal region of white matter, and the deepest gray matter layer that is composed of cerebellar nuclei. The internal region of white matter is called the **arbor vitae** (ar′bōr vī′tē; *arbor* = tree, *vita* = life) because its distribution pattern resembles the branches of a tree.

Three thick nerve tracts, called peduncles, link the cerebellum with the brainstem (see figure 13.20*b*). The **superior cerebellar**

(a) Midsagittal section

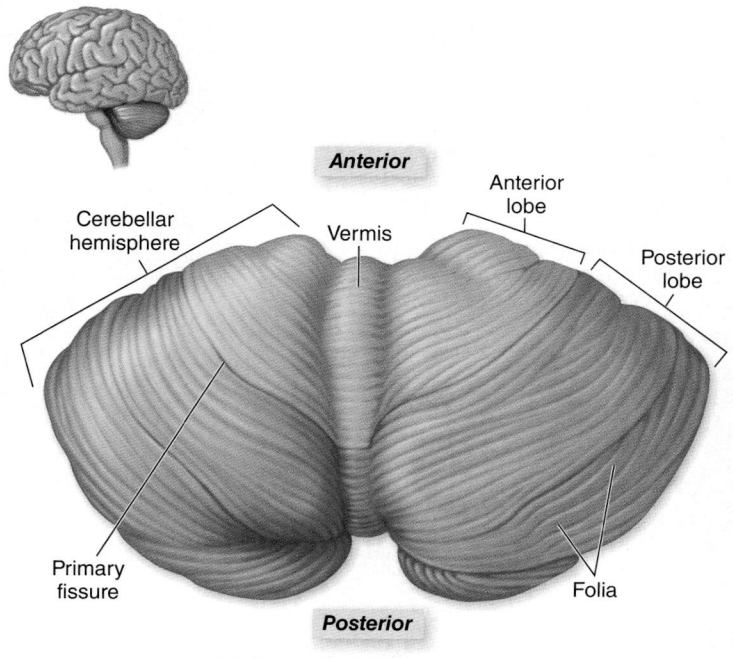

(b) Cerebellum, superior view

Figure 13.24 Cerebellum. The cerebellum lies posterior to the pons and medulla oblongata of the brainstem. (*a*) A midsagittal section shows the relationship of the cerebellum to the brainstem. (*b*) A superior view compares the anterior and posterior lobes of the cerebellum. (Note: The cerebrum has been removed.) AP|R

peduncles connect the cerebellum to the midbrain. The **middle cerebellar peduncles** connect the pons to the cerebellum. The **inferior cerebellar peduncles** connect the cerebellum to the medulla oblongata. These extensive communication lines enable the cerebellum to "fine-tune" skeletal muscle movements and interpret all body proprioceptive movement.

WHAT DID YOU LEARN?

29 What are the primary anatomic components of the cerebellum?

30 The middle cerebellar peduncles connect the cerebellum to which part of the brainstem?

13.6b Functions of the Cerebellum

LEARNING OBJECTIVE

3. Explain the functions of the cerebellum.

The cerebellum does not *initiate* skeletal muscle movement. Rather, it coordinates and "fine-tunes" skeletal muscle movements that were initiated by the cerebrum, and ensures that skeletal muscle contraction follows the correct pattern, leading to smooth, coordinated movements. The cerebellum stores memories of previously learned movement patterns. This function is performed indirectly, by regulating activity along both the voluntary and involuntary motor pathways at the cerebral cortex, cerebral nuclei, and motor centers in the brainstem. The cerebrum initiates a movement and sends a "rough draft" of the movement to the cerebellum, which then coordinates and adjusts it. For example, the controlled, precise movements a classical guitarist makes when playing a concerto result from fine-tuning by the cerebellum. Without the cerebellum, the guitarist's movements would be choppy and sloppy, without precise coordination between the two hands.

The cerebellum has several additional functions. Skeletal muscle activity is adjusted to maintain equilibrium and posture. It also receives proprioceptive (sensory) information from the muscles and joints and uses this information to regulate the body's position. For example, you are able to balance on one foot because the cerebellum takes the proprioceptive information from the body joints and "maps out" a muscle tone plan to keep the body upright.

Voluntary movements
The primary motor cortex and the basal nuclei in the forebrain send impulses through the nuclei of the pons to the cerebellum.

Assessment of voluntary movements
Proprioceptors in skeletal muscles and joints report degree of movement to the cerebellum.

Integration and analysis
The cerebellum compares the planned movements (motor signals) against the results of the actual movements (sensory signals).

Corrective feedback
The cerebellum sends impulses through the thalamus to the primary motor cortex and to motor nuclei in the brainstem.

Primary motor cortex

Cerebral hemisphere

Thalamus

Cerebellar cortex

Corpus callosum

Pontine nucleus

Pons

Direct (pyramidal) pathway

Sagittal section

Figure 13.25 Cerebellar Pathways. Input to the cerebellum from the motor cortex of the cerebrum and the pons (blue arrows), and the tracts between the spinal cord and cerebellum (yellow arrow). Within the cerebellum, the integration and analysis of input information occurs (green arrows). Output from the cerebellum (red arrows) extends through the cerebellar peduncles (not shown).

INTEGRATE

CLINICAL VIEW
Effects of Alcohol and Drugs on the Cerebellum

A variety of drugs, and alcohol in particular, can temporarily or permanently impair cerebellar function. Alcohol intoxication leads to the following symptoms of impaired cerebellar function that are used in the classic sobriety tests performed by police officers:

- **Disturbance of gait.** A person under the influence of alcohol rarely walks in a straight line, but appears to sway and stagger. In addition, falling and bumping into objects are likely, due to the temporary cerebellar disturbance.
- **Loss of balance and posture.** When attempting to stand on one foot, a person who is intoxicated usually tips and falls over.
- **Inability to detect proprioceptive information.** When asked to close the eyes and touch the nose, an intoxicated person frequently misses the mark. This reaction is due to reduced ability to sense proprioceptive information, compounded by uncoordination of skeletal muscles.

Finally, because proprioceptive information from both the body's muscles and joints is sent to the cerebellum, the cerebrum knows the position of each body joint and its muscle tone, even if the person is not looking at the joint. For example, if you close your eyes, you are still aware of which body joints are flexed and which are extended.

The cerebellum continuously receives convergent input from both the various sensory pathways and from the motor pathways in the brain **(figure 13.25)**. In this way, the cerebellum unconsciously perceives the state of the body, receives the plan for movement, and then follows the activity to see if it was carried out correctly. When the cerebellum detects a disparity between the intended and actual

movement, it may generate an error-correcting signal. This signal is transmitted to both the premotor and primary motor cortices via the thalamus and the brainstem. Descending pathways then transmit these error-correcting signals to the motor neurons. Thus, the cerebellum influences and controls movement by indirectly affecting the excitability of motor neurons.

WHAT DID YOU LEARN?

31 What are the functions of the cerebellum?

13.7 Functional Brain Systems

The brain has two important functional systems, which are systems that work together for a common function, even though their structures may be scattered throughout the brain. These systems are the limbic system and the reticular formation.

13.7a Limbic System

LEARNING OBJECTIVES
1. Describe the main functions of the limbic system.
2. List the seven structures that compose the limbic system, and summarize their actions.

The **limbic** (lim'bik) **system** is composed of multiple cerebral and diencephalic structures that collectively process and experience emotions. Thus, the limbic system is sometimes referred to as the *emotional brain*. The structures of the limbic system form a ring or border around the diencephalon (*limbus* = border). Although neuroanatomists continue to debate the components of the limbic system, the brain structures commonly recognized are shown in **figure 13.26** and listed here:

1. The **cingulate** (sin'gū-lāt; *cingulum* = girdle, to surround) **gyrus** is an internal mass of cerebral cortex located within the

Components of the limbic system
- Cingulate gyrus
- Fornix
- Anterior thalamic nucleus
- Septal nucleus
- Mammillary body
- Hippocampus
- Amygdaloid body
- Parahippocampal gyrus
- Olfactory tract
- Olfactory bulb

Corpus callosum

Anterior commissure

Midsagittal section

Figure 13.26 Limbic System. The components of the limbic system affect behavior and emotions. The olfactory cortex of the temporal lobe is not shown. AP|R longitudinal fissure and superior to the corpus callosum. This cortical mass may be seen only in sagittal section, and it surrounds the diencephalon. It receives input from the other components of the limbic system.

2. The **parahippocampal gyrus** is a mass of cerebral cortical tissue in the temporal lobe. Its function is associated with the hippocampus.

3. The **hippocampus** (hip-ō-kam′pŭs; seahorse) is a nucleus located superior to the parahippocampal gyrus that connects to the diencephalon via a structure called the fornix. As its name implies, this nucleus is shaped like a seahorse. Both the hippocampus and the parahippocampal gyrus are essential in storing memories and forming long-term memory.

4. The **amygdaloid body** connects to the hippocampus. The amygdaloid body is involved in several aspects of emotion, especially fear. It can also help store and code memories based on how a person emotionally perceives them—for example, as related to fear, extreme happiness, or sadness.

5. The **olfactory bulbs, olfactory tracts,** and **olfactory cortex** are part of the limbic system as well. You have probably experienced how particular odors can provoke certain emotions or be associated with certain memories.

6. The **fornix** (fōr′niks; arch) is a thin tract of white matter that connects the hippocampus with other diencephalon limbic system structures.

7. Various nuclei in the diencephalon, such as the **anterior thalamic nuclei,** the **habenular nuclei,** the **septal nuclei,** and the **mammillary** (mam′i-lār-ē; *mammilla* = nipple) **bodies,** interconnect other parts of the limbic system and contribute to its overall function.

WHAT DID YOU LEARN?

32 What are the components of the limbic system?

33 What are the main functions of the limbic system?

13.7b Reticular Formation

LEARNING OBJECTIVES

3. Describe the components and function of the reticular formation.

4. Explain anatomy and function of the reticular activating system (RAS).

Projecting vertically through the core of the midbrain, pons, and medulla is a loosely organized core of gray matter called the **reticular formation (figure 13.27).** The reticular formation extends slightly into the diencephalon and the spinal cord as well. This functional brain system has both motor and sensory components.

The motor component of the reticular formation communicates with the spinal cord and is responsible for regulating muscle tone (especially when the muscles are at rest). This motor component also assists in autonomic motor functions, such as respiration, blood pressure, and heart rate, by working with the autonomic centers in the medulla and pons.

The sensory component of the reticular formation is responsible for alerting the cerebrum to incoming sensory information. This sensory component is called the **reticular activating system (RAS),** and it contains sensory axons that project to the cerebral cortex. The

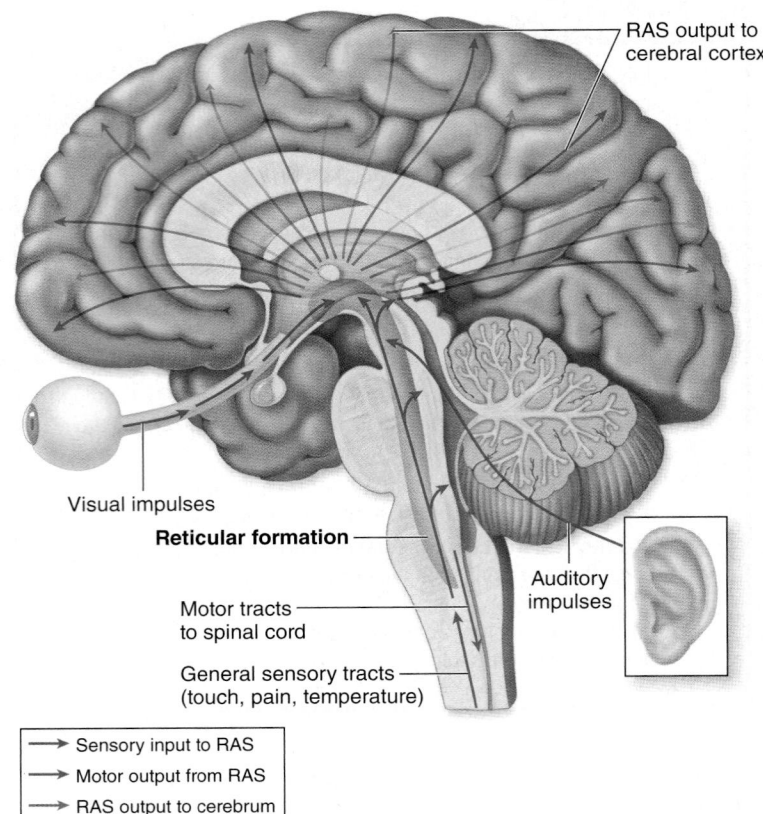

Figure 13.27 The Reticular Formation. The reticular formation receives and processes various types of stimuli (blue arrows). It participates in cyclic activities such as arousing the cortex to consciousness (purple arrows) and controlling the sleep-wake cycle. Some outputs from the reticular formation influence muscle activity (red arrow).

RAS processes visual, auditory, and touch stimuli and uses this information to keep us in a state of mental alertness. Additionally, the RAS arouses us from sleep. The sound of an alarm clock can awaken us because the RAS receives this sensory stimulus and sends it to the cerebrum. Conversely, under conditions of little or no stimuli, such as when you are in bed with the lights out, and no sounds are disturbing you, the RAS is not stimulated and you are able to sleep.

Consciousness includes an awareness of sensation, voluntary control of motor activities, and the activities necessary for higher mental processing. It involves the simultaneous activity of large areas of the cerebral cortex. Levels of consciousness exist on a continuum. The highest state of consciousness and cortical activity is **alertness,** in which the individual is responsive, aware of self, and well-oriented to person, place, and time. People normally alternate between periods of alertness and **sleep,** which is the natural, temporary absence of consciousness from which a person can be aroused by normal stimulation. Cortical activity is depressed during sleep, but functions continue in the vital centers within the brainstem.

WHAT DID YOU LEARN?

34 How is the reticular activating system related to the reticular formation?

CLINICAL VIEW

Pathologic States of Unconsciousness

The level of consciousness of a healthy person varies from wide awake and alert to deep sleep. When a person is asleep, he or she is technically unconscious, but not pathologically so. However, other unconscious conditions are pathologic.

A brief loss of consciousness, termed **fainting,** or **syncope** (sin′kŏ-pē; cutting short), often signals inadequate cerebral blood flow due to low blood pressure, as might follow hemorrhage or sudden emotional stress.

Stupor (stū′per; *stupeo* = to be stunned) is a moderately deep level of unconsciousness from which the person can be aroused only by extreme repeated or painful stimuli. A stupor may be associated with metabolic disorders such as low blood sugar, diseases of the liver or kidney, CVA or other brain trauma, or drug use.

A **coma** is a deep and profound state of unconsciousness from which the person cannot be aroused, even by repeated or painful stimuli. A person in a coma is alive but unable to respond to the environment. A coma may result from severe head injury or CVA, marked metabolic failure (as occurs in advanced liver and kidney disease), very low blood sugar, or drug use.

A **persistent vegetative state** is a condition in which the person has lost his or her thinking ability and awareness of the environment, but noncognitive brain functions continue, such as the brainstem's monitoring of heart rate, breathing, and the sleep-wake cycle. Some people in this state exhibit spontaneous movements, such as moving their eyes, grimacing, crying, and even laughing.

An **electroencephalogram (EEG)** is a diagnostic test where electrodes are attached to the head to record the electrical activity of the brain. Specifically, the test measures and plots four types of brain waves (alpha, beta, theta, and delta). The distribution and frequency of these waves varies, depending upon whether the person is a child or an adult and if the individual is in a deep sleep, having a seizure, or is experiencing a pathologic state of consciousness.

13.8 Integrative Functions and Higher-Order Brain Functions

Higher-order mental functions include learning, memory, and reasoning. These functions occur within the cortex of the cerebrum and involve multiple brain regions connected by complicated networks and arrays of axons. Both conscious and unconscious processing of information are involved in higher-order mental functions, and this processing may be continually adjusted or modified.

13.8a Development of Higher-Order Brain Functions

✓ LEARNING OBJECTIVE

1. Describe the relationship between age and higher-order brain functioning.

From infancy on, our motor control and processing capabilities become increasingly complex as we grow and mature. During the first year of life, the number of cortical neurons continues to increase. The myelination of most CNS axons continues throughout the first 2 years. The brain grows rapidly in size and complexity so that by the age of 5, brain growth is 95% complete. (The rest of the body doesn't reach its adult size until puberty.)

As the CNS continues to develop, many neurons expand their number of connections, providing the increased number of synaptic junctions required for increasingly complex reflex activities and processing. Some CNS axons remain unmyelinated until the teenage years (e.g., some of the axons in the prefrontal cortex). In general, the axons of PNS neurons continue to myelinate past puberty. A person's ability to carry out higher-order mental functions is a direct result of the level of nervous system maturation.

WHAT DID YOU LEARN?

35 What are some implications of the brain's development not being complete until the mid-teens?

13.8b Cognition

✓ LEARNING OBJECTIVES

2. Identify the brain areas in which cognition occurs.

3. Explain how lesions to different regions of the cortex affect cognition.

Mental processes such as awareness, knowledge, memory, perception, and thinking are collectively called **cognition** (kog-ni′shŭn). The association areas of the cerebrum, which form about 70% of the nervous tissue in the brain, are responsible for both cognition and the processing and integration of information between sensory input and motor output areas.

Various studies of individuals suffering from brain lesions (caused by cancer, infection, stroke, and trauma) have provided insight into the functions of these areas of the brain. For example, the frontal association area (prefrontal cortex) integrates information from the sensory, motor, and association areas to enable the individual to think, plan, and execute appropriate behavior. Thus, an individual with a frontal lobe lesion exhibits personality abnormalities.

If an individual loses the ability to detect and identify stimuli (termed loss of awareness) on one side of the body, or on the limbs on that side, the primary somatosensory area in the hemisphere opposite the affected side of the body has been damaged.

An individual who has **agnosia** (ag-nō′zē-ă; *a* = without, *gnosis* = knowledge) displays an inability either to recognize or to understand the meaning of various stimuli. For example, a lesion in the temporal lobe may result in an inability to recognize or understand the meaning of sounds or words. Specific symptoms of agnosia vary, depending upon the location of the lesion within the cerebrum.

WHAT DID YOU LEARN?

36 What association areas are utilized with cognition?

37 Define agnosia, and explain how it affects cognition.

CLINICAL VIEW
Alzheimer Disease: The "Long Goodbye"

Alzheimer disease (AD) has become the leading cause of dementia in the developed world. The images illustrate the anatomic differences between a normal brain and an Alzheimer brain.

What are the classic symptoms of AD?

Typically, AD does not become clinically apparent until after the age of 65, although some individuals have earlier onset; its diagnosis is often delayed because of confusion with other forms of cognitive impairment. Symptoms include slow, progressive loss of higher intellectual functions and changes in mood and behavior. AD gradually causes language deterioration, impaired visuospatial skills, indifferent attitude, and poor judgment, while leaving motor function intact. Patients become confused and restless, often asking the same question repeatedly. AD progresses relentlessly over months and years, and thus has come to be known as "the long goodbye." Eventually, it robs its victims of their memory, their former personality, and even the capacity to speak.

What causes AD?

The underlying cause of AD remains a mystery, although both genetics and environment seem to play a role. Postmortem examinations of the brains of AD patients show marked and generalized cerebral atrophy.

Microscopic examinations of brain tissue reveal a profound decrease in the number of cerebral cortical neurons, while surviving neurons contain abnormal aggregations of protein fibers, termed a **neurofibrillary tangle.** Additionally, an abnormal protein, **amyloid** (am'i-loyd) **precursor protein (APP),** appears in the matrix of the brain as well as in the walls of the cerebral arterioles. Biochemical alterations also occur, most significantly a decreased level of the neurotransmitter acetylcholine in the cerebrum.

Is there a cure or test for AD?

There is no cure at present for AD, although some medications help alleviate the symptoms and seem to slow the progress of the disease. In the meantime, researchers are trying to develop diagnostic tests that can better predict who may be at risk for AD. Until recently, the only way to definitively diagnose AD was at autopsy, when the brain could be macroscopically and microscopically examined. Now, positron emission tomography (PET) scans appear to be able to identify the early brain changes seen with AD.

Recent research has suggested that difficulty or loss in identifying common smells (e.g., lemon, cinnamon) is linked with an increased risk in developing AD. In fact, this loss of smell may be one of the first signs of developing the disease, presumably because the brain regions involved with smell are among the first regions to develop the neurofibrillary tangles of AD. So, in the near future researchers may develop a "scratch and sniff" test to help predict an individual's risk of developing AD.

(a) Normal brain

Enlarged ventricles

Cortical atrophy

(b) Alzheimer brain

Magnetic resonance imaging (MRI) scans show coronal sections of (a) a normal brain and (b) an Alzheimer brain. (Note the large ventricles and wide spaces between gyri in the Alzheimer brain.)

13.8c Memory

LEARNING OBJECTIVES

4. Compare and contrast short-term and long-term memory, and describe the parts of the brain involved with each.

5. Name the two regions of the limbic system involved in conversion of short-term memory to long-term memory.

Memory is a versatile element of human cognition involving different lengths of time and different storage capacities. Storing and retrieving information requires higher-order mental functions and depends on complex interactions among different brain regions. On a broader scale, in addition to memory, information management by the brain entails both learning (the acquisition of new information) and forgetting (the elimination of trivial or nonuseful information).

Neuroscientists classify memory in various ways. For example, **sensory memory** occurs when we form important associations based on sensory input from the environment, such as the sounds coming from a crowded cafeteria, the smell from the food line, and the bright lights from the room. Sensory memory typically lasts for seconds at most.

Short-term memory (STM) follows sensory memory. It is generally characterized by limited capacity (approximately seven small segments of information) and brief duration (ranging from seconds to hours). Suppose that, in a Friday morning anatomy and physiology lecture, your instructor lists the general functions of the cerebral lobes on the board. Unless you study this information over the weekend, you will probably not recall it by Monday's lecture.

Some short-term memory, if adequately repeated and assessed, may be converted to long term memory. Once information is placed into **long-term memory (LTM),** it may exist for limitless periods of time. So, for example, if over the weekend you read and recopy your lecture notes, review the text and figures in the book, and prepare note cards, you will have stored the information about the cerebral lobes as LTM. Not only will you be well prepared for your next examination, but you may even remember this information for years to come. (However, information in LTM needs to be retrieved occasionally or it can be "lost," and our ability to store and retrieve information declines with aging.)

It appears that our brain must organize complex information in short-term memory prior to storing it in long-term memory **(figure 13.28)**. Conversion from STM to LTM is called **encoding,** or *memory consolidation*. Encoding requires the proper functioning of two components of the limbic system: the amygdaloid body and the hippocampus. The hippocampus is required for the formation of STM, whereas long-term memories are stored primarily in the association areas of the cerebral cortex. For example, voluntary motor activity memory is housed in the premotor cortex and the cerebellum, and memory of sounds is stored in the auditory association area.

Because STM and LTM involve different anatomic structures, loss of the ability to form STM does not affect the maintenance or accessibility of LTM.

 WHAT DID YOU LEARN?

38 What types of study habits best convert short-term memories into long-term memories?

13.8d Emotion

LEARNING OBJECTIVE

6. Explain the interactions of the prefrontal cortex and the limbic system in expression of emotions.

INTEGRATE

CLINICAL VIEW
Amnesia

Amnesia (am-nē′zē-ă) refers to complete or partial loss of memory. Most often, amnesia is temporary and affects only a portion of a person's experiences. Causes of amnesia range from psychological trauma to direct brain injury, such as a severe blow to the head or even a CVA.

Because memory processing and storage involve numerous regions of the brain, the type of memory loss that occurs in an episode of amnesia depends upon the area of the brain damaged. The most serious forms of amnesia result from damage to the thalamus and limbic structures, especially the hippocampus. If one or more of these structures is damaged, serious disruption or complete lack of memory storage and consolidation may follow. The nature of the underlying problem determines whether amnesia is complete or partial, and to what degree recovery, if any, is possible.

Emotional expression varies widely. For example, a horrible automobile accident may cause those involved and some observers to cry, scream, or totally lose "emotional control," whereas the responding emergency personnel generally appear stoic, wearing masked expressions as they go about their professional duties.

Expression of our emotions is interpreted by our limbic system but ultimately is controlled by the prefrontal cortex. Irrespective of how we feel, this cortical region decides the appropriate way to show our feelings. Researchers have identified the emotional control centers of the brain by using traditional techniques as well as by examining the behavior of experimental animals and people with brain lesions. Although interpreting the results is often difficult because of the complexities of both the brain and our behavior, researchers have learned that many important aspects of emotion depend upon an intact, functional amygdaloid body and hippocampus (components of the limbic system). If specific regions of either of these structures are damaged or artificially stimulated, we exhibit either deadened or exaggerated expressions of aggression, affection, anger, fear, love, pain, pleasure, or sexuality, as well as anomalies in learning and memory.

 WHAT DID YOU LEARN?

39 What portions of the brain and limbic system are involved with modulation of emotion?

Figure 13.28 Model of Information Processing. Cognitive psychologists have proposed a model to show the relationships between sensory memory and short-term memory. Long-term memory develops later.

Dyslexia

Dyslexia (dis-lek'sē-ă; *dys* = bad, *lexis* = word) is an inherited learning disability characterized by problems with single-word decoding. It often runs in families. Affected individuals not only have trouble reading but may also have problems writing and spelling accurately. These individuals may be able to recognize letters normally, but they demonstrate a level of reading competence far below that expected for their level of intelligence. Their writing may be disorganized and uneven, with the letters of words in incorrect order or even completely reversed. Some individuals appear to outgrow this condition, or at least develop improved reading ability over time. This improvement may reflect neural maturation or retraining of parts of the brain to better decode words and symbols. Some researchers have postulated that dyslexia is a form of **disconnect syndrome,** in which transfer of information between the cerebral hemispheres through the corpus callosum is impaired.

13.8e Language

LEARNING OBJECTIVE

7. List the cerebral centers involved in written and spoken language, and describe how these centers work together.

The higher-order processes involved in language include reading, writing, speaking, and understanding words. Recall that two important cortical areas involved in speech integration are the Wernicke area and the motor speech area (Broca area). The Wernicke area is involved in interpreting what we read or hear, whereas the motor speech area receives axons originating from the Wernicke area and then helps regulate the motor activities needed for us to speak. Thus, the Wernicke area is central to our ability to recognize written and spoken language. Immediately posterior to the Wernicke area is the angular gyrus, a region that processes the words we read into a form that we can speak (**figure 13.29**). First, the Wernicke area sends a speech plan to the motor speech area, which initiates a specific patterned motor program that is transmitted to the primary motor cortex. Next, neurons in the primary motor cortex signal other motor neurons, which then innervate the muscles of the cheeks, larynx, lips, and tongue to produce speech.

The Wernicke area is in the categorical hemisphere in most people. In the representational hemisphere, a cortical region opposite the Wernicke area recognizes the emotional content of speech. A lesion in this area of the cerebrum can make a person unable to understand emotional nuances, such as bitterness or happiness, in spoken words. A lesion in the cortical region of the representational hemisphere opposite the motor speech area results in **aprosodia,** which causes dull, emotionless speech.

WHAT DID YOU LEARN?

40 How is the Wernicke area involved in language processing?

Primary motor cortex

Motor speech area | Wernicke area

(a) Lateral view

Figure 13.29 Functional Areas Within the Cerebral Cortex. (*a*) The left cerebral hemisphere in most people houses the Wernicke area, the motor speech area, and the prefrontal cortex. (*b*) A PET scan shows the areas of the brain that are most active during speech.

① Auditory information about a sentence travels to the primary auditory cortex. The Wernicke area then interprets the sentence.

(b) PET scans

② Information from the Wernicke area travels to the motor speech area.

③ Information travels from the motor speech area to the primary motor cortex, where motor commands involving muscles used for speech are given.

13.9 Cranial Nerves

LEARNING OBJECTIVES

1. List the names and locations of the 12 pairs of cranial nerves.
2. Compare the functions of each of the cranial nerves.

The 12 pairs of cranial nerves are part of the peripheral nervous system (PNS) and originate on the inferior surface of the brain. They are numbered with Roman numerals according to their positions, beginning with the most anteriorly placed nerve, and the number is sometimes preceded by the prefix *CN* (**figure 13.30**).

The name of each nerve generally has some relation to its function. The 12 pairs of cranial nerves are the olfactory (CN I), optic (CN II), oculomotor (CN III), trochlear (CN IV), trigeminal (CN V),

Cranial nerves

- Olfactory bulb, termination of olfactory nerve (CN I)
- Olfactory tract
- Optic chiasm
- Optic nerve (CN II)
- Infundibulum
- Optic tract
- Oculomotor nerve (CN III)
- Trochlear nerve (CN IV)
- Trigeminal nerve (CN V)
- Abducens nerve (CN VI)
- Facial nerve (CN VII)
- Vestibulocochlear nerve (CN VIII)
- Glossopharyngeal nerve (CN IX)
- Vagus nerve (CN X)
- Accessory nerve (CN XI)
- Hypoglossal nerve (CN XII)
- Spinal cord

Pons
Medulla oblongata

Figure 13.30 Cranial Nerves. A view of the inferior surface of the brain shows the 12 pairs of cranial nerves. AP|R abducens (CN VI), facial (CN VII), vestibulocochlear (CN VIII), glossopharyngeal (CN IX), vagus (CN X), accessory (CN XI), and hypoglossal (CN XII).

Table 13.7 summarizes the main motor and sensory functions of each cranial nerve. For easier reference, each main function of a nerve is color-coded. Pink represents a sensory function, blue stands for a somatic motor function (see section 12.1b), and green denotes a parasympathetic motor function. Table 13.8 lists the individual cranial nerves and discusses their functions, origins, and pathways. The color-coding in table 13.7 carries over to table 13.8, so you can easily determine whether a cranial nerve has motor and/or sensory components.

WHAT DID YOU LEARN?

41 Which cranial nerves have sensory functions only?

Table 13.7	Primary Functions of Cranial Nerves		
Cranial Nerve	**Sensory Function**	**Somatic Motor Function**	**Parasympathetic Motor (Autonomic) Function[1]**
I (olfactory)	Olfaction (smell)	*None*	*None*
II (optic)	Vision	*None*	*None*
III (oculomotor)	*None*[2]	Four extrinsic eye muscles (medial rectus, superior rectus, inferior rectus, inferior oblique); levator palpebrae superioris muscle (elevates eyelid)	Innervates sphincter pupillae muscle in eye to make pupil constrict; contracts ciliary muscles to make lens of eye more rounded (as needed for near vision)
IV (trochlear)	*None*[2]	Superior oblique eye muscle	*None*
V (trigeminal)	General sensory from anterior scalp, nasal cavity, nasopharynx, entire face, most of oral cavity, teeth, anterior two-thirds of tongue; part of auricle of ear; meninges	Muscles of mastication, mylohyoid, digastric (anterior belly), tensor tympani, tensor veli palatini	*None*
VI (abducens)	*None*[2]	Lateral rectus eye muscle	*None*
VII (facial)	Taste from anterior two-thirds of tongue	Muscles of facial expression, digastric (posterior belly), stylohyoid, stapedius	Increases secretion from lacrimal gland of eye, submandibular and sublingual salivary glands
VIII (vestibulocochlear)	Hearing (cochlear branch); equilibrium (vestibular branch)	*None*[3]	*None*
IX (glossopharyngeal)	General sensory and taste to posterior one-third of tongue, general sensory to part of pharynx, visceral sensory from carotid bodies	One pharyngeal muscle (stylopharyngeus)	Increases secretion from parotid salivary gland
X (vagus)	Visceral sensory information from heart, lungs, most abdominal organs General sensory information from external acoustic meatus, tympanic membrane, part of pharynx, laryngopharynx, and larynx	Most pharyngeal muscles; all laryngeal muscles	Innervates smooth muscle and glands of heart, lungs, larynx, trachea, most abdominal organs
XI (accessory)	*None*	Trapezius muscle, sternocleidomastoid muscle	*None*
XII (hypoglossal)	*None*	Intrinsic and extrinsic tongue muscles	*None*

1. The autonomic nervous system contains a parasympathetic division and sympathetic division. Some cranial nerves carry parasympathetic axons and are listed in this table. Detailed information about these divisions is found in section 15.2.
2. These nerves do contain some tiny proprioceptive sensory axons in the muscles, but in general, these nerves tend to be described as motor only.
3. A few motor axons travel with this nerve to the inner ear, but they are not considered a significant component of the nerve.

Table 13.8 Cranial Nerves

CN I OLFACTORY NERVE (ol-fak′tŏ-rē; *olfacio* = to smell)

Olfactory tract (to cerebral cortex)
Olfactory bulb
Cribriform plate of ethmoid bone
Axons of olfactory nerves (CN I)

Description	Conducts olfactory (smell) sensations to brain; only type of nervous tissue to regenerate
Sensory function	Olfaction (smell)
Origin	Receptors (bipolar neurons) in olfactory mucosa of nasal cavity
Pathway	Travels through the cribriform foramina of ethmoid bone and synapses in the olfactory bulbs, which are located in the anterior cranial fossa
Conditions caused by nerve damage	Anosmia (partial or total loss of smell)

CN II OPTIC NERVE (op′tik; *ops* = eye)

Eye
Optic nerve (CN II)
Optic chiasm
Optic tract
Lateral geniculate nucleus of thalamus
Optic projection axons
Visual cortex (in occipital lobe)

Description	Special sensory nerve of vision that is an outgrowth of the brain; more appropriately called a brain tract
Sensory function	Vision
Origin	Retina of the eye
Pathway	Enters cranium via optic canal of sphenoid bone; left and right optic nerves unite at optic chiasm; optic tract travels to lateral geniculate nucleus of thalamus; finally, information is forwarded to the occipital lobe
Conditions caused by nerve damage	Anopsia (visual defects)

(continued on next page)

Table 13.8   Cranial Nerves (continued)

CN III OCULOMOTOR NERVE (ok′ū-lō-mō′tŏr; *oculus* = eye, *motorius* = moving)

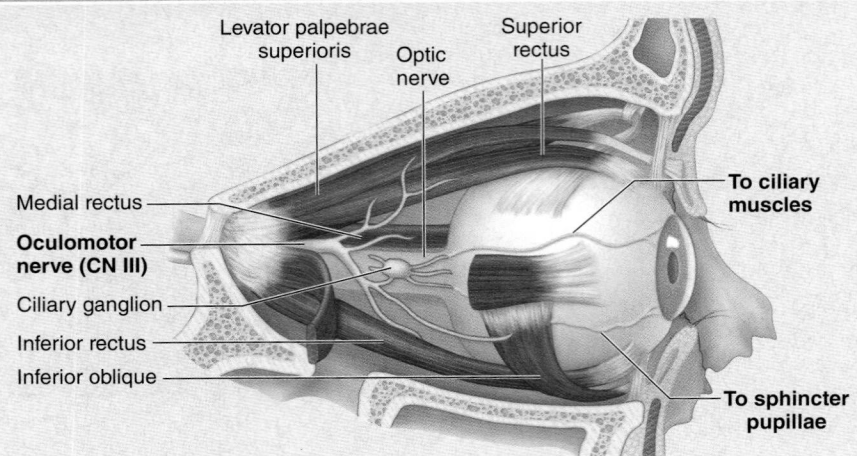

Description	Innervates upper eyelid muscle and four of the six extrinsic eye muscles
Somatic motor function	Supplies four extrinsic eye muscles (superior rectus, inferior rectus, medial rectus, inferior oblique) to move eye Supplies levator palpebrae superioris muscle to elevate eyelid
Parasympathetic motor function	Innervates sphincter pupillae muscle of iris to make pupil constrict Contracts ciliary muscles to make lens of eye more spherical (as needed for near vision)
Origin	Oculomotor and Edinger Westphal nuclei within the midbrain
Pathway	Leaves cranium via superior orbital fissure and travels to eye and eyelid. (Parasympathetic axons travel to ciliary ganglion, and postganglionic parasympathetic axons than travel to iris and ciliary muscles.)
Conditions caused by nerve damage	Ptosis (upper eyelid droop); paralysis of most eye muscles, leading to strabismus (eyes not in parallel/deviated improperly), diplopia (double vision), focusing difficulty

CN IV TROCHLEAR NERVE (trōk′lē-ar; *trochlea* = a pulley)

Description	Innervates one extrinsic eye muscle (superior oblique) that loops through a pulley-shaped ligament
Somatic motor function	Supplies one extrinsic eye muscle (superior oblique) to move eye inferiorly and laterally
Origin	Trochlear nucleus within the midbrain
Pathway	Leaves cranium via superior orbital fissure and travels to superior oblique muscle
Conditions caused by nerve damage	Paralysis of superior oblique, leading to strabismus (eyes not in parallel/deviated improperly), diplopia (double vision)

Table 13.8 Cranial Nerves (continued)

CN V TRIGEMINAL NERVE (trī-jem'i-năl; *trigeminus* = threefold)

Sensory distribution of trigeminal nerve

- Ophthalmic branch (V_1)
- Maxillary branch (V_2)
- Mandibular branch (V_3)

- Ophthalmic branch (V_1)
- Trigeminal ganglion
- **Trigeminal nerve (CN V)**
- Mandibular branch (V_3)
- Chorda tympani (from facial nerve)
- Inferior alveolar nerve
- *To mylohyoid muscle*
- Maxillary branch (V_2)
- Superior alveolar nerves
- *To muscles of mastication*
- Lingual nerve
- Submandibular ganglion
- Mental nerve

Description	This nerve consists of three divisions: ophthalmic (V_1), maxillary (V_2), and mandibular (V_3); receives sensory impulses from face, oral cavity, nasal cavity, meninges, and anterior scalp, and innervates muscles of mastication
Sensory function	Sensory stimuli for this nerve are touch, temperature, and pain. V_1: Conducts sensory impulses from cornea, nose, forehead, anterior scalp, meninges V_2: Conducts sensory impulses from nasal mucosa, palate, gums, cheek, meninges V_3: Conducts sensory impulses from anterior two-thirds of tongue, meninges, skin of chin, lower jaw, lower teeth; one-third from sensory axons of auricle of ear
Somatic motor function	Innervates muscles of mastication (temporalis, masseter, lateral and medial pterygoids), mylohyoid, anterior belly of digastric, tensor tympani muscle, and tensor veli palatini
Origin	Nuclei in the pons
Pathway	V_1: Sensory axons enter cranium via superior orbital fissure and travel to trigeminal ganglion before entering pons V_2: Sensory axons enter cranium via foramen rotundum and travel to trigeminal ganglion before entering pons V_3: Motor axons leave pons and exit cranium via foramen ovale to supply muscles. Sensory axons travel through foramen ovale to trigeminal ganglion before entering pons.
Conditions caused by nerve damage	Trigeminal neuralgia (tic douloureux) is caused by inflammation of the sensory components of the trigeminal nerve and results in intense, pulsating pain lasting from minutes to several hours

(continued on next page)

Table 13.8   Cranial Nerves (continued)

CN VI ABDUCENS NERVE (ab-dū′senz; to move away from)

Abducens nerve (CN VI)
Optic nerve
Lateral rectus (cut)

Description	Innervates lateral rectus eye muscle, which abducts the eye ("pulls away laterally")
Somatic motor function	Innervates one extrinsic eye muscle (lateral rectus) for eye abduction
Origin	Pontine (abducens) nucleus in the pons
Pathway	Leaves cranium through superior orbital fissure and travels to lateral rectus muscle
Conditions caused by nerve damage	Paralysis of lateral rectus limits lateral movement of eye, diplopia (double vision)

CN VII FACIAL NERVE (fā′shăl)

Geniculate ganglion
Pons
Facial nerve (CN VII)
Posterior auricular branch
Stylomastoid foramen
Parotid gland
Branch of lingual nerve of CN V
Cervical branch

Temporal branch
Lacrimal gland
Greater petrosal nerve
Pterygopalatine ganglion
Zygomatic branch
Chorda tympani nerve (traveling to mandibular branch of CN V)
Buccal branch
Submandibular ganglion
Mandibular branch

Description	Innervates muscles of facial expression; lacrimal (tear) gland, and most salivary glands; conducts taste sensations from anterior two-thirds of tongue
Sensory function	Taste from anterior two-thirds of tongue
Somatic motor function	The five major motor branches (temporal, zygomatic, buccal, mandibular, and cervical) innervate the muscles of facial expression, the posterior belly of the digastric muscle, and the stylohyoid and stapedius muscles
Parasympathetic motor function	Increases secretions of the lacrimal gland of the eye as well as the submandibular and sublingual salivary glands
Origin	Nuclei in the pons
Pathway	Sensory axons travel from the tongue via the chorda tympani branch of the facial nerve through a tiny foramen to enter the skull, and axons synapse at the geniculate ganglion of the facial nerve. Somatic motor axons leave the pons and enter the temporal bone through the internal acoustic meatus, project through temporal bone, and emerge through stylomastoid foramen to supply the musculature. Parasympathetic motor axons leave the pons, enter the internal acoustic meatus, leave with either the greater petrosal nerve or chorda tympani nerve, and travel to an autonomic ganglion before innervating their respective glands.
Conditions caused by nerve damage	Decreased tearing (dry eye) and decreased salivation (dry mouth); loss of taste sensation to anterior two-thirds of tongue, nerve paralysis (also known as Bell palsy) characterized by paralyzed facial muscles, lack of orbicularis oculi contraction, sagging at corner of mouth (See section 11.3a for a more complete description of facial nerve paralysis.)

Table 13.8   Cranial Nerves (continued)

CN VIII VESTIBULOCOCHLEAR NERVE (ves-tib′ū-lō-kok′lē-ăr; relating to vestibule and cochlea of the ear)

Description	Conducts equilibrium and auditory (hearing) sensations to brain
Sensory function	Vestibular branch conducts impulses for equilibrium, while cochlear branch conducts impulses for hearing
Origin	Vestibular branch: Hair cells in the vestibule of the inner ear Cochlear branch: Cochlea of the inner ear
Pathway	Sensory cell bodies of the vestibular branch are located in the vestibular ganglion, while sensory cell bodies of the cochlear branch are located in the spiral ganglion near the cochlea. The vestibular and cochlear branches merge, and together enter cranial cavity through internal acoustic meatus and travel to junction of the pons and the medulla oblongata.
Conditions caused by nerve damage	Lesions in vestibular branch produce loss of balance, nausea, vomiting, and dizziness; lesions in cochlear branch result in deafness (loss of hearing)

CN IX GLOSSOPHARYNGEAL NERVE (glos′ō-fă-rin′jē-ăl; *glossa* = tongue)

Description	Receives taste and touch sensations from posterior one-third of the tongue, innervates one pharynx muscle and the parotid salivary gland
Sensory function	General sensation and taste to posterior one-third of tongue; general sensation to most of pharynx, chemoreceptor axons to carotid bodies (structures on the carotid arteries that detect and monitor O_2 and CO_2 levels in the blood)
Somatic motor function	Innervates stylopharyngeus (pharynx muscle)
Parasympathetic motor function	Increases secretion of parotid salivary gland
Origin	Sensory axons originate on taste buds and mucosa of posterior one-third of tongue, as well as the carotid bodies Motor axons originate in nuclei in the medulla oblongata
Pathway	Sensory axons travel from posterior one-third of tongue and carotid bodies along nerve through the inferior or superior ganglion into the jugular foramen, and travel to pons. Somatic motor axons leave cranium via jugular foramen and travel to stylopharyngeus. Parasympathetic motor axons travel to otic ganglion and then to parotid gland.
Conditions caused by nerve damage	Reduced salivary secretion (dry mouth); loss of taste sensations to posterior one-third of tongue

(continued on next page)

Table 13.8	Cranial Nerves (continued)

CN X VAGUS NERVE (vā′gŭs; wandering)

Superior ganglion
Inferior ganglion
Pharyngeal branch
Superior laryngeal nerve
Internal laryngeal nerve
External laryngeal nerve

Right vagus nerve (CN X)   **Left vagus nerve (CN X)**

Right recurrent laryngeal nerve   Left recurrent laryngeal nerve

Cardiac branch

Lung

Pulmonary plexus

Heart

Anterior vagal trunk (formed from left vagus)

Kidney

Spleen

Liver

Stomach
Pancreas

Ascending colon

Small intestine

Appendix

Description	Innervates structures in the head and neck and in the thoracic and abdominal cavities
Sensory function	Visceral sensory information from heart, lungs, and most abdominal organs. General sensory information from external acoustic meatus, eardrum, laryngopharynx and larynx
Somatic motor function	Innervates most pharynx muscles and all larynx muscles
Parasympathetic motor function	Innervates smooth muscle of thoracic and most abdominal organs, cardiac muscle, and glands of heart, lungs, pharynx, larynx, trachea, and most abdominal organs
Origin	Motor nuclei in medulla oblongata
Pathway	Leaves cranium via jugular foramen before traveling and branching extensively in neck, thorax, and abdomen; sensory neuron cell bodies are located in the superior and inferior ganglia associated with the nerve
Conditions caused by nerve damage	Paralysis leads to a variety of larynx problems, including hoarseness, monotone voice, or complete loss of voice. Other lesions may cause difficulty in swallowing or impaired gastrointestinal tract motility.

Table 13.8   Cranial Nerves (continued)

CN XI ACCESSORY NERVE (ak-ses′ō-rē)

Description	Innervates trapezius and sternocleidomastoid muscles; formerly called the *spinal accessory nerve*
Somatic motor function	Cranial root: Travels with CN X axons to pharynx Spinal root: Motor nuclei in spinal cord
Origin	Cranial root: Nucleus in medulla oblongata Spinal root: Nucleus in spinal cord
Pathway	Spinal root travels superiorly to enter skull through foramen magnum; there, cranial and spinal roots merge and leave the skull via jugular foramen. Once outside the skull, cranial root splits to travel with CN X (vagus) to innervate pharynx muscles, and spinal root travels to sternocleidomastoid and trapezius.
Conditions caused by nerve damage	Paralysis of trapezius and sternocleidomastoid, resulting in difficulty in elevating shoulder (trapezius function) or turning head to opposite site (sternocleidomastoid function)

CN XII HYPOGLOSSAL NERVE (hī-pō-glos′ăl; *hypo* = below, *glossus* = tongue)

Description	Innervates intrinsic and extrinsic tongue muscles; name means "under the tongue"
Somatic motor function	Innervates intrinsic and extrinsic tongue muscles
Origin	Hypoglossal nucleus in medulla oblongata
Pathway	Leaves cranium via hypoglossal canal; travels inferior to mandible and to inferior surface of tongue
Conditions caused by nerve damage	Swallowing and speech difficulties due to impaired tongue movement; if a single hypoglossal nerve (either left or right) is paralyzed, a protruded (stuck out) tongue deviates to the side of the damaged nerve

- The brain is composed of the cerebrum, diencephalon, brainstem, and cerebellum. Twelve cranial nerves are associated with the brain.

13.1 Brain Development and Organization 480

13.1a Overview of Brain Anatomy 480

- The brain has two cerebral hemispheres that exhibit folds called gyri with shallow sulci and deep fissures in between. Rostral refers to the anterior region of the brain and caudal to the posterior region.

13.1b Development of Brain Divisions 480

- Three primary vesicles (prosencephalon, mesencephalon, and rhombencephalon) form from the neural tube by the late fourth week of development.

- Five secondary vesicles (telencephalon, diencephalon, mesencephalon, metencephalon, and myelencephalon) form from the primary vesicles by the fifth week of development.

13.1c Gray Matter and White Matter Distribution 488

- Most gray matter (composed of motor neuron and interneuron cell bodies, dendrites, and unmyelinated axons) is located on the periphery of the brain, whereas the white matter (composed primarily of myelinated axons) is located more internally.

13.2 Protection and Support of the Brain 490

- The brain is protected and isolated by the cranium, cranial meninges, cerebrospinal fluid, and a blood-brain barrier.

13.2a Cranial Meninges 490

- The cranial meninges are the pia mater, arachnoid mater, and dura mater.

- The cranial dural septa are folds of dura mater that project between the major parts of the brain and stabilize the brain's position.

13.2b Brain Ventricles 492

- Fluid-filled spaces in the brain are the paired lateral ventricles, the third ventricle, the cerebral aqueduct, and the fourth ventricle.

13.2c Cerebrospinal Fluid 492

- Cerebrospinal fluid (CSF) is a clear fluid that provides buoyancy, protection, and a stable environment for the brain and spinal cord.

- The choroid plexus (formed from ependymal cells and capillaries) produces CSF in the ventricles.

- CSF leaves the ventricles and enters the subarachnoid space, where it circulates around the brain and spinal cord. Excess CSF returns to the venous circulation through the arachnoid villi.

13.2d Blood-Brain Barrier 495

- The blood-brain barrier regulates movement of materials between the blood and the interstitial fluid of the brain.

13.3 Cerebrum 496

- The cerebrum is the center of our sensory perception, thought, memory, judgement, and voluntary motor actions.

13.3a Cerebral Hemispheres 496

- The left and right cerebral hemispheres are separated by a longitudinal fissure.

13.3b Lobes of the Cerebrum 496

- Each hemisphere contains five lobes: four superficial lobes (frontal, parietal, temporal, occipital lobes) and the insula, which is not visible from the surface.

13.3c Functional Areas of the Cerebrum 497

- The primary motor cortex in the frontal lobe directs voluntary movements.

- The primary somatosensory cortex in the parietal lobe collects somatic sensory information.

- Other primary cortices and association areas are housed in each of the five lobes.

13.3d Central White Matter 502

- The central white matter contains three major groups of axons: association tracts, commissural tracts, and projection tracts.

13.3e Cerebral Lateralization 503

- The left hemisphere is the categorical hemisphere in most individuals, and the right is the representational hemisphere.

13.3f Cerebral Nuclei 504

- The cerebral nuclei are masses of gray matter located within the central white matter.

13.4 Diencephalon 505

- The diencephalon is composed of the epithalamus, thalamus, and hypothalamus.

13.4a Epithalamus 505

- The epithalamus forms part of the posterior roof of the diencephalon; it contains the pineal gland (which secretes melatonin) and habenular nuclei (help relay signals from the limbic system to the midbrain).

13.4b Thalamus 505

- The thalamus is the main relay point for integrating, assimilating, and amplifying sensory signals sent to the cerebrum.

13.4c Hypothalamus 508

- The hypothalamus oversees the endocrine and autonomic nervous systems and houses many control and integrative centers.

CHALLENGE YOURSELF

Do You Know the Basics?

_____ 1. Which cranial nerve is responsible for innervating the intrinsic and extrinsic tongue muscles?

    a. accessory (CN XI)

    b. glossopharyngeal (CN IX)

    c. trigeminal (CN V)

    d. hypoglossal (CN XII)

_____ 2. The subdivision of the brain that does not initiate somatic motor movements, but rather coordinates and fine-tunes those movements, is the

    a. medulla oblongata.

    b. cerebrum.

    c. cerebellum.

    d. diencephalon.

3. Which of these is the least likely to affect information transfer from STM (short-term memory) to LTM (long-term memory)?

   a. emotional state
   b. repetition or rehearsal
   c. auditory association cortex
   d. cerebral nuclei

4. Which of the following is *not* a function of the hypothalamus?

   a. controls endocrine system
   b. regulates sleep-wake cycle
   c. controls autonomic nervous system
   d. initiates voluntary skeletal muscle movement

5. Which of the following statements is false about the choroid plexus?

   a. It is located within the ventricles of the brain.
   b. It is composed of ependymal cells and blood capillaries.
   c. It receives and filters all sensory information.
   d. It produces and circulates cerebrospinal fluid.

6. The _____ are descending motor tracts on the anterolateral surface of the midbrain.

   a. cerebral peduncles
   b. inferior colliculi
   c. pyramids
   d. tegmenta

7. Which cerebral lobe is located immediately posterior to the central sulcus and superior to the lateral sulcus?

   a. frontal lobe
   b. parietal lobe
   c. temporal lobe
   d. occipital lobe

8. The primary motor cortex is located in which cerebral structure?

   a. precentral gyrus
   b. postcentral gyrus
   c. motor speech area
   d. prefrontal cortex

9. The _____ are the isolated, innermost gray matter areas near the base of the cerebrum, inferior to the lateral ventricles.

   a. auditory association areas
   b. cerebral nuclei
   c. substantia nigra
   d. corpus callosum axons

10. Which structure contains some autonomic centers involved in regulating respiration?

    a. pons
    b. superior colliculi
    c. cerebellum
    d. thalamus

11. List the five secondary brain vesicles, and describe which adult brain structures are formed from each.

12. Describe (a) how and where the cerebrospinal fluid is formed, (b) its subsequent circulation, and (c) how and where it is reabsorbed into the vascular system.

13. Which specific area of the brain may be impaired if you cannot tell the difference between a smooth and a rough surface using your hands only?

14. What activities occur in the visual association area?

15. Describe the relationship between the cerebral nuclei and the cerebellum in motor activities.

16. List the functions of the hypothalamus.

17. After a severe blow to the head, a patient suddenly lacks the ability to control his emotions and seems unable to tell if he is dehydrated. The attending physician should suspect damage to or a lesion within what general region of the brain?

18. Describe the pathway by which the pressure applied to the right hand during a handshake is transmitted and perceived in the left primary somatosensory cortex.

19. Identify the components of the limbic system.

20. During surgery to remove a tumor from the occipital lobe of the left cerebrum, a surgeon must cut into the brain to reach the tumor. List in order (starting with the covering skin) all of the layers that must be cut through to reach the tumor.

Can You Apply What You've Learned?

Use the following paragraph to answer questions 1 and 2.

Alex went to the dentist to get a cavity filled. The dentist used an anesthetic to numb the teeth prior to drilling.

1. Which nerve likely was anesthetized?

   a. CN IV (trochlear)
   b. CN V (trigeminal)
   c. CN VII (facial)
   d. CN IX (glossopharyngeal)

2. After the filling was inserted, Alex's gums on the same side of the tooth remained numb for a short while. What other problems may Alex temporarily experience until the anesthetic wears off?

   a. inability to close the mouth
   b. inability to protrude the tongue
   c. dry mouth
   d. numbness of the lips

Use the following paragraph to answer questions 3 and 4.

Shannon was the pitcher on her softball team. During one game, a batter hit the ball and it ricocheted off the left side of Shannon's head, knocking her temporarily unconscious. She eventually regained consciousness, but experienced severe pain near her left temple. Within a few hours, Shannon had trouble moving her right upper limb and became lethargic. Her team captain brought her to the emergency room, where the physician diagnosed her with an epidural hematoma.

3. An epidural hematoma causes an accumulation of blood to develop between what two structures?

   a. the skull and the periosteal layer of the dura mater
   b. the periosteal and meningeal layers of the dura mater
   c. the meningeal layer of the dura mater and the arachnoid mater
   d. the arachnoid mater and the pia mater

4. Why did Shannon experience the problems with her right upper limb? The hematoma likely was impinging on what brain structure?

   a. left precentral gyrus   c. left cerebral nuclei
   b. left postcentral gyrus   d. left cerebellum

5. A 25-year-old male named Carlos went to the optometrist with the complaint of double vision (diplopia). The optometrist performed various eye tests on Carlos. Carlos was able to read an eye chart with each individual eye but experienced the double vision when he tried to use both eyes to focus. The optometrist noticed that when he had Carlos look laterally with each eye, Carlos's right eye did not move as far laterally as his left could. Based on these tests, the optometrist suspected that the muscle innervated by _____ was not working properly.

   a. CN II (optic)   c. CN IV (trochlear)
   b. CN III (oculomotor)   d. CV VI (abducens)

Can You Synthesize What You've Learned?

1. Peyton felt strange when she awoke one morning. She could not hold a pen in her right hand when trying to write an entry in her diary, and her muscles were noticeably weaker on the right side of her body. Additionally, her husband noticed that she was slurring her speech, so he took her to the emergency room. What does the ER physician suspect has occurred? Where in the brain might the physician suspect that abnormal activity or perhaps a lesion is located, and why?

2. Parkinson disease is the result of decreased levels of the neurotransmitter dopamine in the brain. However, these patients can't take dopamine in drug form because the drug cannot reach the brain. What anatomic structure prevents the drug from reaching the brain? How could these same anatomic structures be beneficial to an individual under different circumstances?

3. During a robbery at his convenience store, Dustin was shot in the right cerebral hemisphere. He survived, although some specific functions were impaired. Would Dustin have been more likely or less likely to have survived if he had been shot in the medulla oblongata? Why?

INTEGRATE

ONLINE STUDY TOOLS

www.mhhe.com/mckinleyap

Clinical Case Study: A Case of the Shaking Palsy in an Elderly Woman

Interactive Questions: This chapter's content is served up in a number of multimedia question formats for student study.

LearnSmart: Topics and terminology include brain development and organization; protection and support of the brain; cerebrum; diencephalon; brainstem; cerebellum; functional brain systems; integrative functions and higher-order brain functions; cranial nerves

Anatomy & Physiology Revealed: Topics include brain; divisions of the brain; meninges; CSF flow; MRI; thalamus; hypothalamus; brainstem; cerebral peduncle; cerebellum; hippocampus; inferior brain

chapter 14

Nervous System: Spinal Cord and Spinal Nerves

The spinal cord provides a vital link between the brain and the rest of the body, and yet it exhibits some functional independence from the brain. The spinal cord and its attached spinal nerves serve two important functions. First, they are a pathway for sensory and motor nerve signals. Second, the spinal cord and spinal nerves are responsible for reflexes, which are our quickest reactions to a stimulus. This chapter describes the anatomy of the spinal cord and the integrative activities that occur there.

A neurologist is a medical doctor who specializes in the diagnosis and treatment of nervous system disorders. A typical neurologic exam involves testing a patient's reflexes and detecting the patient's perception of various sensations. Hyperactive or hypoactive reflexes, or loss of sensation in specific dermatomes, may help pinpoint disorders in individual nerves, specific segments of the spinal cord, or regions of the brain. The neurologist has a thorough knowledge of the motor and sensory components of the body's nerves, and uses this information to aid her in an accurate diagnosis of the patient.

Anatomy & Physiology | REVEALED®
aprevealed.com

Module 7: Nervous System

14.1 Spinal Cord Gross Anatomy

⚚ LEARNING OBJECTIVES

1. Identify the five anatomic subdivisions of the spinal cord.
2. Explain how the cauda equina arises in development.
3. Describe the spinal nerves and their identification.

A typical adult spinal cord is approximately ¾ of an inch in diameter and ranges between 42 and 45 centimeters (cm) (16 to 18 inches) in length. It extends inferiorly from the brain through the vertebral canal and ends at the level of the L_1 vertebra. Coming off of the spinal cord are rootlets that will form spinal nerves. Some spinal nerves form nerve plexuses (interweaving of spinal nerves). The spinal cord may be subdivided into the following parts (figure 14.1):

- The **cervical part** is the superiormost part of the spinal cord. It is continuous with the medulla oblongata. The cervical part contains neurons whose axons contribute to the cervical spinal nerves (figure 14.1b).
- The **thoracic part** lies inferior to the cervical part. It contains the neurons for the thoracic spinal nerves.

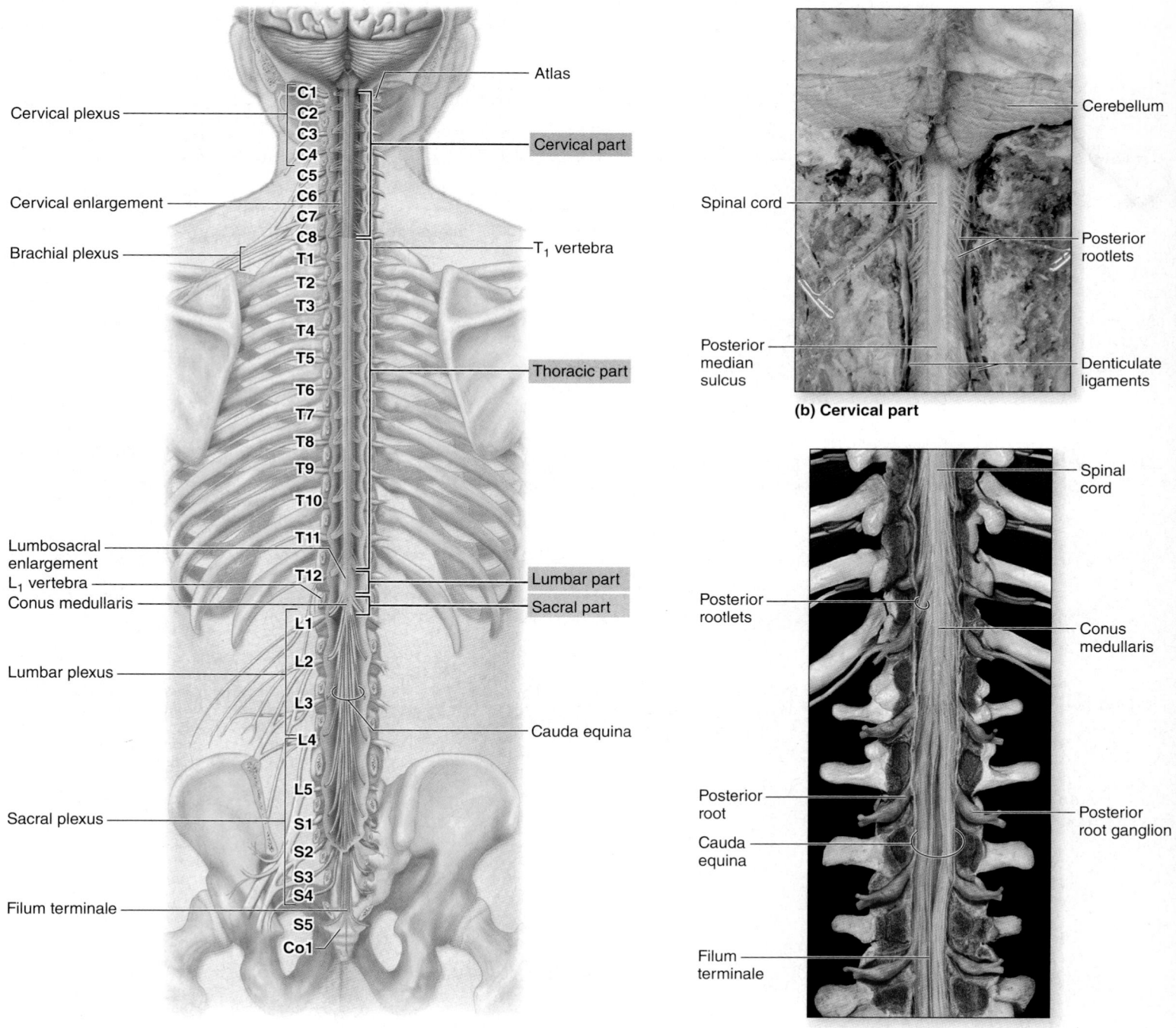

(a) Posterior view

(b) Cervical part

(c) Conus medullaris and cauda equina

Figure 14.1 Gross Anatomy of the Spinal Cord. The spinal cord extends inferiorly from the medulla oblongata through the vertebral canal. (a) The vertebral arches have been removed to reveal the anatomy of the adult spinal cord and its spinal nerves. (b) Cadaver photo of the cervical part of the spinal cord. (c) Cadaver photo of the conus medullaris and the cauda equina. **AP|R**

- The **lumbar part** is a shorter segment of the spinal cord that contains the neurons for the lumbar spinal nerves.
- The **sacral part** lies inferior to the lumbar part and contains neurons for the sacral spinal nerves.
- The **coccygeal** (kok-sij´ē-ăl) **part** is the most inferior tip of the spinal cord. (Some textbooks consider this part a portion of the sacral part of the spinal cord.) One pair of coccygeal spinal nerves arises from this part.

Note that the different *parts* of the spinal cord do not match up exactly with the *vertebrae* of the same name. For example, the lumbar part of the spinal cord is actually closer to the inferior, or lower, thoracic vertebrae than to the lumbar vertebrae. This discrepancy is due to the fact that the vertebrae growth continued longer than the growth of the spinal cord itself. Thus, the spinal cord in an adult is shorter than the vertebral canal that houses it.

The tapering inferior end of the spinal cord is called the **conus medullaris** (kō´nŭs med-ū-lăr´is). The conus medullaris marks the official "end" of the spinal cord proper (usually at the level of the first lumbar vertebra). Inferior to this level, nerve roots (groups of axons) collectively called the **cauda equina** (kaw´dă; *cauda* = tail; ē-kwī´nă; *equus* = horse) project inferiorly from the spinal cord. These nerve roots are so named because they resemble a horse's tail. Within the cauda equina is the **filum terminale** (fi´lŭm ter´mi-nă-lē; *terminus* = end). The filum terminale is a thin strand of pia mater that helps anchor the conus medullaris to the coccyx. Figure 14.1c shows the conus medullaris and the cauda equina.

The spinal cord is associated with 31 pairs of spinal nerves. Spinal nerves are considered *mixed nerves* because they contain

Table 14.1	Cross Sections of Representative Parts of the Spinal Cord			
Spinal Cord Part	**General Size (Diameter)**	**General Shape**	**White Matter/ Gray Matter Ratio**	**Other Characteristics**
Cervical AP|R	Largest of all spinal cord parts (13–14 mm in transverse diameter)	Oval; slightly flattened on both anterior and posterior surfaces	Large proportion of white matter compared to gray matter	In superior segments (C1–C5), anterior horns are relatively small, and posterior horns are relatively large In inferior segments (C6–C8), anterior horns are larger and posterior horns are even more enlarged
Thoracic AP|R	Smaller than the cervical part (9–11 mm in transverse diameter)	Oval; still slightly flattened anteriorly and posteriorly	Larger proportion of white matter than gray matter	Anterior and posterior horns are enlarged only in first thoracic segment; small lateral horns are visible
Lumbar AP|R	Slightly larger than the thoracic part (11–13 mm in transverse diameter)	Less oval, almost circular	Relative amount of white matter is reduced both in proportion to gray matter and in comparison to cervical part	Anterior and posterior horns are very large; small lateral horns present in first two sections of lumbar part only
Sacral AP|R	Very small	Almost circular	Proportion of gray matter to white matter is largest in this spinal cord part	Anterior and posterior horns relatively large compared to the size of the cross section

both sensory axons that relay nerve signals from receptors to the CNS and motor axons that conduct nerve signals from the CNS to effectors (muscles and glands). Each spinal nerve is identified by the first letter of the spinal cord part to which it attaches combined with a number. Thus, each side of the spinal cord contains 8 cervical nerves (called C1–C8), 12 thoracic nerves (T1–T12), 5 lumbar nerves (L1–L5), 5 sacral nerves (S1–S5), and 1 coccygeal nerve (Co1). Spinal nerve names can be distinguished from cranial nerve names (discussed in section 13.9) because cranial nerves are designated by CN followed by a roman numeral.

Viewed in cross section, the spinal cord is roughly cylindrical, but slightly flattened both posteriorly and anteriorly. Its external surface has two longitudinal depressions: a narrow groove, the **posterior** (or *dorsal*) **median sulcus,** dips internally on the posterior surface; and a slightly wider groove, the **anterior** (or *ventral*) **median fissure,** is observed on its anterior surface.

Cross-sectional views of the spinal cord vary, depending upon the part in which the section was taken (table 14.1). These subtle differences make identifying specific spinal cross sections a bit easier. For example, the diameter of the spinal cord changes along its length because the amount of gray matter and white matter and the function of the cord vary in different parts. Therefore, the spinal cord parts that control the upper and lower limbs are larger because more neuron cell bodies are located there, and more space is occupied by axons and dendrites. The **cervical enlargement,** located in the inferior cervical part of the spinal cord, contains the neurons that innervate the upper limbs. The **lumbosacral enlargement** extends through the mid-lumbar part of the spinal cord and innervates the lower limbs.

WHAT DID YOU LEARN?

1 What are the total number of pairs of spinal nerves, and what are the specific types of spinal nerves?

2 What are the functions of the cervical and lumbosacral enlargements?

14.2 Protection and Support of the Spinal Cord

LEARNING OBJECTIVES

1. Describe the locations and function of the spinal cord meninges.

2. Compare and contrast the three spaces associated with the spinal cord meninges.

The spinal cord is protected and encapsulated by **spinal cord meninges** (mĕ-nin'jes, mē'nin-jēz; sing., *meninx,* men'ingks; membrane), which are continuous with the cranial meninges described in section 13.2a. In addition, spaces between some of the meninges have clinical significance. The structures and spaces (both real and

Skin
Subcutaneous layer
Back muscles
Ligamentum flavum
Epidural space
Dura mater and arachnoid mater
Lumbar puncture needle
Subarachnoid space
Cauda equina
L_3
L_4
Vertebral canal

Site of needle insertion for a lumbar puncture.

Posterior

Spinous process of vertebra

Epidural space

Dura mater

Denticulate ligament

Spinal nerve

Subdural space
Arachnoid mater
Subarachnoid space

Pia mater

Intervertebral foramen

Spinal cord

Body of vertebra

Anterior

(a) Cross section of vertebra and spinal cord

White matter
Gray matter

Posterior median sulcus
Central canal
Anterior median fissure
Pia mater

Posterior rootlets

Posterior root

Posterior root ganglion

Spinal nerve

Subarachnoid space

Arachnoid mater

Anterior root

Anterior rootlets

Subdural space

Dura mater

(b) Anterior view

Figure 14.2 Spinal Meninges and Structure of the Spinal Cord. (*a*) A cross section of the spinal cord shows the relationship between the meningeal layers and the superficial landmarks of the spinal cord and vertebral column. (*b*) Anterior view shows the spinal cord and meninges. AP|R potential) that encircle the spinal cord, listed from outermost to innermost, are as follows: vertebra, epidural space, dura mater, subdural space, arachnoid mater, subarachnoid space, and finally the pia mater (**figure 14.2**).

The **epidural** (ep-i-dū'răl) **space** lies between the dura mater and the inner walls of the vertebra, and houses areolar connective tissue, blood vessels, and adipose connective tissue. Epidural anesthetics, such as may be used to lessen pain during childbirth, are introduced into this space. Deep to the epidural space is the most external of the meninges, the **dura mater.** Although the cranial dura mater has an outer periosteal layer and an inner meningeal layer, the spinal dura mater consists of just one layer. The dura mater provides stability to the spinal cord. Additionally, at each intervertebral foramen, the dura mater extends between adjacent vertebrae and fuses with the connective tissue layers that surround the spinal nerves.

WHAT DO YOU THINK?

1 Why doesn't the spinal dura mater have two layers as the cranial dura mater does? What structures that are formed from cranial dura mater must be missing around the spinal cord?

In most anatomic and histologic preparations, a narrow **subdural space** separates the dura mater from the **arachnoid mater.** This space is found only in tissue preparations, and in life it is merely a potential space. Deep to the arachnoid mater is the **subarachnoid space,** which is a space filled with **cerebrospinal fluid (CSF).** The **pia mater,** deep to the subarachnoid space, is a delicate, innermost meningeal layer composed of elastic and collagen fibers. This meninx directly adheres to the spinal cord and supports some of the blood vessels supplying the spinal cord. **Denticulate** (den-tik'ū-lāt; *dentatus* = toothed) **ligaments** are paired, lateral triangular extensions of the spinal pia mater that attach to the dura mater. These ligaments help suspend and anchor the spinal cord laterally (see figures 14.1*b* and 14.2*a*).

WHAT DID YOU LEARN?

3 Where are the epidural, subdural, and subarachnoid spaces located? Which contains CSF?

14.3 Sectional Anatomy of the Spinal Cord

The spinal cord is partitioned into an inner gray matter region and an outer white matter region (**figure 14.3**). The gray matter is dominated by the dendrites and cell bodies of neurons and glial cells and unmyelinated axons, whereas the white matter is composed primarily of myelinated axons that extend to and from the brain.

14.3a Distribution of Gray Matter

LEARNING OBJECTIVES

1. Distinguish the four anatomic locations of gray matter in the spinal cord.
2. Name the types of neurons and functional groups (nuclei) found in each gray matter region.

The **gray matter** in the spinal cord is centrally located, and its shape resembles a letter H, or a butterfly. The gray matter may be subdivided into the following components: anterior horns, lateral horns, posterior horns, and the gray commissure.

Anterior horns are the left and right anterior masses of gray matter. The anterior horns primarily house the *cell bodies of somatic motor neurons,* which innervate skeletal muscle. **Lateral horns** are found in the T1–L2 parts of the spinal cord only. The lateral horns contain the *cell bodies of autonomic motor neurons,* which innervate cardiac muscle, smooth muscle, and glands. **Posterior horns** are the left and right posterior masses of gray matter. The *axons of sensory neurons* and the *cell bodies of interneurons* are located in the posterior horns. (Note that the cell bodies of these sensory neurons are not found in the posterior horns; rather, they are located in the posterior root ganglia, which are described later in this chapter). The **gray commissure** (kom'i-shūr; *commissura* = a seam) is a horizontal bar of gray matter that surrounds a narrow **central canal.**

(a) Gray and white matter

White matter
- Posterior funiculus
- Lateral funiculus
- White commissure
- Anterior funiculus

Posterior

Central canal — Posterior median sulcus

Gray matter
- Posterior horn
- Gray commissure
- Lateral horn
- Anterior horn

Anterior median fissure

Anterior

(b) Transverse section

Posterior

White matter
- Central canal

Gray matter
- Posterior horn
- Gray commissure
- Lateral horn
- Anterior horn

Anterior

Figure 14.3 Gray Matter and White Matter Organization in the Spinal Cord. (*a*) The gray matter is centrally located, and the white matter is externally located. (*b*) Histology of a transverse section of the spinal cord. AP|R

The gray commissure primarily contains unmyelinated axons and serves as a communication route between the right and left sides of the gray matter.

Within these parts of gray matter are various functional groups of neuron cell bodies called **nuclei (figure 14.4)**. **Sensory nuclei** in the posterior horns contain interneuron cell bodies. **Somatic sensory nuclei** receive nerve signals from sensory receptors, such as pain or pressure receptors in the skin, while **visceral sensory nuclei** receive nerve signals from blood vessels and viscera (e.g., from stretched smooth muscle within viscera). **Motor nuclei** in the anterior and lateral horns contain motor neuron cell bodies that send nerve signals to muscles and glands. The **somatic motor nuclei** in the anterior horn innervate skeletal muscle, while the **autonomic motor nuclei** in the lateral horns innervate smooth muscle, cardiac muscle, and glands.

WHAT DID YOU LEARN?

4 What nervous system structures are found in the anterior, lateral, and posterior horns?

14.3b Distribution of White Matter

LEARNING OBJECTIVES

3. Identify the location of white matter in the spinal cord.
4. Name the three anatomic divisions of the white matter, and explain their general composition.

The white matter of the spinal cord is external to the gray matter. White matter on each side of the cord is also partitioned into three regions, each called a **funiculus** (fū-nik′ū-lŭs; pl. *funiculi*,[1] fū-nik′ū-lī; *funis* = cord) (see figure 14.3). A **posterior funiculus** lies between the posterior gray horns on the posterior side of the cord and the posterior median sulcus. The **lateral funiculus** is the white matter region on each lateral side of the spinal cord. The **anterior funiculus** is composed of tracts of white matter that occupy the space on each anterior side of the cord between the anterior

---

1. Note: Anterior and lateral funiculi were formerly called *columns*. The Federative Committee on Anatomical Terminology (FCAT) now states that the term "column" refers to structures within the gray matter of the spinal cord, while "funiculus" refers to the white matter regions.

gray horns and the anterior median fissure; the anterior funiculi are interconnected by the **white commissure.**

The axons within each white matter funiculus are organized into smaller structural units called **tracts** (trakt; *tractus* = a drawing out) or **fasciculi** (fă-sik′ū-lī; *fascis* = bundle). Individual tracts conduct either sensory nerve signals (ascending tracts from the spinal cord to the brain) or motor nerve signals (descending tracts from the brain to the spinal cord) only. Each funiculus (posterior, lateral, and anterior) contains both ascending and descending tracts. Thus, each funiculus contains both motor and sensory axons.

WHAT DID YOU LEARN?

5 What are the three types of funiculi? List the components in each.

14.4 Spinal Cord Conduction Pathways

The CNS communicates with peripheral body structures through **pathways.** These pathways conduct either sensory nerve signals from receptors or motor nerve signals to effectors; processing and integration occur along them. These pathways travel through the white matter of the spinal cord as they connect various CNS regions with spinal nerves.

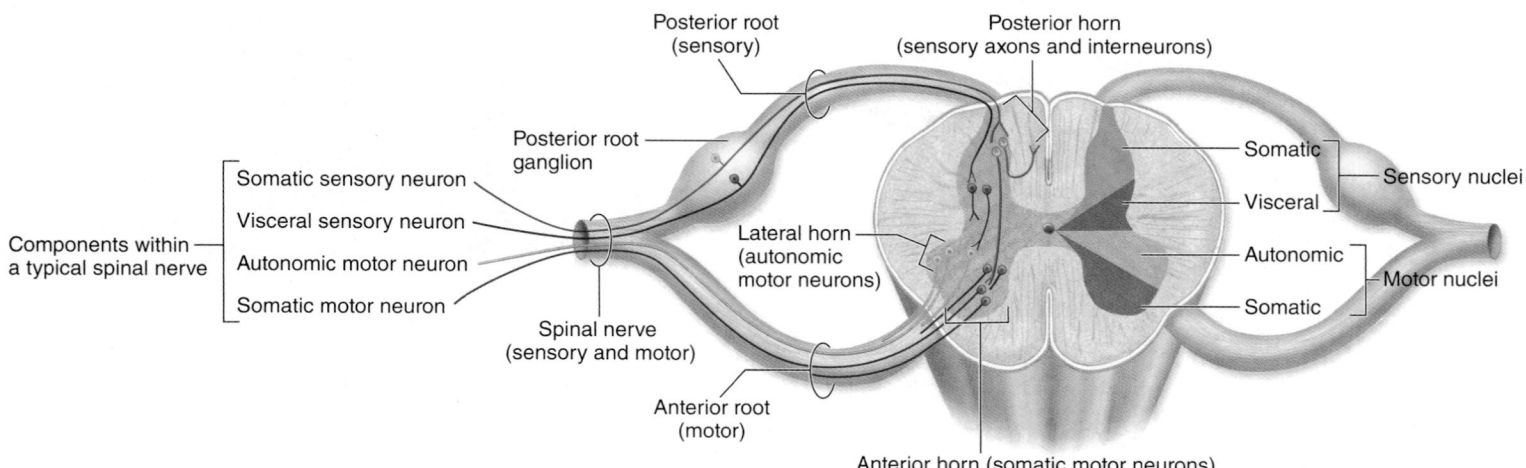

Figure 14.4 Neuron Pathways and Nuclei Locations. The collections of neuron cell bodies within the CNS form specific nuclei. Neurons are color-coded on the left side of the drawing; their respective nuclei are color-coded on the right side of the drawing.

14.4a Overview of Conduction Pathways

✓ LEARNING OBJECTIVES

1. Name the components of a conduction pathway and list the features common to all pathways.
2. Compare and contrast sensory and motor pathways.

A pathway consists of a tract and a nucleus. Recall from table 13.2 that **tracts** are groups or bundles of axons that travel together in the CNS. Each tract may work with multiple nuclei groups in the CNS. A **nucleus** is a collection of neuron cell bodies located within the CNS.

Nervous system pathways are sensory or motor. **Sensory pathways** are also called *ascending pathways* because the nerve signals transmitted by sensory receptors ascends through the spinal cord to the brain. **Motor pathways** are also called *descending pathways* because they transmit nerve signals that descend from the brain through the spinal cord to muscles or glands. Most nervous system pathways share several general characteristics:

- Most pathways **decussate** (dē-kŭ-sāt'; *decusseo* = to make in the form of an X) (cross over) from one side of the body to the other side at some point in its travels. This means that the left side of the brain processes information from the right side of the body, and vice versa. The term **contralateral** (kon-tră-lat′er-ăl; *contra* = opposite, *latus* = side) is used to indicate the relationship to the opposite side, whereas the term **ipsilateral** (ip-si-lat′er-ăl; *ipse* = same) means the same side. Over 90% of all pathways decussate, although the point at which decussation occurs can vary slightly from pathway to pathway.
- All pathways are composed of paired tracts. A pathway on the left side of the CNS has a matching tract on the right side of the CNS.
- Most pathways are composed of a series of two or three neurons that work together. Sensory pathways have primary neurons, secondary neurons, and sometimes tertiary neurons that facilitate the pathway's functioning. In contrast, motor pathways use an upper motor neuron and a lower motor neuron. The cell bodies of these neurons are located in the nuclei associated with each pathway.

💡 WHAT DID YOU LEARN?

6 What are three characteristics common to all nervous system pathways?

14.4b Sensory Pathways

✓ LEARNING OBJECTIVES

3. Define a sensory pathway, and describe its action.
4. List the neurons in the sensory pathway chain, and describe their roles.
5. Describe the three major somatosensory pathways.

Sensory pathways are ascending pathways that conduct information about limb proprioception and the sensations of touch, temperature, pressure, and pain. *Somatosensory pathways* process stimuli received from receptors within the skin, muscles, and joints, while *viscerosensory pathways* process stimuli received from the viscera.

Sensory pathways use a series of two or three neurons to transmit nerve signals from the body to the brain:

- The first neuron in this chain is the **primary neuron** (or *first-order neuron*). The dendrites of this sensory neuron are part of the receptor that detects a specific stimulus. The cell bodies of primary neurons reside in the posterior root ganglia of spinal nerves. The axon of the primary neuron projects to a secondary neuron within the CNS.
- The **secondary neuron** (or *second-order neuron*) is an interneuron. The cell body of this neuron resides within either the posterior horn of the spinal cord or a brainstem nucleus. The axon of a secondary neuron projects either to the thalamus for conscious sensations or to the cerebellum for unconscious proprioception. The secondary neuron to the thalamus synapses with the tertiary neuron, the third neuron in the chain.
  - The **tertiary neuron** (or *third-order neuron*) is also an interneuron, and its cell body resides within the thalamus. Recall that the thalamus is the central processing and coding center for almost all sensory information; thus, it makes sense (pun intended!) that the last neuron in a sensory pathway chain resides in the thalamus. The axon of the tertiary neuron projects to the primary somatosensory cortex of the parietal lobe (see section 13.3c).

The three major types of **somatosensory pathways** are the posterior funiculus–medial lemniscal pathway, the anterolateral pathway, and the spinocerebellar pathway (**figure 14.5**).

Posterior

Posterior funiculus–medial lemniscal pathway
— Fasciculus gracilis
— Fasciculus cuneatus

Spinocerebellar pathway
— Posterior spinocerebellar tract
— Anterior spinocerebellar tract

Anterolateral pathway
— Lateral spinothalamic tract
— Anterior spinothalamic tract

Anterior

Figure 14.5 Sensory Pathways in the Spinal Cord. The major sensory (ascending) pathways are shown in various shades of blue, and are bilaterally symmetrical tracts. The major motor tracts are indicated in pale red.

Posterior Funiculus–Medial Lemniscal Pathway

The **posterior funiculus–medial lemniscal pathway** projects through the spinal cord, brainstem, and thalamus before terminating within the cerebral cortex **(figure 14.6)**. Its name derives from two components: the tracts within the spinal cord, collectively called the **posterior funiculus,** and the tracts within the brainstem, collectively called the **medial lemniscus** (lem-nis′kŭs; *lemniskos* = ribbon). This pathway conducts sensory stimuli concerned with proprioceptive (posture and balance) information about limb position and discriminative touch, precise pressure, and vibration sensations.

The posterior funiculus–medial lemniscal pathway uses a chain of three neurons to signal the brain about a specific stimulus. Axons of the primary neurons reside in spinal nerves and reach the CNS through the posterior roots of spinal nerves. Upon entering the spinal cord, these axons ascend within a specific posterior funiculus, either the **fasciculus cuneatus** (kū′nē-ā-tŭs; *cuneus* = wedge) or the **fasciculus gracilis.** Sensory axons ascending within the posterior funiculi synapse on secondary neuron cell bodies housed within a posterior funiculus nucleus in the medulla oblongata. These secondary neurons then project axons to relay the incoming nerve signals to the thalamus on the opposite side of the brain through the medial lemniscus. Decussation occurs after secondary neuron axons exit their specific nuclei within the medulla oblongata and before they enter the medial lemniscus.

The axons of the secondary neurons synapse on cell bodies of the tertiary neurons within the thalamus, where the sensory information is sorted according to the part of the body involved (somatotopically). Axons from these tertiary neurons transmit nerve signals to a specific location of the primary somatosensory cortex (see figure 13.13).

Anterolateral Pathway

The **anterolateral pathway** (or *spinothalamic pathway*) is located in the anterior and lateral white funiculi of the spinal cord **(figure 14.7)**. It is composed of the **anterior spinothalamic tract** and the **lateral spinothalamic tract.** Axons projecting from primary neurons enter the spinal cord and synapse on secondary neurons within the posterior horns. Axons within these pathways conduct nerve signals related to crude touch and pressure as well as pain and temperature. Typically, sensations that require us to act in response to the stimu-

Figure 14.6 Posterior Funiculus–Medial Lemniscal Pathway. This pathway conducts sensory information about limb position, fine touch, precise pressure, and vibration. This pathway is bilaterally symmetrical—but to avoid confusion, only sensory input from the right side of the body is shown here. Decussation of axons occurs in the medulla oblongata. The primary neuron is purple, the secondary neuron is dark blue, and the tertiary neuron is light green.

Figure 14.7 Anterolateral Pathway. This pathway conducts crude touch, pressure, pain, and temperature sensations toward the brain. Decussation of axons occurs at the level where the primary neuron axon enters the spinal cord. The primary neuron is purple, the secondary neuron is dark blue, and the tertiary neuron is light green.

Cerebellum

Pons

Secondary neuron

Posterior spinocerebellar tract
Anterior spinocerebellar tract
Spinocerebellar pathway

Medulla oblongata

Proprioceptive input
from joints, muscles,
and tendons

Primary neuron

Spinal cord

Pathway direction

Figure 14.8 Spinocerebellar Pathway. This pathway conducts proprioceptive information to the cerebellum through both the anterior and posterior spinocerebellar tracts. Only some axons decussate, and these do so at the level where the primary neuron axon enters the spinal cord. Only primary (purple) and secondary (dark blue) neurons are found in this type of pathway.

lus (such as an itch that makes us want to scratch, or tickling that makes us jerk away) travel through the anterolateral pathway.

Axons of the secondary neurons in the anterolateral pathway decussate through the anterior white commissure and relay nerve signals to the opposite side of the spinal cord before ascending toward the brain. Secondary neuron axons synapse on tertiary neurons located within the thalamus. Axons from the tertiary neurons then conduct nerve signals to the appropriate part of the primary somatosensory cortex.

Spinocerebellar Pathway

The **spinocerebellar pathway** conducts proprioceptive information to the cerebellum for processing to coordinate body movements. The spinocerebellar pathway is composed of anterior and posterior spinocerebellar tracts; these are the major routes for transmitting postural input to the cerebellum (figure 14.8). Note that these spinocerebellar tracts are different from the other sensory pathways in that they do not use tertiary neurons; rather, they have only primary and secondary neurons. Information conducted in spinocerebellar pathways is integrated and acted on at a subconscious level.

Anterior spinocerebellar tracts conduct sensory nerve signals from the inferior parts of the trunk and the lower limbs. Their axons enter the cerebellum through the superior cerebellar peduncles. **Posterior spinocerebellar tracts** conduct sensory nerve signals from the lower limbs, parts of the trunk, and the upper limbs. Their axons enter the cerebellum through the inferior cerebellar peduncles.

Tables 14.2 and 14.3 summarize the characteristics of the three major types of sensory pathways.

WHAT DID YOU LEARN?

7   What are the locations and functions of primary, secondary, and tertiary neurons in sensory pathways?

8   What type of information does the posterior funiculus-medial lemniscal pathway receive?

Table 14.2	Locations and Functions of Principal Sensory Spinal Cord Pathways			
Sensory Pathway	**Funiculus**	**Origin of the Pathway Neuron**	**Termination**	**Function**
POSTERIOR FUNICULUS–MEDIAL LEMNISCAL PATHWAY				
Fasciculus cuneatus	Posterior	Upper limb, superior trunk, neck posterior head	Nucleus cuneatus of medulla oblongata	Conduct nerve signals for proprioceptive information about limb position and discriminative touch, precise pressure, and vibration sensation
Fasciculus gracilis	Posterior	Lower limb, inferior trunk	Nucleus gracilis of medulla oblongata	
ANTEROLATERAL PATHWAY				
Anterior spinothalamic	Anterior	Posterior horn interneurons	Thalamus: Tertiary neurons project to primary somatosensory cortex	Conducts nerve signals for crude touch and pressure
Lateral spinothalamic	Lateral	Posterior horn interneurons	Thalamus: Tertiary neurons project to primary somatosensory cortex	Conducts nerve signals for pain and temperature
SPINOCEREBELLAR PATHWAY				
Anterior spinocerebellar	Lateral	Posterior horn interneurons	Cerebellum	Conducts proprioceptive nerve signals from inferior regions of trunk and lower limbs
Posterior spinocerebellar	Lateral	Posterior horn interneurons	Cerebellum	Conducts proprioceptive nerve signals from lower limbs, regions of trunk, and upper limbs

	Table 14.3		Neuron Cell Body Locations and Decussation Sites of the Principal Sensory Spinal Cord Pathways	

Sensory Pathway	Location of Sensory Neuron Cell Bodies			Structures Involved with Decussation
	Primary Neuron	Secondary Neuron	Tertiary Neuron	
POSTERIOR FUNICULUS–MEDIAL LEMNISCAL PATHWAY				
Fasciculus cuneatus	Posterior root ganglion	Nucleus cuneatus	Thalamus	Axons of secondary neurons decussate prior to entry into medial lemniscus
Fasciculus gracilis	Posterior root ganglion	Nucleus gracilis	Thalamus	Axons of secondary neurons decussate prior to entry into medial lemniscus
ANTEROLATERAL PATHWAY				
Anterior spinothalamic Lateral spinothalamic	Posterior root ganglion	Posterior horn interneurons	Thalamus	Axons of secondary neurons decussate within spinal cord at level of entry
SPINOCEREBELLAR PATHWAY				
Anterior spinocerebellar Posterior spinocerebellar	Posterior root ganglion	Posterior horn interneurons	None	Anterior spinocerebellar: Some axons decussate in spinal cord and pons, while other axons do not decussate

Posterior spinocerebellar: Axons do not decussate |

14.4c Motor Pathways

✓ LEARNING OBJECTIVES

6. Define a motor pathway, and describe its actions.
7. Distinguish between an upper motor neuron and a lower motor neuron, based on function and cell body location.
8. Compare and contrast the direct and indirect motor pathways.

Motor pathways, or *descending tracts,* are descending pathways in the brain and spinal cord that control effectors. Here we discuss the motor pathways that specifically control skeletal muscle. Motor pathways may be formed from the cerebral cortex, cerebral nuclei, the cerebellum, descending projection tracts, or motor neurons. **(figure 14.9).**

Figure 14.9 Motor Pathways in the Spinal Cord. Motor (descending) pathways are bilateral pathways and shown here in red and orange. Sensory (ascending) pathways are shown for comparison in light blue. AP|R

Table 14.4	Principal Motor Spinal Cord Pathways			
Tract	Manner of Decussation	Destination of Upper Motor Neurons	Termination Site	Function
DIRECT PATHWAY				
Corticobulbar tracts	All cranial nerve motor nuclei receive bilateral (both ipsilateral and contralateral) input except CN VI, VII to the lower face, and XII. These nerves receive only contralateral input.	Brainstem only	Cranial nerve nuclei; reticular formation	Voluntary movement of cranial and facial muscles
Lateral corticospinal tracts	All decussate at the pyramids	Lateral funiculus	Gray matter region between posterior and anterior horns; anterior horn; all levels of spinal cord	Voluntary movement of appendicular muscles
Anterior corticospinal tracts	Decussation occurs in spinal cord at level of lower motor neuron cell body	Anterior funiculus	Gray matter region between posterior and anterior horns; anterior horn; cervical part of spinal cord	Voluntary movement of axial muscles
INDIRECT PATHWAY				
Lateral Pathway				
Rubrospinal tract	Decussate at ventral tegmentum	Lateral funiculus	Lateral region between posterior and anterior horns; anterior horn; cervical part of spinal cord	Regulates and controls precise discrete movements and tone in flexor muscles of the limbs
Medial Pathway				
Reticulospinal tract	No decussation (ipsilateral)	Anterior funiculus	Medial region between posterior and anterior horns; anterior horn; all parts of spinal cord	Controls reflexive movements related to posture and maintaining balance
Tectospinal tract	Decussate at dorsal tegmentum	Anterior funiculus	Medial region between posterior and anterior horns; anterior horn; cervical part of spinal cord	Regulates reflexive positional changes of the upper limbs, eyes, head, and neck due to visual and auditory stimuli
Vestibulospinal tract	Some decussate (contralateral) and some do not (ipsilateral)	Anterior funiculus	Medial region between posterior and anterior horns; anterior horn; medial tracts to cervical and superior thoracic parts of spinal cord; lateral tracts to all parts of spinal cord	Regulates reflexive muscular activity that helps maintain balance during sitting, standing, and walking

At least two motor neurons are present in the motor pathway: an upper motor neuron and a lower motor neuron **(table 14.4).** The cell body of an **upper motor neuron** is housed either within the cerebral cortex or a nucleus within the brainstem. Axons of the upper motor neuron synapse either directly on lower motor neurons, or on interneurons that synapse directly on lower motor neurons. The cell body of a **lower motor neuron** is housed either within the anterior horn of the spinal cord or within a brainstem cranial nerve nucleus. Axons of the lower motor neurons exit the CNS and project to the skeletal muscle to be innervated.

The two types of motor neurons perform different activities: The upper motor neuron either excites or inhibits the activity of the lower motor neuron, but the lower motor neuron is always excitatory because its axon connects directly to the skeletal muscle fibers.

The cell bodies of motor neurons and most interneurons involved in the innervation and control of limb and trunk muscles reside in the spinal cord anterior horn and the gray matter zone between the anterior horn and the posterior horn. The neurons that innervate the head and neck are located in the motor nuclei of cranial nerves and in the reticular formation.

Motor neuron axons form two types of motor pathways: direct pathways and indirect pathways. The direct pathways are responsible for conscious control of skeletal muscle activity; the indirect pathways are responsible for subconscious or unconscious control.

Direct Pathway

The **direct pathway,** also called the **pyramidal** (pi-ram'i-dal) **pathway** or *corticospinal pathway,* originates in the pyramidal cells of the primary motor cortex. The name *pyramidal* is derived from the shape of the upper motor neuron cell bodies, which have a tetrahedral, or pyramid-like, shape. Their axons project either into the brainstem or into the spinal cord to synapse directly on lower motor neurons.

The axons from pyramidal cell upper motor neurons descend through the internal capsule, enter the cerebral peduncles, and ultimately form two tracts of the direct pathway: the corticobulbar tracts and the corticospinal tracts.

Corticobulbar Tracts

The **corticobulbar** (kōr'ti-kō-būl'bar) **tracts** originate from the facial region of the motor homunculus within the primary motor cortex (see section 13.3c). The term *bulbar* means resembling a bulb and is used to indicate the embryonic rhombencephalon in the brainstem (see section 13.1b).

Axons of these upper motor neurons extend to the brainstem, where they synapse with lower motor neuron cell bodies that are housed within brainstem cranial nerve nuclei. Axons of these lower motor neurons help form some of the cranial nerves. Thus, note that these tracts differ from the others that we are about to discuss in that 1) they do not pass through the spinal cord, and 2) they involve cranial nerves (and not spinal nerves). We discuss them here because they are considered one type of direct pathway.

Corticospinal Tracts

The **corticospinal tracts** descend from the cerebral cortex through the brainstem and form the pyramids of the medulla oblongata. Then they continue into the spinal cord to synapse on lower motor neurons in the anterior horn of the spinal cord (**figure 14.10**). The corticospinal tracts are composed of two components: lateral and anterior corticospinal tracts.

The **lateral corticospinal tracts** include about 85% of the axons of the upper motor neurons that extend through the medulla oblongata. They decussate within the pyramids of the medulla oblongata and then form the lateral corticospinal tracts in the lateral funiculi of the spinal cord. Axons of the lower motor neurons innervate skeletal muscles that control skilled movements in the *limbs*, such as playing a guitar, dribbling a soccer ball, or typing on your computer keyboard.

The **anterior corticospinal tracts** represent the remaining 15% of the axons of upper motor neurons that extend through the medulla oblongata. The axons of these neurons do not decussate at the level of the medulla oblongata; instead, some decussate at the level of a spinal cord segment through the anterior gray commissure. They subsequently synapse either with interneurons or with lower motor neurons in the anterior horn. Axons of the lower motor neurons innervate *axial* skeletal muscle.

Indirect Pathway

Several nuclei within the midbrain initiate motor commands for activities that occur at a subconscious or reflexive level. The **indirect pathway** is so named because upper motor neurons originate within brainstem nuclei and take a complex, circuitous route through the brain before finally conducting the nerve signal to the spinal cord. The indirect pathway modifies or helps control the pattern of somatic motor activity by exciting or inhibiting the lower motor neurons that innervate the muscles.

The different tracts of the indirect pathway are grouped according to their primary functions. The **lateral pathway** regulates and controls precise, discrete movements and tone in flexor muscles of the limbs—for example, the type of movement required to gently lay a baby in a crib. This pathway consists of the **rubrospinal** (rū'brō-spī'năl; *rubro* = red) **tracts** that originate in the red nucleus of the midbrain.

The **medial pathway** regulates muscle tone and gross movements of the muscles of the head, neck, proximal limb, and trunk. The medial pathway consists of three groups of tracts—reticulospinal tracts, tectospinal tracts, and vestibulospinal tracts:

- The **reticulospinal** (re-tik-ū-lō-spī'năl) **tracts** originate from the reticular formation in the midbrain. They help control more unskilled reflexive movements related to posture and maintaining balance.
- The **tectospinal** (tek-tō-spī'năl) **tracts** conduct motor commands away from the superior and inferior colliculi in the tectum of the midbrain to help regulate positional changes of the arms, eyes, head, and neck as a consequence of visual and auditory stimuli.
- The **vestibulospinal** (ves-tib'ū-lō-spī'năl) **tracts** originate within vestibular nuclei of the brainstem. Nerve signals conducted within these tracts regulate muscular activity that helps maintain balance during sitting, standing, and walking.

Table 14.4 summarizes the characteristics of the principal types of motor pathways. **Figure 14.11** summarizes the main differences between the sensory and motor pathways.

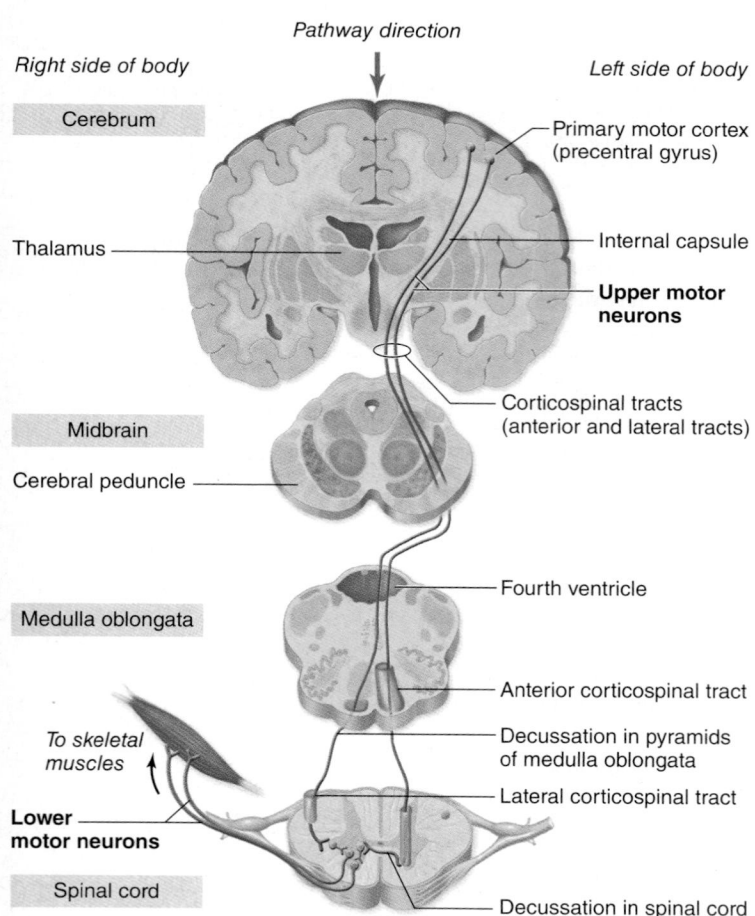

Figure 14.10 Corticospinal Tracts. Corticospinal tracts originate within the cerebrum and synapse on motor neurons within the anterior horns of the spinal cord. The upper motor neuron is dark green and the lower motor neuron is lavender.

Image labels:
Pathway direction
Right side of body
Left side of body
Cerebrum
Primary motor cortex (precentral gyrus)
Thalamus
Internal capsule
Upper motor neurons
Corticospinal tracts (anterior and lateral tracts)
Midbrain
Cerebral peduncle
Fourth ventricle
Medulla oblongata
Anterior corticospinal tract
To skeletal muscles
Decussation in pyramids of medulla oblongata
Lower motor neurons
Lateral corticospinal tract
Spinal cord
Decussation in spinal cord

WHAT DID YOU LEARN?

9 What are the locations and functions of upper and lower motor neurons in the motor pathways?

10 What are the differences between direct and indirect motor pathways?

Figure 14.11 Differences Between Sensory and Motor Pathways.

(*a*) Sensory pathways transmit ascending information to the brain, travel in the posterior and lateral funiculi of the spinal cord, and use up to three neurons to transmit this information (primary, secondary, and tertiary neurons). (*b*) Motor pathways transmit descending information from the brain, typically travel through the anterior and lateral funiculi of the spinal cord, and use two neurons (upper and lower motor neurons).

(a) Sensory Pathways

Nerve signals *ascend* to the brain in sensory pathways.

Most sensory pathways travel in the *posterior* and *lateral* funiculi of the spinal cord.

Posterior funiculus–medial lemniscal pathway

Spinocerebellar pathway (this pathway travels to the cerebellum and not to the thalamus)

Anterolateral pathway

Tertiary sensory neuron

Secondary sensory neuron

Primary sensory neuron

(b) Motor Pathways

Nerve signals *descend* from the brain in motor pathways.

Upper motor neuron

Lower motor neuron

Motor pathways tend to travel through the *anterior* and *lateral* funiculi of the spinal cord.

Lateral corticospinal tract

Rubrospinal tract

Medial pathway

Anterior corticospinal tract

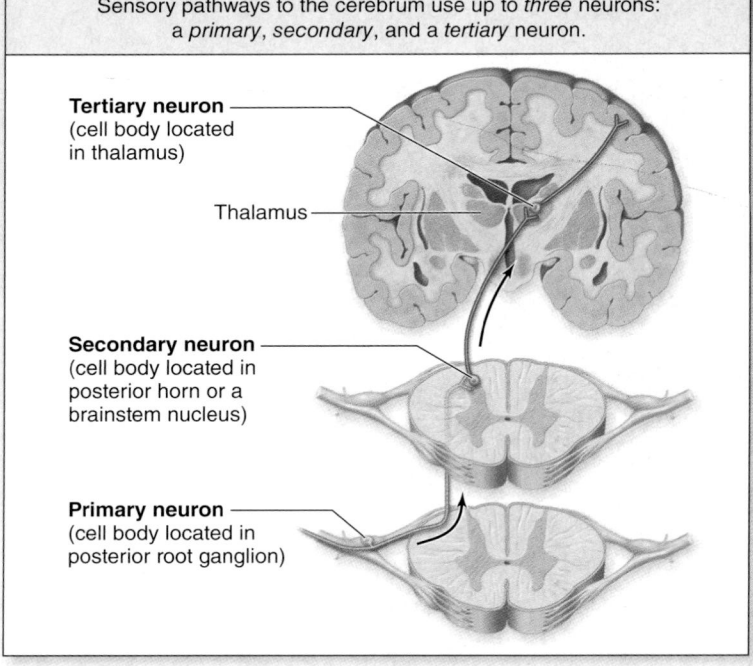

Sensory pathways to the cerebrum use up to *three* neurons: a *primary*, *secondary*, and a *tertiary* neuron.

Tertiary neuron (cell body located in thalamus)

Thalamus

Secondary neuron (cell body located in posterior horn or a brainstem nucleus)

Primary neuron (cell body located in posterior root ganglion)

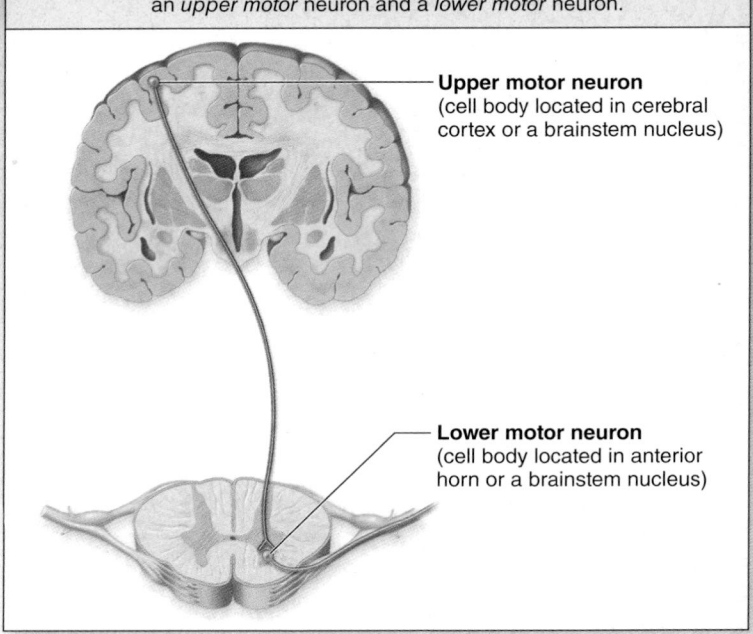

Motor pathways use *two* motor neurons: an *upper motor* neuron and a *lower motor* neuron.

Upper motor neuron (cell body located in cerebral cortex or a brainstem nucleus)

Lower motor neuron (cell body located in anterior horn or a brainstem nucleus)

14.5 Spinal Nerves

The 31 pairs of **spinal nerves** connect the central nervous system to muscles, glands, and receptors. Recall from section 12.2e that a nerve is formed from the union of thousands of motor and sensory axons and is enveloped in the three successive connective tissue wrappings: epineurium, perineurium, and endoneurium.

14.5a Overview of Spinal Nerves

✓ LEARNING OBJECTIVES

1. Describe the components of a typical spinal nerve.
2. Explain the naming convention for spinal nerves as they leave the vertebral canal via intervertebral foramina.
3. Compare and contrast the anterior and posterior rami of a spinal nerve.
4. Define a dermatome, and explain its clinical significance.

Motor axons originate from the spinal cord (see figure 14.2). Anteriorly, multiple **anterior rootlets** arise from the spinal cord and merge to form a single **anterior root** (or *ventral root*), which contains motor axons only. These motor axons arise from cell bodies in the anterior and lateral horns of the spinal cord.

The posterior aspect of the spinal cord also contains multiple **posterior rootlets** that enter the posterior aspect of the spinal cord. These rootlets arise from a single **posterior root** (or *dorsal root*), which contains sensory axons only. The cell bodies of these sensory neurons are located in a **posterior root ganglion,** which is within the posterior root.

Each anterior root and its corresponding posterior root unite within the intervertebral foramen to become a spinal nerve. Thus, a spinal nerve contains both motor axons (from the anterior root) and sensory

axons (from the posterior root). You can compare a spinal nerve to a cable composed of multiple wires. The "wires" within a spinal nerve are the motor and sensory axons.

Each cervical spinal nerve exits the vertebral canal and travels through an intervertebral foramen superior to the vertebra of the same number. For example, the second cervical spinal nerve exits the vertebral canal through the intervertebral foramen between the C_1 and the C_2 vertebrae. The eighth cervical spinal nerve is the exception; it leaves the intervertebral foramen between the C_7 and T_1 vertebrae. The spinal nerves inferior to the C8 nerve exit the vertebral canal and travel through an intervertebral foramen inferior to the vertebra of the same number. So, for example, the second thoracic spinal nerve exits the vertebral canal through the intervertebral foramen between the T_2 and T_3 vertebrae.

Because the spinal cord is shorter than the vertebral canal, the roots of the lumbar and sacral spinal nerves have to travel inferiorly to reach their respective intervertebral foramina before they can merge and form a spinal nerve. Thus, the anterior and posterior roots of the lumbar and sacral spinal nerves are much longer than the roots of the other spinal nerves, and collectively form the cauda equina (described earlier in this chapter).

Distribution of Spinal Nerves

After leaving the intervertebral foramen, a typical spinal nerve almost immediately splits into branches, termed *rami* (**figure 14.12**). The **posterior** (*dorsal*) **ramus** (rā′mŭs; pl., *rami,* rā′mī; = branch) is the smaller of the two main branches. It innervates the deep muscles of the back (e.g., erector spinae and transversospinalis; see section 11.4) and the skin of the back.

The **anterior** (*ventral*) **ramus** is the larger of the two main branches. The anterior ramus splits into multiple other branches, which innervate the anterior and lateral portions of the trunk, the

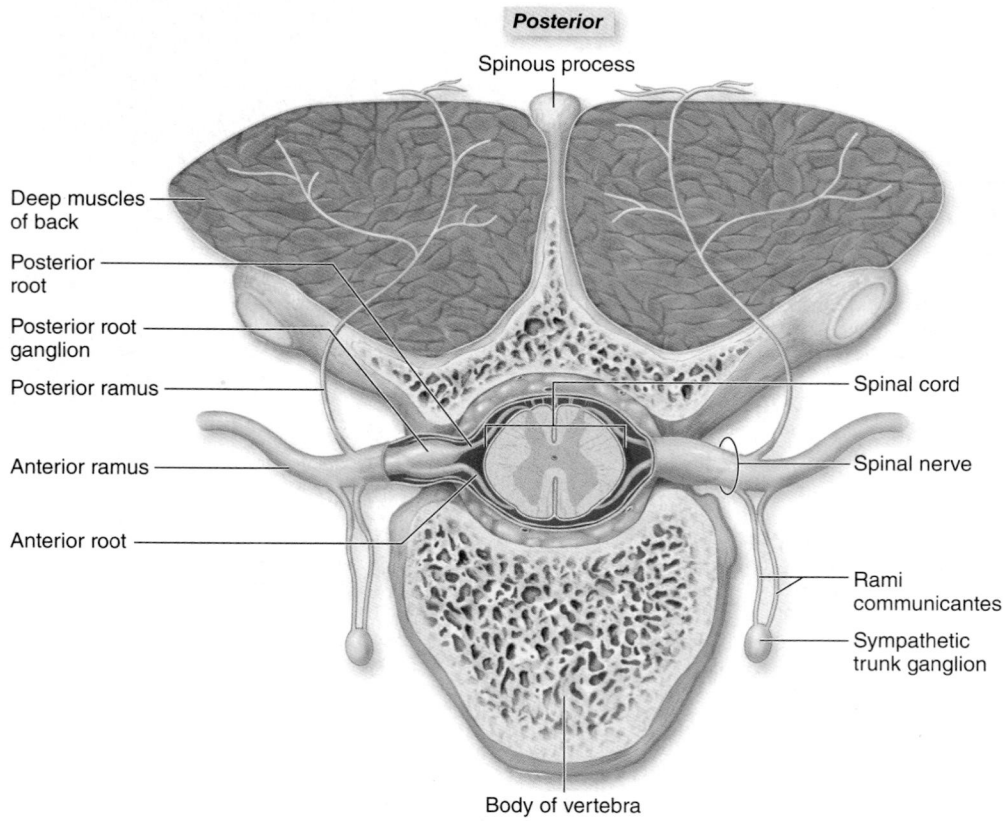

Figure 14.12 Spinal Nerve Branches. The major branches of a spinal nerve are the posterior ramus and the anterior ramus. AP|R

Posterior

Spinous process

Deep muscles of back

Posterior root

Posterior root ganglion

Posterior ramus

Anterior ramus

Anterior root

Spinal cord

Spinal nerve

Rami communicantes

Sympathetic trunk ganglion

Body of vertebra

Anterior

upper limbs, and the lower limbs. Many of the anterior rami go on to form nerve plexuses, which are described in the following sections.

Additional rami, called the *rami communicantes*, are also associated with spinal nerves. These rami contain axons associated with the autonomic nervous system. Each set of rami communicantes extends between the spinal nerve and a ball-like structure called the sympathetic trunk ganglion. These ganglia are interconnected and form a beaded necklacelike structure called the sympathetic trunk, that extends parallel and lateral to the vertebral column. These structures are described in detail in section 15.4.

WHAT DO YOU THINK?

2 Why is an anterior ramus so much larger than a posterior ramus?

Dermatomes

A **dermatome** (der′mă-tōm; *derma* = skin, *tome* = a cutting) is a specific segment of skin supplied by a single spinal nerve. All spinal nerves except for C1 innervate a segment of skin, and so each of these nerves is associated with a dermatome. Thus, the skin of the body may be divided into sensory segments that collectively make up a dermatome map **(figure 14.13)**. For example, the horizontal segment of skin around the umbilicus (navel) region is supplied by the anterior ramus of the T10 spinal nerve.

INTEGRATE

CONCEPT CONNECTION

The spinal nerves transmit nerve signals to the muscular system to control and regulate contraction of selected muscles. In addition, proprioception from the muscular and skeletal system, as well as sensations from the integumentary system, are detected by receptors and transported through the spinal nerves to the central nervous system for processing.

The dermatome map follows a segmental pattern along the body. Dermatomes are clinically important because they can indicate potential damage to one or more spinal nerves. For example, if a patient experiences **anesthesia** (an′es-thē′zē-ă; loss of sensation or numbness) along the medial side of the arm and forearm, the C8 spinal nerve may be damaged.

Dermatomes are also involved in **referred visceral pain,** a phenomenon in which pain or discomfort from one organ is mistakenly referred to a dermatome. For example, the appendix is innervated by axons from the T10 regions of the spinal cord, so appendicitis typically causes referred visceral pain to the T10 dermatome in the umbilicus region rather than in the abdominopelvic

Anterior view

Posterior view

Figure 14.13 Dermatome Maps.

A dermatome is an area of skin supplied by a single spinal nerve. These diagrams only approximate the dermatomal distribution. AP|R

CLINICAL VIEW
Shingles

Some adults (usually after age 50) experience a reactivation of their childhood chickenpox infection, a condition termed **shingles** (shing′glz). Psychological stress, other infections (such as a cold or the flu), and even a sunburn can trigger the development of shingles.

During the initial infection, the chickenpox virus (varicella-zoster) sometimes leaves the skin and invades the posterior root ganglia. There, the virus remains latent until adulthood, when it becomes reactivated and proliferates, traveling through the sensory axons to the dermatome. (The word *shingles* is derived from the Latin word *cingulum,* meaning "girdle,"

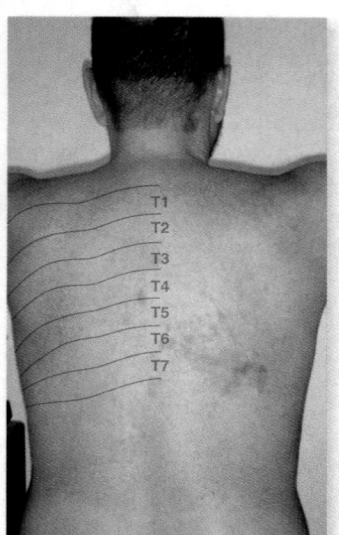

reflecting the dermatomal pattern of its spread.) The virus gives rise to a rash and blisters along the dermatome, which are often accompanied by intense burning or tingling pain.

Antiviral medication (e.g., acyclovir) may reduce the severity and duration of symptoms of shingles. Additionally, older adults may receive a vaccine for shingles, which may help prevent or reduce the severity of the disease.

Typical dermatomal spread of a shingles rash in a 49-year-old man.

region of the appendix itself. Thus, pain in a dermatome typically arises from an organ nowhere near the dermatome. Referred visceral pain is explored further in section 16.2b.

WHAT DID YOU LEARN?

11 What are the components of a typical spinal nerve?

12 How are spinal nerves named? Give specific examples.

13 What are the differences between an anterior ramus and a posterior ramus of a typical spinal nerve?

14 What is a dermatome, and why may a dermatome be clinically significant?

14.5b Nerve Plexuses
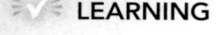 LEARNING OBJECTIVE

5. Define a nerve plexus.

A **nerve plexus** (plek′sŭs; a braid) is a network of interweaving anterior rami of spinal nerves. The anterior rami of most spinal nerves form nerve plexuses on both the right and left sides of the body. These nerve plexuses then split into multiple "named" nerves that innervate various body structures. The main plexuses are the cervical plexuses, brachial plexuses, lumbar plexuses, and sacral plexuses (see figure 14.1).

WHAT DO YOU THINK?

3 What is the benefit of having an intricate nerve plexus, rather than a single nerve that innervates a structure?

Nerve plexuses are organized such that axons from each anterior ramus extend to body structures through several different branches. In addition, each terminal branch of the plexus houses axons from several different spinal nerves. Most of the named nerves from a plexus are composed of axons from multiple spinal nerves. Thus, damage to a single segment of the spinal cord or damage to a single spinal nerve generally does not result in complete loss of innervation to a particular muscle or region of skin.

Most of the thoracic spinal nerves, as well as nerves S5–Co1, do not form plexuses. We discuss the thoracic spinal nerves (called intercostal nerves) first, followed by the individual nerve plexuses.

WHAT DID YOU LEARN?

15 What is the composition of a typical nerve plexus?

14.5c Intercostal Nerves
LEARNING OBJECTIVE

6. Identify the distribution of the intercostal nerves

The anterior rami of spinal nerves T1–T11 are called **intercostal nerves** because they travel in the intercostal space sandwiched between two adjacent ribs **(figure 14.14)**. (T12 is called a **subcostal nerve,** because it arises inferior to the ribs, not between two ribs.) With the exception of T1, the intercostal nerves do not form plexuses. The innervation pattern of the T1–T12 nerves is as follows:

- A portion of the anterior ramus of T1 helps form the brachial plexus, but a branch of it travels within the first intercostal space.
- The anterior ramus of nerve T2 emerges from its intervertebral foramen and innervates the intercostal muscles of the second intercostal space. Additionally, a branch of T2 conducts sensory information from the skin covering the axilla and the medial surface of the arm.
- Anterior rami of nerves T3–T6 follow the costal grooves of the ribs to innervate the intercostal muscles and receive sensations from the anterior and lateral chest wall.
- Anterior rami of nerves T7–T12 innervate not only the inferior intercostal spaces, but also the abdominal muscles and their overlying skin.

WHAT DID YOU LEARN?

16 In general, what do the intercostal nerves innervate?

14.5d Cervical Plexuses
LEARNING OBJECTIVES

7. List the nerves of the cervical plexuses

8. Explain the action of the phrenic nerve.

The left and right **cervical plexuses** are located deep on each side of the neck, immediately lateral to cervical vertebrae C_1–C_4 **(figure 14.15)**. They are formed primarily by the anterior rami of spinal nerves C1–C4. The fifth cervical spinal nerve is not considered part of the cervical plexus, although it contributes some axons to one of the plexus branches. Branches of the cervical

Figure 14.14 Intercostal Nerves. Intercostal nerves are the anterior rami of thoracic spinal nerves. They are typically distributed as shown here.

Posterior root
Anterior root
Posterior root ganglion
Rami communicantes
Sympathetic trunk ganglion
Spinal nerve
Posterior ramus
Anterior ramus
Sympathetic trunk

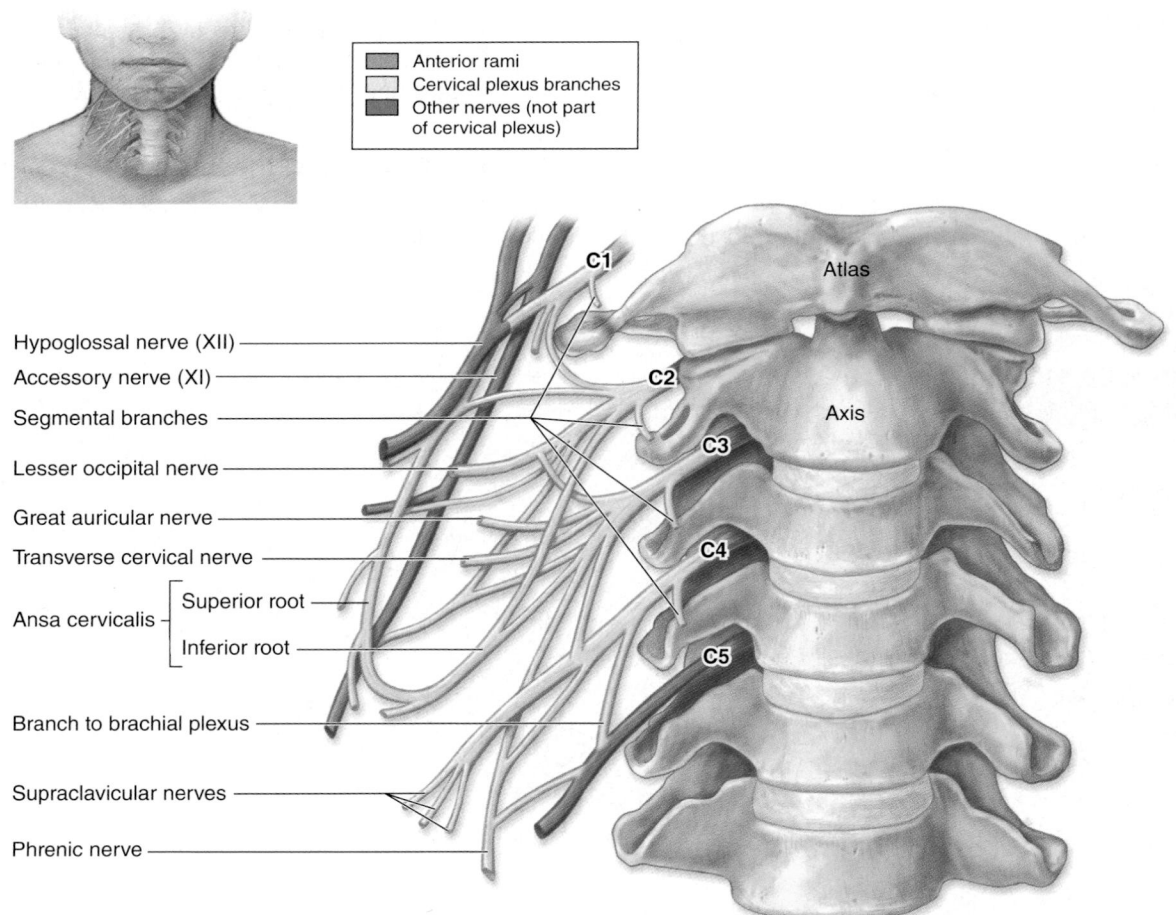

Anterior rami
Cervical plexus branches
Other nerves (not part of cervical plexus)

Hypoglossal nerve (XII)
Accessory nerve (XI)
Segmental branches
Lesser occipital nerve
Great auricular nerve
Transverse cervical nerve
Ansa cervicalis — Superior root
Inferior root
Branch to brachial plexus
Supraclavicular nerves
Phrenic nerve

C1
Atlas
C2
Axis
C3
C4
C5

Figure 14.15 Cervical Plexus. Anterior rami of nerves C1–C4 form the cervical plexus, which innervates the skin and many muscles of the neck. AP|R

INTEGRATE

LEARNING STRATEGY

This mnemonic will help you remember the nerves that innervate the diaphragm: **C three, four, and five keep the diaphragm alive.**

plexuses innervate anterior neck muscles (see section 11.3d) as well as the skin of the neck and portions of the head and shoulders. The branches of the cervical plexuses are described in detail in **table 14.5**.

One important branch of the cervical plexus is the **phrenic** (fren'ik; *phren* = diaphragm) **nerve**, which is formed primarily from the C4 nerve and some contributing axons from C3 and C5. The phrenic nerve travels through the thoracic cavity to innervate the diaphragm (see section 11.5).

 WHAT DID YOU LEARN?

17 What is the action of the phrenic nerve?

14.5e Brachial Plexuses

 LEARNING OBJECTIVES

9. Explain the structure of the brachial plexus, including the three trunks, two divisions, and three cords.

10. Describe the distribution of the five major nerve branches that arise from the three cords.

The left and right **brachial plexuses** are networks of nerves that supply the upper limb. Each brachial plexus is formed by the anterior rami of spinal nerves C5–T1 (**figure 14.16**). The components of the brachial plexus extend laterally from the neck, pass superior to the first rib, and then continue into the axilla.

Each brachial plexus innervates the pectoral girdle and the entire upper limb of one side.

Structure of the Brachial Plexus

Structurally, each brachial plexus is more complex than a cervical plexus and is composed of anterior rami, trunks, divisions, and cords when examined from a medial to lateral perspective. The **anterior rami** (sometimes called *roots*) of the brachial plexus are simply the continuations of the anterior rami of spinal nerves C5–T1. These rami emerge from the intervertebral foramina and travel through the neck. The five rami unite to form the **superior, middle,** and **inferior trunks** in the posterior triangle of the neck. Nerves C5 and C6 unite to form the superior trunk; nerve C7 remains as the middle trunk; and nerves C8 and T1 unite to form the inferior trunk.

Portions of each trunk divide deep to the clavicle into an **anterior division** and a **posterior division** (shown in green and purple, respectively, in figure 14.6). These primarily contain axons that innervate the anterior and posterior parts of the upper limb, respectively.

Upon reaching the axilla, these anterior and posterior divisions converge to form three cords. They are named with respect to their position near the axillary artery:

- The **posterior cord** is posterior to the axillary artery and is formed by the posterior divisions of the superior, middle, and inferior trunks; therefore, it contains portions of C5–T1 nerves.
- The **medial cord** is medial to the axillary artery and is formed by the anterior division of the inferior trunk; it contains portions of nerves C8–T1.
- The **lateral cord** is lateral to the axillary artery and is formed from the anterior divisions of the superior and middle trunks; thus, it contains portions of nerves C5–C7.

Terminal Branches of the Brachial Plexus

Finally, five major **terminal branches** emerge from the three cords: the axillary nerve (from the posterior cord), median nerve (from the

Table 14.5	Branches of the Cervical Plexuses	
Nerves	**Anterior Rami**	**Innervation**
MOTOR BRANCHES		
Ansa cervicalis		Geniohyoid; infrahyoid muscles (omohyoid, sternohyoid, sternothyroid, and thyrohyoid)
Superior root	C1, C2	
Inferior root	C3, C4	
Segmental branches	C1–C4	Anterior and middle scalenes
CUTANEOUS BRANCHES		
Greater auricular	C2, C3	Skin on ear; connective tissue capsule covering parotid gland
Lesser occipital	C2	Skin of scalp superior and posterior to ear
Supraclavicular	C3, C4	Skin on superior part of chest and shoulder
Transverse cervical	C2, C3	Skin on anterior part of neck

Note: Although CN XII (hypoglossal) and the phrenic nerve (C3, C4, C5) travel with the nerves of the cervical plexus, hypoglossal and phrenic are not considered part of the plexus.

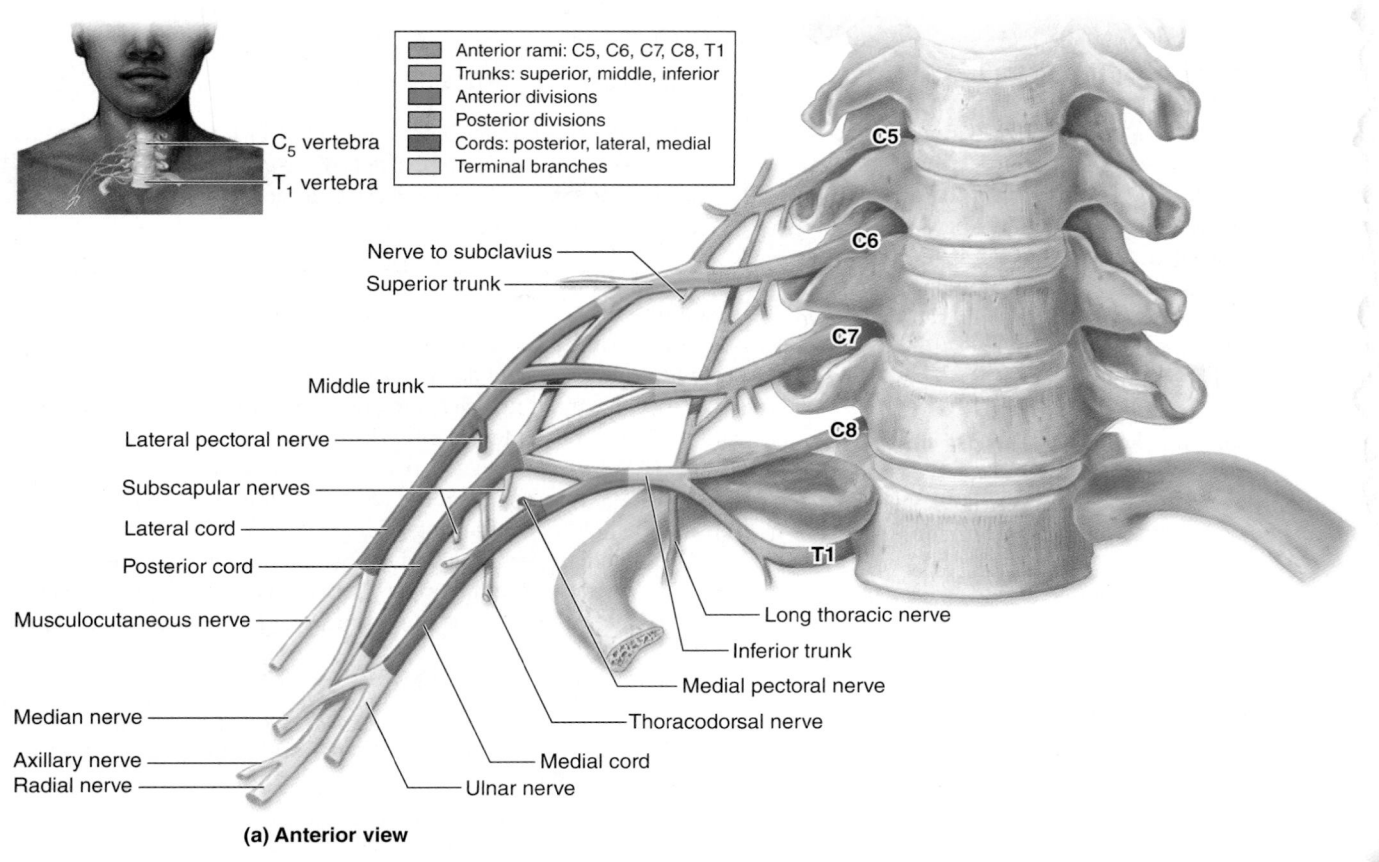

Anterior rami: C5, C6, C7, C8, T1
Trunks: superior, middle, inferior
Anterior divisions
Posterior divisions
Cords: posterior, lateral, medial
Terminal branches

C₅ vertebra
T₁ vertebra

C5
C6
C7
C8
T1

Nerve to subclavius
Superior trunk
Middle trunk
Lateral pectoral nerve
Subscapular nerves
Lateral cord
Posterior cord
Musculocutaneous nerve
Median nerve
Axillary nerve
Radial nerve
Ulnar nerve
Medial cord
Thoracodorsal nerve
Medial pectoral nerve
Inferior trunk
Long thoracic nerve

(a) Anterior view

Lateral cord
Posterior cord
Axillary artery
Musculocutaneous nerve
Axillary nerve
Medial cord
Radial nerve
Median nerve
Ulnar nerve
Long thoracic nerve

(b) Right axilla, anterior view

Clavicle
Lateral cord
Posterior cord
Medial cord
Axillary nerve
Musculocutaneous nerve
Radial nerve
Median nerve
Scapula
Humerus
Ulnar nerve
Superficial branch of radial nerve
Deep branch of radial nerve
Ulna
Ulnar nerve
Median nerve
Radius
Recurrent branch of median nerve
Deep branch of ulnar nerve
Superficial branch of ulnar nerve
Digital branch of median nerve
Digital branch of ulnar nerve

(c) Right upper limb, anterior view

Figure 14.16 Brachial Plexus. Anterior rami of nerves C5–T1 form the brachial plexus, which innervates the upper limb. (*a*) Rami, trunks, divisions, and cords form the subdivisions of this plexus. (*b*) A cadaver dissection identifies major nerves from the brachial plexus. (*c*) Complete pathways of main brachial plexus branches. AP|R medial and lateral cords), musculocutaneous nerve (from the lateral cord), radial nerve (from the posterior cord), and ulnar nerve (from the medial cord). The nerves are compared in **table 14.6**.

The **axillary nerve** traverses through the axilla and posterior to the surgical neck of the humerus. The axillary nerve innervates both the deltoid and teres minor muscles (see section 11.8). It receives sensory nerve signals from the superolateral part of the arm.

The **median nerve** travels along the midline of the arm and forearm, and deep to the carpal tunnel in the wrist. It innervates most of the anterior forearm muscles, the thenar muscles, and the lateral two lumbricals (see section 11.8e). It receives sensory nerve signals from the palmar side of the lateral 3½ fingers (thumb, index finger, middle finger, and the lateral one-half of the ring finger) and from the dorsal tips of these same fingers.

The **musculocutaneous** (mŭs′kū-lō-kū-tā′nē-ŭs) **nerve** innervates the anterior arm muscles (coracobrachialis, biceps brachii, and brachialis), which flex the humerus and/or flex the forearm (see sections 11.8b and c). It also receives sensory information from the lateral surface of the forearm.

The **radial nerve** travels along the posterior side of the arm and then along the radial side of the forearm. The radial nerve innervates the posterior arm muscles (forearm extensors) and the posterior forearm muscles (extensors of the wrist and digits, and the supinator of the forearm, see section 11.8). It receives sensory nerve signals from the posterior arm and forearm surface and the dorsolateral side of the hand.

The **ulnar nerve** descends along the medial side of the arm. It travels posterior to the medial epicondyle of the humerus and then runs along the ulnar side of the forearm. It innervates some of the anterior forearm muscles (the medial region of the flexor digitorum profundus and all of the flexor carpi ulnaris). It also innervates most of the intrinsic hand muscles, including the hypothenar muscles, the palmar and dorsal interossei, and the medial two lumbricals (see section 11.8e). It receives sensory nerve signals from the skin of the dorsal and palmar aspects of the medial 1½ fingers (the pinky finger and the medial half of the ring finger).

The brachial plexus also gives off numerous other nerves that innervate portions of the upper limb and pectoral girdle. These branches are not as large as the terminal branches (see table 14.6).

💡 **WHAT DID YOU LEARN?**

18 Which nerve might you have damaged if you have difficulty abducting your arm, and have anesthesia (lack of sensation) along the superolateral arm?

19 How do the ulnar nerve and radial nerve compare, with respect to motor and cutaneous innervation?

Table 14.6	Branches of the Brachial Plexus			
Terminal Branch		**Anterior Rami**	**Motor Innervation**	**Cutaneous Innervation**
Axillary Nerve Formed from posterior cord, posterior division of the brachial plexus		C5, C6	**Deltoid** (*arm abductor*) **Teres minor** (*lateral rotator of arm*)	Superolateral arm

Posterior cord

Teres minor

Axillary nerve

Deltoid

Posterior

Posterior

Table 14.6   Branches of the Brachial Plexus (continued)

Terminal Branch	Anterior Rami	Motor Innervation	Cutaneous Innervation

Median Nerve
 	
Formed from medial and lateral cords, anterior division of the brachial plexus
 	
Lateral cord
Posterior cord
Medial cord
 	
Median nerve
 	
Pronator teres
Flexor carpi radialis
Palmaris longus
Flexor digitorum superficialis
Flexor pollicis longus
Flexor digitorum profundus (lateral half)
Pronator quadratus
Thenar muscles
Lateral two lumbricals
 	
Anterior
	C5–T1	**Most anterior forearm muscles** (*pronators, flexors of wrist, digits*)
		    Flexor carpi radialis
		    Flexor digitorum superficialis
		    Pronator teres
		    Pronator quadratus
		    Lateral ½ of flexor digitorum profundus
		    Flexor pollicis longus
		
		Thenar (thumb) muscles (*move thumb*)
		    Flexor pollicis brevis
		    Abductor pollicis brevis
		    Opponens pollicis
		
		Lateral 2 lumbricals (*flex MP joints and extend PIP and DIP joints*)
			Palmar aspects and dorsal tips of lateral 3½ digits (*thumb, index finger, middle finger, and ½ of ring finger*)
			
			Posterior
			
			Anterior

Musculocutaneous Nerve
 	
Formed from the lateral cord, anterior division of the brachial plexus
 	
Lateral cord
Coracobrachialis
Musculocutaneous nerve
Biceps brachii
Brachialis
 	
Anterior
	C5–C7	**Anterior arm muscles** (*flex humerus, flex elbow joint, supinate forearm*)
		    Coracobrachialis
		    Biceps brachii
		    Brachialis
			Lateral region of forearm
			
			Anterior
			
			Posterior

(continued on next page)

Table 14.6   Branches of the Brachial Plexus (continued)

Terminal Branch	Anterior Rami	Motor Innervation	Cutaneous Innervation

Radial Nerve
 	
Formed from the posterior cord, posterior division of the brachial plexus
	C5–T1	**Posterior arm muscles** (*extend forearm*)
		  Triceps brachii
		  Anconeus
		Posterior forearm muscles (*supinate forearm, extend wrist, digits, 1 muscle that abducts thumb*)
		  Supinator
		  Extensor carpi radialis muscles
		  Extensor digitorum
		  Extensor carpi ulnaris
		  Extensor pollicis longus
		  Extensor pollicis brevis
		  Abductor pollicis brevis
		  Extensor digiti minimi
		  Extensor indicis
		Brachioradialis (*flexes forearm*)
			Posterior region of arm
			Posterior region of forearm
			Dorsal aspect of lateral 3 digits (except their distal tips)

Ulnar Nerve
 	
Formed from the medial cord, anterior division of the brachial plexus
	C8–T1	**Anterior forearm muscles** (*flexors of wrist and digits*)
		  Medial ½ of flexor digitorum profundus
		  Flexor carpi ulnaris
		Intrinsic hand muscles
		  Hypothenar muscles
		  Palmar interossei (*adduct fingers*)
		  Dorsal interossei (*adduct fingers*)
		  Adductor pollicis (*adducts thumb*)
		  Medial 2 lumbricals (*flex MP joints and extend PIP and DIP joints*)
			Dorsal and palmar aspects of medial 1½ digits (*little finger, medial aspect of ring finger*)

Radial Nerve diagram labels: Lateral cord, Posterior cord, Medial cord, Long head of triceps brachii, Medial head of triceps brachii, Anconeus, Supinator, Extensor carpi ulnaris, Extensor digiti minimi, Extensor digitorum, Extensor pollicis longus and brevis, Extensor indicis, Posterior, Radial nerve, Lateral head of triceps brachii, Brachioradialis, Extensor carpi radialis, Abductor pollicis longus, Posterior

Ulnar Nerve diagram labels: Anterior, Lateral cord, Posterior cord, Medial cord, Ulnar nerve, Flexor carpi ulnaris, Flexor digitorum profundus (medial half), Adductor pollicis, Hypothenar muscles, Medial two lumbricals, Dorsal and palmar interossei, Posterior, Anterior

Table 14.6	Branches of the Brachial Plexus (continued)			
Smaller Branches of the Brachial Plexus	**Anterior Rami**	**Motor Innervation**	**Cutaneous Innervation**	
Dorsal scapular	C5	Rhomboids, levator scapulae		
Long thoracic	C5–C7	Serratus anterior		
Lateral pectoral	C5–C7	Pectoralis major		
Medial pectoral	C8–T1	Pectoralis major Pectoralis minor		
Medial cutaneous nerve of arm	C8–T1		Medial side of arm	
Medial cutaneous nerve of forearm	C8–T1		Medial side of forearm	
Nerve to subclavius	C5–C6	Subclavius		
Suprascapular	C5–C6	Supraspinatus, infraspinatus		
Subscapular nerves	C5–C6	Subscapularis, teres major		
Thoracodorsal (nerve to latissimus dorsi)	C6–C8	Latissimus dorsi		

INTEGRATE

CLINICAL VIEW

Brachial Plexus Injuries

Injuries to parts of the brachial plexus are fairly common, especially in individuals aged 15–25. Minor plexus injuries may be treated by simply resting the limb. More severe brachial plexus injuries may require nerve grafts or nerve transfers, and for very severe injuries, no effective treatment exists.

Axillary Nerve Injury
The axillary nerve can be compressed within the axilla, or it can be damaged if the surgical neck of the humerus is broken (recall that the axillary nerve travels posterior to the surgical neck of the humerus). A patient whose axillary nerve is damaged has great difficulty abducting the arm due to paralysis of the deltoid muscle, as well as anesthesia along the superolateral skin of the arm.

Radial Nerve Injury
The radial nerve is especially subject to injury during humeral shaft fractures or in injuries to the lateral elbow. Nerve damage results in paralysis of the extensor muscles of the forearm, wrist, and fingers. A common clinical sign of radial nerve injury is *wrist drop*, where the patient is unable to extend his or her wrist. The patient also experiences anesthesia along the posterior arm, the forearm, and the part of the hand normally supplied by this nerve.

Posterior Cord Injury
The posterior cord of the brachial plexus (which includes the axillary and radial nerves) may be injured by improper use of crutches, a condition called *crutch palsy*. Similarly, the posterior cord can also be compressed if a person drapes the upper limb over the back of a chair for an extended period of time. Because this can happen if someone passes out in a drunken stupor, this condition is also referred to as *drunkard's paralysis*.

Median Nerve Injury
The median nerve may be impinged or compressed as a result of carpal tunnel syndrome (see Clinical View: "Carpal Tunnel Syndrome," in chapter 11)

or by any deep laceration of the wrist. Median nerve injury often results in paralysis of the thenar group of muscles. The classic sign of median nerve injury is the *ape hand deformity*, which develops over time as the thenar eminence wastes away until the hand eventually resembles that of an ape (apes lack well-developed thumb muscles). The lateral two lumbricals are also paralyzed, and sensation is lost in the part of the hand supplied by the median nerve.

Ulnar Nerve Injury
The ulnar nerve may be injured by fractures or dislocations of the elbow because of this nerve's close proximity to the medial epicondyle of the humerus. When you "hit your funny bone," you actually have hit your ulnar nerve. Most of the intrinsic hand muscles are paralyzed, so the person is unable to adduct or abduct the fingers. In addition, the person experiences sensory loss along the medial side of the hand. A clinician can test for ulnar nerve injury by having a patient hold a piece of paper tightly between the fingers as the doctor tries to pull it away. If the person has weak or paralyzed interossei muscles, the paper can be easily extracted.

Superior Trunk Injury
The superior trunk of the brachial plexus can be injured by excessive separation of the neck and shoulder, as when a person riding a motorcycle is flipped from the bike and lands on the side of the head. A superior trunk injury affects the C5 and C6 anterior rami, so any brachial plexus branch that has these nerves is also affected to some degree.

Inferior Trunk Injury
The inferior trunk of the brachial plexus can be injured if the arm is excessively abducted, as when a neonate's arm is pulled too hard during delivery. In children and adults, inferior trunk injuries happen when grasping something above the head in order to break a fall—for example, grabbing a branch to keep from falling out of a tree. An inferior trunk injury involves the C8 and T1 anterior rami, so any brachial plexus branch that is formed from these nerves (such as the ulnar nerve) also is affected to some degree.

14.5f Lumbar Plexuses

11. Identify the spinal nerves that make up the lumbar plexus.

12. Compare and contrast the femoral and obturator nerve composition and distribution.

The left and right **lumbar plexuses** are formed from the anterior rami of spinal nerves L1–L4 located lateral to the L_1–L_4 vertebrae and along the psoas major muscle in the posterior abdominal wall (**figure 14.17**). The lumbar plexus is structurally less complex than the brachial plexus. However, like the brachial plexus, the lumbar plexus is also subdivided into an anterior division and a posterior division. The primary nerves of the lumbar plexus are listed in **table 14.7**.

Legend:
- Anterior rami
- Posterior divisions
- Anterior divisions

(a) Anterior view

Labels (a): Iliohypogastric nerve, Ilioinguinal nerve, Genitofemoral nerve, Lateral femoral cutaneous nerve, Femoral nerve, Obturator nerve, Lumbosacral trunk; L1, L2, L3, L4, L5

Labels (b): Subcostal nerve, Iliohypogastric nerve, Ilioinguinal nerve, Lateral femoral cutaneous nerve, Genitofemoral nerve, Obturator nerve, Femoral nerve

(b) Right pelvic region, anterior view

Labels (c): Iliohypogastric nerve, Ilioinguinal nerve, Genitofemoral nerve, Femoral nerve, Lateral femoral cutaneous nerve, Obturator nerve, Saphenous nerve (continuation of femoral nerve)

(c) Right lower limb, anterior view

Figure 14.17 Lumbar Plexus. (*a*) Anterior rami of nerves L1–L4 form the lumbar plexus. (*b*) Cadaver photo shows components of the lumbar plexus. (*c*) Pathways of lumbar plexus nerves. AP|R

Table 14.7 Branches of the Lumbar Plexus

Main Branch		Anterior Rami	Motor Innervation	Cutaneous Innervation

Femoral Nerve
Iliacus
Femoral nerve
Sartorius
Rectus femoris
Vastus intermedius
Vastus lateralis
— L2
— L3
— L4
— Psoas major
— Pectineus
— Vastus medialis
— Sartorius
Anterior
		L2–L4	**Anterior thigh muscles**
			  Quadriceps femoris (*knee extensor*)
			  Iliopsoas (*hip flexor*)
			  Sartorius (*hip and knee flexor*)
			  Pectineus[1] (*hip flexor*)
				Anterior thigh
				Inferomedial thigh
				Medial side of leg
				Most medial aspect of foot
				
				Anterior

Obturator Nerve
Obturator externus
Adductor brevis
Adductor longus
Adductor magnus
— L2
— L3
— L4
— **Obturator nerve**
— Adductor longus
— Gracilis
Anterior
		L2–L4	**Medial thigh muscles** (*adductors of thigh*)
			  Adductors
			  Gracilis
			  Pectineus[1]
			  Obturator externus (*lateral rotator of thigh*)
				Superomedial thigh
				
				Medial

1. Pectineus may be innervated by the femoral nerve, obturator nerve, or branches from both nerves.

(continued on next page)

Table 14.7   Branches of the Lumbar Plexus (continued)

Smaller Branches of the Lumbar Plexus	Anterior Rami	Motor Innervation	Cutaneous Innervation
Iliohypogastric	L1	Partial innervation to abdominal muscles (*flex vertebral column*)	Superior lateral gluteal region Inferior abdominal wall
Ilioinguinal	L1	Partial innervation to abdominal muscles (*flex vertebral column*)	Inferior abdominal wall Scrotum (males) or labia majora (females)
Genitofemoral	L1, L2		Small area in anterior superior thigh Scrotum (males) or labia majora (females)
Lateral femoral cutaneous	L2, L3		Anterolateral thigh

The main nerve of the posterior division of the lumbar plexus is the **femoral nerve.** This nerve supplies the anterior thigh muscles, such as the quadriceps femoris (knee extensor) and the sartorius and iliopsoas (hip flexors, see sections 11.9a, b). It also receives sensory nerve signals from the anterior and inferomedial thigh as well as the medial aspect of the leg.

The main nerve of the anterior division is the **obturator nerve,** which travels through the obturator foramen of the os coxae to the medial thigh. There, the nerve innervates the medial thigh muscles (which adduct the thigh, see section 11.9a) and receives sensory nerve signals from the superomedial skin of the thigh. Smaller branches of each lumbar plexus innervate the abdominal wall, portions of the external genitalia, and the inferior portions of the abdominal muscles (see table 14.7 and section 11.6).

 WHAT DID YOU LEARN?

 20 Which nerve of the lumbar plexus might you have damaged if you have difficulty extending your knee?

14.5g Sacral Plexuses

 LEARNING OBJECTIVES

13. List the spinal nerves that form the sacral plexus.

14. Describe the composition of the sciatic nerve and compare its branches.

The left and right **sacral plexuses** are formed from the anterior rami of spinal nerves L4–S4 and are located immediately inferior to the lumbar plexuses (**figure 14.18**). The lumbar and sacral plexuses are sometimes considered together as the *lumbosacral plexus.* The nerves emerging from a sacral plexus innervate the gluteal region, pelvis, perineum, posterior thigh, and almost all of the leg and foot.

The anterior rami of the sacral plexus organize themselves into an anterior division and a posterior division. The nerves arising from the anterior division tend to innervate muscles that flex (or plantar flex) parts of the lower limb, while the posterior division nerves tend to innervate muscles that extend (or dorsiflex) part of the lower limb. **Table 14.8** lists the main and smaller nerves of the sacral plexus.

The **sciatic** (sī-at'ik) **nerve,** also known as the *ischiadic* (is-kē-at'ik; hip joint) *nerve,* is the largest and longest nerve in the body. It is formed from portions of both the anterior and posterior divisions of the sacral plexus. This nerve projects from the pelvis through the greater sciatic notch of the os coxae and extends into the posterior region of the thigh. The sciatic nerve is actually composed of two divisions—the *tibial division* and the *common fibular division*—wrapped in a common sheath.

Just superior to the popliteal fossa, the two divisions of the sciatic nerve split into two nerves. The **tibial nerve** is formed from the anterior divisions of the sciatic nerve. In the posterior thigh, the tibial division of the sciatic nerve innervates the hamstrings (except for the short head of the biceps femoris) and the hamstring part of the adductor magnus. It travels in the posterior compartment of the leg, where it supplies the plantar flexors of the foot and the toe flexors (see section 11.9). In the foot, the tibial nerve splits into the lateral and medial plantar nerves, which innervate the plantar muscles of the foot and receive sensory nerve signals from the skin covering the sole of the foot.

The **common fibular** (*common peroneal*) **nerve** is formed from the posterior division of the sciatic nerve. As the common fibular division of the sciatic nerve, it supplies the short head of the biceps femoris muscle (see section 11.9b). Along the lateral knee, as it wraps around the neck of the fibula, this nerve splits into two main branches: the deep fibular nerve and the superficial fibular nerve.

INTEGRATE

CLINICAL VIEW
Sacral Plexus Injuries

Some branches of the sacral plexus are readily subject to injury. For example, a poorly placed gluteal intramuscular injection can injure the superior or inferior gluteal nerves, and in some cases even the sciatic nerve. Additionally, a herniated intervertebral disc may impinge on the nerve branches that form the sciatic nerve. Injury to the sciatic nerve produces a condition known as **sciatica** (sī-at'i-kă), which is characterized by extreme pain down the posterior of the thigh and leg.

The common fibular nerve is especially prone to injury due to fracture of the neck of the fibula or compression from a leg cast that is too tight. The anterior and lateral leg muscles may be paralyzed and leave the person unable to dorsiflex and evert the foot. One classic sign of fibular nerve injury is *foot drop.* Because the person cannot dorsiflex the foot to walk normally, he or she compensates by flexing the hip to lift the affected area and keep from tripping or stubbing the toes.

Figure 14.18 Sacral Plexus. Anterior rami of nerves L4, L5, and S1–S4 form the sacral plexus. (*a*) The sacral plexus has six roots and both anterior and posterior divisions. (*b*) Cadaver photo reveals the major sacral plexus nerves of the right gluteal region. (*c*) A posterior view shows the distribution of nerves of the sacral plexus.

The **deep fibular** (*deep peroneal*) **nerve** travels in the anterior compartment of the leg and terminates between the first and second toes. It supplies the anterior leg muscles (which dorsiflex the foot and extend the toes) and the muscles on the dorsum of the foot (which extend the toes, see sections 11.9c and d). In addition, this nerve receives sensory nerve signals from the skin between the first and second toes on the dorsum of the foot.

The **superficial fibular** (*superficial peroneal*) **nerve** travels in the lateral compartment of the leg. Just proximal to the ankle, this

nerve becomes superficial along the anterior part of the ankle and dorsum of the foot. The superficial fibular nerve innervates the lateral compartment muscles of the leg (foot evertors and weak plantar flexors, see sections 11.9c and d). It also receives sensory nerve signals from most of the dorsal surface of the foot and the anteroinferior part of the leg.

💡 WHAT DID YOU LEARN?

㉑ What anterior rami form the sacral nerve plexus, and what general areas of the body does it innervate?

Table 14.8　Branches of the Sacral Plexus

Main Branch	Anterior Rami	Motor Innervation	Cutaneous Innervation
Sciatic Nerve (Composed of tibial and common fibular divisions wrapped in a common sheath)	L4–S3	(See tibial and common fibular nerves)	(See tibial and common fibular nerves)
Tibial Nerve	L4–S3	**Posterior thigh muscles** (*extend thigh and flex leg*) 　Long head of biceps femoris 　Semimembranosus 　Semitendinosus 　Part of adductor magnus **Posterior leg muscles** (*plantar flexors of foot, flexors of knee*) 　Flexor digitorum longus 　Flexor hallucis longus 　Gastrocnemius 　Soleus 　Popliteus 　Tibialis posterior (*inverts foot*) **Plantar foot muscles** (*via medial and lateral plantar nerve branches*)	Branches to the heel, and via its medial and lateral plantar nerve branches (which supply the sole of the foot)
Common Fibular Nerve (Divides into deep fibular and superficial fibular branches)	L4–S2	**Short head of biceps femoris** (*knee flexor*); see also deep fibular and superficial fibular nerves	(See deep fibular and superficial fibular nerves)

Table 14.8   Branches of the Sacral Plexus (continued)

Main Branch	Anterior Rami	Motor Innervation	Cutaneous Innervation

Deep Fibular Nerve
 	
 Common fibular nerve
 Superficial fibular nerve
 Extensor digitorum longus
 Fibularis tertius
 Extensor digitorum brevis
 Tibialis anterior
 Deep fibular nerve
 Extensor hallucis longus
 Extensor hallucis brevis
 Anterior
	L4–S1	**Anterior leg muscles** (*dorsiflex foot, extend toes*)
		     Tibialis anterior (*inverts foot*)
		     Extensor hallucis longus
		     Extensor digitorum longus
		     Fibularis tertius
		 Dorsum foot muscles (*extend toes*)
		     Extensor hallucis brevis
		     Extensor digitorum brevis
			Dorsal interspace between first and second toes
			
			 Anterior

Superficial Fibular Nerve
 	
 Common fibular nerve
 Fibularis longus
 Fibularis brevis
 Superficial fibular nerve
 Anterior
	L5–S2	**Lateral leg muscles** (*foot evertors and plantar flexors*)
		     Fibularis longus
		     Fibularis brevis
			Anteroinferior part of leg; most of dorsum of foot
			
			 Anterior

Smaller Branches of the Sacral Plexus	Anterior Rami	Motor Innervation	Cutaneous Innervation
Inferior gluteal nerve	L5–S2	Gluteus maximus (*thigh extensor*)	
Superior gluteal nerve	L4–S1	Gluteus medius, gluteus minimus, and tensor fasciae latae (*abductors of thigh*)	
Posterior femoral cutaneous nerve	S1–S3		Skin on posterior thigh
Pudendal nerve	S2–S4	Muscles of perineum, external anal sphincter, external urethral sphincter	Skin on external genitalia

14.6 Reflexes

Here we consider the characteristics of a reflex, the components of a reflex arc, the different spinal reflexes, and how reflexes are tested in a clinical setting.

14.6a Characteristics of Reflexes

✅ LEARNING OBJECTIVE

1. Describe the properties of a reflex.

Reflexes are rapid, pre-programmed, involuntary reactions of muscles or glands to a stimulus. An example of a reflex occurs when you accidentally touch a hot burner on a stove. Instantly and automatically, you remove your hand from the stimulus (the hot burner), even before you are completely aware that your hand was touching something extremely hot.

All reflexes have similar properties:

- A *stimulus* is required to initiate a response to sensory input.
- A *rapid response* requires that few neurons are involved and synaptic delay is minimal.
- A *pre-programmed response* occurs the same way every time.
- An *involuntary response* requires no conscious intent or pre-awareness of the reflex activity. Thus, reflexes are usually not suppressed.

Awareness of the stimulus occurs after the reflex action has been completed, in time to correct or avoid a potentially dangerous situation. A reflex is a survival mechanism; it allows us to quickly respond to a stimulus that may be detrimental to our well-being without having to wait for the brain to process the information.

💡 WHAT DID YOU LEARN?

㉒ What are the four main properties of a reflex?

14.6b Components of a Reflex Arc

✅ LEARNING OBJECTIVES

2. List the structures involved in a reflex arc and the steps in its action.
3. Distinguish between ipsilateral and contralateral reflexes.
4. Compare and contrast a monosynaptic reflex and a polysynaptic reflex.

A **reflex arc** is the neural "wiring" of a single reflex. It always begins at a receptor in the PNS, communicates with the CNS, and ends at a peripheral effector, either a muscle or gland cell. The number of intermediate steps varies, depending upon the complexity of the reflex. Generally, five steps are involved in a reflex, as illustrated in **figure 14.19** and described here:

① **A stimulus activates a receptor.** Sensory receptors (dendritic endings of a sensory neuron) respond to external and internal stimuli, such as temperature, pressure, or tactile changes.

② **A nerve signal travels through the sensory neuron to the CNS.** A sensory neuron conducts a nerve signal from the receptor to the spinal cord.

③ **Information from the nerve signal is processed in the integration center by interneurons.** More complex reflexes may use a number of interneurons within the CNS to integrate and process incoming sensory nerve signals and transmit information to the motor neuron.

    The simplest reflexes do not involve interneurons; rather, the sensory neuron synapses directly on a motor neuron in the anterior gray horn of the spinal cord.

④ **The motor neuron transmits a nerve signal to an effector.** The motor neuron transmits a nerve signal through the anterior root and spinal nerve to the peripheral effector organ—a gland or muscle.

⑤ **The effector responds to the nerve signal from the motor neuron.** An effector is a peripheral target organ that responds to the nerve signal from the motor neuron. This response is intended to counteract or remove the original stimulus.

Figure 14.19 Simple Reflex Arcs. A reflex arc is a nerve pathway composed of neurons that control rapid, subconscious, pre-programmed responses to a stimulus. AP|R

Reflex arcs may be ipsilateral or contralateral. A reflex arc is termed *ipsilateral* when both the receptor and effector organs of the reflex are on the same side of the spinal cord. For example, an ipsilateral effect occurs when the muscles in your left arm contract to pull your left hand away from a hot object. A reflex arc is *contralateral* when the sensory impulses from a receptor organ cross over through the spinal cord to activate effector organs in the opposite limb. For example, contralateral effect occurs when you step on a sharp object with your left foot and then contract the muscles in your right leg to maintain balance as you withdraw your left leg from the damaging object.

Reflexes may also be monosynaptic or polysynaptic **(figure 14.20)**. A **monosynaptic** (mon′ō-si-nap′tik; *monos* = single) **reflex** is the simplest of all reflexes. The sensory axons

Figure 14.20 Monosynaptic and Polysynaptic Reflexes. The minimal number of neurons and the pathways of a monosynaptic reflex (left) are compared to those of a polysynaptic reflex (right).

synapse directly on the motor neurons, whose axons project to the effector. Interneurons are not involved in processing this reflex. Very minor synaptic delay is incurred in the single synapse of this reflex arc, resulting in a very prompt reflex response. An example of a mono-synaptic reflex is the patellar (knee-jerk) reflex that physicians use to assess the functioning of the spinal cord. By tapping the patellar liga-ment with a reflex hammer, the muscle spindles in the quadriceps muscles are stretched. The brief stimulus causes a reflexive contrac-tion that occurs unopposed and produces a noticeable kick of the leg.

A **polysynaptic** (pol'ē-si-nap'tik; *polys* = many) **reflex** has more complex neural pathways that exhibit a number of synapses involving interneurons within the reflex arc. Because this reflex arc has more components, a more prolonged delay occurs between stimulus and response. An example of a polysynaptic reflex is the withdrawal reflex, which is a reflex initiated by a painful stimulus, such as burning your finger on a candle flame. Sensory input is transmitted by the sensory neurons to the spinal cord, where interneurons receive and process that information. The interneurons then stimulate motor neurons send nerve signals to flexor muscles in the upper limb, so the muscles will contract and the hand is pulled away from the painful stimulus.

⚗ WHAT DID YOU LEARN?

23 What are the five steps involved in action of a reflex?

24 What is the major difference between monosynaptic and polysynaptic reflexes?

14.6c Spinal Reflexes

⟩✓ LEARNING OBJECTIVE

5. Name and describe four common spinal reflexes.

Some common spinal reflexes are the stretch reflex, the Golgi tendon reflex, the withdrawal (flexor) reflex, and the crossed-extensor reflex.

Stretch Reflex

The **stretch reflex** is a monosynaptic reflex that monitors and regu-lates skeletal muscle length. When a stimulus results in the stretching of a muscle, that muscle reflexively contracts (**figure 14.21**; see also figure 14.20).

Stretch in a muscle is monitored by a stretch receptor called a **muscle spindle.** A muscle spindle is composed of **intrafusal muscle fibers** that are surrounded by a connective tissue capsule. These intrafusal muscle fibers lack myofilaments in their central regions and are contractile only at their distal regions. (Actin and myosin are found only at the ends of these fibers.) These muscle fibers are innervated by **gamma (γ) motor neurons,** so named because the term "gamma" refers to motor neurons with small diameter axons. These neurons detect changes *within* the muscle. *Around* the mus-cle spindle are **extrafusal muscle fibers,** which are innervated by **alpha (α) motor neurons,** so named because these motor neurons have the largest diameter axons. (One study tip to remember the

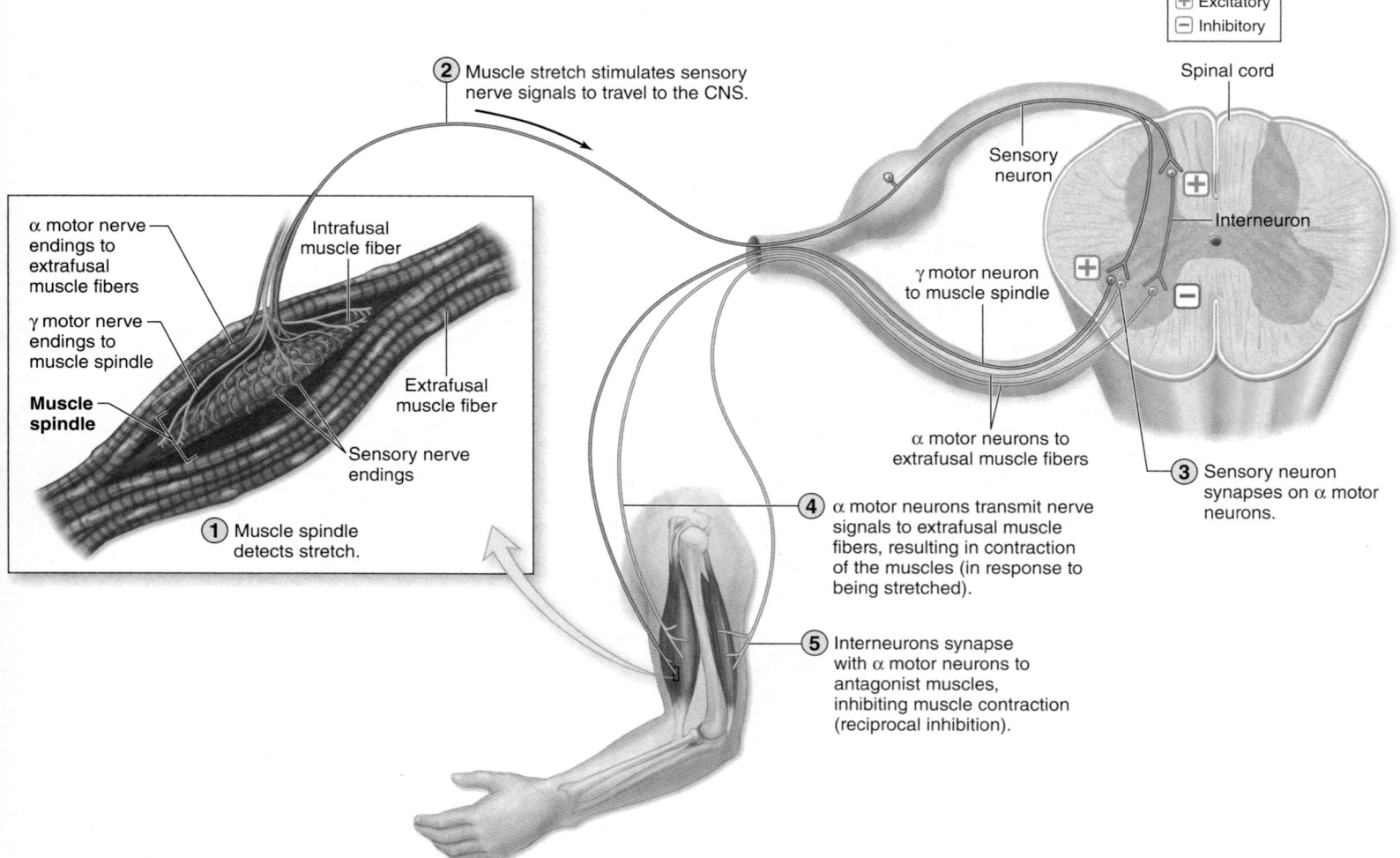

Figure 14.21 Stretch Reflex. A stretch reflex is a simple monosynaptic reflex. A stretching force detected by a muscle spindle results in the contraction of that muscle. Conversely, antagonistic muscle contraction is dampened, in a process called reciprocal inhibition.

difference between the two neuron types is that **G**amma **G**oes within the muscle, and **A**lpha wraps **A**round the muscle.)

A muscle spindle may be stretched if either the entire muscle is stretched or lengthened, or if a portion of the muscle that contains the muscle spindle is lengthened. When the muscle spindle is stretched, the sensation is detected by sensory neurons that are wrapped around the intrafusal muscle fibers of the muscle spindle. The sensory neurons transmit a nerve signal to the spinal cord (CNS), and then synapse with the alpha motor neurons associated with that muscle. The alpha motor neurons then transmit a nerve signal to the extrafusal muscle fibers, which causes the muscle to contract and thus resist the stretch.

The biceps reflex is a monosynaptic reflex that is an example of a stretch reflex. The stimulus (the tap on the bicipital tendon) stretches the muscle spindle in the biceps brachii muscle. Sensory nerve endings transmit a nerve signal to the CNS and synapse with the alpha motor neurons. The alpha motor neurons transmit nerve signals to the extrafusal muscle fibers in biceps brachii, thereby initiating contraction of the muscle and flexing the elbow joint. (Also see in figure 14.21 that the gamma motor neurons are also stimulated by the sensory nerve endings.)

Note in figure 14.21 that a stretch reflex also is indirectly involved in a process called **reciprocal inhibition.** When the sensory nerve signals reach the CNS, some of the sensory axons synapse with interneurons. These interneurons synapse with alpha motor neurons that inhibit antagonistic muscle contraction. In the case of the biceps reflex, the triceps brachii muscles are the inhibited antagonistic muscles. Thus, as the biceps brachii is stimulated, reciprocal inhibition results in the triceps brachii contraction being dampened, so the biceps movement will not be countered by the triceps.

The stretch reflex is a monosynaptic reflex, but the corresponding reciprocal inhibition is polysynaptic in nature, because it uses an interneuron to complete the circuit.

Golgi Tendon Reflex

Whereas the stretch reflex prevents muscles from stretching excessively, the Golgi tendon reflex prevents muscles from doing the opposite: tensing or contracting excessively. The **Golgi tendon reflex** is a polysynaptic reflex that results in muscle lengthening and relaxation in response to increased tension at a structure called a **Golgi tendon organ.** A Golgi tendon organ is composed of sensory nerve endings within a tendon or near a muscle–tendon junction (**figure 14.22**).

Figure 14.22 Golgi Tendon Reflex. Contraction of a muscle generates tension on its tendons and may cause a tendon reflex response. This illustration shows a Golgi tendon organ, which detects the contraction force and results in the relaxation of that muscle. Conversely, antagonistic muscles are stimulated to contract, a process called reciprocal activation.

As a muscle contracts, its associated tendon stretches, resulting in increased tension in the tendon and activation of the Golgi tendon organ. Sensory neurons in the Golgi tendon organ transmit nerve signals to interneurons in the spinal cord, which in turn inhibit the alpha motor neurons in the same muscle. When the motor neurons are inhibited, the associated muscle is allowed to relax, thus protecting the muscle and tendon from excessive tension damage.

Note that the sensory neurons also communicate with other interneurons in the spinal cord that stimulate alpha motor neurons for the *antagonistic* muscles. This process is called **reciprocal activation.** So, for example, if a Golgi tendon organ in the quadriceps femoris muscle detects excessive tension, then the Golgi tendon reflex ultimately relaxes the quadriceps femoris muscle, and reciprocal activation results in the hamstrings being stimulated to contract.

Golgi tendon reflexes help prevent a muscle or tendon from injury due to excessive tension and help ensure that the muscle contraction process occurs smoothly and efficiently. In cases where the muscle is under extreme tension (such as when one lifts a very heavy weight), a Golgi tendon reflex may nullify a stretch reflex (and thus the person drops the weight due to the excessive tension on the muscle). Thus, weightlifters are encouraged to have "spotters" who can help prevent the heavy weight from dropping unexpectedly.

Withdrawal Reflex

A **withdrawal** *(flexor)* **reflex** is a polysynaptic reflex arc that is initiated by a painful stimulus, such as touching something very hot or painful (**figure 14.23**; see also figure 14.20). This stimulation initi-

Figure 14.23 Withdrawal and Crossed-Extensor Reflexes. A withdrawal reflex is a polysynaptic reflex that is initiated by a painful stimulus. The crossed-extensor reflex occurs in response to the withdrawal reflex, by stimulating the extensor muscles in the opposite limb and thereby ensuring the opposite limb supports the body's weight.

ates a nerve signal that is transmitted by a sensory neuron to the spinal cord. Interneurons receive the sensory nerve signal and stimulate motor neurons to the flexor muscles. These flexor muscles contract in response.

For example, when you step on a sharp object, sensory neurons detect the sensation and transmit nerve signals to the spinal cord. They synapse with interneurons, which stimulate motor neurons to contract the flexor muscles (in this case, the hamstrings of the lower limb). You lift the lower limb up and away from the painful stimulus. In addition, reciprocal inhibition occurs with the extensor (quadriceps) muscles, so the hamstrings can contract unimpeded.

Crossed-Extensor Reflex

The **crossed-extensor reflex** often occurs in conjunction with the withdrawal reflex, usually in the lower (weight-bearing) limbs (figure 14.23). In essence, when the withdrawal reflex is occurring in one limb, the crossed-extensor reflex occurs in the other limb. So, when the sensory neurons transmit nerve signals to the spinal cord, some sensory branches synapse with interneurons involved in the stretch reflex, while other sensory branches synapse with interneurons involved in the crossed-extensor reflex. These latter interneurons cross to the other side of the spinal cord through the gray commissure and synapse with motor neurons that control antagonistic muscles in the opposite limb. These motor neurons are stimulated and cause these antagonistic muscles to contract.

Figure 14.23 illustrates how the withdrawal reflex causes the right lower limb to flex at the knee, due to contraction of the right hamstring muscles. In contrast, the crossed-extensor reflex stimulates the left quadriceps femoris muscle to contract, so the left limb remains extended and supports the body weight. Thus, the crossed-extensor reflex helps us maintain balance and shift body weight accordingly in these situations, independently of thought.

 WHAT DID YOU LEARN?

 25 What are the four common spinal reflexes?

14.6d Reflex Testing in a Clinical Setting

LEARNING OBJECTIVE

6. Explain the indications of a hypoactive reflex versus those of a hyperactive reflex.

Reflexes can be an important diagnostic tool. Clinicians use them to test specific muscle groups and specific spinal nerves or segments of the spinal cord (table 14.9). Although some variation in reflexes is normal, a consistently abnormal reflex response may indicate damage to the nervous system or muscles.

A reflex response may be normal, hypoactive, or hyperactive. A **hypoactive reflex** refers to a reflex response that is diminished or absent. A hypoactive reflex may indicate damage to a segment of the spinal cord, or it may suggest muscle disease or damage to the neuromuscular junction.

A **hyperactive reflex** refers to an abnormally strong response. It may indicate damage somewhere in either the brain or spinal cord, especially if it is accompanied by **clonus** (klō′nŭs; *klonus* = tumult), rhythmic oscillations between flexion and extension, when the muscle reflex is tested.

 WHAT DID YOU LEARN?

 26 What problems could a hypoactive reflex suggest?

14.7 Development of the Spinal Cord

 LEARNING OBJECTIVE

1. Describe how the neural tube forms the gray matter structures in the spinal cord.

Recall from section 13.1b that the caudal (inferior) part of the neural tube forms the spinal cord. As the caudal part of the neural tube differentiates and specializes, the spinal cord begins to develop

Table 14.9	Some Clinically Important Reflexes	
Reflex	**Spinal Nerve Segments Tested**	**Normal Action of Effector**
Biceps reflex	C5, C6	Flexes elbow when biceps brachii tendon is tapped
Triceps reflex	C6, C7	Extends elbow when triceps brachii tendon is tapped
Abdominal reflexes	T8–T12	Contract abdominal muscles when one side of the abdominal wall is briskly stroked
Cremasteric reflex	L1, L2	Elevates testis (due to contraction of cremaster muscle in scrotum) when medial side of thigh is briskly stroked
Patellar (knee-jerk) reflex	L2–L4	Extends knee when patellar ligament is tapped
Ankle (Achilles) reflex	S1	Plantar flexes ankle when calcaneal tendon is tapped
Plantar reflex	L5, S1	Plantar flexes foot; flexes toes when plantar side of foot is briskly stroked[1]

1. This is the normal reflex response in adults; in adults with spinal cord damage and in normal infants, the **Babinski sign** occurs, which is extension of the great toe and fanning of the other toes.

(figure 14.24). However, this developmental process is much less complex than that of the brain. A hollow **neural canal** in the neural tube develops into the central canal of the spinal cord. Note that the neural canal doesn't shrink in size; rather, the neural tube around it grows at a rapid rate. Thus, as the neural tube walls grow and expand, the neural canal in the newborn appears as a tiny hole called the central canal.

During the fourth and fifth weeks of embryonic development, the neural tube starts to grow rapidly and unevenly. Part of the neural tube forms the white matter of the spinal cord, while other components form gray matter. By the sixth week of development, a horizontal groove called the **sulcus limitans** (lim'i-tanz; *limes* = boundary) forms in the lateral walls of the central canal (figure 14.24). The sulcus limitans also represents a dividing point in the neural tube as two specific regions become evident: the basal plates and alar plates.

The **basal plates** lie anterior to the sulcus limitans. The basal plates develop into the anterior and lateral horns, motor structures of the gray matter. They also form the anterior part of the gray commissure.

The **alar** (ā'lăr; *ala* = wing) **plates** lie posterior to the sulcus limitans. By about the ninth week of development, the alar plates develop into posterior horns, sensory structures of the gray matter. They also form the posterior part of the gray commissure.

During the embryonic period, the spinal cord extends the length of the vertebral canal. However, during the fetal period, the growth of the vertebral column (and its vertebral canal) outpaces that of the spinal cord. By the sixth fetal month, the spinal cord is at the level of the S_1 vertebra; in contrast, a newborn's spinal cord ends at about the L_3 vertebra. By adulthood, the spinal cord length extends only to the level of the L_1 vertebra. This disproportionate growth explains why the lumbar, sacral, and coccygeal parts of the spinal cord and its associated nerve roots do not lie next to their respective vertebrae.

WHAT DID YOU LEARN?

27 What structures develop from the alar plates, and what structures develop from the basal plates?

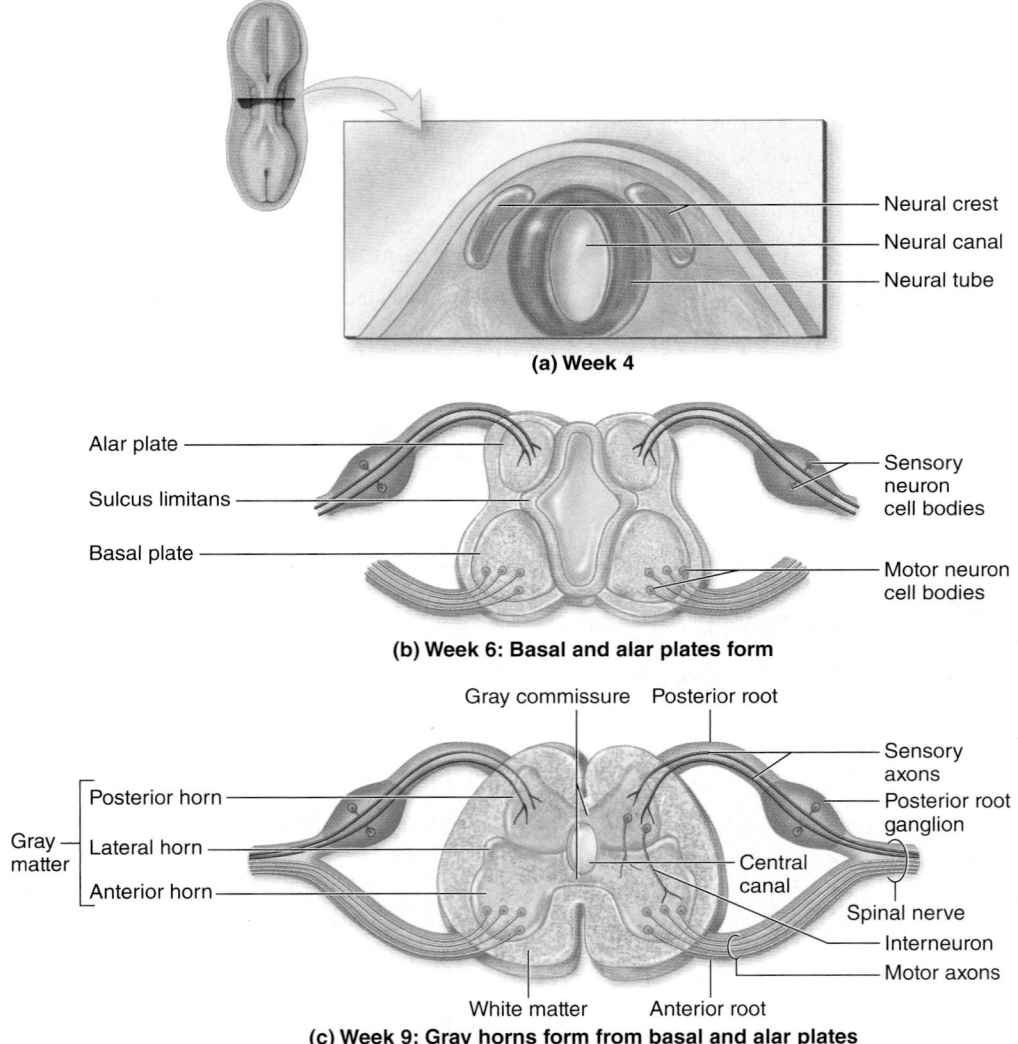

(a) Week 4

(b) Week 6: Basal and alar plates form

(c) Week 9: Gray horns form from basal and alar plates

Figure 14.24 Spinal Cord Development. The spinal cord begins development as a tubular extension of the brain. (*a*) A cross section shows the structures of the neural tube of an embryo in week 4 of development. Transverse sections show (*b*) the formation of the alar and basal plates at week 6 and (*c*) the developing spinal cord at week 9.

- The spinal cord and spinal nerves serve as a pathway for sensory and motor nerve signals and are responsible for reflexes.
- The adult spinal cord traverses the vertebral canal and typically ends at the level of the L_1 vertebra.
- There are 31 pairs of spinal nerves: 8 pairs of cervical nerves, 12 pairs of thoracic nerves, 5 pairs of lumbar nerves, 5 pairs of sacral nerves, and 1 pair of coccygeal nerves.

- The epidural space lies between the vertebral canal and the dura mater.
- A potential subdural space lies between the dura mater and arachnoid mater, while the subarachnoid space lies between the arachnoid mater and pia mater.

- Gray matter is centrally located and composed of cell bodies, unmyelinated axons, and glial cells.
- White matter is peripherally located and composed of myelinated axons.

14.3a Distribution of Gray Matter 539

- Gray matter is composed of three horns: anterior (contains cell bodies of somatic motor neurons), lateral (contains cell bodies of autonomic motor neurons), and posterior (contains sensory axons and interneurons).

14.3b Distribution of White Matter 540

- White matter is organized into three pairs of funiculi, each of which contains sensory (ascending) tracts and motor (descending) tracts.

- The central nervous system (CNS) communicates with the body through conduction pathways in the spinal cord.

14.4a Overview of Conduction Pathways 541

- Sensory pathways carry ascending information to the CNS, while motor pathways transmit descending information from the brain to muscles and glands.

14.4b Sensory Pathways 541

- Sensory pathways use primary, secondary, and tertiary neurons.
- The posterior funiculus–medial lemniscal pathway conducts stimuli of fine touch, precise pressure, and proprioception.
- The anterolateral pathway carries stimuli related to pain, pressure, temperature, and touch.
- The spinocerebellar pathway conducts stimuli to the cerebellum related to tendons, joints, and muscle posture.

14.4c Motor Pathways 544

- Motor pathways use upper and lower motor neurons.
- Somatic motor commands travel through either the direct system (for conscious control) or the indirect system (for unconscious control).
- The direct system consists of the corticobulbar and corticospinal tracts.
- The indirect system consists of the lateral pathway (rubrospinal tracts) and the medial pathway (reticulospinal, tectospinal, and vestibulospinal tracts).

- A spinal nerve is formed from the union of an anterior root and a posterior root.

14.5a Overview of Spinal Nerves 548

- Spinal nerves have two branches: A posterior ramus innervates the skin and deep muscles of the back, and an anterior ramus innervates the anterior and lateral portions of the trunk and the limbs.

14.5b Nerve Plexuses 550

- A nerve plexus is a network of interwoven anterior rami. Nerve plexuses occur in pairs.

14.5c Intercostal Nerves 550

- The anterior rami of spinal nerves T1–T11 form the intercostal nerves. Nerve T12 is called a subcostal nerve.

14.5d Cervical Plexuses 550

- Each cervical plexus is formed from the anterior rami of C1–C4 spinal nerves. It innervates the anterior neck muscles and the skin along the neck and shoulders.

14.5e Brachial Plexuses 552

- Each brachial plexus innervates an upper limb. It is formed from the anterior rami of spinal nerves C5–T1.

14.5f Lumbar Plexuses 558

- Each lumbar plexus innervates the anterior and medial thigh, the lower abdominal wall, and the skin of the medial leg. It is formed from the anterior rami of spinal nerves L1–L4.

14.5g Sacral Plexuses 560

- Each sacral plexus innervates most of the lower limb as well as the perineum. It is formed from the anterior rami of spinal nerves L4–S4.

- A reflex is a rapid, automatic, involuntary motor response of muscles or glands to a stimulus.

14.6a Characteristics of Reflexes 564

- A reflex requires a stimulus to initiate the involuntary response.

14.6b Components of a Reflex Arc 564

- The five steps of a reflex are (1) activation of a receptor by a stimulus, (2) nerve signal conduction along a sensory neuron to the CNS, (3) integration and processing of information by interneurons, (4) nerve signal conduction along a motor neuron, and (5) effector response.
- The simplest reflex arc is a monosynaptic reflex, in which the sensory neuron synapses directly with the motor neuron.
- A polysynaptic reflex involves a sensory neuron, a motor neuron, and at least one interneuron connecting the sensory and motor neurons.

(continued on next page)

14.6 Reflexes (continued)	**14.6c Spinal Reflexes 566**
	• A stretch reflex is monosynaptic and contracts the muscle in response to increased stretch in a muscle spindle.
	• A Golgi tendon reflex is polysynaptic and prevents muscles from tensing excessively.
	• A withdrawal reflex is polysynaptic and activates flexor muscles to immediately remove a body part from a painful stimulus.
	• A crossed-extensor reflex stimulates the extensor muscles in the opposite limb, in response to the withdrawal reflex.
	14.6d Reflex Testing in a Clinical Setting 569
	• Reflex testing can help diagnose nervous system or muscular disorders.
	• Hypoactive reflexes, in which the response is diminished, may indicate spinal cord damage or muscle pathology.
	• Hyperactive reflexes, in which the response is abnormally strong, may indicate damage to the brain or spinal cord.
14.7 Development of the Spinal Cord 569	• The neural tube forms basal plates and alar plates.
	• Basal plates form the anterior horns, lateral horns, and anterior half of the gray commissure.
	• Alar plates form the posterior horns and the posterior half of the gray commissure.

CHALLENGE YOURSELF

Do You Know the Basics?

_____ 1. Identify the meningeal layer immediately deep to the subdural space.
a. arachnoid mater   c. dura mater
b. pia mater   d. epidural space

_____ 2. The anterior root of a spinal nerve contains
a. axons of both motor and sensory neurons.
b. axons of sensory neurons only.
c. interneurons.
d. axons of motor neurons only.

_____ 3. Where are tertiary neurons found?
a. extending between the posterior horn and anterior horn
b. extending between the posterior horn and the brainstem
c. extending between the thalamus and the primary somatosensory cortex
d. extending between the primary motor cortex and the brainstem

_____ 4. Which of the following is an example of a sensory pathway?
a. reticulospinal tract
b. spinocerebellar tract
c. corticobulbar tract
d. tectospinal tract

_____ 5. The radial nerve originates from the _____ plexus.
a. cervical   c. lumbar
b. brachial   d. sacral

_____ 6. Which structure sends motor nerve signals to the deep back muscles and receives sensory nerve signals from the skin of the back?
a. posterior root
b. posterior ramus
c. anterior root
d. anterior ramus

_____ 7. Which statement is true about intercostal nerves?
a. They are formed from the posterior rami of spinal nerves.
b. They form a thoracic plexus of nerves.
c. They originate from the thoracic part of the spinal cord.
d. They innervate the lower limb.

_____ 8. The _____ nerve innervates the anterior thigh muscles and the skin on the anterior thigh.
a. femoral   c. sciatic
b. obturator   d. tibial

_____ 9. A _____ reflex is monosynaptic and responds to stretching in a muscle spindle.
a. withdrawal   c. Golgi tendon
b. crossed-extensor   d. stretch

_____ 10. Which statement is correct about reflexes?
a. The patellar reflex tests the S1-S3 spinal nerve segments.
b. A hypoactive reflex may be indicative of damage to the neuromuscular junction.
c. The more hyperactive the reflex, the healthier the individual.
d. A normal biceps reflex response is extension of the elbow when the biceps tendon is tapped.

11. Identify the spinal cord parts, which spinal nerves are associated with them, and their relationship to the corresponding vertebrae.

12. List the three gray matter horns on each side of the spinal cord, and discuss the neuronal composition of each. In addition, list which types of nuclei (motor or sensory) are located in each horn.

13. Compare the main differences between the posterior funiculus–medial lemniscal pathway and the anterolateral pathway.

14. Describe the location and function of upper and lower motor neurons in the motor pathways.

15. What are the main terminal branches of the brachial plexus, and what muscles do these terminal branches innervate?

16. What anterior rami form the lumbar plexus, and what in general does this plexus innervate?

17. What muscles do the tibial and common fibular nerves innervate?

18. What are the five basic steps involved in a reflex arc?

19. What are the differences between a stretch and Golgi tendon reflex?

20. Where are the basal and alar plates of the neural tube located, and what do each form?

Can You Apply What You've Learned?

Use the following paragraph to answer questions 1–3.

Madeleine is an active 18-year-old who fell off her bike, fracturing the medial epicondyle of her humerus. In addition to experiencing severe pain in her elbow, she experienced numbness along the medial side of her hand. She went to the emergency room and the physician examined her.

1. After x-raying her elbow, the physician performed further tests on Madeline to determine what nerve damage she may have experienced. What nerve likely was injured when she fractured her medial epicondyle?
   a. radial
   b. ulnar
   c. musculocutaneous
   d. median

2. What diagnostic test would best help determine the potential damage to this nerve?
   a. Have Madeline extend her elbow against resistance.
   b. Have Madeline flex her wrist and fingers against resistance.
   c. Have Madeline hold a piece of paper between her fingers while the physician tries to pull the paper away.
   d. Have Madeline flex her elbow while the physician applies gentle pressure to the anterior forearm muscles.

3. What other muscle function could be impaired in this type of injury?
   a. adduction of the thumb
   b. flexion of the thumb
   c. extension of the thumb
   d. abduction of the thumb

4. George tried to lift a heavy box and in the process herniated one of his lumbar intervertebral discs. The herniated disc pinched on nerve roots and most likely caused which of the following ailments?
   a. pain down the back of the leg
   b. inability to flex the thigh
   c. inability to adduct the thigh
   d. pain down the medial side of the leg

5. Carlos experienced some muscle weakness in his right lower limb and went to see his physician. The physician noticed Carlos could not evert his foot and had anesthesia along most of the dorsum of his right foot. Carlos was still able to dorsiflex his foot and invert his foot. Based on these symptoms, what specific nerve likely was injured?
   a. common fibular
   b. tibial
   c. deep fibular
   d. superficial fibular

Can You Synthesize What You've Learned?

1. Arthur dove off a small cliff into water that was shallower than he expected and he hit his head. He is now a quadriplegic, which means that both his upper and lower limbs are paralyzed. Approximately where is the location of his injury? What is the likelihood that Arthur will recover from this injury?

2. Jessica fractured her fibula and had to wear a leg cast for several weeks. When the cast was removed, Jessica had trouble walking normally and experienced "foot drop." What structure likely was pinched by the leg cast, resulting in the foot drop?

3. Juanita was walking barefoot on the sidewalk when she stepped on a piece of glass with her right foot. Her right leg reflexively lifted up, away from the shard of glass. What is this type of reflex called? In addition, Juanita did not fall down when she lifted her leg. What action in her left lower limb helped stabilize her?

INTEGRATE

ONLINE STUDY TOOLS
www.mhhe.com/mckinleyap

  |ANATOMY & PHYSIOLOGY

Clinical Case Study: A Young Man with Rapidly Developing Muscle Weakness

Interactive Questions: This chapter's content is served up in a number of multimedia question formats for student study.

LearnSmart: Topics and terminology include spinal cord gross anatomy; protection and support of the spinal cord; sectional

anatomy of the spinal cord; spinal cord conduction pathways; spinal nerves; reflexes; development of the spinal cord

Anatomy & Physiology Revealed: Topics include cervical, thoracic, lumbar, and sacral regions of spinal cord; spinal nerves; brachial plexus; cervical plexus, lumbosacral plexus; reflex arc

chapter 15
Nervous System: Autonomic Nervous System

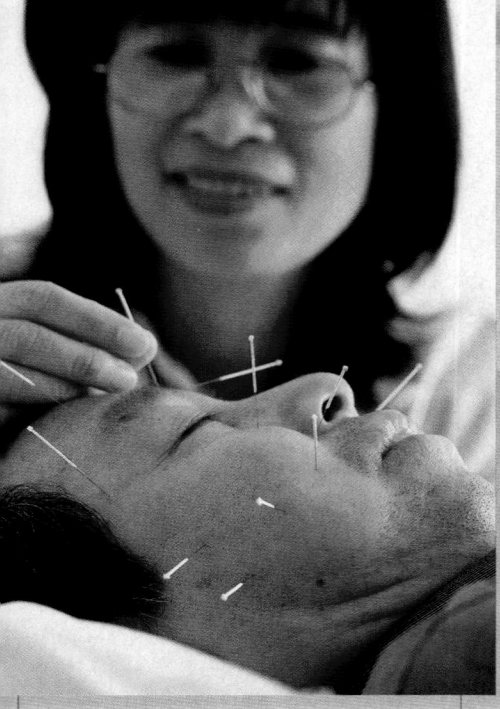

On a twisting downhill slope, an Olympic skier is concentrating on controlling her body to negotiate the course faster than anyone else in the world. Compared to the spectators in the viewing areas, her pupils are dilated, and her heart is beating faster and pumping more blood to her skeletal muscles. At the same time, organ system functions not needed in the race are practically shut down. Digestion, urination, and defecation can wait until the race is over. The skier exhibits a state of heightened readiness, called the "fight-or-flight" response, ➡

Acupuncture is one of the mainstays of traditional Chinese medicine (TCM) as well as complementary and alternative medicine (CAM). TCM believes disease and pathology are due to a blockage of *qi* (vital energy) at some location in the body. An acupuncturist inserts long, thin metallic needles into the skin at specific acupuncture sites to promote *qi* circulation. Acupuncture is effective at relieving some types of pain, and many studies suggest it can relieve nausea associated with chemotherapy or other medical treatments. Acupuncture has also been used to treat depression, anxiety, infertility and some neurological disorders. Some researchers believe that acupuncture manipulates our autonomic nervous system (ANS) in ways that are not yet understood. Since the ANS controls our internal environment and innervates our viscera, practices such as acupuncture may help the workings of these structures.

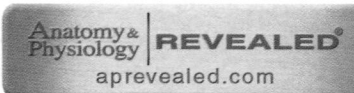

Anatomy & Physiology | REVEALED®
aprevealed.com

Module 7: Nervous System

The autonomic nervous system (ANS) is a complex system of nerves that controls and mediates involuntary actions, regulates body organ activity, and maintains normal internal functions. We begin this chapter by comparing the somatic nervous system (SNS) and the ANS. We then examine the two divisions of the ANS, the parasympathetic and sympathetic divisions, in more detail. We end our discussion with how the autonomic nervous system is regulated by various centers within the central nervous system.

15.1 Comparison of the Somatic and Autonomic Nervous Systems

We introduce this chapter on the autonomic nervous system by first describing how the nervous system is organized into a somatic nervous system and an autonomic nervous system. Included in this section is a description comparing the motor neurons of these two systems.

15.1a Functional Organization

✓ LEARNING OBJECTIVE

1. List the similarities and differences between the SNS and the ANS.

Recall from section 12.1 that anatomists and physiologists have devised various ways to organize the nervous system both structurally and functionally. Here, we introduce a slightly different way of functionally organizing the nervous system into two systems that is based on whether we are conscious of the process. The two components are the somatic nervous system and the autonomic nervous system (**figure 15.1**). Both systems include sensory and motor components.

The **somatic nervous system (SNS)** includes processes that are perceived or controlled consciously (figure 15.1a). The **somatic sensory** portion includes detection of stimuli and transmission of nerve signals from the special senses (e.g., vision, hearing, equilibrium, smell and taste), skin, and proprioceptors (receptors in joints and muscles that detect body position) to the CNS. The sensory portion of the somatic nervous system, for example, allows us to see a beautiful mountain, smell a baby's skin, or taste a delicious dinner. The **somatic motor** portion involves initiation and transmission of nerve signals from the CNS to control skeletal muscles. This is exemplified by voluntary activities such as getting out of a chair, picking up a ball, and throwing a ball for the dog to chase. Both the sensory nerve signals we consciously perceive and the nerve signals that we voluntarily initiate to skeletal muscle involve the cerebrum (section 13.3c). Reflexive skeletal muscle activity is controlled by the brainstem and spinal cord (section 14.6).

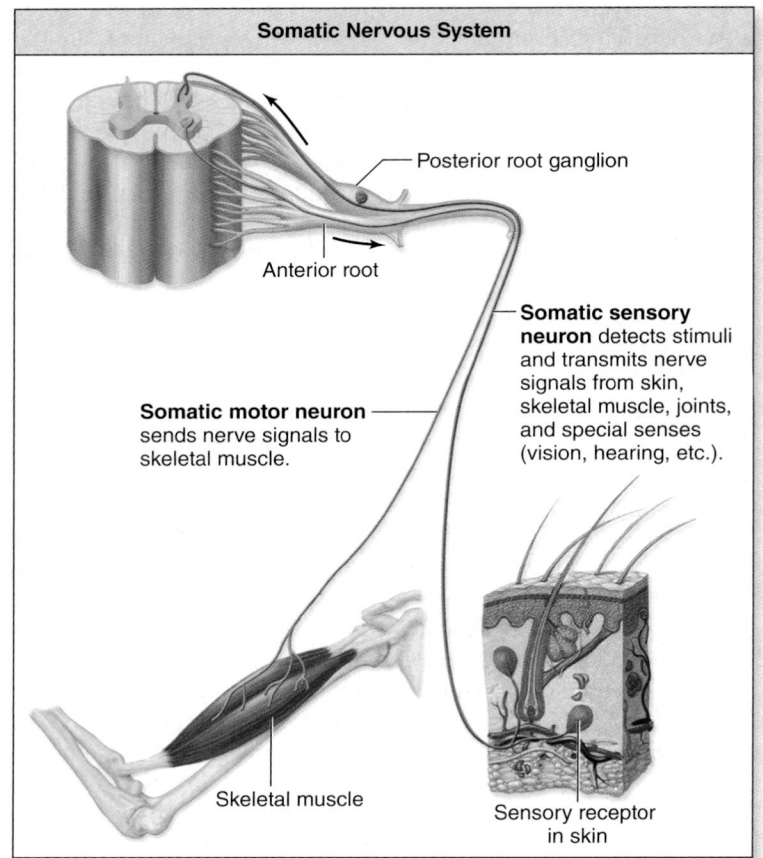

Somatic Nervous System

Posterior root ganglion

Anterior root

Somatic sensory neuron detects stimuli and transmits nerve signals from skin, skeletal muscle, joints, and special senses (vision, hearing, etc.).

Somatic motor neuron sends nerve signals to skeletal muscle.

Skeletal muscle

Sensory receptor in skin

(a)

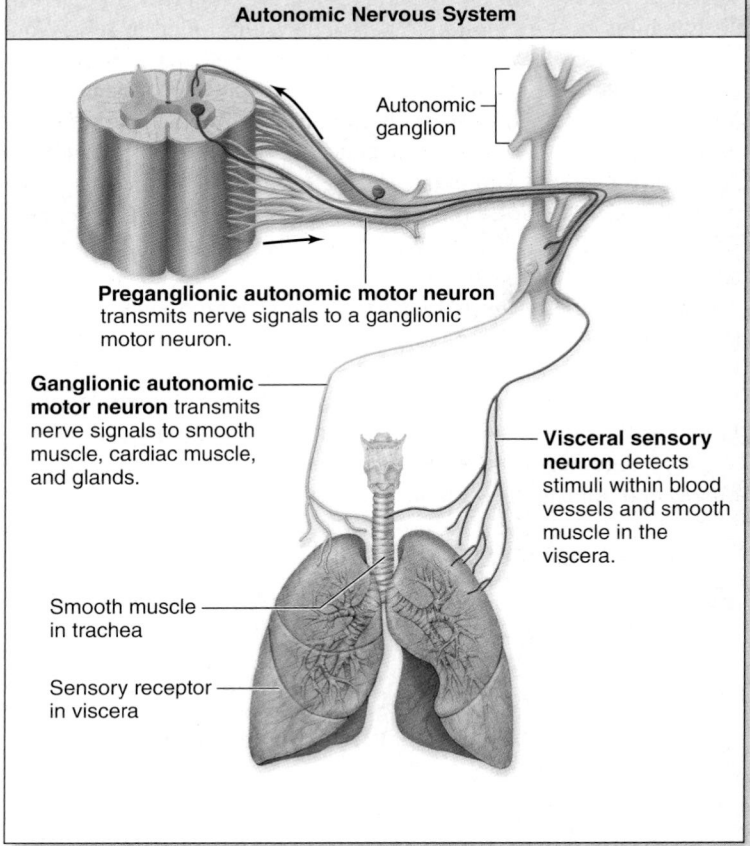

Autonomic Nervous System

Autonomic ganglion

Preganglionic autonomic motor neuron transmits nerve signals to a ganglionic motor neuron.

Ganglionic autonomic motor neuron transmits nerve signals to smooth muscle, cardiac muscle, and glands.

Visceral sensory neuron detects stimuli within blood vessels and smooth muscle in the viscera.

Smooth muscle in trachea

Sensory receptor in viscera

(b)

Figure 15.1 Comparison of Somatic and Autonomic Nervous Systems. The nervous system is functionally organized into the (*a*) somatic nervous system, which involves processes that we consciously perceive and control, and the (*b*) autonomic nervous system, which involves processes that occur below the conscious level.

LEARNING STRATEGY

A good way to understand the two-neuron ANS chain is to compare it to the U.S. airline system, which uses connecting flights and "airport hubs" to transport the maximum number of people in the most cost-effective way.

Imagine that you are flying from Indianapolis to Miami for spring break: Your first flight from Indianapolis to Chicago is the **preganglionic axon.**

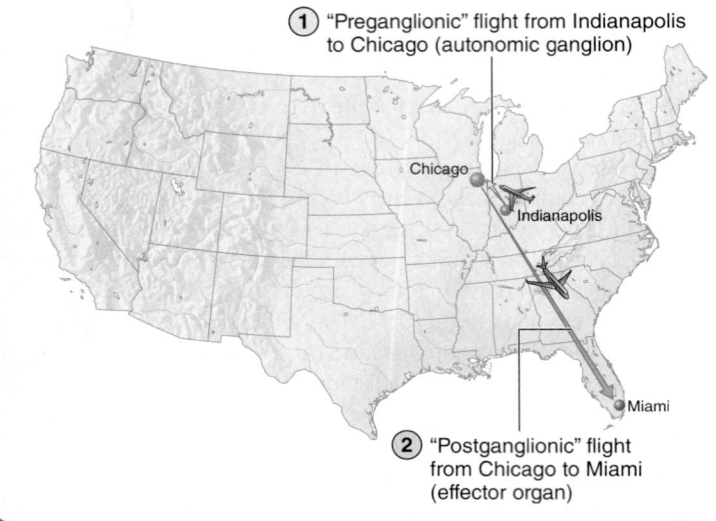

① "Preganglionic" flight from Indianapolis to Chicago (autonomic ganglion)

Chicago
Indianapolis
Miami

② "Postganglionic" flight from Chicago to Miami (effector organ)

Although flying north to Chicago is out of your way, the airline sends you to an airport hub because it is more efficient to send all Indianapolis passengers to this main location before they take different flights throughout the United States.

The airport hub in Chicago is the **autonomic ganglion,** the point where preganglionic and postganglionic "flights" meet up. Other preganglionic flights are arriving at the airport hub, and here all these passengers will connect with other flights.

Your connecting flight from Chicago to Miami is the **ganglionic neuron.** This flight will take you to your final destination, just as a postganglionic axon sends a nerve signal to an effector organ. On the plane with you are people from other preganglionic flights who all want to go to Miami as well.

Is using two different flights the most *direct* way for you to get from Indianapolis to Florida? Of course not. But it is the most *cost-efficient* (or *energy-efficient*) way for the airlines to transport and disperse many passengers with a limited number of planes.

The connecting-flight arrangement also allows for the extensive convergence of passengers to an airport 'hub', and for the extensive divergence of passengers from the 'hubs' to the final destinations. Thus, the two motor neurons used in the ANS allow for neuronal convergence and divergence.

The autonomic nervous system is similar to connecting airline flights and "airport hubs" in that both try to group and disperse many different items (nerve signals or passengers) with a limited number of neurons or flights.

The **autonomic nervous system (ANS)** (aw-tō-nom'ik; *auto* = self, *nomos* = law), also called the *visceral nervous system,* includes processes regulated below the conscious level (figure 15.1b). Thus, all functions of the autonomic nervous system function reflexively and without our awareness. The **visceral sensory** components include receptors that detect stimuli associated with blood vessels and internal organs or viscera. Some of these sensory neurons, for example, monitor carbon dioxide concentration in the blood, whereas others detect pressure by measuring stretch in smooth muscles of visceral walls. The **autonomic motor,** or *visceral motor,* components initiate and transmit nerve signals from the CNS to cardiac muscle, smooth muscle, and glands.

The function of the ANS is to maintain **homeostasis,** or a constant internal environment (see section 1.5). Thus, the ANS regulates all physiological processes that must be maintained by the nervous system to keep the body alive including the regulation of heart rate, blood pressure, body temperature, respiratory rate, sweating, and digestion. The ANS keeps these variables within optimal ranges and adjusts the variables to meet changing body needs.

WHAT DID YOU LEARN?

❶ What criterion is used to organize the nervous system into the SNS and the ANS? What sensory and motor components are associated with each of the two systems?

15.1b Motor Neurons of the Somatic versus Autonomic Nervous System

LEARNING OBJECTIVES

2. Compare and contrast motor neurons in the SNS and ANS.
3. Describe how the two-neuron chain in the ANS facilitates communication and control.

One significant anatomical difference between the somatic nervous system and autonomic nervous system is the number of lower motor neurons that extend from the CNS. A single lower motor neuron extends from the CNS to skeletal muscle fibers in the somatic nervous system (see figure 15.1a). The cell body of a lower motor neuron lies within the brainstem or the spinal cord and its axon exits the CNS in either a cranial nerve or a spinal nerve to a skeletal muscle, respectively. Additionally, the motor neurons of the somatic nervous system are (1) composed of myelinated axons with a large diameter allowing for fast propagation of a nerve signal (section 12.9b), and (2) always release acetylcholine (ACh) neurotransmitter from its synaptic knobs to stimulate or excite the skeletal muscle fiber (section 10.3).

In comparison, a chain of two lower motor neurons extend from the CNS to innervate cardiac muscle, smooth muscle, and glands in the ANS (see figure 15.1b, **figure 15.2**). The first of the two ANS motor neurons is the **preganglionic** (prē'gang-lē-on'ik) **neuron.** Its cell body lies within the brainstem or the spinal cord. A **preganglionic axon** extends from this cell body and exits the CNS in either a cranial nerve or a spinal nerve. This axon projects to an autonomic ganglion in the peripheral nervous system. Preganglionic neurons have myelinated axons that typically are small in diameter, and nerve signals always results in the release of acetylcholine to excite the second neuron.

The second neuron in this pathway is called a **ganglionic neuron.** Its cell body resides within an autonomic ganglion. A **postganglionic axon** extends from the cell body to an effector (cardiac muscle, smooth muscle, or a gland). Ganglionic neurons have unmyelinated axons that are even smaller in diameter than preganglionic axons. The neurotransmitter released from the ganglionic neuron in response to a nerve signal is either ACh or norepinephrine (NE). Both can either excite or inhibit an effector depending on the type of receptors present within the effector

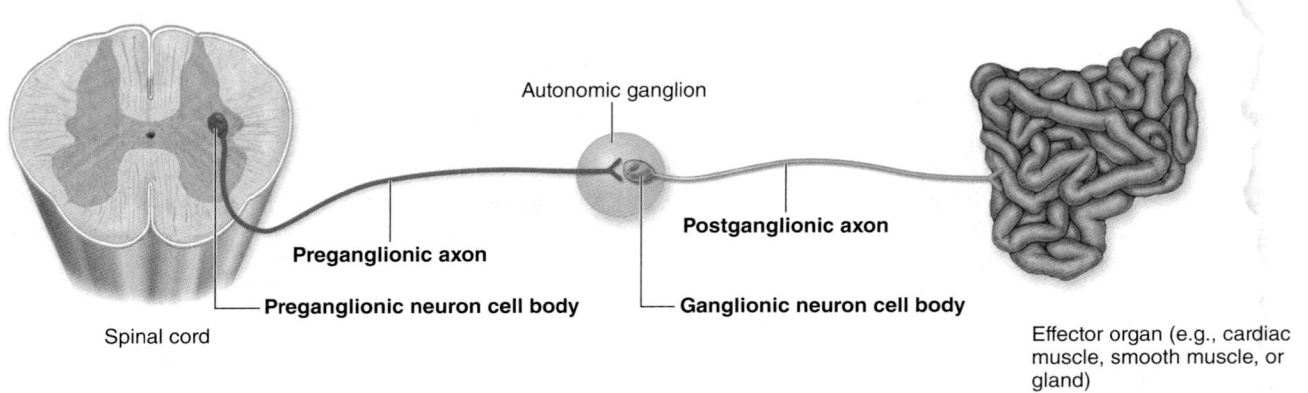

Autonomic ganglion

Postganglionic axon

Preganglionic axon

Ganglionic neuron cell body

Preganglionic neuron cell body

Spinal cord

Effector organ (e.g., cardiac muscle, smooth muscle, or gland)

Figure 15.2 Lower Motor Neurons of the Autonomic Nervous System. The autonomic nervous system employs a chain of two lower motor neurons, a preganglionic neuron and a ganglionic neuron. The dendrites and cell body of a preganglionic neuron are housed within the CNS (brain or spinal cord). The preganglionic axon synapses with a ganglionic neuron within an autonomic ganglion.

(a concept described later in detail). Because motor neurons of the ANS are small or unmyelinated, conduction of nerve signals is relatively slow in comparison to nerve conduction along somatic motor axons.

One significant point must be made concerning the two-neuron motor pathway in the ANS: It has a distinctive advantage in that it allows for increasing communication and control. This occurs because there is neuronal convergence and neuronal divergence (section 12.11). **Neuronal convergence** (kon-ver′jens) occurs because axons from numerous preganglionic neurons synapse with and influence a single ganglionic cell. **Neuronal divergence** (di-ver′jens; *di* = two) occurs because axons from one preganglionic cell synapse with and influence numerous ganglionic cells.

Table 15.1 compares and contrasts the characteristics of the somatic and autonomic nervous systems.

 WHAT DID YOU LEARN?

2 What are the anatomic features that distinguish the motor neurons in the SNS and ANS?

15.2 Divisions of the Autonomic Nervous System

The motor component of the ANS is further subdivided into the parasympathetic division and the sympathetic division. Here we discuss both the functional and anatomical differences between the two divisions, and also the degree of response (local or mass activation) that is possible when each division is activated.

Table 15.1	Comparison of Somatic and Autonomic Motor Nervous Systems	
Feature	**Somatic Nervous System**	**Autonomic Nervous Systems**
Type of Control	Voluntary control (from cerebrum) Reflexive control (brainstem and spinal cord)	Involuntary (or reflexive) control (from brainstem, hypothalamus, and spinal cord)
Number of Neurons in Pathway	One neuron in pathway; somatic motor neuron axon extends from CNS to effector	Two neurons in pathway: preganglionic neuron has preganglionic axon that projects to ganglionic neuron; ganglionic neuron has postganglionic axon that projects to effector
Sensory Input	Special senses, skin; proprioceptors	Visceral senses and some somatic senses
Ganglia Associated with Sensory Input	Posterior root ganglia; sensory ganglia of cranial nerves	Posterior root ganglia; sensory ganglia of cranial nerves
Ganglia Associated with Motor Neurons	None	Autonomic ganglia (terminal ganglia; intramural ganglia; sympathetic trunk ganglia; prevertebral ganglia)
Effector Organs	Skeletal muscle fibers	Cardiac muscle cells, smooth muscle cells, glands
Response of Effector	Excitation only	Either excitation or inhibition of effectors
Neurotransmitter Released	Acetylcholine (ACh)	Preganglionic axons release ACh Postganglionic axons release either ACh or norepinephrine (NE)
Axon Properties	Thicker diameter; myelinated; have fast conduction	Preganglionic axons are thin in diameter and myelinated Postganglionic axons are thinner in diameter and unmyelinated; both have relatively slow conduction

15.2a Functional Differences

✓ LEARNING OBJECTIVE

1. Describe the general functions of parasympathetic and sympathetic divisions of the autonomic nervous system.

The divisions perform dramatically different functions—but instead of being thought of as antagonistic, they should be considered complementary. The **parasympathetic** (par-ă-sim-pa-thet′ik; *para* = alongside, *sympatheo* = to feel with) **division** functions to maintain homeostasis when we are at rest. This division is primarily concerned with conserving energy and replenishing nutrient stores. Because it is most active when the body is at rest or digesting a meal, the parasympathetic division has been nicknamed the "rest-and-digest" division.

The **sympathetic** (sim-pă-thet′ik) **division** is primarily concerned with preparing the body for emergencies. It is often referred to as the "fight-or-flight" division because increased sympathetic activity results in the increased alertness and metabolic activity needed to coordinate and direct body response in stressful or frightening situations. (To help you identify when the sympathetic division is active, remember the "three *E*'s": emergency, exercise, or excitement.)

◦ WHAT DID YOU LEARN?

3 The parasympathetic division is responsible for what main functions?

15.2b Anatomic Differences

✓ LEARNING OBJECTIVE

2. Compare and contrast the anatomic differences in the motor neurons and associated ganglia of the parasympathetic and sympathetic divisions.

Anatomically, these two divisions are similar in that they both use a preganglionic neuron and a ganglionic neuron to innervate muscles or glands. Additionally, both divisions have autonomic ganglia that house the ganglionic neurons. One of the major differences is where the preganglionic neuron cell bodies are housed in the CNS **(figure 15.3)**. Parasympathetic preganglionic neurons originate in either the brainstem or the lateral gray matter of the S2–S4 spinal cord segments, and for this reason this division is also termed the *craniosacral* (krā′nē-ō-sā′krăl) *division*. In comparison, sympathetic preganglionic neurons originate in the lateral horns of the T1–L2 spinal cord segments, and for this reason this division is also termed the *thoracolumbar* (thōr′ă-kō-lŭm′bar) *division*.

Other anatomical differences between the parasympathetic and sympathetic nervous system include **(figure 15.4)**

- **Length of preganglionic and postganglionic axons.** Parasympathetic preganglionic axons are longer, and postganglionic axons are shorter, when compared to their counterparts in the sympathetic division. In the sympathetic division, preganglionic axons are shorter and postganglionic axons are longer.

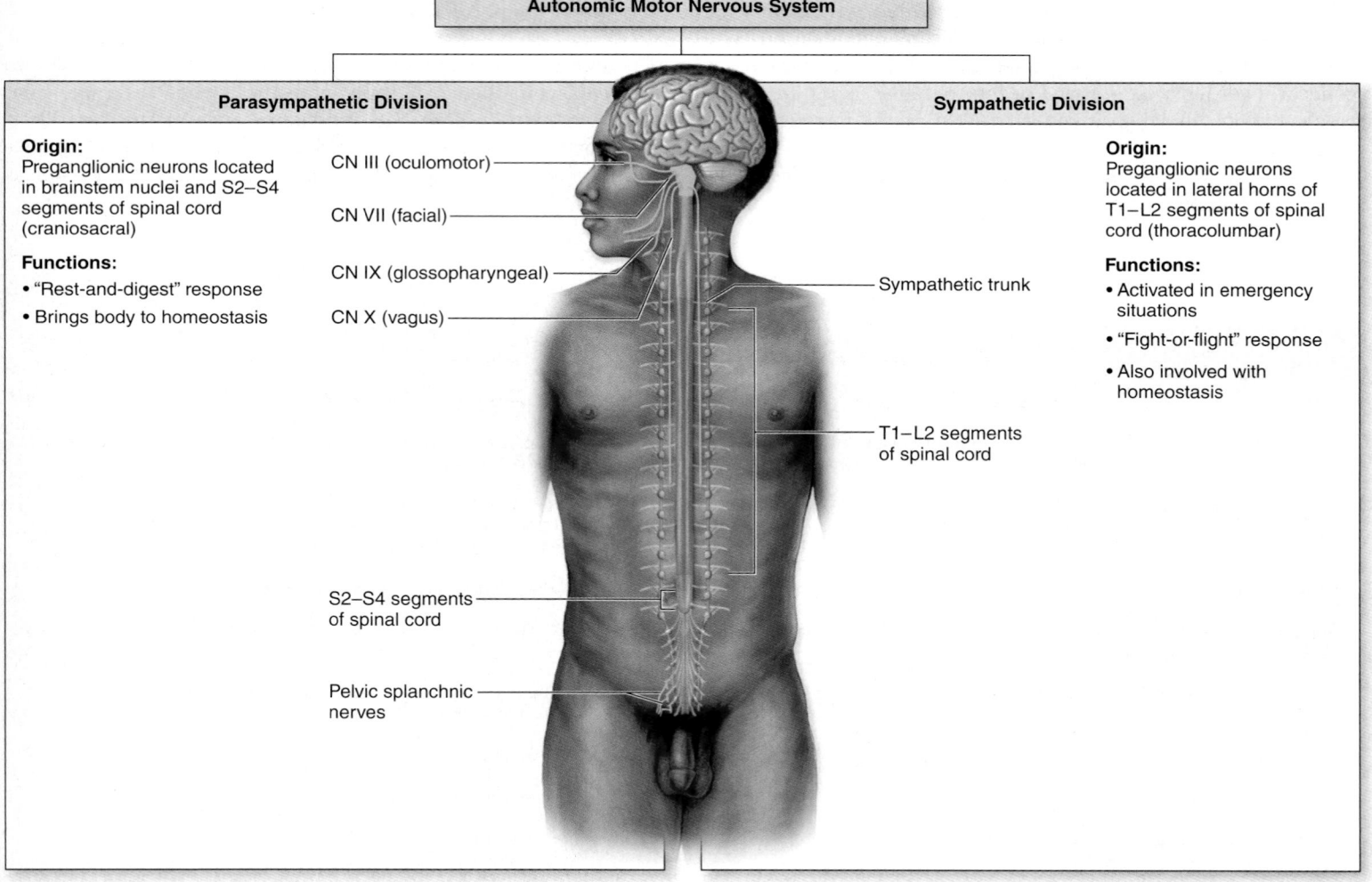

Autonomic Motor Nervous System

Parasympathetic Division

Origin:
Preganglionic neurons located in brainstem nuclei and S2–S4 segments of spinal cord (craniosacral)

Functions:
- "Rest-and-digest" response
- Brings body to homeostasis

CN III (oculomotor)
CN VII (facial)
CN IX (glossopharyngeal)
CN X (vagus)

S2–S4 segments of spinal cord

Pelvic splanchnic nerves

Sympathetic Division

Origin:
Preganglionic neurons located in lateral horns of T1–L2 segments of spinal cord (thoracolumbar)

Functions:
- Activated in emergency situations
- "Fight-or-flight" response
- Also involved with homeostasis

Sympathetic trunk

T1–L2 segments of spinal cord

Figure 15.3 Components of Parasympathetic and Sympathetic Divisions. The motor neurons of the parasympathetic division extend from the brainstem and sacral region, and for this reason is also called the craniosacral division. The motor neurons of the sympathetic division extend from the thoracic and lumbar regions of the spinal cord, and for this reason is also called the thoracolumbar division. AP|R

Parasympathetic Division

Preganglionic neuron
Long preganglionic axon
Ganglionic neuron
Short postganglionic axon
Autonomic ganglion (close to or within effector organ wall)

(a)

Sympathetic Division

Short, branching preganglionic axon
Long postganglionic axon
Preganglionic neuron
Ganglionic neuron
Autonomic ganglion (close to the vertebral column)

(b)

Figure 15.4 Anatomic Differences Between Parasympathetic and Sympathetic Neurons. For both divisions, preganglionic axons are myelinated and relatively larger in diameter, and postganglionic axons are unmyelinated and relatively smaller in diameter. (*a*) The parasympathetic division has longer preganglionic axons and shorter postganglionic axons, its axons exhibit very little branching, and autonomic ganglia lie close to or within the effector organ. (*b*) The sympathetic division has shorter preganglionic axons and longer postganglionic axons, the axons of both neurons show much branching, and autonomic ganglia lie close to the vertebral column.

- **Number of preganglionic axon branches.** Parasympathetic preganglionic axons tend to have few (less than 4) branches, whereas sympathetic preganglionic axons tend to have many branches (more than 20).
- **Location of ganglia.** Parasympathetic autonomic ganglia are either close to or within the effector (terminal ganglia or intramural ganglia). In comparison, sympathetic autonomic ganglia are relatively close to the spinal cord, and are on either side of the spinal cord or anterior to the spinal cord (sympathetic trunk ganglia and prevertebral ganglia). (These ganglia are described later in detail.)

WHAT DID YOU LEARN?

❹ Describe the general anatomic differences in the parasympathetic and sympathetic divisions.

15.2c Degree of Response

LEARNING OBJECTIVE

3. Explain why parasympathetic activation is local and discrete, and sympathetic activation can result in mass activation.

It is the combination of long preganglionic neurons with limited branches that results in a local response when the parasympathetic division is activated. Parasympathetic activity stimulates either one or only a few structures at the same time without necessarily having to "turn on" all the other organs.

In comparison, the combination of short preganglionic neurons with more extensive branching within the sympathetic division facilitates the activation of many structures simultaneously; a process called **mass activation**. Mass activation is especially important in response to stress, when it is necessary to coordinate rapid changes in activity with numerous structures at once. Think of all of the bodily changes that are initiated when you are scared or exercising: changes that include an increase in heart rate and blood pressure, parallel increases in depth and rate of breathing, dilation of the pupils, and mobilization of energy reserves from the liver. Keep in mind, however, that there are times when the sympathetic division may activate a single effector. For example, a single effector is involved when the sympathetic division stimulates smooth muscle to increase the diameter of the pupil of the eye during low-light situations.

Table 15.2 summarizes comparisons between the parasympathetic and sympathetic divisions of the autonomic nervous system.

Table 15.2	Comparison of Parasympathetic and Sympathetic Divisions	
Feature	**Parasympathetic Division**	**Sympathetic Division**
Function	Maintains homeostasis; conserves energy and replenishes energy stores; "rest-and-digest" division	Prepares body to cope with emergencies; releases energy; "fight-or-flight" division
Location of Preganglionic Neuron Cell Bodies	Brainstem and lateral gray matter in S2–S4 segments of spinal cord; thus it is also called the craniosacral division	Lateral horns in T1–L2 segments of spinal cord; thus it is also called the thoracolumbar division
Divergence of Axons	Few (1 axon innervates < 4 ganglionic neurons)	Extensive (1 axon innervates > 20 ganglionic neurons)
Length of Preganglionic Axon and Number of Branches	Long and has relatively few branches	Short and has many branches (over 20)
Length of Postganglionic Axon	Short	Long
Location of Ganglia	Terminal ganglia located close to the target organ; intramural ganglia located within wall of target organ	Sympathetic trunk (paravertebral) ganglia located on either side of vertebral column; prevertebral (collateral) ganglia located anterior to vertebral column and descending aorta
Rami Communicantes	None	White rami attach to T1–L2 spinal nerves; gray rami attach to all spinal nerves
Degree of Response	Local	Mass activation or local

Table 15.3	Parasympathetic Division Outflow		
Nerve(s)	Origin of Preganglionic Neurons	Autonomic Ganglia	Effectors Innervated
CN III (oculomotor)	Midbrain	Ciliary ganglion	Ciliary muscles to control lens for accommodation; sphincter pupillae muscle of eye to constrict pupil
CN VII (facial)	Pons	Pterygopalatine ganglion	Lacrimal glands; glands of nasal cavity, palate, oral cavity
		Submandibular ganglion	Submandibular and sublingual salivary glands
CN IX (glossopharyngeal)	Medulla oblongata	Otic ganglion	Parotid salivary glands
CN X (vagus)	Medulla oblongata	Multiple terminal and intramural ganglia	Thoracic viscera and most abdominal viscera
Pelvic splanchnic nerves	S2–S4 segments of spinal cord	Terminal and intramural ganglia	Some abdominal viscera and pelvic viscera

  WHAT DID YOU LEARN?

5 How does the sympathetic division cause mass activation?

15.3 Parasympathetic Division

Recall that the parasympathetic division is primarily concerned with maintaining homeostasis at rest, and is functionally considered the "rest-and-digest" division. The parasympathetic division is also called the *craniosacral division* because of the anatomic origin of its preganglionic neuron from the brainstem and sacral region of the spinal cord. The two types of ganglia associated with the parasympathetic division are either **terminal** (ter′mi-năl; *terminus* = a boundary) **ganglia,** which are located close to the effector, or are **intramural** (in′tră-mū′răl; *intra* = within, *murus* = wall) **ganglia,** which are located within the wall of the target organ. Here we discuss the details of the structure and function of the cranial and sacral components of the parasympathetic nervous system. **Table 15.3** summarizes the different nerves associated with the parasympathetic division.

15.3a Cranial Components

 LEARNING OBJECTIVE

1. Name the four cranial nerves associated with the parasympathetic division, and describe their actions.

The cranial nerves associated with the parasympathetic division are the oculomotor (CN III), facial (CN VII), glossopharyngeal (CN IX), and vagus (CN X) nerves. (Recall these cranial nerves are paired; they are found on the left and right side of the body.) Review table 13.8 for illustration of the cranial nerve pathways and the locations of their associated parasympathetic ganglia. The first three of these nerves convey parasympathetic innervation to the head, while the vagus nerve is the source of parasympathetic stimulation for the thoracic and most abdominal organs (**figure 15.5**).

Oculomotor Nerve (CN III)

The **oculomotor nerve (CN III)** is formed by axons extending from some cell bodies housed in nuclei in the midbrain. The preganglionic axons extend from CN III to the **ciliary** (sil′ē-ar-ē; *ciliaris* = eyelash) **ganglion** within the orbit. Postganglionic axons project from this ganglion to the ciliary muscle to control focusing of the lens to see close-up objects. Axons from this ganglion also go to the pupillary

constrictor muscle of the iris to to allow less light into the eye, such as when we first walk outside on a bright sunny day (see section 16.4b).

Facial Nerve (VII)

The **facial nerve (CN VII)** contains parasympathetic preganglionic axons that exit the pons and control the production and secretion of tears, mucus, and saliva. Two branches of parasympathetic preganglionic axons exit the facial nerve and terminate at one of two ganglia. One branch (the greater petrosal nerve) terminates at the **pterygopalatine** (ter′i-gō-pal′ă-tīn; *pterygo* = wing shaped, *palatine* = of the palate) **ganglion** near the junction of the maxilla and palatine bones. Postganglionic axons project to the lacrimal glands and small glands of the nasal cavity, oral cavity, and palate to increase secretion by these glands.

The other branch (the chorda tympani) terminates in the **submandibular** (sŭb-man-dib′ū-lăr; *sub* = under) **ganglion** near the angle of the mandible. Postganglionic axons projecting from this ganglion supply the submandibular and sublingual salivary glands in the floor of the mouth, causing an increase in salivary gland secretions (see section 26.2b). Your mouth waters when you smell an aromatic meal due in part to these parasympathetic axons.

  WHAT DO YOU THINK?

1 The pterygopalatine ganglion is sometimes nicknamed the "hay fever ganglion." Why is this nickname appropriate?

Glossopharyngeal Nerve (CN IX)

The **glossopharyngeal nerve (CN IX)** innervates the parotid salivary gland. Parasympathetic stimulation exits the brainstem in the glossopharyngeal nerve. From this nerve, the preganglionic parasympathetic axons branch and synapse on ganglionic neurons in the **otic** (ō′tik; *ous* = ear) **ganglion,** which is positioned anterior to the ear near the foramen ovale. Postganglionic axons from the otic ganglion cause an increase in secretion from the parotid salivary glands.

Vagus Nerve (CN X)

The **vagus nerve (CN X)** is responsible for supplying parasympathetic innervation to the thoracic organs and most of the abdominal organs, as well as the gonads (ovaries and testes).[1] The term vagus means "wanderer," which describes the wandering pathway the

1. It is unclear what function, if any, these parasympathetic axons have on the gonads.

Figure 15.5 Overview of Parasympathetic Pathways. Preganglionic neurons of the parasympathetic division extend from the brain and sacral region of the spinal cord. Ganglionic neurons are located in terminal and intramural ganglia, and extend from these ganglia to innervate the viscera. **AP|R**

vagus nerve makes as it projects inferiorly through the neck and travels throughout the trunk.

Left and right vagus nerves transmit multiple branches to the thoracic organs. As these nerves travel inferiorly, their position changes slightly, and they are referred to as the anterior and pos-

terior vagal trunks. In the thoracic cavity, parasympathetic innervation causes increased mucus production and decreased diameter in the airways, as well as decreases in the heart rate and the force of heart contractions. These trunks pass through the diaphragm and associate with the descending abdominal aorta within the abdominal cavity, where they project to their ganglia located immediately adjacent to (terminal ganglia) or within the wall (intramural ganglia) of their target organs. This parasympathetic innervation also causes increased smooth muscle motility and secretory activity in digestive organs (see chapter 26).

 WHAT DID YOU LEARN?

6 Which four cranial nerves have a parasympathetic component? What organs are innervated by each?

15.3b Pelvic Splanchnic Nerves

 LEARNING OBJECTIVE

2. Explain the actions of the pelvic splanchnic nerves.

The remaining preganglionic parasympathetic axons originate from preganglionic neuron cell bodies housed within the lateral gray regions of the S2–S4 spinal cord segments. These preganglionic axons branch to form the **pelvic splanchnic** (splangk'nik; *splanch-nic* = visceral) **nerves,** which contribute to a superior and inferior hypogastric plexus on each side of the body. The preganglionic axons that continue through each plexus project to the ganglionic neurons within either the terminal or intramural ganglia. The postganglionic axons extend to the effector.

The target organs innervated include the distal portion of the large intestine, the rectum, the urinary bladder, the distal part of the ureter, and most of the reproductive organs. This parasympathetic innervation causes increased smooth muscle motility (muscle contraction) and secretory activity in these portions of digestive tract (see chapter 26), contraction of smooth muscle in the bladder wall (see section 24.8c), and erection of the female clitoris and the male penis (see sections 28.3g and 28.4f).

 WHAT DID YOU LEARN?

7 What organs are innervated by the pelvic splanchnic nerves?

15.4 Sympathetic Division

Recall that the sympathetic division is primarily concerned with preparing the body for emergencies, and is functionally considered the fight-or-flight division because it tends to be activated during emergency situations. The sympathetic division is also called the *thoracolumbar division* because of the anatomic origin of its preganglionic neurons between the first thoracic (T1) and the second lumbar (L2) spinal segments. **Table 15.4** shows how specific organs are affected by the sympathetic division.

15.4a Organization and Anatomy of the Sympathetic Division

 LEARNING OBJECTIVES

1. Give the location of the sympathetic preganglionic neuron cell bodies.

2. Describe the left and right sympathetic trunks and ganglia.

3. Compare and contrast white and gray rami with respect to their location and composition.

4. Explain the differences between the sympathetic trunk ganglia and the prevertebral ganglia.

The sympathetic division is much more anatomically complex than the parasympathetic division so we first describe its anatomic components and then its pathways. The sympathetic preganglionic neuron cell bodies are housed in the **lateral horn** of the T1–L2 regions of the spinal cord. From there, the preganglionic sympathetic axons travel with somatic motor axons to exit the spinal cord and enter first the anterior roots and then the T1–L2 spinal nerves (see figures 14.3 and 14.12). However, these preganglionic sympathetic axons remain with the spinal nerve for only a short distance before they leave the spinal nerve **(figure 15.6).**

Sympathetic Trunks and Ganglia

Immediately anterior to the paired spinal nerves are the left and right **sympathetic trunks,** each of which is located immediately

Table 15.4	Sympathetic Division Pathways			
Pathway	**Destination**	**Spinal Segment Origin**	**Postganglionic Axon Pathway from Sympathetic Trunk**	**Effectors Innervated[1]**
Spinal Nerve	Integumentary structures	T1–L2	Via cervical gray rami to all spinal nerves	Sweat glands, arrector pili muscles, blood vessels in skin of torso, limbs, and neck
Postganglionic Sympathetic Nerve	Head and neck viscera	T1–T2 (primarily from T1)	Via superior cervical ganglion and travel with blood vessels to the head and neck viscera	Sweat glands, arrector pili muscles, and blood vessels in skin of head; dilator pupillae muscle of eye; tarsal glands of eye; superior tarsal muscle of eye; neck viscera
	Thoracic organs	T1–T5	Via cervical and thoracic ganglia to autonomic nerve plexuses near organs	Esophagus, heart, lungs, blood vessels within thoracic cavity
Splanchnic Nerve	Most abdominal organs	T5–T12	Via thoracic splanchnic nerves to prevertebral ganglia (e.g., celiac, superior mesenteric, and inferior mesenteric ganglia)	Abdominal portion of esophagus, stomach, liver, gallbladder, spleen, pancreas, small intestine, most of large intestine, kidneys, ureters, adrenal glands, blood vessels within abdominopelvic cavity
	Pelvic organs	T10–L2	Via lumbar and sacral splanchnic nerves to autonomic nerve plexuses that travel to effectors	Distal part of large intestine, anal canal, and rectum; distal part of ureters; urinary bladder; reproductive organs
Adrenal medulla	Adrenal gland	T8–T12	Via thoracic splanchnic nerves directly to adrenal medulla	Neurosecretory cells of adrenal medulla

1. Sympathetic axons innervate smooth muscle, cardiac muscle, and glands associated with the organs listed.

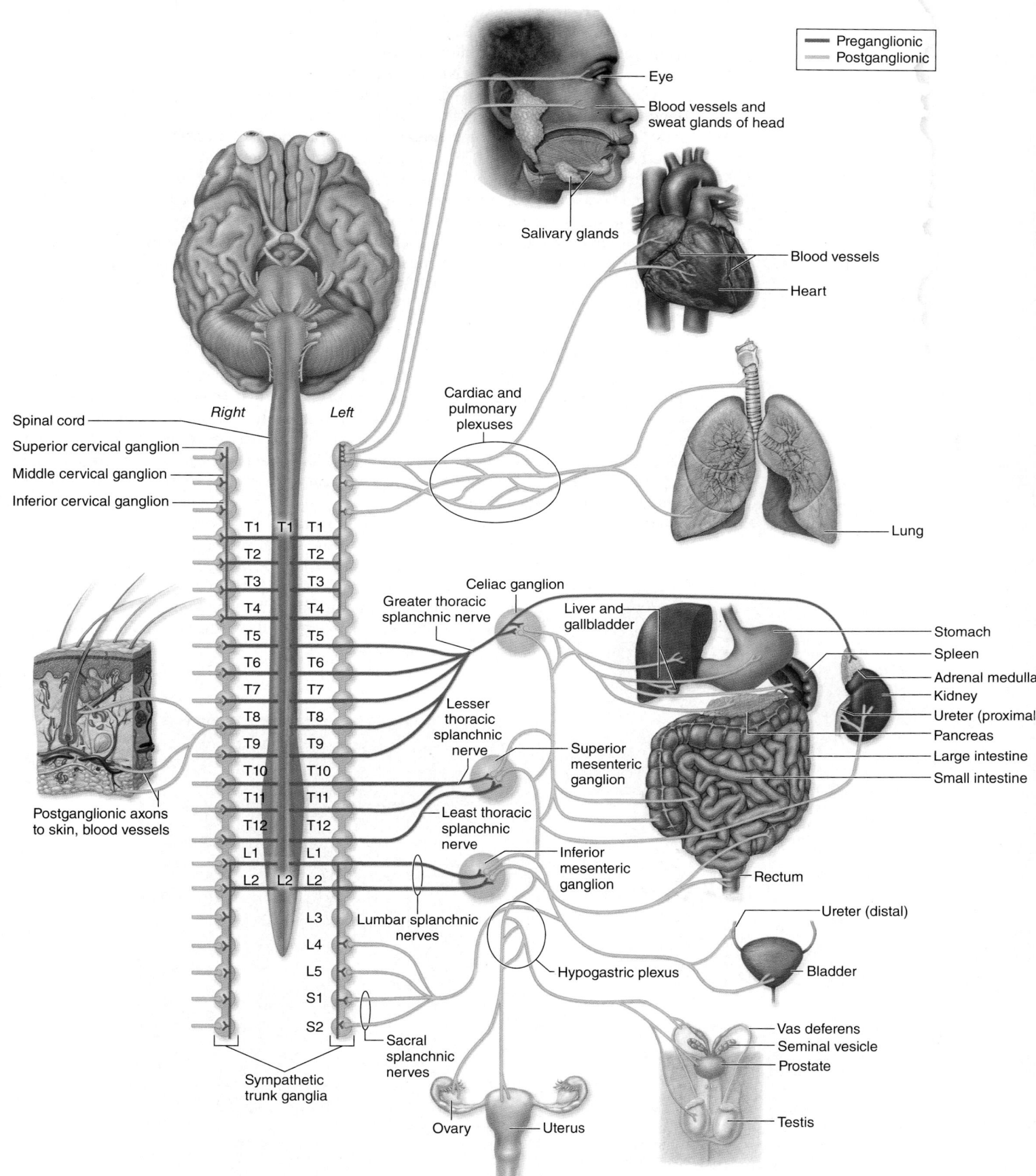

Figure 15.6 Overview of Sympathetic Pathways. (*Left*) The outflow of preganglionic axons and the distribution of postganglionic axons innervating the skin. (*Right*) Sympathetic postganglionic axon pathways through the gray rami, spinal nerves, and splanchnic nerves. **AP|R**

lateral to the vertebral column. A sympathetic trunk looks much like a pearl necklace. The "string" of the necklace is composed of bundles of axons, whereas the "pearls" are the **sympathetic trunk ganglia** (also known as *paravertebral*, or *sympathetic chain ganglia*), which house sympathetic ganglionic neuron cell bodies.

One sympathetic trunk ganglion is approximately associated with each spinal nerve. However, the cervical portion of each sympathetic trunk is partitioned into only three sympathetic trunk ganglia—the superior, middle, and inferior cervical ganglia—as opposed to the eight cervical spinal nerves. The **superior cervical ganglion** contains postganglionic sympathetic neuron cell bodies whose axons are distributed primarily to structures within the head and neck and to some thoracic viscera. These postganglionic axons innervate the sweat glands and smooth muscle in blood vessels of the head and neck, the dilator pupillae muscle of the eye, and the superior tarsal muscle of the eye (which elevates the eyelid). The **middle** and **inferior cervical ganglia** also house neuron cell bodies that extend postganglionic axons to the thoracic viscera. **Figure 15.7** is a photo of the sympathetic trunk on the right side of the body.

White and Gray Rami

Connecting the spinal nerves to each sympathetic trunk are rami communicantes (rā′mī kŏ-mū-ni-kan′tēz; sing., *ramus communicans; rami* = branches, *communico* = to share with someone) (see figure 14.12). **White rami communicantes** (or simply **white rami**) carry *pre*ganglionic sympathetic axons from the T1–L2 spinal nerves to the sympathetic trunk. Thus, white rami are associated only with the T1–L2 spinal nerves. Recall that preganglionic axons are myelinated, giving these rami a whitish appearance. White rami are similar to "entrance ramps" onto a highway.

Gray rami communicantes (or simply **gray rami**) carry *post*ganglionic sympathetic axons from the sympathetic trunk to the spinal nerve. Postganglionic axons are unmyelinated, so these rami have a grayish appearance. Gray rami connect to all spinal nerves, including the cervical, sacral, and coccygeal spinal nerves. By these routes, the sympathetic information that started out in the thoracolumbar region can be dispersed to all parts of the body. Gray rami are similar to "exit ramps" from a highway.

Intercostal nerve

Sympathetic trunk

Gray ramus

White ramus

Sympathetic trunk ganglia

Greater thoracic splanchnic nerve

Superior vena cava

Descending thoracic aorta

Azygos vein

Diaphragm

Figure 15.7 Sympathetic Trunk.
An anterolateral photo of the right side of the thoracic cavity shows the sympathetic trunk, the white and gray rami, their attachment to the intercostal nerves, and the greater thoracic splanchnic nerve. AP|R

Sympathetic Splanchnic Nerves

Sympathetic splanchnic nerves are composed of preganglionic sympathetic axons that did not synapse in a sympathetic trunk ganglion (see figure 15.6). They run anteriorly from the sympathetic trunk to most of the viscera. These splanchnic nerves should not be confused with the pelvic splanchnic nerves associated with the parasympathetic division described earlier. Some of the larger splanchnic nerves have specific names:

- The **greater thoracic splanchnic nerve** forms from preganglionic axons extending from the T5–T9 sympathetic trunk ganglia.
- The **lesser thoracic splanchnic nerve** forms from preganglionic axons extending from the T10–T11 sympathetic trunk ganglia.
- The **least thoracic splanchnic nerve** forms from preganglionic axons extending from the T12 sympathetic trunk ganglia.
- The **lumbar splanchnic nerves** originate from the L1 and L2 sympathetic trunk ganglia.

In addition to these, small *sacral splanchnic nerves* originate from the sacral sympathetic ganglia. Splanchnic nerves typically terminate in three **prevertebral** (or *collateral*) **ganglia**. These ganglia are called prevertebral because they are immediately anterior to the vertebral column on the anterolateral wall of the abdominal aorta. Prevertebral ganglia typically cluster around the origins of the major abdominal arteries and are named for these arteries. Sympathetic postganglionic axons extend away from neurons in these ganglia and innervate many of the abdominal organs.

Types of Prevertebral Ganglia

The prevertebral ganglia differ from the sympathetic trunk ganglia in that (1) they are anterior to the vertebral column (prevertebral) on the anterolateral surface of the aorta; and (2) they are located only in the abdominopelvic cavity. Prevertebral ganglia include the celiac, superior mesenteric, and inferior mesenteric ganglia.

The **celiac ganglia** are adjacent to the origin of the celiac artery. The greater thoracic splanchnic nerves (composed of axons from T5 –T9 segment of the spinal cord) synapse on ganglionic neurons within each celiac ganglion. Postganglionic axons from the celiac ganglia innervate the stomach, spleen, liver, gallbladder, and proximal part of the duodenum (first part of small intestine) and part of the pancreas.

The **superior mesenteric** (mez-en-ter'ik; *mesos* = middle, *enteron* = intestine) **ganglia** are adjacent to the origin of the superior mesenteric artery. The lesser and least thoracic splanchnic nerves project to and terminate within the superior mesenteric ganglia. Thus, these ganglia receives preganglionic sympathetic neurons from the T10–T12 segments of the spinal cord. Postganglionic axons extending from the superior mesenteric ganglia innervate the distal half of the duodenum, the remainder of the small intestine, the proximal part of the large intestine, part of the pancreas, the kidneys, and the proximal parts of the ureters.

The **inferior mesenteric ganglia** are adjacent to the origin of the inferior mesenteric artery. They receive sympathetic preganglionic axons via the lumbar splanchnic nerves, which originate in the L1–L2 segments of the spinal cord. The postganglionic axons project to and innervate the distal part of large intestine, rectum, urinary bladder, distal parts of the ureters, and most of the reproductive organs.

INTEGRATE

CLINICAL VIEW

Horner Syndrome

Horner syndrome is a condition caused by impingement or injury of the cervical sympathetic trunk or the T1 sympathetic trunk ganglion, where postganglionic sympathetic axons traveling to the head originate. Symptoms typically are limited to the same side of the head where the original injury occurred. The patient presents with **ptosis** (tō'sis; a falling), in which the superior eyelid droops because the superior tarsal muscle is paralyzed. Paralysis of the pupil dilator muscle of the eye results in **miosis** (mī-ō'sis; *muein* = to close the eyes), which is a constricted pupil. **Anhydrosis** (an-hī-drō'sis; *an* = without, *hidros* = sweat) occurs because the sweat glands no longer receive sympathetic innervation. A fourth symptom is distinct facial flushing due to lack of sympathetic innervation to blood vessel walls, resulting in vasodilation.

WHAT DID YOU LEARN?

8 What is the difference between sympathetic trunk ganglia and prevertebral ganglia?

9 What are the structural and functional differences between the white and gray rami communicantes?

10 Where are splanchnic nerves in the sympathetic division located, and what is their function?

15.4b Sympathetic Pathways

LEARNING OBJECTIVES

5. Describe the four pathways of sympathetic neurons.

6. Compare and contrast which general effector organs are innervated by each pathway.

All sympathetic preganglionic neurons originate in the lateral gray horns of the T1–L2 regions of the spinal cord. However, the sympathetic pathways of the axons of these neurons vary, depending upon the location and the type of effector organ being innervated.

Recall that preganglionic axons extend from the preganglionic neuron cell bodies via the anterior roots and travel with the T1–L2 spinal nerves. The preganglionic axons immediately leave the spinal nerve and travel through white rami to enter the sympathetic trunk. Once inside the sympathetic trunk, the preganglionic axons may remain at the level of entry, or travel superiorly or inferiorly in the sympathetic trunk.

Axons exit the sympathetic trunk ganglia by one of four pathways (see table 15.4). An axon takes the **spinal nerve pathway** if a preganglionic neuron synapses with a ganglionic neuron in a sympathetic trunk ganglion (**figure 15.8a**). In this case, the postganglionic axon travels through a gray ramus that is at the same "level" as the ganglionic neuron. For example, if the preganglionic and ganglionic neurons synapse in the L4 ganglion, the postganglionic axon travels through the gray ramus at the level of the L4 spinal nerve. After the postganglionic axon travels through the gray ramus, it enters the spinal nerve and extends to its target organ. Skin of the neck, torso, and limbs are innervated via this pathway. Structures innervated include sweat glands, arrector pili muscles ("goosebumps"), and blood vessels in the skin (see chapter 6).

In the **postganglionic sympathetic nerve pathway,** the preganglionic neuron synapses with a ganglionic neuron in a sympathetic trunk ganglion, but the postganglionic axon does

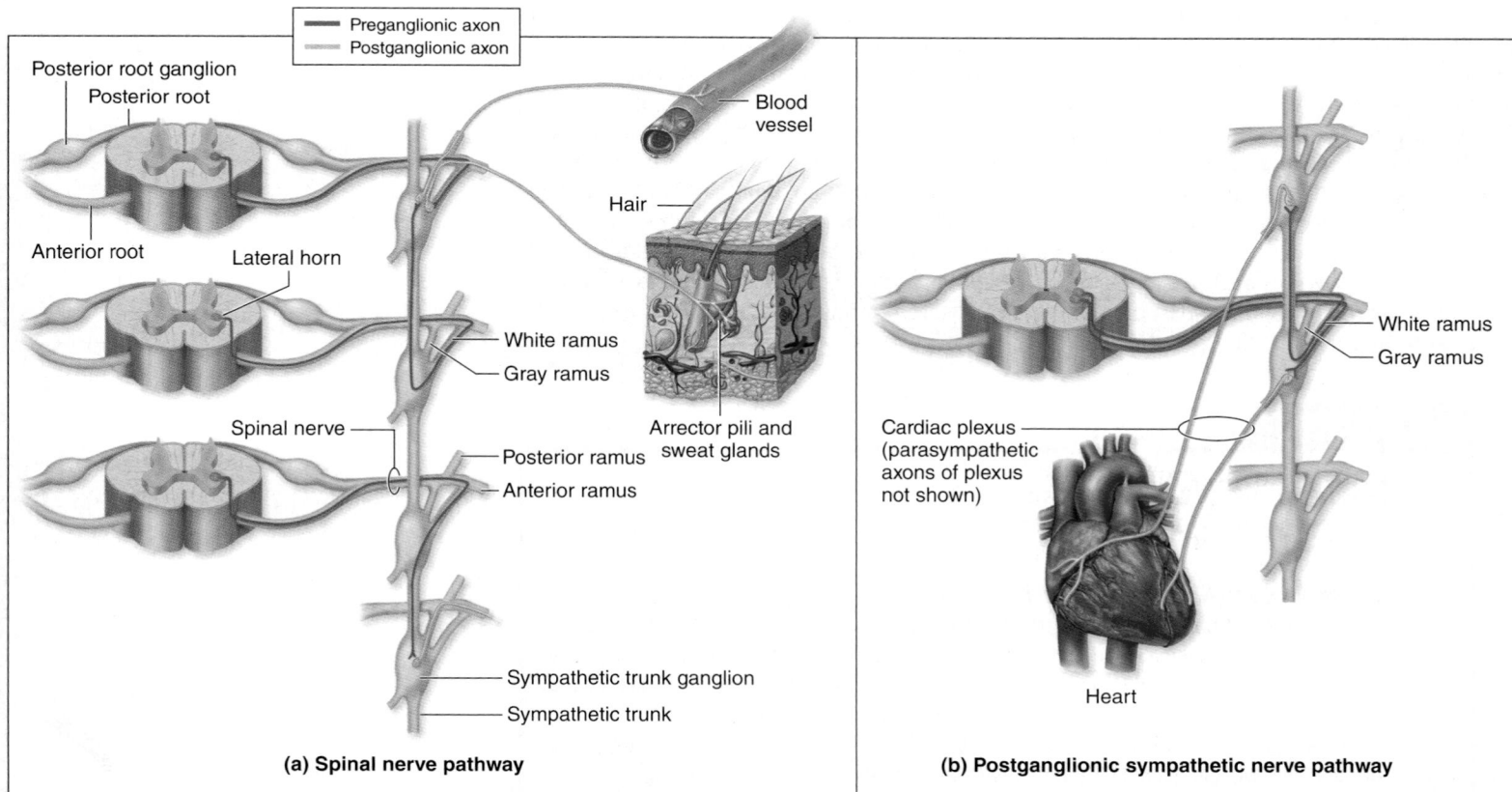

(a) Spinal nerve pathway

(b) Postganglionic sympathetic nerve pathway

Figure 15.8 Types of Sympathetic Pathways. Pathways of (*a*) a spinal nerve, (*b*) a postganglionic sympathetic nerve, (*c*) a splanchnic nerve, and (*d*) the adrenal medulla.

not leave the trunk via a gray ramus (figure 15.8*b*). Instead, the postganglionic axon extends away from the sympathetic trunk ganglion and goes directly to the effector organ. The esophagus, heart, lungs, and thoracic blood vessels typically receive their sympathetic innervation from this pathway. Sympathetic innervation to structures in the head (such as blood vessels and sweat glands in the head, dilator pupillae muscle in the eye, and superior tarsal muscle of the eye) also travel with this pathway (see section 16.4b).

The **splanchnic nerve pathway** uses the splanchnic nerves, which are preganglionic axons that pass through the sympathetic trunk ganglia without synapsing and extend to the prevertebral ganglia (figure 15.8*c*). There, the preganglionic axon synapses with a ganglionic neuron. The postganglionic axon then travels to the effector organs. The abdominal and pelvic organs receive their sympathetic innervation via this pathway.

The final pathway is the **adrenal medulla pathway** (figure 15.8*d*). In this pathway, the internal region of the adrenal gland, called the **adrenal** (ă-drē′năl; *ad* = to, *ren* = kidney) **medulla**, is directly innervated by preganglionic sympathetic axons. (There is no ganglionic neuron.) The axons of the preganglionic neuron extend through both the sympathetic trunk and prevertebral ganglia and then synapse on neurosecretory cells within the adrenal medulla. Stimulation of these cells causes the release of **epinephrine** (ep′i-nef′rin) and **norepinephrine** (nōr-ep-i-nef′rin). These hormones then circulate within the blood and help prolong the fight-or-flight response. Both of these hormones potentiate (prolong) the effects of the sympathetic stimulation. For example, if you narrowly miss getting into a car accident, your heart continues to beat quickly, you breathe rapidly, and you feel tense and alert well after the event because of prolonged effects of the sympathetic stimulation by the adrenal medulla.

WHAT DO YOU THINK?

2 When a person is very stressed and tense, his or her blood pressure typically rises. What aspect of the sympathetic nervous system causes this rise in blood pressure?

WHAT DID YOU LEARN?

11 How do the spinal nerve and splanchnic nerve sympathetic pathways differ, with respect to both the pathway and the organs innervated?

12 In what ways does the adrenal medulla pathway help prolong the effects of the sympathetic stimulation?

(c) Splanchnic nerve pathway

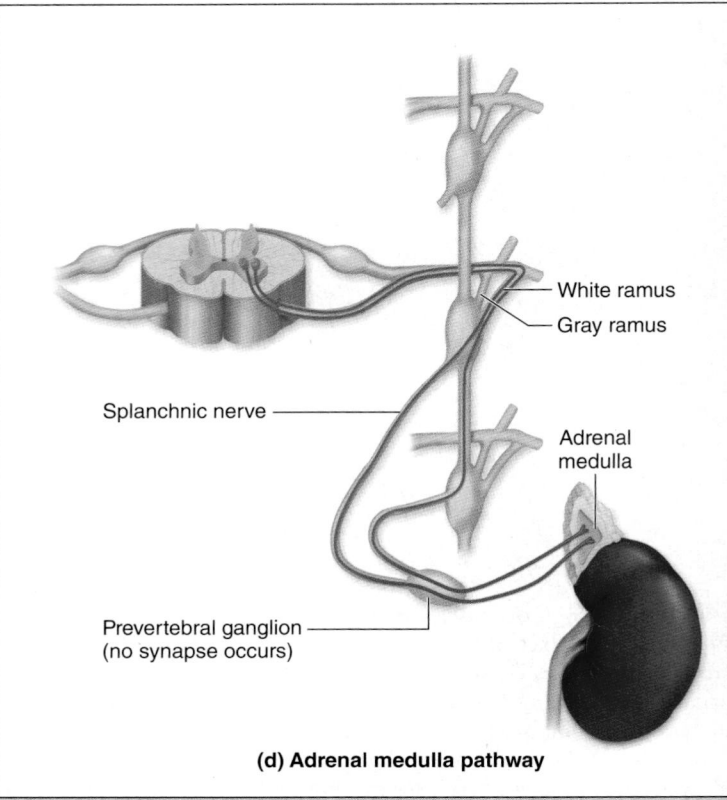

(d) Adrenal medulla pathway

15.5 Comparison of Neurotransmitters and Receptors of the Two Divisions

Transmission of a nerve signal to synaptic knobs causes the release of neurotransmitters into the synaptic cleft. The ANS utilizes several types of neurotransmitters, which are discussed here.

15.5a Overview of ANS Neurotransmitters

LEARNING OBJECTIVE

1. Identify the targets of the cholinergic and adrenergic neurotransmitters of the ANS.

Acetylcholine (ACh) and norepinephrine (NE) are the main neurotransmitters used in the ANS (figure 15.9). These neurotransmitters will bind to specific receptors on the postsynaptic cell. Depending upon the receptor type, the neurotransmitter may cause either stimulation or inhibition.

Neurons that synthesize and release acetylcholine (ACh) are called **cholinergic** (kol-in-er′jik; *ergon* = work) **neurons.** Receptors that bind ACh are called **cholinergic receptors.** We will see in the next section that there are two types of cholinergic receptors (nico-

tinic and muscarinic), and each responds differently to binding of ACh. Cholinergic neurons include the following:

- All sympathetic and parasympathetic preganglionic neurons
- All parasympathetic ganglionic neurons
- The specific sympathetic ganglionic neurons that innervate sweat glands of the skin and blood vessels in skeletal muscle tissue

Neurons that synthesize and secrete norepinephrine (NE) are called **adrenergic** (ad-re-ner′jik) **neurons.** Most other sympathetic ganglionic neurons are adrenergic. Receptors that bind NE (or a related molecule, like epinephrine) are called **adrenergic receptors.** These receptors are subdivided into alpha (α) and beta (β) types, and are discussed in further detail later in this chapter.

The terminal branches of ganglionic sympathetic neurons that secrete NE do not form the usual terminal synaptic knob structure to interface with their target organs (figure 15.10). Rather, they form a network of swellings that give the appearance of a string of beads. Each swollen "bead" is a **varicosity** containing stored NE within vesicles. Numerous varicosities crisscross the surface of the target cells. Upon arrival of a nerve signal, the NE is released along a length of the axon instead of at a single discrete location, to cause a greater target cell response.

WHAT DID YOU LEARN?

13 Which ANS neurons are cholinergic? Which are adrenergic?

Figure 15.9 Comparison of Neurotransmitters in the Autonomic Nervous System. In the parasympathetic pathway, both the preganglionic and postganglionic axons release acetylcholine (ACh). In the sympathetic pathway, all preganglionic axons and a few specific postganglionic axons release ACh. Most postganglionic sympathetic axons release norepinephrine (NE).

Labels in figure:

Parasympathetic Pathway | **Sympathetic Pathways**

Preganglionic axon releases ACh.

Ganglionic neuron cell body and dendrites always contain receptors for ACh.

Postganglionic axon releases ACh or NE.

Target cells contain either ACh receptors (bind ACh) or NE receptors (bind NE).

ACh — Nicotinic receptors — Muscarinic receptors — Target cell

ACh — Nicotinic receptors — Muscarinic receptors — Target cell (e.g., sweat glands and blood vessels in skeletal muscle)

ACh — Nicotinic receptors — NE — Adrenergic receptors — Target cell (e.g., most other body structures)

Figure 15.10 Varicosities in Sympathetic Ganglionic Neurons. Beadlike swellings in sympathetic postganglionic axons contain the neurotransmitter norephinephrine (NE) to stimulate effector cells. Their arrangement on the surface of the target cells permits a widespread stimulation of the target.

15.5b Cholinergic Receptors

✓ LEARNING OBJECTIVE

2. Describe the two types of cholinergic receptors and the action of each when a neurotransmitter binds to them.

Two categories of cholinergic receptors, nicotinic and muscarinic, have been identified in the CNS and PNS. They were differentiated and named because the molecules are similar to ACh, allowing them to bind to and stimulate the receptor type:

Nicotinic receptors were so named because they are sensitive to the drug nicotine. These receptors are found on the cell bodies of all ganglionic neurons (see figure 15.9), as well as on the cells of the adrenal medulla. When nicotinic receptors bind ACh, they open ion channels to allow greater movement of sodium ions (Na⁺) into the cell than potassium ions (K⁺) from the cell. Thus, the membrane depolarizes and an excitatory postsynaptic potential (EPSP) is pro-

duced (see section 12.8a). In other words, ACh binding to nicotinic receptors always produces a stimulatory or excitatory response (This excitatory response to ACh also occurs in the somatic nervous system, and is described for the activation of skeletal muscle fibers in section 10.3b.)

🔆 WHAT DO YOU THINK?

3 What effect, if any, would smoking have on the nicotinic receptors of the ANS?

Muscarinic receptors respond to muscarine, a mushroom toxin. They are found in all target plasma membranes in the parasympathetic division and in the few selected sympathetic target cells (e.g., sweat glands in the skin and blood vessels in skeletal muscle). There are different subtypes of muscarinic receptors, which have different effects on various body systems. These different subclasses of muscarinic receptors are either stimulated or inhibited by binding ACh. For example, the binding of ACh to smooth muscle in the gastrointestinal (GI) tract will result in stimulation and increased motility of the muscle, while binding to muscarinic receptors on cardiac muscle results in decreasing heartbeat rate. All muscarinic receptors use second messenger systems (see section 17.5b).

💡 WHAT DID YOU LEARN?

14 Where are nicotinic and muscarinic receptors each located?

15 When a neurotransmitter binds to a nicotinic effector, is the effect stimulatory or inhibitory?

15.5c Adrenergic Receptors

✓ LEARNING OBJECTIVES

3. List the neurotransmitters categorized as catecholamines.

4. Name the four adrenergic receptors and give the locations of each.

Recall that signaling molecules, such as neurotransmitters, are called **ligands** when they specifically bind to receptors in the plasma membrane (see section 4.4b). The class of ligands that bind to adrenergic receptors in neurons are called **biogenic amines,** or *monoamines*. One category of biogenic amines is called **catecholamines** because of the presence of a catechol ring structure in the molecule. Catecholamines include dopamine, norepinephrine, and epinephrine.

As mentioned earlier, the two types of adrenergic receptors are **alpha (α)** and **beta (β) receptors,** which may be further divided into subclasses such as α_1, α_2, β_1, and β_2. The α receptors typically have stimulatory effects, whereas β receptors may be either stimulatory or inhibitory (note that there are exceptions to this rule). These types of receptors may be further subdivided, as follows:

- α_1 **receptors** are located within plasma membranes of most smooth muscle cells and stimulate smooth muscle contraction. The specific organs with α_1 receptors include most blood vessels (including blood vessels going to the skin, GI tract, and kidneys), arrector pili muscles, uterus, ureters, and internal urethral sphincter. These receptors are involved with vasoconstriction of the above blood vessels, contraction of the uterine wall, contraction of the arrector pili muscles, and closing of the internal urethral sphincter, respectively.

- α_2 **receptors** are located in the pancreas to inhibit insulin secretion. They also are involved with the contraction of the GI tract sphincters and facilitating blood clotting (see section 18.4).

- β_1 **receptors** primarily have stimulatory effects. They are found within the heart, where they increase heart rate and force of contraction (see section 19.5b); and in the kidney, where they stimulate secretion of renin (see section 24.5c).

- **β₂ receptors** primarily have inhibitory effects. They are present in smooth muscle plasma membranes of blood vessels going to the heart, liver, and skeletal muscle. Unlike activation of α₁ receptors, activation of β₂ receptors causes smooth muscle relaxation, resulting in vasodilation of these specific blood vessels. Their stimulation also causes bronchodilation in the lung, relaxation of uterine and GI tract smooth muscle, and relaxation of the detrusor muscle of the urinary bladder.

 WHAT DID YOU LEARN?

16 What are the different types of catecholamines?

17 How is it possible for the stimulation of adrenergic receptors to result in either vasoconstriction or vasodilation of selected blood vessels?

15.6 Interactions Between the Parasympathetic and Sympathetic Divisions

Most organs are innervated by both divisions of the autonomic nervous system, and these stimulate the targets continuously to varying degrees. The parasympathetic and sympathetic division effects are compared in **table 15.5** and **figure 15.11**.

15.6a Autonomic Tone

 LEARNING OBJECTIVE

1. Discuss the nature of autonomic tone and its effects.

The parasympathetic and sympathetic divisions both maintain some continual activity, referred to as the **autonomic tone.** Activity of a stimulated organ may be controlled merely by the change in tone within a single ANS division.

For example, the diameter of most blood vessels is maintained in a partially constricted state by the effects of sympathetic tone. A decrease in stimulation below the sympathetic tone causes vessel dilation, whereas an increase above sympathetic tone brings about vessel constriction. If the initial level of sympathetic tone were not present, then only vasoconstriction could occur as a result of sympathetic division activity.

 WHAT DID YOU LEARN?

18 How does autonomic tone permit the control of blood vessel diameter by sympathetic innervation?

15.6b Dual Innervation

 LEARNING OBJECTIVES

2. Explain what is meant by dual innervation.

3. Describe the antagonistic and cooperative effects of dual innervation.

Many visceral effectors have **dual innervation,** meaning that they are innervated by post-ganglionic axons from both parasympathetic and sympathetic divisions. The actions caused by activities of both the divisions on the same organ usually result in effects that are antagonistic or cooperative.

Antagonistic Effects

Generally, the effects of parasympathetic and sympathetic innervation to the same organ are antagonistic—that is, they oppose each other. Some variations occur in how antagonistic effects are expressed, as follows:

- **Control of heart rate.** Parasympathetic stimulation slows down the heart rate, while sympathetic stimulation speeds up the heart rate. The same heart muscle effector cells receive this opposing stimulation. This is possible because these cells contain both muscarinic receptors to bind ACh released from parasympathetic axons and adrenergic β₁ receptors to bind NE released from sympathetic axons (see section 19.5b).

Table 15.5 — Effects of the Parasympathetic and Sympathetic Divisions

Effector	Parasympathetic Innervation Effects	Sympathetic Innervation Effects
CIRCULATORY SYSTEM		
Heart	Decreases heart rate	Increases heart rate and force of contraction
Blood vessels		
Coronary	Vasodilation	Vasodilation (β receptors) or vasoconstriction (α receptors)
To skeletal muscle	None	Vasodilation (β receptors)
Integumentary and most other blood vessels	None	Vasoconstriction (α receptors)
DIGESTIVE SYSTEM		
Salivary glands	Stimulate watery secretion	Produces more viscous secretion
GI tract gland secretion	Stimulates	Inhibits
Peristalsis (motility)	Stimulates	Inhibits
Sphincters	Relax (open)	Contract (close)
GI tract vasculature	Vasodilation	Vasoconstriction
Liver	Stimulates glycogenesis	Stimulates glycogenolysis
RESPIRATORY SYSTEM		
Bronchi of lungs	Bronchoconstriction (airway narrows)	Bronchodilation (airway widens)
URINARY SYSTEM		
Kidneys	None	Renin secretion
Bladder (muscle wall)	Contraction	Relaxation
Internal urethral sphincter	Relax (open)	Contract (close)
REPRODUCTIVE SYSTEM		
Penile or clitoral erection	Stimulates	None
Penile ejaculation	None	Stimulates
Uterine muscle	None	Contraction
Gland secretion	Stimulates	Inhibits
Vaginal muscular wall	None	Contraction
INTEGUMENTARY SYSTEM		
Arrector pili	None	Contraction to cause hair erection
Sweat glands	None	Secretion
EYE		
Pupil size	Constriction	Dilation
Ciliary muscle	Contraction for near vision	None
Lacrimal gland	Stimulates secretion	None
ADIPOSE CONNECTIVE TISSUE		
	None	Stimulates lipolysis (fat breakdown)
ADRENAL GLAND (MEDULLA)		
	None	Secretion of epinephrine and norepinephrine

- **Control of muscular activity in the gastrointestinal tract.** Parasympathetic stimulation of smooth muscle cells in the gastrointestinal tract wall accelerates their rate of contraction and thus increases gastrointestinal tract motility, whereas sympathetic stimulation decreases motility. Again, both ANS branches innervate the same effector cells, but house two different types of receptors (see chapter 26).
- **Control of pupil diameter in the iris of the eye.** Here, different effectors are innervated by the ANS divisions. Parasympathetic stimulation of the circular muscle layer in the iris causes pupil constriction, whereas sympathetic stimulation of the radial muscle layer in the iris causes pupil dilation (see section 16.4b).

Figure 15.11 **Comparison of the Parasympathetic and Sympathetic Divisions of the ANS.** (a) The parasympathetic division, also known as the "rest-and-digest" system, has its preganglionic neurons located in the cranial region of the brainstem and sacral region of the spinal cord. (b) The sympathetic division contains preganglionic neurons located in the T1–L2 regions of the spinal cord and controls our "fight-or-flight" response.

(a) Parasympathetic Division

The "Rest-and-Digest" Division

Originates in the cranial and sacral regions of the CNS.

CN III
CN VII
Pons
Medulla
CN IX
CN X

Pelvic splanchnic nerves

S2
S3
S4

Tends to have long preganglionic axons and short postganglionic axons.

Preganglionic neuron
Long preganglionic axon
Short postganglionic axon
Ganglionic neuron

Ganglia lie close to organ or within effector wall (e.g., terminal or intramural).

Terminal ganglia
Intramural ganglion
Intramural ganglia

Main effects

Pupil constriction

Returns body to homeostasis

Increases motility and activity of digestive system

Decreases heart rate and causes bronchoconstriction

Stimulates secretion of lacrimal (tear), nasal, and digestive system glands

Storage of fuel molecules in liver and adipose connective tissue.

Neurotransmitters and receptors used

ACh is released from preganglionic axons and binds cholinergic (specifically, nicotinic) receptors.

ACh

Nicotinic receptors

Postganglionic axons release ACh, which binds cholinergic (muscarinic) receptors.

ACh

Muscarinic receptors

Target cell

(b) Sympathetic Division

The "Fight-or-Flight" Division

Tends to have shorter preganglionic axons and longer postganglionic axons. Preganglionic axon has many branches and extensive divergence.

Short, branching preganglionic axon

Long postganglionic axon

Preganglionic neuron

Ganglionic neuron

Originates in the T1–L2 segments of the spinal cord.

Right

Left

T1–L2

Ganglia (sympathetic trunk or prevertebral) lie close to the spinal cord.

Sympathetic trunk ganglia

Prevertebral ganglia

Neurotransmitters and receptors used

ACh

Nicotinic receptors

ACh

Muscarinic receptors

Target cell

ACh is released from preganglionic axons and binds cholinergic (specifically, nicotinic) receptors.

Postganglionic axons release either ACh or NE:

ACh binds cholinergic (muscarinic) receptors for sweat glands and blood vessels to muscle.

NE binds adrenergic receptors (all other structures).

ACh

Nicotinic receptors

NE

Adrenergic receptors

Target cell

Main effects

Pupil dilation

Adrenal gland

Stimulates adrenal medulla to secrete epinephrine and NE to prolong sympathetic effects

Decreases motility and activity of digestive system

Increases heart rate and causes bronchodilation

Increases secretion of sweat glands, contraction of arrector pili

Arrector pili

Sweat gland

Vasoconstricts surface blood vessels and vessels to most visceral organs but vasodilates coronary arteries and arteries to skeletal muscle

Release of fuel molecules from liver and adipose connective tissue into the blood

Cooperative Effects

Cooperative effects are seen when both parasympathetic and sympathetic stimulation cause different effects that together produce a single, distinct result. The best example of cooperative effects occurs in the sexual function of the male reproductive system. The male penis becomes erect as a result of parasympathetic innervation, and ejaculation of semen from the penis occurs as a result of sympathetic innervation (see section 28.4f). This synergistic effort of ANS divisions facilitates reproduction.

 WHAT DID YOU LEARN?

19 What are the antagonistic effects of the sympathetic and parasympathetic divisions on the heart?

20 How do the sympathetic and parasympathetic divisions exhibit cooperative effects on the male reproductive system?

15.6c Systems Controlled Only by the Sympathetic Division

 LEARNING OBJECTIVE

4. Describe the systems innervated only by the sympathetic division and how they function.

In some ANS effectors, opposing effects are achieved without dual innervation. For example, many blood vessels are innervated by sympathetic axons only. Increased sympathetic stimulation increases smooth muscle contraction, resulting in increased blood pressure. An analogy would be when you press down on a gas pedal to cause a car to accelerate. Decreasing the sympathetic stimulation below the autonomic tone will result in vasodilation, just as lifting your foot off of the gas pedal may slow a car down (because you are not supplying the gas). Thus, opposing effects are achieved merely by increasing or decreasing the tone activity in one division.

Other examples of innervation by only the sympathetic division are observed in sweat glands in the trunk (stimulates sweating) and innervation of arrector pili muscles in the skin to cause "goosebumps" (see section 6.2). The neurosecretory cells of the adrenal medulla are innervated only by the sympathetic division. These cells have nicotinic receptors, so upon release of ACh by the postganglionic axon, the adrenal medulla cells are stimulated to release epinephrine and norepinephrine into the blood. There, these molecules act as hormones and prolong the fight-or-flight effects of the sympathetic division.

 WHAT DID YOU LEARN?

21 What are the body structures innervated by the sympathetic division only?

15.7 Control and Integration of Autonomic System Function

Both divisions of the autonomic nervous system innervate organs through specific axon bundles called autonomic plexuses. These are networks of nerves that are located within the thoracic and abdominopelvic cavity. Homeostasis is maintained through autonomic reflexes that occur in the organs innervated by autonomic nerves via the plexuses. Overall, the autonomic functions are controlled by the CNS.

15.7a Autonomic Plexuses

 LEARNING OBJECTIVE

1. Describe the structure and location of the five autonomic plexuses.

Autonomic plexuses are collections of sympathetic postganglionic axons and parasympathetic preganglionic axons, as well as some visceral sensory axons. These sympathetic and parasympathetic axons are close to one another, but they do not interact or synapse with each another. Although these plexuses look like disorganized masses of axons, they provide a complex innervation pattern to their target organs **(figure 15.12).**

In the mediastinum of the thoracic cavity, the **cardiac plexus** consists of sympathetic postganglionic axons that originate in the cervical and thoracic sympathetic trunk ganglia, as well as parasympathetic preganglionic axons from the vagus nerve. Increased sympathetic activity increases heart rate and blood pressure, while increased parasympathetic activity decreases heart rate (section 19.5b).

The **pulmonary plexus** consists of sympathetic postganglionic axons from the cervical and thoracic sympathetic trunk ganglia and parasympathetic preganglionic axons from the

Figure 15.12 **Autonomic Plexuses.** Autonomic plexuses are located in the anterior body cavities in both the thoracic and abdominopelvic cavities. This anterior view shows the cardiac, pulmonary, and esophageal plexuses in the thoracic cavity and the abdominal aortic plexus (celiac, superior mesenteric, inferior mesenteric plexuses) in the abdominopelvic cavity. AP|R

Labels in figure:
- Trachea
- Sympathetic trunk ganglion
- Right vagus nerve (X)
- Left vagus nerve (X)
- Cardiac plexus
- Pulmonary plexus
- Esophageal plexus
- Greater thoracic splanchnic nerve
- Lesser thoracic splanchnic nerve
- Inferior vena cava
- Aorta
- Esophagus
- Diaphragm
- Celiac trunk
- Superior mesenteric artery
- Celiac ganglia and plexus
- Superior mesenteric ganglia and plexus
- Abdominal aortic plexus
- Inferior mesenteric artery
- Inferior mesenteric ganglia and plexus
- Hypogastric plexus

vagus nerve. The axons project to the bronchi of the lungs. Sympathetic innervation causes bronchodilation (increase in the diameter of the bronchi) while stimulation of this parasympathetic pathway causes bronchoconstriction (a reduction in the diameter of the bronchi, see section 23.5c).

The **esophageal plexus** consists of sympathetic postganglionic axons from the cervical and sympathetic trunk ganglia and parasympathetic preganglionic axons from the vagus nerve. Sympathetic innervation will inhibit muscle motility. Smooth muscle activity in the inferior esophageal wall is coordinated by parasympathetic axons that control the swallowing reflex in the inferior region of the esophagus by innervating the cardiac sphincter, a valve through which swallowed food and drink must pass (see section 26.3a).

The **abdominal aortic plexus** consists of the **celiac plexus, superior mesenteric plexus,** and **inferior mesenteric plexus.** It innervates all abdominal and some pelvic organs. The abdominal aortic plexus is composed of sympathetic postganglionic axons projecting from the prevertebral ganglia and parasympathetic preganglionic axons from either the vagus nerve or pelvic splanchnic nerves. Note that the celiac plexus also is known as the *solar plexus,* and it is partly responsible for the sensation of "getting the wind knocked out of you" when you are hit hard in the epigastric region.

The **hypogastric plexus** consists of a complex meshwork of sympathetic postganglionic axons (from the aortic plexus and the lumbar region of the sympathetic trunk) and preganglionic parasympathetic axons from the pelvic splanchnic nerves. Its axons innervate viscera within the pelvic region.

WHAT DID YOU LEARN?

22 What basic structures form an autonomic plexus?

CLINICAL VIEW
Autonomic Dysreflexia

Autonomic dysreflexia is a potentially dangerous vascular condition that causes blood pressure to rise profoundly, sometimes so high that blood vessels rupture. Specifically, it stimulates a sympathetic division reflex that causes systemic vasoconstriction and a marked increase in blood pressure. Autonomic dysreflexia is caused by hyperactivity of the autonomic nervous system in the weeks and months after a spinal cord injury. Often, the initial reaction to spinal cord injury is spinal shock, which is characterized by the loss of autonomic reflexes. However, paradoxically this decrease in reflex activities may cause certain viscera to respond abnormally to the lack of innervation, a phenomenon called **denervation hypersensitivity.** For example, when a person loses the ability to voluntarily evacuate the bladder, the bladder may continue to fill with urine to the point of overdistension. This induces a spinal cord reflex that causes involuntary relaxation of the internal urethral sphincter, allowing the bladder to empty.

15.7b Autonomic Reflexes

LEARNING OBJECTIVES

2. Discuss how autonomic reflexes help maintain homeostasis.
3. Describe some major types of autonomic reflexes.

The autonomic nervous system helps maintain homeostasis through the involuntary activity of **autonomic reflexes,** also termed **visceral reflexes.** These reflexes enable the ANS to control visceral function. Autonomic reflexes consist of smooth muscle contractions, cardiac muscle contractions, or secretion by glands that are mediated by autonomic reflex arcs in response to a specific stimulus. Some autonomic reflexes are described here:

- **Cardiovascular reflex.** A classic autonomic reflex involves the reduction of blood pressure. When blood pressure elevates, stretch receptors in the walls of large blood vessels are stimulated and nerve signals are propagated along visceral sensory neurons to the cardiac center in the medulla oblongata. These nerve signals inhibit sympathetic output and activate parasympathetic output to the heart to slow heart rate and decrease the volume of blood ejected, resulting in a decrease in blood pressure (see section 19.5).

- **Gastrointestinal reflex.** Autonomic reflexes control both the proximal region of the gastrointestinal tract and the activities of the rectum. Gastric glands in the proximal region of the tract are stimulated by parasympathetic innervation to secrete gastric juices merely by the sight or smell of food. In the rectum, fecal matter entry stretches its walls, and a parasympathetic reflex through the sacral region of the spinal cord causes vigorous contraction to aid in elimination of feces from the colon (see section 26.3d).

- **Micturition reflex.** The mechanism leading to bladder emptying is similar to that described for fecal emptying of the colon. In a young child who is not yet toilet trained, stretch receptors send nerve signals to the sacral spinal cord when urine fills the bladder **(figure 15.13)**. The reflex results in contraction of the smooth muscle in the bladder wall and relaxation of the urinary sphincters. (In a toilet-trained individual, sensory nerve signals end at the pons instead of the sacral region of the spinal cord, and urination occurs following voluntary relaxation of the external urethral sphincter. We discuss voluntary control of micturition in section 24.8c).

Figure 15.13 Autonomic Reflexes. An autonomic reflex involves stimulation of an automatic effector. Here, the reflex is initiated as baroreceptors in the bladder wall are stretched and nerve signals are transmitted along sensory neurons to interneurons within the CNS. Nerve signals are then transmitted along motor neurons to stimulate the effector. The effector response is the contraction of the urinary bladder wall and relaxation of the internal urethral sphincter.

LEARNING STRATEGY

The analogy of a corporation can help you understand the hierarchy of control of the ANS:

- The **hypothalamus** is the president of the Autonomic Nervous System corporation. It oversees all activity in this system.
- The **autonomic reflex centers** in the brainstem and spinal cord are the vice presidents of the corporation. They have a lot of control and power, but ultimately they must answer to the president (hypothalamus).
- The **preganglionic and ganglionic neurons** are the workers in the corporation. They are ultimately under the control of both the president and vice presidents. These workers are responsible for production.

Other reflexes alter respiratory rate and depth, regulate digestive system activities, and change pupil diameter.

WHAT DID YOU LEARN?

23 How does the cardiovascular reflex affect blood pressure?

15.7c CNS Control of the ANS

LEARNING OBJECTIVE

4. Describe the CNS hierarchy that controls the autonomic nervous system.

Several levels of CNS complexity are required to coordinate and regulate ANS function. Thus, despite the name "autonomic," the ANS is a regulated nervous system, not an independent one. Autonomic function is influenced by four CNS regions: the cerebrum, hypothalamus, brainstem, and spinal cord (**figure 15.14**).

ANS activities are affected by conscious activities in the cerebral cortex and subconscious communications between association areas in the cortex and the centers of parasympathetic and sympathetic control in the hypothalamus. Additionally, sensory processing in the thalamus and emotional states controlled in the limbic system directly affect the hypothalamus.

The hypothalamus is the integration and command center for autonomic functions (see section 13.4c). It contains nuclei that control visceral functions in both divisions of the ANS, and it communicates with other CNS regions, including the cerebral cortex, thalamus, brainstem, cerebellum, and spinal cord. The hypothalamus is the central brain structure involved in emotions and drives that act through the ANS. For example, the sympathetic nervous system fight-or-flight response originates in the sympathetic nucleus in this brain region.

The brainstem nuclei mediate visceral reflexes (see section 13.5). These reflex centers control changes in blood pressure, blood vessel diameter, digestive activities, heart rate, pupil size, and eye lens shape for focusing on close-up objects.

Some autonomic responses, notably the parasympathetic activities associated with defecation and urination (in children), are processed and controlled at the level of the spinal cord without the involvement of the brain. However, the higher centers in the brain may consciously prevent defecation and urination by controlling the external sphincters.

WHAT DID YOU LEARN?

24 What CNS structure is the integration and command center for autonomic function?

Figure 15.14 Control of Autonomic Functions by Higher Brain Centers. ANS functions are influenced by activities within the cerebrum and hypothalamus, which in turn control ANS regions in the brainstem and spinal cord.

CHAPTER SUMMARY

15.1 Comparison of the Somatic and Autonomic Nervous Systems 575	• The autonomic nervous system controls the internal environment and helps maintain homeostasis. • The nervous system can be functionally organized into the somatic nervous system and autonomic nervous based on whether the sensory input and motor output can be consciously regulated. **15.1a Functional Organization 575** • The somatic nervous system includes sensory input from the special senses, skin, muscles and joints, and motor ouput to control skeletal muscle. • The autonomic nervous system includes sensory input from blood vessels and viscera, and involuntary motor ouput to cardiac muscle, smooth muscle, and glands. **15.1b Motor Neurons of the Somatic versus Autonomic Nervous System 576** • A single motor neuron innervates skeletal muscle fibers in the SNS, while the ANS has a two-neuron pathway consisting of preganglionic neurons in the CNS and ganglionic neurons in the PNS.

(continued on next page)

15.2 Divisions of the Autonomic Nervous System 577	**15.2a Functional Differences 578** • The parasympathetic division is primarily concerned with conserving energy and replenishing nutrient stores. • The sympathetic division is primarily concerned with preparing the body for emergencies.

15.2b Anatomic Differences   578
- Parasympathetic preganglionic neurons reside in the brainstem and sacral regions of the spinal cord, whereas sympathetic preganglionic axons reside in the thoracic and lumbar regions of the spinal cord.

15.2c Degree of Response 579
- The parasympathetic response tends to be discrete and localized, whereas the sympathetic response has the potential to produce a mass activation effect.

15.3 Parasympathetic Division   580
- The parasympathetic preganglionic neurons is also known as the craniosacral system, because of the location of the preganglionic neurons.

15.3a Cranial Components   580
- Parasympathetic preganglionic axons extend through the oculomotor, facial, glossopharyngeal, and vagus cranial nerves.

15.3b Pelvic Splanchnic Nerves   582
- The remaining preganglionic parasympathetic cell bodies are housed within the S2–S4 segments of the spinal cord and form pelvic splanchnic nerves.

15.4 Sympathetic Division   582
- The sympathetic division is also known as the thoracolumbar division, since its preganglionic neurons reside in the T1-L2 segments of the spinal cord.
- Sympathetic pathways prepare the body for fight or flight.
- A single effector may control one tissue, but many effectors often respond together, a phenomenon called mass activation.

15.4a Organization and Anatomy of the Sympathetic Division   582
- Preganglionic neuronal cell bodies are housed within the lateral gray horn of the spinal gray matter and their axons enter the sympathetic trunk through white rami communicantes.
- Gray rami communicantes carry postganglionic sympathetic axons from the sympathetic trunk to the spinal nerve.
- Some preganglionic axons pass through the sympathetic trunk without synapsing and form splanchnic nerves that project to the prevertebral ganglia. Postganglionic axons travel from the prevertebral ganglia to the target organ.

15.4b Sympathetic Pathways   586
- In the spinal nerve pathway, the postganglionic axon enters the spinal nerve through the gray ramus and travels to the blood vessels and glands distributed throughout the limbs and body wall of the trunk.
- In the postganglionic sympathetic nerve pathway, the postganglionic axon leaves the sympathetic trunk and extends directly to the target organ.
- In the splanchnic nerve pathway, the preganglionic axon passes through the sympathetic trunk and travels to the prevertebral ganglia, where it synapses with a ganglionic neuron.
- In the adrenal medulla pathway, the preganglionic axon extends through both a sympathetic trunk ganglion and prevertebral ganglion without synapsing. It synapses on secretory cells in the adrenal medulla that release epinephrine and norepinephrine.

15.5 Comparison of Neuro-transmitters and Receptors of the Two Divisions   588
- The two main types of receptors are cholinergic and adrenergic receptors.

15.5a Overview of ANS Neurotransmitters   588
- Acetylcholine (ACh) is the cholinergic neurotransmitter used by all preganglionic neurons as well as all ganglionic parasympathetic neurons. ACh also is used by some ganglionic sympathetic neurons to sweat glands and blood vessels in skeletal muscle.
- Norepinephrine (NE) is the adrenergic neurotransmitter used by all other sympathetic postganglionic neurons.

15.5b Cholinergic Receptors   589
- Nicotinic receptors are located on all ganglionic neurons and cells in the adrenal medulla, and are always stimulatory.
- Muscarinic receptors are located on all parasympathetic target cells, on sweat glands in the skin, and on blood vessels in skeletal muscle.

15.5c Adrenergic Receptors   589
- NE binds to alpha and beta adrenergic receptors. There are two subsets for both alpha and beta types.

15.6 Interactions Between the Parasympathetic and Sympathetic Divisions   590
- Most organs are innervated by both divisions of the ANS.

15.6a Autonomic Tone   590
- Both ANS divisions maintain some continual activity, which is called the autonomic tone for that division.

15.6b Dual Innervation   590
- Many visceral effectors have dual innervation, meaning they are innervated by axons from both ANS divisions. The actions of the divisions oppose each other, and thus they exert antagonistic effects on the same organ.

15.6c Systems Controlled Only by the Sympathetic Division   594
- Most blood vessels, the adrenal medulla, and sweat glands of the skin are innervated by sympathetic axons only.

15.7 Control and Integration of Autonomic System Function 594	• Autonomic functions ultimately are controlled by the CNS.
	15.7a Autonomic Plexuses 594
	• Autonomic plexuses are meshworks of sympathetic postganglionic axons and parasympathetic preganglionic axons, as well as some visceral sensory axons.
	15.7b Autonomic Reflexes 596
	• The autonomic nervous system helps maintain homeostasis through involuntary activity of autonomic reflexes, which are also called visceral reflexes.
	15.7c CNS Control of the ANS 597
	• Autonomic function is influenced by four CNS regions: cerebrum, hypothalamus, brainstem, and spinal cord.

CHALLENGE YOURSELF

Do You Know the Basics?

_____ 1. A splanchnic nerve in the sympathetic division of the ANS

    a. connects neighboring sympathetic trunk ganglia.

    b. controls parasympathetic functions in the thoracic cavity.

    c. is formed by preganglionic axons that travel to prevertebral ganglia.

    d. travels through parasympathetic pathways in the head.

_____ 2. Some parasympathetic preganglionic neuron cell bodies are housed within the

    a. hypothalamus.

    b. sacral region of the spinal cord.

    c. cerebral cortex.

    d. thoracolumbar region of the spinal cord.

_____ 3. Which of the following is *not* a function of the sympathetic division of the ANS?

    a. increases heart rate and breathing rate

    b. prepares for emergency

    c. increases digestive system motility and activity

    d. dilates pupils

_____ 4. Maintaining a resting level of ANS activity in a cell is called

    a. autonomic tone.   c. cooperative effect.

    b. dual innervation.   d. antagonistic effect.

_____ 5. Sympathetic division preganglionic axons travel to the _____ ganglia via the _____ rami.

    a. terminal; white

    b. sympathetic trunk; gray

    c. prevertebral; gray

    d. sympathetic trunk; white

_____ 6. All parasympathetic division synapses use _____ as a neurotransmitter.

    a. dopamine   c. acetylcholine

    b. norepinephrine   d. epinephrine

_____ 7. Which autonomic nerve plexus innervates the pelvic organs?

    a. cardiac plexus

    b. esophageal plexus

    c. hypogastric plexus

    d. inferior mesenteric plexus

_____ 8. A sympathetic postganglionic axon is

    a. long and unmyelinated.

    b. short and myelinated.

    c. short and unmyelinated.

    d. long and myelinated.

_____ 9. Nicotinic receptors are located on which of the following?

    a. cell membranes of ganglionic neurons

    b. target cells that receive parasympathetic innervation

    c. blood vessels in skeletal muscles

    d. sweat glands

_____ 10. Which of the following is true about a beta receptor?

    a. It binds acetylcholine.

    b. Its effects are stimulatory only.

    c. It causes general vasoconstriction.

    d. It increases heart rate.

11. What are the four CNS regions that control autonomic function?

12. For the following ganglia, identify the location and the division of the ANS each is part of: sympathetic trunk ganglia, prevertebra ganglia, and terminal ganglia.

13. Compare and contrast the postganglionic axons of the parasympathetic and sympathetic divisions. Examine the axon length, myelination (or lack thereof), and the neurotransmitter used.

14. Compare and contrast sympathetic and parasympathetic innervation effects on digestive system structures.

15. Explain responses of nicotinic receptors and muscarinic receptors to simulation by ACh.

16. Describe the differences between cooperative effects and complementary effects in dual innervation of target organs.

17. Describe how the general functions of the sympathetic and parasympathetic divisions of the ANS differ.

18. What may occur with the mass activation of the sympathetic division of the ANS?

19. Describe the process of micturition reflex.

20. How does sympathetic innervation regulate vasoconstriction or vasodilation in the same blood vessels?

Can You Apply What You've Learned?

Use the following paragraph to answer questions 1 and 2.

Arlene was crossing the street when a car ran a red light and nearly hit her. Arlene was not hurt, but she was very frightened and was in a heightened state of alertness well after the incident.

1. Arlene likely experienced all of the following physiological effects *except*
   a. increased heart rate.
   b. pupil constriction.
   c. increased respiratory rate.
   d. sweaty palms.

2. Arlene was in a heightened state of alertness well after the incident because
   a. the adrenal medulla secreted epinephrine and norepinephrine.
   b. the parasympathetic division stimulated regions of the brain.
   c. the sympathetic division decreased overall autonomic tone of blood vessels.
   d. All of these are correct.

3. George has hypertension (high blood pressure). His physician prescribed the drug propranolol, which is described as a beta-blocker, to reduce his blood pressure What do you suppose could be a side effect of propranolol?
   a. reduced heart rate
   b. increased blood clotting
   c. vasoconstriction of blood vessels to the skin
   d. bronchodilation

4. Albuterol is a drug designed to counteract the effects of asthma—namely, the medication, which may be used in an inhaler, facilitates bronchodilation. What receptors would you expect this drug to bind?
   a. α-1 receptors
   b. α-2 receptors
   c. β-1 receptors
   d. β-2 receptors

5. One surgical treatment for gastric ulcers is a selective vagotomy, where branches of the vagus nerve to the upper GI tract are cut. How would you suppose a vagotomy would help the treatment of a gastric ulcer?
   a. It would stimulate vasodilation of the blood vessels serving the stomach.
   b. It would reduce gastric gland secretion.
   c. It would promote faster movement of materials through the stomach.
   d. All of these are correct.

Can You Synthesize What You've Learned?

1. Our body expends a lot of energy activating and propagating the mass activation response of the sympathetic nervous system. Why is it necessary for us to have such an "expensive" mechanism at our disposal?

2. When you were younger, your parents may have told you to wait until 1 hour after you've eaten before you go swimming. Based on what you've learned about the ANS, can you hypothesize why swimming right after a meal may be problematic?

3. Some faculty dislike teaching lecture classes after lunch, complaining that the students do not pay attention at this time. From a physiologic viewpoint, what is happening to these students?

INTEGRATE

ONLINE STUDY TOOLS
www.mhhe.com/mckinleyap

Clinical Case Study: A Secret Life Leading to an Unexpected Death

Interactive Questions: This chapter's content is served up in a number of multimedia question formats for student study.

LearnSmart: Topics and terminology include comparison of the somatic and autonomic nervous systems; divisions of the autonomic

nervous system; parasympathetic division; sympathetic division; comparison of neurotransmitters and receptors of the two divisions; interactions between the parasympathetic and sympathetic divisions; control and integration of autonomic system function

Anatomy & Physiology Revealed: Topics include sympathetic and parasympathetic overviews; thoracic region

chapter 16
Nervous System: Senses

We are barraged continuously with sensory information about the state of the environment—both outside and inside our bodies. This information must be detected by various sensory receptors and transmitted to the brain so that it can be analyzed and the appropriate responses initiated. The sensory information comes in many different forms. Touch receptors react to physical contact, receptors for taste detect chemicals in the food we eat, receptors for vision receive and respond to light waves, hearing receptors ➤

A pediatrician focuses on the health and well-being of children, from birth to early adulthood. This health care professional is especially knowledgeable about normal development of growing children and ailments that are prevalent in this population. One of the more common ailments of children is ear pain, which typically occurs as a result of a respiratory infection that has spread to the middle ear. Thus, knowledge of ear anatomy and physiology is essential for this health care professional. A pediatrician uses a tool called an otoscope to examine the ear canal, eardrum, and middle ear for possible infection. This chapter provides examples of how the otoscope visualizes healthy versus infected middle ears, and why middle ear infections are more prevalent in children under 5.

Anatomy & Physiology | REVEALED®
aprevealed.com

Module 7: Nervous System

detect and react to sound waves, and blood vessels respond to stretch. Here you'll learn the structure of sensory receptors and how these receptors may be classified. We will discuss the functions of the general senses and explore the clinically relevant phenomenon of referred visceral pain. We then examine in detail the actions of the more complex special senses (smell, taste, vision, hearing, and equilibrium). As you will see, the physiology of these sensory structures varies, and they are often highly elaborate—yet all inform the central nervous system of what is going on within and around us.

16.1 Introduction to Sensory Receptors

Receptors (*recipio* = to receive) range in complexity from the relatively simple, bare dendritic ending of a single sensory neuron (e.g., touch receptors; see figure 16.3) to complex structures called sense organs whose nerve endings are associated with epithelial tissue, connective tissue, or muscular tissue (e.g., the eye; see figure 16.13). The feature common to all receptors is the ability to respond to a stimulus and initiate sensory input to the central nervous system (CNS). Here we define stimuli and sensations, provide an overview of the basic properties of sensory receptors, and describe how receptors are classified.

16.1a Stimuli and Sensations

 LEARNING OBJECTIVE

1. Differentiate between a stimulus and a sensation.

Stimuli (stim′ū-lī; sing., *stimulus* = a goad) are the changes in the sensory information our receptors detect in our external or internal environment. Some stimuli give us pleasure, as when we watch a funny movie, listen to a CD, touch a baby's face, or eat a tasty meal. Other stimuli alert us to potential dangers, as when we see a stranger lurking in the dark, smell smoke upon walking into a room, or detect an extremely hot object in the kitchen. Still others provide routine, moment-to-moment information about our external surroundings, such as air temperature and our internal environment such as whether blood pressure is high or low.

INTEGRATE

CONCEPT CONNECTION

Our sensory receptors initiate communication among most body systems. For example, sensory receptors in our integument signal our central nervous system to initiate cooling or heating mechanisms if the environmental temperature is either too hot or too cold. Chemoreceptors in the blood vessels monitor oxygen and carbon dioxide levels within the blood, and when their balance is changed both the cardiovascular system and respiratory system are stimulated to bring these levels back to homeostasis. Receptors associated with our musculoskeletal system alert the nervous system about the body's position and balance. Finally, sensory receptors in the digestive tract allow us to perceive tastes in our food, detect textures and consistencies of foods, and let us know when our stomach has been extensively stretched when we have eaten too much.

Sensation is our conscious awareness of incoming sensory information. It occurs when we recognize a child's face or realize that the room is too warm. Only a stimulus that reaches the cerebral cortex of the brain results in our conscious awareness.

Although your body is constantly bombarded by sensory stimuli, you are consciously aware of only a fraction of them. Much of the sensory input is only relayed to lower areas of the brain (e.g., the brainstem or the hypothalamus), where a response is initiated without your awareness. Sensory stimuli regarding your blood pressure, blood carbon dioxide levels, and chemical composition of material within the small intestine are examples of sensory information that is detected and responded to on a subconscious level.

WHAT DID YOU LEARN?

❶ For a stimulus to be consciously perceived, the sensory input must be sent to what area of the brain?

16.1b Properties of Sensory Receptors

LEARNING OBJECTIVES

2. Describe the general function of sensory receptors.
3. Explain the significance of a receptive field.
4. Distinguish between tonic receptors and phasic receptors.

Important functional characteristics are associated with receptors including how they serve as transducers, the size of their receptive fields, and the two basic patterns of how the receptors communicate with the CNS.

Receptors as Transducers

Sensory receptors act as transducers. **Transducers** (tranz-dū′sĕr; *trans* = across, *duco* = to lead) change one form of energy into a different form. The original energy form detected is specific to the type of receptor (e.g., light energy is detected by the eye, sound energy by the ear, and mechanical energy by blood vessels). However, the form the energy is transduced or changed to is always electrical energy, and it is conducted along a sensory neuron. This sensory information is relayed to the CNS for interpretation.

Two features are critical to allow sensory receptors to function as transducers: (1) Receptors, like neurons and muscle cells, establish and maintain a resting membrane potential (RMP) across their plasma membrane (see section 12.7b). (2) Receptors contain modality gated channels within their plasma membranes. A modality gated channel opens in response to a stimulus other than a chemical or a voltage change at the plasma membrane. (Recall that chemically gated channels open in response to a neurotransmitter and voltage-gated channels open in response to a voltage change; see section 12.6a.)

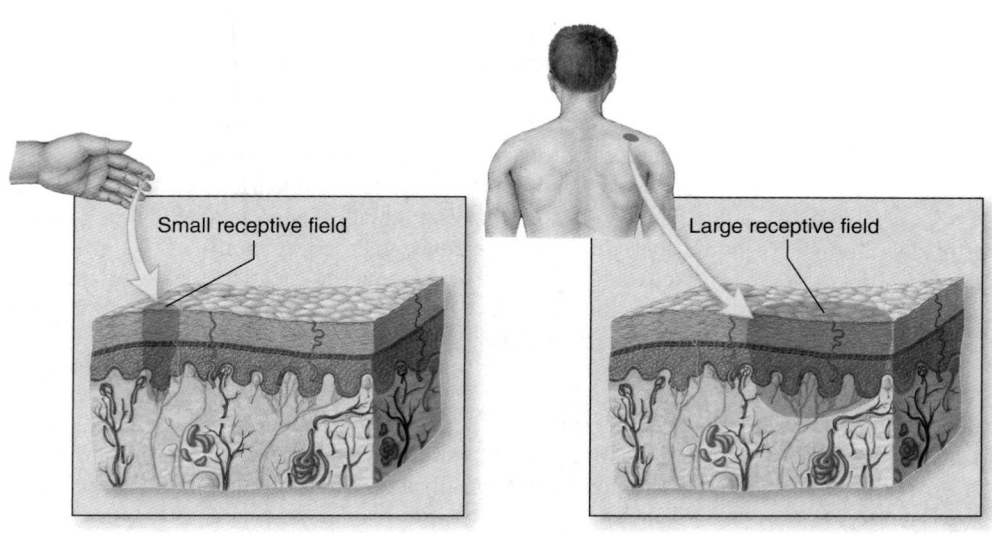

Small receptive field

Large receptive field

Figure 16.1 Receptive Fields. The specific area monitored by each sensory receptor is called its receptive field. A smaller receptive field offers greater specificity of localization than does a larger receptive field.

The details for the various types of receptors and the opening of their specialized modality gated channels are explained in detail throughout the later sections of this chapter.

Receptive Field

The **receptive field** of a receptor is the entire area through which the sensitive ends of the receptor cell are distributed. This is most clearly shown with a comparison of receptive fields within the skin (**figure 16.1**).

An inverse relationship exists between the size of the receptive field and our ability to identify the exact location of a stimulus. If the receptive field is small, precise localization of the stimulus and sensitivity are determined easily. In contrast, a broad receptive field detects only the general region of the stimulus.

Although it might seem advantageous for all receptors to have small receptive fields, the number of receptors in the body would have to markedly increase to detect environmental stimuli if all receptive fields were very small. Not only would organ size and total body surface need to increase markedly to accommodate all of these extra receptors, but the increase in energy costs to maintain activity in such a large number of receptors would be enormous.

Tonic and Phasic Receptors

Sensory receptors may respond continuously to a stimulus or only to changes in a stimulus (**figure 16.2**). **Tonic receptors** respond continuously to stimuli at a constant rate; examples are the balance receptors within the inner ear that help us keep our head upright. The sensitivity of these receptors stays the same over time.

Phasic receptors detect a new stimulus or a change in a stimulus that has already been applied, but over time their sensitivity decreases. An example is the tactile receptors of the skin that sense the increased pressure when we are touched. Phasic receptors can undergo a change called **adaptation,** which is a reduction in sensitivity to a continually applied stimulus. For example, when we sit down in a chair, we are immediately aware of the pressure increase wherever our body contacts the chair. But soon, we lose awareness or do not notice this pressure because adaptation has occurred in the deep pressure receptors of the skin. It is advantageous for us to not be continuously bombarded by this sensory information.

WHAT DID YOU LEARN?

2 How does a receptor function as a transducer?

3 What is the difference between tonic and phasic receptors?

Tonic Receptors

Tonic receptors receive and process stimuli continuously at a constant rate (e.g., balance receptors within the inner ear).

Response

— Stimulus

Strength of response

Time

With continued exposure, sensitivity to the stimulus remains constant.

Phasic Receptors

Phasic receptors detect a new stimulus or a change in a stimulus that has already been applied (e.g., tactile receptors in the skin).

Response

— Stimulus

Strength of response

Time

Detection of a new or changed stimulus produces a response. With continued exposure, sensitivity to the stimulus diminishes, resulting in adaptation.

Figure 16.2 Receptor Activities. Tonic receptor activity continuously responds to stimuli, whereas phasic receptor activity decreases over time.

16.1c Receptor Classification

LEARNING OBJECTIVES

5. Identify and describe the three criteria used to describe receptors.
6. Classify the various types of sensory receptors based on each of the three criteria.

Three criteria are used to describe receptors—receptor distribution, stimulus origin, and modality of stimulus. These classification criteria are summarized in **table 16.1**.

Receptor Distribution

Receptors may be classified based on their distribution in the body. The two distribution types are the general senses and the special senses.

General senses receptors are distributed throughout the body and are located in the skin and internal organs. General sense receptors are typically simple in structure. The receptors for general senses are subdivided into two categories based on their location in the body. **Somatic sensory receptors** are housed within the skin for monitoring tactile sensations (e.g., pressure, vibration, and pain) and within joints, muscles, and tendons for detection of stretch and pressure relative to position and movement of the skeleton and skeletal muscles. **Visceral sensory receptors** are located in the walls of the viscera (internal organs); they respond to temperature, chemicals, stretch, and pain.

Receptors of the **special senses** are located only within the head and are specialized, complex sense organs. The five special senses are gustation (taste), olfaction (smell), vision (sight), hearing (audition), and equilibrium (balance and acceleration).

We use receptor distribution as the criterion for organizing our discussion on receptors. General senses are first described followed by the details of the special senses.

Stimulus Origin

Receptors can also be classified based on where the stimulus originates. These classifications include exteroceptors, interoceptors, and proprioceptors.

Exteroceptors (eks′ter-ō-sep′ter, -tōr; *exterus* = external) detect stimuli from the external environment. For example, the receptors in your skin (called *cutaneous receptors*) are exteroceptors because external stimuli typically cause sensations to the skin. Likewise, our receptors for special senses are considered to be exteroceptors because they are excited by external stimuli, such as the taste of the

Table 16.1	Criteria for Classifying Receptors	
Classification	**Description**	**Examples**
RECEPTOR DISTRIBUTION (BODY LOCATION)		
General senses	Distributed throughout the body; structurally simple	
Somatic sensory receptors	Located in skin; located in joints, muscles, and tendons	Tactile (touch) receptors Proprioceptors in joints
Visceral sensory receptors	Located within walls of viscera	Stretch receptors in blood vessels
Special senses	Located only in the head; structurally complex	Receptors for smell, taste, vision, hearing, and equilibrium
STIMULUS ORIGIN (LOCATION OF STIMULUS)		
Exteroceptors	Detect stimuli in the external environment	Receptors within skin or mucous membranes Receptors for smell, taste, vision, hearing and equilibrium
Interoceptors (visceroceptors)	Detect stimuli within the body	Receptors with blood vessels or viscera
Proprioceptors	Detect stimuli within skeletal muscles, tendons, and joint capsules that sense position or state of contraction of the muscle	Muscle spindle, Golgi tendon organ, joint receptors
MODALITY OF STIMULUS (STIMULATING AGENT)		
Chemoreceptors	Detect chemicals dissolved in fluid	Taste receptors, receptors in blood vessels that monitor hydrogen ions (H^+)
Thermoreceptors	Detect changes in temperature	Receptors within skin and hypothalamus
Photoreceptors	Detect changes in light intensity, color, and movement of light rays	Eye
Mechanoreceptors	Detect physical deformation due to touch, pressure, vibration, and stretch	Primarily cutaneous tactile receptors
Baroreceptors	Detect changes in stretch or distension of an organ	Blood vessels, urinary bladder
Nociceptors	Detect painful stimuli	Pain receptors present in almost all organs

food you are eating or the music you are listening to on your iPod. Exteroceptors are also found within the mucous membranes that are exposed to the environment outside of our body, such as the membranes lining the nasal cavity, oral cavity, vagina, and anal canal.

Interoceptors (in'ter-ō-sep'ter; *inter* = between), also called *visceroceptors,* detect stimuli in internal organs. These receptors are primarily stretch receptors in the smooth muscle within the walls of these organs. Most of the time we are unaware of these receptors, but when the smooth muscle stretches to a certain point (e.g., when the eating of a large meal stretches our stomach wall), we may become aware of these sensations. Interoceptors also report on temperature, pressure, chemical changes, and perceived pain in the visceral tissue.

Proprioceptors (prō'prē-ō-sep'ter; *proprius* = one's own) are located in our muscles, tendons, and joints. They detect body and limb movements, skeletal muscle contraction and stretch, and changes in joint capsule structure. Thus, even if you are not looking at your body joints, you are aware of their position and the state of contraction of your skeletal muscles, because proprioceptors continuously send this information to the CNS.

Modality of Stimulus

Finally, receptors may be classified according to the stimulus they perceive, which is called the **modality of stimulus,** or the *stimulating agent.* Thus, some receptors respond only to temperature changes, while others respond to chemical changes. There are six groups of receptors, based on their modality of stimulus: chemoreceptors, thermoreceptors, photoreceptors, mechanoreceptors, baroreceptors, and nociceptors:

- **Chemoreceptors** (kē'mō-rē-sep'tōr, -ter) detect chemicals, either molecules or ions dissolved in fluid. These chemicals include the food and drink we have ingested, the composition of our body fluids, and the relative components of our inhaled air. The receptors in the taste buds on our tongue are chemoreceptors, because they respond to the specific molecules in our ingested food to provide information to us about what is present in what we are eating. Likewise, chemoreceptors in some of our blood vessels monitor the concentration of oxygen and carbon dioxide in our blood, to help influence our respiratory rate (see section 23.5c).

- **Thermoreceptors** (ther'mō-rē-sep'tōr; *therme* = heat) respond to changes in temperature. Thermoreceptors are present in both the skin and the hypothalamus. These receptors are components of reflexes that regulate and maintain body temperature.

- **Photoreceptors** (fō'tō-rē-sep'tōr; *phot* = light) are located in the eye, where they detect changes in light intensity, color, and movement.

- **Mechanoreceptors** (me-kăn'ō-rē-sep'tōr; *mechane* = machine) respond to touch, pressure, vibration, and stretch. Most of the cutaneous receptors are mechanoreceptors, because they respond to pressure and touch on the skin. Mechanoreceptors are also located in the ear for hearing and equilibrium.

- **Baroreceptors** (bar'ō-rē-sep'tōr; *baros* = weight) detect changes in stretch or distension within body structures. These sensory receptors branch repeatedly within the connective tissues in vessel or organ walls, especially the elastic layers. Any pressure stimulus that causes wall deformation results in a change in the nerve signal rates from the receptors to the CNS. These are involved, for example in the regulation of blood pressure (see section 20.5a).

- **Nociceptors** (nō'si-sep'tōr; *noci* = pain) respond to painful stimuli. The purpose of nociceptors is to inform the body of injury or other damage so that an appropriate response may be made. **Somatic nociceptors** detect chemical, heat, or mechanical damage to the body surface or skeletal muscles. For example, our exposure to acid, touching a hot pan, or suffering a sprained ankle stimulates somatic nociceptors. **Visceral nociceptors** detect internal body damage within the viscera. When we feel discomfort in our internal organs, it often occurs because (1) a tissue has been deprived of oxygen—for example, as a result of a heart attack or a blocked blood vessel elsewhere; (2) the smooth muscle in the wall of the organ has been stretched so much that we are uncomfortable; or (3) the tissue has suffered trauma, and damaged cells have released chemicals that stimulate specific nociceptors.

Classifying a Receptor

A given receptor is described based on each classification criterion: receptor distribution, stimulus origin, and modality of stimulus. The eyes, for example, are special senses because they are located in the head (receptor distribution); exteroceptors because they detect stimuli outside the body (stimulus origin); and photoreceptors because they detect light (modality of stimulus). In comparison, receptors that detect stretch of blood vessels are classified as general senses because they are distributed throughout the body, interoceptors because they detect stimuli within the body, and baroreceptors because they detect changes in distension of the organ wall.

WHAT DID YOU LEARN?

4 Describe the following sensory receptors based on the three classification criteria: the ear and the sense of hearing, the tongue and the sense of taste, and stretch receptors in the urinary bladder wall.

INTEGRATE

LEARNING STRATEGY

When you eat a very spicy meal, your mouth stings because the nociceptors in your mouth are somatic nociceptors. When you swallow that spicy meal and it travels through your gastrointestinal (GI) tract, you may not experience the stinging, burning sensation because the nociceptors here are visceral nociceptors that respond only to abnormal muscle stretch, oxygen deprivation, or chemical imbalance in the tissue. When the waste products from that spicy meal are expelled from the body, the anus may sting because the nociceptors around the anus and inferior anal canal are somatic nociceptors.

16.2 The General Senses

Receptors for general senses are distributed throughout the skin and viscera and are usually simple in structure. Here we discuss tactile receptors of the skin and referred pain.

16.2a Tactile Receptors

✔ LEARNING OBJECTIVE

1. Compare and contrast unencapsulated and encapsulated receptors.

Tactile (tak′til; *tango* = to touch) **receptors** are the most numerous type of receptor **(figure 16.3)**. They are mechanoreceptors located in the dermis and the subcutaneous layer (see section 6.1), which respond to touch, pressure, and vibration stimuli. Tactile receptors range from simple, dendritic ends of sensory neurons with no protective connective tissue wrapping (called unencapsulated) to more complex structures that are wrapped with connective tissue or enclosed with glial cells (called encapsulated) **(table 16.2)**.

Unencapsulated Tactile Receptors

Unencapsulated tactile receptors are dendritic ends of sensory neurons with no protective coat. The three types of unencapsulated receptors are free nerve endings, root hair plexuses, and tactile discs.

Free nerve endings are terminal branches of dendrites. They are the least complex of the tactile receptors and reside closest to the surface of the skin, usually in the papillary layer of the dermis. Often, some dendritic branches extend into the deepest epidermal strata and terminate between the epithelial cells. Free nerve endings are also located in mucous membranes. These tactile receptors primarily detect pain and temperature stimuli, but some also detect light touch and pressure.

Root hair plexuses are specialized free nerve endings that form a weblike sheath around hair follicles in the reticular layer of the dermis. Any movement or displacement of the hair changes the arrangement of these branching dendrites, initiating a nerve signal. These receptors quickly adapt; thus, although we feel the initial contact of a long-sleeved shirt on our arm hairs when we put on the garment, our conscious awareness subsides immediately until we move and the root hair plexuses are restimulated.

Tactile discs, previously called *Merkel discs,* are flattened nerve endings that extend to specialized **tactile cells** (*Merkel cells*), which are located in the stratum basale of the epidermis. These discs function as tonic receptors for fine touch and are important in distinguishing the texture and shape of a object.

Encapsulated Tactile Receptors

Encapsulated tactile receptors are either wrapped by connective tissue or covered by glial cells. Encapsulated tactile receptors include end bulbs, lamellated corpuscles, bulbous corpuscles, and tactile corpuscles.

End bulbs, or *Krause bulbs,* are dendritic endings of sensory neurons ensheathed in connective tissue. They are located in the dermis of the skin near the border of the stratified squamous epithelium, and in the mucous membranes of the oral cavity, nasal cavity, vagina, and anal canal. End bulbs detect light pressure stimuli and low-frequency vibration.

Lamellated (lam′e-lāt-ed) **corpuscles,** previously called *Pacinian corpuscles,* are composed of several dendritic endings ensheathed with an inner core of neurolemmocytes (type of glial cell) and outer concentric layers of connective tissue. They are found deep within the reticular layer of the dermis of the skin; in the subcutaneous tissue of the palms of the hands, soles of the feet, breasts, and external genitalia; in the synovial membranes of joints; and in the walls of some organs. The structure of lamellated corpuscles ensures that only deep-pressure and vibration stimuli will activate the receptor.

Bulbous corpuscles, or *Ruffini corpuscles,* are sensory dendritic endings within connective tissue that are housed within the dermis and subcutaneous layer, as well as in joint capsules. They detect both continuous deep pressure and distortion in the skin. These are tonic receptors that do not exhibit adaptation.

Tactile corpuscles, previously called *Meissner corpuscles,* are large, encapsulated oval receptors. They are formed from highly intertwined dendrites enclosed by modified neurolemmocytes, which are then covered with dense irregular connective tissue. They are housed within the dermal papillae of the skin, especially in the lips, palms, eyelids, nipples, and genitals. Tactile corpuscles are phasic

Unencapsulated tactile receptors
Tactile disc
Free nerve ending
Root hair plexus

Encapsulated tactile receptors
Tactile corpuscle
End bulb
Bulbous corpuscle
Lamellated corpuscle

Figure 16.3 Tactile Receptors. Various types of tactile receptors in the skin receive information about touch, pressure, or vibration in our immediate environment. Unencapsulated tactile receptors have no connective tissue covering around them while encapsulated tactile receptors are enclosed by either connective tissue or glial cells.

Table 16.2   Types of Tactile Receptors

UNENCAPSULATED TACTILE RECEPTORS

Tactile cell   Tactile disc

Receptor Type	Free Nerve Ending	Root Hair Plexus	Tactile (Merkel) Disc
Structure	Dendritic endings of sensory neurons	Dendritic endings of sensory neurons that surround hair follicles	Flattened dendritic endings of sensory neurons that end adjacent to specialized tactile cells
Location	Deep epidermis and papillary layer of the dermis; some dendritic endings extend into the deepest layers of the epidermal strata	Reticular layer of the dermis	Stratum basale of epidermis
Function	Thermoreceptors; nociceptors; or mechanoreceptors that detect pressure	Mechanoreceptors that detect movement of the hair	Mechanoreceptors for light touch

ENCAPSULATED TACTILE RECEPTORS

Receptor Type	End Bulb	Lamellated Corpuscle	Bulbous Corpuscle	Tactile Corpuscle
Structure	Dendritic endings of sensory neurons ensheathed in connective tissue	Dendritic endings of sensory neurons ensheathed with an inner core of neurolemmocytes and outer concentric layers of connective tissue	Dendritic endings of sensory neurons within connective tissue	Highly intertwined dendrites enclosed by modified neurolemmocytes and dense irregular connective tissue
Location	Dermis, mucous membranes of oral cavity, nasal cavity, vagina, and anal cavity	Dermis, subcutaneous tissue, synovial membranes, and some viscera	Dermis and subcutaneous layer; joint capsules	Dermal papillae, especially in lips, palms, eyelids, nipples, genitals
Function	Mechanoreceptors that detect light pressure and low-frequency vibration	Mechanoreceptors that detect deep pressure and high-frequency vibration	Mechanoreceptors that detect continuous deep pressure and skin distortion	Mechanoreceptors for discriminative touch to determine textures and shapes; light touch

receptors for discriminative touch to determine textures and shapes of an object and for light touch.

 WHAT DID YOU LEARN?

 5 What are the three types of unencapsulated receptors, and where are they located?

16.2b Referred Pain

 LEARNING OBJECTIVE

2. Define referred pain, and explain its significance in diagnosis.

Referred pain occurs when sensory nerve signals from certain viscera are perceived as originating not from the organ, but in dermatomes of

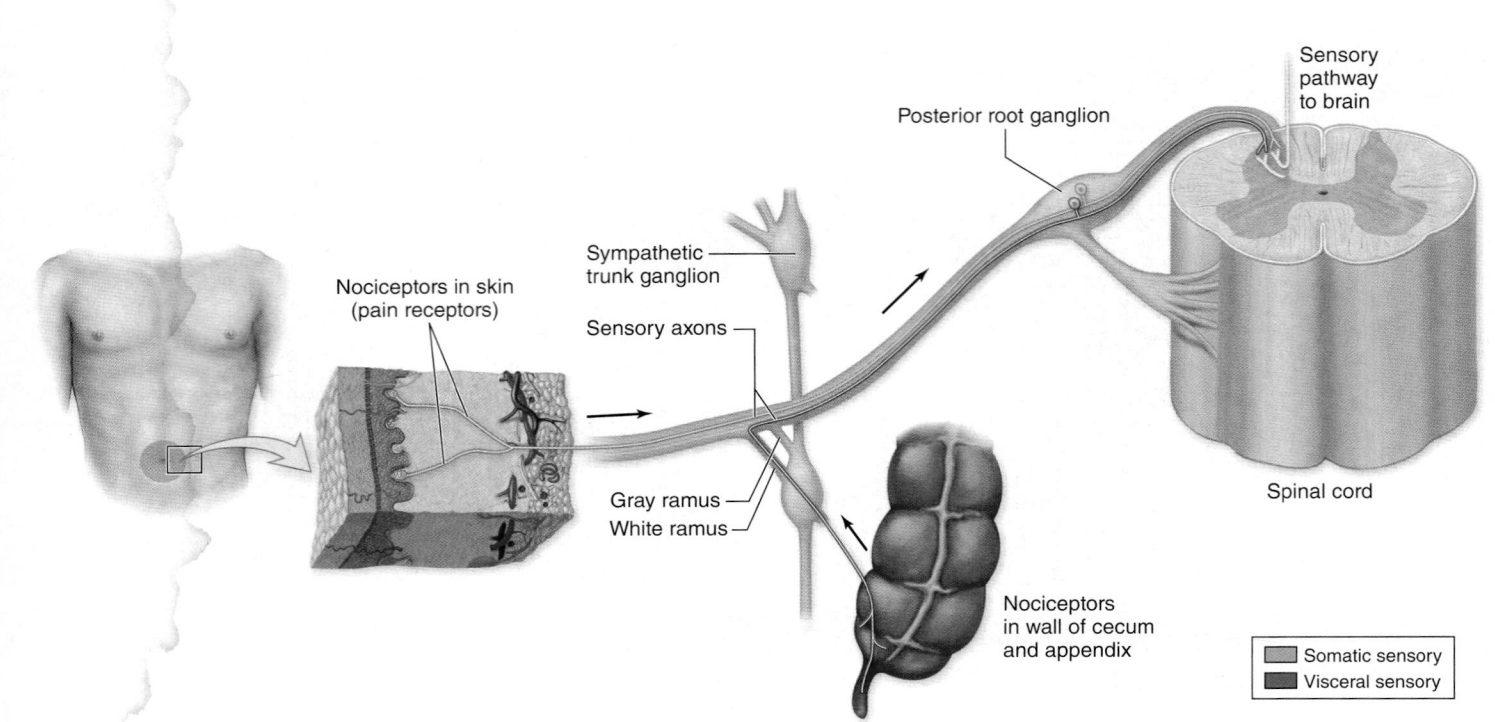

Figure 16.4 Source of Referred Pain. Misinterpretation of a pain source occurs when sensory impulses from two different organs are conducted to the brain in a common pathway. For example, pain that is perceived as originating from the umbilical region of the skin actually has its source within the cecum and appendix.

the skin (see figure 14.13). Numerous cutaneous and visceral sensory neurons conduct nerve signals on the same ascending tracts within the spinal cord **(figure 16.4)**. As a result, the sensory cortex in the brain is unable to differentiate between actual and false sources of the stimulus, and thus the stimulus may be localized incorrectly.

Clinically, some common sites of referred pain are useful in medical diagnosis **(figure 16.5)**. For example, cardiac problems are often a source of referred pain because the heart receives its sympathetic innervation from the T1–T5 segments of the spinal cord (see section 15.4). Pain associated with a myocardial infarction (heart attack) may be referred to the skin dermatomes innervated by the

T1–T5 spinal nerves, which lie along the pectoral region and the medial side of the arm. Thus, some individuals who are experiencing heart problems may feel pain along the medial side of the left arm, where the T1 dermatome lies. By the same token, kidney and ureter pain may be referred along the T10–L2 dermatomes, which typically overlie the inferior abdominal wall in the groin and loin regions.

Visceral pain is usually referred along the sympathetic nerve pathways, but sometimes it can follow parasympathetic pathways as well. Referred pain from the urinary bladder often can follow the parasympathetic pathways (via the pelvic splanchnic nerves; see section 15.3b). Since the pelvic splanchnic nerves lie in the S2–S4

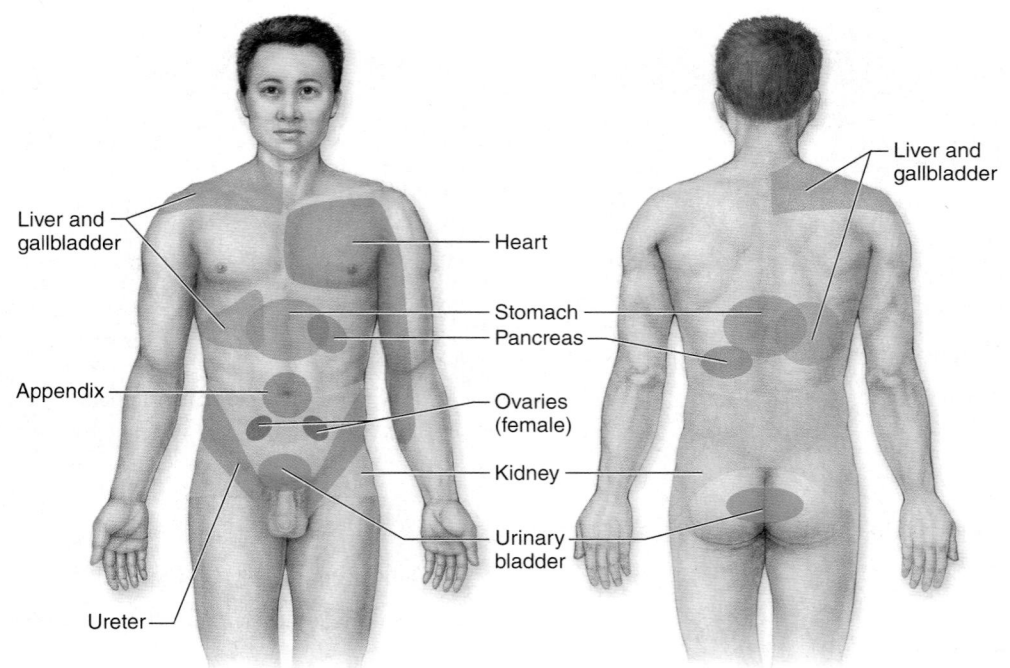

Figure 16.5 Common Sites of Referred Pain.

CLINICAL VIEW
Phantom Pain

Phantom (fan'tŏm; a ghost) **pain** is a sensation associated with a body part that has been removed. Following the amputation of an appendage, a patient often continues to experience pain apparently from that removed part. For example, a patient may feel pain that seems localized in a foot that is no longer there. The stimulation of a sensory neuron pathway from the removed limb anywhere on the remaining intact portion of the pathway propagates nerve signals and conducts them to the CNS, where they are interpreted as originating in the amputated limb. In other words, the cell bodies of the sensory neurons that provided sensation to the limb remain alive because they were not part of the limb. This so-called **phantom limb syndrome** can be quite debilitating. Some people experience extreme pain, whereas others have an insatiable desire to scratch a nonexistent itch.

region of the spinal cord, pain may be referred to the S2–S4 dermatomes, which overlie the medial buttocks regions.

WHAT DID YOU LEARN?

6 Explain the clinical significance of referred pain.

16.3 Olfaction and Gustation

Chemoreceptors are specialized neurons that detect a specific chemical and initiate a nerve signal. The stimulating chemical must be dissolved in the aqueous environment around the receptor to be detected. Here, we consider chemoreceptors for the senses of olfaction (smell) and gustation (taste). As you will see later, the appreciation of taste also involves our sense of smell.

16.3a Olfaction: The Sense of Smell

LEARNING OBJECTIVES

1. Name the components of the olfactory organs and their mode of action.
2. Identify areas in the brain that receive sensory input from the olfactory chemoreceptors.

Olfaction (ol-fak'shŭn; *olfacio* = to smell) is the sense of smell, whereby volatile molecules (called **odorants**) must be dissolved in the mucus in our nasal cavity to be detected. We use this sense to sample our environment for information about the food we will eat, the presence of other individuals in the room, or potential danger (spoiled food or smoke from a fire).

Compared to many other animals, our olfactory ability is vastly less sensitive and not as highly developed, because we do not rely as greatly on olfactory information to find food or communicate with others. Yet we do have the ability to distinguish one odor among thousands of different ones, a capability that we very much appreciate as we walk through a garden of flowers.

Olfactory Organs

Within the nasal cavity, paired **olfactory organs** are the organs of smell. They are composed of several components **(figure 16.6)**. In our nasal cavity, an **olfactory epithelium** lines the superior region of the nasal cavity, including both the superior nasal conchae and the inferior surface of the cribriform plate of the ethmoid bone (see section 8.2). This specialized epithelium is composed of three distinct cell types:

- **Olfactory receptor cells** (also called *olfactory neurons),* which detect odors
- **Supporting cells** (also called *sustentacular cells*) that sandwich the olfactory neurons and sustain the receptors
- **Basal cells** functioning as neural stem cells to continually replace olfactory receptor cells

Figure 16.6 Olfactory Organs. Olfactory organ cells detect chemical stimuli in the air we breathe. When receptor cells within the olfactory epithelium are stimulated, they initiate nerve signals in axons that pass through the cribriform plate and synapse on neurons within the olfactory bulb. AP|R

Olfactory receptor cells are one of the few neuronal types that are replaced. Olfactory receptor neurons are regenerated every 40 to 60 days by basal cells within the olfactory epithelium. (This process decreases with age, and the remaining olfactory neurons lose their sensitivity to odors. Thus, an elderly individual has a decreased ability to recognize odor molecules.)

Internal to the olfactory epithelium is an areolar connective tissue layer called the **lamina propria** (lam′i-nă prō′prī-ă). Housed within the collagen fibers and ground substance of this layer are mucin-secreting **olfactory glands** (or *Bowman glands*) and many blood vessels and nerves. Secretions from both supporting cells and olfactory glands form the mucus that covers the exposed surface of the olfactory epithelium.

Olfactory Receptor Cells

Olfactory receptor cells are bipolar neurons that have undergone extensive differentiation and modification, and serve as the primary neuron in the sensory pathway for smell. Olfactory receptor cells have both a single dendrite and an unmyelinated axon. Dendrites extend into the overlying mucus. Projecting from the dendrites are numerous thin, unmyelinated extensions called **olfactory hairs,** which are immobile and usually appear as a tangled mass within the layer of mucus. Olfactory hairs house receptor proteins for detecting one specific odorant molecule. Depending upon which olfactory receptor cells are stimulated, different smells will be perceived. Axons of olfactory cells, in comparison, form bundles (fascicles) of the **olfactory nerves (CN I)** (see section 13.9). These fascicles project through foramina in the cribriform plate of the ethmoid bone to enter a pair of olfactory bulbs.

Olfactory Nerve Structures and Pathways

Olfactory bulbs are the terminal ends of olfactory tracts located inferior to the frontal lobes of the brain (see section 13.9). Axons of fascicles of olfactory nerves synapse with both *mitral cells* and *tufted cells* (which are secondary neurons) within the olfactory bulbs. The resulting spherical structures are called **olfactory glomeruli** (glō-mar′yū-lī; sing., glomerulus; *glomerulus* = small ball). We have about 2000 glomeruli in our olfactory bulbs, and numerous olfactory receptor cells converge on each olfactory glomerulus. The convergence of signals within the glomerulus facilitates our ability to detect faint odors.

Axon bundles of the mitral and tufted cells, form the paired **olfactory tracts** that project posteriorly along the inferior frontal lobe surface directly to the primary olfactory cortex in the temporal lobe (see table 13.3) and selected different regions of the brain, including the hypothalamus and amygdala. Unlike other sensory information, olfactory pathways do not project to the thalamus and therefore do not undergo any thalamic processing prior to reaching the cerebrum.

Detecting Smells

During normal relaxed breathing, most of the inhaled air does not pass across the olfactory epithelium. To be sure to detect different smells, we must sniff repeatedly or breathe deeply. Deep breathing causes the inhaled air to mix and swirl in the superior region of the nasal cavity, so that odor molecules diffuse into the mucus layer covering the olfactory receptor cells. Within the mucus, soluble proteins called **odorant-binding proteins** display an affinity for a variety of odorants, and assist in the concentration and binding of odorants to olfactory hair receptors.

Olfactory cells are stimulated by contact of odorant-binding proteins with olfactory cell receptors. The olfactory pathway is so

sensitive that only a few stimulating molecules are needed to bind to receptors and initiate olfactory sensation. Stimulation of olfactory cells involves G protein molecules that are located on the inner surface of the plasma membrane (see section 4.4b). Odorants may activate G proteins, which directly results in the opening of ion channels. Sometimes, activation of G proteins works through an intermediary molecule called a second messenger (see section 17.6). The second messenger starts a cascade of events that ultimately results in opening of ion channels. In either case, opening of ion channels results in the flow of ions across the plasma membrane that results in generation of local receptor potentials within the olfactory hairs. These local potentials will initiate an action potential that is propagated through the axon of olfactory receptor cells, causing the release of neurotransmitter from the terminal ends of the axon. This results in stimulation of different patterns of the approximately 2000 glomeruli. Consider for example that cooking a meal causes the release of numerous odorants, but the smell of the meal concoction has a unique "signature" recognized by the excitation pattern observed within the glomeruli.

Binding of neurotransmitter by secondary neurons results in propagation of nerve signals through the various olfactory pathways. Sensory information reaches different regions of the brain including the (1) cerebral cortex, which allows us to consciously perceive and identify the smell; (2) hypothalamus, which controls visceral reactions to smell, such as salivation, sneezing, or gagging; and (3) amygdala, which is a center for recognition of odors and often tying those odors to a particular emotion (see section 13.8c).

Note that once the receptors are stimulated, changes to the ion channels alter the flow of ions. This results in interfering with the subsequent generation of receptor potentials within olfactory receptor cells, and adaptation of smell occurs rapidly. Thus, an initially strong smell (such as rotting food in a trash can) may seem to dissipate as your olfactory receptor cells adapt to the foul odor.

WHAT DID YOU LEARN?

7 What is the role of the mucus in detection of smells?

8 Why do some smells stimulate an emotional reaction?

16.3b Gustation: The Sense of Taste

LEARNING OBJECTIVES

3. Describe the structure and function of papillae of the tongue.

4. Discuss the structure, location, and innervation pathways of gustatory chemoreceptors.

5. List the five types of tastes and explain the association of smell with taste.

Our sense of taste, called **gustation** (gŭs-tā′shŭn; *gusto* = to taste), occurs when we come in contact with the molecules of what we eat and drink. Gustatory cells are taste receptors housed in specialized, cylindrical sensory organs termed taste buds on the surface of the tongue and on the soft palate. The tongue also houses mechanoreceptors and thermoreceptors to provide us with information about the texture and temperature of our food, respectively.

Papillae and Taste Buds of the Tongue

On the dorsal surface of the tongue are epithelial and connective tissue elevations called **papillae** (pă-pil'ē; *papula* = a small nipple), which are of four types: filiform, fungiform, vallate, and foliate (**figure 16.7a, b**):

Filiform (fil'i-form; *filum* = thread) **papillae** are short and spiked; they are distributed on the anterior two-thirds of the tongue surface. These papillae do not house taste buds and thus, have no role in gustation. Instead, their bristlelike structure serves a mechanical function; they assist in detecting texture and manipulating food.

Fungiform (fŭn'ji-form; = mushroom-shaped) **papillae** are blocklike projections primarily located on the tip and sides of the tongue. Each contains only a few taste buds.

Vallate (val'āt; *vallo* = to surround) **papillae,** or *circumvallate papillae,* are the least numerous (about 10 to 12) yet are the largest papillae on the tongue. They are arranged in an inverted V shape on the posterior dorsal surface of the tongue. Each papilla is surrounded by a deep, narrow depression. Most of our taste buds are housed within the walls of these papillae along the side facing the depression.

Foliate (fō'lē-āt; = leaflike) **papillae** are not well developed on the human tongue. They extend as ridges on the posterior lateral sides of the tongue and house only a few taste buds during infancy and early childhood.

A taste bud has the appearance of an onion (figure 16.7c, d). Within each taste bud are numerous taste receptors called **gustatory cells** (or *gustatory receptors*) that are enclosed by **supporting cells.** A population of **basal cells** (stem cells) constantly replaces the gustatory cells that have a 7-to-10-day life span. Beginning at about age 50, our ability to distinguish between different tastes declines due to a reduction in both gustatory cell replacement and the number of taste buds.

Gustatory Cells

Gustatory cells within the taste buds are specialized neuroepithelial cells. The dendritic ending of each gustatory cell is formed by a slender **gustatory microvillus,** sometimes called a *taste hair.* The taste hair extends through an opening in the taste bud, called the **taste pore,** to the surface of the tongue. This is the receptive portion

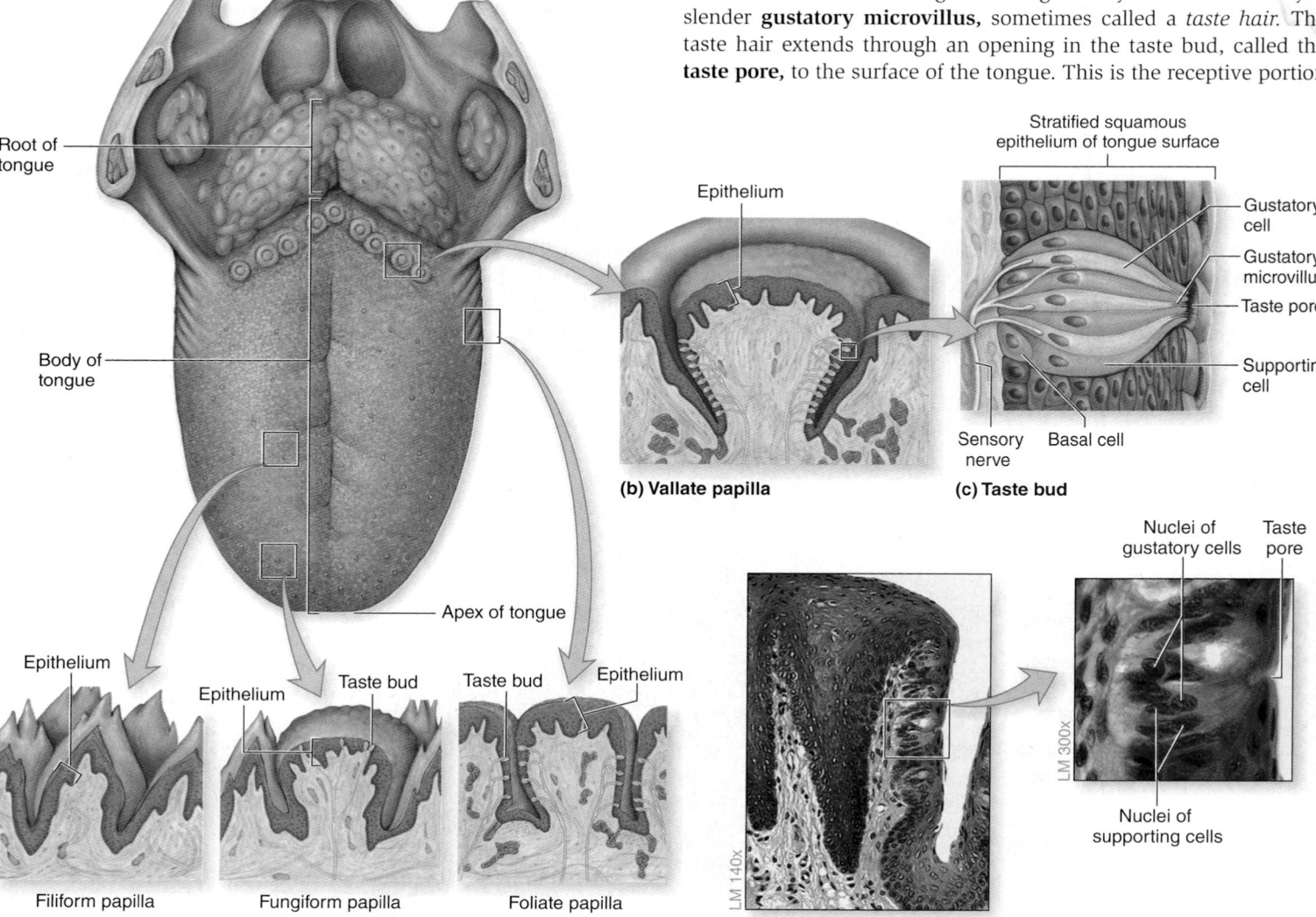

(a) Dorsal surface of tongue

(b) Vallate papilla

(c) Taste bud

(d) Histology of taste bud

Figure 16.7 Tongue Papillae and Taste Buds. (*a*) Papillae are small elevations on the tongue surface that exist in four types: filiform, fungiform, foliate, and vallate (shown in [*b*]). (*b*) A vallate papilla exhibits many taste buds, one of which is shown in detail (*c*). (*d*) Photomicrographs show the histologic structure of a taste bud. AP|R of the cell. Within the oral cavity, saliva keeps the environment moist; the **tastants** (taste-producing molecules) in our food dissolve in the saliva, and then they are able to contact and stimulate gustatory receptors through the taste pore. Thus, these receptors are classified as chemoreceptors because food molecules must be dissolved in saliva before they can be tasted.

Gustatory Pathways

Dendritic endings of primary neurons are associated with gustatory cells, with each sensory neuron contacting several gustatory cells. These sensory neurons are primarily components of the facial nerve (CN VII), which innervates taste buds from the anterior two-thirds of the tongue and the glossopharyngeal nerve (CN IX), which innervates taste buds from the posterior one-third of the tongue **(figure 16.8)**. Axons within these nerves project first to the medulla oblongata (specifically the nucleus solitarius) to synapse with secondary neurons. These neurons project to the thalamus, and axons of tertiary neurons project to the primary gustatory cortex in the insula of the cerebrum (see section 13.9 and table 13.3).

Gustatory Discrimination and Physiology of Taste

In contrast to the large number of olfactory receptors we have in our nose, our tongue detects just five basic **taste sensations**: sweet, salty, sour, bitter, and umami:

- **Sweet** tastes are produced by organic compounds such as sugar or other molecules (e.g., artificial sweeteners).
- **Salt** tastes are produced by metal ions, such as sodium (Na^+) and potassium (K^+).
- **Sour** tastes are associated with acids in the ingested material, such as hydrogen ions (H^+) in vinegar.
- **Bitter** tastes are produced primarily by alkaloids such as quinine, unsweetened chocolate, nicotine, and caffeine.
- **Umami** stimuli: *Umami* is a Japanese word meaning "delicious flavor." It is a taste related to amino acids, such as glutamate and aspartate, to produce a meaty flavor.

Researchers previously thought certain tastes were best interpreted along specific regions of the tongue; however, research has found these "taste maps" to be incorrect and has shown that taste sensations are spread over broader regions of the tongue than previously thought.

The tastants in our food bind to specific receptor cell membrane proteins. The initial binding of a specific tastant molecule to its receptor prompts a response for each of the basic taste sensations, but the manner in which cell depolarization occurs varies. In general, sweet, bitter and umami stimuli bind to receptors on the taste bud surface, which activate a G protein. The G protein activation causes the formation of a secondary messenger, which results in cell depolarization. In contrast, salt and sour stimuli do not use a G protein and depolarize the cell directly.

Depolarization of a receptor taste cell generates local receptor potentials that initiate action potentials that cause the release of neurotransmitter at its basal side. This stimulates a sensory neuron connected to the receptor cell to convey the appropriate taste sensation information through CN VII (facial) and CN IX (glossopharyngeal) to the brain.

Sensory information first reaches the nucleus solitarius within the medulla oblongata to trigger reflexes that increase salivation and release of stomach secretions in anticipation of the arrival of food. A gag or vomiting reflex may also occur in response to a nauseating substance. Sensory information is then relayed to the thalamus and to the primary gustatory cortex for the conscious perception of taste. This requires integrating taste sensations with those of temperature, texture, and smell.

WHAT DO YOU THINK?

1. When a person has a stuffy nose from a "cold" or hay fever, he or she typically can't detect tastes as well. Why?

Note that our ability to taste what we eat relies heavily on our olfactory sense. Recall the last time you had a severe cold or sinus infection. The aroma of the food could not reach your olfactory receptors, so the food was bland and almost tasteless. Together, taste and smell give our food its flavor. We then perceive the taste of the food when the brain interprets both the stimulation pattern from gustatory receptor sensory neurons and the aroma information from olfactory receptors.

Figure 16.8 Gustatory Pathway. Taste sensations are carried by the paired facial nerves (CN VII) from the anterior two-thirds of the tongue and by the glossopharyngeal nerves (CN IX) from the posterior one-third of the tongue. These taste sensations are transmitted to the nucleus solitarius of the medulla oblongata before being conducted to the thalamus and finally entering the gustatory cortex of the cerebrum.

WHAT DID YOU LEARN?

9 What is the basic composition of a taste bud, and which papillae have taste buds?

10 What are the five basic taste sensations, and what is the specific stimuli detected by each?

16.4 Visual Receptors

Visual stimuli help us form specific, detailed visual images of objects in our environment. The sense of vision uses photoreceptors in the eyes to detect light, color, and movement. Refer to section 8.2d to review the orbital complex, section 11.3b to review the extrinsic eye muscles and their functions, and section 13.9 to review the cranial nerves associated with vision and moving the extrinsic eye muscles.

16.4a Accessory Structures of the Eye

LEARNING OBJECTIVE

1. Describe the accessory structures of the eye, and list their functions.

The accessory structures of the eye prevent foreign objects from coming into contact with the eye (eyebrows, eyelashes, and eyelids); keep the exposed surface moist, clean, and lubricated (lacrimal glands); and provide a superficial covering over its anterior exposed surface (conjunctiva) **(figure 16.9)**.

External Accessory Structures

The **eyebrows** are slightly curved rows of thick, short hairs at the superior edge of the orbit along the supraorbital ridge. They function primarily to prevent sweat from dripping into the open eyes. **Eyelashes** extend from the margins of the eyelids and prevent large foreign objects from coming into contact with the anterior surface of the eye.

The **eyelids,** also called the *palpebrae* (pal-pē'brē; sing., *palpebra*), form the movable anterior protective covering over the surface of the eye. Each eyelid is formed by a fibrous core (the **tarsal plate**), tarsal muscles, tarsal glands, the palpebral part of the orbicularis oculi muscle, the palpebral conjunctiva, and a thin covering of skin. **Tarsal glands,** previously called *Meibomian glands,* are sebaceous glands that produce a secretion to prevent tear overflow from the open eye and keep the eyelids from adhering together. The eyelids' free margins are separated by a central **palpebral fissure** (or "eyeslit").

The eyelids are united at the **medial** and **lateral palpebral commissures.** At the medial commissure is a small, reddish body called the **lacrimal caruncle** (kar'ŭng-kl; *caro* = flesh) that houses ciliary glands. Ciliary glands are modified sweat glands that form the thick secretory products that contribute to the gritty, particulate material often noticed around the eyelids after awakening.

WHAT DO YOU THINK?

2 When a person cries, tears spill onto the cheeks, and the person usually gets a temporary runny nose. Based on your knowledge of the lacrimal apparatus, what is happening?

Conjunctiva

A specialized stratified squamous epithelium termed the **conjunctiva** (kon-jŭnk-tī'vă) forms a continuous lining over the external, anterior surface of the eye (the **ocular conjunctiva**) and the internal surface of the eyelid (the **palpebral conjunctiva**). The space formed by the junction of the ocular conjunctiva and palpebral conjunctiva is called the **conjunctival fornix** (fōr'niks; = vault or arch).

The conjunctiva contains numerous goblet cells, which lubricate and moisten the eye. Additionally, the conjunctiva contains many blood vessels, which supply nutrients to the avascular sclera ("white") of the eye, as well as abundant nerve endings that detect foreign objects as they contact the eye. The conjunctiva does not cover the surface of the cornea (the transparent center of the external eye), so no blood vessels interfere with passage of light into the eye.

Figure 16.9 External Anatomy of the Eye and Surrounding Accessory Structures. (*a*) Accessory structures protect the eye. (*b*) A sagittal section shows the eye and its accessory structures. AP|R

Conjunctivitis (kon-jŭnk-ti-vī'tis) is the most common nontraumatic eye complaint seen by physicians. It presents as inflammation and reddening of the conjunctiva, and is often called *pink eye*. Conjunctivitis frequently results from a viral infection, but also can be a response to a bacterial infection, airborne allergens (pollen or animal dander), chemicals, or physical irritants, such as contact lenses left in too long.

Trachoma is a chronic, contagious form of conjunctivitis caused by *Chlamydia trachomatis*. Infection by this bacterium results in inflammation because of hypertrophy of the conjunctiva. The condition is accompanied by the appearance of newly formed, minute gray-yellow granules in the conjunctiva. Trachoma is a common cause of neonatal blindness in developing countries; the newborn becomes infected as it passes through the birth canal. Blindness occurs when the inflammatory process causes scarring and thickening of the conjunctiva.

Lacrimal Apparatus

A **lacrimal** (lak'ri-măl; *lacrima* = a tear) **apparatus** is associated with each eye; it produces, collects, and drains lacrimal fluid (tears) from the eye **(figure 16.10)**. Lacrimal fluid lubricates the anterior surface of the eye to reduce friction from eyelid movement; continuously cleanses and moistens the eye surface; and helps prevent bacterial infection because it contains an antibacterial enzyme called lysozyme.

A **lacrimal gland** is located within the superolateral depression of each orbit. It is composed of an orbital or superior part and a palpebral or inferior part. The gland continuously produces lacrimal fluid. The blinking motion of the eyelids "washes" the lacrimal fluid released from its excretory ducts over the eyes. Gradually, the lacrimal fluid is transferred to the lacrimal caruncle at the medial surface of the eye. On the superior and inferior sides of the lacrimal caruncle are two small openings called the **lacrimal puncta** (pungk'tă; sing., *punctum* = to prick). (If you examine your own eye, each punctum appears as a "hole" in the lacrimal caruncle.) Each lacrimal punctum has a **lacrimal canaliculus** (kan-ă-lik'yū-lŭs; = small canal) that drains lacrimal fluid into a rounded **lacrimal sac.** Finally, a **nasolacrimal duct** receives the lacrimal fluid from the lacrimal sac. This duct drains lacrimal fluid into the lateral side of the nasal cavity, where it mixes with mucus.

WHAT DID YOU LEARN?

11 Where is the conjunctiva located, and what is its function?

12 How is lacrimal fluid spread across the eye and removed from the orbital region?

16.4b Eye Structure

LEARNING OBJECTIVE

2. Describe the structures and function of the components of the eye.

The eye is an almost spherical organ that measures about 2.5 centimeters (1 inch) in diameter. Most of the eye is receded into the orbit of the skull, a space also occupied by the lacrimal gland, extrinsic eye muscles, numerous blood vessels, and the cranial nerves that innervate the eye and other structures in the orbit. **Orbital fat** cushions the posterior and lateral sides of the eye (see figure 16.9*b*), providing support, protection, and facilitating oxygen and nutrient delivery by the blood.

Three principal layers form the wall of the eye: the fibrous tunic (external layer), the vascular tunic (middle layer), and the retina (inner layer) **(figure 16.11 and table 16.3).**

Figure 16.10 Lacrimal Apparatus. The lacrimal apparatus continually produces lacrimal fluid (tears) that cleanse and maintain a moist condition on the anterior surface of the eye. Lacrimal fluid production and drainage occur in a series of steps.

① Lacrimal fluid (tears) is produced in the lacrimal gland.

② Lacrimal fluid is dispersed across eye surface when we blink.

③ Lacrimal fluid enters the lacrimal puncta, drains into the lacrimal canaliculi, and collects in the lacrimal sac.

④ Lacrimal fluid from the lacrimal sac drains through the nasolacrimal duct.

⑤ Lacrimal fluid enters the nasal cavity.

The interior of the eye consists of two cavities that are filled with fluid. The *lens,* which focuses light rays onto the retina, lies between these two cavities.

Fibrous Tunic

The external layer of the eye wall is called the **fibrous tunic,** or *external tunic.* It is composed of the posterior sclera and the anterior cornea.

Most of the fibrous tunic (the posterior five-sixths) is the tough **sclera** (sklĕr′ă; *skleros* = hard), a part of the outer layer that is called the "white" of the eye. It is composed of dense irregular connective tissue that includes both collagen and elastic fibers. The sclera provides for eye shape, protects the eye's delicate internal components, and serves as attachment site for extrinsic eye muscles. Posteriorly, the sclera becomes continuous with the dura mater that surrounds the optic nerve.

The **cornea** (kōr′nē-ă) is a convex, transparent structure that forms the anterior one-sixth of the fibrous tunic; its outer edge adjoins the sclera. The structural continuity between

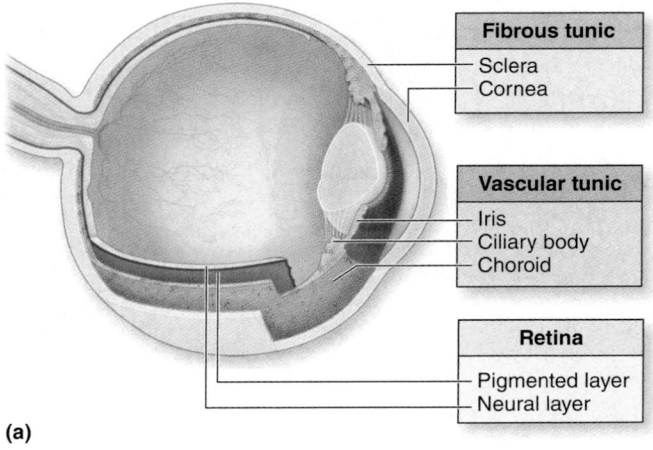

Fibrous tunic
- Sclera
- Cornea

Vascular tunic
- Iris
- Ciliary body
- Choroid

Retina
- Pigmented layer
- Neural layer

(a)

Figure 16.11 Anatomy of the Internal Eye. Sagittal views depict (*a*) the three tunics of the eye, and (*b*) internal eye structures. AP|R

Ora serrata

Central artery of retina
Central vein of retina

Ciliary muscle ⎤
Ciliary process ⎦ Ciliary body

Suspensory ligaments

Limbus

Scleral venous sinus

CN II (optic)

Lens

Iris

Cornea

Optic disc

Pupil

Fovea centralis

Posterior cavity

Retina

Choroid

Anterior chamber ⎤
Posterior chamber ⎦ Anterior cavity

Sclera

(b)

Table 16.3   Tunics of the Eye

Structures	Components	Location	Function
FIBROUS TUNIC (EXTERNAL LAYER)			
Sclera	Dense irregular connective tissue	Posterior covering of the eye (forms the remaining five-sixths of the external eye layer); the "white" of the eye	Supports eye shape Protects delicate internal structures Extrinsic eye muscle attachment site
Cornea	Two layers of epithelium with collagen fiber layer in between; avascular	Forms the anterior one-sixth of the external eye layer	Protects anterior surface of the eye Refracts (bends) incoming light
VASCULAR TUNIC (MIDDLE LAYER)			
Choroid	Areolar connective tissue; highly vascularized	Forms posterior two-thirds of middle wall of eye	Supplies nourishment to retina Pigment absorbs extraneous light
Ciliary body	Ciliary smooth muscle and ciliary processes; covered with a secretory epithelium	Between choroid posteriorly and iris anteriorly	Holds suspensory ligaments that attach to the lens and change lens shape for far and near vision Epithelium secretes aqueous humor
Iris	Two layers of smooth muscle (sphincter pupillae and dilator pupillae) with a central opening called the pupil	Anterior region of middle layer	Controls pupil diameter and thus the amount of light entering the eye
RETINA (INTERNAL LAYER)			
Pigmented layer	Pigmented epithelial cells and supporting cells	Outermost portion of retina that directly adheres to choroid	Absorbs extraneous light Provides vitamin A for photoreceptor cells
Neural layer	Photoreceptors, bipolar neurons, and ganglion cells	Inner portion of retina	Detects incoming light rays; light rays are converted to nerve signals and transmitted to brain

the cornea and sclera is called the **limbus** (lim′bŭs), or the *corneal scleral junction.* The cornea is a composed of an inner simple squamous epithelium, a middle layer of collagen fibers, and an outer stratified squamous epithelium, called the corneal epithelium. The edge of the corneal epithelium is continuous with the ocular conjunctiva. The cornea contains no blood vessels. Nutrients and oxygen are supplied to the external corneal epithelium by fluid from the lacrimal glands, whereas the internal epithelium obtains needed gases and nutrients from the fluid (aqueous humor) in the anterior chamber of the eye (described shortly). The convex shape of the cornea refracts (bends) light rays coming into the eye.

Vascular Tunic

The middle layer of the eye wall is the **vascular tunic,** also called the *uvea* (ū′vē-ă; *uva* = grape). The vascular tunic houses an extensive array of blood vessels, lymph vessels, and the intrinsic muscles of the eye. It is composed of three distinct regions; from posterior to anterior, they are the choroid, the ciliary body, and the iris.

The **choroid** (kōr′oyd) is the most extensive and posterior region of the vascular tunic. It houses a vast network of capillaries that supply the retina, the inner layer of the eye wall, with oxygen and nutrients. Cells of the choroid are filled with pigment from the numerous melanocytes in this region. The melanin pigment is needed to absorb extraneous light that enters the eye, thus allowing the retina to absorb the remaining light rays and form a visual image.

The **ciliary** (sil′ē-ar-ē; *cilium* = eyelid) **body** is located immediately anterior to the choroid, and is composed of both ciliary muscles

Figure 16.12 Pupil Diameter. Pupillary constriction decreases the diameter of the pupil to reduce the amount of light entering the eye. Pupillary constriction is controlled by the parasympathetic division of the ANS. Pupillary dilation increases pupil diameter to increase light entry into the eye and is controlled by the sympathetic division.

and ciliary processes. **Ciliary muscles** are bands of smooth muscle. Extending from the ciliary muscle to the capsule surrounding the lens are suspensory ligaments, which anchor the lens. Relaxation and contraction of the ciliary muscles change the tension on the suspensory ligaments, thereby altering the shape of the lens. The ciliary processes contain capillaries that secrete a fluid called aqueous humor (both processes of the ciliary body are discussed later in detail).

The most anterior region of the vascular tunic is the **iris** (ī′ris; = rainbow), which is the colored portion of the eye. The iris is composed of two layers of pigment-forming cells, two groups of smooth muscle fibers, and an array of vascular and nervous structures. The peripheral edge of the iris is continuous with the ciliary body. In the center of the iris is a black opening called the **pupil** (pū′pil). The iris controls pupil size or diameter—and thus the amount of light entering the eye—using its two smooth muscle layers (**figure 16.12**). The **sphincter pupillae muscle** (or *pupillary constrictor*) is arranged in a pattern that resembles concentric circles around the pupil. Under the control of the parasympathetic division via axons from CN III (see section 13.9), this muscle constricts the pupil. The **dilator pupillae muscle** (or *pupillary dilator*) is

organized in a radial pattern extending peripherally through the iris. It is controlled by the sympathetic division of the ANS to dilate the pupil. Only one set of these smooth muscle layers can contract at a time. When stimulated by bright light the parasympathetic division causes the pupillary constrictors to contract and thus decrease pupil diameter, whereas low light levels activate the sympathetic division to cause pupil dilation.

Retina

The internal layer of the eye wall, called the **retina** (ret′i-nă; *rete* = a net) also is known as the *internal tunic* or *neural tunic*. It is composed of two layers: an outer pigmented layer and an inner neural layer (**figure 16.13**). The **pigmented layer** is immediately

Figure 16.13 Structure and Organization of the Retina.
The retina is composed of two distinct layers: the outer pigmented layer and the inner neural layer, also called the neural retina. (*a*) The optic nerve is composed of ganglionic cell axons that originate in the neural retina. (*b*) The neural retina is composed of three primary cellular layers (in bold): the outer photoreceptor cells (rods and cones), the middle bipolar cells, and the inner ganglion cells. (*c*) Histologic section of the retina. AP|R

CLINICAL VIEW
Detached Retina

A **detached retina** occurs when the outer pigmented and inner neural layers of the retina separate. Detachment may result from head trauma (soccer players and high divers are especially susceptible), or it may have no overt cause. Individuals who are nearsighted, due to a more elliptical eyeball, are at increased risk for detachment because their retina is typically thinned or stretched more than that of a normal eye. There is also increased risk for retinal detachment in diabetics and older individuals. A detached retina results in deprivation of nutrients for cells in the inner neural layer because it is pulled away from the vascularized choroid layer. Degeneration and death of nervous tissue result if the blood supply is not restored.

Symptoms of a detached retina include a large number of "floaters" (small, particle-like objects) in the vision; the appearance of a "curtain" in the affected eye; flashes of light; and decreased, watery, or wavy vision.

Pneumatic retinopexy is a treatment for upper retinal detachment. The physician inserts a needle into the anesthetized eye and injects a gas bubble into the vitreous humor. The gas bubble rises and pushes against the upper retinal detachment, forcing the two layers back together again. The gas bubble absorbs and disappears over 1 to 2 weeks, and then a laser may be used to tack the two layers of the retina together. The **scleral buckle** is another treatment, and uses a silicone band to press inward on the sclera in order to hold the retina in place. A laser is then used to reattach the retina.

internal to the choroid and attached to it. This layer provides vitamin A for the photoreceptor (light-detecting) cells. Light rays that pass through the inner neural layer are absorbed by the pigmented layer. The inner **neural layer** houses all of the photoreceptors and their associated neurons. This layer of the retina is responsible for absorbing light rays and converting them into nerve signals that are transmitted to the brain.

The edge of the retina is the **ora serrata** (ō'ră sē-ră'tă; serratus = sawtooth), which is a jagged margin between the photosensitive posterior region of the retina and the nonphotosensitive anterior region of the retina that continues anteriorly to cover the ciliary body and the posterior side of the iris (see figure 16.11b).

Cells of the Neural Layer
Three distinct layers of cells form the neural layer: photoreceptor cells, bipolar cells, and ganglion cells. Incoming light must pass through almost the entire neural layer before reaching the photoreceptors.

The outermost layer of cells in the neural layer is composed of **photoreceptor** (phot = light) **cells,** which contain pigment molecules that react to light energy. The two types of photoreceptor cells are **rods,** which have a rod-shaped outer part and function in dim light, and **cones,** which have a cone-shaped outer part and function in high-intensity light and in color vision. These cells are described in more detail later in this chapter.

Immediately internal to the photoreceptor layer is a layer of **bipolar cells.** Rods and cones form synapses on the dendrites of the bipolar neurons. There are far fewer bipolar neurons than photoreceptors, and thus information must converge as visual signals are directed toward the brain from the stimulated photoreceptors.

Ganglion cells are neurons that form the innermost layer in the neural layer and are adjacent to the posterior cavity. Neuronal con-

vergence continues between the bipolar neurons and ganglionic neurons. Axons extend from the ganglionic cells into and through the optic disc (described shortly).

Other cells that function in transmission of light stimuli include horizontal cells and amacrine cells. **Horizontal cells** are sandwiched between the photoreceptor layer and the bipolar cells in a thin web. These horizontal cells regulate and integrate the stimuli sent from the photoreceptors to the other cell layers. **Amacrine** (am'ă-krin) **cells** are positioned between the bipolar and ganglion cells and help process and integrate visual information as it passes between bipolar and ganglionic neurons. Only the amacrine and ganglion cells in the retina produce action potentials; the other cells generate graded potentials (see section 12.7c).

Components of the Retina   The distribution of rods and cones, the two types of photoreceptors, is not uniform throughout the retina. Three specific regions are identified as a result including the optic disc, macula lutea, and peripheral retina **(figure 16.14)**. The **optic disc** contains no photoreceptors. This is because the ganglion axons toward the brain (see figure 16.13a). It is commonly called the **blind spot** because it lacks photoreceptors, and no image forms there. The **macula lutea** (mak'ū-lă lū'tē-a; macula = small spot; lutea = saffron-yellow) is a rounded, yellowish region just lateral to the optic disc (figure 16.14). Within the macula lutea is a depressed pit called the **fovea centralis** (fō'vē-ă sen'tră'lis; fovea = pit; centralis = central), which contains the highest proportion of cones

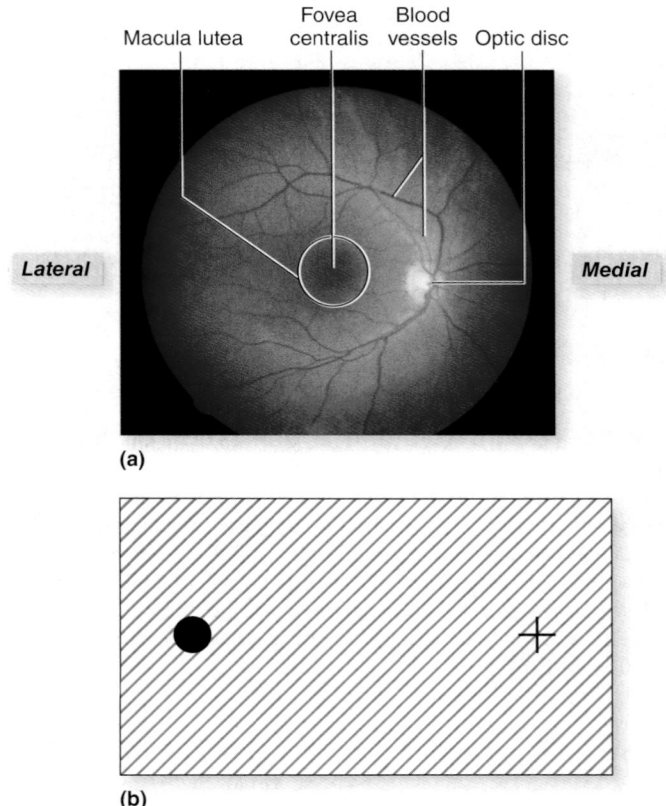

(a)

(b)

Figure 16.14 Internal View of the Retina Showing the Optic Disc (Blind Spot). (a) An ophthalmoscope is used to view the retina through the pupil. Blood vessels travel through the optic nerve to enter the eye at the optic disc. (b) Check your blind spot! Close your left eye. Hold this figure in front of your right eye, and stare at the black spot. Move the figure toward your open eye. At approximately 6 inches from your eye, the image of the plus sign is over the optic disc and the plus sign seems to disappear.

Macular degeneration, which is the physical deterioration of the macula lutea, is the leading cause of blindness in developed countries. Although the majority of cases are reported in people over 55, the condition may occur in younger people as well. Most non-age-related cases are associated with conditions such as diabetes, an ocular infection, hypertension, or trauma to the eye.

Macular degeneration is typically the loss of visual acuity in the center of the visual field; diminished color perception and "floaters."

At present, there is no cure for macular degeneration. However, its progression may be slowed. Early detection has become an important element in treatment. To track the progression of the disease, doctors rely heavily on self-monitoring, in which the patient regularly performs a simple visual test using the *Amsler grid*. While staring at the dot, the patient looks for wavy lines, blurring, or missing parts of the grid, which would indicate degenerative changes in the macula.

Normal vision.

The same scene as viewed by a person with macular degeneration.

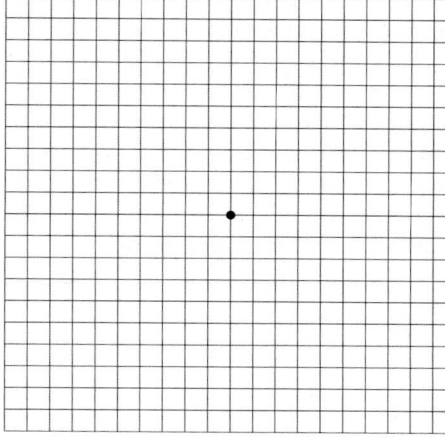

Amsler grid, seen with normal vision.

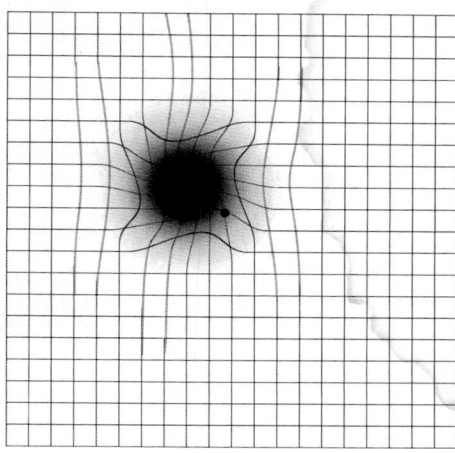

Amsler grid, as viewed by a person with macular degeneration.

and almost no rods. This pit is the area of sharpest vision; when you read the words in your text, they are precisely focused here. Although the other regions of the retina also receive and interpret light rays, no other region can focus as precisely as can the fovea centralis because of its high concentration of cones. The remaining regions of the retina are called the **peripheral retina,** which contains primarily rods and functions most effectively in low light.

Lens

The **lens** is a strong yet deformable, transparent structure bounded by a dense, fibrous, elastic capsule. Internally, it is composed of precisely arranged layers of cells that have lost their organelles and are filled completely by a protein called *crystallin*. The lens focuses incoming light onto the retina, and its shape determines the degree of light refraction.

The **suspensory** (sŭs-pen'sŏ-rē; *suspendo* = to hang up) **ligaments** attach to the lens capsule at its periphery, where they transmit tension that enables the lens to change shape. The tension in the suspensory ligaments comes from contraction of the **ciliary muscles** in the ciliary body. When the ciliary muscles relax, the ciliary body moves posteriorly, away from the lens, and so the tension on the suspensory ligaments increases. This constant tension causes the lens to flatten (**figure 16.15a**). A flattened lens is necessary for viewing distant objects. This shape of the lens is the "default" position of the lens.

(a) Lens shape for distant vision

(b) Lens shape for near vision (accommodation)

Figure 16.15 Lens Shape in Far Vision and Near Vision. (*a*) To focus a distant object on the retina, the ciliary muscles within the ciliary body relax, which tenses the suspensory ligaments and flattens the lens. (*b*) Accommodation occurs when a nearby object is focused on the retina. The ciliary muscles contract, causing the suspensory ligaments to relax and the lens to thicken (become more spherical or "puffy").

Cataracts (kat′ă-rakt) are small opacities within the lens that, over time, may coalesce to completely obscure the lens. Most cases occur as a result of aging, although other factors include diabetes, intraocular infections, excessive ultraviolet light exposure, and glaucoma. The resulting vision problems include difficulty focusing on close objects, reduced visual clarity due to clouding of the lens, "milky" vision, and reduced intensity of colors.

A cataract needs to be removed only when it interferes with normal daily activities. Newer surgical techniques include **phacoemulsification** (făk′ō-i-mul′se-fi-kā′shen), a process by which the opacified center of the lens is fragmented using ultrasonic sound waves, thus making it easier to remove. The destroyed lens is then replaced with an artificial intraocular lens, which becomes a permanent part of the eye.

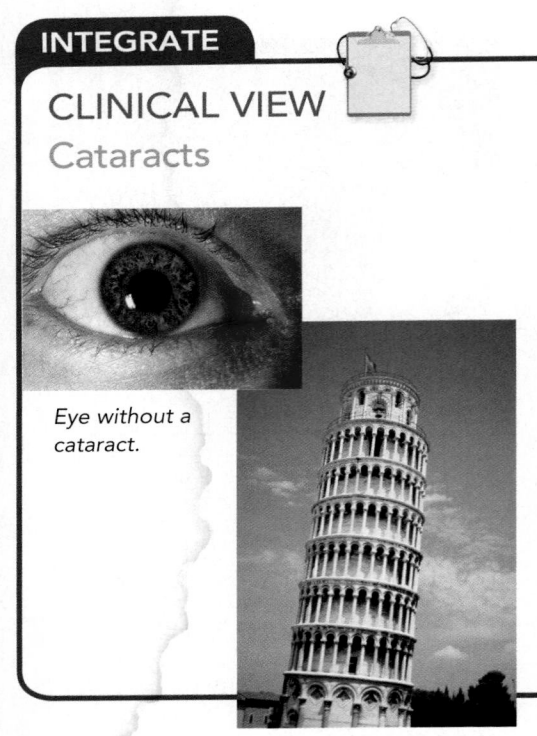

Eye without a cataract.

Normal vision.

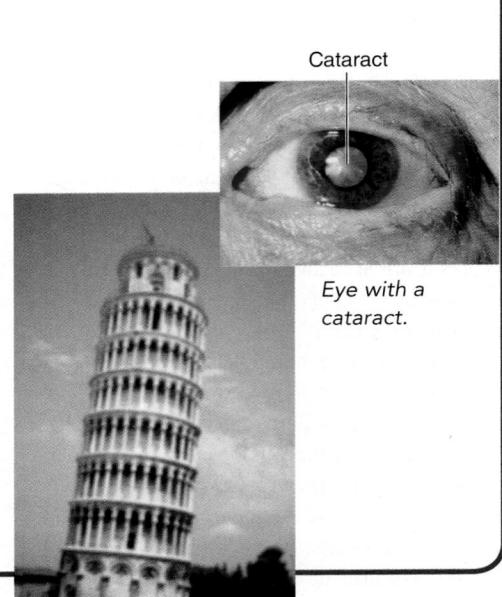

Cataract

Eye with a cataract.

Image seen through cataract.

In contrast, when we wish to see close objects, the lens must become more spherical or "puffy" to properly refract (bend) the light rays and focus an image on the retina. The process of making the lens more spherical in order to view close-up objects is called **accommodation** (ă-kom′ŏ-dā′shŭn; *accommodo* = to adapt) (figure 16.15b). Accommodation is controlled by parasympathetic axons extending within the oculomotor nerve (CN III); see section 13.9. Stimulation of the ciliary muscle by the parasympathetic division causes the muscle to contract. When the ciliary muscle contracts, the entire ciliary body moves anteriorly and thus moves closer to the lens itself. This process reduces the suspensory ligaments' tension and releases some of their pull on the lens, so the lens can become more spherical.

Cavities of the Eye

The internal space of the eye is subdivided by the lens into two separate cavities: the anterior cavity and the posterior cavity (see figure 16.11). The **posterior cavity** is posterior to the lens and anterior to the retina. It is occupied by **vitreous humor** (vit′rē-ŭs; *vitrum* = glassy), or *vitreous body*. This transparent, gelatinous fluid completely fills the space between the lens and the retina. The vitreous humor helps maintain eye shape, supports the retina to keep it flush against the back of the eye, and transmits light from the lens to the retina.

The **anterior cavity** is the space anterior to the lens and posterior to the cornea. The iris subdivides the anterior cavity further into two chambers: The **anterior chamber** is between the iris and cornea, whereas the **posterior chamber** is between the lens and the iris (figure 16.16). The anterior cavity contains a fluid called **aqueous humor** (ak′qwē-ŭs hū′mer; = watery fluid). It is a filtrate of blood plasma that resembles cerebrospinal fluid (CSF) and is produced by the ciliary processes. The aqueous humor is secreted into the posterior chamber. From the posterior chamber, it flows through the pupil into the anterior chamber. The aqueous humor is continually resorbed into a vascular space, called the **scleral venous sinus** (previously called the *canal of Schlemm*), located in the limbus between the cornea and the sclera. The scleral venous sinus drains into nearby veins. Thus, as with cerebrospinal fluid, excess aqueous humor is removed from these eye chambers and transported into the venous circulation. The circulation of aqueous humor provides nutrients and oxygen to both the lens and cornea and helps maintain the chemical environment within the anterior cavity of the eye.

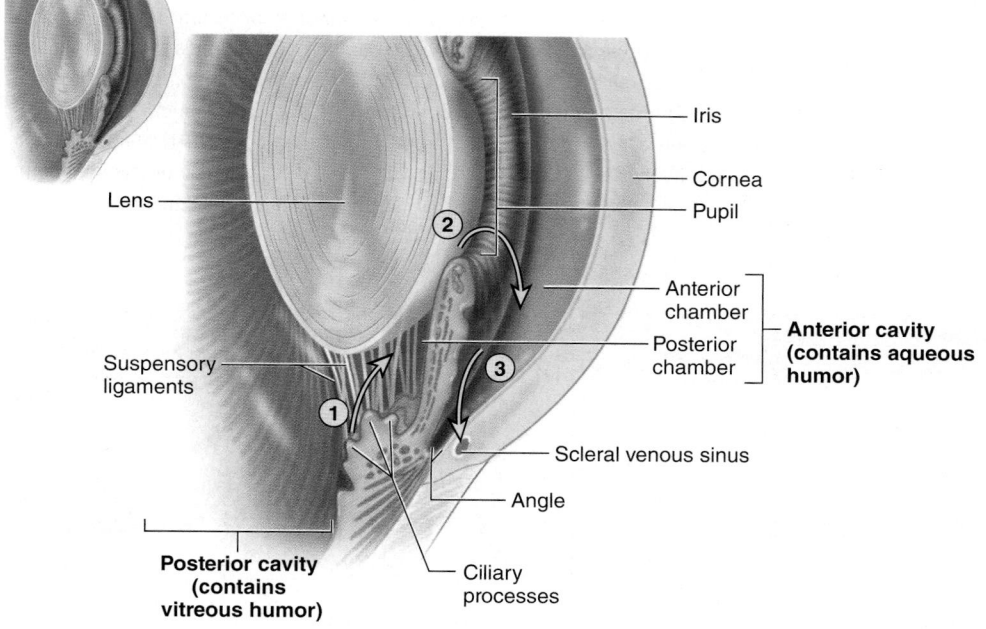

Figure 16.16 Aqueous Humor: Secretion and Resorption. Aqueous humor is a watery secretion that is continuously produced and circulated through the eye, helping to maintain the chemical environment and removing waste products.

Anterior cavity
■ Anterior chamber
▨ Posterior chamber
▢ Posterior cavity

Iris

Lens

Cornea

Pupil

Suspensory ligaments

Anterior chamber

Posterior chamber

Anterior cavity (contains aqueous humor)

Scleral venous sinus

Angle

Posterior cavity (contains vitreous humor)

Ciliary processes

(1) Aqueous humor is secreted by the ciliary processes into the posterior chamber.

(2) Aqueous humor moves from the posterior chamber, through the pupil, to the anterior chamber.

(3) Excess aqueous humor is resorbed via the scleral venous sinus.

 WHAT DID YOU LEARN?

(13) What are the three eye tunics; what is the primary function of each tunic?

(14) How is the lens able to change shape?

(15) What are the functions of the aqueous humor and the vitreous humor?

 INTEGRATE

CLINICAL VIEW
Glaucoma

Glaucoma (glaw-kō′mă) is a disease that exists in three forms, all characterized by increased intraocular pressure: primary angle-closure glaucoma, open-angle glaucoma, and congenital or juvenile glaucoma.

Angle-closure glaucoma and *open-angle glaucoma* both involve the angle formed in the anterior chamber of the eye by the union of the choroid and the corneal-scleral junction (see figure 16.16). If this angle narrows, aqueous humor and pressure build up within the anterior chamber. Primary angle-closure glaucoma develops as a direct consequence of the narrowing of this angle, whereas open-angle glaucoma occurs if the drain angles are adequate but fluid transport out of the anterior chamber is impaired. *Congenital glaucoma* occurs only rarely and is due to hereditary factors or intrauterine infection.

Regardless of the cause, fluid buildup causes a posterior dislocation of the lens and a substantial increase in pressure in the posterior cavity. Compression of the choroid layer may occur, constricting the blood vessels that nourish the retina. Retinal cell death and increased pressure may distort the axons within the optic nerve. Eventually, the patient may experience such symptoms as reduced field of vision, dim vision, and halos around lights. These symptoms are often unrecognized until it is too late and the damage is irreversible, so it is essential individuals get regular eye screenings where early stages may be detected by an optometrist or ophthalmologist.

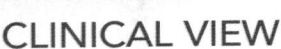

CLINICAL VIEW
Functional Visual Impairments

Emmetropia (em-ĕ-trō′pē-ă; *emmetros* = according to measure, *ops* = eye) is the condition of normal vision, in which parallel rays of light are focused exactly on the retina. Any variation in the curvature of either the cornea or the lens, or in the overall shape of the eye, causes entering light rays to form an abnormal focal point. Conditions that can result include hyperopia, myopia, and astigmatism.

People with **hyperopia** (hī-per-ō′pē-ă) have trouble seeing close-up objects, and so are called *farsighted.* In this optical condition, only convergent rays (those that come together from distant points) can be brought to focus on the retina. The cause of hyperopia is a short eyeball; parallel light rays from objects close to the eye focus posterior to the retina. By contrast, people with **myopia** (mī-ō′pē-ă; *myo* = to shut) have trouble seeing faraway objects, and so are called *nearsighted.* In myopia, only rays relatively close to the eye focus on the retina. The cause of this condition is a long eyeball; parallel light rays from objects at some distance from the

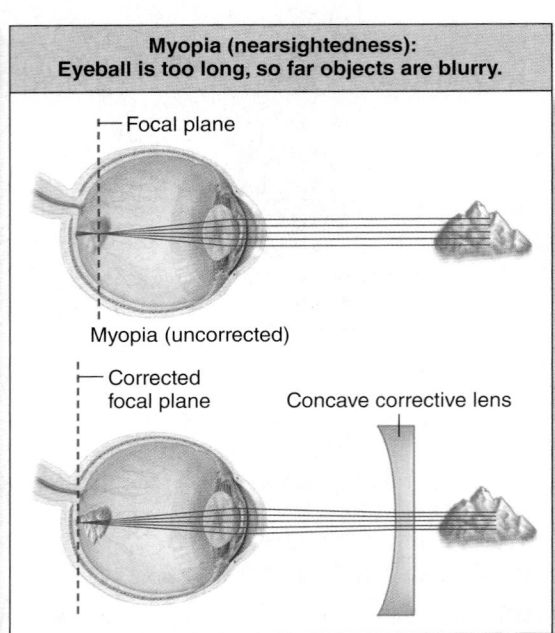

Vision correction using convex and concave lenses.

16.4c Physiology of Vision

LEARNING OBJECTIVES

3. Compare and contrast the two general types of photoreceptors, including their photopigments.
4. Define phototransduction.
5. Explain the bleaching reaction and how it relates to dark adaptation and light adaptation.

We focus different parts of the visual field onto the retina of each eye by our stereoscopic vision. The visual field is the entire area observed in our vision during the time the eye is focused on a central point. The cornea and lens focus the left region of our visual field on the right side of each retina at the same time the right region is being focused on the left side. The two images from each eye are then sent to the brain for interpretation.

Visual acuity is the clearness or sharpness of our vision. The clearness of an observed image formed on the retina is dependent upon bending (refraction) of light rays as they enter the eye, the sensitivity of neuronal elements in the retina, and our ability to interpret the image in the brain. Often this is portrayed as the ability to differentiate between two objects (usually small black dots) that are very close together. We call this ability to form separate and distinct images of close objects the **resolving power** of the optical system.

Here we describe several concepts associated with vision, including a brief description of refraction and focusing of light, and a detailed discussion of photoreceptors and stimulation of photoreceptors to produce a nerve signal.

① Cornea is sliced with a sharp knife. Flap of cornea is reflected, and deeper corneal layers are exposed.

② A laser removes microscopic portions of the deeper corneal layers, thereby changing the shape of the cornea.

③ Corneal flap is put back in place, and the edges of the flap start to fuse within 72 hours.

LASIK laser vision correction procedure.

eye focus anterior to the retina within the vitreous body. Another variation is **astigmatism** (ă-stig′mă-tizm), which causes unequal focusing and blurred images due to unequal curvatures in one or more of the refractive surfaces (cornea, anterior surface, or posterior surface of the lens).

With increasing age, the lens becomes less resilient and less able to become spherical. Thus, even if the suspensory ligaments relax, the lens may not be able to spring out of the flattened position into the more spherical shape needed for near vision, and reading close-up words becomes difficult. This age-related change is called **presbyopia** (prez-bē-ō′pē-ă; *presbys* = old man, *ops* = eye).

The typical treatment for vision disturbances is eyeglasses. A concave eyeglass lens is used to treat myopia, because the concave lens bends the light rays to make the focused image appear directly on the retina, instead of too far in front of it. A convex lens is used to treat both hyperopia and presbyopia.

Corneal incision surgical techniques may help treat hyperopia, myopia, and astigmatism (which are all visual disturbances that involve the cornea). These techniques involve cutting the cornea to change its shape, and thereby change its ability to refract light. One type of procedure, called a

radial keratotomy (ker′ă-tot′ō-mē; *tome* = incision), or **RK**, treats nearsightedness. The ophthalmologist makes radial-oriented cuts in the cornea, which flatten the cornea and allow it to refract the light rays so that they focus on the retina.

Laser vision correction uses a laser to change the shape of the cornea. Two of the more popular types of laser vision correction are photorefractive keratectomy and laser-assisted in situ keratomileusis.

Photorefractive keratectomy (PRK) is called a *photoablation procedure* because the laser removes (ablates) tissue directly from the surface of the cornea. The removal of corneal tissue results in a newly shaped cornea that can focus better. This procedure is becoming less popular, because its regression rate is high—that is, the epithelial tissue that covers the surface of the cornea can regrow and regenerate, leading to partial return to uncorrected vision.

Laser-assisted in situ keratomileusis (ker′ă-tō-mī-lū′sis) (or **LASIK**) is rapidly becoming the most popular laser vision correction procedure. It can treat nearsightedness, farsightedness, and astigmatism. LASIK removes tissue from the inner, deeper layer of the cornea, which is less likely to regrow than surface tissue, so less vision regression occurs.

Refraction and the Focusing of Light

Light rays are refracted (bent) when (1) they pass between two media of different densities, and (2) these media meet at a curved surface. Each medium—such as air, water, and other clear fluids, and even clear solids such as glass—is assigned a *refractive index,* a number that represents its comparative density. The refraction of light rays is greatest when a large difference in refractive index is observed between adjacent media, such as between air and water (figure 16.17).

Before light can reach the photoreceptors, it must pass from the air, through the cornea, the aqueous humor, lens, and the vitreous humor, as well as through the inner two layers of the retina. Refraction of light for vision is greatest as light rays pass from air into the cornea, because their difference in refractive index is maximal. Although the shape of the cornea cannot be altered, lens shape is changeable in order to focus light rays onto the retina. Recall that ciliary muscles contract and relax to alter the curvature of the lens. The refracted image that focuses on the retina appears upside down and backward; the brain sorts this out to provide our upright interpretation of objects.

Photoreceptors

The two types of photoreceptor cells, rods and cones (see figure 16.13), were briefly described earlier. Recall that the rod and cone photoreceptors are present in different numbers and distribution patterns in our retinas. The ratio of rods to cones is highest in the periphery of the retina and lowest in and around the fovea centralis.

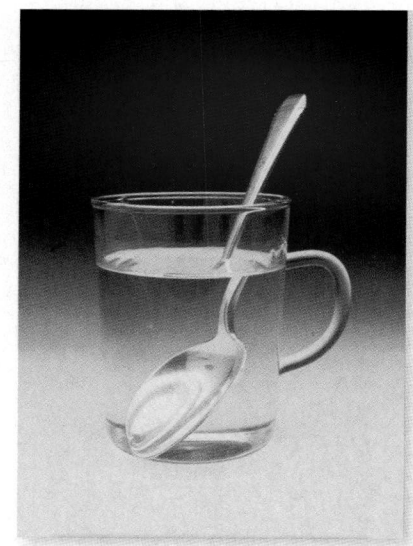

Figure 16.17 Refraction. Light waves change in speed as they pass between media of different densities. This results in the distortion of the image.

Each type of photoreceptor has both an outer segment that extends into the pigmented layer of the retina (rod-shaped in rods and conical-shaped in cones) and an inner segment (figure 16.18). The **outer segment** of each photoreceptor is composed of hundreds of discs that are flattened membranous sacs containing photopigments that are capable of absorbing light energy. These discs are constantly being replaced. New discs are added at the base of the outer segment and begin to move externally toward the tip, where old, worn-out discs are removed by phagocytic cells. Usually it takes about 10 days for a disc to traverse this distance. The **inner segment** contains the organelles for the cell, such as mitochondria. The inner segment connects directly to the **cell body.**

Rods   Rods are longer and narrower than cones. Each eye contains more than 100 million rods, and they are primarily located in the peripheral regions of the neural layer. Rods are especially important when the light is dim. They detect movement well but are poor at sharpness of vision. Additionally, rods pick up contrasting dark and light tones but cannot distinguish color. Thus, when you are trying to see at night, it is primarily the rods that are working. The rods can perceive objects, but your vision may not be particularly sharp, and you may find it difficult to see any color variation.

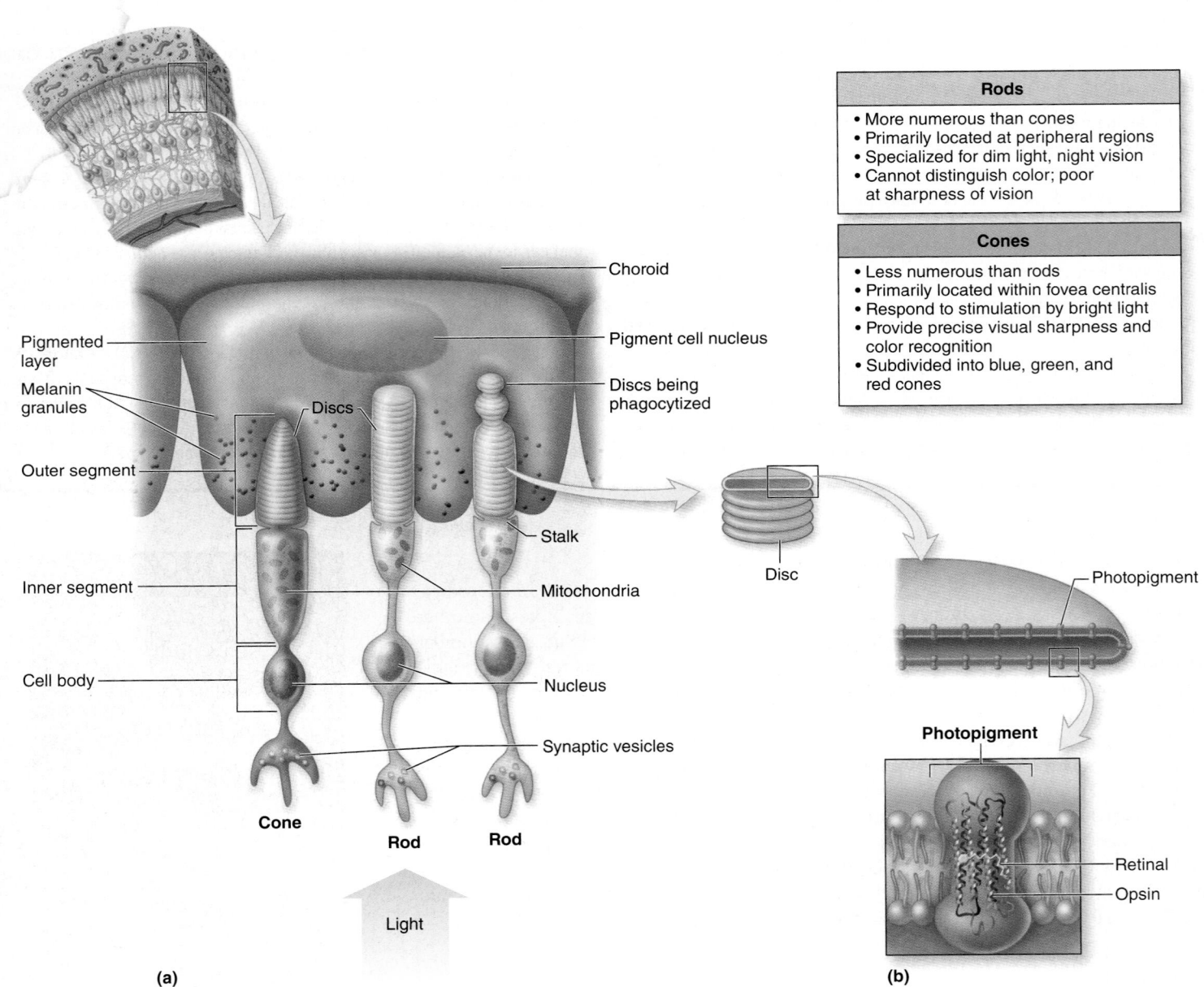

Rods
- More numerous than cones
- Primarily located at peripheral regions
- Specialized for dim light, night vision
- Cannot distinguish color; poor at sharpness of vision

Cones
- Less numerous than rods
- Primarily located within fovea centralis
- Respond to stimulation by bright light
- Provide precise visual sharpness and color recognition
- Subdivided into blue, green, and red cones

Figure 16.18 Photoreceptors. (*a*) The outer segments of both rods and cones consist of stacks of discs embedded in pigment cells. The inner segments contain some cellular organelles. (*b*) Membranes of the discs contain photopigments. Each photopigment is composed of an opsin and a retinal.

Cones Cones occur at a density of less than 10 million per eye. Cones are activated by high-intensity light and provide precise visual sharpness and color recognition. Thus, when you notice the fine details in a colorful picture, the cones of your retina are responsible. Cones are concentrated in the fovea centralis, the place of our most acute vision.

Three different types of cones have been distinguished on the basis of the wavelength they most optimally detect. They are categorized as **blue cones,** which best detect wavelengths of light at about 420 nanometers (nm), **green cones,** which best detect light at 531 nm, and **red cones,** which best detect light at 558 nm **(figure 16.19)**.

Photopigments A photopigment is composed of a protein called an **opsin** (op′sin; *opsis = vision*) and a light-absorbing molecule called a **retinal** (or a *retineme*). This molecule is formed from vitamin A (see figure 16.18). There are several different types of opsins, and each type transduces different wavelengths of light. Thus, some opsins may transduce greater wavelength light like reds, while other opsins may transduce lower wavelength light like blues. However, each photoreceptor expresses only one opsin type.

The opsin in rods is called **rhodopsin** (rō-dop′sin; *rhodon = a rose*). This opsin is involved in the transduction of dim light and is most sensitive to light at a 500-nm wavelength. It is less sensitive to other light wavelengths.

In the cone cells that provide color vision, each cone has a retinal that is associated with a specific opsin called **photopsin.** There are three different photopsin proteins that provide for the difference found in the wavelength absorption maxima noted earlier.

Thus, specific colors are best perceived by specific cones. But what about conditions where there is a mixture of colors (such as a greenish-blue hue)? In this case, we perceive intricate colors based on patterns of nerve signals arriving from all of these cones. Note from figure 16.19 that at about 470 nm, only the blue and green cones are stimulated; however, they are not stimulated at their peak. Instead, both types of cones are stimulated at about 50% capacity. When the blue and green cones initiate nerve signals, the brain interprets the color as a blue-green.

Phototransduction

Phototransduction is the process by which photoreceptors become activated when the photopigments within the discs of the cells are altered by light entering the eye. The photoreceptor responds to light stimulation by changing its resting membrane potential, resulting in a change in the neurotransmitter it releases.

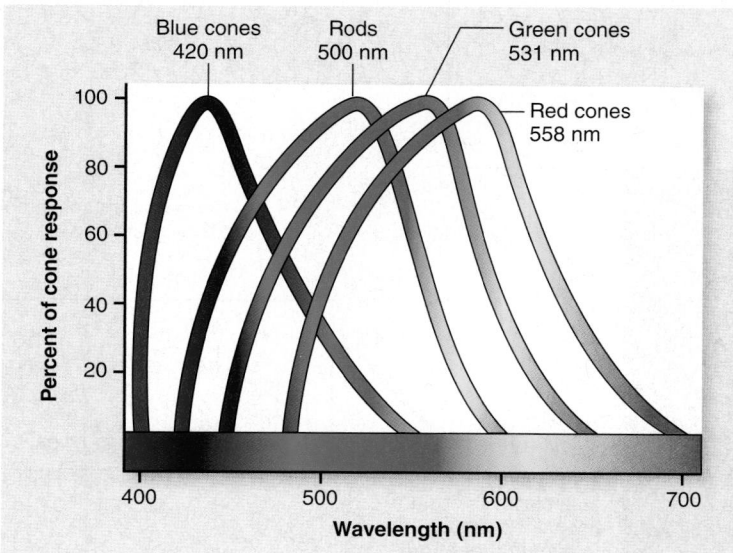

Figure 16.19 Absorption Wavelengths. Each photoreceptor detects a range of wavelengths, but not all wavelengths are detected with equal strength. For example, blue cones reach their peak stimulation at wavelengths of 420 nm—yet at 450 nm these blue cones respond at about 70% of their maximum. Mixtures of colors (such as a blue-green, at 470 nm) stimulate green and blue cones at about 50% of their maximum.

We first discuss what happens with rods. Prior to being activated by light, the retinal portion of the rhodopsin is in a bent, twisted shape called *cis*-retinal. Upon exposure to light, the retinal straightens out and reconfigures into a form called ***trans*-retinal (figure 16.20)**. *Trans*-retinal disassociates from the opsin (rhodopsin in rods) and phototransduction occurs. This dissociation of rhodopsin into its two components is a process termed a **bleaching reaction** because the rhodopsin goes from a bluish-purple color to colorless. Bleaching reduces rhodopsin amounts in rods and temporarily affects our ability to see in dim light conditions.

Rhodopsin must be regenerated for the rod cell to continue to function. Its regeneration occurs as follows: The disassociated *trans*-retinal is transported to the pigmented layer where the retinal is converted back to its bent *cis*-retinal form. The *cis*-retinal is transported back to the rod where is associates with the opsin and re-forms the rhodopsin. This process is relatively slow; typically only half of your bleached rhodopsin is regenerated after about 5 minutes. Light will interfere with this process, and rhodopsin will bleach as fast as it is re-formed. For this reason, rods are essentially nonfunctional in bright light situations; the bleaching reaction in the neural retina occurs more quickly than rhodopsin re-formation in the pigmented layer.

A similar process occurs for the photopsin of cone cells. *Cis*-retinal transforms to *trans*-retinal, and a bleaching reaction occurs. However, the regeneration of photopsin occurs much more quickly

than the regeneration of rhodopsin; thus, cone cells are not as negatively affected by bright light as rods.

Recall a time when you went quickly from bright light conditions outside on a sunny day into a darkened movie theater. You probably remember the slow return of your sensitivity to low light levels. This phenomenon, called **dark adaptation,** occurs because initially our cones become nonfunctional in the low light, but our rods are still bleached from the bright light conditions from outside. It may take 20 to 30 minutes for your rhodopsin to be regenerated sufficiently that you can see well in low-light conditions.

Light adaptation is the process by which your eyes adjust from low light to bright light conditions, such as when you wake up at night and turn on the bright light in the bathroom. Even though your pupils constrict to reduce the amount of light entering your eyes, you are temporarily blinded as the rods become inactive and the cones, which initially were overstimulated, gradually adjust to the brighter light. In about 5 to 10 minutes, the cones can produce sufficient visual acuity and color vision.

Details of Phototransduction

Photoreceptors are depolarized when it is completely dark and photoreceptors are not being stimulated by light **(figure 16.21a)**. Depolarized photoreceptors exhibit a membrane potential of about −40 millivolts (mV). In a photoreceptor cell, the depolarized (or

Figure 16.20 Bleaching Reaction and Regeneration of Rhodopsin. When light waves reach the rod, *cis*-retinal is transformed to *trans*-retinal, which then disassociates from opsin in a process called the bleaching reaction. *Trans*-retinal is converted back to *cis*-retinal. Rhodopsin is re-formed when *cis*-retinal reunites with opsin.

In the dark

Rod

Na⁺ channels are kept open by high levels of cGMP

Na⁺
Na⁺ channel (open)

Dark current is caused by Na⁺ entry.

K⁺
K⁺ channel

Graded potential

OFF

Ca²⁺
Ca²⁺ channel (open)

Inhibitory neurotransmitter is released continuously in the dark.

Inhibitory neurotransmitter

Bipolar cell
Ca²⁺ channel (closed)

Ganglion cell

1. Dark current (caused by influx of Na⁺) causes photoreceptor cell to be depolarized at −40 mV. Graded potential is transmitted along cell.

2. Ca²⁺ channels open, and an inhibitory neurotransmitter (glutamate) is released from photoreceptor to bipolar cell.

3. IPSPs hyperpolarize the bipolar cell, causing it to become inhibited.

4. Ca²⁺ channels are closed in the bipolar cell, and the bipolar cell releases no excitatory neurotransmitter.

5. No nerve signal is generated.

(a)

In the light

Rhodopsin bleaches, leading to a drop in cGMP. Drop in cGMP levels closes Na⁺ channels.

Na⁺ channel (closed)
Dark current stops because of decrease in Na⁺ entry.

Mitochondria

K⁺

ON

Ca²⁺ channel (closed)

No inhibitory neurotransmitter is released in the light.

Ca²⁺
Ca²⁺ channel (open)

Excitatory neurotransmitter

Ganglion cell

Nerve signal

1. Stimulation by light causes the photoreceptor cell to become hyperpolarized at −70 mV.

2. Ca²⁺ channels close, and no inhibitory neurotransmitter is released.

3. The bipolar cell is no longer inhibited and thus it depolarizes.

4. Ca²⁺ channels in the bipolar cell open, and the bipolar cell releases excitatory neurotransmitter.

5. The excitatory neurotransmitter binds to receptors in the ganglion cell, and a nerve signal is initiated.

(b)

Figure 16.21 Phototransduction in Rod Photoreceptors. (*a*) Depolarization of photoreceptors in the absence of light causes a dark current. (*b*) In the presence of light, the photoreceptors hyperpolarize and initiate a chain reaction that ultimately stimulates the ganglion cell, and it propagates a nerve signal along the optic nerve.

"resting") state is maintained by cyclic guanosine monophosphate (cGMP). When elevated concentrations of cGMP are present, then Na^+ channels in the photoreceptor plasma membrane are kept open and Na^+ enters the photoreceptor. This is called the **dark current** (or *sodium current*), and it fosters the depolarization of the cell.

As a result of this dark current, calcium channels in the photoreceptor open, and ultimately there is a continuous (tonic) release of inhibitory neurotransmitter (glutamate) from the photoreceptors to bind with bipolar cells. The bipolar cells are inhibited as inhibitory postsynaptic potentials (IPSPs) hyperpolarize the bipolar cells to −70 mV. The bipolar cells thus do not release their own neurotransmitter and do not stimulate the ganglion cell. Because the ganglion cell is unstimulated, no nerve signal is generated, and therefore the brain does not perceive light.

So what happens in the presence of light? Stimulation by light causes the plasma membrane of the photoreceptor to hyperpolarize to −70 mV (figure 16.21*b*). This action is not what we have observed before for nerve and muscle cells; usually, stimulation of the excitable cell causes its depolarization—that is, greater positivity (or lesser negativity). This hyperpolarization due to stimulation is a unique characteristic of photoreceptors.

Hyperpolarization specifically occurs as follows: Light rays activate the opsin and cause the *cis*-retinal to change in shape and become *trans*-retinal. This results in bleaching of the photoreceptors and activates the photopigments. When rhodopsin changes conformation (i.e., it is bleached), a series of reactions occur that lead to a drop in cGMP levels. Chemically-gated Na^+ channels regulated by cGMP then close, resulting in a reduction in Na^+ entry.

When the photoreceptor cell is hyperpolarized, the calcium channels also are closed, and this ultimately blocks the release of the inhibitory neurotransmitter. Without the inhibitory neuro-transmitter, the bipolar cells become depolarized, their own calcium channels open, and they release their own neurotransmitter (which is excitatory in nature). This excitatory neurotransmitter binds to receptors in the ganglion cells, generating nerve signals that are transmitted via the optic nerve to the brain. This process continues as long as light stimulates the photoreceptors.

WHAT DID YOU LEARN?

16 What are the differences between rods and cones with respect to their anatomy, their photopigments, and what light they process?

17 How does dark adaptation differ from light adaptation?

18 What occurs during phototransduction of light?

16.4d Visual Pathways

LEARNING OBJECTIVES

6. Describe the visual pathway from the photoreceptors to the brain.

7. Explain how stereoscopic vision provides depth perception.

The visual image that is formed in the brain is a result of the processing and summation of information as it is collected and integrated within the retina. Because of this continual processing and integration activity, fewer cells are found in each layer of the retina, from photoreceptor to ganglionic neuron (as described).

Ganglionic axons converge to form the **optic nerve.** Optic nerves project from each eye through paired optic foramina and converge at the **optic chiasm** immediately anterior to the pituitary gland (**figure 16.22**; see also section 13.9). The ganglionic axons originating from the medial region of each retina cross to the opposite side of the brain at the optic chiasm. The optic chiasm is a flattened structure anterior to the infundibulum that is the location of decussation (or crossing) of optic nerve axons. Ganglionic axons originating from the lateral region of each retina remain on the same side of the brain and do not cross. **Optic tracts** extend laterally from the optic chiasm as a composite of ganglionic axons originating from the retinas of each eye.

Some axons within each optic tract project to the **superior colliculi** upon entry into the brain. These projecting axons and the indirect motor pathway they stimulate are called collectively the **tectal system.** This system coordinates the reflexive movements of eyes, head, and neck to respond to visual stimuli.

The remainder of the optic tract axons extend to the thalamus, specifically to the **lateral geniculate** (je-nik′ū-lāt; *genu* = knee, referring to its appearance) **nucleus,** where visual

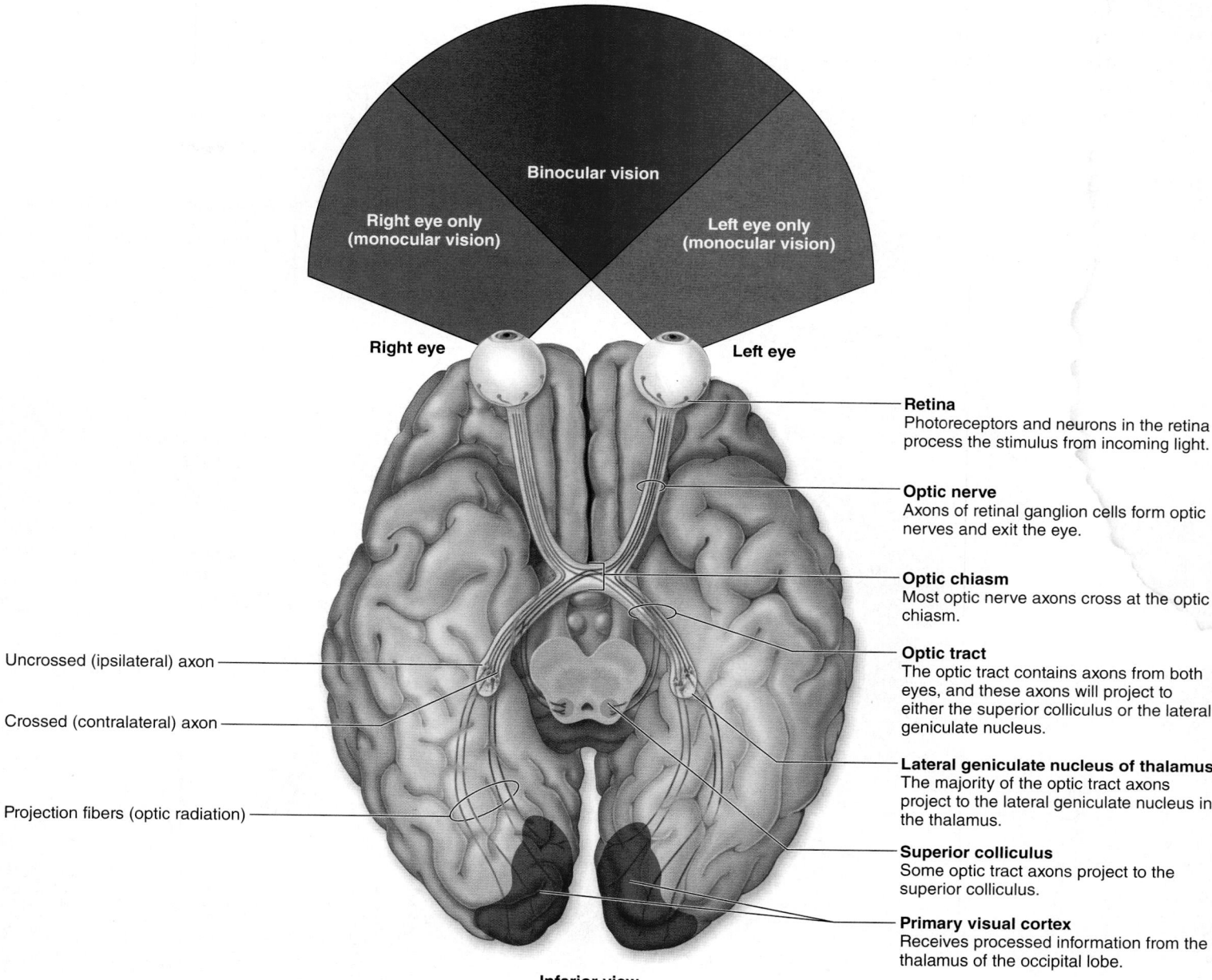

Binocular vision

Right eye only (monocular vision)

Left eye only (monocular vision)

Right eye

Left eye

Retina
Photoreceptors and neurons in the retina process the stimulus from incoming light.

Optic nerve
Axons of retinal ganglion cells form optic nerves and exit the eye.

Optic chiasm
Most optic nerve axons cross at the optic chiasm.

Optic tract
The optic tract contains axons from both eyes, and these axons will project to either the superior colliculus or the lateral geniculate nucleus.

Lateral geniculate nucleus of thalamus
The majority of the optic tract axons project to the lateral geniculate nucleus in the thalamus.

Superior colliculus
Some optic tract axons project to the superior colliculus.

Primary visual cortex
Receives processed information from the thalamus of the occipital lobe.

Uncrossed (ipsilateral) axon

Crossed (contralateral) axon

Projection fibers (optic radiation)

Inferior view

Figure 16.22 Visual Pathways. Each optic nerve conducts visual stimuli information. At the optic chiasm, some axons from the optic nerve decussate. The optic tract on each side then contains axons from both eyes. Visual stimuli information is processed by the thalamus and then interpreted by visual association areas in the cerebrum. **AP|R**

information is processed within each thalamic body. Neurons from the thalamus then project axons to the visual cortex of the occipital lobe for interpretation of incoming visual stimuli.

Note that the left and right eyes have somewhat overlapping visual fields. In order for the brain to interpret these two distinct visual images, it must process or unite them into one. These overlapping images then provide us with **stereoscopic vision,** or **depth perception,** which is the ability to determine how close or far away an object is. Animals that don't have overlapping visual fields (such as horses or deer) may have a greater visual range, but they cannot perceive visual depths.

The Anatomy and Physiology of Vision

Let's integrate what we've learned about how visual information is processed. Refer to **figure 16.23** as we review the anatomy and physiology of vision.

The process of vision begins when light rays reach the eye and then are refracted by the cornea. The pupil either constricts (in bright light situations) or dilates (in low light situations) to regulate how much of this light passes through the pupil. The light rays are further refracted

Figure 16.23 **How We See.** (*a*) Light is refracted and then focused on the retina. (*b*) Light rays are transduced to nerve signals, and (*c*) these nerve signals are transmitted to the brain.

(a) Refraction and Focusing of Light

Flattened lens

Far/distant vision

Puffy lens

Near vision

③ Light passes through the pupil and is refracted by the lens. The lens flattens for distant vision, while the lens becomes puffy as the eye accommodates for near vision.

① Light rays enter the eye and are refracted by the cornea.

② Pupils dilate for low light or constrict for bright light.

⑧ Visual image is perceived by the brain.

Lens

Pupil

Cornea

Iris

Light rays

Low light: pupils dilate

Bright light: pupils constrict

Sclera
Choroid
Retina
Optic disc

Optic nerve

Fovea centralis

④ An inverted image is focused on the retina.

Rod   Cone

Choroid

Pigmented layer

Retina

Neural layer

Axons of ganglion cells to optic nerve

Light

(b) Phototransduction

⑤ Photoreceptors hyperpolarize in the presence of light.

Rod

Outer segment

Inner segment

Cell body

Cones provide sharp color vision in the presence of bright light.

Rods detect movement and work best in dim light.

⑥ Hyperpolarized photoreceptors no longer inhibit bipolar cells, allowing them to stimulate ganglion cells, which initiate nerve signals that are propogated along the optic nerve.

Bipolar cell

Ganglion cell

Nerve signal

(c) Visual Pathway

Optic tracts

Right eye

Right eye only (monocular vision)

⑦d   ⑦c

⑦b   ⑦a

Primary visual cortex of occipital lobe

Binocular vision

Superior colliculi

Optic chiasm

Left eye only (monocular vision)

Lateral geniculate nucleus

Optic nerve

Left eye

⑦a Nerve signals generated from each eye travel via each optic nerve.

⑦b Some axons from each eye cross at the optic chiasm.

⑦c Each optic tract transmits nerve signals from both eyes, which are relayed to both the superior colliculi and each lateral geniculate nucleus.

⑦d Nerve signals are propogated from the lateral geniculate nuclei to the left and right primary visual cortices. Each visual cortex receives visual information from both eyes.

by the lens. The lens is flattened when we are viewing faraway objects and rounded when we are viewing close-up objects.

Light rays focus an inverted image on a specific part of the retina. Photoreceptors in this region hyperpolarize in the presence of light. As a result, the photoreceptors stop inhibiting the bipolar cells, which allow the bipolar cells to release their own neurotransmitter that attaches to receptors on the ganglion cells. This causes the production of nerve signals in the ganglion cells that are propagated along the optic nerve.

Each optic nerve transmits nerve signals from its respective eye. At the optic chiasm, some of the axons from each nerve cross, thereby ensuring that each hemisphere of the brain receives visual information from both eyes. From the optic chiasm, optic tracts (composed of axons from both left and right eyes) extend to the superior colliculi to coordinate reflexive movement of eyes, head, and neck in response to visual stimuli. Tracts also extend to the lateral geniculate nucleus in the thalamus. Axons from the thalamus then are directed to the left and right primary visual cortices within the occipital lobe, where the (upright) image is produced and perceived by the brain.

WHAT DID YOU LEARN?

19 What is the significance of some ganglionic axons' crossing to the opposite side of the brain?

20 Why would it be an advantage for a deer to have a wide visual field, as compared to overlapping, stereoscopic vision?

16.5 Hearing and Equilibrium Receptors

The ear is the organ that detects both sound and movements of the head. These stimuli are transduced into nerve signals that are transmitted via vestibulocochlear nerve (CN VIII) (see section 13.9), resulting in the sensations of hearing and equilibrium or balance.

16.5a Ear Structure

LEARNING OBJECTIVES

1. Describe the structures of the outer, middle, and inner ear.
2. Name the auditory ossicles and explain how they function in hearing.
3. Compare and contrast the bony labyrinth and the membranous labyrinth.

The ear is partitioned into three distinct anatomic regions: external, middle, and inner **(figure 16.24)**. The external ear is located mostly on the outside of the body, and the middle and inner areas are housed within the petrous part of the temporal bone (see section 8.2).

External Ear

The most visible part of the external ear is a skin-covered, elastic cartilage–supported structure called the **auricle** (aw'ri-kl; *auris* =

Figure 16.24 Anatomic Regions of the Right Ear. The ear is divided into external, middle, and inner regions. AP|R

CLINICAL VIEW
Otitis Media

Otitis (ō-tī′tis; *itis* = inflammation) **media** (mē′dē-ă; *medius* = middle) is an infection of the middle ear. It is most often experienced by young children, whose auditory tubes are horizontal, relatively short, and underdeveloped. If a young child has a respiratory infection, the causative agent may spread from the phyarynx (throat) through the auditory tube. Fluid then accumulates in the middle ear cavity, resulting in pressure, pain, and sometimes impaired hearing. An **otoscope** (ō′tō-skōp; *skopeo* = to view) is an instrument used to examine the tympanic membrane, which normally appears white and "pearly," but in cases of severe otitis media is red (due to inflammation and sometimes bleeding) and may even bulge due to fluid pressure in the middle ear.

Repeated ear infections, or a chronic ear infection that does not respond to antibiotic treatment, usually calls for a surgical procedure called a **myringotomy** (mir-ing-got′ō-mē; *myringa* = membrane), whereby a ventilation tube is inserted into the tympanic membrane. This procedure allows the infection to heal and the pus and mucus to drain from the middle ear into the external auditory meatus and offers immediate relief from the pressure. Eventually, the inserted tube is sloughed, and the tympanic membrane heals.

When a child is about 5 years old, the auditory tube has become larger, more vertically angled, and better able to drain fluid and prevent infection from reaching the middle ear. Thus, the occurrence rate for ear infections drops dramatically at this time.

Normal tympanic membrane

Otitis media

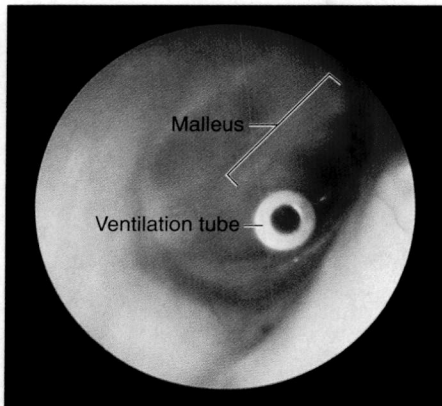

Myringotomy

Middle ear views as seen with an otoscope.

ear), or *pinna* (pin′ă; wing). The auricle is funnel-shaped, and it serves both to protect the entry into the ear and to direct sound waves into the bony tube called the **external acoustic meatus,** which extends and slightly superiorly from the lateral surface of the head. The external acoustic meatus terminates at the **tympanic** (tim-pan′ik; *tympanon* = drum) **membrane,** or *eardrum,* a delicate, funnel-shaped epithelial sheet that is the partition between the external and middle ear. The tympanic membrane vibrates when sound waves hit it. Its vibrations provide the means for transmission of sound wave energy into the middle and inner ear.

The narrow external opening in the external acoustic meatus prevents large objects from entering and damaging the tympanic membrane. Near its entrance, fine hairs help guard the opening. Deep within the canal, ceruminous glands produce a waxlike secretion called **cerumen,** which combines with dead sloughed skin cells to form earwax. This material may help reduce infection within the external acoustic meatus by impeding microorganism growth.

Middle Ear

The middle ear contains an air-filled **tympanic cavity** (figure 16.25). Medially, a bony wall that houses the oval window and round window (discussed later)

Figure 16.25 Middle Ear. The middle ear contains the auditory ossicles and associated structures within the tympanic cavity.

Labels on figure:
Temporal bone (petrous part)
Auditory ossicles
Malleus
Incus
Stapes
Oval window
Stapedius
Tensor tympani (cut)
Round window
Auditory tube
Tympanic membrane
External acoustic meatus
Tympanic cavity

separates the middle ear from the inner ear. The tympanic cavity maintains an open connection with the atmosphere through the **auditory tube** (also called the *pharyngo-tympanic tube* or *Eustachian tube*). This passageway extends from the middle ear into the nasopharynx (portion of upper throat posterior to the nasal cavity). It has a normally closed, slitlike opening at its connection to the nasopharynx. Air movement through this tube occurs as a result of chewing, yawning, and swallowing, which allows the pressure to equalize within the middle ear.

Sound is transmitted through the tympanic cavity via the auditory ossicles, described next.

WHAT DO YOU THINK?

3 When an airplane descends to a lower altitude, you may feel greater pressure in your ears, followed by a popping sensation—then more normal pressure resumes. What do you think has happened?

Auditory Ossicles

The tympanic cavity of both middle ears houses the three smallest bones of the body, the **auditory ossicles** (os′i-kl). These bones are, from lateral to medial, the malleus (hammer), the incus (anvil), and the stapes (stirrup). The **malleus** (mal′ē-ŭs) is attached to the medial surface of the tympanic membrane, and suspended by ligaments bound to the inner wall of the tympanic cavity. It resembles a large hammer in shape. The **incus** (ing′kŭs) resembles an anvil and is the middle auditory ossicle. The **stapes** (stā′pēz) resembles a stirrup on a

Figure 16.26 Inner Ear. The inner ear is composed of a bony labyrinth cavity that houses a fluid-filled membranous labyrinth. Within the bony labyrinth are the portions of the membranous labyrinth for equilibrium and balance (saccule, utricle, and semicircular ducts) and the cochlear duct for hearing. **AP|R**

saddle. It has a cylindrical, disclike footplate that fits into the oval window, an opening that marks the lateral wall of the inner ear.

The auditory ossicles are responsible for both amplifying sound waves and transmitting them into the inner ear via the oval window. When sound waves strike the tympanic membrane, the three middle ear ossicles vibrate along with the tympanic membrane, causing the footplate of the stapes to move in and out of the oval window. The movement of this ossicle initiates pressure waves in the fluid within the closed compartment of the inner ear. Since the tympanic membrane is 20 times greater in diameter than the footplate of the stapes in the oval window, sounds transmitted across the middle ear are amplified 20-fold. This permits us to be able to detect very faint sounds. Two tiny skeletal muscles, the **stapedius** (attached to the stapes) and the **tensor tympani** (attached to the malleus), are located within the middle ear. These muscles restrict ossicle movement when loud noises occur, and thus protect the sensitive receptors in the inner ear.

Inner Ear

The inner ear is located within the petrous part of the temporal bone, where there are spaces or cavities called the **bony labyrinth** (lab'i-rinth; an intricate, mazelike passageway) **(figure 16.26)**. Within the bony labyrinth are membrane-lined, fluid-filled tubes and spaces, called the **membranous labyrinth.** Receptors for both equilibrium and hearing are housed along with supporting cells within a sensory epithelium lining part of the membranous labyrinth.

The space between the outer walls of the bony labyrinth and the membranous labyrinth is filled with a fluid called **perilymph** (per'i-limf) that is similar in composition to interstitial fluid. In the inner ear, the perilymph suspends, supports, and protects the membranous labyrinth from the wall of the bony labyrinth. The membranous labyrinth contains a unique fluid called **endolymph** (en'dō-limf). Endolymph exhibits a low sodium and high potassium electrolyte concentration, similar to that of intracellular fluid.

The bony labyrinth is structurally and functionally partitioned into three distinct regions: the **cochlea** (kok'lē-ă = snail shell), the **vestibule** (ves'ti-būl; *vestibulum* = entrance court), and the **semicircular canals.** The cochlea houses a membranous labyrinth called the **cochlear duct,** to be described later. The vestibule and semicircular canals compose a general area called the **vestibular complex.** The vestibule of the vestibular complex contains two saclike, membranous labyrinth parts—the **utricle** (ū'tri-kl; *uter* = leather bag) and the **saccule** (sak'ūl; *saccus* = sack)—which are positioned at right angles to each other and interconnected through a narrow passageway. Within the semicircular canals of the vestibular complex, the membranous labyrinth collectively forms and is called the **semicircular ducts.**

Table 16.4 summarizes the structures of the inner ear and clarifies which ones are part of the bony labyrinth and which are part of the membranous labyrinth.

WHAT DID YOU LEARN?

21 What is the function of the external acoustic meatus?

22 Where are the auditory ossicles located, and what is their function?

23 What structures compose the bony labyrinth, and what structures form the membranous labyrinth?

Table 16.4	Inner Ear Structures		
Bony Labyrinth Structure	**Membranous Labyrinth Structure Housed in Bony Labyrinth**	**Structure(s) Housing Receptors**	**Function of Receptors**
Cochlea	Cochlear duct	Spiral organ	Hearing
Vestibule	Utricle, saccule	Maculae	Detect linear movements of the head and static equilibrium of head
Semicircular canals	Semicircular ducts	Ampullae	Detect rotational movements of the head

16.5b Physiology of Hearing

LEARNING OBJECTIVES

4. Explain the components of the cochlea and how they function in the sense of hearing.

5. Trace the path of a sound wave from outside the ear to stimulation of vestibulocochlear nerve (CN VIII).

6. Distinguish between frequency and intensity of sound.

Here we follow the progression of sound from the environment to the brain, where it is interpreted. First, we consider the structures in the inner ear that are related to sound detection.

Structures for Hearing

Hearing organs are housed within the cochlea in both inner ears. Within the cochlea is the spiral organ, where hair cells detect wave motion and transmit this as sound information.

Cochlea The **cochlea** is a snail-shaped spiral chamber within the bone of the inner ear. It has a spongy bone axis, called the **modiolus** (mō-dī′ō-lŭs; = hub of a wheel). Protected within the core of the cochlea, the membranous labyrinth houses the **spiral organ** (formerly called the *organ of Corti*), which is responsible for hearing **(figure 16.27)**.

The **cochlear duct,** or *scala* (skā′lă; = stairway) *media*, is the membranous labyrinth that extends through the cochlea. The roof and floor of the cochlear duct are formed by the vestibular and basilar membranes, respectively. These membranes partition the bony labyrinth of the cochlea into two smaller chambers, both filled with perilymph. The superior chamber is the **scala vestibuli** (*vestibular duct*), and the inferior chamber is the **scala tympani** (*tympanic duct*). The scala vestibuli and scala tympani merge through a small channel called the **helicotrema** (hel′i-kō-trē′mă; *helix* = spiral, *trema* = hole) at the apex of the cochlea (figure 16.26).

Spiral Organ Within the cochlear duct, the spiral organ is a thick sensory epithelium consisting of both hair cells and supporting cells that rests on the basilar membrane (figure 16.27). **Hair cells** are the sensory receptors of the inner ear for hearing. They continuously release neurotransmitter molecules to the sensory neurons that monitor their activity. The apical surface of each hair cell has a covering of numerous (more than 50) long, stiff microvilli that are called **stereocilia** (ster′ē-ō-sil′ē-ă; *stereos* = solid).

The hair cells extend stereocilia into an overlying gelatinous structure called the **tectorial** (tek-tōr′ē-ăl; *tectus* = to cover) **membrane.** Any movement of the basilar membrane causes distortion of the stereocilia, with subsequent change in neurotransmitter release resulting in stimulation of sensory neurons. The cell bodies of these sensory neurons are housed within the **spiral ganglia** in the modiolus medial to the cochlear duct. The distortion is caused by pressure waves in the fluid of the inner ear as a consequence of sound waves arriving at the tympanic membrane that are transmitted via ossicles to the oval window to initiate pressure waves in the perilymph. The pressure waves cause the basilar membrane to flutter or "bounce," resulting in the distortion of the stereocilia.

INTEGRATE

CLINICAL VIEW
Cochlear Implants

A **cochlear implant** is an electronic device that assists some hearing-impaired people. It is not a hearing aid and does not restore normal hearing; rather, it compensates for damaged or nonfunctioning parts of the inner ear. The components of a cochlear implant include (1) an external microphone to detect sound (typically worn behind one ear), (2) a speech processor to arrange the sounds from the microphone, and (3) a transmitter connected to a receiver/stimulator (placed within the cochlea) to convert the processed sound into electrical impulses.

A cochlear implant parallels normal hearing by selecting sounds, processing them into electrical signals, and then sending sound information to the brain for interpretation. However, this type of "hearing" is considerably different from normal hearing. Patients with implants report that voices sound squeaky and high-pitched, but this limitation does not prevent people with implants from having oral communication capabilities.

Although tens of thousands of people have received cochlear implants, some controversy accompanies their increasing use. First, any surgical installation procedure is always accompanied by a small risk for infection or complication. Second, cochlear implants do not always improve hearing quality. Cochlear implant opponents also have expressed concern that the implant represents a threat to the unique, sign-based culture of deaf people. Others question the use of implants in children, who may not have made the decision for themselves.

① Antenna, transmitter, and receiver are inserted in skin posterior and superior to the auricle. The transmitter lead is inserted into the inner ear.

Transmitter lead — Spiral organ

— Transmitter
— Receiver
— Antenna

Cochlea cutaway

Transmitter lead

② Sound waves are detected by the receiver and turned into electrical impulses, which travel through the transmitter.

③ Electrical impulses from the transmitter stimulate the cochlear nerve, which then transmits nerve signals to the brain.

Cochlear implant.

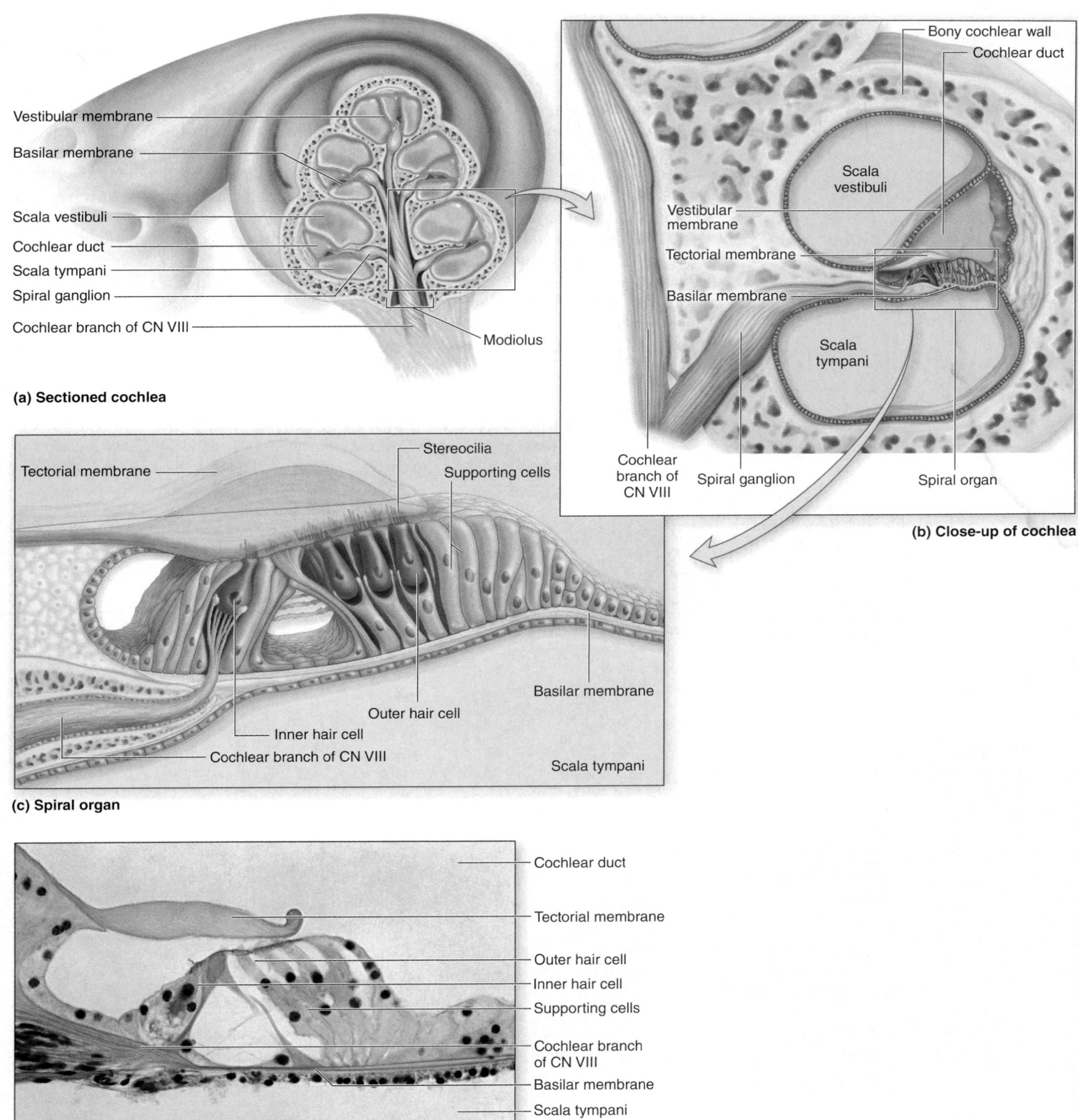

(a) Sectioned cochlea

Vestibular membrane
Basilar membrane
Scala vestibuli
Cochlear duct
Scala tympani
Spiral ganglion
Cochlear branch of CN VIII
Modiolus

(b) Close-up of cochlea

Bony cochlear wall
Cochlear duct
Scala vestibuli
Vestibular membrane
Tectorial membrane
Basilar membrane
Scala tympani
Cochlear branch of CN VIII
Spiral ganglion
Spiral organ

(c) Spiral organ

Tectorial membrane
Stereocilia
Supporting cells
Outer hair cell
Inner hair cell
Cochlear branch of CN VIII
Basilar membrane
Scala tympani

(d) Spiral organ

Cochlear duct
Tectorial membrane
Outer hair cell
Inner hair cell
Supporting cells
Cochlear branch of CN VIII
Basilar membrane
Scala tympani

LM 75x

Figure 16.27 Structure of the Cochlea and Spiral Organ. The cochlea exhibits a snail-like spiral shape and is composed of three fluid-filled ducts. (*a*) A section through the cochlea details the relationship among the three ducts: the cochlear duct, scala tympani, and scala vestibuli. (*b*) A magnified view of the cochlea. (*c*) Hair cells rest on the basilar membrane of the spiral organ in the scala media. (*d*) Light micrograph of the spiral organ. **AP|R**

The Pathway from Sound Wave to Nerve Signal

Recall that the cochlea is a curled structure. In the next few sets of figures, we have straightened out the cochlea so you may be better able to visualize the sound wave pathway through the inner ear (**figure 16.28**).

Sound waves are collected and funneled by the auricle of the external ear. From there, sound waves enter the external acoustic meatus and make the tympanic membrane vibrate. The vibration of the tympanic membrane causes movement of the auditory ossicles. Sound waves are amplified, allowing even faint sounds to cause vibration. The foot of the stapes moves like a piston on the oval window, thereby transmitting the effect of sound waves into pressure waves within the inner ear.

These pressure waves originate within the inner ear at the oval window and travel through the perilymph in the scala vestibuli. Pressure waves in the scala vestibuli cause deformation of the cochlear duct. Pressure waves in the cochlear duct displace specific regions of the basilar membrane, relating to frequency (described shortly). Hair cells in the spiral organ of this region are distorted, initiating nerve signals in the cochlear branch of CN VIII. Simultaneously, the pressure wave vibrations in the scala media are transmitted to

Figure 16.28 Sound Wave Pathways Through the Ear. Sound waves enter the external ear, are conducted through the ossicles of the middle ear, and then are detected by a specific region of the spiral organ in the inner ear. **AP|R**

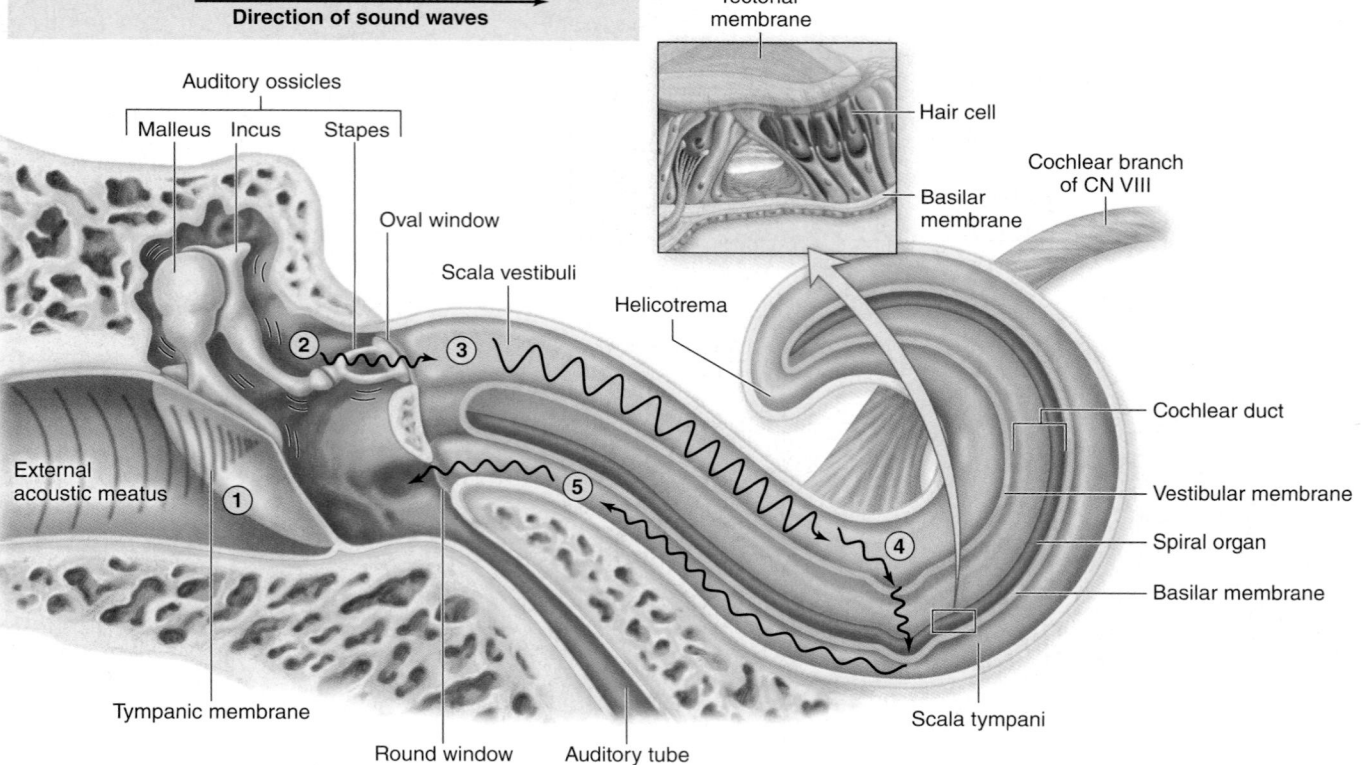

① Sound waves enter ear and cause the tympanic membrane to vibrate.

② Tympanic membrane vibration moves auditory ossicles; sound waves are amplified.

③ The stapes at the oval window generates pressure waves in the perilymph within the scala vestibuli.

④ Pressure waves cause the vestibular membrane to move, resulting in pressure wave formation in the endolymph within the cochlear duct and displacement of a specific region of the basilar membrane. Hair cells in the spiral organ are distorted, initiating a nerve signal in the cochlear branch of CN VIII.

⑤ Remaining pressure waves are transferred to the scala tympani and exit the inner ear via the round window.

the perilymph of the scala tympani, and are absorbed at the round window, as the window bulges slightly.

The sound waves that give rise to pressure waves in the inner ear are characterized by their frequency and intensity. **Frequency** is the number of waves that move past a point during a specific amount of time. Frequency is measured in *hertz* (*Hz*), and is classified as high, medium, or low **(figure 16.29)**. Frequency is interpreted as the pitch of a sound. The region of the spiral organ stimulated by pressure waves in the perilymph varies according to the frequency of the sound: High-frequency sounds stimulate it near the oval window, while low-frequency sounds stimulate the spiral organ far away from the oval window. **Intensity** refers to a sound's loudness and is measured in units called *decibels* (*dB*). An inaudible sound has no decibels. Louder sounds increase the rate of nerve signals relayed to the brain.

WHAT DID YOU LEARN?

24 What are the steps for detecting sounds?

25 How does frequency of sound differ from intensity of sound?

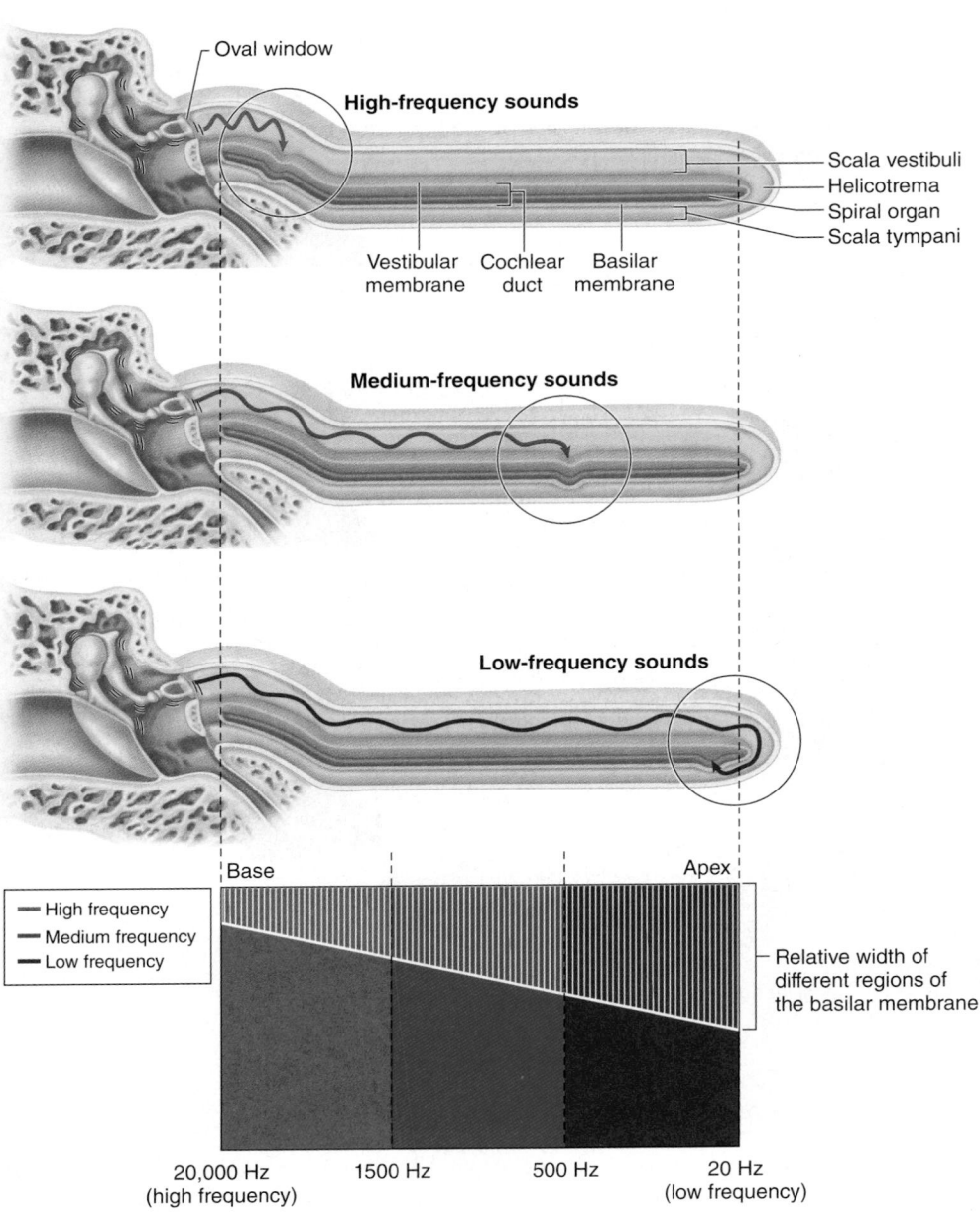

Figure 16.29 Sound Wave Interpretation at the Basilar Membrane. Sound waves are interpreted at specific sites along the basilar membrane within a cochlea that has been straightened from its normal spiral shape. High-frequency sounds (red arrow) generate pressure waves that cause the basilar membrane to displace close to the base of the cochlea. Medium-frequency sounds (green arrow) generate pressure waves that cause the basilar membrane to displace near the center of the cochlea. Low-frequency sounds (blue arrow) generate pressure waves that cause the basilar membrane to displace near the helicotrema.

16.5c Auditory Pathways

✓ LEARNING OBJECTIVE

7. Describe the auditory pathway from stimulation of CN VIII to the brain.

We discussed how sound waves travel through the inner ear in the previous section. But what is the nerve pathway that the initated nerve signals travel to in the brain? This auditory pathway is shown in **figure 16.30** and described here:

1. When the basilar membrane moves, the stereocilia on the spiral organ hair cells distort because they are anchored by the tectorial membrane. This initiates nerve signals that are transmitted through the cochlear nerve branches that attach to the hair cells. The sensory axons of the cochlear nerve (the primary neurons in this sensory pathway) terminate in the **cochlear nucleus** within the brainstem. These sensory neurons synapse with secondary neurons housed within this nucleus.

2. After integration and processing of the incoming information within the cochlear nucleus, axons from secondary neurons in this nucleus take one of two pathways: (a) the axons of some secondary axons project directly to the inferior colliculus of the midbrain, while (b) other secondary axons first project to the superior olivary nucleus within the pons (see section 13.5b) and synapse with other sensory neurons that then project to the inferior colliculi. Nerve signals arriving at the **superior olivary nuclei** function to both localize the sound and are involved in the reflex to loud sounds that transmits nerve signals to the tensor tympani and stapedius to contract and decrease the vibration of the ossicles. Nerve signals arriving at the **inferior colliculi** of the midbrain (see section 13.5a) are also involved in a reflex to loud sounds; here nerve signals are relayed to skeletal muscles of the body that cause us to jump and turn our head in response to loud sounds.

(1) Movement of basilar membrane produces nerve signals that are propogated along cochlear nerve axons. Cochlear nerve axons terminate in the cochlear nucleus in the medulla oblongata. Two sensory pathways extend from the nucleus.

(2a) Axons from secondary neurons in the cochlear nucleus project directly to the inferior colliculus.

(2b) Axons from some secondary neurons in the cochlear nucleus project to the superior olivary nucleus first, before synapsing with other neurons that project to the inferior colliculus.

(3) Axons from neurons in the inferior colliculus project to the medial geniculate nucleus of the thalamus.

(4) Axons from thalamic neurons project to the primary auditory cortex, where the nerve signals are perceived as sound.

Thalamus

Primary auditory cortex

Medial geniculate nucleus

Cochlear branch of CN VIII

Primary auditory cortex

Inferior colliculus

Superior olivary nucleus

Cochlear nucleus

Figure 16.30 Central Nervous System Pathways for Hearing. Nerve signals are propogated along the cochlear branch of CN VIII to the superior olivary nucleus and inferior colliculus of the brainstem, and then stimuli are sent to the thalamus before the information is finally transmitted to the primary auditory cortex.

3. Nerve signals are transmitted from an inferior colliculus to the **medial geniculate nucleus** of the thalamus (see section 13.4b) for initial processing and filtering of auditory sensory information.
4. Axons from the tertiary neurons in the thalamus extend to the primary auditory cortex within the temporal lobe, where nerve signals are perceived as sounds.

To integrate what you've learned about how sounds are processed and interpreted by the brain, refer to **figure 16.31** to review the anatomy and physiology of hearing.

WHAT DID YOU LEARN?

26 What are the major brain structures involved in the auditory pathway, and what is the function of each?

16.5d Mechanisms of Equilibrium and Head Movement

LEARNING OBJECTIVES

8. Describe the structures of the inner ear involved in equilibrium.
9. Explain how the utricle and saccule detect static equilibrium and linear movements of the head, and how the semicircular ducts function to detect rotational movements of the head.
10. Summarize the nerve pathways involved in equilibrium.

The term **equilibrium** refers to our awareness and monitoring of head position. Sensory receptors in the utricle, saccule, and semicircular ducts help monitor and adjust our equilibrium. Our brain receives this sensory information and, along with visual sensory input and input from our proprioceptors, integrates this information so we may keep our balance and make positional adjustments as necessary.

The utricle and saccule detect head position during **static equilibrium**—that is, when the body is stationary. So for example, when you are standing in the anatomic position, it is the utricle and saccule that inform your brain that your head is also upright. The utricle and saccule also detect **linear acceleration** changes of the head. This occurs when you tilt your head downward to look at your shoes.

The semicircular ducts, in contrast, are responsible for detecting **angular acceleration,** or rotational movements of the head. When a figure skater does a lengthy spin on the ice, it is the sensory receptors in her semicircular ducts that are informing her brain about the position of her moving head.

Saccule, Utricle, and Linear Acceleration of the Head
The sensory epithelium in the utricle and saccule forms a covering on a small, raised oval area called the **macula** located along the internal wall of both sacs. Each macula is

Figure 16.31 **How We Hear.** Sound waves enter the external ear and then (*a*) are transmitted to the middle ear. (*b*) Sound is amplified and transmitted to the inner ear, where (*c*) sound is converted to nerve signals that (*d*) are transmitted to the brain.

Primary auditory cortex

(a) Transmitting Sound Waves from External to Middle Ear

① Sound waves are directed to the external ear.

② Sound waves travel through the external acoustic meatus and vibrate the tympanic membrane.

External ear | Middle ear | Inner ear

Sound waves

Cochlea

Tympanic membrane

External acoustic meatus

Auditory tube

(d) Auditory Pathway

⑧ Nerve signals travel from the cochlear branch of CN VIII to the brainstem and then through the medial geniculate nucleus of the thalamus, and ultimately go to the primary auditory cortex, where they are perceived as sounds.

Thalamus

Medial geniculate nucleus

Cochlear branch of CN VIII

Primary auditory cortex

Inferior colliculus

Superior olivary nucleus

Cochlear nucleus

(b) Amplification and Transmission of Sound from Middle to Inner Ear

3 The tympanic membrane vibration causes the auditory ossicles to vibrate, and they amplify the sound.

Auditory ossicles
- Malleus
- Incus
- Stapes

Tympanic membrane
Tympanic cavity

4 The stapes moves the oval window, generating pressure waves in the perilymph of the inner ear.

Oval window
Scala vestibuli
Cochlear branch of CN VIII
Cochlear duct
Vestibular membrane
Basilar membrane
Round window
Scala tympani
Auditory tube

(c) Conversion of Sound to Nerve Signals

Cochlear duct
Scala vestibuli
Vestibular membrane
Tectorial membrane
Basilar membrane
Scala tympani

5 Pressure waves travel through perilymph in the scala vestibuli, cause vibration of the vestibular membrane and movement of endolymph within the cochlear duct.

Tectorial membrane   Stereocilia

Cochlear branch of CN VIII
Basilar membrane
Nerve signal
Hair cell

6 The pressure waves displace one part of the basilar membrane, depending upon the frequency of the sounds.

Cochlear duct
High-frequency sounds
Basilar membrane

Medium-frequency sounds

Low-frequency sounds

7 The displacement of the basilar membrane causes the stereocilia on the hair cells to bend, and nerve signals are propogated along the cochlear branch of CN VIII.

composed of a mixed layer of hair cells and supporting cells (**figure 16.32**). These hair cells not only have stereocilia, but each hair cell also has one long cilium, called a **kinocilium** (kī-nō-sil′-ē-ŭm; *kino* = movement) on its apical surface. Both the stereocilia and kinocilia may be physically bent or displaced, resulting in changes in the amount and rate of neurotransmitter release from the hair cell. Stereocilia and kinocilia projecting from the hair cells embed within a gelatinous mass that completely covers the apical surface of the epithelium. This gelatinous layer is covered by a mass of small calcium carbonate crystals called **otoliths** (ō′tō-lith; *oto* = ear; *lithos* = stone), or *statoconia*. Together, the gelatinous layer and the crystals form the **otolithic membrane** (or *statoconic membrane*). The otoliths push on the underlying gelatin, thereby increasing the weight of the otolithic membrane covering the hair cells.

The position of the head influences the position of the otolithic membrane (**figure 16.33**). When the head is held erect, the otolithic membrane applies pressure directly onto the hair cells, and minimal stimulation of the hair cells occurs. However, tilting the head causes the otolithic membrane to shift its position on the macula surface, thus distorting the stereocilia. Bending of the stereocilia results in a change in the amount of neurotransmitter released from the hair cells and a simultaneous change in the stimulation of the sensory neurons of the vestibular branch of CN VIII.

Bending of the stereocilia toward the kinocilium causes the hair cells to depolarize and increase their rate of neurotransmitter release (figure 16.33*b*). A greater frequency of nerve signals is generated in the vestibular branch of CN VIII as a result. In contrast, bending of the stereocilia away from the kinocilium causes the hair cells to hyperpolarize and thus decrease their rate of neurotransmitter release. Ultimately, fewer and less frequent nerve signals are generated in the axons of the vestibular branch as time elapses. The brain interprets the change in nerve signals to determine the direction the head has tilted.

Semicircular Ducts and Rotational Movements of the Head

Within each semicircular canal is a semicircular duct connected to the utricle. Contained within each semicircular duct is an expanded region, called the **ampulla** (am-pul′lă;

Figure 16.32 Macula Structure. Maculae detect both the orientation of the head when the body is stationary and linear acceleration of the head. (*a*) The maculae are located within the walls of the saccule and utricle. (*b*) An enlarged view of a macula shows the apical surface of the hair cells covered by a gelatinous layer overlaid with otoliths, called the otolithic membrane. (*c*) An individual hair cell has numerous microvilli called stereocilia and a single, long kinocilium.

Head upright

Otoliths
Gelatin layer — Otolithic membrane

Kinocilium

Stereocilia

Otolithic membrane

Stereocilia parallel to kinocilium

- Neurotransmitter released at regular interval
- Steady rate of nerve signals are transmitted along vestibular branch of CN VIII

Hair cell

Standard nerve signal frequency

Vestibular branch of CN VIII

Supporting cell

(a) Macula in upright head position

Head tilted upward

Stereocilla bent toward kinocilium

- Hair cells depolarize, increasing neurotransmitter release
- Increased nerve signal frequency along vestibular branch of CN VIII

Excitation

Stereocilia of hair cells bend.

Otolithic membrane moves.

Gravitational force

Head tilted downward

Stereocilla bent away from kinocilium

- Hair cells hyperpolarize, inhibiting neurotransmitter release
- Decreased nerve signal frequency along vestibular branch of CN VIII

Inhibition

(b) Macula in altered head position

Figure 16.33 How the Maculae Detect Linear Acceleration of the Head. (*a*) When the head is in an upright position, hair cells and stereocilia are in parallel and supported by the otolithic membrane. (*b*) Tilting the head causes the otolithic membrane to move slightly, causing the stereocilia to bend and alter the frequency of propagated nerve signals, which reports the change in head position. When the stereocilia are bent toward the kinocilium, the hair cell depolarizes and thus increases frequency of nerve signal propagation. Conversely, when stereocilia are bent away from the kinocilium, the hair cell hyperpolarizes and thus decreases frequency of nerve signal propagation.

pl., *ampullae*, am-pul′lē; bottle shaped), located at the end farthest from the utricle connection **(figure 16.34)**. The ampulla contains an elevated region, called the **crista ampullaris** (or *ampullary crest*), which is covered by an epithelium of hair cells and supporting cells. These hair cells embed both their kinocilia and stereocilia into an overlying gelatinous dome called the **cupula** (kū′pū-lă). This accessory structure extends completely across the semicircular duct to the roof over the ampulla.

Receptors in the semicircular ducts detect rotational movements of the head **(figure 16.35)**. When the head first rotates, inertia causes endolymph to lag behind. This endolymph pushes against the cupula, causing bending of the stereocilia. Stereocilia bending results in altered neurotransmitter release from the hair cells and simultaneous stimulation of the sensory neurons. As previously described, bending of the stereocilia in the direction of the kinocilium results in depolarization of the hair cells and increased frequency of nerve signals, whereas bending in the opposite direction results in hyperpolarization of the hair cells and decreased frequency of nerve signals (see figure 16.33*b*). Interestingly, the ampullae respond primarily to changes in velocity—meaning they respond to rotational acceleration or deceleration. If the head is rotating at a constant speed, eventually the movement of the endolymph catches up with the ampulla, and so the stereocilia on the hair cells are no longer bent, and the hair cells no longer are stimulated.

You may have done the following as a small child: You stood upright, closed your eyes, and then you spun in a clockwise direction for about 1 minute. Initially, you felt your head spinning, but after about 30 seconds that spinning sensation may have disappeared. The reason is that the endolymph movement caught up with the ampulla's rotational movement. When you stopped spinning, your head may still have felt like it was moving even though you were standing still. When you came to a stop (and decelerated), the endolymph's momentum resulted in endolymph movement after the body stopped.

Vestibular Sensation Pathways

The vestibular branch of CN VIII receives all equilibrium stimuli from the inner ear **(figure 16.36)**. Sensory neurons housed within the vestibular ganglia monitor changes in the activities of the hair cells within the vestibule and the semicircular canals. Vestibular nerve axons either project first to paired **vestibular nuclei** within the superior region of the medulla oblongata, or project directly to the cerebellum. Both the vestibular nuclei and the cerebellum integrate the stimuli related to balance and equilibrium, and transmit nerve signals through the descending vestibulospinal tracts to skeletal muscle to maintain muscle tone and balance.

Additionally, the vestibular nuclei sends nerve signals to selected cranial nerve nuclei to control reflexive motor activities associated with head and eye movements. Specifically, axons project to the nuclei for CN III, IV, and VI (the nerves responsible for controlling the reflexive eye muscle movements by the extrinsic muscles). The nerve signals generated from the changing equilibrium are also sent from the vestibular nuclei and cerebellum to the thalamus and even-

tually the cerebral cortex for further processing and for our awareness of body position.

WHAT DID YOU LEARN?

27 How does the otolithic membrane participate in detecting head movement?

28 What type of movement does the macula detect, and how does it detect this movement?

29 What type of movement do the ampullae detect, and how do they detect this movement?

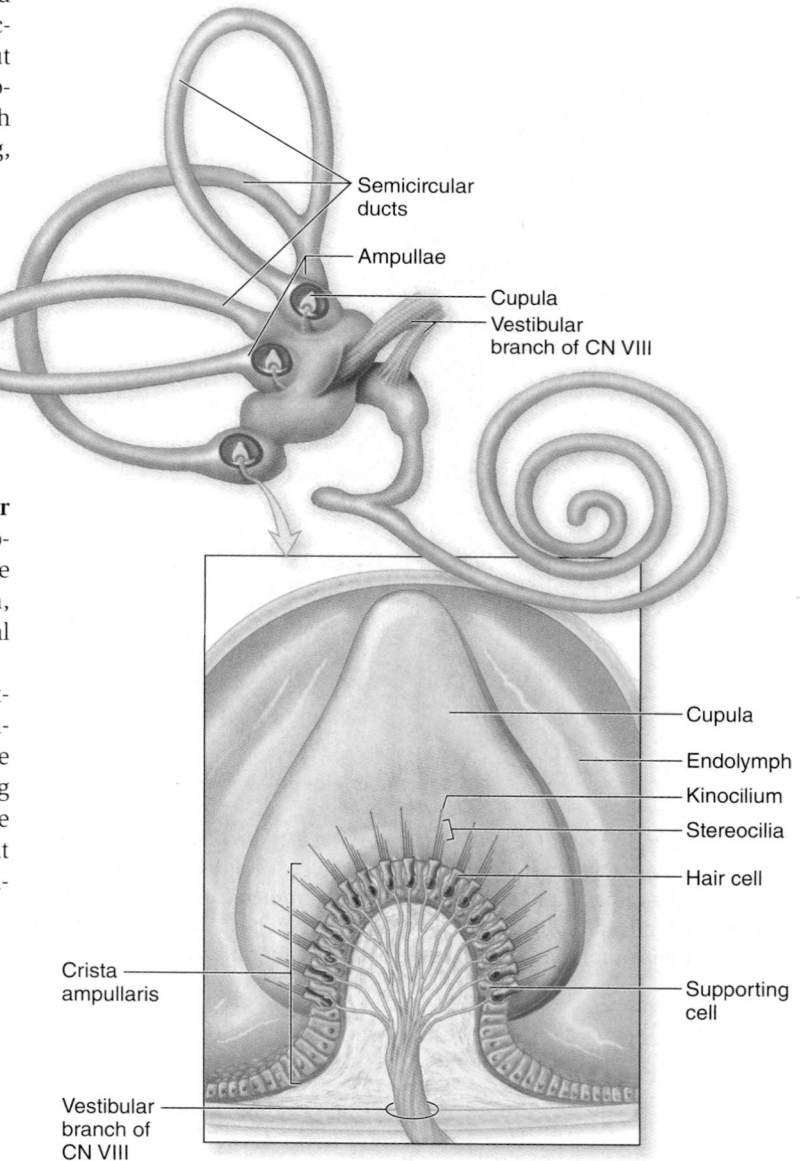

Figure 16.34 Ampulla. A diagrammatic section through an ampulla in a semicircular duct details the relationships among the hair cells and supporting cells, the cupula, and the endolymph in detecting rotational movement of the head.

Figure 16.35 Function of the Crista Ampullaris. Rotation of the head causes endolymph within the semicircular duct to push against the cupula covering the hair cells, resulting in bending of their stereocilia and an alteration in the frequency of nerve signal propagation.

Head still

Ampulla

Section of ampulla filled with endolymph

Axons of vestibular branch of CN VIII

Head rotating

Ampulla

Cupula being moved by the inertia of the endolymph

Bending stereocilia

Nerve signals sent to brain

- Nuclei for eye movement CN III, IV, and VI (compensatory eye movements)
- Motor coordinator
- Awareness of body position
- Thalamus
- Vestibular nucleus

Cerebral cortex

3c
3b CN IV
CN III
CN VI
CN VIII
2
1

Vestibular branch of CN VIII

Vestibular nucleus

Vestibulospinal tracts

Vestibular complex

Cerebellum

3a

① Equilibrium stimuli are transmitted as nerve signals along the vestibular branch of CN VIII.

② Vestibular branch axons project to the vestibular nuclei and the cerebellum.

③a Equilibrium information is projected through the vestibulospinal tracts to maintain muscle tone and balance.

③b Vestibular nuclei also transmit nerve signals to several cranial nerve nuclei to control reflexive eye and head movements.

③c Nerve signals are also transmitted to the thalamus and then the cerebral cortex for further processing and for conscious awareness of body position.

Vestibular receptors

Cerebellum ⟷ Vestibular nuclei in medulla oblongata

Conscious awareness of equilibrium (thalamus and cerebral cortex)

Muscle tone and balance (vestibulospinal tracts)

Oculomotor control (CN III, IV, VI)

Figure 16.36 Vestibular Pathways. Information from the vestibular complex is sent to multiple parts of the brain, so posture and body movement may be adjusted accordingly.

- Receptors range in complexity from a single neuron to multicellular organs.
- The feature common to all receptors is the ability to respond to a stimulus and initiate sensory nerve signals to the central nervous system.

16.1 Introduction to Sensory Receptors 602

16.1a Stimuli and Sensations   602
- A stimulus is a change in the internal or external environment that is detected by a receptor and causes a response.
- A sensation is a stimulus that is consciously perceived by the cerebral cortex. Most stimuli are not consciously perceived.

16.1b Properties of Sensory Receptors   602
- Sensory receptors act as transducers, detecting specific stimuli via modality gated channels and ultimately causing a nerve signal to be propagated along a sensory neuron.
- A receptive field encompasses the area of distribution of the receptor's sensitive ends. A smaller receptive field allows a more precise identification of stimulus location.
- Sensory impulses may be from either tonic (continuously stimulated) or phasic (on-and-off stimulation) receptors.

16.1c Receptor Classification   604
- Receptors are defined and characterized by receptor distribution (general senses and special senses); stimulus origin (exteroceptors, interoceptors, and proprioceptors); and modality of stimulus (chemoreceptors, thermoreceptors, photoreceptors, mechanoreceptors, baroreceptors, and nociceptors).

16.2 The General Senses 606
- General sense receptors are located throughout the body and are typically simple in structure.

16.2a Tactile Receptors   606
- Tactile receptors are the most numerous type of sensory receptors.
- Unencapsulated receptors include free nerve endings, such as pain receptors and temperature receptors; root hair plexuses, which detect movement of hairs; and tactile discs that detect fine texture and shape.
- Encapsulated receptors include end bulbs, which detect light pressure stimuli; lamellated corpuscles and bulbous corpuscles, which detect deep pressure; and tactile corpuscles for fine touch and texture.

16.2b Referred Pain   607
- Referred pain is pain that is perceived as if it originates in a dermatome but actually is caused by sensory nerve signals from an internal organ.

16.3 Olfaction and Gustation 609
- Both olfactory and gustatory receptors are chemoreceptors.

16.3a Olfaction: The Sense of Smell   609
- Olfaction is the chemical sense of smell. Paired olfactory organs are composed of a lining olfactory epithelium (olfactory receptor cells, supporting cells, and basal cells), a lamina propria, and olfactory glands.
- Olfactory receptor cells are bipolar neurons with olfactory hairs.
- Olfactory tracts project directly to the olfactory cortex without first synapsing in the thalamus.

16.3b Gustation: The Sense of Taste   610
- Gustatory cells are housed in taste buds that also have supporting cells and basal cells.
- The five basic taste sensations are sweet, salt, sour, bitter, and umami.
- CN VII (facial) and CN IX (glossopharyngeal) are involved in conducting taste information through gustatory pathways.

16.4 Visual Receptors 613
- The eyes house photoreceptors that detect light, color, and movement.

16.4a Accessory Structures of the Eye   613
- Accessory structures include eyebrows, eyelashes, eyelids, conjunctiva, and lacrimal glands.
- The conjunctiva is a membrane that lines the sclera of the eye (the ocular conjunctiva) and the internal surface of the eyelid (the palpebral conjunctiva).
- Each lacrimal apparatus includes a lacrimal gland that distributes lacrimal fluid to cleanse the eye surface and moisten the conjunctiva. Lacrimal fluid is collected into the lacrimal puncta, which drain into the nasolacrimal duct and then the nasal cavity.

_____ 1. Unencapsulated, terminal branches of dendrites are called
  a. lamellated corpuscles.
  b. free nerve endings.
  c. bulbous corpuscles.
  d. end bulbs.

_____ 2. Which receptor is *not* matched with its correct function?
  a. chemoreceptor; detects specific molecules dissolved in fluid
  b. nociceptor; detects tissue damage or pain
  c. proprioceptor; detects change in muscle tension
  d. thermoreceptor; detects change in pressure

_____ 3. Which of the following is accurate about the macula of the vestibular complex?
  a. They detect rotational movements of the head.
  b. They are located in the semicircular canal.
  c. Nerve signals are generated when the otolithic membrane bends the stereocilia of the hair cells.
  d. They are the organs of hearing.

_____ 4. When viewing a close-up object, all of the following processes occur *except*
  a. the eyes accommodate to focus on the close-up object.
  b. the ciliary body contracts, so the suspensory ligaments become less taut.
  c. the lens becomes more rounded to better refract light rays.
  d. the pupils dilate to let in more light for the retina.

_____ 5. All of the following are accurate about the conjunctiva *except*
  a. it contains blood vessels that nourish the sclera.
  b. it covers the cornea.
  c. it secretes mucus as a lubricant.
  d. if the conjunctiva becomes inflamed, the eye appears reddish and mucus secretion is thick.

_____ 6. The arrangement of tunics in the eye, from the innermost to outermost aspect of the eye, is
  a. retina, vascular, fibrous.
  b. vascular, retina, fibrous.
  c. vascular, fibrous, retina.
  d. retina, fibrous, vascular.

_____ 7. Which ear structure is correctly matched with its function?
  a. round window; transmits sound waves into the inner ear
  b. external acoustic meatus; directs sound waves to the tympanic membrane

  c. auditory ossicles; dampen sound waves before they reach the inner ear
  d. vestibular membrane; bends the stereocilia on hair cells to produce a nerve signal

_____ 8. The only sensations to reach the cerebral cortex without first processing through the synapses in the thalamus are
  a. olfaction.
  b. vision.
  c. proprioception.
  d. touch.

_____ 9. Lacrimal fluid (tears) performs all of the following functions *except*
  a. cleansing the eye surface.
  b. preventing bacterial infection.
  c. humidifying the orbit.
  d. moistening the eye surface.

_____ 10. Which statement is accurate about the cochlear duct?
  a. It detects linear acceleration of the head when the otolithic membrane bends the hair cells.
  b. It is filled with perilymph.
  c. It contains hair cells that convert sound waves into nerve signals.
  d. It contains a spiral organ that rests on a vestibular membrane.

11. What are the six classifications of receptors according to modality of stimulus? Give an anatomic example of each.

12. How are visceral nociceptors different from somatic nociceptors, and how do they relate to the phenomenon known as "referred pain"?

13. What are the pathways by which taste sensations reach the brain?

14. Describe the pathway by which olfactory stimuli travel from the nasal cavity to the brain.

15. What structures in the wall of the eye help control the amount of light entering the eye?

16. How is the lens able to focus images from a book that you are reading, and then immediately also focus the image of children playing in your backyard?

17. Discuss the formation, circulation, and reabsorption of aqueous humor in the eye.

18. Briefly describe the structural relationship between the membranous labyrinth and the bony labyrinth.

19. Describe the pathway by which sound waves enter and exit the ear, and how that sound is converted into a nerve signal.

20. Explain how the vestibule and semicircular canals detect equilibrium.

Can You Apply What You've Learned?

1. You are babysitting a 5-year-old child who does not want to eat his broccoli. He states that the broccoli tastes yucky. You tell him to hold his nose closed while he eats a piece of broccoli and see how it tastes. He says it doesn't taste as yucky when he holds his nose (although he still doesn't want to eat the broccoli). Why did the broccoli taste "less yucky" when the child held his nose?
   a. Cranial nerve IX was pinched when the child held his nose, so tastes could not be perceived as clearly.
   b. The activity of holding his nose took the child's mind off of eating the broccoli.
   c. Olfaction is responsible for a large component of taste, so by not smelling the broccoli, its taste is diminished.
   d. Holding the nose closed facilitated odiferous molecules to enter the mouth, thereby increasing the number of molecules that could be tasted by the taste buds.

2. Horner syndrome is a condition where sympathetic innervation to one side of the head and neck is damaged. What visual disturbances would you expect a person to have if she had Horner syndrome?
   a. inability to accommodate the eyes for near vision
   b. constricted pupil
   c. lens is permanently flattened
   d. abduction of the individual's affected eye

3. You may be familiar with "mosquito tones" for your cell phones—these are ringtones that are of a relatively high pitch that most children and teenagers can hear, but most adults cannot. Why do you think adults cannot hear these tones as well?
   a. Hair cells close to the oval window of the inner ear probably have become damaged as we age.
   b. The tympanic membrane loses its flexibility as we age, so it is not as able to transmit sound waves to the middle ear.
   c. Adults likely have damaged the spiral organ near the helicotrema, resulting in their inability to hear the tones.
   d. As we age, there is a gradual accumulation of cerumen that blocks the external auditory meatus and makes hearing sounds more difficult.

4. Individuals with macular degeneration may experience loss of vision in their central vision area, but their peripheral vision either is not affected or not as greatly affected. Why is this the case?
   a. Macular degeneration damages the optic disc, making central vision impaired but leaving peripheral vision intact.
   b. Only a single optic tract typically is damaged, so using your peripheral vision allows you to use the normal optic tract.
   c. Only rods are damaged in macular degeneration, so peripheral vision (where there are fewer rods) is not as affected.
   d. The central vision loss is due to damage to the fovea centralis; the peripheral retina is not greatly affected.

5. An elderly gentleman is brought in to the emergency room. He is complaining of pain radiating down his left arm and has shortness of breath. The ER physician suspects the gentleman is suffering a heart attack. Why would the man be experiencing pain down his left arm if the problem is with his heart?
   a. Chemoreceptors in the blood vessels of the left arm detected a change in oxygen levels in the blood and initiated the pain sensations.
   b. The cerebral cortex mistakenly located the source of the stimulus as being from a dermatome in the arm instead of the heart.
   c. The patient was experiencing phantom pain in the upper limb.
   d. A heart attack stimulates baroceptors in the blood vessels of the upper limb.

Can You Synthesize What You've Learned?

1. Savannah is an active 3-year-old who began to cough and sniffle. Then she experienced an earache and a marked decrease in hearing acuity. During a physical examination, her pediatrician noted the following signs: elevated temperature, a reddened tympanic membrane with a slight bulge, and some inflammation in the pharynx. What might the pediatrician call this condition, and how would it be treated? How does Savannah's age relate to her illness?

2. After Alejandro quit smoking, he discovered that foods seemed much more flavorful than when he had smoked. How are smoking and taste perceptions linked?

3. George is unclear why nearsighted persons may need bifocal eyeglasses (which have two lenses—one for reading and one for nearsightedness) when they get older. He does not understand why the same set of glasses wouldn't work for both reading and for the nearsighted correction. Can you explain to George the difference between the two conditions, and why the treatment for both may appear to be similar?

chapter 17

Endocrine System

Some days are just more hectic than others. We don't have time for breakfast and then have classes that meet over the lunch hour, allowing us only enough time to grab something from the snack machine before heading off to work in the afternoon. Finally, upon returning home for the evening, we are so hungry we eat rapidly and have a second helping. Fortunately, our endocrine system has come to our rescue, maintaining blood glucose levels within normal homeostatic limits during this period of erratic food intake. Through the release of ➡

An endocrinologist is a physician that specializes in the treating of endocrine disorders. The thyroid gland is the most commonly treated endocrine gland. This gland is located on the anterior side of the neck. It produces and releases thyroid hormone to regulate and control metabolism. Palpation of a physical anomaly of the thyroid gland is often the first indication of a thyroid gland disorder (e.g., goiter or Grave's disease).

apsrevealed.com

Module 8: Endocrine System

hormones, the endocrine system provides the means to regulate and control many diverse metabolic processes of the body, including regulating blood sugar.

This chapter has two primary purposes. The first is to provide an introduction and general discussion of the endocrine system's central concepts, including endocrine glands, hormone structure, hormone transport in the blood, and how hormones interact with body cells. The second is a unique component that presents the detailed processes by which selected representative hormones maintain body homeostasis. Examples include three hormones that are regulated by the hypothalamus and pituitary gland and two hormones released from the pancreas. Details of the action of most other hormones—which require an understanding of specific anatomic structures covered in other chapters—are described in those chapters; for example, sex hormones are discussed in the chapter on reproduction (see chapter 28). Because this chapter is the central reference location for the endocrine system, we have included an overview table (see table 17.2) of the body's major hormones, providing the hormone's general function and identifying the specific chapter for its detailed discussion. Please note that each major hormone described in this text can be quickly accessed in the summary tables provided in the appendix.

17.1 Introduction to the Endocrine System

The **endocrine** (en′dō-krin) **system** is composed of endocrine glands located throughout the body that synthesize and secrete molecules called **hormones** (hōr′mōn; *hormao* = to rouse). Endocrine glands lack ducts and hormones are released into the blood and transported throughout the body (see section 5.1d where endocrine and exocrine glands are first discussed). Cells with specific receptors for a hormone are called **target cells**. They bind the hormone, which initiates or inhibits selective metabolic activities within these cells. Thus, the endocrine system serves as one of the two major control systems in the body; the other is the nervous system, which was described in the preceding chapters.

There are four central concepts of the endocrine system discussed in the next several sections, including (1) the endocrine glands that are the structures that release hormones; (2) hormones, which are the molecules released from endocrine glands; (3) hormone transport, which is the movement of a hormone within the blood to target cells following its release from an endocrine gland; and (4) target cells that have receptors for a specific hormone.

We first provide a general comparison of the endocrine system with the nervous system and describe the general functions of the endocrine system.

17.1a Comparison of the Two Control Systems

✓ LEARNING OBJECTIVE

1. Compare and contrast the actions of the endocrine system and the nervous system to control body function.

The endocrine system and nervous system work together to control and regulate the human body. The endocrine system has several features in common with the nervous system. In response to stimuli, both systems release chemical substances (hormones or neurotransmitters) called **ligands** to communicate with particular target cells. A ligand binds to a cellular receptor in target cells to initiate a cellular change. However, the methods and effects of the two systems differ.

The nervous system exercises control between two specific locations in the body by way of neurons **(figure 17.1a)**. There is a rapid conduction of a nerve signal that triggers the release of neurotransmitter. The neurotransmitter crosses the synaptic cleft and binds to another neuron, a muscle cell, or a gland cell to initiate a

(a) Nervous system   **(b) Endocrine system**

Figure 17.1 Nervous and Endocrine System Communication Methods. (*a*) In the nervous system, neurons release neurotransmitters into a synaptic cleft to stimulate their target cells. (*b*) In the endocrine system, hormones are secreted by endocrine cells. The hormones enter the blood and travel throughout the body to reach their target cells.

Table 17.1	Comparison of the Nervous System and the Endocrine System	
Features	**Nervous System**	**Endocrine System**
Communication Method	A nerve signal causes neurotransmitter release from a neuron into a synaptic cleft	Secretes hormones into blood; hormones transported within the blood are distributed to target cells throughout body
Target of Stimulation	Other neurons, muscle cells, and gland cells	Any cell in the body with a receptor for the hormone
Response Time	Rapid reaction time: Typically milliseconds or seconds	Relatively slow reaction time: Seconds to minutes to hours
Effect of Stimulation	Causes stimulation (or inhibition) of another neuron, contraction (or relaxation) of muscles, or change in secretion from glands	Causes metabolic activity changes in target cells
Range of Effect	Typically has localized, specific effects in the body	Typically has widespread effects throughout the body
Duration of Response	Short-term: Milliseconds; terminates with removal of stimulus	Long-lasting: Minutes to days to weeks; may continue after stimulus is removed

response, such as muscle contraction or gland secretion. The neurotransmitter is quickly degraded or taken back into the neuron.

The endocrine system communicates with target cells through secretion of hormones (figure 17.1*b*). Hormones are released from endocrine glands and transported within the blood to reach a target. This can be any cell in the body that contains a receptor for the hormone. As you might predict, the endocrine system generally exhibits a longer response time, but it has both more widespread and longer-lasting effects than the nervous system. The general characteristics of the endocrine and nervous systems are compared in **table 17.1**.

 WHAT DID YOU LEARN?

❶ How does the endocrine system differ from the nervous system with respect to their target cells?

17.1b General Functions of the Endocrine System

 LEARNING OBJECTIVE

2. Describe the general functions controlled by the endocrine system.

The target cells of the nervous system are limited to other neurons, muscles, and glands, whereas the endocrine system through the release of hormones can communicate with any body cell that has receptors for it. Thus, the endocrine system is able to coordinate and regulate potentially any cell in the body. Consequently, its functions are much more diverse. We have organized the functions of the endocrine system into the following four broad categories:

- **Maintaining homeostasis of blood composition and volume.** Hormones regulate the amount of specific substances dissolved within blood, such as glucose, cations (positively charged ions such as calcium [Ca^{2+}], potassium [K^+], and sodium [Na^+]), and anions (negatively charged ions such as chloride [Cl^-] and phosphate [PO_4^-]). Additionally, hormones also regulate other characteristics of blood, including its volume, its cellular concentration (erythrocytes and leukocytes), and number of platelets.
- **Controlling reproductive activities.** Hormones affect both development and function of the reproductive system as well as expression of sexual behaviors.
- **Regulating development, growth, and metabolism.** Hormones have regulatory roles in embryonic cell division and differentiation of cells during development. They are important in both anabolic (synthesis) and catabolic (degradation) processes involving proteins, carbohydrates, and lipids for growth and metabolism.
- **Controlling digestive processes.** Several hormones influence both the secretory processes and the movement of materials through the digestive tract.

 WHAT DID YOU LEARN?

❷ Diabetes mellitus is noted by sustained high blood glucose levels. Which of the four functions listed is the most directly affected?

17.2 Endocrine Glands

Endocrine glands are composed of secretory endocrine cells derived from an epithelium that is supported by a connective tissue framework. Although the arrangement and organization of cells differs between endocrine glands, a consistent feature among these ductless glands is their extensive blood supply. This facilitates the rapid uptake of hormones from cells of the gland into the blood. See **figure 17.2** to view a representative histologic image of the pancreas (pancreatic islets). Note the secretory epithelial cells embedded in areolar connective tissue and the numerous associated capillaries. Here we discuss the location of the major endocrine glands and the general mechanisms for stimulating their release of hormones.

17.2a Location of the Major Endocrine Glands

 LEARNING OBJECTIVES

1. Distinguish between the two types of organization of endocrine cells.
2. Identify the major endocrine glands and their location within the body.

Endocrine cells are organized in two general ways: either as a single organ with only endocrine function or as cells housed in small clusters within organs that have some other primary function (**figure 17.3**).

LM 100x

Capillary

Secretory epithelial cells

Areolar connective tissue

Pancreatic islet

Figure 17.2 Histology of a Representative Endocrine Gland (Pancreas). The hormone-producing epithelial cells are embedded in a connective tissue framework, which is vascularized with numerous capillaries. AP|R

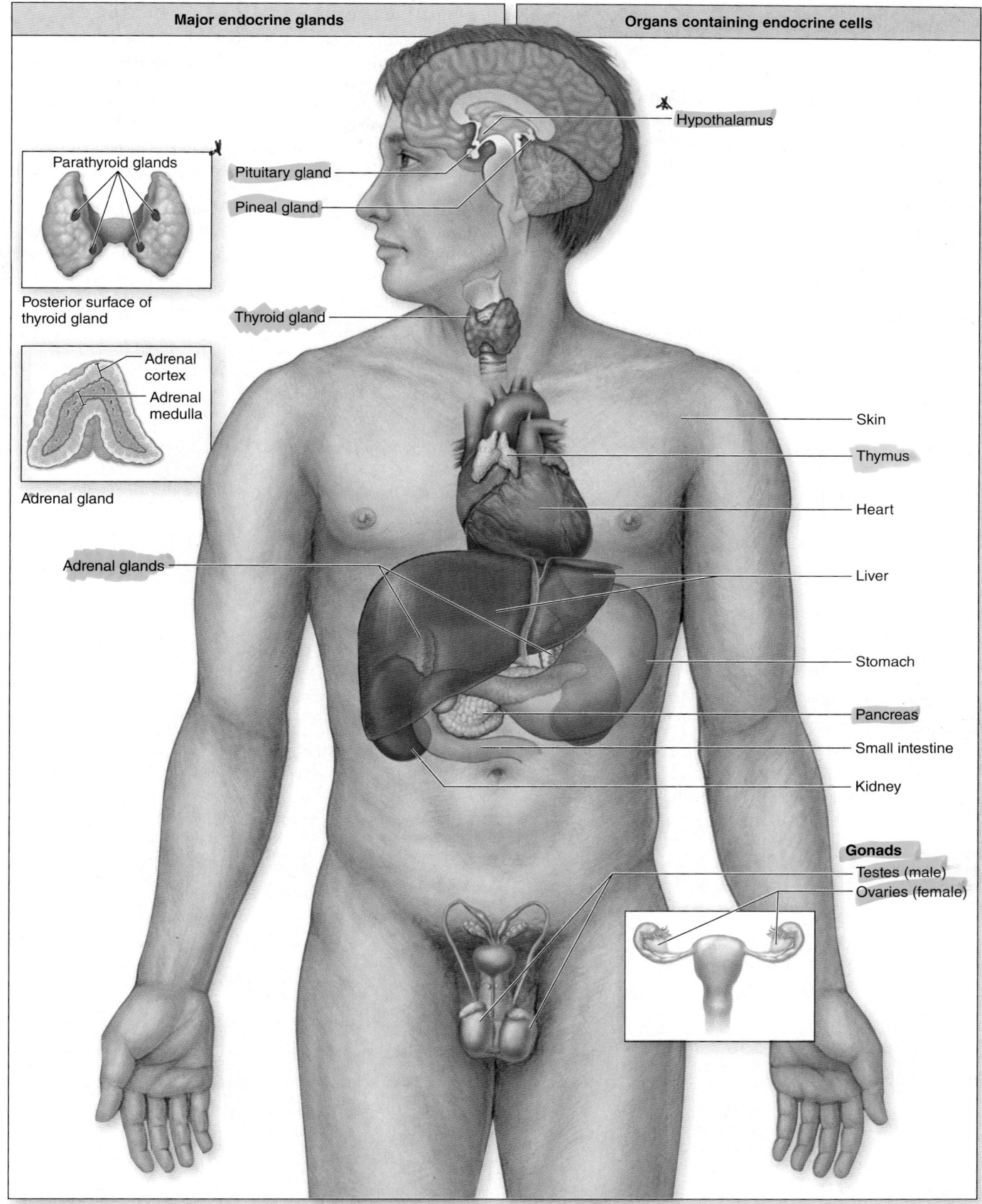

Major endocrine glands

Parathyroid glands

Posterior surface of thyroid gland

Adrenal cortex
Adrenal medulla

Adrenal gland

Pituitary gland
Pineal gland

Thyroid gland

Adrenal glands

Organs containing endocrine cells

Hypothalamus

Skin
Thymus
Heart

Liver

Stomach

Pancreas
Small intestine
Kidney

Gonads
Testes (male)
Ovaries (female)

Figure 17.3 Location of the Major Endocrine Glands and Organs Containing Endocrine Cells. AP|R

CONCEPT CONNECTION

Capillaries are microscopic vessels about 1 millimeter in length (see section 20.1c). The fluid of the blood with its dissolved substances, including hormones, moves out of the blood on one end of a capillary to become part of the interstitial fluid that "bathes" the cells. Most of the fluid is then reabsorbed back into the capillary on its other end. This provides the means for a hormone to both enter the blood from an endocrine gland and to make contact with its target cells (cells that possess its specific receptor).

Endocrine Organs

An **endocrine organ** is a single organ that is entirely endocrine in function. Endocrine organs include the pituitary gland, pineal gland, thyroid gland, parathyroid glands, and adrenal glands.

The five major endocrine glands are described in this chapter. Here we briefly cover the details of the general structure and function of the pineal gland and parathyroid glands. The pituitary gland, thyroid gland, and adrenal glands are discussed in detail later in the chapter.

Pineal Gland The **pineal** (pin'ē-al; *pineus* = relating to the pine) **gland** is also called the *pineal body*. It is a small, cone-shaped structure forming the posterior region of the epithalamus (see section 13.4a), which decreases in size as we age. It is composed primarily of

Table 17.2	Endocrine Glands and Organs Containing Endocrine Cells		
Gland	**Hormones Produced**	**General Function**	**Chapter Reference**
Pineal gland	Melatonin	Helps regulate the body's circadian rhythm	Chapter 17
Pituitary gland			
Posterior pituitary*	Oxytocin (OT)	Uterine contractions; breast milk release	Chapters 28, 29
	Antidiuretic hormone (ADH)	Fluid balance	Chapters 24, 25
Anterior pituitary	Thyroid-stimulating hormone (TSH)	Stimulates thyroid gland to release thyroid hormone	Chapter 17
	Prolactin (PRL)	Breast milk production	Chapters 28, 29
	Follicle-stimulating hormone (FSH)	Development of gametes (and follicle in female)	Chapter 28
	Luteinizing hormone (LH)	Development of gametes (and ovulation in female)	Chapter 28
	Adrenocorticotropic hormone (ACTH)	Stimulates adrenal cortex to release corticosteroids	Chapter 17
	Growth hormone (GH)	Stimulates cell growth and division	Chapter 17
Thyroid gland	Thyroid hormone (TH)	Increases metabolism	Chapter 17
	Calcitonin	Decreases blood calcium levels	Chapter 7
Parathyroid glands	Parathyroid hormone (PTH)	Increases blood calcium levels	Chapters 7, 17
Adrenal glands			
Adrenal medulla	Catecholamines (epinephrine and norepinephrine)	Prolong fight-or-flight response	Chapter 15
Adrenal cortex	Mineralocorticoids (e.g., aldosterone)	Regulate blood sodium and potassium levels	Chapters 24, 25
	Glucocorticoids (e.g., cortisol)	Participate in stress response	Chapter 17
	Gonadocorticoids (e.g., androgens)	Stimulates maturation and functioning of reproductive system	Chapters 28, 29
Organs Containing Endocrine Cells	**Hormones Produced**	**General Function**	**Chapter Reference**
Hypothalamus	See table 17.4	Regulates hormone release from pituitary gland	Chapter 17
Skin	Vitamin D (later converted to calcitriol through enzymes in liver and kidney)	Promotes absorption of calcium from gastrointestinal (GI) tract into blood	Chapter 7
Thymus	Thymosin, thymulin, thymopoietin	Stimulates maturation of T-lymphocytes	Chapters 21, 22
Heart	Atrial natriuretic peptide (ANP)	Regulates blood sodium levels and blood volume	Chapters 24, 25
Stomach	Gastrin	Increases secretions and motility of the stomach	Chapter 26
Liver	Angiotensinogen	Regulates blood volume and blood pressure	Chapters 20, 24, 25
	Erythropoietin (EPO)	Increases production of erythrocytes	Chapter 18
Pancreas	Insulin	Decreases blood glucose	Chapter 17
	Glucagon	Increases blood glucose	Chapter 17
Small intestine	Secretin	Regulates digestive processes of the small intestine	Chapter 26
	Cholecystokinin		
Kidneys	Erythropoietin (EPO)	Increases production of erythrocytes	Chapter 18
Testes (gonads)	Androgens (testosterone), inhibin	Stimulate maturation and function of male reproductive system	Chapters 28, 29
Ovaries (gonads)	Estrogen, progesterone, inhibin	Stimulate maturation and function of female reproductive system	Chapters 28, 29

*Oxytocin and antidiuretic hormone are produced in the hypothalamus and stored and released from the posterior pituitary.

pinealocytes, which secrete **melatonin** (mel-ā-tōn′in; *melas* = dark hue, *tonas* = contraction). Melatonin makes us drowsy, and its production tends to be cyclic; it increases at night and decreases during the day, with the lowest levels around lunchtime. Melatonin, along with the hypothalamus, helps regulate the circadian rhythm (24-hour body clock).

Melatonin also appears to affect the synthesis of a hypothalamic hormone (gonadotropin-releasing hormone). This hormone is responsible for regulating synthesis of two hormones from the anterior pituitary (follicle-stimulating hormone and luteinizing hormone), which in turn regulate the reproductive system. The role of melatonin in sexual maturation is not well understood. However, excessive melatonin secretion is known to delay puberty in humans.

Parathyroid Gland   The small, brownish-red **parathyroid** (par-ā-thī′royd) **glands** are located on the posterior surface of the thyroid gland. The parathyroid glands are usually four small nodules, but some individuals may have as few as two or as many as six of these glands.

There are two different types of cells in the parathyroid glands: chief cells and oxyphil cells. The **chief cells,** or *principal cells,* are the source of parathyroid hormone (PTH) that is released in response to decreased blood calcium to return blood calcium to within normal homeostatic levels; functional details of PTH are described in section 7.6b. The role of oxyphil cells is not known, although these cells are associated with a rare form of cancer called *oxyphil cell adenoma.*

Endocrine Cells Within Other Organs

Some endocrine cells are housed in tissue clusters within specific organs. These cells secrete one or more hormones, but the organs have some other primary function as well. These organs include the hypothalamus, skin, thymus, heart, liver, stomach, pancreas, small intestine, kidneys, and gonads (testes and ovaries) (figure 17.3). All of these organs are described in detail in other sections of the text—either later in this chapter or in another chapter.

The endocrine glands and other organs containing endocrine cells are listed in **table 17.2**. Note that the term "endocrine gland" will be used throughout the rest of this chapter when referring to either an endocrine gland or an organ containing endocrine cells.

WHAT DID YOU LEARN?

3 What are the major endocrine organs in the human body? What are the organs that have another primary function and contain endocrine cells?

4 One of the general functions of the endocrine system is to maintain homeostasis of blood composition and volume. Identify the hormones listed in table 17.2 that regulate the following: (a) blood glucose, (b) blood calcium, and (c) blood sodium.

17.2b Stimulation of Hormone Synthesis and Release

LEARNING OBJECTIVE

3. Explain the three reflex mechanisms for regulating secretion of hormones.

The regulated secretion of a hormone from an endocrine gland is controlled through a reflex. Recall from section 14.6 that a reflex is a preprogrammed response that occurs when activated by certain stimuli. Reflexes occur in both the nervous system and the endocrine system. Endocrine reflexes are initiated by one of three types of stimulation: hormonal stimulation, humoral stimulation, or nervous stimulation (**figure 17.4**).

- **Hormonal stimulation.** The stimulus for the release of many hormones from its endocrine gland is stimulation by another hormone. An example occurs when thyroid-stimulating hormone released from the anterior pituitary stimulates the thyroid gland to secrete thyroid hormone.

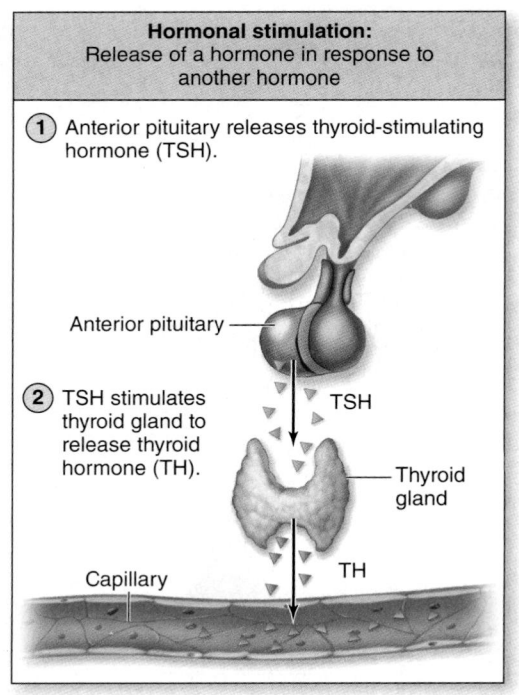

Hormonal stimulation:
Release of a hormone in response to another hormone

1 Anterior pituitary releases thyroid-stimulating hormone (TSH).

Anterior pituitary

2 TSH stimulates thyroid gland to release thyroid hormone (TH).

TSH

Thyroid gland

Capillary

TH

(a)

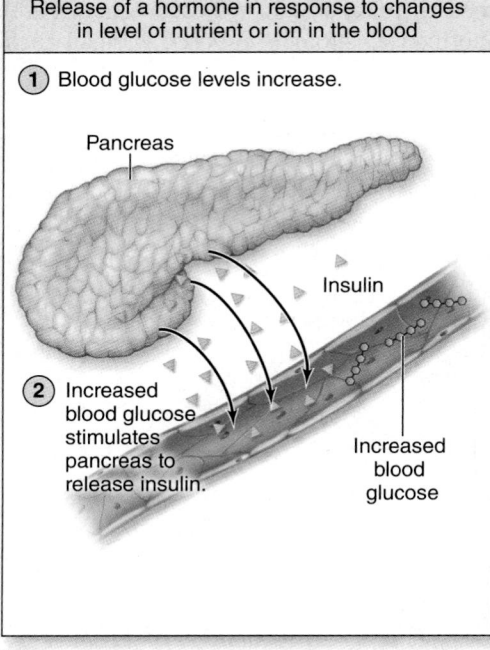

Humoral stimulation:
Release of a hormone in response to changes in level of nutrient or ion in the blood

1 Blood glucose levels increase.

Pancreas

Insulin

2 Increased blood glucose stimulates pancreas to release insulin.

Increased blood glucose

(b)

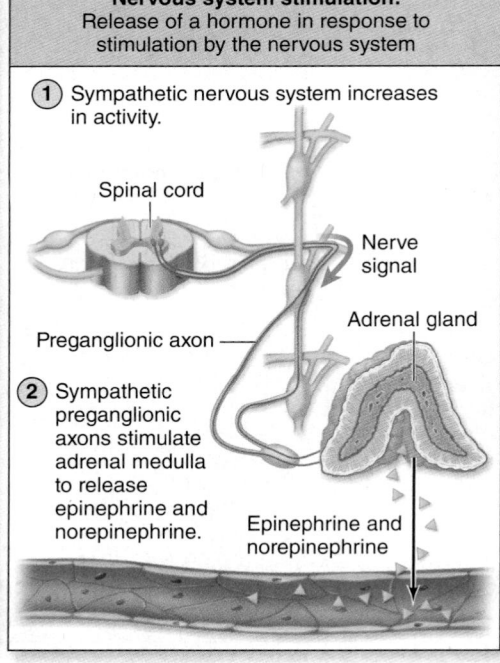

Nervous system stimulation:
Release of a hormone in response to stimulation by the nervous system

1 Sympathetic nervous system increases in activity.

Spinal cord

Nerve signal

Preganglionic axon

Adrenal gland

2 Sympathetic preganglionic axons stimulate adrenal medulla to release epinephrine and norepinephrine.

Epinephrine and norepinephrine

(c)

Figure 17.4 Types of Endocrine Stimulation. An endocrine gland can be stimulated to release its hormone in response to (*a*) hormonal stimulation, (*b*) humoral stimulation, or (*c*) nervous stimulation. AP|R

- **Humoral stimulation.** Some endocrine glands are stimulated to release their hormones in response to a changing level of nutrients or ions within the blood. (The term "humoral" is a historical term related to blood's being one of the four "humors," or fluids, of the body.) When either nutrient or ion levels decrease or increase within the blood, responsive cells of an endocrine gland release hormones that act on target cells to either offset further loss or store or eliminate the excess.

- **Nervous stimulation.** A few endocrine glands are stimulated to release hormone(s) by direct stimulation from the nervous system. The classic example is the release of epinephrine and norepinephrine by the adrenal medulla in response to sympathetic nervous stimulation as part of the "fight-or-flight" response (see section 15.4b).

INTEGRATE

CONCEPT CONNECTION

The regulation of blood Ca^{2+} (see section 7.6) is an endocrine reflex that is initiated by humoral stimulation. It involves multiple body systems. Parathyroid hormone (PTH) is released from the parathyroid gland in response to low blood Ca^{2+} levels by humoral stimulation. Following its release into the blood, PTH stimulates several target organs, including (1) bone connective tissue to release Ca^{2+} into the blood; (2) the kidneys to complete the final enzymatic step to produce calcitriol (a hormone that increases Ca^{2+} absorption from the GI tract); and (3) the kidneys to decrease the loss of Ca^{2+} in the urine. The net result is that blood Ca^{2+} level rises, returning to its normal concentration.

WHAT DID YOU LEARN?

5 Adrenocorticotropic hormone (ACTH) stimulates the adrenal cortex to release its hormones. This is an example of what type of stimulation: (a) hormonal, (b) humoral, or (c) nervous?

17.3 Hormones

All circulating hormones are synthesized within endocrine cells from either cholesterol or amino acids. Recall that cholesterol is a type of lipid with a ring structure (see section 2.7b) and amino acids are the building block components of proteins (see section 2.7e).

17.3a Categories of Circulating Hormones

LEARNING OBJECTIVES

1. Name the three structural categories of circulating hormones, and give examples within each category.
2. Distinguish the hormones that are lipid-soluble from those that are water-soluble.

Circulating hormones are grouped according to their chemical structure into three general categories: steroid hormones, protein hormones, and biogenic amines. An example of each category is shown in **figure 17.5**. As you read about the chemical structure of these hormones, please note whether the molecules in each category are water-soluble or lipid-soluble. This difference in solubility influences both the transport of the hormone in the blood and how it interacts with its target cells.

Steroid Hormones

Steroid hormones are lipid-soluble molecules synthesized from cholesterol (figure 17.5a). This category includes both the steroids produced in the gonads (e.g., estrogen and progesterone in the ovaries and testosterone in the testes) and the hormones synthesized by the adrenal cortex (e.g., corticosteroids such as cortisol).

Calcitriol is the hormone produced from vitamin D (see section 7.6a), and it is sometimes classified as a steroid hormone. However, it is more accurately classified as a *sterol* hormone, a slightly different molecule but one that is also lipid-soluble.

Protein Hormones

Most hormones are **protein hormones.** These are molecules composed of small chains of amino acids (figure 17.5b). All hormones

Steroid hormone
- Lipid-soluble
- Formed from cholesterol
- Produced by gonads and adrenal cortex

Example: Cortisol

(a)

Protein hormone
- Water-soluble
- Consists of amino acid chains
- Three subgroups
  Polypeptides
  Oligopeptides
  Glycoproteins

Example: Parathyroid hormone

(b)

Biogenic amine
- Water-soluble (except thyroid hormone)
- Derived from amino acid that is modified (e.g., tyrosine)

Example: Norepinephrine

(c)

Figure 17.5 Hormone Types. (*a*) Steroid hormones are lipid-soluble and formed from cholesterol, whereas (*b*) protein hormones and (*c*) biogeneic amines typically are water-soluble and formed from amino acids.

in this category are water-soluble. These hormones include the following three subgroups:

- *Polypeptides* are hormones that contain between 14 to 199 amino acids. Examples include insulin and glucagon, which are released from the pancreas, and parathyroid hormone (PTH) released from the parathyroid gland.
- *Oligopeptides* are hormones that have only 3 to 10 amino acids. Examples include oxytocin (OT) and antidiuretic hormone (ADH), both of which are released from the posterior pituitary.
- *Glycoproteins* are hormones composed of proteins with attached carbohydrate. Examples include follicle-stimulating hormone (FSH) and thyroid-stimulating hormone (TSH), both released from the anterior pituitary.

Biogenic Amines

Biogenic amines are also called *monoamines*. They are modified amino acids (modification involves removal of a carboxyl functional group from an amino acid) (figure 17.5c). Biogenic amines include the catecholamines (e.g., epinephrine and norepinephrine) released from the adrenal medulla and thyroid hormone released from the thyroid gland. Biogenic amines are water-soluble except for thyroid hormone. Thyroid hormone is lipid-soluble because it is produced from two tyrosine amino acids (see figure 2.26), which are amino acids that contain a nonpolar ring.

 WHAT DID YOU LEARN?

6 Identify which of the following hormone categories is lipid-soluble: (a) reproductive hormones produced in the gonads, (b) adrenal cortex hormones, and (c) thyroid hormone

7 What two events or processes associated with a hormone are influenced by whether a hormone is lipid-soluble or water-soluble?

17.3b Local Hormones

 LEARNING OBJECTIVES

3. Describe the general structure, formation, and function of local hormones.

4. Compare autocrine and paracrine signaling that occurs through local hormones.

Local hormones are a large group of signaling molecules that do not circulate within the blood. Instead, these molecules are released from the cells that produce them and bind with the same cell that produced them or neighboring cells. For this reason, some biologists do not classify these signaling molecules as hormones.

Eicosanoids (ī′kō-să-noydz; *eicosa* = twenty, *eidos* = formed) are a primary type of local hormones. The name "eicosanoids" is derived from the fact that this group of signaling molecules is formed from fatty acids that contain a chain of 20 carbon atoms. The source of these fatty acids is phospholipids within a cell's plasma membrane.

Eicosanoids are synthesized through a series of enzymes called an enzymatic cascade **(figure 17.6)**. This process is initiated by an enzyme (phospholipase A₂) that removes a fatty acid from a phospholipid within a plasma membrane. The fatty acid that is released is called *arachidonic acid*. Other specific enzymes then act on arachidonic acid to convert its chemical structure to various

Figure 17.6 Eicosanoid Formation. Eicosanoids are synthesized by an enzymatic cascade that begins with phospholipids from within a plasma membrane. Subsequent to their formation, eicosanoids may stimulate the cell from which it is released (autocrine stimulation) or neighboring cells (paracrine stimulation).

types of eicosanoids, which include leukotrienes, prostaglandins, and thromboxanes.

Subsequent to their synthesis, eicosanoids initiate cellular changes in either (1) the same cell from which they were formed, a process called **autocrine stimulation,** or (2) neighboring cells, a process called **paracrine stimulation.**

A major function of eicosanoids is their role in inflammation as part of the body's defense (see section 22.3d). They also serve other local signaling functions, such as initiation of smooth muscle contraction and stimulation of pain receptors, as described in various sections throughout the text.

 WHAT DID YOU LEARN

8 Leukotrienes from damaged tissue cause smooth muscle in local blood vessels to vasodilate (increase the diameter of the vessel lumen). Is this an example of (a) autocrine stimulation or (b) paracrine stimulation? Explain.

17.4 Hormone Transport

Hormone molecules are transported within the blood and carried to target cells following their release from the endocrine gland that synthesized them. Here we consider how both water-soluble and lipid-soluble hormones are transported and the factors that influence the level of circulating hormone.

17.4a Transport in the Blood

 LEARNING OBJECTIVE

1. Compare the transport of water-soluble hormones with that of lipid-soluble hormones.

Transport of water-soluble hormones within the blood from an endocrine gland to target cells is relatively straightforward. Chemical interactions between the water-soluble hormone and the fluid of the blood (blood plasma) permit the hormone molecules to readily dissolve (see section 2.4c).

Lipid-soluble hormones (e.g., steroids, calcitriol, and thyroid hormone) do not readily dissolve within the aqueous environment of the blood. Thus, the transport of lipid-soluble hormones in the blood requires carrier molecules. These molecules are water-soluble proteins synthesized by the liver. You may find it helpful to think of these proteins as small boats that "ferry" the hormone molecules within the blood. Some hormone carrier proteins may be very selective, binding and transporting only one specific lipid-soluble molecule (e.g., thyroxine-binding globulin), whereas others are non-selective (e.g., albumin), meaning they bind and transport numerous lipid-soluble molecules.

The binding between a lipid-soluble hormone and a carrier protein is temporary. Hormone molecules bind to the carrier molecule, detach from the carrier and float free within the blood, and then may later reattach to a different carrier molecule. Any hormone that is attached to a carrier is a **bound hormone,** whereas an unattached hormone is an **unbound (free) hormone.** Only unbound hormone, which represents a very small fraction of the hormone transported within the blood (0.1% to 10%), is generally able to exit the blood and bind to cellular receptors of target organs.

A transport carrier protein also protects the hormone molecule it is carrying and prevents its early destruction. Consequently, the association of a hormone with a carrier protein often acts as a safeguard to help prolong the life of the hormone. It is for this reason that some water-soluble hormones are transported by carrier protein molecules.

 WHAT DID YOU LEARN?

9 Why are carrier proteins necessary for lipid-soluble hormones?

17.4b Levels of Circulating Hormone

 LEARNING OBJECTIVES

2. Describe the two primary factors that affect the concentration level of a circulating hormone.

3. Explain what is meant by the half-life of a hormone.

Hormones exert their physiologic effects primarily as a result of their blood concentration. Consequently, the amount of each hormone must be tightly regulated to prevent potential clinical consequences, such as organ or tissue malfunction and disease. For example, gigantism is due to high blood levels of growth hormone, whereas decreased metabolic rate is caused by low blood levels of thyroid hormone.

Two primary factors interact to influence hormone concentration—hormone synthesis and hormone elimination:

- **Hormone synthesis.** Hormone synthesis occurs in an endocrine gland. If the rate of synthesis and release increases, then the concentration of the hormone within the blood is greater. In contrast, if synthesis and release of the hormone decreases, hormone concentration in the blood is lower.

- **Hormone elimination.** Hormones are typically eliminated through either (1) enzymatic degradation, which usually occurs in liver cells, or (2) removal of the hormone from the blood either by its excretion by the kidneys or by its uptake into target cells. The faster the rate of hormone elimination, the lower the hormone concentration within the blood, whereas the slower the rate of hormone elimination, the higher the hormone concentration within the blood.

To maintain homeostatic levels of each hormone, a balance is required between its rate of synthesis by its endocrine gland and its elimination from the blood by the activities of the liver, kidney, and target cells.

 WHAT DO YOU THINK?

1 What effect would impaired function of the liver or kidneys potentially have on hormone concentration in the blood: increase, decrease, or no change? Explain.

Half-Life

The **half-life** is the amount of time necessary to reduce the hormone concentration within the blood to one-half of what had been secreted originally (or measured previously). Generally, water-soluble hormones have a relatively short half-life that amounts to a few minutes or less for small peptide hormones, and about an hour for larger polypeptide hormones. Steroid hormones generally have the longest half-life. The half-life of testosterone, for example, is 12 days. Note that the shorter the half-life of a hormone, the more frequently it must be replaced to maintain its normal concentration in the blood.

 WHAT DID YOU LEARN?

10 What is the relationship of hormone synthesis to the concentration of that hormone in the blood?

17.5 Target Cells: Interactions with Hormones

Hormones have contact with essentially all tissues of the body through their transport in the blood and exit from capillaries. However, hormones interact only with target cells (cells with receptors for that hormone) to initiate a specific cellular response. A specific hormone generally has different types of target cells. The hormone insulin, for example, binds with muscle cells, hepatocytes (liver cells), and adipose connective tissue cells. The greater the number of different target cells, the wider the potential influence that may be exhibited by a given hormone.

The specific process of how hormones interact with cell receptors, and the cellular changes that are initiated, is significantly different for lipid-soluble hormones and water-soluble hormones. We first describe the action of lipid-soluble hormones and then discuss the action of water-soluble hormones.

17.5a Lipid-Soluble Hormones

 LEARNING OBJECTIVE

1. Describe how lipid-soluble hormones reach their target cell receptors and the type of cellular change they initiate.

Lipid-soluble hormones are relatively small, nonpolar molecules that are **lipophilic** (lip′ō-fil′ik), or lipid-loving. Recall that the plasma membrane is not an effective barrier to small, nonpolar substances (see section 4.2). Consequently, unbound lipid-soluble hormones such as steroid hormones are able to diffuse across the plasma membrane. Upon entering the cell, the hormone binds to intracellular receptors located in either the cytosol or nucleus to form a **hormone-receptor complex** (figure 17.7).

The hormone-receptor complex formed within the target cell then binds to a particular DNA sequence in regions of chromatin within the nucleus called **hormone-response elements (HREs).** Binding to a specific DNA sequence results in transcription of messenger ribonucleic acid (mRNA). Subsequent translation of this mRNA by ribosomes synthesizes a specific protein (see section 4.7). The change in protein synthesis pattern within the cell may result in either an alteration in cell structure (e.g., as occurs with sex hormones during puberty) or a shift in the target cells' metabolic activities if the newly synthesized proteins are enzymes.

Consider, for example, that testosterone results in larger muscles due to formation of contractile proteins, a deeper voice from longer and thicker vocal cords, and facial hair growth. These effects induced by testosterone reflect a cellular increase in protein synthesis.

 WHAT DID YOU LEARN?

11 Where are lipid-soluble hormone receptors located? What is the general cellular change that occurs with binding of a lipid-soluble hormone?

17.5b Water-Soluble Hormones

 LEARNING OBJECTIVE

2. Describe how water-soluble hormones induce cellular change in their target cells.

Water-soluble hormones (e.g., proteins and biogenic amines, except TH) are polar molecules and are unable to cross the plasma membrane. Denied entry into the cell, water-soluble hormones instead must use an alternative, slightly more complex way to stimulate a target cell. This stimulation is initiated when the hormone binds to a plasma membrane receptor.

The binding of water-soluble hormones to a plasma membrane receptor initiates a series of biochemical events across the membrane called a **signal transduction pathway.** In this pathway, the hormone is the signaling molecule, or **first messenger.** Its "docking" with the receptor results in the formation of a different molecule

1 The unbound lipid-soluble hormone diffuses readily through the plasma membrane and binds with an intracellular receptor, either within the cytosol or the nucleus to form a hormone-receptor complex.

2 The hormone-receptor complex then binds with a specific DNA sequence called a hormone-response element.

3 This binding stimulates mRNA synthesis.

4 mRNA exits the nucleus and is translated by a ribosome in the cytosol. A new protein is synthesized.

Figure 17.7 Lipid-Soluble Hormones and Intracellular Receptors. Lipid-soluble hormones enter a cell and ultimately cause the formation of new protein. AP|R within the cell called the **second messenger.** The second messenger then modifies some cellular activity. The mechanisms of initiating cellular changes are described here for the two most common signal transduction pathways. We first describe the activation of the G protein complex, which is common to both of these pathways.

Hormone Binding and the Activation of G Protein

Both of the two common signal transduction pathways function through an internal plasma membrane protein complex called a **G protein** (first introduced in section 4.4b). This protein is named based upon its ability to bind guanine nucleotide (a nucleotide containing the base guanine; see section 2.7d). Guanine diphosphate (GDP) is bound when G protein is in the inactive state, and guanine triphosphate (GTP) is bound when G protein is in the activated state. The binding of hormone to a plasma membrane receptor causes a change in G protein from its inactive form to its activated form. The sequence of this occurrence is depicted and described in detail in **figure 17.8**.

Subsequent to its formation, activated G protein then generally activates one of two plasma membrane enzymes associated with different intracellular enzymatic cascades: adenylate cyclase or phospholipase C. A cell may have either or both enzymatic cascades.

Adenylate Cyclase Activity

Activated G protein moves along the inside of the plasma membrane, where it binds to the plasma membrane protein **adenylate** (a-den′i-lāt) **cyclase (figure 17.9a)**. Activated adenylate cyclase increases the formation of the second messenger, cAMP (3′,5′-cyclic adenosine monophosphate) from ATP. The cAMP then activates a **protein kinase** (protein kinase A), a protein that phosphorylates (adds phosphate to) other molecules (see section 3.3g). Phosphorylation results in activation or inhibition of these molecules. Examples of hormones that function through the activation of adenylate cyclase include glucagon, antidiuretic hormone, epinephrine, thyroid-stimulating hormone, and follicle-stimulating hormone.

Phospholipase C Activity

The second possibility as a result of G protein activation occurs when it binds with a different plasma membrane protein called **phospholipase C** (fos′fō-lip′ās) (figure 17.9b). Activation of phospholipase C results in the splitting of **PIP$_2$** (phosphatidylinositol bisphosphate), a phospholipid molecule within the plasma membrane. The splitting of PIP$_2$ results in the formation of two secondary messenger molecules: **DAG (diacylglycerol;** dī′as-il′glis′ĕr-ōl) and **IP$_3$ (inositol;** in-ō′si-tōl, -tol) **triphosphate.**

Action of DAG DAG is a second messenger that remains in the plasma membrane. It is similar in action to cAMP in that it activates a protein kinase (here, protein kinase C). This enzyme in turn phosphorylates other molecules.

Action of IP$_3$ IP$_3$ is a second messenger that diffuses from the plasma membrane into the cytosol. It increases intracellular Ca^{2+} concentration by interacting with either the endoplasmic reticulum, causing the release of stored Ca^{2+}, or with Ca^{2+} channels in the plasma

Figure 17.8 Activation of G Proteins. G proteins are activated in response to water-soluble hormone binding to a plasma membrane receptor.

① Activated G protein binds to and causes activation of the plasma membrane enzyme adenylate cyclase.

② Adenylate cylase converts ATP molecules to cAMP molecules.

③ cAMP serves as the "second messenger" by activating protein kinase A (a phosphorylating enzyme that adds phosphate to other molecules; these molecules may be activated or inhibited as a result).

(a) Activated G protein "turns on" adenylate cyclase.

① Activated G protein binds to and causes activation of the plasma membrane enzyme phospholipase C.

② Phospholipase C splits PIP_2 into two second messengers: DAG (diaclyglycerol) and IP_3 (inositol triphosphate).

③a DAG activates protein kinase C (a phosphorylating enzyme).

③b IP_3 increases Ca^{2+} in cytosol (by stimulating Ca^{2+} release from the endoplasmic reticulum [ER] and entry across the plasma membrane from the interstitial fluid).

③c Ca^{2+} acts as a third messenger to activate protein kinase enzymes (Ca^{2+} does this directly or by first binding to calmodulin). Ca^{2+} may also alter activity of ion channel within the plasma membrane.

(b) Activated G protein "turns on" phopholipase C.

Figure 17.9 Action of G Proteins. Following its activation, G protein is an intracellular molecule that moves along the inside of the plasma membrane and can stimulate other molecules. Two of the most common are (*a*) adenylate cyclase, which forms cyclic AMP second messenger, and (*b*) phospholipase C, which causes formation of DAG and IP_3 second messengers. Pathways involving G protein ultimately result in the activation of kinase enzymes that activate or inhibit other enzymes through phosphorylation, change cell permeability, or both. **AP|R**

membrane (not shown in figure), permitting Ca^{2+} entry from the interstitial fluid. Increased intracellular Ca^{2+} acts as a third messenger within the cytosol to (1) activate protein kinase enzymes directly, or by first binding with an intracellular protein called calmodulin; or (2) alter plasma membrane permeability by binding to specific ion channels located within the plasma membrane and changing the flow of that specific ion either into or out of the cell. Examples of hormones that function through the activation of phospholipase C include oxytocin, antidiuretic hormone, and epinephrine.

Action of Water-Soluble Hormones

Hormone binding and the subsequent production of second (and third) messengers results in protein kinase activity, alteration of cell permeability to ions, or both. Ultimately, the action may result in either activation or inhibition of enzymatic pathways, stimulation of growth through cellular reproduction (mitosis), stimulation of cellular secretions, changes in membrane permeability, and muscle contraction or relaxation. The specific response in each cell type is dependent upon the hormone that binds to a cellular receptor, the types of second (and third) messengers (cAMP, DAG, IP_3, and Ca^{2+}) that a given cell can produce, and the different enzymes within a cascade that are phosphorylated. For example:

- Glucagon is released from pancreatic cells in response to low blood glucose levels. Glucagon combines with receptors in plasma membranes of liver cells to cause an increase in cAMP synthesis and activation of kinase A enzymes.

Kinase A enzymes phosphorylate specific enzyme pathways (e.g., glycogenolysis; see section 2.7c) that lead to the release of glucose from liver cells. Glucose enters the blood and helps to return blood glucose levels to within a normal homeostatic range.

- Oxytocin is released from the posterior pituitary during active labor for childbirth (section 29.6). It binds with membrane receptors of smooth muscle cells in the uterus to increase production of IP_3, thus increasing intracellular Ca^{2+} and causing stronger uterine muscle contractions that help expel the baby.

Intracellular Enzyme Cascade and Amplification of Response

Recall that the hormone molecule is not actually moved along a signaling pathway. The binding of the hormone results in specific "information" being passed in a signal conduction pathway called an *intracellular enzyme cascade.* The cascade includes G protein, transmembrane enzyme (adenylate cyclase or phospholipase C), second messenger, and protein kinase enzymes. The activated protein kinase enzymes may either stimulate or inhibit enzymatic pathways within the cell, alter cell permeability to an ion, or both. Signaling pathways have two advantages:

- The signaling pathway amplifies the signal at each enzymatic step to activate more molecules than were present in the previous step, which ultimately leads to a greater specific response. Consequently, the binding of a relatively small number of hormone molecules to their receptors in the membrane of a cell may result in the activation or inhibition of millions of molecules within a cell.

- Multistep signaling pathways provide more places and opportunities to fine-tune and regulate the pathway activities.

We have emphasized the amplification pathways in this discussion. However, metabolic cascade controls require precise regulation to be effective. Cells must have efficient mechanisms to quickly inactivate intermediates, including breakdown of second messenger molecules, and to terminate the activity of enzymes that had been activated during amplification (e.g., phosphodiester-

ase degrades cyclic AMP, limiting the response of those signaling pathways).

WHAT DID YOU LEARN?

⑫ What is the specific role of the protein kinase enzymes in the signal transduction pathway initiated by water-soluble hormones?

17.6 Target Cells: Degree of Cellular Response

A cell's response to a hormone is not an isolated event. This is because a single target cell (1) displays differing numbers of receptors for the same hormone and can bind varying amounts of the same hormone simultaneously; and (2) may possess receptors for many different hormones, and thus it is able to respond to more than one type of hormone at the same time. Hepatocytes, for example, have changing numbers of receptors for both insulin and glucagon and respond to both of them. Consequently, the response of a given cell is dependent upon the net effect of both its displayed receptors and the amounts and kinds of hormone that it binds.

17.6a Number of Receptors

 LEARNING OBJECTIVES

1. Describe the conditions that influence the number of receptors available for a specific hormone.

2. Define up-regulation and down-regulation.

The number of available receptors in a cell fluctuates, and both the direction and degree that it fluctuates are tightly regulated. This is necessary because the number of receptor molecules available for hormone binding directly influences the degree of cellular response. Cells may increase the number of receptors, thereby increasing cell sensitivity to a hormone, a process called **up-regulation.** In contrast, a cell may decrease its number of receptors and reduce the cell's sensitivity to a hormone through **down-regulation.**

Cells alter the number of receptors available in response to changes in hormone concentration within the blood. A cell may increase its number of receptors when there is a lower than normal hormone concentration level, or decrease its number of receptors in response to an elevated hormone level (**figure 17.10a**). The ability of a cell to change the number of its available receptors helps to maintain a normal level of cellular response, preventing either understimulation or overstimulation of the cell.

WHAT DO YOU THINK?

② What cellular response (up-regulation or down-regulation) would you predict occurs in response to high doses of a drug that binds to a specific hormone receptor? Will more or less of the drug be required for the same response over time? Explain.

Changes in receptor number also occur as a consequence of developmental maturity, the cell's state of activity, and the different stages of the cell cycle. For example, when a secretory cell becomes a mature cell, it may become less responsive to growth

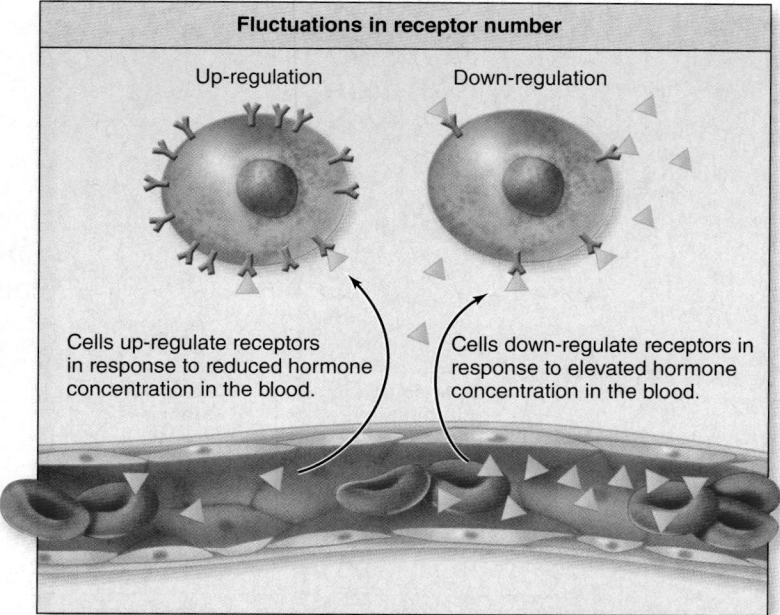

Fluctuations in receptor number

Up-regulation — Down-regulation

Cells up-regulate receptors in response to reduced hormone concentration in the blood.

Cells down-regulate receptors in response to elevated hormone concentration in the blood.

(a)

Hormone interactions

Target cell receptors

Different target cells can house various types of receptors, allowing them to bind multiple hormones simultaneously.

Adipose cell   Liver cell   Muscle cell

Representative target cell

When multiple hormones bind to a target cell simultaneously, their interactions can produce different effects.

Synergistic	Permissive	Antagonistic
Hormones work together to produce greater effect.	First hormone allows action of second hormone.	One hormone causes opposite effect of another.

(b)

Figure 17.10 Cellular Response to Hormones. A cell's response to hormones is dependent upon several factors, including the (*a*) number of cellular receptors available to bind a specific hormone and (*b*) possible interactions caused by more than one type of hormone binding to its different cellular receptors.

hormone (GH) because it no longer needs to continue growing at an accelerated rate. Thereafter, the mature secretory cell develops the ability to respond to hormones that stimulate it to secrete its product. This response occurs because the secretory cell now produces and displays receptors for different hormones.

 WHAT DID YOU LEARN?

13 How does down-regulation of cellular receptors change responsiveness to a given hormone?

17.6b Receptor Interactions

LEARNING OBJECTIVE

3. Compare and contrast the three types of hormone interactions.

A target cell can simultaneously bind different hormones. The cellular response to binding more than one type of hormone is often such that some integration occurs within their signaling pathways. There are three principal ways in which hormones interact: synergistically, permissively, or antagonistically (figure 17.10*b*).

Synergistic interaction occurs when the activity of one hormone reinforces the activity of another hormone. Synergy means "working together." For example, female reproductive structures are more powerfully influenced by the presence of both estrogen and progesterone than by either hormone alone.

Permissive interaction takes place when the activity of one hormone requires a second hormone—as if one hormone "gives permission" for a different hormone to function. For example, prolactin is required to produce breast milk, and oxytocin is required for milk ejection from the breast. Oxytocin is unable to cause milk ejection without the previous, or accompanying, prolactin release to produce the milk.

Antagonistic interaction occurs when the effects of one hormone oppose the effects of another hormone. An example is the opposing effects on blood glucose levels exhibited by glucagon, which initiates cellular changes that increase blood glucose levels, and insulin, which initiates cellular changes that decrease blood glucose levels.

Figure 17.11 provides a visual overview of the general concepts of the endocrine system, as previously discussed.

 WHAT DID YOU LEARN?

14 What effects are seen when hormones act synergistically?

INTEGRATE

CLINICAL VIEW

Hormone Analogs

Specificity of receptors allows the pharmaceutical industry to produce hormone analogs for use as medicines to inhibit or activate particular cellular functions. The drugs may activate a receptor and mimic the effect of the native hormone. One potential consequence of long-term or high-dose hormone analog use is that a patient's cells may down-regulate hormone receptors, an unintended effect. Consequently, following administration of the drug, the individual must be "weaned" from the medication (i.e., administered progressively smaller doses over several days). Weaning allows time for the body's cells to up-regulate the specific receptor to the normal level. You may be familiar with weaning an individual from steroids following treatment for inflammation (e.g., inflammation associated with asthma, allergic reactions, or rheumatoid arthritis).

Figure 17.11 Endocrine System: Major Control System of the Body. Hormones are produced by the glands of the endocrine system, released into the blood and transported to target organs. Lipid-soluble hormones enter target cells, whereas water-soluble hormones bind to receptors within the plasma membrane to induce cellular changes. A cell's response is determined both by its number of receptors and the different types of receptors that are available. Hormones are eliminated by the liver and kidney.

(b) Hormones and Hormone Transport

Blood vessel

Bound hormone

Hormone

Carrier protein

Lipid-soluble hormones	Water-soluble hormones
• Steroid hormones • Calcitrol • Thyroid hormone (TH)	• Proteins • Biogenic amines (except TH)

(a) Endocrine System

Hormone level increases in blood with release from endocrine cells

Endocrine glands and cells synthesize and release hormones into the blood in response to hormonal, humoral, or nervous system stimulation.

Endocrine glands

- Pineal
- Pituitary
- Thyroid
- Parathyroid

Posterior surface of thyroid gland

- Adrenal

Organs containing endocrine cells

- Hypothalamus
- Skin
- Thymus
- Heart
- Liver
- Stomach
- Kidney
- Pancreas
- Small intestine
- Gonads
  - Ovary (female)
  - Testis (male)

(f) Elimination of Hormones

Liver degrades hormones.

Kidney excretes hormones.

(c) Target Cell and Cellular Response

Lipid-soluble hormones and gene activation

Amino acids

Ribosome

Protein

Hormone

Receptor

Hormone-receptor complex

Unbound hormone

Carrier protein

Hormone binds to intracellular receptor to form hormone-receptor complex.

mRNA synthesis

mRNA

Result

New protein is synthesized.

Complex binds to DNA segment and mRNA transcribed.

Water-soluble hormones and activation of kinase enzymes and changes to ion permeability

① Activate G protein with binding of hormone (first messenger)

② Activate effector protein: adenylate cyclase or phospholipase C

③ Formation of second messengers (cAMP or DAG and IP_3)

④ cAMP, Ca^{2+}, DAG activate protein kinase enzymes to phosphorylate other molecules

Possible results

- Stimulate or inhibit enzyme pathways
- Include growth or release of cellular secretions
- Change membrane permeability
- Initiate muscle contraction or relaxation

Inactive G protein GDP

Activated G protein GTP

Hormone

Hormone

①

②

Adenylate cyclase

ATP

cAMP

Active protein kinases

Inactive protein kinases

④

Phospholipase C

PIP_2

③

IP_3

$*Ca^{2+}$

DAG

$*Ca^{2+}$ may also bind with ion channels in plasma membrane to increase the cell's ion permeability

Ion

Open ion channel

(e) Simultaneous Binding of Different Hormones

When multiple hormones bind a target cell, their interactions can produce different effects.

Synergistic	Permissive	Antagonistic
Hormones work together to produce greater effect.	First hormone allows action of second hormone.	One hormone causes opposite effect of another hormone.

(d) Altering Number of Receptors

Down-regulation	Up-regulation
Cells down-regulate receptors in response to elevated hormone concentration in the blood.	Cells up-regulate receptors in response to reduce hormone concentration in the blood.
	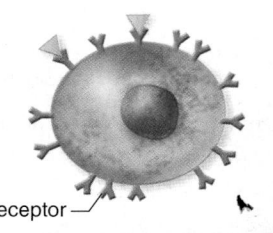
Receptor	Receptor

17.7 Nutrient Metabolism

LEARNING OBJECTIVES

1. Identify the three primary nutrients within the blood.
2. Describe the enzymatic pathways that alter nutrient levels within the blood.

All of the hormones described later in this chapter influence nutrient metabolism. To help you understand the action of these hormones, we briefly present relevant and necessary information on nutrient metabolism.

Recall that some organic molecules including glucose, fatty acids, and some amino acids can be oxidized by cells to provide energy to form ATP molecules (see section 3.4). For simplicity, we collectively refer to organic molecules derived from foods to generate ATP as "nutrients."

The primary nutrients circulate in the blood in their simple form as glucose, fatty acids, and amino acids. Glucose and fatty acids are also stored within cells in the complex forms of glycogen and triglycerides (fats), respectively. Proteins are not stored, but serve specific structural and functional roles within a cell. Several structures in the body are significant for regulating nutrient blood levels, including the liver, adipose connective tissue, and skeletal muscle tissue. Through intracellular enzymatic pathways, nutrients can be "deposited" in these structures when there is excess in the blood and later may be "withdrawn" when blood levels are falling.

Figure 17.12 illustrates how nutrients move between the blood and the body cells that store nutrients (liver, adipose connective tissue, muscle) and the enzymatic processes that are involved.

The enzymatic pathways for nutrient processing in the liver include glycogenesis, glycogenolysis, and gluconeogenesis (figure 17.12a). **Glycogenesis** (glī′kō-jen′ĕ-sis; *glycol* = sugar,

glycogen, *genesis* = creation) is the synthesis of glycogen from glucose obtained from the blood; this enzymatic pathway is also active in muscle cells. In contrast, glucose is added to the blood as a result of both glycogenolysis and gluconeogenesis. **Glycogenolysis** (glī′kō-je-nol′i-sis; *lysis* = destruction) is the breakdown of stored glycogen into glucose, whereas **gluconeogenesis** (glū′kō-nē′ō-jen′ĕ-sis; *gluco* = glucose, *neo* = new) is the production of glucose from noncarbohydrate molecules such as amino acids, fatty acids, or lactate. Muscle cells engage in glycogenolysis, but do not release glucose into the blood; instead these cells use glucose to support their own high energy needs.

Adipose connective tissue cells use two enzymatic pathways: lipogenesis and lipolysis (figure 17.12b). **Lipogenesis** (lip′ō′jen′ĕ-sis; *lipo* = fatty) is the synthesis of triglycerides for storage from fatty acids and glycerol obtained from the blood. **Lipolysis** (li-pol′i-sis) involves the breakdown of triglycerides into glycerol and fatty acids that are then released into the blood.

All cells, especially muscle cells, employ enzymatic pathways that produce protein (figure 17.12c). **Protein anabolism** (synthesis) is stimulated with increased uptake of amino acids from the blood to produce protein. **Protein catabolism** (degradation) is the breakdown of protein to release amino acids—however, cells generally do not break down protein for the purpose of supplying amino acids as fuel except under specific conditions (e.g., stress and the release of cortisol, or when starvation occurs). This nutrient source is generally used for "emergency" purposes.

WHAT DID YOU LEARN?

15. Identify the nutrient (e.g., glucose, fatty acids, amino acids) that enters the blood as a result of (a) glycogenolysis and gluconeogenesis, (b) lipolysis, and (c) protein catabolism.

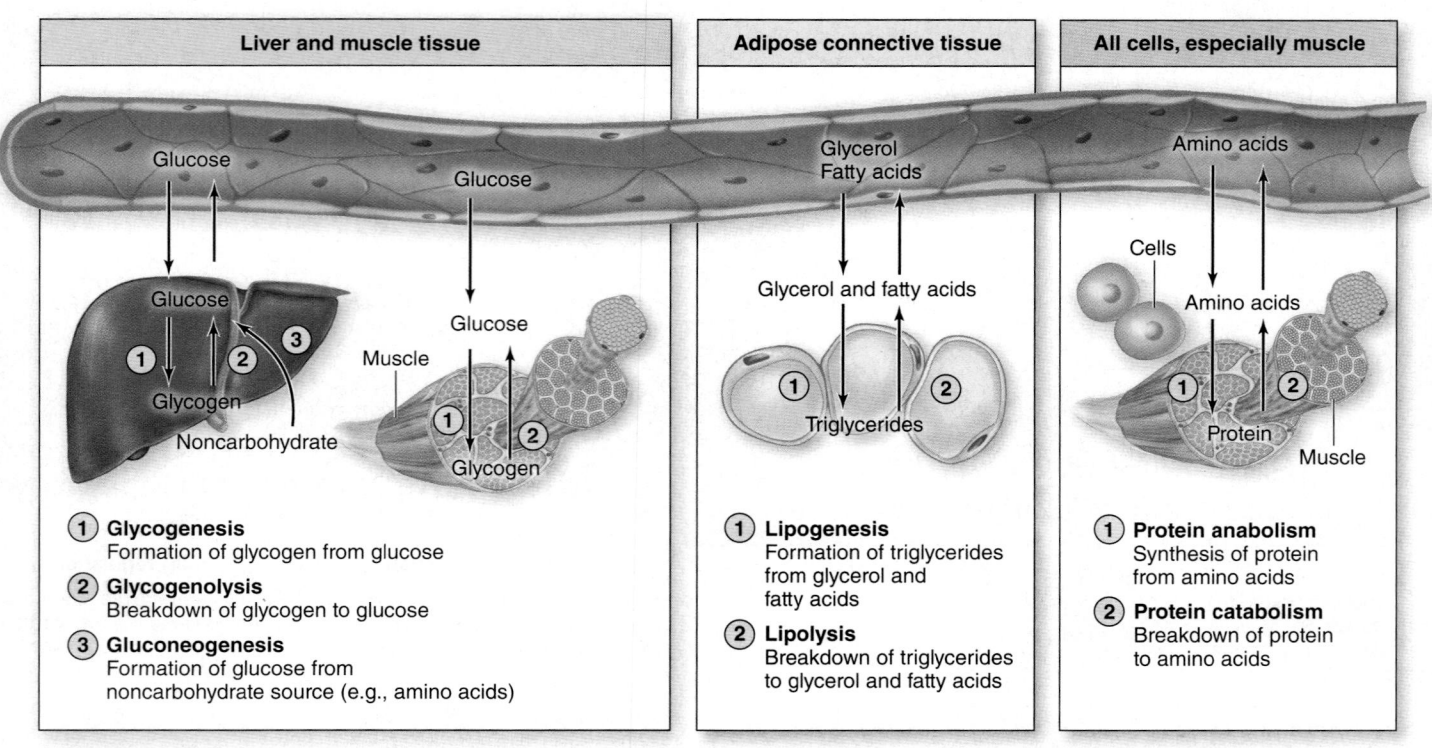

Liver and muscle tissue

① **Glycogenesis**
Formation of glycogen from glucose

② **Glycogenolysis**
Breakdown of glycogen to glucose

③ **Gluconeogenesis**
Formation of glucose from noncarbohydrate source (e.g., amino acids)

(a) Glucose metabolism

Adipose connective tissue

① **Lipogenesis**
Formation of triglycerides from glycerol and fatty acids

② **Lipolysis**
Breakdown of triglycerides to glycerol and fatty acids

(b) Lipid metabolism

All cells, especially muscle

① **Protein anabolism**
Synthesis of protein from amino acids

② **Protein catabolism**
Breakdown of protein to amino acids

(c) Protein metabolism

Figure 17.12 Movement of Nutrients Between the Blood and Cells. Maintaining normal blood levels of nutrients (e.g., glucose, fatty acids, and amino acids) involves the processes of (*a*) glucose metabolism, (*b*) lipid metabolism, and (*c*) protein metabolism.

17.8 The Hypothalamus and the Pituitary Gland

Although some endocrine glands function primarily as independent structures (e.g., the parathyroid glands), many endocrine glands are under the influence or control of the hypothalamus. The hypothalamus has direct control over the release of hormones from the pituitary gland, and it has indirect control over the release of hormones from the thyroid gland, adrenal gland, liver, testes, and ovaries. Thus, the hypothalamus controls a number of physiologic processes. We first describe the anatomic relationship between the hypothalamus and pituitary gland.

17.8a Anatomic Relationship of the Hypothalamus and the Pituitary Gland

LEARNING OBJECTIVES

1. Describe the anatomic relationship of the hypothalamus and the pituitary gland.

2. Identify the specific structures associated with the posterior pituitary and the anterior pituitary.

The **pituitary gland** is also called the *hypophysis* (hī-pof′i-sis; undergrowth). It lies inferior to the hypothalamus (**figure 17.13**). This small, slightly oval gland, which is approximately the size of a pea, is housed within the sella turcica of the sphenoid bone (see section 8.2b).

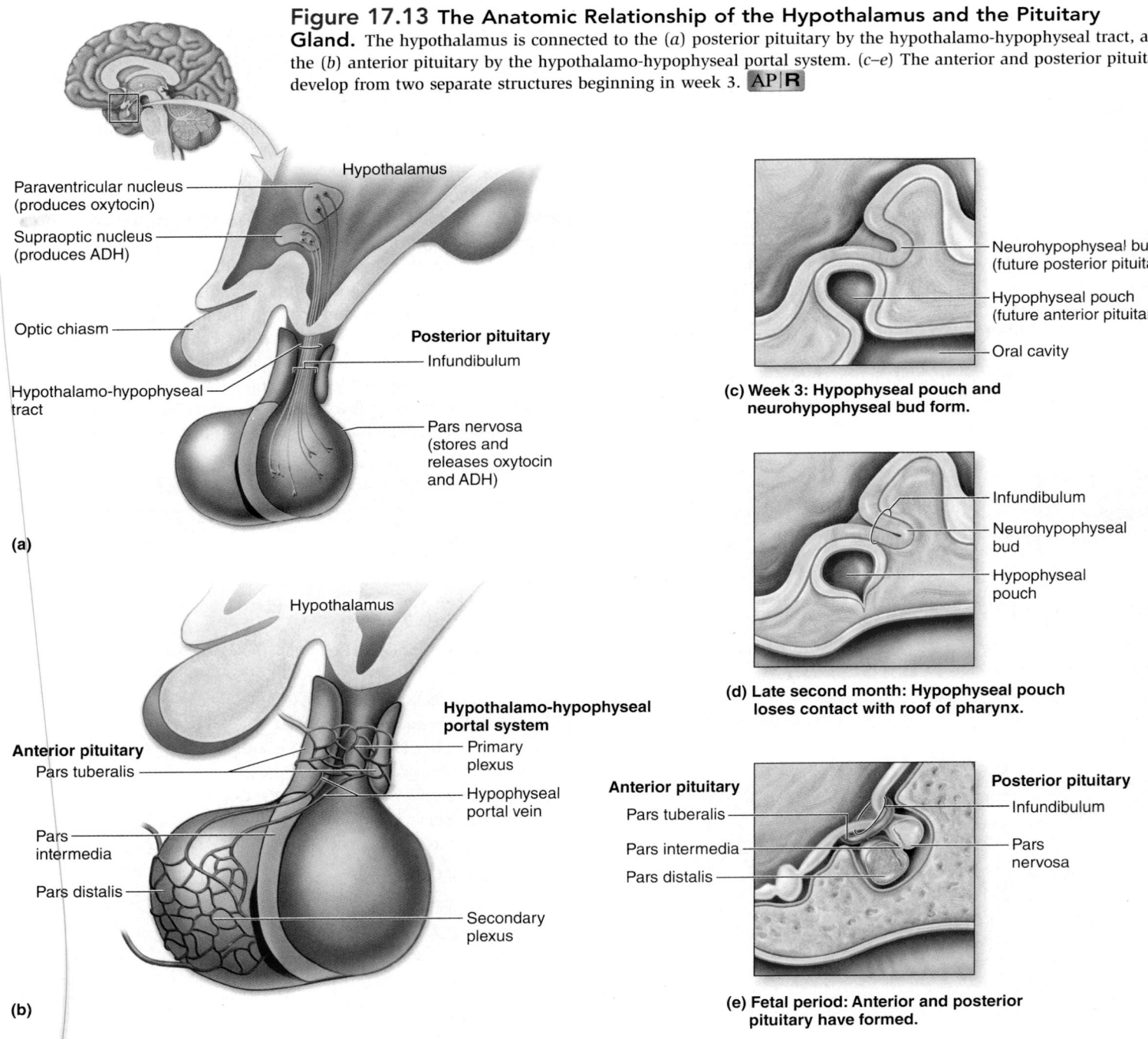

Figure 17.13 The Anatomic Relationship of the Hypothalamus and the Pituitary Gland. The hypothalamus is connected to the (a) posterior pituitary by the hypothalamo-hypophyseal tract, and the (b) anterior pituitary by the hypothalamo-hypophyseal portal system. (c–e) The anterior and posterior pituitary develop from two separate structures beginning in week 3. AP|R

(a)
- Paraventricular nucleus (produces oxytocin)
- Supraoptic nucleus (produces ADH)
- Optic chiasm
- Hypothalamo-hypophyseal tract
- Hypothalamus
- Posterior pituitary
- Infundibulum
- Pars nervosa (stores and releases oxytocin and ADH)

(b)
- Hypothalamus
- Anterior pituitary
- Pars tuberalis
- Pars intermedia
- Pars distalis
- Hypothalamo-hypophyseal portal system
- Primary plexus
- Hypophyseal portal vein
- Secondary plexus

(c) **Week 3: Hypophyseal pouch and neurohypophyseal bud form.**
- Neurohypophyseal bud (future posterior pituitary)
- Hypophyseal pouch (future anterior pituitary)
- Oral cavity

(d) **Late second month: Hypophyseal pouch loses contact with roof of pharynx.**
- Infundibulum
- Neurohypophyseal bud
- Hypophyseal pouch

(e) **Fetal period: Anterior and posterior pituitary have formed.**
- Anterior pituitary
- Pars tuberalis
- Pars intermedia
- Pars distalis
- Posterior pituitary
- Infundibulum
- Pars nervosa

The pituitary gland is connected to the hypothalamus by a very thin stalk, called either the **infundibulum** (in-fŭn′dib′ū-lŭm; a funnel), or *infundibular stalk*. The pituitary gland is partitioned both structurally and functionally into a posterior pituitary and an anterior pituitary and sometimes referred to as just the *posterior lobe* and *anterior lobe*, respectively. The characteristics of the posterior pituitary and anterior pituitary are summarized in **table 17.3**.

Posterior Pituitary

The **posterior pituitary** is also called *neurohypophysis* (nū′rō-hī-pof′i-sis). It is a neural part of the pituitary gland that develops beginning at about the third week of development as a bud that grows from the developing hypothalamus. The posterior pituitary is composed of a rounded lobe called the *pars nervosa* and the infundibulum; it makes up approximately one-quarter of the mass of the pituitary gland.

Axons from groups of neurons (approximately 10,000) extend from the hypothalamus to the pars nervosa of the posterior pituitary. The dendrites and cell bodies of these neurons are within the hypothalamus. Unmyelinated axons from these neurons extend through the infundibulum as the **hypothalamo-hypophyseal tract.** The ends of the axons, including synaptic knobs, are within the pars nervosa. Two specific hypothalamic nuclei are recognized as being associated with the posterior pituitary: the **supraoptic** (sū-pră-op′tik) **nucleus** and the **paraventricular** (par-ă′ven-trik′ū-lĕr) **nucleus.**

Anterior Pituitary

Most of the pituitary gland (about three-quarters of the mass of the pituitary gland) is composed of the **anterior pituitary,** or *adenohypophysis* (ad′ĕ-nō-hī-pof′i-sis; *adenos* = gland). It develops beginning at about the third week of development as an invagination of the ectoderm in the developing oral cavity to form the hypophyseal pouch (figure 17.13c–e). The anterior pituitary is partitioned into three distinct areas (figure 17.13b). The *pars distalis* is the large anterior rounded portion of the anterior pituitary. The *pars tuberalis* is a thin wrapping around the infundibulum. A thin *pars intermedia* is a scant region between the pars distalis and the posterior pituitary.

The connection between the hypothalamus and the anterior pituitary involves two capillary plexuses interconnected by **portal veins** (a portal vessel is any vessel located between two capillary beds; see section 20.1e). The very porous capillary network associated with the hypothalamus is the **primary plexus,** or *primary capillary plexus*. The capillary network associated with the anterior pituitary is the **secondary plexus,** or *secondary capillary plexus*. Blood is drained from the primary plexus of the hypothalamus and transported to the secondary plexus of the anterior pituitary by the **hypophyseal portal veins.** This blood vessel network is called the **hypothalamo-hypophyseal** (hī′pō-thal′ă-mō-hī-pō-fiz′ē-ăl) **portal system**. Thus, the hypothalamo-hypophyseal portal system provides a direct blood pathway between the hypothalamus and the anterior pituitary.

 WHAT DID YOU LEARN?

16   What is the anatomic connection between the hypothalamus and the posterior pituitary?

17.8b Interactions Between the Hypothalamus and the Posterior Pituitary Gland

LEARNING OBJECTIVE

3.   Identify the two hormones released from the posterior pituitary and describe how the hypothalamus controls their release.

The posterior pituitary stores two hormones (figure 17.13*a*): **oxytocin (OT)** (ok-sē-tō′sin; *okytokos* = swift birth) and **antidiuretic** (an′tē-dī-ū-ret′-ik) **hormone (ADH).** Both hormones are synthesized in the hypothalamus: The paraventricular nucleus primarily produces oxytocin, and the supraoptic nucleus primarily forms ADH. For this reason, these neurons in the hypothalamus are called **neurosecretory** (nūr′ō-sē′krĕ-tōr-ē) **cells.** Following their synthesis in the hypothalamus, the hormones are packaged within secretory vesicles and transported by fast axonal transport (section 12.2c) through the unmyelinated axons to the synaptic knobs within the posterior pituitary. Note that the posterior pituitary does not produce

Table 17.3	Comparison of Posterior and Anterior Pituitary	
Characteristic	**Posterior Pituitary**	**Anterior Pituitary**
Structure	¼ of mass of pituitary gland; nervous tissue	¾ of mass of pituitary gland; endocrine tissue
Mechanism of control	Nervous	Hormonal

Hormones synthesized by hypothalamus	*Synthesized and transported to posterior pituitary*
	
	    Oxytocin (OT)
	    Antidiuretic hormone (ADH)
		Synthesized and released into hypothalamo-hypophyseal portal system
		
		    Thyrotropin-releasing hormone (TRH)
		    Prolactin-releasing hormone (PRH)
		    Gonadotropin-releasing hormone (GnRH)
		    Corticotropin-releasing hormone (CRH)
		    Growth hormone–releasing hormone (GHRH)
		    Prolactin-inhibiting hormone (PIH)
		    Growth-inhibiting hormone (GIH)

Hormones released, or synthesized and released, by pituitary gland	*Released only*
	
	    Oxytocin (OT)
	    Antidiuretic hormone (ADH)
		Tropic hormones synthesized and released
		
		    Thyroid-stimulating hormone (TSH)
		    Prolactin (PRL)
		    Follicle-stimulating hormone (FSH)
		    Luteinizing hormone (LH)
		    Adrenocorticotropic hormone (ACTH)
		    Growth hormone (GH)

hormones; it is simply a storage site for these two hormones synthesized in the hypothalamus.

Hormone is released from the posterior pituitary when a nerve signal is sent from the hypothalamus along the hypothalamo-hypophyseal tract. Specifically, nerve signals from the paraventricular nucleus primarily stimulate release of oxytocin and those from the supraoptic nucleus primarily cause release of ADH. These molecules are considered hormones, and not neurotransmitters, because they enter into the blood when released, even though they are released from synaptic knobs of neurons. (For detailed descriptions of these hormones see sections 24.6d and 25.4b for ADH, and section 29.6 for oxytocin.)

⚡ WHAT DID YOU LEARN?

17 How is ADH released from the posterior pituitary when the hypothalamus detects an increase in blood osmolarity (concentration)?

17.8c Interactions Between the Hypothalamus and the Anterior Pituitary Gland

✓ LEARNING OBJECTIVES

4. Explain how the hypothalamus controls the release of hormones from the anterior pituitary.

5. List the hormones released from the hypothalamus that control the anterior pituitary.

6. Identify and briefly describe the function of the six tropic hormones produced by the anterior pituitary.

Hormonal stimulation triggers the release of hormones from the anterior pituitary. This occurs when specific hormones produced within the hypothalamus are released into the primary plexus and then transported via the hypophyseal portal vein to reach the secondary plexus within the anterior pituitary. The anterior pituitary then releases its hormones into the blood of the general circulation through which they reach target cells.

Hormones of the Hypothalamus

The hormones released from the hypothalamus are called **regulatory hormones** because they are molecules secreted into the blood to regulate secretion of anterior pituitary hormones. Regulatory hormones fall into one of two groups: **releasing hormones (RHs)** that stimulate the production and secretion of specific anterior pituitary hormones, and **inhibiting hormones (IHs)** that deter the production and secretion of specific anterior pituitary hormones. The hormones released from the hypothalamus that control the release of anterior pituitary hormones are listed in **table 17.4**. The arrival of these hypothalamic hormones controls specific cells of the anterior pituitary to release their hormone molecules **(figure 17.14)**.

Hormones of the Anterior Pituitary

The anterior pituitary secretes six major hormones. Five of the six hormones are called **tropic** (trōp′ik) **hormones** because they

Figure 17.14 Tropic Anterior Pituitary Hormones. The hypothalamus releases seven regulatory hormones, and the anterior pituitary releases six tropic hormones. AP|R

Table 17.4 Hypothalamic Hormones that Stimulate the Anterior Pituitary

Hormone	Effect on Anterior Pituitary	Indirect Effect on Other Organs
Thyrotropin-releasing hormone (TRH)	Increases secretion of thyroid-stimulating hormone (TSH)	TSH stimulates release of thyroid hormone (TH) from the thyroid gland
Prolactin-releasing hormone (PRH)	Increases secretion of prolactin (PRL)	PRL regulates breast milk production in females; may help androgen production in males
Gonadotropin-releasing hormone (GnRH)	Increases secretion of follicle-stimulating hormone (FSH) and luteinizing hormone (LH)	FSH and LH regulate production and maturation of gametes (sperm and oocytes) and hormone synthesis by the gonads
Corticotropin-releasing hormone (CRH)	Increases secretion of adrenocorticotropic hormone (ACTH)	ACTH stimulates the adrenal cortex to produce and secrete corticosteroid hormones (e.g., cortisol)
Growth hormone–releasing hormone (GHRH)	Increases secretion of growth hormone (GH)	GH stimulates cell growth either directly or indirectly (through release of insulin-like growth factor [IGF]), especially in cartilage, bone, muscle tissue, and adipose connective tissue

stimulate other endocrine glands or cells to secrete other hormones. These tropic hormones include thyroid-stimulating hormone, follicle-stimulating hormone, luteinizing hormone, adrenocorticotropic hormone, and growth hormone. (Prolactin is not considered a tropic hormone because it does not stimulate hormone secretion by other endocrine cells of the body.) The primary function of each of these hormones is discussed here:

- **Thyroid-stimulating hormone (TSH),** also called *thyrotropin* (thī-rō-trō′pin), regulates the release of thyroid hormone from the thyroid gland (described later).
- **Prolactin** (prō-lak′tin; *lac* = milk) **(PRL).** Prolactin primarily regulates mammary gland growth and breast milk production in females and may help androgen production in males (see sections 28.3f and 29.8c).
- **Follicle-stimulating hormone (FSH)** and **luteinizing** (lū′tē-in-ī-zing) **hormone (LH)** are collectively called **gonadotropins.** These hormones act in both females and males, regulating hormone synthesis by the gonads and the production and maturation of gametes (see sections 28.3b and 28.4b).
- **Adrenocorticotropic** (ă-drē′nō-kōr′ti-kō-trō′pik) **hormone (ACTH)** is also called *corticotropin*. ACTH stimulates the adrenal cortex to produce and secrete glucocorticoids (e.g., cortisol) (described later).
- **Growth hormone (GH)** is also called *somatotropin*. GH stimulates cell growth as well as cell division and affects most body cells, particularly those within the skeletal and muscular systems. GH exhibits its tropic effects by stimulating the liver to release **insulin-like growth factor 1 and 2 (IGF-1** and **IGF-2).** These are also called *somatomedins*

(sō′mă-tō-mē′din) and are hormones that have overlapping functions with growth hormone (described later).

Melanocyte-Stimulating Hormone

The anterior pituitary also releases **melanocyte-stimulating hormone (MSH).** MSH stimulates the rate of melanin synthesis by melanocytes in the integument and the distribution of melanocytes in the skin. Its secretion has little effect in humans and usually ceases prior to adulthood, except in certain diseases.

 WHAT DID YOU LEARN?

18 What are the six primary hormones released from the anterior pituitary? How is the release of each of these hormones regulated by the hypothalamus?

17.9 Representative Hormones Regulated by the Hypothalamus

Regulatory hormones secreted by the hypothalamus (TRH, PRH, GnRH, CRH, GHRH, PIH, and GIH) influence the secretion of the hormones from the anterior pituitary, as just described. Here we examine regulatory hormone effects on three of the six specific tropic hormones: growth hormone, thyroid hormone, and glucocorticoids (e.g., cortisol). The other three—FSH, LH, and prolactin, which participate in regulation of the reproductive system—are described in detail in chapters 28 and 29.

CLINICAL VIEW
Disorders of Growth Hormone Secretion

Pituitary dwarfism

Gigantism

Pituitary dwarfism is a condition that exists at birth as a result of inadequate growth hormone production due to a hypothalamic or pituitary problem. Growth retardation is typically not evident until a child reaches 1 year of age, because the influence of growth hormone (GH) is minimal during the first 6 to 12 months of life. In addition to short stature, children with pituitary dwarfism often have periodic low blood sugar (hypoglycemia). Injections of growth hormone over a period of many years can bring about improvement, but not a normal state.

Too much growth hormone causes excessive growth and leads to increased levels of blood sugar. Oversecretion of growth hormone in childhood causes **pituitary gigantism.** Beyond extraordinary height (sometimes up to 8 feet), these people have enormous internal organs, a large and protruding tongue, and significant problems with blood glucose management. If untreated, a pituitary giant dies at a comparatively early age, often from complications of diabetes or heart failure.

Excessive growth hormone production in an adult results in **acromegaly.** The individual does not grow in height, but the bones of the face, hands, and feet enlarge and widen (appositional growth), along with growth in cartilage. An increase in mandible size leads to a protruding jaw (prognathism). Internal organs, especially the liver, increase in size, and increased release of glucose lead to the development of diabetes in virtually everyone with acromegaly. Acromegaly may result from loss of feedback control of growth hormone at either the hypothalamic or pituitary level, or it may develop because of a GH-secreting tumor of the pituitary. Removal of the pituitary alleviates the effects of acromegaly, but this drastic treatment results in the loss of all pituitary hormones.

Age 9

Age 16

Age 33

Age 52

Acromegaly

17.9a Growth Hormone

1. Describe the homeostatic system involving growth hormone.

Growth hormone (GH) has numerous functions, including the stimulation of linear growth at the epiphyseal plate by causing an increase in mitosis and matrix formation within cartilage and bone, hypertrophy of muscle, and many other physiologic changes.

The release of GH (**figure 17.15**) from the anterior pituitary is controlled by the release of **growth hormone–releasing hormone (GHRH)** from the hypothalamus. GHRH is produced

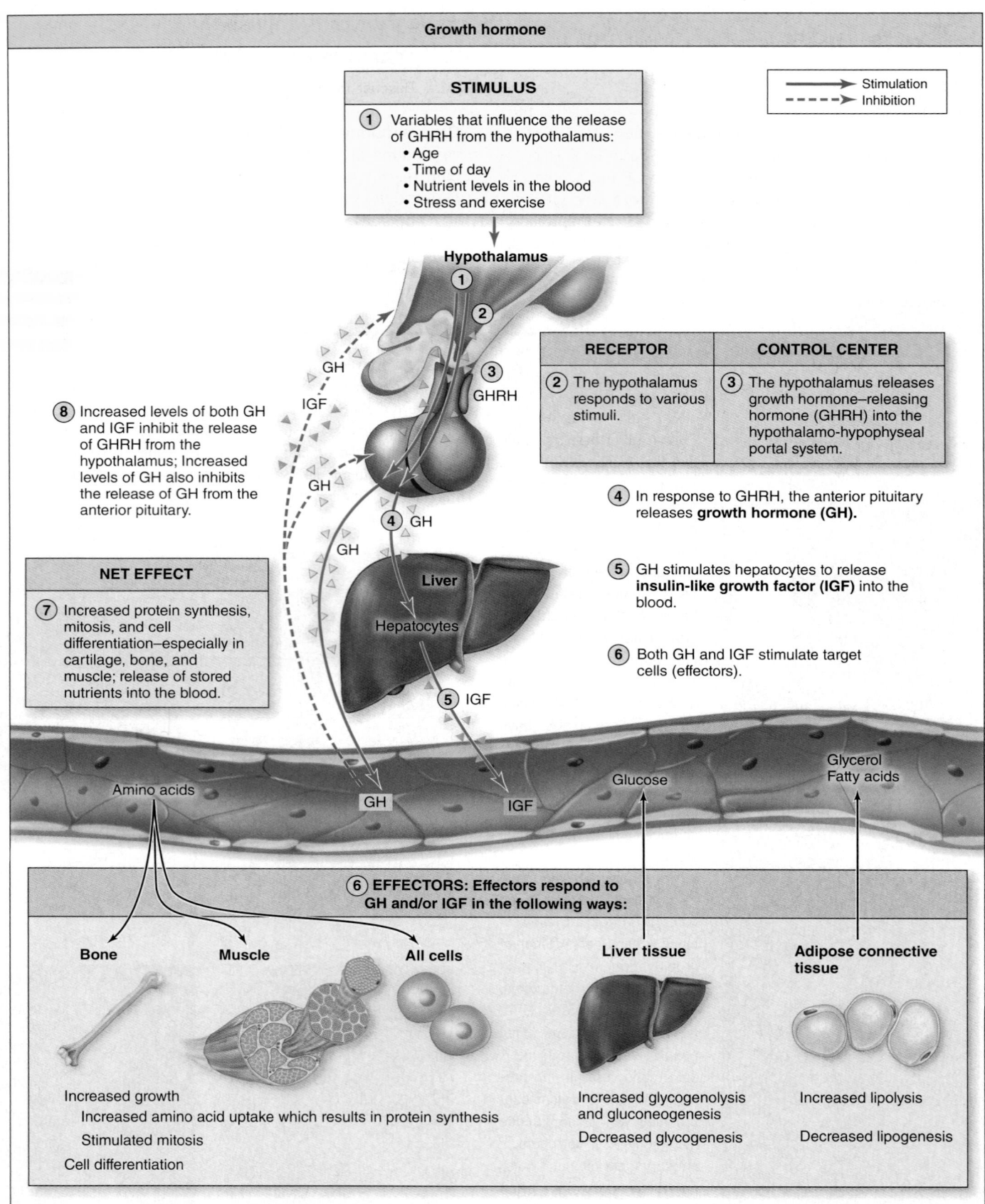

Growth hormone

Stimulation → (solid arrow)
Inhibition → (dashed arrow)

STIMULUS

① Variables that influence the release of GHRH from the hypothalamus:
- Age
- Time of day
- Nutrient levels in the blood
- Stress and exercise

Hypothalamus

① ② ③

GH

IGF

GHRH

⑧ Increased levels of both GH and IGF inhibit the release of GHRH from the hypothalamus; Increased levels of GH also inhibits the release of GH from the anterior pituitary.

RECEPTOR

② The hypothalamus responds to various stimuli.

CONTROL CENTER

③ The hypothalamus releases growth hormone–releasing hormone (GHRH) into the hypothalamo-hypophyseal portal system.

④ In response to GHRH, the anterior pituitary releases **growth hormone (GH).**

GH

④ GH

GH

Liver

NET EFFECT

⑦ Increased protein synthesis, mitosis, and cell differentiation—especially in cartilage, bone, and muscle; release of stored nutrients into the blood.

Hepatocytes

⑤ GH stimulates hepatocytes to release **insulin-like growth factor (IGF)** into the blood.

⑥ Both GH and IGF stimulate target cells (effectors).

⑤ IGF

Glycerol
Fatty acids

Amino acids

Glucose

GH

IGF

⑥ **EFFECTORS:** Effectors respond to GH and/or IGF in the following ways:

Bone   **Muscle**   **All cells**   **Liver tissue**   **Adipose connective tissue**

Increased growth
  Increased amino acid uptake which results in protein synthesis
Stimulated mitosis
Cell differentiation

Increased glycogenolysis and gluconeogenesis

Decreased glycogenesis

Increased lipolysis

Decreased lipogenesis

Figure 17.15 Regulation and Action of Growth Hormone. The hypothalamus responds to particular stimuli by releasing growth hormone–releasing hormone (GHRH), which stimulates the anterior pituitary to release growth hormone (GH). GH stimulates the release of insulin-like growth factor (IGF) from the liver. Together, GH and IGF stimulate growth and alter the availability of nutrient molecules within the blood to support the growth. (Direction of arrows between the blood and effectors indicates the net movement of the nutrients.)

and released from the hypothalamus in response to a number of factors, including a person's age, the time of day, nutrient levels in the blood, stress, and exercise (figure 17.16). GHRH enters the hypothalamo-hypophyseal portal system and is transported to the anterior pituitary (figure 17.15). GHRH binds to receptors in specific cells of the anterior pituitary (somatotropic cells) and stimulates the release of GH into the general circulation to be transported throughout the body.

One of the primary targets of GH is hepatocytes. Hepatocytes release the peptide **insulin-like growth factor (IGF),** also called somatomedin, into the general circulation when stimulated by GH. GH and IGF have overlapping functions, but IGF is responsible for the greater response from the target cells. This results from the difference in their individual half-lives: GH (a protein hormone) has a half-life of 6 to 20 minutes, and IGF (also a protein hormone) has a half-life of approximately 20 hours because it is transported in the blood by carrier proteins that help protect IGF from destruction.

All cells of the body have receptors for GH, IGF, or both. Binding of the hormones activates second messengers within the target cells, altering enzymatic pathways to increase protein synthesis, mitosis, cell differentiation, or a combination of these. Bone and muscle tissue in particular are affected by these hormones. In muscle fibers, uptake of amino acids increases and use of glucose decreases.

Hepatocytes are also stimulated by GH to increase both glycogenolysis and gluconeogenesis; at the same time, the glycogenesis pathway is inhibited. Blood glucose levels rise as a result. This rise in blood glucose is referred to as a **diabetogenic** (dī′ă-bet′ō-jen-ik) effect due to the similarity of elevated blood glucose levels in individuals with diabetes mellitus.

Adipose connective tissue cells are stimulated by GH and IGF to increase lipolysis and decrease lipogenesis, thus causing an increase

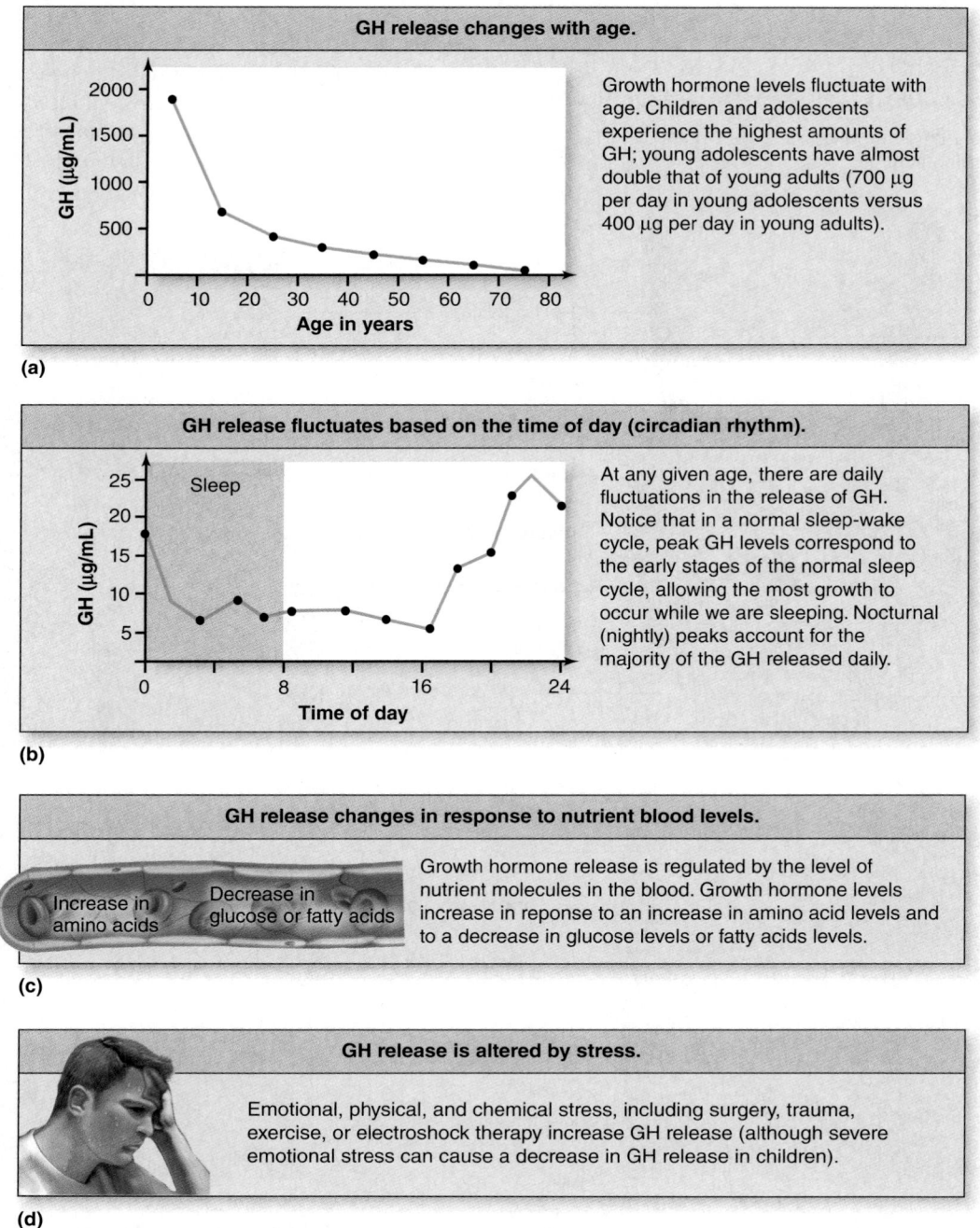

(a)

GH release changes with age.

Growth hormone levels fluctuate with age. Children and adolescents experience the highest amounts of GH; young adolescents have almost double that of young adults (700 μg per day in young adolescents versus 400 μg per day in young adults).

(b)

GH release fluctuates based on the time of day (circadian rhythm).

At any given age, there are daily fluctuations in the release of GH. Notice that in a normal sleep-wake cycle, peak GH levels correspond to the early stages of the normal sleep cycle, allowing the most growth to occur while we are sleeping. Nocturnal (nightly) peaks account for the majority of the GH released daily.

(c)

GH release changes in response to nutrient blood levels.

Increase in amino acids
Decrease in glucose or fatty acids

Growth hormone release is regulated by the level of nutrient molecules in the blood. Growth hormone levels increase in reponse to an increase in amino acid levels and to a decrease in glucose levels or fatty acids levels.

(d)

GH release is altered by stress.

Emotional, physical, and chemical stress, including surgery, trauma, exercise, or electroshock therapy increase GH release (although severe emotional stress can cause a decrease in GH release in children).

Figure 17.16 Variables That Influence Growth Hormone Levels. Release of growth hormone is influenced by: (a) an individual's age, (b) time of day, (c) nutrient blood levels, and (d) stress.

in the level of glycerol and fatty acids in the blood. Growth is an energy-requiring process. The additional glucose released from the liver, and the fatty acids released from adipose connective tissue, together provide nutrient molecules required in cellular respiration for generating ATP (section 3.4). Additional responses to the release of GH are listed in the summary table on GH in the appendix (Table B.3).

The release of both GHRH from the hypothalamus and GH from the anterior pituitary are regulated by negative feedback in the following ways: In response to increased levels of GH or increased levels of IGF, the hypothalamus is stimulated to release **growth hormone–inhibiting hormone (GHIH),** which inhibits the release of GH from the anterior pituitary. GH also directly inhibits its own release from the anterior pituitary.

WHAT DO YOU THINK?

3 You may have heard someone describe a teenager going through puberty as having "thinned out." Which cellular process stimulated by GH directly accounts for the loss of fat tissue: glycogenolysis, lipolysis, or protein anabolism?

WHAT DID YOU LEARN?

19 How do GHRH, GH, and IGF function together to regulate growth?

20 What are the primary target organs/tissues of GH and IGF? Describe the effect on each.

17.9b Thyroid Gland and Thyroid Hormone

LEARNING OBJECTIVES

2. Describe thyroid gland location and anatomy.
3. Discuss how thyroid hormones are produced, stored, and secreted.
4. Explain the control of thyroid hormone by the hypothalamus and pituitary.

The largest structure in the body entirely devoted to endocrine activities is the **thyroid** (thī′royd; *thyreos* = an oblong shield) **gland (figure 17.17).** Thyroid hormone produced by the thyroid gland increases metabolic rate and body temperature. Release of thyroid hormone is under the control of the hypothalamus via the anterior pituitary.

Anatomy of the Thyroid Gland

The thyroid gland in an adult weighs between 25 and 30 grams and is located immediately inferior to the thyroid cartilage of the larynx and anterior to the trachea. It is covered by a connective tissue capsule.

The thyroid gland exhibits a distinctive "butterfly" shape due to its **left** and **right lobes,** which are connected at the anterior midline by a narrow **isthmus** (is′mŭs). Both lobes of the thyroid gland are highly vascularized, giving the gland an intense reddish coloration.

(a)

(b)

Figure 17.17 The Thyroid Gland. (*a*) A drawing and cadaver photo illustrate that the thyroid gland is located anterior to the thyroid cartilage and has a rich blood supply. (*b*) Microscopic anatomy of thyroid follicles, illustrating the simple cuboidal epithelium of the follicular cells, colloid within the follicle lumen, and the relationship of parafollicular cells (which produce calcitonin) to a follicle. **AP|R**

The gland is supplied by the superior and inferior thyroid arteries. Thyroid veins return venous blood from the thyroid and also transport thyroid hormone (and calcitonin, see section 7.6) from the thyroid gland into the general circulation.

The thyroid gland at the histologic level is composed of numerous microscopic, spherical structures called **thyroid follicles** (figure 17.17*b*). The wall of each follicle is formed by simple cuboidal epithelial cells, called **follicular cells,** which surround a central lumen. That lumen houses a viscous, protein-rich fluid termed **colloid** (kol′oyd). Thus, follicles are microscopic fluid-filled spheres.

The follicular cells produce and later release **thyroid hormone (TH)** by first synthesizing a glycoprotein called **thyroglobulin (TGB)** and secreting it by exocytosis into the colloid fluid. In brief, iodine molecules must be combined with the thyroglobulin in the colloid to produce hormone precursors, which are TGB molecules that contain immature thyroid hormone within their structure. The precursors are stored in the colloid until the secretion of thyroid hormone is needed.

When the thyroid gland is stimulated to secrete thyroid hormone, some of the colloid with thyroid hormone precursors is internalized by endocytosis into a follicular cell. It travels to a lysosome, where an enzyme releases the immature thyroid hormone molecules from the precursor in preparation for its secretion from the follicular cells. The details of thyroid hormone synthesis and release are covered in **figure 17.18**.

WHAT DO YOU THINK?

④ Have you ever noticed that the salt you buy in the grocery store is "iodized"? What is the function of iodine added to our salt?

① **I⁻ uptake.** Iodide ion (I⁻) is moved by active transport into follicular cells.

②a **I₂ formation.** Two I⁻ join to form molecular iodine (I₂).

②b **Thyroglobulin synthesis.** Thyroglobulin protein, containing tyrosine amino acids, is synthesized in follicular cells.

③ **Transport to colloid.** Both I₂ and thyroglobulin are transported into colloid.

④ **MIT and DIT formation.** One I₂ binds to tyrosine within thyroglobulin to form MIT; two I₂ bind to tyrosine to form DIT.

⑤ **Pre-T₃, pre-T₄ formation.** Within thyroglobulin molecules, one DIT and one MIT join to form pre-T₃; or, two DIT join to form pre-T₄.

⑥ **Endocytosis into follicular cell.** The modified protein strand containing pre-T₃ and pre-T₄ is endocytosed into follicular cell and taken to a lysosome.

⑦ **T₃, T₄ release.** T₃ and T₄ are excised from molecule and released into the blood.

MIT: monoiodotyrosine   T₃: triiodothyronine
DIT: diiodotyrosine   T₄: tetraidothyronine

Figure 17.18 Thyroid Hormone: Synthesis, Storage, and Release. Iodine is attached to tyrosine amino acids of thyroglobulin within the colloid of thyroid follicles. Then pre-T3 and pre-T4 structures are formed. Thyroglobulin with pre-T3 and pre-T4 is later transported into the follicular cells. Within lysosomes of follicular cells, thyroid hormone is cleaved from thyroglobulin and released into the blood.

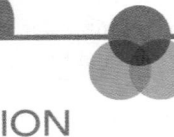
Action of Thyroid Hormone

Thyroid hormone is released from the thyroid gland as a result of the integrated activities of the hypothalamus and anterior pituitary. This physiologic relationship is referred to as the **hypothalamic-pituitary-thyroid axis.** A description of how this axis works is explained next **(figure 17.19).**

The hypothalamus releases thyrotropin-releasing hormone (TRH), which enters into the hypothalamo-hypophyseal portal system in response to a decrease in blood levels of thyroid hormone. Other stimuli that may cause increased release of TRH include cold weather, pregnancy, high altitude, hypoglycemia—and in children, decreased body temperature.

TRH binds to receptors in cells of the anterior pituitary (thyrotropic cells) and stimulates the anterior pituitary to release thyroid-stimulating hormone (TSH) into the general circulation.

TSH binds to receptors of the follicular cells of the thyroid gland and stimulates the release of thyroid hormone (TH). TH has two forms—**triiodothyronine (T_3)** and **tetraiodothyronine (thyroxine) (T_4)**—which are released into the circulation.

T_3 and T_4 are transported within the blood bound by carrier molecules (e.g., albumin, thyroxine-binding globulin, also called TBG). T_3 and T_4 randomly become unbound from the carrier protein and can then exit from the blood.

A transport system moves TH into target cells, where it binds to intracellular receptors. T_3 is the most active form of TH. Most cells, however, have an enzyme to remove one iodine in order to convert T_4 to T_3. This increases a cell's response to thyroid hormone because a much greater amount of T_4 ($\sim 90\%$) is produced than T_3 ($\sim 10\%$).

TH is a lipid-soluble hormone that ultimately increases protein synthesis in all cells, especially neurons. TH specifically stimulates the synthesis of sodium-potassium (Na^+/K^+) pumps in nervous tissue, and the action of these additional ion pumps generates heat. The rise in temperature is referred to as the **calorigenic** (kǎ-lōr′i-jen′ik; *calor* = heat, *genesis* = production) **effect.**

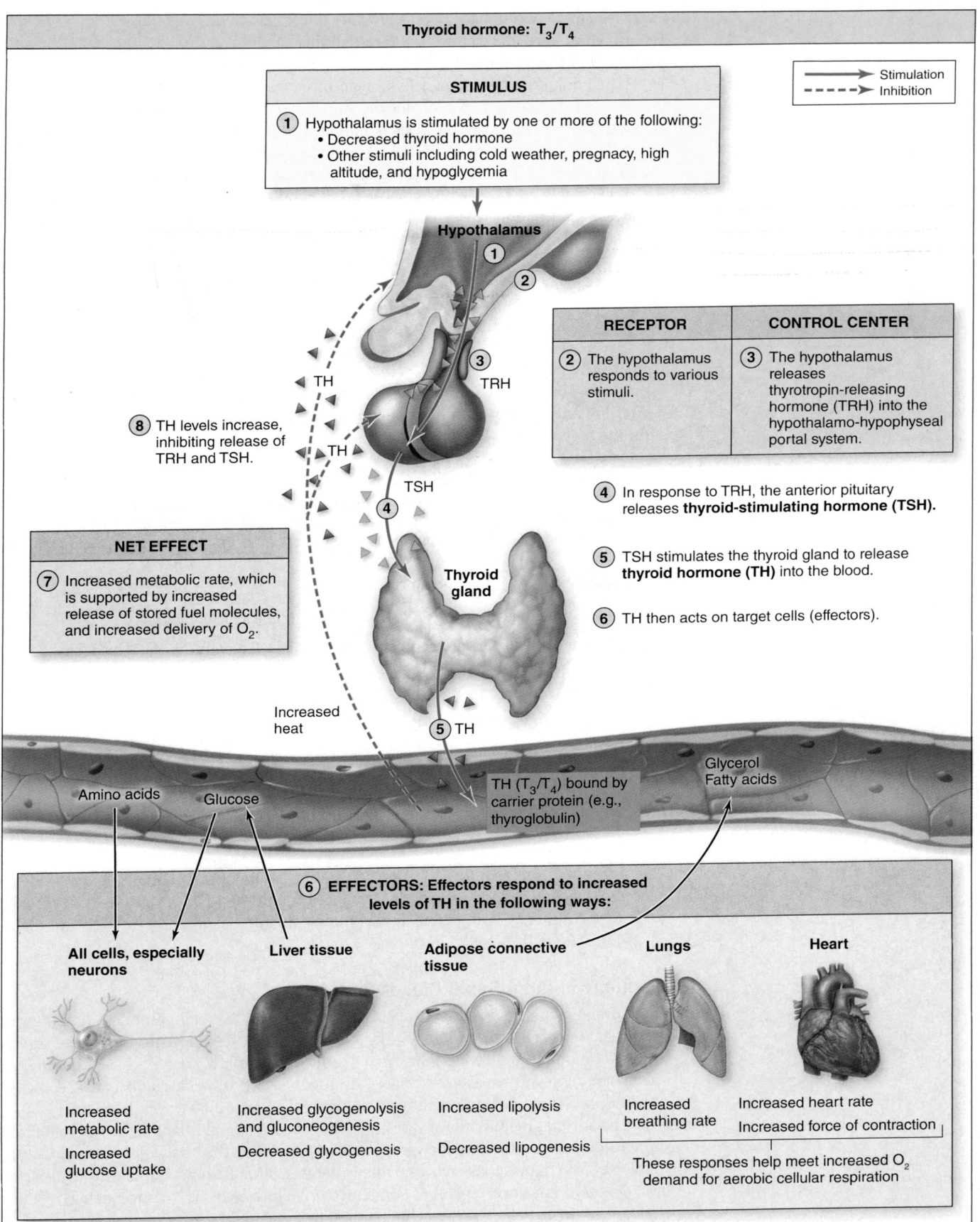

Thyroid hormone: T_3/T_4

→ Stimulation
---→ Inhibition

STIMULUS

① Hypothalamus is stimulated by one or more of the following:
• Decreased thyroid hormone
• Other stimuli including cold weather, pregnacy, high altitude, and hypoglycemia

Hypothalamus

① ②

③

TH   TRH

⑧ TH levels increase, inhibiting release of TRH and TSH.

TH

TSH

④

RECEPTOR	CONTROL CENTER
② The hypothalamus responds to various stimuli.	③ The hypothalamus releases thyrotropin-releasing hormone (TRH) into the hypothalamo-hypophyseal portal system.

④ In response to TRH, the anterior pituitary releases **thyroid-stimulating hormone (TSH).**

⑤ TSH stimulates the thyroid gland to release **thyroid hormone (TH)** into the blood.

NET EFFECT

⑦ Increased metabolic rate, which is supported by increased release of stored fuel molecules, and increased delivery of O_2.

Thyroid gland

⑥ TH then acts on target cells (effectors).

Increased heat

⑤ TH

Amino acids   Glucose

TH (T_3/T_4) bound by carrier protein (e.g., thyroglobulin)

Glycerol Fatty acids

⑥ **EFFECTORS: Effectors respond to increased levels of TH in the following ways:**

All cells, especially neurons   **Liver tissue**   **Adipose connective tissue**   **Lungs**   **Heart**

Increased metabolic rate

Increased glucose uptake

Increased glycogenolysis and gluconeogenesis

Decreased glycogenesis

Increased lipolysis

Decreased lipogenesis

Increased breathing rate

Increased heart rate

Increased force of contraction

These responses help meet increased O_2 demand for aerobic cellular respiration

Figure 17.19 Regulation and Action of Thyroid Hormone. The hypothalamus responds to particular stimuli by releasing thyrotropin-releasing hormone (TRH), which stimulates the anterior pituitary to release thyroid-stimulating hormone (TSH). TSH stimulates the thyroid gland to release TH. TH increases the body's metabolic rate and alters the availability of nutrient molecules within the blood to support the higher metabolic rate. (Direction of arrows between the blood and effectors indicates the net movement of the nutrients.)

Increased amino acid uptake by cells provides the structural building blocks for these processes. TH also stimulates all cells to increase their glucose uptake. Concomitant with this increase is buildup in the number of cellular respiration enzymes within mitochondria.

TH stimulates other target cells to help meet the additional requirements for ATP due to the elevated metabolic rate. Hepatocytes are stimulated to increase both glycogenolysis and gluconeogenesis, while glycogenesis is inhibited, thus additional glucose is released into the blood. Adipose connective tissue cells respond to TH by both stimulating lipolysis and inhibiting lipogenesis. As a result, both glycerol and fatty acids are released into blood as alternative fuel molecules. This saves blood glucose for the brain and is called the **glucose-sparing effect.**

Respiration rate increases in response to TH to meet the additional demands for oxygen. Additionally, both heart rate and force of heart contraction increase blood flow to the tissues to deliver more nutrients and oxygen. This is a result of the heart cells increasing their number of cellular receptors for epinephrine and norepinephrine, ensuring that the heart continues to be more responsive to these hormones (see section 19.9b). Additional responses to the release of thyroid hormone are listed in the summary table on thyroid hormone in the appendix (Table B.4).

The release of both TRH from the hypothalamus and TSH from the anterior pituitary are regulated by negative feedback. Increased thyroid hormone inhibits the release of both TRH from the hypothalamus and the release of TSH from the anterior pituitary. Increased TH also causes the release of growth hormone inhibiting hormone, which inhibits the release of TSH from the anterior pituitary (not shown on figure 17.19).

WHAT DO YOU THINK?

5 Predict the signs/symptoms that a person with hyperthyroidism would exhibit in each of the following circumstances: (a) high temperature or low temperature, (b) elevated pulse or decreased pulse, (c) elevated breathing or decreased breathing, and (d) plump or thin body.

WHAT DID YOU LEARN?

21 What is the relationship of TRH, TSH, and TH in regulating metabolism?

22 What are the primary target organs/tissues of TH? Describe the effect on each.

17.9c Adrenal Glands and Cortisol

LEARNING OBJECTIVES

5. Describe the structure and location of the adrenal glands.

6. Name the three zones of the adrenal cortex and the hormones produced in each zone.

7. Describe how the hypothalamus controls the release of glucocorticoid (cortisol) and the effects of cortisol.

The **adrenal** (ă-drē′năl; *ad* = to, *ren* = kidney) **glands,** or *suprarenal glands,* are paired, pyramid-shaped endocrine glands anchored on the superior surface of each kidney **(figure 17.20).** The two regions that comprise an adrenal gland, the cortex and the medulla, secrete different types of hormones.

Anatomy of the Adrenal Glands

The adrenal glands are retroperitoneal (posterior to the parietal peritoneum) and embedded within fat and fascia to minimize their movement. These endocrine glands are supplied by multiple suprarenal arteries that branch from larger abdominal arteries. Venous drainage occurs through the suprarenal veins. The inner region of each gland is called the adrenal medulla and the outer region the adrenal cortex (figure 17.20c).

The **adrenal medulla** forms the inner core of each adrenal gland. It has a pronounced red-brown color due to its extensive vascularization. It releases the catecholamines epinephrine and norepinephrine in response to sympathetic nervous stimulation (as described in section 15.4).

The **adrenal cortex** exhibits a distinctive yellow color as a consequence of the stored lipids within its cells. These cells synthesize more than 25 different corticosteroids. The adrenal cortex is partitioned into three separate regions: the outer zona glomerulosa, the middle zona fasciculata, and the inner zona reticularis (figure 17.20d). Different functional categories of steroid hormones are synthesized and secreted in the separate zones.

Hormones of the Adrenal Cortex

The **zona glomerulosa** (zō′nă glō-mĕr-ū-lōs′ă; *glomerulus* = ball of yarn) is the thin, outer cortical layer composed of dense, spherical clusters of cells. These cells synthesize

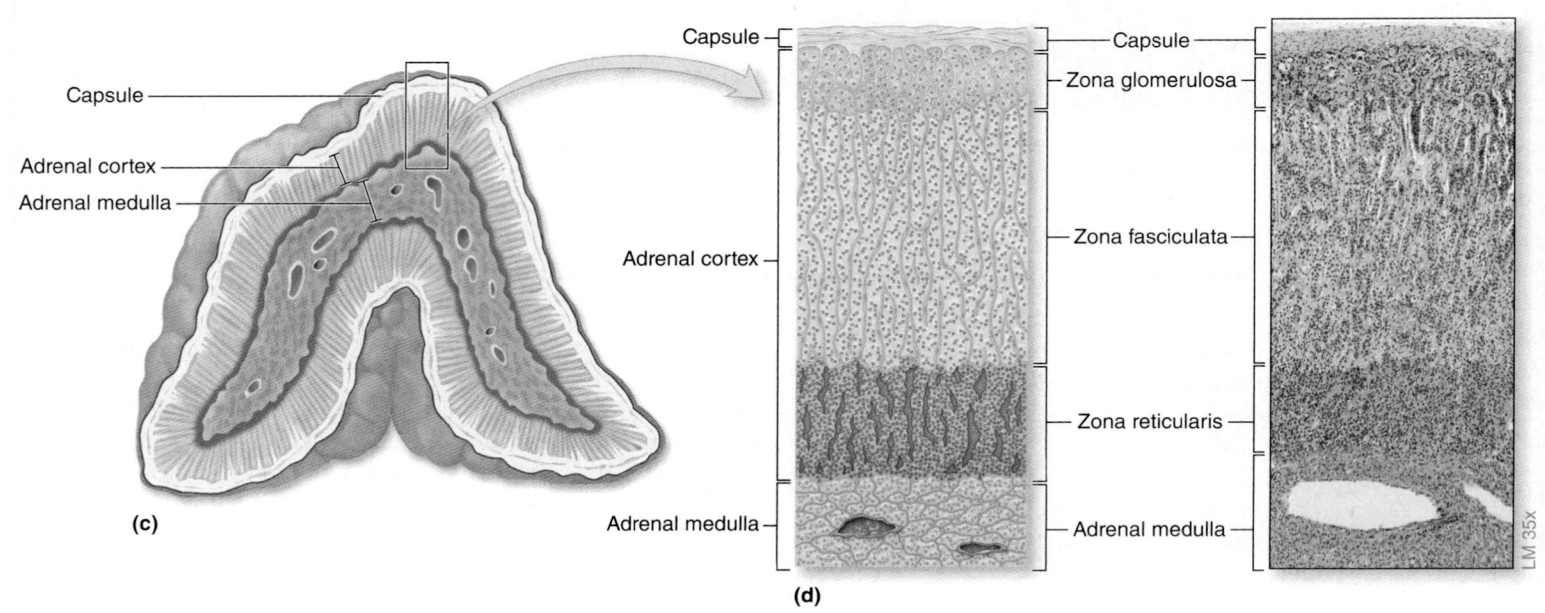

Figure 17.20 Adrenal Glands. Each adrenal gland is a two-part gland that secretes stress-related hormones. The adrenal cortex produces corticosteroid hormones (e.g., cortisol), and the adrenal medulla produces epinephrine and norepinephrine. (*a*) An anterior view and (*b*) a cadaver photo show the relationships of the kidneys and adrenal glands. (*c*) A sectioned adrenal gland shows the outer cortex and the inner medulla. (*d*) A diagram and a micrograph illustrate the three zones of the adrenal cortex, as well as the relationship of the cortex to the external capsule and the internal medulla. AP|R

Labels for (a):

Right inferior phrenic artery
Left inferior phrenic artery
Right superior suprarenal arteries
Right middle suprarenal artery
Celiac trunk
Right adrenal gland
Left superior suprarenal arteries
Left middle suprarenal artery
Left adrenal gland
Left inferior suprarenal arteries
Right inferior suprarenal artery
Right suprarenal vein
Right renal artery
Right renal vein
Right kidney
Left suprarenal vein
Left renal artery
Left renal vein
Superior mesenteric artery
Left kidney
Inferior vena cava
Abdominal aorta

(a)

Labels for (b):

Right adrenal gland
Diaphragm
Left renal vein
Inferior vena cava
Abdominal aorta
Right renal vein
Right kidney

(b)

Labels for (c):

Capsule
Adrenal cortex
Adrenal medulla

(c)

Labels for (d):

Capsule
Adrenal cortex
Adrenal medulla
Capsule
Zona glomerulosa
Zona fasciculata
Zona reticularis
Adrenal medulla

LM 35x

(d)

CLINICAL VIEW
Disorders in Adrenal Cortex Hormone Secretion

Three abnormal patterns of adrenal cortical function are Cushing syndrome, Addison disease, and androgenital syndrome.

Cushing syndrome results from the chronic exposure of the body's tissues to excessive levels of glucocorticoid hormones. This complex of symptoms is seen most frequently in people taking corticosteroids as therapy for autoimmune diseases such as rheumatoid arthritis, although some cases result when the adrenal gland produces too much of its own glucocorticoid hormones. Corticosteroids are powerful immunosuppressant drugs, but they have serious side effects, such as osteoporosis, muscle weakness, redistribution of body fat, and salt retention (resulting in overall swelling of the tissues). Cushing syndrome is characterized by body obesity, especially in the face (called "moon face") and back ("buffalo hump"). Other symptoms include hypertension, excess hair growth, kidney stones, and menstrual irregularities.

Addison disease is a form of adrenal insufficiency that develops when the adrenal glands fail, resulting in a chronic shortage of glucocorticoids and sometimes mineralocorticoids. Adrenal cortical failure may develop because the pituitary stops supplying ACTH to stimulate the adrenal cortex, or because the adrenal glands themselves are diseased and cannot respond

JFK prior to being treated for Addison disease.

JFK following cortiocosteroid therapy for Addison disease.

to ACTH. Addison disease is a rare disorder, occurring in about 1 in 100,000 people of all ages and affecting men and women equally. The symptoms include weight loss, general fatigue and weakness, hypotension, and darkening of the skin. Therapy consists of oral corticosteroids taken for the rest of the patient's life. Perhaps the most well-known person with Addison disease was John Fitzgerald Kennedy (JFK), who was quietly treated by specialists throughout his presidency. It is now thought that these steroid treatments may have contributed to this president's other medical problems, among them osteoporosis and back pain.

Adrenogenital syndrome, or **congenital adrenal hyperplasia,** first manifests in the embryo and fetus. It is characterized by the inability to synthesize corticosteroids. The anterior pituitary, sensing the deficiency of corticosteroids, releases massive amounts of ACTH in an unsuccessful effort to bring the glucocorticoid content of the blood up to a healthy level. This large amount of ACTH produces *hyperplasia* (increased size) of the adrenal cortex and causes the release of intermediary hormones that have a testosterone-like effect. The result is *virilization* (masculinization) in a newborn. Virilization in girls means the clitoris is enlarged, sometimes to the size of a male penis. The effect may be so profound that the sex of a newborn female is questioned or even mistaken. A virilized male may have an enlarged penis and exhibit signs of premature puberty as early as age 6 or 7. About 75% of affected newborns also have a salt-losing problem, owing to their bodies' inability to manufacture mineralocorticoids and glucocorticoids. Treatment consists of oral corticosteroids, which boost the body's level of corticosteroids and inhibit the pituitary from releasing excessive amounts of ACTH.

Photo prior to onset of Cushing syndrome.

Symptoms resulting from the excessive glucocorticoid secretion in Cushing syndrome include "buffalo hump" and "moon face."

mineralocorticoids (min′er-al-ō kōr′ti-koyd), a group of hormones that help regulate the composition and concentration of electrolytes (ions) in body fluids. The principal mineralocorticoid is **aldosterone** (al-dos′ter-ōn), which regulates the ratio of Na$^+$ and K$^+$ in our blood and body fluids by altering the amounts excreted by the kidney into the urine. Aldosterone stimulates Na$^+$ retention and K$^+$ secretion. Severe imbalances in this ratio can result in death (see section 25.4c for details of regulation).

The **zona fasciculata** (fă-sik′ū-lă′tă; *fascicle* = bundle of parallel sticks) is the middle layer and largest region of the adrenal cortex. It is composed of parallel cords of lipid-rich cells that have a bubbly, almost pale appearance. The primary **glucocorticoids** synthesized in this region are cortisol and corticosterone. Details of cortisol regulation and function are described shortly.

The innermost region of the cortex, the **zona reticularis** (rĕ-tik′ū-lăr′is; *reticulum* = network), is a narrow band of small, branching cells. They are capable of secreting minor amounts of sex hormones called **gonadocorticoids.** The primary gonadocorticoids secreted are male sex hormones called **androgens.** The androgens in females are converted to estrogen. The amount of androgen secreted by the adrenal cortex is small compared to that secreted by the gonads; however, adrenal gland tumors in a female can result in elevated levels of testosterone and varying degrees of masculinization.

Action of Cortisol

Cortisol (kōr′ti-sol) (or *hydrocortisone*) and **corticosterone** (kōr′ti-kos′ter-ōn) are the most common glucocorticoids released from the adrenal gland. Glucocorticoids increase nutrient levels in the blood (glucose, fatty acids, and amino acids), especially in an attempt to resist stress and help repair injured or damaged tissues. Other physiologic changes are stimulated by glucocorticoids and become most evident when present in high doses.

Cortisol release from the adrenal cortex occurs through hypothalamic regulation by means of **corticotropin-releasing hormone (CRH)** and the subsequent release of **adrenocorticotropic hormone (ACTH)** from the anterior pituitary. This physiologic relationship is referred to as the **hypothalamic-pituitary-adrenal axis.** A description of how this axis works to release cortisol is discussed next **(figure 17.21)**.

A decrease in cortisol level within the blood stimulates the hypothalamus to release CRH. The time of day and stress also influence the release of CRH and thus the release of cortisol **(figure 17.22)**.

Figure 17.21 Regulation and Action of Cortisol Hormone. The hypothalamus responds to particular stimuli by releasing corticotropin-release hormone (CRH), which stimulates the anterior pituitary to release adrenocorticotropic hormone (ACTH). ACTH stimulates the adrenal gland to release cortisol. Cortisol increases the the availability of nutrient molecules to support the response to stress. (Direction of arrows between the blood and effectors indicates the net movement of the nutrients.)

CRH travels through the hypothalamo-hypophyseal portal system to the anterior pituitary, where it binds to receptors in corticotropic cells of the anterior pituitary and stimulates the release of adrenocorticotropic hormone (ACTH) into general circulation (figure 17.21). ACTH then binds to receptors within adrenal cortex cells (zona fasciculata) and stimulates the release of cortisol and corticosterone. Cortisol accounts for 95% of the glucocorticoid activity. Cortisol is transported within the blood by carrier proteins (*corticosteroid-binding globulin,* or *CBG,* also called transcortin or serum albumin). Cortisol circulates in the blood and randomly becomes unbound from its carrier protein and exits from the blood.

Cortisol readily passes through the plasma membrane and binds to intracellular receptors to form a hormone-receptor complex. This complex binds to DNA and stimulates cellular changes through the activation of genes. The cellular changes depend upon the tissue being stimulated. For example, hepatocytes are stimulated by cortisol to increase glycogenolysis and gluconeogenesis. At the same time, they are inhibited from using the glycogenesis pathway, so that blood glucose levels rise. Some cortisol is converted to cortisone in the liver.

Adipose connective tissue cells are stimulated by cortisol to increase lipolysis and decrease lipogenesis, resulting in the release of glycerol and fatty acids into blood. This provides alternative nutrients for gluconeogenesis.

Most cells, including muscle cells, lymphatic tissue cells, skin cells, and bone cells, increase protein catabolism in response to cortisol. An exception to this occurs in hepatocytes. In liver cells, additional amino acid released into the blood provides alternative nutrient molecules for gluconeogenesis. Cortisol additionally stimulates most cells to decrease glucose uptake. This is the glucose-sparing effect, which saves blood glucose for use in the brain.

Corticosterone is used as a treatment for chronic inflammation. The side effects, especially when administered in high doses, include retention of Na^+ and water; inhibited release of inflammatory agents (the anti-inflammatory effect); suppression of the immune system; and inhibited connective tissue repair. Note that suppression of the immune system increases an individual's susceptibility to infection and risk of cancer.

The release of both CRH from the hypothalamus and ACTH from the anterior pituitary is regulated by negative feedback. Increasing levels of cortisol inhibit the release of CRH from the hypothalamus and ACTH from the anterior pituitary. The details for cortisol are listed in the summary table on cortisol in the appendix (Table B.5).

Cortisol release fluctuates based on the time of day (circadian rhythm).

Cortisol levels fluctuate throughout the day. Notice that in a normal sleep-wake cycle, peak levels of cortisol correspond to the late stages of a normal sleep cycle. About half of all cortisol release occurs when you are asleep, with cortisol levels peaking right before waking in the morning. This rhythm of release is regulated by light and dark cycles detected by the retina as nerve signals are relayed to the hypothalamus. (Between individuals, there is significant variation in normal levels.)

(a)

Cortisol level is increased by stress.

Both emotional stress (e.g., anxiety, anger, fear) and physical stress (e.g., fever, trauma, or intense exercise) increase the release of cortisol.

(b)

Figure 17.22 Variables That Influence Blood Levels of Cortisol. Blood levels of cortisol (*a*) fluctuate throughout the day, and (*b*) rise with increased stress, which is why cortisol is sometimes called the "stress hormone."

The Stress Response (General Adaptation Syndrome)

Stressors may fall under the category of either *emotional stress* (e.g., anxiety, anger, fear, and excitement) or *physical stress* (e.g., fever, trauma, hemorrhage, surgery, and malnutrition). Stressors elicit the **stress response** (or general adaptation syndrome), which was defined by Hans Selye (a pioneer in the endocrinology of stress) as "the nonspecific response of the body to any demand made upon it." The body's response to stress is initiated by the hypothalamus and involves both the nervous system and the endocrine system. In 1936, Hans Selye described the response to stressors in three stages: the alarm reaction, the stage of resistance, and the stage of exhaustion.

The Alarm Reaction

The alarm reaction is the initial reaction to stress and is regulated primarily by the sympathetic division of the autonomic nervous system. The hypothalamus activates the sympathetic division with subsequent stimulation of the adrenal medulla to release epinephrine and norepinephrine into the blood. The following changes occur to the body (see table 15.5):

- Pupils dilate.
- Bronchioles dilate.
- Respiration rate increases.
- Blood pressure increases as both the heart rate and force of contraction increase.
- Blood vessels vasoconstrict.
- Sodium and water are retained, resulting in an increase in blood volume.
- Potassium and hydrogen ions are excreted.
- Both glucose and lipid levels in the blood increase.
- Sweating increases.
- Both digestion and urine production activities decrease.

The Stage of Resistance

The stage of resistance occurs after a few hours as glycogen stores in the liver are depleted. This stage is regulated primarily by the endocrine system. The major changes are induced by the release of glucocorticoids (e.g., cortisol). The principle function of this stage is to provide glucose to meet the increased energy demands. Glucose is especially important for nervous tissue because it is the main fuel molecule these tissues can use. To meet the increased demands for energy, gluconeogenesis is increased in the liver, and glucose is released into the blood. Fatty acids increase in the blood due to increased lipolysis in adipose connective tissue cells. Amino acids increase as a result of increased protein catabolism (and decreased protein synthesis) in most cells. Fatty acids and amino acids provide the liver with alternative nutrients for gluconeogenesis. Additionally, glucose uptake is inhibited in most cells. The net result is elevated blood glucose levels.

The Stage of Exhaustion

The stage of exhaustion occurs after weeks or months, as fat stores in adipose connective tissue are depleted. With fat stores depleted, and as structural proteins of the body's cells continue to be broken down for gluconeogenesis, the body becomes progressively weaker. Additionally, elevated levels of aldosterone may cause fluid, electrolyte, and pH imbalances. The combination of body weakness, electrolyte imbalances, and other factors may ultimately cause organ failure and death.

 WHAT DID YOU LEARN?

23 What is the relationship of CRH, ACTH, and cortisol?

24 What are the primary target organs/tissues of cortisol? Describe the effect on each.

17.10 Pancreatic Hormones

The pancreatic hormones, insulin and glucagon, function in regulating nutrient levels in the blood—both of which are released from the pancreas and regulate blood glucose levels. We begin with a brief description of the anatomy of the pancreas before looking at the specifics of pancreatic hormone actions.

17.10a Anatomy of the Pancreas

LEARNING OBJECTIVES

1. Describe the gross anatomy and cellular structure of the pancreas.
2. Identify the primary types of pancreatic islet cells and the hormones they produce.

INTEGRATE

CONCEPT CONNECTION

The pancreas functions as both an endocrine gland and an exocrine gland. Endocrine glands release their secretions (hormones) into the blood. The pancreas releases both insulin and glucagon into the blood. In contrast, exocrine glands release their secretions into ducts. The pancreas also releases pancreatic juice into ducts that empty into the small intestine (duodenum), as described in section 26.3c.

The **pancreas** (pan′krē-as; *pan* = all, *kreas* = flesh) is an elongated, nodular organ situated between the duodenum of the small intestine and the spleen (**figure 17.23a**) and directly posterior to the stomach. The pancreas performs both exocrine and endocrine activities; thus, it is considered a *heterocrine*, or mixed, gland. The pancreas is mostly composed of groups of cells called **pancreatic acini** (sing., *acinus* = grape). **Acinar cells** are involved in exocrine activities and produce an alkaline pancreatic secretion (juice) that is secreted through pancreatic ducts into the small intestine. This pancreatic juice aids digestion (see section 26.3c).

Scattered among the pancreatic acini are small clusters of endocrine cells called **pancreatic islets** (ī′let), also known as *islets of Langerhans* (figure 17.23b). Estimates of the number of islets in a pancreas range between 1.5 and 2 million; however, these endocrine cell clusters form only about 1% of the total pancreatic volume. A pancreatic islet is composed of two primary types of cells: **alpha cells** that secrete **glucagon** (glū′kă-gon), and **beta cells** that secrete **insulin** (in′sū-lin; *insula* = island).

Minor cells within the pancreatic islets include delta cells, which secrete somatostatin (also described as growth hormone–inhibiting hormone) and F cells, which secrete pancreatic polypeptide. These minor cells and their hormones will not be addressed.

WHAT DID YOU LEARN?

25 Why is the pancreas considered both an exocrine gland and an endocrine gland?

(a)

(b)

Figure 17.23 Pancreas. The pancreas performs both exocrine and endocrine activities. (*a*) An illustration and cadaver photo show the relationship between the pancreas and both the duodenum and spleen. (*b*) A diagram and micrograph reveal the histology of a pancreatic islet. Different types of islet cells are shown in the diagram. AP|R

17.10b Effects of Pancreatic Hormones

✓ LEARNING OBJECTIVES

3. Describe the action of insulin in lowering blood glucose concentration.
4. Explain the action of glucagon in raising blood glucose concentration.

The primary endocrine function of the pancreas is to maintain the concentration of glucose in the blood within a normal range of 70 of 110 milligrams of glucose per deciliter (mg/dL; a deciliter is an amount equivalent to 100 milliliters). Chronically high blood glucose levels can be very damaging to blood vessels and the kidneys, so this excess glucose must be transported into other body cells that can use or store this resource. Conversely, low blood glucose levels result in lethargy, impairment of mental and physical function, and death if glucose levels drop too low. Thus, blood glucose levels must be closely regulated. The homeostatic mechanisms for insulin and glucagon are described next and are summarized in the table in the appendix (Table B.1).

Lowering High Blood Glucose Levels with Insulin

Insulin is generally released from the pancreas following food intake (figure 17.24). Chemoreceptors in the beta cells of the pancreas detect an increase in blood glucose (readings greater than the normal 70–110 mg/dL) and are stimulated to release insulin (a protein hormone). Insulin circulates in the blood and randomly exits from the blood into the interstial fluid as it passes through capillaries. Target cells bind insulin, which activates second messengers within the

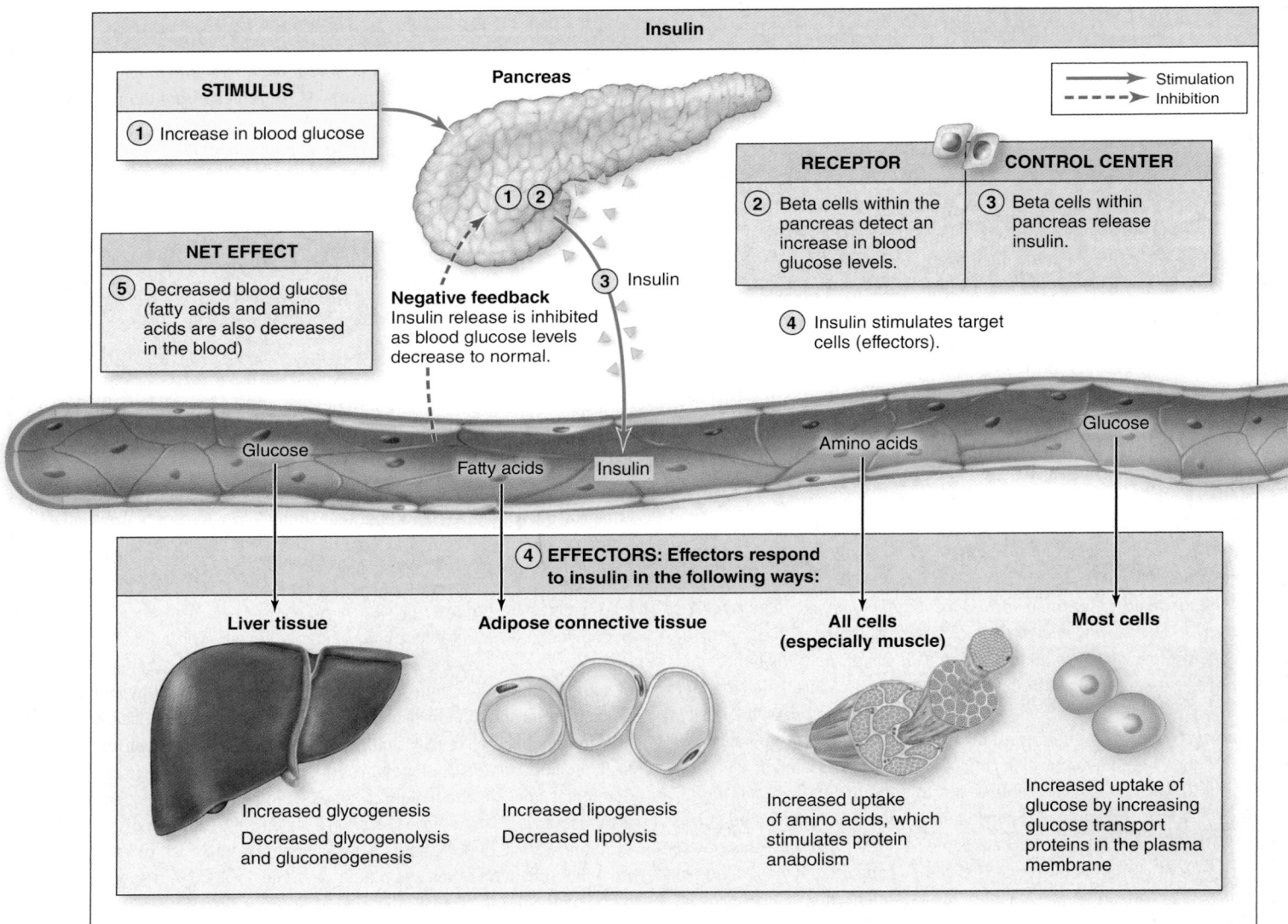

Figure 17.24 Regulation and Action of Insulin. Insulin decreases the level of all nutrient molecules (glucose, fatty acids, and amino acids) in the blood. The uptake of fatty acids and amino acids from the blood limits their availability making it more likely that cells will use glucose as their fuel molecule. Thus, blood glucose more quickly returns to within normal homeostatic levels.

target cell. (Additionally, recent evidence suggests that insulin may also enter the cell and directly bind to intracellular receptors.) Specific enzymatic pathways are altered as follows:

- Glycogenesis in hepatocytes is stimulated, and both glycogenolysis and gluconeogenesis are inhibited, resulting in glucose molecules being removed from the blood and stored as glycogen within liver cells.

- Lipogenesis in adipose connective tissue cells is stimulated, and lipolysis is inhibited. Fatty acid levels in the blood decrease, and the storage of fat is increased as a result.

- Most cells are stimulated to increase their cellular uptake of (1) amino acids (especially muscle cells), a change that induces cells to increase protein anabolism; and (2) glucose, especially by the cells of muscle and adipose connective tissue. The uptake of glucose occurs as intracellular vesicles containing glucose transport proteins (specifically Glut4 transport proteins) fuse with the plasma membrane. Additional glucose transport molecules are placed within the plasma membrane of cells, providing the glucose carrier molecules needed to bring more glucose into the cell. (These carriers are later removed as insulin levels decrease.)

In summary, the release of insulin results in both a decrease in *all* nutrients in the blood and in an increase in the synthesis of the storage form of these molecules within body tissues. By decreasing alternative nutrients (fatty acids and amino acids), the cells of the body are more likely to use the available glucose and help return blood glucose to a normal level. The release of insulin is controlled by negative feedback; as blood glucose levels decrease, less insulin is released from the pancreas.

Note that some cells do not require insulin for glucose uptake. These cells include nervous tissue cells, kidney cells, hepatocytes, and erythrocytes (red blood cells). Each of these cells takes up glucose independently without external stimulation.

 WHAT DO YOU THINK?

6 Body builders have been known to inject insulin to increase muscle bulk. Explain their reasoning. What is the risk of an insulin overdose?

Raising Low Blood Glucose Levels with Glucagon

All nervous tissue depends almost exclusively upon glucose for cellular respiration. To prevent impairment of mental function,

CLINICAL VIEW
Conditions Resulting in Abnormal Blood Glucose Levels

Diabetes Mellitus

Diabetes mellitus (dí-ă-bē′tez = a siphon, me-lī′tŭs = sweetened with honey) is a metabolic condition marked by inadequate uptake of glucose from the blood. The name is derived from the phrase "sweet urine" because some of the excess glucose may be filtered into the urine, a condition called *glycosuria*. Chronically elevated blood glucose levels damage blood vessels, especially the smaller arterioles. Because of its damaging effects on the vascular system, diabetes is the leading cause of retinal blindness, kidney failure, and nontraumatic leg amputations in the United States. Diabetes is also associated with increased incidence of heart disease and stroke. In fact, heart disease or stroke is the cause of death in approximately 65% of individuals with diabetes.

Measuring the amount of glucose attached to hemoglobin molecules within erythrocytes is an accurate means for determining the degree of risk for an individual. The greater the amount of attached glucose, the higher the risk.

Three categories of diabetes mellitus are type 1 diabetes, type 2 diabetes, and gestational diabetes.

Type 1 diabetes is also referred to as *insulin-dependent diabetes mellitus (IDDM)* or *juvenile diabetes*. It is characterized by absent or diminished production and release of insulin by the pancreatic islet cells. This type tends to occur in children and younger individuals, and is not directly associated with obesity. Type 1 diabetes may develop in a person who harbors a genetic predisposition, although some kind of triggering event is required to start the process. Often, the trigger is a viral infection leading to an autoimmune condition in which the beta cells of the pancreatic islets are destroyed. Treatment of type 1 diabetes requires daily injections of insulin. Newer monitoring instruments now allow rapid and almost continual monitoring of blood glucose. The recent use of stem cells shows promise as an effective means in treating type 1 diabetes.

Type 2 diabetes, also known as *insulin-independent diabetes mellitus (IIDM),* results from either decreased insulin release from the pancreatic beta cells or decreased insulin effectiveness at peripheral tissues. This type of diabetes was previously referred to as *adult-onset diabetes* because it tended to occur in people over the age of 30. However, type 2 diabetes is now often found in adolescents and young adults. Obesity plays a major role in the development of type 2 diabetes, and more young people today are considered overweight than ever before. Most patients with type 2 diabetes can be successfully treated with a combination of diet, exercise, and medications that enhance insulin release or increase sensitivity to insulin at the tissue level. A person with type 2 diabetes must take insulin injections in more severe cases.

Gestational diabetes is seen in some pregnant women, typically in the latter half of the pregnancy. If untreated, gestational diabetes can pose a risk to the fetus as well as increase delivery complications. Most at risk for developing this condition are women who are overweight; those of African American, Native American, or Hispanic ancestry; or those who have a family history of diabetes. Although gestational diabetes usually resolves after giving birth, a woman having this condition has a 20% to 50% chance of developing type 2 diabetes within 10 years.

Hypoglycemia

Hypoglycemia occurs when blood glucose levels drop below 60 mg/dL. Hypoglycemia is not a disease; however, it may be a nonspecific indicator of some underlying homeostatic imbalance. The causes of hypoglycemia are numerous and include insulin overdose, prolonged and intense exercise, drinking alcohol on an empty stomach, liver or kidney dysfunction, deficiency of either glucocorticoids or growth hormone, and certain genetic conditions. Symptoms may include hunger, dizziness, nervousness, confusion, feeling anxious or weak, sweating, sleepiness, or any combination of these. The symptoms are thought to occur from insufficient glucose to the brain or from the activation of the sympathetic nervous system in response to low blood glucose levels.

If an individual is unable to eat or drink safely, such as if unconscious, unresponsive, or having convulsions, glucagon can be administered by injection. This provides a safe means to offset the low blood glucose level.

lethargy, and possibly death, blood glucose levels must be prevented from dropping too low. Glucagon is one of the important hormones released in response to low blood glucose levels (figure 17.25).

Chemoreceptors in the alpha cells of the pancreas detect decreased blood glucose levels and subsequently release glucagon (a polypeptide hormone) into the blood. Nutrients are stored in various body tissues, and glucagon facilitates the breakdown of these nutrients and their release into the blood. Glucagon binds to plasma membrane receptors to activate second messengers (cAMP) that cause the following:

- Glycogenolysis and gluconeogenesis in hepatocytes are stimulated, and glycogenesis is inhibited; glucose is released into the blood, thereby increasing blood glucose levels. (Glucose within muscle cells is not released but remains within muscle cells and is oxidized in cellular respiration.)
- Lipolysis in adipose connective tissue cells is stimulated, and lipogenesis is inhibited. Fatty acids and glycerol are released from fat storage and are increased within the blood.

In summary, the release of glucagon results in an increase in glucose, glycerol, and fatty acids in the blood and in a decrease in the storage form of these molecules within body tissues. An increase in blood glucose levels results in a decrease in glucagon release by negative feedback.

Note that glucagon has no effect on the structural and functional protein components of the body. The physiologic significance of this lack of effect is that the ongoing, and regular, release of this hormone (e.g., during periods between meals) does not tear down the muscles and other protein components of the body to maintain blood glucose levels in "nonemergency" situations.

Interestingly, paramedics may administer glucagon subcutaneously under certain conditions when low blood glucose is detected. This may be done if the individual is unconscious and is unable to be given sugar orally to directly raise blood glucose.

WHAT DID YOU LEARN?

26 Is the stimulus for insulin and glucagon release from the pancreas hormonal, humoral, or nervous?

27 What is the stimulus, receptor, control center, and effector response to the release of insulin? Indicate what happens to nutrient levels in the blood.

28 Which of these hormones causes release of glucose into the blood: growth hormone, thyroid hormone, cortisol, insulin, or glucagon?

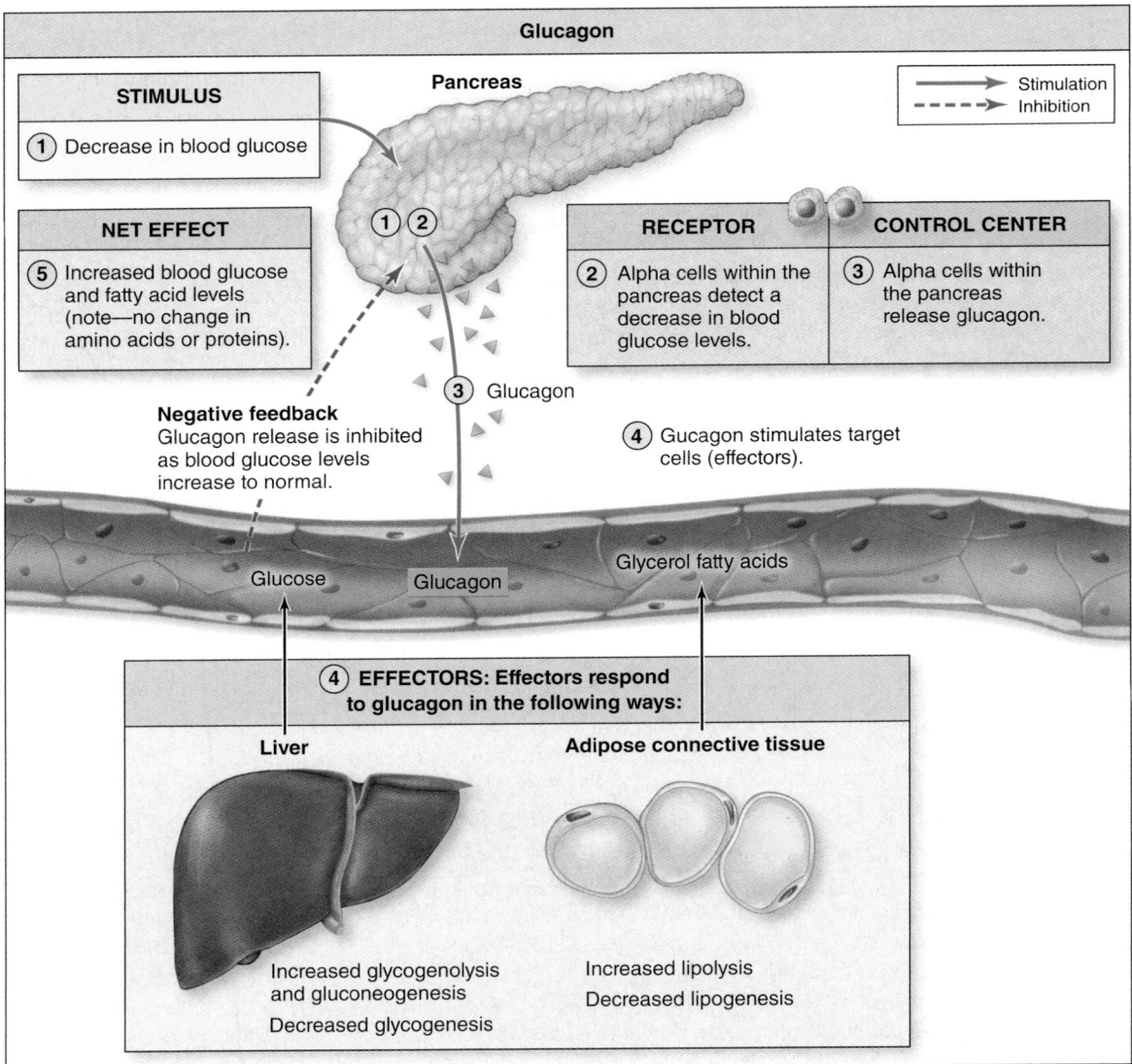

Figure 17.25 Regulation and Action of Glucagon. Glucagon is released in response to low blood glucose. Glucagon binds with target cells that increase both glucose, glycerol, and fatty acid levels in the blood.

17.11 Aging and the Endocrine System

1. Describe how endocrine activity changes as people age.

The secretory activity of endocrine glands typically wanes as we age. Aging reduces the efficiency of endocrine system functions, and often normal levels of hormones decrease. Many conditions experienced after middle age, such as abdominal weight gain or muscle loss, are directly related to diminishing or reduced endocrine gland function.

One example is that the secretion of GH and sex hormones often decreases. Reduction in GH levels leads to loss of weight and body mass in the elderly, although continued exercise reduces this effect.

In addition, testosterone or estrogen levels decline as males and females age. Often hormone replacement therapy (HRT), or "trying to turn back the clock," attempts to supplement GH and sex hormone levels that have naturally diminished with age.

 WHAT DID YOU LEARN?

29 What general changes occur to the ability of endocrine glands to produce hormones as we age?

CHAPTER SUMMARY

17.1 Introduction to the Endocrine System 653	• The endocrine system is composed of endocrine glands that produce chemical communication molecules called hormones. • The two control systems of the body include the nervous system and endocrine system. **17.1a Comparison of the Two Control Systems 653** • The nervous and endocrine systems complement each other to maintain homeostasis. **17.1b General Functions of the Endocrine System 654** • The primary processes controlled by hormones include maintaining homeostasis of blood composition and volume; controlling reproductive activities; regulating development, growth, and metabolism; and controlling digestive processes.
17.2 Endocrine Glands 654	• Endocrine glands are located throughout the body and are regulated to secrete their hormones into the blood. **17.2a Location of the Major Endocrine Glands 654** • Endocrine organs include the pineal gland, pituitary gland, thyroid gland, parathyroid glands, and adrenal glands. • Endocrine tissue is housed in small clusters within the hypothalamus, skin, thymus, heart, stomach, liver, pancreas, small intestine, kidneys, and gonads. **17.2b Stimulation of Hormone Synthesis and Release 657** • Release of hormones from endocrine cells is controlled through reflexes. There are three ways to stimulate these cells: (1) hormonal stimulation, (2) humoral stimulation by something in the blood other than another hormone, and (3) nervous system stimulation.
17.3 Hormones 658	• All hormones are synthesized within endocrine gland cells from either cholesterol or amino acids. **17.3a Categories of Circulating Hormones 658** • The three general categories of circulating hormones include steroid hormones, protein hormones, and biogenic amines. **17.3b Local Hormones 659** • Eicosanoids are local hormones; they are synthesized from a polyunsaturated fatty acid (arachidonic acid).
17.4 Hormone Transport 659	• The mechanism of hormone transport is dependent upon whether the hormone is lipid-soluble or water-soluble. **17.4a Transport in the Blood 660** • Water-soluble hormones readily dissolve in the aqueous environment of the blood. • Lipid-soluble hormones must attach to a carrier protein molecule to be transported within the blood. **17.4b Levels of Circulating Hormone 660** • The two primary factors that influence hormone concentration are hormone synthesis by endocrine glands and hormone elimination by the liver, kidneys, and target cells.
17.5 Target Cells: Interactions with Hormones 660	• Hormones bind with receptors of target cells. **17.5a Lipid-Soluble Hormones 660** • Hormones that are lipid-soluble (steroid hormones, calcitriol, and thyroid hormone) stimulate cellular activity by binding to intracellular receptors: The hormone-receptor complex activates a region of DNA, resulting in the production of new proteins. **17.5b Water-Soluble Hormones 661** • Hormones that are water-soluble (protein hormones and biogenic amines, except thyroid hormone) bind with plasma membrane receptors; the hormone is the first messenger, and it causes the activation of G protein and the formation of a second messenger through an intracellular enzyme cascade. • The cellular response may include activation or inhibition of enzymatic pathways, stimulation of growth through cellular reproduction, stimulation of cellular secretions, change membrane permeability, and muscle contraction or relaxation.

CHALLENGE YOURSELF

Do You Know the Basics?

____ 1. Which of the following is *not* a general process controlled by the endocrine system?

a. development, growth, and metabolism

b. control of reproductive activities

c. maintenance of homeostasis of blood composition

d. programmed cell death/destruction of aged cells

____ 2. This hormone's primary function is to regulate metabolism.

a. calcitonin

b. thyroid hormone

c. growth hormone

d. glucagon

____ 3. Which of the following are components of intracellular enzyme cascades initiated by hydrophilic hormones?

a. G proteins

b. cAMP

c. protein kinase enzymes

d. All of these are correct.

____ 4. A tropic hormone released from the anterior pituitary is

a. glucagon.

b. growth hormone.

c. melatonin.

d. epinephrine.

____ 5. The action of hydrophilic hormones may include all of the following *except*

a. activation or inhibition of enzymatic pathways.

b. formation of hormone-responsive element.

c. muscle contraction or relaxation.

d. stimulation of cellular secretions.

____ 6. The enzymatic pathways for synthesizing glycogen from individual glucose molecules occurs in liver and muscle cells and is called

a. glycogenolysis.

b. gluconeogenesis.

c. glycogenesis.

d. lipogenesis.

____ 7. The pancreas is composed of

a. endocrine and exocrine tissue.

b. endocrine tissue only.

c. exocrine tissue only.

d. neither endocrine or exocrine tissue.

____ 8. Glucocorticoids (e.g., cortisol) are produced in the adrenal cortex to help regulate

a. Na$^+$ and K$^+$ levels in body fluids.

b. blood pressure.

c. calcium levels in the blood.

d. glucose levels in the blood.

____ 9. Thyroid-stimulating hormone stimulates the

a. anterior pituitary to release its hormones.

b. hypothalamus to release its hormones.

c. thyroid gland to release its hormones.

d. All of these are correct.

____ 10. All of the following hormones are released from the hypothalamus to control the anterior pituitary gland *except*

a. growth-releasing hormone.

b. antidiuretic hormone.

c. prolactin-releasing hormone.

d. corticotropin-releasing hormone.

11. Describe similarities and differences between the endocrine system and the nervous system in their method of operation and effects.

12. List the four primary functions of the endocrine system.

13. Explain the three mechanisms used to stimulate hormone release from a target cell to initiate an endocrine reflex.

14. Identify the three chemical classes of hormones, and give an example of each. Most hormones belong to which class?

15. Describe how local hormones differ from circulating hormones.

16. Explain the function of carrier proteins in transporting lipid-soluble hormones in the blood, and how these hormones interact with cells.

17. Describe how water-soluble hormones interact with cells.

18. Explain how the hypothalamus oversees and controls endocrine system function of the posterior pituitary.

19. Explain how the hypothalamus oversees and controls endocrine system function of the anterior pituitary.

20. Discuss the homeostatic system involving insulin.

Can You Apply What You've Learned?

1. George is a 43-year-old construction worker who has developed a swelling in his neck that is painful and continues to grow. He visited the doctor and confided to his clinician that he has also lost weight and has become very hyperactive. What gland does the clinician suspect is functioning abnormally?

a. pituitary

b. thyroid

c. adrenal

d. pancreas

2. What is the best diagnostic test to determine if this gland is not functioning normally?

a. measuring the amount of radioactive iodine taken up by the thyroid

b. doing body temperature scans every morning and evening at the same time

c. watching weight fluctuation over a 1-month time period

d. taking a blood sample to measure the amount of thyroid hormone (T_3 and T_4) present

3. Jelena is late for work and is rushing to get out the door. Her commute to work is slow due to rush-hour traffic, and she begins to become anxious and upset. As she is attempting to park, someone hits her car and she becomes angry. What specific hormones are released to help her during this "emergency"?

a. insulin/glucagon

b. epinephrine/cortisol

c. insulin/thyroid hormone

d. melatonin/epinephrine

4. Blood samples from a young woman named Michelle indicate an elevated blood glucose level. This homeostatic imbalance is most likely caused by an insufficient amount, or decreased sensitivity, to which hormone?

a. growth hormone

b. glucagon

c. insulin

d. cortisol

5. Stephen is taking a new weight-loss supplement that is known to not only decrease the amount of adipose connective tissue (as advertised) but to also decrease glycogen stores in the liver and causes breakdown of muscle protein (protein catabolism). What substance in this weight-loss supplement is responsible for these changes?

a. growth hormone

b. glucagon

c. insulin

d. cortisol

Can You Synthesize What You've Learned?

1. After seeing a physician for a sudden weight loss, 19-year-old Harold is diagnosed with type 1 diabetes, which is a condition in which the beta cells of the pancreas are producing insufficient amounts of hormone. Explain to Harold why results from his blood lab report indicate that he has an elevated blood glucose level.

2. Susan is a 35-year-old mother of two who works as an admissions officer at the university. She was recently diagnosed with a pituitary tumor. Consider the potential challenges she may experience by listing the hormones released by both the posterior pituitary and the anterior pituitary.

3. Henry is a well-informed patient who is interested in understanding how thyroid hormone is controlled by thyrotropin-releasing hormone (TRH) and thyroid-stimulating hormone (TSH). Briefly explain to him the hypothalamic-pituitary-thyroid axis.

chapter 18

Cardiovascular System: Blood

Within our bodies is a connective tissue so valuable that donating a portion of it to someone else can save that person's life. This tissue is regenerated continuously and is responsible for transporting the gases, nutrients, and hormones our bodies need for proper functioning. Losing too much of this tissue can be fatal and yet is something we frequently take for granted.

This valuable connective tissue is blood. Blood is considered a fluid connective tissue because it contains formed elements (red blood cells, white blood cells, platelets) and ➡

A blood bank technician is responsible for sampling and testing donated blood. This testing involves determining the blood type of the donated sample and whether the sample has been infected with serious diseases such as hepatitis or HIV. The technician has a thorough understanding of blood composition and the importance of matching donor and recipient blood types prior to a transfusion.

Anatomy & Physiology | REVEALED®
aprevealed.com

Module 9: Cardiovascular System

dissolved proteins in a liquid ground substance called plasma. Four to six liters of this warm, alkaline, viscous fluid is continuously pumped through our blood vessels. It may help to think of the circulation of blood as a "fluid conveyor belt" where cells, ions, and molecules are both continuously added to it and dropped off from it. As a result, the composition of blood is ever changing as it is pumped by our heart and makes its continuous journey through our vessels. Because of its intimate contact with the cells of the body, various blood tests can be performed, providing a physician with important information for an accurate diagnosis.

In this chapter, we describe the function of blood and the various blood components. We then examine how these components are formed, how they function, and discuss hemostasis (blood clotting). We finish with a discussion of development and aging of blood.

18.1 Functions and General Composition of Blood

Blood is the specialized fluid that is transported through the **cardiovascular** (kar′dē-ō-vas′kū-lăr; *cardio* = heart, *vascular* = vessels) **system,** which is composed of the heart (cardio) and blood vessels (vascular). Blood vessels form a circuit away from the heart and back to the heart that includes the arteries, capillaries, and veins. **Arteries** transport blood away from the heart, whereas **veins** transport blood toward the heart. **Capillaries** (kap′i-lār-ēz; *capillaries* = relating to hair) are permeable, microscopic vessels between arteries and veins. Capillaries serve as the sites of exchange between the blood and body tissues; it is from our capillaries that oxygen and nutrients exit the blood, and carbon dioxide and cellular wastes enter the blood.

Blood is composed of **formed elements** (erythrocytes, leukocytes, and platelets) and plasma. **Erythrocytes** (ĕ-rith′rō-sīt; *erthyros* = red, *kytes* = cell) (or *red blood cells*) function to transport respiratory gases in the blood. **Leukocytes** (or *white blood cells*) contribute to defending the body against pathogens, and **platelets** help clot the blood and prevent blood loss from damaged vessels. **Plasma** is the fluid portion of blood containing plasma proteins and dissolved solutes. We begin by describing the general functions of blood, its physical characteristics, and its general components.

18.1a Functions of Blood

 LEARNING OBJECTIVE

1. Describe the general functions of blood.

Blood carries out a variety of important functions as it circulates throughout the body; these functions can be grouped as transportation, regulation, and protection.

Transportation

Blood transports formed elements and dissolved molecules and ions throughout the body. Consider that as blood is transported through the blood vessels it carries oxygen from and carbon dioxide to the lungs, nutrients absorbed from the gastrointestinal tract, hormones released by endocrine glands, and heat and waste products from the systemic cells. Even when you take a medication, it is the blood that delivers it to the cells of your body. Thus, it is the blood that serves as the "delivery system" for the body.

Regulation

Blood participates in the regulation of body temperature, body pH, and fluid balance:

- **Body temperature.** Blood helps regulate body temperature. This is possible because blood absorbs heat from body cells, especially skeletal muscle, as it passes through blood vessels of body tissues. Heat is then released from blood at the body surface as blood is transported through blood vessels of the skin.
- **Body pH.** Blood, because it absorbs acids and base from body cells, helps maintain the pH of cells. Blood contains chemical buffers (e.g., proteins, bicarbonate) that bind and release hydrogen ions (H^+) to maintain blood pH until the excess is eliminated from the body (see chapter 25).
- **Fluid balance.** Water is added to the blood from the gastrointestinal (GI) tract and lost in numerous ways (e.g., urine, skin). In addition, there is a constant exchange of fluid between the blood plasma in the capillaries and the interstitial fluid surrounding the cells of the body's tissues. Blood contains proteins and ions that exert osmotic pressure to pull fluid back into the capillaries to help maintain normal fluid balance (see section 20.2).

Protection

Blood contains leukocytes, plasma proteins, and various molecules that help protect the body against potentially harmful substances. These substances are part of the immune system that is described in detail in chapter 22. Components of blood, including platelets and plasma proteins, also protect the body against blood loss, as described later in this chapter.

 WHAT DID YOU LEARN?

❶ What are some of the materials that blood transports?

❷ How does blood help regulate body temperature and fluid levels in the body?

18.1b Physical Characteristics of Blood

2. Name six characteristics that describe blood, and explain the significance of each to health and homeostasis.

Blood is a type of connective tissue (see section 5.2d) that can be described based on its physical characteristics including color, volume, viscosity, plasma concentration, temperature, and pH:

- **Color.** The color of blood depends upon whether it is oxygen-rich or oxygen-poor. Oxygen-rich blood is bright red or almost scarlet. Contrary to popular belief, oxygen-poor blood is not blue; rather, oxygen-poor blood is dark red. The bluish appearance of our veins can be attributed to both (1) the fact that we can see the blood traveling through the superficial veins through the skin; and (2) how light is reflected back to the eye from different colors. Lower-energy light wavelengths, like red, are absorbed by the skin and *not* reflected back to the eye, but higher-energy wavelengths like blue *are* reflected back to the eye, so the eyes can perceive only the blue coloration from the veins.

- **Volume.** The average volume of blood in an adult is 5 liters (L). Males tend to have more blood (5 to 6 L) than do females (4 to 5 L) because of their larger size. Sustaining a normal blood volume is essential in maintaining blood pressure.

- **Viscosity.** Blood is about 4 to 5 times more *viscous* than water, meaning that it is thicker. Viscosity of blood depends upon the amount of dissolved substances in the blood relative to the amount of fluid; that is, viscosity is increased if the amount of substances (primarily erythrocytes) increases, the amount of fluid decreases, or both.

- **Plasma concentration.** Although viscosity is a characteristic of whole blood (plasma plus formed elements), another important physical characteristic is the plasma concentration, or the relative concentration of solutes, in plasma. The relative concentration of solutes (e.g., proteins and ions) determines whether fluids move into or out of the plasma by osmosis as blood is transported through capillaries. For example, when an individual is dehydrated, the plasma becomes hypertonic (see section 4.3b), and fluid moves into the plasma from the surrounding tissues. Additionally, the plasma concentration is used to determine intravenous (IV) solution concentrations, which are usually isotonic to plasma.

- **Temperature.** The temperature of blood is about 1°C higher than measured body temperature; thus, if your body temperature is 37°C (98.6°F), your blood temperature is about 38°C (100.4°F). Therefore blood warms areas through which it travels.

- **Blood pH.** Blood plasma is slightly alkaline, with a pH between 7.35 and 7.45. Plasma proteins, like all proteins of the body, have a three-dimensional shape that is dependent upon H^+ concentration. If the pH is altered from the normal range, plasma proteins become denatured and are unable to carry out their functions (see section 2.8b).

The physical characteristics of blood are summarized in **table 18.1**.

Table 18.1	Physical Characteristics of Blood	
Characteristics	**Normal Values**
Color	Scarlet (oxygen-rich) to dark red (oxygen-poor)
Volume	4–5 L (females); 5-6 L (males)
Viscosity (relative to water)	4.5–5.5 × (whole blood)
Temperature	38°C (100.4°F)
pH	7.35–7.45

WHAT DO YOU THINK?

1 If a woman has 5 L of blood and she donates 1 pint (about 0.5 L), what approximate percentage is she donating: 1%, 5%, 10%, or 15%? Why do you think individuals below a certain weight (i.e., less than 110 pounds) are not allowed to give blood?

WHAT DID YOU LEARN?

3 Will blood be able to properly carry out its functions if blood pH is significantly altered? Why or why not?

18.1c Components of Blood

3. List the three components of a centrifuged blood sample.

4. Define hematocrit, and explain how the medical definition differs from the clinical usage.

5. Name the three formed elements of the blood, and compare their relative abundance.

INTEGRATE

CONCEPT CONNECTION

Recall from section 2.5c that an **acid** increases the concentration of H^+ by releasing it into the solution. Examples include hydrochloric acid (HCl) and carbonic acid (H_2CO_3). In contrast, a **base** decreases the concentration of H^+ in the solution. Examples include bicarbonate ions (HCO_3^-) and hydroxide ions (OH^-). The **pH** is a measure of the relative amounts of H^+ in solution. A **buffer** helps prevent pH changes by binding or releasing excess H^+ to maintain the normal H^+ concentration in a solution.

Centrifuged Blood

Whole blood (plasma and formed elements) can be separated into its liquid and cellular components by using a **centrifuge,** a device that spins the sample of blood in a tube so that heavier components collect at the bottom. **Figure 18.1** shows the resulting three components separated in the test tube. From bottom to top, these components are as follows:

- Erythrocytes, which form the lower layer of the centrifuged blood. They typically make up about 44% of a blood sample.

Whole blood

Centrifuge

(1) Withdraw blood into a syringe and place it into a glass centrifuge tube.

(2) Place the tube into a centrifuge and spin for about 10 minutes.

(3) Components of blood separate during centrifugation to reveal plasma, buffy coat, and erythrocytes.

Plasma (55% of whole blood)		
Water 92% by weight	**Proteins** 7% by weight	**Other solutes** 1% by weight
	Albumins 58% Globulins 37% Fibrinogen 4% Regulatory proteins <1%	Electrolytes Nutrients Respiratory gases Waste products

Buffy coat (<1% of whole blood)

Platelets 150–400 thousand per cubic mm

Leukocytes 4.5–11 thousand per cubic mm

Neutrophils 50–70%

Lymphocytes 20–40%

Monocytes 2–8%

Eosinophils 1–4%

Basophils 0.5–1%

Formed elements

Erythrocytes (44% of whole blood)

Erythrocytes 4.2–6.2 million per cubic mm

—55%—

—<1%—

—44%—

Figure 18.1 Whole Blood Separation and Composition. Whole blood contains plasma (average is about 55%) and formed elements (average is about 45%). The percentages presented in this figure are average numbers of cells, and the numbers for components of the buffy coat represent average ranges. A cubic millimeter of blood is equivalent to a microliter (μL). **AP|R**

- A thin **buffy coat** makes up the middle layer. This slightly gray-white layer is composed of leukocytes and platelets. The buffy coat forms less than 1% of a blood sample.
- Plasma is a straw-colored liquid that rises to the top in the test tube; it generally makes up about 55% of blood.

The percentage of the volume of all formed elements (erythrocytes, leukocytes, and platelets) in the blood is called the **hematocrit** (hē′mă-tō-krit, hem′ă-; *hemato* = blood, *krino* = to separate). This medical dictionary definition of the true hematocrit differs slightly from the clinical definition, which equates the hematocrit to the percentage of only erythrocytes. (In practice, the true hematocrit and the clinical hematocrit are virtually the same.)

Hematocrit values vary somewhat and are dependent upon the age and sex of the individual. Adult males tend to have a hematocrit ranging between 42% and 56%, whereas adult females' hematocrits range from 38% to 46%. Males have a higher hematocrit because testosterone stimulates the kidney to produce the hormone erythropoietin (EPO), which promotes erythrocyte production (discussed later).

Blood Smear

All of the components of the formed elements can be viewed by preparing a **blood smear**. A blood smear and the steps to produce a smear are shown in **figure 18.2**. Note the following:

- **Erythrocytes** are the most numerous of the formed elements. These are anucleate cells and appear as pink or pale purple, biconcave discs.
- **Leukocytes** are larger than erythrocytes. The nucleus is very noticeable in leukocytes. Several leukocytes (a lymphocyte, neutrophil, and two monocytes) are shown in figure 18.2.
- **Platelets** appear as small fragments of cells.

WHAT DID YOU LEARN?

4 What are the three components visible in a centrifuged blood sample?

5 How does hematocrit vary among individuals?

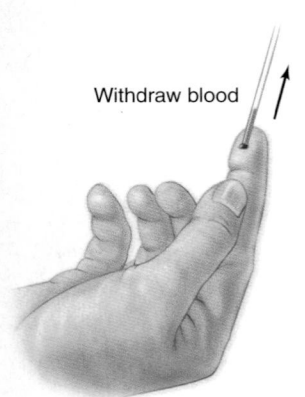

1 Prick finger and collect a small amount of blood using a micropipette.

2 Place a drop of blood on a slide.

3a Using a second slide, pull the drop of blood across the first slide's surface, leaving a thin layer of blood on the slide.

3b After the blood dries, apply a stain for contrast. Place a coverslip on top.

4 When viewed under the microscope, blood smear reveals the components of the formed elements.

Figure 18.2 Preparing a Blood Smear.

18.2 Composition of Blood Plasma

Plasma is composed primarily of water (about 92% of its volume), plasma proteins (about 7% of its volume), and dissolved organic and inorganic molecules and ions (about 1% of its volume) **(table 18.2)**. Plasma is an extracellular fluid (ECF) because it is body fluid found outside of cells. Plasma is similar to interstitial fluid, in that both have similar concentrations of nutrients, waste products, and electrolytes. However, one of the most significant differences is that protein concentration is higher in plasma than in the interstitial fluid. We first describe plasma proteins and then the specific substances transported in the plasma.

Always ask "What is the point?"

18.2a Plasma Proteins

 LEARNING OBJECTIVES

1. Define colloid osmotic pressure.
2. Identify the various types of plasma proteins, and explain the general function of each.

Blood is considered a **colloid** (see section 2.6a) because it contains proteins in the plasma. Plasma proteins include albumin, globulins, fibrinogen and other clotting proteins, and regulatory proteins such as enzymes and some hormones. Most of these proteins are produced in the liver, including albumin, alpha- and beta-globulins, fibrinogen, and proteins involved with clotting. Other plasma proteins, such as gamma-globulins and regulatory proteins, are produced by leukocytes and other organs, respectively.

Collectively, these plasma proteins exert osmotic pressure and prevent the loss of fluid from the blood as it moves through the capillaries. Osmotic pressure exerted by plasma proteins is called **colloid osmotic pressure.** This osmotic force is responsible for drawing fluids into the blood and preventing excess fluid loss between blood capillaries and the interstitial fluid (see section 20.2), thus helping to maintain blood volume and

Table 18.2	The Composition of Blood Plasma
Plasma Component (Percentage of Plasma)	**Functions**
Water (~92% of plasma)	The solvent in which formed elements are suspended and proteins and solutes are dissolved
PLASMA PROTEINS (~7% OF PLASMA): All proteins serve to buffer against pH changes	
Albumin (~58% of plasma proteins)	Exerts osmotic force to retain fluid within the blood Contributes to blood's viscosity Responsible for some fatty acid and hormone transport
Globulins (~37% of plasma proteins)	Alpha-globulins transport lipids and some metal ions. Beta-globulins transport iron ions and lipids in blood. Gamma-globulins are antibodies that immobilize pathogens.
Fibrinogen (~4% of plasma proteins)	Participates in blood coagulation (clotting)
Regulatory proteins (<1% of plasma proteins)	Consists of enzymes and hormones
OTHER SOLUTES (~1% OF BLOOD PLASMA)	
Electrolytes (e.g., sodium, potassium, calcium, chloride, iron, bicarbonate, and hydrogen)	Help establish and maintain membrane potentials, maintain pH balance, and regulate osmosis (control of the percentages of water and salt in the blood)
Nutrients (e.g., amino acids, glucose, cholesterol, vitamins, fatty acids)	Energy source; precursor for synthesizing other molecules
Respiratory gases (e.g., oxygen: <2% dissolved in plasma, 98% bound to hemoglobin within erythrocytes; and carbon dioxide: ~7% dissolved in plasma, ~27% bound to hemoglobin within erythrocytes, ~66% converted to HCO_3^-)	Oxygen is needed for aerobic cellular respiration; carbon dioxide is a waste product produced by cells during this process.
Wastes (breakdown products of metabolism) (e.g., lactic acid, creatinine, urea, bilirubin, ammonia)	Waste products serve no function in the blood plasma; rather, they merely are being transported to the liver and kidneys where they can be removed from the blood.

consequently blood pressure. If plasma protein levels decrease, such as might occur due to liver disease (resulting in decreased production of plasma proteins) or kidney damage (resulting in increased elimination of plasma proteins), colloid osmotic pressure also decreases. This decrease results in fluid loss from the blood and fluid retention in the interstitial space (i.e., edema).

Albumins (al-bū'min; *albumen* = white of egg) are the smallest and most abundant of the plasma proteins, making up approximately 58% of total proteins. Because albumin is the most abundant plasma protein, it exerts the greatest colloid osmotic pressure to maintain blood volume and blood pressure. Secondarily, albumins act as transport proteins that carry ions, hormones, and some lipids in the blood.

Globulins (glob'ū-lin; *globules* = globule) are the second largest group of plasma proteins, forming about 37% of all plasma proteins. The smaller **alpha-globulins** and the larger **beta-globulins** primarily bind and transport certain water-insoluble molecules and hormones, some metals (e.g., iron), and ions (e.g., calcium ions [Ca^{2+}]). **Gamma-globulins** are also called *immunoglobulins*, or *antibodies*, which play a part in the body's defenses (see section 22.8).

Fibrinogen (fi'brin-ō-jen; *fibra* = fiber) makes up about 4% of all plasma proteins. Fibrinogen as well as other clotting proteins are responsible for blood clot formation. Following trauma to the walls of blood vessels, fibrinogen is converted into long, insoluble strands of *fibrin*, which help form a blood clot. When the clotting proteins are removed from plasma, the remaining fluid is termed **serum** (ser'um; = whey). Blood clotting is described in more detail later in this chapter.

Regulatory proteins form a very minor class of plasma proteins (less than 1% of total plasma proteins). This group of proteins includes enzymes to accelerate chemical reactions in the blood and some hormones (e.g., insulin) being transported throughout the body to target cells (see section 17.3).

WHAT DID YOU LEARN?

6 How are plasma protein levels related to colloid osmotic pressure?

7 What is the most abundant type of plasma protein, and what are its functions?

18.2b Other Solutes

LEARNING OBJECTIVE

3. List dissolved substances in plasma by category.

Table 18.3	Common Electrolytes in Arterial Plasma		
Electrolytes (Ions)	**Normal Ranges (Values)**	**Function**	**Substances That Regulate Electrolyte Blood Level**
CATIONS			
Sodium (Na^+)	135–145 milliequivalents per liter (mEq/L)	Neuron and muscle function; fluid balance; cotransporter	Aldosterone, atrial natriuretic peptide (ANP), estrogen, progesterone, glucocorticoids
Potassium (K^+)	3.5–5.0 mEq/L	Neuron and muscle function	Aldosterone, ANP
Calcium (Ca^{2+})	8.4–10.2 milligrams per deciliter (mg/dL)	Hardens bone; release of neurotransmitter; muscle contraction; blood clotting; second messenger	Parathyroid hormone, calcitriol, calcitonin
Hydrogen (H^+)	pH 7.35–7.45	pH balance	Buffering systems—chemicals in blood, kidney, respiratory system
ANIONS			
Chloride (Cl^-)	96–106 mEq/L	Anion bound to sodium; component of gastric acid (HCl); chloride shift	Regulated indirectly through sodium
Bicarbonate (HCO_3^-)	23.1–26.7 mEq/L	pH balance	Dependent upon carbon dioxide and H^+ blood levels
Hydrogen phosphate (HPO_4^{3-})	1.4–2.7 mEq/L	Binds with calcium and deposited in bone	Parathyroid hormone

Table 18.4	Common Nutrients Found in Blood Plasma	
Nutrients	**Normal Ranges (Values)**	**Function**
Glucose	Fasting: 70–100 mg/dL; 2 hours after a meal: < 145 mg/dL	Fuel molecule for cellular respiration (primary energy source for nervous tissue); tightly regulated by a number of hormones, including insulin and glucagon
Amino acids	*(Varies, based on specific amino acid being measured)*	Monomers for synthesizing protein; also regulated by some of the same hormones as glucose
Lactic acid	4.5–14.4 mg/dL	By-product of anaerobic cellular respiration
Iron	Male: 50–175 micrograms per deciliter (μg/dL) Female: 40–150 μg/dL	Component of hemoglobin
Lipids		Molecules that generally do not dissolve in water
Cholesterol	100–200 mg/dL	Plasma membrane component; synthesis of steroid hormones; bile salts
HDL	40–80 mg/dL	Transports lipids to the liver
VLDL/LDL	10–100 mg/dL	Transports lipids from the liver
Triglycerides	30–149 mg/dL	Fuel molecules
Phospholipids	6–12 mg/dL	Molecules that form cell membrane bilayer

Blood is also considered a *solution* because it contains dissolved organic and inorganic molecules and ions (see section 2.4). These substances include electrolytes, nutrients, gases, and waste products. Recall from sections 2.3c and 17.3 that polar or charged substances (e.g., glucose and salts) dissolve readily in the blood, and nonpolar molecules (e.g., cholesterol, triglycerides, and fatty acids) do not readily dissolve in blood and require a transporter protein (some of which were just described). **Tables 18.3** and **18.4** list the normal ranges and functions of common solutes dissolved in blood plasma.

 WHAT DID YOU LEARN?

8 What are the main dissolved substances found in plasma?

18.3 Formed Elements in the Blood

Collectively, the erythrocytes, leukocytes, and platelets are called the formed elements and make up approximately 45% of whole blood. It is best not to refer to these structures as cells because some (mature erythrocytes) contain neither nuclei nor organelles, and others (the platelets) are merely fragments broken off from a larger cell. **Table 18.5** summarizes the characteristics of the formed elements.

Table 18.5	Characteristics of the Formed Elements			
Formed Element	**Size (Diameter)**	**Function**	**Life Span**	**Density (Average Number per mm³ of Blood = μL)**
Erythrocytes	7.5 μm	Transport oxygen and carbon dioxide	~120 days	Females: ~4.8 million Males: ~5.4 million
Leukocytes (e.g., neutrophils, eosinophils, basophils, monocytes, and lymphocytes)	1.5 to 3 times larger than an erythrocyte; 11.25–22.5 μm	Initiate immune response; defend against potentially harmful substances	Varies from 12 hours (neutrophils) to years (lymphocytes)	4500–11,000
Platelets	< ¼ the size of an erythrocyte; ~2 μm	Participate in blood clotting	~8–10 days	150,000–400,000

18.3a Hemopoiesis

1. Define hemopoiesis, and explain the role of colony-stimulating factors.
2. Describe the four cellular stages of erythropoiesis.
3. Compare the production of granulocytes, monocytes, and lymphocytes in leukopoiesis.
4. Summarize the process by which platelets are formed in thrombopoiesis.

Formed elements have a relatively short life span; new ones are continually produced by the process of **hemopoiesis** (hē′mō-poy-ē′sis; *poiesis* = a making), also called *hematopoiesis*. Hemopoiesis occurs in red bone marrow (myeloid tissue) of certain bones.

The process of hemopoiesis starts with hemopoietic stem cells called **hemocytoblasts** (hē′-mō-sī′tō-blasts) **(figure 18.3)**. Hemocytoblasts are considered pluripotent cells (see Clinical View: "Stem Cells" in section 5.1), meaning that they can differentiate and develop into many different kinds of cells. Hemocytoblasts produce two different lines for blood cell development: The **myeloid** (mī′ĕ-loyd; *myelos* = marrow, *eidos* = appearance) **line** forms (1) erythrocytes, (2) all leukocytes except lymphocytes (this would include granulocytes and monocytes), and (3) megakaryocytes (cells that produce platelets). The **lymphoid** (lim′foyd) **line** forms only lymphocytes.

The maturation and division of hemopoietic stem cells is influenced by **colony-stimulating factors (CSFs),** or *colony-forming units* (*CFUs*). These molecules are all growth factors (except erythropoietin, which is a hormone). They include the following:

- **Multi-colony-stimulating factor (multi-CSF)** increases the formation of erythrocytes, as well as all classes of granulocytes, monocytes, and platelets from myeloid stem cells.
- **Granulocyte-macrophage colony-stimulating factor (GM-CSF)** accelerates the formation of all granulocytes and monocytes from their progenitor cells.
- **Granulocyte colony-stimulating factor (G-CSF)** stimulates the formation of granulocytes from myeloblast cells.
- **Macrophage colony-stimulating factor (M-CSF)** stimulates the production of monocytes from monoblasts.
- **Thrombopoietin** stimulates both the production of megakaryocytes in the bone marrow and the subsequent formation of platelets.
- **Erythropoietin (EPO)** is a hormone that is produced primarily by the kidneys (small amounts are produced by the liver) to increase the rate of production and maturation of erythrocyte progenitor and erythroblast cells.

Erythropoiesis

Erythrocytes make up more than 99% of formed elements with a concentration between 4.2 and 6.2 million per cubic millimeter. The process of erythrocyte production is called **erythropoiesis** (ĕ-rith′rō-poy-ē′sis; *erythro* = red or red blood cell). Normally, erythrocytes are produced at the rate of about 3 million per second. The hormone erythropoietin (EPO) controls this rate by increasing the rate of erythrocyte formation (described later). Dietary requirements for normal erythropoiesis include iron, B vitamins (e.g., folic acid, riboflavin), and amino acids (to build proteins).

The process of erythropoiesis begins with a **myeloid stem cell,** which under the influence of multi-CSF forms a progenitor cell. The progenitor cell forms a **proerythroblast,** which is a large, nucleated cell. It then becomes an **erythroblast,** which is a slightly smaller cell that is producing hemoglobin in its cytoplasm. The next stage, called a **normoblast,** is a still smaller cell with more hemoglobin in the cytoplasm; its nucleus has been ejected. A cell called a **reticulocyte** (re-tik′ū-lō-sīt) eventually is formed. The reticulocyte has lost all organelles except some ribosomes, but it continues to produce hemoglobin. The transformation from myeloid stem cell to reticulocyte takes about 5 days.

Some reticulocytes finish maturation while circulating in blood vessels (and in normal circumstances, make up 0.5–2.0% of the circulating blood). One to two days after entering the circulation, the organelles in the reticulocyte degenerate, and the reticulocyte becomes a mature erythrocyte. Without a nucleus and cellular organelles, the mature erythrocyte is essentially a plasma membrane "bag" containing hemoglobin.

Figure 18.3 Origin, Differentiation, and Maturation of Formed Elements. All formed elements are derived from common hemopoietic stem cells, called hemocytoblasts. Both myeloid stem cells and lymphoid stem cells are derived from hemocytoblasts. Myeloid stem cells give rise to erythrocytes, platelets, and to all leukocytes except lymphocytes. Lymphoid stem cells give rise to lymphocytes and natural killer (NK) cells. **AP|R**

Leukopoiesis

Leukocytes make up less than 0.01% of formed elements with a concentration between 4500 and 11,000 per cubic millimeter. The production of leukocytes is called **leukopoiesis** (lū'kō-poy-ē'sis; *leuko* = white). Leukopoiesis involves three different types of maturation processes: granulocyte maturation, monocyte maturation, and lymphocyte maturation.

All three types of granulocytes (neutrophils, basophils, and eosinophils) are derived from a myeloid stem cell. This stem cell is stimulated by multi-CSF and GM-CSF to form a progenitor cell. The granulocyte line develops when the progenitor cell forms a **myeloblast** (mī'ĕ-lō-blast) under the influence of G-CSF. The myeloblast ultimately differentiates into one of three types of granulocytes.

Like granulocytes, monocytes are also derived from a myeloid stem cell. The myeloid stem cell differentiates into a progenitor cell, and under the influence of M-CSF this cell forms a **monoblast.** This is the monocyte line. Eventually, the monoblast forms a promonocyte that differentiates and matures into a **monocyte.**

Lymphocytes are derived from a **lymphoid stem cell** through the lymphoid line. The lymphoid stem cell differentiates into **B-lymphoblasts** and **T-lymphoblasts.** B-lymphoblasts mature into B-lymphocytes, whereas T-lymphoblasts mature into T-lymphocytes. Some lymphoid stem cells differentiate directly into natural killer (NK) cells. (Lymphocyte development and maturation is further described in section 22.5)

Thrombopoiesis

Platelets (or *thrombocytes*) make up less than 1% of formed elements with a concentration between 150,000 and 400,000 per cubic millimeter. The production of platelets is called **thrombopoiesis** (throm'bō-poy-ē'sis; *thrombos* = clot). From the myeloid stem cell, a committed cell called a **megakaryoblast** (meg-ă-kar'ē-ō-blast; *mega* = big) is produced. It matures under the influence of thrombopoietin to form a **megakaryocyte** (meg-ă-kar'ē-ō-sīt) **(figure 18.4)**. Megakaryocytes are easily distinguished both by their large size (about

Megakaryocyte

LM 1600x

(a) Red bone marrow with megakaryocytes

Megakaryocytes

Blood flow

Figure 18.4 Platelet Formation.
Platelets are derived from megakaryocytes in the red bone marrow. (*a*) Photomicrograph of megakaryocytes in red bone marrow. (*b*) Megakaryocytes extend long processes (called proplatelets) through the blood vessel wall. These proplatelets are spliced by the force of the blood flow into platelets, which then circulate in the blood. AP|R

Endothelial cells   Proplatelets   Platelets

(b) Platelets forming in blood vessel

100 micrometers [μm] in diameter) and their dense, multilobed nucleus. Each megakaryocyte then produces thousands of platelets.

Until recently, the process of how megakaryocytes produce platelets was in question. However, researchers in 2007 reported that megakaryocytes produce long extensions from themselves called *proplatelets*. While still attached to the megakaryocyte, these proplatelets extend through the blood vessel wall (between the endothelial cells) in the red bone marrow. The force from the blood flow "slices" these proplatelets into the fragments we know as platelets.

WHAT DID YOU LEARN?

9 What are the roles of the different colony-stimulating factors (CSFs) in hemopoiesis?

10 What precursor cells ultimately form leukocytes?

18.3b Erythrocytes

LEARNING OBJECTIVES

5. Describe the structure of erythrocytes.
6. List the events by which erythrocyte production is stimulated.
7. Explain the process by which erythrocyte components are recycled.
8. Compare and contrast the different blood types and their importance when transfusing blood.

Erythrocytes are very small, flexible cells, with a diameter of approximately 7.5 μm **(figure 18.5)**. Although erythrocytes are commonly referred to as red blood cells, or RBCs, the term "red blood cell" is a misnomer because a mature erythrocyte is not really a cell; it lacks a nucleus and cellular organelles. As a result, it is more appropriate to call it a *formed element*. An erythrocyte has a unique biconcave disc structure (at its narrowest point about 0.75 μm and at its widest point about 2.6 μm). It is composed of a plasma membrane within which are housed about 280 million hemoglobin molecules.

Erythrocytes transport oxygen and carbon dioxide between the tissues and the lungs. The fact that erythrocytes lack a nucleus and organelles enables them to carry respiratory gases more efficiently. The biconcave shape allows erythrocytes to stack and line up in single file, termed a **rouleau** (rū-lō′; pl., *rouleaux* = cylinder), as they pass through the smallest blood vessels called capillaries. A latticework of spectrin protein supports the plasma membrane of the erythrocyte on its internal surface and provides flexibility to the erythrocyte as it moves through the capillaries.

WHAT DO YOU THINK?

2 What does an erythrocyte gain by the loss of its nucleus and organelles? What three cellular processes can it no longer engage in due to the loss of its (a) nucleus and (b) mitochondria?

Figure 18.5 Erythrocyte Structure. (*a*) Erythrocytes have the gross structure of a biconcave disc, as shown here in sectional and superior views. (*b*) LM of erythrocytes shows their three-dimensional structure and a rouleau. AP|R

Hemoglobin

Hemoglobin (hē'mō-glō-bin) is a red-pigmented protein that transports oxygen and carbon dioxide. When blood is maximally loaded with oxygen, it is termed **oxygenated** (and appears bright red). Conversely, when some oxygen is lost and carbon dioxide is gained during respiratory gas exchange, blood is called **deoxygenated** (and appears dark red). Depending upon what gases it is binding, hemoglobin can be referred to as oxyhemoglobin (hemoglobin bound to oxygen), deoxyhemoglobin (hemoglobin without oxygen), and carbaminohemoglobin (hemoglobin with carbon dioxide bound to an amino group).

Each hemoglobin molecule consists of four protein building blocks called **globins.** Two of these globins are called **alpha (α) chains,** and the other two, which are slightly different, are called **beta (β) chains (figure 18.6).** All globin chains contain a **heme** group, which is composed of a porphyrin (organic compound) ring, with an iron ion (Fe^{2+}) in its center. Oxygen binds to the Fe^{2+} in heme groups for transport in the blood.

Because each molecule of hemoglobin has four heme groups, it has four Fe^{2+} and is capable of binding four molecules of oxygen. The oxygen binding is fairly weak; this allows rapid attachment of oxygen with hemoglobin when erythrocytes pass through the blood capillaries of the lungs, and rapid detachment when erythrocytes pass through the systemic capillaries of body tissues.

Carbon dioxide and the globin molecule (not the Fe^{2+}) have a similar weak attachment relationship for the transport of carbon dioxide molecules. Carbon dioxide binds to the globin protein molecule as blood moves through systemic capillaries and is released as blood moves through the capillaries of the lungs.

Erythrocyte Production

Erythrocyte production is controlled by the hormone **erythropoietin (EPO).** The kidneys are the primary producers of EPO, although the liver also secretes a small amount of EPO as well. The process by which EPO release is stimulated is shown in **figure 18.7.** The initial stimulus is a decrease in blood oxygen levels. This decrease may be caused by the continuous removal of aged erythrocytes, exercise, blood loss, or exposure to high altitudes (where atmospheric oxygen levels are lower). Chemoreceptors within the kidney detect low blood oxygen levels as the blood travels through blood vessels within the kidney. As a result, certain cells in the kidney release the hormone EPO into the blood. EPO travels through the blood and reaches the red bone marrow. There, EPO stimulates myeloid cells in the red bone marrow to increase the rate of erythrocyte production. Additional erythrocytes are released into circulation (a process that takes a few days), more oxygen can be transported from the lungs and delivered to the cells. Blood oxygen levels increase as a result. Increased oxygen levels inhibit release of EPO from kidney cells through negative feedback.

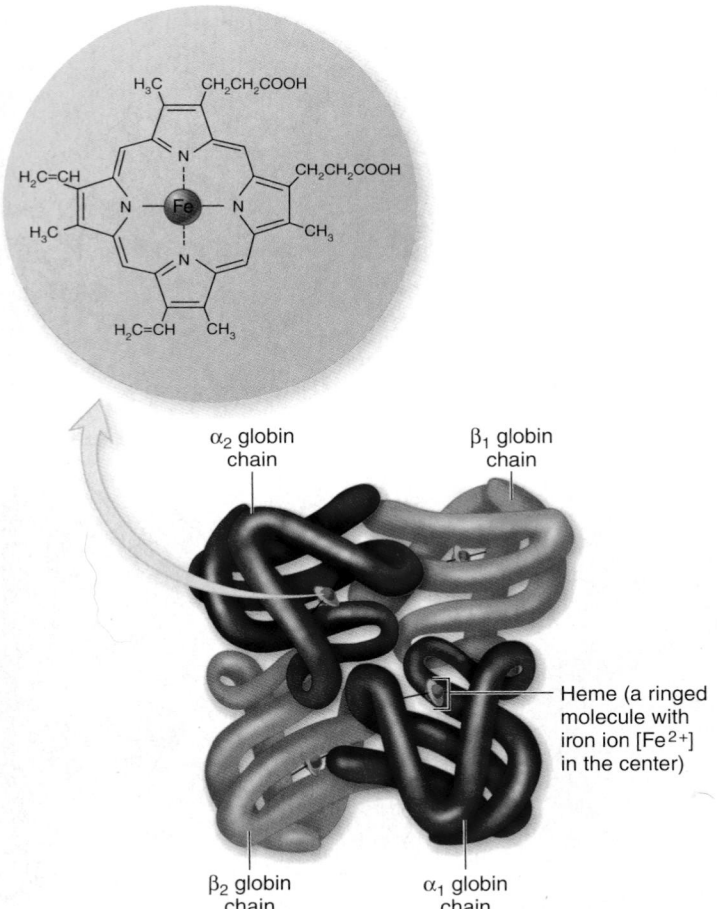

Figure 18.6 Molecular Structure of Hemoglobin. A single molecule of hemoglobin is composed of four protein subunits, called globins, each containing a lipid heme group that holds a single iron ion (Fe^{2+}) in its center. Each hemoglobin molecule transports four oxygen molecules that are weakly attracted to the Fe^{2+}. **AP|R**

INTEGRATE

CLINICAL VIEW
Blood Doping

To enhance their performance in endurance events, some athletes may try to boost their bodies' ability to deliver oxygen to the muscles by increasing the number of erythrocytes in their blood. This can be accomplished in several ways. First, the number of erythrocytes can be increased naturally by living and training at high altitude. The body compensates for the decreased oxygen concentration in the atmosphere by increasing the rate of erythrocyte production, thus increasing the number of erythrocytes per unit volume of blood.

An illegal procedure used by some athletes is called **blood doping.** There are two different methods for blood doping. In the first (and older) method) the athlete essentially donates erythrocytes to himself or herself. Prior to competition, the athlete has a unit of blood removed and stored. As the kidneys detect the decreased blood oxygen, the hormone erythropoietin (EPO) is released by the kidneys and the bone marrow responds by increasing production of erythrocytes. This causes the body to increase erythrocyte production to make up for the ones just removed. A few days before the competition, the erythrocytes from the donated unit are transfused back into the athlete's body. The increased number of erythrocytes increases the amount of oxygen transported in the blood and is thought to favorably affect muscle performance, thereby improving athletic performance. The second method of blood doping has occurred with the development of pharmaceutical EPO, which is used to treat anemia. In this method of blood doping, an athlete is injected with pharmaceutical EPO to further increase erythrocyte levels

Potentially deadly dangers are inherent in blood doping, however. By increasing the number of erythrocytes per measured volume of blood, blood doping also increases the viscosity of the blood. Thus, the heart must work harder to pump this more cellular and viscous blood. Eventually, temporary athletic success may be overshadowed by permanent cardiovascular damage that can even lead to death, as has occurred with some Olympic athletes. Thus, blood doping has now been banned by athletic competition governing bodies.

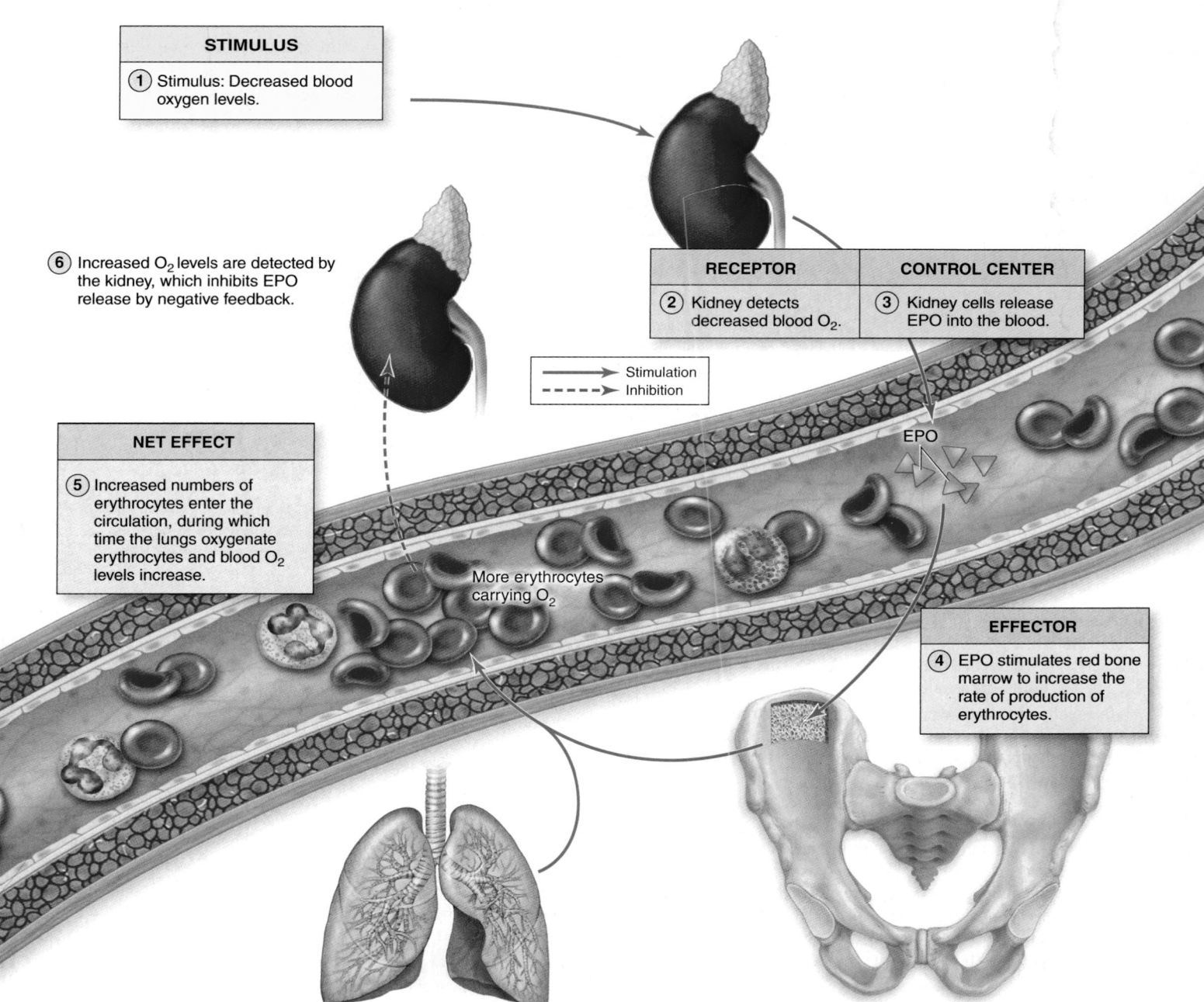

Figure 18.7 How EPO Regulates Erythrocyte Production. Low blood oxygen levels are detected by kidney chemoreceptors, which triggers the release of erythropoietin (EPO) into the blood. EPO stimulates the red bone marrow to produce more erythrocytes. EPO release is then inhibited when blood oxygen levels rise.

The adrenal gland secretes small amounts of testosterone in both sexes, and the testes secrete large amounts of testosterone in males (section 17.9c). In addition to its many other functions, testosterone stimulates the kidney to produce more EPO. Because males have higher levels of testosterone, they also usually have a higher erythrocyte count and a higher hematocrit.

Environmental factors, such as altitude, can affect EPO release and ultimately affect the hematocrit. Let us say a woman moves to a cabin high in the Rocky Mountains, where the atmospheric pressure is lower than it is at sea level. (As you'll learn in section 23.8, a lower atmospheric pressure means less oxygen availability.) Each time she takes a breath at this altitude, she takes in relatively less oxygen than she would on an ocean beach. Her body compensates

by releasing more EPO and making more erythrocytes over time; more erythrocytes in the blood can carry more oxygen to the tissues. However, having more erythrocytes increases the blood's viscosity, which could increase the chance of cardiovascular complications, such as major blood clots that lead to heart attacks or strokes.

Erythrocyte Destruction

The absence of both a nucleus and cellular organelles comes at a cost to the erythrocyte and affects its longevity. A mature erythrocyte cannot synthesize proteins either to repair itself or to replace damaged membrane regions. Aging and the wear-and-tear of circulation through blood vessels cause erythrocytes to become more fragile and less flexible. Therefore, the erythrocyte has a finite maximum life span of about 120 days. Every day, just under 1% of the oldest circulating erythrocytes are removed from circulation. These old erythrocytes are phagocytized in both the spleen and liver by cells called **macrophages.**

Three molecular components must be accounted for in the destruction of hemoglobin: the globin protein, iron ion, and the heme group. Two of the components are stored in other organs for recycling; the other component is metabolically altered and then excreted from the body, as shown in **figure 18.8.**

Globin proteins and erythrocyte membrane proteins are broken down into free amino acids, most of which are used by the body for protein synthesis to make new erythrocytes or other body proteins.

The number of erythrocytes in a person's blood can vary from the normal range, leading to various clinical disorders. In general, these conditions are classified as either anemia or polycythemia.

Anemia (ă-nē′mē-ă; *an* = without, *haima* = blood) is any condition in which either the percentage of erythrocytes is lower than normal or the oxygen-carrying capacity of the blood is reduced (such as may occur if the hemoglobin is abnormal). In either case, there is decreased oxygen delivery to body tissues—and consequently, the heart must work harder to supply oxygen to the body. Symptoms of anemia include lethargy, shortness of breath, pallor of the skin and mucous membranes, fatigue, and heart palpitations. The types of anemia include the following:

- **Aplastic anemia** is characterized by significantly decreased formation of both erythrocytes and hemoglobin. This condition results from defective red bone marrow, perhaps as a result of poisons, toxins, or radiation exposure.

- **Congenital hemolytic anemia** occurs when destruction of erythrocytes is more rapid than normal. It is usually due to a genetic defect, which results in the production of abnormal membrane proteins that make the erythrocyte plasma membrane very fragile.

- **Erythroblastic anemia** is characterized by the presence of large numbers of immature, nucleated cells (called erythroblasts and normoblasts) in the circulating blood. An accelerated pace of cell maturation causes immature cells to be present in the blood. These cells cannot function normally and thus anemia results.

- **Familial microcytic anemia** is a rare type of inherited anemia associated with a defect in iron uptake and use.

- **Hemorrhagic anemia** results from heavy blood loss. The hemorrhage may be caused, for example, by chronic ulcers or by heavy or prolonged menstrual flow.

- **Macrocytic anemia** occurs when the average size of circulating erythrocytes is too large. Deficiencies in both vitamin B_{12} and folic acid presence or uptake cause the production of enlarged erythrocytes.

- **Pernicious anemia** is a chronic progressive anemia of adults caused by failure of the body to absorb vitamin B_{12}. This vitamin is found in fish and meat, so most individuals receive enough B_{12} in their diet, unless they are vegans or strict vegetarians. (Thus, it is recommended that all vegetarians take a B_{12} vitamin supplement.) A defect in the production of **intrinsic factor,** a glycoprotein secreted by stomach lining cells to protect B_{12} in the stomach and enhance B_{12} absorption in the small intestine, leads to pernicious anemia. Individuals who have pernicious anemia due to defective intrinsic factor production must receive B_{12} intramuscular or subcutaneous injections, since they are unable to absorb oral B_{12} supplements.

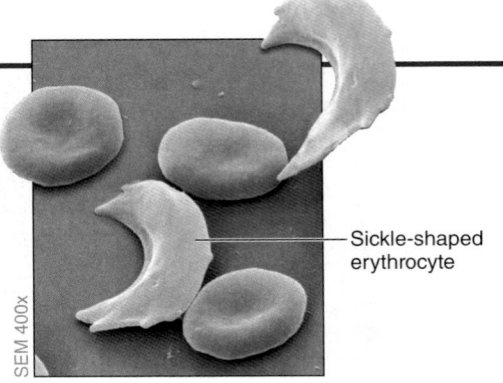

SEM of blood from a person with sickle-cell disease.

SEM 400x

Sickle-shaped erythrocyte

- **Sickle-cell disease** is an autosomal recessive anemia that occurs when a person inherits two copies of the sickle-cell gene. Erythrocytes become sickle-shaped at lower blood oxygen concentrations, making them unable to flow efficiently through the blood vessels to body tissues and more prone to destruction (a process called *hemolysis*).

Most anemias are treated by letting the patient's own bone marrow replace the erythrocytes. This process may be facilitated through the use of pharmaceutical EPO. However, anemia is often a symptom of another disease or problem. For example, while many anemias are due to iron deficiency, the iron deficiency often is not because of diet, but rather the result of chronic blood loss, a process that depletes the body of its iron stores over months or years. The three most common causes of such chronic blood loss are excessive menstrual bleeding, undiagnosed stomach ulcer, and colon cancer. So, while restoring the patient's erythrocyte count, a physician should also look for any underlying cause of the anemia.

Polycythemia (pol′ē-sī-thē′mē-ă; *poly* = many, *kytos* = cell) is the condition of having a normal blood volume but a higher percentage of erythrocytes in the blood (otherwise known as an elevated hematocrit). The blood becomes thick and viscous, putting a tremendous strain on the heart. Following are some of the different types of polycythemia:

- **Compensatory polycythemia** results from chronic **hypoxia** (inadequate oxygen supply to tissues). Smokers develop this condition when long-term exposure to tobacco smoke and chronically high levels of carbon monoxide damage their lungs.

- **Relative polycythemia** is an increase in the number of erythrocytes in the blood per unit volume as a result of a decrease in blood plasma. For example, suppose that a child is severely dehydrated due to a serious case of diarrhea. As the child progressively loses water, his or her blood becomes more concentrated. This type of polycythemia is a temporary condition, and the ratio of erythrocytes to plasma returns to normal when the child becomes rehydrated.

- **Erythrocytosis** is an increase in erythrocytes due to an increase in the level of the hormone EPO.

- **Polycythemia vera** is a chronic form characterized by an increase in blood volume and the number of erythrocytes. This condition results when erythrocyte growth in the red bone marrow is not regulated. Erythrocyte precursors continue to grow and mature, irrespective of the presence or absence of EPO.

Figure 18.8 **Recycling and Elimination of Erythrocyte Components.** Erythrocytes circulate in the blood for about 120 days, after which they are phagocytized in the liver and spleen. Various components are recycled; other components are altered and expelled as waste.

① Erythrocytes form in red bone marrow.

② They circulate in the blood for about 120 days.

Aged erythrocyte

Liver

Spleen

Macrophage

③ Aged erythrocytes are phagocytized by macrophages in the liver and spleen. The three components of hemoglobin are separated.

Globin proteins are broken down into amino acids and enter the blood. Some of these amino acids may be used to make new erythrocytes.

Iron is transported by transferrin into the red bone marrow as needed for erythrocyte production.

Fe^{2+}

Globin

Iron ion

Fe^{2+}

Heme (minus the iron) is converted to

Biliverdin

Bilirubin

④ Some components of hemoglobin (i.e., globin and heme) are broken down. Some of the broken down components are recycled, while others are expelled as waste. (Iron ions are not broken down, but are recycled.)

Iron is stored in the liver attached to ferritin and hemosiderin.

Small amounts of iron are lost in feces, sweat, and urine daily; iron is also lost via injury and menstruation.

Bilirubin is transported to the liver and then released as a component of bile in the small intestine.

Bilirubin is converted to **urobilinogen** in the small intestine.

Some urobilinogen is absorbed back into the blood and converted to **urobilin** and excreted in the urine.

Most urobilinogen continues to the large intestine and is converted to **stercobilin** and expelled in feces.

The iron component in hemoglobin is removed and transported by a globulin protein called **transferrin** (trans-fer′in; *trans* = across, *ferrum* = iron) to the liver where the Fe^{2+} then is bound to storage proteins called **ferritin** (fer′i-tin) and **hemosiderin** (hē′mō-sid′ĕr-in). Ferritin is a large water-soluble protein that serves as the primary storage mechanism for iron. Iron is stored mainly in the liver and spleen, and it is transported by transferrin to the red bone marrow as needed for erythrocyte production. However, small amounts of iron, approximately 0.9 mg, are lost daily in feces, sweat, and urine. In females, additional iron is lost in the monthly menstrual flow.

The heme group (minus the Fe^{2+}) released from hemoglobin is converted within macrophages first into a green pigment called **biliverdin** (bil-i-ver′din; *bilis* = bile, *verd* = green). Biliverdin is eventually converted into a yellowish pigment called **bilirubin** (bil-i-rū′bin; *rubin* = reddish), which is transported by albumin to the liver. Bilirubin is a component of a digestive secretion called bile, which is produced by liver and released into the small intestine.

Bilirubin is converted to **urobilinogen** in the small intestine. Urobilinogen can either (1) continue through the large intestine and eventually be converted by the intestinal bacteria to **stercobilin,** a brown pigment that is expelled from the body as a component of feces; or (2) be absorbed back into the blood. In this latter case, it is converted to **urobilin,** a yellow pigment that is excreted by the kidneys.

Blood Types

The plasma membrane of an erythrocyte has numerous molecules called **surface antigens** (or *agglutinogens*), which project from the surface. These antigens have significant implications for blood transfusion, and in some cases, pregnancy.

ABO Blood Group The best-known antigens are those that form the **ABO blood group.** This group consists of two surface antigens called **A** and **B.** The presence or absence of the A antigen, the B antigen, or both is the criterion that determines your **ABO blood type,** as shown in **figure 18.9** and listed here:

- **Type A** blood has erythrocytes with surface antigen A.
- **Type B** blood has erythrocytes with surface antigen B.
- **Type AB** blood has erythrocytes having both surface antigens A and B.
- **Type O** blood has erythrocytes with neither surface antigen A nor B.

INTEGRATE

CLINICAL VIEW

Transfusions

Transfusion is the transfer of blood or blood components from a donor to a recipient. Whole blood is almost never transfused today, and it is not generally available. Rather, when you donate a unit of blood, it is almost immediately divided into three components: erythrocytes, clotting factors, and platelets. When a person needs one of these blood products, the physician administers only what is required, thus allowing one whole blood donation to serve up to three people.

To prevent health-related problems, donor blood must be collected under sterile conditions. The donated blood is first mixed with an anticoagulant to prevent clotting and is immediately refrigerated. Then the donated unit is tested for a variety of infectious diseases, including hepatitis and AIDS. Next, the blood is separated into erythrocytes, clotting factors, and platelets. Should leukocytes be needed, they must be collected in a special apparatus that effectively filters the leukocytes from the blood and then returns the blood to the donor. (A donor with healthy red bone marrow can quickly replace the donated leukocytes.)

(a)

	ABO Blood Types			
Blood type	**Type A**	**Type B**	**Type AB**	**Type O**
Erythrocytes	Surface antigen A	Surface antigen B	Surface antigens A and B	Neither surface antigen A nor B
Plasma	Anti-B antibodies	Anti-A antibodies	Neither anti-A nor anti-B antibodies	Both anti-A and anti-B antibodies

(b)

	Rh Blood Types	
Blood type	**Rh positive**	**Rh negative**
Erythrocytes	Surface antigen D	No surface antigen D
Plasma	No anti-D antibodies	No anti-D antibodies unless exposed to Rh positive blood

Figure 18.9 ABO Blood Types. The blood type of an individual is determined by the specific antigens (agglutinogens) exposed on the surface of the erythrocyte membrane. Likewise, plasma contains antibodies (agglutinins) that react with antigens from outside the body. (*a*) ABO blood types. (*b*) Rh blood types.

The ABO surface antigens on erythrocytes are accompanied by specific **antibodies** (or *agglutinins*) that travel in the blood plasma. In general, an antibody is a Y-shaped protein that is designed to recognize and immobilize a specific antigen it perceives as foreign to the body (see section 22.4). The ABO blood group has both **anti-A** and **anti-B antibodies** that react with the surface antigen A and the surface antigen B, respectively. You do not have antibodies in your blood plasma to recognize the surface antigens on your erythrocytes. Within the ABO blood group, the following blood types and antibodies are normally associated:

- Type A blood has anti-B antibodies in its blood plasma.
- Type B blood has anti-A antibodies in its blood plasma.
- Type AB blood has *neither* anti-A nor anti-B antibodies in its blood plasma.
- Type O blood has *both* anti-A and anti-B antibodies in its blood plasma.

Blood types become clinically important when a patient needs a blood transfusion. Compatibility between donor and recipient must be ascertained prior to blood transfusions. If a person is transfused with blood of an incompatible type, antibodies in the plasma bind to surface antigens of the transfused erythrocytes, and clumps of erythrocytes bind together in a process termed **agglutination** (ă-glū-tin-ā′shŭn; *ad* = to, *gluten* = glue). Clumped erythrocytes can block blood vessels and prevent the normal circulation of blood (figure 18.10). Eventually, some or all of the clumped erythrocytes may rupture, a process called **hemolysis** (hē-mol'i-sis; *lysis* = destruction). The release of erythrocyte contents and fragments into the blood often causes further hemolytic reactions and ultimately may damage organs. Therefore, compatibility between donor and recipient must be determined prior to blood donations and transfusions using an agglutination test.

⟨?⟩ WHAT DO YOU THINK?

3 Why is an individual with type O⁻ blood called a "universal donor"? Likewise, why is an individual with type AB⁺ blood called a "universal recipient"?

Rh Factor   Another common surface antigen on erythrocyte membranes determines the Rh blood type. The **Rh blood type** is determined by the presence or absence of the Rh surface antigen, often called either **Rh factor,** or **surface antigen D.** When the Rh factor is present, the individual is said to be **Rh positive (Rh⁺)**. Conversely, an individual is termed **Rh negative (Rh⁻)** when the surface antigen is lacking (see figure 18.9b).

In contrast to the antibodies of the ABO blood group, which may be found in the blood even without prior exposure to a foreign antigen, antibodies to the Rh factor (termed **anti-D antibodies**) appear in the blood only when an Rh negative individual is exposed to Rh positive blood. Often this occurs as a result of an inappropriate blood

Figure 18.10 Agglutination Reaction. (*a*) If a person receives mismatched blood, antibodies in the blood plasma bind to their respective surface antigens within the erythrocyte plasma membranes; erythrocytes agglutinate (clump) and may block small blood vessels. (*b*) In a test between plasma and erythrocyte samples, a successful match (no clumping) is compared to an unsuccessful match (clumping).

(a) Erythrocyte agglutination

(b) Agglutination test

CLINICAL VIEW
Rh Incompatibility and Pregnancy

The potential presence of anti-D antibodies is especially important in pregnant women who are Rh negative and have an Rh positive fetus. An Rh incompatibility may result during pregnancy if the mother has been previously exposed to Rh positive blood (such as can occur with a previously carried Rh positive fetus, typically at the time of childbirth). As a result of the prior exposure, the mother has anti-D antibodies that may cross the placenta and destroy the fetal erythrocytes, resulting in severe illness or death. The illness that occurs in the newborn is called **hemolytic disease of the newborn (HDN)**, or *erythroblastosis fetalis*. The newborn typically presents with anemia and hyperbilirubinemia (increased bilirubin in the blood) due to erythrocyte destruction. In severe cases, the infant may develop heart failure and must be given a blood transfusion to survive.

Giving a pregnant Rh negative woman special immunoglobulins (e.g., RhoGAM) between weeks 28–32 of her pregnancy and at birth prevents the mother from developing anti-D antibodies. Specifically, these immunoglobulins bind to fetal erythrocyte surface antigens—and in so doing, prevent the mother's immune system from recognizing Rh antigens and being stimulated to produce anti-D antibodies.

Hemolytic disease of the newborn.

	Mother Rh Blood Types		Fetus Rh Blood Types	
	Pregnancy #1	**Pregnancy #2**	**Pregnancy #1**	**Pregnancy #2**
Blood type	**Rh negative**	**Rh negative**	**Rh positive**	**Rh positive**
Erythrocytes	No antigen D	No antigen D	Antigen D	Antigen D
Plasma	No anti-D antibodies	Anti-D antibodies (due to prior exposure)	No anti-D antibodies	No anti-D antibodies. Anti-D antibodies from mother cross placenta and attack fetal erythrocytes causing **hemolytic disease of the newborn**

transfusion. Individuals who are Rh positive never exhibit anti-D antibodies, because they possess the Rh antigen on their erythrocytes. Only individuals who are Rh negative can exhibit anti-D antibodies, and that can occur only after exposure to Rh antigens.

The ABO and Rh blood types are usually reported together. For example, types AB and Rh⁺ together are reported as AB⁺. However, remember that ABO and Rh blood types are independent of each other, and neither of them interacts with or influences the presence or activities of the other group.

WHAT DID YOU LEARN?

11. What is the main function of an erythrocyte, and in what ways is an erythrocyte designed to efficiently carry out its function?

12. How do transferrin, ferritin, and hemosiderin participate in recycling erythrocyte components?

13. What are the structural and molecular differences between type A⁺ blood and type B⁻ blood?

18.3c Leukocytes

LEARNING OBJECTIVES

9. Explain the main function of leukocytes.

10. Distinguish between granulocytes and agranulocytes, and compare and contrast the various types.

11. Explain what is meant by a differential count and how it is clinically useful.

Leukocytes help defend the body against pathogens. Leukocytes are "true" cells in that they contain a nucleus and cellular organelles. Leukocytes also differ from erythrocytes in that they are about 1.5 to 3 times larger in diameter, and they do not contain hemoglobin. The number of leukocytes in the blood normally ranges between 4500 and 11,000 per cubic millimeter (or microliter) of blood.

Leukocytes are motile (capable of movement within interstitial fluid) and remarkably flexible. In fact, most leukocytes are found within body tissues, as opposed to in the blood. Leukocytes enter the tissues from blood vessels by a process called **diapedesis** (dī′ă-pĕ-dē′sis; *dia* = through, *pedesis* = a leaping), whereby they squeeze between the endothelial cells of the blood vessel walls. **Chemotaxis** (kē-mō-tak′sis) is a process in which leukocytes are attracted to a site of infection by the presence of molecules released by damaged cells, dead cells, or invading pathogens. These processes are part of the inflammatory response discussed in depth in section 22.3d.

The five types of leukocytes are divided into two distinguishable classes—granulocytes and agranulocytes—based upon the visible presence or absence of cytoplasmic secretory vesicles termed *specific granules*. The leukocytes are summarized in **table 18.6**.

Granulocytes

Granulocytes (gran′ū-lō-sīt) have specific granules in their cytoplasm that are clearly visible when viewed with a microscope. When a blood smear is stained to provide contrast, three types of granulocytes can be distinguished: neutrophils, eosinophils, and basophils. Their names refer to the granules' affinities for certain stains.

Neutrophils   The most numerous leukocyte in the blood is the **neutrophil** (nū′trō-fil; *neuter* = neither, *philos* = fond), constituting about 50–70% of the total number of leukocytes. The neutrophil is named for its neutral or pale-colored granules within a light lilac–colored cytoplasm. A neutrophil is about 1.5 times larger in diameter than an erythrocyte. Neutrophils exhibit a multilobed nucleus; as many as five lobes are interconnected by thin strands. For this reason, neutrophils also may be called *polymorphonuclear* (*PMN*) *leukocytes* because of the number of lobes and various shapes of their nuclei.

Neutrophils usually remain in circulation for about 10 to 12 hours before they exit the blood vessels and enter the tissue spaces, where they phagocytize infectious pathogens, especially bacteria. The mechanisms that help destroy bacteria are described in section 22.3b. The number of neutrophils in a person's blood rises dramatically in the presence of a chronic bacterial infection, as more neutrophils are produced that target the bacteria.

Eosinophils   **Eosinophils** (ē-ō-sin′ō-fil; *eos* = dawn) have reddish or pink-orange granules in their cytoplasm. Typically, eosinophils constitute about 1–4% of the total number of leukocytes. Their nucleus is bilobed, and the two lobes are connected by a thin strand. An eosinophil is about 1.5 times larger in diameter than an erythrocyte. Eosinophils phagocytize numerous antigen-antibody complexes or allergens (antigens that initiate a hypersensitive or allergic reaction). If the body is infected by parasitic worms, the eosinophils release chemical mediators that attack the worms.

Basophils   **Basophils** (bā′sō-fil; *basis* = base) are usually about 1.5 times larger than erythrocytes. They are the least numerous of the granulocytes; typically, basophils constitute about 0.5–1% of the total number of leukocytes. Basophils exhibit a bilobed nucleus and abundant deep blue-violet granules in the cytoplasm. The primary components of basophil granules are histamine and heparin. When histamine is released from these granules, it causes both an increase in the diameter of blood vessels (called **vasodilation**) and increased capillary permeability. The classic allergic symptoms of swollen nasal membranes, itchy and runny nose, and watery eyes are partially attributed to the release of histamine. The release of heparin from basophils inhibits blood clotting (a process called **anticoagulation**).

Agranulocytes

Agranulocytes are leukocytes that have such small specific granules in their cytoplasm that they are not clearly visible under the light microscope—hence the name agranulocyte (*a* = without). Agranulocytes include both lymphocytes and monocytes.

Lymphocytes   As their name implies, most **lymphocytes** (lim′fō-sīt) reside in lymphatic organs and structures (e.g., lymph nodes, spleen). Usually, lymphocytes constitute about 20–40% of the total number of leukocytes in the blood. Their dark-staining nucleus is typically rounded, and smaller lymphocytes exhibit only a thin rim of blue-gray cytoplasm around the nucleus. A lymphocyte usually is about the same size as or slightly larger than an erythrocyte. When activated, lymphocytes grow larger and have proportionally more cytoplasm. Thus, some of the smaller, nonactivated lymphocytes have a diameter less than that of an erythrocyte, whereas activated lymphocytes may be two times the diameter of an erythrocyte.

There are three categories of lymphocytes. **T-lymphocytes** (*T-cells*) manage and direct an immune response; some directly attack foreign cells and virus-infected cells. **B-lymphocytes** (*B-cells*) are stimulated to become plasma cells and produce antibodies. **NK cells** (*natural killer cells*) attack abnormal and infected tissue cells. Lymphocytes are examined in detail in chapter 22.

Monocytes   A **monocyte** (mon′ō-sīt) can be up to three times the diameter of an erythrocyte. Monocytes usually constitute about 2–8% of all leukocytes. The nucleus of a monocyte is kidney-shaped or C-shaped. After approximately 3 days in circulation, monocytes exit blood vessels and take up residence within the tissues, where they transform into large phagocytic cells called **macrophages** (mak′rō-fāj; *macros* = large, *phago* = to eat). Macrophages phagocytize bacteria, viruses, cell fragments, dead cells, and debris.

Differential Count and Changes in Leukocyte Profiles

Abnormal numbers of leukocytes result from various pathologic conditions. For example, a reduced number of leukocytes causes a serious disorder called **leukopenia** (lū-kō-pē′nē-ă; *penia* = poverty).

Table 18.6   Leukocytes

Type	Characteristics	Functions	Approximate %
GRANULOCYTES			
Neutrophils AP|R	Nucleus is multilobed (as many as 5 lobes) Cytoplasm contains neutral or pale, specific granules (when stained)	Phagocytize pathogens, especially bacteria Release enzymes that target pathogens	50–70% of total leukocytes (1800–7800 cells per microliter)
Eosinophils AP|R	Nucleus is bilobed Cytoplasm contains reddish or pink-orange specific granules (when stained)	Phagocytize antigen-antibody complexes and allergens Release chemical mediators to destroy parasitic worms	1–4% of total leukocytes (100–400 cells per microliter)
Basophils AP|R	Nucleus is bilobed Cytoplasm contains deep blue-violet specific granules (when stained)	Release histamine (vasodilator and increases capillary permeability) and heparin (anticoagulant) during inflammatory reactions	0.5–1% of total leukocytes (20–50 cells per microliter)
AGRANULOCYTES			
Lymphocytes AP|R	Round or slightly indented nucleus (fills the cell in smaller lymphocytes) Nucleus is usually darkly stained Thin rim of cytoplasm surrounds nucleus	Coordinate immune cell activity Attack pathogens and abnormal and infected cells Produce antibodies	20–40% of total leukocytes (1000–4800 cells per microliter)
Monocytes AP|R	Kidney-shaped or C-shaped nucleus Nucleus is generally pale staining Abundant cytoplasm around nucleus	Exit blood vessels to become macrophages Phagocytize pathogens (e.g., bacteria, viruses), cellular fragments, dead cells, debris	2–8% of total leukocytes (100–700 cells per microliter)

This decreased number of leukocytes may increase the risk of a person developing an infection or decrease their ability to fight infection effectively. Conversely, **leukocytosis** (lū′kō-sī-tō′sis) results from a slightly elevated leukocyte count and may be caused by a variety of factors, such as a recent infection or stress.

The term **differential count,** or *white blood cell differential count,* measures the amount of each type of leukocyte in your blood, and determines whether any of the circulating leukocytes are immature. The normal range of leukocytes in circulating blood ranges from 4500 to 11,000 cells per microliter, where 50–70% (1800 to 7800 cells per microliter) of these are neutrophils, 20–40% (1000 to 4800 cells per microliter) are lymphocytes, 2–8% (100 to 700 cells per microliter) are monocytes, 1–4% (100 to 400 cells per microliter) are eosinophils, and less than 1% (20 to 50 cells per microliter) are basophils. Infection, tissue necrosis, bone marrow failure, cancers, or some other stresses to the body can affect the total ranges or percentages of a specific type of leukocyte, so differential counts are useful for diagnosing ailments.

Acute bacterial infections, acute stress, and tissue necrosis typically are associated with an increase in neutrophils, called **neutrophilia.** Their numbers will be in the tens of thousands, and some ailments may cause neutrophil counts of up to 50,000. In addition, as the body tries to produce more and more neutrophils, some immature neutrophils (called *band neutrophils,* or *band cells*) enter the circulation and are detected by the differential count. Increased presence of these immature neutrophils is referred to as a **left-shifted differential.** This phrase reflects that historically a lab printout listed numbers of cells according to maturity from left to right, so that an increased number of immature neutrophils was listed on the left. Decreased neutrophil count, called **neutropenia,** may occur with certain anemias, drug or radiation therapy, and from other causes.

Viral infections, such as mumps, rubella, or mononucleosis, typically produce **lymphocytosis,** which is an increased number of lymphocytes. Lymphocyte values can increase to 20,000 in extreme cases. Additionally, the lymphocytes develop morphologic changes, in which their cytoplasm appears watery. Other conditions that can cause lymphocytosis include chronic bacterial infections, some leukemias, and

multiple myeloma (a cancer of plasma cells, which are derived from B-lymphocytes). Decreased lymphocyte counts (**lymphocytopenia**) can occur with HIV infection, other leukemias, and sepsis, which is the presence of a pathogenic organism or substance in the blood.

Eosinophil numbers can increase in response to allergic reactions, parasitic infections, or some autoimmune diseases. Monocyte numbers may increase with chronic inflammatory disorders or tuberculosis, and may decrease due to prolonged prednisone (steroid) drug therapy. Finally, basophil counts can increase due to myeloproliferative disorders (which result from an overproduction of some formed elements in the bone marrow) and can decrease due to acute allergic and stress reactions.

WHAT DID YOU LEARN?

14 What type of leukocyte may increase in number if you develop "strep throat" (an infection of the throat by *Streptococcus* bacteria)?

15 A person undergoes a routine blood test and is found to have a leukocyte count of 7000 cells per cubic millimeter, and 60% of the cells are neutrophils. Is the individual healthy? Explain.

18.3d Platelets

LEARNING OBJECTIVE

12. Explain the structure and function of platelets.

Platelets are irregular-shaped, membrane-enclosed cellular fragments that are about 2 μm in diameter (less than one-fourth the size of an erythrocyte). In stained preparations, they exhibit a dark central region. Platelets are sometimes called *thrombocytes* (throm′bō-sīt; *thrombos* = clot); as with erythrocytes, that name is inappropriate because they are not true cells. Platelets are cell fragments, and unlike erythrocytes, they never had a nucleus. Recall that platelets are continually produced in the red bone marrow by megakaryocytes. Platelets serve an important function in hemostasis **(figure 18.11).**

Normally, the concentration of platelets in an adult ranges from 150,000 to about 400,000 per cubic millimeter of blood, although the count may rise further during times of stress. Platelets can circulate in the blood for 8 to 10 days, unless they are needed earlier for hemostasis. Thereafter, they are broken down, and their contents are recycled. Approximately 30% of platelets are stored in the spleen (see section 21.4b). An abnormally small number of platelets in circulating blood is termed **thrombocytopenia.**

WHAT DID YOU LEARN?

16 What is the function of platelets, and what is their life span?

SEM 4100x

Fibrin

Platelets

Erythrocytes

Figure 18.11 Blood Clotting. This SEM shows erythrocytes, fibrin, and platelets within a forming clot.

18.4 Hemostasis

When your blood vessels are healthy and functioning well, blood flows through them freely and does not clot unnecessarily. But if there is damage to a blood vessel, hemostasis occurs. **Hemostasis** (hē′mō-stā′sĭs; *hemo* = blood, *stasis* = stability) is a process where the blood clots and stops blood flow through a small injured blood vessel wall. It consists of three sequential phases, although there is some overlap between phases: vascular spasm, platelet plug formation, and coagulation phase (figure 18.12).

18.4a Vascular Spasm

LEARNING OBJECTIVES
1. Describe vascular spasm, the first phase of hemostasis.
2. Name conditions that bring about vascular spasm.

When a blood vessel is injured, the first phase in hemostasis to occur is a **vascular spasm,** whereby the blood vessel constricts suddenly and, in so doing, limits the amount of blood that can leak from this damaged vessel. The spasm continues during the next phase, as both platelets and the endothelial cells of the blood vessel wall release an array of chemicals to further stimulate the vascular spasms.

The vascular spasm phase usually lasts from a few to many minutes. The more extensive the vessel and tissue damage, the greater the degree of vasoconstriction.

WHAT DID YOU LEARN?
17 What occurs during a vascular spasm, and how long does this phase last?

18.4b Platelet Plug Formation

LEARNING OBJECTIVE
3. Describe what happens when platelets encounter damage in a blood vessel.

The next phase in hemostasis is the formation of a **platelet plug.** Normally, the endothelial wall (inner lining of a blood vessel) is smooth and is coated with an eicosanoid (see section 17.3b) called

prostacyclin, which activates a pathway in both platelets and endothelial cells that involves production of cAMP to ultimately inhibit platelet activation. The end result is that prostacyclin serves as a platelet repellent.

Once a blood vessel is damaged, however, the collagen fibers within the connective tissue beneath the endothelial cells in the vessel wall become exposed. Platelets begin to stick to the exposed collagen fibers. Platelets adhere to the collagen fibers with the assistance of a plasma protein called *von Willebrand factor,* which serves as a bridge between platelets and collagen fibers.

As the platelets start to stick to the vessel wall, their morphology changes dramatically; they develop long processes that further adhere them to the blood vessel wall. As more and more platelets aggregate to the site, a platelet plug develops to close off the injury. The timing of this entire phase typically is less than a few minutes for a small- to medium-sized injury. Again, this is a temporary measure to block the flow of blood to an area where a vessel wall is damaged.

Platelets undergo this morphologic change and become activated: their cytoplasm degranulates, releasing chemicals to assist with hemostasis. The following processes occur in response to these different chemicals:

- **Prolonged vascular spasms** with the release of *serotonin* and *thromboxane A_2* (an eicosanoid)
- **Attraction of other platelets** with the release of *adenosine diphosphate (ADP)* and *thromboxane A_2,* which facilitates the degranulation and release of these chemicals in other platelets
- **Stimulation of coagulation** with the release of *procoagulants* that enhance blood clotting (the third phase)
- **Repair of the blood vessel** as platelets secrete substances to stimulate epithelial tissue, smooth muscle, and fibroblasts (cells of connective tissue) to replicate

① **Vascular spasm**
Blood vessel constricts to limit blood escape.

② **Platelet plug formation**
Platelets arrive at site of injury and stick to exposed collagen fibers.

③ **Coagulation phase**
Coagulation cascade converts inactive proteins to active forms and forms a blood clot.

Figure 18.12 Hemostasis. Trauma to a blood vessel causes the blood to coagulate in a process called hemostasis.

WHAT DO YOU THINK?

4 Is the formation of the platelet plug an example of negative feedback or positive feedback?

Note that platelets are not only involved in the second phase of platelet plug formation, but they also increase events of the first and third phases, vascular spasm and coagulation phase. Thus, through the release of specific substances, platelets increase *all three* processes of hemostasis.

The formation of the platelet plug is an example of positive feedback and typically is formed within 1 minute. But what is to prevent a platelet plug from becoming too big and growing out of control? As just mentioned, endothelial cells normally release prostacyclin. The healthy endothelial cells near the site of injury are still releasing their prostacyclin, so the plug does not grow larger than what is needed. The next phase, the coagulation phase, is beginning.

WHAT DID YOU LEARN?

18 What prevents platelets from forming plugs in healthy blood vessels? What substances assist platelets with forming plugs in damaged blood vessels?

INTEGRATE

CLINICAL VIEW
Bleeding and Blood Clotting Disorders

If hemostasis fails to occur when needed, uncontrolled bleeding and death could result. On the other hand, if hypercoagulation develops, then unwanted blood clots could form in the blood and lead to the risk of deep vein thrombosis (blood clot in the leg), pulmonary embolism (blood clot in the lung), stroke (blood clot in the brain), or heart attack. Here we discuss several blood clotting disorders.

Bleeding Disorders

Hemophilia is a group of bleeding disorders caused by specific genetic mutations. The two most common types of hemophilia are hemophilia A and hemophilia B, both of which are inherited in an X-linked recessive pattern. Females typically are carriers of the gene but may not experience symptoms because they have two X chromosomes, and one of the two X chromosomes may be normal. In contrast, males typically exhibit the full-blown disease because they have only one X chromosome.

Hemophilia A, also known as *classic hemophilia,* represents the vast majority of all hemophilias. It results in a deficiency or complete lack of normal factor VIII protein in the clotting cascade; the protein is abnormal and typically cannot participate in the proper clotting of the blood. This hemophilia occurs in approximately 1 in 5000 males in the United States. **Hemophilia B** is a deficiency of factor IX. It occurs in approximately 1 in 25,000 males in the United States. **Hemophilia C** is a relatively rare autosomal dominant deficiency of factor XI.

Vitamin K is a fat-soluble vitamin used by liver cells to produce many of the clotting factors. **Vitamin K deficiency** is more common in newborns (because their livers are immature and breast milk contains little vitamin K) and in individuals with liver or biliary diseases or chronic problems with fat absorption.

Thrombocytopenia is a deficiency in platelet count. This may be caused by an increased breakdown of platelets or decreased production of new platelets, as may occur with some bone marrow infections or cancers.

Various drugs, such as aspirin, ibuprofen (and other nonsteroidal anti-inflammatory drugs [NSAIDs]), and warfarin (Coumadin) and some herbal supplements (e.g., ginkgo biloba, garlic supplements) interfere with blood clotting and may cause bleeding if taken at sufficiently high doses. Physicians always should be monitoring their patients for bleeding disorders if they are taking any of these medications regularly. Additionally, they should ask their patients what herbal supplements they may be taking, so as to avoid any herbal supplement–drug interactions.

Hypercoagulation Problems

The term **hypercoagulation** refers to an increased tendency to clot blood. Hypercoagulation can lead to a **thrombus** (throm′bŭs; *thrombos* = clot), which is a clot within a blood vessel. If the thrombus dislodges and travels within the blood, it is called an **embolus** (em-bō′lŭs; *embolus* = wedge or stopper). An embolus is particularly dangerous because it can wedge within an artery and obstruct blood flow. A **pulmonary embolism** occurs in the pulmonary circulation of the lungs and can lead to breathing problems and perhaps death if not treated, whereas an embolism that travels to the blood vessels of the brain can cause a stroke. Treatment for a thrombus or embolus typically is with blood thinning medication (e.g., warfarin, heparin, or low-molecular-weight heparin).

Hypercoagulation can also have drug-related, environmental, and genetic causes. Certain medications such as birth control pills or hormone replacement therapy are associated with an increased risk of developing blood clots. Smoking greatly increases your risk, as nicotine is a vasoconstrictor, and it appears smoking increases levels of blood components related to clotting. Environmental causes include prolonged bedrest, surgery, pregnancy, or sitting in an airplane seat for a long time. In all of these cases, blood may pool in veins that are not being worked by exercise, and clotting can occur.

Genetic causes of hypercoagulation can be due to mutations of several genes, the most common of which is the **Leiden mutation,** which is a mutation of the gene for the synthesis of factor V. This mutation is present in 3% of the population and 3–15% of all Caucasians, and it accounts for 20–40% of all venous thromboses. Individuals with this mutation are unable to inactivate factor V in the clotting cascade, causing hypercoagulation and increased risk of thrombus formation. Young (under age 50), active individuals who present with a thrombus or embolus, and who don't have other significant risk factors for clotting, may need to be screened for these genetic mutations.

18.4c Coagulation Phase

✅ LEARNING OBJECTIVES

4. Compare and contrast the intrinsic pathway and the extrinsic pathway for activating blood clotting.

5. Describe events in the common pathway.

6. Discuss the survival response that occurs when blood loss exceeds 10%.

Perhaps the most important and most complex component of hemostasis is **coagulation,** or blood clotting. A blood clot has an insoluble protein network composed of fibrin, which is derived from soluble fibrinogen. This meshwork of protein traps other elements of the blood, including erythrocytes, leukocytes, platelets, and plasma proteins, to form the clot (figure 18.11).

Substances Involved in Coagulation

Blood coagulation is a process that requires numerous substances, including calcium, clotting factors, platelets, and vitamin K. The specific clotting factors, including their numerical designation, name, function, pathway, and disorders associated with the factor are listed in **table 18.7.** Note that the clotting factor numbers are *in order of their discovery,* and not their position in the clotting pathway.

Table 18.7	Clotting Factors			
Factor Designator[1]	**Name**	**Function**	**Extrinsic or Intrinsic Pathway**	**Clinical Syndrome (if Clotting Factor Is Deficient)**
I	Fibrinogen	Activated to fibrin	Both	Afibrinogemia (autosomal recessive disorder); during pregnancy can cause premature separation of placenta
II	Prothrombin	Protease; activated to thrombin	Both	Hypoprothrombinemia (autosomal recessive disorder); decreased synthesis in liver generally due to insufficient vitamin K (Note that mutation in the prothrombin gene causes hypercoagulation problems[2].)
III	Tissue factor (thromboplastin)	Cofactor; activates factor VII	Extrinsic	None known
IV	Calcium	Ion essential to both pathways	Both	None known
V	Proaccelerin	Cofactor; activates factor VII; combines with factor X to form prothrombin activator	Both	Parahemophilia (autosomal recessive) (Note that Leiden mutation causes hypercoagulation problems[2].)
VI	Accelerin	Redundant to activated factor V	Both	None known
VII	Proconvertin	Protease; activates factor X	Extrinsic	Hypoconvertinemia (autosomal recessive)
VIII	Antihemophilic factor A	Cofactor; activates factor X	Intrinsic	Hemophilia A (classical hemophilia); congenital X-linked trait
IX	Antihemophilic factor B (Christmas factor)	Protease; activates factor VIII	Intrinsic	Hemophilia B (Christmas disease[3]); congenital X-linked trait
X	Thrombokinase	Protease; combines with factor V to form prothrombin activator	Both	Stuart-Prower factor deficiency (autosomal recessive)
XI	Antihemophilic factor C	Protease; activates factor IX	Intrinsic	Hemophilia C, also known as plasma thromboplastin antecedent (PTA) deficiency (autosomal dominant)
XII	Hageman factor	Protease; activates factor XI and plasmin; converts prekallikrein to kallikrein	Intrinsic	Hageman trait (autosomal recessive disorder)
XIII	Fibrin-stabilizing factor	Cross-links fibrin	Both	The rarest of all of the clotting deficiencies; bleeding disorders apparent at birth (autosomal recessive disorder)

1. All proteins produced by the liver except tissue thrombplastin (factor III) formed by perivascular tissue; fibrin-stabilizing factor (factor XIII) produced by platelets and plasma; and factor IV, which is simply Ca^{2+} (not a protein). Hageman factor is produced by both the liver and platelets. Additional factors released from platelets: platelet factors 1, 2, 3, and 4.

2. This item is a hypercoagulation problem and not due to deficient clotting factor.

3. Named for the first person diagnosed with the disease.

Most clotting factors are inactive enzymes, and most of these are produced by the liver. Vitamin K is a fat-soluble vitamin that is required for the synthesis of clotting factors II, VII, IX, and X; it acts as a coenzyme (see section 3.3c). Proteases such as factor VII and IX, when activated, act like scissors to "release" another separate factor from its inactive to its active form. This active factor acts like scissors to convert yet another inactive factor to its active form; thus, the formation of a blood clot involves a cascade of changes.

Initiation of the Coagulation Cascade

The initiation of blood clotting can occur by two separate mechanisms: the intrinsic pathway (also known as the *contact activation pathway*) or the extrinsic pathway (the *tissue factor pathway*) (**figure 18.13**). Both pathways converge, through a series of complicated steps, to the common pathway.

The **intrinsic pathway** is initiated by damage to the *inside* of the vessel wall and is initiated by platelets. This pathway typically takes approximately 3 to 6 minutes:

1. Platelets adhering to a damaged vessel wall release factor XII.
2. Factor XII converts the inactive factor XI to the active factor XI.
3. Factor XI changes inactive factor IX to active factor IX.
4. Factor IX binds with Ca^{2+} and platelet factor 3 to form a complex that converts inactive factor VIII to active factor VIII.
5. Factor VIII changes inactive factor X to active factor X.

In contrast, the **extrinsic pathway** is initiated by damage to the tissue that is *outside* the vessel, and this pathway usually takes approximately 15 seconds:

1. Tissue thromboplastin released from damaged tissues combines with factor VII and Ca^{2+} to form a complex.
2. This complex converts inactive factor X to active factor X.

Factor X, activated by either the extrinsic or intrinsic pathway, is the first step in the **common pathway:**

1. Factor X combines with factors II and V, Ca^{2+}, and platelet factor 3 to form prothrombin activator.
2. Prothrombin activator activates prothrombin to thrombin.
3. Thrombin converts soluble fibrinogen into insoluble fibrin.
4. In the presence of Ca^{2+}, factor XIII is activated. Factor XIII cross-links and stabilizes the fibrin monomers into a fibrin polymer that serves as the "framework" of the clot.

Other components of blood become trapped in this spiderweb-like protein mesh. Like platelet plug formation, the clotting cascade is regulated by positive feedback. Once initiated by the intrinsic or extrinsic pathway, the events of the clotting cascade continue until a clot is formed (the climactic event). The size of the clot is limited because thrombin is either trapped within the clot or thrombin is quickly degraded by enzymes within the blood.

The Sympathetic Response to Blood Loss

In severe cases, when over 10% of the blood has been lost from the blood, a survival response is initiated.

As blood volume decreases, blood pressure decreases. If greater than 10% of the blood volume is lost from the blood vessels, the sympathetic division of the autonomic nervous system (ANS) is activated (see section 15.4), bringing about increased vasoconstriction of blood vessels, increased heart rate, and increased force of heart contraction in an attempt to maintain blood pressure. Blood flow is also redistributed to the heart and brain. These processes are

LEARNING STRATEGY

In both the intrinsic or extrinsic processes of clotting initiation, the final result is the production of factor X (factor 10). Use these tips to remember the sequence of factors:

- In the intrinsic pathway, a series of steps takes you to X by counting backward from 12 to 8—factors XII, XI, IX, and VIII (simply skip 10 because that is "the goal").
- The extrinsic pathway involves the coming together of factors VII and III, and if you add 7 and 3, the result is 10 (X).

effective in maintaining blood pressure until approximately 40% of the blood is lost. Blood loss greater than 40% results in insufficient blood volume within the blood vessels, and blood pressure decreases to levels unable to support life.

WHAT DID YOU LEARN?

19 In what ways do the intrinsic and extrinsic pathways of the clotting cascade differ?

20 What is the sequence of events in the common pathway?

21 At what point in blood loss is the sympathetic nervous system typically activated, and what physiologic changes occur?

18.4d Elimination of the Clot

LEARNING OBJECTIVE

7. Explain the processes of clot retraction and fibrinolysis.

A blood clot is a temporary measure to stop blood loss through a damaged vessel wall. To return to normal, the blood vessel wall must be repaired and the clot eliminated. Elimination of the blood clot includes both clot retraction and fibrinolysis.

Clot retraction occurs as the clot is forming when actinomyosin, a contractile protein within platelets, contracts and squeezes the serum out of the developing clot. This makes the clot smaller as the sides of the vessel wall are pulled closer together.

To destroy the fibrin framework of the clot, **plasmin** (plaz'min) (or *fibrinolysin*) degrades the fibrin strands through **fibrinolysis.** This is a process that begins within 2 days of the clot formation and occurs slowly over a number of days.

A "balancing act" is occurring continually within your blood between clot formation processes and those processes that prevent clot formation. The balance can be "tipped" so that blood clotting is initiated. A damaged blood vessel, impaired blood flow, atherosclerosis, or inflammation of the blood vessels can all potentially initiate blood clotting. Additionally, certain nutrients and vitamins must be present and available for blood clotting to occur normally. For example, calcium is used during the clotting process, and vitamin K is required for the synthesis of certain plasma proteins by the liver. Problems with the balance can lead to either bleeding or blood clotting disorders.

WHAT DO YOU THINK?

5 Predict why an individual confined to a wheelchair is more likely to develop unwanted clots.

WHAT DID YOU LEARN?

22 What is fibrinolysis, and what is its purpose?

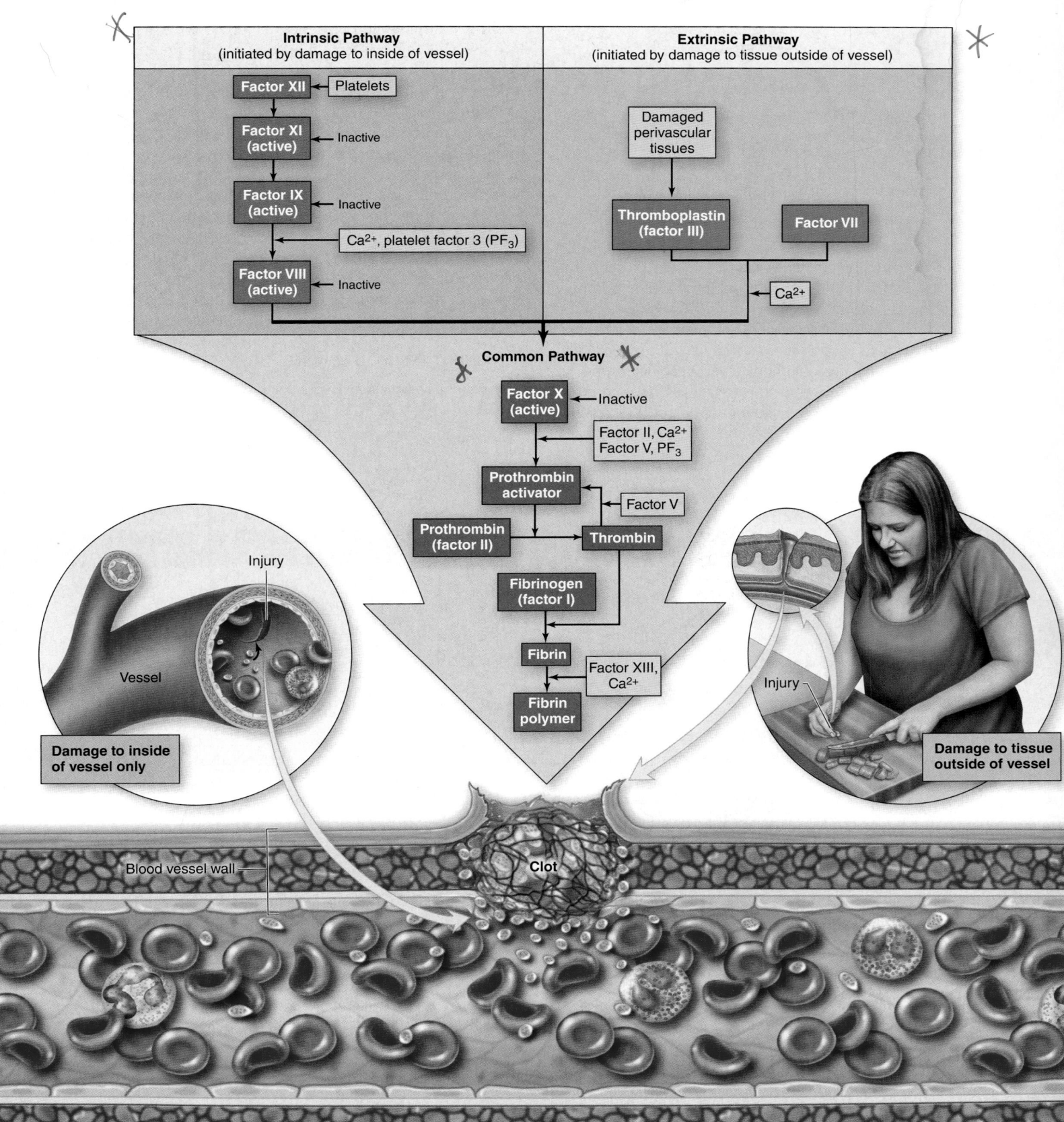

Figure 18.13 Coagulation Pathways. The process of coagulation typically involves both an intrinsic and an extrinsic pathway. Both pathways "merge" into a common pathway that converts prothrombin (factor II) into thrombin, and fibrinogen (factor I) into fibrin.

18.5 Development and Aging of Blood

LEARNING OBJECTIVES

1. Describe when and how blood is formed in the embryo, fetus, childhood, and adulthood.

2. List some conditions that occur with the bone marrow and blood in the elderly.

The first primitive hemopoietic stem cells develop in the yolk sac wall of the embryo by the third week of development. The primitive hemopoietic stem cells go on to colonize other organs, such as the liver, spleen, and thymus. In these organs, these very primitive stem cells develop into the hemocytoblasts that produce all of the formed elements. Later in fetal development (perhaps beginning at 10 weeks), the hemocytoblasts begin to colonize red bone marrow, although the liver doesn't completely give up its blood cell production until close to birth.

Recall from section 7.2d that hemopoiesis occurs in most bones in young children, but as an individual reaches adulthood, hemopoiesis is restricted to selected bones in the axial skeleton (e.g., flat bones of the skull, sternum, ribs, hip bones, and proximal epiphyses of each humerus and femur).

More red bone marrow is replaced with fat as individuals continue to age. Thus, older individuals have relatively less red bone marrow and may be more prone to developing anemia, which is a decrease in the number of circulating erythrocytes. In addition, older bone marrow may be less able to meet any demands for an increased number of formed elements. The leukocytes in the elderly may be less efficient and active than those in younger individuals, and the elderly also may have decreased numbers of leukocytes. Certain types of leukemias also are more prevalent among the elderly, probably due to the immune system (and its leukocytes) being less efficient.

 WHAT DID YOU LEARN?

 23 Where does hemopoiesis occur in (a) the fetus, (b) a child, and (c) an adult?

 24 What are some ways that red bone marrow changes in the elderly?

CHAPTER SUMMARY

- Blood is a fluid connective tissue composed of formed elements, plasma, plasma proteins, and dissolved solutes that is transported through the cardiovascular system.

18.1a Functions of Blood   695
- Blood transports nutrients, wastes, and respiratory gases; regulates body temperature, pH, and fluid levels; and protects the body against the activities of pathogens and the loss of blood.

18.1b Physical Characteristics of Blood   696
- The physical characteristics of blood include color, volume, viscosity, plasma concentration, temperature, and pH.

18.1c Components of Blood   696
- Centrifugation separates blood into three components: erythrocytes, a buffy coat composed of leukocytes and platelets, and plasma.
- Hematocrit represents the percentage of formed elements in blood. Males have higher hematocrits than females.
- Formed elements can be viewed in a blood smear.

- Blood plasma is a mixture of water, plasma proteins, and other solutes. It forms about 55% of whole blood.

18.2a Plasma Proteins   699
- Plasma has a greater osmolarity than interstitial fluid due to its abundant plasma proteins.
- Plasma proteins include albumin, globulins, fibrinogen and other clotting proteins, and regulatory proteins.

18.2b Other Solutes   700
- Other solutes include electrolytes, nutrients, respiratory gases, and waste products.

- Formed elements include erythrocytes that transport respiratory gases, leukocytes that serve some roles in protecting the body from harmful substances, and platelets that help clot blood.

18.3a Hemopoiesis   702
- Hemopoiesis is the process by which formed elements develop.
- Formed elements develop in the red bone marrow via stem cells called hemocytoblasts.

18.3b Erythrocytes   705
- Erythrocytes exhibit a biconcave disc structure that facilitates the exchange of respiratory gases into and out of the cells.
- Hemoglobin is a pigmented protein that fills mature erythrocytes; it transports oxygen and carbon dioxide.
- Erythrocyte production is controlled by erythropoietin (and indirectly by testosterone).
- Aged erythrocytes are broken down and their components recycled after about 120 days in the blood.
- The ABO blood group consists of surface antigens (A or B) on the erythrocytes and plasma antibodies (anti-A or anti-B). Blood type is determined by the surface antigens on the erythrocytes (type O blood has no antigens). Individuals have plasma antibodies in their blood that are different from their surface antigens.
- The Rh blood group is determined by the presence or absence of the Rh surface antigen, called surface antigen D.

18.3c Leukocytes 713
- Leukocytes are white blood cells that defend against invading pathogens and remove damaged cells, debris, and antigen-antibody complexes.
- The types of leukocytes are neutrophils, eosinophils, basophils, lymphocytes, and monocytes.

18.3d Platelets 716
- Platelets are cellular fragments derived from megakaryocytes and function to clot blood.

18.4 Hemostasis 717
- Hemostasis is a process to halt bleeding. There are three phases of hemostasis: vascular spasm, platelet plug formation, and the coagulation phase.

18.4a Vascular Spasm 717
- When a blood vessel wall is damaged, the vessel undergoes vascular spasms and constricts.

18.4b Platelet Plug Formation 717
- Platelets stick to the exposed collagen fibers within the damaged vessel wall, the platelets degranulate, and they release an array of chemicals to attract more platelets to the site.
- The platelets form a plug to close off the broken part of the blood vessel wall.

18.4c Coagulation Phase 719
- Coagulation is a clotting cascade involving the activation of numerous clotting factors that will turn the liquid blood into a more solid form.
- The clotting cascade consists of an intrinsic pathway (which is initiated within a blood vessel by platelets), an extrinsic pathway (which is initiated by substances released outside the blood vessel), and a common pathway that produces fibrin.

18.4d Elimination of the Clot 720
- The blood clot is removed through clot contraction and fibrinolysis.

18.5 Development and Aging of Blood 722
- The first hemopoietic stem cells arise from the yolk sac wall in the embryo.
- In the fetus, hemopoiesis shifts to the liver, and then shifts to red bone marrow.
- Older individuals may have decreased production of formed elements.

CHALLENGE YOURSELF

Do You Know the Basics?

_____ 1. In an adult, the stem cells for leukocytes reside in the
   a. blood.
   b. red bone marrow.
   c. liver.
   d. muscle.

_____ 2. Which type of leukocyte increases during allergic reactions and parasitic worm infections?
   a. basophil
   b. eosinophil
   c. lymphocyte
   d. neutrophil

_____ 3. Which cell type forms platelets in the red bone marrow?
   a. lymphocyte
   b. megakaryocyte
   c. eosinophil
   d. reticulocyte

_____ 4. Which of the following is *not* a function of blood?
   a. prevention of fluid loss
   b. transport of nutrients and waste
   c. maintenance of constant pH levels
   d. production of hormones

_____ 5. A person with blood type A has
   a. anti-B antibodies in her blood plasma.
   b. anti-A antibodies in her blood plasma.
   c. both anti-A and anti-B antibodies in her blood plasma.
   d. no antibodies in her blood plasma.

_____ 6. The hematocrit is a measure of
   a. water concentration in the plasma.
   b. the percentage of formed elements in the blood.
   c. the number of platelets in the blood.
   d. antibody concentration in the plasma.

_____ 7. Oxygen attaches to a(n) _____ ion in hemoglobin.
   a. calcium
   b. sodium
   c. iron
   d. potassium

_____ 8. During the recycling of components following the normal destruction of erythrocytes, globin is broken down, and its components are
   a. used to synthesize new proteins.
   b. stored as iron in the liver.
   c. eliminated from the body in the bile.
   d. removed in the urine.

____ 9. The extrinsic pathway of coagulation is initiated by

    a. platelets.

    b. fibrinogen.

    c. factor VIII.

    d. damage to tissue.

____ 10. A clot is best described as

    a. an aggregation of platelets.

    b. a fibrin network with trapped formed elements.

    c. agglutination of erythrocytes.

    d. All of these are correct.

11. How does blood help regulate body temperature?

12. What are alpha- and beta-globulins? What do they do?

13. When blood is centrifuged, a thin, whitish-gray layer called the buffy coat covers the packed erythrocytes. What are the components of the buffy coat?

14. What is the shape of an erythrocyte, and why is this shape advantageous to its function?

15. How are respiratory gases (oxygen and carbon dioxide) transported by erythrocytes?

16. What are the anatomic characteristics of each type of leukocyte? How can you tell these leukocytes apart when you view a blood smear under the microscope?

17. How do the functions of basophils differ from those of lymphocytes?

18. Briefly describe the origin, structure, and functions of platelets.

19. What is hemopoiesis? What is a hemocytoblast? Briefly describe the two lines of blood cells that develop during hemopoiesis.

20. Describe the three phases of hemostasis, and list the major events that occur in each phase.

Can You Apply What You've Learned?

Use the following paragraph to answer questions 1–5.

Taylor is an active 25-year-old woman. She was brought into the emergency room after being hit by a car. Taylor suffered extensive blood loss, and the physicians felt she might be in need of a transfusion. They began the procedure of typing her blood.

1. Taylor's blood type was determined to be type A$^-$. This meant she could be transfused with type

    a. A$^+$.

    b. O$^+$.

    c. AB$^-$.

    d. O$^-$.

    e. b and d are both correct.

2. Taylor was weak but conscious. The physicians asked her what medications, if any, she had taken. They asked her to list herbal supplements, pain relievers, and any multivitamins she took over the last few days. Her list included Advil (ibuprofen)—2 tablets that morning, 2 tablets that afternoon; a multivitamin—daily; birth control pill—daily; and an iron supplement—daily. Which of these medications, if any, would exacerbate and prolong Taylor's bleeding?

    a. Advil

    b. multivitamin

    c. birth control pills

    d. iron supplements

    e. None of these are correct.

3. Which sequence or pathway best describes the process of hemostasis that must occur in Taylor to stop her bleeding?

    a. intrinsic pathway ⟶ common pathway ⟶ clotting

    b. common pathway ⟶ extrinsic pathway ⟶ clotting

    c. extrinsic pathway ⟶ common pathway ⟶ clotting

    d. intrinsic pathway ⟶ extrinsic pathway ⟶ clotting

    e. common pathway ⟶ intrinsic pathway ⟶ extrinsic pathway ⟶ clotting

4. Taylor was given the proper blood type and was admitted into the hospital to recoup from her injuries. The following evening, Taylor presented with a high fever, and the physicians suspected she had the complication of a bacterial infection. They sent her blood to the lab for a differential count. Assuming the physicians' guess was correct, the lab results would be returned with which of the following?

    a. increased number of eosinophils

    b. decreased number of basophils

    c. increased number of neutrophils

    d. increased number of lymphocytes

    e. decreased number of monocytes

5. Taylor recovered from her injuries and left the hospital. Several months later, Taylor discovered that she was pregnant with her first child. Her OB/GYN told her she needed to take RhoGAM to ensure this pregnancy would culminate normally and there would be no problems for her child. If Taylor did *not* take RhoGAM, what complication could occur?

    a. The baby would develop anti-D antibodies to Taylor's A$^-$ blood.

    b. The anti-D antibodies in Taylor's blood could attack the erythrocytes of all subsequent babies that Taylor carried.

    c. The child could survive only if it also had an A$^+$ blood type.

    d. The child would present with a lack of bilirubin in its system.

    e. The anti-D antibodies in the baby's blood would attack Taylor's erythrocytes.

Can You Synthesize What You've Learned?

1. While taking a clinical laboratory class, Marilyn prepared and examined blood smears from several donors. One of the smears had an increased percentage (about 10% of observed leukocytes) of cells containing reddish-orange granules. Discuss the type of cell described and the condition that may have caused this increase in the donor.

2. Abby is a nurse on duty in a hospital emergency room when a critically injured patient is brought in. The physician calls for an immediate blood transfusion, but the patient's blood type is unknown. What blood type should the patient be given and why?

3. Your roommate and you are watching the track and field events at the Olympics. One of the sportscasters mentions that a particular athlete has been banned from competing because he was found guilty of blood doping. Your roommate asks you what is blood doping, and why an athlete would be banned for doping his blood. How would you answer your roommate?

chapter 19

Cardiovascular System: Heart

A paramedic is an allied healthcare professional who administers initial treatment at the scene of a medical emergency or trauma. It is important for them to understand the cardiovascular system because one of their central responsibilities is to assess cardiovascular health and administer certain preliminary treatments.

aprevealed.com

Module 9: Cardiovascular System

Who hasn't heard the saying "stay healthy, live longer"? When we think about staying healthy, many thoughts may come to mind: eating a diet that includes plenty of fruits and vegetables with limited amounts of fat and salt, participating in regular aerobic exercise, getting plenty of rest, and avoiding unhealthy behaviors such as smoking and heavy drinking. One significant reason for following this advice is to minimize our risk for developing cardiovascular disease. The importance of doing so becomes more obvious when we ➡

realize that cardiovascular disease—which is any disease that affects the heart or blood vessels—is the leading cause of death both worldwide and in the United States.

We discuss the cardiovascular system in both this chapter on the heart and the next chapter on blood vessels. Our goal is to provide a clear and straightforward discussion on both a normal, healthy cardiovascular system and some of the more common malfunctions (e.g., myocardial infarction, heart murmurs, atherosclerosis, and circulatory shock). We hope to help you to develop both an understanding of, and an appreciation for, this system—a system so central to life that unfortunately when it fails, the outcome often proves fatal.

19.1 Introduction to the Cardiovascular System

Blood must circulate continuously to maintain homeostasis in the body: It must do so whether you are resting in bed or participating in intensive exercise. Circulation of blood is accomplished by the

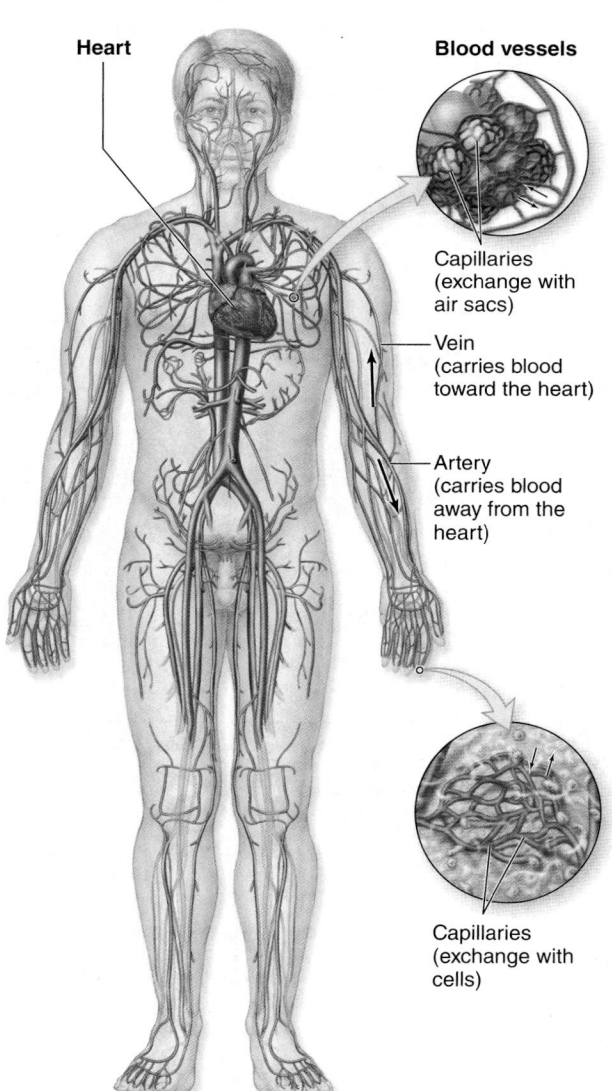

Heart

Blood vessels

Capillaries (exchange with air sacs)

Vein (carries blood toward the heart)

Artery (carries blood away from the heart)

Capillaries (exchange with cells)

Figure 19.1 The Cardiovascular System.
The cardiovascular system consists of the heart (a pump) and three major types of blood vessels (the delivery system), including arteries, capillaries, and veins. Capillaries are the sites of exchange between both the blood and air sacs in the lungs and blood and body cells. AP|R

cardiovascular (kar′dē-ō-vas′kū-lăr; *cardio* = heart, *vascular* = vessels) **system,** which is composed of both the heart and blood vessels **(figure 19.1)**. We first examine the general function of this system and then include an overview of its components.

19.1a General Function

LEARNING OBJECTIVE

1. Describe the general function of the cardiovascular system.

The general function of the cardiovascular system is to transport blood throughout the body to allow the exchange of substances (e.g., respiratory gases, nutrients, and waste products) between the blood of capillaries and the body's cells. The "goal" of the cardiovascular system is to provide adequate perfusion of all body tissues. **Perfusion** (per-fyū′zhŭn; *perfusio* = pouring) is the delivery of blood per time per gram of tissue; typically expressed in milliliters per minute per gram (mL/min/g). *Adequate* perfusion involves delivering sufficient blood to maintain the health of all body cells.

The continual pumping action of the heart and healthy, patent (open and unblocked) vessels are essential to maintain good blood circulation and ample perfusion. If the heart fails to pump sufficient volumes of blood, or the vessels become hardened or occluded (blocked), then an inadequate amount of blood may be supplied to cells. Tissues are deprived of needed oxygen and nutrients, waste products accumulate, and cell death may occur.

WHAT DID YOU LEARN?

❶ What are the potential consequences of a failing cardiovascular system?

19.1b Overview of Components

LEARNING OBJECTIVES

2. Differentiate between the three primary types of blood vessels.

3. Describe the general structure and function of the heart.

4. Compare and contrast pulmonary circulation and systemic circulation of the cardiovascular system. Trace blood flow through both circuits.

Here we provide an overview description of (1) the primary types of blood vessels, through which blood travels; (2) the heart, which pumps the blood; and (3) the two closed circulations of blood vessels that begin and end with the heart.

Blood Vessels

Blood vessels are the conduits or "soft pipes" of the cardiovascular system that transport blood throughout the body (figure 19.1). They are categorized into three primary types: **Arteries** (ar′ter-ēz) carry blood away from the heart; **veins** (vānz) carry blood back to the heart; and **capillaries** (kap′i-lār-ēz; capillaries = relating to hair) serve as the sites of exchange, either between the blood and the air sacs (alveoli) of the lungs or the blood and body cells. (The details of blood vessels are described in section 20.1.)

A common error is to describe arteries as the vessels that always carry **oxygenated** (ok′si-je-nāt-ed) blood (blood high in O_2 and low in CO_2) and veins as the vessels that always transport **deoxygenated** blood (blood low in O_2 and high in CO_2). As you will see, this is *not* an accurate generalization; in some parts of the cardiovascular system, the reverse is true. The defining factor is whether the blood is moving away from the heart or toward it.

The Heart

At the center of the cardiovascular system is the **heart,** which is a hollow, four-chambered organ. Three anatomic features are signifi-

cant in the normal function of the heart: (1) its two-pump structure; (2) the great vessels that lead to and from the heart; and (3) the two sets of valves that are located within the heart **(figure 19.2)**.

First, the heart is composed of two pumps, one on the right side and one on the left side (figure 19.2a). The two-pump structure of the heart allows separation of circulating oxygenated and deoxygenated blood. The right side receives deoxygenated blood from the body and pumps it to the lungs, and the left side receives oxygenated blood from the lungs and pumps it to the body. A superior chamber for receiving blood is called an **atrium** (ā′trē-ŭm; entrance hall), and an inferior chamber for pumping blood away from the heart is called a **ventricle** (ven′tri-kl; *venter* = belly). Blood is received into an atrium; it then moves from the atrium inferiorly into the ventricle to be pumped. Both types of chambers are associated with each pump. Thus, four chambers in the heart are identified: right atrium and right ventricle on the right side of the heart, and the left atrium and left ventricle on the left side of the heart.

Second, blood is transported directly to and from the chambers of the heart by the **great vessels** that are continuous with each chamber (figure 19.2b). These vessels include both arteries and veins. There are two large arteries (or *arterial trunks*) attached to the superior border of the ventricles: They transport blood away from the heart. The **pulmonary trunk** (which splits into the pulmonary arteries) receives deoxygenated blood from the right ventricle, and the **aorta** (ā-ōr′tă), which receives oxygenated blood from the left ventricle. Large veins deliver blood to the atria on the more posterior

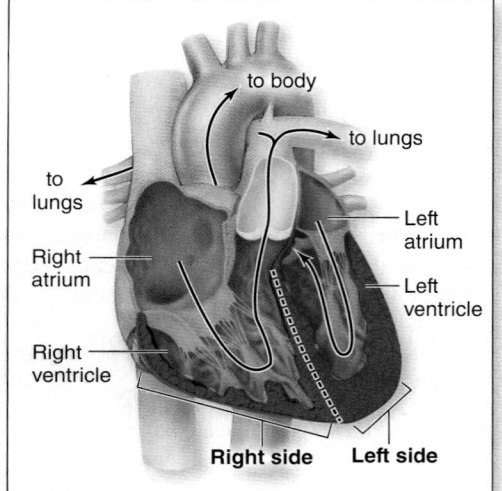

Two pumps

Each pump has a receiving chamber (atrium) and a pumping chamber (ventricle).

- Right side: pumps deoxygenated blood to the lungs
- Left side: pumps oxygenated blood to the body

(a)

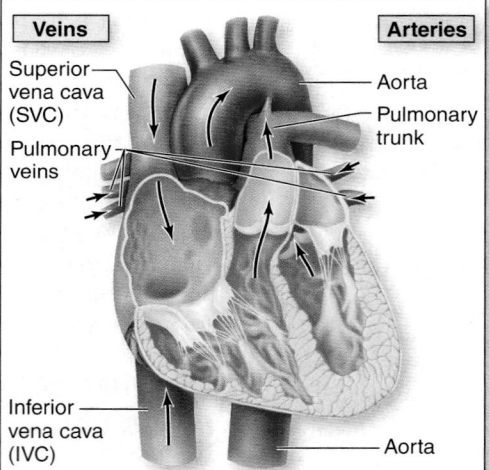

Great vessels

Arteries (arterial trunks) transport blood away from the heart.

- Pulmonary trunk transports from right side
- Aorta transports from left side

Veins transport blood toward the heart

- Vena cavae (SVC and IVC) drain into right side
- Pulmonary veins drain into left side

(b)

Valves

Heart valves prevent backflow to ensure one-way blood flow.

- Atrioventricular (AV) valves (i.e., right AV valve and left AV valve) are between atrium and ventricle
- Semilunar valves (i.e., pulmonary semilunar valve and aortic semilunar valve) are between ventricle and arterial trunk

(c)

Figure 19.2 Significant Anatomic Features of the Heart. The heart is a two-pump structure (*a*) with attached great vessels (*b*) and two sets of valves (*c*) that permit one-way flow of blood. AP|R aspect of the heart. These include the **superior vena cava** and **inferior vena cava,** which drain deoxygenated blood into the right atrium, and the **pulmonary veins,** which drain oxygenated blood into the left atrium. Remember, ventricles pump blood into the greater arterial trunks, and atria receive blood from the veins.

✎ WHAT DO YOU THINK?

❶ What vessels attached to the heart contain oxygenated blood? Are they both arteries? Explain.

Third, two sets of valves are located within the heart (figure 19.2c). The **atrioventricular** (ā'trē-ō-ven-trik'ū-lăr) **(AV) valves** are between the atrium and ventricle of each side of the heart. The **right AV valve,** also called the *tricuspid valve*, is located between the right atrium and the right ventricle. (Remember that the **TRI**cuspid is on the **RI**ght side.) The **left AV valve,** also called the *bicuspid valve*, or *mitral valve*, is located between the left atrium and left ventricle.

The other set of valves is the **semilunar valves**, which mark the boundary between a ventricle and its associated arterial trunk. The **pulmonary semilunar valve** is between the right ventricle and the pulmonary trunk, and the **aortic semilunar valve** is between the left ventricle and the aorta. The valves open to allow blood to flow through the heart and then close to prevent its backflow. This ensures one-way, or unidirectional, flow of blood through the heart.

Circulation Routes

The blood vessels and the two pumps of the heart are arranged in two circuits: the pulmonary circulation and systemic circulation (**figure 19.3**).

The **pulmonary** (pŭl'mō-nār-ē; *pulmo* = lung) **circulation** conveys deoxygenated blood from the right side of the heart through blood vessels to the lungs for the pickup of oxygen and the release of carbon dioxide, and then back through blood vessels to the left side of the heart.

The **systemic circulation** moves oxygenated blood from the left side of the heart. The blood moves through blood vessels to the systemic cells such as those of the liver, skin, muscle, and brain for the exchange of nutrients, respiratory gases, and wastes before returning the blood in vessels that enter the right side of the heart. Thus, the basic pattern of blood flow is the right side of the heart ⟶ lungs ⟶ the left side of the heart ⟶ systemic tissues of the body ⟶ back to the right side.

Note that equal amounts of blood are normally pumped by the two ventricles through the two circulations, a condition called **ventricular balance.** Sustained pumping of *unequal* amounts of blood may result in **edema** (e-dē'mă; *aoidema* = swelling), which is excess fluid in the interstitial space or within cells. (See Clinical View: "Systemic and Pulmonary Edema").

One of the critical concepts in understanding the function of the cardiovascular system is the flow of blood through the heart and the two circulatory routes. This flow pattern is summarized in **figure 19.4** and **table 19.1**.

INTEGRATE
CLINICAL VIEW
Systemic and Pulmonary Edema

Edema may be the result of a change in the systemic circulation or the pulmonary circulation. **Systemic edema** may occur if the *right* ventricle is impaired. If the right ventricle cannot keep up with the left ventricle, more blood remains in the systemic circulation. Systemic edema results as additional fluid leaves the systemic capillaries to enter the interstitial space and into the cells. **Pulmonary edema** may occur if the *left* ventricle pumps less blood than the right side of the heart. Here, additional blood remains in the pulmonary circulation because the left side of the heart receives blood from the lungs. The result is swelling and fluid accumulation in the lungs. Some symptoms of pulmonary edema include pale skin, coughing up blood, and breathing difficulties. It leads to impaired gas exchange and may cause respiratory failure and death if not treated.

Figure 19.3 Cardiovascular System Circulations.
The cardiovascular system is composed of the pulmonary circulation and the systemic circulation. AP|R

Figure 19.4 **Blood Flow Through the Heart and Circulatory Routes.** The two circulations are the (a) pulmonary circulation, which includes the pumping of blood by the right side of the heart to the lungs and the return of blood to the left side of the heart, and (b) systemic circulation, which includes the pumping of blood by the left side of the heart to the body's cells and the return of blood to the right side of the heart.

(a) Pulmonary Circulation

Transports blood from the right side of the heart to the alveoli of the lungs for gas exchange and back to the left side of the heart

Pulmonary capillaries of right lung

Right pulmonary artery

Superior vena cava (SVC)

Right pulmonary veins

Right atrium

Right AV valve

Right ventricle

Inferior vena cava (IVC)

Pulmonary semilunar valve

Pulmonary capillaries of left lung

Left pulmonary artery

Pulmonary trunk

Left atrium

Left pulmonary veins

Blood flow through pulmonary circulation

1. Deoxygenated blood enters the right atrium from the vena cavae (SVC and IVC) and coronary sinus (not shown).

2. Blood passes through the right AV valve (tricuspid valve).

3. Blood enters the right ventricle.

4. Blood passes through the pulmonary semilunar valve.

5. Blood enters the pulmonary trunk.

6. Blood continues through the right and left pulmonary arteries to both lungs.

7. Blood enters pulmonary capillaries of both lungs for gas exchange.

8. Oxygenated blood exits the pulmonary capillaries of the lungs and returns to the heart by right and left pulmonary veins.

9. Blood enters the left atrium of the heart.

(b) Systemic Circulation

Transports blood from the left side of the heart to the systemic cells of the body for nutrient and gas exchange, and back to the right side of the heart

Systemic capillaries
of head, neck, and upper limbs

Systemic veins

Systemic arteries

Aorta

Superior vena cava (SVC)

Left atrium

Left AV valve

Right atrium

Inferior vena cava (IVC)

Left ventricle

Aortic semilunar valve

Systemic veins

Systemic arteries

Systemic capillaries of trunk and lower limbs

Blood flow through systemic circulation

(1) Oxygenated blood enters the left atrium.

(2) Blood passes through the left AV valve (bicuspid or mitral valve).

(3) Blood enters the left ventricle.

(4) Blood passes through aortic semilunar valve.

(5) Blood enters the aorta.

(6) Blood is distributed by the systemic arteries.

(7) Blood enters systemic capillaries for nutrient and gas exchange.

(8) Deoxygenated blood exits systemic capillaries and returns to the heart by systemic veins that ultimately drain into the SVC, IVC, and coronary sinus (not shown).

(9) Blood enters right atrium.

Table 19.1	Blood Flow Through the Heart		
Heart Chamber	**Receives Blood From**	**Sends Blood To**	**Valve Through Which Blood Flows**
Right atrium	Superior vena cava Inferior vena cava Coronary sinus[1]	Right ventricle	Right atrioventricular (AV) valve
Right ventricle	Right atrium	Pulmonary trunk	Pulmonary semilunar valve
Left atrium	Pulmonary veins	Left ventricle	Left AV valve
Left ventricle	Left atrium	Aorta	Aortic semilunar valve

1. Drains deoxygenated blood from the heart wall.

WHAT DID YOU LEARN?

2 What generalization can be made about all arteries? What generalization can be made about all veins?

3 What path does blood follow through the heart? Identify all structures that it passes through, including each chamber, valve, and great vessel. Begin at the right atrium.

4 Why must ventricular output be balanced?

19.2 Location of the Heart and the Pericardium

The heart is located within the thoracic cavity and is enclosed within a fibroserous sac; both of these structures have roles in protection and support of the heart.

19.2a Location and Position of the Heart

LEARNING OBJECTIVE

1. Describe the location and position of the heart in the thoracic cavity.

The heart is located posterior to the sternum left of the body midline between the lungs in the **mediastinum** (me′dē-as-tī′nŭm; *medius* = middle) **(figure 19.5)**. The position of the heart is slightly rotated such that its right side or right border (primarily formed by the right atrium and a small part of the right ventricle) is located more anteriorly, while its left side or left border (primarily formed by the left atrium and left ventricle) is located more posteriorly. The postero-superior surface of the heart is called the **base.** The inferior, conical end of the heart is called the **apex** (ā′peks; tip). It projects slightly anteroinferiorly toward the left side of the body with the right ventricle lying on the diaphragm. You may find it helpful to think of the heart's position like an "upside down" pyramid with the apex below the base.

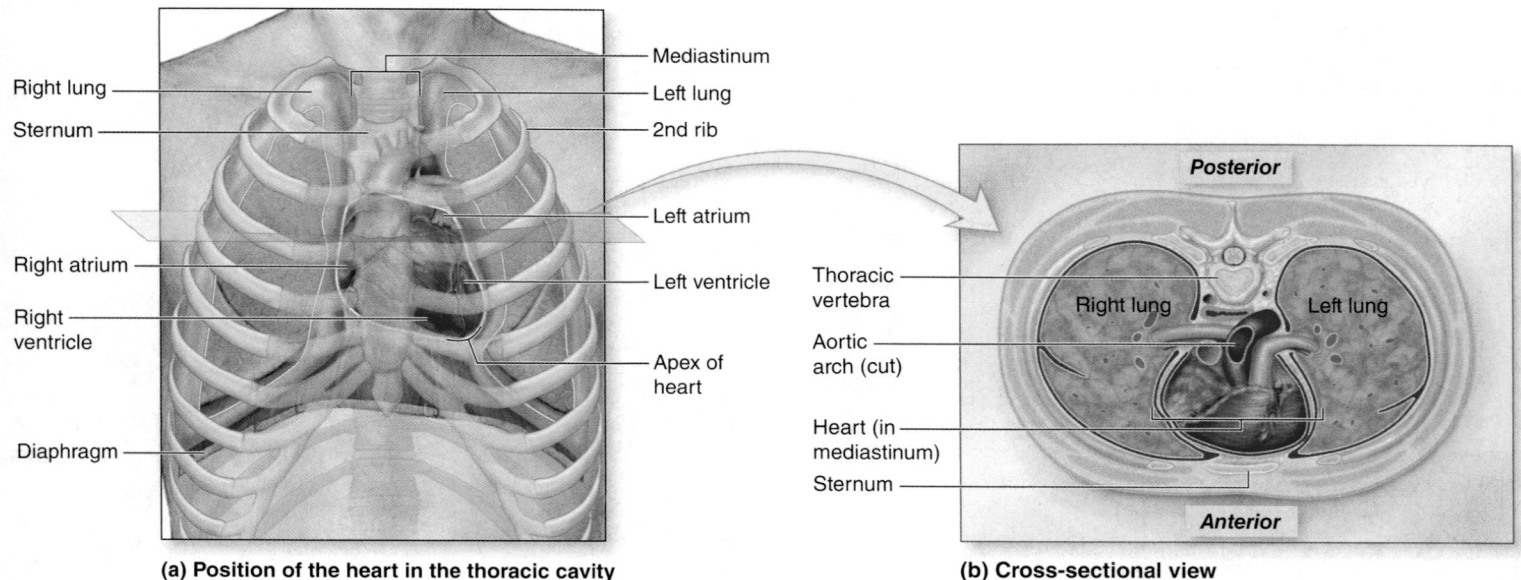

(a) Position of the heart in the thoracic cavity

(b) Cross-sectional view

Figure 19.5 Heart Position Within the Thoracic Cavity. (*a*) The heart is located within the mediastinum of the thoracic cavity between the lungs. (*b*) A cross-sectional view depicts the heart's relationship to the other organs in the thoracic cavity. AP|R

⑤ Which side of the heart is more visible in an anterior view?

19.2b Characteristics of the Pericardium

✓ **LEARNING OBJECTIVES**

2. List the structural components of the pericardium.

3. Describe the function of the pericardium and the purpose of the serous fluid within the pericardial cavity.

The heart is enclosed in the **pericardium** (per-i-kar′dē-ŭm; *peri* = around, *kardia* = heart) **(figure 19.6)**. The outermost covering is a double-layered fibroserous sac called the **pericardial sac.** The outer portion of the sac is a tough, dense irregular connective tissue layer called the **fibrous pericardium.** This layer is attached inferiorly to the diaphragm and superiorly to the base of the great arterial trunks (pulmonary trunk and aorta). It restricts movements so that the heart does not bounce and move about in the thoracic cavity, and it prevents the heart from overfilling with blood. The inner portion of the sac is a thin, serous membrane identified as the **parietal layer of serous pericardium** (or *parietal pericardium*). Tightly adhered to the heart is a second serous membrane called the **visceral layer of serous pericardium** (or *visceral pericardium*). The visceral layer is also called the *epicardium.*

The parietal and visceral layers of the pericardium are continuous with each other and reflect along, and attach to the great arterial

- Fibrous pericardium
- Parietal layer of serous pericardium
- Pericardial cavity (contains serous fluid)
- Visceral layer of serous pericardium (epicardium)

- Fibrous pericardium
- Parietal layer of serous pericardium
- Visceral layer of serous pericardium (epicardium)

Pericardial sac

Diaphragm

Figure 19.6 Pericardium. The protective layers of the heart include the pericardial sac composed of an outer fibrous pericardium and an inner serous membrane called the parietal layer of serous pericardium. Tightly adhered to the heart is a serous membrane called the visceral layer of serous pericardium. The space between the parietal and visceral layers is called the pericardial cavity, which contains serous fluid produced by both serous membranes. **AP|R**

 INTEGRATE

CLINICAL VIEW
Pericarditis

Pericarditis (per′i-kar-dī′tis; *itis* = inflammation) is an inflammation of the pericardium typically caused by viruses, bacteria, or fungi. The inflammation is associated with an increase in capillary permeability; the blood vessels become more "leaky," resulting in fluid accumulation in the pericardial cavity. At this point, the potential space of the pericardial cavity becomes a real space as it fills with fluid. In severe cases, the excess fluid accumulation limits the heart's movement and keeps the heart chambers from filling with an adequate amount of blood. The heart is unable to pump blood, leading to a medical emergency called **cardiac tamponade** (tam′pŏ-nād′) and possibly resulting in heart failure and death.

A helpful physical finding in diagnosing pericarditis is **friction rub**, a crackling or scraping sound heard with a stethoscope that is caused by the movement of the inflamed pericardial layers against each other.

trunks. The potential space between the parietal and visceral layers is called the **pericardial cavity.** Serous fluid is secreted by both layers and released into the pericardial cavity to lubricate the membranes and facilitate the almost frictionless movement of the heart when it beats.

 WHAT DID YOU LEARN?

⑥ Describe the three layers that cover the heart. Where is the pericardial cavity relative to these layers?

19.3 Heart Anatomy

When the pericardial sac is cut and reflected, the heart can be removed from the mediastinum and examined in greater detail. It is a relatively small, conical, muscular organ approximately the size of a person's clenched fist. In the average normal adult, it weighs about 300 grams (0.7 pound), but certain diseases may cause heart size to increase dramatically. Here we examine the heart's external and internal structures.

19.3a Superficial Features of the Heart

✓ **LEARNING OBJECTIVE**

1. Compare the superficial features of the anterior and posterior aspects of the heart.

The heart was previously described as being composed of four hollow chambers: two smaller atria and two larger ventricles **(figure 19.7)**. The atria are separated from the ventricles externally by a relatively deep groove called the **coronary** (kōr′o-nār-ē; *corona* = crown) **sulcus** (or *atrioventricular sulcus*) that extends around the circumference of the heart. An **interventricular** (in-ter-ven-trik′ū-lăr; *inter* = between) **sulcus** is a groove between the ventricles that extends inferiorly from the coronary sulcus toward the heart apex, and delineates the superficial boundary between the right and left ventricles. The **anterior interventricular sulcus** is located on the anterior side of the heart, and the **posterior interventricular sulcus**

Superior vena cava

Branches of right
pulmonary artery

Right pulmonary veins

Right auricle

Right atrium

Right coronary artery
(in coronary sulcus)

Right ventricle

Right marginal artery

Inferior vena cava

Ascending aorta

Aortic arch

Ligamentum arteriosum

Left pulmonary artery

Pulmonary trunk

Left pulmonary veins

Left auricle

Left coronary artery
(in coronary sulcus)

Circumflex artery
(in coronary sulcus)

Anterior interventricular artery
(in anterior interventricular sulcus)

Left ventricle

Apex of heart

Descending aorta

Branches of right
pulmonary artery

Right pulmonary vein

Right auricle

Right atrium

Right coronary artery
(in coronary sulcus)

Right ventricle

Right marginal artery

Ascending aorta

Aortic arch

Ligamentum arteriosum

Left pulmonary artery

Pulmonary trunk

Left pulmonary vein

Left auricle

Left coronary artery
(in coronary sulcus)

Anterior interventricular artery
(in anterior interventricular sulcus)

Left ventricle

Apex of heart

(a) Anterior view

Figure 19.7 External Anatomy and Features of the Heart. A drawing and a cadaver photo show the superficial features of the heart. (*a*) Anterior view. AP|R

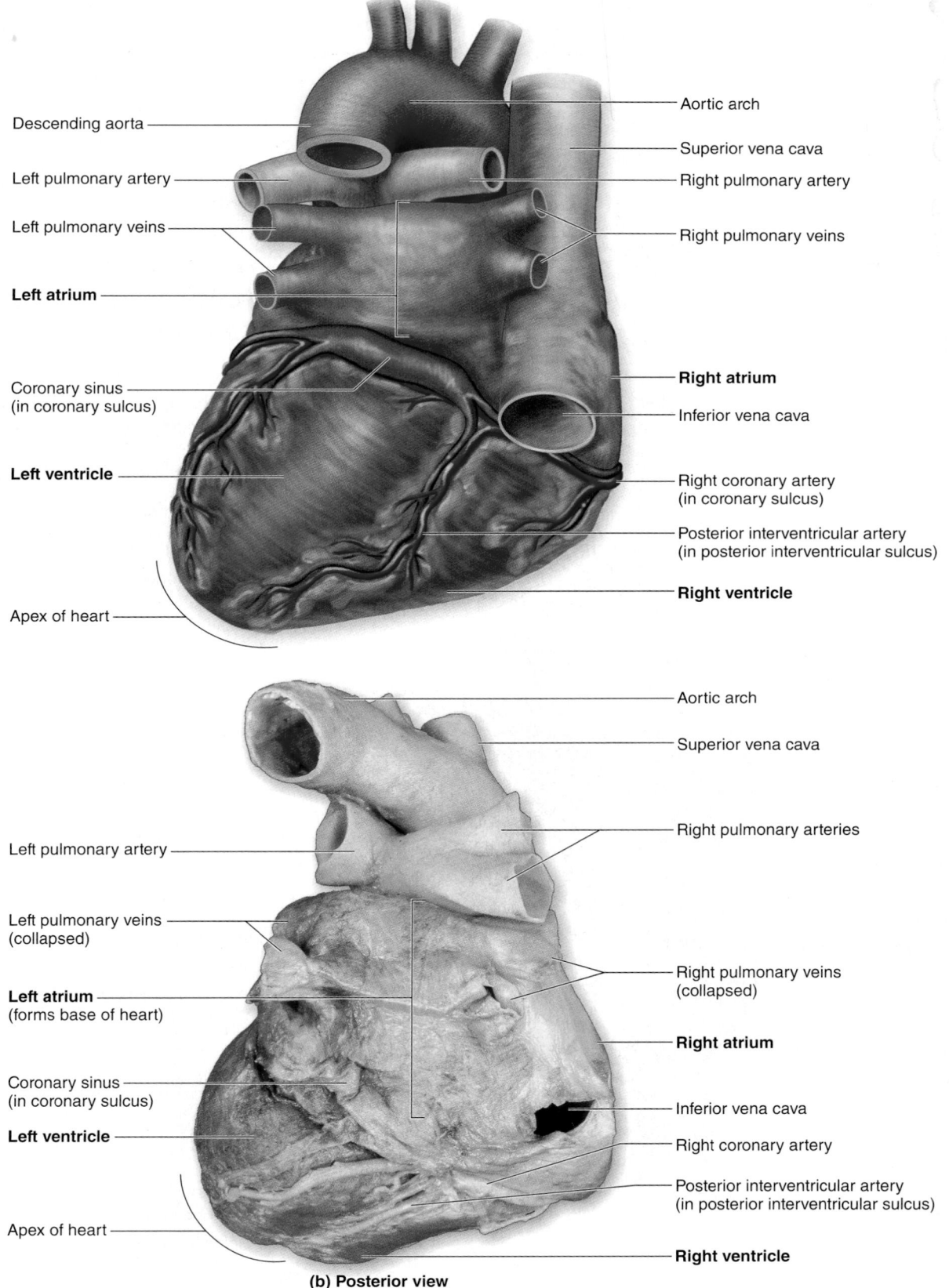

Descending aorta
Left pulmonary artery
Left pulmonary veins
Left atrium
Coronary sinus
(in coronary sulcus)
Left ventricle
Apex of heart

Aortic arch
Superior vena cava
Right pulmonary artery
Right pulmonary veins
Right atrium
Inferior vena cava
Right coronary artery
(in coronary sulcus)
Posterior interventricular artery
(in posterior interventricular sulcus)
Right ventricle

Left pulmonary artery
Left pulmonary veins
(collapsed)
Left atrium
(forms base of heart)
Coronary sinus
(in coronary sulcus)
Left ventricle
Apex of heart

Aortic arch
Superior vena cava
Right pulmonary arteries
Right pulmonary veins
(collapsed)
Right atrium
Inferior vena cava
Right coronary artery
Posterior interventricular artery
(in posterior interventricular sulcus)
Right ventricle

(b) Posterior view

Figure 19.7 External Anatomy and Features of the Heart (*continued*). (*b*) Posterior view. AP|R is located on the posterior side of the heart. Located within all of these sulci are coronary vessels associated with supplying blood to the heart wall. Coronary vessels are described in detail shortly.

Anterior View

The right atrium and right ventricle are prominent when viewing the heart from an anterior view as just described (figure 19.7a). The portion of the right atrium that is most noticeable is its wrinkled, flaplike extension called the **right auricle** (aw′ri-kl); *auris* = ear). You may find it helpful to think of an auricle as an "ear" of the atrium. Also seen in this view are both the aorta and pulmonary trunk, a small portion of the **left auricle** of the left atrium, the anterior interventricular sulcus, and part of the coronary sulcus.

Posterior View

The left atrium and left ventricle are prominent when seeing the heart from a posterior view (figure 19.7b). The left atrium primarily forms the base on the posterosuperior surface of the heart. The

pulmonary veins are attached to the left atrium. Also seen in this view are both the superior and inferior vena cavae, pulmonary arteries, the posterior interventricular sulcus, and part of the coronary sulcus that houses the coronary sinus (the vessel that drains blood from the heart wall).

WHAT DID YOU LEARN?

7 Where is the coronary sulcus located? Is the coronary sinus visible from both the anterior view and posterior view?

19.3b Layers of the Heart Wall

LEARNING OBJECTIVE

2. Name the three layers of the heart wall and the tissue components of each.

If a coronal section is made through the heart, it is possible to view the internal structures of the heart (**figure 19.8**). First, observe the

Figure 19.8 Internal Anatomy of the Heart.
(a) A coronal section reveals the internal structure of the heart, including the heart wall, chambers, and valves. (b) The heart wall contains an outer epicardium; a thick, middle myocardium; and an inner endocardium. AP|R

heart wall of the different heart chambers. Notice that the walls of the ventricles are thicker than the walls of the atria; this is because the ventricles are the "pumping chambers." Also note that the wall of the left ventricle is typically three times thicker than the right ventricular wall. This difference is because the left ventricle—although it pumps the same amount of blood as the right ventricle—must generate enough pressure to force the blood through the entire systemic circulation. The right ventricle, in contrast, merely has to pump blood to the nearby lungs. This difference in thickness can also be seen when a transverse section is made through the heart (figure 19.9).

Three distinctive layers compose the wall of each chamber: an external epicardium, a thick middle myocardium, and an internal endocardium (figure 19.8b).

The **epicardium** (ep-i-kar′dē-ŭm; epi = upon) is the outermost heart layer and is also called the visceral layer of serous pericardium. The epicardium is a serous membrane composed of simple squamous epithelium and an underlying layer of areolar connective tissue. As we age, the epicardium thickens as it becomes more invested with adipose connective tissue.

The **myocardium** (mī-ō-kar′dē-ŭm; mys = muscle) is the middle layer of the heart wall. It is composed of cardiac muscle tissue (see section 5.3) and is the thickest of the three heart wall layers. Contraction of cardiac muscle in the myocardium generates the force necessary to pump blood. The ventricular myocardium may change in thickness as we age. For example, it hypertrophies in response to narrowing of systemic arteries. We consider the microscopic anatomy of cardiac muscle later in this chapter.

The internal surface of the heart and the external surfaces of the heart valves are covered by **endocardium** (en-dō-kar′dē-ŭm; endon = within). The endocardium is composed of a simple squamous epithelium called an endothelium (see section 5.1c), and an underlying layer of areolar connective tissue. It is continuous with the inner lining of blood vessels.

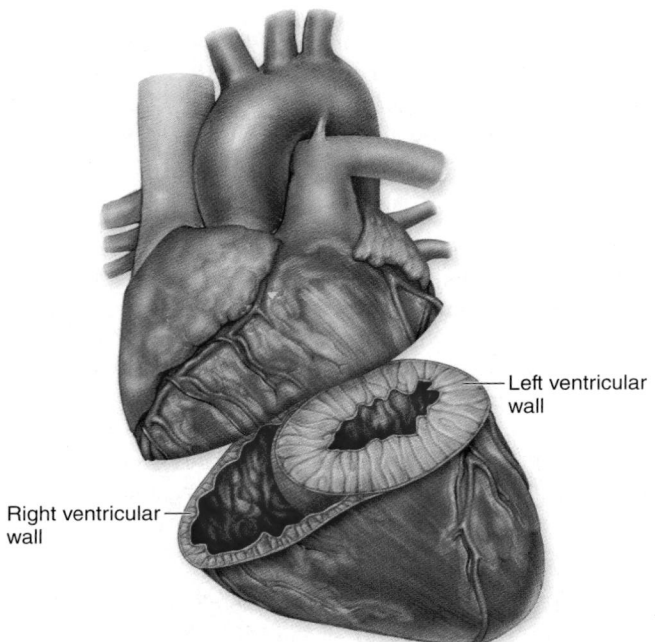

Figure 19.9 Comparison of Right and Left Ventricular Wall Thickness. The wall of the left ventricle is about three times thicker than that of the right ventricle, because the left ventricle must generate a force sufficient to push blood through the systemic circulation.

  WHAT DID YOU LEARN?

8 What are the layers of the heart (in order) that a scalpel would pass through during dissection?

19.3c Heart Chambers

 LEARNING OBJECTIVE

3. Characterize the four chambers of the heart and their functions.

Figure 19.8 also depicts the internal anatomy and structural organization of the four heart chambers. The right and left atrial chambers are separated by a thin wall called the **interatrial** (in-ter-ā′trē-ăl) **septum,** and the right and left ventricles are separated by a thick wall called the **interventricular septum.** The position of the interventricular septum is delineated on the heart's superficial surface with the interventricular sulci (see figure 19.7).

Right Atrium

The internal wall of the right atrium is smooth on its posterior surface, but it exhibits muscular ridges, called **pectinate** (pek′ti-nāt; teeth of a comb) **muscles** on its anterior wall and within the auricle (see figure 19.8a). Inspection of the interatrial septum reveals an oval depression called the **fossa ovalis** (fos′ă; trench; ō-va′lis). It occupies the former location of the fetal **foramen ovale** (ō-val′ē), which shunted blood from the right atrium to the left atrium, bypassing the lungs during fetal life (fetal circulation is described in section 20.12). Immediately inferior to the fossa ovalis is the opening of the coronary sinus, which drains blood from the heart wall. Openings of the superior and inferior vena cavae are also visible. Separating the right atrium from the right ventricle is the right atrioventricular opening that contains the right AV valve.

Right Ventricle

The internal wall surface of the right ventricle displays characteristic large, smooth, irregular muscular ridges, called the **trabeculae carneae** (tră-bek′ū-lē; trabs = beam, kar′nē-ē; carne = flesh). Extending from the internal wall of the right ventricle are typically three cone-shaped, muscular projections called **papillary** (pap′i-lăr-ē; papilla = nipple) **muscles.** (The number of papillary muscles in the right ventricle can range from 2 to 9.) Papillary muscles anchor thin strands of collagen fibers called **chordae tendineae** (kōr′dē ten′di-nē-ē), which are attached to the right atrioventricular valve. At its superior end, the right ventricle narrows into a smooth-walled, conical region leading into the pulmonary trunk. The pulmonary semilunar valve is positioned between the right ventricle and pulmonary trunk.

Left Atrium

Like the right atrium, the left atrium has pectinate muscles in its auricle. Openings of the pulmonary veins are visible. (Two are seen in figure 19.8.) Separating the left atrium from the left ventricle is the left atrioventricular opening that is marked by the left AV valve.

Left Ventricle

The internal wall surface of the left ventricle also displays characteristic trabeculae carneae. It has two papillary muscles that are anchored by chordae tendineae. The entrance into the aorta is located at the

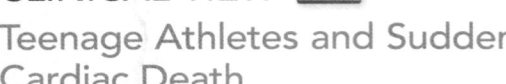

CLINICAL VIEW

Teenage Athletes and Sudden Cardiac Death

Sudden deaths of high school athletes have occurred during athletic events. These deaths were apparently caused by underlying, previously undetected cardiovascular disease. The *Journal of the American Medical Association* published a study of hundreds of cases that occurred between 1985 and 1995. This study indicated that no forewarning of a problem preceded these deaths. Autopsies revealed that most deaths were due to congenital heart defects and coronary artery anomalies. The result from these anomalies was cardiomegaly, which led to sudden death.

Cardiomegaly is one term used to indicate an increase in the thickness of the heart muscle wall (hypertrophy) or an obvious increase or enlargement in heart size (dilation) due to stress applied to the heart. Other terms used are *hypertrophic heart, heart enlargement,* or *athlete's heart.* Usually, cardiomegaly refers to a pathologic condition that implies either that the heart is overworked, it is excessively abnormal, or it is accompanied by

other cardiovascular problems. Often, symptoms accompanying an enlarged heart include swelling in the limbs, dizziness, arrhythmia (an irregular heartbeat), and shortness of breath.

A standard x-ray that may accompany a physical examination often reveals the condition. The confirmation of this condition depends upon an echocardiogram that is used to evaluate the heart's function and its structure.

As a result, many school districts are weighing the costs of requiring these x-rays against the potential benefits of identifying student athletes who may be at risk for cardiomegaly.

Cardiomegaly in an adult female. Note how the heart shadow encompasses most of the width of the thorax.

Cardiomegaly

superior end of the left ventricle. The aortic semilunar valve can be seen there at the boundary of the left ventricle and aorta.

 WHAT DID YOU LEARN?

9 What is the structure that separates the two ventricles? What is the superficial landmark that identifies the location of this structure?

19.3d Heart Valves

 LEARNING OBJECTIVE

4. Compare and contrast the structure and function of the two types of heart valves.

Effective blood flow requires both uninterrupted heart beating (discussed later) and valves to control blood flow and ensure it is "one-way." Recall that the two categories of heart valves are the atrioventricular valves and the semilunar valves. Each valve consists of endothelium-lined fibrous connective tissue flaps called cusps, or leaflets **(figure 19.10)**.

Atrioventricular Valves

The right AV valve covers the right atrioventricular opening, and it has three cusps; the left AV valve covers the left atrioventricular opening, but it has only two cusps. The AV valves are shown in both the open and closed position in figure 19.10b. When open, the cusps of the valve extend into the ventricles. This allows blood to move from an atrium into the ventricle. When the ventricles contract, blood is forced superiorly as ventricular pressure rises. This causes the AV valves to close. The papillary muscles secure the thin chordae tendineae that attach to the lower surface of each AV valve cusp. This prevents the valve from inverting and being "pushed open" into the atrium when the valve is closed. By being properly held in place, the cusps of the AV valves prevent blood flow back into the atrium.

Semilunar Valves

The pulmonary semilunar valve is located between the right ventricle and the pulmonary trunk, and the aortic semilunar valve is located between the left ventricle and the aorta. Each valve is composed of three half-moon-shaped, pocketlike semilunar cusps (figure 19.10a, c). Neither papillary muscles nor chordae tendineae are associated with these valves. The semilunar valves are shown in both the open and closed position.

The semilunar valves open when the ventricles contract and the force of the blood pushes the semilunar valves open and blood enters the arterial trunks. The valves close when the ventricles relax and the pressure in the ventricle becomes less than the pressure in a great

Figure 19.10 Heart Valves. (*a*) Location of heart valves as viewed in coronal section and transverse section. (*b*) Atrioventricular valves in open and closed position. (*c*) Semilunar valves in open and closed position. AP|R

arterial trunk. Blood in the arteries begins to fall backward toward the ventricle and is caught in the cusps of the semilunar valves, and they close. The closure of the semilunar valves prevents blood flow back into the ventricle.

Both flexibility and elasticity of connective tissue composing heart valves decrease with aging. This may cause the heart valves to become inflexible. As a result, blood flow through the heart may be altered, and a heart murmur may be detected (see Clinical View: Heart Sounds and Heart Murmurs). The location, structure, and function of the four heart valves are summarized in **table 19.2**.

WHAT DID YOU LEARN?

10 What are the functions of the chordae tendineae and papillary muscles?

Table 19.2	Heart Valves		
Valve	**Location**	**Structure**	**Prevents Backflow**
Right atrioventricular (AV) valve	Between right atrium and right ventricle	Three cusps with chordae tendineae attached to free edges of cusps	From right ventricle into right atrium
Left atrioventricular (AV) valve	Between left atrium and left ventricle	Two cusps with chordae tendineae attached to free edges of cusps	From left ventricle into left atrium
Pulmonary semilunar valve	Between right ventricle and pulmonary trunk	Three half-moon shaped cusps; no chordae tendineae	From pulmonary trunk into right ventricle
Aortic semilunar valve	Between left ventricle and aorta	Three half-moon shaped cusps; no chordae tendineae	From aorta into left ventricle

19.3e Microscopic Structure of Cardiac Muscle

✓ LEARNING OBJECTIVES

5. Describe the general structure of cardiac muscle.
6. Explain the intercellular structures of cardiac muscle.
7. Discuss how cardiac muscle meets its energy needs.

The myocardium is composed of cardiac muscle tissue (see section 5.3). This muscle tissue is made up of relatively short, branched cells that usually house one or two central nuclei (**figure 19.11**). These cells are supported by areolar connective tissue, called an endomysium, that surrounds the cells. Other anatomic structures of cardiac muscle cells include the following:

- The sarcolemma (plasma membrane), which invaginates to form T-tubules that extend into the sarcoplasmic reticulum (SR).

The T-tubules of cardiac muscle invaginate once per sarcomere and overlie Z discs.

- The SR surrounds bundles of myofilaments called myofibrils in cardiac muscle, but it is less extensive than the SR of skeletal muscle and lacks both terminal cisternae (the "end sacs" of sarcoplasmic reticulum) and a tight association with transverse tubules (figure 19.11c).

- Myofilaments are arranged in sarcomeres—thus, cardiac muscle appears striated when viewed under a microscope (figure 19.11d). Interestingly, maximum overlap of thin and thick filaments within the sarcomeres does *not* occur when cardiac muscle is at rest (as is the case within skeletal muscle; see length-tension relationship in section 10.7c). Instead, maximum overlap of thin and thick filaments occurs when cardiac muscle is stretched as blood is added to a heart

(a) Cross section of cardiac muscle cells

(b) Intercellular junctions

(c) Longitudinal view of cardiac muscle cell

(d) Longitudinal section of cardiac muscle

Figure 19.11 Histology of Cardiac Muscle. Cardiac muscle cells form the myocardium. (*a*) Individual cells are relatively short, branched, and striated. (*b*) They are connected to adjacent cells by intercalated discs composed of both desmosomes and gap junctions. (*c*) T-tubules are invaginations of the sarcolemma that extend internally to the sarcoplasmic reticulum. (*d*) Light micrograph of cardiac muscle in longitudinal section. Intercalated discs are visible as dark lines perpendicular to the cardiac muscle cells. AP|R chamber. As we will see, this provides a means of forming additional crossbridges between the thin and thick filaments and cardiac muscle contracting with increasingly greater degrees of force as additional blood enters the chamber.

Intercellular Structures

Neighboring cardiac muscle cells have an extensively folded sarcolemma that permits adjoining membranes to interconnect, markedly increasing exposed surface areas between neighboring cells (figure 19.11b). This increases structural stability of the myocardium and facilitates communication between cardiac muscle cells.

Unique structures called **intercalated** (in-ter′kǎ-lā-ted) **discs** are found at these cell-to-cell junctions. They link cardiac muscle cells together both mechanically and electrically and contain two distinctive structural features:

- **Desmosomes.** These are protein filaments that anchor into a protein plaque located on the internal surface of the sarcolemma (see section 4.5d). They act as mechanical junctions to prevent cardiac muscle cells from pulling apart.
- **Gap junctions.** These are protein pores between the sarcolemma of adjacent cardiac muscle cells. They provide a low-resistance pathway for the flow of ions between the cardiac cells. Gap junctions allow an action potential to move continuously along the sarcolemma of cardiac muscle cells, resulting in synchronous contraction of that chamber. Thus, a chamber functions as a single unit, or **functional syncytium**.

Metabolism of Cardiac Muscle

Cardiac muscle has features that support its great demand for energy, including an extensive blood supply, numerous mitochondria, and other structures such as myoglobin and creatine kinase (section 10.4a).

Cardiac muscle relies almost exclusively on aerobic cellular respiration (section 3.4). Its cellular structures and metabolic processes support this. Cardiac muscle has a large number of mitochondria (comprising approximately 25% of its volume compared to about 2% of the volume in skeletal muscle). It is also versatile in being able to use different types of fuel molecules, including fatty acids, glucose, lactic acid, amino acids, and ketone bodies. The relative amounts of fuel molecules that cardiac muscle cells use fluctuates depending upon conditions. For example, during intense exercise and increased production and release of lactic acid into the blood by skeletal muscle, cardiac muscle will absorb and use this resource.

Yet, as a consequence of its reliance on aerobic metabolism, cardiac muscle is quite susceptible to failure if ischemic (low-oxygen) conditions prevail. Cardiac muscle has limited capability in using anaerobic (glycolysis) pathways (see section 3.4b) or accruing an oxygen debt (see section 10.4b) in its activities. Therefore, anything that interferes with blood flow to the heart muscle, such as narrowing of the coronary arteries, can cause damage or death.

WHAT DID YOU LEARN?

⑪ Which features of cardiac muscle support aerobic cellular respiration?

19.3f Fibrous Skeleton of the Heart

LEARNING OBJECTIVE

8. Describe the location and function of the fibrous skeleton.

The heart is supported internally by a **fibrous skeleton** composed of dense irregular tissue (**figure 19.12**). This fibrous skeleton performs the following functions:

- Provides structural support at the boundary between the atria and the ventricles
- Forms supportive fibrous rings to anchor the heart valves
- Provides a rigid framework for the attachment of cardiac muscle tissue
- Acts as an electric insulator because it does not conduct action potentials and thus prevents the atrial chambers from contracting at the same time as the ventricular chambers

Notice that cardiac muscle cells are arranged in spiral bundles around the heart chambers attached to the fibrous skeleton (figure 19.12b). When the atria contract, they compress the wall of the chambers inward to move the blood into the ventricles. When the ventricles contract, the action is similar to the wringing of a mop that begins at the apex of the heart and compresses superiorly, moving the blood into the great arterial trunks.

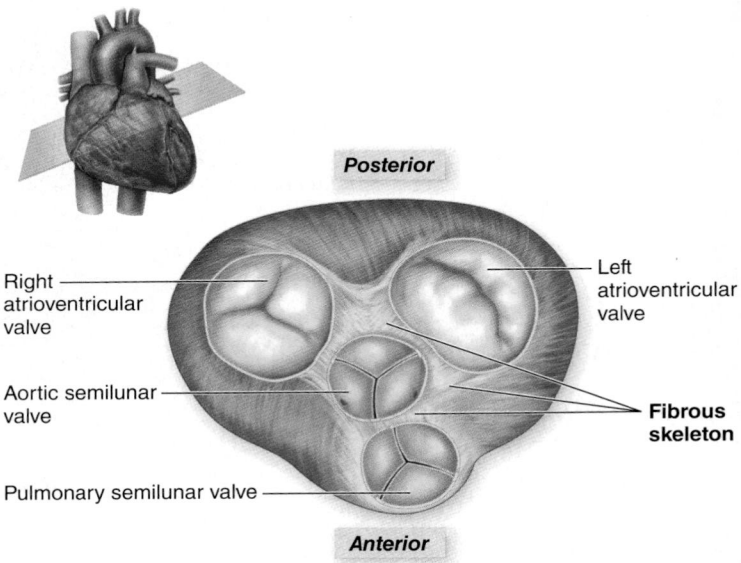

Posterior

Right atrioventricular valve

Left atrioventricular valve

Aortic semilunar valve

Fibrous skeleton

Pulmonary semilunar valve

Anterior

(a)

Contraction of bundles:
→ Narrows heart
→ Shortens heart

Cardiac muscle bundles

Spiral arrangement of cardiac muscle

(b)

Figure 19.12 Fibrous Skeleton of the Heart. (a) The fibrous skeleton is composed of dense irregular connective tissue that provides both mechanical support and electrical insulation within the heart. Shown in superior view, its structural support of heart valves is especially evident. (b) Diagram and photo of spiral pattern of cardiac muscle attached to the fibrous skeleton.

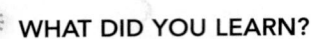

WHAT DID YOU LEARN?

12 Which function of the fibrous skeleton allows the atria to contract separately from the ventricles?

cate distribution system called the **coronary circulation** handles the task (figure 19.13). The vessels that transport oxygenated blood to the wall of the heart are called coronary arteries, whereas coronary veins transport deoxygenated blood away from the heart wall.

19.4 Coronary Vessels: Blood Supply of the Heart Wall

Although the heart continuously pumps blood through its chambers, it cannot absorb the oxygen and nutrients it requires from this blood. The diffusion of oxygen and nutrients at the needed rates through the thick wall of the heart is not possible; instead, an intri-

19.4a Coronary Arteries

LEARNING OBJECTIVES

1. Identify the coronary arteries, and describe the specific areas of the heart supplied by their major branches.

2. Explain the significance of coronary arteries as functional end arteries.

3. Describe blood flow through the coronary arteries.

(a) Coronary arteries

(b) Coronary veins

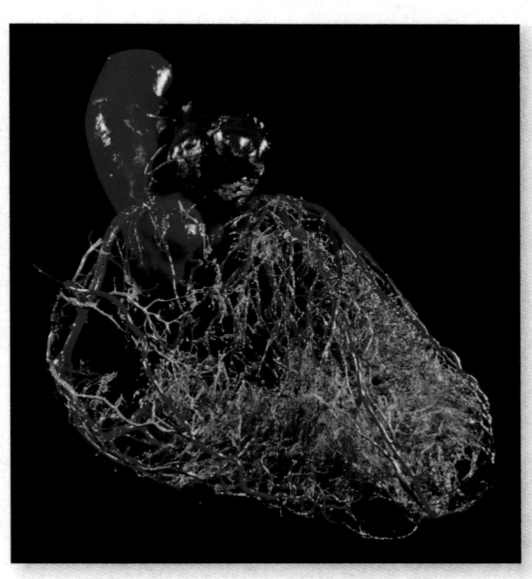

(c) Polymer cast of coronary vessels

Figure 19.13 Coronary Circulation. Diagram of the (*a*) anterior view of coronary arteries that transport blood to cardiac muscle tissue and (*b*) coronary veins that transport blood from cardiac muscle tissue. (*c*) Photo of polymer cast of coronary vessels. AP|R

Right and **left coronary arteries** travel within the coronary sulcus of the heart to supply the heart wall (figure 19.13a). These arteries are the first and only branches of the ascending aorta and originate immediately superior to the aortic semilunar valve.

The right coronary artery typically branches into the **right marginal artery** to supply the right border of the heart, and the **posterior interventricular artery** to supply the posterior surface of both the left and right ventricles. The left coronary artery typically branches into the **circumflex** (ser'kum-fleks; around, *flexus* = to bend) **artery** to supply the left atrium and ventricle, and the **anterior interventricular artery** (also called the *left anterior descending artery*) to supply the anterior surface of both ventricles and most of the interventricular septum. However, this arterial pattern can vary greatly among individuals. Note that the anterior interventricular artery is nicknamed the 'widowmaker', because if this artery becomes occluded, there is a very high risk of a fatal heart attack and make a 'widow' of the spouse.

Functional End Arteries

Some arteries may share connections, called arterial **anastomoses** (see section 20.1e). Other arteries terminate in capillary beds only, and are called **end arteries.** The left and right coronary arteries are considered **functional end arteries** because, although these coronary arteries have anastomoses, if one of the arteries becomes blocked these anastomoses are too tiny to shunt sufficient blood from one artery to the other. For example, if a branch of the left coronary artery becomes blocked, as may happen with coronary artery disease, the right coronary artery cannot shunt enough blood to the part of the heart supplied by this occluded branch. As a result, the part of the heart wall that was supplied by the left coronary artery branch will die due to lack of blood flow to the tissue.

Blood Flow

Coronary arterial blood flow to the heart wall is intermittent. This occurs because coronary vessels are patent when the heart is relaxed and blood flow is possible. However, coronary vessels are compressed when the heart contracts, temporarily interrupting blood flow. Thus, blood flow to the heart wall is not a steady stream; it is impeded and then flows, as the heart rhythmically contracts and relaxes.

 WHAT DO YOU THINK?

2   What happens to the length of time the coronary arteries are compressed when a heart beats at a faster rate, such as during exercise?

 WHAT DID YOU LEARN?

13   What areas of the heart are deprived of blood when there is a blockage in the posterior interventricular artery?

19.4b Coronary Veins

 LEARNING OBJECTIVE

4. Identify the coronary veins, and describe the specific areas of the heart drained by their major branches.

Venous return occurs through one of several cardiac veins (figure 19.13b). These include the **great cardiac vein** within the anterior interventricular sulcus, positioned alongside the anterior interventricular artery; the **middle cardiac vein** within the posterior interventricular sulcus, positioned alongside the posterior interventricular artery; and a **small cardiac vein** that travels alongside the right marginal artery. These cardiac veins all drain into the **coronary sinus,** a large vein that lies within the posterior aspect of the coronary sulcus. The coronary sinus collects venous blood and drains deoxygenated blood from the heart wall directly into the right atrium of the heart.

 WHAT DID YOU LEARN?

14 What is the function of the coronary sinus?

19.5 Anatomic Structures Controlling Heart Activity

The heart pumps blood continuously and depends upon rhythmic stimulation of cardiac muscle cells. Precise electrical events are orchestrated by the heart's conduction system, beginning with stimulation by the "*pacemaker*" and then transmission of an action potential by specialized conduction fibers of the heart to ensure that the atria are stimulated to contract prior to the ventricles. These events are influenced by the activity of the autonomic nervous system.

19.5a The Heart's Conduction System

 LEARNING OBJECTIVE

1. Identify and locate the components of the heart's conduction system.

Specialized cardiac muscle cells are found within the heart and are collectively called the heart's **conduction system (figure 19.14a)**. These distinct cardiac cells do not contract, but rather they initiate and conduct electrical signals. The conduction system includes the following structures:

- The **sinoatrial** (sī′nō-ā′trē-ăl) **(SA) node** is located in the posterior wall of the right atrium, adjacent to the entrance of the superior vena cava. The cells here initiate the heartbeat and are commonly referred to as the "pacemaker" of the heart.
- The **atrioventricular (AV) node** is located in the floor of the right atrium between the right AV valve and the opening for the coronary sinus.
- The **atrioventricular (AV) bundle** (*bundle of His*) extends from the AV node into and through the interventricular septum. It divides into **left** and **right bundles.**
- The **Purkinje** (pŭr-kin′jē) **fibers** extend from the left and right bundles from the apex of the heart and then continue through the walls of the ventricles.

 WHAT DID YOU LEARN?

15 Why is the SA node referred to as the pacemaker?

19.5b Innervation of the Heart

LEARNING OBJECTIVE

2. Compare and contrast parasympathetic and sympathetic innervation to the heart.

While the heart rate is initiated by the SA node, both heart rate and the strength of contraction are regulated by the autonomic nervous system. Parasympathetic and sympathetic pathways extend from the **cardiac center** within the medulla oblongata to the heart (see section 13.5c). This center houses both the cardioaccelerary and cardioinhibitory centers (figure 19.14b). The innervation from this center does not initiate the heartbeat; it merely modifies cardiac activity.

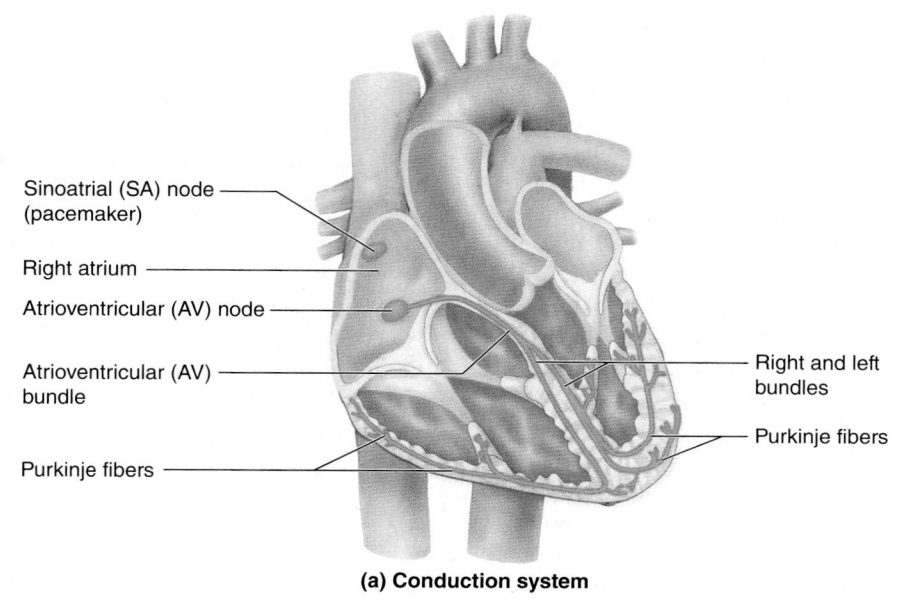

Sinoatrial (SA) node (pacemaker)

Right atrium

Atrioventricular (AV) node

Atrioventricular (AV) bundle

Purkinje fibers

Right and left bundles

Purkinje fibers

(a) Conduction system

Sympathetic innervation	Parasympathetic innervation
Cardioacceleratory center sends nerve signals along sympathetic nerves, which results in an increase in both heart rate and force of contraction.	Cardioinhibitory center sends nerve signals along vagus nerves (CN X), which results in a decrease in heart rate.

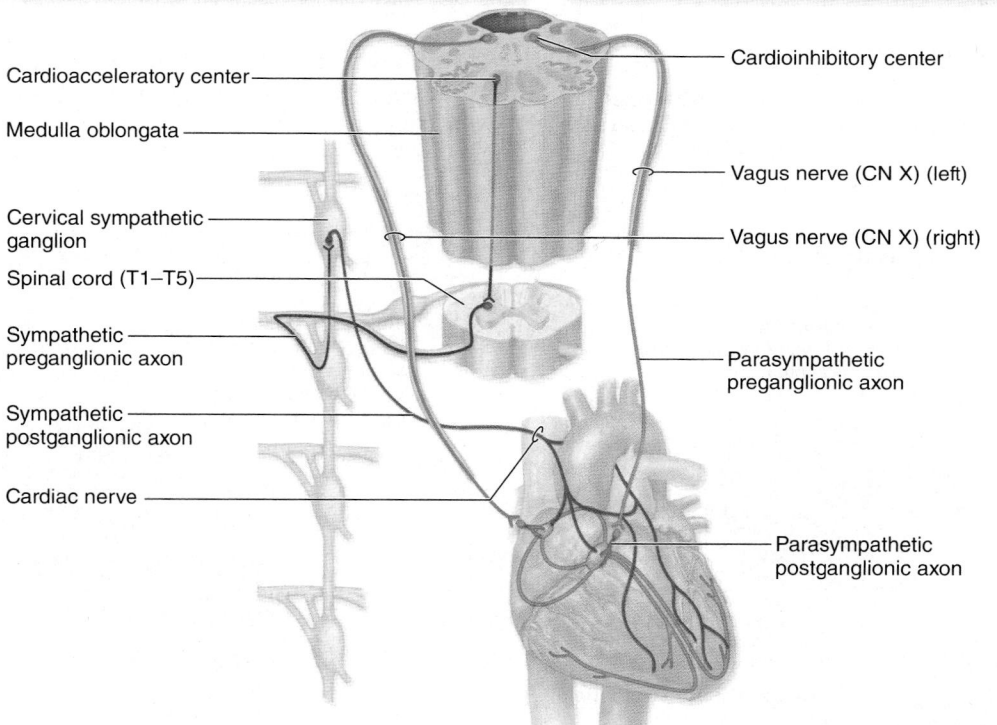

Cardioacceleratory center

Medulla oblongata

Cervical sympathetic ganglion

Spinal cord (T1–T5)

Sympathetic preganglionic axon

Sympathetic postganglionic axon

Cardiac nerve

Cardioinhibitory center

Vagus nerve (CN X) (left)

Vagus nerve (CN X) (right)

Parasympathetic preganglionic axon

Parasympathetic postganglionic axon

(b) Innervation of the heart

Figure 19.14 Anatomic Structures Controlling Heart Activity. (*a*) The heart's conduction system initiates and conducts the electrical activity to cause heart contraction. (*b*) Heart rate and force of contraction are modified by autonomic centers (cardioacceleratory and cardioinhibitory centers) in the brainstem. (*Left*) Sympathetic axons extend from the cardioacceleratory center with nerve signals carried through the cardiac nerves. (*Right*) Parasympathetic axons extend from the cardioinhibitory center with nerve signals transmitted through the vagus nerves.

Parasympathetic innervation comes from the **cardioinhibitory center** via the left and right vagus nerves (CN X). As these nerves descend into the thoracic cavity, they give off branches that supply the heart (see section 15.3). Primarily, the right vagus nerve innervates the SA node, and the left vagus nerve innervates the AV node. Parasympathetic stimulation decreases heart rate but generally has no direct effect on the force of contraction.

Sympathetic innervation arises from the **cardioacceleratory center.** Neurons within the T1–T5 segments of the spinal cord extend to the SA node, AV node, and the myocardium (see section 15.4). Stimulation by the sympathetic division increases both heart rate and the force of heart contraction. There is also some sympathetic innervation to the coronary arteries, causing dilation of these vessels to support increased blood flow to the myocardium.

Parasympathetic and sympathetic influence on heart rate are controlled by reflexes. The cardiac center receives and reflexively responds to sensory information from baroreceptors (blood pressure changes) and chemoreceptors (concerning carbon dioxide and hydrogen ion [H^+] levels) to alter parasympathetic and sympathetic nerve signals to the heart as needed to maintain homeostasis.

Atrial Reflex

One specific reflex is the **atrial reflex,** also called the *Bainbridge reflex,* which protects the heart from overfilling. It is initiated when baroreceptors (stretch receptors) in the atrial walls are stimulated by an increase in venous return. Nerve signals are increased along sensory neurons to the cardioacceleratory center, resulting in an increase in nerve signals relayed along sympathetic axons to the heart. Heart rate increases so blood moves more quickly through the heart, thus decreasing atrial stretch. Arterial reflexes associated with regulating blood pressure are described in section 20.5a.

WHAT DID YOU LEARN?

16 Which autonomic division is associated with the cardioacceleratory center in the brainstem, and how does it generally affect heart activity?

19.6 Stimulation of the Heart

The physiologic processes associated with heart contraction that ultimately result in pumping of blood throughout the cardiovascular system are organized into two major events. These are presented diagrammatically in **figure 19.15** and include the following:

- **Conduction system.** Electrical activity is initiated at the SA node, and an action potential is then transmitted through the conduction system.
- **Cardiac muscle cells.** The action potential spreads across the sarcolemma of the cardiac muscle cells, causing sarcomeres within cardiac muscle cells to contract. These events occur *twice* in cardiac muscle cells during a heartbeat, first in the cells of the atria and then in the cells of the ventricles.

Here we describe the events associated with the conduction system. The physiologic processes of cardiac muscle cells are described shortly.

19.6a Overview of Pumps and Channels of Nodal Cells

LEARNING OBJECTIVE

1. Describe the pumps and channels associated with cardiac nodal cells.

Nodal cells in the SA node are the pacemaker cells that initiate a heartbeat. These cells generate an action potential, and thus they have properties similar to neurons.

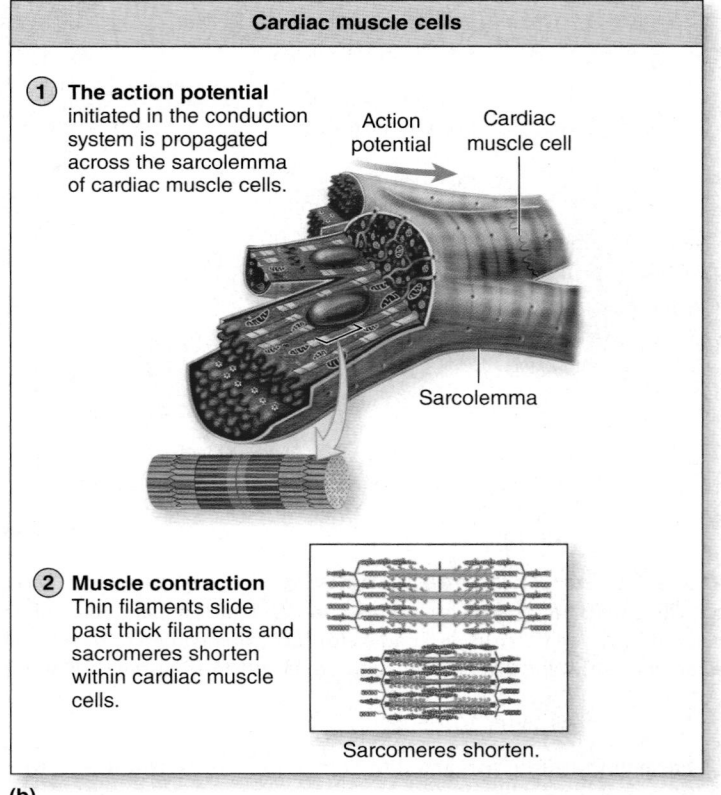

(a) Conduction system

1 Initiation
SA node initiates action potential.

Nodal cell

SA node

2 Spread of action potential
An action potential is propagated throughout the atria, the conduction system.

(b) Cardiac muscle cells

1 The action potential
initiated in the conduction system is propagated across the sarcolemma of cardiac muscle cells.

Action potential

Cardiac muscle cell

Sarcolemma

2 Muscle contraction
Thin filaments slide past thick filaments and sarcomeres shorten within cardiac muscle cells.

Sarcomeres shorten.

Figure 19.15 Physiologic Processes Associated with Heart Contraction. The two physiologic processes required for heart contraction occur in the conduction system and in cardiac muscle cells. (*a*) The SA node of the conduction system initiates an action potential that spreads throughout the heart. (*b*) Action potentials spread along the sarcolemma of cardiac muscle cells, triggering contraction of sarcomeres within these cells. Events of cardiac muscle cells occur twice in one cycle: once in the cells of the atria and once in the cells of the ventricles.

INTEGRATE

CONCEPT CONNECTION

Nodal cells and the conduction system of the heart have properties similar to neurons: Both establish and maintain a resting membrane potential and conduct action potentials. Neurons are discussed in detail in chapter 12.

Nodal cells, like neurons, have sodium-potassium (Na^+/K^+) pumps, as well as sodium ion (Na^+) leak channels and potassium ion (K^+) leak channels to establish and maintain a **resting membrane potential (RMP)** with a greater concentration of Na^+ outside the nodal cells and a greater concentration of K^+ inside (see section 12.7b). The RMP value of nodal cells, however, is -60 millivolts (mV) (in comparison to -70 mV for neurons). Nodal cells also contain calcium ion (Ca^{2+}) pumps that create a Ca^{2+} concentration gradient with more Ca^{2+} outside the cell than inside.

Additionally, nodal cells contain specific voltage-gated channels, including slow voltage-gated Na^+ channels, fast voltage-gated Ca^{2+} channels, and voltage-gated K^+ channels (**figure 19.16a**).

WHAT DID YOU LEARN?

17 What is the resting membrane potential value of nodal cells?

19.6b Electrical Events at the SA Node: Initiation of the Action Potential

LEARNING OBJECTIVES

2. Define autorhythmicity.

3. Describe the steps for SA nodal cells to spontaneously depolarize and serve as the pacemaker cells.

SA nodal cells are unique in that they exhibit **autorhythmicity** (or *automaticity*), meaning that they are capable of depolarizing and firing an action potential spontaneously without any external influence. The following series of events occur within SA nodal cells, as depicted in figure 19.16b:

1 **Reaching threshold.** Slow voltage-gated Na^+ channels open (this is caused by repolarization from the previous cycle). The Na^+ flows into the nodal cells, changing the resting membrane potential from -60 mV to -40 mV, which is the **threshold** value. Notice that the threshold is reached without outside stimulation.

2 **Depolarization.** Changing of the membrane potential to the threshold triggers the opening of fast voltage-gated Ca^{2+} channels, and Ca^{2+} entry into the nodal cell causes a change in the membrane potential from -40 mV to a slightly positive membrane potential (just above 0 mV). This reversal of polarity is called **depolarization**.

3 **Repolarization.** Calcium channels close and voltage-gated K^+ channels open; K^+ flows out to change the membrane potential from a positive value to -60 mV, which is the RMP. The process of reestablishing the RMP is called **repolarization.** Repolarization triggers the reopening of slow voltage-gated Na^+ channels, and the process begins again.

This process typically takes approximately 0.8 second, at rest; this results in a resting heart rate of 75 beats per minute. Interestingly, the inherent rhythm that SA nodal cells spontaneously depolarize is at a much faster rate of approximately 100 times per minute. (This inherent rhythm is determined when excised cardiac muscle cells are placed into cell culture, without autonomic nerve innervation.) The normal resting heart rate of 75 beats per minute is due to continuous parasympathetic stimulation of the SA node by the vagus nerve. This slowing of the heart rate is called **vagal tone.**

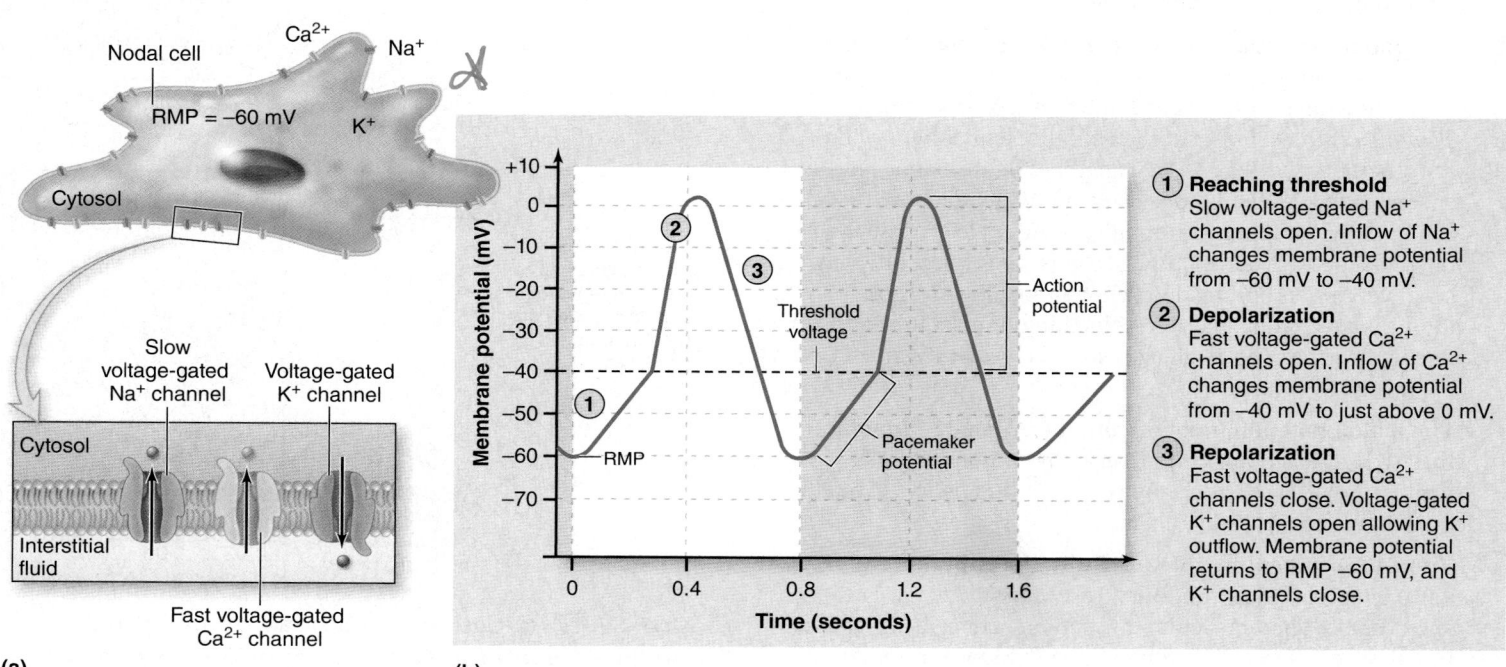

Figure 19.16 SA Node Cellular Activity. (*a*) Nodal cells have a resting membrane potential of -60 mV. Voltage-gated channels located in the plasma membrane of nodal cells open in response to changes in membrane potential. (*b*) Graph of the sequential electrical changes occurring in SA nodal (pacemaker) cells to initiate stimulation of the heart.

3 What specific type of channel is unique to cardiac nodal cells? What is the significance of this channel?

Comparison of Cardiac Nodal Cells and Neurons

Nodal cells are like neurons. However, a significant difference between them is that neurons require stimulation (in the form of neurotransmitters or a modality), whereas nodal cells do not. This is because nodal cells do not have a stable resting membrane potential. Instead the RMP gradually increases to threshold when slow Na^+ channels reopen. This ability to reach the threshold without stimulation is called a **pacemaker potential.** Another difference between neurons and nodal cells is that depolarization occurs by the entrance of Na^+ into neurons—but with entrance of Ca^{2+} into nodal cells.

WHAT DID YOU LEARN?

18 What is autorhythmicity? Describe how nodal cells function as autorhythmic cells to serve as the pacemaker of the heart.

19.6c Conduction System of the Heart: Spread of the Action Potential

LEARNING OBJECTIVE

4. Describe the spread of the action potential through the heart's conduction system.

Cardiac muscle stimulation requires that the action potential initiated by the SA node be spread through the conduction system. The sequence of events occurs as follows **(figure 19.17)**:

① **Action potential is distributed throughout both atria and is relayed to the AV node.** The action potential initiated in the SA node is spread between cardiac muscle cells in the atria by gap junctions that allow almost instantaneous excitation of all muscle cells in the atrial walls. This electrical stimulation ultimately results in cardiac muscle cells of both atria contracting at the same time.

② **The action potential is delayed at the AV node.** AV nodal cells have both smaller fiber diameters and fewer numbers of gap junctions—thus, they exhibit characteristics that *slow the conduction rate* of the action potential by serving as "a bottleneck." This is facilitated by the insulating characteristics of the fibrous skeleton, which only allow the action potential to move through the AV node. The delay in conduction (about 100 milliseconds, or 0.1 second) may seem very brief, but it is long enough to allow the atria to finish contracting and force blood into the ventricles to complete ventricular filling before the ventricles are stimulated to contract.

③ **The action potential travels from the AV node through the AV bundle to purkinje fibers.** The action potential spreads from the AV node along the AV bundle to the bundle branches to the Purkinje fibers.

④ **The action potential spreads throughout both ventricles via gap junctions.** The action potential is then spread between ventricular cardiac muscle cells by gap junctions that allow the almost simultaneous stimulation of the cardiac muscle cells in the ventricular walls. Generally, these cells begin to contract within 120 to 200 milliseconds after the firing of the SA nodal cells.

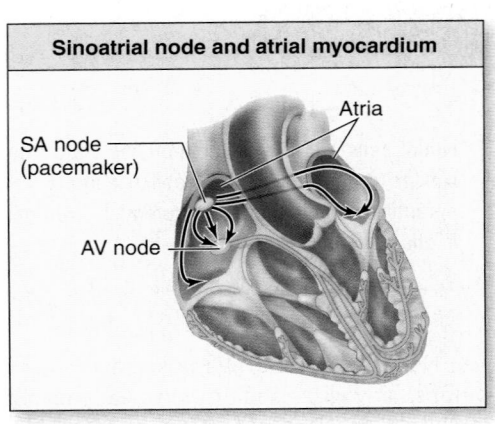

① An action potential is generated at the sinoatrial (SA) node. It spreads via gap junctions between cardiac muscle cells throughout the atria to the atrioventricular (AV) node.

Sinoatrial node and atrial myocardium

Atria
SA node (pacemaker)
AV node

② The action potential is delayed at the AV node before it passes to the AV bundle within the interventricular septum.

Atrioventricular (AV) node

AV node
AV bundle

③ The AV bundle conducts the action potential along the left and right bundle branches to the Purkinje fibers.

Bundle branches and Purkinje fibers

AV bundle
Left and right bundle branches
Purkinje fibers

④ The action potential is spread via gap junctions between cardiac muscle cells throughout the ventricles.

Ventricular myocardium

Purkinje fibers
Ventricles

Figure 19.17 Initiation and Spread of an Action Potential Through the Cardiac Conduction System. The initiation and spread of an action potential begins at the SA node and is propagated through the cardiac conduction system. The average rate at rest is one per 0.8 second. AP|R

Specialized Features Associated with Ventricles

The efficient functioning of the ventricles requires that there be a coordination of contraction that includes the following features:

- Purkinje fibers are larger in diameter than other cardiac conduction fibers, so action potential propagation is extremely rapid through ventricular cells and then spreads immediately throughout the ventricular myocardium. Thus, the cardiac muscle cells of both ventricles contract at the same time.

- Papillary muscles within the ventricles are stimulated to contract immediately. These muscles anchor the chordae tendineae to the AV valve cusps; they tighten the relaxed cords and cause them to start to pull on the AV valve cusps just prior to the increase in pressure within the ventricles.

Thus, the valves are "braced" and better able to prevent backflow of blood into the atria.

- The stimulation of the ventricles begins at the apex of the heart. This feature ensures that blood is efficiently ejected superiorly toward the arterial trunks.

 WHAT DID YOU LEARN?

19 What is the path of an action potential through the conduction system of the heart?

20 What anatomic feature(s) slows the conduction rate of the action potential as it passes through the AV node? What is the function of this delay?

19.7 Cardiac Muscle Cells

Two significant and interrelated events occur within cardiac muscle cells following their stimulation by the conduction system. These include propagation of an action potential at the sarcolemma and contraction of sarcomeres within the cardiac muscle cells. Remember that the events of cardiac muscle cells occur twice: first in the cardiac muscle cells of the atria, and then in the cardiac muscle cells of the ventricles.

19.7a Overview of Pumps and Channels Within Cardiac Muscle Cells

LEARNING OBJECTIVE

1. Describe the pumps and channels within cardiac muscle cells.

Conduction of an action potential along the sarcolemma of cardiac muscles cells requires various types of pumps and channels within the sarcolemma, which are first described.

The sarcolemma of cardiac muscle cells, like nodal cells, has Na^+/K^+ pumps, as well as Na^+ leak channels and K^+ leak channels to establish and maintain a resting membrane potential with a greater concentration of Na⁺ outside the nodal cells and a greater concentration of K⁺ inside. The RMP value of cardiac muscle cells, however, is -90 millivolts (mV) (in comparison to -60 mV for nodal cells). Cardiac muscle cells also contain Ca^{2+} pumps that form a Ca^{2+} concentration gradient with more Ca^{2+} outside the cell than inside.

The sarcolemma of cardiac muscle cells have fast voltage-gated Na⁺ channels that participate in depolarization at the membrane, and K⁺ voltage-gated channels in the sarcolemma that participate in repolarization of the membrane. Additionally, cardiac cells have slow voltage-gated Ca^{2+} channels within the sarcolemma. Slow voltage-gated Ca^{2+} channels, when open, allow Ca^{2+} into the cell (figure 19.18a). The movement of Ca^{2+} is significant in the normal function of cardiac muscle cells, as we will describe shortly.

WHAT DID YOU LEARN?

21 In which direction does Ca^{2+} move in response to the opening of voltage-gated Ca^{2+} channels: into or out of the cardiac muscle cells?

19.7b Electrical and Mechanical Events of Cardiac Muscle Cells

LEARNING OBJECTIVES

2. List the electrical events of an action potential that occur at the sarcolemma.

3. Briefly summarize the mechanical events of muscle contraction.

As the heart contracts, we can distinguish certain electrical and mechanical events.

Electrical Events

Electrical events of cardiac muscle occur as follows (figure 19.18b):

1 **Depolarization.** An action potential transmitted through the conduction system (or via gap junctions) triggers the opening of fast voltage-gated Na⁺ channels in the sarcolemma.

Sodium ion enters the cardiac muscle cell, causing depolarization. The resting membrane potential changes from -90 mV to $+30$ mV. Voltage-gated Na⁺ channels close to inactivated state.

2 **Plateau.** Depolarization triggers the opening of voltage-gated K⁺ channels, and K⁺ leaves the cardiac muscle cells. There is a slight change in the membrane potential. Almost immediately, slow voltage-gated Ca^{2+} channels in the sarcolemma also open, and Ca^{2+} enters from the interstitial fluid into the cardiac muscle cells. The entering of Ca^{2+} stimulates the sarcoplasmic reticulum to release more Ca^{2+} (more than 80% of the Ca^{2+} is released from the SR). The exit of positively charged K⁺ from the sarcoplasm and the simultaneous entrance of positively charged Ca^{2+} into the sarcoplasm results in no electrical change at the sarcolemma. Thus, the sarcolemma of the cardiac muscle cell remains in a "depolarized state." This "leveling off" is referred to as the **plateau.**

3 **Repolarization.** Voltage-gated Ca^{2+} channels then close, and K⁺ channels remain open to complete repolarization as K⁺ exits the cardiac muscle cell. The membrane potential reverses, and the resting membrane potential of -90 mV is reestablished. This allows a muscle cell to propagate a new action potential when the cardiac muscle is stimulated again.

Mechanical Events (Crossbridge Cycling)

The entry of Ca^{2+} into the sarcoplasm from both the interstitial fluid and SR (as described in step 2) initiates the internal mechanical events of muscle contraction. Calcium ions now bind to troponin to begin crossbridge cycling within a sarcomere, similar to the way in which skeletal muscle contracts (see section 10.3).

The closing of voltage-gated Ca^{2+} channels (as described in step 3), reuptake of Ca^{2+} into the sarcoplasmic reticulum, and removal of Ca^{2+} from the cell by plasma membrane pumps decrease calcium levels in the sarcoplasm. Calcium is released from troponin with the subsequent decrease in crossbridges between the thin and thick filaments. Sarcomeres return to their resting length as the cardiac muscle cell now relaxes.

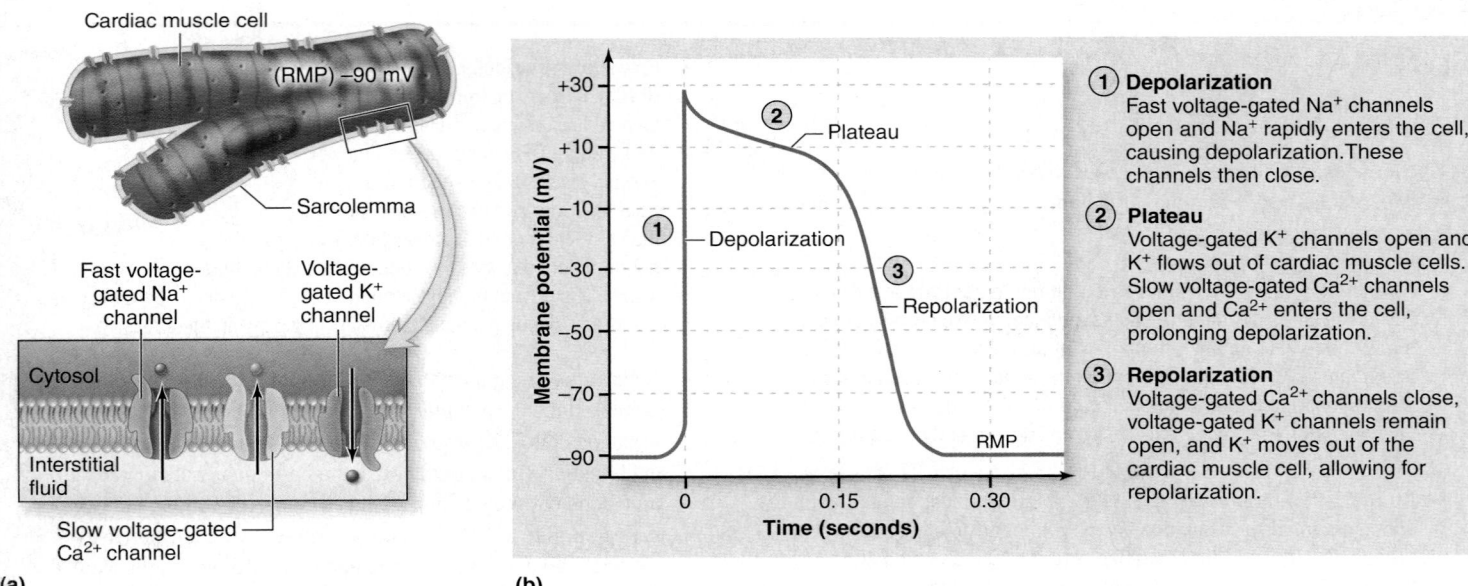

Figure 19.18 Electrical Events of Cardiac Muscle Cells. (a) Cardiac muscle cells have a resting membrane of -90 mV. Voltage-gated channels in the sarcolemma open in response to changes in membrane potential. (b) Graph of the sequential electrical events of an action potential at the sarcolemma of cardiac muscle cells.

WHAT DO YOU THINK?

④ Calcium channel–blocking drugs are sometimes given to patients with heart problems. If a patient is given a Ca^{2+} channel blocker, how will this affect both heart rate and force of contraction? Explain.

WHAT DID YOU LEARN?

㉒ What three electrical events occur at the sarcolemma of cardiac muscle cells? Explain each event.

19.7c Repolarization and the Refractory Period

✔️ **LEARNING OBJECTIVES**

4. Define the refractory period.

5. Explain the significance of the plateau phase.

Recall from section 10.3b that the time between depolarization and repolarization when the muscle cannot be restimulated to contract is called the **refractory period.** Both cardiac muscle cells and skeletal muscle fibers exhibit an absolute refractory period prior to their repolarization.

Figure 19.19 is a comparison of action potentials at the sarcolemma, change in muscle tension, and the refractory period for both skeletal and cardiac muscle. Examine the two graphs, and notice that in both skeletal muscle fibers and cardiac muscle cells the action potential (blue line on graph) is composed of depolarization and repolarization, and muscle tension (red line on the graph) involves muscle contraction and relaxation. Notice also that the action potential occurs prior to muscle contraction in both muscle types, and there is a latent time that coincides with propagation of depolarization along the sarcolemma and into the T-tubule prior to

the subsequent release of Ca^{2+} to initiate crossbridge cycling within the muscle cell to cause muscle contraction.

One significant difference is exhibited between the action potential of skeletal muscle fibers and that of cardiac muscle cells: In skeletal muscle fibers, repolarization occurs immediately following depolarization, and the refractory period is approximately 1 to 2 milliseconds (with muscle contraction occurring over 15 to 100 milliseconds). This difference allows skeletal muscle to be restimulated to contract prior to its complete relaxation, making a sustained contraction or **tetany** possible. In comparison, a distinct, extended plateau occurs in the action potential in cardiac muscle cells, with a refractory period of 250 milliseconds (with muscle contraction occurring in about 200 milliseconds).

 WHAT DO YOU THINK?

⑤ What would you predict is the function of the plateau in cardiac muscle cells?

Remember that a muscle cannot be stimulated to contract again until the sarcolemma has repolarized and reestablished the RMP. The plateau extends the refractory period and delays the repolarization of the cardiac muscle cells at the sarcolemma. This allows time for the sarcomeres of cardiac muscle within the heart chamber wall to fully contract and relax before being stimulated again. Without the plateau, sarcomeres might be stimulated so quickly that they would contract and not relax and instead would experience a sustained contraction—this would be similar to a "pump ceasing or locking up." Thus, the plateau allows the heart chambers to contract and relax to continue their pumping action.

 WHAT DID YOU LEARN?

㉓ What is the significance of the extended absolute refractory period in cardiac muscle?

(a) Skeletal muscle

(b) Cardiac muscle

Figure 19.19 Comparison of Electrical and Mechanical Events in Skeletal Muscle Cells and Cardiac Muscle Cells. The electrical changes associated with an action potential propagated along the sarcolemma and the mechanical changes associated with generating muscle tension when a muscle contracts is shown for (a) skeletal muscle and (b) cardiac muscle. The extended refractory period in cardiac muscle cells allows time for cardiac muscle to contract and relax before being stimulated again. Thus, a sustained contraction (tetany) is prevented.

19.7d The ECG Recording

LEARNING OBJECTIVE

6. Identify the components of an ECG recording.

Electrical changes within the heart can be detected during a routine physical examination using monitoring electrodes attached to the skin—usually at the wrists, ankles, and six separate locations on the chest. The electrical signals are collected and charted as an **electrocardiogram** (ē-lek-trō-kar′dē-ō-gram; *gramma* = drawing), also called an **ECG** or **EKG**. When readings from the different electrodes are compared, they collectively provide an accurate, comprehensive assessment of the electrical changes of the heart.

Waves and Segments

An ECG provides a composite tracing of all cardiac action potentials generated by myocardial cells. A typical ECG tracing for one heart cycle has three principal deflections: a P wave above the baseline, a QRS complex that begins (Q) and ends (S) with small downward deflections from the baseline and has a large deflection (R) above the baseline, and a T wave above the baseline **(figure 19.20)**. These waves indicate the electrical changes associated with depolarization and repolarization within specific heart regions:

1. The **P wave** reflects electrical changes of *atrial depolarization* that originates in the SA node. An event that typically lasts 0.08 to 0.1 second.
2. The **QRS complex,** which usually lasts between 0.06 to 0.1 second, represents the electrical changes associated with *ventricular depolarization*. Note that the atria are simultaneously repolarizing; however, this repolarization signal is masked by the greater electrical activity of the ventricles.
3. The **T wave** is the electrical change associated with *ventricular repolarization*.

The two segments between the waves correspond with a plateau (where there is essentially no electrical change). During these time periods, the sarcomeres are shortening within the cardiac muscle cells. The **P-Q segment** is associated with the atrial plateau at the sarcolemma when the cardiac muscle cells within the atria are contracting, and the **S-T segment** is the ventricular plateau when the cardiac muscle cells within the ventricles are contracting.

(a)

(b)

Figure 19.20 The Electrocardiogram.
(*a*) A tracing of an electrocardiogram with the location of three waves, including the P wave, QRS complex, and T wave. Two segments are located between the waves and include the P-Q segment and the S-T segment. The P-R interval and Q-T interval are also shown. (*b*) A graph of electrical changes within atria and ventricles is superimposed on an ECG to help you to see the relationship of these electrical changes and their relationship to the waves of an ECG.

Figure 19.20b shows two of the graphs of the electrical changes associated with the atria and ventricles (see figure 19.18) superimposed on the ECG. Notice how the waves of an ECG reflect electrical changes—either depolarization or repolarization—and how the flat or level portions in the segments correspond to a plateau when there is no electrical change. The flat line between cycles represents when the heart is resting between beats.

Intervals

Additional characteristics of an ECG include two intervals: the P-R interval and the Q-T interval (figure 19.20a). Changes in length of an interval may reflect abnormal changes to the heart. The **P-R interval** represents the period of time from the beginning of the P wave (atrial depolarization) to the beginning of the QRS deflection (ventricular depolarization). This interval of time normally ranges from 0.12 to 0.20 second. It is the time required to transmit an action potential through the entire conduction system. P-R intervals that extend longer than 0.20 second generally indicate an impaired conduction within the ventricles, often indicating a *heart block* (see Clinical View: "Heart Blocks").

The **Q-T interval** represents the time from the beginning of the QRS (ventricular depolarization) to the end of the T wave (ventricular repolarization). This is the time required for the action potential to occur within the ventricles. This interval depends upon heart rate and ranges from 0.2 to 0.4 second. Changes in the Q-T intervals may result in a fast, irregular heart rate, which recall is called **tachyarrhythmia** (tak′ē′ă′ridh′mē-ă; tachys = speed).

An ECG is a common diagnostic tool that is used in physical exams and after surgery to detect many changes to the heart, including abnormal heart rhythms (fast, slow, arrhythmia), hypertrophy of the heart, low blood flow to the heart (ischemia), and damage to the heart from myocardial infarction or high blood pressure. Although it is a very effective tool in diagnosing many conditions, it does not detect all abnormalities. Thus, it is one of several diagnostic tools used by cardiologists and other physicians in determining a diagnosis and development of a treatment plan.

 WHAT DID YOU LEARN?

 24 What events in the heart are indicated by each of the following: P wave, QRS complex, and T wave? Identify the two segments of an ECG that reflects the plateau.

19.8 The Cardiac Cycle

A **cardiac cycle** is the inclusive changes within the heart from the initiation of one heartbeat to the start of the next. One heartbeat involves the contraction and relaxation of the heart chambers. **Systole** (sis′tō-lē) is contraction of a heart chamber, and **diastole** (dī-as′tō-lē; dilation) is relaxation of a heart chamber.

19.8a Overview of the Cardiac Cycle

 LEARNING OBJECTIVES

1. Identify the two processes within the heart that occur due to pressure changes associated with the cardiac cycle.

2. List the five events of the cardiac cycle.

The alternating contraction and relaxation of both the atria and ventricles cause pressure changes within the chambers. Pressure increases during contraction and decreases during relaxation. These alternating pressure changes are responsible for two significant physiologic processes:

- Unidirectional movement of blood through the heart chambers, as blood moves along a pressure gradient (i.e., from an area of greater pressure to an area of lesser pressure)
- Opening and closing of heart valves to ensure that blood continues to move in a "forward" direction without backflow

The most important driving force to move blood through the heart, and to open and close heart valves during the cardiac cycle, is contraction and relaxation of the ventricles:

- **Ventricular contraction.** Ventricles contract and ventricular pressure rises. The one-way flow of blood occurs as both AV valves are pushed and kept closed, preventing

LEARNING STRATEGY

You may find it helpful to think of how changing ventricular pressure has opposite effects on the two sets of valves by imagining yourself in a small room with two spring-loaded doors: One is open, and the other is closed. You apply pressure to the open door and it closes, and then you apply pressure to the closed door and it opens. You then release the pressure on the two spring-loaded doors in the reverse order. What happens? Each door returns to its original position—the one that was pushed open closes, and the door pushed closed opens.

backflow of blood into each atrium, and then the semilunar valves are pushed open, forcing blood from a ventricle into an arterial trunk (aorta or pulmonary trunk).

- **Ventricular relaxation**. Ventricles relax and ventricular pressure decreases. Now, the semilunar valves close (because there is no longer pressure pushing them open), and then the AV valves open (because there is no longer pressure pushing them closed).

Five events describe the cardiac cycle: atrial systole, early ventricular systole, late ventricular systole, early ventricular diastole, and late ventricular diastole. These events are summarized in **figure 19.21**. Consider the following as you read through the description of each of the events of the cardiac cycle: (1) whether the atria and ventricles are contracted or relaxed, (2) whether the pressure in the ventricles is higher or lower than the pressure in the atria and higher or lower than in the arterial trunks (aorta and pulmonary trunk), and (3) if the AV valves and semilunar valves are opened or closed.

WHAT DID YOU LEARN?

25 Pressure changes that occur during the cardiac cycle are responsible for what two physiologic processes within the heart?

---

① Atrial systole

Chambers	Atria contract Ventricles relax
Ventricular pressure	< Atrial pressure < Arterial trunk pressure
Valves	AV valves open Semilunar valves closed

Atria contract

② Early ventricular systole

Atria relax

AV valves closed

Ventricles contract

EDV

Chambers	Atria relax Ventricles contract
Ventricular pressure	> Atrial pressure < Arterial trunk pressure
Valves	AV valves closed Semilunar valves closed

③ Late ventricular systole

SV

Semilunar valves open

Ventricles contract

Chambers	Atria relax Ventricles contract
Ventricular pressure	> Atrial pressure > Arterial trunk pressure
Valves	AV valves closed Semilunar valves open

⑤ Late ventricular diastole

AV valves open

Chambers	Atria relax Ventricles relax
Ventricular pressure	< Atrial pressure < Arterial trunk pressure
Valves	AV valves open Semilunar valves closed

④ Early ventricular diastole

Semilunar valves closed

ESV

Ventricles relax

Chambers	Atria relax Ventricles relax
Ventricular pressure	> Atrial pressure < Arterial trunk pressure
Valves	AV valves closed Semilunar valves closed

**Figure 19.21
Phases of the
Cardiac Cycle.**
Contraction and relaxation of heart chambers, changes in ventricular pressure, and opening and closing of heart valves occur during the phases of the cardiac cycle. AP|R

SV: Stroke volume
EDV: End diastolic volume
ESV: End systolic volume

19.8b Events of the Cardiac Cycle

3. Explain what is occurring in the activity of the heart when it is at rest immediately prior to atrial systole.

4. List and describe what occurs during the five events of the cardiac cycle.

Because this is a cycle, we could start at any point and describe the events. However, for orientation and convenience we begin when all chambers are at rest and the atria are just initiating the contraction phase.

As the Cardiac Cycle Begins

We can observe the following characteristics of the heart prior to atrial systole as a new round of the cardiac cycle begins.

- All four chambers are at rest.
- Blood continues to return to the right atrium through the superior vena cava, inferior vena cava, and the coronary sinus, and to the left atrium through the pulmonary veins.
- Passive filling of the ventricles is under way. No contraction of the atria is needed at this time to assist with the continual ventricular filling.
- The AV valves are open because the pressure exerted by the blood filling the atria is greater than the pressure exerted by the blood remaining in the resting ventricles.
- The semilunar valves are closed because the pressure exerted by the blood remaining in the filling ventricles is lower than the pressure exerted by the blood in the arterial trunks.

Atrial Systole

The atria are contracting and the ventricles are relaxed during **atrial systole.** Atrial systole is a brief contraction of the atrial myocardium (duration about 100 milliseconds) initiated by the SA node. This contraction moves the remainder of blood that was within each atrium into the right or left ventricle. The AV valves remain open, and the semilunar valves remain closed.

The contraction of the atria compresses the openings for the great veins. This prevents both additional blood from entering the atria from their supplying veins and backflow of blood from the atria into these veins. Ventricular filling is complete upon the termination of atrial systole. The atria enter and remain in diastole until the beginning of the next cardiac cycle.

Note that the ventricles are filled and now hold their maximum blood volume. This is appropriately called the **end-diastolic volume (EDV)** because it is the volume of blood in the ventricle at the end of rest. In a resting adult, this value is approximately 130 milliliters (mL) of blood.

Early Ventricular Systole

Early ventricular systole is the beginning of ventricular contraction. Ventricular systole is contraction of the ventricular myocardium initiated by the Purkinje fibers of the conduction system. This contraction moves blood within each ventricle into the arterial trunks (pulmonary trunk or aorta).

As pressure in the ventricles increases and exceeds pressure on the blood that is now filling the atrium, the AV valves are forced closed to prevent backflow of blood into the atria. These valves are braced by the chordae tendineae anchored to the papillary muscles. Pressure continues to rise in the ventricles; however, the semilunar valves remain closed because the pressure in the contracting ventricle is still less than pressure exerted within the attached arterial trunk.

Note that all heart valves are closed at this time—thus, no blood may enter or leave the ventricles. Cardiac muscle cells are contracting, but the volume in the ventricular chambers remains the same. Consequently, early ventricular systole is also referred to as the time of **isovolumetric** (ī′sō-vol′yū-met′rik; *iso* = same) **contraction** of the ventricles.

Late Ventricular Systole

The ventricles continue to contract during **late ventricular systole.** Now the semilunar valves are forced open because pressure on blood within the ventricles becomes greater than blood pressure in the attached arterial trunks. Blood is ejected into the trunks, and this event is termed **ventricular ejection.** The amount of blood pumped out during ventricular systole is termed the **stroke volume.** Generally, this volume is approximately 70 mL of blood.

Not all of the blood in either ventricle is ejected. The blood remaining in a ventricle at the end of systole is called the **end-systolic volume (ESV).** ESV is determined by subtracting SV from EDV: 130 mL − 70 mL = 60 mL. The AV valves stay closed, and atria remain in diastole during this phase.

Early Ventricular Diastole

Early ventricular diastole is the beginning of ventricular relaxation, and the ventricular chamber starts to expand back to its resting size. Pressure on the remaining blood in the ventricles falls below the pressure on the blood within the attached arterial trunks. Blood initially flows backward slightly within the arterial trunks but is caught in the semilunar valves, causing them to close. This closure of the semilunar valves prevents blood backflow into the ventricles. The AV valves remain closed and atria remain in diastole during early ventricular diastole.

Late Ventricular Diastole

The continuation of ventricular relaxation is **late ventricular diastole,** and it is also the start of ventricular filling. The AV valve is forced open when pressure on the blood in the relaxed but filling atrium exceeds pressure on the blood in the relaxing ventricle. Now, passive filling of the ventricle begins; it is the time when most of the ventricular filling (about 70%) occurs. The semilunar valves remain closed to prevent blood backflow from the arterial trunks into the ventricles. The atria remain in diastole during this phase.

Figure 19.22 summarizes the events of each stage of the cardiac cycle, including the electrical events that control heart contraction, as depicted on an ECG; atrial and ventricular contraction and relaxation; the pressure changes within the left atrium, left ventricle, and aorta; opening and closing of heart valves; and blood volume changes in the left ventricle.

WHAT DID YOU LEARN?

26 What is occurring during late ventricular systole?

27 What pressure changes cause the closing of the AV valves and the opening of the semilunar valves?

28 Define end-diastolic volume, end-systolic volume, and stroke volume. How are they related?

19.9 Cardiac Output

The function of the cardiovascular system is to move blood throughout the body to transport respiratory gases, nutrients, and other substances. Cardiac output is a measure of how effective the cardiovascular system is in fulfilling its function. In a healthy individual, cardiac output increases during strenuous effort or exercise to meet the additional cellular demands for oxygen and nutrients and eliminating waste products. In contrast, individuals with impaired heart function may not experience an increase in cardiac output, thus limiting their ability to engage in physically demanding activities. Here we first define cardiac output and then discuss the variables that influence it.

Figure 19.22 Changes Associated with a Cardiac Cycle. Each cardiac cycle is initiated by action potentials that spread across the atria and then the ventricles. (*a*) An ECG is a graph of the electrical changes. (*b*) Heart chambers are stimulated to contract and relax, which (*c*) causes pressure changes in the atria, ventricles, and arterial trunks. (Left atrium, left ventricle, and aorta are shown.) These pressure changes cause both the (*d*) valves to open and close and (*e*) movement of blood through the heart. (Changes in ventricular blood volume are shown.)

→ Path of blood flow

(a) ECG

Initiates contraction of ventricles

R

Initiates contraction of atria

P

Q   S

T

ECG is a graphic recording of electrical changes in the heart that initiate atrial and ventricular contraction

(b) Chambers

	①	②	③	④	⑤
Atria	Relax	Contract	Relax	Relax	Relax
Ventricles	Relax	Relax	Contract	Contract	Relax

① **Atrial systole**
Chambers: Atria contracting and ventricles relaxed.
Pressure: Ventricular pressure (blue line) < atrial pressure (green line) and < pressure in aorta (red line).
Valves: AV valves open, semilunar valves closed.
Ventricular Blood Volume: Increases slightly.

(c) Pressure in left atrium, left ventricle, and aorta

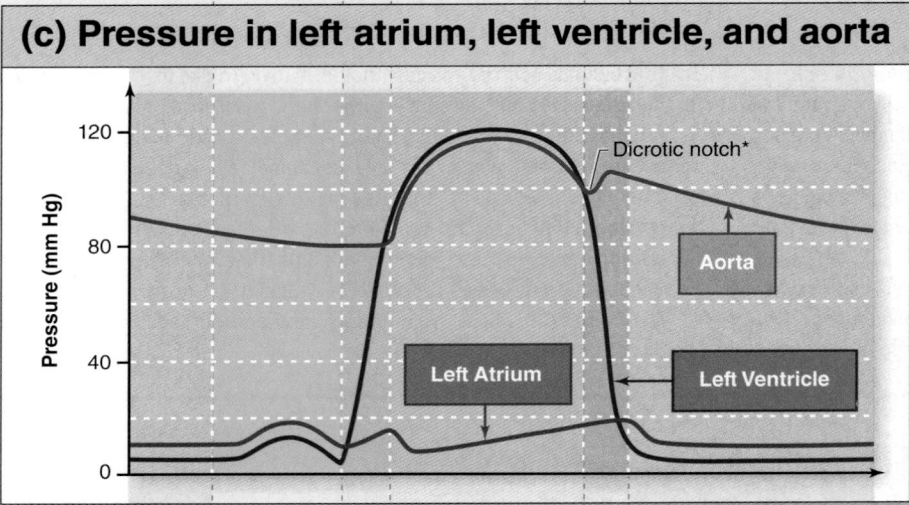

Pressure (mm Hg)

120

80

40

0

Dicrotic notch*

Aorta

Left Atrium

Left Ventricle

② **Early ventricular systole**
Chambers: Atria relaxed and ventricles contracting.
Pressure: Ventricular pressure > atrial pressure and < pressure in aorta.
Valves: AV valves closed, semilunar valves remain closed.
Ventricular Blood Volume: Remains the same (isovolumetric; notice the flat line in [e]).

③ **Late ventricular systole**
Chambers: Atria relaxed and ventricles contracting.
Pressure: Ventricular pressure > atrial pressure and > pressure in aorta.
Valves: AV valves remain closed, semilunar valves open.
Ventricular Blood Volume: Decreases (as blood is ejected).

(d) Heart valves

AV	Open	Closed	Open
Semilunar	Closed	Open	Closed

④ **Early ventricular diastole**
Chambers: Atria relaxed and ventricles relaxing.
Pressure: Ventricular pressure > atrial pressure and < pressure in aorta.
Valves: AV valves remain closed, semilunar valves closed.
Ventricular Blood Volume: Remains the same.

(e) Blood volume in left ventricle

Ventricular volume (mL)

130

100

70

End diastolic volume (EDV)

Stroke volume (SV)

End systolic volume (ESV)

0   0.2   0.4   0.6   0.8

Time (msec)

⑤ **Late ventricular diastole**
Chambers: Atria relaxed and ventricles relaxing.
Pressure: Ventricular pressure < atrial pressure and < pressure in aorta.
Valves: AV valves open, semilunar valves remain closed.
Ventricular Blood Volume: Increases (as blood flows from the atrium).

*Dicrotic notch: A temporary drop in pressure in the aorta that occurs when the aortic semilunar valve closes.

CLINICAL VIEW
Heart Sounds and Heart Murmurs

There are two normal heart sounds associated with each heartbeat that collectively form the lubb-dupp sounds. The "lubb" sound is also known as the S1 sound and represents the closing of the atrioventricular valves. The "dupp" sound is also known as the S2 sound and is the closing of the semilunar valves. These heart sounds provide clinically important information about heart activity and the action of heart valves.

The place where sounds from each AV valve and each semilunar valve may best be heard does not correspond with the location of the valve, because some overlap of valve sounds occurs near their anatomic locations:

- The aortic semilunar valve is best heard in the second intercostal space to the right of the sternum.

- The pulmonary semilunar valve is best heard in the second intercostal space to the left of the sternum.

- The right AV valve is best heard by the right side of the sternum, inferior end.

- The left AV valve is best heard near the apex of the heart (at the level of the left fifth intercostal space, about 9 centimeters from the midline of the sternum).

An abnormal heart sound, generally called a **heart murmur,** is the first indication of heart valve problems. A heart murmur is usually the result of turbulence of the blood as it passes through the heart, and may be caused by valvular leakage, decreased valve flexibility, or a misshapen valve. Sometimes heart murmurs are of little consequence, but all of them need to be evaluated to rule out a more serious heart problem. Two types of heart murmurs are valvular insufficiency and valvular stenosis.

Valvular insufficiency, also termed *valvular incompetence,* occurs when one or more of the cardiac valves leaks because the valve cusps do not close tightly enough. Inflammation or disease may cause the free edges of the valve

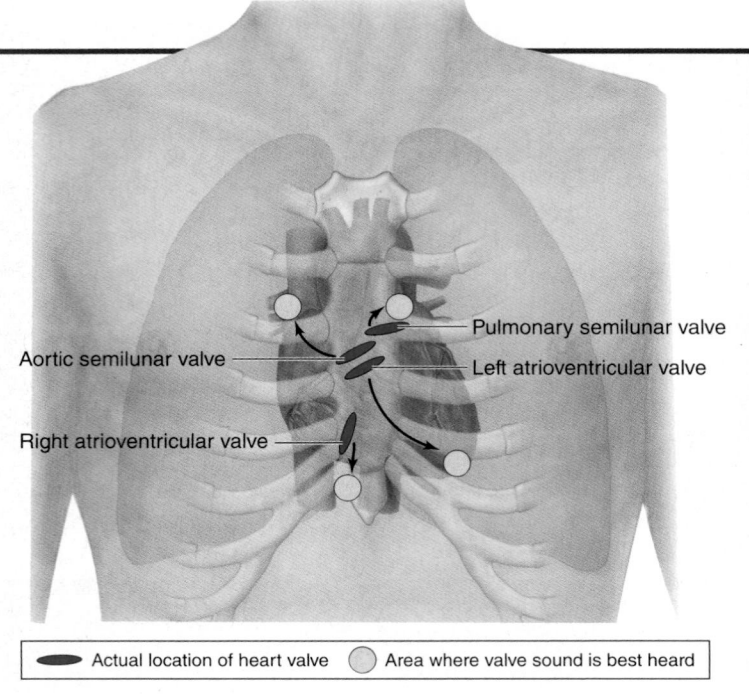

| Actual location of heart valve | Area where valve sound is best heard |

Locations of individual heart valves and the ideal listening sites for each valve are shown.

cusps to become scarred and constricted, allowing blood to regurgitate back through the valve and may cause further heart enlargement.

Valvular stenosis (ste-nō′sis; narrowing) is scarring of the valve cusps so that they become rigid or partially fused and cannot open completely. A stenotic valve is narrowed and presents resistance to the flow of blood, decreasing chamber output. Often the affected chamber undergoes hypertrophy and dilates—both conditions that may have dangerous consequences. A primary cause of valvular stenosis is **rheumatic** (rū-mat′ik) **heart disease,** which may follow a streptococcal infection of the throat.

19.9a Introduction to Cardiac Output

LEARNING OBJECTIVES

1. Define cardiac output.

2. Explain what is meant by cardiac reserve.

Cardiac output is defined as the amount of blood that is pumped by a *single* ventricle (left or right) in 1 minute and is typically expressed as liters per minute. Recall that both ventricles eject equal amounts of blood (i.e., balanced ventricular output), so either the left or right ventricle can be used.

Cardiac output is determined by heart rate and stroke volume. **Heart rate (HR)** is the number of beats per minute (bpm). **Stroke volume (SV)** is the volume of blood ejected during one beat and is expressed as milliliters per beat. Cardiac output (CO) is determined as follows:

$$HR \quad \times \quad SV \quad = \quad CO$$

HR	×	SV	=	CO
Beats per minute		mL ejected per beat		mL ejected per minute

So, for example, when a person is at rest and the HR is 75 beats per minute and SV is 70 mL per beat, then the CO is 5250 milliliters per minute (5250 mL/min) or 5.25 liters per minute (5.25 L/min).

The total volume of blood in the body is approximately 5 L (see section 18.1b). Thus, with a cardiac output of approximately 5 L per minute, the total blood volume is pumped through both the pulmonary circulation and systemic circulation every minute. This is equivalent to moving approximately 7500 L of blood daily!

Maintaining Resting Cardiac Output

The ability to maintain normal resting cardiac output is a function of both heart rate and stroke volume, and the value of one influences the value of the other. For example, individuals with a smaller heart produce a smaller stroke volume. Consequently, their resting heart rates must be higher to maintain normal resting cardiac output. This accounts for women's typically faster resting heart rate compared to men, and it also explains why infants and young children with their relatively small hearts have a faster resting heart rate than adults. Newborns, for example, typically have a resting heart rate between 120 to 160 beats per minute.

In comparison, highly trained athletes tend to have larger and stronger hearts. This is because the cardiac muscle cells of the heart wall hypertrophy in response to the additional cardiovascular demands made during strenuous effort. The larger heart generates a greater stroke volume. Thus, an athlete's normal resting cardiac output is maintained with a larger stroke volume and a lower heart rate. An example is Lance Armstrong, the seven-time winner of the Tour de France, who at the peak of his training had a resting heart rate of about 33 beats per minute.

Cardiac Reserve

An increase in both heart rate and stroke volume results in an increase in cardiac output. During physical exertion, heart rate can be accelerated to more than 170 beats per minute. Likewise, stroke volume can be increased to more than 100 mL. **Cardiac reserve** is an increase in cardiac output above its level at rest. It can be determined by subtracting cardiac output at rest from the cardiac output during exercise.

Cardiac reserve is a measure of the level and duration of physical effort in which an individual can engage. Cardiac output may be increased by about four-fold in a healthy, nonathletic individual (to approximately 20 L/min), and up to seven-fold in a highly trained athlete (to approximately 35 L/min). In comparison, individuals with a weakened heart may have little cardiac reserve and thus experience limitations in exerting themselves.

 WHAT DID YOU LEARN?

29 What are the two factors that determine cardiac output?

30 What is the cardiac output at rest and during exercise, and the cardiac reserve if (a) the heart rate is 75 beats per minute and stroke volume is 70 mL at rest, and (b) if the heart rate is 150 beats per minute and stroke volume is 100 mL during exercise?

19.9b Variables That Influence Heart Rate

 LEARNING OBJECTIVE

3. Define chronotropic agents, and describe how they affect heart rate.

Cardiac output is directly influenced by both heart rate and stroke volume. Both heart rate and stroke volume, in turn, have variables that influence each of them. Here we describe the variables that influence heart rate and then in the next section discuss the variables that influence stroke volume.

The heart rate can be altered by external factors that act on the SA node and the AV node. The primary external factors to increase and decrease heart rate come from autonomic innervation and varying levels of some hormones. These factors that change heart rate are called **chronotropic** (kron'ō-trop'ik; *chrono* = time, *tropos* = change) **agents.** Chronotropic agents alter activity of nodal cells either directly or indirectly by acting on nerves that innervate the SA node or the AV node.

Positive chronotropic agents cause an increase in heart rate and include sympathetic nerve stimulation and certain types of hormonal stimulation. Sympathetic axons release the neurotransmitter norepinephrine to act directly on the heart and cause release of epinephrine and norepinephrine from the adrenal medulla into the blood. Both norepinephrine and epinephrine bind to β_1-adrenergic receptors (see section 15.5c) of the heart. This binding initiates an intracellular pathway involving adenylate cyclase with the accompanying production of the second messenger, cAMP (see section 17.5b). Ultimately, protein kinase enzymes phosphorylate Ca^{2+} channels, causing them to open. Positively charged Ca^{2+} enters the nodal cells, and nodal cells reach threshold more quickly, increasing the firing rate of the SA node. Sympathetic stimulation of AV node also increases calcium influx into these cells. The delay in the AV node is decreased, and the conduction rate is increased. Thus, heart rate increases.

Thyroid hormone is also a positive chronotropic agent because it makes nodal cells more responsive to norepinephrine and epinephrine by increasing the number of β_1-adrenergic receptors. Additionally, caffeine (which inhibits cAMP breakdown) increases heart rate. You may have, for example, observed an increase in your heart rate after drinking a cup of coffee. Certain drugs such as nicotine (which stimulates release of norepinephrine) and cocaine (that inhibits reuptake of norepinephrine) also increase heart rate. In fact, large doses of cocaine can result in both a fast and arrhythmic (erratic) heartbeat or tachyarrhythmia, which can be fatal.

In contrast, **negative chronotropic agents** decrease heart rate. Parasympathetic innervation is one of the most important. Parasympathetic axons release acetylcholine that binds to voltage-gated K^+ channels of nodal cells. These channels open, and K^+ moves down its concentration gradient to exit the cells. This loss of positive ion causes hyperpolarization (membrane potential becomes more negative) of nodal cells, and it takes a longer period of time for these cells to reach threshold—thus, the heart rate is slower. Beta-blocker drugs (which interfere with binding of norepinephrine and epinephrine to beta receptors) are another type of negative chronotropic agents that are used to treat high blood pressure.

WHAT DID YOU LEARN?

31 Distinguish the effect of a positive chronotropic agent and a negative chronotropic agent on heart rate, and give examples of each.

32 Explain how movement of Ca^{2+} increases heart rate, whereas movement of K^+ decreases heart rate.

19.9c Variables That Influence Stroke Volume

LEARNING OBJECTIVES

4. List the three variables that may influence stroke volume.

5. Define each of the three variables, and describe the factors that influence each one and how it affects stroke volume.

Stroke volume is the volume of blood pumped per beat and is influenced by several variables (figure 19.23). These include (1) venous return, which is the amount of blood returned to the heart; (2) inotropic agents, which are external factors that alter the force of contraction of the myocardium; and (3) afterload, which is the resistance in the arteries to the ejection of blood from the heart.

Venous Return

Venous return is the volume of blood returned to the heart via the great veins and is directly related to stroke volume. Venous return determines the amount of blood in the ventricle at the end of rest immediately prior to contraction (i.e., end-diastolic volume, or EDV). This volume of blood, in turn, determines the preload on the heart. **Preload** is stretch of the heart wall due to "the load to which a cardiac muscle is subjected before shortening."

The direct relationship of venous return on stroke volume can be explained by the **Frank-Starling law** of the heart (or simply *Starling's law*). This law essentially states that as the volume of blood entering the heart increases, there is greater stretch of the heart wall (or preload). This results in greater overlap of the thick and thin filaments in the sarcomeres of the cardiac muscle cells composing the myocardium, allowing formation of greater numbers of crossbridges. (Recall that cardiac muscle does not exhibit maximum overlap of thin and thick filaments at rest.) Consequently, a more forceful ventricular contraction is generated, and stroke volume increases.

In contrast, as venous return decreases, there is less stretch of the heart wall (smaller preload), and this results in less overlap of the thick and thin filaments and fewer crossbridges form. Consequently, a less forceful ventricular contraction is generated, and stroke volume decreases.

So, what causes venous return, and thus preload, to either increase or decrease? Venous return is increased by either an increase in venous pressure or an increase in time to fill, and venous return may be decreased by a decrease in either of these two factors. You might find the analogy of filling a balloon helpful. The water pressure and the time to fill the balloon will determine how much water you can add to the balloon in a given period of time.

Venous return increases, for example, during exercise because of greater venous pressure. Veins are "squeezed" by skeletal muscles, which help return blood to the heart (see section 20.4a). Greater muscular movement increases the action of the skeletal muscle pump. During exercise, venous return can approximately double in comparison to its rate at rest. Venous return also increases with a slower heart rate. The slower heart rate allows a greater amount of time for blood to enter the heart. This is most noticeable in high-caliber athletes that have a very low resting heart rate.

In comparison, low blood volume (e.g., due to hemorrhage) or an abnormally high heart rate, decreases venous return. The result is a smaller end diastolic volume and preload, and a smaller stroke volume.

Balanced ventricular output is primarily a function of the inherent ability of the heart to contract more forcefully in response to increased venous return. Consider, for example, that when you first start to exercise venous return into the right side of the heart increases, causing it to contract more forcefully and increasing stroke volume. Increased amount of blood then moves through the pulmonary circulation and returns to the left ventricle. The left ventricle, in turn, will experience greater stretch of its chamber wall and will contract more forcefully.

Inotropic Agents

Stroke volume, like heart rate, is altered by external factors. The primary external factors to increase and decrease heart rate come from autonomic innervation and varying levels of some hormones. These factors that change stroke volume are called **inotropic** (in′ō-trop′ik; *ino* = fiber) **agents.** Inotropic agents alter **contractility,** which is the force of contraction at a given stretch of the cardiac cells. An increase or decrease in the force of contraction is generally due to a change in the available Ca^{2+} in the sarcoplasm. Changes in Ca^{2+} alter the number of crossbridges formed and thus the force of contraction generated.

A positive inotropic agent increases available Ca^{2+}, which results in formation of additional crossbridges. Positive inotropic agents include release of norepinephrine from sympathetic axons and subsequent release of epinephrine and norepinephrine from the adrenal medulla. Thyroid hormone is also a positive inotropic agent because it increases the number of receptors for epinephrine. Certain drugs (e.g., digitalis) are positive inotropic agents used to treat abnormally low cardiac output that accompanies some heart conditions (e.g., congestive heart failure).

In comparison, a negative inotropic agent decreases contractility by decreasing available Ca^{2+} and fewer numbers of crossbridges are formed. Electrolyte imbalances (see sections 25.3 and 25.6) including an increase in either K^+ or H^+ are negative inotropic agents. Certain drugs (e.g., nifedipine, a Ca^{2+} channel–blocking drug) are negative inotropic agents and are given to decrease cardiac output, typically in an effort to treat high blood pressure.

Afterload

Afterload is the resistance in arteries to the ejection of blood by the ventricles, and it represents the pressure that must be exceeded before blood is ejected from the chamber. Afterload generally becomes a consideration only in older individuals. As we age, arteries typically develop atherosclerosis, a condition in which

(a) Venous return

Volume of blood returned to the heart per unit

Increased venous return (occurs with greater venous pressure or slower heart rate)

↓

Increases stretch of the heart wall (preload), which results in greater overlap of thick and thin filaments within the sarcomeres of the myocardium

↓

Additional crossbridges form, and ventricles contract with greater force

↓

Stroke volume increases

The opposite is seen with smaller venous return (e.g., occurs with hemorrhage or extremely rapid heart rate)

(c) Afterload

Resistance in arteries to ejection of blood

Atherosclerosis, which is deposition of plaque on the inner lining of arteries, is typically only a factor as we age

↓

Arteries become more narrow in diameter

↓

Increases the resistance to pump blood into the arteries

↓

Stroke volume decreases

(b) Inotropic agents

Substances that act on the myocardium to alter contractility

Positive inotropic agents (e.g., stimulation by sympathetic nervous system)

↓

Increased Ca^{2+} levels in the sarcoplasm results in greater binding of Ca^{2+} to troponin of thin filaments within sarcomeres of the myocardium

↓

Additional crossbridges form, and ventricles contract with greater force

↓

Stroke volume increases

The opposite is seen with negative inotropic agents (e.g., calcium channel blockers)

Figure 19.23 Variables That Influence Stroke Volume. Three variables influence stroke volume, which is the amount of blood ejected from the heart per beat. These include (*a*) venous return, (*b*) inotropic agents, and (*c*) afterload.

plaque accumulates on the inner linings of a blood vessel. The smaller arterial lumen exerts greater resistance to the movement of blood into the arterial trunks, and stroke volume decreases.

WHAT DID YOU LEARN?

33 Which of the following increases stroke volume: (a) increased venous return, (b) increased Ca^{2+} in sarcoplasm, or (c) afterload? Explain.

19.9d Variables That Influence Cardiac Output

LEARNING OBJECTIVE

6. Summarize the variables that influence cardiac output.

The factors that influence heart rate and stroke volume and ultimately cardiac output are integrated in a flowchart in **figure 19.24**. Note the following:

- **Heart rate.** An increase or decrease in heart rate is dependent upon chronotropic agents that influence the *conduction*

INTEGRATE

CLINICAL VIEW

Bradycardia and Tachycardia

A persistently low resting heart rate in adults below 60 beats per minute is called **bradycardia**. Bradycardia is considered a normal change in highly trained athletes who engage in a sustained aerobic exercise program. Abnormal conditions that cause bradycardia include hypothyroidism, electrolyte imbalances, and congestive heart failure. In comparison, a persistently high resting heart rate in adults above 100 beats per minute is called **tachycardia**. Tachycardia is caused by abnormal conditions such as heart disease, fever, or anxiety.

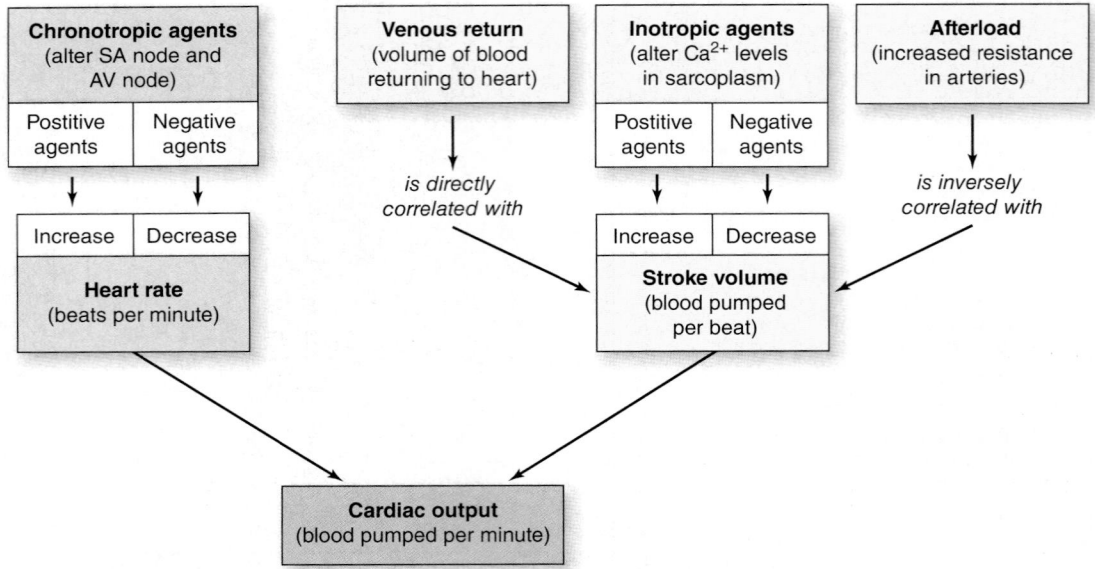

Figure 19.24 Factors Affecting Cardiac Output. Cardiac output is influenced by both heart rate and stroke volume. Heart rate is altered by stimulation of the SA node and the AV node. Stroke volume is altered by changes to the myocardium, which include an increase or decrease in stretch of the heart wall (preload), the amount of Ca^{2+} in the sarcoplasm caused by inotropic agents, and changes in resistance (afterload) in the arteries that must be overcome for the heart to eject blood.

system. These agents stimulate the SA node to change its firing rate or the AV node to alter the amount of delay.

- **Stroke volume.** An increase or decrease in stroke volume is generally due to changes in the *myocardium.* Venous return (which alters the stretch of the heart) and inotropic agents (which change the Ca^{2+} level in the sarcoplasm) influence the number of crossbridges, which alters the force of contraction. The only exception is afterload, which reflects increased resistance in arteries, making it more difficult for the heart to pump blood. Afterload is generally a factor only as we age.

- **Cardiac output.** Both heart rate and stroke volume are directly related to cardiac output. When both heart rate and stroke volume increase, cardiac output increases. In contrast, when both heart rate and stroke volume decrease, cardiac output decreases. It is not possible to predict the net effect on cardiac output (i.e., whether it will increase or decrease) if the heart rate and stroke volume change in the opposite direction to one another (e.g., stroke volume decreases from blood loss, and heart rate increases in an attempt to maintain cardiac output). The net effect will be determined by the relative change to both heart rate and stroke volume.

 WHAT DID YOU LEARN?

 If both heart rate and stroke volume increase, cardiac output (a) stays the same, (b) increases, or (c) decreases? Thus, is the relationship between these two variables and cardiac output direct or inverse?

19.10 Development of the Heart

LEARNING OBJECTIVES

1. Explain how postnatal heart structures develop from the primitive heart tube.

2. Describe septal defects that may occur during development.

Development of the heart commences in the third week, when the embryo becomes too large to receive its nutrients through diffu-

sion alone. The steps involved in heart development are complex, because the heart must begin working before its development is complete **(figure 19.25).**

By day 19 (middle of week 3), two **heart tubes** (*endocardial tubes*) form from mesoderm in the embryo. By day 21, these paired tubes fuse, forming a single primitive heart tube (figure 19.25*a*). By day 22, the heart begins to beat, and later in the fourth week, this single heart tube bends and folds upon itself to form the external heart shape (figure 19.25*b*). This tube develops the following named expansions that give rise to postnatal heart structures (listed from inferior to superior): **sinus venosus, primitive atrium, primitive ventricle,** and **bulbus cordis** (bŭl'bŭs kōr'dis). The sinus venosus and primitive atrium form parts of the left and right atria. The primitive ventricle forms most of the left ventricle. The bulbus cordis may be further subdivided into a **trabeculated part of the right ventricle,** which forms most of the right ventricle; the **conus cordis,** which forms the outflow tracts for the ventricles; and the **truncus arteriosus,** which forms the ascending aorta and pulmonary trunk (figure 19.25*c*).

The next major steps in heart development occur during weeks 5–8, when the single heart tube becomes partitioned into four chambers (two atria and two ventricles), and the great vessels form. This partitioning is complex, and errors in development lead to many of the more common congenital heart malformations.

The common atrium is subdivided into a left and right atrium by an interatrial septum, which consists of two parts (**septum primum** and **septum secundum**) that partially overlap (figure 19.25*d*). These two parts connect to tissue masses called endocardial cushions. An opening in the septum secundum (which is covered by the septum primum) is called the foramen ovale. Because the embryonic lungs are not functional, much of the blood is shunted from the right atrium to the left atrium by traveling through the foramen ovale and pushing the septum primum into the left atrium. Blood cannot flow back from the left atrium to the right atrium, because the septum primum's movement is stopped when it comes against the septum secundum. Thus, the septum primum acts as a unidirectional flutter valve.

When the baby is born and the lungs are fully functional, the blood from the left atrium pushes the septum primum and secundum together, closing the interatrial septum. The only remnant of

Figure 19.25 Development of the Heart. The heart develops from mesoderm. By day 19, paired heart tubes are present in the cardiogenic region of the embryo. (*a*) These paired tubes fuse by day 21. (*b*) The single heart tube bends and folds upon itself, beginning on day 22. (*c*) By day 28, the heart tube is S-shaped. (*d*) By early week 7, the interatrial septum is formed by two overlapping septa. The foramen ovale is a passageway that detours blood away from the pulmonary circulation into the systemic circulation prior to birth.

the embryonic opening is an oval-shaped depression in the interatrial septum called the **fossa ovalis.**

Left and right ventricles are partitioned by an **interventricular septum** that grows superiorly from the floor of the ventricles. The AV valves, papillary muscles, and chordae tendineae all form from portions of the ventricular walls as well. The superior part of the interventricular septum develops from superior structures (the aorticopulmonary septum, which is a spiral-shaped mass that also subdivides the truncus arteriosus into the pulmonary trunk and the ascending aorta).

Many congenital heart malformations result from incomplete or faulty development during these weeks. For example, in an **atrial septal defect,** the postnatal heart still has an opening between the left and right atria. Thus, blood from the left atrium (the higher-pressure system) is shunted to the right atrium (the

lower-pressure system). This can lead to enlargement of the right side of the heart.

Ventricular septal defects can occur if the interventricular septum is incompletely formed. A common malformation called **tetralogy of Fallot** occurs when the aorticopulmonary septum divides the truncus arteriosus unevenly. As a result, the patient has a ventricular septal defect, a very narrow pulmonary trunk (pulmonary stenosis), an aorta that overlaps both the left and right ventricles, and an enlargement of the right ventricle (right ventricular hypertrophy).

WHAT DID YOU LEARN?

35 What would be the path of blood flow through the heart if the foramen ovale did not close shortly after birth?

CHAPTER SUMMARY

- The cardiovascular system is composed of the heart and blood vessels organized into the pulmonary circulation and systemic circulation.

19.1a General Function   727

- The function of the cardiovascular system is to transport substances throughout the body and provide adequate perfusion to all tissues.

19.1b Overview of Components   727

- The primary types of blood vessels include arteries, capillaries, and veins.

- The heart acts as two "side-by-side" pumps with the right side composed of a right atrium and right ventricle and the left side composed of a left atrium and left ventricle. Valves within the heart help ensure a one-way flow of blood.

- The circulation routes include the pulmonary circulation and systemic circulation.

- The heart is a located in the thoracic cavity and is enclosed within a fibroserous sac.

19.2a Location and Position of the Heart   732

- The heart is located left of the body midline, posterior to the sternum in the mediastinum with its apex projecting anteroinferiorly.

19.2b Characteristics of the Pericardium   733

- The pericardium that encloses the heart includes the pericardial sac, which has an outer fibrous pericardium and an inner parietal layer of serous pericardium, and a visceral layer of serous pericardium (epicardium) that forms the outer layer of the heart wall.

- The pericardial cavity is a potential space between the layers of the serous pericardium that contain serous fluid, which is produced by the serous membranes and lubricates the surfaces to reduce friction.

- The right side of the heart is more visible from the anterior view, and the left side of the heart is more visible from the posterior view.

19.3a Superficial Features of the Heart   733

- The coronary sulcus and interventricular sulci are visible from the external surface of the heart. These grooves house coronary vessels.

19.3b Layers of the Heart Wall   736

- The heart wall has an epicardium (visceral layer of serous pericardium), myocardium, and endocardium.

19.3c Heart Chambers   737

- Atria are separated by an interatrial septum, and ventricles are separated by an interventricular septum.

- The four heart chambers include the right atrium, right ventricle, left atrium, and left ventricle.

19.3d Heart Valves   738

- The atrioventricular valves are located between an atrium and ventricle, and the semilunar valves are between a ventricle and an arterial trunk (pulmonary trunk or aorta).

19.3e Microscopic Structure of Cardiac Muscle   740

- Cardiac muscle cells are small, have one or two centrally located nuclei, and are branched.

- Intercalated discs tightly link the cardiac muscle cells together and permit the passage of action potentials.

- Cardiac muscle cells rely almost exclusively on aerobic cellular respiration for supplying ATP.

19.3f Fibrous Skeleton of the Heart   741

- The fibrous skeleton provides an attachment site for heart valves and cardiac muscle, and prevents action potentials from spreading between the atria and ventricles except through the AV node.

- The coronary circulation is the circulation of blood to and from the heart wall.

19.4a Coronary Arteries   742

- Coronary arteries supply blood to the heart wall and include the left and right coronary arteries that branch off the aorta.

19.4b Coronary Veins   744

- Venous return is through the cardiac veins into the coronary sinus, which drains into the right atrium of the heart.

- Heart activity is regulated by the conduction system and the autonomic nervous system.

19.5a The Heart's Conduction System   744

- Stimulation of the heart involves initiation of an action potential at the SA node and its transmission through the conduction system.

- The conducting system includes sinoatrial (SA) node, atrioventricular (AV) node, AV bundle, and Purkinje fibers, which are composed of specialized cardiac cells that initiate and conduct action potentials, resulting in a heartbeat.

19.5b Innervation of the Heart   744

- Parasympathetic innervation comes from the cardioinhibitory center to decrease the heart rate. Sympathetic innervation comes from the cardioacceleratory center to increase the heart rate and increase force of contraction.

19.6a Overview of Pumps and Channels of Nodal Cells   746

- The pumps and channels associated with neurons are also in the plasma membrane of nodal cells. A type of channel unique to nodal cells is the slow voltage-gated Na^+ channel that allows the nodal cells to spontaneously depolarize.

19.6b Electrical Events at the SA Node: Initiation of the Action Potential   747

- The three events of SA nodal cells include (1) reaching the threshold as Na^+ enters the nodal cells through open voltage-gated Na^+ channels, (2) depolarization as Ca^{2+} enters the nodal cells through open voltage-gated Ca^{2+} channels, and (3) repolarization as K^+ exits the nodal cells through open voltage-gated K^+ channels.
- At rest, the parasympathetic nervous system decreases the inherent rhythm of nodal cells from a firing rate of 100 per minute to approximately 75 per minute.

19.6c Conduction System of the Heart: Spread of the Action Potential   748

- The action potential travels through the conduction system as follows: (1) SA node, (2) AV node, (3) AV bundle, (4) bundle branches, and (5) Purkinje fibers.

19.7 Cardiac Muscle Cells   749

- Following stimulation by the conduction system, there is a propagation of the action potential at the sarcolemma and contraction of sarcomeres within the cardiac muscle cells.

19.7a Overview of Pumps and Channels Within Cardiac Muscle Cells   749

- The pumps and channels associated with skeletal muscle fibers are also in the plasma membrane of cardiac muscle cells. A type of channel unique to the function of cardiac muscle cells in transmitting an action potential is the voltage-gated Ca^{2+} channel.

19.7b Electrical and Mechanical Events of Cardiac Muscle Cells   750

- The electrical events of cardiac muscle include depolarization, plateau, and repolarization at the sarcolemma.
- The mechanical events are similar to those of skeletal muscle fibers and involve crossbridge cycling and the shortening of sarcomeres within cardiac muscle cells.

19.7c Repolarization and the Refractory Period   751

- Cardiac muscle exhibits a longer refractory period than skeletal muscle fibers to allow time for contraction and relaxation of the muscle cells before they are stimulated again—a necessary requirement for the "pumping action" of the heart.

19.7d The ECG Recording   752

- An electrocardiogram (ECG) is a graphic recording of the electrical changes in the heart and is used in the diagnosis and treatment of abnormal heart function.

19.8 The Cardiac Cycle   753

- A cardiac cycle is the inclusive period of time from initiation of one heartbeat to the start of the next.

19.8a Overview of the Cardiac Cycle   753

- Systole refers to contraction of a chamber; diastole refers to its relaxation.

19.8b Events of the Cardiac Cycle   755

- Atrial systole is the contraction of atria to finish filling the ventricles, which are in diastole.
- Early ventricular systole is a time of isovolumetric contraction: Ventricles begin to contract, AV valves are pushed closed, and no blood leaves the ventricles yet.
- Late ventricular systole is the time of ventricular ejection: Semilunar valves are pushed open, and blood is forced through the semilunar valves into the arterial trunk.
- Early ventricular diastole is the beginning of ventricular relaxation: AV valves remain closed, and semilunar valves close.
- Late ventricular diastole is a time to begin ventricular filling as AV valves open and passive filling of the ventricle begins.

19.9 Cardiac Output   756

- Cardiac output is a measure of how effective the cardiovascular system is in transporting substances through the body.

19.9a Introduction to Cardiac Output   758

- Cardiac output (CO) is defined as the amount of blood pumped by a single ventricle in 1 minute.
- Cardiac output is the heart rate multiplied by the stroke volume.
- Cardiac reserve is a measure of the ability of the heart to increase pumping capacity beyond the normal resting CO.

19.9b Variables That Influence Heart Rate   759

- Heart rate is altered through chronotropic agents, which change SA node and AV node activity. Postive chronotropic agents increase the heart rate and negative chronotropic agents decrease the heart rate.

19.9c Variables That Influence Stroke Volume   760

- Stroke volume is influenced by venous return, inotropic agents, and afterload. Venous return is directly correlated with stroke volume. Postive inotropic agents increase stroke volume, negative inotropic agents decrease stroke volume, and afterload is inversely correlated with stroke volume.

19.9d Variables That Influence Cardiac Output   761

- Heart rate is altered by stimulating the conducting system, and stroke volume is usually altered by changes in the myocardium.
- Both heart rate and stroke volume are directly related to cardiac output.

19.10 Development of the Heart   762

- Development of the heart commences in the third week.
- Mesodermal cells in the cardiogenic region of the embryo form two heart tubes, which fuse by day 21, forming a single primitive heart tube.
- The foramen ovale connects the two atria, allowing most of the blood to bypass the pulmonary circulation. This foramen closes shortly after birth.

CHALLENGE YOURSELF

Do You Know the Basics?

____ 1. Which of the following is the correct circulatory sequence for blood to pass through part of the heart?

a. right atrium ⟶ left AV valve ⟶ right ventricle ⟶ pulmonary semilunar valve

b. right atrium ⟶ right AV valve ⟶ right ventricle ⟶ pulmonary semilunar valve

c. left atrium ⟶ right AV valve ⟶ left ventricle ⟶ aortic semilunar valve

d. left atrium ⟶ left AV valve ⟶ left ventricle ⟶ pulmonary semilunar valve

____ 2. The pericardial cavity is located between the

a. fibrous pericardium and the parietal layer of the serous pericardium.

b. parietal and visceral layers of the serous pericardium.

c. visceral layer of the serous pericardium and the epicardium.

d. myocardium and the visceral layer of the serous pericardium.

____ 3. How is blood prevented from backflowing from the pulmonary trunk into the right ventricle?

a. closing of the right AV valves

b. opening of the pulmonary semilunar valve

c. contraction of the right atrium

d. closing of the pulmonary semilunar valve

____ 4. Venous blood draining the heart wall (coronary sinus) enters the right atrium through the

a. coronary sinus.

b. inferior vena cava.

c. pulmonary veins.

d. superior vena cava.

____ 5. Calcium channels in the nodal cells function to

a. cause depolarization and initiate the cardiac action potential.

b. assure excess calcium can leave the cell.

c. bring the cell quickly to its resting membrane potential.

d. sustain contraction of the cell.

____ 6. Action potentials are spread rapidly between cardiac muscle cells by

a. sarcomeres.

b. intercalated discs.

c. chemical neurotransmitters.

d. the fibrous skeleton.

____ 7. Why is it necessary to stimulate papillary muscles in the ventricle slightly earlier than the rest of the ventricular wall myocardium?

a. to assure rapid conduction speed of the action potential

b. to pull on AV valve cusps to prevent backflow

c. to assure blood will surge toward the semilunar valves

d. to assure coordinated contraction of the ventricular myocardium

____ 8. Preload is a measure of

a. heart chamber volume prior to contraction.

b. contraction rate in cardiac muscle.

c. reduced filling during exercise.

d. autonomic nervous system stimulation of the heart.

____ 9. All of the following occur when the ventricles contract *except*

a. the AV valves close.

b. blood is ejected into the aorta.

c. the semilunar valves open.

d. blood from the pulmonary trunk enters the atria.

____ 10. What occurs during the atrial reflex?

a. Atria slow their filling rate.

b. There is a decrease in heart rate due to an increase in blood pressure.

c. The SA node rhythm decreases.

d. An increase in heart rate occurs in response to an increase in blood volume within the atria.

11. Describe and compare the differences between the pulmonary and systemic circulations.

12. Compare the structure, location, and function of the parietal and visceral layers of the serous pericardium.

13. Why are the chordae tendineae required for the proper functioning of the AV valves?

14. Explain why the walls of the atria are thinner than those of the ventricles, and why the walls of the right ventricle are relatively thin when compared to the walls of the left ventricle.

15. Describe the structure and function of intercalated discs in cardiac muscle tissue.

16. Explain the general location and function of coronary vessels.

17. Describe the functional differences in the effects of the sympathetic and parasympathetic divisions of the autonomic nervous system on the activity of the heart.

18. Provide an overview of the two events for cardiac muscle contraction to occur that include the conduction system and cardiac muscle cells.

19. List the five events of the cardiac cycle, and indicate for each if the atria are contracted or relaxed, if the ventricles are contracted or relaxed, if the AV valves are open or closed, and if the semilunar valves are open or closed.

20. Define cardiac output, and explain how it is influenced by both heart rate and stroke volume.

Can You Apply What You've Learned?

Use the following paragraph to answer questions 1 and 2.

A young man was doing some vigorous exercise when suddenly he felt chest pains just before he passed out. Upon being revived, he was taken to the hospital for examination. The medical personnel ran standard tests and ECG tracings, then said it would fine for him to resume his normal activities and workouts.

1. Why might the increase in heart rate associated with a vigorous exercise program be the cause of his becoming unconscious?
   a. increase in blood pressure throughout the body
   b. failure of the conduction system
   c. increase in return volume of blood to the heart
   d. coronary blood flow reduction due to tachycardia

2. Which of the following treatments would *not* be used to rule out that a myocardial infarction had occurred?
   a. doing an ECG
   b. performing constant blood pressure monitoring
   c. measuring blood levels of creatine kinase released from damaged heart muscle
   d. measuring blood levels of troponin released from damaged heart muscle

3. Calcium channel blockers are drugs that are given to cause
   a. an increase in the volume of blood being pumped.
   b. the afterload to be increased.
   c. contractility to decrease.
   d. preload to decrease.

4. A patient has been in a serious car accident and is hemorrhaging. Which of the following changes would be seen in this patient?
   a. a decrease in stroke volume
   b. an increase in heart rate
   c. a possible decrease in cardiac output
   d. All of these are correct.

5. During surgery, the right vagus nerve was accidently cut. Explain the effect to the heart rate.
   a. There is no change to the heart rate because the vagus nerve does not innervate the heart.
   b. The heart rate increases to the inherent rhythm of SA nodal cells.
   c. The heart stops beating, and heart rate becomes zero.
   d. The heart rate decreases to the inherent rhythm of SA nodal cells.

Can You Synthesize What You've Learned?

1. A young couple that you are friends with gave birth to a new baby. They were told by their physician that the foramen ovale did not close between the right atrium and left atrium (i.e., that their baby has "a hole in her heart"). They know that you are a nurse and have come to you to help them to understand what is going on. Explain both the normal flow of blood through the heart and the flow with the foramen ovale still open. Include in your description the concept of oxygenated and deoxygenated blood.

2. Josephine is a 55-year-old overweight woman who has a poor diet and does not exercise. One day while walking briskly, she experienced pain in her chest and down her left arm. Her doctor told her that she was experiencing angina due to heart problems. Josephine asks you to explain what causes angina, and why she was feeling pain in her arm even though the problem was with her heart. What do you tell her?

3. Your grandfather was told that his SA node (pacemaker) has stopped functioning. Explain how his heart is still beating at a rate of 40 to 50 times per minute. Are the atria stimulated to contract? Explain.

INTEGRATE

ONLINE STUDY TOOLS

www.mhhe.com/mckinleyap

Concept Overview Interactive: Figure 19.23: Cardiac Cycle

Clinical Case Study: A Middle-Aged Woman with Back Pain

Interactive Questions: This chapter's content is served up in a number of multimedia question formats for student study.

LearnSmart: Topics and terminology include introduction to the cardiovascular system; location of the heart and the pericardium; heart anatomy; coronary vessels: blood supply of the heart wall; anatomic structures controlling heart activity; stimulation of

the heart; the cardiac cycle; cardiac output; development of the heart

Anatomy & Physiology Revealed: Topics include cardiovascular system overview; heart fly-through; blood flow through the heart; thoracic arteries; heart vasculature; internal features of the heart; cardiac muscle; cardiac cycle

Animations: Topics include action potentials in the sinoatrial node; cardiac cycle; mechanical events of the cardiac cycle; conduction system of the heart; cardiac EC coupling

chapter 20

Cardiovascular System: Vessels and Circulation

Many of us are aware that high blood pressure (hypertension) is not healthy. Hypertension can damage blood vessels and lead to cardiovascular disease. But a minimal amount of blood pressure is needed to effectively pump blood (and the nutrients and respiratory gases it transports) throughout the body and transport these materials to the body tissues. If blood pressure drops too low, the body will be deprived of nutrients and death may occur. Multiple body systems (including the endocrine, nervous, ➡

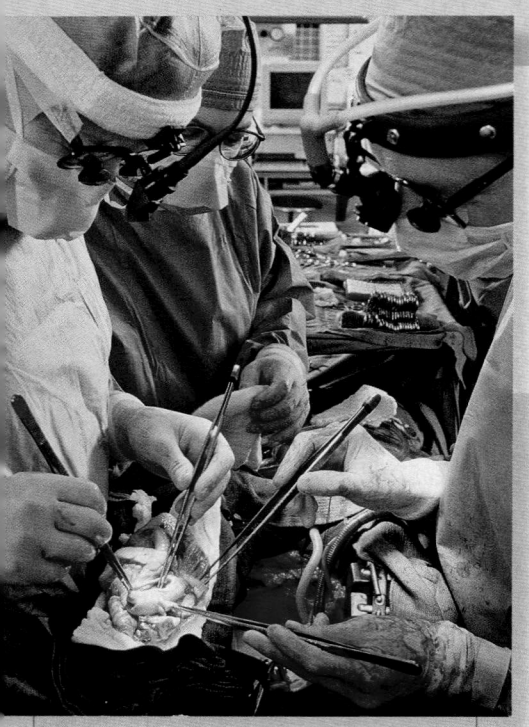

Cardiovascular surgery is the medical specialty involving the diagnosis and treatment of disorders of the heart and blood vessels. One of the most common blood vessel disorders is atherosclerosis, where plaques develop in the vessels and result in lumen narrowing. If these vessels become completely blocked, the tissues they supply may die. Cardiovascular surgeons are trained to remove blockages in vessels or add blood vessel bypasses to restore blood supply to an affected organ. They also use medical imaging to help direct catheters through blood vessels and insert stents in blocked vessels.

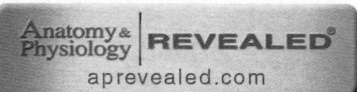

aprevealed.com

Module 9: Cardiovascular System

and urinary systems) participate in maintaining adequate blood pressure to ensure tissues are adequately perfused (supplied with blood) for the activity at hand.

We begin this chapter by describing the general anatomy of blood vessels, processes of capillary exchange, and factors that influence both blood flow and blood pressure in vessels. Pulmonary circulation and the major arteries and veins of systemic circulation are then described, and we conclude with a comparison of fetal versus adult circulation.

20.1 Structure and Function of Blood Vessels

Blood vessels are classified into three primary types based on function. **Arteries** (ar'ter-ē) convey blood away from the heart to the capillaries. **Capillaries** (kap'i-lar-ē; *capillaris* = relating to hair) are microscopic, relatively porous blood vessels for the exchange of substances between blood and tissues. **Veins** (vān) drain blood from the capillaries, transporting it back to the heart.

20.1a General Structure of Vessels

✓ LEARNING OBJECTIVES

1. Describe the three tunics common to most vessels.
2. Explain the distinguishing features of the tunics found in arteries, capillaries, and veins.

Vessel walls are composed of layers called **tunics** (tū'nik; *tunica* = coat). The tunics surround the **lumen** (lū'men), or inside space of the vessel, through which blood flows. The three tunics are the tunica intima, tunica media, and tunica externa **(figure 20.1)**.

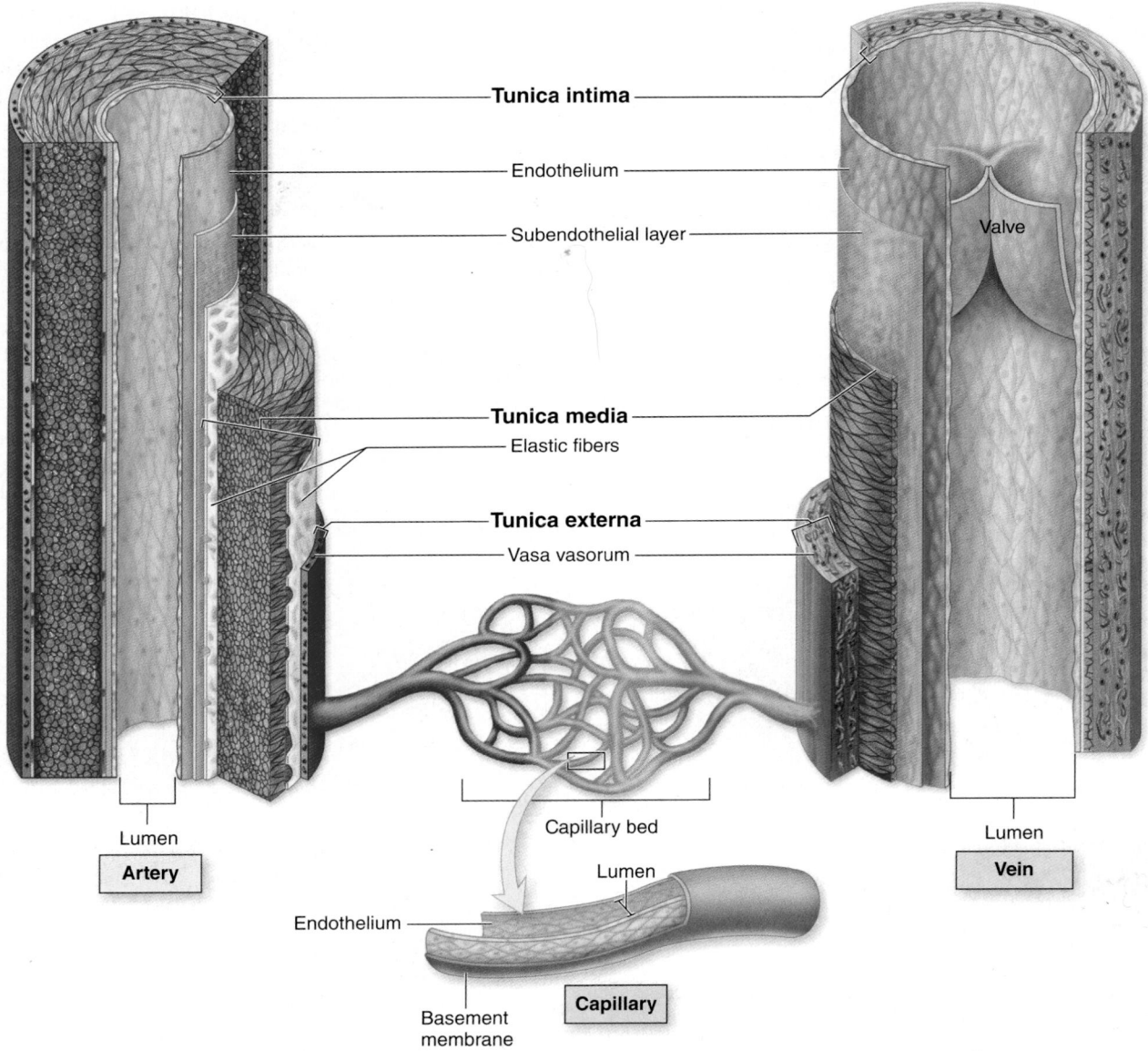

Tunica intima
Endothelium
Subendothelial layer
Valve
Tunica media
Elastic fibers
Tunica externa
Vasa vasorum
Lumen
Artery
Capillary bed
Lumen
Endothelium
Basement membrane
Capillary
Lumen
Vein

Figure 20.1 Walls of an Artery, a Capillary, and a Vein. Both arteries and veins have a tunica intima, tunica media, and tunica externa. However, an artery has a thicker tunica media and a relatively smaller lumen, whereas a vein's thickest layer is the tunica externa, and it has a larger lumen. Some veins also have valves. Capillaries typically have only a tunica intima (basement membrane and endothelium), but they do not have a subendothelial layer.

Arteries, capillaries, and veins differ in the specific composition of the tunics; the differences reflect their functions.

Tunics

The innermost layer of a blood vessel wall is the **tunica intima** (tū′ni-kă in-ti′mă; *intimus* = inmost), or *tunica interna*. It is composed of an **endothelium** (a simple squamous epithelium) that faces the blood vessel lumen and a thin subendothelial layer made up of areolar connective tissue. This layer provides a smooth surface as the blood moves through the lumen of the blood vessel. It is continuous with the endocardium, which is the inner lining of the heart (section 19.3b).

The **tunica media** (mē′dē-ă; *medius* = middle) is the middle layer of the vessel wall. It is composed predominantly of circularly arranged layers of smooth muscle cells that are supported by elastic fibers. Contraction of smooth muscle in the tunica media results in **vasoconstriction** (vā′sō-kon-strik′shŭn), or narrowing of the blood vessel lumen; relaxation of the smooth muscle causes **vasodilation** (vā′sō-dī-lā′shŭn), or widening of the blood vessel lumen.

The **tunica externa** (eks-ter′nă; *externe* = outside), or *tunica adventitia*, is the outermost layer of the blood vessel wall. It is composed of areolar connective tissue that contains elastic and collagen fibers. The tunica externa helps anchor the vessel to other structures. Very large blood vessels require their own blood supply to the tunica externa in the form of a network of small arteries called the **vasa vasorum** (vā-să vā-sŏr′ŭm; vessels of vessels). The vasa vasorum extend through the tunica externa.

Comparison of the Different Vessel Types

Arteries and veins that supply the same body region and tend to lie next to one another are called **companion vessels. Figure 20.2** is a histologic image of a companion artery and vein. Compared to their venous companions, arteries have a thick tunica media, a narrower lumen, and more elastic and collagen fibers. These differences mean that arterial walls can spring back to shape, and are more resilient and resistant to changes in blood pressure than are veins. In addition, an artery remains patent (open) even without blood in it.

In contrast, veins have a thicker tunica externa, a larger lumen, and less elastic and collagen fibers than a companion artery. The wall of a vein is typically collapsed if no blood is in it. The characteristics of arteries and veins are summarized in **table 20.1**.

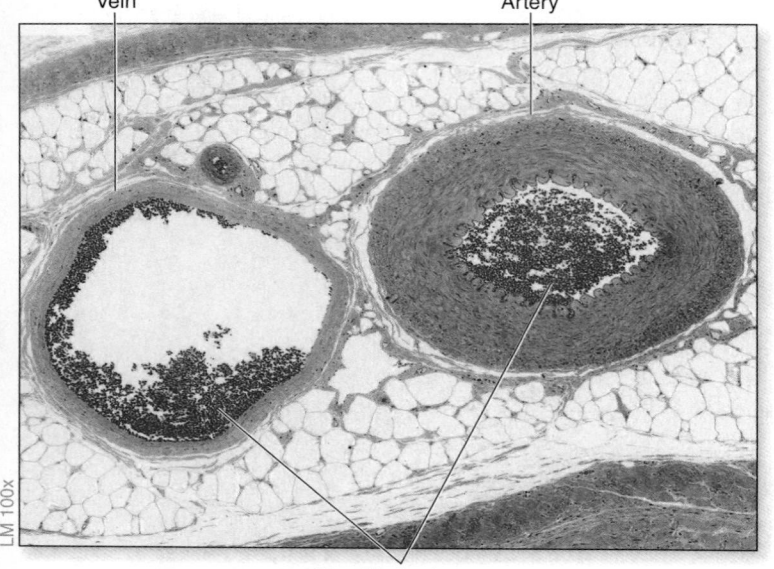

Vein | Artery

LM 100x

Blood in the lumen

Figure 20.2 Microscopic Comparison of an Artery and Vein. The artery generally maintains its shape in tissues as a result of its thicker wall. The wall of a companion vein often collapses when it is not filled with blood (although in the above photo, the vein is not collapsed). AP R

Table 20.1	Comparison of Companion Arteries and Veins	
Characteristic	**Artery**	**Vein**
Lumen Diameter	Narrower than vein lumen	Wider than artery lumen
General Wall Thickness	Thicker than vein	Thinner than artery
Cross-Sectional Shape	Retains its circular cross-sectional shape	Cross section tends to flatten out (collapse) if no blood is in the vein
Thickest Tunic	Tunica media	Tunica externa
Elastic and Collagen Fibers in Tunics	More than in vein	Less than in artery
Valves	None	Present in most veins
Blood Pressure Range	Higher than in veins (100 mm Hg in larger arteries to 40 mm Hg in smaller arterioles)	Lower than in arteries (20 mm Hg in venules to 0 mm Hg in vena cavae)
Blood Flow	Transports blood away from heart to the body	Transports blood from the body to the heart
Blood Oxygen Levels	Systemic arteries carry blood high in O_2 Pulmonary arteries carry blood low in O_2	Systemic veins carry blood low in O_2 Pulmonary veins carry blood high in O_2

Capillaries are unique in that they contain only the tunica intima composed of an endothelium and its underlying basement membrane; there is no subendothelial layer. Having only the tunica intima allows for rapid gas and nutrient exchange between the blood in capillaries and the tissues.

WHAT DID YOU LEARN?

1 What are three differences in anatomic structure between arteries and veins?

20.1b Arteries

LEARNING OBJECTIVE

3. Distinguish between elastic arteries, muscular arteries, and arterioles.

Arteries branch into smaller and smaller vessels as they extend from the heart to the capillaries. There is both a corresponding decrease in lumen diameter and a change in the composition of the tunic wall that includes both a decrease in the relative amount of elastic fibers and an increase in the relative amount of smooth muscle. Arteries may be classified into three basic types: elastic arteries, muscular arteries, and arterioles (**figures 20.3** and **20.4**).

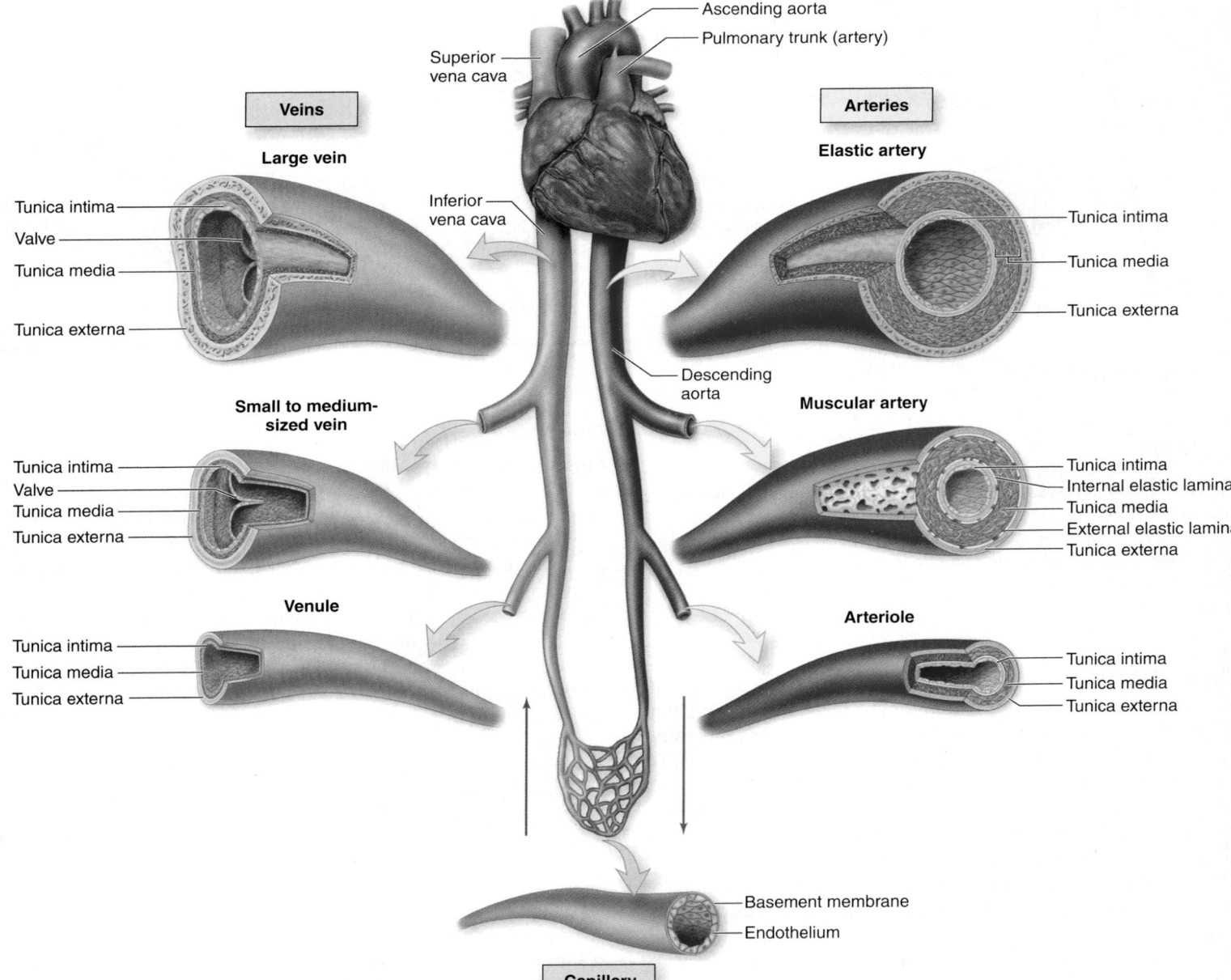

Figure 20.3 Comparison of Companion Vessels. The thickness of the tunics in companion arteries and veins differs, depending upon the size of the vessels.

(a) Elastic artery

- Lumen
- Tunica intima
- Tunica media
- Elastic fibers throughout tunica media
- Tunica externa

LM 100x

(b) Muscular artery

- Tunica intima
- Internal elastic lamina
- Lumen
- Tunica media
- External elastic lamina
- Tunica externa

LM 100x

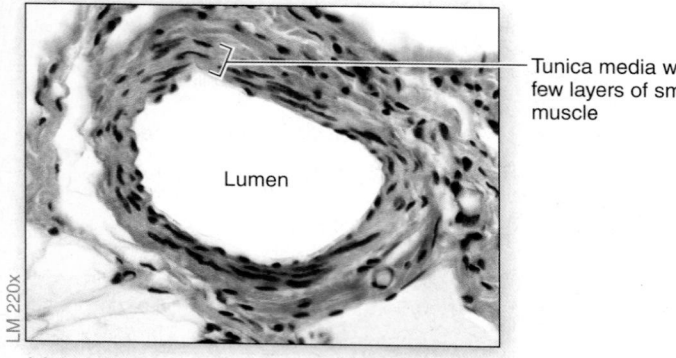

(c) Arteriole

- Tunica media with few layers of smooth muscle
- Lumen

LM 220x

Figure 20.4 Types of Arteries. Light micrograph images of three types of arteries. (*a*) Elastic arteries have vast arrays of elastic fibers in their tunica media. (*b*) Muscular arteries have a tunica media with numerous layers of smooth muscle flanked by elastic laminae. (*c*) Arterioles typically have a tunica media composed of six or fewer layers of smooth muscle cells.

Elastic Arteries

Elastic arteries are the largest arteries, with diameters ranging from 2.5 to 1 centimeter. They are also called *conducting arteries* because they conduct blood—from the heart to the smaller muscular arteries. As their name suggests, these arteries have a large proportion of elastic fibers throughout all three tunics, especially in the tunica media. The abundant elastic fibers allow the artery to stretch and accommodate the blood when a heart ventricle ejects blood into it during ventricular systole (contraction) and then recoil, which helps propel the blood through the arteries during ventricular diastole (relaxation).

Examples of elastic arteries include the aorta and the pulmonary trunk, and brachiocephalic, common carotid, subclavian, and common iliac arteries (see figure 20.19*a*). Elastic arteries branch into muscular arteries.

Muscular Arteries

Muscular arteries typically have diameters ranging from 1 centimeter to 0.3 millimeters. These medium-sized arteries are also called *distributing arteries* because they distribute blood to specific body regions and organs.

Muscular arteries have a proportionately thicker tunica media, with multiple layers of smooth muscle cells. Unlike in elastic arteries, the elastic fibers in muscular arteries are confined to two circumscribed sheets: The **internal elastic lamina** (lam'i-nă) separates the tunica intima from the tunica media, and the **external elastic lamina** separates the tunica media from the tunica externa. The greater amount of muscle and lesser amount of elastic tissue result in a better ability to vasoconstrict and vasodilate, although a lessened ability to stretch in comparison to elastic arteries.

Most named arteries (e.g., the brachial, anterior tibial, coronary, and inferior mesenteric arteries) are examples of muscular arteries (see figure 20.19*a*). Muscular arteries branch into arterioles.

Arterioles

Arterioles are the smallest arteries, with diameters ranging from 0.3 millimeters to 10 micrometers. In general, arterioles have fewer than six layers of smooth muscle in their tunica media. Larger arterioles have all three tunics, whereas the smallest arterioles may have a thin layer of endothelium surrounded by a single layer section 22.3d). Low-density lipoproteins and very-low-density lipoproteins (LDLs and VLDLs) enter the tunica intima, combine with oxygen, and remain stuck to the vessel wall. This oxidation of lipoproteins attracts monocytes, which adhere to the endothelium and migrate into the wall. As the monocytes migrate into the wall, they digest the lipids and develop into structures called **foam cells.** Eventually, smooth muscle cells from the tunica media migrate into the atheroma and proliferate, causing further enlargement of the atheroma and narrowing of the lumen of the blood vessel, thereby restricting blood flow to the regions the artery supplies.

Atherosclerosis is a progressive disease. The plaques typically begin to develop in early adulthood and grow and enlarge as we age. People are unaware of the plaques until they become large enough to restrict blood flow in an artery and cause vascular complications.

Risk Factors

Some individuals are genetically prone to atherosclerosis. **Hypercholesterolemia** (an increased amount of cholesterol in the blood), which also tends to run in families, has been positively associated with the rate of development and severity of atherosclerosis. Additionally, males tend to be affected more than females, and symptomatic atherosclerosis increases with age. Finally, smoking and hypertension both cause vascular injury, which increases the risk.

Treatment Options

If an artery is occluded (blocked) in one or just a few areas, a treatment called **angioplasty** (an'jē-ō-plas-tē; *angeion* = vessel, *plastos* = formed) is used. A physician inserts a balloon-tip catheter into an artery, and positions it at the site where the lumen is narrowed. Then the balloon is inflated, forcibly expanding the narrowed area, and a stent is placed in the vessel. A stent is a piece of wire-mesh that springs open to keep the vessel lumen open. For occluded coronary arteries, sometimes a much more invasive

treatment known as coronary bypass surgery may be needed. A vein (e.g., the great saphenous vein) or artery (e.g., the internal thoracic artery) is detached from its original location and grafted from the aorta to the coronary artery system, thus bypassing the area(s) of atherosclerotic narrowing.

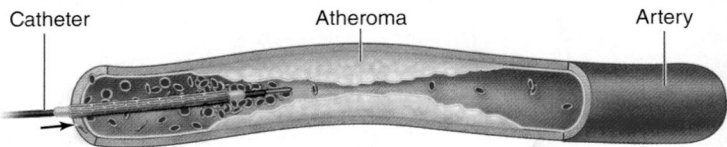

Catheter   Atheroma   Artery

① An uninflated balloon and compressed stent are passed through a catheter to the area of the artery that is obstructed.

Balloon   Stent

② Balloon inflates, which expands the stent and inserts it in place and also compresses the atheroma.

③ The stent remains in the vessel as the balloon is deflated and the catheter is withdrawn.

Angioplasty is used to expand the narrowed region of an artery.

of smooth muscle cells. Smooth muscle in the arterioles usually is at least slightly constricted (just as your skeletal muscles often are in a partial state of contraction; see section 10.7a). This slightly constricted state is called **vasomotor tone** and is regulated by the vasomotor center in the brainstem. Arterioles have a significant role in regulating systemic blood pressure and blood flow to different areas of the body. These functions are described in later sections of the chapter.

 WHAT DID YOU LEARN?

② What changes are seen in the composition of the tunic wall of arteries as they branch into smaller and smaller vessels?

INTEGRATE

CLINICAL VIEW

Aneurysm AP|R

Many of the elastic and muscular arteries are less able to withstand the forces from the pulsating blood as we age. Systolic blood pressure may increase with age, exacerbating this problem. As a result, older

Normal aorta   *Large abdominal aortic aneurysm*

individuals are more apt to develop an **aneurysm** (an'ū-riz-m; *aneurysma* = a dilation), whereby part of the arterial wall thins and balloons out. This wall is more prone to rupture, which can cause massive bleeding and may lead to death. Aneurysms most commonly occur in the arteries at the base of the brain or in the aorta.

Table 20.2 — Types of Capillaries

Characteristics	(a) Continuous Capillary	(b) Fenestrated Capillary
Structure	Basement membrane; Pinocytotic vesicles; Erythrocyte; Intercellular cleft; Lumen; Nucleus of endothelial cell	Basement membrane; Fenestrations; Erythrocyte; Intercellular cleft; Lumen; Nucleus of endothelial cell
Description	Lining of endothelial cells is complete around lumen; basement membrane is complete; intercellular clefts between endothelial cells	Same as continuous capillaries, except also contain fenestrations (range from 10 to 100 nanometers in diameter)
Materials That Pass Through Vessel Wall	Some leukocytes, plasma and its contents (except most proteins)	Large amounts of materials are filtered, released, or absorbed; some smaller proteins
Locations	Most capillaries (e.g., capillaries within muscles, skin, thymus, lungs, and central nervous system [CNS])	Small intestine; for absorbing nutrients Ciliary process; to produce aqueous humor Choroid plexus; to produce cerebrospinal fluid [CSF] in the brain Most endocrine glands; permit absorption of hormones into the blood Kidneys; for filtering blood

20.1c Capillaries

LEARNING OBJECTIVES

4. Describe the general anatomic structure and function of capillaries.
5. Compare the anatomic structure, function, and location of continuous capillaries, fenestrated capillaries, and sinusoids.
6. Trace the movement of blood through a capillary bed.

Capillaries are the smallest blood vessels. They connect arterioles to venules (the smallest veins). The average capillary is approximately 1 mm in length with a diameter of 8 to 10 micrometers, just slightly larger than the diameter of a single erythrocyte. The narrow vessel diameter means erythrocytes must travel in single file (termed **rouleau**) through each capillary (see section 18.3b). Capillaries consist solely of an endothelial layer resting on a basement membrane. The narrow vessel diameter and the thin wall are optimal for exchange of substances between blood and body tissues.

Types of Capillaries

Capillaries are differentiated based on their relative degree of permeability and include continuous capillaries, fenestrated capillaries, and sinusoids **(table 20.2)**.

Continuous capillaries are the most common type of capillary. The endothelial cells form a complete, *continuous* lining around the lumen that rests on a complete basement membrane. Tight junctions (see section 4.5d) secure endothelial cells to one another; however, they do not form a complete "seal." The gaps between the endothelial cells are called **intercellular clefts.** Materials can move into or out of the blood either through endothelial cells by cellular transport processes (e.g., diffusion, pinocytosis; see section 4.3), or between endothelial cells through intercellular clefts by diffusion and bulk flow (described shortly).

The size of intercellular clefts prevent movement of large substances, including formed elements and plasma proteins, while allowing the movement of fluid containing small substances (smaller than about 5 nanometers), such as glucose, amino acids, and ions. Continuous capillaries are found in muscle, the skin, lungs, and central nervous system.

(c) Sinusoid

Discontinuous basement membrane

Large openings

Erythrocyte

Lumen

Intercellular cleft

Nucleus of endothelial cell

Lining of endothelial cells is incomplete around lumen; basement membrane is incomplete or absent

Large substances (formed elements, large plasma proteins) and plasma

Bone marrow (where formed elements enter the blood)

Liver and spleen (where old erythrocytes are phagocytized by macrophages and taken out of circulation)

Some endocrine glands (anterior pituitary, adrenal, and parathyroid)

Fenestrated (fen′es-trā′ted; *fenestra* = window) **capillaries** are also composed of a complete, continuous lining of endothelial cells, and a complete basement membrane. However, small regions of the endothelial cells (typically 10 to 100 nanometers in diameter) are extremely thin; these thin areas are called **fenestrations** (or *pores*). Fenestrations are small enough to prevent formed elements from passing through the wall, yet large enough to allow movement of some smaller plasma proteins. Fenestrated capillaries are seen where a great deal of fluid transport between the blood and interstitial tissue occurs, such as in the small intestine for the absorption of nutrients, the ciliary process of the eye in the production of aqueous humor, choroid plexus of the brain in the production of cerebrospinal fluid, most of the endocrine glands to facilitate the absorption of hormones into the blood, and the kidney for the filtering of blood.

Sinusoids (si′nŭ-soyd; *sinus* = cavity, *eidos* = appearance), or *discontinuous capillaries*, have an incomplete lining of the endothelial cells with large openings or gaps, and the basement membrane is either discontinuous or absent. These openings allow for transport of large substances (formed elements, large plasma proteins), as well as plasma between the blood and tissues. Sinusoids are found in bone marrow for entrance of formed elements into the circulation, the liver and spleen for removing aged erythrocytes from circulation, and some endocrine glands for facilitating the movement of hormone molecules into the blood.

INTEGRATE

CONCEPT CONNECTION

The blood-brain barrier (BBB) (see section 13.2d) is formed by modified continuous capillaries that have thickened basement membranes and no intercellular clefts. Substances can pass through endothelial cells only by regulated cellular processes. However, movement of nonpolar substances is not regulated by cells and so these nonpolar substances (e.g., nicotine, alcohol) may pass through the cells by simple diffusion and enter the brain.

Capillary Beds

Capillaries do not function independently; rather, a group of capillaries (10 to 100) function together and form a **capillary bed** (figure 20.5). A capillary bed is fed by a **metarteriole** (met′ar-tēr′ē-ōl; *meta* = after), which is a vessel branch of an arteriole. The proximal part of the metarteriole is encircled by scattered smooth muscle cells, while the distal part of the metarteriole (called the **thoroughfare channel**) has no smooth muscle cells. The thoroughfare channel connects to a **postcapillary venule** (ven′ūl, vē′nūl), which drains the capillary bed.

Vessels called **true capillaries** branch from the metarteriole and make up the bulk of the capillary bed. At the origin of each true capillary, a smooth muscle ring called the **precapillary sphincter** controls blood flow into the true capillaries. Sphincter relaxation permits blood to flow into the true capillaries, whereas sphincter contraction causes blood to flow directly from the metarteriole and thoroughfare channel into the postcapillary venule with blood bypassing the capillary bed. The precapillary sphincters go through cycles of contracting and relaxing at a rate of about 5 to 10 cycles per minute. This cyclical process is called **vasomotion.**

At any given time only about one-quarter of the capillary beds are open, because there are over 60,000 miles of capillaries and only about 250 to 300 milliliters (mL) of blood (about 5% of the total blood volume) moving through the capillaries at any particular moment. There is simply not enough blood available to fill all capillaries at the same time. The specific amount of blood entering capillaries per unit time per gram of tissue is called **perfusion,** typically expressed in milliliters per minute per gram (mL/min/g).

WHAT DID YOU LEARN?

3 What type of capillary is the most permeable, and where in the body are they found?

(a) Sphincters relaxed; capillary bed well perfused

(b) Sphincters contracted; blood bypasses capillary bed

Figure 20.5 Capillary Bed Structure and Perfusion Through the Bed. A capillary bed originates from a metarteriole. The metarteriole directly connects to a thoroughfare channel that merges with the postcapillary venule. True capillaries branch from the thoroughfare channel, and blood flow into these true capillaries is regulated by the precapillary sphincters. (*a*) A well-perfused capillary bed, with all of the precapillary sphincters relaxed, and (*b*) a capillary bed where most blood is shunted away due to contracted precapillary sphincters.

20.1d Veins

✅ LEARNING OBJECTIVES

7. Describe the structure and general function of veins.

8. Explain how veins serve as a blood reservoir for the cardiovascular system.

Veins merge into larger and larger vessels with a corresponding increase in lumen diameter as they extend from the capillaries to the heart (see figure 20.3).

Venules

Venules are the smallest veins, measuring from 8 to 100 micrometers in diameter. Venules are companion vessels with arterioles. The smallest venules, called postcapillary venules, drain capillaries. Smaller venules merge to form larger venules. The largest venules have all three tunics. Venules merge to form veins.

Small, Medium-Sized, and Large Veins

A venule becomes a vein when its diameter is greater than 100 micrometers. Small and medium-sized veins are companion vessels with muscular arteries, whereas the largest veins travel with elastic arteries. Blood pressure in veins is typically too low to overcome the forces of gravity. Most veins contain numerous **valves,** so as to prevent blood from pooling in the limbs. The valves are formed primarily of tunica intima and strengthened by elastic and collagen fibers. Valves have an anatomic structure similar to semilunar valves of the heart (see section 19.3d).

Systemic Veins as Blood Reservoirs

The percentage of the total blood that is moving through each of the different components of the cardiovascular system while *at rest* is

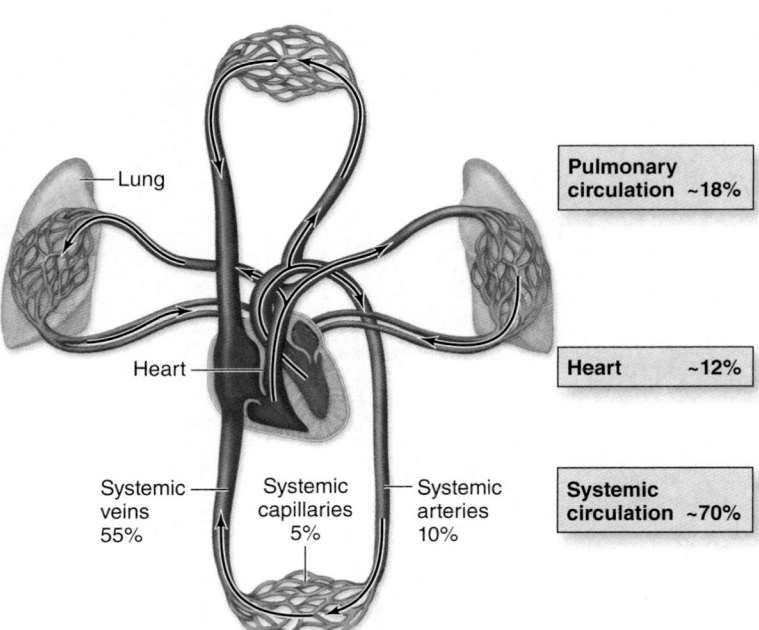

Figure 20.6 Blood Distribution at Rest. Different components of the cardiovascular system vary in the amounts of blood moving through them, with systemic veins containing the largest percentage.

illustrated in **figure 20.6**. Relatively small amounts of blood are within the pulmonary circulation (about 18%) and the heart (about 12%). The largest percentage of blood is within the systemic circulation (about 70%), with the greatest amount (about 55%) within the body's systemic veins. The relatively large amount of blood within veins allows veins to function as **blood reservoirs.** Blood may be shifted from venous reservoirs into circulation through vasoconstriction of veins, when more blood is needed with increased physical exertion—and shifted back into venous reservoirs through vasodilation of veins, when less blood is needed at rest.

Figure 20.7 illustrates how each specific blood vessel structure is adapted for the specific functions of that vessel.

💡 WHAT DID YOU LEARN?

4 How does a vein serve as a blood reservoir?

20.1e Pathways of Blood Vessels

✅ LEARNING OBJECTIVE

9. Compare and contrast the simple and alternative pathways of blood vessels.

Blood vessels are arranged in either simple or alternative pathways **(figure 20.8)**. Each pathway is described in detail.

Simple Pathway

In the simple pathway, one major artery delivers blood to the organ or body region and then branches into smaller and smaller arteries to become arterioles. Each arteriole feeds into a single capillary bed. A venule drains blood from the capillaries and merges with other venules to form one major vein that drains blood from the organ or body region. Thus, the simple pathway includes one artery, capillary bed, and vein associated with an organ or body region.

Blood transported to and from the spleen is an example of a simple blood flow pathway. The single splenic artery delivers oxygenated blood to the spleen with the exchange made in a capillary bed of the spleen, and a single splenic vein drains deoxygenated blood from the spleen. Arteries that provide only one pathway through which blood can reach an organ are referred to as **end arteries.**

Alternative Pathways

Several alternative circulatory pathways are possible, and these include various types of anastomoses and the portal systems. They differ from the simple pathway in the number of arteries, capillary beds, or veins that serve an organ or body region.

Figure 20.7 **How Blood Vessel Form Influences Function.** The anatomy and physiology of (a) arteries, (b) capillaries, and (c) veins are compared.

(a) Arteries

All systemic arteries transport oxygenated blood away from the heart. (Note that pulmonary arteries transport deoxygenated blood to the lungs.) Larger arteries branch into progressively smaller arteries that lead into arterioles.

Elastic arteries
stretch to accommodate the pulses of blood ejected from the heart and recoil to help propel blood through the arteries.

Muscular arteries
regulate distribution of blood through vasoconstriction and vasodilation.

Arterioles
regulate distribution of blood through vasoconstriction and vasodilation.

Artery anatomy

- Tunica intima
  - Endothelium
  - Subendothelial layer
- Tunica media
  - Elastic fibers
- Tunica externa

Lumen

(c) Veins

All systemic veins transport deoxygenated blood toward the heart. (Note that pulmonary veins transport oxygenated blood from the lungs.) Small veins drain blood into progressively larger veins.

Large veins
serve as a blood reservoir (at rest ~ 55% total blood).

Small/medium veins
Blood drains sequentially from venules, into small veins, then into medium-size veins, which drain into large veins.

Valves prevent backflow of blood

Vein anatomy

- Tunica intima
- Endothelium
- Subendothelial layer
- Tunica media
- Tunica externa
- Vasa vasorum

Valve

Lumen

Venules
receive blood from the capillaries.

(b) Capillaries

Capillaries receive blood from arterioles and allow for exchange of substances between the blood and cells.

Precapillary sphincters
regulate blood flow through capillary beds.

Precapillary sphincter contracted

Precapillary sphincter relaxed

Blood flow

Capillary bed

Continuous capillary

Least permeable

Fenestrated capillary

Varying degrees of permeability determine the size and amount of substances exchanged across capillary walls.

Sinusoid

Most permeable

(a) Simple pathway

(b) Alternative pathways
Anastomoses

Venous
anastomoses

Arterial
anastomoses

Arteriovenous anastomosis (shunt)

Portal system
Capillary bed   Capillary bed
Portal vein

Figure 20.8 Comparison of Simple and Alternative Blood Flow Pathways. (*a*) Simple pathways use one major artery, one capillary bed, and one major vein to deliver blood to a body region. (*b*) Alternative pathways include anastomoses and portal systems. Anastomoses differ in the number of either arteries, capillary beds, or veins that serve a body region. In a portal system, venous blood is directed through the capillary bed of another organ (like the liver) first before going back to the heart.

Three of the alternative pathways are designated as anastomoses. An **anastomosis** (a-nas′tō-mō′sis; pl., *anastomoses*) is the joining together of blood vessels. An **arterial anastomosis** includes two or more *arteries* converging to supply the same body region. (For example, figure 20.22*a* shows anastomoses among the superior and inferior epigastric arteries that serve the abdominal wall.) Other vessels, such as the coronary arteries, may have anastomoses that are so tiny that the function of the arteries may almost be considered end arteries; these arteries are called **functional end arteries** (see section 19.4a).

A **venous anastomosis** includes two or more *veins* draining the same body region. Veins tend to form many more anastomoses than

do arteries. Veins that drain the upper limb including the basilic, brachial, and cephalic veins provide an example of a venous anastomosis (see figure 20.19*b*).

An **arteriovenous anastomosis,** or *shunt*, transports blood from an artery directly into a vein, bypassing the capillary bed. These shunts are present in the fingers, toes, palms, and ears, and they allow these areas to be bypassed if the body is becoming hypothermic (cold).

A different type of blood vessel arrangement is a **portal system.** Blood flows through *two* capillary beds, with the two capillary beds separated by a portal vein. A **portal vein** delivers blood to another organ first, before the blood is sent back to the heart. Thus, the sequence of blood vessels is as follows: an artery, capillary bed, portal vein, capillary bed, and a vein. One example is the hypothalamo-hypophyseal portal system that extends between the hypothalamus and the anterior pituitary (see section 17.8a). This portal system provides a more direct means of delivering hypothalamic hormones to the anterior pituitary. Another is the hepatic portal system, which is described later in this chapter.

💡 WHAT DID YOU LEARN?

5 How does each of the various alternative blood vessel pathways differ from the simple pathway?

20.2 Capillary Exchange

The function of capillaries is to allow for the exchange of substances (e.g., respiratory gases, nutrients, wastes, and hormones) between the blood and the surrounding tissues. Exchange processes include diffusion, vesicular transport, and bulk flow.

20.2a Diffusion and Vesicular Transport

✓ LEARNING OBJECTIVE

1. Explain the process of diffusion and vesicular transport between capillaries and tissues.

Within systemic capillaries, substances such as oxygen, hormones, and nutrients move by **diffusion** (section 4.3b) from their relatively high concentration in the blood into the interstitial fluid and then into the tissue cells, where the concentration of these materials is lower. Conversely, carbon dioxide and waste products diffuse from the higher concentration in the tissue cells to the lower concentration in the blood. Very small solutes (e.g., O_2, CO_2, glucose, ions) and fluids may diffuse via the endothelial cells or intercellular clefts, while larger solutes, such as small proteins, must pass through the fenestrations in fenestrated capillaries or gaps in sinusoids.

Vesicular transport occurs when endothelial cells use pinocytosis (see section 4.3c) to fuse fluid-filled vesicles with the plasma membrane and transport their contents either from the blood to the interstitial fluid or from the interstitial fluid into the blood. Solutes such as certain hormones (e.g., insulin) and fatty acids are transported across the endothelial cells by this method.

💡 WHAT DID YOU LEARN?

6 What substances are transported by diffusion through the capillaries? Which substances leave the capillaries by vesicular transport?

20.2b Bulk Flow

✔ LEARNING OBJECTIVES

2. Explain the processes of bulk flow, filtration, and reabsorption.

3. Compare and contrast hydrostatic pressure and colloid osmotic pressure in the capillaries.

Bulk flow refers to the movement of large amounts of fluids and their dissolved substances in one direction down a pressure gradient. **Filtration,** a process that occurs on the arterial end of a capillary, is the movement of fluid by bulk flow out of the blood through the openings in the capillaries (e.g., intercellular clefts, fenestrations). During this process, fluids and small solutes flow through easily, while large solutes are generally blocked. In contrast, reabsorption occurs on the venous end of a capillary. **Reabsorption** is the movement of fluid by bulk flow in the opposite direction, back into the blood (figure 20.9).

How is it possible to have filtration on the arterial end, and reabsorption on the venous end, of a capillary? The direction of movement is dependent upon the net pressure of two opposing forces at the capillary level—hydrostatic pressure and colloid osmotic pressure; both are measured in millimeters of mercury (mm Hg).

Hydrostatic Pressure (HP)

Hydrostatic pressure (HP) is the physical force exerted by a fluid on a structure. For example, **blood hydrostatic pressure (HP_b)** (or simply *blood pressure*) is the force exerted per unit area by the blood as it presses against the vessel wall. Blood hydrostatic pressure promotes filtration from the capillary.

The interstitial fluid also has its own hydrostatic pressure, called **interstitial fluid hydrostatic pressure (HP_{if}),** which is the force of the interstitial fluid on the external surface of the blood vessel. For most tissues, the interstitial fluid hydrostatic pressure is very small and for simplicity's sake is assumed to be close to zero. Thus, for our discussion, the main hydrostatic pressure is the blood hydrostatic pressure, which pushes materials *out* of the capillary.

Colloid Osmotic Pressure (COP)

The other main force regulating filtration and reabsorption is osmotic pressure, which refers to the "pull" of water into an area by osmosis due to the higher relative concentration of solutes. **Colloid osmotic pressure (COP)** refers to the pull of water back into a tissue by the tissue's concentration of proteins (colloid).

The **blood colloid osmotic pressure (COP_b)** is the force that draws fluid back into the blood due to the proteins in blood, such as albumin. Blood colloid osmotic pressure opposes hydrostatic pressure, and thus promotes reabsorption. Clinicians also use the term **oncotic** (*onkosis* = swelling) **pressure** to describe the blood colloid osmotic pressure.

An **interstitial fluid colloid osmotic pressure (COP_{if})** also exists, but its value is relatively low because few proteins are present in the interstitial fluid. COP_{if} may range from 0 to 5 mm Hg. By knowing the specific values for the hydrostatic and osmotic pressures, the direction of bulk flow can be determined through the calculation of net filtration pressure.

💡 WHAT DID YOU LEARN?

7 What is the difference between hydrostatic pressure and osmotic pressure?

Figure 20.9 Bulk Flow at Capillaries. Blood hydrostatic pressure is greater at the arterial end of the capillary and less at the venous end of the capillary. The osmotic pressures remain relatively constant, resulting in a net filtration out of the arterial end of the capillary, and a net reabsorption into the venous end of the capillary. AP|R

20.2c Net Filtration Pressure

LEARNING OBJECTIVES

4. Define net filtration pressure (NFP).
5. Calculate net filtration pressure for both the arterial end and the venous end of a capillary.

Net filtration pressure (NFP) is the difference between the net hydrostatic pressure (difference between the blood and interstitial fluid hydrostatic pressures) and the net colloid osmotic pressure (difference between the blood and the interstitial fluid colloid osmotic pressures) and is shown in figure 20.9. The net filtration pressure may be determined by the following equation:

$$NFP = (HP_b - HP_{if}) - (COP_b - COP_{if})$$

where HP_b = the hydrostatic pressure of blood, HP_{if} = the hydrostatic pressure of the interstitial fluid, COP_b = the colloid osmotic pressure of blood, and COP_{if} = the colloid osmotic pressure of the interstitial fluid. This equation is a variation of **Starling's law,** developed by the physiologist Ernest Starling. Starling was among the first to discover that hydrostatic and osmotic forces work against one another to drive the filtration and reabsorption of materials across a capillary membrane.

Net filtration pressure changes as the blood moves from the arterial end of the capillary to the venous end of the capillary. On the arterial end of a capillary, HP_b is typically around 35 mm Hg, HP_{if} is assumed to be 0 mm Hg, COP_b is around 26 mm Hg, and COP_{if} is around 5 mm Hg. The net filtration pressure is calculated as follows:

$$(35 \text{ mm Hg} - 0 \text{ mm Hg}) - (26 \text{ mm Hg} - 5 \text{ mm Hg})$$
$$= 35 \text{ mm Hg} - 21 \text{ mm Hg}$$
$$= 14 \text{ mm Hg}$$

Notice that NFP has a positive value of 14 mm Hg at the arterial end. A positive value indicates that the hydrostatic pressure pushing fluids out of the blood is greater than the net colloid osmotic pressure pulling the fluid back into the capillary. Consequently, *filtration,* or the net movement of fluid out of the blood vessel into the surrounding tissue, occurs on the arterial end of a capillary.

Now consider the events on the venous end of a capillary. Blood hydrostatic pressure decreases continuously as it moves through the capillary to reach the venule end, since there is a net movement of fluids out of the capillary as blood moves through the length of the capillary. This smaller amount of blood means the blood hydrostatic pressure at the venous end of a capillary is lower—usually around 16 to 20 mm Hg.

In contrast, the colloid osmotic pressures of both the blood and the interstitial fluid remain relatively constant throughout the capillary and have values similar to those on the arterial end of the capillary: COP_b is around 26 mm Hg and COP_{if} is around 5 mm Hg. Again, HP_{if} is assumed to be 0 mm Hg. Net filtration pressure is calculated on the venous end as follows:

$$(16 \text{ mm Hg} - 0 \text{ mm Hg}) - (26 \text{ mm Hg} - 5 \text{ mm Hg})$$
$$= 16 \text{ mm Hg} - 21 \text{ mm Hg}$$
$$= -5 \text{ mm Hg}$$

Notice that in this case, NFP has a negative value (–5 mm Hg). A negative value for NFP occurs because blood hydrostatic pressure is less than net osmotic pressure. Consequently, reabsorption occurs on the venous end of the capillary with a net movement of fluid back into the blood vessel from the surrounding tissue.

Keep in mind that the numbers for the pressures used to calculate net filtration pressure are examples only. The specific values depend upon the part of the body, the amount of blood entering a specific capillary bed, and the general health of the individual.

WHAT DO YOU THINK?

1. Is it possible for blood pressure to decrease to such a degree that capillary exchange ceases? Explain.

WHAT DID YOU LEARN?

8. How does the hydrostatic pressure change from the arterial end of a capillary to the venous end of a capillary? Do you see similar changes in colloid osmotic pressure?

9. Which two pressures have the largest values? Explain how each of these specifically influences filtration and reabsorption.

20.2d The Role of the Lymphatic System

LEARNING OBJECTIVE

6. Explain the lymphatic system's role at the capillary bed.

Although net filtration occurs at the arterial end of a capillary and net reabsorption at its venous end, not all of the fluid is reabsorbed at the venous end of the capillary. The capillary typically reabsorbs only about 85% of the fluid that has passed into the interstitial fluid. What happens to the excess 15% of fluid that wasn't reabsorbed?

Another body system, the **lymphatic system,** is responsible for picking up this excess fluid and returning it to the blood. Lymph vessels reabsorb this excess fluid, filter it, and return it to the venous circulation. These lymph vessels and the lymphatic system in general are described in detail in chapter 21.

WHAT DID YOU LEARN?

10. If these lymph vessels were nonfunctional, what would happen to the amount of interstitial fluid around the capillary bed?

20.3 Local Blood Flow

Recall that there is simply not enough blood in the body to fill all capillaries at the same time. Blood must therefore be directed to organs and tissues where it is most needed and away from areas where it is not. **Local blood flow** is the blood delivered locally to the capillaries of a specific tissue and is measured in milliliters per minute. Recall that the specific amount of blood entering capillaries per unit time per gram of tissue is called perfusion. The ultimate goal of the cardiovascular system is for *adequate perfusion of all tissues.*

The amount of blood delivered to a specific organ or tissue is dependent upon several factors, including (1) the degree of vascularization of the tissue, (2) local regulatory factors that alter blood flow, and (3) total blood flow.

20.3a Degree of Vascularization and Angiogenesis

LEARNING OBJECTIVES

1. Describe what is meant by degree of vascularization.
2. Explain the process of angiogenesis and how it aids perfusion.

The **degree of vascularization,** or the extent of blood vessel distribution within a tissue, determines the potential ability of blood delivery. Organs that are very active metabolically, such as the brain, skeletal muscle, the heart, and the liver generally are highly vascularized. In comparison, some structures, such as tendons and ligaments, have little vascularization; blood delivery to these tissues is limited.

The amount of vascularization in a given tissue may change over time through the process of angiogenesis. **Angiogenesis** (an'jē-ō-jen'ĕ-sis; *angio* = vessel, *genesis* = production) is the formation of new blood vessels in tissues that require them. This process helps provide adequate perfusion through long-term anatomic changes that occur over several weeks to months. For example, angiogenesis is stimulated in skeletal muscle in response to aerobic training; in adipose tissue, angiogenesis occurs when an individual gains weight in the form of fat deposits. Angiogenesis also occurs in response to occlusion (blockage) of coronary vessels, thus providing alternative routes to deliver blood to the heart wall.

Regression (or return to previous state) of vessels is also possible. For example, some skeletal muscle blood vessels regress when an individual who was physically active becomes sedentary, or blood vessels in adipose tissue regress when the amount of adipose tissue is decreased through restriction of food and increased physical activity.

WHAT DID YOU LEARN?

11 In what ways is angiogenesis stimulated in skeletal muscle? In adipose tissue?

20.3b Local, Short-Term Regulation

LEARNING OBJECTIVES

3. Compare and contrast a vasodilator and a vasoconstrictor.

4. Explain how a tissue autoregulates local blood flow based on metabolic needs.

5. Describe how local blood flow is altered by tissue damage and as part of the body's defense.

Local regulation of blood flow occurs on a continual basis in response to changes in metabolic activity of tissues. Local blood flow is also altered in response to tissue damage or as part of the body's defense systems. The stimulus is changing concentrations of certain chemicals, collectively called **vasoactive chemicals.** They are classified according to their action as either vasodilators or vasoconstrictors. **Vasodilators** are substances that both dilate arterioles and relax precapillary sphincters, so there is increased blood flow into a capillary bed. **Vasoconstrictors** are substances that both constrict arterioles and cause contraction of precapillary sphincters to decrease blood flow into a capillary bed (see figure 20.5).

Autoregulation and Changing Metabolic Activity

Autoregulation is the process by which a tissue itself regulates or controls its local blood flow in response to its changing metabolic needs. The initial stimulus typically is inadequate perfusion due to increased metabolic activity of the tissue. If the tissue is not receiving adequate blood perfusion, then the oxygen and nutrient levels decline, while there is an increase in carbon dioxide, lactic acid, hydrogen ion (H^+), and potassium ion (K^+) levels. These altered levels act as local vasodilators, and as a result additional blood enters the capillaries serving the tissue. As perfusion increases in the tissue and these levels adjust back to homeostatic values, the vessels constrict. Thus, there is a negative feedback loop between elevated levels of these molecules and the degree of vasodilation.

Autoregulation is most noticeable when blood supply is temporarily disrupted and then restored. When the blood flow is temporarily disrupted, the tissue is deprived of needed oxygen and nutrients, and metabolic wastes accumulate. When the local blood flow is restored, there is a marked increase in blood flow to the affected tissue—a condition called **reactive hyperemia.** The additional blood is required to resupply the oxygen and nutrients and eliminate the accumulated wastes.

An example of reactive hyperemia occurs when you enter a warm room after being outside in the cold, and your cheeks turn bright red. When you were outside in the cold, the blood vessels in the dermis constricted, forcing more blood away from the dermis through an arteriovenous shunt to conserve heat. When you leave the cold, the reddish color of your cheeks is due to increased blood flow in the dermis. After a short period of time, the reddish color subsides, as normal blood flow in the skin resumes.

Short-Term Regulation Due to Damaged Tissue or as Part of the Body's Defense System

Local blood flow is also regulated when vasoactive chemicals are released from damaged tissue, leukocytes, and platelets in response to tissue damage or as part of the body's defense. This process is referred to as *inflammation* and is discussed in detail in section 22.3d.

Table 20.3	Substances and Systems That Affect Blood Pressure and Flow	
Effect	**Local Substances**	**Hormones and Neurotransmitters**
Vasodilators	Decreased oxygen levels Decreased nutrient levels Increased CO_2, H^+, K^+, lactic acid levels Histamine Bradykinin Nitric oxide	Atrial natriuretic peptide (ANP) Epinephrine (bound to β-adrenergic receptors within coronary and skeletal muscle blood vessels)
Vasoconstrictors	Increased oxygen levels Increased nutrient levels Decreased CO_2, H^+, K^+, lactic acid levels Endothelins Prostaglandins Thromboxanes	Angiotensin II Aldosterone Antidiuretic hormone (ADH) Norepinephrine (bound to α-adrenergic receptors of most blood vessels including the skin and abdominal organs)[1]

1. A *decrease* in sympathetic stimulation will result in a decrease in the listed effect, much like taking the foot off of the gas pedal will slow down a car.

For example, **histamine** and **bradykinin** are released in response to a trauma, allergic reaction, infection, or even exercise. These chemicals may cause vasodilation by directly stimulating arterioles or indirectly by stimulating endothelial cells of the vessel to release nitric oxide. **Nitric oxide** is a very powerful, but short-lived, vasodilator.

Other vasoactive substances, such as **prostaglandins** and **thromboxanes,** can cause vasoconstriction (see description of local hormones in section 17.3b). Recall from section 18.4a that if endothelial cells are damaged, they release an array of chemicals that are powerful vasoconstrictors to help prevent blood loss through the damaged vessel. See **table 20.3** for a list of vasodilators and vasoconstrictors.

 WHAT DID YOU LEARN?

12 What relationship exists between metabolic activity and local blood flow?

20.3c The Relationship of Local and Total Blood Flow

LEARNING OBJECTIVE

6. Explain the general relationship of total blood flow to local blood flow.

Maintaining sufficient local blood flow transported throughout the body (to ensure adequate perfusion of all tissues) is ultimately dependent on total blood flow. **Total blood flow** is the amount of blood transported throughout the entire vasculature in a given period of time (usually expressed in liters per minute). Total blood flow equals cardiac output. The average cardiac output at rest is 5.25 liters per minute (L/min), and may increase substantially during exercise (see section 19.9). If cardiac output increases, total blood flow increases, and additional blood is available to body tissues. If cardiac output decreases, total blood flow decreases, and less blood is available to the tissues. The factors that regulate total blood flow are dependent upon the two components of the cardiovascular system (both the heart and blood vessels), as well the blood that is transported through them. These factors are described in detail the next section.

 WHAT DID YOU LEARN?

13 How is local blood flow dependent on total blood flow?

20.4 Blood Pressure, Resistance, and Total Blood Flow

Here we integrate concepts on the heart, blood vessels, and blood to describe: first, blood pressure and how the pumping action of the heart establishes a pressure gradient to drive the blood through the vasculature; second, how blood experiences resistance as it is transported through blood vessels; and third, how together blood pressure and resistance determine total blood flow.

20.4a Blood Pressure

✔ LEARNING OBJECTIVES

1. Define blood pressure and a blood pressure gradient.
2. Compare and contrast blood pressure and blood pressure gradients in the arteries, capillaries, and veins.
3. Calculate pulse pressure and mean arterial pressure (MAP) in the arteries.
4. Explain the mechanisms that help overcome the small pressure gradient in veins to return blood to the heart.

Blood pressure is the force per unit area that blood exerts against the inside wall of a vessel (as described earlier in the section on bulk flow). A **blood pressure gradient** is the change in blood pressure from one end of a blood vessel to its other end. A blood pressure gradient exists in the vasculature because blood pressure is highest in the arteries as the heart rhythmically contracts, and it is lowest in the veins. Blood pressure gradients are both clinically and physiologically significant because they are the driving force that propels blood through the vessels. Please refer to **figure 20.10** as you read through this section.

Arterial Blood Pressure

Blood flow is pulsing, or *pulsatile*, in arteries as a consequence of the ventricles contracting and relaxing. The highest blood pressure generated in arteries is during ventricular systole when the artery is maxi-

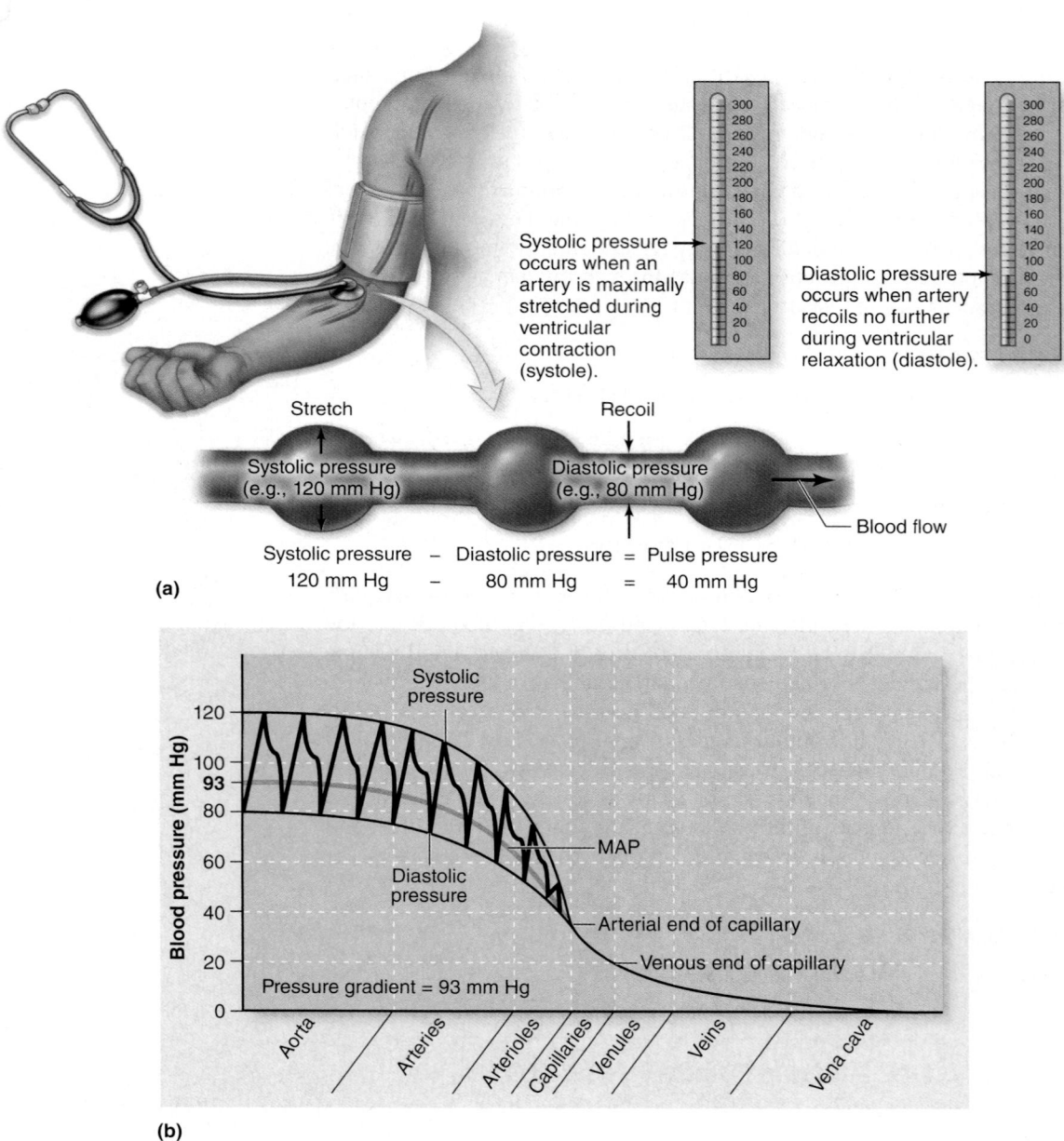

Figure 20.10 Blood Pressure. (*a*) Blood pressure within the arteries is pulsatile. Systolic pressure is when the artery is maximally stretched during ventricular contraction. Diastolic pressure is when the vessel recoils no further, which occurs during ventricular relaxation. Pulse pressure is the additional pressure placed on the artery from when the heart is relaxing to when it is contracting. (*b*) A tracing compares the blood pressure changes as blood flows through the different vessels in the cardiovascular system.

CLINICAL VIEW
Detecting a Pulse Point

A **pulse** refers to the rhythmic throbbing of an arterial wall as blood is being pumped through it. A pulse reflects the pulse pressure. Measuring the pulse is clinically significant for the following reasons:

1. It allows us to indirectly determine the rate of our heartbeat.
2. The force of the pulse can inform us about blood pressure, as high blood pressure will produce a more forceful pulse, and low blood pressure will produce a weaker pulse.

3. The absence of a pulse can allow us to determine if blood flow to a body part is lacking.

Pulse points can be found throughout the body and typically are located where an artery may be compressed against a bone or other solid structure. Two fingers are used to palpate the pulse, but the thumb is typically not used because it has a weak pulse of its own, which may interfere with pulse detection. Some common pulse locations are shown and listed in **table 20.4**. See if you can palpate these pulse points on yourself.

Table 20.4	Common Pulse Locations	
Artery	**Best Location to Detect Pulse**	
Superficial temporal	Anterior to the ear superior to the root (origin) of the zygomatic process of the temporal bone	
Facial	Immediately anterior to the angle of the mandible and the masseter muscle	
Common carotid	Anterior to the sternocleidomastoid muscle and lateral to the larynx and trachea	
Brachial	Along the medial surface of the arm, midway between the axilla and antecubital regions	
Radial	Radial side of the wrist, between the brachioradialis and flexor carpi radialis tendons	
Femoral	Immediately inferior to the inguinal ligament (groin), approximately halfway between the pubis and the anterior superior iliac spine	
Popliteal	Popliteal fossa, with the knee flexed slightly	
Posterior tibial	Posteroinferior to the medial malleolus of the tibia	
Dorsalis pedis	Either over the navicular (on the dorsal medial side of the foot) or between the dorsal interspace between the first and second toes	

Superfical temporal artery
Facial artery
Common carotid artery
Brachial artery
Radial artery
Femoral artery
Popliteal artery
Posterior
Posterior tibial artery
Dorsalis pedis artery

mally stretched; this value is recorded as the **systolic pressure.** The lowest pressure is during ventricular diastole when the artery recoils no further; this value is recorded as the **diastolic pressure.** Arterial blood pressure is expressed as a ratio, in which the numerator (upper number) is the systolic pressure and the denominator (lower number) is the diastolic pressure. The average adult has a blood pressure of 120/80 mm Hg, but blood pressure can vary greatly among individuals. Two values can be calculated from systolic pressure and diastolic pressure: pulse pressure and mean arterial pressure.

Pulse Pressure **Pulse pressure** is the additional pressure placed on the arteries from when the heart is resting (diastolic

blood pressure) to when the heart is contracting (systolic blood pressure). Pulse pressure can be calculated by taking the difference between the systolic and the diastolic blood pressure. So, for an individual with a blood pressure of 120/80 mm Hg, the pulse pressure would be 40 mm Hg (120 mm Hg − 80 mm Hg = 40 mm Hg).

Pulse pressure is significant because it is a measure of the elasticity and recoil of arteries. Healthy elastic arteries expand and recoil easily, assisting in the movement of blood through the cardiovascular system. However, as vessels age or become diseased (e.g., with atherosclerosis), arteries lose their elasticity and expand and recoil less readily, making it more difficult for the heart to pump blood.

Thus, although temporary changes in pulse pressure are associated with increased cardiac output, such as would occur during exercise, permanent changes in pulse pressure may be an indication of unhealthy arteries.

The rhythmic throbbing sensations associated with pulse pressure are palpated in superficial elastic and muscular arteries to determine one's "pulse" (see table 20.4).

Mean Arterial Pressure **Mean arterial pressure (MAP)** is the average (or mean) measure of the blood pressure forces on the arteries. Because diastolic pressure usually lasts slightly longer than systolic pressure, MAP is not simply an average of these two pressures. Rather, MAP may be estimated as follows:

$$\text{MAP} = \text{Diastolic pressure} + \frac{1}{3}\text{Pulse pressure}$$

So for a person with average blood pressure of 120/80 mm Hg, his or her MAP would be approximately 93 mm Hg (80 + 40/3 = 93).

Mean arterial pressure is clinically significant because it provides a numerical value for how well body tissues and organs are perfused. A MAP of 70 to 110 mm Hg typically indicates good perfusion. A MAP lower than 60 mm Hg may indicate insufficient blood flow, and a very high MAP could indicate the delivery of too large of blood flow to body tissues with the possibility of causing edema (swelling) in the interstitial tissues (see Clinical View "Cerebral Edema").

Pulse pressure and mean arterial pressure are highest in the arteries closest to the heart, such as the aorta. As the arteries branch into smaller vessels and travel greater distances from the ventricles, both of these pressures decrease. The pressure gradient in arteries is relatively steep and facilitates the movement of blood through the arteries (see figure 20.10b).

Capillary Blood Pressure

By the time the blood reaches the capillaries, fluctuations between systolic and diastolic blood pressure disappear, so the pulse pressure disappears. Blood flow is smooth and even as it enters the capillaries.

Capillary blood pressure must be sufficient for exchange of substances between the blood and surrounding tissue, but not be so high that it would damage the fragile vessels. Blood pressure on the arterial end of the capillary is about 40 mm Hg and drops quickly (along the approximately 1-millimeter length of a capillary) to below 20 mm Hg on the venous end of the capillary. These blood pressure values are used to determine net filtration pressure for capillary exchange as previously described. Recall that the relatively high blood pressure on the arteriole end of the capillary accounts for filtration, and the relatively low blood pressure on the venous end allows for reabsorption as colloid osmotic pressure pulls fluids back into the blood.

Venous Blood Pressure

The movement of blood from the capillaries back to the heart via the veins is called **venous return.** Blood pressure in the venules and veins is not pulsatile because the blood is far removed from (and thus not influenced by) the pumping action of the heart. Therefore, veins also have no demonstrable pulse pressure. Blood pressure is 20 mm Hg in the venules and almost 0 mm Hg by the time blood travels through the inferior vena cava to the right atrium of the heart. Thus, the pressure gradient in the veins is only 20 mm Hg. This relatively small blood pressure gradient is generally insufficient to move blood through the veins under given conditions, such as

CLINICAL VIEW
Circulatory Shock

Circulatory shock is any state in which there is insufficient blood flow for adequate perfusion of the body's tissues, typically due to impaired pumping of the heart (e.g., caused by congestive heart failure or a malfunctioning pacemaker) or to low venous return. Circulatory shock associated with low venous return can result from:

- Decreased blood volume due to hemorrhage, dehydration, or systemic release of histamine in an allergic reaction that increases capillary permeability
- An obstructed vein
- Venous pooling caused by extended immobility or by extensive vasodilation (resulting from certain bacterial toxins or from brainstem trauma that results in loss of vasomotor tone)

when an individual is standing. Thus, venous return must be facilitated by valves within veins and two "pumps"—the skeletal muscle pump and the respiratory pump **(figure 20.11)**.

The **skeletal muscle pump** assists the movement of blood primarily within the limbs. As skeletal muscles contract, veins are squeezed to help propel the blood toward the heart, and valves prevent blood backflow. When skeletal muscles are more active—for example, when a person is walking—blood is pumped more quickly and efficiently toward the heart by the skeletal muscle pump. Con-

versely, extended inactivity leads to blood pooling in the leg veins, which increases an individual's risk for development of deep vein thrombosis (see Clinical View: "Deep Vein Thrombosis").

The **respiratory pump** assists the movement of blood within the thoracic cavity. The diaphragm contracts and flattens as we inspire (inhale). Intra-abdominal pressure increases and places pressure on the vessels within the abdominal cavity. Concomitantly, thoracic cavity volume increases and intrathoracic pressure decreases. Blood is propelled from the vessels in the abdominopelvic cavity into the vessels in the thoracic cavity. When we expire (exhale), the diaphragm relaxes and returns to its dome shape. Thoracic cavity volume decreases and intrathoracic pressure increases, which places pressure on vessels within the thoracic cavity. Blood moves from the vessels in the thoracic cavity back into the heart. In addition, intra-abdominal pressure decreases, allowing blood to move from the lower limbs into the abdominal vessels. When breathing rate increases—for example, when a person is exercising—blood is moved more quickly back to the heart by the respiratory pump.

Blood Pressure Gradient in the Systemic Circulation

We now know the normal range of blood pressure values in the various portions of the vasculature (along with significant concepts related to each type of vessel). We can use the average blood pressure in the arteries close to the heart and the blood pressure in the inferior vena cava to calculate the total blood pressure gradient in the systemic circulation. This can be determined by viewing figure 20.10. The average or mean blood pressure (MAP) in the arteries is 93 mm Hg. The blood pressure in the inferior vena cava is 0 mm Hg. Thus, the blood pressure gradient established by the pumping action of the heart is 93 mm Hg (93–0).

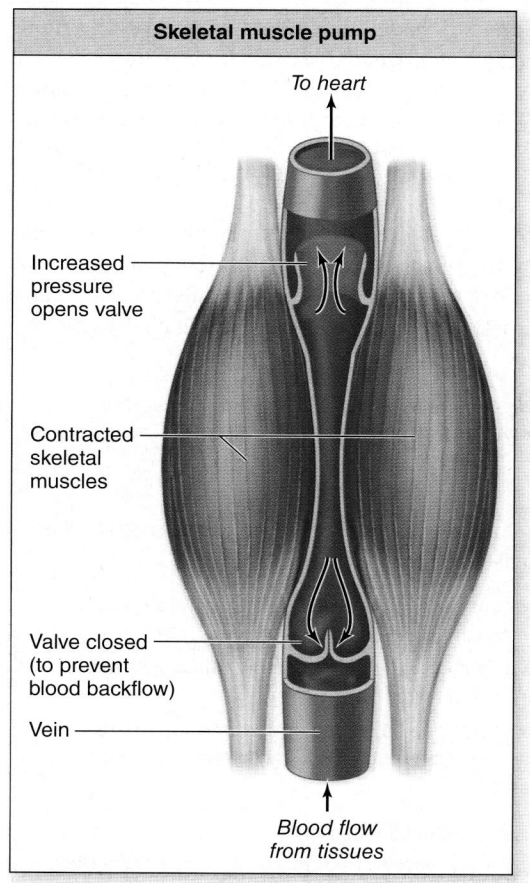

Skeletal muscle pump

To heart

Increased pressure opens valve

Contracted skeletal muscles

Valve closed (to prevent blood backflow)

Vein

Blood flow from tissues

(a)

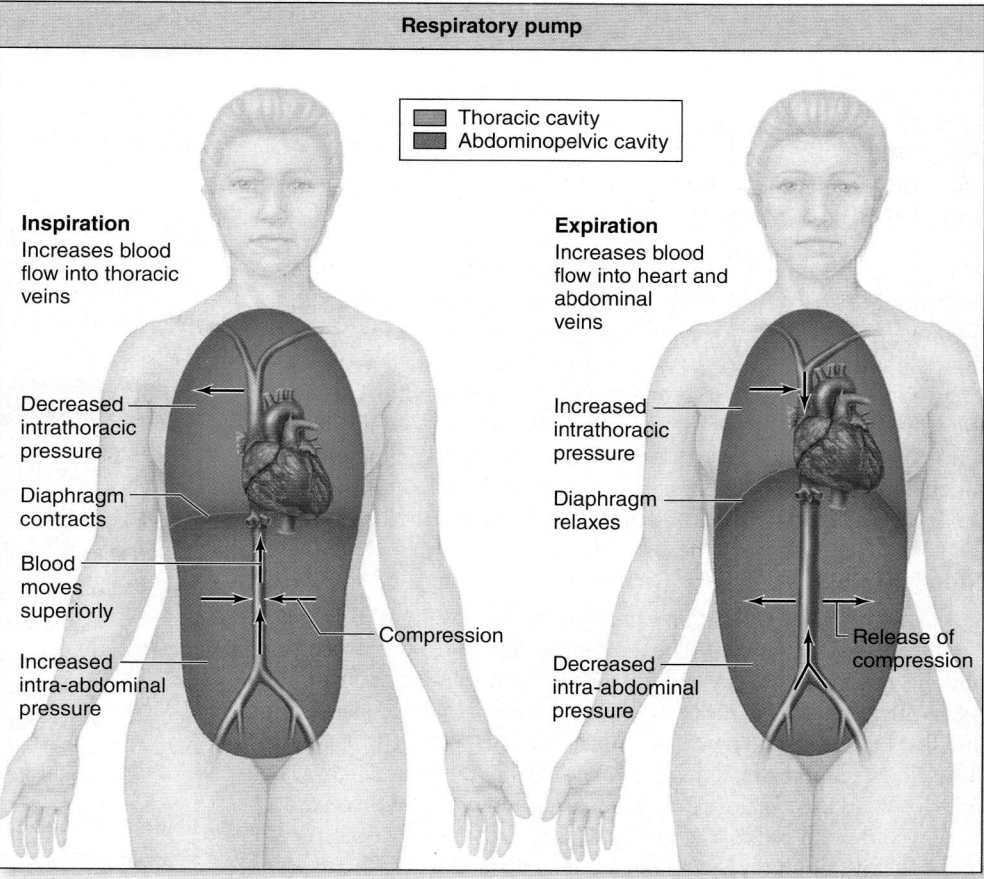

Respiratory pump

Thoracic cavity
Abdominopelvic cavity

Inspiration
Increases blood flow into thoracic veins

Decreased intrathoracic pressure

Diaphragm contracts

Blood moves superiorly

Compression

Increased intra-abdominal pressure

Expiration
Increases blood flow into heart and abdominal veins

Increased intrathoracic pressure

Diaphragm relaxes

Release of compression

Decreased intra-abdominal pressure

(b)

Figure 20.11 Factors That Influence Venous Return. To help overcome the small pressure gradient in veins, blood return to the heart via veins is facilitated by both (*a*) a skeletal muscle pump within the limbs, and (*b*) the respiratory pump within the torso.

INTEGRATE

LEARNING STRATEGY

A blood pressure gradient is established by the heart when it pumps blood through the vessels, much like a pressure gradient is created by a water pump to force water through pipes. In both cases, the stronger the pump, the greater the pressure gradient that can be established, and the greater the flow that is possible.

Most importantly, this blood pressure gradient is the driving force to move blood through the vasculature. Changes in the blood pressure gradient are directly correlated with changes in total blood flow. An increase in the blood pressure gradient increases total blood flow, whereas a decrease in the blood pressure gradient decreases total blood flow.

How is it possible to change the steepness of the pressure gradient? The blood pressure gradient is altered by changes in cardiac output. An increase in cardiac output will increase the pressure gradient. Conversely, a decrease in cardiac output will decrease the pressure gradient (see section 19.9).

WHAT DID YOU LEARN?

14 A 55-year-old female has an arterial blood pressure reading of 155/95 mm Hg. What is her pulse pressure and her mean arterial pressure?

15 What is the physiologic significance of capillary blood pressure?

16 How is the small pressure gradient in veins overcome?

17 How is the pressure gradient to move blood through the systemic circulation calculated? What is the significance of this pressure gradient?

20.4b Resistance

LEARNING OBJECTIVE

5. Define resistance, and explain how it is influenced by blood viscosity, vessel length, and vessel radius.

Resistance also influences total blood flow. **Resistance** is defined as the amount of friction the blood experiences as it travels through the blood vessels. Blood flow is always opposed by resistance. This friction is due to the contact between blood and the blood vessel wall. The term **peripheral resistance** is typically used when discussing the resistance of blood in the blood vessels (as opposed to the resistance of blood in the heart). Several factors affect peripheral resistance, including blood viscosity, blood vessel length, and the size of the lumen of blood vessels (as indicated by vessel radius).

Blood Viscosity

Viscosity refers to the resistance of a fluid to its flow. More generally, it is the "thickness" of a fluid. The thicker the fluid, the more viscous it is, and the greater its resistance to flow. The thickness is dependent on the relative percentage of particles in the fluid and their interactions with one another. Because blood contains formed elements, plasma proteins, and platelets, it is approximately 4.5 to 5.5 times more viscous than water. As a result, blood has greater resistance to flow than water would.

A change in blood's viscosity causes a change in resistance of blood flow through a vessel. For example, if someone is anemic (and has a lower than normal number of erythrocytes), then that person's blood viscosity would be lower, and the blood would have less resistance to flow. Conversely, if someone has a greater than normal

amount of formed elements (e.g., if an individual tries to increase the number of erythrocytes in his or her blood; see Clinical View: "Blood Doping" in chapter 18), or the individual is dehydrated, then the blood would be more viscous and have greater resistance to flow.

Vessel Length

Increasing vessel length increases resistance, because the longer the vessel, the greater the friction the fluid experiences as it travels through the vessel. Consequently, shorter vessels offer less resistance than longer vessels with comparable diameters. Normally, vessel length in a person remains relatively constant. However, if one gains a large amount of weight, the body must produce miles of additional vessel length by angiogenesis for blood to travel through the extra fat. Thus, vessel resistance increases if one gains weight, and decreases if someone loses a lot of weight (because those vessels are no longer needed and regress).

Vessel Radius

Blood viscosity and vessel length remain relatively constant in a typical healthy individual. The major way resistance may be regulated is by altering vessel lumen radius (and thus changing the vessel diameter.)

How specifically does vessel radius influence resistance? Blood tends to flow fastest in the center of the vessel lumen, while blood near the sides of the vessels slows, because it encounters resistance from the nearby vessel wall. This difference in flow rate within a blood vessel (or in any conduit) is called **laminar flow.** You can see evidence of laminar flow by studying a river: The water flow near the banks or edges of the river is a bit slower or sluggish, while the water flow near the center of the river is quite fast in comparison. So, if vessel diameter increases, relatively less blood flows near the edges and overall blood flow increases. In contrast, if vessel radius decreases, relatively more blood flows near the edges and overall blood flow decreases.

The relationship between blood flow and the radius of blood vessel lumen may be stated as follows (where the symbol $\propto$ means "is proportional to"):

$$F \propto r^4$$

where F = flow and r = radius of the lumen of a vessel. This mathematical expression reflects that flow is directly proportional to the fourth power of a radius. If a vessel vasodilates and its radius increases from 1 millimeter (mm) to 2 mm, the overall change in flow

INTEGRATE

LEARNING STRATEGY

Drinking through a straw provides an easy way to demonstrate the variables that influence resistance:

- **Viscosity.** Water or soda moves through a straw more easily than does a thick vanilla milkshake.
- **Vessel length.** It is easier to drink through a relatively short straw compared with a very long, twisty straw.
- **Vessel radius.** Water can be sipped through a normal-sized straw more easily than through a hollow coffee stirrer with its smaller diameter.

Greater resistance is experienced when drinking thick liquids, using a longer straw, or using a more narrow straw. In the same way, an increase in resistance is exhibited with more viscous blood, increased total length of blood vessels, and vasoconstriction of blood vessels.

is 16 times greater: If r = 1 mm, then r^4 = 1, and F = 1 mm per second; and when r = 2 mm, then r^4 = 16, and F = 16 mm per second. In contrast, if a vessel vasoconstricts and its radius decreases from 2 mm to 1 mm, the overall change in flow is 16 times less.

Any vessel may vasoconstrict or vasodilate; however, resistance usually is regulated specifically by vasoconstriction and vasodilation of the arterioles, a change systemically controlled by the sympathetic division of the ANS. Thus, because there are so many arterioles (and the overall vessel length of all arterioles is so great), even small changes in vessel radius significantly change resistance, and therefore can have dramatic effects on blood flow.

Note that atherosclerosis (see Clinical View: "Atherosclerosis") is a disease process where a plaque narrows the lumen of blood vessels. Thus, resistance is increased as blood moves through the atherosclerotic blood vessels.

WHAT DID YOU LEARN?

18 How is resistance defined?

19 What are the three factors that alter resistance? How does each affect blood flow in vessels?

20.4c The Relationship of Blood Flow to Blood Pressure Gradients and Resistance

LEARNING OBJECTIVES

6. Explain the relationship of both blood pressure gradients and resistance to total blood flow.

7. Discuss why blood pressure increases with increased resistance in the systemic circulation.

Total blood flow is the amount of blood that moves through the cardiovascular system per unit time and is influenced by both blood pressure gradients and resistance, as previously described. This relationship is expressed mathematically as follows:

$$F \propto \frac{\Delta P}{R}$$

where F = blood flow, ΔP = pressure gradient $(P_1 - P_2)$, and R = resistance.

Systemic Blood Pressure Gradient

The preceding formula demonstrates that blood flow is *directly* related to the pressure gradient. Thus, as the blood pressure gradient increases, total blood flow is greater, and as the blood pressure gradient decreases, total blood flow lessens (assuming resistance remains the same). Recall that an increase in cardiac output will increase the pressure gradient, while a decrease in cardiac output will decrease the pressure gradient. Consequently, increasing blood flow is possible with a steeper blood pressure gradient—however, it is a change exhibited only with greater effort exerted by the heart.

Resistance

The preceding mathematical expression also demonstrates that blood flow is inversely related to resistance. If resistance increases, then blood flow lessens, whereas if resistance decreases, blood flow increases (assuming the pressure gradient remains the same).

Recall that resistance is increased with (1) an increase in blood viscosity (e.g., as occurs with greater concentration of erythrocytes); (2) an increase in blood vessel length (e.g., a change that accompanies weight gain); and (3) a decrease in vessel lumen diameter (e.g., a change that occurs with a net increase in vasoconstriction and in individuals with atherosclerosis).

Relationship of Systemic Blood Pressure and Resistance

Individuals with *sustained* increased resistance (e.g., that accompanies significant weight gain, or with atherosclerosis) generally exhibit elevated arterial blood pressure readings. This condition is clinically significant; it occurs because a greater pressure gradient must be produced to overcome the higher resistance and ensure normal blood flow and adequate perfusion of all tissues. The relationship of blood flow, blood pressure gradients, and resistance is summarized in **figure 20.12**.

WHAT DID YOU LEARN?

20 In general, would you predict a higher blood pressure, lower blood pressure, or a normal blood pressure in individuals with sustained increased resistance? Explain.

Total blood flow $\propto \dfrac{\text{Pressure gradient (established by the heart)}}{\text{Resistance (experienced by blood as it moves through the vessels)}}$

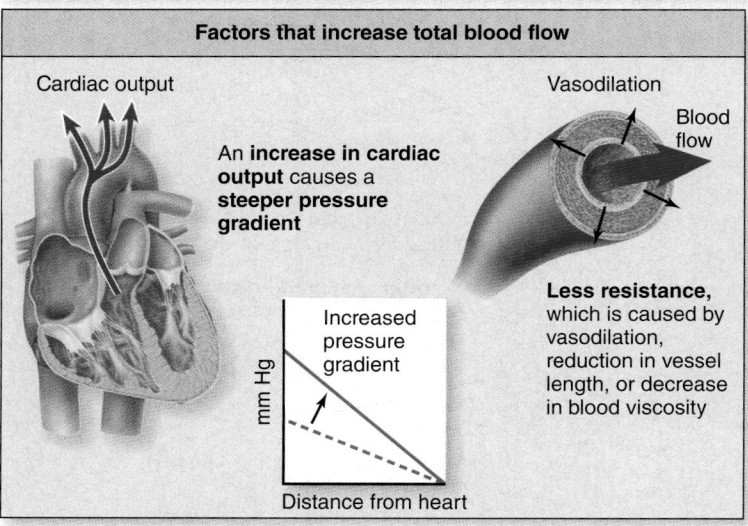

Factors that increase total blood flow

Cardiac output

An **increase in cardiac output** causes a **steeper pressure gradient**

Increased pressure gradient

mm Hg

Distance from heart

Vasodilation

Blood flow

Less resistance, which is caused by vasodilation, reduction in vessel length, or decrease in blood viscosity

(a)

Factors that decrease total blood flow

Cardiac output

A **decrease in cardiac output** causes a **smaller pressure gradient**

Decreased pressure gradient

mm Hg

Distance from heart

Vasoconstriction

Blood flow

Greater resistance, which is caused by vasoconstriction, increase in vessel length, or increase in blood viscosity

(b)

Figure 20.12 Factors That Influence Total Blood Flow. Maintaining adequate perfusion of systemic tissues is dependent upon maintaining total blood flow. Total blood flow is a function of the pressure gradient and resistance and can be either (a) increased or (b) decreased.

20.5 Regulation of Blood Pressure and Blood Flow

Blood pressure must be high enough to propel blood through the cardiovascular system to maintain adequate perfusion of all tissues, yet not so high that it causes damage to the blood vessels. Blood pressure is dependent on three primary variables: cardiac output, resistance, and blood volume. Regulation of these variables is critical in maintaining homeostasis and occurs through short-term mechanisms of the nervous system, long-term mechanisms of the endocrine system, or both.

20.5a Neural Regulation of Blood Pressure

✔ LEARNING OBJECTIVES

1. Describe the anatomic components associated with regulating blood pressure through short-term mechanisms.

2. Explain the autonomic reflexes that alter blood pressure.

Short-term regulation of blood pressure occurs through autonomic reflexes involving nuclei within the medulla oblongata (see section 13.5c). These reflexes adjust blood pressure quickly, such as occurs when you arise from a sitting to a standing position; by altering cardiac output, resistance, or both. We first describe the ana- tomic structures involved in the autonomic reflexes and then discuss how they function to maintain a normal blood pressure. Please refer to figure 20.13 as you read through this section.

Cardiovascular Center

Two distinct groups of autonomic nuclei in the medulla oblongata participate in the regulation of blood pressure, specifically the **cardiac center** and the **vasomotor center.** Collectively, these two centers are called the **cardiovascular center.** The cardiac center regulates heart activity (and thus cardiac output), and the vasomotor center controls the degree of vasoconstriction of blood vessels (and thus, regulates resistance).

Cardiac Center Recall that two regulatory nuclei are housed within the cardiac center: the **cardioacceleratory center** and the **cardioinhibitory center** (see section 19.5b). Sympathetic division pathways extend from the cardioacceleratory center to both the sinoatrial (SA) node and to the myocardium. Increased sympathetic motor output from the cardioacceleratory center increases both heart rate and force of contraction, increasing cardiac output. Parasympathetic division pathways extend from the cardioinhibitory center to the SA node and atrioventricular (AV) node. Increased parasympathetic motor output from the cardioinhibitory center decreases heart rate and slows the conduction of electrical signals through the heart's conducting system, decreasing cardiac ouput.

Figure 20.13 Cardiovascular Center. The cardiovascular center regulates blood pressure via a negative feedback loop. It receives sensory input about blood pressure from baroreceptors and chemoreceptors within the carotid arteries and aortic arch. This center then regulates blood pressure (through motor output from sympathetic nerves and vagus nerves) by adjusting cardiac output and peripheral resistance experienced by blood in blood vessels. AP|R

Vasomotor Center Sympathetic division pathways extend from the vasomotor center to blood vessels. Blood vessel response to sympathetic stimulation is dependent upon the type of cellular receptor associated with the smooth muscle within the wall of each blood vessel. The two primary receptors are **alpha (α) receptors** and **beta (β) receptors** (see section 15.5c).

Blood vessels containing α receptors contract in response to sympathetic stimulation, resulting in vasoconstriction; these include most vessels of the body. In contrast, blood vessels with β receptors relax in response to epinephrine, resulting in vasodilation; these include blood vessels in skeletal muscle and the coronary vessels. (Epinephrine is released from the adrenal medulla when stimulated by the sympathetic nervous system.) Simply put, sympathetic stimulation constricts blood vessels with α receptors and epinephrine dilates blood vessels with β receptors.

Activation of the vasomotor center and increased nerve signals along sympathetic pathways cause the following:

- **Increased peripheral resistance.** More blood vessels are stimulated to vasoconstrict than vasodilate because there are more blood vessels that house α receptors than β receptors; consequently, peripheral resistance is increased, raising blood pressure.
- **Larger circulating blood volume.** Vasoconstriction of veins shifts blood from venous reservoirs and circulating blood volume increases, thus increasing blood pressure.
- **Redistribution of blood flow.** More blood flow reaches skeletal muscles and the heart, and less blood flow goes to most other structures. Thus, organs requiring additional nutrients and oxygen have adequate perfusion.

A decrease in sympathetic stimulation from the vasomotor center to blood vessels reverses these changes: Peripheral resistance decreases, blood shifts to venous reservoirs, and blood flow distribution returns toward its previous levels.

Baroreceptors

Baroreceptors are specialized sensory nerve endings that respond to the stretch in blood vessel walls. The two main baroreceptors for the cardiovascular system are the aortic arch baroreceptors and carotid sinuses.

The **aortic arch baroreceptors** are located in the tunica externa of the aortic arch. They transmit nerve signals back to the cardiovascular center through the vagus nerve (CN X). The aortic arch baroreceptors are important in regulating systemic blood pressure.

The **carotid sinuses** are baroreceptors located in the tunica externa of each internal carotid artery, near the artery's initial bifurcation (branching) from the common carotid artery. Each carotid sinus transmits nerve signals back to the cardiovascular center through the glossopharyngeal nerve (CN IX). The carotid sinuses monitor blood pressure changes in the head and neck—thus, it is important in monitoring blood pressure affecting the brain. Baroreceptors in the carotid sinuses are more sensitive to blood pressure changes than baroreceptors in the aortic arch—a condition that is not surprising given the importance of delivering sufficient blood to the brain.

Baroreceptors transmit nerve signals to the cardiovascular center at a particular rate. Their firing rate changes when the stretch in the blood vessel wall changes.

Autonomic Reflexes

Baroreceptors are activated in response to changes in stretch to initiate autonomic reflexes that help regulate blood pressure. These reflexes are appropriately called **baroreceptor reflexes.** These reflexes are initiated by either a decrease or an increase in blood pressure.

If blood pressure decreases:

1. Decreased stretch in the blood vessel wall (reflecting a decrease in blood pressure, such as might occur when you arise from bed in the morning) is detected by baroreceptors in aortic arch baroreceptors, carotid sinuses, or both.
2. The baroreceptors decrease their firing rate along sensory neurons within the vagus and glossopharyngeal nerves that extend to both the cardiac center and vasomotor center.
3. The cardioacceleratory center of the cardiac center *increases* nerve signals along sympathetic pathways extending to the heart. The SA node increases its firing rate and the myocardium contracts with greater force. Concomitantly, the cardioinhibitory center of the cardiac center *decreases* nerve signals along parasympathetic pathways that extend to the SA node and to the AV node. Consequently, both heart rate and stroke volume increase, producing a greater cardiac output.
4. Simultaneously, the vasomotor center *increases* nerve signals along sympathetic pathways that extend to blood vessels, resulting in net vasoconstriction and an increase in peripheral resistance, along with shifting of blood from venous reservoirs.

The resulting increase in cardiac output, increase in resistance, and larger circulating blood volume quickly elevate blood pressure to maintain sufficient blood pressure to move blood through the vasculature.

If blood pressure increases:

1. Increased stretch in the blood vessel wall (reflecting an increase in blood pressure) is detected by baroreceptors in the carotid sinuses, aortic arch baroreceptors, or both.
2. The baroreceptors increase their firing rate to both components of the cardiovascular center in the brainstem.
3. The cardioacceleratory center of the cardiac center *decreases* nerve signals along sympathetic pathways to a) the SA node to slow down the heart rate, and b) the myocardium to decrease stroke volume. Concomitantly, the cardioinhibitory center *increases* nerve signals along parasympathetic pathways to the SA node to slow the firing rate, and to the AV node to further delay the nerve signals. Consequently, both heart rate and stroke volume decrease, resulting in a decrease in cardiac output.
4. Simultaneously, the vasomotor center *decreases* nerve signals along sympathetic pathways to blood vessels, resulting in net vasodilation and a decrease in resistance, along with shifting of blood to venous reservoirs.

The resulting decrease in cardiac output, decrease in resistance, and smaller circulating blood volume lower blood pressure, and blood flow returns to its resting levels.

Baroreceptors respond best to sudden, short-term changes in blood pressure, but they are not effective long-term or chronic blood pressure regulators. If someone has chronically high blood pressure, eventually the baroreceptors will adapt to the change in blood pressure and thus adjust their normal "set point" (see section 1.5).

WHAT DO YOU THINK?

2. Nicotine stimulates the heart and raises cardiac output. It also causes arteriole vasoconstriction. Given this information, would you expect the blood pressure of a smoker to be relatively higher or lower than that of a nonsmoker? Explain.

INTEGRATE

CLINICAL VIEW

Hypertension and Hypotension

Hypertension is chronically elevated blood pressure, defined as a systolic pressure greater than 140 mm Hg and/or a diastolic pressure greater than 90 mm Hg. Hypertension may damage blood vessel walls, making arteries more likely to develop atherosclerosis, or it may thicken the arteriole walls and reduce their luminal diameter, a condition called **arteriolosclerosis.** Hypertension also is a major cause of heart failure owing to the extra workload placed on the heart.

In contrast, **hypotension** is a chronically low blood pressure that results in symptoms such as fatigue, dizziness, and fainting. Some physicians define hypotension as a systolic pressure below 90 mm Hg or a diastolic pressure below 60 mm Hg, while other physicians state that "normal" low blood pressure for one individual may be hypotensive for another.

Orthostatic hypotension, or *postural hypotension,* is a drop in blood pressure when an individual suddenly changes position, such as when a person stands up after lying down. As a result, the person may experience dizziness, light-headedness, and fainting after this positional change. Essentially, orthostatic hypotension occurs when the nervous system responses that help regulate blood pressure do not function quickly enough, and MAP decreases below 60 mm Hg. Thus, the blood remains pooled in the veins and not enough reaches the cerebral vasculature, resulting in the above symptoms.

Chemoreceptor Reflexes

Chemoreceptors, although more important in regulating respiration, are also secondarily involved in regulating blood pressure. When chemoreceptors are stimulated, they initiate **chemoreceptor reflexes,** which are negative feedback loops that ultimately bring blood chemistry levels back to normal.

The two main peripheral chemoreceptors are the **aortic bodies** and **carotid body.** The aortic bodies are located in the arch of the aorta while a carotid body is located at the bifurcation of each common carotid as it splits into an external cartotid and an internal carotid artery. Both aortic and carotid bodies send sensory input to the cardiovascular center; the aortic bodies send nerve signals via the vagus nerve, and the carotid body along the glossopharyngeal nerve.

High carbon dioxide levels, low pH, and very low oxygen levels stimulate the chemoreceptors, and their increased firing primarily stimulates the vasomotor center. The vasomotor center responds by increasing nerve signals along sympathetic pathways to blood vessels, which increases resistance and shifts blood from venous reservoirs to increase venous return. The changes raise blood pressure and increase blood flow, including blood flow to the lungs, which allows for an accompanying change in respiratory gas exchange. As a result, blood gas levels return to normal. (Regulation of breathing is discussed in sections 23.5 and 23.6.)

Higher Brain Centers

Blood pressure is also influenced by higher brain centers. For example, increases in body temperature, or experiencing the fight-or-flight response associated with exercise or an emergency, result in the hypothalamus increasing cardiac output and resistance.

Even anxiety over a new or dangerous experience, such as skydiving, can increase blood pressure. In addition, the limbic system alters blood pressure in response to emotions or emotional memories (see section 13.8d).

WHAT DID YOU LEARN?

21 When are the short-term mechanisms for regulation of blood pressure important?

22 What is the initial change to blood pressure when you arise in the morning? Describe the autonomic reflex to maintain your blood pressure when you arise.

20.5b Hormonal Regulation of Blood Pressure

LEARNING OBJECTIVES

3. Describe the hormones that regulate blood pressure.

4. Explain the renin-angiotensin system and its influence on blood pressure.

5. Contrast the effects of aldosterone, antidiuretic hormone, and angiotensin II on blood pressure with those of atrial natriuretic peptide.

Several hormones, in addition to epinephrine and norepinephrine, participate in regulating blood pressure. These include angiotensin II, antidiuretic hormone, aldosterone, and atrial natriuretic peptide. These typically regulate blood pressure by altering resistance, blood volume, or both. Blood volume is regulated by stimulating fluid intake (assuming fluid intake occurs) or altering urine output. A general description of each hormone is presented next. A more detailed discussion of these hormones is included in chapters 24 and 25.

Renin-Angiotensin System

The **renin-angiotensin system** "straddles" short-term neural regulation and long-term hormonal regulation because the synthesis of the angiotensin II is initiated by the nervous system (short-term mechanisms), and angiotensin II causes the release of other hormones (long-term mechanisms).

In response to low blood pressure in the kidney or stimulation by the sympathetic division, the enzyme **renin** is released from the kidney into the blood (**figure 20.14**). Renin initiates an enzymatic chemical reaction by converting **angiotensinogen,** an inactive hormone previously produced by the liver and secreted into the blood, into **angiotensin I.** Angiotensin I is then converted to **angiotensin II** by **angiotensin-converting enzyme (ACE),** an enzyme associated with the capillary endothelium. ACE is found in very high concentrations on the pulmonary capillary endothelium, so most (but not all) angiotensin conversion occurs in the lungs.

Having most of the ACE enzyme in pulmonary capillary endothelium helps ensure that sufficient angiotensin I is converted to angiotensin II. This is because all blood moves through the pulmonary circulation to be oxygenated, so contact between angiotensin I and ACE is maximized.

Angiotensin II has several effects: It is a powerful vasoconstrictor—much more powerful than comparable hormones, such as norepinephrine—and thus it increases peripheral resistance and raises blood pressure to a a greater extent. Angiotensin II stimulates the thirst center; fluid intake increases blood volume, which

Figure 20.14 Renin-Angiotensin System. The enzyme renin, released by the kidney in response to low blood pressure, initiates a series of enzymatic chemical reactions within the blood that ultimately help raise blood pressure.

(1) Kidney receptors detect low blood pressure or are stimulated by the sympathetic nervous system; renin enzyme is released.

Liver

Kidney

Angiotensinogen is continuously produced by the liver and circulates in the bloodstream.

Angiotensin-converting enzyme (ACE) is anchored to the internal walls in capillaries, especially capillaries in the lungs.

Lungs

Angiotensinogen (inactive hormone)   Renin   Angiotensin I (inactive hormone)   ACE   Angiotensin II (active hormone)

(2) Renin converts angiotensinogen into angiotensin I.

(3) ACE converts angiotensin I into angiotensin II.

(4) Angiotensin II increases blood pressure by:
- Causing vasoconstriction
- Stimulating thirst center
- Decreasing urine formation to increase blood pressure

increases blood pressure. Angiotensin II also regulates blood volume by direct action in the kidneys to decrease urine formation, and by indirect action through stimulation of other hormones (aldosterone and antidiuretic hormone). A decrease in urine formation results in less fluid lost from the blood; this helps maintain blood volume and thus blood pressure.

  WHAT DO YOU THINK?

(3) Do you think an ACE inhibitor drug would be used to treat hypertension or hypotension? Explain.

Aldosterone and Antidiuretic Hormone

Aldosterone is released from the adrenal cortex in response to several stimuli, including angiotensin II. Aldosterone increases the absorption of sodium ion (Na^+) and water in the kidney, decreasing their loss in the urine; this helps maintain blood volume and blood pressure.

Antidiuretic hormone (ADH) is released from the posterior pituitary in response to nerve signals from the hypothalamus (see section 17.8b). The hypothalamus stimulates the posterior pituitary subsequent to either detection of increased concentration of blood (typically correlated with low blood volume), or stimulation of the hypothalamus by angiotensin II. ADH increases the absorption of water in the kidney, decreasing its loss in the urine; this helps maintain blood volume and blood pressure. ADH also stimulates the thirst center so there is fluid intake, and blood volume increases. During extreme cases of low blood volume, such as might occur with hemorrhaging, extensive release of ADH occurs, which causes vasoconstriction. This vasoconstriction increases peripheral resistance and blood pressure. This is why ADH is also referred to as *vasopressin*.

In summary, angiotensin II and ADH (in high doses) increase peripheral resistance and blood pressure; and angiotensin II, aldosterone, and ADH decrease urine output to help maintain blood volume and blood pressure (or increase blood volume and blood pressure following fluid intake).

Atrial Natriuretic Peptide

Atrial natriuretic peptide (ANP) is released from the atrium of the heart in response to an increase in stretch of the atrial walls due to increased blood volume and increased venous return. ANP stimulates vasodilation, which decreases peripheral resistance and increases urine output, which decreases blood volume. The net effect is a decrease in blood pressure.

Integration of Variables That Influence Blood Pressure

Homeostatic mechanisms to maintain a normal blood pressure are dependent on three primary variables: cardiac output, resistance, and blood volume. All three of these variables are *directly* related to blood pressure. An increase in any of the three increases blood pressure, and a decrease in any of the three decreases blood pressure. The relationship of these primary variables is summarized in **figure 20.15**.

 WHAT DID YOU LEARN?

(23) How is angiotensinogen activated to become angiotensin II? How does angiotensin II influence blood pressure?

(24) Which hormone decreases blood pressure?

Figure 20.15 **Factors That Regulate Blood Pressure.**
Three primary factors influence blood pressure: (a) cardiac output, (b) peripheral resistance, and (c) blood volume.

(a) Cardiac Output (CO)

Cardiac output is the volume of blood pumped per minute. CO is a function of heart rate (HR) and stroke volume (SV): **CO = HR × SV**.

Heart rate (HR)

Cardiac output increases.

120 bpm

Cardiac output decreases.

65 bpm

Increased heart rate increases cardiac output and blood pressure.

Decreased heart rate decreases cardiac output and blood pressure.

Stroke volume (SV)

Cardiac output increases.

Cardiac output decreases.

Force of contraction

Force of contraction

Increased stroke volume increases cardiac output and blood pressure.

Decreased stroke volume decreases cardiac output and blood pressure.

INTEGRATE

CLINICAL VIEW
Measuring Blood Pressure

Arterial blood pressure is measured indirectly using a **sphygmomanometer** (sfig´mō-mă-nom´ ĕ-ter; *phygmos* = pulse, *metron* = measure). A cuff is wrapped around the arm, and a stethoscope is placed just distal to the compressed artery, allowing a practitioner to listen for pulse sounds. The cuff is inflated until the brachial artery is completely compressed, temporarily stopping blood flow. The pressure in the cuff is then decreased as air is gradually released. Two values are recorded (e.g., 120/80), and the unit of measurement is millimeters of mercury (mm Hg).

Brachial artery
Stethoscope

Blood pressure cuff

Stretch

Recoil

Systolic pressure (e.g., 120 mm Hg)

Diastolic pressure (e.g., 80 mm Hg)

Blood flow

Systolic pressure

The "top" number of a blood pressure recording represents systolic pressure, which is pressure in the arteries when the heart contracts. This value is recorded when the first sound is heard. The sound occurs when pressure in the brachial artery is sufficient to overcome the pressure in the cuff, reestablishing blood flow.

300
280
260
240
220
200
180
160
140
120
100
80
60
40
20
0

300
280
260
240
220
200
180
160
140
120
100
80
60
40
20
0

Diastolic pressure

The "bottom" number of a blood pressure recording represents the diastolic pressure, which is the pressure in the arteries when the heart relaxes. This value is recorded when sounds are no longer heard. The absence of sound occurs when blood flow in the brachial artery is smooth because pressure in the cuff is no longer compressing the artery.

(b) Peripheral Resistance

Peripheral resistance is the opposition to flow of blood in vessels, and is a function of vessel radius, vessel length, and blood viscosity.

Vessel radius	Vessel length	Blood viscosity
Vasoconstriction narrows vessel and forces blood through a narrower lumen, increasing peripheral resistance and blood pressure.	Longer vessels increase peripheral resistance, which raises blood pressure.	Increased viscosity creates an opposition to blood flow, increasing peripheral resistance and blood pressure.
Vasodilation widens vessel, decreasing peripheral resistance and blood pressure.	Shorter vessels decrease peripheral resistance, which lowers blood pressure.	Decreased viscosity allows blood to flow more freely through vessels, decreasing peripheral resistance and blood pressure.

(c) Blood Volume

Blood volume is a function of fluid intake and fluid output. Fluid intake increases blood volume and blood pressure. Fluid output decreases blood volume and blood pressure.

Fluid intake (~2500 mL/day)	Fluid output (~2500 mL/day)

Food and drink

Metabolic water

Moisture in expired air

Sweat and transpiration

Urine

Feces

Sufficient blood pressure is required to maintain adequate perfusion of systemic tissues during capillary exchange.

20.6 Velocity of Blood Flow

Blood flow velocity is the rate of blood transported per unit time and typically measured in millimeters per minute (or centimeters per second). Blood flow velocity through the arteries, capillaries, and veins is dependent upon the total cross-sectional area of each of the vessel types. (Total cross-sectional area is estimated by determining the aggregate diameter across the total number of a given type of vessel if they were positioned side-by-side.)

Figure 20.16 depicts both total cross-sectional area and velocity of blood flow. Arteries have a relatively small total cross-sectional area, whereas capillaries have the largest total cross-sectional area, because there are thousands of miles of capillaries. The total cross-sectional area of all capillaries has a value of approximately 4500 square centimeters (cm^2). The veins have a total cross-sectional area much closer to that of the arteries.

Notice that the velocity of a fluid is inversely related to the total cross-sectional area of the conduit through which it flows. Velocity of blood flow is relatively fast in the arteries, slowest in the capillaries, and moves relatively fast again as it moves through the veins. The greater the total cross-sectional area of a vessel, the slower the flow rate, and vice versa. Consider the analogous phenomenon of water flow in a river. In regions where the river is narrow, the river moves more quickly, and where the river is wider, the river moves more slowly. Of course, the amount of water flow is the same in these different regions and always moves toward the ocean down the gradient. Likewise, blood moves along a blood pressure gradient as it is transported through the vasculature of the cardiovascular system, but its velocity is altered as it moves through the different portions of the vasculature.

What is the significance of the much slower rate of blood flow through the capillaries? The slower blood flow rate allows sufficient time for efficient capillary exchange of nutrients, respiratory gases, hormones, and wastes between the tissues and the blood.

WHAT DID YOU LEARN?

25 In which type of vessel is blood flow the slowest? Explain the anatomic structure that accounts for this and the physiologic significance.

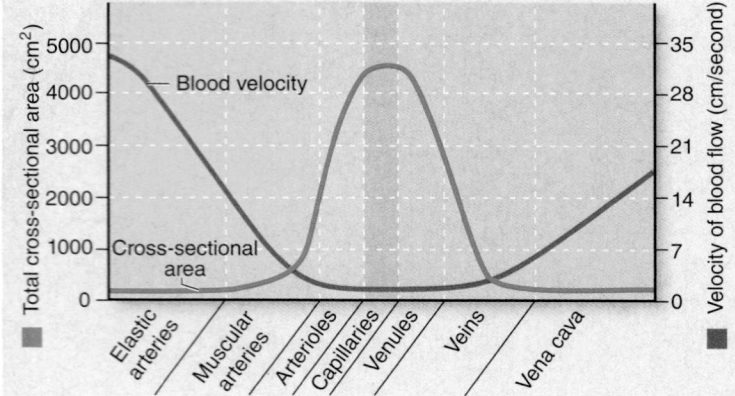

Figure 20.16 Relationship of Total Cross-Sectional Area and Velocity of Blood Flow. The greater the total cross-sectional area, the slower the blood flow. Notice that capillaries have the greatest cross-sectional area and the slowest blood flow—conditions that facilitate the exchange of substances between the blood and tissues.

20.7 Blood Flow Distribution During Exercise

During exercise, there is both an increase in total blood flow due to a faster and stronger heartbeat and because blood is removed from the "reservoirs" of the veins to the active circulation. There is also a redistribution of blood. Both of these changes help ensure that the most metabolically active tissues are receiving adequate blood flow to meet the needs of the tissue cells.

Figure 20.17 provides an example in which blood flow changes from 5.25 L/min (5250 mL/min) at rest to 17.5 L/min (17,500 mL/min) during exercise. The following increases in blood flow to specific regions or organs can be noted:

- Blood flow to the coronary vessels of the heart increases approximately three-fold (from 250 mL/min to 750 mL/min), a change that helps to ensure that sufficient oxygen reaches the cardiac muscle within the heart wall.
- Skeletal muscle blood flow increases an amazing 11-fold (from 1100 mL/min to 12,500 mL/min)—which is approximately 70% of the total cardiac output—a change needed to meet the high metabolic demands experienced by skeletal muscle during exercise.
- The percentage of blood flow to the skin increases to almost five times its resting level (from 400 mL/min to 1900 mL/min) to dissipate heat.

In contrast, relatively less total blood flow is distributed to the abdominal organs slowing digestive processes; less is transported to the kidneys, which decreases urine output to maintain blood volume and blood pressure. Smaller amounts reach other structures that are not as metabolically active during exercise.

WHAT DID YOU LEARN?

26 Which organs have an increased proportion of cardiac output during exercise? Which receive a decreased proportion of cardiac output during exercise?

20.8 Pulmonary Circulation

The pulmonary circulation is responsible for carrying deoxygenated blood from the right side of the heart to the lungs and then returning the newly oxygenated blood to the left side of the heart.

20.8a Blood Flow Through the Pulmonary Circulation

In the pulmonary circulation, deoxygenated blood is pumped out of the right ventricle into the **pulmonary trunk (figure 20.18)**. This vessel bifurcates into a **left** and **right pulmonary artery** that go to the corresponding lungs. The pulmonary arteries divide into smaller arteries that continue to subdivide to form arterioles. These arterioles finally branch into pulmonary capillaries, where gas exchange occurs. Carbon dioxide diffuses from the blood and enters the tiny air sacs (alveoli) of the lungs, while oxygen moves in the opposite direction, from the air sacs into the blood.

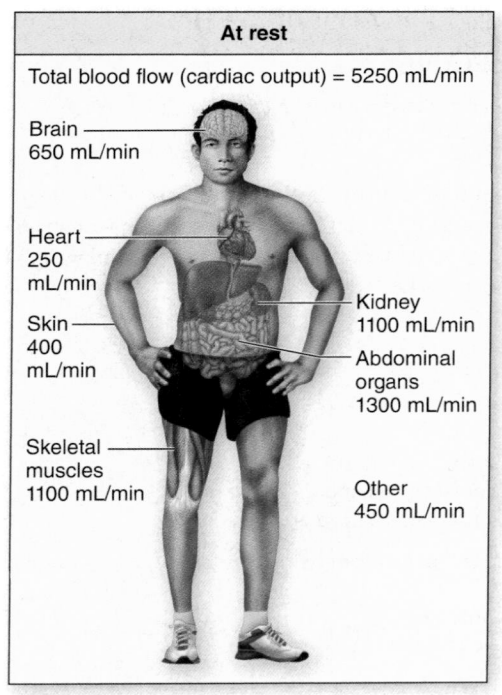

At rest

Total blood flow (cardiac output) = 5250 mL/min

Brain
650 mL/min

Heart
250
mL/min

Skin
400
mL/min

Kidney
1100 mL/min

Abdominal
organs
1300 mL/min

Skeletal
muscles
1100 mL/min

Other
450 mL/min

(a)

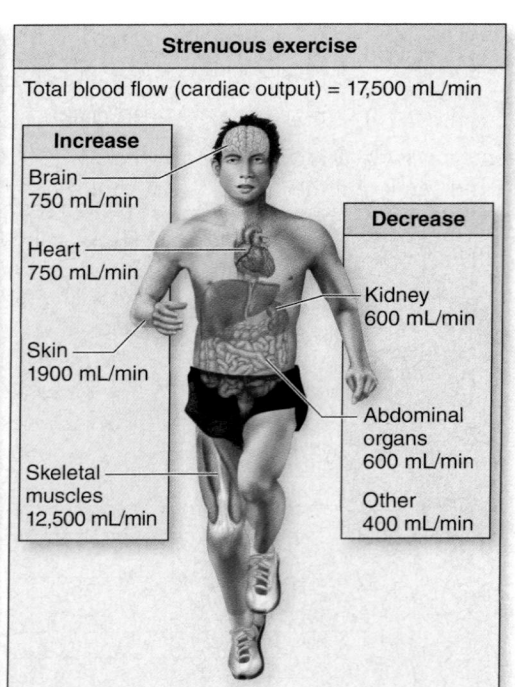

Strenuous exercise

Total blood flow (cardiac output) = 17,500 mL/min

Increase

Brain
750 mL/min

Heart
750 mL/min

Decrease

Kidney
600 mL/min

Skin
1900 mL/min

Abdominal
organs
600 mL/min

Skeletal
muscles
12,500 mL/min

Other
400 mL/min

(b)

Figure 20.17 Comparison of Systemic Circulation Blood Flow During Rest and Strenuous Exercise. (*a*) At rest, cardiac output is approximately 5.25 L/min (5250 mL/min). (*b*) Cardiac output increases to 17.5 L/min (1750 mL/min) during strenuous exercise in this example. A greater percentage of blood is directed to the coronary vessels of the heart, skeletal muscles, and skin, and relatively less blood is sent to the abdominal organs, kidneys, and other less metabolically active tissues.

The capillaries merge to form venules and then the **pulmonary veins.** Typically, two left and two right pulmonary veins carry the newly oxygenated blood to the left atrium of the heart.

WHAT DID YOU LEARN?

27 What is the percentage of blood returning to the right side of the heart that is then pumped to the lungs?

20.8b Characteristics of the Pulmonary Circulation

LEARNING OBJECTIVE

2. Identify features of the pulmonary circulation that distinguish it from systemic circulation.

Pulmonary arteries have less elastic connective tissue and wider lumens than systemic arteries. Compared to the systemic circulation, pulmonary vessels are relatively short, since the lungs are close to the heart. As a result, blood pressure is lower throughout the pulmonary circulation in comparison to the systemic circulation. The pressure changes associated with the pulmonary circulation are as follows:

- Blood leaves the right ventricle with a systolic pressure of about 15 to 25 mm Hg, depending upon whether the body is resting or active.

- Blood pressure drops as the blood passes through the pulmonary trunk and right and left pulmonary arteries, reaching an overall pressure of about 10 mm Hg in the pulmonary capillaries of the alveoli. This lower pressure means that the blood moves more slowly in pulmonary capillaries than in systemic capillaries, facilitating gas exchange within the lungs.

- Blood exits the pulmonary capillaries into progressively larger veins that become the pulmonary veins; blood pressure is almost 0 mm Hg as these veins empty into the left atrium.

WHAT DID YOU LEARN?

28 How does blood pressure in the pulmonary circulation compare to the pressure in the systemic circulation?

Deoxygenated blood is transported to the lungs.

① Right atrium
② Right ventricle
③ Pulmonary trunk
④ Pulmonary arteries
⑤ Pulmonary arterioles

⑪ Aorta
⑩ Left ventricle
⑨ Left atrium
⑧ Pulmonary veins
⑦ Pulmonary venules

Oxygenated blood is transported from the lungs.

⑥ Gas exchange occurs in the pulmonary capillaries.

Figure 20.18 Pulmonary Circulation. The pulmonary circulation conducts blood to and from the gas exchange surfaces of the lungs. Blood circulation through the heart is indicated by colored arrows: deoxygenated blood (blue arrows), oxygenated blood (red arrows). **AP|R**

20.9 Systemic Circulation: Vessels from and to the Heart

We discuss the vessels from and to the heart and then look at the circulatory routes for each body region: the head and trunk and the upper and lower limbs. As you read these descriptions, refer to **figure 20.19**, which shows the locations of the major arteries and veins.

20.9a General Arterial Flow Out of the Heart

LEARNING OBJECTIVE

1. List the arteries that carry blood away from the left ventricle of the heart to the major areas of the body.

Oxygenated blood is pumped out of the left ventricle of the heart and enters the ascending aorta. The **left** and **right coronary arteries** emerge immediately from the wall of the ascending aorta and supply the heart wall (figure 20.19 *inset*).

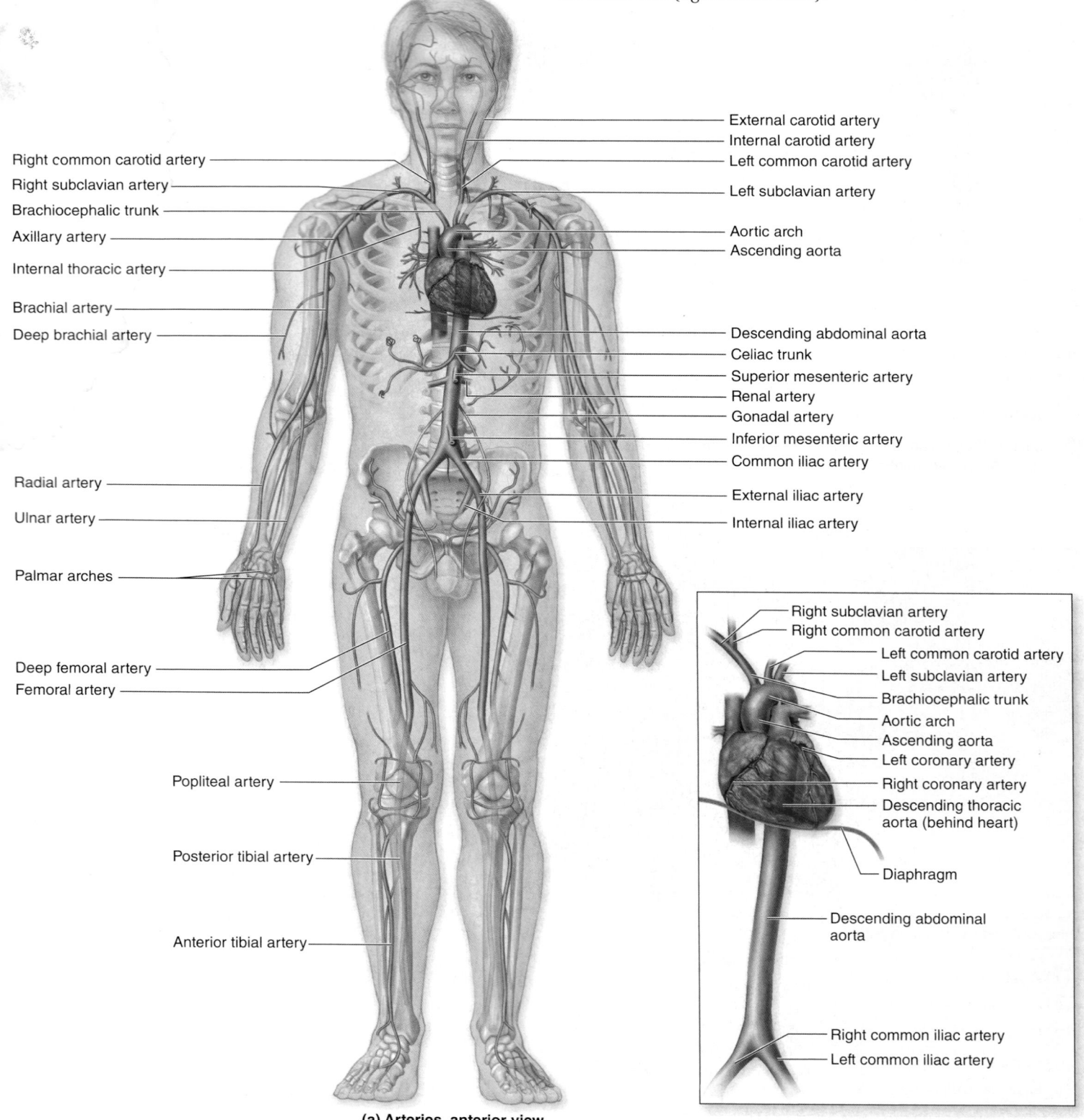

(a) Arteries, anterior view

Figure 20.19 General Vascular Distribution. Arteries in the systemic circulation carry blood from the heart to systemic capillary beds; systemic veins return this blood to the heart. (*a*) Anterior view of the systemic arteries, with an inset of the heart and aorta. AP|R

The ascending aorta curves toward the left side of the body and becomes the **aortic arch** (also called the *arch of the aorta*). Recall that the aortic bodies for regulating blood pressure are within the tunica externa of the aortic arch. Three main arterial branches emerge from the aortic arch:

1. The **brachiocephalic** (brā-kē-ō-se-fal'ik) **trunk,** which bifurcates into the **right common carotid** (ka-rot'id) **artery,** supplying arterial blood to right side of the head and neck, and the **right subclavian** (sŭb-klā've-an; *sub* = beneath + clavicle) **artery,** supplying the right upper limb and some thoracic structures

2. The **left common carotid artery,** supplying the left side of the head and neck

3. The **left subclavian artery,** supplying the left upper limb and some thoracic structures

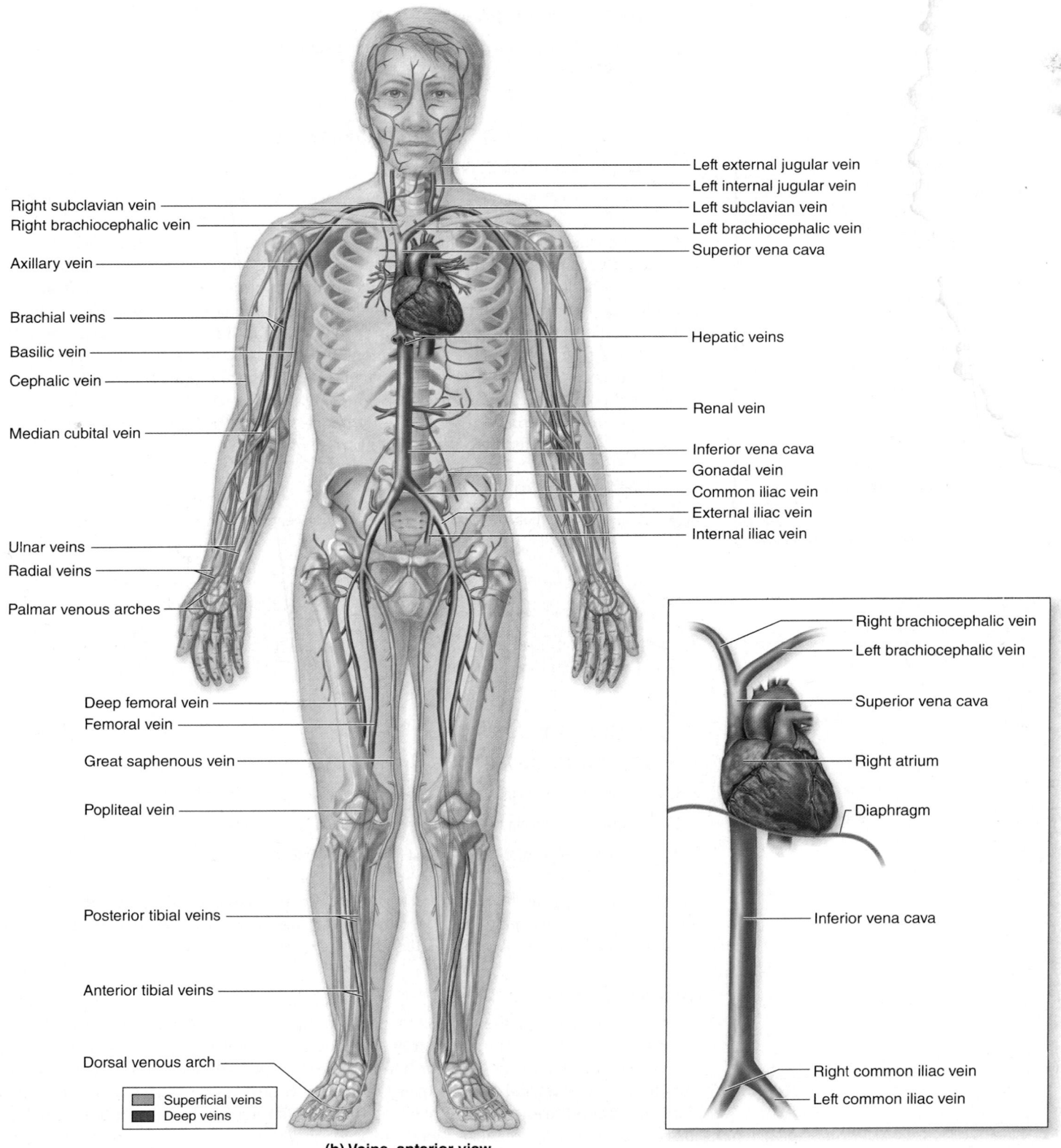

(b) Veins, anterior view

Figure 20.19 General Vascular Distribution (*continued*). (*b*) Anterior view of the systemic veins, with an inset of the major veins that drain into the heart.

The aortic arch curves and projects inferiorly as the **descending thoracic aorta,** several branches of which supply the thoracic wall and viscera. As this artery extends inferiorly through the aortic opening (hiatus) in the diaphragm, it is renamed the **descending abdominal aorta,** where it supplies the abdominal wall and organs.

At the level of the fourth lumbar vertebra, the descending abdominal aorta bifurcates into **left** and **right common iliac** (il'ē-ak; *ileum* = groin) **arteries.** Each of these arteries further divides into an internal iliac artery (to supply pelvic and perineal structures) and an external iliac artery (to supply the lower limb).

 WHAT DID YOU LEARN?

29 What are the three main branches off of the aortic arch? What areas in general do these branches serve?

20.9b General Venous Return to the Heart

 LEARNING OBJECTIVE

2. Name the veins that return blood from the systemic circulation to the right atrium of the heart.

Blood is returned to the right atrium of the heart by three vessels: the superior vena cava, the inferior vena cava, and the coronary sinus (figure 20.19b). The veins that drain the head, neck, upper limbs, and thoracic and abdominal walls merge to form the **left** and **right brachiocephalic veins,** which in turn merge to form the **superior vena cava.** The veins inferior to the diaphragm merge to collectively form the **inferior vena cava.** The inferior vena cava is responsible for carrying venous blood toward the heart from the lower limbs, pelvis and perineum, and abdominal structures. It lies to the right side of the descending abdominal aorta and extends through an opening (caval opening) in the diaphragm.

Recall from section 19.4b that the **coronary sinus** also drains into the right atrium, delivering deoxygenated blood from the heart myocardium.

 WHAT DID YOU LEARN?

30 Which body regions are drained by the superior vena cava and the inferior vena cava?

20.10 Systemic Circulation: Head and Trunk

Blood flow to the head and to the thoracic and abdominal organs is critical to survival, so it is not surprising that these regions receive blood flow soon after it leaves the heart.

20.10a Head and Neck

 LEARNING OBJECTIVES

1. Name the arteries and veins associated with the head and neck structures.

2. Diagram and explain the cerebral arterial circle and its function.

3. Describe the general structure and function of dural venous sinuses.

Arterial supply to the head and neck comes from the branches of the aortic arch. Venous drainage of the head and neck is through the jugular veins, which then drain into the brachiocephalic veins. We discuss the arterial supply first.

Arterial Supply

Most of the blood to the head and neck is supplied by the **common carotid arteries (figure 20.20a).** The common carotid arteries travel parallel immediately lateral to either side of the trachea. At the superior border of the thyroid cartilage of the larynx, each artery divides into an **external carotid artery** that supplies structures external to the skull, and an **internal carotid artery** that supplies internal skull structures. Recall that the carotid sinus, a receptor that helps regulate blood pressure, is within the internal carotid artery near its bifurcation from the common carotid artery.

Branches of common carotid artery

Internal carotid artery (brain and orbit)

External carotid artery (superficial head and neck structures)

Paired arteries to head and neck

Thyrocervical trunk (thyroid gland, part of neck and shoulder)

Costocervical trunk (deep neck and upper intercostal muscles)

Vertebral artery (brain)

Common carotid artery

Branches of external carotid artery

Superficial temporal artery (parotid gland, part of scalp)

Maxillary artery (teeth, gums, nasal cavity, mastication muscles, meninges)

Posterior auricular artery (ears and part of scalp)

Occipital artery (posterior scalp)

Facial artery (face)

Lingual artery (tongue)

Ascending pharyngeal artery (pharynx)

Superior thyroid artery (thyroid gland and larynx)

Thyroid cartilage

Brachiocephalic artery

Subclavian artery

(a) Arteries, right lateral view

Anterior

Internal carotid artery

Anterior cerebral artery

Ophthalmic artery

Middle cerebral artery

Anterior communicating artery (connects right and left anterior cerebral arteries)

Anterior cerebral arteries (R/L)

Internal carotid artery

Posterior communicating arteries (R/L)

Posterior cerebral arteries (R/L)

Cerebral arterial circle (circle of Willis)

Posterior cerebral artery

Basilar artery

Vertebral artery

Posterior

(b) Arteries of the brain, inferior view

Figure 20.20 Arterial Blood Flow to the Head and Neck. (*a*) Right lateral view shows the branches that supply blood to the head and neck. (*b*) An inferior view of the brain shows the branches of the internal carotid and vertebral arteries that supply the brain. An inset shows an enlarged view of the cerebral arterial circle, which is an anastomosis of blood vessels that surrounds the sella turcica of the sphenoid bone. **AP|R**

Additional blood to the head and neck comes from the **vertebral artery, thyrocervical** (thy′rō-ser′vi-kal) **trunk,** and **costocervical** (kos′tō-ser′vi-kal) **trunk.** These are all branches of the subclavian artery.

External Carotid   The external carotid artery supplies blood to several branches that include the **superior thyroid artery, ascending pharyngeal** (fă-rin′jē-ăl; *pharynx* = throat) **artery, lingual** (lin′gwăl) **artery, facial artery, occipital artery** and **posterior auricular artery.** Thereafter, the external carotid artery divides into the **maxillary artery** and the **superficial temporal artery.** The specific regions supplied by these arteries are listed in figure 20.20*a*.

Internal Carotid   The internal carotid artery branches only after it enters the skull through the carotid canal. Once inside the skull, it forms multiple branches, including the **anterior** and **middle cerebral arteries,** which supply the brain, and the **ophthalmic** (op-thal′mik; *ophthalmos* = eye) **arteries,** which supply the eyes and some of the surrounding structures (figure 20.20*b*).

Vertebral Arteries   The **vertebral arteries** emerge from the subclavian arteries and travel through the transverse foramina of the cervical vertebrae before entering the skull through the foramen magnum, where they merge to form the **basilar** (bas′i-lăr; *basis* = base) **artery.** The basilar artery travels immediately anterior to the pons and extends many branches prior to subdividing into the **posterior cerebral arteries,** which supply the posterior portion of the cerebrum.

Cerebral Arterial Circle   The **cerebral arterial circle** (*circle of Willis*) is an important arterial anastomosis around the sella turcica (see inset, figure 20.20*b*). The circle is formed from posterior cerebral arteries, **posterior communicating arteries** (branches of the posterior cerebral arteries), internal carotid arteries, anterior cerebral arteries, and an **anterior communicating artery** (which connects the two anterior cerebral arteries). This arterial circle equalizes blood pressure in the brain and can provide collateral channels should one vessel become blocked.

Venous Drainage

Three primary pairs of veins drain the neck and head **(figure 20.21)**. On each side of the head is a **vertebral vein** and an **external jugular vein,** both of which empty into the subclavian vein. The third vein is an **internal jugular vein,** which joins with the subclavian vein to form the brachiocephalic vein. The external jugular primarily drains superficial head and neck structures, while the internal jugular drains blood from the cranial cavity. The right and left brachiocephalic veins join to form the superior vena cava.

Cranial Cavity   Some cranial venous blood is drained by the vertebral veins that extend through the transverse foramina of the cervical vertebrae and drain into the brachiocephalic veins. However, most of the venous blood of the cranium drains through several large veins collectively known as the **dural** (dū′răl) **venous sinuses.** Recall that these large modified veins are formed between the two layers of dura mater and also receive excess cerebrospinal fluid (see section 13.2a). Blood from the dural venous sinus system is drained primarily into the internal jugular vein.

WHAT DID YOU LEARN?

31 What four arteries extend from each subclavian artery to supply the head and neck? What three primary veins drain these regions?

32 What is the function of the dural venous sinuses?

Veins of neck and superficial head structures

Occipital vein
Superficial temporal vein
Maxillary vein
Posterior auricular vein
Retromandibular vein
Facial vein
Lingual vein

Superior thyroid vein

Major veins draining head and neck

Vertebral vein
External jugular vein
Internal jugular vein

Right subclavian vein
Right brachiocephalic vein

(a) Veins, right lateral view

Superior sagittal sinus
Inferior sagittal sinus

Straight sinus
Occipital sinus
Marginal sinuses
Transverse sinus
Sigmoid sinus

Cavernous sinus

Superior petrosal sinus
Inferior petrosal sinus
Ophthalmic veins

Facial vein

Internal jugular vein

(b) Dural venous sinuses, right superior anterolateral view

Figure 20.21 Venous Blood Flow from the Head and Neck. (*a*) Right lateral view shows the major veins and their tributaries that drain blood from the neck and head. (*b*) Venous drainage of the cranium from a superior anterolateral view. The dural venous sinuses are labeled in bold. AP|R

20.10b Thoracic and Abdominal Walls

✓ LEARNING OBJECTIVES

4. Describe the pairs of arteries that supply the thoracic wall.

5. Discuss the arteries that supply the abdominal wall.

6. List veins that drain the thoracic and abdominal walls and delineate their pathways.

The systemic circulation to the walls of the trunk region is primarily via paired vessels that have extensive anastomoses. The venous drainage is more complex than the arterial supply.

Arterial Supply

The thoracic and abdominal walls are both supplied by several pairs of arteries (figure 20.22a). A left and right internal thoracic

artery emerge from each subclavian artery to supply the anterior thoracic wall and mammary gland. Each internal thoracic artery is located lateral to the sternum and has the following branches: the first six anterior intercostal arteries and a musculophrenic (mŭs′kū-lō-fren′ik; phren = diaphragm) artery that divides into anterior intercostal arteries 7–9. The intercostal arteries supply the contents of the intercostal spaces. The internal thoracic artery then becomes the superior epigastric (ep-i-gas′trik; epi = upon, gastric = stomach) artery, which carries blood to the superior abdominal wall.

The inferior epigastric artery, a branch of the external iliac artery, supplies the inferior abdominal wall. This artery anastomoses extensively with the superior epigastric artery.

The supreme intercostal artery is a branch of the costocervical trunk; it branches into the first and second posterior intercostal arteries. Posterior intercostal arteries 3–11 are branches of the

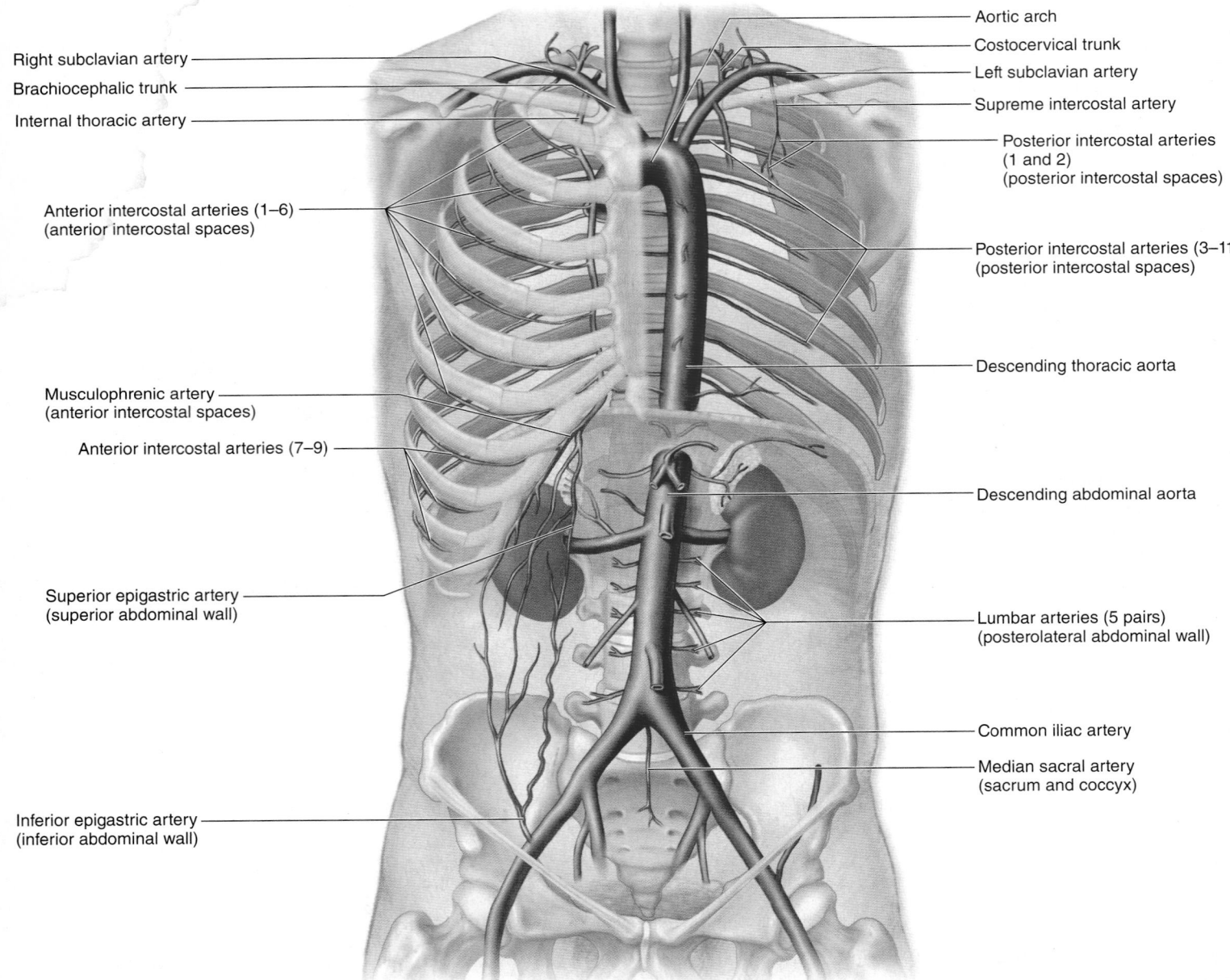

Right subclavian artery

Brachiocephalic trunk

Internal thoracic artery

Anterior intercostal arteries (1–6) (anterior intercostal spaces)

Musculophrenic artery (anterior intercostal spaces)

Anterior intercostal arteries (7–9)

Superior epigastric artery (superior abdominal wall)

Inferior epigastric artery (inferior abdominal wall)

Aortic arch

Costocervical trunk

Left subclavian artery

Supreme intercostal artery

Posterior intercostal arteries (1 and 2) (posterior intercostal spaces)

Posterior intercostal arteries (3–11) (posterior intercostal spaces)

Descending thoracic aorta

Descending abdominal aorta

Lumbar arteries (5 pairs) (posterolateral abdominal wall)

Common iliac artery

Median sacral artery (sacrum and coccyx)

(a) Arteries, anterior view

Figure 20.22 Circulation to the Thoracic and Abdominal Body Walls. (a) The arteries that supply the thoracic and abdominal wall are shown. Notice the anastomoses of the superior and inferior epigastric arteries. AP|R descending thoracic aorta. The posterior and anterior intercostal arteries anastomose, and each pair forms a horizontal vessel arc that spans a segment of the thoracic wall.

Finally, five pairs of **lumbar arteries** branch from the descending abdominal aorta to supply the posterolateral abdominal wall. In addition, a single **median sacral artery** arises at the bifurcation of the aorta in the pelvic region to supply the sacrum and coccyx.

Venous Drainage

Venous drainage of the thoracic and abdominal walls is a bit more complex than the arterial pathways (figure 20.22b). **Anterior intercostal veins, a musculophrenic vein,** and **superior epigastric vein** all merge into the **internal thoracic vein,** which drains into the brachiocephalic vein.

The **inferior epigastric vein** merges with the **external iliac vein.** The first and second **posterior intercostal veins** merge with the **supreme intercostal vein** that drains into the brachiocephalic vein.

The **lumbar veins** and **posterior intercostal veins** drain into the azygos system of veins along the posterior thoracic wall. The **hemiazygos** (hem′ē-az′ī-gos) and **accessory hemiazygos veins** on the left side of the vertebrae drain the left-side veins. The **azygos vein** drains the right-side veins and also receives blood from the hemiazygos veins. The azygos vein drains into the superior vena cava. A schematic for venous return can be viewed in figure 20.22c.

WHAT DID YOU LEARN?

33 Does the azygos system, which receives venous blood from the thoracic and abdominal wall, drain into the superior vena cava or the inferior vena cava?

Right subclavian vein

Right brachiocephalic vein

Superior vena cava

Internal thoracic vein

Anterior intercostal veins

Azygos vein

Posterior intercostal vein

Inferior vena cava

Musculophrenic vein

Superior epigastric vein

Inferior epigastric vein

Left subclavian vein

Left brachiocephalic vein

Supreme intercostal vein

Posterior intercostal veins (1–3)

Accessory hemiazygos vein

Posterior intercostal vein

Hemiazygos vein

Diaphragm

Inferior vena cava

Lumbar veins

Median sacral vein

Common iliac vein

External iliac vein

Internal iliac vein

(b) Veins, anterior view

Figure 20.22 Circulation to the Thoracic and Abdominal Body Walls (*continued*). (*b*) The venous drainage of the thoracic and abdominal wall is more complex than its arterial supply. AP|R

(continued on next page)

Figure 20.22 Circulation to the Thoracic and Abdominal Body Walls (*continued*). (*c*) A schematic of the venous drainage.

20.10c Thoracic Organs

✓ LEARNING OBJECTIVE

7. Describe the vessels that supply and drain the lungs, esophagus, and diaphragm.

The main thoracic organs include the heart, lungs, esophagus, and diaphragm. The vessels supplying and draining the heart were described in section 19.4. The vessels of the other thoracic organs are discussed here **(figure 20.23)**.

Lungs

The bronchi and bronchioles (airways of the lung) and connective tissue of the lungs are supplied by three or four small **bronchial arteries** that emerge as tiny branches from the anterior wall of the descending thoracic aorta. Left and right **bronchial veins** (not shown) drain into the azygos system of veins and the pulmonary veins. The rest of the lung receives its oxygen via diffusion directly from the tiny air sacs (alveoli) of the lungs.

Esophagus

Several small **esophageal** (ē-sof′a-jē′ăl, ĕ′sŏ-faj′ē-ăl) **arteries** emerge from the anterior wall of the descending thoracic aorta and supply the esophagus. Additionally, the left gastric artery forms several **esophageal branches** that supply the abdominal portion of the esophagus. **Esophageal veins** drain the esophageal wall and may take either of two routes: into the azygos vein or into the left gastric vein (not shown). The latter merges with the hepatic portal vein (described in the next section).

Diaphragm

Arterial blood is supplied to the diaphragm by paired vessels. **Superior phrenic** (fren′ik; *phren* = diaphragm) **arteries** emerge from the descending thoracic aorta; **inferior phrenic arteries**

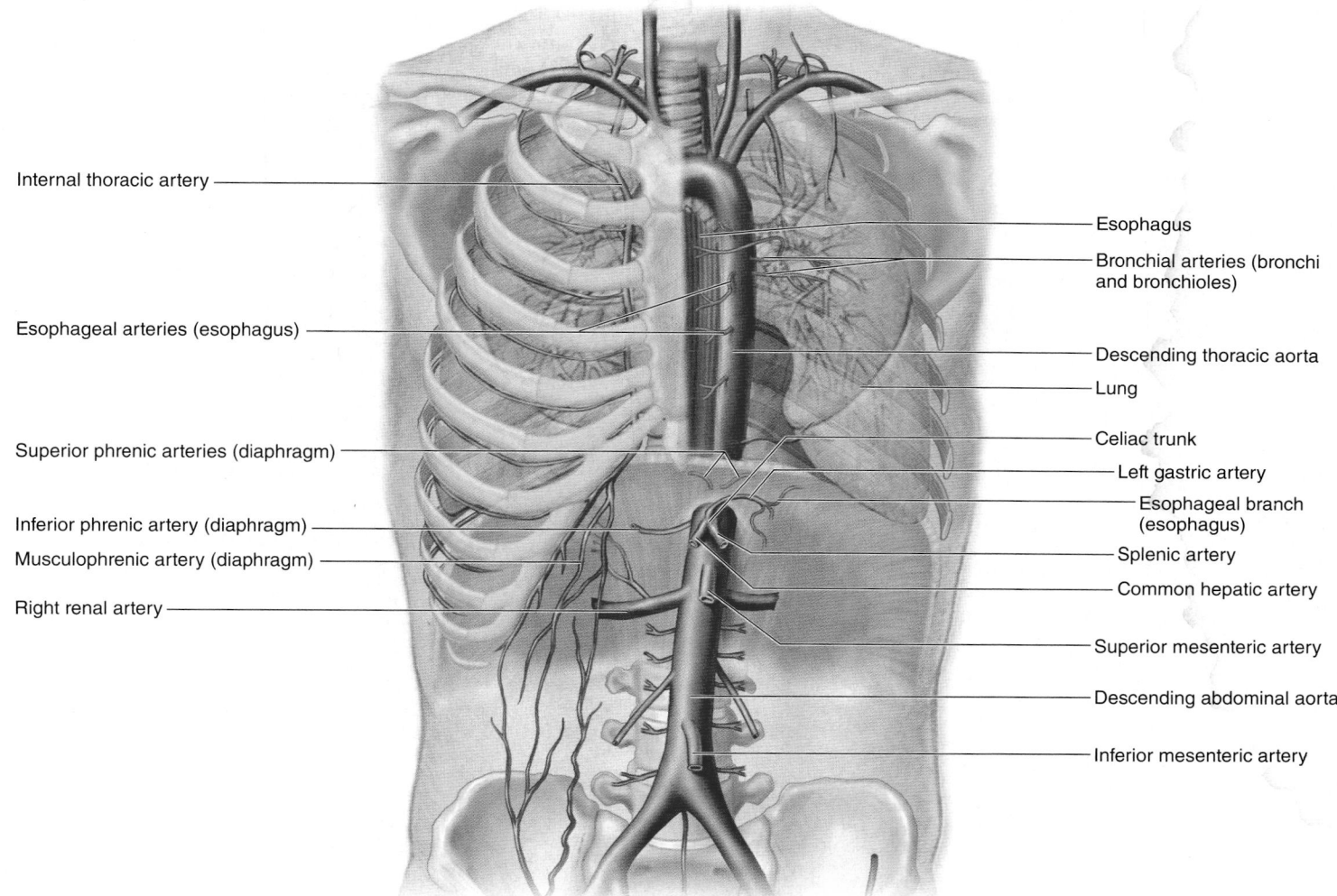

Internal thoracic artery

Esophageal arteries (esophagus)

Superior phrenic arteries (diaphragm)

Inferior phrenic artery (diaphragm)

Musculophrenic artery (diaphragm)

Right renal artery

Esophagus

Bronchial arteries (bronchi and bronchioles)

Descending thoracic aorta

Lung

Celiac trunk

Left gastric artery

Esophageal branch (esophagus)

Splenic artery

Common hepatic artery

Superior mesenteric artery

Descending abdominal aorta

Inferior mesenteric artery

Figure 20.23 Arterial Blood Supply of Organs of the Thoracic Cavity and Diaphragm. The blood vessels to the bronchi (airways), esophagus, and diaphragm are shown. The ribs and superficial vessels have been removed from the left side of the body so as to see the deeper vessels. **AP|R**

emerge from the descending abdominal aorta to supply the diaphragm; and both **musculophrenic arteries** and pericardiacophrenic arteries (not shown) arise from the internal thoracic artery. Superior phrenic and inferior phrenic veins drain with the inferior vena cava, while the musculophrenic drains into the internal thoracic veins that merge with the brachiocephalic veins. These veins are not illustrated.

WHAT DID YOU LEARN?

34 What are the systemic arteries that supply oxygenated blood to the lungs? What specific structures of the lung receive the blood?

20.10d The Gastrointestinal Tract

LEARNING OBJECTIVES

8. Name the three major arteries that branch from the descending aorta to supply the gastrointestinal tract, and list their major branches.

9. Explain the function of the hepatic portal system.

10. Trace the route of blood from the gastrointestinal tract to the inferior vena cava.

The gastrointestinal (GI) tract receives arterial blood from unpaired arteries that arise from the abdominal aorta. Venous blood travels through a hepatic portal system before draining into the inferior vena cava.

Arterial Supply to the Abdomen

Three unpaired arteries emerge from the anterior wall of the descending abdominal aorta to supply the GI tract. From superior to inferior, these arteries are the celiac trunk, superior mesenteric artery, and inferior mesenteric artery (see figure 20.22a).

Celiac Trunk The **celiac** (sē′lē-ak; *koilia* = belly) **trunk** is located immediately inferior to the aortic opening (hiatus) of the diaphragm. Three branches emerge from this arterial trunk **(figure 20.24)**: (1) the **left gastric artery**, (2) the **splenic artery**, and (3) the **common hepatic artery**. The common hepatic artery

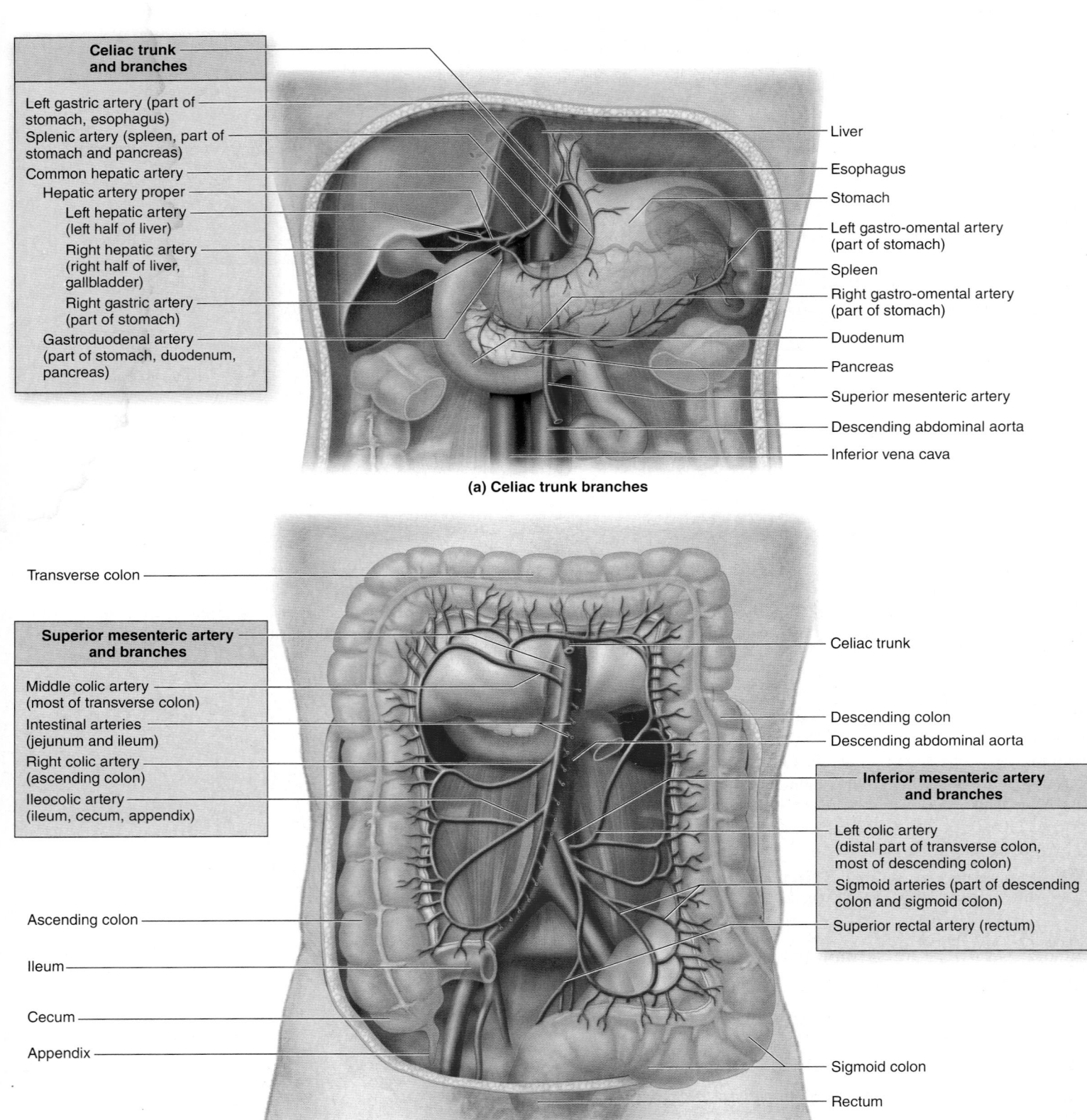

Celiac trunk and branches

Left gastric artery (part of stomach, esophagus)
Splenic artery (spleen, part of stomach and pancreas)
Common hepatic artery
Hepatic artery proper
Left hepatic artery (left half of liver)
Right hepatic artery (right half of liver, gallbladder)
Right gastric artery (part of stomach)
Gastroduodenal artery (part of stomach, duodenum, pancreas)

Liver
Esophagus
Stomach
Left gastro-omental artery (part of stomach)
Spleen
Right gastro-omental artery (part of stomach)
Duodenum
Pancreas
Superior mesenteric artery
Descending abdominal aorta
Inferior vena cava

(a) Celiac trunk branches

Transverse colon

Superior mesenteric artery and branches

Middle colic artery (most of transverse colon)
Intestinal arteries (jejunum and ileum)
Right colic artery (ascending colon)
Ileocolic artery (ileum, cecum, appendix)

Ascending colon
Ileum
Cecum
Appendix

Celiac trunk
Descending colon
Descending abdominal aorta

Inferior mesenteric artery and branches

Left colic artery (distal part of transverse colon, most of descending colon)
Sigmoid arteries (part of descending colon and sigmoid colon)
Superior rectal artery (rectum)

Sigmoid colon
Rectum

(b) Superior and inferior mesenteric arteries

Figure 20.24 Arterial Supply to the Gastrointestinal Tract and Abdominal Organs. The celiac trunk, superior mesenteric artery, and inferior mesenteric artery supply most of the abdominal organs. (*a*) Branches of the celiac trunk supply part of the esophagus, stomach, spleen, pancreas, liver, and gallbladder. (*b*) Branches of the superior mesenteric and inferior mesenteric arteries primarily supply the intestines.

divides into the **hepatic artery proper** and the **gastroduodenal** (gas′trō-dū′ō-dē′năl) **artery.**

Superior Mesenteric Artery

The **superior mesenteric** (mez-en-ter′ĭk; *mesos* = middle, *enteron* = intestine) **artery** is located immediately inferior to the celiac trunk. Its branches include 18–20 **intestinal arteries,** the **middle colic artery,** the **right colic artery,** and the **ileocolic** (il′ē-ō-kol-ik) **artery.**

Inferior Mesenteric Artery

The **inferior mesenteric artery** emerges approximately 5 centimeters superior to bifurcation of the aorta at about the level of the L$_3$ vertebra. Its branches include the **left colic artery,** the **sigmoid arteries,** and the **superior rectal** (rek′tăl; *rectus* = straight) **artery.** The specific regions that each arterial branch supplies blood to are included in figure 20.24.

Venous Return from the Abdomen and the Hepatic Portal System

Blood that has passed through the capillaries of digestive organs and then drained by its respective veins is not directly returned to the inferior vena cava and returned to the heart **(figure 20.25).** Instead, the blood is transported from the veins of the digestive organs into a **hepatic portal system** that drains the blood into the liver before this blood drains to the inferior vena cava.

The hepatic portal system is needed because the veins of the GI tract absorb digested nutrients, and these nutrients must be processed by the liver. The liver also detoxifies any harmful agents absorbed by the gastrointestinal blood vessels. The hepatic portal system allows for the most efficient route for handling these absorbed substances. The hepatic portal system also receives products of erythrocyte destruction from the spleen, so that the liver can recycle some of these components.

Within the hepatic portal system, blood from the digestive organs drains into three main venous branches:

1. The **splenic vein,** a horizontally positioned vein
2. The **inferior mesenteric vein,** a vertically positioned vein
3. The **superior mesenteric vein,** another vertically positioned vein on the right side of the body

All three of these drain into the **hepatic portal vein** that connects to the liver. Some small veins, such as the left and right gastric veins, drain directly into the hepatic portal vein. The venous blood in the hepatic portal vein flows through the sinusoids of the liver. In these sinusoids, the venous blood mixes with arterial oxygenated blood entering the liver via the hepatic arteries. Thus, deoxygenated but high-nutrient-filled blood from digestive organs and oxygenated blood from the hepatic artery flow within the liver sinusoids.

Blood leaves the liver through **hepatic veins** that merge with the inferior vena cava.

WHAT DID YOU LEARN?

35 What are the three branches off of the celiac trunk, and which organs do these vessels supply?

36 What are the three primary veins that drain into the hepatic portal vein of the hepatic portal system? What is the function of the hepatic portal system?

Figure 20.25 Hepatic Portal System. The hepatic portal system is a network of veins that transports venous blood from the GI tract to the liver for nutrient processing. AP|R

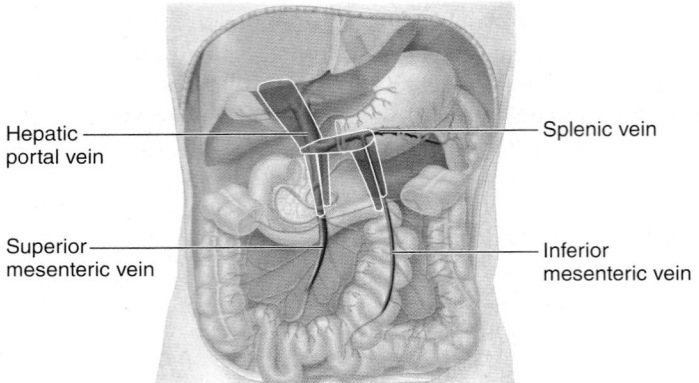
20.10e Posterior Abdominal Organs, Pelvis, and Perineum

LEARNING OBJECTIVES

11. Describe the arteries and veins that supply and drain the adrenal glands, kidneys, and gonads.

12. Name the main vessels associated with the pelvis and perineum.

Branches from the descending abdominal aorta and the internal iliac arteries supply the posterior abdominal organs and pelvis, and veins having the same names drain them **(figure 20.26)**. Several paired arterial branches emerge from the sides of the descending abdominal aorta in addition to the arteries already mentioned.

Posterior Abdominal Organs

The **middle suprarenal artery** supplies each adrenal gland; the **renal artery** supplies each kidney; and the **gonadal artery** supplies each gonad. Subsequently, these organs are drained by veins having the same name as the arteries.

Pelvis and Perineum

The aorta divides at its inferior end into the right and left common iliacs. Each common iliac further divides into an internal iliac artery and an external iliac artery. The **internal iliac artery** is the primary arterial supply to the pelvis and perineum. Some branches of the internal iliac artery include the **superior** and **inferior gluteal** (glū'tē-ăl) **arteries,** the **superior vesical artery,** the **middle rectal artery,** the **vaginal artery** and **uterine artery** (in females), the **internal pudendal** (pū-den'dăl; *pudeo* = to feel ashamed) **artery,** and the **obturator** (ob'tū-rā-tŏr) **artery.** Remnant vessels of fetal circulation are the **medial umbilical ligaments**—previously, umbilical arteries that transported blood from the fetus to the placenta.

The pelvis and perineum are drained by veins with the same name as the supplying arteries (see figure 20.22*b*). The veins merge with the internal iliac vein that merges with the common iliac vein, which subsequently drains into the inferior vena cava.

WHAT DID YOU LEARN?

37 What arteries supply the kidneys? The adrenal glands? The female uterus?

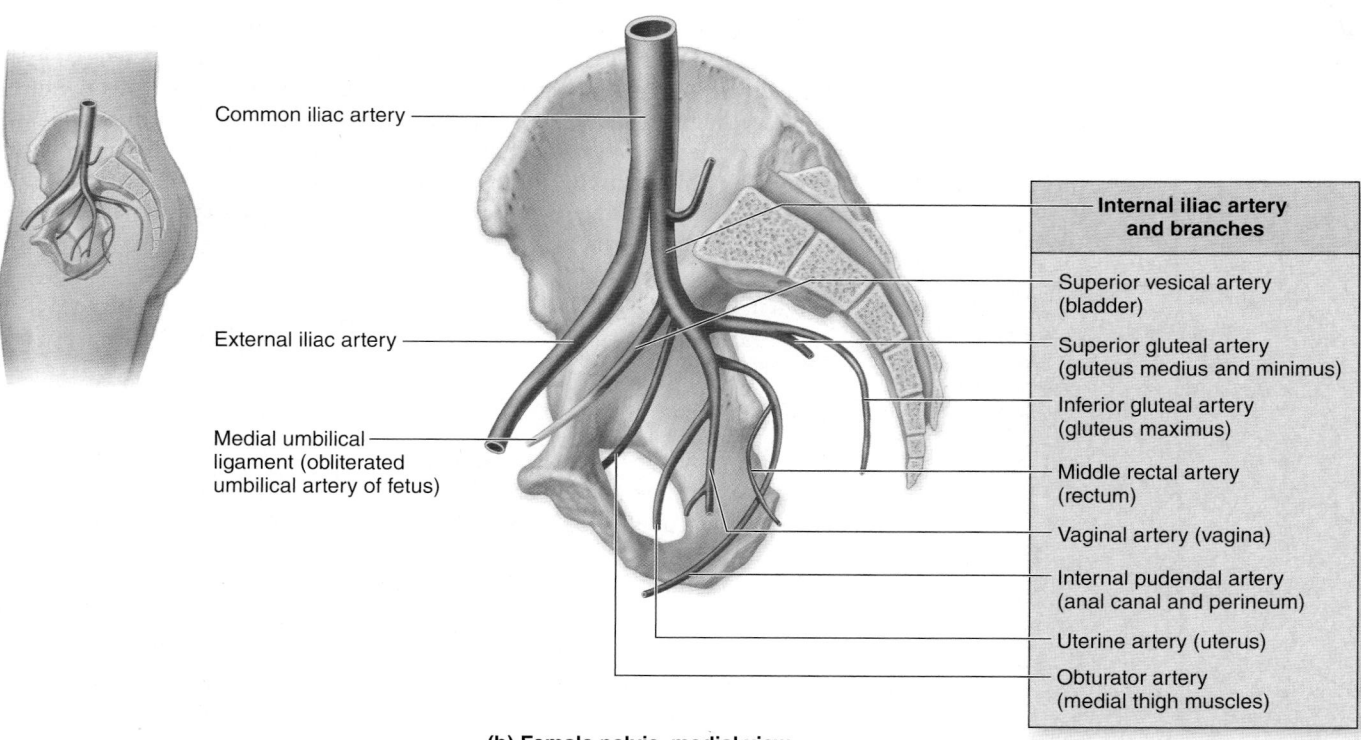

Unpaired arteries

Celiac trunk

Superior mesenteric artery

Descending abdominal aorta

Inferior mesenteric artery

Median sacral artery

Paired arteries

Inferior phrenic artery (diaphragm and part of adrenal gland)

Middle suprarenal artery (adrenal gland)

Renal artery (kidney and part of adrenal gland)

Gonadal artery (gonads)

Common iliac artery

Internal iliac artery (pelvis and perineum)

External iliac artery (inferior abdominal wall, external genitalia, lower limb)

(a) Abdominal wall, anterior view

Common iliac artery

External iliac artery

Medial umbilical ligament (obliterated umbilical artery of fetus)

Internal iliac artery and branches

Superior vesical artery (bladder)

Superior gluteal artery (gluteus medius and minimus)

Inferior gluteal artery (gluteus maximus)

Middle rectal artery (rectum)

Vaginal artery (vagina)

Internal pudendal artery (anal canal and perineum)

Uterine artery (uterus)

Obturator artery (medial thigh muscles)

(b) Female pelvis, medial view

Figure 20.26 Arterial Supply to the Abdominal Organs, Pelvis, and Perineum. (*a*) Paired arteries directly off the descending abdominal aorta supply blood to the adrenal gland, kidney, gonads, and pelvis. (*b*) Branches of the right internal iliac artery distribute blood to the pelvic organs. Shown is a female pelvis; a male pelvis would have no uterine artery, and instead of a vaginal artery, would have an inferior vesical artery (not all internal iliac artery branches are labeled).

20.11 Systemic Circulation: Upper and Lower Limbs

Blood flow through the upper and the lower limbs mirror one another. Both the upper and lower limbs (1) are supplied by a main arterial vessel: the subclavian artery for the upper limb, and the external iliac artery for the lower limb; (2) have their main artery bifurcating at either the elbow or the knee; (3) have arterial and venous arches; and (4) have superficial and deep networks of veins.

20.11a The Upper Limb

☑ LEARNING OBJECTIVES

1. Trace the arteries of the upper limb from the subclavian artery to the fingers.

2. Compare and contrast the superficial venous drainage and the deep venous drainage of the upper limb.

Each arm is supplied by a subclavian artery and drained by a subclavian vein. The venous system includes both deep and superficial drainage.

Arterial Flow to the Upper Limb

A **subclavian artery** supplies blood to each upper limb. The left subclavian artery emerges directly from the aortic arch, while the right subclavian artery is a division of the brachiocephalic trunk (see figure 20.19*a*).

Before extending into the arm, the subclavian artery extends multiple branches to supply parts of the body's upper region: the vertebral artery, the thyrocervical trunks, the costocervical trunk, and the internal thoracic artery, as described earlier.

After the subclavian artery passes over the lateral border of the first rib, it is renamed the **axillary** (ak′sil-ār-ē) **artery (figure 20.27)**. The axillary artery extends many branches to the shoulder and thoracic region. When the axillary artery passes the inferior border of the teres major muscle, it is renamed the **brachial** (brā′kē-ăl) **artery.** One of its branches is the **deep brachial artery,** which supplies blood to most brachial (arm) muscles. In the cubital fossa, the brachial artery divides into a **radial artery** and an **ulnar artery.** Both arteries supply the forearm and wrist before they anastomose and form two arterial arches in the palm: the **deep palmar arch** (formed primarily from the radial artery), and the **superficial palmar arch** (formed primarily from the ulnar artery). **Digital arteries** emerge from the arches to supply the fingers.

WHAT DO YOU THINK?

4 If the left ulnar artery is cut, would any blood be able to reach the left hand and fingers? Why or why not?

Venous Drainage of the Upper Limb

Venous drainage of the upper limb, which converges on the axillary vein and into the subclavian vein, is accomplished through two groups of veins: superficial and deep.

Superficial Venous Drainage On the dorsum of the hand, a dorsal venous network (or arch) of veins drains into both the medially located **basilic** (ba-sil′ik) **vein** and the laterally located **cephalic** (se-fal′ik) **vein.** These veins drain into the axillary vein, and they also have perforating branches that allow them to connect to the deeper veins.

In the cubital region, an obliquely positioned **median cubital vein** connects the cephalic and basilic veins. The median cubital vein is a common site for venipuncture, in which a vein is punctured with a hollow needle to draw blood or inject a solute. All of these superficial veins are highly variable among individuals and have multiple superficial tributaries draining into them.

Deep Venous Drainage The **digital veins** and **deep** and **superficial palmar venous arches** drain into *pairs* of **radial veins** and **ulnar veins** that run parallel to arteries of the same name. At the level of the cubital fossa, the radial and ulnar veins merge to form a pair of **brachial veins** that travel with the brachial artery. Brachial veins and the basilic vein merge to form the **axillary vein.**

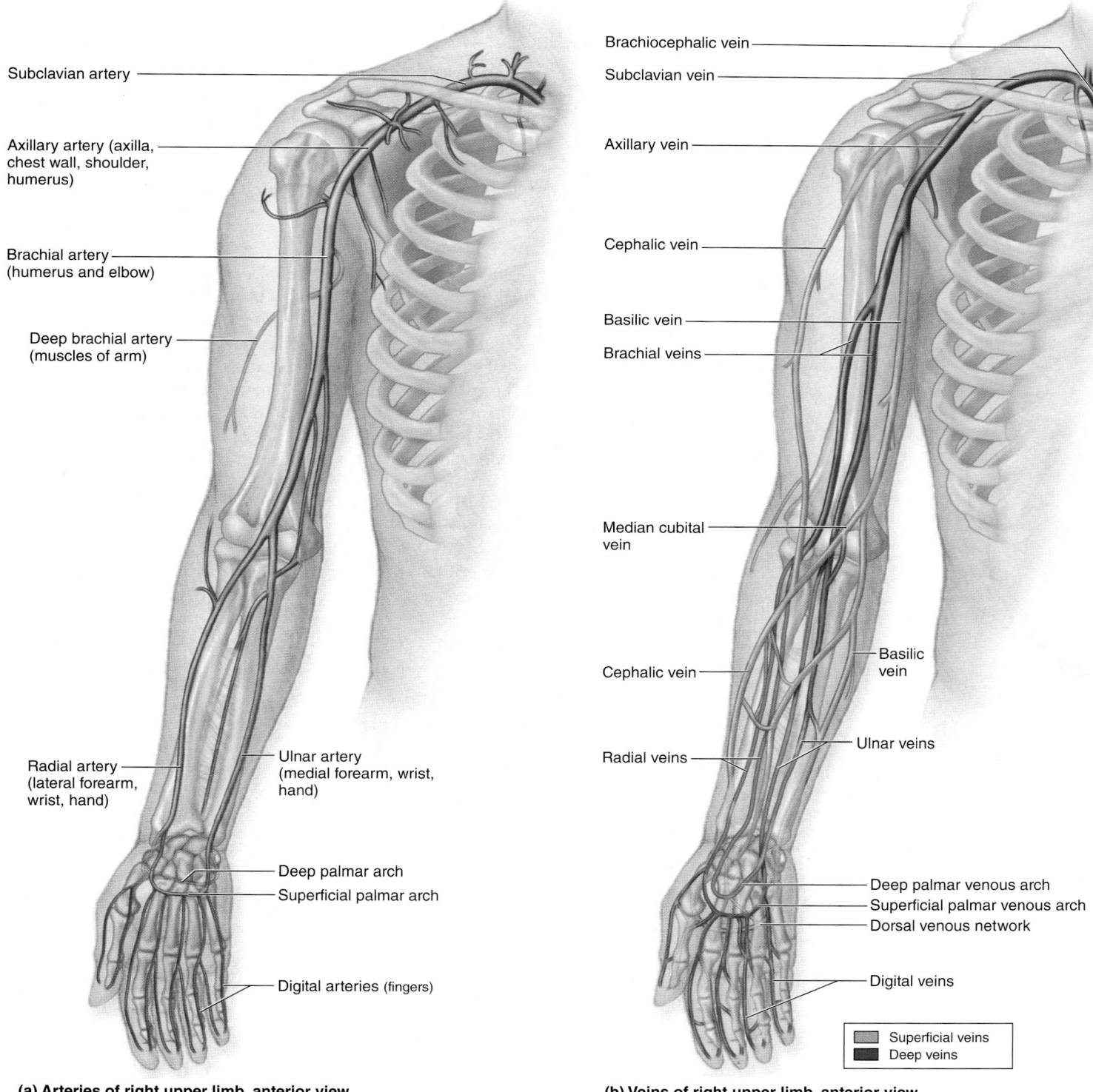

(a) Arteries of right upper limb, anterior view

(b) Veins of right upper limb, anterior view

Figure 20.27 Vascular Supply to the Upper Limb. The subclavian artery carries oxygenated blood to the upper limb; veins merge to return deoxygenated blood to the heart. (*a*) Arteries that supply the upper limb. (*b*) Superficial and deep veins that return blood from the upper limb. **AP|R**

Superior to the lateral border of the first rib, the axillary vein is renamed the **subclavian vein** (see figure 20.19*b*). When the subclavian vein and internal jugular veins of the neck merge, they form the brachiocephalic vein. As we have seen, the left and right brachiocephalic veins form the superior vena cava.

WHAT DID YOU LEARN?

38 What is the sequence of vessels from the subclavian artery to the digital artery of the thumb?

39 What are the primary superficial veins of the upper limb?

3. Trace the arteries of the lower limb from the external iliac artery to the toes.

4. Compare and contrast the superficial venous drainage and the deep venous drainage of the lower limb.

The arterial and venous blood flow of the lower limb is very similar to that of the upper limb. As we discuss lower limb blood flow, compare it with that of the upper limb.

Arterial Flow to the Lower Limb

The main arterial supply for the lower limb is the **external iliac artery,** which is a branch of the common iliac artery **(figure 20.28a)**. The external iliac artery travels inferior to the inguinal ligament, where it is renamed the **femoral** (fem′ŏ-răl) **artery.** The **deep femoral artery** (or *deep artery of the thigh*) emerges from the femoral artery to supply the hip joint (via medial and lateral femoral circumflex arteries) and many of the thigh muscles, before traversing posteromedially along the thigh. When the femoral artery enters the popliteal fossa, it is renamed the **popliteal** (pop-lit′ē-ăl, pop-li-tē′ăl) **artery.** The popliteal artery supplies the knee joint and muscles in this region.

The popliteal artery divides into an **anterior tibial artery** that supplies the anterior compartment of the leg, and a **posterior tibial artery** that supplies the posterior compartment of the leg. The posterior tibial artery extends a branch called the **fibular artery,** which supplies the lateral compartment leg muscles.

The posterior tibial artery continues to the plantar side of the foot, where it branches into **medial** and **lateral plantar arteries.** The anterior tibial artery crosses over the anterior surface of the ankle, where it is renamed the **dorsalis pedis artery** (*dorsal artery of the foot*). The dorsalis pedis artery and a branch of the lateral plantar artery unite to form the **plantar arterial arch** of the foot. **Digital arteries** extend from the plantar arch and supply the toes.

Venous Drainage of the Lower Limb

Venous drainage of the lower limb is also through superficial and deep veins (figure 20.28b).

Superficial Venous Drainage On the dorsum of the foot, a dorsal venous arch drains into the **great saphenous** (să-fē′nŭs) **vein** and the **small saphenous vein.** The great saphenous vein originates in the medial ankle and extends adjacent to the medial surface of the entire lower limb before it drains into the femoral vein. The small saphenous vein extends adjacent to the lateral ankle and then travels along the posterior calf, before draining into the popliteal vein. These superficial veins have perforating branches that connect to the deeper veins. If the valves in these veins (or the perforating branches) become incompetent, varicose veins develop. (See Clinical View: "Varicose Veins.")

Deep Venous Drainage The **digital veins** and deep veins of the foot drain into pairs of **medial** and **lateral plantar veins.** These veins and a pair of **fibular veins** drain into a pair of **posterior tibial veins.** On the dorsum of the foot and ankle, deep veins drain into a pair of **anterior tibial veins,** which traverse alongside the anterior tibial artery. The **anterior** and **posterior tibial veins** merge to form a **popliteal vein** that curves to the anterior portion of the thigh and is renamed the **femoral vein.** Once this vein passes superior to the inguinal ligament, it is renamed as the **external iliac vein.** The external and internal iliac veins merge in the pelvis, forming the common iliac vein. Left and right common iliac veins then merge to form the inferior vena cava.

💡 **WHAT DID YOU LEARN?**

40 Can you trace one pathway that blood may travel through from the external iliac artery to the digital arteries?

41 How do the great saphenous vein and small saphenous vein compare in terms of their anatomic position and length?

Anterior

External iliac artery

Common iliac artery

Internal iliac artery

Inguinal ligament

Femoral artery
(knee, leg)

Deep femoral artery
(hip joint, femur, most thigh muscles)

Popliteal artery
(knee, popliteus muscle)

Anterior tibial artery
(anterior compartment of leg)

Posterior tibial artery
(posterior compartment of leg)

Fibular artery
(lateral compartment of leg)

Dorsalis pedis artery
(foot)

Plantar arterial arch
(formed from a branch of dorsalis
pedis and lateral plantar artery)

Digital arteries (toes)

Posterior

Femoral artery
(knee, leg)

Deep femoral artery
(hip joint, femur, most thigh muscles)

Popliteal artery
(knee, popliteus muscle)

Anterior tibial artery
(anterior compartment of leg)

Posterior tibial artery
(posterior compartment of leg)

Fibular artery
(lateral compartment of leg)

Lateral plantar artery
(part of plantar surface
of foot)

Medial plantar artery
(part of plantar
surface of foot)

Digital arteries (toes)

(a) Arteries of right lower limb

Figure 20.28 Vascular Supply to the Lower Limb. The external iliac artery carries oxygenated blood to the lower limb; veins merge to return deoxygenated blood to the heart. (*a*) Anterior and posterior views of arteries distributed throughout the lower limb. AP|R

(continued on next page)

Anterior

Common iliac vein

External iliac vein

Internal iliac vein

Deep femoral vein

Femoral vein

Great saphenous vein

Popliteal vein

Anterior tibial veins

Fibular veins

Posterior tibial veins

Great saphenous vein

Dorsal venous arch

Posterior

Fibular veins

Small saphenous vein

Medial plantar veins

Lateral plantar veins

Digital veins

Deep veins
Superficial veins

(b) Veins of right lower limb

Figure 20.28 Vascular Supply to the Lower Limb (*continued*). (*b*) Anterior and posterior views of the superficial and deep veins that return blood from the lower limb.

20.12 Comparison of Fetal and Postnatal Circulation

The cardiovascular system of the fetus is structurally and functionally different from that of the newborn. Whereas the fetus receives oxygen and nutrients directly from the mother through the placenta, the newborn's postnatal cardiovascular system must be independent. Additionally, since the fetal lungs are not functional, the blood pressure in the pulmonary arteries and right side of the heart is greater than the pressure in the left side of the heart. Finally, several fetal vessels help shunt blood directly to the organs in need and away from the organs that are not yet functional. As a result, the fetal cardiovascular system has some structures that are modified or that cease to function once the human is born.

20.12a Fetal Circulation

LEARNING OBJECTIVE

1. Trace the pathway of blood circulation in the fetus.

The fetal circulatory route is listed here and shown in **figure 20.29**:

(1) Oxygenated blood from the placenta enters the body of the fetus through the **umbilical vein.**

(2) The blood from the umbilical vein is shunted away from the liver and directly toward the inferior vena cava through the **ductus venosus** (dŭk′tŭs vē-nō′sŭs).

(3) Oxygenated blood in the ductus venosus mixes with deoxygenated blood in the inferior vena cava.

(4) Blood from the superior and inferior venae cavae empties into the right atrium.

(5) Because pressure is greater on the right side of the heart as compared to the left side, most of the blood is shunted from the right atrium to the left atrium via the **foramen ovale.** This blood flows into the left ventricle and then is pumped out through the aorta.

(6) A small amount of blood enters the right ventricle and pulmonary trunk, but much of this blood is shunted from the pulmonary trunk to the aorta through a vessel detour called the **ductus arteriosus** (ar-tēr′ē-ō′sŭs).

(7) Blood travels to the rest of the body, and the deoxygenated blood returns to the placenta through a pair of **umbilical arteries.**

(8) Nutrient and gas exchange occurs at the placenta, and the cycle repeats.

At birth, the fetal circulation begins to change into the postnatal pattern. When the baby takes its first breath, pulmonary resistance drops, and the pulmonary arteries dilate. As a result, pressure on the right side of the heart decreases so that the pressure is greater on the left side of the heart, which handles the systemic circulation.

WHAT DID YOU LEARN?

42 List the five structures of fetal circulation and identify the function of each.

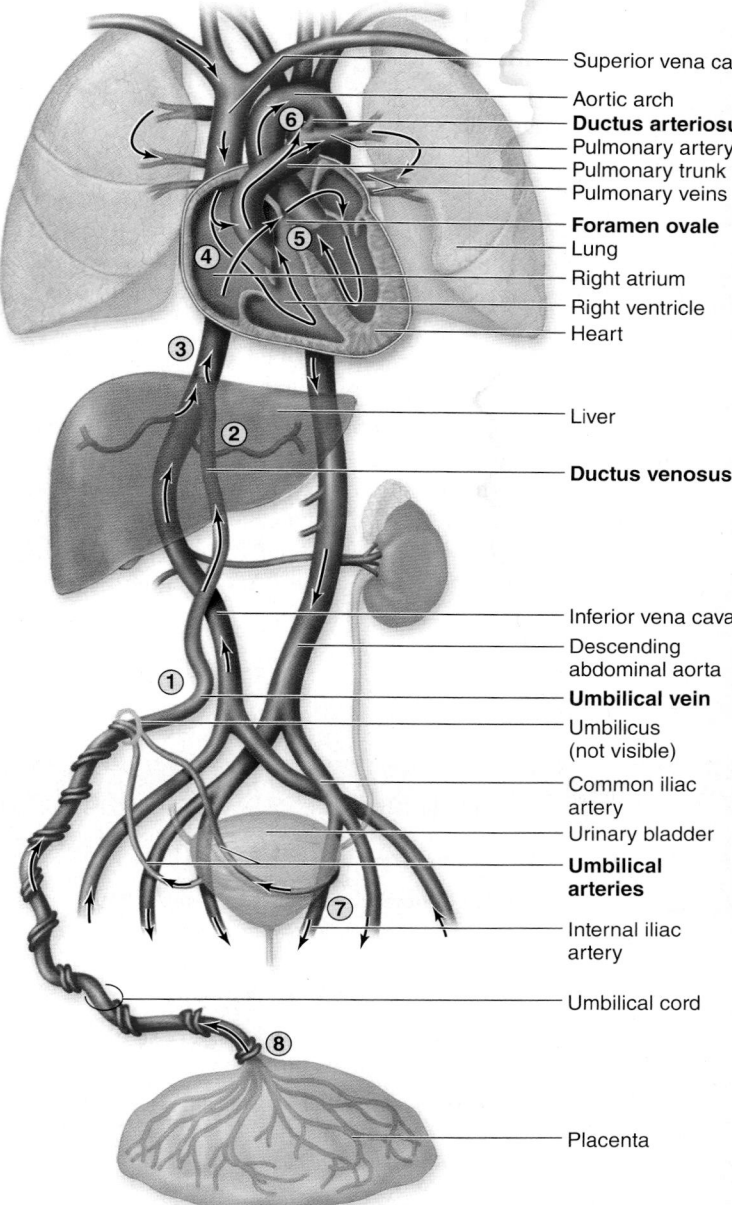

Figure 20.29 Fetal Circulation. Structural changes in both the heart and blood vessels accommodate the different needs of the fetus and the newborn. The pathway of blood flow is indicated by black arrows. The chart at the bottom of the drawing summarizes the fate of each fetal cardiovascular structure.

Fetal cardiovascular structure	Postnatal structure
Ductus arteriosus	Ligamentum arteriosum
Ductus venosus	Ligamentum venosum
Foramen ovale	Fossa ovalis
Umbilical arteries	Medial umbilical ligaments
Umbilical vein	Round ligament of liver (ligamentum teres)

20.12b Postnatal Changes

✓ LEARNING OBJECTIVE

2. Describe the changes that occur after the baby is born and must utilize the pulmonary circulation.

The postnatal changes occur as follows:

- The umbilical vein and umbilical arteries constrict and become nonfunctional. They turn into the **round ligament of the liver** (or *ligamentum teres*) and the **medial umbilical ligaments,** respectively.
- The ductus venosus ceases to be functional and constricts, becoming the **ligamentum venosum.**
- Because pressure is now greater on the left side of the heart, the two flaps of the interatrial septum close off the foramen ovale. The only remnant of the foramen ovale is a thin, oval depression in the wall of the septum called the **fossa ovalis.**
- Within 10 to 15 hours after birth, the ductus arteriosus closes and becomes a fibrous structure called the **ligamentum arteriosum.**

INTEGRATE

CLINICAL VIEW
Patent Ductus Arteriosus

In some infants, especially those born prematurely, the ductus arteriosus fails to close after birth. A **patent** (open) **ductus arteriosus** serves as a conduit through which blood from the aorta can enter the pulmonary system; it can result in high blood pressure in the pulmonary circulation and in mixing of deoxygenated blood with oxygenated blood from the aorta. Because prostaglandins help keep the ductus arteriosus open during fetal life, a patent ductus arteriosus may be treated with prostaglandin-inhibiting medication. Surgery to remove the ductus arteriosus is a second treatment option.

💡 WHAT DID YOU LEARN?

43 Why is it important for the ductus arteriosus and foramen ovale to both close after birth?

CHAPTER SUMMARY

20.1 Structure and Function of Blood Vessels 769

- Arteries take blood away from the heart, capillaries are responsible for gas and nutrient exchange, and veins take blood to the heart.

20.1a General Structure of Vessels 769

- Arteries and veins have a tunica intima (innermost layer) a tunica media (middle layer), and a tunica externa (outermost layer).
- Capillaries have a tunica intima, composed of an endothelial layer and a basement membrane only.

20.1b Arteries 771

- Elastic arteries have the largest diameter and the greatest proportion of elastic fibers in their walls.
- Muscular arteries are medium-sized arteries with more smooth muscle and fewer elastic fibers to ensure vasodilation and vasoconstriction.
- Arterioles are the smallest arteries.

20.1c Capillaries 774

- Capillaries, the smallest blood vessels, connect arterioles with venules. Gas and nutrient exchange occurs in the capillaries.
- The three types of capillaries are continuous capillaries, fenestrated capillaries, and sinusoids.

20.1d Veins 777

- Venules are small veins that merge into larger veins. One-way valves prevent blood backflow in veins.
- Blood pressure is low in the veins, which act as reservoirs and hold about 55% of the body's blood at rest.

20.1e Pathways of Blood Vessels 777

- Blood vessels may be arranged in simple pathways (artery ⟶ arterioles ⟶ capillary bed ⟶ venules ⟶ veins ⟶ heart) or in alternative pathways, which include anastomoses and portal venous systems.

20.2 Capillary Exchange 779

- Materials may pass through the capillary walls via diffusion, vesicular transport, and bulk flow.

20.2a Diffusion and Vesicular Transport 779

- Oxygen, carbon dioxide, nutrients, and waste products move between blood and interstitial fluid via diffusion.
- Certain hormones, such as insulin and fatty acids, are transported via vesicular transport.

20.2b Bulk Flow 780

- Bulk flow refers to the net filtration and reabsorption that occurs at the capillary level due to hydrostatic pressure and osmotic pressure.

20.2c Net Filtration Pressure 781

- The net filtration pressure is the difference between the net hydrostatic pressure and the net colloid osmotic pressure.
- The net filtration pressure is positive at the arterial end of the capillary, resulting in filtration, and is negative at the venous end of the capillary, resulting in reabsorption.

(continued on next page)

20.9 Systemic Circulation: Vessels from and to the Heart 798

20.9a General Arterial Flow Out of the Heart 798

- Oxygenated blood is pumped from the left ventricle through the ascending aorta; the coronary arteries branch from the ascending aorta.
- Three branches of the aortic arch are the brachiocephalic trunk, the left common carotid, and the left subclavian.
- The descending abdominal aorta bifurcates into the left and right common iliac arteries.

20.9b General Venous Return to the Heart 800

- Veins from the head, neck, upper limbs, and thoracic and abdominal walls merge to form left and right brachiocephalic veins, which merge to form the superior vena cava.

20.10 Systemic Circulation: Head and Trunk 800

20.10a Head and Neck 800

- The common carotid artery supplies most of the blood to the head and neck and divides into the external carotid artery and internal carotid artery.
- The external carotid artery supplies superficial regions of the head and organs of the neck while the internal carotid artery supplies the brain and orbits.
- Blood from the cranium drains via the vertebral veins and the dural venous sinuses. Venous return is via the internal and external jugular veins.

20.10b Thoracic and Abdominal Walls 804

- Two internal thoracic arteries as well as other arteries supply the thoracic and abdominal wall.
- Venous return from the thoracic and abdominal walls is complex and involves the azygos system of veins.

20.10c Thoracic Organs 806

- The lungs are supplied by bronchial arteries branching from the descending thoracic aorta; they are drained by bronchial veins.
- The esophagus receives blood from the esophageal arteries that branch from the aorta and from the esophageal branches of the left gastric artery; it is drained via the esophageal veins.
- The diaphragm is supplied by a number of phrenic arteries and drained by the phrenic veins.

20.10d The Gastrointestinal Tract 807

- The three major unpaired arteries from the descending abdominal aorta that supply the abdominal organs are the celiac trunk, the superior mesenteric artery, and the inferior mesenteric artery.
- The hepatic portal vein receives oxygen-poor but nutrient-rich blood from the gastrointestinal (GI) organs and takes it to the liver for processing. Blood leaves the liver via the hepatic veins.

20.10e Posterior Abdominal Organs, Pelvis, and Perineum 810

- Paired branches of the descending abdominal aorta supply the posterior abdominal organs, pelvis, and perineum. Venous drainage is by veins of the same name as the arteries.

20.11 Systemic Circulation: Upper and Lower Limbs 812

- The upper and lower limbs are each supplied by a single artery that branches into multiple vessels. Both superficial and deep veins drain the limbs.

20.11a The Upper Limb 812

- The upper limb is supplied by the subclavian artery and its branches and is drained into the subclavian vein.

20.11b The Lower Limb 814

- The lower limbs are supplied by the external iliac arteries and veins.

20.12 Comparison of Fetal and Postnatal Circulation 817

20.12a Fetal Circulation 817

- In the fetus, oxygenated blood is supplied by the umbilical vein from the placenta, and deoxygenated blood leaves through a pair of umbilical arteries.
- The fetal cardiovascular system bypasses the liver via the ductus venosus and bypasses the pulmonary circulation via the foramen ovale and ductus arteriosus.

20.12b Postnatal Changes 818

- In the newborn, the umbilical vein and arteries degenerate, and the ductus venosus, foramen ovale, and ductus arteriosus close as the infant is able to breathe on its own.

CHALLENGE YOURSELF

Do You Know the Basics?

_____ 1. Which of the following is *not* a characteristic of a capillary?

    a. Fenestrated capillaries have pores that allow for relatively large materials to slip out of the capillary.

    b. Sinusoid capillaries are main type of capillary around the brain.

    c. Capillaries often are arranged in a capillary bed that is supplied by an arteriole.

    d. The capillary wall consists of an endothelium and basement membrane only—there is no subendothelial layer.

_____ 2. Which statement is accurate about veins?

    a. Veins always carry deoxygenated blood.

    b. Veins drain into smaller vessels called venules.

    c. The largest tunic in a vein is the tunica externa.

    d. The lumen of a vein tends to be smaller than that of a comparably sized artery.

_____ 3. Vasa vasorum are found in the tunica _____ of a large blood vessel.

    a. intima

    b. media

    c. externa

    d. All of these are correct.

_____ 4. Which of the following decreases perfusion of a tissue?

    a. decreased total blood flow

    b. vasodilators

    c. angiogenesis

    d. increased carbon dioxide, increased H^+, and low O_2

_____ 5. The _____ is a type of vessel with the smallest pressure gradient that must be overcome by contraction of skeletal muscles and breathing.

    a. artery

    b. vein

    c. capillary

    d. sinusoid

_____ 6. An increase in _____ will result in an increase in blood flow to an area.

    a. vessel length

    b. vessel diameter

    c. blood viscosity

    d. the number of formed elements

_____ 7. Which of the following is accurate?

    a. Total blood flow increases with a steeper pressure gradient (assuming resistance stays the same).

    b. Total blood flow decreases with increased resistance (assuming cardiac output stays the same).

    c. Total blood flow is significant in maintaining adequate perfusion of all tissues.

    d. All of these are correct.

_____ 8. Velocity of blood flow is the slowest in

    a. muscular arteries.

    b. capillaries.

    c. veins.

    d. elastic arteries.

_____ 9. Blood pressure is regulated by the

    a. cardiac center.

    b. vasomotor center.

    c. hormones.

    d. All of these are correct.

_____ 10. Name the correct pathway that blood flows through in the upper limb arteries.

    a. subclavian $\longrightarrow$ axillary $\longrightarrow$ ulnar $\longrightarrow$ radial $\longrightarrow$ brachial

    b. subclavian $\longrightarrow$ axillary $\longrightarrow$ brachial $\longrightarrow$ cephalic $\longrightarrow$ basilic

    c. subclavian $\longrightarrow$ ulnar $\longrightarrow$ brachial $\longrightarrow$ radial

    d. subclavian $\longrightarrow$ axillary $\longrightarrow$ brachial $\longrightarrow$ radial and ulnar

11. List and describe the three tunics found in most blood vessels.

12. Compare and contrast arteries and veins with respect to function, tunic size, lumen size, and blood pressure.

13. Explain the difference between hydrostatic and osmotic pressure. How do these pressures change from the arteriole end of a capillary to the venule end of a capillary?

14. Write the formula for determining net filtration pressure in the capillaries.

15. Describe the relationship of vessel radius, vessel length, blood viscosity, and blood pressure to blood flow.

16. How is it possible for the sympathetic division to cause vasoconstriction in most blood vessels, but vasodilation in coronary and skeletal muscle blood vessels? Explain.

17. Briefly explain how changes in cardiac output, resistance, and blood volume influence blood pressure.

18. Compare how the cardiac center and vasomotor center regulate blood pressure and blood flow.

19. Compare the systemic circulation and pulmonary circulation. Discuss the function of arteries and veins in each system.

20. What postnatal changes occur in the heart and blood vessels? Why do these occur?

Can You Apply What You've Learned?

1. If a patient has cirrhosis of the liver and is unable to produce sufficient albumin and other plasma proteins, then what variable is changed in capillary exchange, and what is the effect?

   a. There is no change in the capillary exchange process.

   b. Hydrostatic pressure in the blood decreases, and fluid remains in the blood.

   c. Colloid osmotic pressure in the capillary increases, and blood volume increases in the blood vessels.

   d. Colloid osmotic pressure in the capillary decreases, and fluid remains in the interstitial fluid, potentially causing edema.

2. Arlene heads to the gym and initiates a vigorous exercise regimen. Which hormone will *not* be released?

   a. epinephrine

   b. atrial natriuretic peptide

   c. angiotensin II

   d. norepinephrine

3. After her workout, Arlene lies down on a mat to stretch out her leg muscles. She stands up suddenly after stretching and feels a bit light-headed. However, the light-headed feeling passes quickly. What physiologic process occurred that resulted in her light-headed feeling passing?

   a. The aortic bodies detected an increase in blood pressure in the head, and initiated a chemoreceptor reflex that decreased blood pressure.

   b. The carotid bodies detected low CO_2 and high O_2 levels from exercising, and stimulated the vasomotor center to vasoconstrict the vessels of the head and neck.

   c. Only α receptors in the head and neck initially were being stimulated, resulting in the light-headed feeling.

   d. The carotid sinuses detected decreased stretch in the carotid vessel wall and initiated a baroreceptor reflex to increase blood flow to the head and neck.

4. Over a period of 6 months, Harold loses 40 pounds. When Harold next visits his doctor, he discovers that his blood pressure levels have fallen too. Which of the following best explains why Harold's blood pressure dropped?

   a. When fat is lost, the extra length in blood vessels supplying the fat is lost too. Decreased blood vessel length resulted in decreased blood pressure.

   b. Most of the fat that Harold lost was around his thoracic organs, which compressed these organs. By losing the weight, he removed this compressive force.

   c. The resistance in the blood vessels increased due to the fat loss, resulting in decreased blood pressure.

   d. The fat previously constricted the blood vessels. When Harold lost the fat, the blood vessels were allowed to dilate, and thus blood pressure was reduced.

5. Alejandro was hit by a car, which resulted in massive injury and bleeding to his right foot. You realize that you have to compress a lower limb artery so that Alejandro will not lose too much blood. Which vessel, if compressed, will completely stop the flow of blood to the foot?

   a. anterior tibial artery

   b. posterior tibial artery

   c. deep femoral artery

   d. popliteal artery

Can You Synthesize What You've Learned?

1. Your patient is Thomas, a 50-year-old man that rarely exercises, is overweight, and only occasionally eats healthy meals, which puts him at risk for atherosclerosis. Explain to him the relationship between atherosclerosis and high blood pressure.

2. Arteries tend to have a lot of vascular anastomoses around body joints, such as the elbow and knee. Can you think of a reason why this would be beneficial?

3. Explain why an overweight individual with high blood pressure is advised to lose weight. Include in your response the relationship of blood vessel length, resistance, and blood pressure.

chapter 21
Lymphatic System

It is not uncommon for young children to develop tonsillitis—a condition in which the tonsils become inflamed and enlarged. Often, the lymph nodes in the neck are swollen, and the spleen may also become enlarged. You might initially be curious about why, if a child has tonsillitis, the lymph nodes and the spleen are also affected. Recall from chapter 1 that all of these structures—the tonsils, lymph nodes, and the spleen—are components of the lymphatic system. What you may not yet know is that these ➤

Nurses, physical therapists, occupational therapists, and massage therapists may earn a certification as a lymphedema therapist. These therapists use massage, compression wraps/garments, and exercise with patients to alleviate edema, a common condition if lymph vessels and lymph nodes are removed as a part of the treatment for cancer. Massage assists the movement of lymph in the lymph vessels and its return to venous circulation.

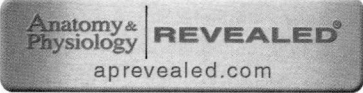

Anatomy & Physiology | REVEALED®
aprevealed.com

Module 10: Lymphatic System

organs function in helping the immune system defend the body against microbes and other infectious agents. The inflammation and enlargement that occur in lymphatic structures are signs that these organs are actively engaged in defending the body against potentially harmful substances.

The lymphatic system has two significant functions, both of which provide support to another system. The lymphatic system transports and houses lymphocytes and other immune cells that help the immune system defend against foreign substances. In addition, the lymphatic system aids the cardiovascular system by returning excess fluid to the blood to maintain fluid balance, blood volume, and blood pressure. Interestingly, the lymphatic system has no unique function of its own.

Here, we first describe lymph vessels and the absorption of excess fluid from the interstitial space and then discuss lymphatic organs, including lymph nodes and the spleen. Integrated within the chapter are brief descriptions of some of the common malfunctions of the lymphatic system. The details of the immune system are described in the next chapter.

21.1 Lymph and Lymph Vessels

The **lymphatic** (lim-fat′ik) **system** is composed of lymph vessels and lymphatic tissues and organs **(figure 21.1)**. Lymph is the fluid transported within lymph vessels. We begin by describing the formation and characteristics of lymph. We then discuss its transport through progressively larger lymph vessels until the lymph is returned to the cardiovascular system.

21.1a Lymph and Lymphatic Capillaries

 LEARNING OBJECTIVES

1. Describe lymph and its contents.
2. Discuss the location and anatomic structure of lymphatic capillaries.
3. Explain how fluid enters lymphatic capillaries.

Lymph originates as interstitial fluid surrounding tissue cells; it moves passively into the lymphatic capillaries due to a pressure gradient. Lymphatic capillaries merge to form larger lymph vessels.

Characteristics of Lymph

Approximately 15% of the fluid that enters the interstitial space surrounding the cells is not reabsorbed back into the blood capillaries during capillary exchange (see section 20.2). This interstitial fluid amounts to about 3 liters daily and is normally absorbed into lymphatic capillaries.

Once inside the lymph vessels, the interstitial fluid is called **lymph** (limf; *lympha* = clear spring water). The components of lymph include water, dissolved solutes (e.g., ions), a small amount of protein (approximately 100 to 200 grams that leaked into the interstitial space during capillary exchange), sometimes foreign material that includes both cell debris and pathogens, and perhaps metastasized cancer cells (see Clinical View: "Metastasis").

Lymphatic Capillaries

The lymph vessel network begins with **lymphatic capillaries**, which are the smallest lymph vessels **(figure 21.2)**. Lymphatic capillaries are microscopic, closed-ended vessels that absorb interstitial fluid. They are interspersed throughout areolar connective tissue among most blood capillary networks, except those within the red bone marrow and the central nervous system. Note that lymphatic capillaries are absent within avascular tissues such as epithelia.

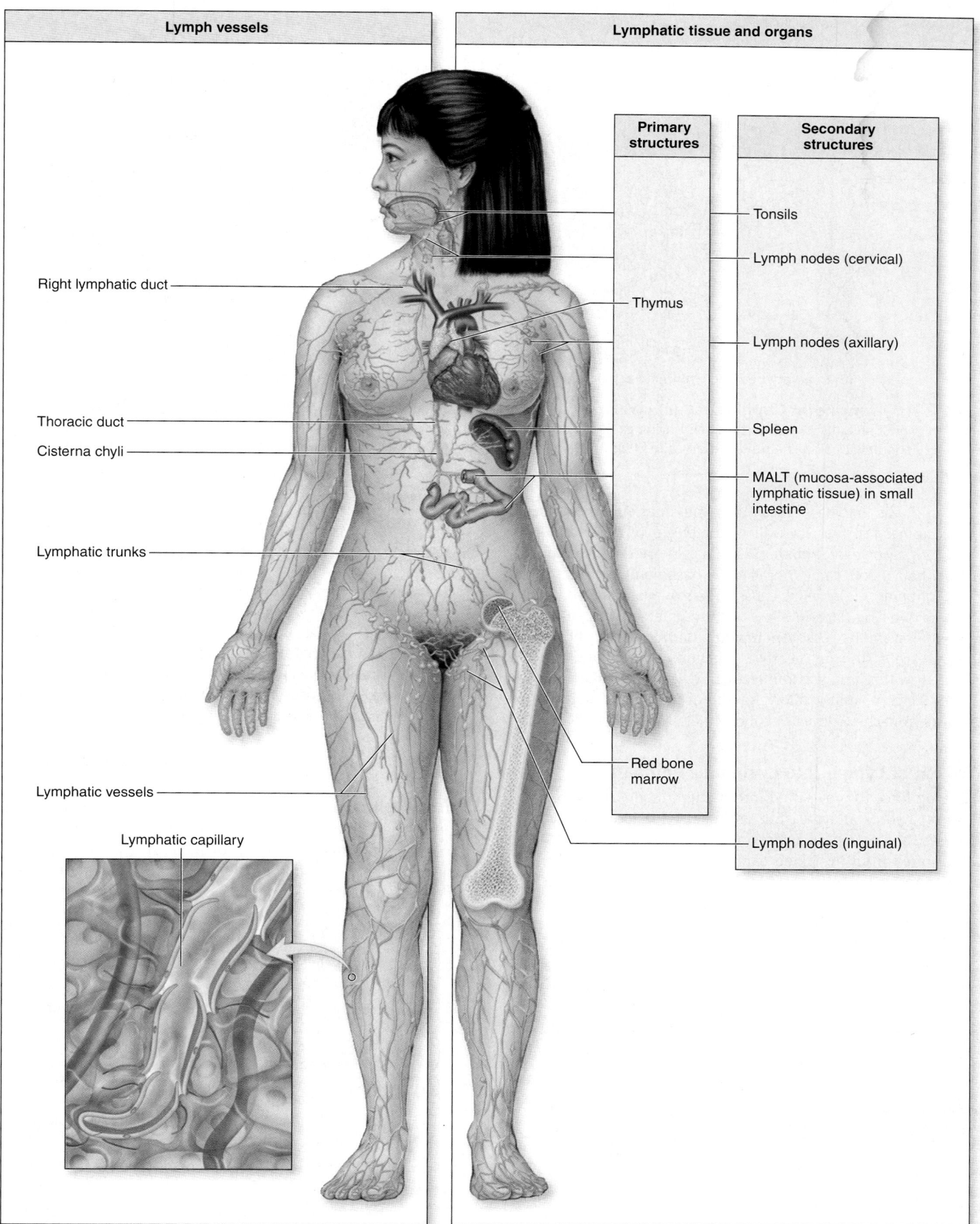

Lymph vessels

Right lymphatic duct

Thoracic duct

Cisterna chyli

Lymphatic trunks

Lymphatic vessels

Lymphatic capillary

Lymphatic tissue and organs

Primary structures

Thymus

Red bone marrow

Secondary structures

Tonsils

Lymph nodes (cervical)

Lymph nodes (axillary)

Spleen

MALT (mucosa-associated lymphatic tissue) in small intestine

Lymph nodes (inguinal)

Figure 21.1 Lymphatic System. The lymphatic system is made up of both lymph vessels and lymphatic tissue and organs. Lymphatic tissue and organs are organized into primary and secondary structures.

Interstitial fluid   Capillary bed   Venule

Lymphatic capillaries

Tissue cells

Arteriole

Anchoring filament

Lymph

Opening

Interstitial fluid

Endothelium of lymphatic capillary

(a) Capillary bed and lymphatic capillaries   **(b) Lymphatic capillary**

Figure 21.2 Lymphatic Capillaries. (*a*) Lymphatic capillaries arise as blind-end vessels within connective tissue among most blood capillary networks and absorb excess fluid left during capillary exchange. (*b*) A lymphatic capillary takes up excess interstitial fluid through overlapping endothelial cells. The fluid is then called lymph. Here, the black arrows show blood flow and the green arrows show lymph flow. AP|R

A lymphatic capillary resembles the anatomic structure of a blood capillary in that its wall is composed of an endothelium (figure 21.2*b*). However, lymphatic capillaries are typically larger in diameter than blood capillaries, lack a basement membrane, and have overlapping endothelial cells. These overlapping endothelial cells act as one-way flaps to allow fluid to enter the lymphatic capillary, but prevent its loss. **Anchoring filaments** help hold these endothelial cells to the nearby structures. Lymphatic capillaries located within the gastrointestinal (GI) tract, called **lacteals** (lak′tē-ăl; lactis = milk), allow for the absorption of lipid-soluble substances from the GI tract, a concept detailed in section 26.4c.

Movement of Lymph into Lymphatic Capillaries

The driving force to move fluid into the lymphatic capillaries is an increase in hydrostatic pressure within the interstitial space (see section 20.2b). Interstitial hydrostatic pressure rises as additional fluid is filtered from the blood capillaries. An increase in pressure at the margins of the lymphatic capillary endothelial cells "pushes" interstitial fluid into the lymphatic capillary lumen. The higher the interstitial fluid pressure, the greater the amount of fluid that enters the lymphatic capillary. The anchoring filaments extending between the lymphatic capillary cells and the surrounding tissue prevent the collapse of the lymphatic capillaries as pressure exerted by the interstitial fluid increases.

The pressure exerted by lymph after it enters the lymphatic capillary forces the endothelial cells of these vessels to close.

INTEGRATE

CONCEPT CONNECTION

Specific lymphatic capillaries in the small intestine are called lacteals. These vessels absorb dietary lipids and lipid-soluble vitamins that are unable to enter the blood directly from the gastrointestinal (GI) tract (see section 26.4c). The lymph from the GI tract has a milky color due to the lipid, and for this reason the GI tract lymph is also called chyle.

INTEGRATE

LEARNING STRATEGY

Fluid entry into a lymphatic capillary is analogous to the movement of the entryway door to your house or apartment. Imagine that the door is unlocked and the knob is turned. Putting pressure on the outside of the door (like the pressure of interstitial fluid on the outside of the lymphatic capillary wall) causes it to open to the inside so you can enter. Once inside, pressure applied to the inside surface of the door (or fluid pressure against the inside lymphatic capillary surface) causes it to close.

Thus, lymph becomes "trapped" within the lymphatic vessel and cannot be released back into the interstitial space. Lymph is then transported through a network of increasingly larger vessels that include lymphatic capillaries, lymphatic vessels, lymphatic trunks, and lymphatic ducts.

WHAT DID YOU LEARN?

❶ What substances typically are absorbed from the interstitial space into lymphatic capillaries?

❷ How does fluid enter and become "trapped" in the lymphatic capillaries?

21.1b Lymphatic Vessels, Trunks, and Ducts

LEARNING OBJECTIVES

4. Explain the mechanisms that move lymph through lymphatic vessels, trunks, and ducts.

5. Name the five types of lymphatic trunks and the regions of the body from which they drain lymph.

6. Describe the regions that are drained by the right lymphatic duct and by the thoracic duct.

After lymph enters the lymphatic capillaries, it continues to flow into increasingly larger lymphatic vessels, trunks, and ducts. Ultimately, the lymph empties into the blood circulation.

Lymphatic Vessels

Lymphatic capillaries merge to form larger structures that are called **lymphatic vessels** (see figure 21.1). Superficial lymphatic vessels are generally positioned adjacent to the superficial veins of the body; in contrast, deep lymphatic vessels are next to deep arteries and veins. Lymphatic vessels resemble small veins because both contain all three vessel tunics (intima, media, and externa) and have **valves** within their lumen. Valves are required to prevent lymph from pooling in the vessel and help prevent lymph backflow because the lymphatic vessel network is a low-pressure system, These valves are especially important in areas where lymph flow is against the direction of gravity, such as in the lower limbs.

The lymphatic system lacks a pump; thus, it relies on several mechanisms to move lymph through its vessels: (1) contraction of nearby skeletal muscles in the limbs (skeletal muscle pump) and the respiratory pump in the torso (as described in section 20.4a), (2) the pulsatile movement of blood in nearby arteries, and (3) rhythmic contraction of smooth muscle in walls of larger lymph vessels (trunks and ducts).

Some lymphatic vessels connect directly to lymphatic organs called lymph nodes. Foreign or pathogenic material is filtered as lymph passes through lymph nodes. Lymph nodes are described in more detail later in this chapter.

Lymphatic Trunks

Lymphatic vessels feed into **lymphatic trunks** on both the right and left side of the body (**figure 21.3**). Each lymphatic trunk removes lymph from a specific major body region:

- *Jugular trunks* drain lymph from both the head and neck.
- *Subclavian trunks* remove lymph from the upper limbs, breasts, and superficial thoracic wall.
- *Bronchomediastinal trunks* drain lymph from deep thoracic structures.
- *Intestinal trunks* drain lymph from most abdominal structures.
- *Lumbar trunks* remove lymph from the lower limbs, abdominopelvic wall, and pelvic organs.

WHAT DO YOU THINK?

1 Predict what may occur with respect to lymphatic drainage if a group of lymph nodes and their associated lymph vessels are surgically removed, such as might occur when breast cancer has metastasized.

Lymphatic Ducts

Lymphatic trunks drain into the largest lymph vessels called **lymphatic ducts.** There are two lymphatic ducts: the right lymphatic duct and the thoracic duct. Both of these convey lymph back into the venous blood circulation.

(a) Posterior thoracic wall, anterior view

Figure 21.3 Lymphatic Trunks and Ducts.
Lymph drains from lymphatic trunks into two lymphatic ducts (right lymphatic duct and thoracic duct) that empty into the junctions of the right jugular and right subclavian veins and left jugular and subclavian veins, respectively. (*a*) An anterior view of the posterior thoracic wall illustrates the major lymphatic trunks and ducts and the site of lymph drainage into the venous circulation of the cardiovascular system. (*b*) Areas of lymph drainage into the right lymphatic duct and the thoracic duct. AP|R

(b) Lymph drainage pattern

CLINICAL VIEW

Lymphedema

Lymphedema (limf′e-dē′mă; *oidema* = a swelling) is recognized as an accumulation of interstitial fluid that occurs due to interference with lymphatic drainage in a part of the body. Interstitial fluid accumulates, and the affected area both swells and becomes painful. If lymphedema is left untreated, the protein-rich interstitial fluid may interfere with wound healing and can even contribute to an infection by acting as a growth medium for bacteria.

Most cases of lymphedema are *obstructive*, meaning they are caused by blockage of lymph vessels. There are several causes of obstructive lymphedema:

- Trauma or infection of the lymph vessels
- The spread of malignant tumors within the lymph nodes and lymph vessels
- Radiation therapy that results in scar formation in lymph vessels or nodes
- Any surgery that requires removal of a group of lymph nodes (e.g., breast cancer surgery when the axillary lymph nodes are removed)

Although lymphedema has no cure, it can be controlled. Patients may wear compression stockings or other compression garments to reduce swelling and assist interstitial fluid return to the circulation. Certain exercise and massage regimens may improve lymphatic drainage as well.

Millions of individuals in Southeast Asia and Africa have developed lymphedema as a result of infection by threadlike, parasitic filarial worms. In **lymphatic filariasis** (fil-ă-rī′ă-sis; *filum* = thread), filarial worms lodge in the lymphatic system, live and reproduce there for years, and eventually obstruct lymphatic drainage. Mosquitoes are the most common vector for transmitting filariasis, although some filarial worms gain entrance through cracks in the skin of the foot. An affected body part can swell to many times its normal size. In these extreme cases, the condition is known as **elephantiasis** (el′ĕ-fan-tī′ă-sis). Patients are treated with antiparasitic medications to kill the filarial worms, although the damage to the lymphatic system may be irreversible.

Elephantiasis

Right Lymphatic Duct The **right lymphatic duct** is located near the right clavicle. It receives lymph from the lymphatic trunks that drain the following areas: (1) the right side of the head and neck, (2) the right upper limb, and (3) the right side of the thorax. It returns the lymph into the junction of the right subclavian vein and the right internal jugular vein. Thus, the right lymphatic duct drains lymph from the upper right quadrant of the body.

Thoracic Duct The larger of the two lymphatic ducts is the **thoracic duct.** It has a length of about 37.5 to 45 centimeters (15 to 18 inches) and extends from the diaphragm inferiorly to the junction of the left subclavian and left jugular veins superiorly. The thoracic duct drains lymph from the remaining areas of the body (left side of head and neck, left upper limb, left thorax, all of the abdomen, and both lower limbs).

At the base of the thoracic duct and anterior to the L_2 vertebra is a rounded, saclike structure called the **cisterna chyli** (sis-ter′nă kī′lī). The cisterna chyli gets its name from the milky, lipid-rich lymph called **chyle** (kīl; *chylos* = juice) it receives from vessels that drain the small intestine of the gastrointestinal (GI) tract. Both left and right intestinal and lumbar trunks drain into the cisterna chyli. The thoracic duct travels superiorly from the cisterna chyli and lies directly anterior to the vertebral bodies. It passes through the aortic opening of the diaphragm then ascends to the left of the vertebral body midline.

WHAT DID YOU LEARN?

3 What distinguishes a lymphatic trunk from a lymphatic duct?

4 Which major body regions drain lymph to the right lymphatic duct?

21.2 Overview of Lymphatic Tissue and Organs

 LEARNING OBJECTIVE

1. Name the two categories of lymphatic tissue and organs, and identify components of the body that belong to each category.

The lymphatic system also is made up of specialized lymphatic (lymphoid) tissue and organs. These tissues and organs include red bone marrow, the thymus, lymph nodes, the spleen, tonsils, MALT (mucosa-associated lymphatic tissue), and diffuse lymphatic nodules (see figure 21.1; diffuse lymphatic nodules not shown).

Lymphatic system tissues and organs are categorized as either primary or secondary structures:

- **Primary lymphatic structures** are involved in the formation and maturation of lymphocytes. Both the red bone marrow and thymus are considered primary lymphatic structures.
- **Secondary lymphatic structures** are not involved in lymphocyte formation, but instead serve to house both lymphocytes and other immune cells following their formation. Secondary lymphatic structures provide the site where an immune response is initiated (see section 22.6). The major secondary lymphatic structures include the lymph nodes, spleen, tonsils, lymphatic nodules, and MALT.

Each component is described in more detail in the next several sections and is summarized in **table 21.1**.

 WHAT DID YOU LEARN?

5 How are primary lymphatic structures and secondary lymphatic structures differentiated? What are examples of each?

Table 21.1	Lymphatic Structures		
Component	**Primary or Secondary Lymphatic Structures**	**Location**	**Function**
Red bone marrow	Primary structure	Spaces in spongy bone within certain bones	Formation of all formed elements
Thymus	Primary structure	Superior mediastinum (in adults); anterior and superior mediastinum (in children)	Site of T-lymphocyte maturation and differentiation
Lymph nodes	Secondary structure	Along length of lymphatic vessels; clusters are present in axillary, inguinal, and cervical regions	Filter lymph; where immune response is initiated against a substance in the lymph
Spleen	Secondary structure	Left upper quadrant of abdomen, near 9th–11th ribs, "wraps" partway around stomach	Filters blood; where immune response is initiated against a substance in the blood; removes aged erythrocytes and platelets; serves as platelet reservoir
Tonsils	Secondary structure	Within pharynx (throat)	Protect against inhaled and ingested substances
MALT (mucosa-associated lymphatic tissue)	Secondary structure	Within walls of gastrointestinal (GI) tract, respiratory, reproductive, and urinary tracts	Initiate an immune response against a substance that comes in contact with a mucosal membrane

21.3 Primary Lymphatic Structures

The general structure and function of the primary lymphatic structures are described in this section. These include the red bone marrow and the thymus.

21.3a Red Bone Marrow

✓ LEARNING OBJECTIVES

1. Describe the location and general function of red bone marrow.
2. Identify the two major types of lymphocytes.

Red bone marrow is located within the spaces between trabeculae in selected portions of spongy bone within the skeleton. In adults, these include the flat bones of the skull, the vertebrae, the ribs, the sternum, the ossa coxae, and proximal epiphyses of each humerus and femur (see section 7.2d).

Red bone marrow is responsible for hemopoiesis, which was described in section 18.3. Recall that the

Figure 21.4 Formed Elements of Hemopoiesis. Red bone marrow produces all formed elements through the process of hemopoiesis. Immature T-lymphocytes (pre-T-lymphocytes) migrate from the bone marrow to the thymus to complete their maturation.

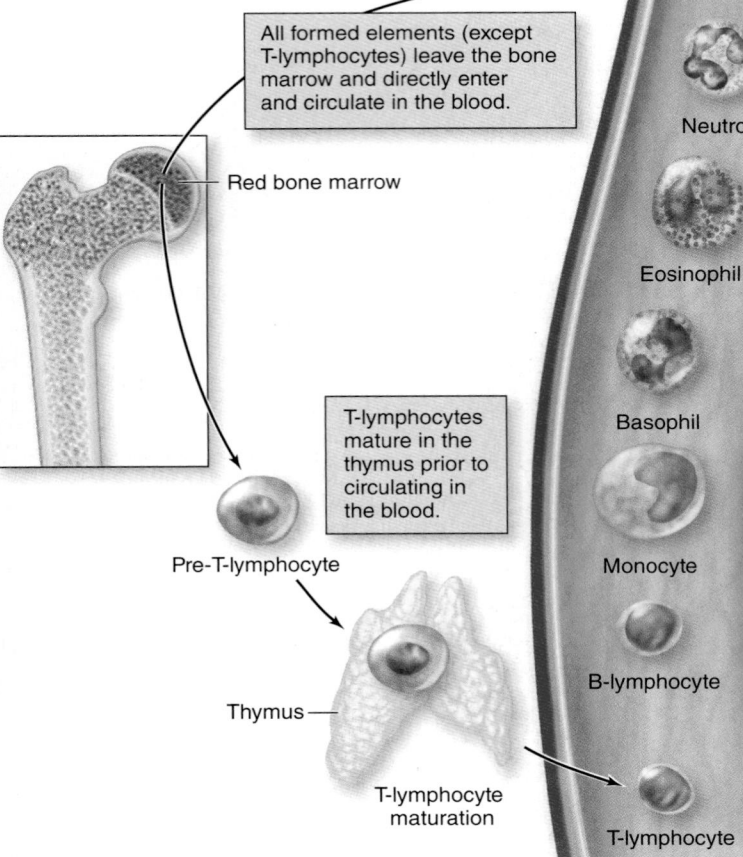

All formed elements (except T-lymphocytes) leave the bone marrow and directly enter and circulate in the blood.

Red bone marrow

T-lymphocytes mature in the thymus prior to circulating in the blood.

Pre-T-lymphocyte

Thymus

T-lymphocyte maturation

Erythrocyte

Platelets

Neutrophil

Eosinophil

Basophil

Monocyte

B-lymphocyte

T-lymphocyte

formed elements include erythrocytes, platelets, granulocytes (neutrophils, eosinophils, and basophils), and agranulocytes (monocytes and lymphocytes) (figure 21.4). The two major types of lymphocytes are **T-lymphocytes** (also called *T-cells*) and **B-lymphocytes** (also called *B-cells*). The formed elements move from the red bone marrow into the blood following hemopoiesis. Unlike the other formed elements, T-lymphocytes must migrate to the thymus to complete their maturation. The functions of both T-lymphocytes and B-lymphocytes are described in detail in chapter 22. It is interesting to note that the "T" in the name "T-lymphocytes" originates from the requirement of these cells to complete their maturation in the thymus.

💡 WHAT DID YOU LEARN?

6. Why is red bone marrow considered a primary lymphatic structure?

21.3b Thymus

✓ LEARNING OBJECTIVE

3. Describe the structure and general function of the thymus.

The **thymus** (thī′mŭs) is a bilobed organ that is located in the superior mediastinum and functions in T-lymphocyte maturation (figure 21.5). In infants and young children, the thymus is quite large and extends into the anterior mediastinum as well. The thymus continues to grow until puberty, when it reaches a maximum weight of 30 to 50 grams. Cells within the thymus begin to regress after it reaches this size. Thereafter, much of the thymic tissue is replaced by adipose connective tissue.

The thymus, when in its prime, consists of two fused **thymic lobes,** each surrounded by a connective tissue **capsule** (cap′sūl). Fibrous extensions of the capsule, called **trabeculae** (tră-bek′ū-lē), or *septa*, subdivide the thymic lobes into **lobules.** Each lobule is arranged into an outer **cortex** and inner **medulla.** Both parts are composed primarily of epithelial tissue infiltrated with T-lymphocytes in varying stages of maturation. The cortex contains immature T-lymphocytes (pre-T-lymphocytes) and the medulla contains mature T-lymphocytes. The epithelial cells secrete thymic hormones that participate in the maturation of T-lympho-

INTEGRATE

CONCEPT CONNECTION

In our discussion of the endocrine system (see chapter 17) we describe how some organs, in addition to their primary function, also house clusters of endocrine tissue that produce hormones. The thymus is an example of this type of organ. It contains (1) lymphatic tissue and is considered part of the lymphatic system, and (2) epithelial tissue that produces and secretes hormones and is considered part of the endocrine system. The hormones produced by the thymus include thymosin, thymulin, and thymopoietin that stimulate the maturation of T-lymphocytes.

Thyroid gland

Trachea

Thymus

Lungs

Heart

Diaphragm

(a) Child (left) and adult (right) thorax, anterior view

Trabecula

Cortex

Capsule

Medulla

LM 20x

(b) Micrograph of child's thymus

Thymic tissue

Adipose connective tissue

LM 5x

(c) Micrograph of adult's thymus

Figure 21.5 Thymus. (*a*) The thymus is a bilobed lymphatic organ that is most prominent in children. (*b*) A micrograph of a child's thymus reveals the arrangement of the cortex and the central medulla within a lobule. (*c*) A micrograph of an adult's thymus showing gain of adipose connective tissue and loss of thymic tissue. AP|R

cytes. Because the thymus contains both lymphatic cells and epithelial tissue, it is described as a *lymphoepithelial organ*. The details of T-lymphocyte maturation are described in section 22.5.

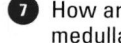 **WHAT DID YOU LEARN?**

7 How are the two types of T-lymphocytes arranged in the cortex and medulla?

21.4 Secondary Lymphatic Structures

Structures that house both lymphocytes and other immune cells are called secondary lymphatic structures. These structures are composed of lymphatic cells that are enmeshed within a reticular extracellular connective tissue matrix.

Secondary lymphatic structures are organized into both **lymphatic organs** and aggregates of **lymphatic nodules.** They are differentiated by the presence or absence of a capsule composed of dense irregular connective tissue that encloses the lymphatic structure. A *complete* capsule is present in lymphatic organs; these structures include lymph nodes and the spleen. A capsule is either *incomplete* or *absent* in other lymphatic structures, which include tonsils, MALT, and diffuse lymphatic nodules.

21.4a Lymph Nodes

 LEARNING OBJECTIVES

1. Describe the structure of lymph nodes.

2. Explain the function of lymph nodes.

Lymph nodes are small, round, or oval encapsulated structures located along the pathways of lymph vessels, where they serve as the main lymphatic organ. Lymph nodes function in the filtering of lymph and removal of unwanted substances.

INTEGRATE

CONCEPT CONNECTION

Dendritic cells are specialized phagocytic cells that are formed in bone marrow and are housed in epithelial tissue of skin and mucosal membranes. Those within the skin are specifically called epidermal dendritic cells or Langerhans cells (see section 6.1). Dendritic cells migrate from the skin and mucosal membranes to a lymph node following endocytosis of foreign substances (see section 22.2a).

Lymph nodes vary in both their size (from 1 to 25 millimeters) and their number (estimated 500 to 700). Lymph nodes are located both deep and superficially within the body and typically occur in clusters that receive lymph from selected body regions. Some examples of clustered lymph nodes include the *axillary lymph nodes* in the armpit that receive lymph from the breast, axilla, and upper limb; *inguinal lymph nodes* in the groin that receive lymph from the lower limb and pelvis; and *cervical lymph nodes* that receive lymph from the head and neck (see figure 21.1). In addition to clusters, lymph nodes are found individually throughout the body.

Numerous **afferent lymphatic vessels** bring lymph into a lymph node **(figure 21.6)**. There is typically only one **efferent lymphatic vessel,** which originates at the involuted portion of the lymph node called the **hilum** (hī′lŭm), or *hilus*. Lymph is drained via the efferent lymphatic vessel from this region of the lymph node.

The capsule of a lymph node is composed of connective tissue that both encapsulates the node and sends internal extensions into it that are called **trabeculae.** They subdivide the node into compartments. The connective tissue provides a pathway through which blood vessels and nerves may enter the lymph node.

The lymph node regions deep to the capsule are subdivided into an outer **cortex** and an inner **medulla.** The cortex is composed in part of multiple **lymphatic nodules.** Each lymphatic nodule within the lymph node is composed of reticular fibers that support an

Figure 21.6 Lymph Nodes. (*a*) Lymph nodes are small, encapsulated organs that filter the lymph within lymphatic vessels. Green arrows indicate the direction of lymph flow into and out of the lymph node. (*b*) The arrangement of regions within the cortex and medulla of a lymph node. (*c*) A micrograph of a lymph node shows the cortex and medulla. AP|R

(a) Lymph node

(b) Cortex and medulla

(c) Lymph node section

CLINICAL VIEW
Lymphoma

A **lymphoma** (lim-fō′mă; *oma* = tumor) is a malignant neoplasm that develops from lymphatic structures. Usually (but not always) a lymphoma presents as a nontender, enlarged lymph node, often in the neck or axillary region. Some patients have no further symptoms, while others may experience night sweats, fever, and unexplained weight loss in addition to the nodal enlargement. Lymphomas are grouped into two categories: Hodgkin lymphoma and non-Hodgkin lymphoma.

Hodgkin lymphoma (or *Hodgkin disease*) is characterized by the presence of the **Reed-Sternberg cell**, a large cell whose two nuclei resemble owl eyes, surrounded by lymphocytes within the affected lymph node. Hodgkin lymphoma affects young adults (ages 16–35) and people over 60. It arises in a lymph node and then spreads to other nearby lymph nodes. If caught early, Hodgkin lymphoma can be treated and cured by excision of the tumor, followed by radiation, chemotherapy, or both.

Non-Hodgkin lymphomas are much more common than Hodgkin lymphomas. These lymphomas typically develop from abnormal B-lymphocytes, and less commonly from T-lymphocytes. Some kinds of non-Hodgkin lymphoma are aggressive and often fatal, whereas others are slow-growing and more responsive to treatment. Treatment depends on the type of non-Hodgkin lymphoma, the extent of its spread at the time of discovery, and the rate of progression of the malignancy.

Reed-Sternberg cell

LM 1000x

Reed-Sternberg cell, a characteristic of Hodgkin lymphoma.

---

inner **germinal center** that houses both proliferating B-lymphocytes and some macrophages surrounded by an outer region called a **mantle zone,** which contains T-lymphocytes, macrophages, and dendritic cells (described in section 22.2a). The medulla differs because it has strands of B-lymphocytes, T-lymphocytes, and macrophages supported by connective tissue fibers called **medullary cords.**

Both the cortex and medulla of a lymph node contain tiny open channels called lymphatic sinuses (**cortical sinus** and **medullary sinus,** respectively); these spaces are lined with macrophages.

Lymph Flow Through Lymph Nodes

Lymph enters a lymph node through numerous afferent lymphatic vessels and makes its way through the lymph node sinuses. Lymph is continuously monitored for the presence of foreign or pathogenic material as it passes through nodes. Macrophages residing in the lymph node remove foreign debris from the lymph. Lymph then exits the lymph node through an efferent lymphatic vessel. Recall that lymph nodes are often found in clusters, so after one lymph node receives and filters lymph, the lymph is passed to another lymph node in the cluster, then to another, and so on. Thus, lymph is repeatedly screened for unwanted substances.

Lymphocytes housed within the lymph node also come into contact with foreign substances. An immune response may be generated after this contact, during which lymphocytes undergo cell division, especially in the germinal centers. Some of these new lymphocytes remain within the lymph node, while others are transported in the lymph and then enter into the blood, to ultimately reach areas of infections (see section 22.6).

When a person has an infection, often some lymph nodes are swollen and tender to the touch. This is a condition erroneously termed *swollen glands.* These enlarged nodes are a sign that lymphocytes are proliferating and attempting to fight an infection. Swollen superficial lymph nodes can generally be palpated (felt), including those in the neck and axilla.

WHAT DID YOU LEARN?

8 How does lymph flow through a lymph node, and how is it monitored by macrophages and lymphocytes?

21.4b Spleen

✔ LEARNING OBJECTIVES

3. Describe the spleen and its location.
4. Distinguish between white pulp and red pulp.
5. List the functions of the spleen.

The **spleen** (splēn) is the largest lymphatic organ in the human body. It is located in the left upper quadrant of the abdomen, inferior to the diaphragm and adjacent to ribs 9–11 **(figure 21.7)**. This deep red organ lies lateral to the left kidney and posterolateral to the stomach. The spleen can vary considerably in size and weight, but typically is about 12 centimeters (5 inches) long and 7 centimeters (3 inches) wide.

The spleen's posterolateral aspect (called the *diaphragmatic surface*) is convex and rounded; the concave anteromedial border (the *visceral surface*) contains the **hilum** (or *hilus*), where blood vessels and nerves enter and leave the spleen. A **splenic** (splen'ik) **artery** delivers blood to the spleen, while blood is drained by a **splenic vein.**

The spleen is surrounded by a connective tissue capsule from which trabeculae extend into the organ. The spleen lacks a cortex and medulla. Rather, the trabeculae subdivide the spleen into white pulp and red pulp. **White pulp** consists of spherical clusters of T-lymphocytes, B-lymphocytes, and macrophages. Within the white pulp is a **central artery.**

The remaining splenic tissue, called **red pulp,** contains erythrocytes, platelets, macrophages, and B-lymphocytes. The cells in red pulp are housed in reticular connective tissue and form structures called **splenic cords** (*cords of Bilroth*). **Splenic sinusoids** are associated with red pulp. (Recall from section 20.1c that sinusoids are very permeable capillaries that

(a) Abdominal cavity, anterior view

(c) Red and white pulp of spleen

(b) Spleen, medial surface

(d) Histology of spleen

Figure 21.7 Spleen. (*a*) A cadaver photo shows the position of the spleen within the body. The pancreas has been moved inferiorly in this photo to show more clearly the splenic vessels. (*b*) A second photo shows the medial surface of the spleen including the hilum where the splenic artery and splenic vein enter. A diagram (*c*) and micrograph (*d*) of spleen histology depict the microscopic arrangement of red pulp and white pulp. **AP|R**

have a discontinuous basal lamina, so blood cells can easily enter and exit across the vessel wall.) The sinusoids drain into small venules that ultimately lead into a **splenic vein.**

The platelets stored within the red pulp of the spleen serve as a reservoir for platelets (about 30% of all platelets are stored in the spleen). In situations where more platelets are needed, such as during hemorrhage, these stored platelets reenter the blood (see section 18.3d).

WHAT DO YOU THINK?

2 Predict the consequences to the spleen during an accident if an individual wears his or her seatbelt high across the abdomen instead of lower across the pelvis.

Monitoring Blood as It Flows Through the Spleen

The spleen functions to filter *blood* (not lymph). As blood enters the spleen and flows through the central arteries, the white pulp lymphatic cells monitor the blood for foreign materials, bacteria, and other potentially harmful substances.

After passing through a central artery, blood travels through sinusoids of red pulp. As blood moves through the sinusoids, it is in contact with cells of the splenic cords of red pulp. Macrophages lining the sinusoids phagocytize bacteria and foreign debris from the blood, as well as both old and defective erythrocytes and platelets. Thus, the general flow of blood through the spleen is the splenic artery, the central artery (of white pulp), the splenic sinusoid (of red pulp), venules (that drain sinusoids), and ultimately the splenic vein (figure 21.7c).

In summary, the spleen serves several functions, including (1) phagocytosis of bacteria and other foreign materials in the blood as part of the body's defense (red and white pulp); (2) phagocytosis of old, defective erythrocytes and platelets from circulating blood (red pulp); and (3) serving as a reservoir for platelets (red pulp).

During fetal development through the fifth month, the spleen also engages in the formation of blood cells, a function performed after birth by the bone marrow. This function remains latent in the spleen and may be reactivated under certain conditions.

WHAT DID YOU LEARN?

9 What are the general functions of the spleen? Indicate whether red pulp or white pulp is responsible for each function.

10 Which lymphatic structures filter lymph? Which filter blood?

21.4c Tonsils

LEARNING OBJECTIVE

6. Identify the main groups of tonsils and their location and function.

Tonsils (ton'sillz; *tonsilla* = a stake) are secondary lymphatic structures that are not completely surrounded by a connective tissue capsule. They are found in the pharynx (throat). A **pharyngeal tonsil** is found in the posterior wall of the nasopharynx; when this tonsil becomes enlarged, it is called **adenoids** (ad'ĕ-noydz; *aden* = gland). **Palatine tonsils** are in the posterolateral region of the oral cavity, and **lingual tonsils** are along the posterior one-third of the tongue **(figure 21.8)**. Tonsils help protect against foreign substances that may be either inhaled or ingested.

Invaginated outer edges called *tonsillar crypts* increase the surface area to help trap material. Lymphatic nodules, some containing germinal centers, are housed with the tonsils.

(a) Tonsils — Pharyngeal tonsil, Palatine tonsil, Lingual tonsil

(b) Tonsil — Germinal centers, Tonsillar crypts, LM 5x

(c) Lymphatic nodules of a tonsil — Lymphatic nodule, Germinal center, LM 40x

Figure 21.8 Tonsils. (*a*) Tonsils reside in the wall of the pharynx. A micrograph shows (*b*) tonsillar crypts that help trap foreign substances and (*c*) the germinal centers within the lymphatic nodules of the tonsils. AP|R

CLINICAL VIEW
Tonsillitis and Tonsillectomy

The tonsils are designed to protect the pharynx from infection. They frequently become inflamed and infected, a condition called **acute tonsillitis** (ton'si-lī'tis). The palatine tonsils are most commonly affected. The tonsils redden and enlarge; in severe cases, they may partially obstruct the pharynx and cause respiratory distress.

Tonsils may be infected by viruses such as adenoviruses or bacteria such as *Streptococcus*. Streptococcal tonsillitis often results in very red tonsils that have whitish specks (called whitish exudate). The symptoms of tonsillitis include fever, chills, sore throat, and difficulty swallowing.

Persistent or recurrent infections may result in permanent enlargement of the tonsils and development of a condition that is called **chronic tonsillitis.** If medical treatment does not help the chronic tonsillitis, surgical removal of the tonsils **(tonsillectomy)** may be indicated. Medical guidelines suggest performing a tonsillectomy only if the person has had 7 throat infections (e.g., tonsillitis, strep throat) in 1 year, 5 infections in 2 years, or 3 infections per year for 3 years. Research indicates that tonsillectomy does not significantly affect the body's response to new infections.

Tonsillitis

WHAT DID YOU LEARN?

11 What are the three main groups of tonsils and their function?

21.4d Lymphatic Nodules and MALT

LEARNING OBJECTIVES

7. Describe the composition of individual lymphatic nodules.

8. Compare the locations of MALT and Peyer patches.

Lymphatic nodules and MALT make up the last category of secondary lymphatic structures. These relatively small masses of lymphatic tissue are located throughout the body.

Lymphatic Nodules

Lymphatic nodules (nod'ūlz), or *lymphatic follicles,* are small, oval clusters of lymphatic cells with some extracellular matrix that are *not* completely surrounded by a connective tissue capsule. Scattered lymphatic nodules are referred to as *diffuse lymphatic tissue.* This tissue can be found in every body organ and within the wall of the appendix helping to defend against infections in these structures. However, in some areas of the body, many lymphatic nodules group together to form larger structures, such as MALT.

MALT

MALT (mucosa-associated lymphatic tissue) is located in the lamina propria of the mucosa (see section 5.5b) of the gastrointestinal, respiratory, genital, and urinary tracts. The lymphatic cells in the MALT help defend against foreign substances that come in contact with mucosal membranes.

MALT is very prominent in the mucosa of the small intestine, primarily in the ileum. There, collections of lymphatic nodules called **Peyer patches** can become quite large and bulge into the gut lumen (see figure 26.15).

Figure 21.9 is a visual representation of the role of the lymphatic system, which assists the cardiovascular system in maintaining fluid balance by returning excess fluid from the interstitial space to the blood, and assists the immune system by participating in defending the body against potentially harmful substances.

WHAT DID YOU LEARN?

12 What is the function of MALT in the mucosal linings of the gastrointestinal, respiratory, genital, and urinary tracts?

Figure 21.9 **Relationship of the Lymphatic System to Both the Cardiovascular System and Immune System.** The lymphatic system assists both (*a*) the cardiovascular system by returning fluid from the interstitial space back into the blood to help maintain fluid balance, blood volume, and blood pressure, and (*b*) the immune system in the body's defense.

(a) Lymphatic Structures That Assist the Cardiovascular System

Lymphatic trunks and ducts

Lymph is transported through progressively larger lymph vessels that include lymphatic capillaries, lymphatic vessels, lymphatic trunks, and lymphatic ducts. Lymphatic ducts drain lymph into the venous circulation.

Lymphatic vessels

Lymph is transported through lymphatic vessels. Lymphatic vessels drain into lymph nodes, which monitor lymph.

Lymph node

Lacteals

Lymphatic capillaries in the small intestine called lacteals absorb lipid-soluble substances from gastrointestinal (GI) tract.

Lymphatic capillary

Interstitial fluid is absorbed into lymphatic capillaries.

Spleen: Red pulp

Phagocytizes old or defective erythrocytes and platelets from circulating blood; serves as a reservoir for platelets

(b) Lymphatic Structures That Assist the Immune System

PRIMARY LYMPHATIC STRUCTURES

Red bone marrow

Produces formed elements, including lymphocytes

Thymus

Site of T-lymphocyte maturation and differentiation

SECONDARY LYMPHATIC STRUCTURES

Lymph nodes

Monitor lymph for foreign materials (e.g., bacteria and viruses)

Spleen: White pulp

Monitors blood for foreign materials (e.g., bacteria and viruses)

Tonsils

Provide defense against pathogens in air and ingested food

Lymph nodules/MALT

Protects body organs (lymphatic nodules) and mucosal linings (MALT) against potentially harmful substances

CHAPTER SUMMARY

- Lymphatic system supports the functions of the cardiovascular and immune system.
- Lymph is transported in lymph vessels.

21.1a Lymph and Lymphatic Capillaries   824

- Lymph is interstitial fluid containing solutes and sometimes foreign material that is absorbed into lymphatic capillaries and transported through lymph vessels and returned to the blood.
- Lymphatic capillaries are endothelium-lined vessels with overlapping endothelial cells that regulate lymph entry.

21.1b Lymphatic Vessels, Trunks, and Ducts   826

- Lymphatic vessels form from merging lymphatic capillaries. They have valves to prevent lymph backflow.
- Lymphatic trunks are formed from merging lymphatic vessels; each trunk drains a major body region. Lymphatic trunks drain into one of two lymphatic ducts.
- The right lymphatic duct drains the right side of the head and neck, the right upper limb, and the right side of the thorax.
- The thoracic duct drains lymph from the left side of the head and neck, the left upper limb, the left thorax, and all body regions inferior to the diaphragm.

- Primary lymphatic structures are involved in the formation and maturation of lymphocytes.
- Secondary lymphatic structures house lymphocytes and other immune cells, serving as sites to initiate the immune response.

21.3a Red Bone Marrow   830

- Red bone marrow produces all formed elements including lymphocytes.

21.3b Thymus   830

- The thymus is a bilobed organ found in the mediastinum. It is most active in childhood until puberty, and then it declines in size and function.
- T-lymphocytes mature and differentiate within the thymus under stimulation by thymic hormones.

- Secondary lymphatic structures may be organized into lymphatic organs, which are enclosed within a complete capsule, and lymphatic nodules that have an incomplete or absent capsule.
- Both lymphatic organs and lymphatic nodules are composed of an extracellular connective tissue matrix that houses lymphatic cells.

21.4a Lymph Nodes   831

- Lymph nodes are numerous, small, encapsulated lymphatic organs that filter lymph.

21.4b Spleen   834

- The spleen is the largest lymphatic organ and it is partitioned into white pulp and red pulp.
- The white pulp consists of clusters of lymphatic cells that generate an immune response when exposed to antigens in the blood.
- The red pulp consists of splenic cords and sinusoids containing erythrocytes, platelets, macrophages, and B-lymphocytes. Macrophages phagocytize bacteria, foreign debris, and old erythrocytes.

21.4c Tonsils   835

- Tonsils are large clusters of partially encapsulated lymphatic cells. They include the pharyngeal tonsil, palatine tonsils, and lingual tonsils.

21.4d Lymphatic Nodules and MALT   836

- Lymphatic nodules can be found in every organ throughout the body.
- MALT (mucosa-associated lymphatic tissue) is composed of large groups of lymphatic nodules housed in the walls of the gastrointenstinal tract, respiratory tract, reproductive tract, and urinary tract.

CHALLENGE YOURSELF

Do You Know the Basics?

_____ 1. What body systems are supported by the lymphatic system?

    a. cardiovascular and urinary

    b. cardiovascular and immune

    c. respiratory and cardiovascular

    d. respiratory and urinary

_____ 2. Lymph is drained into the thoracic duct from which of the following body regions?

    a. right lower limb

    b. right upper limb

    c. right side of the head

    d. right side of the thorax

_____ 3. All of the following are accurate descriptions of lymphatic nodules _except_

    a. the center has proliferating B-lymphocytes and some macrophages.

    b. T-lymphocytes are located along the periphery of germinal centers.

    c. lymphatic nodules are completely surrounded by a connective tissue capsule. (no) surrounded

    d. clusters of lymphatic nodules in the small intestine are called Peyer patches.

_____ 4. What is the function of the thymus?

    a. It is the site of T-lymphocyte maturation.

    b. It filters lymph.

    c. It filters blood.

    d. It produces the formed elements of the blood.

_____ 5. Which type of lymph vessel consists solely of an endothelium and has one-way flaps that allow interstitial fluid to enter but not exit?

    a. lymphatic vessel

    b. lymphatic capillary

    c. lymphatic duct

    d. lymphatic trunk

_____ 6. Which statement is accurate about lymph nodes?

    a. Lymph nodes do not become swollen and tender.

    b. Lymph nodes filter blood.

    c. Lymph enters the lymph node through afferent lymphatic vessels.

    d. Lymphatic sinuses are located in the cortex of a lymph node only.

_____ 7. In an early _Streptococcus_ infection of the throat, all of the following structures may swell _except_ the

    a. pharyngeal tonsil.   c. cervical lymph node.

    b. spleen.   d. palatine tonsil.

_____ 8. Each of the following is a function of the spleen _except_

    a. it phagocytizing erythrocytes.

    b. it serves as a platelet reservoir.

    c. it normally serves as a site for hemopoiesis during adult life.

    d. it eliminates potentially harmful substances, such as bacteria and viruses from the blood.

_____ 9. Aged erythrocytes are removed from circulation by the

    a. mucosa-associated lymphatic tissue.

    b. lymph nodes.

    c. thymus.

    d. spleen.

_____ 10. Interstitial fluid that is absorbed into lymph vessels will be monitored by the _____ before the fluid is dumped into venous circulation.

    a. mucosa-associated lymphatic tissue

    b. spleen

    c. thymus

    d. lymph nodes

11. List the anatomic structures of the lymphatic system, including lymph vessels, primary lymphatic structures, and secondary lymphatic structures.

12. Explain what distinguishes a primary lymphatic structure from a secondary lymphatic structure.

13. Describe what lymph is, and draw a flowchart that illustrates what structures the lymph travels through to return to the blood.

14. Which body regions have their lymph drained to the thoracic duct?

15. Describe how the thymus's anatomy changes as we age.

16. Describe the basic anatomy of a lymph node, how lymph enters and leaves the node, and the functions of this organ.

17. Compare and contrast the red and white pulp of the spleen with respect to the anatomy and functions of each.

18. Describe the specific locations of the tonsils.

19. Describe the basic composition of a lymphatic nodule, and give examples in the body where lymphatic nodules may be found.

20. Explain how the lymphatic system supports the functions of both the cardiovascular system and the immune system.

Can You Apply What You've Learned?

1. A tick has embedded itself in the scalp of a young boy. His mother is most likely to find which lymph nodes to be swollen?

   a. cervical
   b. inguinal
   c. axillary
   d. femoral

2. A child born without his thymus would not have mature

   a. macrophages.
   b. B-lymphocytes.
   c. dendritic cells.
   d. T-lymphocytes.

3. A young woman was in a car accident and had to have her spleen removed as a consequence of its rupture during the accident. She now has a greater risk of

   a. an overactive immune response.
   b. bacterial infections.
   c. low blood pressure.
   d. a pathogen surviving in her lymph.

4. One of the postoperative complications from the removal of lymph nodes during a mastectomy would be

   a. edema in the upper limb.
   b. regrowth of the lymph nodes.
   c. an overactive immune system.
   d. tender and swollen lymph nodes in other regions of the body.

5. All of the following can result in lymphedema (the accumulation of interstitial fluid due to interference with lymphatic drainage) *except*

   a. surgical removal of a group of lymph nodes.
   b. obstruction of lymph vessels that drain a lymph node, such as might occur with a tumor or infection.
   c. radiation therapy, which may cause scar formation of lymph vessels.
   d. exercise that increases the flow of lymph in the lymph vessels.

Can You Synthesize What You've Learned?

1. Arianna was diagnosed with mononucleosis, an infectious disease that targets B-lymphocytes. The doctor palpated her left side, just below the rib cage, and told Arianna she was checking to see if a certain organ was enlarged, a complication that can occur with mononucleosis. What lymphatic organ was the doctor checking, and why would it become enlarged? Include some explanation of the anatomy and histology of this organ in your answer.

2. Jordan has an enlarged lymph node along the side of his neck, and he is worried that the structure may be a lymphoma. Explain how malignant cells may have reached the lymph node.

3. Mark has come to the emergency care facility complaining of a sore throat. Upon examination, his tonsils appear swollen. When questioned further, he reports that although he has no history of his tonsils being swollen, his throat has been sore for almost a week. He is concerned that he will need to go to the hospital to have his tonsils removed. Explain the conditions that would generally require a tonsillectomy.

---

chapter 22

Immune System and the Body's Defense

Immunology is the branch of medicine that studies the characteristics and components of the immune system. Practicing specialists and research scientists study and analyze its normal activities, malfunctions, and the best means of treating disorders involving this system. Hypersensitivity disorders including allergies is one common malfunction. Skin tests for allergies are performed on an area of the back by placing allergens into the epidermis and observing the reaction that occurs. The formation of a rash where the substance is tested indicates that the individual is allergic to that substance.

apreveaIed.com

Module 10: Lymphatic System

There are children born without an **immune** (i-myūn′) **system**—a condition called severe combined immune deficiency syndrome (SCIDS). The most famous of these children was a boy named David Vetter, born in 1971. He was dubbed by the media as "The Boy in the Bubble" because without an immune system, David literally had to live in a sterile plastic bubble. At the age of 12, David received a bone marrow transplant from his sister with the hope of his being able to live outside the bubble. This new ➤

841

bone marrow would have the ability to produce the immune cells that David's bone marrow was unable to form. Sadly, residing in his sister's bone marrow was a dormant (not active) virus called Epstein-Barr. This virus is generally kept under control by a healthy immune system. However, because David did not have an immune system, the bone marrow with the Epstein-Barr virus induced formation of cancerous tumors throughout his body, and he died several months later.

Most of us may take for granted that we have a functioning immune system. While each of us may catch a cold or the flu on occasion, most of the time our immune system is—without our typically being aware of it—protecting us from infectious agents and other harmful substances. This system is unique because unlike all other body systems, the immune system is not made up of organs. Rather, it is composed of numerous cellular and molecular structures located throughout the body, which function together in the body's defense to provide us with **immunity** (i-myū'ni-tē).

The types of immunity within the body are organized into two categories: innate immunity and adaptive immunity. In this chapter, we present the details of both types of immunity. Visual summaries that integrate the many different means the body has to defend itself are included for both. We first, however, provide a brief overview of the different infectious agents. This is a necessary preliminary step because immune system function is often dependent upon the specific type of infectious agent against which it must defend.

22.1 Overview of Diseases Caused by Infectious Agents

LEARNING OBJECTIVES

1. Compare and contrast the five major classes of infectious agents.
2. Describe prions, and name a disease they cause.

Infectious agents are organisms that cause damage, or possibly death, to the host organism that they invade. Infectious agents that cause harm to the host are said to be **pathogenic.** The five major categories of infectious agents include bacteria, viruses, fungi, protozoans, and multicellular parasites. These classes, including examples of each, are summarized and compared in **table 22.1** and described here:

- **Bacteria** are microscopic, single-celled organisms 1 to 2 micrometers in size that are enclosed by a cell wall. Bacterial cells are fundamentally different from the cells of humans and other living things so are called *prokaryotic cells.* The cells of humans and other living organisms are termed *eukaryotic cells.* Different species of bacteria are spherical, rodlike, or coiled in shape, and thus are referred to as cocci, bacilli, and spirilla, respectively. Certain bacteria can cause disease, but the vast majority of bacterial species do not.

  Some bacteria have increased **virulence** (vir'yū-lĕns)— the ability to cause serious illness—due to the presence of an external, sticky polysaccharide capsule. Additionally, some pathogenic bacteria cause disease by releasing enzymes or toxins that interfere with the function of cells; an example is the bacterium *Clostridium tetani* (see Clinical View: "Muscular Paralysis and Neurotoxins" in section 10.3).

- **Viruses** are *not* cells. Viruses are much smaller than a bacterial cell at about one-hundredth of a micrometer, and

they are composed of DNA or RNA within a protein capsid, or shell. The protein capsid of some viruses may also be enclosed within a membrane. Viruses are **obligate intracellular parasites;** that is, they must enter a cell to reproduce. The process of viral reproduction includes directing the infected cell to synthesize copies of both the viral DNA or RNA molecule and its capsid protein. Newly formed *viral particles* are then formed within the infected cells and released from them to infect surrounding cells. A

Table 22.1	Major Categories of Infectious Agents	
Characteristic	**Bacteria**	
Structure		
Cellular Characteristic	Prokaryotic	
Significant Features	Intracellular and extracellular parasites; some produce enzymes, toxins	
Selected Diseases Caused by the Agent	Streptococcal infections (e.g., Strep throat), staphylococcal infections, tuberculosis, syphilis, diphtheria, tetanus, Lyme disease, salmonella, and anthrax	

virus, or the immune system's response to it, ultimately kills the cells it invades.

Viruses cause different diseases depending upon the type of cell they infect. Examples of viral diseases include the common cold, chickenpox, and HIV.

- **Fungi** (fun′jī) are eukaryotic cells that have a cell wall external to the plasma membrane. This group includes molds, yeasts, and multicellular fungi that produce spores. Proteolytic enzymes released from fungi induce inflammation that causes redness and swelling of the infected area.

  Fungal diseases (*mycoses*) in healthy individuals in the United States are usually limited to superficial infections of the skin, scalp, and nails, such as ringworm and "athlete's foot." Other fungal diseases involve infections of mucosal linings (e.g., vaginal yeast infections) or may cause internal fungal infections (e.g., histoplasmosis, which affects the respiratory system).

- **Protozoans** are also eukaryotic cells, but they lack a cell wall. Protozoan infections include malaria and trichomoniasis.

- **Multicellular parasites** are nonmicroscopic organisms (larger than a centimeter in size) that reside within a host from which they take nourishment. Parasitic worms such as tapeworms, for example, infect the intestinal tract of humans and other mammals.

Prions (prī′on) are small fragments of infectious proteins that cause disease in nervous tissue. Variant Creutzfeldt-Jakob disease (also known as *bovine spongiform encephalopathy*, or "mad cow disease") is an example. This prion disease can be spread from cows to humans by consuming infected meat. Prions are neither cells nor viruses, and research into how they cause disease is ongoing.

  WHAT DID YOU LEARN?

1 Which pathogen must enter a cell to replicate? Which type of pathogen consists of prokaryotic cells?

22.2 Overview of the Immune System

Cells, plasma proteins, and secreted products of the immune system protect the body from infectious agents and other potentially harmful substances. Here we provide a brief introduction to the immune cells, as well as the specialized hormonelike chemicals called cytokines that regulate them. We then give an overview of how the immune system is organized into two overlapping and complementary components: the innate immune component and the adaptive immune component.

22.2a Immune Cells and Their Locations

LEARNING OBJECTIVE

1. List the types of leukocytes of the immune system, and describe where they may be found.

Leukocytes are formed in the red bone marrow (section 18.3d) prior to circulating in the blood. They include (1) the three types of granulocytes (neutrophils, eosinophils, and basophils); (2) monocytes that become macrophages when they exit blood vessels and take up residence in the tissues; and (3) the three types of lymphocytes, which include T-lymphocytes (or T-cells), B-lymphocytes (or B-cells), and NK (natural killer) cells.

Viruses	Fungi	Protozoans	Multicellular Parasites
Not a cell; DNA or RNA within a capsid protein	Eukaryotic	Eukaryotic	Eukaryotic
Obligate intracellular parasites; must enter cell to replicate	Produce spores; release proteolytic enzymes	Intracellular and extracellular parasites that interfere with normal cellular functions	Live within a host; grow in size with nutrients provided by the host
Common cold, influenza, polio, mumps, measles, hepatitis, rubella, chickenpox, herpes, and HIV (that leads to AIDS)	Ringworm, diaper rash, jock itch, athlete's foot, yeast infections, and histoplasmosis	Malaria, toxoplasmosis, giardiasis, amoebiasis, leishmaniasis, trichomoniasis, and African sleeping sickness	Parasitic infection from tapeworms, lung flukes, liver flukes, blood flukes, hookworms, *Trichinella*, *Ascaris*, whipworms, and pinworms

Structures That House Immune System Cells

Most leukocytes are found in body tissues (as opposed to in the blood). The primary locations that house immune cells include lymphatic tissue, select organs, epithelial layers of the skin and mucosal membranes, and connective tissue of the body (figure 22.1):

- **Lymphatic tissue.** T-lymphocytes, B-lymphocytes, macrophages, and NK cells are housed in secondary lymphatic structures of lymph nodes, the spleen, tonsils, MALT (mucosa-associated lymphatic tissue), and lymphatic nodules (see section 21.4).
- **Select organs.** Macrophages are also housed in other organs; some are specifically named based on their location, such as alveolar macrophages of the lungs, and microglia of the brain. Macrophages may be permanent residents, referred to as fixed macrophages, or migrate through tissues as wandering macrophages.
- **Epithelial layers of the skin and mucosal membranes.** Dendritic cells are located in the skin and mucosal membranes, and are typically derived from monocytes. These cells in the epidermis of the skin are more specifically called *epidermal dendritic cells* (see section 6.1a). Dendritic cells engulf pathogens in the skin and mucosal membranes and subsequently migrate to a lymph node through lymph vessels that drain the tissue.

- **Connective tissue.** Mast cells (cells similar to basophils) are located in the connective tissue throughout the body, typically in close proximity to small blood vessels (see section 5.2a). They are especially abundant in the dermis of the skin and the mucosal linings of the respiratory, digestive, and urogenital tracts. However, they are also housed in connective tissue of organs, such as the endomysium that ensheathes muscle fibers (see section 10.2a).

WHAT DID YOU LEARN?

❷ What types of immune cells are housed in lymphatic tissue? What two types of immune cells are located in the skin and mucosal membranes?

22.2b Cytokines

LEARNING OBJECTIVES

2. Define cytokines and describe their similarities to hormones.
3. List the general categories of cytokines.

Cytokines (sī′tō-kīn; *cyto* = cell, *kinesis* = movement) are small, soluble proteins produced by cells of both the innate and adaptive immune system to regulate and facilitate immune system activity. Cytokines serve as a means of communication between the cells; control the development and behavior of effector cells of immunity;

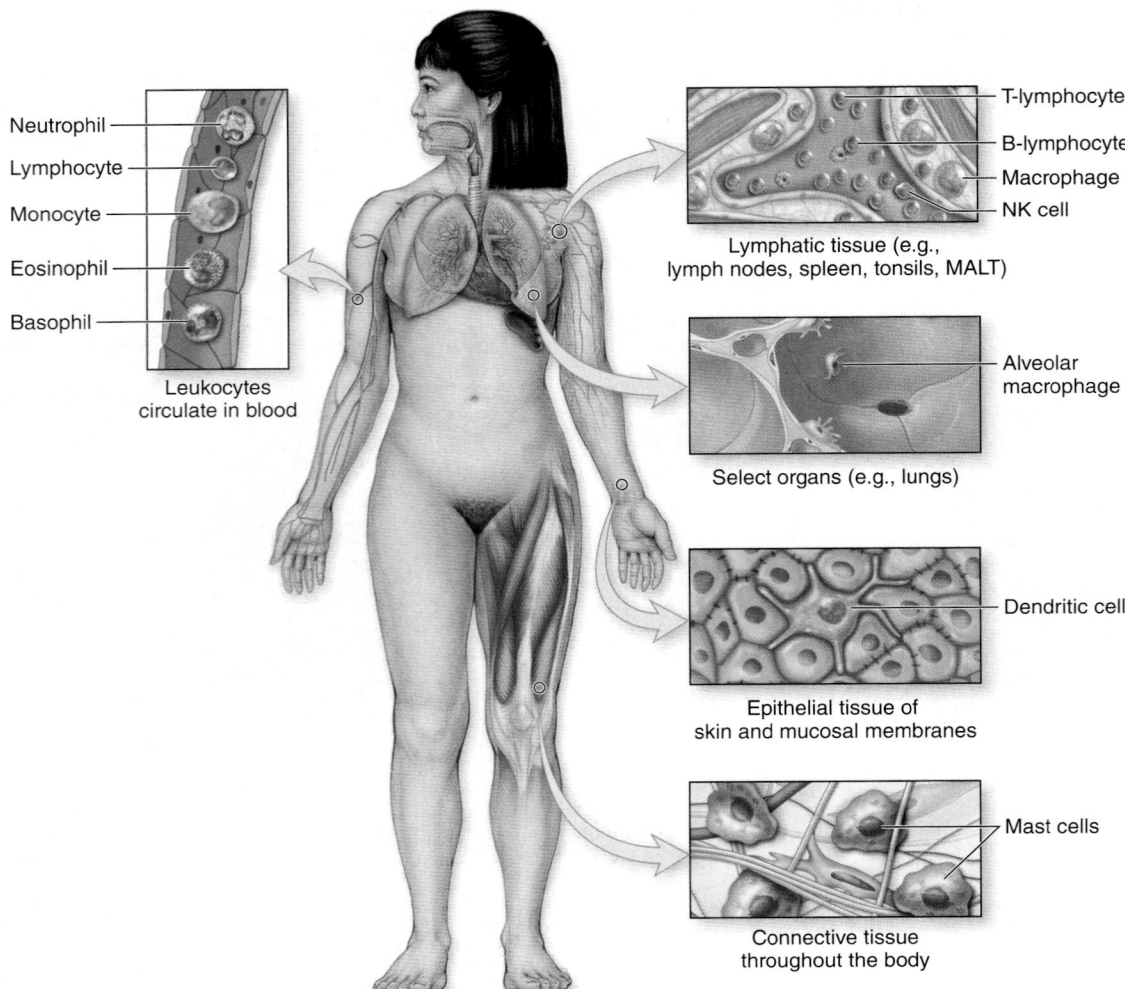

Figure 22.1 Primary Location of Immune Cells. Immune cells circulate in the blood, but are primarily located in lymphatic tissue, other organs, epithelial tissue of the skin and mucosal membranes, and connective tissue throughout the body.

Table 22.2	Major Classes of Cytokines			
Category	**Primary Function**	**Source**	**Designation**	**Examples**
Interleukin (IL)	Regulates immune cells	T-lymphocytes, macrophages, and other various cells	IL followed by number	IL-1 IL-2
Tumor necrosis factor (TNF)	Destroys tumor cells; may have other functions as well	T-lymphocytes, macrophages, mast cells	TNF followed by Greek letter	TNF-α
Colony-stimulating factor (CSF)	Stimulates leukopoiesis in bone marrow to increase synthesis of a specific type (colony) of leukocytes	T-lymphocytes, monocytes	First letter of cell(s) it is regulating followed by CSF	G-CSF (granulocyte CSF) GM-CSF (granulocyte-macrophage CSF)
Interferon (IFN)	Two classes: IFN-α and IFN-β are antiviral agents, and IFN-γ is a pro-inflammatory agent	Leukocytes, fibroblasts	IFN followed by Greek letter	IFN-α

regulate the inflammatory response of the innate immunity; and in some cases, serve as weapons to destroy cells. Cytokines have also recently been shown to influence other, non-immune cells such as those of the nervous system.

A cytokine is released from one cell and binds to a specific receptor of a target cell, where its action is similar to that of a hormone. Cytokines can act on the cell that released it (autocrine), local neighboring cells (paracrine), or circulate in the blood to cause systemic effects (endocrine). To prevent continuous stimulation, cytokines have a short half-life (see section 17.4b).

Although the terminology of cytokines continues to evolve within the discipline of immunology, a current method of organizing cytokines identifies these different categories: interleukin (IL), tumor necrosis factor (TNF), colony-stimulating factor (CSF), and interferon (IFN). **Table 22.2** summarizes the cytokine categories.

 WHAT DID YOU LEARN?

3 What is the definition of a cytokine? How are cytokines similar to hormones?

INTEGRATE

LEARNING STRATEGY

A military analogy can help describe how the cells of the immune system function in the body's defense. The cells are the "troops," the pathogen is the "opposition," and cytokines serve as both a means of communication and as weapons available to the troops to fight infection.

22.2c Comparison of Innate Immunity and Adaptive Immunity

LEARNING OBJECTIVE

4. Compare and contrast innate and adaptive immunity.

The cells, cytokines, and processes of the immune system are organized into two categories based on the type of immunity that is provided. The two categories are innate immunity and adaptive immunity (**figure 22.2**). Although both work to protect us from potentially harmful agents, the two differ in several respects

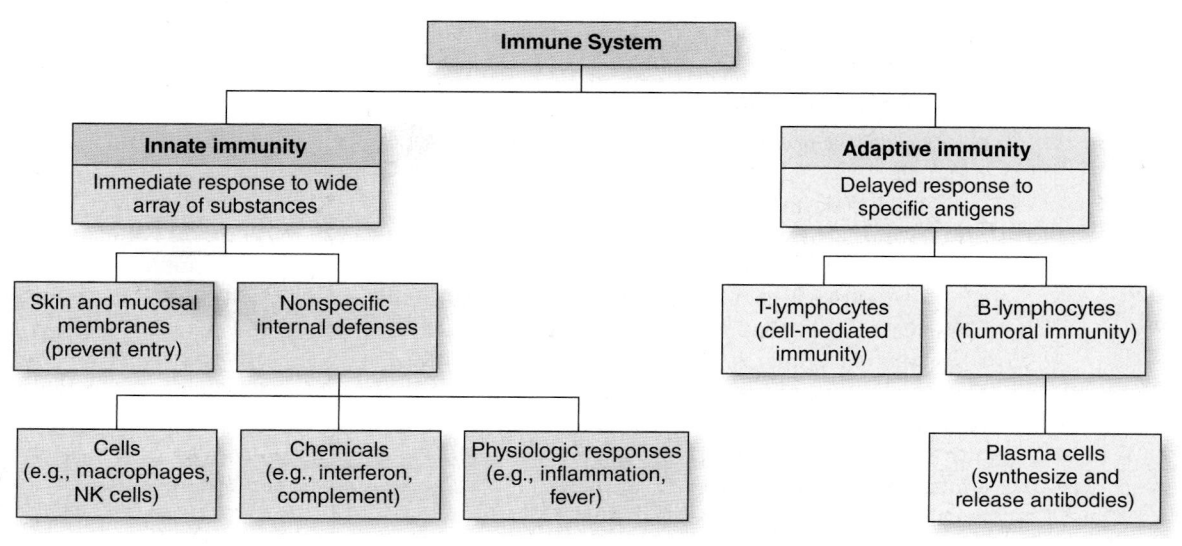

Figure 22.2 Overview of the Immune System. The immune system is composed of two overlapping and complementary components: innate immunity, which is initiated immediately against a wide array of substances; and adaptive immunity, which involves a delayed response to a specific antigen.

including the participating cells that are involved, the specificity with which the cells respond, the mechanisms involved in eliminating harmful substances, and the amount of time required for a response.

Innate Immunity

Some defense mechanisms of the immune system serve to protect us against numerous different substances, and because we are born with these defenses, this type of immunity is referred to as **innate immunity** (or *nonspecific immunity*). Innate immunity includes the barriers of the skin and mucosal membranes that prevent entry, as well as nonspecific cellular and molecular internal defenses. The structures and mechanisms associated with innate immunity do not require previous exposure to a foreign substance, and they respond immediately to any potentially harmful agent.

Adaptive Immunity

Adaptive immunity (or *acquired immunity*) involves specific T-lymphocytes and B-lymphocytes, which respond to different foreign substances (or antigens) to which we are exposed during our lifetime. For example, one lymphocyte may respond to the virus that causes chickenpox, but this same lymphocyte does not respond if it encounters the bacteria that causes strep throat. Lymphocytes provide a powerful means of eliminating foreign substances. However, although the process begins immediately, adaptive immunity typically takes several days to be effective.

In the past, the immune system was defined as the functional system composed only of lymphocytes and their response to specific foreign substances. That is, it was synonymous with adaptive immunity. The definition of the immune system has since changed because of a greater understanding of the interdependency of adaptive immunity and innate immunity, and it now includes the structures and processes of both. Although we consider these two components of immunity separately, you will see that innate and adaptive immunity work together to defend the body.

 WHAT DID YOU LEARN?

4 What are the cells of adaptive immunity?

22.3 Innate Immunity

Innate immunity includes all body structures and processes that (1) prevent entry of potentially harmful substances and (2) respond nonspecifically to a wide range of potentially harmful substance following their entry into the body—that is, nonspecific internal defenses (figure 22.2). If you imagine your body to be like a fortress, the skin and mucosal membranes provide it with its *first line of defense*. The internal processes of innate immunity are considered the body's *second line of defense*. These internal defenses include (1) activities of various types of cells including neutrophils, macrophages, and NK cells; (2) chemicals such as interferon and complement; and (3) physiologic processes that include the inflammatory response and development of a fever. We describe each of these defenses next.

22.3a Preventing Entry

LEARNING OBJECTIVE

1. Describe the physical, chemical, and biological barriers to entry of harmful agents into the body.

The epithelial tissues of the epidermis and connective tissue of the dermis of the skin provide a physical barrier that very few microbes can penetrate, if the skin is intact. The cells of the skin also release a number of antimicrobial substances, including immunoglobulin A (IgA), lysozyme, sebum, and defensins. Additionally, nonpathogenic microorganisms, termed the *normal flora*, reside on the skin and help prevent the growth of pathogenic microorganisms.

Mucosal membranes that line the openings of the body produce mucin that when hydrated forms mucus. In addition, harmless bacteria also live in the linings of the various tracts of the body and suppress the growth of other potentially more virulent types. The various mechanisms used by the skin, mucosal membranes, and other structures to help prevent entry are summarized in **table 22.3**.

Table 22.3	First Line of Defense: Preventing Entry of Pathogens	
Structure, Substance, or Process	**Description**	**Function**
SKIN		
Epidermis; dermis	Stratified squamous epithelium forms epidermis; areolar and dense irregular connective tissue forms dermis	Provides a physical, chemical, and biological barrier for body surface
Normal flora	Commensal flora, including nonpathogenic bacteria	Help prevent growth of pathogenic microbes
Exfoliation	Sloughing off of epidermal cells	Removes potential pathogens from skin surface
Hyaluronic acid	Mucopolysaccharide with a gel-like consistency that is located in areolar tissue of the dermis	Slows migration of microbes that have penetrated the epidermis
Sebaceous (oil) gland secretions	Secretions that contain lactic acid and fatty acids	Creates a low pH (3-5) that interferes with the growth of microbes
Sweat gland secretions	Secretions that contain lysozyme, defensins, and dermicidin	Helps wash away microbes; contains antibacterial and antifungal substances
MUCOUS MEMBRANES		
Epithelial and connective tissue	Lining of respiratory, gastrointestinal, and urogenital tracts	Provides a physical, chemical, and biological barrier of body structures exposed to the external environment
Normal flora	Commensal flora, including nonpathogenic bacteria	Help prevent growth of pathogenic microbes
Mucus	Secretion containing lysozyme, defensins, and IgA	Thick secretion that helps trap microbes; contains antimicrobial substances
RESPIRATORY TRACT		
Nasal secretions	Secretions that contain lysozyme, defensins, and IgA	Contains antimicrobial substances
Vibrissiae	Hairs in nasal cavity	Traps microbes in the nose
Cilia	Extensions of plasma membranes	Sweep mucus upward so that it can be expectorated or swallowed
Coughing and Sneezing	Blasts of expired air	Mechanical elimination of microbes or other foreign substances from the respiratory tract
GASTROINTESTINAL TRACT		
Saliva	Secretions released into the mouth from the salivary glands; contains lysozyme and IgA	Helps wash away microbes; contains antimicrobial substances
Hydrochloric acid (HCl)	Strong acid produced within the stomach	Creates very low pH (pH ~ 2) that destroys many bacteria, bacterial toxins, and other microbes that enter the stomach
Defecation and Vomiting	Removal of waste from the digestive tract	Eliminate microbes before they can be absorbed into the blood
UROGENITAL TRACT		
Urine	Urine formed in kidneys is transported out of the body through the urinary tract	Flow of urine flushes microbes from urinary tract
Lactic acid	Weak acid	Produced by the vagina; creates a low pH that slows or prevents the growth of microbes
SECRETIONS PRODUCED BY THE SKIN AND MUCOUS MEMBRANES		
Lysosome	Antibacterial enzyme	Attacks the cell wall of some bacterial (gram positive bacteria)
Defensins	Small proteins	Create pores in the plasma membrane of microbes, compromising their integrity
Dermicidin	Small proteins produced by the skin	Antibacterial agent against both gram positive and gram negative bacteria; antifungal agent
Immunoglobulin A (IgA)	Specific type of antibody present in areas exposed to the environment	Binds with a specific foreign substance (antigen)
OTHER SECRETIONS		
Lacrimal fluid	Fluid produced by lacrimal glands; contains lysozyme and IgA	Washes microbes away from surface of eyes; contains antimicrobial agents
Cerumen	Waxy secretions within external auditory meatus	Waterproofs external auditory meatus; may trap microbes in external ear

These mechanisms generally are very successful. However, if microbes are present in sufficient numbers, or the barrier is compromised, such as occurs with a puncture or burns, microbes may be able to penetrate into the underlying connective tissue and establish an infection. At this point, the internal processes of both innate immunity (the *second line of defense*) and adaptive immunity (the *third line of defense*) are both set in motion to eliminate the infectious agent.

 WHAT DID YOU LEARN?

 ⑤ What is the role of the skin and mucosal membranes in the body's defenses?

22.3b Cellular Defenses

 LEARNING OBJECTIVE

2. Describe the six types of cells that function in innate immunity.

Cells of innate immunity include neutrophils and macrophages, basophils and mast cells, NK cells, and eosinophils (see section 18.3c). The structure and function of each is described here. Please refer to **figure 22.3** as you read through this section.

Neutrophils and Macrophages

Neutrophils are the most prevalent leukocyte in the blood and the first to arrive during the inflammatory response (described later). **Macrophages** (mak′rō-fāj; *macros* = large, *phago* = to eat) are cells that reside in tissues throughout the body; they arrive later after the inflammatory response begins and stay longer than neutrophils (figure 22.3*a*). (Recall from section 18.3c that monocytes transform into macrophages when they exit the blood vessels and enter the tissues.)

Neutrophils and macrophages function to engulf unwanted substances such as infectious agents and cellular debris through phagocytosis. Following endocytosis, the vesicle containing the unwanted substance (a *phagosome*) merges with a lysosome to form a phagolysosome. Within the *phagolysosome,* digestive enzymes contributed from the lysosome chemically digest the unwanted substances. Destruction of microbes and viruses is facilitated by the production of reactive oxygen contain molecules, such as nitric oxide, hydrogen peroxide, and superoxide; the release of these molecules is called a **respiratory burst** (or *oxidative burst*). Degraded residues of the engulfed substance are then released from the cell by exocytosis.

Basophils and Mast Cells

Basophils and **mast cells** are both proinflammatory chemical-secreting cells (figure 22.3*b*). Recall that basophils circulate in the blood, and mast cells reside in connective tissue of the skin, mucosal linings, and various internal organs. Substances secreted by basophils and mast cells increase fluid movement from the blood to an injured tissue. They also serve as *chemotactic chemicals* (chemicals that attract immune cells as part of the inflammatory response).

Basophils and mast cells release granules during the inflammatory response. These cellular granules contain various substances including **histamine,** which increases both vasodilation and capillary permeability, and **heparin,** an anticoagulant. They also release **eicosanoids** from their plasma membrane (see section 17.3b), which increase inflammation (described later).

Natural Killer Cells

NK (natural killer) cells destroy a wide variety of unwanted cells, including virus-infected cells, bacteria-infected cells, tumor cells,

(a)

(b)

(c)

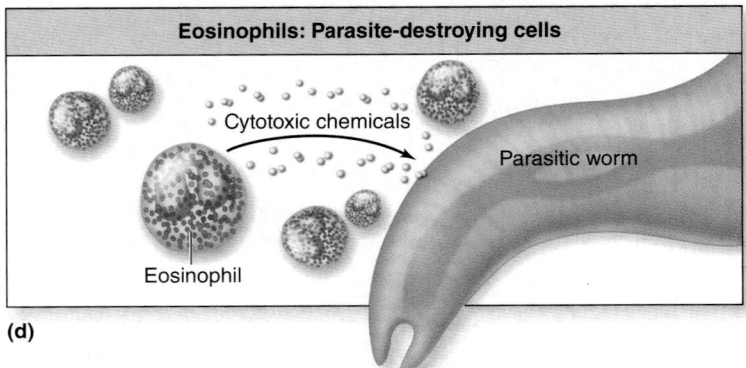

(d)

Figure 22.3 Cells of Innate Immunity. The cells of innate immunity use multiple tactics to combat pathogens, including (*a*) phagocytosis (example shown is of macrophage), (*b*) chemical secretion that increases inflammation (example shown is of basophil), (*c*) chemical secretion that destroys unhealthy cells by inducing apoptosis, and (*d*) chemical secretion that helps eliminate parasites. AP|R

The cells associated with innate immunity have a "military-like" function:

- **Neutrophils** are the "foot soldiers" that are the first to arrive at the site of infection.
- **Macrophages** are the "big eaters"—the cleanup crew that arrives at the injured or infected scene late and stays longer.
- **Basophils/mast cells** engage in chemical warfare that causes inflammation.
- **NK cells** serve as security guards that search and destroy unwanted cells.
- **Eosinophils** are the heavy artillery to take on the "big guys" (parasites).

and cells of transplanted tissue (figure 22.3c). NK cells are formed in the bone marrow, circulate in the blood, and accumulate in secondary lymphatic structures of the lymph node, tonsils, and spleen.

NK cells patrol the body in an effort to detect unhealthy cells, a process referred to as **immune surveillance.** NK cells make physical contact with unhealthy cells and destroy them by release of cytotoxic chemicals. These cytotoxic chemicals include *perforin,* which forms a transmembrane pore in the unwanted cells, and *granzymes,* which then enter the cell through the perforin hole initiating apoptosis. Apoptosis (see section 4.9) is a form of cellular death in which the cell does not lyse, but rather "shrivels"; this helps limit the spread of the infectious agent.

Eosinophils

Eosinophils target parasites (figure 22.3d). Mechanisms of destruction include degranulation and release of enzymes and other substances (e.g., reactive oxygen-containing compounds, neurotoxins) that are lethal to the parasite. Like NK cells, eosinophils also can

Earlier we discussed the differential count of white blood cells (see section 18.3c), a process that measures the amount of each type of leukocyte in your blood. Differential counts are useful in diagnosing different types of infections. For example:

- An increase in neutrophils is associated with an acute bacterial infection.
- Monocytes may increase with chronic inflammatory disorders or tuberculosis.
- An increase in eosinophils occurs in response to a parasitic infection.
- An altered number of lymphocytes generally are associated with viral infections or with chronic bacterial infections.

In contrast, decreased lymphocyte counts can occur with HIV infection and sepsis (presence of a large number of pathogens in the blood).

release proteins that form a transmembrane pore to destroy cells of the multicellular organism.

Eosinophils also participate in the immune response associated with allergy and asthma (see Clinical View: "Hypersensitivities" at end of chapter), and engage in phagocytosis of antigen-antibody complexes.

WHAT DID YOU LEARN?

6 What distinguishes neutrophils from macrophages? How do basophils differ from mast cells?

7 How do NK cells accomplish the task of eliminating unwanted cells?

22.3c Antimicrobial Proteins

LEARNING OBJECTIVES

3. Explain the general function of interferons.
4. Define the complement system and describe how it is activated.
5. Describe the four major means by which complement participates in innate immunity.

Antimicrobial proteins are components of the innate immune system that function against microbes. Two of those, interferons and complement, are described in this section.

Interferons

Interferons (IFNs) are a class of cytokines released from a variety of cells, including leukocytes and fibroblasts. IFN serves as a non-specific defense mechanism against the spread of any viral infection. A virus-infected cell, although "doomed" because either the virus or the immune cells will destroy it, helps prevent further spread of the virus by releasing IFN. Following its release, IFN has two primary actions **(figure 22.4)**:

- IFN binds to receptors of neighboring cells, preventing them from becoming infected. IFN triggers synthesis of enzymes that destroy viral RNA or DNA and that inhibit synthesis of viral proteins.

- IFN stimulates macrophages and NK cells to destroy virus-infected cells.

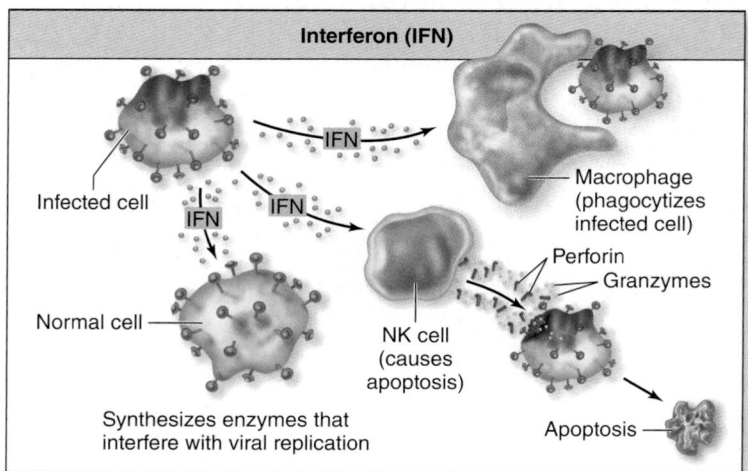

Figure 22.4 Effects of Interferon. Interferon (IFN) is one class of cytokine released from a variety of cells. A viral-infected cell releases IFN, which stimulates antiviral changes to neighboring cells to prevent their infection and induces macrophages and NK cells to destroy viral-infected cells.

Complement System

One of the most important antimicrobial groups of substances of innate immunity is the **complement system**. It is composed of at least 30 plasma proteins that make up approximately 10% of the serum proteins in the blood. These proteins are collectively referred to as **complement**. The name is derived from how they complement, or work along with, antibodies (proteins produced by differentiated B-lymphocytes, which are described later). Individual complement proteins are generally identified with the letter "C" followed by a number (e.g., C1, C2).

The liver continuously synthesizes and releases inactive complement proteins into the blood. Once in the blood, inactive complement proteins are activated by an enzyme cascade.

Activation occurs following entry of a pathogen into the body. Two of the major means of activation include the **classical pathway,** in which a complement protein binds to an antibody that has previously attached to a foreign substance (e.g., a portion of a bacterium); and the **alternative pathway,** in which surface polysaccharides of certain bacterial and fungal cell walls bind directly with a complement protein. Note that antibody is required in the classical pathway of activation, but not for activation by the alternative pathway.

The complement system mediates several important defense mechanisms, and it is especially potent against bacterial infections (**figure 22.5**).

- **Opsonization** (op'sŏn-ī-zā'shŭn) is the binding of a protein (in this case, complement) to a portion of bacteria or other cell type that enhances phagocytosis. The binding protein is called an **opsonin** (op'sŏ-nin). The binding of complement makes it more likely that a substance is identified and engulfed by phagocytic cells.

- **Inflammation.** Complement increases the inflammatory response through the activation of mast cells and basophils and by attracting neutrophils and macrophages.

- **Cytolysis.** Various complement components (e.g., C5–C9) trigger direct killing of a target by forming a protein channel in the plasma membrane of a target cell called a **membrane attack complex (MAC).** The MAC protein channel compromises the cell's integrity, allowing an influx of fluid that causes lysis of the cell.

- **Elimination of immune complexes.** Complement links immune (antigen-antibody) complexes to erythrocytes so they may be transported to the liver and spleen. Erythrocytes

are stripped of these complexes by macrophages in these organs, and the erythrocytes then continue circulating in the blood.

WHAT DID YOU LEARN?

8 How is the complement system defined? What are the four major means by which complement participates in innate immunity?

22.3d Inflammation

LEARNING OBJECTIVES

6. Define inflammation, and describe the basic steps involved.
7. Explain what is meant by exudate, and discuss its role in eliminating harmful substances.
8. List the cardinal signs of inflammation, and explain why each occurs.

Inflammation, or the **inflammatory response,** is an immediate, local, nonspecific event that occurs in vascularized tissue against a great variety of injury-causing stimuli. Inflammation occurs, for example, in response to a scratch of your skin, a bee sting, overuse of a body structure such as a pitching arm, or from proteolytic enzymes released by fungi. This physiologic process is the major effector response of innate immunity and is successful in helping to eliminate most infectious agents and other unwanted substances from the body.

Events of Inflammation

Inflammation involves several steps (**figure 22.6**). The first step involves the release of various chemicals. Damaged cells of injured tissue, basophils and mast cells, and infectious organisms release numerous chemicals, including histamine, leukotrienes, prostaglandins, and chemotactic factors. **Table 22.4** lists various chemicals of inflammation, describes their function, and identifies their source.

Opsonization	Inflammation	Cytolysis	Elimination of immune complexes
Complement (C) binds to pathogen; acts as opsonin	Complement activates and attracts various cells of innate immunity.	Complement proteins create MAC to lyse cell.	Complement (C) cross-links immune (antigen-antibody) complexes to erythrocyte and transports to liver and spleen.

Figure 22.5 The Complement System. Upon activation, complement (C) proteins serve to protect the body through various mechanisms, including opsonization, increasing inflammation, cytolysis of target cells, and elimination of immune complexes.

Figure 22.6 Inflammation. Inflammation involves several steps including the release of chemicals, vascular changes, recruitment of cells, and delivery of plasma proteins. A critical event of inflammation is the formation of exudate that helps to "wash" the area of injurious or infectious agents.

Table 22.4	Chemicals of Inflammation	
Substance	**Function in Inflammation**	**Source**
Histamine	Vasodilation; increased permeability of capillaries; conversion of an inactive plasma protein (kininogen) into active peptides called kinins; released early in inflammation	Mast cells, basophils, platelets
Bradykinin	Vasodilation and increased permeability of capillaries; stimulates sensory pain receptors	Plasma protein produced by the liver and other cells as kininogen; activated by tissue injury
Leukotrienes (slow-reacting substance of anaphylaxis [SRS-A])	Effects similar to histamine; released later in the inflammatory response than histamine and longer lasting	Eicosanoids produced from arachidonic acid molecules of mast cell plasma membranes
Prostaglandins	Vasodilation, fever, stimulates sensory pain receptors (categories include E, D, A, F, and B)	Eicosanoids produced from arachidonic acid molecules of mast cell plasma membranes
Chemotactic factor	Attracts immune cells; release of specific chemotactic factors attract a specific type of cell (e.g., neutrophil chemotactic factor attracts neutrophils early in the inflammatory response; with a parasitic infection, eosinophil chemotactic factor attracts eosinophils)	Mast cells
Serotonin	Effects similar to histamine	Platelets
Nitric oxide	Vasodilation; may inhibit mast cells and platelets	Endothelium of blood vessels
Alpha-1 antitrypsin	Inhibits damage to connective tissue by enzymes released from destroyed phagocytes	Plasma protein formed by the liver
C-reactive protein	Activates complement by binding to polysaccharides on bacteria surface	Liver

The second step encompasses vascular changes. Released chemicals cause a variety of responses in local blood vessels, including vasodilation, increase in capillary permeability, and stimulation of the capillary endothelium to provide molecules for leukocyte adhesion (**cell-adhesion molecules,** or **CAMs**).

The third step involves the recruitment of leukocytes. Leukocytes make their way from the blood to the infected tissue through the following processes:

- **Margination** is the process by which CAMs on leukocytes adhere to CAMs on the endothelial cells of capillaries within the injured tissue. The result is similar to "cellular Velcro." Neutrophils are generally the first to arrive and are short-lived, followed later by the longer-lived macrophages.
- **Diapedesis** is the process by which cells exit the blood by "squeezing out" between vessel wall cells, usually in the postcapillary venules, and then migrate to the site of infection (see section 18.3c).
- **Chemotaxis** is migration of cells along a chemical gradient (see section 18.3c). Chemicals released from damaged cells, dead cells, or invading pathogens diffuse outward and create a chemical gradient that attracts immune cells. Recruited cells also participate in the inflammatory response through the release of specific cytokines, such as granulocyte-macrophage colony-stimulating factor (GM-CSF), that stimulate leukopoiesis (see section 18.3a). This helps account for the increase in leukocyte count that occurs during an active infection. Macrophages may also release pyrogens, such as interleukin 1 (IL-1), that induce a fever.

Selective plasma proteins are also brought into the injured or infected site, including immunoglobulins (described later), complement (described previously), clotting proteins, and kinins. **Clotting proteins** lead to formation of a clot that walls off microbes and prevents them from spreading into blood and other tissues (see section 18.4c). However, some bacterial species can dissolve clots. **Kinins** (kī′nin) are produced from kininogens, which are inactive plasma proteins produced by the liver (and released into the blood) and locally by numerous other cells. Kinins, including bradykinin, have similar effects to histamine; they increase capillary permeability and the production of CAMs by the capillary endothelium. Kinins also stimulate pain receptors and are the most significant stimulus for causing the pain associated with inflammation.

Effects of Inflammation

One of the most important consequences produced by the inflammatory response is a net movement of fluid from the blood through the infected or injured area and then into the lymph. Increased fluid, protein, and immune cells leave the capillaries and then enter the interstitial space of the tissue; this material is collectively referred to as **exudate** (eks′ū-dāt). Exudate delivers cells and substances needed to eliminate the injurious agent and promote healing.

The increase in interstitial fluid raises hydrostatic pressure, resulting in additional fluid uptake by lymphatic capillaries (see section 21.1a). The newly formed lymph carries with it unwanted substances that include infectious agents, dead cells, and cellular debris. The contents of lymph can then be monitored as it passes through a series of lymph nodes. You may find it helpful to think of the inflammatory response as "washing" the infected or injured area.

The inflammatory response typically slows down and tissue healing begins within 72 hours. Monocytes exit the blood and become macrophages to begin the cleanup of the affected area. Bacteria, damaged host cells, and dying neutrophils are engulfed and destroyed by macrophages. Tissue repair begins as fibroblasts multiply and synthesize collagen, forming new connective tissue. (Connective tissue formation may lead to the formation of scar tissue in the case of an extensive injury.)

WHAT DO YOU THINK?

1 How can you tell by looking at an injured area of the skin that inflammation has occurred?

Cardinal Signs of Inflammation

Inflammation is accompanied by certain cardinal signs that may include the following:

- **Redness,** due to increased blood flow
- **Heat,** due to increased blood flow and increased metabolic activity within the area
- **Swelling,** resulting from increase in fluid loss from capillaries into the interstitial space
- **Pain** caused by stimulation of pain receptors from compression due to accumulation of interstitial fluid, and chemical irritation by kinins, prostaglandins, and substances released by microbes
- **Loss of function** (may occur in more severe cases of inflammation due to pain and swelling)

The inflammatory response typically lasts no longer than 8 to 10 days under normal conditions. The ending of the normal **acute inflammatory response** (the process just described) is necessary to prevent the unwanted detrimental effects of **chronic inflammation** (see Clinical View: "Chronic Inflammation").

 WHAT DID YOU LEARN?

9 What is inflammation and what are the basic steps involved in the inflammatory response?

10 In what ways does exudate assist in the body's defense?

22.3e Fever

 LEARNING OBJECTIVES

9. Define fever, and describe how it occurs.

10. List the benefits and risks of a fever.

A fever may accompany the inflammatory response. A **fever** is defined as an abnormal elevation of body temperature **(pyrexia)** of at least 1°C (1.8°F) from the typically accepted core body temperature of 37°C (98.6°F). It results from release of **pyrogens** such as IL-1, TNF-α, and IL-6; toxins produced by infectious agents, or in response to trauma, drug reactions, and brain tumors.

Events of Fever

Pyrogens are released and circulate in the blood; they target the hypothalamus (see section 13.4c) and cause release of prostaglandin E_2 (PGE_2); PGE_2 raises the temperature set point of the hypothalamus from its normal 37°C. The following stages of a fever occur in response: onset, stadium, and defervescence. (Keep in mind that these stages can be cyclical until the pathogen is eliminated or at least brought under control.)

During the **onset** of a fever, the hypothalamus stimulates blood vessels in the dermis of the skin to vasoconstrict to decrease heat loss through the skin, and a person shivers to increase heat production through muscle contraction (see section 1.5). Consequently, body temperature rises. The person may experience chills during this stage, which leads to the shivering.

The period of time where the elevated temperature is maintained is referred to as **stadium.** The metabolic rate increases to promote physiologic processes involved in eliminating the harmful substance. The liver and spleen bind zinc and iron (minerals needed by microbes) to slow microbial reproduction.

Defervescence (def'ĕr-ves'ents) occurs when the temperature returns to its normal set point. This happens when the hypothalamus is no longer stimulated by pyrogens, prostaglandin release decreases, and the temperature set point reverts to its normal value. The hypothalamus stimulates the mechanisms to release heat from the body, including vasodilation of blood vessels in the skin and sweating. The person may appear flushed and the skin warm to the touch. An increase in fluid intake should occur during a fever to prevent dehydration caused by an increased loss of body fluid.

Benefits of Fever

Fever actually has numerous benefits. A fever inhibits reproduction of bacteria and viruses, promotes interferon activity, increases activity of adaptive immunity, and accelerates tissue repair. Most recently, it has been demonstrated that a fever also increases CAMs on the endothelium of capillaries in the lymph nodes, resulting in additional immune cells migrating out of the blood and into the lymphatic tissue. Thus, it is not necessary (and may be detrimental) to treat a mild fever. Most physicians now recommend letting a fever "run its course" and give fever-reducing medication only if the fever becomes very high or if the patient is in significant discomfort from the fever.

Risks of a High Fever

A fever is significant when it is above 100°F. High fevers (103°F in children, and slightly lower in an adult) are potentially dangerous because of the changes in metabolic pathways and denaturation of body proteins (section 2.8b). Seizures may occur at sustained body temperature above 102°F (although generally they occur at much higher temperatures), irreversible brain damage may occur at body temperatures that are sustained at greater than 106°F, and death is likely when body temperature reaches 109°F.

Figure 22.7 is a visual summary of innate immunity. Both the structures and processes that prevent entry (first line of defense) and the internal nonspecific structures and processes (second line of defense) are included. Internal nonspecific defenses are generally effective in eliminating most pathogens.

INTEGRATE

CLINICAL VIEW
Chronic Inflammation

Chronic inflammation is the condition in which inflammation continues for longer than 2 weeks. Chronic inflammation elicits all the discomfort of the inflammatory response without necessarily ridding the body of the foreign substance. Whereas the acute inflammatory response is generally characterized by neutrophils, chronic inflammation is generally characterized by the presence of cells that arrive later in the inflammatory response, such as macrophages and lymphocytes.

One primary cause of chronic inflammation is from overuse injuries that occur as a result of repetitive minute trauma to a given area of the body. These include tennis elbow, swimmer's shoulder, or shin splints.

Some forms of chronic inflammation occur when the processes of acute inflammation do not eliminate the pathogen or injurious agent such as with tuberculosis, allergens, a splinter that is not removed, injury to a blood vessel, or from an autoimmune disorder (e.g., rheumatoid arthritis, shown below). Unfortunately, chronic inflammation can lead to tissue destruction and formation of scar tissue (fibrosis).

Figure 22.7 **Innate Immunity.** Innate immunity is the nonspecific means of defending the body against potentially harmful substances. These include the (*a*) first line of defense (cellular and molecular structures that help prevent entry), and (*b*) second line of defense (all internal, nonspecific means of eliminating a foreign substance).

(a) First Line of Defense | Prevent Entry of Infectious Agents

Skin and mucosal membranes provide a physical, chemical, and biological barrier.

Skin: Covers body surface

Normal flora help prevent growth of pathogenic organisms.

Epidermis exfoliates, which removes potential pathogens.

Dermis contains gel-like hyaluronic acid; limits spread of microbes.

Sebaceous (oil) gland secretions are low in pH and contain antibacterial and antifungal substances.

Sweat gland secretions help wash away microbes; contain lysozyme, defensins, and dermicidin.

Mucosal membranes: Line tracts

Normal flora

Mucus traps microbes, and contains lysozyme, defensins, and IgA to defend against potential pathogens.

Cilia sweep material along some tracts.

Epithelium provides a physical barrier.

Connective tissue contains hyaluronic acid; limits spread of infection.

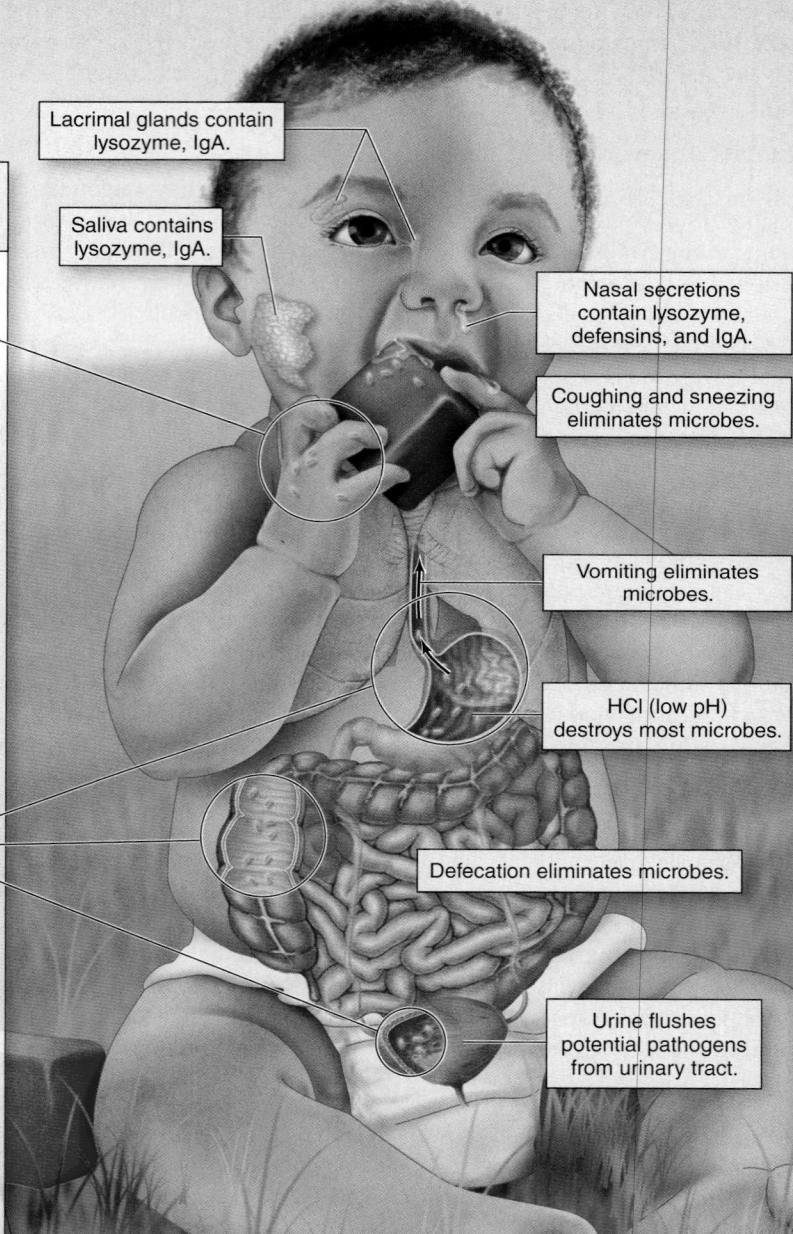

Lacrimal glands contain lysozyme, IgA.

Saliva contains lysozyme, IgA.

Nasal secretions contain lysozyme, defensins, and IgA.

Coughing and sneezing eliminates microbes.

Vomiting eliminates microbes.

HCl (low pH) destroys most microbes.

Defecation eliminates microbes.

Urine flushes potential pathogens from urinary tract.

(b) Second Line of Defense | Nonspecific Cellular and Molecular Defenses for Protecting the Body

FEVER

Hypothalamus regulates body temperature including a fever. Benefits of fever include inhibition of microbe reproduction, enhanced immune response, and accelerated tissue repair.

INFLAMMATION

Inflammation

Inflammation delivers needed substances to defend against injurious agents, and flushes unwanted substances into the lymphatic capillaries.

CELLULAR DEFENSES

Basophils and mast cells: Release chemicals that initiate and enhance inflammation

Heparin is an anticoagulant.

Histamine increases capillary permeability.

Eicosanoids (e.g., leukotrienes) enhance inflammation.

Basophil

Mast cell

Neutrophils and macrophages: Phagocytic cells that engulf and destroy microbes

Neutrophils

Macrophage

Pathogen

NK cells: Destroy abnormal cells by release of cytotoxic chemicals

Perforin

Granzymes

NK cell

Unhealthy or unwanted cell

Apoptosis

Gastrointestinal tract

Cytotoxic chemicals

Eosinophils: Destroy parasites by release of cytotoxic chemicals

Eosinophil

Parasitic worm

ANTIMICROBIAL PROTEINS AND CHEMICALS

Interferons (IFN): Antiviral substances that help prevent spread of virus

Infected cell

IFN

IFN

IFN

Macrophage

Perforin/granzyme

Apoptosis

Normal cell

NK cell

Complement system: Cascade of plasma proteins that is especially effective against bacteria

Complement increases inflammation through activation of basophils, mast cells, and attraction of macrophages and neutrophils.

Complement

Neutrophil

Basophil

Macrophage

Mast cell

Complement promotes opsonization by binding to pathogens to increase phagocytosis by immune cells.

Bacterium

Macrophage

Ab

Ag

Complement eliminates immune complexes by attaching immune (antigen-antibody) complexes to erythrocytes.

Complement induces cytolysis through formation of a MAC transmembrane protein.

Erythrocyte

Complement

MAC

Bacterium

WHAT DID YOU LEARN?

11 What is a fever and what are the three stages of a fever?

12 What are the benefits and risks of a fever?

22.4 Adaptive Immunity: An Introduction

Adaptive immunity is also initiated upon entry of a foreign substance (or antigen); however, it takes longer to respond than innate immunity. Contact with an antigen causes a lymphocyte to proliferate and differentiate to form a specialized clone, or "army," of lymphocytes against that antigen. The lymphocytes formed and the products they secrete in the body's defense are collectively referred to as the **immune response.** At least several days are generally required to develop an immune response, and it is for this reason that adaptive immunity is considered the *third line of the body's defense.*

The immune response involving T-lymphocytes is more specifically called **cell-mediated immunity** (or *cellular immunity*), and the immune response involving B-lymphocytes that develop into plasma cells to synthesize and release antibodies is termed **humoral immunity** (or *antibody-mediated immunity*). These two branches of immunity are compared in **table 22.5.**

In this section, we introduce adaptive immunity by describing several central concepts, including a description of antigens, the general structure of lymphocytes, MHC molecules (structures that interact with T-lymphocytes), and an overview of the critical events in the life cycle of a lymphocyte.

22.4a Antigens

LEARNING OBJECTIVES

1. Describe the features of an antigen, and explain what is meant by antigenic determinant.
2. Explain immunogenicity, and list attributes that affect it.
3. Discuss how haptens stimulate immune responses.

Pathogenic organisms and other foreign substances are detected by T-lymphocytes and B-lymphocytes because they contain antigens. An **antigen** (an'ti-gen; *anti[body]* + *gen* = producing) is a substance that binds to a component of adaptive immunity (an antibody or a T-lymphocyte).

The molecular structure of an antigen is usually a protein or a large polysaccharide (section 2.7). Examples of antigens include parts of infectious agents such as the protein capsid of viruses, cell wall of bacteria or fungi, and bacterial toxins. Tumor cells also con-

Figure 22.8 Antigens and Antigenic Determinants. An antigenic determinant is the specific portion of an antigen to which the components of the adaptive immune system bind. Typically each antigen has several antigenic determinants. **AP|R**

tain antigens. In the case of cancerous cells, mutations occur that generally result in the production of unique (abnormal) proteins designated as *tumor antigens.*

Foreign antigens or *nonself-antigens* bind with the body's immune components because they are different enough in structure from the human body's molecules. In contrast, the body's molecules (structures called **self-antigens**) typically do not bind with the body's immune components. The immune system is generally very effective in distinguishing a self-antigen from foreign antigen. One malfunction of the immune system, however, involves the immune system reacting to self-antigens as if they were foreign. These conditions are collectively called **autoimmune disorders** (see Clinical View: "Autoimmune Disorders"). (Note that plastic and some metals are generally not antigens. This accounts for why plastics and metals, including titanium, stainless steel, and cobalt chrome, are used in artificial implants such as for a hip replacement.)

Lymphocytes normally have contact with only a portion of the antigen. The specific site on the antigen molecule that is recognized by components of the immune system is referred to as the **antigenic determinant,** or *epitope.* Each type of antigenic determinant has a different shape, and a pathogenic organism can have numerous different antigenic determinants. **Figure 22.8** shows an antigen and several antigenic determinants.

An antigen that induces an immune response is more specifically called an **immunogen,** and its ability to cause an immune response is termed its **immunogenicity.** Important attributes that affect an antigen's immunogenicity include degree of foreignness, size, complexity, and the quantity of the antigen. An increase in one or more of these attributes increases the antigen's ability to elicit an immune response, and thus its immunogenicity.

Table 22.5	Comparison of Cell-Mediated and Humoral Immunity	
Characteristic	**Cell-Mediated Immunity**	**Humoral Immunity**
Participating lymphocyte	T-lymphocyte	B-lymphocyte
Effective against	Antigen within cells	Antigen outside of cells
Does it require antigen-presenting cells?	Yes	No
Antigen molecule structure	Proteins digested into peptide fragments	Proteins and some nonprotein molecules (e.g., complex carbohydrates)
General effector response	Release cytokines for activating other immune cells or for destroying infected cells	Synthesize and release antibodies

INTEGRATE

CLINICAL VIEW
Autoimmune Disorders

Autoimmune disorders occur when the immune system does not have tolerance for a specific self-antigen and subsequently initiates an immune response to these self-antigens as if they were foreign. Lack of tolerance and the development of autoimmune disorders can result from cross reactivity, altered self-antigens, or when immune cells enter an area of immune privilege.

Cross-reactivity occurs when a foreign antigen is similar in structure to a self-antigen, and the immune system is unable to distinguish between the two. For example, antigens of *Streptococcus* bacteria are similar to certain heart proteins, and immune cells damage the bicuspid (mitral) and aortic valves, resulting in *rheumatic heart disease.*

Altered self-antigens occur when a microbe induces changes in a specific protein in the body (self-antigen) and the immune cells now respond to it as if it were foreign. Examples of diseases include the following:

- *Type 1 (insulin-dependent) diabetes,* which is thought to result from a microbe's inducing changes in the proteins of the beta cells of the pancreatic islets in the pancreas; the immune system then destroys these cells (see Clinical View: "Diabetes" in chapter 17).
- *Multiple sclerosis,* which results from the destruction of the myelin sheath formed by oligodendrocytes; this destruction occurs by T-lymphocytes (see Clinical View: "Nervous System Disorders Affecting Myelin" in chapter 12).

Areas of **immune privilege** are structures that prevent or limit access of immune cells (e.g., the brain, eye, testes, ovaries, and placenta). Previously, it was thought that these areas were protected passively by the blood-tissue barrier and lack of lymphatic drainage. However, recent studies have shown that these areas actively participate in maintaining immune privilege by producing various molecules, including specific immuno-suppressive cytokines and special plasma proteins that actively destroy T-lymphocytes that infiltrate the area. If large numbers of immune cells enter an immune privileged area, they can destroy structures that are "perceived" as foreign. For example, if a male takes a hard blow to the scrotum that destroys the blood-testis barrier, immune cells may destroy developing sperm cells and cause sterility.

Some substances are too small to function as an antigen alone, but when attached to a carrier molecule in the host, become antigenic and trigger an immune response; these molecules are called **haptens** (hap′ten; *hapto* = to grasp). An example is the lipid toxin in poison ivy, which penetrates the skin and triggers an immune response after combining with a body protein. Hapten-stimulating immune responses account for hypersensitivity reactions to drugs, such as penicillin, and to chemicals in the environment, such as pollen, animal dander, mold, and snake or bee venom (see Clinical View: "Hypersensitivities").

WHAT DID YOU LEARN?

13 How is an antigenic determinant related to an antigen?

14 What distinguishes a hapten from an antigen?

22.4b General Structure of Lymphocytes

LEARNING OBJECTIVE

4. Describe receptors of both T-lymphocytes and B-lymphocytes.

T-lymphocytes and B-lymphocytes differ from other immune cells because each lymphocyte has a unique **receptor complex,** which may be composed of several different and separate proteins. There are typically about 100,000 receptor complexes per cell. A receptor complex will bind one specific antigen. The antigen receptor (which is a portion of a receptor complex) of a T-lymphocyte is referred to as the **TCR** (or *T-cell receptor*), and the antigen receptor of a B-lymphocyte is called a **BCR** (or *B-cell receptor*) **(figure 22.9)**.

WHAT DO YOU THINK?

2 If an antigen mutates, will the same lymphocytes recognize it?

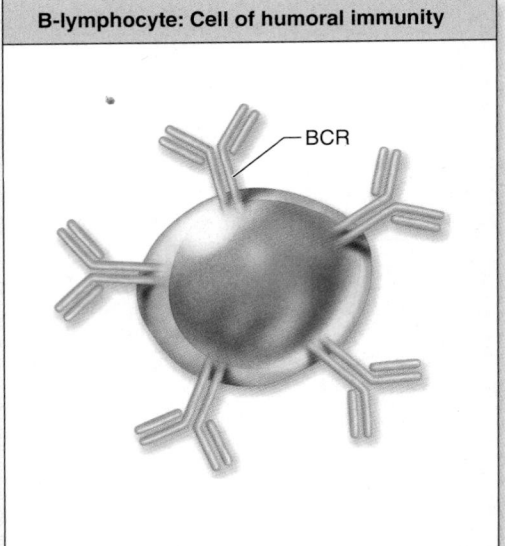

T-lymphocytes: Cells of cell-mediated immunity	B-lymphocyte: Cell of humoral immunity

CD4 protein — CD8 protein — BCR

TCR — TCR

Helper T-lymphocyte — Cytotoxic T-lymphocyte

Each cell has approximately 100,000 receptors.

(a)

(b)

Figure 22.9 T-Lymphocytes and B-Lymphocytes. The receptors of T-lymphocytes and B-lymphocytes are plasma membrane molecules. (*a*) Helper T-lymphocytes contain TCRs (T-cell receptors) and CD4 proteins, whereas cytotoxic T-lymphocytes contain TCRs and CD8 protein. (*b*) B-lymphocytes contain BCRs (B-cell receptors). AP|R

The initial contact made between a BCR or TCR of a lymphocyte and the antigen it recognizes is different in B-lymphocytes and T-lymphocytes. B-lymphocytes can make direct contact with an antigen. In contrast, T-lymphocytes must first have the antigen processed and presented in the plasma membrane of another type of cell. T-lymphocytes simply are not able to "see" the antigen without this preliminary step.

T-lymphocytes have additional receptor molecules (called coreceptors) that facilitate T-lymphocyte physical interaction with a cell presenting antigen. One significant category of coreceptors is the CD molecules. In fact, the two major types of T-lymphocytes—helper T-lymphocytes and cytotoxic T-lymphocytes—can be distinguished based on the specific CD protein associated with the TCR (figure 22.9a). The plasma membranes of helper T-lymphocytes contain the CD4 protein, and the plasma membranes of cytotoxic T-lymphocytes contain the CD8 protein.

Please note that the terminology associated with T-lymphocytes can be confusing because they may have several designations. Keep in mind that their names reflect either the lymphocyte's function or the type of membrane protein receptor associated with the TCR:

- **Helper T-lymphocytes** (T_H) "help" activate B-lymphocytes (and other immune cells), and because they contain the CD4 plasma membrane protein are also classified as **CD4$^+$** (or CD4) **cells.**

- **Cytotoxic T-lymphocytes** (T_C) release chemicals that are toxic to cells, resulting in their destruction, and because they contain the CD8 plasma membrane protein are also classified as **CD8$^+$** (or CD8) **cells.**

WHAT DID YOU LEARN?

15 What features distinguish the receptors of helper T-lymphocytes, cytotoxic T-lymphocytes, and B-lymphocytes?

22.4c Antigen Presentation and MHC Molecules

LEARNING OBJECTIVES

5. Define antigen presentation.

6. Describe antigen-presenting cells, and list cells that serve this function.

7. Explain the process of formation of MHC class I molecules in nucleated cells and MHC class II molecules in professional antigen-presenting cells.

8. Diagram the general interaction of TCR and CD receptors of a T-lymphocyte with antigen associated with MHC molecules of other cells.

Antigen presentation is the display of antigen on a cell's plasma membrane surface. This is a necessary process performed by other cells so that T-lymphocytes can "see" an antigen. Generally, two categories of cells present antigen to T-lymphocytes: all nucleated cells of the body (i.e., all cells except erythrocytes) and a category of cells called antigen-presenting cells. The term **antigen-presenting cell (APC)** is used to describe any immune cell that functions specifically to communicate the presence of antigen to *both* helper T-lymphocytes and cytotoxic T-lymphocytes. Dendritic cells, macrophages, and B-lymphocytes function as APCs.

Antigen presentation requires the physical attachment of antigen to a specialized transmembrane protein called **MHC.** MHC is an abbreviation for **major histocompatibility** (his′tō-kom-pat′i-bil′i-tē; *histo* = tissue) **complex.** This name refers to the group of genes that code for MHC molecules embedded within plasma membranes. There are two primary categories of MHC molecules: MHC class I molecules and MHC class II molecules. All nucleated cells present antigen with MHC class I molecules, whereas APCs display antigen with both an MHC class I molecule and with MHC class II molecules (a molecule displayed only by APCs).

Synthesis and Display of MHC Class I Molecules on Nucleated Cells

MHC class I molecules are glycoproteins; they are genetically determined and are unique to each individual (see Clinical View: "Organ Transplants and MHC Molecules").

MHC class I molecules are continuously synthesized by the rough endoplasmic reticulum (RER), inserted into the ER, shipped and modified by the endomembrane system (see section 4.5a), and then embedded wtihin the plasma membrane (**figure 22.10a**).

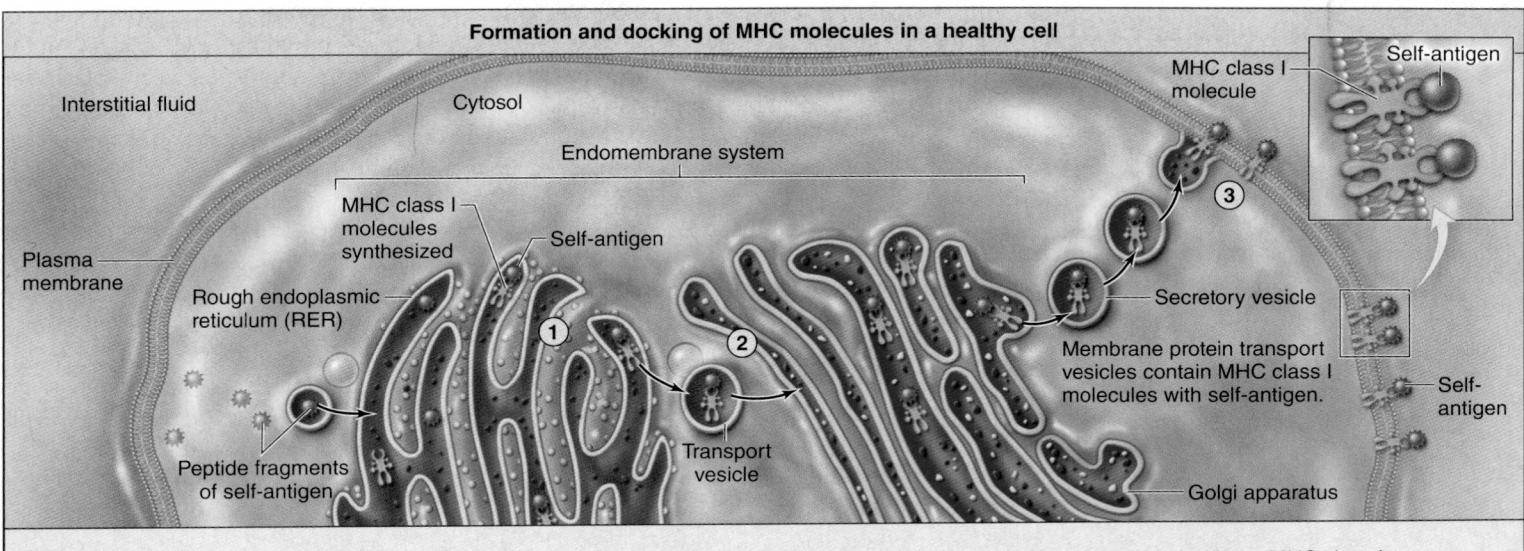

Formation and docking of MHC molecules in a healthy cell

Interstitial fluid

Cytosol

Endomembrane system

Plasma membrane

Rough endoplasmic reticulum (RER)

MHC class I molecules synthesized

Self-antigen

Peptide fragments of self-antigen

Transport vesicle

MHC class I molecule

Self-antigen

Secretory vesicle

Membrane protein transport vesicles contain MHC class I molecules with self-antigen.

Self-antigen

Golgi apparatus

① MHC class I molecules are synthesized by the RER. During production, peptide fragments of the cell (self-antigens) bind with the MHC class I molecules.

② Transport vesicles are produced from the RER that contain MHC class I molecules with bound self-antigen. They are shipped by the endomembrane system through the Golgi apparatus to the plasma membrane.

③ MHC class I molecules with bound self-antigen are displayed within the plasma membrane following fusion of the secretory vesicles with the plasma membrane.

(a)

Formation and docking of MHC molecules in an unhealthy cell (e.g., viral-infected cell)

RER

Viral particles

Proteasome digests protein of viral particles.

Peptide fragments of viral particles

Viral peptide fragments attach to MHC class I molecules.

MHC class I molecule

Transport vesicle

Viral peptide (foreign antigen)

Membrane protein transport vesicles contain MHC class I molecules with foreign antigen.

Foreign antigen (e.g., viral antigen)

Golgi apparatus

MHC class I molecule

Foreign antigen

Proteins of viral particles (or other microbes) are digested by proteasomes into peptide fragments; peptide fragments are taken up into the RER.

① As MHC class I molecules are synthesized by the RER, peptide fragments of the viral particle (foreign antigen) become attached to MHC class I molecules.

② Transport vesicles are produced from the RER that contain MHC class I molecules with viral peptide fragments. They are shipped by the endomembrane system through the Golgi apparatus to the plasma membrane.

③ MHC class I molecules with bound foreign antigen are displayed within the plasma membrane following fusion of the secretory vesicles with the plasma membrane.

(b)

Figure 22.10 Formation and "Docking" of MHC Class I Molecules in Nucleated Cells. MHC class I molecules are produced and shipped to the plasma membrane of all nucleated cells. (*a*) A normal, healthy cell only displays self-antigens with the MHC class I molecules. (*b*) An infected or unhealthy cell displays foreign antigen with the MHC class I molecules. This "alerts" cytotoxic T-lymphocytes that this cell is infected or unhealthy and should be destroyed.

A significant event occurs during the synthesis and transport of MHC class I molecules to the cell surface: Peptide fragments in the cell randomly bind with the MHC class I molecules. This occurs within the RER. These peptide fragments in uninfected, healthy cells are simply partially degraded proteins of the cell and are considered "self." Consequently, in uninfected, healthy cells MHC class I molecules are displaying self-antigens on their surface. These self-antigens are ignored or tolerated by the immune system cells.

However, if the cell is infected, the antigens presented are foreign antigens (figure 22.10b). Proteins of an intracellular infectious agent (e.g., viral particle) are cleaved by a proteasome in the cytosol into peptide fragments of 3 to 15 amino acids; these degraded peptide fragments of the infectious agent are considered "nonself." The peptide fragments of the infectious agent that are in the cytosol are shipped into the RER, where the peptide fragments combine with MHC class I molecules within the RER. Through the endomembrane system, the MHC class I molecules carrying the foreign antigens are shipped to the plasma membrane at the cell surface, where they are displayed. We will see that the display of foreign antigens with an MHC class I molecule provides the means of communicating specifically with *cytotoxic* T-lymphocytes and will result in the destruction of these cells.

Synthesis and Display of MHC Class II Molecules on Professional Antigen-Presenting Cells

Recall that APCs display both MHC class I and MHC class II molecules. MHC class I molecules are synthesized in an APC in a manner similar to other nucleated cells. Here we describe the synthesis and display of MHC class II molecules.

The **MHC class II molecule,** like the MHC class I molecule, is a glycoprotein continuously synthesized by the rough endoplasmic reticulum (RER), modified by the endomembrane system, and then embedded within the plasma membrane **(figure 22.11)**. However, antigens are presented with MHC class II molecules only after an APC engulfs

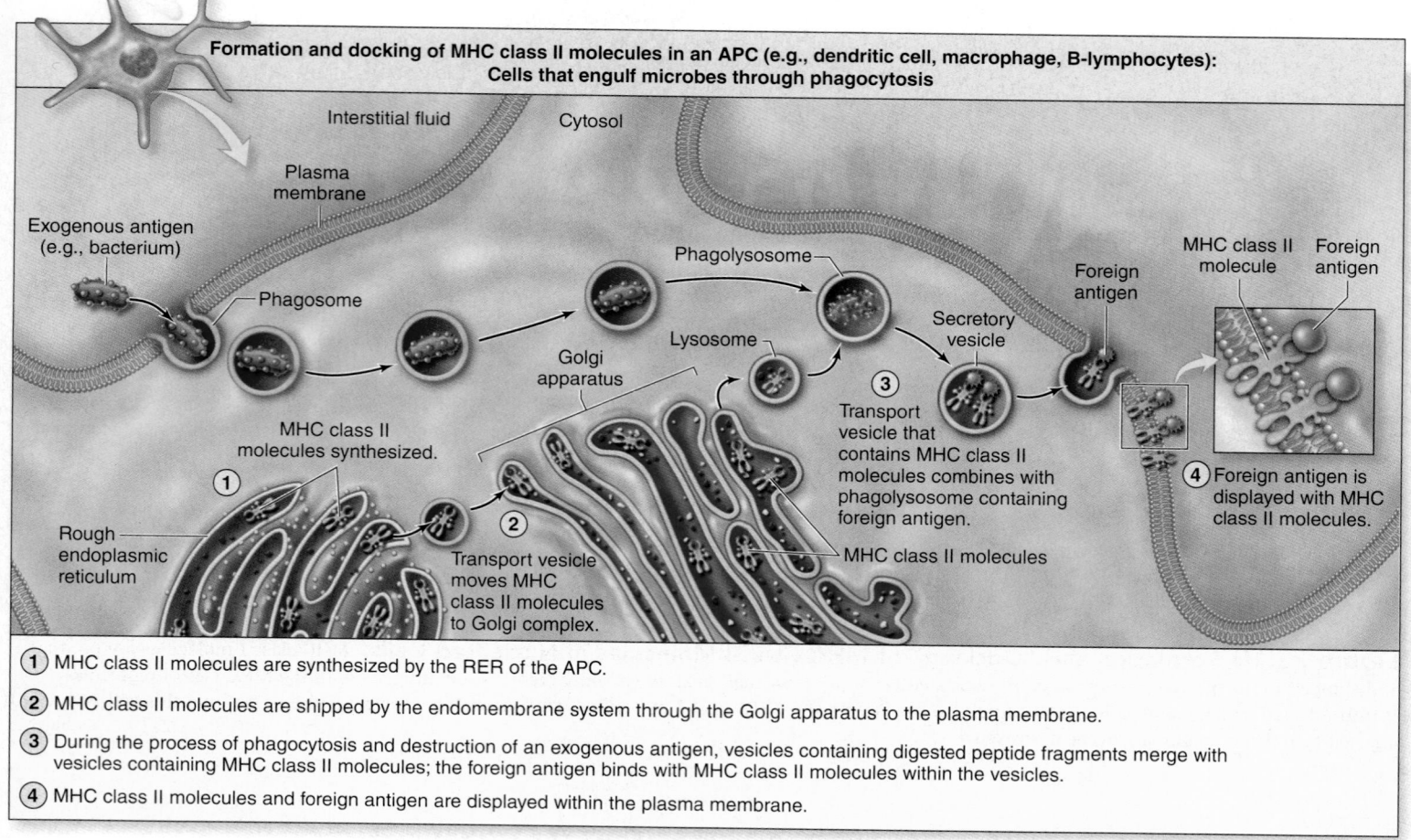

Formation and docking of MHC class II molecules in an APC (e.g., dendritic cell, macrophage, B-lymphocytes): Cells that engulf microbes through phagocytosis

① MHC class II molecules are synthesized by the RER of the APC.

② MHC class II molecules are shipped by the endomembrane system through the Golgi apparatus to the plasma membrane.

③ During the process of phagocytosis and destruction of an exogenous antigen, vesicles containing digested peptide fragments merge with vesicles containing MHC class II molecules; the foreign antigen binds with MHC class II molecules within the vesicles.

④ MHC class II molecules and foreign antigen are displayed within the plasma membrane.

Figure 22.11 Formation and "Docking" of MHC Class II Molecules in Antigen-Presenting Cells. Antigen-presenting cells (APCs) include dendritic cells, macrophages, and B-lymphocytes display both MHC class I and MHC class II molecules. Here we see the engulfment of exogenous antigen (Ag) (antigen from outside of a cell) and its presentation with MHC class II molecules in the plasma membrane.

Image labels: TCRs · Nucleated cell · MHC class I or II with antigen · Either CD4 or CD8 · MHC class I or II · TCR · Antigen · T-lymphocyte · CD4 or CD8 · **CD4** interacts specifically with **MHC class II** molecules. **CD8** interacts specifically with **MHC class I** molecules.

exogenous antigens (pathogens, cellular debris, or other potentially harmful substances located *outside* of cells).

Exogenous antigen, through the process of endocytosis, is brought into the cell. A phagosome (vesicle) is formed. The phagosome containing foreign antigen merges with a lysosome to form a phagolysosome, where the substance is digested into peptide fragments. The vesicle containing peptide fragments (antigens) then merges with vesicles containing newly synthesized MHC class II molecules. The peptide fragments are then "loaded" into the MHC class II molecules. These vesicles in turn then merge with the plasma membrane of the APC, with exogenous antigen now displayed bound to MHC class II molecules. This display of foreign antigen with an MHC class II molecule provides the means of communicating specifically with *helper* T-lymphocytes. Degraded components of the engulfed exogenous antigen are also removed from the cell by exocytosis.

Figure 22.12 illustrates a general example of how the receptors of a T-lymphocyte (TCR and CD4 or CD8) interact with an MHC class I or II molecule that contains antigen. Details of these interactions are described later.

INTEGRATE

CLINICAL VIEW

Organ Transplants and MHC Molecules

An **organ transplant** involves the transfer of an organ from one individual to another (see Clinical View: "Tissue Transplants" in section 5.6c). Examples of transplanted organs include the kidney, liver, heart, and lungs. Prior to the transplant, the donor and recipient are tested for the major histocompatibility complex (MHC) antigens and the ABO blood group antigens. No two individuals (except identical twins) have the same MHC genes, so no two individuals have exactly the same MHC molecules.

Organ transplants are risky because the MHC molecules of the cells of the transplanted tissue or organ may be detected by the immune system as foreign. Consequently, components of both the adaptive and innate immune system attempt to destroy it. Thus, the recipient's immune system is suppressed with drugs that make it less likely that it will detect the foreign antigens and cause rejection. However, these immunosuppressive drugs increase the risk of infectious agents and tumor cells going undetected.

The cornea of the eye is in an area of immune privilege (i.e., an area where immune cells are generally prevented from entering). Thus, a cornea can be transplanted from one individual to another without the need for matching of the tissue or for the administration of immunosuppressive drugs.

16 Which type of MHC class molecules is found on all nucleated cells and is used to communicate with cytotoxic T-lymphocytes? Which class is found only on APCs and is used to communicate with helper T-lymphocytes?

22.4d Overview of Life Events of Lymphocytes

☑️ **LEARNING OBJECTIVE**

9. Identify the three significant events that occur in the lifetime of a lymphocyte.

Figure 22.13 Overview of Life Events of Lymphocytes. (*a*) Lymphocyte formation occurs in primary lymphatic structures (bone marrow and thymus), and mature (immunocompetent) cells migrate to secondary lymphatic structures. (*b*) Activation occurs in secondary lymphatic structures. (*c*) The effector response occurs at the site of infection.

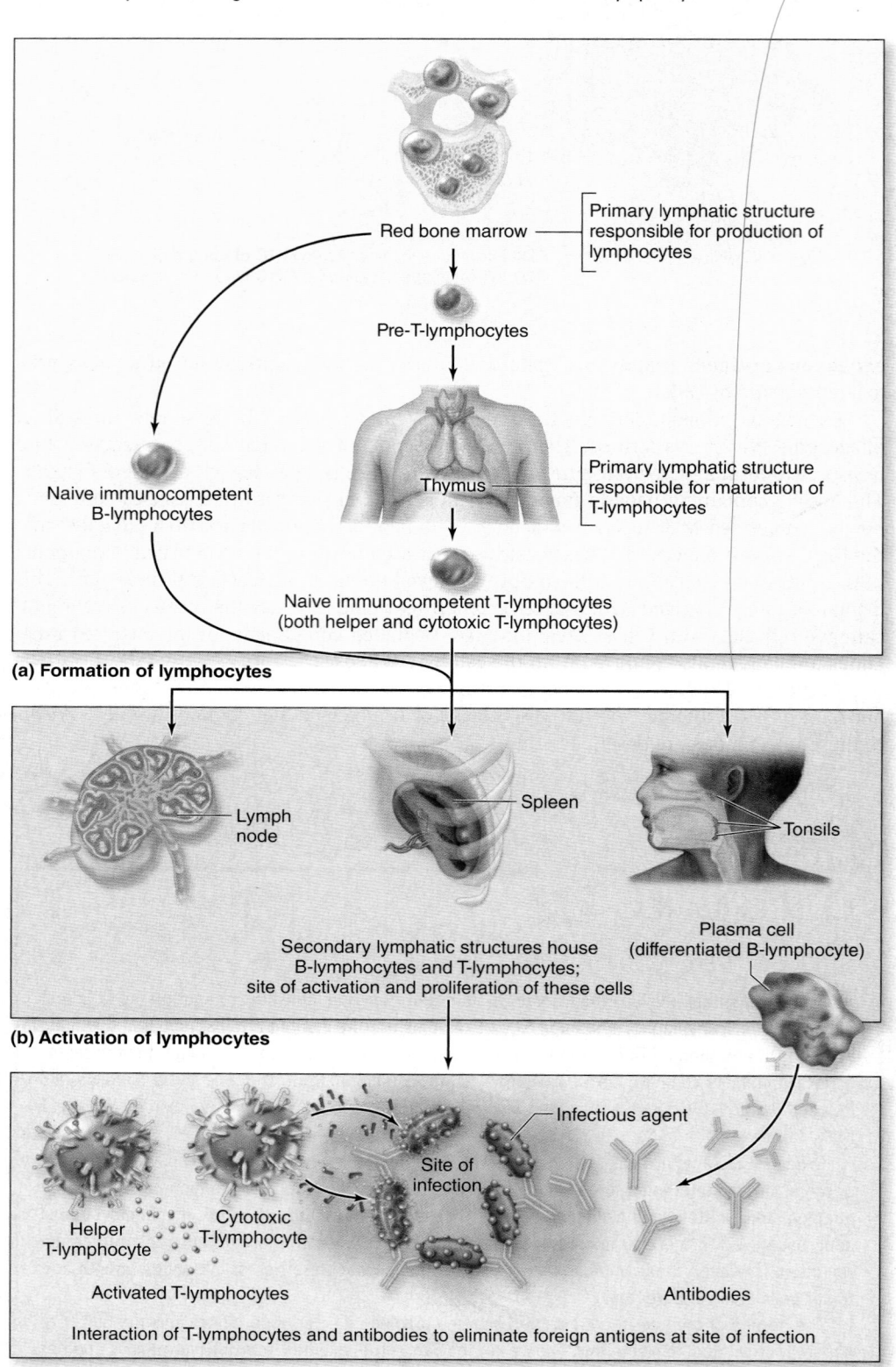

Red bone marrow — Primary lymphatic structure responsible for production of lymphocytes

Pre-T-lymphocytes

Thymus — Primary lymphatic structure responsible for maturation of T-lymphocytes

Naive immunocompetent B-lymphocytes

Naive immunocompetent T-lymphocytes (both helper and cytotoxic T-lymphocytes)

(a) Formation of lymphocytes

Lymph node

Spleen

Tonsils

Secondary lymphatic structures house B-lymphocytes and T-lymphocytes; site of activation and proliferation of these cells

Plasma cell (differentiated B-lymphocyte)

(b) Activation of lymphocytes

Infectious agent

Site of infection

Helper T-lymphocyte

Cytotoxic T-lymphocyte

Activated T-lymphocytes

Antibodies

Interaction of T-lymphocytes and antibodies to eliminate foreign antigens at site of infection

(c) Effector response

Participation of lymphocytes in the body's defense involves three significant events (figure 22.13):

- **Formation of lymphocytes.** The formation and maturation of lymphocytes occurs within primary lymphatic structures (red bone marrow and the thymus; see section 21.3). Here T-lymphocytes and B-lymphocytes become able to recognize only one specific foreign antigen.
- **Activation of lymphocytes.** Following their formation, lymphocytes then migrate to secondary lymphatic structures (e.g., lymph nodes, the spleen, tonsils, MALT) where they are housed (see section 21.4). Typically, these locations are where lymphocytes have their first exposure to the antigen that they bind, and thus become activated. In response to activation, lymphocytes replicate to form many identical lymphocytes.
- **Effector response.** The effector response is the specific action of the T-lymphocytes and B-lymphocytes to help eliminate the antigen at the site of infection. T-lymphocytes leave the secondary lymphatic structures, migrating to the site of infection. B-lymphocytes (as differentiated plasma cells) remain within the secondary lymphatic structures, synthesizing and releasing large quantities of antibodies against the antigen. The antibodies enter the blood and lymph and are transported to the site of infection.

Please note that these processes are sequential but generally differ in where they take place in the body: lymphocyte development in primary lymphatic structures, activation of lymphocytes in secondary lymphatic structures, and effector response at the site of infection.

 WHAT DID YOU LEARN?

 17 Where does a lymphocyte typically encounter an antigen for the first time: primary lymphatic structure, secondary lymphatic structure, or site of infection?

22.5 Formation and Selection of Lymphocytes

Lymphocytes originate in red bone marrow (see section 18.3c). Following their formation, lymphocytes are "tested" to see whether they are able to bind antigen and respond to it—that is, whether they are **immunocompetent.** This process occurs primarily during development and shortly after birth in primary lymphatic structures (bone marrow and thymus). We describe how this occurs in T-lymphocytes.

22.5a Formation of T-Lymphocytes

 LEARNING OBJECTIVE

1. Explain how T-lymphocytes mature.

T-lymphocytes originate in red bone marrow and then migrate to the thymus to complete their maturation. (The "T" of T-lymphocytes reflects the role of the thymus in its maturation.) Millions of pre-T-lymphocytes migrate from the red bone marrow to the thymus; they possess a unique TCR receptor *and* initially both the CD4 and CD8 proteins (referred to as "double positive"). These cells are immature T-lymphocytes with a TCR that was produced randomly through "gene shuffling," a concept beyond the scope of this text.

Each T-lymphocyte must have its TCR "tested" to determine not only whether it is able to bind to the MHC molecule with presented antigen, but also whether it binds only to antigen that is foreign or "nonself." This testing results in T-lymphocyte selection.

 WHAT DID YOU LEARN?

 18 Where does the maturation of T-lymphocytes take place?

22.5b Selection of T-Lymphocytes

✅ **LEARNING OBJECTIVE**

> 2. Compare and contrast positive and negative selection of T-lymphocytes.

T-lymphocytes go through two selection processes in the thymus, collectively called *thymic selection* (see **figure 22.14** as you read through this section):

1. **Positive selection.** The TCR embedded in the plasma membrane of a T-lymphocyte must be able to recognize and bind an MHC molecule. This is "tested" by having T-lymphocytes bind with thymic epithelial cells that have MHC molecules. Those T-lymphocytes that can bind MHC survive, and those that cannot are eliminated. Thus, those T-lymphocytes that perform this function are selected *for*, a process referred to as **positive selection.**

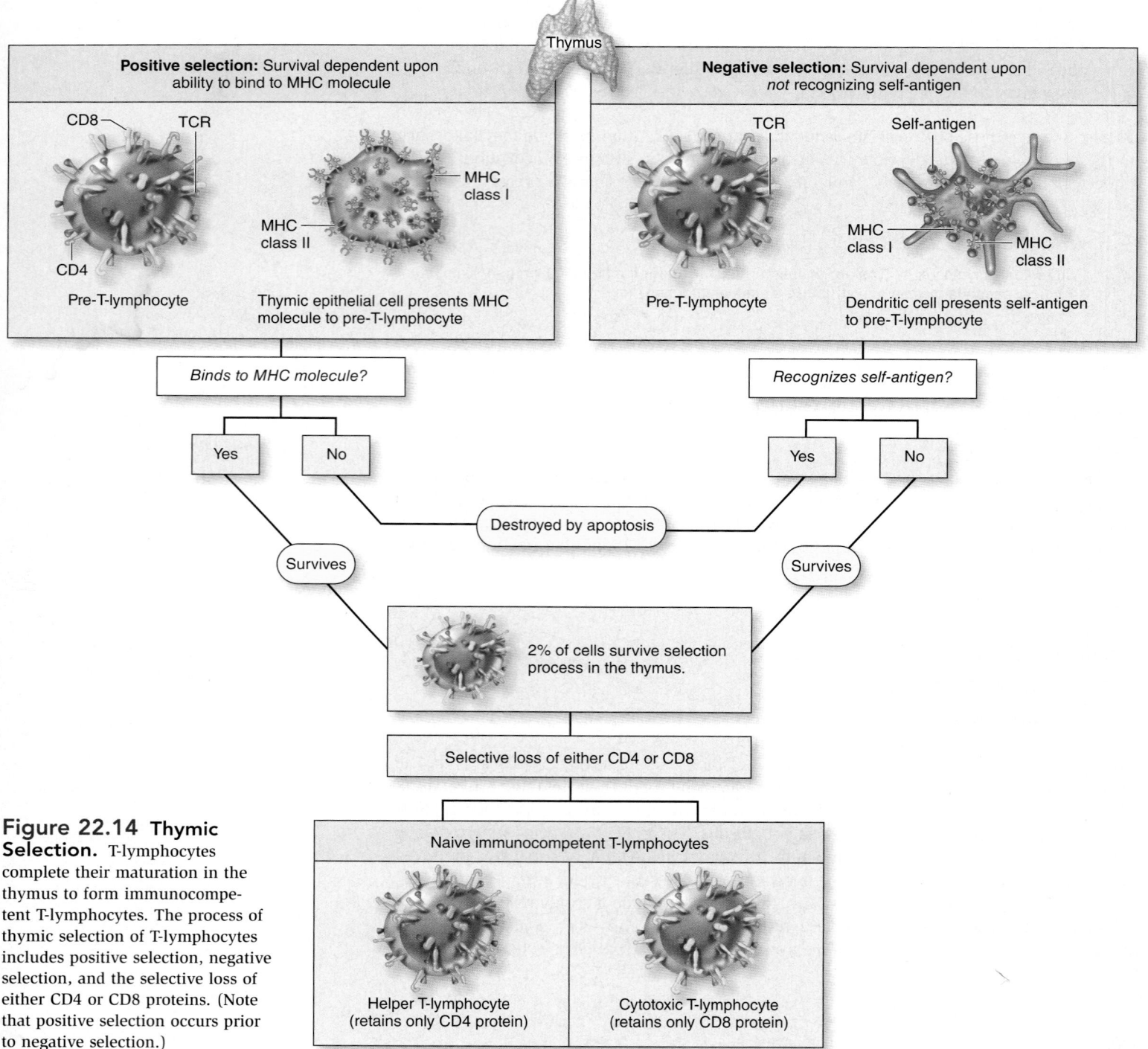

Figure 22.14 Thymic Selection. T-lymphocytes complete their maturation in the thymus to form immunocompetent T-lymphocytes. The process of thymic selection of T-lymphocytes includes positive selection, negative selection, and the selective loss of either CD4 or CD8 proteins. (Note that positive selection occurs prior to negative selection.)

2. Negative selection. The newly formed T-lymphocyte must also *not* bind to any self-antigens that are presented within an MHC molecule. This is "tested" by thymic dendritic cells presenting self-antigens with MHC class I and II molecules. If the T-lymphocyte does bind to the self-antigen, then it is destroyed. Thus, those T-lymphocytes that perform this function are selected *against,* a process referred to as **negative selection.** This is the process by which cells learn to "ignore" molecules of the body or self-antigens, a state referred to as **self-tolerance.**

Consequently, T-lymphocytes that survive both positive and negative selection can bind an MHC molecule and recognize foreign antigen. Only approximately 2% of the originally formed T-lymphocytes survive both selection processes; the remaining 98% are eliminated in the thymus by apoptosis (see section 4.9).

  WHAT DID YOU LEARN?

19 What would happen if a T-lymphocyte that failed the negative selection test was not destroyed?

22.5c Differentiation and Migration of T-Lymphocytes

 LEARNING OBJECTIVE

3. Explain the additional changes to T-lymphocytes after selection.

The final step in T-lymphocyte selection is that each T-lymphocyte differentiates into either a helper T-lymphocyte (CD4$^+$ cell) by the selective loss of the CD8 protein, or a cytotoxic T-lymphocyte (CD8$^+$ cell) by the selective loss of CD4 protein. Consequently, two primary types of immunocompetent T-lymphocytes leave the thymus: helper T-lymphocytes and cytotoxic T-lymphocytes. (There are other T-lymphocytes, including regulatory T-lymphocytes that decrease the immune response; however, we do not discuss the details of these other subtypes.)

The T-lymphocytes that leave the thymus are immunocompetent cells. However, each of these T-lymphocytes is also classified as a **naive T-lymphocyte** because it has not yet been exposed to the specific foreign antigen it recognizes. Naive helper T-lymphocytes and naive cytotoxic T-lymphocytes migrate from the thymus to secondary lymphatic structures, where they are housed (figure 22.13*b*).

A similar process to form and select B-lymphocytes occurs in the red bone marrow. Naive B-lymphocytes also then migrate to secondary lymphatic structures where they are housed, and come in contact with foreign antigen that stimulates them to proliferate and differentiate. New T- and B-lymphocytes continue to form throughout one's lifetime, and these cells participate in the immune response when exposed to a particular foreign antigen.

  WHAT DID YOU LEARN?

20 What types of lymphocytes can be found in secondary lymphatic structures, and where do they originate?

22.6 Activation and Clonal Selection of Lymphocytes

Lymphocyte activation involves physical contact between a lymphocyte and the antigen it recognizes and the subsequent proliferation and differentiation of lymphocytes into a clone of identical cells that have the same TCR or BCR that matches that specific antigen. This process of forming a clone in response to a specific antigen is called **clonal selection.**

The first encounter between an antigen and lymphocyte is called an **antigen challenge.** It typically occurs in secondary lymphatic structures. The specific secondary lymphatic structure in the body in which the antigen challenge occurs generally depends upon the point of entry of the antigen. Antigen in the blood is taken to the spleen; antigen that penetrates the skin is engulfed and transported by epidermal dendritic cells to a lymph node; and antigen that enters through the mucosal membrane of the respiratory, gastrointestinal, or urogenital tracts comes into contact with the tonsils or MALT (mucosa-associated lymphatic tissue).

Costimulation to activate T-lymphocytes for clonal selection

Helper T-lymphocyte

- Naive helper T-lymphocyte
- TCR
- IL-2
- CD4
- IL-2
- APC
- MHC class II with antigen

② Second stimulation: Helper T-lymphocyte releases IL-2, which stimulates the helper T-lymphocyte.

① First stimulation: CD4 binds with MHC class II molecule of APC; TCR interacts with antigen within MHC class II molecule.

Activated helper T-lymphocyte proliferates and differentiates to form a clone of activated and memory helper T-lymphocytes.

(a)

Cytotoxic T-lymphocyte

① First stimulation: CD8 binds with MHC class I molecule of infected cell; TCR interacts with antigen within MHC class I molecule.

- CD8
- Naive cytotoxic T-lymphocyte
- TCR
- MHC class I with antigen
- Infected cell

② Second stimulation: IL-2 released from activated helper T-lymphocyte stimulates the cytotoxic T-lymphocyte.

IL-2

Activated cytotoxic T-lymphocyte proliferates and differentiates to form a clone of activated and memory cytotoxic T-lymphocytes.

(b)

Figure 22.15 Activation of Lymphocytes. Activation of lymphocytes occurs in secondary lymphatic structures, usually the lymph nodes or spleen. Activation results in their proliferation and differentiation to form a clone of identical cells that includes memory cells. Two forms of stimulation (costimulation) are required to activate each type of lymphocyte: (*a*) helper T-lymphocyte, (*b*) cytotoxic T-lymphocyte, and (*c*) B-lymphocyte. **AP|R**

22.6a Activation of T-Lymphocytes

✓ LEARNING OBJECTIVES

1. Describe how both helper T-lymphocytes and cytotoxic T-lymphocytes are activated.
2. Explain the role played by IL-2 in both activations.

Both types of T-lymphocytes must undergo activation before they can carry out immune system functions. Activation of both types of T-lymphocytes requires two forms of stimulation (costimulation); however, the specific process differs between the two types.

Activation of Helper T-Lymphocytes

The specifics of activation of helper T-lymphocytes is shown in **figure 22.15a**. The **first stimulation** is direct physical contact between an antigen-presenting cell (APC) and a helper T-lymphocyte. Antigen previously engulfed by an APC is presented on its surface with MHC class II molecules. The APC is either housed in the secondary lymphatic structure (e.g., macrophage) or migrates there from the skin (e.g., dendritic cells).

A helper T-lymphocyte binds to the APC to inspect the antigen: The specific TCR of a T-lymphocyte binds with the peptide fragment presented with an MHC *class II* molecule of the APC. This interaction is stabilized by the CD4 molecule of the helper T-lymphocyte binding to other regions of the MHC class II molecule. If the TCR does not recognize the presented antigen, it disengages from the APC. If it does recognize the antigen, contact between the two cells lasts several hours.

The **second stimulation** takes place when the helper T-lymphocytes begin to secrete the cytokine interleukin 2 (IL-2), a process that occurs

within about 24 hours. IL-2 acts as an autocrine hormone to further stimulate the helper T-lymphocyte from which it was released.

T-lymphocytes in response proliferate to form a "clone" of helper T-lymphocytes (T-lymphocytes that possess TCRs that bind that specific antigen). Some of the cells produced are *activated helper T-lymphocytes* that continue to produce IL-2, and some are *memory helper T-lymphocytes,* cells available for subsequent encounters with the specific antigen.

Activation of Cytotoxic T-Lymphocytes

The **first stimulation** for a cytotoxic T-lymphocyte is similar to the first stimulation for a naive helper T-lymphocyte (figure 22.15b). However, direct physical contact is made between the TCR of a cytotoxic T-lymphocyte and a peptide fragment presented with an MHC *class I* molecule of an infected cell. This interaction is stabilized by the CD8 of the cytotoxic T-lymphocyte binding to other regions of the MHC class I molecule. The **second stimulation** is the binding of IL-2 that is released from *helper* T-lymphocytes. IL-2 acts as a paracrine hormone to stimulate the cytotoxic T-lymphocyte.

Upon activation, cytotoxic T-lymphocytes proliferate and differentiate into clones, some becoming *activated cytotoxic T-lymphocytes*, and others developing into *memory cytotoxic T-lymphocytes* that are activated upon reexposure to the same antigen.

💡 WHAT DID YOU LEARN?

21 What type of cell is required to activate both helper T-lymphocytes and cytotoxic T-lymphocytes?

22 How do cytokines released by helper T-lymphocytes participate in activation of both helper and cytotoxic T-lymphocytes?

Costimulation to activate a B-lymphocyte for clonal selection

B-lymphocyte

Naive B-lymphocyte
- Antigen
- BCR
- Antigen cross-links BCRs

Activated helper T-lymphocyte

IL-4

CD4
TCR

MHC II with antigen

Antigen is presented with MHC class II molecules.

① First stimulation: Free antigen binds to BCR; B-lymphocyte engulfs and presents antigen to activated helper T-lymphocyte.

② Second stimulation: IL-4 released from activated helper T-lymphocyte stimulates B-lymphocyte.

Activated B-lymphocyte proliferates and differentiates to form a clone of plasma cells and memory B-lymphocytes.

Memory B-lymphocytes

Antibodies

Plasma cells produce antibodies.

(c)

22.6b Activation of B-Lymphocytes

✔ LEARNING OBJECTIVE

3. Compare the activation of B-lymphocytes with that of T-lymphocytes.

Immunocompetent but naive B-lymphocytes are also activated by a specific antigen in secondary lymphatic structures. As with T-lymphocytes, two forms of stimulation are required. However, B-lymphocytes do not require antigen to be presented by other non-lymphocyte cells. B-lymphocytes "see" and respond to antigens *outside of cells,* such as antigens of viral particles, bacteria, bacterial toxins, or yeast spores.

The **first stimulation** occurs when intact antigen binds to the BCR, and the antigen cross-links BCRs (figure 22.15c). The stimulated B-lymphocyte engulfs, processes, and presents the antigen to the helper T-lymphocyte that recognizes that antigen. (This is similar to the action of other APCs.) The **second stimulation** occurs when an activated helper T-lymphocyte releases IL-4 to stimulate the B-lymphocyte.

Activation of B-lymphocytes causes the B-lymphocytes to proliferate and differentiate. Most of the *activated B-lymphocytes* differentiate into **plasma cells** that produce antibodies, and the remainder become *memory B-lymphocytes* that are activated upon reexposure of the same antigen. Memory B-lymphocytes differ from plasma cells in some respects: (1) The memory B-lymphocytes retain their BCRs, and (2) memory B-lymphocytes have a much longer life span (months to years) than plasma cells (typically 5 to 7 days). Note that B-lymphocytes can be stimulated by antigen without direct contact between a B-lymphocyte and helper T-lymphocyte under certain conditions. However, the production of memory B-lymphocytes and the various forms of anti-bodies (described later) requires helper T-lymphocyte participation during B-lymphocyte activation.

💡 WHAT DID YOU LEARN?

㉓ Is a separate APC required for B-lymphocyte activation, or is a B-lymphocyte able to serve the role of an APC?

㉔ Explain the role of cytokines that are released from helper T-lymphocytes in the activation of B-lymphocytes.

22.6c Lymphocyte Recirculation

✔ LEARNING OBJECTIVE

4. Describe lymphocyte recirculation and explain its general function.

One of the hurdles facing adaptive immunity is the requirement of direct physical contact between antigen and the specific lymphocyte with the unique receptor that recognizes the antigen. It is estimated that only 1 in every 100,000 to 1,000,000 T-lymphocytes or B-lymphocytes can bind with a specific antigen on the first exposure to that antigen—that is, during the antigen challenge. The "odds" for contact are increased because lymphocytes reside only temporarily in any given secondary lymphatic structure, and after a period of time they exit and then circulate through blood and lymph every several days. This process is referred to as **lymphocyte recirculation.** Lymphocyte recirculation provides a means of delivering different lymphocytes to secondary lymphatic structures, making it more likely that a lymphocyte will encounter its antigen, if present.

💡 WHAT DID YOU LEARN?

㉕ What advantage is provided by lymphocyte recirculation?

22.7 Effector Response at Infection Site

The **effector response** comprises the specific mechanisms that activated lymphocytes use to help eliminate the antigen. Each type of lymphocyte has a unique function. Helper T-lymphocytes release IL-2 and other cytokines that regulate (or stimulate) cells of both adaptive and innate immunity. Cytotoxic T-lymphocytes destroy unhealthy cells by apoptosis. Plasma cells (differentiated B-lymphocytes) produce antibodies.

22.7a Effector Response of T-Lymphocytes

LEARNING OBJECTIVES

1. Explain the effector response of helper T-lymphocytes.
2. Explain how an unhealthy cell is destroyed by cytotoxic T-lymphocytes.
3. Explain why the processes of T-lymphocytes are collectively called the cell-mediated branch of adaptive immunity.

Just as with activation, the effector response of helper T-lymphocytes and cytotoxic T-lymphocytes differs, as is reflected in their names.

Effector Response of Helper T-Lymphocytes

Activated and memory helper T-lymphocytes leave the secondary lymphatic structure after several days of exposure to antigen. They migrate to the site of infection, where they continue to release the cytokines to regulate other immune cells **(figure 22.16a)**.

Although helper T-lymphocytes are named based on their function in helping activate B-lymphocytes, their contributions are much more encompassing. Helper T-lymphocytes activate cytotoxic T-lymphocytes, as described previously, through the release of cytokines (e.g., IL-2); they also enhance formation and activity of cells of the innate immune system, including macrophages and NK cells. Thus, healthy helper T-lymphocytes play a central role in a normal functioning immune system (see Clinical View: "HIV and AIDS").

 WHAT DO YOU THINK?

③ HIV (the virus that causes AIDS) specifically targets the helper T-lymphocytes, causing the destruction of these cells. Given the role of helper T-lymphocytes, why does this disease increase a person's susceptibility to infectious diseases?

Effector Response of Cytotoxic T-Lymphocytes

Like helper T-lymphocytes, activated and memory cytotoxic T-lymphocytes also leave the secondary lymphatic structure after several days and migrate to the site of infection in the body's tissue. Cytotoxic T-lymphocytes destroy infected cells that display the antigen. The effector response of cytotoxic T-lymphocytes is initiated when physical contact is made between a cytotoxic T-lymphocyte and an unhealthy or foreign *cell*, such as a virus-infected cell, bacteria-infected cell, tumor cell, or foreign transplanted cell (figure 22.16b).

If the cytotoxic T-lymphocyte recognizes the antigen presented by the infected cell (with MHC class I molecules), it destroys the cell by releasing granules containing the cytotoxic chemicals perforin and granzymes (the same substances released from NK cells described earlier in this chapter). Perforin forms a channel in the target cell membrane that increases the cell's permeability; granzymes enter the cell through the perforin channels. Granzymes induce cell death by apoptosis, which helps to limit spread of the infectious agent. It is because the immune response of T-lymphocytes is effective against antigens associated with cells that it is referred to as cell-mediated immunity.

Infection

Effector response of helper T-lymphocytes

Activated helper T-lymphocyte

Cytokines (e.g., IL-2)

Synthesis and release of various cytokines (e.g., IL-2) regulate the cells of the immune system (both adaptive and innate).

(a)

Effector response of cytotoxic T-lymphocytes

Activated cytotoxic T-lymphocyte

Perforin and granzymes

Apoptosis of abnormal cell

Perforin

Granzymes

Abnormal cell (e.g., infected cell, tumor cell, transplanted cell)

Release of cytotoxic chemicals induces apoptosis of abnormal cells.

(b)

Figure 22.16 Effector Response of T-Lymphocytes. The effector response of helper T-lymphocytes and cytotoxic T-lymphocytes occurs at the site of infection. (*a*) Helper T-lymphocytes release various cytokines, and (*b*) cytotoxic T-lymphocytes destroy abnormal cells through the release of the cytotoxic chemicals perforin and granzymes.

Figure 22.17 Antibody Structure. The structure of an antibody is a Y-shaped protein that includes two variable regions that bind antigen and one constant region that determines its biological activity.

LEARNING STRATEGY ✐

The "military" contribution of the different lymphocytes of adaptive immunity can be thought of as follows:

- **Helper T-lymphocytes** are generals of the army; they recruit and regulate other immune cells.
- **Cytotoxic T-lymphocytes** are elite military forces; they engage in "cell-to-cell" combat against a specific foe.
- **B-lymphocytes** are the elite military forces that release "munitions" (antibodies) that act at a distance.

WHAT DID YOU LEARN?

26 Are cells of both innate immunity and adaptive immunity regulated by cytokines released by helper T-lymphocytes?

27 Cell-mediated immunity is effective against what types of substances?

22.7b Effector Response of B-Lymphocytes

✓ LEARNING OBJECTIVES

4. Describe the function of plasma cells in the effector response of B-lymphocytes.

5. Define antibody titer.

Antibodies are the effectors of humoral immunity. Antibodies are formed by plasma cells (although limited amounts are produced by B-lymphocytes). Plasma cells typically remain in the lymph nodes, continuing to synthesize and release antibodies. Antibodies circulate throughout the body in the lymph and blood, ultimately coming in contact with antigen at the site of infection. Plasma cells, over their life span of about 5 days, produce hundreds of millions of antibodies against the specific antigen.

The circulating blood concentration of antibody against a specific antigen is referred to as the **antibody titer.** This can be a measure of immune response. The details of antibody structure and function are described next.

WHAT DID YOU LEARN?

28 What is the specific role of plasma cells?

22.8 Immunoglobulins

An **antibody** is an **immunoglobulin** (im′ū-nō-glob′ū-lin) **(Ig)** protein produced against a particular antigen **(figure 22.17)**. The structure of antibodies reflects their ability to target specific antigens that they may encounter. Antibodies do not destroy pathogens directly but facilitate the destruction by other immune cells. You may find it helpful to think of the function of antibodies as "tagging" a specific antigen so that it can be eliminated. Here we consider both the structure of immunoglobulins and their actions.

22.8a Structure of Immunoglobulins

✓ LEARNING OBJECTIVE

1. Describe the general structure of an immunoglobulin molecule, including its two functional regions.

An immunoglobulin molecule is a Y-shaped, soluble protein composed of four polypeptide chains: two identical heavy chains and two identical light chains, with flexibility at the hinge region of the two heavy chains. These four polypeptide chains are held together by disulfide bonds to form an **antibody monomer** (i.e., a single Y-shaped protein). Two important functional regions of the antibody monomer are the variable regions and the constant region.

Variable Regions

The **variable regions** located at the ends of the "arms" of the antibody contain the antigen-binding site, which attach to a specific antigenic determinant of an antigen. Most antibodies have two antigen-binding sites, which allow each antibody to bind to two antigenic determinants. The variable region binds the antigen through weak intermolecular forces, including hydrogen bonds, electrostatic interactions, van der Waals forces, and hydrophobic interactions (see section 2.3d).

Constant Region

The **constant region** contains the **Fc region**, which is the portion of the antibody that determines the biological functions of the antibody. The constant region is the same or nearly the same in structure for antibody molecules of a given class; there are five major classes of immunoglobulins: IgG, IgM, IgA, IgD, and IgE. These classes are described in greater detail later in this chapter.

WHAT DID YOU LEARN?

29 What is the significance of the variable regions of an immunoglobulin molecule?

CONCEPT CONNECTION

Recall from section 18.2a that most plasma proteins, including albumin, clotting proteins, and alpha- and beta-globulins, are produced by the liver. In contrast, antibodies (immunoglobulins), which are the most significant gamma-globulins, are produced by plasma cells.

22.8b Actions of Antibodies

✓ LEARNING OBJECTIVE

2. List the functions of the antigen-binding site and Fc region of antibodies, and briefly describe how each occurs.

Antibodies are effective against antigens through the binding of the antigen-binding region with the antigen to cause the following (figure 22.18):

- **Neutralization.** An antibody physically covers an antigenic determinant of a pathogen to make it ineffective in establishing an infection or causing harm. For example, neutralization occurs when an antibody covers the region of a virus used to bind to a cell receptor, preventing entry of the virus into a cell. A similar process neutralizes toxins.
- **Agglutination.** Antibody cross-links antigens of foreign cells, causing them to agglutinate or "clump." This is especially effective against bacterial cells and mismatched erythrocytes in a blood transfusion (section 18.3b).
- **Precipitation.** Antibody can cross-link soluble, circulating antigens such as viral particles (not whole cells) to form an

antigen-antibody complex. These complexes become insoluble and precipitate out of body fluids. The precipitated complexes are then engulfed and eliminated by phagocytic cells such as macrophages.

The Fc region of the antibody projects externally after the variable region of the antibody binds to the antigen. The exposed Fc region may participate in several important actions including the following:

- **Complement fixation.** The Fc region of certain classes of antibodies (IgG and IgM) can bind specific complement proteins to cause activation of complement by the classical pathway. The functions of complement were described earlier, and include opsonization, increasing inflammation, inducing cytolysis, and elimination of immune complexes.
- **Opsonization.** The Fc region of certain classes of antibodies (e.g., IgG) can also cause opsonization (making it more likely that a target is "seen" by phagocytic calls). Phagocytic cells such as neutrophils and macrophages have receptors for the Fc region of certain antibody classes. The phagocytic receptors bind in a "zipperlike" fashion to the Fc region of the antibodies to engulf both the antigen and antibody.

Figure 22.18 Antibody Functions. Antibody (Ab) functions to "tie up" the antigen (Ag) until it can be eliminated. (*a*) Three functions of antibodies involve the binding of the antigen-binding site to an antigen to cause neutralization, agglutination, or precipitation. (*b*) Three other functions first require the binding of antibody to an antigen; the Fc region of the antibody projects externally. The Fc region can then bind complement, enhance opsonization, and activate NK cells.

- **Activation of NK cells.** The Fc region of certain classes of antibodies (IgG) can also trigger the activity of NK cells. Recall that NK cells destroy abnormal cells by the release of cytotoxic chemicals that cause apoptosis of the cell. This process is called **antibody-dependent cell-mediated cytotoxicity (ADCC).**

The antibodies immobilize specific antigens and ultimately cause their elimination by other immune cells. Antibodies are especially effective in binding to viral particles, bacteria, toxins, and yeast spores. It is because the immune response of B-lymphocytes is effective against soluble antigens (antigens dissolved in the body's "humors") that it is referred to as humoral immunity.

WHAT DID YOU LEARN?

30 What are the six major functions of antibodies? Which occur due to antigen-binding and which depend on the Fc region?

22.8c Classes of Immunoglobulins

LEARNING OBJECTIVE

3. Describe the structure, location, and specific function of the five major classes of immunoglobulins.

The five classes of immunoglobulins are IgG, IgM, IgA, IgD, and IgE. These may be remembered with the acronym G-MADE. Each class

of immunoglobulin is unique in a number of aspects. **Table 22.6** summarizes the characteristics of the five immunoglobulin classes.

IgG is the major class of immunoglobulins. It comprises 75–85% of antibody in the blood and is the predominant antibody in the lymph, cerebrospinal fluid, serous fluid, and peritoneal fluid. IgG can participate in all of the functions previously listed for actions of antibodies including the neutralization of toxins such as snake venom. Additionally, IgG antibodies cross the placenta and can be responsible for hemolytic disease of the newborn (see Clinical View: "Erythroblastosis Fetalis" in chapter 18).

IgM is normally a pentamer (composed of five monomers) found mostly in the blood. IgM is not as versatile in its biological functions as IgG. For example, IgM is not efficient at virus neutralization. However, IgM is the most effective at causing agglutination of cells and binding complement. Additionally, naturally occurring IgM antibodies are responsible for rejection of mismatched blood transfusions (see Clinical View: "Transfusions" in chapter 18).

IgA is found in areas exposed to the environment, such as skin, mucosal membranes, and tonsils, and it is produced in various secretions, including mucus, saliva, tears, and breastmilk. IgA plays a significant role in protecting the respiratory and gastrointestinal tract. In secretions, IgA is a dimer (i.e., composed of two antibody molecules). It helps to prevent pathogens (e.g., viruses, bacteria) from adhering to epithelial tissue and penetrating underlying tissue by neutralization. IgA is especially effective at agglutination.

IgD (along with a monomer form of IgM) functions as the antigen-specific B-lymphocyte receptor. It also functions to identify when immature B-lymphocytes may be ready for activation to participate in adaptive immunity.

IgE has a very low rate of synthesis and is generally formed in response to allergic reactions and to parasitic infections. IgE causes release of histamine and other mediators from basophils and mast cells, and it attracts eosinophils. The formation of IgE and its response to allergens is described in detail (see Clinical View: "Hypersensitivities" at the end of the chapter).

Figure 22.19 is a visual summary of adaptive immunity. Adaptive immunity is considered the third line of defense because on the first exposure to an antigen (which although is initiated immediately), there is a lag time that occurs from the time of exposure to the development of the immune response. This process may take several days.

Table 22.6	Major Classes of Immunoglobulins				
Characteristic	**IgG**	**IgM**	**IgA**	**IgD**	**IgE**
Primary locations	Body fluids including blood, lymph, cerebrospinal fluid, serous fluid, peritoneal fluid	Blood (monomer is B-lymphocyte receptor)	External secretions (skin, mucus, saliva, tears, breastmilk, and colostrum)	B-lymphocyte receptor	Blood
Actions	Neutralization (viruses, bacteria, toxins); agglutination; precipitation; complement activation; opsonization; natural killer cell activation; (antibody-dependent cell-mediated cytotoxicity)	Neutralization, agglutination (great potential), complement binding (great potential)	Neutralization, agglutination (great potential)	BCR (B-cell receptor)	Produced during allergic reactions or as a result of a parasitic infection; activation of mast cells and basophils
Half-Life (Days) in Blood	23	5	5.5	2.8	2.0
Unique Characteristics	Used for passive immunity; crosses placenta	First produced antibody; only antibody produced in fetus	Associated with mucosal membranes; helps protect against local respiratory or gastrointestinal (GI) infections	Identifies when immature B-lymphocytes may be ready for activation	Causes release of products from basophils and mast cells; attracts eosinophils

Figure 22.19 Adaptive Immunity. Adaptive immunity is considered the third line of defense. It is the specific means by which lymphocytes defend the body against potentially harmful substances. Adaptive immunity requires three events in the life of lymphocytes: (a) formation of lymphocytes in primary lymphatic structures, (b) activation and clonal selection of lymphocytes in secondary lymphatic structures, and (c) effector response of T-lymphocytes and antibodies at the site of infection.

(a) Formation of Lymphocytes

Primary lymphatic structure

T-lymphocyte and B-lymphocyte formation and maturation into naive immunocompetent lymphocytes occurs in red bone marrow during development and throughout one's lifetime. These cells migrate to secondary lymphatic structures.

T-lymphocytes (maturation is completed in thymus)

B-lymphocyte (maturation complete in red bone marrow)

CD4 receptor

TCR

CD8 receptor

TCR

BCR

Helper T-lymphocyte

Cytotoxic T-lymphocyte

Red bone marrow

Lymph node

Site of infection

(b) Activation and Clonal Selection of Lymphocytes

The first exposure to antigen (the antigen challenge) typically occurs in secondary lymphatic structures (e.g., lymph nodes, spleen, tonsils, MALT). Clones of activated and memory helper and cytotoxic T-lymphocytes, and plasma cells and memory B-lymphocytes are formed.

Secondary lymphatic structure

Naive helper T-lymphocyte
CD4
TCR
Ag
APC
MHC class II with antigen
IL-2
IL-2

Naive cytotoxic T-lymphocyte
CD8
TCR
Ag
Infected cell
MHC class I with antigen
IL-2

Activated helper T-lymphocyte
CD4
TCR
Ag
IL-4
MHC class II with antigen
Naive B-lymphocyte (serves as APC)

Antibodies
Plasma cells produce antibodies.

Memory B-lymphocytes

Activated helper T-lymphocyte proliferates and differentiates to form a clone of activated and memory helper T-lymphocytes.

Activated cytotoxic T-lymphocyte proliferates and differentiates to form a clone of activated and memory cytotoxic T-lymphocytes.

Activated B-lymphocyte proliferates and differentiates to form a clone of plasma cells and memory B-lymphocytes.

(c) Effector Response

Site of infection

CELL-MEDIATED IMMUNITY

Activated helper T-lymphocyte releases cytokines to stimulate activity of B-lymphocytes and cytotoxic T-lymphocytes, and regulate cells of innate immunity.

Cytokines (e.g., IL-2)
Helper T-lymphocyte
Erythrocyte

Activated cytotoxic T-lymphocytes release cytotoxic molecules (perforin and granzymes) causing apoptosis of foreign or abnormal cells.

Perforin
Granzymes
Cytotoxic T-lymphocyte
Abnormal cell
Apoptosis of abnormal cell

HUMORAL IMMUNITY

Fab region of antibody binds to antigen to cause several consquences including: neutralization of microbial cells (e.g., bacteria) and particles (e.g., virus, toxins); agglutination of cells; and precipitation of particles (e.g., toxins).

Fab region
Bacterium
Virus
Neutralization
Soluble particles
Bacteria
Precipitation
Agglutination

Fc region of antibody serves as point of interaction with several structures including: complement to cause complement activation; phagocytic cells to increase the likelihood of the antigen being engulfed (opsonization); and NK cells to trigger NK cells to induce apoptosis of unwanted cells.

Complement
Binding **complement**
Fc region
Phagocyte
Binding phagocytic cells through **opsonization**
NK cell
Binding **NK cells** to cause apoptosis of unwanted cells

INTEGRATE

CONCEPT CONNECTION

The fetus produces only IgM, and the mother supplies the fetus with IgG, the only antibody that crosses the placenta. IgG, IgA, and IgM in the breastmilk of the nursing mother protects the newborn, and eventually the child produces its own IgA to protect its intestines.

WHAT DID YOU LEARN?

31 Which subclass of antibodies is most prevalent? Which specific functions of antibodies can it engage in?

22.9 Immunologic Memory and Immunity

One of the central features of adaptive immunity is the development of "memory" that provides immunity against a specific antigen. Here we discuss immunologic memory and how immunity is obtained through both active and passive means.

22.9a Immunologic Memory

✓ LEARNING OBJECTIVE

1. Define immunologic memory and explain how it occurs.

Activation of the adaptive immunity requires direct physical contact between a lymphocyte and an antigen. On the first exposure to an antigen (the antigen challenge), limited numbers of helper T-lymphocytes, cytotoxic T-lymphocytes, and B-lymphocytes recognize the antigen (about 1 in 100,000 to 1,000,000). Generally a lag time occurs between the body's initial exposure to the antigen and the physical contact with lymphocytes required to develop an immune response.

The antigen challenge, however, causes the formation of memory cells in response to the activation of T-lymphocytes and B-lymphocytes, as described in earlier sections. These long-lived lymphocytes represent an "army" of thousands against specific antigens and are responsible for immunologic memory.

On subsequent exposures to an antigen, these vast number of memory cells make contact with the antigen more rapidly and produce a more powerful response, which is referred to as the **secondary response,** *memory response,* or *anamnestic* (an'am-nes'tik; *an* = not, *amnesia* = forgetfulness) *response.* On each subsequent exposure to a specific pathogen, the pathogen is typically eliminated even before disease symptoms develop. For example, a person who develops measles will not develop measles again, even if reexposed to that virus. The virus is eliminated by activated memory T- lymphocytes, memory B-lymphocytes, and antibodies before it causes harm. This feature of immunologic memory makes adaptive immunity a highly potent protector. Vaccines are typically effective in developing memory, and a secondary response is seen on exposure to the substance vaccinated against (see Clinical View: "Vaccinations").

WHAT DID YOU LEARN?

32 Briefly describe immunologic memory, and explain its significance.

22.9b Measure of Immunologic Memory

✓ LEARNING OBJECTIVE

2. Discuss the difference between the primary response and the secondary response to antigen exposure.

Antibody titer (concentration) in blood serum is one measure of immunologic memory. The graphs shown in **figure 22.20** reflect the changes in serum antibody titer (specifically, the amount of IgM and IgG in the blood) over time in response to both the initial exposure and subsequent exposure to an antigen. The *degree* of protection is indicated by levels of circulating IgG.

Initial Exposure and the Primary Response

The initial exposure to a specific antigen can be in the form of an active infection or a vaccine. The measurable response of antibody production to the first exposure is called the **primary response** (figure 22.20*a*):

- **Lag or latent phase.** There is initially a period of no detectable antibody in the blood. This period may extend 3 to 6 days. Antigen detection, activation,

Lag phase

Primary response

Serum antibody titer

IgM

IgG

0 5 10 15 20 25

Days from first exposure to antigen

Secondary response

Serum antibody titer

IgG

IgM

0 5 10 15 20 25

Days from reexposure to same antigen

Figure 22.20 Primary and Secondary (Anamnestic) Response in Humoral Immunity. Graph of the primary response that shows the level of IgM and IgG antibody produced by plasma cells on the first exposure to a given antigen. Graph of the secondary response that depicts the level of these antibodies on all subsequent exposures to the same antigen.

proliferation, and differentiation of lymphocytes, including development of memory lymphocytes, occur during the lag phase.

- **Production of antibody.** Within 1 to 2 weeks, plasma cells produce IgM and then IgG. Antibody titer levels peak and then generally decrease over time.

Subsequent Exposures and the Secondary Response

Subsequent exposures to an antigen can occur after varying lengths of time following the initial exposure, and the measurable response to subsequent exposure is called the **secondary response** (figure 22.20b):

- **Lag or latent phase.** A much shorter lag phase occurs with subsequent exposures to the same antigen. This difference is due to the presence of memory lymphocytes.
- **Production of antibody.** Antibody levels rise more rapidly, with a greater proportion of the IgG class of antibodies. This higher level of IgG production may continue for longer periods, perhaps even years.

 WHAT DID YOU LEARN?

 How does the secondary response differ from the primary response? What is the advantage of the secondary response?

INTEGRATE

CLINICAL VIEW
Vaccinations

A **vaccine** is an attenuated (weakened) or dead microorganism, or some component of the microorganism (may be bioengineered) that is administered through one of several routes: oral, intradermal, intravenous (IV), intraperitoneal, or intranasal.

The function of a vaccine is to stimulate the immune system to develop memory B-lymphocytes, (predominantly) while providing a relatively safe means for the initial exposure to a microorganism. The risk is relatively low because the microorganism (or its components) has no ability (or limited ability) to establish an infection. If an individual is later exposed to the same antigens, the secondary response is triggered and it will be swift and powerful; the individual is generally not even aware of contact with the microbe.

However, a vaccine is different from having an active infection in these ways:

- The immune response to a vaccine is predominantly from the humoral-mediated branch (e.g., oral polio vaccine). The reason is that B-lymphocytes bind unattached microbes to induce humoral-mediated immunity, but few, if any, of the weakened or dead microbes in the vaccine can infect cells to induce T-lymphocytes to establish cell-mediated immunity. (The B-lymphocytes present the antigen to T-lymphocytes in some instances.)
- Depending upon the life span of the particular memory B-lymphocytes, the vaccine may provide lifelong immunity, or periodic **booster shots** may be needed to ensure continued protection against the antigen. For example, booster shots are needed every 10 years for protection against tetanus.

22.9c Active and Passive Immunity

LEARNING OBJECTIVES

3. Define active immunity and passive immunity.

4. Describe how both active and passive immunity can be acquired naturally and artificially.

Immunity can be active or passive. **Active immunity** results from a direct encounter with a pathogen or foreign substance and can be obtained naturally or artificially. *Naturally* acquired active immunity occurs when an individual is directly exposed to the antigen of an infectious agent. *Artificially* acquired active immunity takes place when the exposure occurs through a vaccine. In both cases, memory cells against that specific antigen are formed.

In contrast to active immunity, **passive immunity** is obtained from another individual, and it can also be obtained naturally or artificially. Naturally acquired passive immunity occurs from the transfer of antibodies from the mother to the fetus across the placenta (IgG) or to the baby in mother's breastmilk (IgA, IgM, and IgG). In contrast, when serum containing antibodies against a specific antigen is transferred from one individual to another, this process is referred to as artificially acquired passive immunity. For example, serum containing antibodies against the toxins associated with tetanus and botulism, can be transferred to an individual who is at risk from one of these toxins. Antibodies to a poisonous snake venom (antivenom) can also be transferred to an individual who has been bitten by that species of snake. The antibodies neutralize the toxin or venom to prevent it from doing harm until the body is able to eliminate it.

In both types of passive immunity, the individual has not had an antigenic challenge and has not produced memory cells. Passive immunity lasts only as long as the antibody proteins are present in the individual. For example, the half-life of IgG in the blood is 23 days; IgM is 5 days (table 22.6). **Table 22.7** compares the characteristics of active and passive immunity.

WHAT DID YOU LEARN?

 34 Which type of immunity—active or passive—results in the production of memory cells and generally provides lifelong protection from that antigen?

Table 22.7	Comparison of Active and Passive Immunity	
Characteristic	**Active Immunity**	**Passive Immunity**

Direct contact with an antigen	Yes
	  Naturally acquired—involves infectious agent
	  Artificially acquired—occurs through vaccine
		No

Development of memory cells	Yes	No

Antibodies provided from other source	No	Yes
		  Naturally acquired—occurs from mother to child
		  Artificially acquired—is the transfer of cells or antibodies from another individual

CLINICAL VIEW
Hypersensitivities

Hypersensitivity is an abnormal and exaggerated response of the immune system to an antigen. The various types of hypersensitivities are categorized based on the amount of time required for the immune response to occur following exposure to an antigen: **Acute hypersensitivities** occur within seconds; **subacute hypersensitivities** with 1 to 3 hours, and **delayed hypersensitivities** occur within 1 to 3 days. The difference in time of onset reflects the components of the immune system that are involved. Both acute and subacute hypersensitivity reactions involve humoral immunity. Immunoglobulin E (IgE) antibodies are involved in acute hypersensitivities, whereas subacute hypersensitivity reactions are triggered by immunoglobulin G (IgG) and immunoglobulin M (IgM). In contrast, delayed hypersensitivity reactions involve cell-mediated immunity. We limit our discussion to acute hypersensitivities.

Acute Hypersensitivity (Allergies)

An acute hypersensitivity is more commonly referred to as an **allergy** (or *type I hypersensitivity*), and it is an overreaction of the immune system to a noninfectious substance, or **allergen.** Examples of different allergens include pollen, latex, peanuts, and bee venom. Following exposure to the allergen, an allergic reaction occurs within seconds and continues for about a half hour.

There are three major phases associated with an allergic reaction:

1. **Sensitization phase.** An individual is exposed to an allergen. The allergen is engulfed by an antigen-presenting cell (APC) and presented to a helper T-lymphocyte. The helper T-lymphocytes release cytokines that cause the B-lymphocytes to mature into plasma cells that produce IgE antibodies against the allergen. The IgE antibodies bind to basophils and mast cells (by the Fc region of

the antibody), and may remain bound to these cells for several weeks or longer.

2. **Activation phase.** If the individual is reexposed to the same allergen, the allergen binds to the IgE antibodies that are bound to the basophils and mast cells, cross-linking the receptors.

3. **Effector phase.** The mast cells or basophils release chemicals (histamine, heparin, and eicosanoids) that cause an inflammatory response. The inflammatory response is responsible for the symptoms associated with allergies. The symptoms an individual experiences depend upon where the inflammatory response occurs in the body:

- Contact with the mucous membranes of the nasal passage and conjunctiva of the eye result in a runny nose and watery eyes (**allergic rhinitis**, or "*hay fever*"). This is the most common site with approximately 20% of the general population experiencing allergic rhinitis.
- Exposure of the skin surface can result in red welts and itchy skin (**hives**).
- Entrance into the respiratory passageway causes bronchoconstriction and increases secretion of mucus, causing labored breathing and coughing (**allergic asthma**).
- Entrance into the digestive tract causes increased fluid secretions and peristalsis that may cause vomiting and diarrhea (not shown in figure).
- Circulation in the blood through a bee sting or injection by needle causes systemic vasodilation and inflammation. In extreme cases, extensive loss of fluid from the blood into the interstitial space results in a marked decrease in blood volume and blood pressure. Consequently, the individual may have insufficient blood pressure to maintain adequate perfusion (**anaphylactic shock**).

Type I (IgE) hypersensitivity

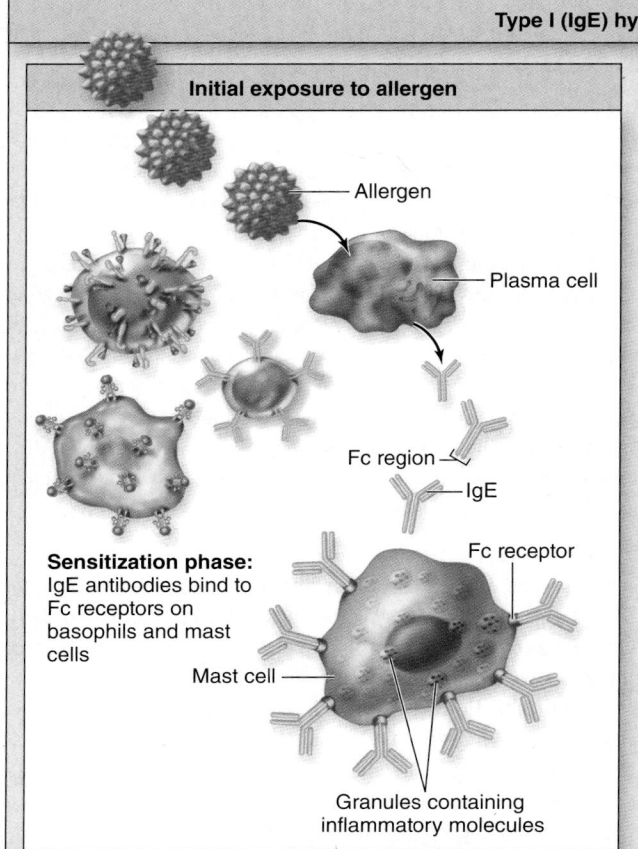

Initial exposure to allergen

Allergen

Plasma cell

Fc region

IgE

Fc receptor

Sensitization phase:
IgE antibodies bind to Fc receptors on basophils and mast cells

Mast cell

Granules containing inflammatory molecules

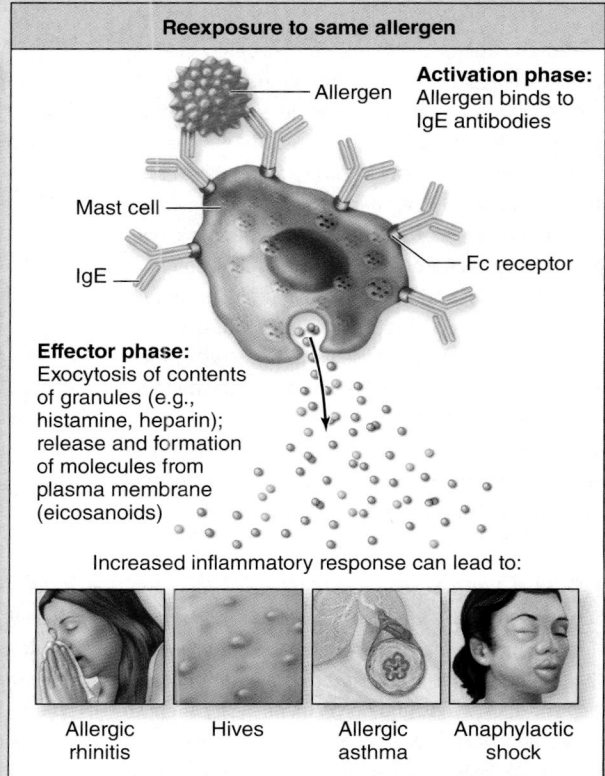

Reexposure to same allergen

Allergen

Activation phase:
Allergen binds to IgE antibodies

Mast cell

IgE

Fc receptor

Effector phase:
Exocytosis of contents of granules (e.g., histamine, heparin); release and formation of molecules from plasma membrane (eicosanoids)

Increased inflammatory response can lead to:

Allergic rhinitis — Hives — Allergic asthma — Anaphylactic shock

Acute hypersensitivity reactions involve the IgE antibody. The three stages of acute hypersensitivity include the sensitization phase, activation phase, and effector phase.

CLINICAL VIEW
HIV and AIDS

AIDS (acquired immunodeficiency syndrome) is a life-threatening condition that is the result of the **human immunodeficiency virus (HIV)**. An HIV infection targets the immune system—in particular, the helper T-lymphocyte (CD4⁺ T-cell). HIV infects and destroys these helper T-lymphocytes over a period of time (months to years). Prolonged HIV infection leads to the devastating effects of AIDS.

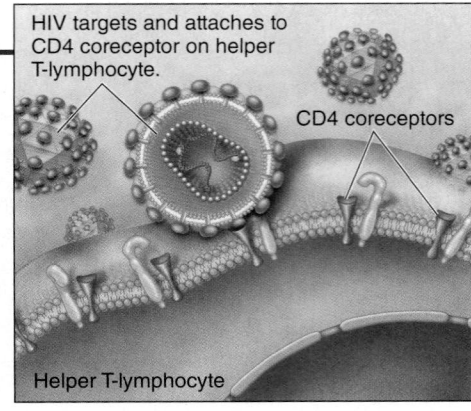

Process of the human immunodeficiency virus (HIV) infecting a cell.

HIV targets and attaches to CD4 coreceptor on helper T-lymphocyte.

CD4 coreceptors

Helper T-lymphocyte

Epidemiology

HIV resides in the body fluids of infected individuals, including their blood, semen, vaginal secretions, or even breast milk. HIV can be transmitted during activities that transmit these bodily fluids, such as unprotected sexual (vaginal or anal) intercourse, sharing hypodermic needles with other intravenous drug users, or breastfeeding an infant. Current evidence indicates HIV is *not* spread by casual kissing, sharing eating utensils, using a public toilet, or casual physical contact. First seen in the United States in the early 1980s among the homosexual male population, it is now a prominent disease among heterosexual populations. The United Nations program on AIDS (UNAIDS) estimates that 90% of all HIV infections are currently transmitted heterosexually. Prior to 1985, before HIV and AIDS were well known, HIV could be transmitted through the donated blood supply. Individuals who received blood transfusions sometimes received HIV-infected blood, thereby infecting them as well. This discovery has led to more stringent screening of blood donors.

Since the early 1980s, over 60 million people have become infected with HIV, and over 27 million people have died. The incidence of AIDS is increasing throughout the world, but the disease is particularly rampant on the continents of Africa and Asia. The AIDS epidemic in Africa has led to massive numbers of deaths, and children are frequently orphaned as both parents succumb to the disease. Asian countries are seeing a surge of new HIV and AIDS cases, especially among sex workers and their clients.

Prevention

The key to limiting the spread of HIV infection is to refrain from behaviors that allow the virus's transmission. Unprotected sexual intercourse (especially anal intercourse) can spread HIV, so individuals should either practice abstinence or protect themselves with the use of condoms. HIV can also be spread through oral sex. (Other contraceptives like birth control pills do *not* protect an individual from HIV infection.) Both partners in a monogamous relationship should be tested for presence of the HIV virus (done via a simple blood test) before engaging in sexual intercourse. Intravenous drug users should not share needles. Health-care workers should wear gloves and be careful around patient bodily fluids. HIV-infected pregnant women need special prenatal care to help prevent the transmission of the virus to their fetus. In addition, HIV-infected mothers are discouraged from breastfeeding their infants, as the virus is present in breast milk.

HIV cannot survive for long periods of time outside the human body. The virus can be eliminated from medical equipment or personal care items by cleaning them with a common disinfectant (such as bleach or hydrogen peroxide) or by heating them to temperatures above 135°F.

How HIV Causes Its Damage

Helper T-lymphocytes are destroyed by HIV infection. This destruction occurs in several ways. Some helper T-lymphocytes are programmed to produce HIV RNA at such a fast rate that the cell undergoes lysis, or bursts. Other helper T-lymphocytes are targeted and destroyed by other immune cells, such as macrophages or cytotoxic T-lymphocytes. Over a period of months to years, the helper T-lymphocyte population declines to a dangerously low level. Helper

T-lymphocytes initiate and oversee the body's immune response; therefore, a decrease in helper T-lymphocytes results in a loss of normal immune function.

Early Symptoms

Approximately several weeks to several months after initial HIV infection, many individuals will experience flulike symptoms, including sore throat, fever, fatigue, headache, and swollen lymph nodes. Some people also may experience night sweats as well, while still others may be completely asymptomatic. Often, these symptoms disappear after a few weeks when the body's other immune cells target and destroy HIV infected cells. Healthy helper T-lymphocytes divide to replace those cells that were destroyed. However, HIV continues to replicate at a faster rate than the immune system can rid itself of infected cells; in addition, the virus mutates to avoid detection. Over a period of years, the helper T-lymphocyte population drops to very low numbers, setting the stage for AIDS.

What Do HIV Blood Tests Look For?

HIV blood tests look for the evidence of HIV antibodies in the blood. These antibodies are produced by plasma cells about a month after initial infection. These antibodies indicate the body is responding to HIV infection. It can take up to 6 months for antibody levels in the blood to rise to a point where they can be detected by the blood test. Thus, individuals who have been exposed to HIV but get tested within the first 6 months may receive false negative results and are still at risk for infecting others.

When Does HIV Become AIDS?

HIV infection is diagnosed as AIDS when either a person's helper T-lymphocyte count drops to below 200 cells per cubic milliliter (in comparison to 800 to 1200 cells per cubic millimeter for a healthy individual) or a person develops an opportunistic infection or illness.

Opportunistic infections are those that thrive due to the compromised immune system. Some examples of opportunistic illness include protozoan infections (e.g., toxoplasmosis and pneumonia caused by *Pneumocystis jiroveci*); fungal infections (e.g., candidiasis, histoplasmosis), some bacterial infections; and neoplasms (cancers; e.g., Kaposi's sarcoma, aggressive non-Hodgkin lymphoma, and cervical cancer). Opportunistic infections account for up to 80% of all AIDS-related deaths. Additionally, many AIDS patients have some form of central nervous system (CNS) complications, including meningitis, encephalitis, neurologic deficits, and neuropathies.

Treatment Options

There is no cure for HIV, so HIV infection is a lifelong illness. Current pharmaceutic treatments alleviate symptoms or help prevent the spread of HIV in the body, but they cannot eradicate HIV from an infected individual. Most of these drugs also have unpleasant side effects.

Unfortunately, HIV drugs are expensive and not widely available in developing countries, where their need is greatest. One hopeful sign is that pharmaceutical companies are negotiating with these governments to make cheaper forms of the drug available. In the meantime, education about preventing HIV infection continues throughout the world.

CHAPTER SUMMARY

- The immune system is a functional system composed of cells, plasma proteins, and other substances that protect the body from harmful agents.

22.1 Overview of Diseases Caused by Infectious Agents 842

- The five major classes of infectious agents are bacteria, viruses, fungi, protozoans, and parasites.

- Bacteria are composed of prokaryotic cells; viruses are composed of either DNA or RNA in a protein capsid; and fungi, protozoans, and parasites are composed of eukaryotic cells.

22.2 Overview of the Immune System 843

- The immune system is composed of immune cells and cytokines, and it is organized into innate immunity and adaptive immunity.

22.1a Immune Cells and Their Locations 843

- Immune cells circulate in the blood and are also located in body tissues, including lymphatic structures, other body organs, epithelial tissue of the skin and mucosal membranes, and connective tissue throughout the body.

22.2b Cytokines 844

- Cytokines are small, soluble proteins produced by immune cells that function similarly to hormones; cytokines include interleukins, tumor-necrosis factors, colony-stimulating factors, and interferons.

22.2c Comparison of Innate Immunity and Adaptive Immunity 845

- Innate immunity encompasses defenses we are born with and includes barriers to prevent entry and nonspecific internal defenses.

- Adaptive immunity encompasses defenses developed in response to exposure to specific antigens and includes both cell-mediated immunity (T-lymphocytes) and humoral immunity (B-lymphocytes).

22.3 Innate Immunity 846

- The advantages of innate immunity are that the components develop an immediate response against a wide array of potentially harmful substances; however, the responses do not result in memory.

22.3a Preventing Entry 846

- The skin and mucosal membranes provide a physical, chemical, and biological barrier that is usually successful in preventing entry of harmful substances. These are considered the body's first line of defense.

22.3b Cellular Defenses 848

- Cells of innate immunity include neutrophils, macrophages, basophils and mast cells, NK (natural killer) cells, and eosinophils.

22.3c Antimicrobial Proteins 849

- Antimicrobial proteins include interferon and the complement system.

22.3d Inflammation 850

- Inflammation is an immediate, local, nonspecific response that occurs in vascularized tissue against a great variety of injury-causing stimuli.

22.3e Fever 853

- A fever is an abnormal elevation of body temperature of at least 1°C (1.8°F), and three phases associated with a fever are onset, stadium, and defervescence. Mild fevers are beneficial, while high fevers may be detrimental.

22.4 Adaptive Immunity: An Introduction 856

- Adaptive immunity is developed when T-lymphocytes and B-lymphocytes are stimulated by antigen.

22.4a Antigens 856

- An antigen is a substance that binds to a component of adaptive immunity.

22.4b General Structure of Lymphocytes 857

- Helper T-lymphocytes contain TCRs (T-cell receptors) and CD4, cytotoxic T-lymphocytes contain TCRs and CD8, and B-lymphocytes contain BCRs (B-cell receptors).

- TCRs bind with presented antigen, and BCRs bind with free antigen (e.g., viral particles).

22.4c Antigen Presentation and MHC Molecules 858

- Major histocompatibility complex (MHC) molecules, which are plasma membrane proteins, display antigen on a cell's surface so the antigen can be encountered by T-lymphocytes.

- All nucleated cells present antigen with MHC class I molecules, and antigen-presenting cells (APCs) present antigen with both MHC class I and MHC class II molecules.

22.4d Overview of Life Events of Lymphocytes 862

- Three significant events occur in the lifetime of a lymphoycte: formation, activation, and participation in an effector response.

22.5 Formation and Selection of Lymphocytes 863

22.5a Formation of T-Lymphocytes 863

- Formation of T-lymphocytes begins in the red bone marrow and is completed in the thymus to produce immunocompetent but naive lymphocytes, a process that contributes to self-tolerance.

22.5b Selection of T-Lymphocytes 864

- T-lymphocytes undergo positive selection, in which their ability to recognize foreign antigen attached to MHC is determined, and negative selection, in which their tolerance for self-antigens attached to MHC is tested. Only those lymphocytes that successfully pass both types of selection are allowed to survive.

(continued on next page)

22.5 Formation and Selection of Lymphocytes *(continued)*	**22.5c Differentiation and Migration of T-Lymphocytes 865** • T-lymphocytes differentiate into helper T-lymphocytes or cytotoxic T-lymphocytes. These naive but immunocompetent lymphocytes then migrate from the thymus to secondary lymphatic structures. • A similar process of selection takes place in red bone marrow to produce B-lymphocytes.
22.6 Activation and Clonal Selection of Lymphocytes 865	• Activation requires the binding of antigen by a specific lymphocyte. Once activated, large numbers of identical cells (clones) of the lymphocyte that binds the specific antigen are produced. • Antigen challenge is the first encounter between an antigen and lymphocyte. **22.6a Activation of T-Lymphocytes 866** • Activation of both helper T-lymphocytes and cytotoxic T-lymphocytes requires presentation of antigen by APCs and stimulation by interleukin 2 (IL-2). **22.6b Activation of B-Lymphocytes 867** • Activation of B-lymphocytes requires binding and engulfing antigen that is presented to a helper T-lymphocyte that recognizes the same antigen, and stimulation by IL-2 released by the helper T-lymphocyte. **22.6c Lymphocyte Recirculation 867** • The probability of an encounter occurring between a lymphocyte and the antigen it responds to is increased by lymphocyte recirculation, the circulation of lymphocyte through the blood and lymph every several days.
22.7 Effector Response at Infection Site 868	**22.7a Effector Response of T-Lymphocytes 868** • Activated helper T-lymphocytes play a central role in the immune response by releasing cytokines that regulate the activation of other lymphocytes and the activity of cells of the innate immune system. • Activated cytotoxic T-lymphocytes go to the site of infection and produce cytotoxic chemicals that kill the unwanted cells (infected cells, transplanted cells, or cancer cells) that contain antigen it recognizes. **22.7b Effector Response of B-Lymphocytes 869** • Plasma cells (differentiated B-lymphocytes) produce large amounts of antibody against a specific antigen.
22.8 Immunoglobulins 869	**22.8a Structure of Immunoglobulins 869** • An antibody is an immunoglobulin that is produced against a specific antigen. • An immunoglobulin is a Y-shaped protein. It has two identical variable regions in the arms that include the antigen-binding sites and an Fc region that determines the molecules biological activity. **22.8b Actions of Antibodies 870** • An antibody binds antigen and cause neutralization, agglutination, and precipitation of pathogens. • Once antibody is bound with antigen, the Fc region of an antibody can bind complement, cause opsonization, and initiate destruction of a cell through NK cells. **22.8c Classes of Immunoglobulins 871** • There are five major classes of immunoglogulins: IgG, IgM, IgA, IgD, and IgE. Of these, IgG is the most prevalent.
22.9 Immunologic Memory and Immunity 874	• Memory is a significant feature of acquired immunity that protects us from subsequent exposures to a given antigen. **22.9a Immunologic Memory 874** • The level of immune response can be gauged by measuring the antibody titer of a specific antibody. The first exposure results in the primary response, and subsequent exposures to the same antigen result in the secondary response. **22.9b Measure of Immunologic Memory 874** • Blood concentration levels of IgM and IgG (i.e., antibody titers) can be used to measure the primary response and secondary response of the immune system. **22.9c Active and Passive Immunity 876** • Active immunity involves the production of memory cells and can be acquired through contact with an infectious agent (natural) or through a vaccine (acquired). • Passive immunity does not involve the production of memory cells because protection comes from another individual, either from the mother across the placenta or in breastmilk (natural), or from the serum of another individual (artificial).

CHALLENGE YOURSELF

Do You Know the Basics?

_____ 1. All of the following are phagocytic cells *except*

   a. neutrophils.   c. macrophages.

   b. T-lymphocytes.   d. eosinophils.

_____ 2. This cell releases cytokines to activate B-lymphocytes, increase the activity of macrophages, and in general regulates the overall immune response.

   a. cytotoxic T-lymphocyte

   b. helper T-lymphocyte

   c. natural killer cell

   d. basophil

_____ 3. This cell is activated by binding antigen, and then engulfing and presenting the antigen with MHC class II molecules to helper T-lymphocytes. The helper T-lymphocytes release cytokines as the second form of stimulation.

   a. NK (natural killer) cell

   b. macrophage

   c. B lymphocyte

   d. cytotoxic T-lymphocyte

_____ 4. These two cells destroy an infected cell by releasing chemicals that cause apoptosis.

   a. NK cell and cytotoxic T-lymphocyte

   b. macrophage and NK cell

   c. helper T-lymphocyte and cytotoxic T-lymphocyte

   d. B-lymphocyte and T-lymphocyte

_____ 5. All of the following are functions of antibodies *except*

   a. neutralization of pathogen.

   b. destruction of antigen.

   c. agglutination of antigen.

   d. opsonization.

_____ 6. The four characteristics of adaptive immunity include all of the following *except*

   a. activation by a specific antigen.

   b. memory.

   c. production of clones of cells that have the same TCR or BCR.

   d. each lymphocyte is effective against a wide array of pathogens.

_____ 7. During which process does additional fluid enter an injured or infected area from the blood and additional fluid is removed by the lymph vessels?

   a. fever

   b. clonal selection

   c. inflammation

   d. activation of helper T-lymphocytes

_____ 8. This chemical is released by virus-infected cells to decrease the spread of virus to nearby cells.

   a. interferon

   b. bradykinin

   c. perforin

   d. complement

_____ 9. The correct sequence of the major events in the life of a lymphocyte includes

   a. effector response, formation, and activation.

   b. activation, formation, and effector response.

   c. activation, effector response, and formation.

   d. formation, activation, and effector response.

_____ 10. Two of the major actions of complement include

   a. increasing the inflammatory response and cytolysis.

   b. recognizing and destroying a specific antigen and cytolysis.

   c. producing antibody and increasing the inflammatory response.

   d. releasing cytokines to increase the immune response and production of antibody.

11. Compare the general characteristics of innate immunity and adaptive immunity in terms of the cells involved, specificity, general mechanisms, and time required.

12. Define the inflammatory response, and explain its benefits.

13. Describe an antigen.

14. Describe class I and class II MHC molecules, and explain how they function in assisting T-lymphocytes in "seeing" an antigen.

15. Explain positive and negative selection that occurs during selection of T-lymphocytes.

16. Describe how helper T-lymphocytes play a pivotal role in a healthy, normal functioning immune system.

17. Explain the general function of cytotoxic T-lymphocytes.

18. Describe both the function of antibodies and complement in defending the body.

19. There are two branches of acquired immunity: cell-mediated and humoral immunity. Distinguish the types of antigens they are each effective against.

20. Explain the difference between the primary and secondary immune response.

Can You Apply What You've Learned?

1. Maria, who is 3 years old, was stung by a bee. The area where the stinger entered the skin became red, warm, and swollen. This is a normal response to the foreign venom called

   a. a fever.

   b. the complement cascade.

   c. an inflammatory response.

   d. an antigen challenge.

2. A young mother must take her baby to the pediatrician several times in the first year of the child's life. These visits will stimulate the baby to make memory cells against specific antigens. Why are these visits necessary?

   a. The baby is being vaccinated.

   b. This is to verify that the baby has a normal inflammatory response.

   c. The baby must have an unusual immune deficit that must be monitored.

   d. To cleanse the blood of any foreign antigen.

3. A young woman has just been diagnosed with the human immunodeficiency virus (HIV). This virus is especially devastating because it infects the cell that regulates the immune response. The cells HIV infects are

   a. B-lymphocytes.

   b. helper T-lymphocytes.

   c. NK cells.

   d. cytotoxic T-lymphocytes.

4. One-year-old Matthew always seems to be sick. When his blood is tested, there are no antibodies. The physician concludes that the child is lacking

   a. the ability to develop an inflammatory response.

   b. helper T-lymphocytes.

   c. cytotoxic T-lymphocytes.

   d. humoral immunity.

5. Upon further testing, it is found that Matthew does have normal cellular immunity. However, without antibodies Matthew will be less able to

   a. destroy cancer cells.

   b. destroy viral-infected cells.

   c. bind viral particles.

   d. destroy intracellular pathogens.

Can You Synthesize What You've Learned?

1. Dianne is an avid tennis player but has recently been complaining of tendonitis in her elbow. She knows that you work in health care and asks you to explain what caused this flare-up.

2. Stephanie is in her first year of college and has recently come down with a cold. She is running a slight fever of 100°F. Explain to her why a fever is beneficial.

3. Identify the numerous components of the first line of defense that prevent entry of potentially harmful agents.

---

chapter 23

Respiratory System

The **respiratory** (res′pi-rǎ-tōr′ē; *respire* = to breathe) **system** provides the means for gas exchange necessary for living cells. As cells engage in aerobic cellular respiration they need both an uninterrupted supply of oxygen and the removal of carbon dioxide waste that is produced. The continuous exchange of oxygen and carbon dioxide between the atmosphere and body cells occurs through collective processes called **respiration.** Respiration requires both coordinated and integrated physiologic processes of a ➡

Allied health professionals depend on Respiratory Therapists to assess breathing disorders and be integral in their treatment. These may include acute conditions often encountered in operating rooms that may accompany stroke and heart attack or chronic conditions such as bronchitis, asthma, emphysema, and chronic obstructive pulmonary disease.

Module 11: Respiratory System

Anatomy & Physiology | REVEALED®
aprevealed.com

number of systems, including the respiratory, skeletal, muscular, nervous, and cardiovascular systems. The respiratory system is responsible for the exchange of gases between the atmosphere and the lungs. The skeletal and muscular systems alter the volume and pressure within the thoracic cavity to facilitate movement of air into and out of the lungs, and the nervous system stimulates and coordinates the contraction of skeletal muscles associated with breathing. The cardiovascular system transports oxygen and carbon dioxide between the lungs and the cells.

We begin by discussing the general functions and anatomic structures of the respiratory system components. Next, we consider how the respiratory, skeletal, muscular, and nervous systems function together during breathing (pulmonary ventilation). We then look closely at and explore the exchange of respiratory gases between the lungs and blood (alveolar gas exchange) and between the blood and tissue cells (systemic gas exchange). The specifics of gas transport by the cardiovascular system are described before we conclude by considering the influence of breathing rate on homeostasis.

23.1 Introduction to the Respiratory System

The respiratory system consists of the respiratory passageways extending through the head, neck, and trunk, and the lungs themselves. Here we examine how the respiratory system serves numerous functions in the body, is organized both structurally and functionally, and is lined and protected with a mucosal lining.

23.1a General Functions of the Respiratory System

LEARNING OBJECTIVE

1. State the functions of the respiratory system.

The primary, and perhaps only, function most of us associate with the respiratory system is breathing. However, it has several functions that include the following:

- **Air Passageway.** The respiratory tract is a passageway for air between the external environment and the alveoli (air sacs) of the lungs. Air is moved from the atmosphere to alveoli as we breathe in and then expelled into the atmosphere as we breathe out.
- **Site for the Exchange of Oxygen and Carbon Dioxide.** A thin barrier between the alveoli and the pulmonary capillaries provides the site for exchange of oxygen and carbon dioxide. Oxygen diffuses from the alveoli into the blood, while carbon dioxide diffuses from the blood into the alveoli.

Figure 23.1 General Anatomy of the Respiratory System. Structurally, the respiratory system is organized into the upper and lower respiratory tract. Functionally, the respiratory system is divided into the conducting and respiratory zones.

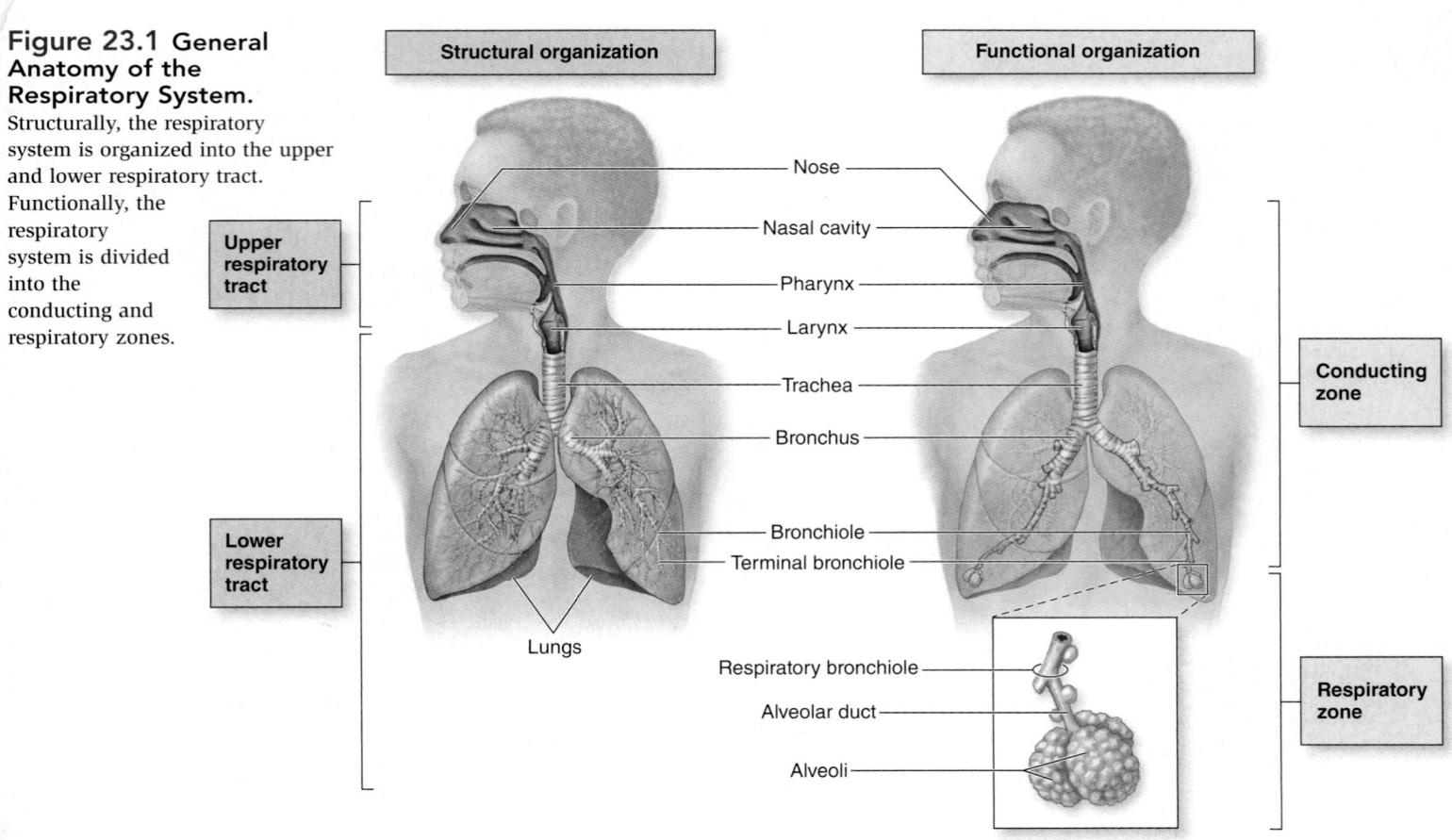

Structural organization · Functional organization

Upper respiratory tract

Lower respiratory tract

Nose · Nasal cavity · Pharynx · Larynx · Trachea · Bronchus · Bronchiole · Terminal bronchiole · Lungs

Conducting zone

Respiratory zone

Respiratory bronchiole · Alveolar duct · Alveoli

- **Detection of Odors.** Olfactory receptors located in the superior regions of the nasal cavity detect odors as air moves across them. Sensory input from these receptors is then relayed to the various regions of the brain for interpretation.
- **Sound Production.** The vocal cords of the larynx (voice box) vibrate as air moves across them to produce sound; these sounds then resonate in upper respiratory structures.

Additionally, the rate and depth of breathing influence the blood levels of oxygen (O_2), carbon dioxide (CO_2), hydrogen ion (H^+), and also influences the venous return of blood and lymph due to changes in compression within the thoracic cavity that occur during breathing. How breathing rate and depth influence both blood composition and blood and lymph transport is described in detail at the end of the chapter.

WHAT DID YOU LEARN?

1 Which respiratory structure is associated with the exchange of respiratory gases?

23.1b General Organization of the Respiratory System

LEARNING OBJECTIVE

2. Distinguish between the structural organization and the functional organization of the respiratory system.

The respiratory system is organized into two structural regions: an upper respiratory tract and a lower respiratory tract (**figure 23.1**). The nose, nasal cavity, and pharynx form the **upper respiratory tract.** The larynx, trachea, bronchi, bronchioles (including terminal and respiratory bronchioles), alveolar ducts, and alveoli are components of the **lower respiratory tract.**

The structures of the respiratory system are also categorized based on function. Passageways that serve primarily to transport or conduct air are part of the **conducting zone;** these structures include the passageways from the nose to the end of the terminal bronchioles. Structures that participate in gas exchange with the blood—including the respiratory bronchioles, alveolar ducts, and alveoli—are part of the **respiratory zone.**

WHAT DID YOU LEARN?

2 What structures compose the upper respiratory tract? What structures compose the respiratory zone?

23.1c Mucosal Lining

LEARNING OBJECTIVES

3. Describe the structure of the mucous membrane that lines the respiratory tract and the structural changes observed along its length.

4. Explain the function of mucus produced by the mucous membrane.

The respiratory passageway is exposed to the external environment and is lined internally by a **mucous membrane,** called a **mucosa.** In general, the mucous membrane is composed of an epithelium resting upon a basement membrane, and an underlying lamina propria composed of areolar connective tissue. The epithelium is ciliated in most portions of the respiratory tract conducting zone.

A general pattern of structural change is observed in the epithelium along the length of the respiratory tract. The epithelium becomes progressively thinner from the nasal cavity to the alveoli; it changes from pseudostratified ciliated columnar to simple ciliated columnar to simple cuboidal to simple squamous (see section 5.1). Some exceptions to this general pattern occur in parts of the respiratory tract.

These include (1) portions of the pharynx that serve as a passageway for both air and food, and (2) components of the larynx that include the vocal cords and the area immediately superior to them. These areas are lined by a nonkeratinized stratified squamous epithelium to withstand potential abrasion. **Figure 23.2** summarizes the types of epithelia found in the mucosa along the respiratory tract.

General structure of mucosa

Mucus
Goblet cell
Epithelium
Basement membrane
Lamina propria
Blood vessel

The mucosa is composed of an epithelium resting on a basement membrane and an underlying lamina propria composed of areolar connective tissue. The epithelium becomes progressively thinner from the nasal cavity to the alveoli with some exceptions.

(a)

Progressively thinner epithelium

Pseudostratified ciliated columnar epithelium lines the nasal cavity, paranasal sinuses, nasopharynx, trachea, main and lobar bronchi.

Simple ciliated columnar epithelium lines the segmental bronchi and large bronchioles.

Simple ciliated cuboidal epithelium lines the small terminal and respiratory bronchioles (with progressive loss of cilia).

Simple squamous epithelium lines the alveolar ducts and forms alveoli.

(b)

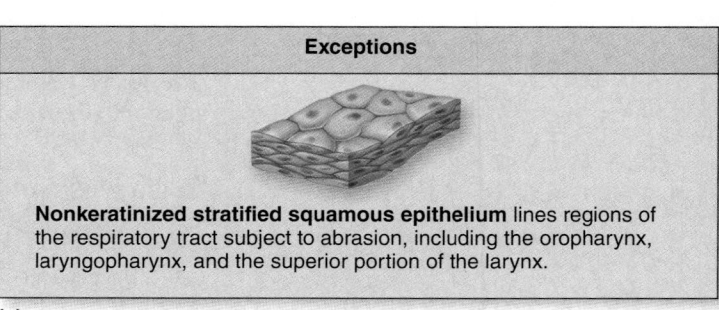

Exceptions

Nonkeratinized stratified squamous epithelium lines regions of the respiratory tract subject to abrasion, including the oropharynx, laryngopharynx, and the superior portion of the larynx.

(c)

Figure 23.2 Mucous Membrane. A mucosa forms the inner lining of the respiratory tract. (*a*) The general structure of mucosa includes three major layers: an epithelium, basement membrane, and an underlying lamina propria. (*b*) The types of epithelia in the mucosa become progressively thinner along the length of the respiratory tract. (*c*) Exceptions to the general thinning pattern occur in places subject to abrasion. **AP|R**

Figure 23.3
Upper Respiratory Tract. (*a*) Anatomic regions that compose the upper respiratory tract, (*b*) supporting structures of the nose, (*c*) midsagittal section of the nasal cavity, and (*d*) coronal view of the nasal cavity in a cadaver.

AP|R

(a) Upper respiratory tract

Nose
Nasal cavity
Pharynx
Nasopharynx
Oropharynx
Laryngopharynx

(b) External nose

Nasal bones
Septal cartilage
Lateral cartilage
Alar cartilages
Dense irregular connective tissue
Nostril

The epithelium lining most of the respiratory tract contains goblet cells, and the underlying lamina propria houses both mucous and serous glands. Mucus is produced from the combined secretions of these cells and glands. The amount of mucus produced daily is approximately 1 to 7 tablespoons, but that amount increases with exposure to irritants. Mucous secretions contain **mucin,** a protein that increases viscosity of mucus to more effectively trap inhaled dust, dirt particles, microorganisms, and pollen. The secretions also contain specific substances to help defend the body against microbes, including lysozyme (an antibacterial enzyme), defensins (antimicrobial proteins), and immunoglobulin A (antibodies).

When mucus mixes with saliva and materials it entraps, it may be coughed up as a viscous substance called **sputum.** Physicians may request sputum samples from their patients to diagnose potential respiratory infections.

 WHAT DID YOU LEARN?

 ❸ In what ways does the epithelium of the upper respiratory tract differ from the epithelium in the alveoli?

23.2 Upper Respiratory Tract

The upper respiratory tract, as described previously, includes the nose, nasal cavity, and pharynx (**figure 23.3a**).

23.2a Nose and Nasal Cavity

 LEARNING OBJECTIVES

1. Describe the structure and function of the nose.
2. Name and describe the three regions of the nasal cavity.

The **nose** is the main conducting passageway for inhaled air (figure 23.3b); it is formed by bone, hyaline cartilage, and dense irregular connective tissue covered with skin externally. Paired nasal bones form the bridge of the nose and support it superiorly. Anteroinferiorly from the bridge, there is one pair of **lateral cartilages** and there are two pairs of **alar cartilages.**

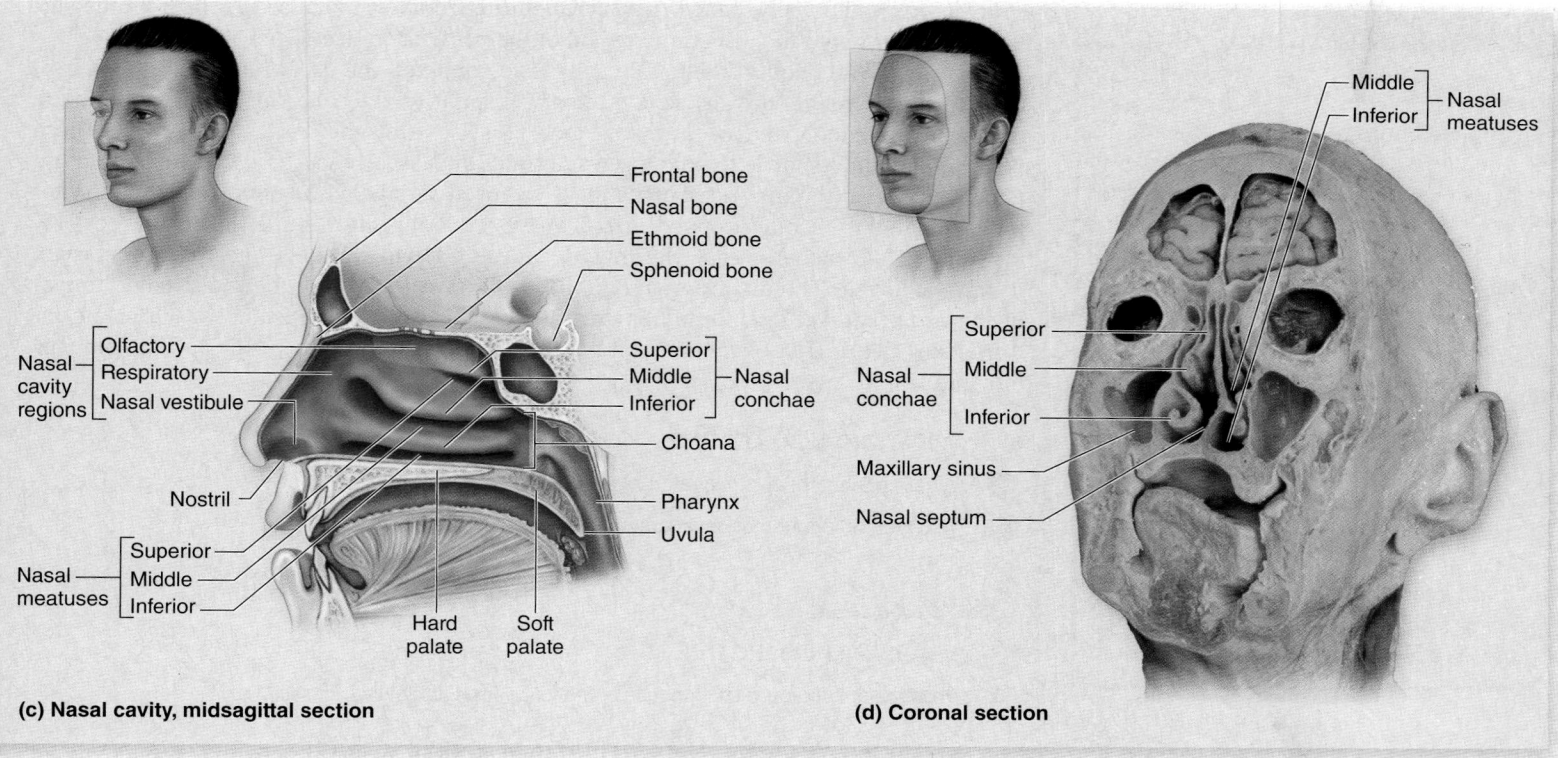

Frontal bone
Nasal bone
Ethmoid bone
Sphenoid bone

Nasal cavity regions
Olfactory
Respiratory
Nasal vestibule

Superior
Middle
Inferior
— Nasal conchae

Choana

Nostril

Nasal meatuses
Superior
Middle
Inferior

Hard palate
Soft palate

Pharynx
Uvula

(c) Nasal cavity, midsagittal section

Middle
Inferior
— Nasal meatuses

Nasal conchae
Superior
Middle
Inferior

Maxillary sinus
Nasal septum

(d) Coronal section

The flared components of the paired **nostrils,** or *nares* (nā′res; sing., *naris*) are composed of dense irregular connective tissue. The nostrils open into the inferior surface of the nose that leads into the nasal cavity.

The **nasal cavity** is an internal space formed by the nose anteriorly and the skull superiorly and posteriorly (figure 23.3c, d). The cavity is oblong-shaped, and it extends from the nostrils to paired openings called **choanae** (kō′an-ē; sing., *choana*) or *posterior nasal apertures*. The choanae lead into the pharynx. The floor of the nasal cavity is formed by the hard and soft palate, and the roof is composed of the nasal, frontal, ethmoid, and sphenoid bones, and some cartilage of the nose. The **nasal septum** divides the nasal cavity into left and right portions. The septum is formed anteriorly by the **septal nasal cartilage** and posteriorly by a thin, bony sheet composed of the perpendicular plate of the ethmoid superiorly and the vomer bone inferiorly. (See section 8.2d.)

WHAT DO YOU THINK?

1 What is a deviated nasal septum, and how would it affect breathing?

Three paired, bony projections are located along the lateral walls of the nasal cavity: the **superior, middle,** and **inferior nasal conchae** (kon′kē; sing., *concha;* a shell). Because the conchae help produce turbulence in the inhaled air, they are sometimes called the *turbinate* bones. The conchae partition the nasal cavity into separate air passages (or "valleys"), each called a **nasal meatus** (mē-ā′tŭs). A meatus is located immediately inferior to its corresponding nasal conchae.

The nasal cavity is divided into three parts (figure 23.3c): the nasal vestibule, olfactory region, and respiratory region. The **nasal vestibule** is immediately internal to the nostrils and is lined by skin and coarse hairs called **vibrissae** (vi-bris′ē; sing., *vibrissa; vibro* = to quiver) to trap large particulates.

The **olfactory region** is the superior portion of the nasal cavity. It contains the olfactory epithelium (pseudostratified ciliated columnar epithelium and olfactory receptors). Airborne molecules that dissolve in the mucus covering the olfactory epithelium stimulate olfactory receptors to detect different odors (section 16.3a).

The **respiratory region** of the nasal cavity is lined by a mucosa composed of pseudostratified ciliated columnar epithelium. The lamina propria of this mucosal lining has an extensive vascular network. Nosebleeds (*epistaxis*) are especially common because of both the vast distribution of blood vessels and their superficial location (just deep to the epithelium). Additionally, paired **nasolacrimal ducts** drain lacrimal secretions from the surface of each eye into the respiratory region of the nasal cavity (see figure 16.10).

A primary function of the nasal cavity is to condition the air (which means to warm, cleanse, and humidify the air) as it enters the respiratory tract. The air is warmed to body temperature by the extensive array of blood vessels within the nasal cavity lining. These vessels dilate in response to cold air, resulting in increased blood flow that helps to more effectively warm the inhaled air. The air is cleansed as inhaled microbes, dust, and other foreign material become trapped in the mucus covering the inner lining of the respiratory tract. Cilia then "sweep" the mucus and its trapped contents towards the pharynx to be swallowed. The air is also humidified as it passes through the moist environment of the nasal passageway. Conditioning of air is enhanced by conchae, which create air turbulence that increases the amount of contact between the inhaled air and the mucous membranes.

WHAT DID YOU LEARN?

4. What changes occur to inhaled air as it travels through the nasal cavity?

5. What is the function of nasal conchae?

23.2b Paranasal Sinuses

LEARNING OBJECTIVE

3. Describe the structure and function of the four paired paranasal sinuses.

The **paranasal** (par-ă-nā'săl; *para* = alongside) **sinuses**, first described in section 8.2d, are associated with the nasal cavity (**figure 23.4**). These sinuses are spaces within the skull bones and named for the specific skull bones in which they are housed. Thus, from a superior to inferior direction, they are the paired **frontal, ethmoidal,** and **maxillary sinuses;** the **sphenoidal sinuses** are located posterior to the ethmoidal sinuses. Ducts connect all sinuses to the nasal cavity. Both the sinuses and their ducts are lined by a pseudostratified ciliated columnar epithelium that is continuous with the mucosa of the nasal cavity. The mucus, with its trapped particulate matter, is swept by cilia from each paranasal sinus into the nasal cavity and then into the pharynx, where it is swallowed.

WHAT DID YOU LEARN?

6. How are the paranasal sinuses connected to the nasal cavity?

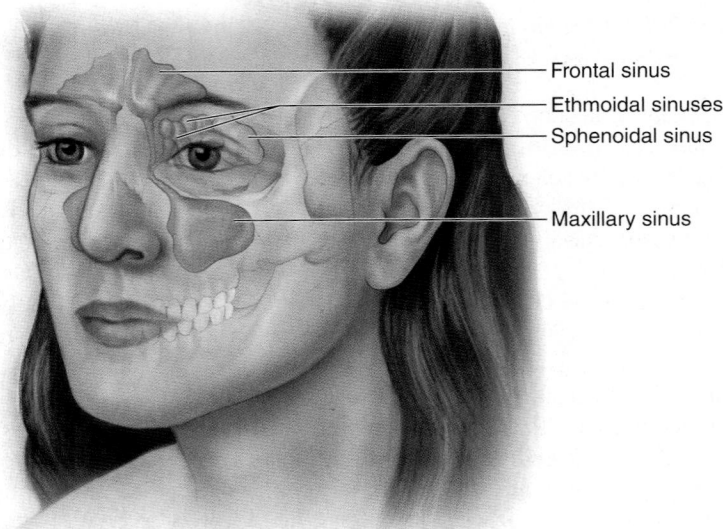

Frontal sinus
Ethmoidal sinuses
Sphenoidal sinus

Maxillary sinus

Anterolateral view

Figure 23.4 Paranasal Sinuses. The paranasal sinuses are air-filled cavities named for the bones in which they occur: frontal, ethmoidal, sphenoidal, and maxillary.

23.2c Pharynx

LEARNING OBJECTIVE

4. Compare the three regions of the pharynx, and describe their associated structures.

The **pharynx** (far′ingks), commonly called the *throat,* is a funnel-shaped passageway that averages 13 centimeters (5.1 inches) in length (**figure 23.5**). It is located posterior to the nasal cavity, oral cavity, and larynx. Air is conducted along its entire length, and both air and food along its inferior portions. The lateral walls of the pharynx are composed of skeletal muscles that contribute to both the flexibility and distensibility needed to accommodate swallowed food, and help force these materials into the esophagus. The pharynx is partitioned into three regions—from superior to inferior, they are the nasopharynx, oropharynx, and laryngopharynx.

Nasopharynx

The **nasopharynx** (nā′zō-far′inks) is the superiormost region of the pharynx. Located directly posterior to the nasal cavity and superior to the soft palate, the nasopharynx, like the nasal cavity, is lined by a pseudostratified ciliated columnar epithelium. Normally, only air passes through the nasopharynx. Material from both the oral cavity and oropharynx typically is blocked from entering the nasopharynx by the soft palate, which elevates when we swallow. However, sometimes food or drink enters the nasopharynx and the nasal cavity, as when a person tries to swallow and then laughs at the same time. The soft palate cannot form a good seal for the nasopharynx, and the force from the laugh may propel some of the material into the nasal cavity. If the laugh is forceful enough, the material may come out the nostrils.

The nasopharynx lateral walls house paired openings into **auditory tubes** (*eustachian tubes,* or *pharyngotympanic tubes*) that connect the nasopharynx to the middle ear. These tubes equalize air pressure between the middle ear and the atmosphere by allowing excess air pressure to be released into the nasopharynx (section 16.5a). A collection of lymphatic nodules, called the tubal tonsils, are located near the pharyngeal opening of these tubes. The posterior nasopharynx wall also houses a single **pharyngeal tonsil.** When this tonsil is enlarged, clinicians refer to it as the **adenoids** (ad′ĕ-noydz; *aden* = gland, *eidos* = resemblance). Both the tubal and pharyngeal tonsils are composed of lymphatic tissue and help to prevent the spread of infections.

Oropharynx

The middle pharyngeal region, called the **oropharynx** (ōr′ō-far′ingks), is immediately posterior to the oral cavity. The oropharynx extends from the level of soft palate superiorly to the hyoid bone inferiorly. The **palatine tonsils** are located on lateral walls of the oropharynx, and

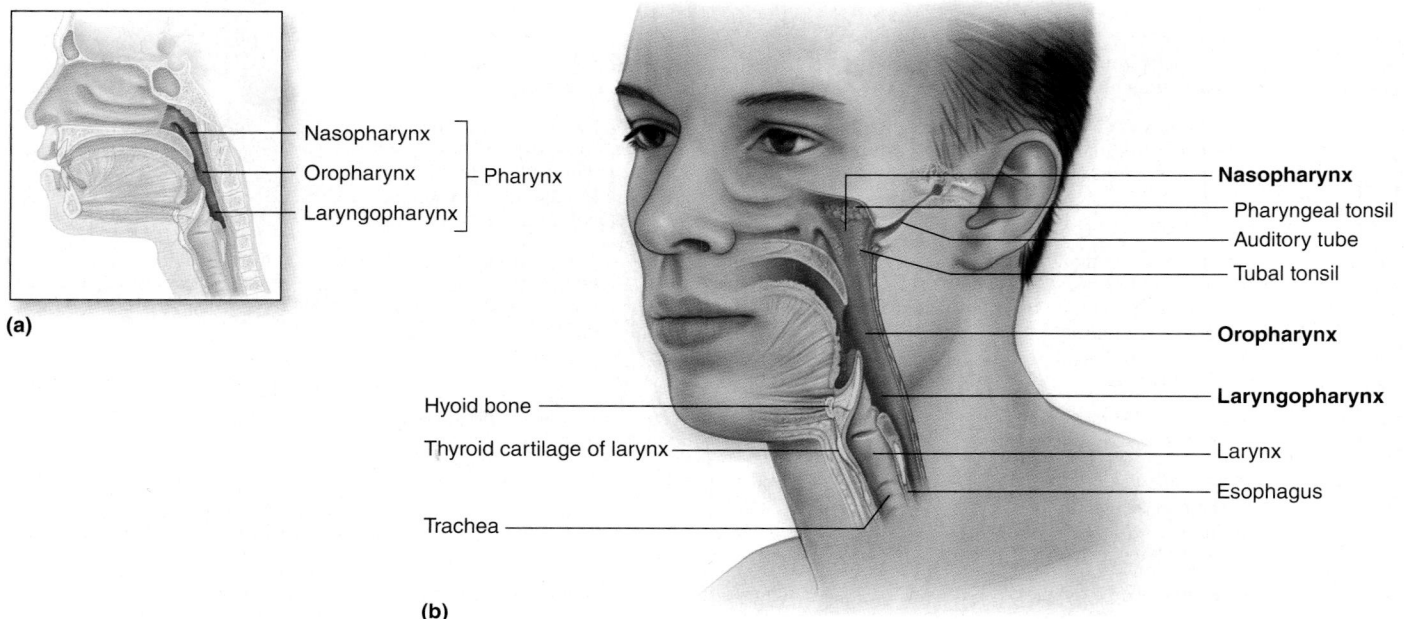

(a)

Nasopharynx
Oropharynx — Pharynx
Laryngopharynx

Nasopharynx
Pharyngeal tonsil
Auditory tube
Tubal tonsil

Oropharynx

Hyoid bone

Laryngopharynx

Thyroid cartilage of larynx

Larynx

Esophagus

Trachea

(b)

Figure 23.5 Pharynx. (*a*) The three specific regions of the pharynx (nasopharynx, oropharynx, and laryngopharynx) are highlighted in a sagittal section. (*b*) The pharynx is shown in relationship to the larynx, trachea, and esophagus in an anterolateral view. AP|R the **lingual tonsils** are at the base of the tongue (and thus are in the anterior region of oropharynx), providing the "first line of defense" against ingested or inhaled foreign materials (see figure 21.9).

Laryngopharynx

The inferior, narrowed region of the pharynx is the **laryngopharynx** (lă-ring′gō-far′ingks), which is located directly posterior to the larynx. It extends from the level of the hyoid bone and is continuous on its inferior end with both the larynx anteriorly and the esophagus posteriorly. Both the oropharynx and laryngopharynx serve as a common passageway for food and air. They are lined by a nonkeratinized stratified squamous epithelium (see figure 23.2).

 WHAT DID YOU LEARN?

7 What two regions of the pharynx contain tonsils? What is their purpose?

23.3 Lower Respiratory Tract

The structures of the **lower respiratory tract** include both conducting pathways (the larynx, trachea, bronchi, and bronchioles) and those involved in gas exchange (respiratory bronchioles, alveolar ducts, and alveoli) (see figure 23.1). **Table 23.1** summarizes the structures of the lower respiratory tract. A lower respiratory tract infection affects some or all of these structures.

23.3a Larynx

 LEARNING OBJECTIVES

1. Describe the general functions and structure of the larynx.
2. Explain how the larynx functions in sound production.

The **larynx** (lar′ingks), also called the *voice box,* is a somewhat cylindrical airway that averages about 4 centimeters (1.6 inches) in length (see figure 23.5). It is continuous superiorly with the laryngopharynx and inferiorly with the trachea.

Functions of the Larynx

The larynx has several major functions:

- **Serves as a passageway for air.** The larynx is normally open to allow the passage of air.
- **Prevents ingested materials from entering the respiratory tract.** During swallowing, the superior opening of the larynx is covered to prevent ingested materials from entering the lower respiratory passageway.
- **Produces sound for speech.** Ligaments within the larnyx, called vocal cords, vibrate as air is passed over them during an expiration.
- **Assists in increasing pressure in the abdominal cavity.** The epiglottis closes over the larynx so air cannot escape, while simultaneously abdominal muscles contract to increase abdominal pressure. This action is referred to as

Table 23.1	Structures of the Lower Respiratory Tract			
Structure[1]	**Anatomic Description**	**Wall Support**	**Epithelial Lining**	**Function**
Larynx	A somewhat cylindrical airway structure between the pharynx and trachea	Nine pieces of cartilage; supported by ligaments and skeletal muscle	Nonkeratinized stratified squamous epithelium superior to vocal folds; pseudostratified ciliated columnar epithelium inferior to vocal folds	Conducts air; prevents ingested material from entering trachea; produces sound; assists in increasing pressure in abdominal cavity; participates in both a sneeze and cough reflex
Trachea	Flexible, semirigid tubular organ connecting larynx to primary bronchi	C-shaped cartilage rings keep trachea patent (open)	Pseudostratified ciliated columnar epithelium	Conducts air
Bronchi	Largest airways of bronchial tree; consist of main, lobar, segmental, and smaller bronchi	Incomplete rings and irregular plates of cartilage; some smooth muscle	Larger bronchi lined by pseudostratified ciliated columnar epithelium; smaller bronchi lined by simple ciliated columnar epithelium	Conducts air
Bronchioles	Smaller conducting airways of bronchial tree; larger bronchioles branch into smaller bronchioles; terminal bronchioles are last part of conducting zone	No cartilage; proportionately greater amounts of smooth muscle in walls	Ranges from simple ciliated columnar epithelium (for largest bronchioles) to simple cuboidal epithelium (for smaller bronchioles)	Conducts air; smooth muscle in walls allows bronchoconstriction and bronchodilation
Respiratory bronchioles	First structures of respiratory zone	No cartilage; smooth muscle is scarce in walls	Simple cuboidal epithelium	Gas exchange
Alveolar ducts	Tiny airways that branch off respiratory bronchioles; multiple alveoli found along walls of alveolar duct	No cartilage, no smooth muscle	Simple squamous epithelium	Gas exchange
Alveoli	Tiny microscopic air sacs	No cartilage, no smooth muscle	Simple squamous epithelium	Gas exchange

1. Structures are listed in the order that air passes through them during inspiration.

the **Valsalva maneuver** (see Integrate: Concept Connection). You can experience the increase in abdominal pressure associated with the Valsalva maneuver by holding your breath while forcefully contracting your abdominal muscles.

- **Participates in both a sneeze and cough reflex.** Both a sneeze and a cough result in an explosive blast of exhaled air. This occurs when the abdominal muscles contract forcefully and the vocal cords are initially closed and then open abruptly as the pressure increases in the thoracic cavity. Sneezing is initiated by irritants in the nasal cavity and coughing by irritants in the trachea and bronchi. Both help remove irritants from the respiratory tract.

Larynx Anatomy

The opening that connects the pharynx and larynx is called the **laryngeal inlet,** *laryngeal aperture,* or *laryngeal aditus.* The larynx is formed and supported by a framework of nine pieces of cartilage that are held in place by ligaments and muscles. The anatomic arrangement of the nine cartilages include: the single thyroid, cricoid, and epiglottis cartilages, and the paired arytenoid, corniculate, and cuneiform cartilages as shown in **figure 23.6**.

The **thyroid cartilage** is the largest laryngeal cartilage. Shaped like a shield, it forms the lateral and anterior walls of the larynx. The almost V-shaped anterior projection of the thyroid cartilage is called the **laryngeal** (lă-rin′jē-ăl) **prominence** (commonly referred to as the *Adam's apple*). This protuberance is generally larger in males because (1) the laryngeal inlet is narrower in males (90 degrees) than in females (120 degrees), and (2) it enlarges at puberty due to testosterone-induced growth.

INTEGRATE

CONCEPT CONNECTION

The Valsalva maneuver facilitates several physiologic processes including: elimination of both urine from the urinary bladder (section 24.7c) and feces from the gastrointestinal tract (section 26.3d), and the expulsion of a baby during childbirth (section 29.6d).

The thyroid cartilage is attached to the lateral surface of the ring-shaped **cricoid** (krī′koyd; *kridos* = a ring) **cartilage** located inferior to the thyroid cartilage. The large, spoon- or leaf-shaped **epiglottis** (ep-i-glot′is; *epi* = on; *glottis* = mouth of windpipe) is anchored to the inner aspect of the thyroid cartilage and projects posterosuperiorly into the pharynx. It closes over the laryngeal inlet during swallowing. The three smaller, paired cartilages, the **arytenoid** (ar-i-tē′noyd), **corniculate** (kōr′-ni-kū-lāt; *corniculatus* = horned), and **cuneiform** (kū′nē-i-fōrm; *cuneus* = wedge) **cartilages** are located internally. All cartilages of the larynx, except the epiglottis, are composed of hyaline cartilage. The epiglottis, which opens and closes over the laryngeal inlet, is composed of the more flexible elastic cartilage.

Laryngeal ligaments are classified as either extrinsic ligaments or intrinsic ligaments. **Extrinsic ligaments** attach to the external surface of laryngeal cartilages and extend to other structures that include the hyoid bone and trachea.

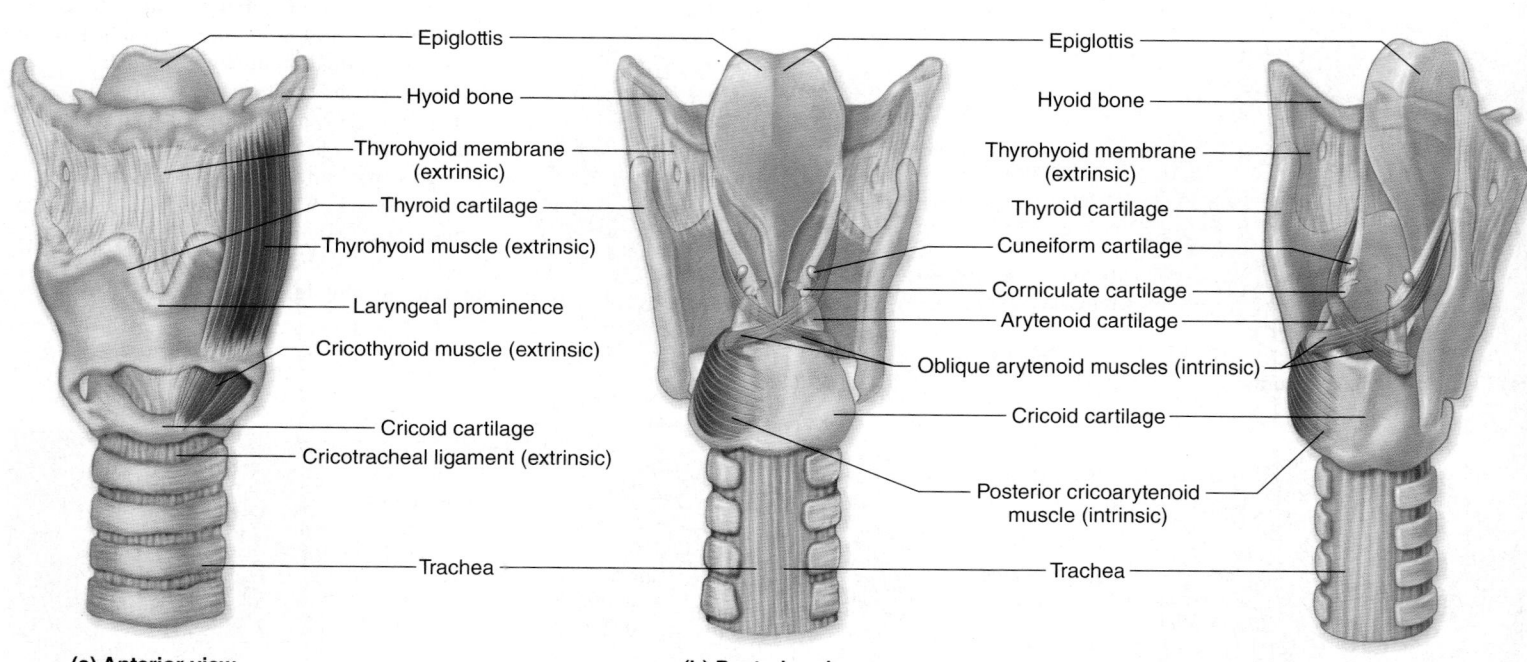

(a) Anterior view **(b) Posterior view** **(c) Posterior oblique view**

Figure 23.6 Larynx. The larynx shown in an (*a*) anterior view, (*b*) posterior view, and (*c*) posterior oblique view. It is composed of nine cartilages, various ligaments, and skeletal muscle. The nine cartilages, as well as extrinsic and intrinsic ligaments, form the flexible support of the larynx. Extrinsic muscles participate in the elevation of the larynx, and intrinsic muscles function in sound production. AP|R

The **intrinsic ligaments** are located within the larynx and include both vocal ligaments and vestibular ligaments (**figure 23.7**). The **vocal ligaments** are composed primarily of elastic connective tissue and extend anterior to posterior between the thyroid cartilage and the arytenoid cartilages. These ligaments are covered with a mucous membrane to form the **vocal folds.** Vocal folds also are called the *true vocal cords* because they produce sound when air passes between them. They are distinctive from the surrounding tissue because they are avascular and white in color. The opening between these folds is called the **rima glottidis** (rī′mă; slit; glo-tī′dis; *rima* = slit). Together the vocal folds and the rima glottidis form the **glottis.**

The **vestibular ligaments** form the other intrinsic ligaments. These extend between the thyroid cartilage to the arytenoid and corniculate cartilages. Together with the mucosa covering them, they form the **vestibular folds** located superior to the vocal folds. The opening between the vestibular folds is called the **rima vestibuli.** These folds also are called the *false vocal cords* because they have no function in sound production, but serve to protect the vocal folds.

Skeletal muscles compose part of the larynx wall and are classified as either extrinsic or intrinsic muscles. The **extrinsic muscles** originate on either the hyoid bone or the sternum and insert on the thyroid cartilage. Extrinsic muscles normally stabilize the larynx and help move it during swallowing (section 26.2c).

The **intrinsic muscles** are located within the larynx and attach to both the arytenoid and corniculate cartilages. Contraction of the intrinsic muscles causes the arytenoid cartilages to pivot resulting in a change in the dimension of the rima glottidis. The opening becomes narrower as the vocal folds are adducted and becomes wider if the vocal folds are abducted. They function in voice production and help close off the larynx when swallowing.

Sound Production

Sound production originates as the vocal folds begin to vibrate. This occurs when the intrinsic laryngeal muscles narrow the opening of the rima glottidis and air is forced past the vocal cords during an expiration.

The characteristics of the sound include range, pitch, and loudness. The **range** of a voice (be it soprano or bass) is determined by the length and thickness of the vocal folds. Males generally have longer and thicker folds than do females, and thus males produce sounds that are in a lower range. Our vocal folds increase in length as we grow, which is why our voices become lower or deeper as we mature to adulthood.

Pitch refers to the frequency of sound waves. Pitch is determined by the amount of tension or tautness on the vocal folds as regulated primarily by the intrinsic laryngeal muscles. Increasing the tension on the vocal folds causes the vocal folds to vibrate more when air passes by them and thus to produce a higher sound. Conversely, the less taut the vocal folds, the less they vibrate, and the lower the pitch of the sound.

Loudness depends on the force of the air passing across the vocal cords. A lot of air forced through the rima glottidis produces a loud sound. whereas a little air produces a soft sound. When you whisper, only the most posterior portion of the rima glottidis is open, and the vocal folds do not vibrate. Because the vocal folds are not vibrating, the whispered sounds are all of the same pitch.

Speech also requires the participation of the spaces in the pharynx, nasal and oral cavities, and the paranasal sinuses, which serve as resonating chambers for sound, and the structures of the lips, teeth, and tongue that help form different sounds. Young children tend to have high, nasal-like voices because their sinuses are not yet

Adducted (closed) vocal folds

Abducted (open) vocal folds

Anterior

Thyroid cartilage

Cricoid cartilage

Vocal ligaments (intrinsic)

Vestibular ligaments (intrinsic)

Arytenoid cartilage

Corniculate cartilage

Posterior

(a) Cartilages and ligaments

Figure 23.7 Vocal Folds. The vocal folds (true vocal cords) are elastic ligaments covered with a mucous membrane that extend between the thyroid and arytenoid cartilages. These folds surround the rima glottidis and are involved in sound production. Adducted (closed) and abducted (open) vocal folds are shown in (*a*) a superior view of the cartilages and ligaments only, and (*b*) a diagrammatic laryngoscopic view of the coverings around these cartilages and ligaments. (*c*) A photo of a superolateral laryngoscopic view, showing the vestibular folds, the vocal folds, and the rima glottidis opening into the trachea.

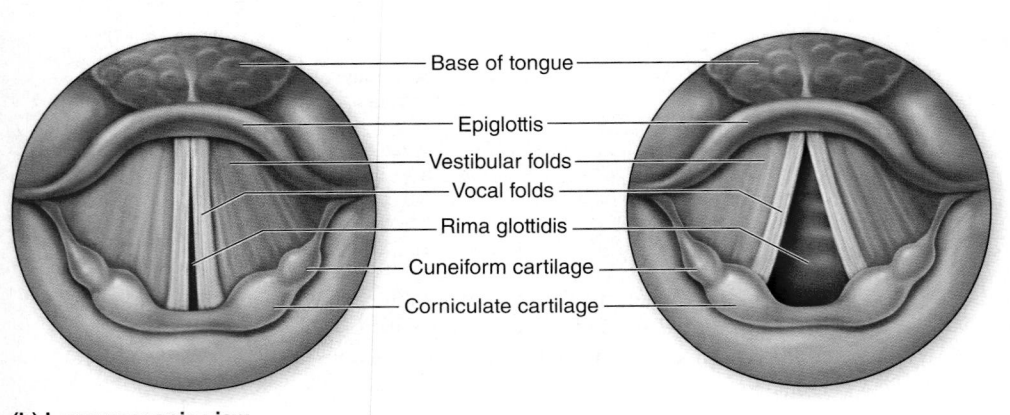

Base of tongue

Epiglottis

Vestibular folds

Vocal folds

Rima glottidis

Cuneiform cartilage

Corniculate cartilage

(b) Laryngoscopic view

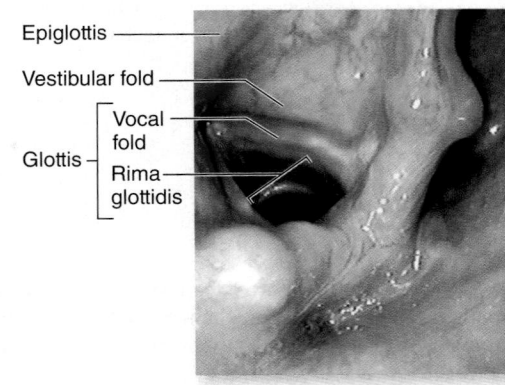

Epiglottis

Vestibular fold

Glottis — Vocal fold / Rima glottidis

(c) Larynx, superolateral view

well developed, so they lack large resonant chambers. When you hold your nose and speak, your voice sounds quite different because air doesn't pass through the nasal cavity.

WHAT DID YOU LEARN?

8 How does the larynx assist in increasing abdominal pressure?

9 What are the three unpaired cartilages in the larynx?

10 What are the structural and functional differences between the vocal folds and vestibular folds?

23.3b Trachea

LEARNING OBJECTIVES

3. Describe the structure of the trachea.

4. Explain the structure and function of the tracheal cartilages.

The **trachea** (trā'kē-ă; = rough) is a flexible, slightly rigid, tubular organ often referred to as the "windpipe" **(figure 23.8)**. It extends inferiorly through the neck into the mediastinum from the larynx to the main bronchi. The trachea lies immediately anterior to the esophagus and posterior to part of the sternum.

Figure 23.8 Trachea. (*a*) The trachea connects to the larynx superiorly and to the main bronchi inferiorly. (*b*) A cross-sectional photomicrograph shows the relationship of the trachea and the esophagus. (*c*) A photo of the trachea leading into the main bronchi. Located at this split is the carina, which houses sensory receptors that when stimulated by irritants induce a cough. (*d*) The inner surface of the tracheal wall, showing the upward movement of mucus toward the pharynx. AP|R

Esophagus

Larynx

Thyroid cartilage

Cricoid cartilage

Trachea

Tracheal cartilage

Anular ligament

Right main bronchus   Left main bronchus

(a)

Posterior

Esophagus

Trachealis muscle

Lumen of trachea

Mucosa

Submucosa

Tracheal cartilage

LM 8x

(b)   Anterior

Trachea

Carina (internal projection)

Right main bronchus

Left main bronchus

(c) Carina

Mucosa

Pseudostratified ciliated columnar epithelium   Lamina propria

Basement membrane

Submucosa

Mucus

Lumen

(d)

Gross Anatomy of the Trachea

The trachea averages approximately 13 centimeters (5.1 inches) in length and 2.5 centimeters (1 inch) in diameter. The anterior and lateral walls of the trachea are supported by 15 to 20 C-shaped "rings" of hyaline cartilage called **tracheal cartilages.** The tracheal cartilages are connected superiorly and inferiorly with one another by elastic connective tissue sheets called **anular** (an'ū-lăr; *anulus* = ring) **ligaments.** An internal ridge of mucosal covered cartilage called the **carina** (kă-rī'nă) is located at the bifurcation (split) of the main bronchi (figure 23.8c). The sensory receptors of the carina are extremely sensitive and can induce a forceful cough when stimulated by irritants.

Each C-shaped tracheal cartilage is ensheathed in a perichondrium and a dense fibrous membrane. The open ends of the cartilage rings are attached posteriorly by both the **trachealis muscle** and an elastic ligamentous membrane. These rings reinforce and provide some rigidity to the tracheal wall to ensure that the trachea remains open (patent) at all times, whereas the more flexible trachealis muscle and ligamentous membrane on the posterior aspect of the trachea allows for distension during swallowing of food through the esophagus. The trachealis contracts during coughing to reduce the diameter of the trachea, thus facilitating the more rapid expulsion of air, helping to dislodge material (foreign objects or food) from the air passageway.

Tracheotomy (trā-kē-ot'ō-mē; *tome* = incision) is one of the oldest surgical procedures: it involves making an incision into the trachea to facilitate breathing when a patient's airway is blocked or respiratory ventilation is compromised by disease or injury. Although a tracheotomy is a potentially life-saving procedure, it is not without risks and should be undertaken only by trained medical personnel.

Histology of the Tracheal Wall

The innermost to outermost layers that form the wall of the trachea are (1) the **mucosa,** which is composed of a pseudostratified ciliated columnar epithelium with goblet cells and a lamina propria; (2) the **submucosa,** consisting of areolar connective tissue that houses larger blood vessels, nerve endings, serous and mucous glands, and lymphatic tissue; (3) **tracheal cartilage** (described earlier); and (4) the **adventitia,** composed of elastic connective tissue (not labeled in figure).

The movement of cilia in the mucosal epithelium propels mucus laden with dust, microbes, and other particles superiorly toward the larynx and the pharynx, where it may be swallowed or expelled (figure 23.8d).

WHAT DO YOU THINK?

2 The lining of the trachea and bronchi in chronic smokers changes from pseudostratified ciliated columnar epithelium to stratified squamous epithelium. Why do you think this change occurs, and what are some consequences of this change?

WHAT DID YOU LEARN?

11 What is the function of the C-shaped tracheal cartilages? How does the function of the trachealis muscle and elastic ligamentous membrane that complete each ring posteriorly?

23.3c Bronchial Tree

LEARNING OBJECTIVES

5. Describe the structural subdivisions of the bronchial tree.

6. Explain the processes of bronchoconstriction and bronchodilation.

The **bronchial** (brong'kē-ăl) **tree** is a highly branched system of air-conducting passages that originates at the main bronchi and progressively branches into narrower tubes that diverge throughout the lungs before ending in the smallest bronchiole passageway **(figure 23.9).**

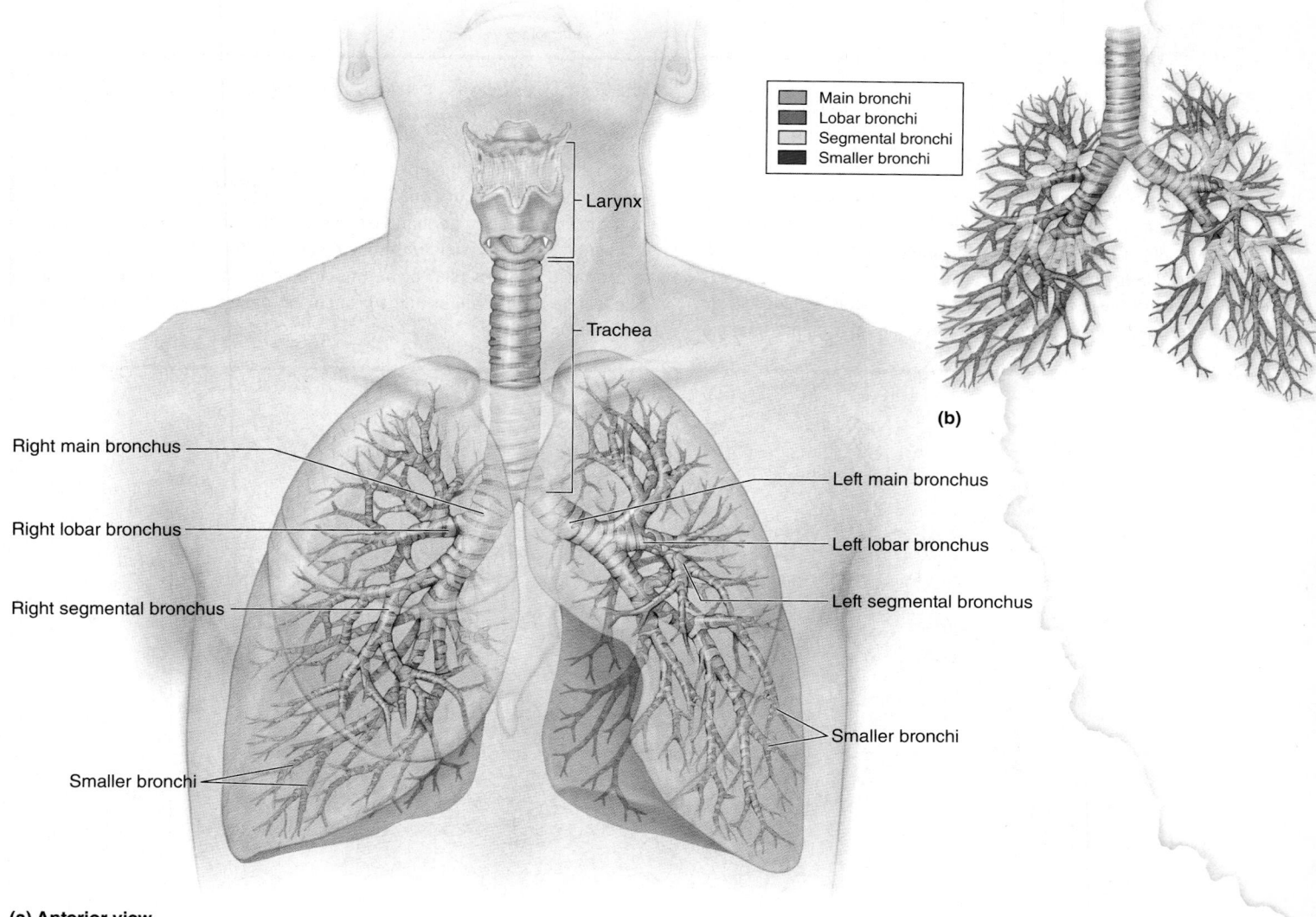

(a) Anterior view

Larynx

Trachea

Right main bronchus

Right lobar bronchus

Right segmental bronchus

Smaller bronchi

Left main bronchus

Left lobar bronchus

Left segmental bronchus

Smaller bronchi

Main bronchi
Lobar bronchi
Segmental bronchi
Smaller bronchi

(b)

Figure 23.9 Bronchial Tree. The bronchial tree is composed of conducting passageways that originate at the two main bronchi and end at the terminal bronchioles. (*a*) Larynx, trachea, and bronchi are shown. (*b*) The major divisions of the bronchial tree are color-coded. AP|R

Gross Anatomy of the Bronchial Tree

The trachea bifurcates at the level of the sternal angle (where the manubrium and body of the sternum articulate) into the right and left **main bronchi** (brong′kī; sing., *bronchus*), also known as *primary bronchi*. Each main bronchus projects inferiorly and laterally toward a lung. The right main bronchus is shorter, wider, and more vertically oriented than the left main bronchus—thus, foreign particles are more likely to lodge in the right main bronchus. Both main bronchi, along with all associated pulmonary vessels, lymph vessels, and nerves, enter a lung on its medial surface.

Each main bronchus then branches into **lobar bronchi,** or *secondary bronchi,* that extend to each lobe of the lung. The right lung with three lobes has three lobar bronchi, and the left lung with two lobes has two lobar bronchi. Lobar bronchi are smaller in diameter than main bronchi. They further divide into **segmental bronchi,** or *tertiary bronchi* that serve a division of the lung called a bronchopulmonary segment (described later). The right lung is supplied with 10 segmental bronchi, and the left lung is supplied by 8 to 10 segmental bronchi. The bronchial tree continues to divide into more numerous and smaller passageways. There are approximately 9 to 12 different levels or generations of bronchial branch divisions; the main, lobar, and segmental bronchi are the first, second, and third generations of bronchi, respectively.

Bronchi lead into tubes that have a diameter of less than 1 millimeter called **bronchioles** (brong′kē-ōl). **Terminal bronchioles** are the last portion of the conducting pathway. They lead into respiratory bronchioles, the first segments of the respiratory zone.

CLINICAL VIEW
Bronchitis

Bronchitis (brong-kī'tis) is inflammation of the bronchi caused by a viral or bacterial infection, or by inhaling irritants such as vaporized chemicals, particulate matter, or cigarette smoke. Clinically, bronchitis is divided into two categories: acute and chronic.

Acute bronchitis develops rapidly either during or after an infection, such as a cold. Symptoms include coughing, sneezing, pain upon inhalation, and fever. Most cases of acute bronchitis resolve completely within 10 to 14 days.

Chronic bronchitis results from long-term exposure to irritants. Chronic bronchitis is defined medically as the production of large amounts of mucus, associated with a cough lasting 3 continuous months. If exposure to the irritant persists, permanent changes to the bronchi occur, including thickened bronchial walls with subsequent narrowing of their lumens and overgrowth (hyperplasia) of the mucin-secreting cells of the bronchi. These long-term changes in the bronchi increase the likelihood of future bacterial infections.

Figure 23.10 Structure of the Bronchial Wall. Irregular cartilage plates of decreasing size support the branching bronchi. In contrast, bronchioles do not contain cartilage, but rather have a proportionately thicker layer of smooth muscle. This smooth muscle layer allows bronchoconstriction and bronchodilation that changes the size of the lumen, regulating the amount of air reaching the alveoli.

CLINICAL VIEW

Asthma (az'mă) is a chronic condition characterized by episodes of bronchoconstriction coupled with wheezing, coughing, shortness of breath, and excess pulmonary mucus. Typically, the affected person develops sensitivity to an airborne agent, such as pollen, smoke, mold spores, dust mites, or particulate matter. Upon reexposure to this triggering substance, a localized immune reaction occurs in the bronchi and bronchioles, resulting in bronchoconstriction, swollen submucosa, and increased production of mucus. Episodes typically last an hour or two. Continual exposure to the triggering agent increases the severity and frequency of asthma attacks.

The walls of the bronchi and bronchioles eventually may become permanently thickened, leading to chronic and unremitting airway narrowing and shortness of breath. If airway narrowing is extreme during a severe asthma attack, death could occur.

The primary treatment for asthma consists of administering inhaled steroids (cortisone-related compounds) to reduce the inflammatory reaction, combined with bronchodilators to alleviate the bronchoconstriction. Allergy shots have proven helpful for some patients. Individuals with severe asthma may need oral doses of steroids to help control the allergic hyper-response and reduce the inflammation.

Airway constriction occurs during an asthma attack.

Constriction of respiratory passageways

Mucus
Mucosa
Submucosa
Muscularis

Cross section of a normal bronchiole

Extra mucus
Mucosa
Swollen submucosa
Muscularis

Cross section of a bronchiole during an asthma attack

Histology of the Bronchial Tree

Incomplete rings or plates of hyaline cartilage support the walls of the main bronchi to ensure that they remain open **(figure 23.10)**. The extent of wall support lessens as bronchi divide and their diameter decreases. It first appears as various-sized irregular plates of cartilage in their walls that continue to decrease in size and number as the branching of smaller air passageways continues. Unlike bronchi, bronchioles have no cartilage in their walls, because their small diameter alone normally prevents collapse. Instead, bronchioles have a proportionately thicker layer of smooth muscle than do bronchi. Contraction of this smooth muscle narrows the diameter of the bronchiole, referred to as **bronchoconstriction,** and decreases the amount of air passing through the bronchial tree. In comparison, the expansion of the diameter of the bronchiole from relaxation of the smooth muscle, called **bronchodilation,** increases the amount of air passing through the bronchial tree. The changes in the epithelium of the bronchial tree are summarized in figure 23.2.

WHAT DID YOU LEARN?

12   What are the significant structural differences between bronchi and bronchioles?

23.3d Respiratory Zone: Respiratory Bronchioles, Alveolar Ducts, and Alveoli

LEARNING OBJECTIVES

7. Describe the structure and function of the other lower respiratory tract structures and organs.

8. List three types of cells found in alveoli and their functions.

The respiratory zone was described earlier as being composed of respiratory bronchioles, alveolar ducts, and alveoli. These are all microscopic structures. The smallest **respiratory bronchioles** subdivide into thin airways called **alveolar ducts** that lead into **alveolar sacs,** a grape-like cluster of alveoli at the end of an alveolar duct (**figure 23.11**). Both respiratory bronchioles and alveolar ducts are airways that contain small (about 0.25 to 0.5 millimeters in diameter) saccular outpocketings called **alveoli** (al-vē′ō-lī; sing., al-vē′ō-lŭs; *alveus* = hollow sac). Respiratory bronchioles typically are lined by a simple cuboidal epithelium, and both the alveolar ducts and alveoli are lined by a simple squamous epithelium (see

figure 23.2). The epithelium within the respiratory zone is much thinner than in the conducting portion, thus facilitating gas diffusion between the alveolus and pulmonary capillaries.

Each lung contains approximately 300 to 400 million alveoli by the time a person is about 8 years old. The packing of these millions of air-filled alveoli give the lung its spongy nature.

Alveoli abut one another, so their sides become slightly flattened. Thus, an alveolus in cross section actually looks more hexagonal or polygonal in shape than circular. Small openings in the walls, called **alveolar pores,** occur between some adjacent alveoli; these openings provide for collateral ventilation of alveoli. Blood capillaries surround each alveolus to facilitate gas exchange. The interalveolar septum contains elastic fibers that contribute to the ability of the lungs to stretch during inspiration and recoil during expiration.

Two cell types form the alveolar wall: the simple squamous alveolar type I cell, and the almost cuboidal-shaped alveolar type II cell (**figure 23.12a**). The predominant **alveolar type I cell** is also called a *squamous alveolar cell*. It comprises approximately

Figure 23.11 Bronchioles and Alveoli. Bronchioles and alveoli form the terminal ends of the respiratory passageway. (*a*) Terminal bronchioles branch into respiratory bronchioles in the respiratory zone, which then branch into alveolar ducts and alveoli. A pulmonary vessel travels with the bronchioles, and the pulmonary capillaries wrap around the alveoli for gas exchange. Elastic tissue is also wrapped around alveoli. (*b*) A photomicrograph shows the relationship of respiratory bronchioles, alveolar ducts, and alveoli. (*c*) SEM of a terminal bronchiole, a respiratory bronchiole, alveolar duct, and alveoli reveals the honeycomb appearance of alveoli. AP|R

95% of the alveolar surface area and forms part of a thin barrier that separates the air in the alveoli from the blood in pulmonary capillaries. The internal surface of alveoli formed by type I cells is moist, thus making alveoli prone to collapse because the moist inner surface creates a high surface tension. The smaller population of **alveolar type II cells,** also called *septal cells,* secrete an oily fluid, called **pulmonary surfactant** (ser-fak'tănt), which coats the inner alveolar surface. If an alveolus begins to collapse, such as would occur during expiration, the pulmonary surfactant molecules become more tightly packed together and tend to collectively oppose the collapse of the alveolus.

A third type of cell that is part of the alveolus is the **alveolar macrophage,** also called a *dust cell.* This cell is a leukocyte that may be either fixed or free. Fixed alveolar macrophages remain within the connective tissue of the alveolar walls, whereas free alveolar macrophages are migratory cells that continually crawl across the alveolar surface within the alveoli. Both types of alveolar macrophages engulf any microorganisms or particulate material that reach the alveoli. The alveolar macrophages are able to leave the lungs either by entering the lymph vessels or by being coughed up in sputum and then expectorated from the mouth.

WHAT DID YOU LEARN?

13 Which of the following respiratory structures are supported by cartilage: nose, larynx, trachea, bronchi, bronchioles, and alveolar sacs?

14 The respiratory tract can be damaged from desiccation (drying out), cold air, microbes, or exposure to chemicals or particulate matter. Which of the following help protect the respiratory tract: nasal hairs, mucus, tonsils, cilia, macrophages, sneezing, or coughing? Explain how for each.

15 List the conducting and respiratory structures (in order) that air passes through from the atmosphere to the alveoli.

23.3e Respiratory Membrane

LEARNING OBJECTIVE

9. Explain the structure of the respiratory membrane.

The **respiratory membrane** (figure 23.12b) is the thin barrier (only 0.5 micrometer thick) that oxygen and carbon dioxide diffuse across during gas exchange between the alveoli and the blood in the pulmonary capillaries. It consists of an alveolar epithelium and its basement membrane, and a capillary endothelium and its basement membrane. The two basement membranes are fused. Oxygen diffuses from the alveolus across the respiratory membrane into the pulmonary capillary, thereby allowing the erythrocytes in the blood to become oxygenated. Oxygen is then transported by the blood to tissue cells. Conversely, carbon dioxide diffuses from the blood through the respiratory membrane into the capillary to enter each alveolus. Once in the alveoli, carbon dioxide is expired from the respiratory system into the external environment.

WHAT DID YOU LEARN?

16 List, in order, the structures of the respiratory membrane that oxygen must cross to move from an alveolus into the blood.

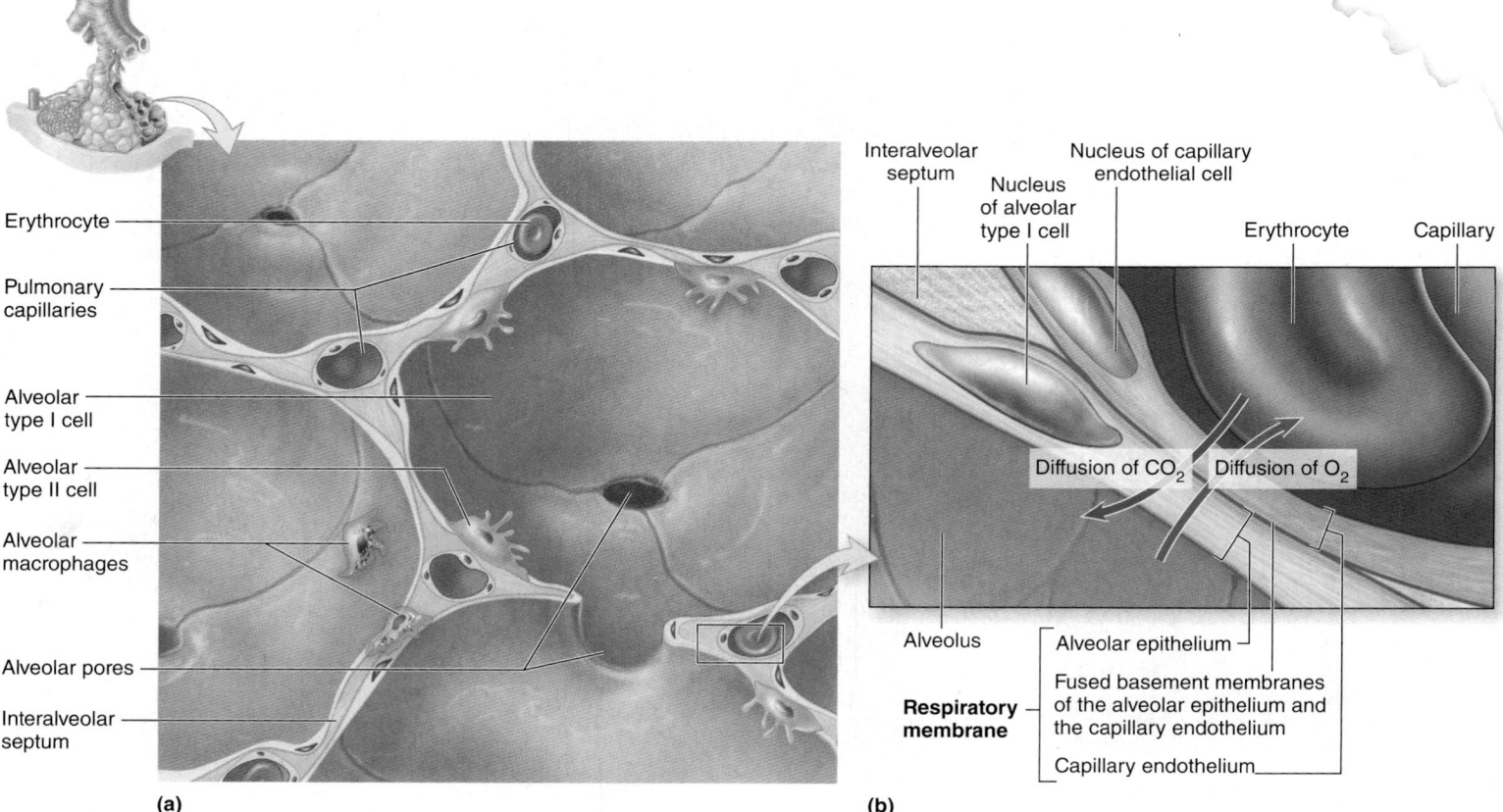

(a)

(b)

Figure 23.12 Alveoli and the Respiratory Membrane. (*a*) Microscopic alveoli form the terminal end of the air passageway. (*b*) Gas exchange between the alveoli and the pulmonary capillaries occurs across a thin respiratory membrane. The respiratory membrane consists of an alveolar type I cell, an endothelial cell of a capillary, and their fused basement membranes. Oxygen diffuses from an alveolus into the blood within the capillary, and carbon dioxide diffuses in the opposite direction. (Note that the pulmonary surfactant covering layer is not shown here.) AP|R

23.4 Lungs

The paired lungs house both the bronchial tree and all the respiratory portions of the respiratory system. Here we examine the position of the lungs in the thoracic cavity and their anatomic structure. We also discuss circulation to and innervation of the lungs, pleural membranes, and how lung inflation is maintained.

23.4a Gross Anatomy of the Lung

✓ LEARNING OBJECTIVES

1. Describe the location and general structure of the lungs.
2. Compare and contrast the right versus left lung.

The paired lungs are located within the thoracic cavity on either side of the mediastinum, the median region that houses the heart. The lungs are enclosed and protected by the thoracic cage (**figure 23.13**). Each lung has a wide, concave **base** that rests inferiorly upon the muscular diaphragm, and an **apex** (or *cupula*) that is slightly superior and posterior to the clavicle. The lung surfaces are adjacent to the ribs, mediastinum, and diaphragm, and are respectively referred to as the **costal surface, mediastinal surface,** and **diaphragmatic surface** of the lungs.

Each lung has a conical shape with an indented region on its mediastinal surface called the **hilum,** through which pass the bronchi, pulmonary vessels, lymph vessels, and the pulmonary plexus autonomic nerves (**figure 23.14**). Collectively, these structures that extend from the hilum are termed the **root** of the lung.

Figure 23.13 Position of the Lungs. Within the thoracic cavity, the lungs are bordered and protected by the thoracic cage. They are lateral to the mediastinum. The base of each lung rests on the diaphragm, and its apex is slightly superior and posterior to the clavicle. AP|R

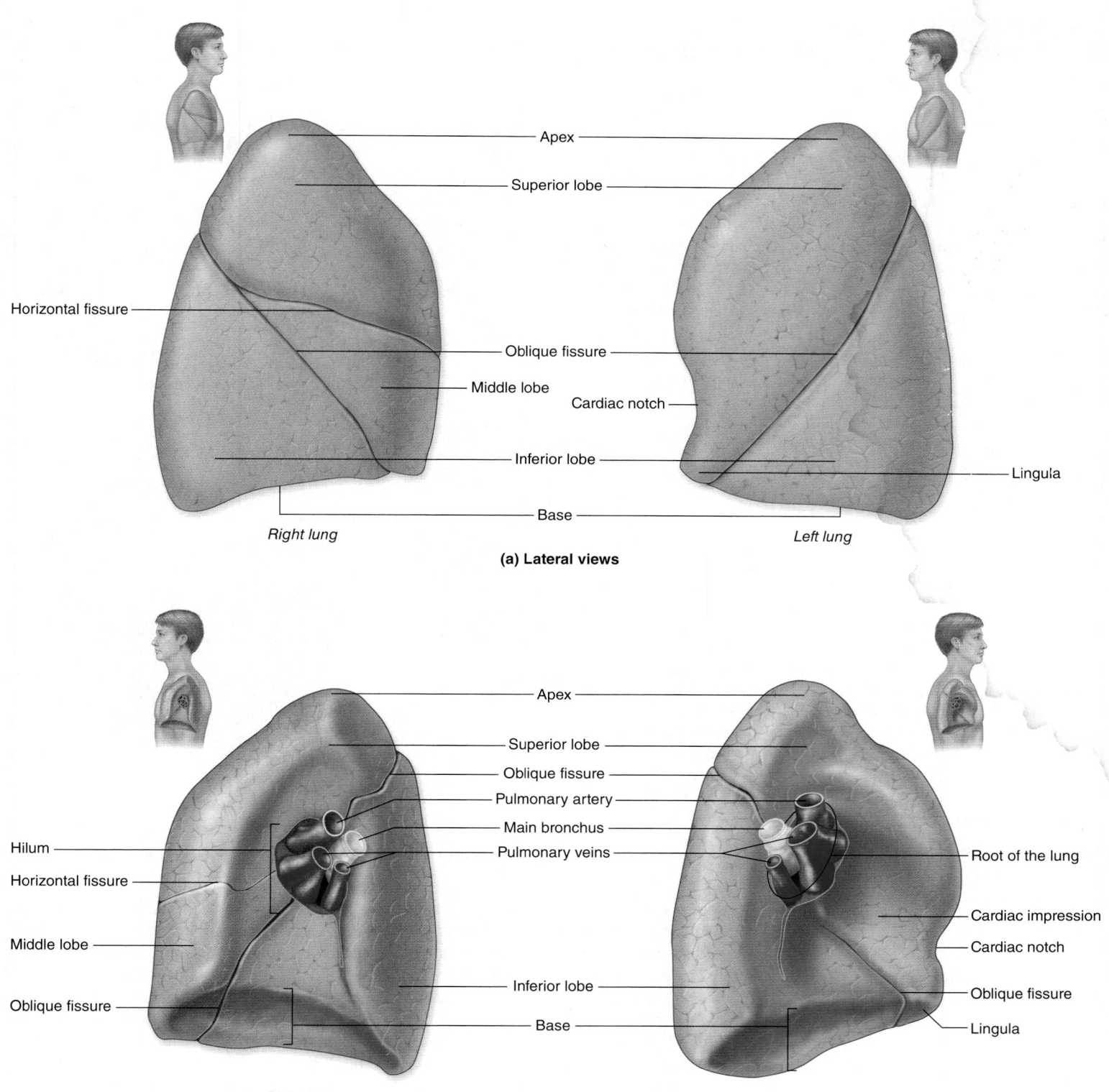

Figure 23.14 Lungs. The lungs are composed of lobes separated by distinct depressions called fissures. (*a*) Lateral views show the three lobes of the right lung and the two lobes of the left lung. (*b*) Medial views show the hilum of each lung, where the pulmonary vessels and bronchi enter and leave as part of the root of the lung. AP|R

The right and left lungs exhibit some obvious structural differences. The right lung is larger and wider than the left lung, and is subdivided by two fissures into three lobes. The **horizontal fissure** separates the **superior** (*upper*) **lobe** from the **middle lobe,** whereas the **oblique fissure** separates the middle lobe from the **inferior** (*lower*) **lobe.** In contrast, the left lung—which is slightly smaller than the right lung because the heart projects into the left side of the thoracic cavity—has only two lobes. The left lung has an oblique fissure that separates the superior lobe from the inferior lobe. The **lingula** of the left lung is a projection from the

CLINICAL VIEW
Smoking

Smoking results in the inhalation of over 200 chemicals into the respiratory passageways of the lungs. These chemicals blacken the respiratory passageways and cause respiratory changes that increase the risk of (1) respiratory infections, including the common cold, influenza, pneumonia, and tuberculosis; and (2) cellular and genetic damage to the lungs that may lead to emphysema or lung cancer.

The deleterious effects of smoking are not limited to the respiratory system. Nicotine causes vasoconstriction in the cardiovascular system, carbon monoxide interferes with oxygen binding to hemoglobin, and the risk and severity of atherosclerosis is increased. These changes decrease blood flow, thus resulting in decreased delivery of nutrients and oxygen to cells of systemic tissues. Women who smoke during pregnancy typically have babies with lower birth weight. This condition occurs in part because the umbilical arteries vasoconstrict, decreasing blood flow to the placenta.

Smoking increases the risk of both stomach ulcers caused by *Helicobacter pylori* infection and the risk of cancer of the esophagus, stomach, and pancreas. In the reproductive system, smoking increases the risks associated with human papillomavirus (HPV) infection. HPV is linked with increased risk of cervical cancer. Smoking also increases the risk of Alzheimer disease.

Current studies indicate an association between secondhand smoke exposure and increased risk of bronchitis, asthma, and ear infections in children. New evidence also shows that third-hand smoke, the toxins that are present in clothes, furniture, carpet, and other materials even after the cigarette is extinguished, poses a health risk— especially to infants and young children.

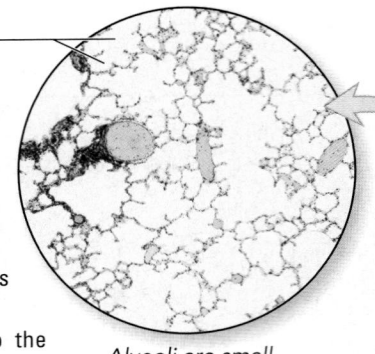

Alveoli

Alveoli are small, numerous, and well formed.

Nonsmoker's lungs: lungs are pink

Deposits

Enlarged alveolus

Alveoli are enlarged, less numerous, and contain black deposits.

Smoker's lungs: lungs are blackened

---

superior lobe that is homologous to the middle lobe of the right lung. The left lung also has two surface indentations to accommodate the heart: the **cardiac impression** on its medial surface and a **cardiac notch** on its anterior surface. In addition, a groovelike impression on the medial surface of the left lung accommodates the descending thoracic aorta.

The left and right lungs are partitioned into **bronchopulmonary** (brong′kō-pul′mō-nār′ē) **segments;** there are 10 segments in the right lung and typically 8 to 10 in the left lung (**figure 23.15**). (The discrepancy in segment number for the left lung comes from the merging of some left segments into combined ones.) Each bronchopulmonary segment is an autonomous unit, encapsulated within connective tissue, and supplied by its own segmental bronchus, a branch of both the pulmonary artery and vein, and lymph vessels. Consequently, if a portion of a lung is diseased, a surgeon can remove the entire bronchopulmonary segment that is affected, and the remaining healthy segments continue to function.

Within each segment, the lung is organized into **lobules,** each of which is surrounded by connective tissue and supplied by a terminal bronchiole, arteriole, venule, and lymph vessel.

 WHAT DID YOU LEARN?

17 Match the component of the lung with its air passageway.

main bronchus	bronchopulmonary segment
lobar bronchus	lobe
segmental bronchus	lobule
terminal bronchiole	lung (right and left)

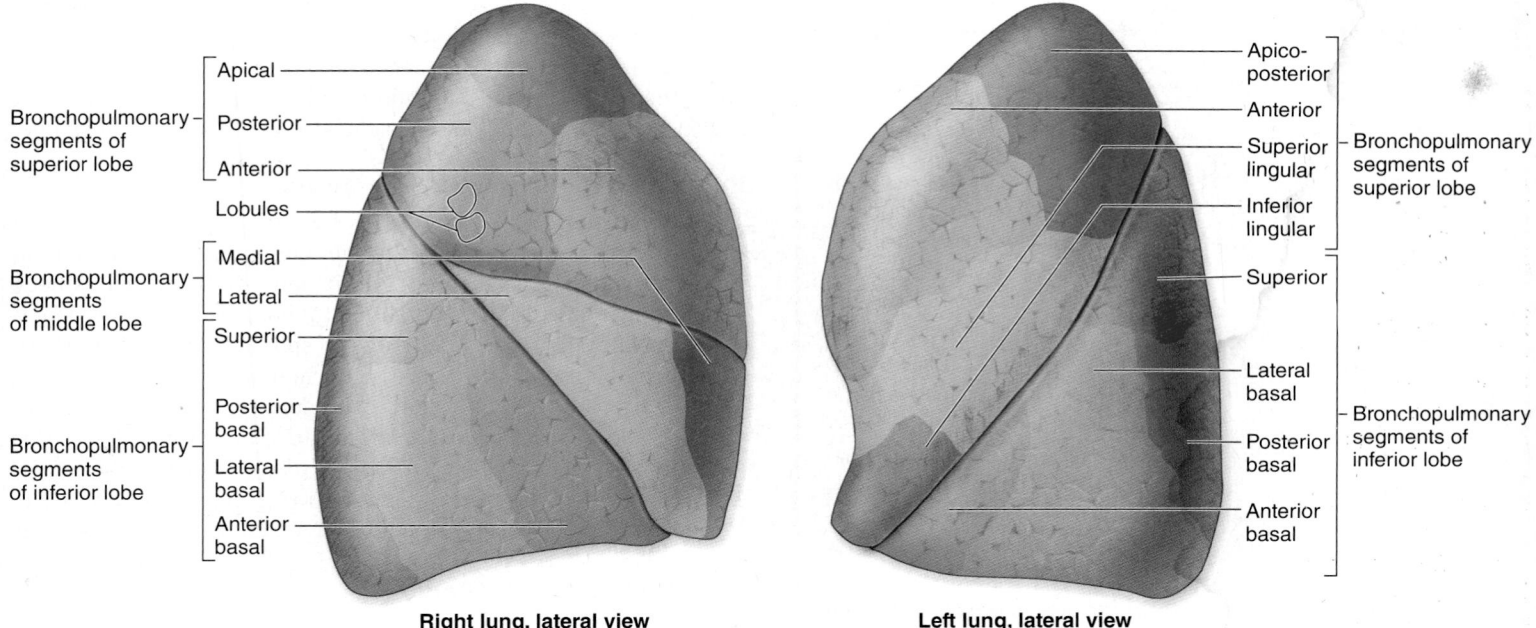

Figure 23.15 Bronchopulmonary Segments and Lobules of the Lungs. Both lungs are partitioned into self-contained bronchopulmonary segments (represented by different colors), each supplied by a segmental bronchus. Lobules are visible in each bronchopulmonary segment. (Not all bronchopulmonary segments are shown in this view.)

23.4b Circulation to and Innervation of the Lungs

✔ LEARNING OBJECTIVES

3. Distinguish between the two types of blood circulation through the lungs.

4. Describe the innervation of lung structures by the autonomic nervous system.

The circulation of blood to and from the lungs, lymph circulation from the lungs, and innervation of the lungs by autonomic axons are described here.

Blood Supply

Two types of blood circulation are associated with the lungs: the pulmonary circulation and the bronchial circulation. Recall from our examination of the heart and blood vessels that the **pulmonary circulation** (figure 23.16) conducts blood to and from the gas

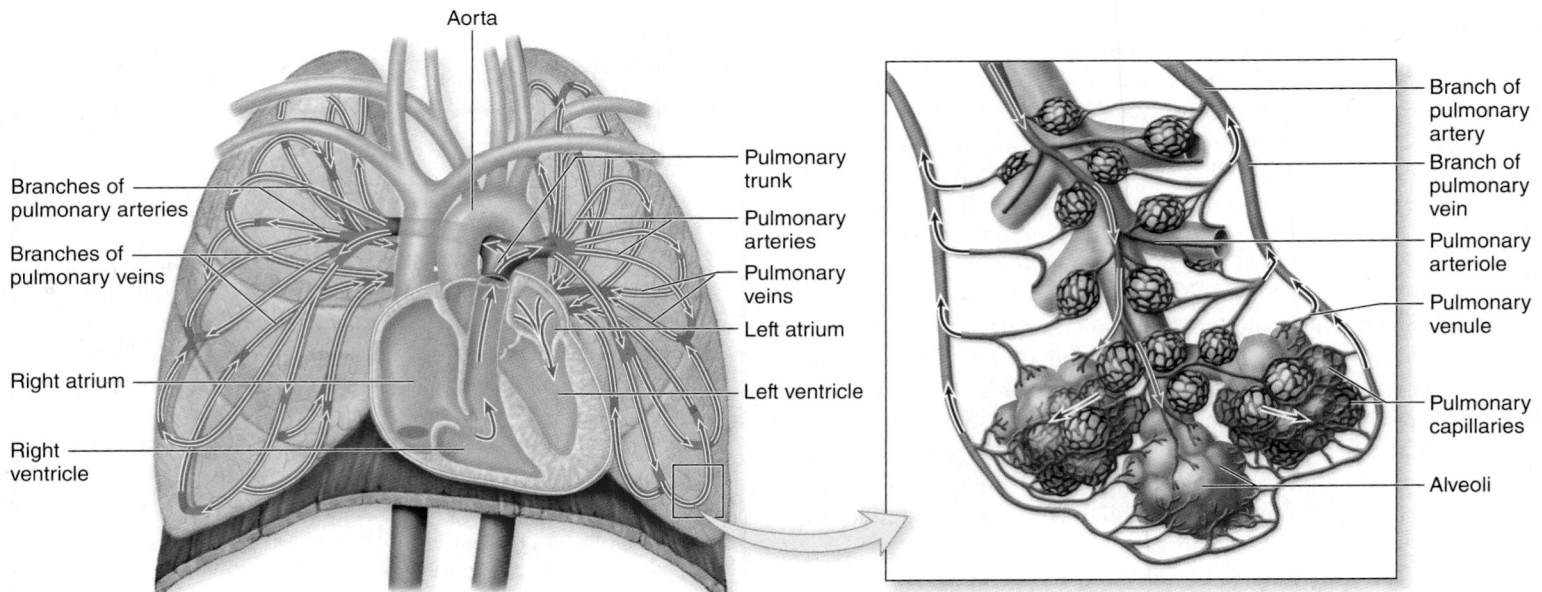

Figure 23.16 Pulmonary Circulation of the Lungs. Pulmonary circulation delivers blood to the lungs for reoxygenation. AP|R

exchange surfaces of the lungs to replenish its depleted oxygen levels and get rid of excess carbon dioxide. Pulmonary arteries carry deoxygenated blood to pulmonary capillaries within the lungs. The deoxygenated blood that enters these capillaries is reoxygenated here before it returns to the left atrium through a series of pulmonary venules and veins.

In comparison, the **bronchial circulation** is a component of the systemic circulation and transports oxygenated blood to the tissues of the lungs (see figure 20.23). It consists of both small bronchial arteries and veins that supply the bronchi and bronchioles. The cells of the smallest respiratory structures (such as alveoli and alveolar ducts) exchange their respiratory gases directly with the inhaled air. Approximately three or four **bronchial arteries** branch from the anterior wall of the descending thoracic aorta (or its branches). Thereafter, bronchial arteries then divide to form capillary beds supplying structures in the bronchial tree. **Bronchial veins** collect venous blood from these capillary beds. Some of this deoxygenated blood drains into pulmonary veins, where it mixes with the freshly oxygenated blood. Consequently, blood exiting the lungs within the pulmonary veins, which will be returned to the left side of the heart and circulated throughout the body, is slightly less oxygenated than the blood immediately leaving the pulmonary capillaries following gas exchange.

Lymph Drainage

Lymph vessels and nodes are located within the connective tissue of the lung, around the bronchi and in the pleura. Lymph vessels are important in removing excess fluid from the lungs. Lymph, absorbed by lymph vessels, is filtered through lymph nodes, which collect carbon, dust particles, and pollutants that were not "swept out" by cilia lining the respiratory tract. Lymph nodes may become dark in color as they accumulate the microscopic matter we inhale over a lifetime.

Innervation of the Respiratory System

The smooth muscle and glands of the larynx, trachea, bronchial tree, and lungs are innervated by the autonomic nervous system. The bronchioles receive both sympathetic and parasympathetic innervation. Sympathetic innervation to the lungs originates generally from the T1–T5 segments of the spinal cord (section 15.4). This innervation primarily causes bronchodilation.

Parasympathetic innervation to the lungs is from vagus nerves (CN X), and it stimulates bronchoconstriction (section 15.3). The vagus nerves are also the primary source of innervation to the larynx. Thus, damage to one of the vagus nerves going to the larynx can cause a person to develop a monotone or a permanently hoarse voice.

WHAT DID YOU LEARN?

18 Which arteries deliver oxygenated blood to tissues of the lungs and which veins drain deoxygenated blood from the lungs? What vessels receive some of this deoxygenated blood?

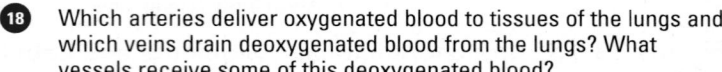

23.4c Pleural Membranes and Pleural Cavity

LEARNING OBJECTIVES

5. Describe the pleural membranes and pleural cavity.
6. Explain the function of serous fluid in the pleural cavity.

The outer lung surfaces and the adjacent internal thoracic wall are lined by a serous membrane called **pleura** (ploor′ă). It is composed of simple squamous epithelium. The **visceral pleura** tightly adheres to the lung surface, whereas the **parietal pleura** lines the internal thoracic walls, the lateral surfaces of the mediastinum, and the superior surface of the diaphragm (**figure 23.17**). The pleural layers are continuous at the hilum of each lung. Each lung is enclosed in a separate visceral pleural membrane, and the heart in a visceral pericardial membrane (see section 19.2b); thus, these organs are compartmentalized, which helps limit spread of infections.

Figure 23.17 Pleural Membranes and Pressures
Associated with the Lungs. The two pleural membranes include
the visceral pleura, which covers the outer surface of the lungs and the
parietal pleura, which lines the inner surface of the thoracic wall.
Between the two pleural membranes is a potential space called the pleural
cavity. Two pressures associated with the lungs include the
intrapulmonary pressure (the pressure within the lungs) and the
intrapleural pressure (pressure within the pleural cavity). **AP|R**

The **pleural cavity** is located between the visceral and parietal
serous membrane layers. When the lungs are fully inflated, the
pleural cavity is considered a *potential space* because the visceral
and parietal pleurae are almost in contact with each other. An oily,
serous fluid is produced by the serous membranes and covers their
surface within the pleural cavity. Serous fluid acts as a lubricant,
ensuring the pleural surfaces slide by each other with minimal friction during breathing. Each pleural cavity normally contains less
than 15 mL of serous fluid and is drained continuously by lymph
vessels within the visceral pleura. A balance normally exists
between formation and removal of serous fluid in the pleural
cavity.

 WHAT DID YOU LEARN?

19 What is the function of serous fluid within the pleural cavity?

23.4d How Lungs Remain Inflated

 LEARNING OBJECTIVE

7. Explain the anatomic properties that keep lungs inflated.

Lung inflation occurs due to the expanding properties of the chest
wall, the recoiling properties of the lungs, and the anatomic
arrangement of the pleural cavity between chest wall and lungs.

The chest wall is anatomically configured to expand outwardly.
This is readily observed when the thoracic cage is opened surgically, because cutting through the chest wall causes it to "spring"
open. The lungs cling to the internal surface of the chest wall as it
expands outward because of the surface tension caused by the
serous fluid within the pleural cavity. However, the lungs are
composed of vast amounts of elastic connective tissue that is

"stretched" as the lungs expand. The natural tendency of elastic
connective tissue is to recoil, which causes the lungs to exhibit a
noticeable inward pull.

The contrasting outward pull of the chest wall and the opposing inward pull of the lungs create a vacuum or "suction" within
the pleural cavity. Consequently, the pressure generated in the
pleural cavity, called the **intrapleural pressure,** is lower than the
pressure inside the lungs, called the **intrapulmonary** (or *intra-
alveolar*) **pressure** (figure 23.17). This difference in pressure keeps
the lungs inflated. The lungs remain inflated similar to the way in
which a balloon remains inflated—namely, the pressure inside is
greater than the pressure outside. Note that when intrapleural pressure becomes equal to intrapulmonary pressure the lungs deflate,
like the deflation of a balloon when the stem is released.

 WHAT DID YOU LEARN?

20 Why is the intrapleural pressure normally lower than
intrapulmonary pressure?

23.5 Respiration: Pulmonary Ventilation

Respiration is a general term for the exchange of respiratory gases
(oxygen and carbon dioxide) between the atmosphere and the tissue
cells of the body—it is organized into four continuous and simultaneously occurring processes:

- **Pulmonary ventilation**—movement of respiratory gases
  between the atmosphere and the alveoli of the lungs
- **Alveolar gas exchange** (or *external respiration*)—exchange
  of respiratory gases between the alveoli and the blood
- **Gas transport**—transport of respiratory gases within the
  blood between the lungs and systemic cells of the body
- **Systemic gas exchange** (or *internal respiration*)—exchange
  of respiratory gases between the blood and systemic cells of
  the body

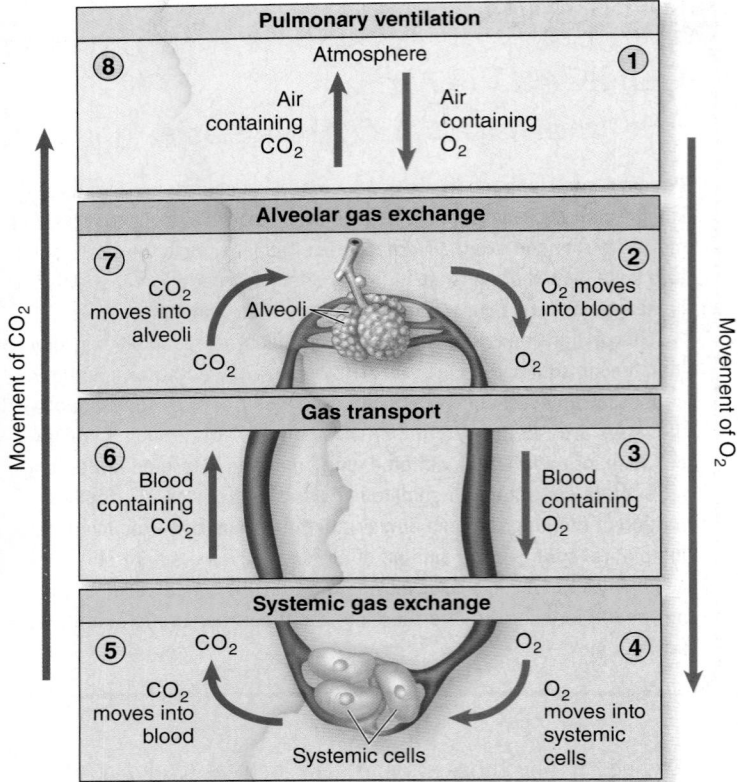

Figure 23.18 Overview of Respiration. Respiration involves four processes that include pulmonary ventilation, alveolar gas exchange, gas transport, and systemic gas exchange.

Table 23.2	Respiration Processes	
Process	**Description**	**Body Systems**
Pulmonary ventilation	Movement of air between atmosphere and the alveoli • Net movement of oxygen from atmosphere to alveoli during inspiration (step 1) • Net movement of carbon dioxide from alveoli to atmosphere during expiration (step 8)	Respiratory, skeletal, muscular, and nervous
Alveolar gas exchange	Exchange of respiratory gases between alveoli of the lungs and the blood • Oxygen diffuses from alveoli into blood (step 2) • Carbon dioxide diffuses from blood into alveoli (step 7)	Respiratory and cardiovascular
Gas transport	Blood transport of respiratory gases between lungs and tissue cells of the body • Oxygen is transported from lungs to tissue cells (step 3) • Carbon dioxide is transported from systemic cells to lungs (step 6)	Cardiovascular
Systemic gas exchange	Exchange of respiratory gases between blood and systemic cells • Oxygen diffuses from blood into tissue cells (step 4) • Carbon dioxide diffuses from systemic cells into blood (step 5)	Cardiovascular

Figure 23.18 and **table 23.2** provide a summary for the movement of respiratory gases involving these four processes. Notice that the net movement of oxygen is from the atmosphere to the systemic cells, and involves the following:

1. Air containing oxygen is inhaled into the alveoli during the inspiratory phase of pulmonary ventilation.

2. Oxygen diffuses from alveoli into the blood of pulmonary capillaries during alveolar gas exchange.

3. Gas transport of oxygen occurs within the blood from the lungs to the systemic cells of the body.

4. Oxygen diffuses from the blood within the systemic capillaries into the systemic cells during systemic gas exchange.

5. Carbon dioxide diffuses from systemic cells into the blood within systemic capillaries during systemic gas exchange.

6. Carbon dioxide is transported within the blood from systemic cells to the lungs.

7. Carbon dioxide diffuses from the blood within the pulmonary capillaries into the alveoli during alveolar gas exchange.

8. Air containing carbon dioxide is then exhaled from the alveoli into the atmosphere during the expiratory phase of pulmonary ventilation.

Pulmonary ventilation is discussed in this section. The other three processes of respiration are covered later in this chapter.

23.5a Introduction to Pulmonary Ventilation

LEARNING OBJECTIVE

1. Give an overview of the process of pulmonary ventilation.

Pulmonary ventilation is known as *breathing,* which is the movement of air between the atmosphere and the alveoli. It consists of two cyclic phases: **inspiration,** also called *inhalation,* which brings air into the lungs and **expiration,** also called *exhalation,* which forces air out of the lungs. Breathing may be either quiet or forced. **Quiet breathing** is the rhythmic breathing that occurs at rest; **forced breathing** is vigorous breathing that accompanies exercise or hard exertion.

The principles involved in breathing, whether quiet or forced, use the same physiologic processes. Autonomic nuclei in the brainstem stimulate the skeletal muscles involved with breathing to cyclically contract and relax, resulting in thoracic cavity volume changes. Dimensional changes within the thoracic cavity during breathing result in pressure changes, establishing a changing pressure gradient between the lungs and the atmosphere. Air moves down the pressure gradient either to enter the lungs during inspiration or to exit the lungs during expiration. Three major topics are addressed in this section: how pressure gradients are established during breathing (mechanics of breathing), how breathing is controlled by the central nervous system, and the different pulmonary measurements associated with breathing.

WHAT DID YOU LEARN?

21. What are the general steps of pulmonary ventilation beginning with the autonomic nuclei?

23.5b Mechanics of Breathing

☑ LEARNING OBJECTIVES

2. Explain how pressure gradients are established and result in pulmonary ventilation.

3. State the relationship between pressure and volume as described by Boyle's law.

4. Distinguish between quiet and forced breathing.

The mechanics of breathing involve several integrated aspects: (1) the specific actions of the skeletal muscles of breathing; (2) dimensional (volume) changes within the thoracic cavity; (3) pressure changes resulting from volume changes (Boyle's gas law); (4) pressure gradients; and (5) volumes and pressures associated with breathing. Individual aspects of breathing are discussed and then this information is integrated to describe how breathing occurs.

Skeletal Muscles of Breathing

The skeletal muscles of breathing are classified into the following three categories: muscles of quiet breathing, muscles of forced inspiration, and muscles of forced expiration **(figure 23.19)**.

Figure 23.19 Skeletal Muscles of Breathing.

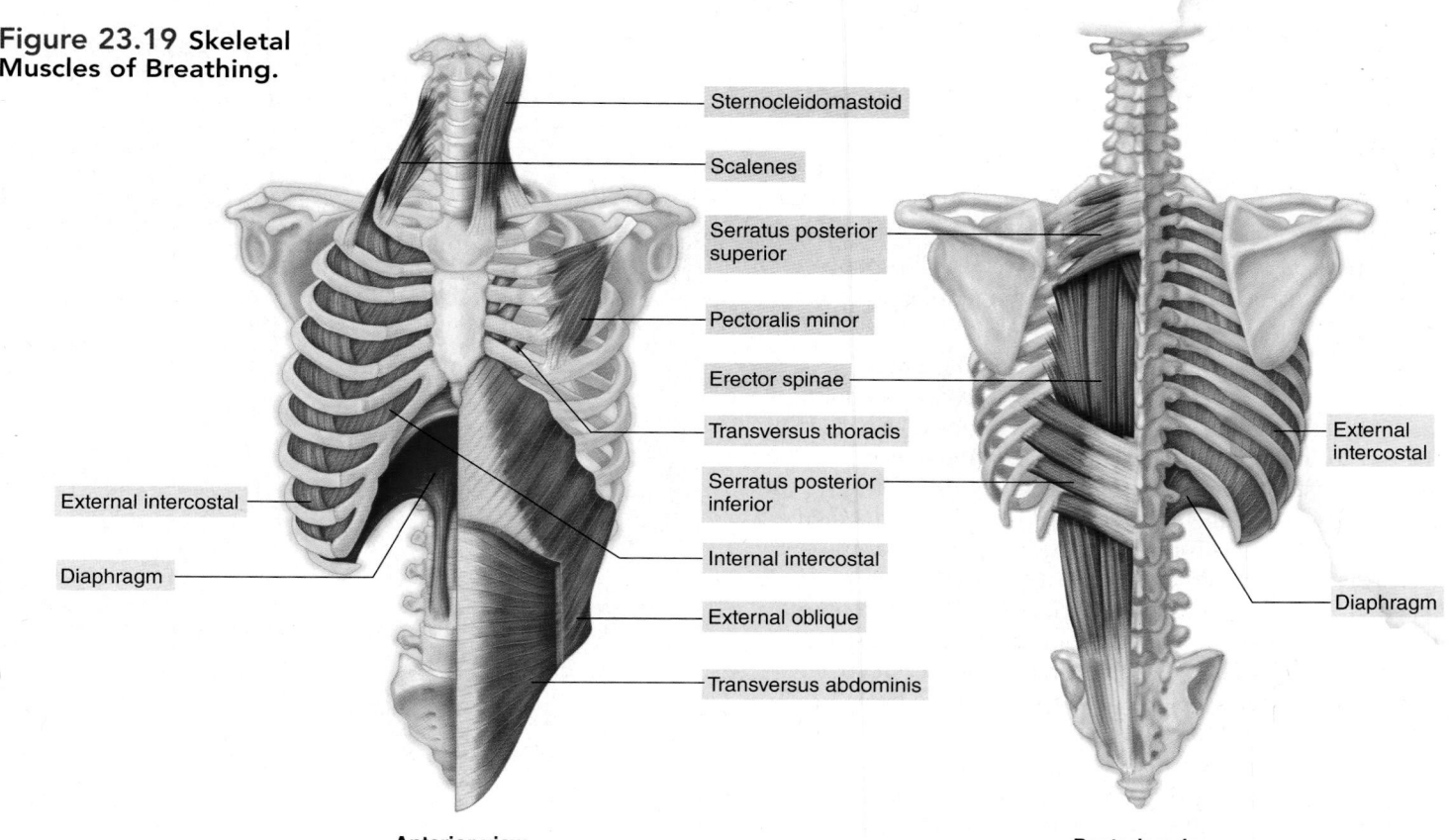

Anterior view   Posterior view

	Muscles of Breathing
Muscles of quiet breathing	The **diaphragm** forms the rounded "floor" of the thoracic cavity and is dome-shaped when relaxed. It alternates between the relaxed domed position and the contracted flattened position and changes the vertical dimensions of the thoracic cavity.
	The **external intercostals** extend from a superior rib inferiomedially to the adjacent inferior rib. These elevate the ribs and increase the transverse dimensions of the thoracic cavity.
Muscles of forced inspiration	The **sternocleidomastoid** attaches to sternum and clavicle; lifts rib cage.
	The **scalenes** attach to ribs 1 and 2; elevates ribs 1 and 2.
	The **pectoralis minor** attaches to ribs 3–5; elevates ribs 3–5.
	The **serratus posterior superior** attaches to ribs 2–5 on its anterior surface; lifts ribs 2–5.
	The **erector spinae** is a group of deep muscles along the length of the vertebral column; extends the vertebral column.
Muscles of forced expiration	The **internal intercostals** lie deep and at right angles to the external intercostals; depress the ribs and decrease the transverse dimensions of the thoracic cavity.
	The **abdominal muscles** (primarily the external obliques and transversus abdominis) compress the abdominal contents, forcing the diaphragm into a higher domed position and the rectus abdominus pulls the sternum and rib cage inferiorly.
	The **transversus thoracis** extends across the inner surface of the thoracic cage and attaches to ribs 2–6; depresses ribs 2–6 .
	The **serratus posterior inferior** extends between the ligamentum nuchae and the lower border of ribs 9–12; depresses ribs 9–12.

CONCEPT CONNECTION

Cellular respiration is the metabolic pathway whereby glucose and other fuel molecules, such as fatty acids, are oxidized and their chemical energy transferred to form adenosine triphosphate (ATP) as described in section 3.4. The carbon atoms of the oxidized fuel molecules are released as carbon dioxide, a waste product. Oxygen eventually "catches electrons" and joins with hydrogen ions to form water as the final step in the electron transport system. The respiratory system and cardiovascular system support the process of cellular respiration by delivering the oxygen and removing the carbon dioxide waste.

- **Muscles of quiet breathing** are the skeletal muscles involved in normal rhythmic breathing that occurs at rest. They are the **diaphragm** and the **external intercostals.** These muscles alternately contract and relax, resulting in movement of air into and out of the lungs.

- **Muscles of forced inspiration** are used during a deep inspiration, such as occurs during heavy exercise or prior to "holding a long note" while singing. These muscles include the **sternocleidomastoid, scalenes, pectoralis minor, serratus posterior superior,** and **erector spinae.** These muscles, except for the erector spinae, are located in a more superior location relative to the thoracic cavity and can effectively move the rib cage superiorly, laterally, and anteriorly, resulting in a greater increase in the volume of the thoracic cavity than occurs during quiet breathing. Located along the length of the vertebral column, the erector spinae muscles also aid in lifting the rib cage, but do so by extending the vertebral column.

- **Muscles of forced expiration** contract during a hard expiration, for example, when one blows up a balloon or coughs. The muscles of forced expiration include the **internal intercostals, abdominal muscles, transversus thoracis,** and **serratus posterior inferior.** In general, these muscles either pull the rib cage inferiorly, medially, and posteriorly or compress the abdominal contents to move the diaphragm superiorly into the thoracic cavity, resulting in a large decrease in volume within the thoracic cavity.

The muscles of forced inspiration and forced expiration are collectively referred to as the *accessory muscles of breathing.*

Volume Changes in the Thoracic Cavity

The cyclic activity of breathing muscles causes thoracic cavity volume changes that occur in three dimensions: vertically, laterally, and in an anterior-posterior direction (**figure 23.20**).

Vertical dimension changes of the thoracic cavity result from the movement of the diaphragm as it contracts and relaxes. The diaphragm forms the rounded "floor" of the thoracic cavity and is dome-shaped when relaxed. When it contracts, its central portion flattens and moves inferiorly to press against the abdominal viscera—consequently, the vertical dimensions of the thoracic cavity increase. When the diaphragm relaxes and returns to its original position, the vertical dimensions decrease.

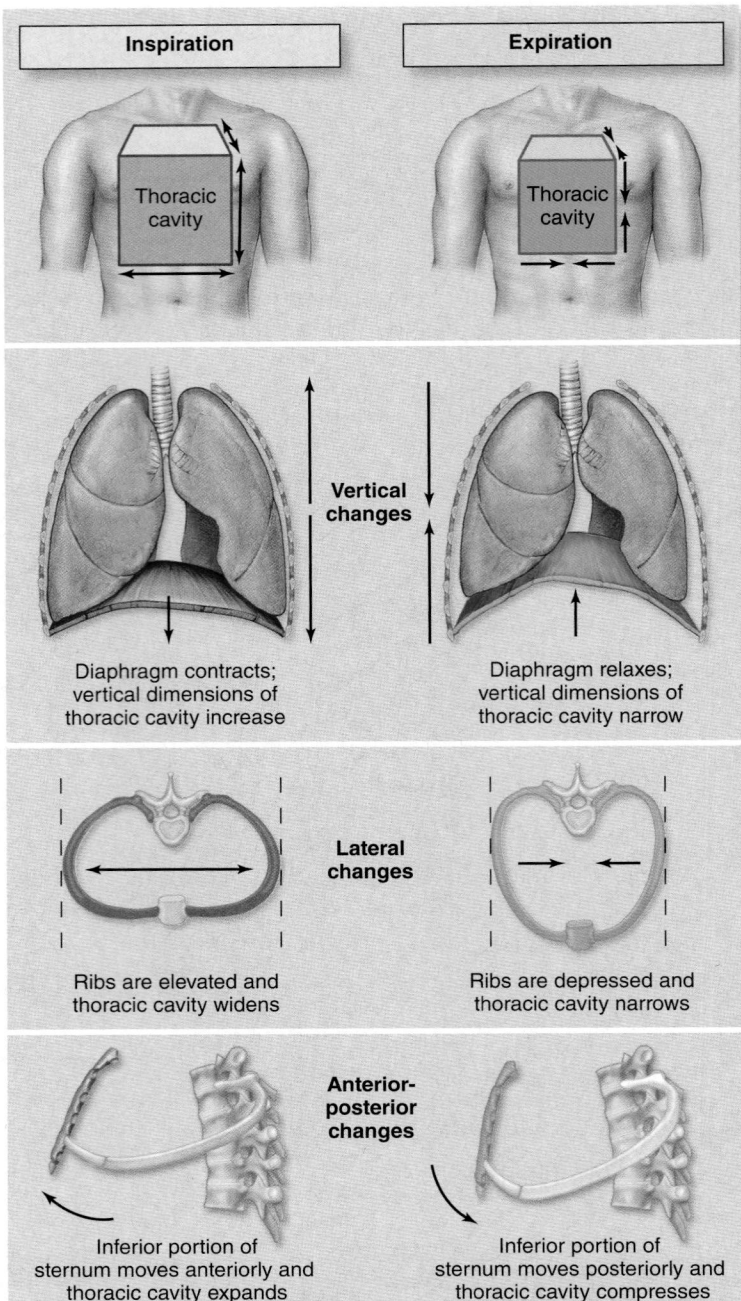

Figure 23.20 Thoracic Cavity Dimensional Changes Associated with Breathing. The box-like thoracic cavity changes size during inspiration and expiration. The box increases in vertical, lateral, and anterior-posterior dimensions during inspiration due to movement of the diaphragm, ribs, and sternum, respectively. These dimensions decrease upon expiration, and the thoracic cavity becomes smaller.

Only small movements of the diaphragm are required for breathing, and usually the changes in vertical dimension measure only a few millimeters during quiet breathing. Greater changes in the superior movement of the diaphragm occur during forced expiration because of contraction of the abdominal muscles.

Lateral dimension changes occur either as the rib cage is elevated and the thoracic cavity widens, or as the rib cage depresses and thoracic cavity narrows. This action can be mimicked by placing your hands at the sides of your ribs and then abducting and adducting your hands relative to your ribs.

(a) Boyle's Law

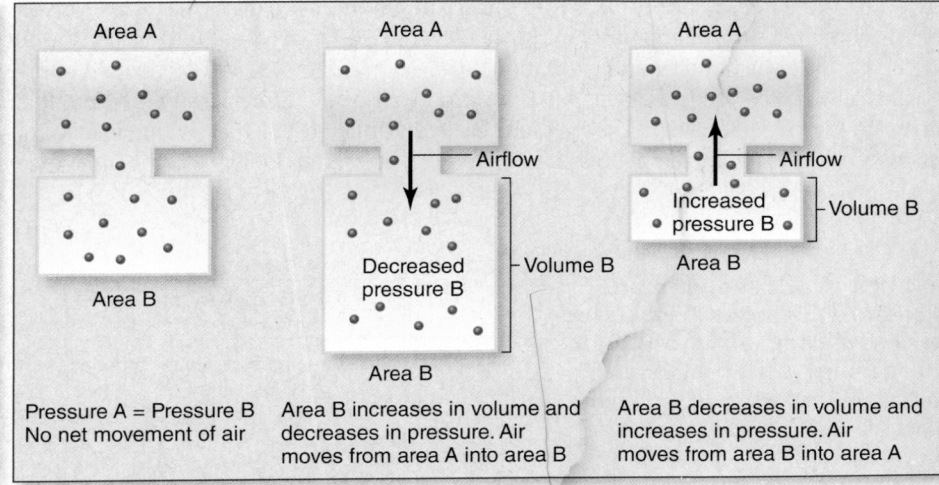

(b) Pressure gradients

Pressure A = Pressure B
No net movement of air

Area B increases in volume and decreases in pressure. Air moves from area A into area B

Area B decreases in volume and increases in pressure. Air moves from area B into area A

(c) Volumes and pressures with breathing (at the end of an expiration)

Figure 23.21 Boyle's Law and Pressure Gradients.
(*a*) Boyle's law states that volume and pressure are inversely related. (*b*) The figure shows that air does not move if the pressure is equal between two areas. It also shows how air moves from an area of high pressure to an area of low pressure when pressure gradients are established by changes in volume. (*c*) Three significant pressures are associated with breathing. Atmospheric pressure is a set value of 760 mm Hg at sea level. The other two are the intrapulmonary pressure and the intrapleural pressure, which both change during breathing as a result of changing volumes. AP|R

Anterior-posterior dimension changes occur as the inferior portion of the sternum moves anteriorly and then posteriorly. This action can be visualized by placing one hand on the front of your lower chest and lifting it outwardly away from the chest and then back. In general, lateral and anterior-posterior dimensional changes both occur as a result of the contraction and relaxation of all muscles of breathing shown in figure 23.19, except for the diaphragm.

Boyle's Gas Law: Relationship of Volume and Pressure

Dimensional volume changes cause gas pressure changes in the thoracic cavity. **Boyle's law** states that at a constant temperature, the pressure (*P*) of a gas decreases if the volume (*V*) of the container increases, and vice versa. The law may be expressed by the following formula:

$$P_1V_1 = P_2V_2$$

where P_1 and V_1 represent the initial conditions, and P_2 and V_2 represent the changed conditions for pressure and volume, respectively. This formula expresses an inverse relationship that exists between gas pressure and volume. **Figure 23.21*a*** visually helps you to understand this relationship.

Pressure Gradients

An air pressure gradient occurs when the force per unit area is greater in one place than in another. If a pressure gradient exists

between two regions, and they are interconnected, then air moves from the region of higher pressure to the region of lower pressure until the pressure in the two regions becomes equal. Figure 23.21*b* shows this relationship.

Volumes and Pressures Associated with Breathing

A similar relationship exists with respect to the atmosphere and the lungs, which are interconnected by the respiratory passageway (figure 23.21*c*).

The **atmosphere** is the air in the environment that surrounds us. **Atmospheric pressure** is the pressure (weight) gases in the air exert in the environment. Its value changes with altitude. The standard value is given at sea level because air becomes less dense or "thins" with increased altitude. The "thinner air" exerts a correspondingly lower atmospheric pressure. The value for atmospheric pressure at sea level can be expressed in several ways: 14.7 pounds per square inch = 1 atmosphere (atm) = 760 mm Hg. The value used in this text is 760 mm Hg. (Note that 1 millimeter of mercury is expressed as 1 mm Hg, and it is the pressure exerted by a column of mercury that is 1 millimeter high in a glass tube.) Atmospheric pressure does not change in the context of breathing.

The thoracic cavity contains the lungs. The collective volume of the alveoli within the lungs is called the **alveolar volume,** and its associated pressure is the intrapulmonary pressure (described earlier). This pressure fluctuates with breathing and may be higher, lower, or the same as atmospheric pressure. Intrapulmonary pressure is equal to atmospheric pressure (at sea level = 760 mm Hg) at the end of both inspiration and expiration.

Recall that the lungs are separated from the wall of the thoracic cavity by the pleural cavity. The pressure exerted within the pleural cavity is called the intrapleural pressure. Intrapleural pressure also fluc-tuates with breathing and is always lower than intrapulmonary pressure so that the lungs remain inflated. Prior to inspiration, it is generally about 4 mm Hg lower than intrapulmonary pressure (756 mm Hg).

Note that a volume change in the thoracic cavity occurring during inspiration and expiration establishes a pressure gradient between the atmosphere and the thoracic cavity that determines the direction

Figure 23.22 Volume and Pressure Changes Associated with the Mechanics of Quiet Breathing. Circled numbers correspond to the steps described in the text. (*a*) Schematic of changes in volume, pressure, and air flow that are associated with breathing. (*b*) Approximately 500 mL of air is inspired and then expired during quiet breathing, these volumes are associated with (*c*) relatively small changes in intrapulmonary and intrapleural pressures.

of airflow. Thus, an increase in volume of the thoracic cavity, with an accompanying decrease in pressure, results in air moving into the lungs during inspiration. In contrast, a decrease in volume of the thoracic cavity, with an accompanying increase in pressure, results in air moving out of the lungs during expiration.

Quiet Breathing

Recall that quiet breathing is the normal breathing that occurs when you are relaxed. Refer to **figure 23.22** as you read through this description of the stepwise sequence of events that occurs during quiet breathing.

Inspiration

1. Initially, both intrapulmonary pressure and atmospheric pressure are 760 mm Hg at sea level prior to inspiration. Intrapleural pressure is slightly lower at approximately 756 mm Hg, or about 4 mm Hg lower than intrapulmonary pressure.

2. The diaphragm contracts, increasing the thoracic cavity vertical dimensions, and the external intercostals contract, increasing both lateral and anterior-posterior dimensions. During quiet breathing, diaphragmatic movement may account for about two-thirds of the thoracic cavity volume change, and external intercostal movement for about one-third.

   - Muscle contraction results in pleural cavity volume increasing with an accompanying decrease in intrapleural pressure from approximately 756 to 754 mm Hg.
   - Simultaneously, the lungs expand because of the surface tension caused by serous fluid in the pleural cavity. The intrapulmonary pressure decreases from 760 to 759 mm Hg as the alveolar volume increases.
   - When the intrapulmonary pressure decreases below atmospheric pressure, air moves down the pressure gradient from the environment, ultimately into the lungs, until the intrapulmonary pressure is once again equal to atmospheric pressure. The approximate volume of air that moves from the atmosphere into the lungs during a single breath in quiet breathing is approximately 500 milliliters (mL) or 0.5 liters (L). This volume of air is called the tidal volume.

Expiration

3. Initially, the intrapulmonary pressure has equalized with atmospheric pressure (both at 760 mm Hg) prior to quiet expiration, and intrapleural pressure is about 754 mm Hg, still lower than intrapulmonary pressure.

4. The diaphragm and external intercostals relax, decreasing the dimensions of the thoracic cavity.

   - The pleural cavity volume decreases as the diaphragm relaxes and the thoracic wall recoils. Intrapleural pressure now increases from 754 mm Hg to return to 756 mm Hg.
   - Simultaneously, the alveolar volume decreases because the lungs are pulled inward by the recoil of elastic connective tissue in the lungs. Intrapulmonary pressure now increases from 760 to 761 mm Hg.
   - When intrapulmonary pressure exceeds atmospheric pressure, air is forced out of the alveoli into the atmosphere. This continues until the intrapulmonary pressure is once again equal to atmospheric pressure. Approximately 500 mL of air moves out of the lungs.

The changes in thoracic cavity volume and both intrapulmonary and intrapleural pressures that are associated with quiet breathing are shown in figure 23.22b, c. The events of quiet inspiration and quiet expiration are summarized in **table 23.3**.

Forced Breathing

Forced breathing involves steps similar to quiet breathing. However, both forced inspiration and expiration are active processes, requiring contraction of additional muscles (see figure 23.19). Their activity causes greater changes in both the thoracic cavity volume and intrapulmonary pressure. Consequently, more air moves into and out of the lungs. Significant chest volume changes are apparent that accompany forced breathing, unlike the barely perceptible changes in the chest cavity volume that occur during quiet breathing.

 WHAT DID YOU LEARN?

22. Describe the sequence of events of quiet inspiration.

23. How are larger amounts of air moved between the lungs and atmosphere during forced inspiration and forced expiration? Is more energy expended during forced breathing? Why?

23.5c Nervous Control of Breathing

LEARNING OBJECTIVES

5. Describe how pulmonary ventilation is controlled by the central nervous system.

6. Explain the different reflexes that alter breathing rate and depth.

7. Distinguish between nervous system control of breathing and nervous system control of anatomic structures of the respiratory system.

The skeletal muscles of breathing are coordinated by nuclei within the brainstem. These regulatory nuclei are housed specifically in the **medullary respiratory center** within the medulla

Table 23.3	Changes Associated with Quiet Breathing		
Variable	**Inspiration**		**Expiration**
Diaphragm and external intercostals	Contracting (active)		Relaxing (passive)
Pleural cavity	Volume increases; Pressure decreases		Volume decreases; Pressure increases
Lungs	Volume increases; Pressure decreases		Volume decreases; Pressure increases
Air movement	Into lungs		Out of lungs

oblongata and the **pontine respiratory center** (also called the *pneumotaxic center*) within the pons. These two centers are collectively called the **respiratory center.** Although there is much still unknown about how breathing is completely controlled, the following description provides some insight into what is generally accepted. Please refer to **figure 23.23** throughout this section.

Respiratory Center: Controlling Quiet Breathing

There are two distinct groups of nuclei in the medulla oblongata. The **ventral respiratory group (VRG)** is a column of neurons located in the ventrolateral region of the medulla that contains both inspiratory and expiratory neurons. Posterior to the VRG in the dorsomedial region of the medulla is the **dorsal respiratory group (DRG),** which relays its input to the VRG. The VRG initiates neural signals for inspiration and expiration; previously, physiologists thought the DRG controlled this activity. Axons from upper motor neurons extend from the VRG into the spinal cord. Axons from lower motor neurons extend from the spinal cord and form both the **phrenic nerves** that innervate the diaphragm and **intercostal nerves** that innervate the intercostal muscles.

Action potentials are initiated during quiet breathing by inspiratory neurons in the VRG and sent through these nerve pathways for approximately 2 seconds. The intensity of the action potentials increases over these 2 seconds. Additionally, nerve signals are sent from the VRG inspiratory neurons to VRG expiratory neurons.

The inspiratory neuron stimulation causes both the diaphragm and external intercostal muscles to contract, resulting in an increase in thoracic cavity volume. Ultimately, inspiratory neurons are inhibited by the expiratory neurons of the VRG and the pontine respiratory group. Consequently, inspiratory impulses cease for approximately 3 seconds. Lack of nerve stimulation causes both the diaphragm and external intercostal muscles to relax, and the thoracic cavity volume subsequently decreases.

The **pontine respiratory center** is located within the pons and modifies the activity of the nuclei in the medulla. It appears to provide for a smooth transition between inspiration and expiration by sending impulses to the VRG. Erratic breathing results if this area is damaged.

A breathing rhythm that involves 2 seconds of inspiration followed by 3 seconds of expiration results in an average respiratory rate of 12 times per minute. The average range for the rate of quiet breathing is generally between 12 and 15 times per minute—a rate referred to as **eupnea** (yūp-nē-ă).

WHAT DO YOU THINK?

3 The phrenic nerves extend from the cervical plexus formed by the rami of spinal nerves C1–C4, and intercostal nerves are the anterior rami of spinal nerves T1–T11. Predict the consequences to breathing for each condition if a spinal cord injury is above C2–C4, between C5 and T12, or below T12.

Altering Breathing Rate and Depth

Breathing rate and depth are altered by a number of reflexes that respond to sensory input from receptors, including chemoreceptors, proprioceptors, stretch receptors, and irritant receptors, as well as input from higher brain centers. Nerve signals are sent along sensory neurons to the DRG. When the DRG is activated, nerve signals are subsequently relayed to the VRG, resulting in a change in the rhythm and force of breathing. Change in the *rate* of breathing is accomplished by altering the amount of time spent in both inspiration and expiration, whereas altering the depth of breathing is accomplished through stimulation of accessory muscles, which results in greater thoracic volume changes.

Reflexes Involving Chemoreceptors Internal chemoreceptors include both central chemoreceptors and peripheral chemoreceptors. They perform a critical role in regulating changes in our breathing rate by monitoring fluctuations in chemical concentration of both hydrogen ions (H^+) and respiratory gases in the blood and cerebrospinal fluid (CSF). Levels of respiratory gases are expressed as the partial pressure of carbon dioxide (P_{CO_2}) and the partial pressure of oxygen (P_{O_2}). Partial pressures are discussed in more detail later in the chapter. For now, just remember that the higher the partial pressure for a gas, the greater its concentration.

Central chemoreceptors are located specifically on the ventrolateral surface of the medulla. This is an area that is in close proximity to the medullary respiratory center. Central chemoreceptors monitor only pH changes of CSF induced by changes in blood P_{CO_2}. Carbon dioxide diffuses from the blood into the CSF. In the CSF, carbonic anhydrase catalyzes the formation of carbonic acid from carbon dioxide and water. The carbonic acid then dissociates into bicarbonate and hydrogen ions. The formation of H^+ causes a drop in CSF pH, and this change is detected and relayed to the medullary respiratory center. Respiration rate and depth are increased and additional carbon dioxide is expelled, ultimately returning blood P_{CO_2} and CSF pH to normal levels. Conversely, a decrease in P_{CO_2} would cause an increase in pH, and breathing rate and depth would decrease.

Peripheral chemoreceptors are housed within the walls of specific blood vessels. They are the **carotid bodies** located at the split of the common carotid artery into the external and internal

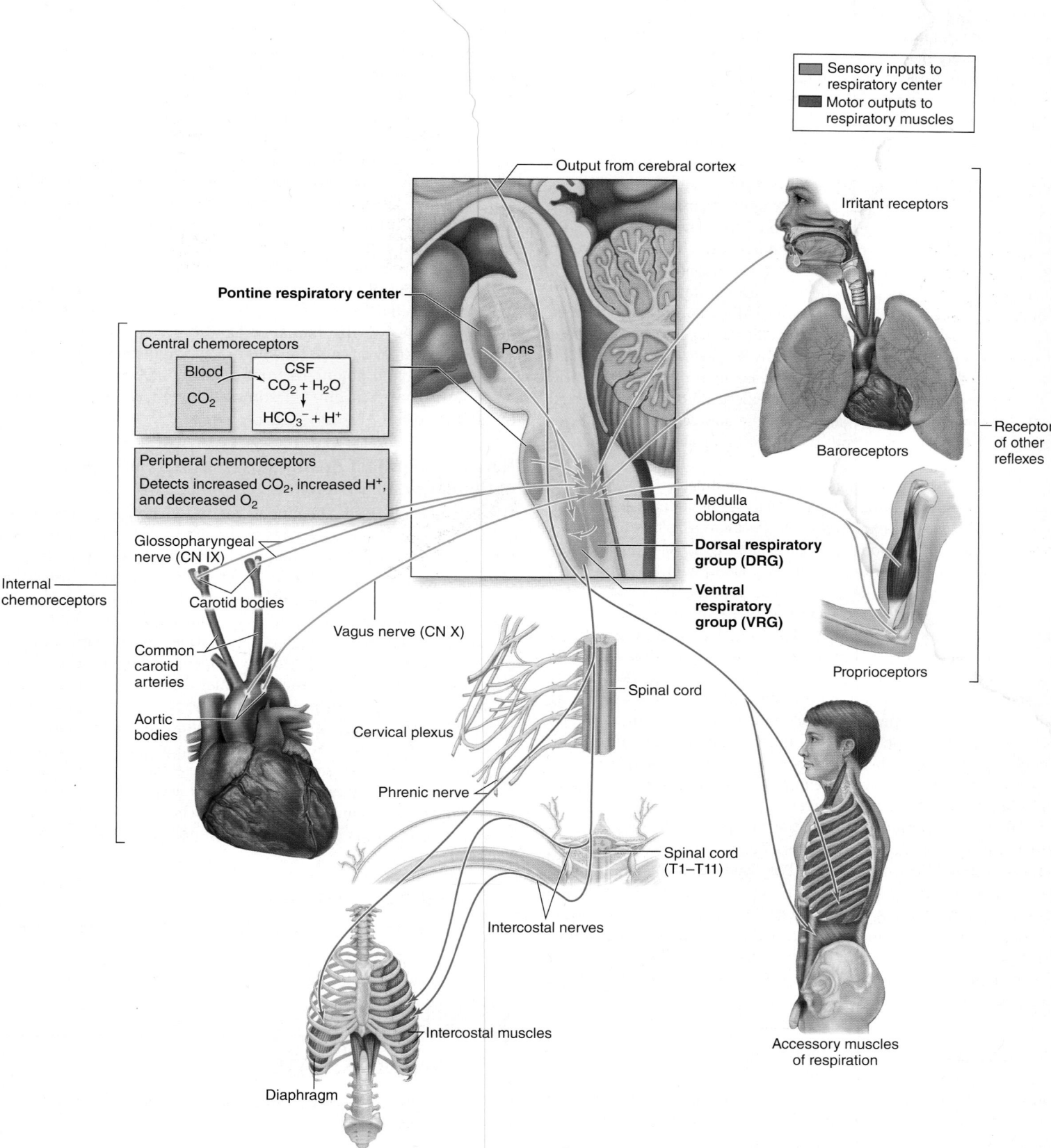

Figure 23.23 Respiratory Center. The respiratory center rhythmically sends motor output to the diaphragm and external intercostals to regulate quiet breathing. The respiratory center is stimulated to alter its breathing rate and depth by sensory input from central chemoreceptors in the brain. Additional sensory input comes from peripheral receptors, including chemoreceptors within the carotid and aortic bodies, irritant receptors of the mucosal lining of the respiratory tract, stretch receptors of the lungs and visceral pleura, and proprioceptors of muscles, tendons, and joints. Breathing can be consciously controlled by the cerebral cortex; its motor output bypasses the respiratory center to directly stimulate lower motor neurons innervating skeletal muscles of breathing. AP|R

carotid arteries, and the **aortic bodies** housed in the aortic arch. Peripheral chemoreceptors detect changes in arterial blood. When stimulated either by changes in blood respiratory gases or blood pH, the carotid bodies send nerve impulses through the glossopharyngeal nerves, and the aortic bodies send nerve impulses through the vagus nerves to the respiratory center. This center alters action potentials to breathing muscles, resulting in either an increase or decrease in rate and depth. The specific types of stimulation for peripheral chemoreceptors are described next.

Both central and peripheral chemoreceptors monitor pH changes induced by changes in blood P_{CO_2}. The peripheral chemoreceptors differ from central chemoreceptors because they are also stimulated by changes in H^+ produced independently of P_{CO_2}. This occurs, for example, when H^+ accumulates either during metabolic acidosis, as a result of either kidney failure (kidneys normally eliminate H^+), or when ketoacidosis develops, in the case of diabetes mellitus (keotacids are a by-product from metabolism of fatty acids, section 25.6c). An increase in H^+ concentration in the blood is detected by peripheral chemoreceptors and is relayed to the respiratory center regardless of the source. The result is an increase in the rate and depth of breathing in an attempt to reestablish homeostasis.

Peripheral chemoreceptors are also stimulated by blood P_{O_2} changes. Generally, changes in blood P_{O_2} levels influence breathing rate by causing the chemoreceptors to be more sensitive to changes in blood P_{CO_2}. This relationship has a synergistic effect: The combination of decreased P_{O_2} and increased P_{CO_2}, along with the subsequent production of H^+, causes greater stimulation of the respiratory center.

Note that the arterial oxygen level in the blood must decrease substantially from its normal P_{O_2} level of 95 mm Hg to an abnormally low level of 60 mm Hg before it can stimulate the chemoreceptors independently of P_{CO_2}. This relationship can have deadly consequences to swimmers who hyperventilate before swimming underwater. This hyperventilation reduces the swimmer's blood CO_2 level to the point where chemoreceptors are not stimulated. Their blood O_2 level is being depleted at the same time by exertion, but not enough to stimulate chemoreceptors. A swimmer may lose consciousness and drown as a result.

The most important stimulus affecting breathing rate and depth is blood P_{CO_2}. The respiratory center is very sensitive to changes in carbon dioxide levels; increases in P_{CO_2} levels as small as 5 mm Hg will double the breathing rate. The changes in P_{CO_2} can stimulate respiratory rate changes most powerfully when the carbon dioxide is joined to water, forming carbonic acid in the CSF because, unlike the blood, the CSF lacks proteins to buffer the gain or loss of H^+. Consequently, pH changes in the CSF most accurately reflect the changes in P_{CO_2}.

Other Reflexes   **Proprioceptors** within joints and muscles are stimulated by body movement. These sensory receptors relay nerve signals to the respiratory center in response to increases in body movement with a subsequent increase in breathing depth. **Baroreceptors** are stretch receptors located within both the visceral pleura and bronchiole smooth muscle. These sensory receptors initiate a reflex to prevent overstretching of the lungs by inhibiting inspiration activities. This reflex is referred to as the **inhalation reflex,** or *Hering-Breuer reflex*. It effectively protects the lungs from damage due to overinflation. When overstretched, these baroreceptors send nerve signals through the vagus nerves to the respiratory center to shut off inspiration activity, thus resulting in expiration.

This may be a normal means of controlling respiration in infants, but it is thought to serve only as a protective reflex after infancy.

Sneezing and coughing are reflexes that involve an exaggerated intake of breath, the closure of the larynx and contraction of abdominal muscles, followed by an explosive blast of exhaled air when the vocal cords open abruptly.

Action of Higher Brain Centers   Higher brain centers, including the hypothalamus, limbic system, and cerebral cortex, can influence breathing rate. The hypothalamus increases the breathing rate if the body is warm and decreases it if the body is cold. The limbic system alters the breathing rate in response to emotions and emotional memories. The frontal lobe of the cerebral cortex controls voluntary changes in our breathing pattern for various activities, such as talking, singing, breath-holding, performing the Valsalva maneuver, and other actions. Unlike the other higher areas of the brain that relay impulses to the respiratory center, action potentials from the cerebral cortex bypass the respiratory center to directly stimulate lower motor neurons in the spinal cord.

Nervous Control of Breathing Versus Nervous Control of the Respiratory System

We distinguish between the innervation for breathing and the innervation of the anatomic structures of the respiratory system. Respiratory structures, which are composed of both smooth muscle and glands, are innervated by the axons of lower motor neurons of the autonomic nervous system and controlled by brainstem nuclei. In contrast, breathing muscles, which are composed of skeletal muscle tissue, are innervated by axons of the lower motor neurons of the somatic nervous system. The control of the breathing muscles comes from nuclei in both the brainstem and the cerebral cortex. The nuclei composing the respiratory center regulate normal breathing with their rhythmic output along the lower motor neurons of the phrenic and intercostal nerves, and this center alters breathing rate and depth in response to various sensory input. The cerebral cortex consciously regulates breathing by directly stimulating lower motor neurons that extend to the skeletal muscles of breathing. This diverse input from the nervous system allows breathing to be controlled both reflexively and consciously.

 WHAT DID YOU LEARN?

 24 What are the functions of the VRG and DRG within the respiratory centers?

INTEGRATE

LEARNING STRATEGY

This summary can help you to remember what is monitored by the two different types of chemoreceptors.

- **Central chemoreceptors** *monitor CSF:* H^+ in CSF (which is produced from blood CO_2).

- **Peripheral chemoreceptors** *monitor blood:* (1) H^+ in blood (which is produced from blood CO_2). (2) the H^+ from metabolic acid, such as occurs in ketoacidosis; and (3) the P_{O_2} in blood.

25 Which of the following stimuli will cause an increase in the respiratory rate: (a) increase in blood P_{CO_2}, (b) increase in blood H^+, (c) increase in H^+ within the CSF, and (d) increase in blood P_{O_2}?

26 Are the skeletal muscles of breathing innervated by somatic nerves or autonomic nerves? Explain.

23.5d Airflow, Pressure Gradients, and Resistance

✔ LEARNING OBJECTIVES

8. Define airflow.

9. Explain how pressure gradients and resistance determine airflow.

Airflow is the amount of air that moves into and out of the lungs with each breath. Sufficient exchange of air must be maintained for normal body functions; this exchange is in part determined by airflow and variables that affect it. Airflow is a function of two factors: (1) the *pressure gradient* established between atmospheric pressure and intrapulmonary pressure, and (2) the *resistance* that occurs due to conditions within the airways, lungs, and chest wall. The formula for airflow is expressed here:

$$F = \frac{\Delta P}{R} \quad \text{or} \quad F = \frac{P_{atm} - P_{alv}}{R}$$

The parameters are F = flow, ΔP = difference in pressure between atmosphere (atm) and the intrapulmonary pressure within the alveoli (alv), and R = resistance.

This mathematical expression demonstrates that flow is *directly* related to the pressure gradient between atmosphere and lungs and *inversely* related to resistance. If the pressure gradient increases, then airflow into the lungs increases, but if the pressure gradient decreases, airflow into the lungs lessens (assuming resistance remains the same). In contrast, if resistance increases, then airflow lessens, whereas if resistance decreases, airflow increases (assuming the pressure gradient remains the same).

The **pressure gradient** (ΔP) is the difference between atmospheric pressure and intrapulmonary pressure ($P_{atm} - P_{alv}$). It can be changed by altering the volume of the thoracic cavity. The contraction of both the diaphragm and external intercostals during quiet breathing cause small volume changes that allow approximately 500 mL of air to enter into the lungs. The thoracic cavity volume is further increased if accessory muscles of forced inspiration are stimulated, causing a larger decrease in intrapulmonary pressure. Airflow into the lungs increases because a steeper pressure gradient is established between atmospheric pressure and intrapulmonary pressure.

Airflow is always opposed by resistance. **Resistance** includes all the factors that make it more difficult to move air from the atmosphere through the respiratory passageway into the alveoli. Resistance may be altered in three possible ways: (1) a decrease in elasticity of the chest wall and lungs, (2) a change in the bronchiole diameter or the size of the passageway through which air moves, and (3) the collapse of alveoli.

A decrease in elasticity of the chest wall and lungs results in an increase in resistance. Young, healthy chest walls and lung tissue are naturally elastic. However, as we age, elastic connective tissue decreases in both the chest wall and the lungs. Elasticity of these structures is decreased when (1) an individual has vertebral column malformation, such as scoliosis; (2) arthritis develops within the thoracic cage; or (3) elastic connective tissue in the lungs is replaced with inflexible scar tissue, which occurs with pulmonary fibrosis.

Bronchiole diameter also influences resistance. Resistance increases with bronchoconstriction caused by parasympathetic stimulation, histamine release, or exposure to cold. In addition, decreasing lumen size through accumulation of mucus or inflammation in bronchioles also increases resistance. Resistance decreases with bronchodilation caused by sympathetic stimulation and the subsequent release of epinephrine from the adrenal medulla, or with external administration of epinephrine.

Increase in surface tension occurs if alveolar type II cells are not producing sufficient pulmonary surfactant because this condition increases resistance. This variable is generally important only with premature infants that are unable to produce sufficient pulmonary surfactant (healthy lungs continue to produce pulmonary surfactant beginning approximately 2 months prior to birth). Without pulmonary surfactant, the alveoli in the lungs of these premature infants collapse with each expiration. With each inspiration, the high surface tension created by the wet inner surface of the alveoli must be overcome for air to enter and reinflate the alveoli for gas exchange. These infants, therefore, experience greater resistance to airflow. This condition is referred to as **acute respiratory distress syndrome (ARDS)**.

Both surface tension and elasticity of the chest wall and lung determine compliance. **Compliance** is the ease with which the lungs and chest wall expand. Thus, the easier the lung expansion, the greater the compliance. In contrast, the more difficult it is for the lungs to expand, the lower the compliance.

✎ WHAT DO YOU THINK?

4 Epinephrine is administered in the treatment of asthma. Does epinephrine increase or decrease airway resistance? Does epinephrine increase or decrease airflow?

Respiratory diseases and anatomic abnormalities that increase resistance to airflow are associated with either a decrease in the size of the lumen of bronchioles (e.g., asthma) or a decrease in compliance (e.g., pulmonary fibrosis), or both. In either case, it produces an increase in resistance. If adequate airflow is to be maintained, the increased resistance must be met with more forceful inspirations to establish a steeper pressure gradient.

The muscles of inspiration must work harder, and a greater amount of the body's metabolic energy must be spent on breathing, for more forceful inspirations to occur. Approximately 5% of the total energy expenditure of the body normally is spent for quiet breathing. This value increases as airway resistance increases, and it can reach 20–30% of energy expenditure. This four-fold to six-fold increase in energy is so demanding that individuals with these disorders can become exhausted simply from breathing.

INTEGRATE

CONCEPT CONNECTION

A similar mathematical relationship expresses flow as a function of a pressure gradient and resistance exists for blood flow. The blood pressure gradient is established by the heart, and the resistance is experienced by the blood as it is transported through the blood vessels (section 20.4c).

27 The two factors that determine airflow are the pressure gradient and resistance. What are the three major factors that increase resistance to airflow? What changes to breathing must occur to maintain adequate airflow if resistance is increased?

23.5e Pulmonary and Alveolar Ventilation

LEARNING OBJECTIVES

10. Distinguish between pulmonary ventilation and alveolar ventilation, and discuss the significance of each.

11. Explain the relationship between anatomic dead space and physiologic dead space.

Previously we described the process of moving air into and out of the lungs and referred to it as pulmonary ventilation. The term **pulmonary ventilation** may also refer to the amount of air that is moved between the atmosphere and alveoli in 1 minute. The normal adult breathes approximately 500 mL per breath (tidal volume), and this occurs about 12 times per minute. The amount of air taken in during 1 minute (pulmonary ventilation) is calculated using the following formula:

Tidal volume × Respiration rate = Pulmonary ventilation
(amount of air   (number of breaths
per breath)   per minute)

500 mL × 12 breaths/min = 6000 mL/min = 6 L/min

WHAT DO YOU THINK?

5 Is *all* of the air taken in during pulmonary ventilation available for gas exchange? Why or why not?

Note that only the air reaching the alveoli is available for gas exchange. When air is moved from the atmosphere into the respiratory tract, a portion of it remains in the conducting zone. This collective space, where there is no exchange of respiratory gases, is referred to as the **anatomic dead space,** and it has an average volume of approximately 150 mL. The amount of air that reaches the alveoli and is available for gas exchange per minute is termed **alveolar ventilation.** This volume is less than pulmonary ventilation because the volume of air in the anatomic dead space must be subtracted from the volume of air inhaled with each breath. Thus, alveolar ventilation is calculated using the following mathematical formula:

(Tidal volume − anatomic dead space) × Respiration rate
= Alveolar ventilation
(500 mL − 150 mL) × 12 =
350 mL × 12 = 4200 mL/min = 4.2 L/min

Deeper breathing is more effective for maximizing alveolar ventilation than faster, shallower breathing. Assuming you take one deep breath, you have to overcome the dead air space only one time. All the additional air inhaled in that breath is available for gas exchange. If you take two quick breaths, you have to fill the dead air space twice.

Some respiratory disorders result in a decreased number of alveoli participating in gas exchange. This decrease can be due either to damage to the alveoli or a change in the respiratory membrane, such as when fluid accumulates in the lungs with pneumonia. The difference in volume of air available for gas exchange is accounted for by the more inclusive term **physiologic dead space,** which is the normal anatomic dead space plus any loss of alveoli. The anatomic dead space is equivalent to the physiologic dead space in a healthy individual, because the usual loss of alveoli should be minimal.

WHAT DID YOU LEARN?

28 A person in yoga class is encouraged to take long, deep breaths. Would this person have greater or lesser alveolar ventilation than an individual with a more shallow breathing? Explain.

23.5f Volume and Capacity

LEARNING OBJECTIVES

12. Define the four different respiratory volume measurements.

13. Explain the four respiratory capacities that are calculated from the volume measurements.

14. Give the meaning of forced expiratory volume (FEV) and maximum voluntary ventilation (MVV)

The volume of air that enters and leaves the lungs can be measured with an instrument called a **spirometer.** Respiratory volumes vary throughout a 24-hour period and during different stages of your life. They also vary from individual to individual. The variation is significant enough to be used as a diagnostic tool for determining the health of an individual's respiratory system. Values are compared to standard values of a reference population. Respiratory measurements are often used to diagnose respiratory disease, monitor changes in respiratory impairment over time, and assess effectiveness of treatment.

Four major respiratory volumes are typically measured (**figure 23.24** and **table 23.4**). **Tidal volume (TV)** is the amount of air inhaled or exhaled per breath during quiet breathing. **Inspiratory reserve volume (IRV)** is the amount of air that can be forcibly inhaled beyond the tidal volume (after a normal inspiration). IRV is a measure of lung compliance. **Expiratory reserve volume (ERV)** is the amount that can be forcibly exhaled beyond the tidal volume (after a normal expiration). ERV is a measure of lung and chest wall elasticity. Finally, **residual volume (RV)** is the amount of air left in the lungs even after the most forceful expiration.

There are four major respiratory capacities that can be calculated from the summation of two or more of these respiratory volumes. **Inspiratory capacity (IC)** is the sum of the tidal volume plus the inspiratory reserve volume. **Functional residual capacity (FRC)** is the sum of the expiratory reserve volume plus the residual volume. It is the volume of air that is normally left in the lungs after a

---

INTEGRATE

CLINICAL VIEW

Minimal Volume

Prior to birth, the fetus's respiratory system is nonfunctional because gas exchange occurs between fetal blood and maternal blood at the placenta. The lungs and pulmonary vessels of the fetus are collapsed; most of the blood is shunted to the systemic circulation.

When a newborn takes its first breath, the alveoli inflate. Thereafter, a small amount of air, termed **minimal volume,** remains in the lungs even if they later collapse. In contrast, a stillborn infant never takes a breath. The test at autopsy of whether an infant has been stillborn is to immerse its lungs in water. If the infant was stillborn, the lungs sink because they contain no minimal volume of air.

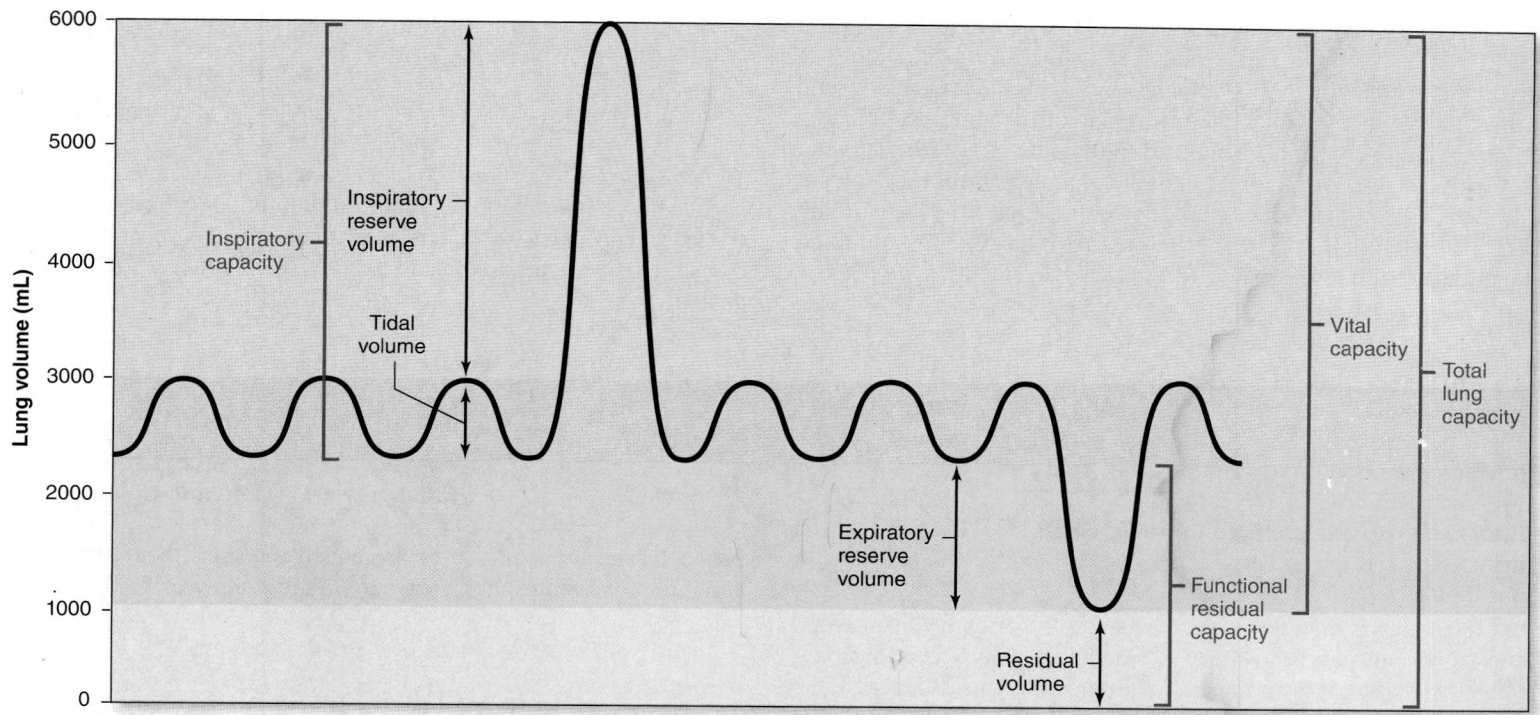

Figure 23.24 Respiratory Volumes and Capacities. Pulmonary volumes include tidal volume, inspiratory reserve volume, expiratory reserve volume, and residual volume. Capacities are the sum of two or more volumes. Inspiratory capacity includes tidal volume and inspiratory reserve volume. Functional residual capacity includes expiratory reserve volume and residual volume. Vital capacity includes tidal volume, inspiratory reserve volume and expiratory reserve volume. Total lung capacity is the sum of all four volumes.

Table 23.4	Respiratory Volumes and Capacities			
VOLUMES				
Volume	**Definition**		**Normal Values (Male)**	**Normal Values (Female)**
Tidal volume (TV)	Volume of air taken into or expelled out of lungs during a quiet breath		500 mL	500 mL
Inspiratory reserve volume (IRV)	The amount of air taken into the lungs during a forced inspiration, following a quiet inspiration; IRV is a measure of lung compliance		3100 mL	1900 mL
Expiratory reserve volume (ERV)	The amount of air expelled from the lungs during a forced expiration, following a quiet expiration; ERV is a measure of lung and chest wall elasticity		1200 mL	700 mL
Residual volume (RV)	Amount of air left in lungs following a forced expiration		1200 mL	1100 mL
CAPACITIES				
Capacity	**Formula**	**Definition**	**Normal Values (Male)**	**Normal Values (Female)**
Inspiratory capacity	TV + IRV	Total ability to inspire	3600 mL	2400 mL
Functional residual capacity	ERV + RV	Amount of air normally left (residual) in lungs after you expire quietly	2400 mL	1800 mL
Vital capacity	TV + IRV + ERV	Measure of the strength of respiration	4800 mL	3100 mL
Total lung capacity	TV + IRV + ERV + RV	Total amount of air that can be in lungs	6000 mL	4200 mL

quiet expiration. **Vital capacity (VC)** is the sum of the tidal volume plus both the inspiratory and expiratory reserve volumes. The residual volume is not part of the vital capacity. VC is significant because it is a measure of the total amount of air that a person can exchange through forced breathing. Finally, **total lung capacity (TLC)** is the sum of all the volumes, including the residual volume, and is the maximum volume of air that the lungs can hold.

Two additional common respiratory measurements of note are forced expiratory volume and maximum voluntary ventilation.

Forced expiratory volume (FEV) is the percentage of the vital capacity that can be expelled in a specific period of time. For example, FEV_1 is the vital capacity percentage that is expired in 1 second. This value is obtained by inspiring as much air as possible and then expelling the air from the lungs as quickly as possible. A healthy person should be able to expel 75–85% of the vital capacity in 1 second. Individuals with decreased ability to expire (e.g., individuals with emphysema) typically exhibit decreased FEV values.

Maximum voluntary ventilation (MVV) is the greatest amount of air that can be taken into, and then expelled from, the lungs in 1 minute. MVV levels are obtained by breathing as quickly and as deeply as possible for 1 minute. Maximum voluntary ventilation can be as high 30 L/min (compared to the pulmonary ventilation at rest of 6 L/min). All individuals with respiratory disorders have an impaired ability to inspire, expire, or both—thus, they will exhibit lower than normal MVV values. Note that both the FEV and MVV amounts are timed and reflect *rates* of air movement.

 WHAT DID YOU LEARN?

 29 How are capacities calculated?

23.6 Respiration: Alveolar and Systemic Gas Exchange

Gas exchange is the movement of respiratory gases between blood and either alveoli or cells of systemic tissues. The movement of these gases between blood in pulmonary capillaries and the alveoli of the lungs is called alveolar gas exchange, whereas the movement of respiratory gases between blood in systemic capillaries and systemic cells is called systemic gas exchange. Here we describe the general chemical principles of gas exchange, then we describe the specifics of alveolar gas exchange in the lungs and systemic gas exchange at systemic cells.

23.6a Chemical Principles of Gas Exchange

LEARNING OBJECTIVES

1. Define partial pressure and the movement of gases relative to a partial pressure gradient.
2. Describe the partial pressures that are relevant to gas exchange.
3. Explain the laws that govern gas solubility.

The gases in air move collectively down a (total) pressure gradient during breathing, as previously described in the section on pulmonary ventilation. In contrast, each gas moves independently down its own partial pressure gradient during gas exchange. Additionally, each gas also moves between air (in the alveoli) and a liquid (blood).

Partial Pressure and Dalton's Law

Partial pressure is the pressure exerted by each gas within a mixture of gases and is measured in mm Hg; it is written with a P followed by the symbol for the gas. For example, the partial pressure for oxygen is written as P_{O_2}. We can use atmospheric pressure and the mixture of gases in air to more fully explain partial pressure.

Atmospheric pressure is the total pressure all gases collectively exert in the environment. These molecules include nitrogen (N_2), oxygen (O_2), carbon dioxide (CO_2), water vapor (H_2O), and a number of other minor gases. We have seen that at sea level atmospheric pressure has a value of 760 mm Hg. The amount each gas in the atmosphere contributes to the total pressure—that is, its partial pressure—is determined by multiplying the total pressure exerted by the gas mixture by the percent of the specific gas of interest:

Total pressure × % of gas = Partial pressure of that gas

Thus, the partial pressure exerted for each gas in the atmosphere can be calculated from the total pressure (760 mm Hg at sea level) and the percentage of each of the most common gases: nitrogen (78.6%), oxygen (20.9%), carbon dioxide (0.04%), and water vapor (0.46%) as follows:

$$
\begin{array}{llll}
P_{N_2} & 760 \text{ mm Hg} \times 78.6\% & = 597 \text{ mm Hg} \\
P_{O_2} & 760 \text{ mm Hg} \times 20.9\% & = 159 \text{ mm Hg} \\
P_{CO_2} & 760 \text{ mm Hg} \times 0.04\% & = 0.3 \text{ mm Hg} \\
P_{H_2O} & 760 \text{ mm Hg} \times 0.46\% & = \underline{3.5 \text{ mm Hg}} \\
& \text{Total pressure} & = 760 \text{ mm Hg}
\end{array}
$$

When these partial pressures are added together, their sum must equal the total atmospheric pressure. As just shown,

$$P_{N_2} + P_{O_2} + P_{CO_2} + P_{H_2O} = 760 \text{ mm Hg}$$

The relationship of partial pressure to total pressure is summarized by **Dalton's law,** which states that the total pressure in a mixture of gases is equal to the sum of all of the individual partial pressures.

Partial Pressure Gradients

A **partial pressure** gradient exists when the partial pressure for a specific gas is higher in one region than in another. If a partial pressure gradient exists between two regions for a given gas, then the gas moves from the region of its higher partial pressure to the region of its lower partial pressure, and it may continue to move until the partial pressures in the two regions become equal. The exchange of respiratory gases in both alveolar gas exchange and systemic gas exchange are dependent upon partial pressure gradients.

Relevant Partial Pressures in the Body

The partial pressures that are relevant for understanding respiratory gas exchange are both the P_{O_2} and P_{CO_2} within alveoli in the lungs, systemic cells, and in circulating blood. Refer to **figure 23.25** as you read through this section.

P_{O_2} and P_{CO_2} in the Alveoli   Although air from the environment is inhaled directly into the lungs, the partial pressures of the gases within the alveoli are different from the respective atmospheric partial pressures measured for several reasons: (1) air from the environment mixes with the air remaining in the anatomic dead space in the respiratory tract; (2) oxygen diffuses out of the alveoli into the blood, and carbon dioxide diffuses from the blood into the alveoli; and (3) more water vapor is present within the alveoli because of the higher humidity there. Consequently, within the alevoli the percentage of oxygen is lower (13.7%) and the percentage of carbon dioxide is higher (5.2%) than in the atmosphere. The calculation of the partial pressure of the respiratory gases in the alveoli is as follows (figure 23.25*b*):

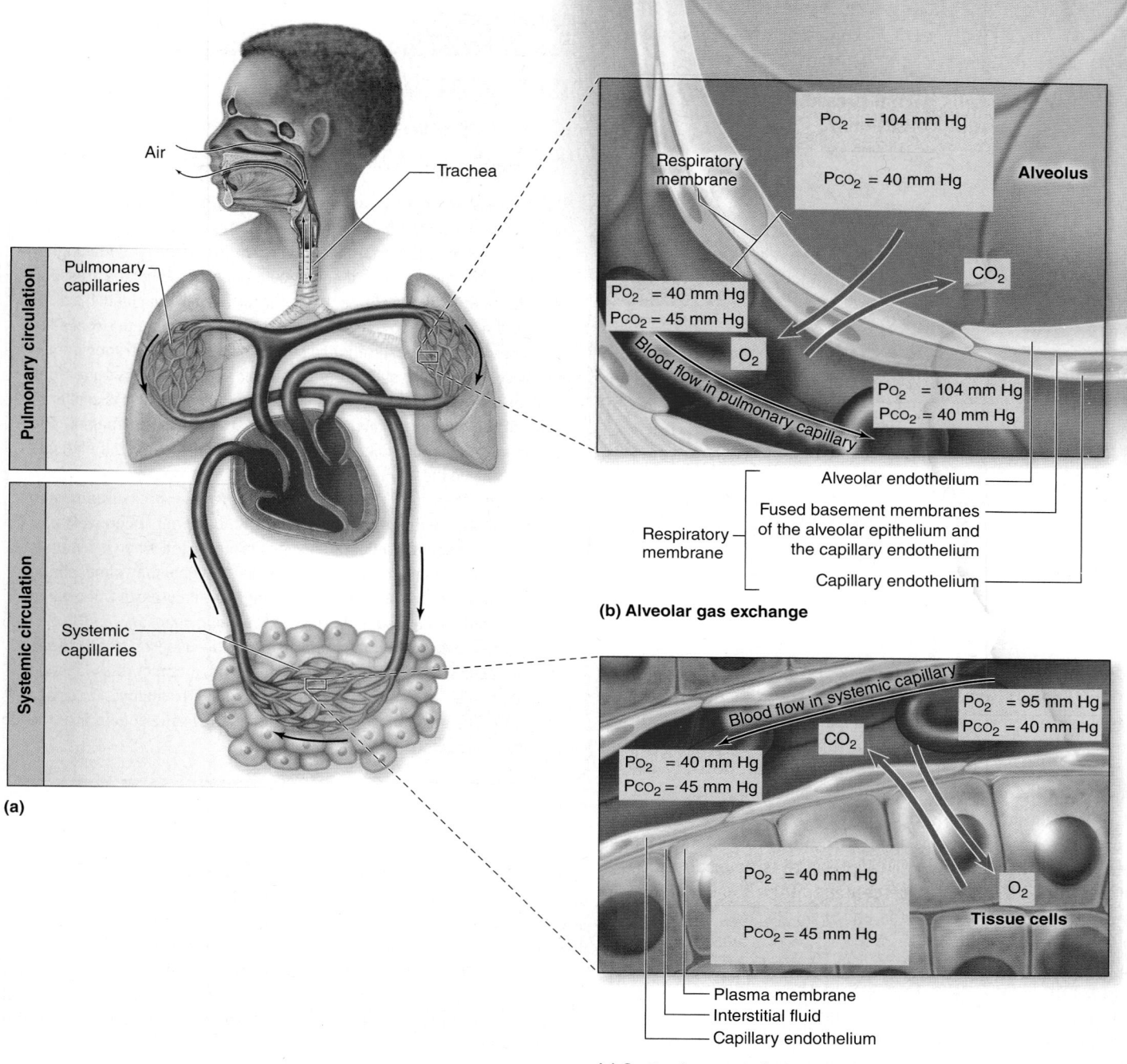

Figure 23.25 Alveolar and Systemic Gas Exchange. (*a*) Pulmonary circulation delivers blood to and from the lungs, and systemic circulation delivers blood to and from systemic cells. (*b*) Alveolar gas exchange occurs when respiratory gases are exchanged between the alveoli and the pulmonary capillaries across the respiratory membrane. Oxygen diffuses from the alveoli into the blood of the pulmonary capillaries. Carbon dioxide simultaneously diffuses in the reverse direction. (*c*) Oxygen diffuses from the blood in the systemic capillaries during systemic gas exchange, while carbon dioxide simultaneously diffuses in the reverse direction. (Values for P_{CO_2} are shown in blue; values for P_{O_2} are shown in pink.) **AP|R**

Alveolar Partial Pressures (at Sea Level)

P_{O_2} 760 mm Hg × 13.7% = 104 mm Hg

P_{CO_2} 760 mm Hg × 5.2% = 40 mm Hg

The P_{O_2} is *lower* in the alveoli (P_{O_2} = 104 mm Hg) than it is in the atmosphere (P_{O_2} = 159 mm Hg), and the P_{CO_2} is *higher* in the alveoli (P_{CO_2} = 40 mm Hg) than it is in the atmosphere (P_{CO_2} = 0.3 mm Hg). Note that under normal circumstances, the alveolar partial pressures remain constant because we are rhythmi-

cally exchanging air between the atmosphere and the alveoli of the lungs as we breathe.

P_{O_2} and P_{CO_2} in Systemic Cells The partial pressures of both O_2 and CO_2 in systemic cells reflect the activities of cellular respiration. Cells use oxygen during cellular respiration and produce carbon dioxide as a waste product. So in comparison to the percentages in alveoli, the percentage of oxygen in the systemic cells is lower and the percentage of carbon dioxide is higher. The partial pressures of the respiratory gases in systemic cells at rest usually exhibit the measured values as shown here (figure 23.25c):

Systemic cells partial pressures
(Resting conditions)

P_{O_2} 40 mm Hg

P_{CO_2} 45 mm Hg

Note that under normal, resting conditions, the partial pressures in systemic cells remain constant because the oxygen is continuously used and carbon dioxide is continuously produced by cells during cellular respiration.

P_{O_2} and P_{CO_2} in the Circulating Blood   Both P_{O_2} and P_{CO_2} levels in the blood (figure 23.25b, c) are not set values, unlike the relatively constant values in the alveoli and systemic cells. The P_{O_2} and P_{CO_2} in the blood change continuously as the blood flows through the lung capillaries, where oxygen enters the blood and carbon dioxide leaves the blood. In addition, as blood flows through systemic capillaries, the reverse occurs: Oxygen leaves the blood and carbon dioxide enters the blood. We explain in a later section how the values for blood P_{O_2} and blood P_{CO_2} change during alveolar and systemic gas exchange.

Gas Solubility and Henry's Law

Specific additional chemical principles govern the exchange of gas between air (a gas) and blood (a liquid). These principles are summarized by **Henry's law,** which states that at a given temperature, the solubility of a gas in a liquid (i.e., how much gas can either enter or leave the liquid) is dependent upon (1) the partial pressure of the gas in the air and (2) the solubility coefficient of the gas in the liquid.

The partial pressure of a gas is the driving force to move it into a liquid. Recall that a given partial pressure is determined by the total pressure and the specific percentage of the gas of interest within the mixture—if either of these changes, the amount of the gas that enters the liquid changes. Carbon dioxide gas in a soft drink is an example of forcing more gas into a liquid by increasing its partial pressure. The CO_2 is forced into the soda under high pressure, and then the container is sealed. When the can is opened and the pressure released, carbon dioxide leaves the soda because of the lower P_{CO_2} of the atmosphere; over time, the soda becomes "flat."

The **solubility coefficient** is the volume of gas that dissolves in a specified volume of liquid at a given temperature and pressure. This coefficient is a constant that depends upon the interactions between molecules of both the gas and the liquid. The more favorable these molecular interactions are for a given partial pressure, the greater the amount of gas that dissolves in the liquid.

Gases vary in their solubility in water. For example, oxygen has a very low solubility in water (solubility coefficient = 0.024), whereas carbon dioxide has solubility about 24 times that of oxygen (solubility coefficient = 0.57). Nitrogen is the least soluble of these three major gases in the atmosphere and is about half as soluble as oxygen. The order of solubility for the three gases would be

$$CO_2 > O_2 > N_2$$

Because the amount of a gas that dissolves in a liquid is dependent upon both its partial pressure and its solubility coefficient, gases with low solubility coefficients require larger pressure gradients to "push" the gas into the liquid. You can see this

relationship when comparing the partial pressure gradients for oxygen and carbon dioxide. Nitrogen, with its very low solubility, does not dissolve in the blood in significant amounts under conditions at or above sea level. However, as mentioned in the Clinical View on decompression sickness, divers using compressed air may be subject to dangerous effects of increased nitrogen forced into the blood because of the greater pressures experienced when submerged.

WHAT DID YOU LEARN?

30 Given the same partial pressure for oxygen and carbon dioxide, which respiratory gas enters a water solution more readily? Explain using Henry's Law.

23.6b Alveolar Gas Exchange (External Respiration)

LEARNING OBJECTIVES

4. Describe alveolar gas exchange and the partial pressure gradients responsible.

5. Name the two anatomic features of the respiratory membrane that contribute to efficient alveolar gas exchange.

6. Explain ventilation-perfusion coupling and how it maximizes alveolar gas exchange.

The partial pressure gradients between the alveoli and blood, and the subsequent movement of respiratory gases across the respiratory membrane during alveolar gas exchange, are described in this section. The factors that contribute to the efficiency of alveolar gas exchange follow.

Figure 23.25b depicts events that occur in alveolar gas exchange. Notice that the P_{O_2} in the alveoli is 104 mm Hg, and the blood entering the pulmonary capillaries has a P_{O_2} of 40 mm Hg. Oxygen diffuses across the respiratory membrane from the alveoli into the capillaries because of the P_{O_2} partial pressure gradient, until the P_{O_2} in the blood is equal to that of the alveoli at 104 mm Hg. Thus, blood P_{O_2} has increased from 40 to 104 mm Hg as blood moves through the pulmonary capillaries. However, the P_{O_2} in the alveoli remains constant because oxygen is continuously entering the alveoli through the respiratory passageways.

Simultaneously, CO_2 is diffusing in the opposite direction; the P_{CO_2} in the alveoli is 40 mm Hg and that of the blood entering the pulmonary capillaries is 45 mm Hg. Carbon dioxide diffuses down its partial pressure gradient from the blood into the alveoli until the P_{CO_2} in the blood is equal to that of the alveoli at 40 mm Hg. Thus, blood P_{CO_2} has decreased from 45 to 40 mm Hg as blood moves through the pulmonary capillaries. As with oxygen, the P_{CO_2} in the alveoli also remains constant because carbon dioxide is continuously leaving the alveoli through the respiratory passageways.

Efficiency of Gas Exchange at the Respiratory Membrane

The efficiency of both O_2 and CO_2 diffusion during alveolar gas exchange is dependent upon anatomic features of the respiratory membrane. These features include both its large surface area and minimal thickness. The aggregate surface area of the respiratory membrane in a healthy lung measures approximately 70 square meters—a little less than half the size of a tennis court. The minimal thickness of this barrier measures approximately 0.5 micrometers.

Physiologic adjustments also contribute to maximizing gas exchange at the alveoli. Some alveoli, at any given time, are well ventilated and some are not; similarly, some regions of the lung have ample blood moving through pulmonary capillaries, and some do not. The smooth muscle of both the bronchioles that lead into the alveoli and the arterioles that carry blood to pulmonary capillaries

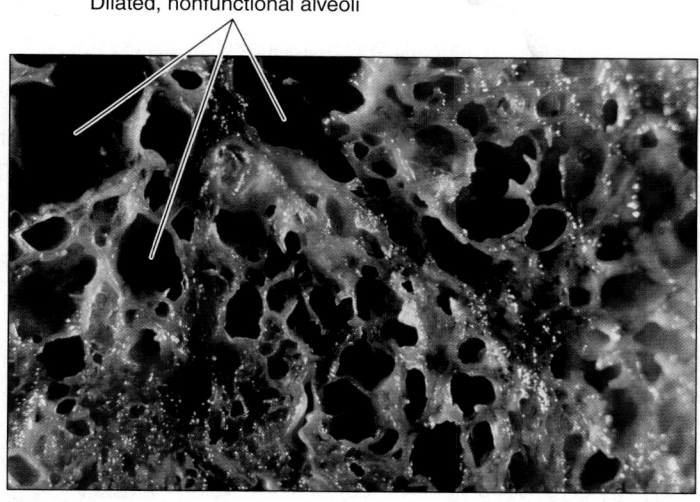

can contract and relax to maximize gas exchange. This inherent ability of bronchioles to regulate airflow and arterioles to regulate blood flow simultaneously is called **ventilation-perfusion coupling** (figure 23.26).

   Ventilation is altered by changes in bronchodilation and bronchoconstriction. Bronchioles dilate in response to an increase in P_{CO_2}, whereas they constrict in response to a decrease in P_{CO_2}.

   Perfusion is altered by changes in pulmonary arteriole dilation and pulmonary arteriole constriction. These arterioles dilate in response to either an increase in P_{O_2} or a decrease in P_{CO_2}, whereas they constrict in response to either a decrease in P_{O_2} or an increase in P_{CO_2}. Note these changes in bronchioles and pulmonary arterioles occur independently of one another.

💡 WHAT DID YOU LEARN?

31 How do the partial pressures of oxygen and carbon dioxide in blood change during alveolar gas exchange?

32 Which of the following would decrease alveolar gas exchange: loss of alveoli, fluid accumulation in the lungs, arteriole vasoconstriction, and bronchiole dilation?

23.6c Systemic Gas Exchange (Internal Respiration)

✓ LEARNING OBJECTIVES

7. Explain the partial pressure gradients between systemic cells and the blood in capillaries.

8. Differentiate between alveolar and systemic gas exchange.

Gases move between the blood and systemic cells of the body during systemic gas exchange (see figure 23.25c). Oxygen diffuses out of systemic capillaries into the interstitial fluid around systemic cells, prior to crossing the plasma membrane to enter a cell. At the same time, carbon dioxide exits the cell moving in the opposite direction to enter the blood in systemic capillaries. The driving

force is the same as in alveolar gas exchange—the partial pressure gradient that exists for both O_2 and CO_2.

   Notice that the P_{O_2} in the systemic cells is 40 mm Hg, and the blood as it enters the surrounding systemic capillaries has a P_{O_2} of 95 mm Hg. Therefore, oxygen diffuses out of the systemic capillaries down its partial pressure gradient into the cells until the blood P_{O_2} is equal to the partial pressure in the cells at 40 mm Hg. Thus, blood

Figure 23.26 Ventilation-Perfusion Coupling. (*a*) Bronchioles dilate or constrict in response to changes in CO_2 in air within the bronchioles. (*b*) Pulmonary arterioles dilate or constrict in response to changes in either blood P_{O_2} or blood P_{CO_2}.

Table 23.5	Gas Exchange[1]	
Characteristic	**Alveolar Gas Exchange**	**Systemic Gas Exchange**
Definition	Exchange of respiratory gases between alveoli in lungs and blood in pulmonary capillaries	Exchange of respiratory gases between systemic cells and blood in systemic capillaries
Changes in Blood P_{O_2}	Blood P_{O_2} increases from 40 to 104 mm Hg	Blood P_{O_2} decreases from 95 to 40 mm Hg
Changes in Blood P_{CO_2}	Blood P_{CO_2} decreases from 45 to 40 mm Hg	Blood P_{CO_2} increases from 40 to 45 mm Hg

1. General Conditions: Location is at sea level and individual is at rest

P_{O_2} has decreased from 95 to 40 mm Hg as blood moves through the systemic capillaries.

Simultaneously, carbon dioxide is diffusing in the opposite direction. The P_{CO_2} in systemic cells is 45 mm Hg, and the blood entering the systemic capillaries is 40 mm Hg. Carbon dioxide diffuses down its partial pressure gradient from the cells into the blood until blood P_{CO_2} is 45 mm Hg. Thus, blood P_{CO_2} has increased from 40 to 45 mm Hg as blood moves through the systemic capillaries.

Unless conditions change, such as when engaging in strenuous activity, the partial pressure of each gas in the cells remains relatively constant because the continuous delivery of oxygen and removal of carbon dioxide correspond with the amounts associated with cellular respiration. The results of both alveolar and systemic gas exchange are summarized in **table 23.5**.

Integration of Alveolar and Systemic Gas Exchange

During alveolar gas exchange, blood P_{CO_2} decreases from 45 to 40 mm Hg; during systemic gas exchange, blood P_{CO_2} increases from 40 to 45 mm Hg (see figure 23.25b, c). Notice that the P_{CO_2} values reverse as the blood makes its way through the two cardiovascular circuits: 45 to 40 mm Hg in the pulmonary capillaries, 40 to 45 mm Hg in the systemic capillaries.

 WHAT DO YOU THINK?

6 What can account for the blood P_{O_2} arriving at systemic capillaries with a lower P_{O_2} value than when it left the pulmonary capillaries?

Blood P_{O_2} increases from 40 to 104 mm Hg during alveolar gas exchange, and blood P_{O_2} decreases from 95 to 40 mm Hg during systemic gas exchange. When we discussed pulmonary blood circulation earlier, we noted that bronchial veins dump small amounts of deoxygenated blood into the pulmonary veins prior to the blood returning to the heart, where it is subsequently pumped by the left ventricle through the systemic circulation. This input of deoxygenated blood accounts for the decrease in P_{O_2} from 104 to 95 mm Hg.

 WHAT DID YOU LEARN?

33 How do the partial pressures of oxygen and carbon dioxide in blood change during systemic gas exchange?

23.7 Respiration: Gas Transport

The fourth process of respiration is gas transport. Gas transport is the movement of respiratory gases within the blood between the lungs and systemic cells.

23.7a Oxygen Transport

☑ LEARNING OBJECTIVE

1. Explain why hemoglobin is essential to oxygen transport.

Oxygen is transported in blood from the alveoli through pulmonary veins of the pulmonary circulation to the left side of the heart. Next, oxygen is pumped into the aorta and through arteries of the systemic circulation to enter systemic capillaries (see figure 19.4). Oxygen then diffuses from the blood in systemic capillaries into systemic cells. The ability of blood to transport oxygen is dependent upon two factors: the solubility coefficient of oxygen in blood plasma and the presence of hemoglobin (Hb).

Our discussion of gas solubility and Henry's law pointed out that the solubility coefficient of oxygen is very low (0.024). This means that only small amounts of oxygen (less than 2%) are dissolved in the plasma. Consequently, about 98% of the oxygen in the blood must be transported within erythrocytes where it attaches to the iron within hemoglobin molecules (see figure 18.6). Oxygen bound to hemoglobin is referred to as **oxyhemoglobin** (abbreviated HbO_2). Hemoglobin without bound oxygen is called **deoxyhemoglobin** (abbreviated as HHb):

HHb (deoxyhemoglobin) + O_2 ↔ HbO_2 (oxyhemoglobin)

 WHAT DID YOU LEARN?

34 Why is such a small percentage (about 2%) of oxygen dissolved in plasma and most transported on hemoglobin?

23.7b Carbon Dioxide Transport

LEARNING OBJECTIVES

2. Describe the three ways carbon dioxide is transported in the blood.

3. Explain the conversion of CO_2 to and from HCO_3^- within erythrocytes.

Cells typically produce about 200 mL/min of carbon dioxide as a waste product during cellular respiration. Carbon dioxide is transported from systemic cells within deoxygenated blood through veins of the systemic circulation to the right side of the heart, then pumped into the pulmonary trunk and pulmonary arteries to enter pulmonary capillaries (see figure 19.4). Carbon dioxide then diffuses from the blood within capillaries into the alveoli.

Whereas hemoglobin is the major means of transporting oxygen, carbon dioxide has three means of being transported in the blood from the systemic cells to the alveoli: (1) CO_2 dissolved in plasma, (2) CO_2 attached to globin portion of hemoglobin, and (3) as bicarbonate (HCO_3^-) dissolved in plasma.

We previously noted that the solubility coefficient of carbon dioxide is 0.57. Due to both this value and the small partial pressure gradient for CO_2, approximately 7% of carbon dioxide is transported to the alveoli as a dissolved gas within the plasma of blood.

Hemoglobin is capable of transporting about 23% of the CO_2 as a carbaminohemoglobin compound. The CO_2 is attached to amine groups (—NH_2) in the globin protein:

$$CO_2 + Hb \leftrightarrow HbCO_2 \text{ (carbaminohemoglobin)}$$

The remaining 70% of the CO_2 diffuses into erythrocytes and combines with water to form bicarbonate (HCO_3^-) and H^+:

$$CO_2 + H_2O \leftrightarrow H_2CO_3 \leftrightarrow HCO_3^- + H^+$$

HCO_3^- then diffuses into the plasma. Thus, the largest percentage of CO_2 is carried from the systemic cells to the lungs in plasma as dissolved HCO_3^-. Carbon dioxide is regenerated when blood moves through pulmonary capillaries and this process is reversed. **Figure 23.27** provides a synopsis of the details of this conversion and its reversal within erythrocytes.

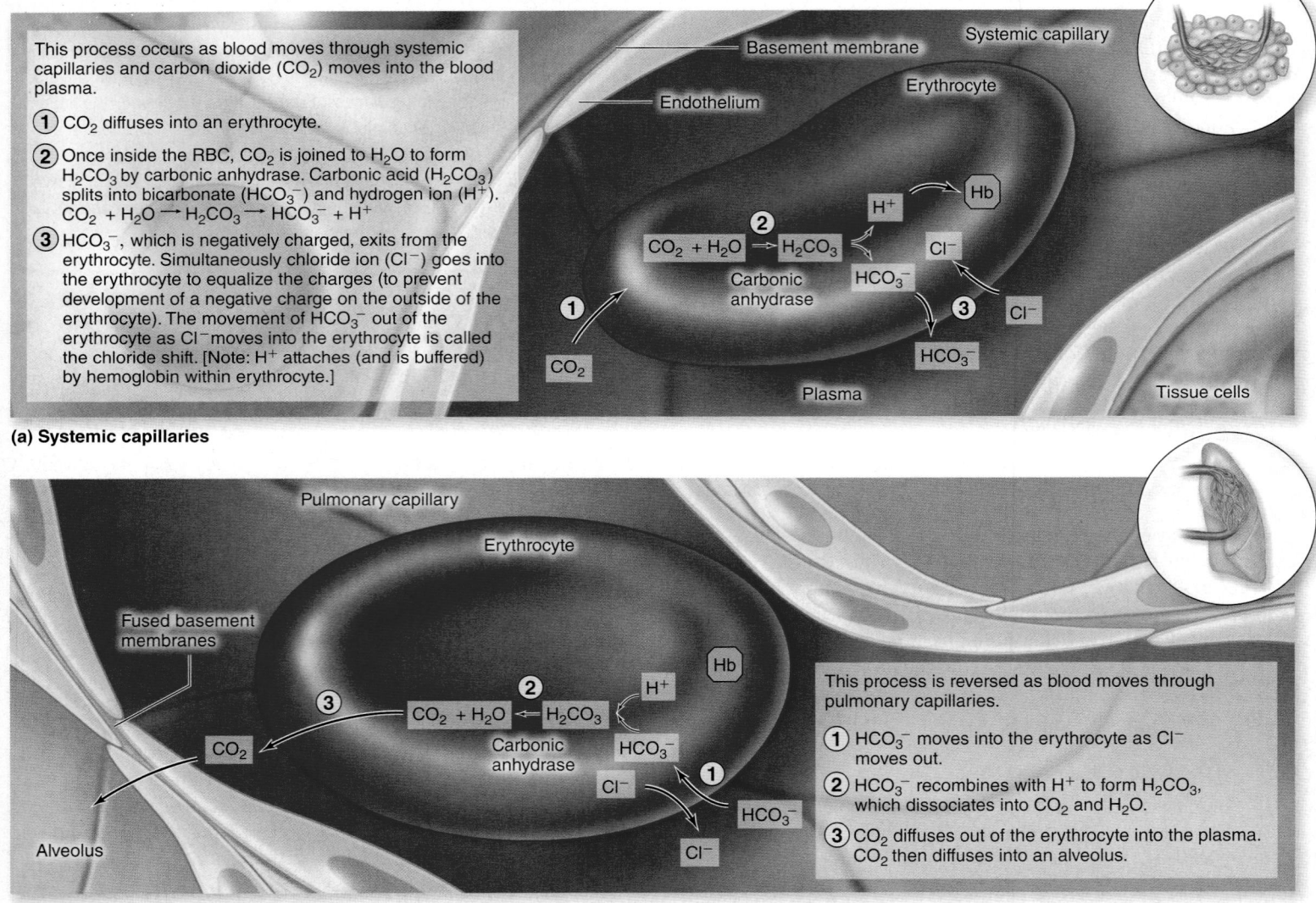

This process occurs as blood moves through systemic capillaries and carbon dioxide (CO_2) moves into the blood plasma.

① CO_2 diffuses into an erythrocyte.

② Once inside the RBC, CO_2 is joined to H_2O to form H_2CO_3 by carbonic anhydrase. Carbonic acid (H_2CO_3) splits into bicarbonate (HCO_3^-) and hydrogen ion (H^+).
$CO_2 + H_2O \rightarrow H_2CO_3 \rightarrow HCO_3^- + H^+$

③ HCO_3^-, which is negatively charged, exits from the erythrocyte. Simultaneously chloride ion (Cl^-) goes into the erythrocyte to equalize the charges (to prevent development of a negative charge on the outside of the erythrocyte). The movement of HCO_3^- out of the erythrocyte as Cl^- moves into the erythrocyte is called the chloride shift. [Note: H^+ attaches (and is buffered) by hemoglobin within erythrocyte.]

(a) Systemic capillaries

This process is reversed as blood moves through pulmonary capillaries.

① HCO_3^- moves into the erythrocyte as Cl^- moves out.

② HCO_3^- recombines with H^+ to form H_2CO_3, which dissociates into CO_2 and H_2O.

③ CO_2 diffuses out of the erythrocyte into the plasma. CO_2 then diffuses into an alveolus.

(b) Pulmonary capillaries

Figure 23.27 Conversion of Carbon Dioxide to Bicarbonate. (*a*) In systemic capillaries, CO_2 enters erythrocytes, where it combines with H_2O to form carbonic acid (H_2CO_3): this compound is then converted to bicarbonate ion (HCO_3^-) and hydrogen ion (H^+). HCO_3^- leaves the erythrocyte and is replaced by Cl^-. HCO_3^- is transported in plasma. H^+ produced during the chloride shift binds with and is buffered by hemoglobin, thus helping to prevent a decrease in pH. (*b*) The process is reversed in pulmonary capillaries. Cl^- leaves the erythrocyte and HCO_3^- enters. HCO_3^- recombines with H^+ to reform CO_2 and H_2O. CO_2 exits the erythrocyte. It then diffuses into the alveoli and is expelled.

WHAT DID YOU LEARN?

35 How is the majority of carbon dioxide transported within the blood?

23.7c Hemoglobin as a Transport Molecule

LEARNING OBJECTIVES

4. Name the three substances carried by hemoglobin.

5. Explain the significance of the oxygen-hemoglobin saturation curve for both alveolar and systemic gas exchange.

Hemoglobin transports three substances relative to respiration activities: (1) oxygen attached to iron, (2) carbon dioxide bound to the globin, and (3) hydrogen ions bound to the globin. A critical aspect of this transport is that the binding or release of one substance causes a conformational change that temporarily alters the shape of the hemoglobin molecule. This change influences the ability of hemoglobin to bind or release the other two substances.

Oxygen-Hemoglobin Saturation Curve

Because one hemoglobin molecule has four iron atoms, each hemoglobin molecule may bind a maximum of four O_2 molecules. The amount of oxygen bound to hemoglobin is expressed as the *percent O_2 saturation of hemoglobin*. For example, when oxygen is bound to one-quarter of the available iron binding sites, the hemo-globin is said to be 25% saturated, and if all iron sites are occupied by oxygen, hemoglobin is 100% saturated.

Hemoglobin saturation is determined by several variables. The most important variable is the Po_2. Predictably, as the Po_2 increases, hemoglobin saturation increases. The binding of each O_2 molecule causes a conformational change in hemoglobin that makes it progressively easier for each additional O_2 molecule to bind to an available iron. This increase in the ease of oxygen binding is termed the **cooperative binding effect** of O_2 loading.

The graph shown in **figure 23.28** relates the Po_2 and percent O_2 saturation of hemoglobin called the **oxygen-hemoglobin saturation curve** (or *oxyhemoglobin dissociation curve*). Notice that the relationship between Po_2 and hemoglobin saturation is not linear (a straight line). The plotted points on the graph produce an S-shaped, or sigmoidal curve.

Relatively large changes occur in the hemoglobin saturation as the Po_2 increases initially. For example, a change in Po_2 from 20 to 40 mm Hg, a relatively small difference, results in the hemoglobin saturation increasing from about 35% to 75% saturated as a result of the cooperative binding effect. The curve is very steep in this part of the graph. A Po_2 of at least 60 mm Hg causes hemoglobin to become over 90% saturated. When Po_2 values are higher than 60 mm Hg, only relatively small changes in hemoglobin saturation occur. A small change in Po_2 from 80 to 100 mm Hg changes the hemoglobin saturation from 95% to 98% saturated—a very small change of only 3%. Figure 23.28 has application to the physiologic processes of oxygen loading that occurs during alveolar gas exchange in the lungs and oxygen unloading that occurs during systemic gas exchange at the systemic cells as described next.

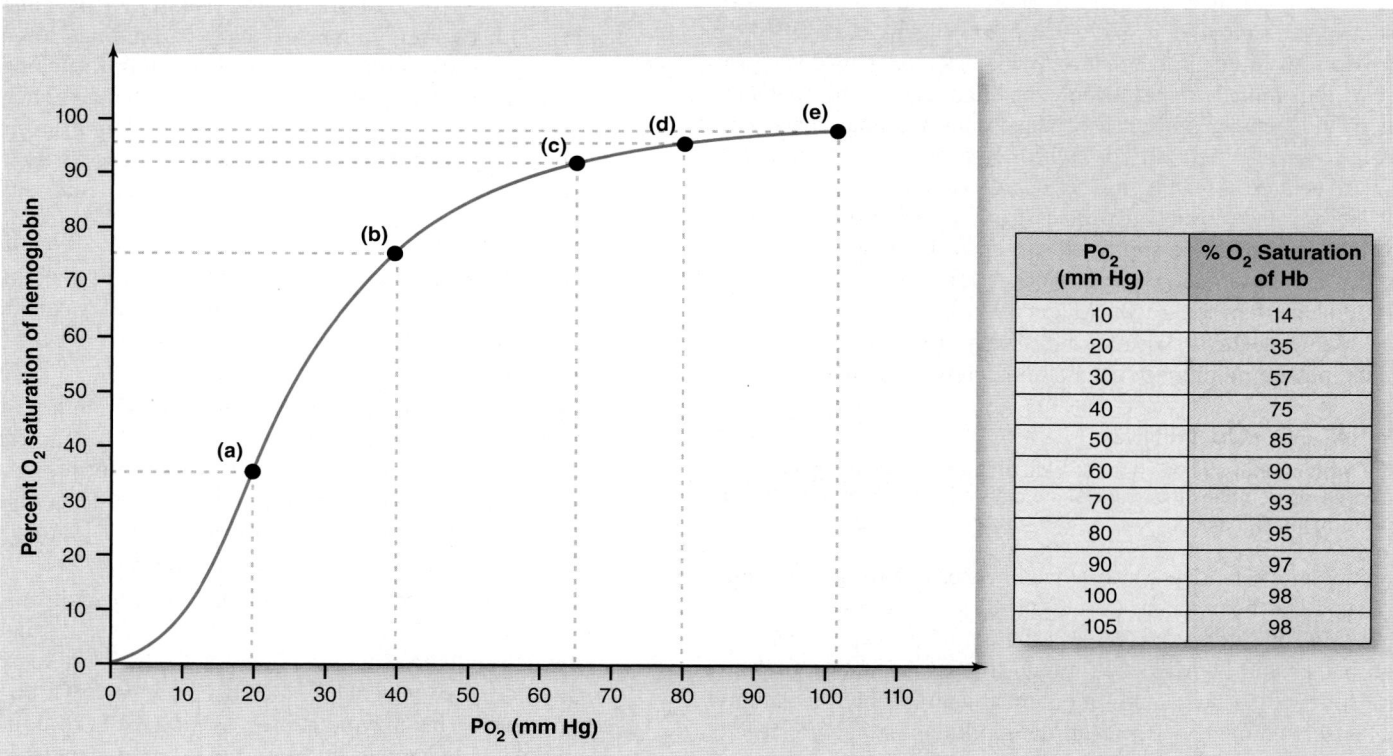

Po_2 (mm Hg)	% O_2 Saturation of Hb
10	14
20	35
30	57
40	75
50	85
60	90
70	93
80	95
90	97
100	98
105	98

Figure 23.28 Oxygen-hemoglobin Saturation Curve. The percent O_2 saturation of hemoglobin increases as Po_2 increases. Relatively large changes in percent O_2 saturation of hemoglobin occur as Po_2 changes from 0 to 60 mm Hg. At Po_2 greater than 60 mm Hg changes in percent O_2 saturation of hemoglobin are much smaller. (The letter labels are discussed in text.)

The Oxygen-Hemoglobin Saturation Curve and Alveolar Gas Exchange Hemoglobin loads with oxygen as blood moves through the pulmonary capillaries in the lungs. The alveolar P_{O_2} is 104 mm Hg at sea level. What would hemoglobin saturation be after the blood is transported through the pulmonary capillaries? The graph in figure 23.28 (label e) helps us determine that hemoglobin would be approximately 98% saturated.

If we ascend a high mountain, the air thins and environmental P_{O_2} decreases; this is accompanied by a decrease in alveolar P_{O_2}. How does this influence the hemoglobin saturation that occurs during alveolar gas exchange? Figure 23.28 can be used to determine approximate oxygen percent saturation values by selecting several specific alveolar P_{O_2} values that that are correlated with given altitudes. For example, if the alveolar P_{O_2} value is 81 mm Hg (which corresponds to an elevation of about 5000 feet), hemoglobin saturation would be approximately 95% (figure 23.38, label d); and if the P_{O_2} value is 65 mm Hg (altitude 9000 feet), the hemoglobin saturation would be about 91% (figure 23.28, label c). In comparison, if alveolar P_{O_2} is 40 mm Hg (altitude 17,000 feet), hemoglobin saturation would be only 75% (figure 23.28, label b).

Increases in altitude from sea level (with accompanying decreases in alveolar P_{O_2}) initially result in only small changes in hemoglobin saturation; thus, changes in oxygen delivery are minimal. However, ascending to a very high altitude, with its accompanying large decrease in alveolar P_{O_2}, results in large decreases in hemoglobin saturation. The adverse physiologic effects from a decrease in alveolar P_{O_2}, referred to as **altitude sickness,** can occur in some individuals at altitudes as low as 6600 feet but occur for most individuals at altitudes greater than 8200 feet. Milder symptoms of altitude sickness include headache, nausea, and difficulty sleeping; more severe symptoms include pulmonary edema and cerebral edema.

 WHAT DO YOU THINK?

7 If a professional athlete is on the side of the field breathing pure oxygen, do you think this will make a difference in his or her athletic performance? Explain.

One additional observation can be made concerning oxygen loading in the alveoli and hemoglobin saturation. Because a person's hemoglobin is 98% saturated at sea level, if the partial pressure of oxygen is raised higher and higher (say, through the administration of pure oxygen), little would be gained—a potential gain of only the saturation of the remaining 2%. However, the binding of oxygen to reach 100% hemoglobin saturation can be reached only if atmospheric pressure is increased from 1 atm to 3 atm (760 to 2280 mm Hg), pressures that generally can be simulated only in hyperbaric oxygen chambers.

The Oxygen-Hemoglobin Saturation Curve and Systemic Gas Exchange Oxygen is released from hemoglobin while trav-

eling through systemic capillaries to supply the needs of the body's tissues. The partial pressure of oxygen in systemic cells during resting conditions is approximately 40 mm Hg, and hemoglobin saturation is therefore 75% (figure 23.28, label b). Hemoglobin in the blood is 98% saturated with oxygen as it leaves the lungs, and then after it flows through the systemic capillaries during resting conditions it is still relatively saturated with oxygen at approximately 75%. Therefore, under resting conditions only a small percentage of the oxygen (approximately 20–25%) transported by the hemoglobin is released as it passes through systemic capillaries.

The amount of oxygen that remains bound to the hemoglobin after passing through the systemic capillaries is referred to as the **oxygen reserve.** The oxygen reserve provides a means for additional oxygen to be delivered to systemic cells under increased metabolic demands, such as occurs during exercise. If systemic cell P_{O_2} decreases to 20 mm Hg, such as occurs during vigorous exercise, then what is the hemoglobin saturation? Vigorous exercise produces a large decrease in the hemoglobin saturation, meaning that more oxygen is unloaded. The hemoglobin saturation in the blood leaving systemic capillaries would be only 35% (figure 23.28, label a).

 WHAT DO YOU THINK?

8 Is more or less oxygen delivered to the systemic cells under the conditions of the lower cellular P_{O_2} (such as during exercise)? Is the oxygen reserve higher or lower?

Other Variables That Influence Oxygen Release from Hemoglobin During Systemic Exchange

Although blood P_{O_2} is the most significant factor in hemoglobin's ability to bind and release oxygen (**figure 23.29a**), other factors—such as changes in temperature, changes in pH [H^+], synthesis of the molecule 2,3-BPG (2,3-bisphosphoglycerate) in an alternative biochemical pathway in erythrocytes, and CO_2 binding to hemoglobin—can influence the amount of oxygen binding to hemoglobin. Each of these variables causes a conformational change in hemoglobin that decreases the ability of iron within the heme to bind O_2. Consequently, additional oxygen is released. We discuss how these variables influence the release of oxygen within systemic capillaries (figure 23.29).

- **Temperature.** Metabolic activities increase body temperature. This elevated temperature interferes with hemoglobin's ability to bind and hold oxygen, so additional oxygen is released from hemoglobin (figure 23.29b).
- **H^+ binding to hemoglobin.** H^+ produced when CO_2 enters erythrocytes (carbonic anhydrase reaction) binds to the globin protein in hemoglobin, causing a conformational change in hemoglobin and additional oxygen to be released. This H^+-induced decrease in affinity of O_2 for hemoglobin is known as the **Bohr effect** (figure 23.29c).
- **Presence of 2,3-BPG.** 2,3-BPG binds to hemoglobin, causing the release of additional oxygen as blood moves through systemic capillaries (figure 23.29d). 2,3-BPG is produced in an alternative (glycolytic) metabolic pathway within erythrocytes. The enzymatic process for 2,3-BPG production is stimulated by certain hormones that bind receptors in erythrocytes, including thyroid hormone, epinephrine, growth hormone, and testosterone.
- **CO_2 binding to hemoglobin.** The binding of carbon dioxide to globin also causes the release of more oxygen from hemoglobin (figure 23.29e).

(a) Po₂ levels within the blood and cells

(b) Temperature increase

(c) H⁺ increase (Bohr effect)

(d) 2,3-BPG binding

(e) CO₂ binding

Releasing O₂

Figure 23.29 Hemoglobin and Oxygen Release. (*a*) The most important variable that influences oxygen release from hemoglobin during systemic gas exchange is blood Po₂. Other variables cause a conformational change in hemoglobin that increases the release of oxygen, including (*b*) an increase in temperature; (*c*) an increase in H⁺ (referred to as the Bohr effect); (*d*) the presence of 2,3-BPG; and (*e*) the presence of carbon dioxide. The influence of temperature and H⁺ levels on the oxygen-hemoglobin saturation curve are shown in figure (*b*) and figure (*c*), respectively.

More oxygen is released as temperature increases.

More oxygen is released as pH decreases.

Interestingly, the release of oxygen during systemic gas exchange also causes a conformational change in hemoglobin that enhances its ability to bind CO_2. Consequently, the more oxygen that is released from hemoglobin, the more carbon dioxide that binds to it—this is called the **Haldane effect.**

Examination of the oxygen-hemoglobin saturation curve reveals the effects two of these variables (temperature and pH) have on oxygen release (figure 23.29, graphs). When temperature increases from 38°C to 43°C, at any given Po₂, hemoglobin saturation is lower than when the temperature is 38°C (figure 23.29*b*, graph). If temperature decreases, hemoglobin saturation increases. Similar changes in hemoglobin saturation are observed with changes in pH (figure 23.29*c*, graph). Factors that bring about a decrease in oxygen affinity (e.g., increase in temperature, increase in H⁺) to hemoglobin and the additional release of oxygen are said to cause a **shift right** in the saturation curve. In contrast, the variables that bring about an increase in oxygen affinity to hemoglobin (e.g., decrease in temperature, decrease in H⁺) result in release of less oxygen and are said to cause a **shift left.**

Summary of Respiration

Figure 23.30 is a visual overview of the four events of respiration, the seemingly effortless task of supplying oxygen and removing carbon dioxide between our systemic cells and the environment for the purpose of generating ATP through cellular respiration. Remember that all of the processes are occurring simultaneously and continuously.

1 PULMONARY VENTILATION: INSPIRATION

- Respiratory center stimulates respiratory muscles to contract.
- Pleural cavity and thoracic cavity volumes increase and intrapleural and intrapulmonary pressures decrease.
- Air containing oxygen moves from the atmosphere into alveoli down the pressure gradient.

Inspired air

754 mm Hg (intrapleural)

759 mm Hg (intrapulmonary)

Inspired air

(a) Oxygen transport from the atmosphere into the cells. (Steps 1–4)

2 ALVEOLAR GAS EXCHANGE: OXYGEN DIFFUSES INTO BLOOD

Alveolus

Respiratory membrane

$P_{O_2} = 104$ mm Hg

Pulmonary capillary

$P_{O_2} = 104$ mm Hg

O_2 diffuses into blood

Blood flow

$P_{O_2} = 40$ mm Hg

Oxygen diffuses down its partial pressure gradient. The amount of oxygen that moves into the blood is dependent upon surface area and thickness of the respiratory membrane, and ventilation-perfusion coupling.

3 GAS TRANSPORT OF OXYGEN WITHIN THE BLOOD

>98% of O_2 binds to iron of hemoglobin

<2% of O_2 is dissolved in plasma

4 SYSTEMIC GAS EXCHANGE: OXYGEN DIFFUSES INTO SYSTEMIC CELLS

$P_{O_2} = 40$ mm Hg

O_2 diffuses into systemic cells

Systemic cells

$P_{O_2} = 95$ mm Hg

Systemic capillary

Blood flow

$P_{O_2} = 40$ mm Hg

Additional oxygen is released from hemoglobin with: an increase in temperature, H^+, 2,3-BPG, and CO_2 binding.

O_2 O_2

Increased temperature

O_2 O_2

Increased H^+ (Bohr effect)

O_2 O_2 2,3-BPG

Increased 2,3-BPG

O_2 O_2

Increased CO_2

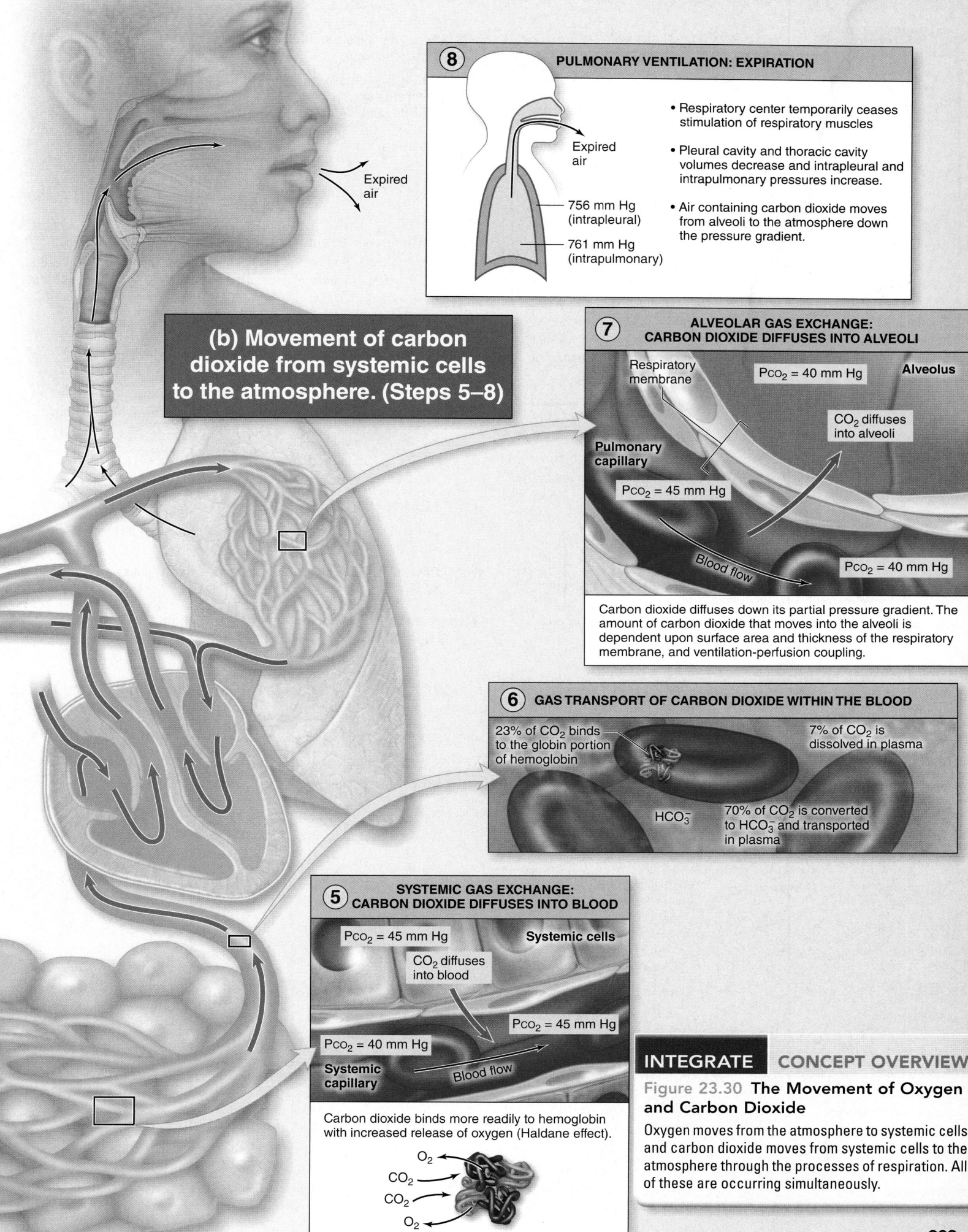

(b) Movement of carbon dioxide from systemic cells to the atmosphere. (Steps 5–8)

8 PULMONARY VENTILATION: EXPIRATION

Expired air

756 mm Hg (intrapleural)

761 mm Hg (intrapulmonary)

- Respiratory center temporarily ceases stimulation of respiratory muscles
- Pleural cavity and thoracic cavity volumes decrease and intrapleural and intrapulmonary pressures increase.
- Air containing carbon dioxide moves from alveoli to the atmosphere down the pressure gradient.

Expired air

7 ALVEOLAR GAS EXCHANGE: CARBON DIOXIDE DIFFUSES INTO ALVEOLI

Respiratory membrane

$P_{CO_2} = 40$ mm Hg   **Alveolus**

CO_2 diffuses into alveoli

Pulmonary capillary

$P_{CO_2} = 45$ mm Hg

Blood flow

$P_{CO_2} = 40$ mm Hg

Carbon dioxide diffuses down its partial pressure gradient. The amount of carbon dioxide that moves into the alveoli is dependent upon surface area and thickness of the respiratory membrane, and ventilation-perfusion coupling.

6 GAS TRANSPORT OF CARBON DIOXIDE WITHIN THE BLOOD

23% of CO_2 binds to the globin portion of hemoglobin

7% of CO_2 is dissolved in plasma

HCO_3^-

70% of CO_2 is converted to HCO_3^- and transported in plasma

5 SYSTEMIC GAS EXCHANGE: CARBON DIOXIDE DIFFUSES INTO BLOOD

$P_{CO_2} = 45$ mm Hg   **Systemic cells**

CO_2 diffuses into blood

$P_{CO_2} = 45$ mm Hg

$P_{CO_2} = 40$ mm Hg

Systemic capillary   Blood flow

Carbon dioxide binds more readily to hemoglobin with increased release of oxygen (Haldane effect).

O_2
CO_2
CO_2
O_2

INTEGRATE   CONCEPT OVERVIEW

Figure 23.30 The Movement of Oxygen and Carbon Dioxide

Oxygen moves from the atmosphere to systemic cells and carbon dioxide moves from systemic cells to the atmosphere through the processes of respiration. All of these are occurring simultaneously.

929

38 Does hemoglobin saturation increase or decrease during alveolar gas exchange?

39 How is oxygen released from hemoglobin during systemic gas exchange altered by: P_{O_2}, temperature, H^+ concentration, 2,3-BPG, and CO_2?

INTEGRATE

CLINICAL VIEW

Fetal Hemoglobin and Physiologic Jaundice

A different type of hemoglobin molecule, called **fetal hemoglobin**, is found in the erythrocytes of unborn babies. Fetal hemoglobin has a greater affinity for binding oxygen than adult hemoglobin, ensuring a net movement of oxygen from the mother's blood to the blood of the fetus. After the infant is born, the erythrocytes with fetal hemoglobin are replaced with erythrocytes containing adult hemoglobin. The infant may exhibit **physiologic jaundice**—a yellowish tinge to the skin due to elevated levels of bilirubin— as the fetal hemoglobin breaks down. This condition lasts about a week, and sometimes 2 weeks in premature infants. To facilitate and accelerate the breakdown of bilirubin, an infant with jaundice may be placed under a bili light or partially "wrapped" in a biliblanket.

If any of the systems involved in respiration—respiratory, skeletal, muscular, nervous, or cardiovascular—are unable to function normally, a homeostatic imbalance in respiratory gas exchange occurs. **Table 23.6** summarizes many of the causes of these homeostatic imbalances.

WHAT DID YOU LEARN?

36 How does oxygen movement occur during alveolar gas exchange, gas transport, and systemic gas exchange?

37 How does carbon dioxide movement occur during systemic gas exchange, gas transport, and alveolar gas exchange?

23.8 Breathing Rate and Homeostasis

The respiratory center stimulates breathing to occur at a rate of 12 to 15 times per minute and a tidal volume depth of 500 mL at rest. The respiratory center adjusts the rate and depth of breathing to maintain homeostasis in response to various stimuli, including changes in blood P_{CO_2}, levels of blood H^+, and changes in blood P_{O_2}. Recall that blood P_{CO_2} level is the most important stimulus.

Changes in breathing rate generally help to maintain homeostatic levels of respiratory gases and pH in the blood. However, changes in breathing rate may also result in homeostatic imbalances. Here we cover the changes that occur with hyperventilation, hypoventilation, and during exercise, including how homeostasis may be affected.

23.8a Effects of Hyperventilation and Hypoventilation on Cardiovascular Function

LEARNING OBJECTIVES

1. Explain how hyperventilation and hypoventilation influence the chemical composition of blood.
2. Describe how breathing rate and depth effects venous return of blood and lymph.

Hyperventilation is a breathing rate or depth that is increased above the body's demand. Hyperventilation may be caused by anxiety,

Table 23.6	Causes of Respiratory Homeostatic Imbalances	
System	**Physiologic Consequences**	**Clinical Example**
RESPIRATORY SYSTEM		
Airway obstruction	Decreased airflow into alveoli	Asthma, bronchitis
Thickened respiratory membrane	Decreased alveolar gas exchange	Pulmonary edema, pneumonia
Loss of respiratory membrane surface	Decreased alveolar gas exchange	Emphysema, lung cancer
SKELETAL SYSTEM		
Arthritis or deformities of thoracic cage or vertebral column	Impaired ability to cause dimensional volume changes in thoracic cavity	Rheumatoid arthritis, congenital deformities
MUSCULAR SYSTEM		
Paralysis of respiratory muscles	Impaired ability to cause dimensional volume changes in thoracic cavity	Polio, muscular dystrophy
NERVOUS SYSTEM		
Brainstem injury / Oversedation of respiratory center	Decreased ability to stimulate muscles of breathing	Trauma, drug use
Spinal cord injuries	Decreased ability to stimulate muscles of breathing	Trauma (e.g., diving or motorcycle accident)
CARDIOVASCULAR SYSTEM		
Pulmonary embolism	Blockage in pulmonary artery, and blood does not reach lung capillaries for gas exchange	Slowed blood flow from immobilization (e.g., prolonged bedrest, long plane flight, confined to wheelchair)
Anemia	Decreased erythrocytes or hemoglobin concentration with decreased gas transport	Low iron, pernicious anemia (inability to absorb B_{12})
Impeded blood flow	Decreased gas transport and gas exchange	Atherosclerosis, congestive heart failure, hemorrhage

panic, or ascending to a high altitude (as the individual breathes faster to compensate for the lower oxygen levels). Hyperventilation may also be performed voluntarily when you consciously inspire and expire excessively at an advanced rate. P_{O_2} levels increase and P_{CO_2} levels decrease in the alveoli. This increases the partial pressure gradients between alveoli and blood for both P_{O_2} and P_{CO_2}. These changes affect the blood as follows: (1) Additional oxygen does not enter the blood despite the steeper P_{O_2} gradient because hemoglobin is generally 98% saturated even during quiet breathing. (2) However, additional carbon dioxide leaves the blood to enter the alveoli due to a steeper P_{CO_2} gradient. Consequently, blood P_{CO_2} decreases below normal levels, a condition called **hypocapnia** (hī′pō-kap′nē-ă).

Low blood P_{CO_2} causes vasoconstriction of blood vessels. The blood vessels within the brain are especially vulnerable to these changes. Ironically, one result of hyperventilation is *decreased* oxygen delivery to the brain due to this generalized vasoconstriction. Low blood P_{CO_2} may also result in a decrease in blood H^+ concentration, if the body's buffering capacity is exceeded. This may result in **respiratory alkalosis,** a condition discussed in more detail in section 25.6.

Symptoms that accompany hyperventilation may include feeling faint or dizzy, numbness, tingling of the mouth and fingertips, muscular cramps, and tetany. If hyperventilation is prolonged, it can cause disorientation, loss of consciousness, coma, and possibly death. If the cause is panic, breathing rate typically returns to a normal level once the individual loses consciousness. A person who is hyperventilating is sometimes directed to breathe into and out of a paper bag, because this action is thought to slow the loss of CO_2.

Hypoventilation is breathing that is either too slow (called **bradypnea,** brad-ip-nē′-ă) or too shallow (called **hypopnea,** hī-pop′nē-ă) to adequately meet the metabolic needs of the body. Causes of hypoventilation are varied and include airway obstruction, pneumonia, brainstem injury, obesity (which restricts lung expansion), and any other condition that interferes with pulmonary ventilation or alveolar gas exchange. Oxygen levels decrease and carbon dioxide levels increase in the alveoli. This results in smaller partial pressure gradients between the alveoli and blood for both O_2 and CO_2. Thus, the diffusion of the respiratory gases is altered during alveolar gas exchange as follows:

- Lower amounts of oxygen diffuse from the alveoli into the blood, and blood P_{O_2} decreases. This is a condition called **hypoxia** (hī-pok′sē-ă).
- Lower amounts of carbon dioxide diffuse from the blood into the alveoli. This causes blood P_{CO_2} to increase, a condition called **hypercapnia** (hī′pěr-kap′nē-ă).

Low blood oxygen levels may result in insufficient oxygen delivery to systemic cells, with a subsequent decrease in aerobic cellular respiration (see section 3.4).

High blood P_{CO_2} may result in an increase in blood H^+ concentration (decrease in pH) if the body's buffering capacity is exceeded. This shift may lead to **respiratory acidosis,** described in more detail in section 25.6.

Symptoms resulting from either insufficient blood P_{O_2}, increased blood P_{CO_2}, or both, include lethargy, sleepiness, headache, polycythemia (low oxygen triggers release of erythropoietin), and cyanotic tissues in which skin color appears blue as a consequence of low oxygen saturation of hemoglobin. If hypoventilation is prolonged, it may lead to convulsions, unconsciousness, and possibly death.

Hypoventilation, or even the cessation of breathing, can be performed voluntarily. However, you cannot hold your breath long enough to die. The accumulation of CO_2 in the blood stimulates chemoreceptors to stimulate inspiration before or after loss of consciousness—but always before the brain suffers damage from lack of oxygen.

CONCEPT CONNECTION

Breathing rate also influences venous return of blood and lymph, as is described in the cardiovascular system (see section 20.4a) and lymphatic system (see section 21.1b). The contraction and relaxation of the skeletal muscles of breathing cause rhythmic pressure changes while breathing, and this cycle is referred to as the *respiratory pump.* The action of the respiratory pump increases during hyperventilation, increasing venous return of blood and lymph, whereas during hypoventilation, decreased action of the respiratory pump decreases venous return of blood and lymph.

 WHAT DID YOU LEARN?

40 How does blood P_{O_2} and P_{CO_2} change if an indvidual is hyperventilating?

23.8b Breathing and Exercise

 LEARNING OBJECTIVE

3. Explain the changes in breathing that accompany exercise.

A number of observations have been made regarding breathing and exercise, although not all aspects are fully understood.

While participating in vigorous exercise, a person's breathing *depth* increases while the breathing *rate* remains the same. This type of breathing, which is deeper, but not faster, is referred to as **hyperpnea** (hī′pĕr-nē-ă). Hyperpnea can be differentiated from hyperventilation in that hyperventilation is a condition where both breathing depth and rate are increased.

Both oxygen consumption and carbon dioxide production increase in response to elevated rates of cellular respiration during exercise. However, blood P_{O_2} and P_{CO_2} levels remain relatively the same. This occurs because deeper breathing, increased cardiac output, and increased blood flow are able to deliver the additional oxygen needed and eliminate the greater amount of carbon dioxide produced (i.e., supply increases to meet demand). Thus, blood P_{O_2} and P_{CO_2} levels are not thought to be the stimuli that cause breathing to change because they remain relatively constant during exercise. Although questions remain as to the exact cause, stimulation of the respiratory center generally is thought to occur from one or more of the following causes, including

- Sensory signals relayed from proprioceptors in joints, muscles, and tendons in response to movement
- Motor output originating in the cerebral cortex that initiate muscular movement during exercise, simultaneously relaying signals to the respiratory center
- The conscious anticipation of participating in exercise

 WHAT DO YOU THINK?

9 Does exercise increase or decrease venous return of blood and lymph? Will the change in blood return affect heart rate? Why or why not?

 WHAT DID YOU LEARN?

41 How does blood P_{O_2} and P_{CO_2} change during exercise?

42 What are three possible reasons that breathing changes during exercise?

CHAPTER SUMMARY

- The respiratory system consists of the lungs and the respiratory passageways extending through the head, neck, and trunk.
- The functions, organization, and mucosal lining are described for the respiratory system.

23.1a General Functions of the Respiratory System 884
- The primary functions of the respiratory system include serving as a passageway for air between the atmosphere and the alveoli, site for gas exchange between the alveoli and blood, detection of odors, and sound production.
- Breathing rate influences blood levels of oxygen, carbon dioxide, and hydrogen ion (pH), as well as venous return of blood and lymph.

23.1b General Organization of the Respiratory System 885
- Structurally, the respiratory tract is composed of the upper respiratory tract and the lower respiratory tract.
- Functionally, the respiratory tract is composed of the conducting zone and respiratory zone.

23.1c Mucosal Lining 885
- The respiratory tract is lined by a mucous membrane (mucosa) that has protective, secretory, and sensory functions.
- The epithelium of the mucosa exhibits trends of "thinning" along its length, except for areas that must withstand abrasion.

- The upper respiratory tract includes the nose, nasal cavity, and pharynx.

23.2a Nose and Nasal Cavity 886
- The nose leads into the nasal cavity, a space formed by the nose and skull that can be divided into the nasal vestibule, olfactory region, and respiratory region.

23.2b Paranasal Sinuses 888
- The four paranasal sinuses—frontal, ethmoidal, sphenoidal, and maxillary—have ducts that lead into the nasal cavity.

23.2c Pharynx 889
- The pharynx is portioned into three regions: the nasopharynx, oropharynx, and laryngopharynx.

- The lower respiratory tract is composed of the structures from the larynx to the alveoli.

23.3a Larynx 890
- The larynx is a passageway for air, closes off the respiratory tract during swallowing, is involved in sound production, assists in increasing pressure in the abdominal cavity, and participates in both a sneeze and cough reflex.

23.3b Trachea 893
- The trachea is a flexible tube with C-shaped cartilage "rings" that extends from the larynx to the primary bronchi.

23.3c Bronchial Tree 894
- The bronchial tree is a highly branched system of air-conducting passages that originate from the left and right main bronchi and end in the terminal bronchioles.
- Airflow is regulated through the bronchial tree by contraction (bronchoconstriction) and relaxation (bronchodilation) of smooth muscle, especially within bronchioles.

23.3d Respiratory Zone: Respiratory Bronchioles, Alveolar Ducts, and Alveoli 898
- The respiratory zone includes the regions of the respiratory tract with a wall thin enough for gas exchange: it extends from respiratory bronchioles, alveolar ducts, and alveoli.
- Alveoli are composed of alveolar type I cells, which are the barrier between the air sacs and pulmonary capillaries; alveolar type II cells, which produce surfactant to decrease surface tension; and alveolar macrophages, which engulf microorganisms and particulate matter.

23.3e Respiratory Membrane 899
- The respiratory membrane is the boundary between the alveolar lumen and the lumen of the pulmonary capillary.
- Respiratory gases cross this barrier in alveolar gas exchange between the alveoli of the lungs and the blood.

- Lungs are located in the thoracic cavity lateral to the mediastinum and enclosed in the thoracic cage.

23.4a Gross Anatomy of the Lung 900
- Each lung is conical in shape and divided into lobes.

23.4b Circulation to and Innervation of the Lungs 903
- Pulmonary circulation transports deoxygenated blood to the gas exchange surface of the lung for re-oxygenation, and bronchial circulation delivers oxygenated blood to the bronchi and bronchioles.
- The smooth muscle of the larynx and bronchioles are innervated by the autonomic nervous system.

23.4c Pleural Membranes and Pleural Cavity 904
- The lung surface and the internal thoracic walls are lined by serous pleural membranes.
- The pleural cavity is sandwiched between the pleural layers and contains serous fluid.

23.4d How Lungs Remain Inflated 905
- The intrapleural pressure (the pressure in the pleural cavity) is lower than the intrapulmonary pressure (the pressure in the lungs), and this pressure difference keeps the lungs inflated.

Do You Know the Basics?

____ 1. Respiration normally requires the

   a. respiratory system.
   b. muscular system.
   c. nervous system.
   d. All of these are correct.

____ 2. Arrange the following from largest to smallest for the divisions of the lung.

   a. lobes, bronchopulmonary segments, lobules, alveoli
   b. lobes, alveoli, lobules, bronchopulmonary segments
   c. alveoli, lobules, bronchopulmonary segments, lobes
   d. lobules, bronchopulmonary segments, lobes, alveoli

____ 3. The lungs do not normally collapse because

   a. they are attached to the thoracic wall with parietal ligaments.
   b. they are attached to the thoracic wall with the visceral ligaments.
   c. the pressure in the intrapleural cavity is lower than the pressure in the intrapulmonary space (lungs).
   d. the pressure in the intrapleural cavity is greater than the pressure in the intrapulmonary space (lungs).

____ 4. Which of the following correctly represents the sequence of events associated with the thoracic cavity to produce inspiration?

   a. muscle contraction, increase in volume, decrease in pressure
   b. decrease in pressure, increase in volume, muscle contraction
   c. muscle contraction, decrease in pressure, increase in volume
   d. increase in volume, muscle contraction, decrease in pressure

____ 5. The diaphragm and the external intercostals relax. Volume decreases and pressure increases in the thoracic cavity. This (by itself) describes

   a. quiet inspiration.
   b. quiet expiration.
   c. forced inspiration.
   d. forced expiration.

____ 6. Which areas of the brain contain the respiratory center?

   a. medulla oblongata and hypothalamus
   b. hypothalamus and pons
   c. medulla oblongata and pons
   d. medulla oblongata and cerebrum

____ 7. The amount of which substance in the blood normally sets the respiratory pace?

   a. oxygen
   b. carbon dioxide

   c. hydrogen gas (H_2)
   d. bicarbonate

____ 8. The movement of oxygen from the blood into the systemic cells is referred to as

   a. pulmonary ventilation.
   b. alveolar gas exchange.
   c. systemic gas exchange.
   d. gas transport.

____ 9. Most carbon dioxide is transported in the blood

   a. dissolved in the plasma as carbon dioxide.
   b. in association with hemoglobin.
   c. as bicarbonate ion.
   d. in combination with oxygen.

____ 10. All of the following are accurate statements about hemoglobin except

   a. hemoglobin carries oxygen on the Fe ion.
   b. hemoglobin carries carbon dioxide on the globin.
   c. hemoglobin carries only a small portion of the total carbon dioxide in the blood (less than 25%).
   d. hemoglobin releases oxygen at the level of the cell, making hemoglobin more saturated.

11. List, in order, all the structures air must pass through to move from the atmosphere into the alveoli.

12. Describe the relationship of the visceral pleura, parietal pleura, pleural cavity, and serous fluid to keep the lungs inflated.

13. List the four processes of respiration, in order, for moving oxygen from the atmosphere to the body's tissues. List, in order, the processes for the movement of carbon dioxide.

14. Describe the muscles, volume changes, and pressure changes involved with quiet inspiration and expiration.

15. Explain how additional air is moved during a forced inspiration or expiration.

16. Describe how quiet breathing is controlled by the respiratory center.

17. Explain alveolar and systemic gas exchange.

18. List the two means by which oxygen is transported in the blood and the three means by which carbon is transported.

19. Describe the relationship of P_{O_2} and hemoglobin percent saturation.

20. List the variables that increase the release of oxygen (by decreasing the affinity of oxygen to hemoglobin) as blood passes through systemic capillaries.

Can You Apply What You've Learned?

1. Paramedics arrived at a car accident to find an elderly gentleman breathing erratically. He was not wearing his seat belt and had hit his head on the windshield. Given his erratic breathing, they were concerned that he had damage to the

   a. medulla oblongata.
   b. cerebral cortex.
   c. pons.
   d. spinal cord.

Use the following to answer questions 2–4.

Michelle, age 45, has been smoking for over 30 years. She now is beginning to have trouble breathing. Her physician sent her to have her respiratory function tested. The results showed that she has emphysema, which is characterized by a decreased surface area for alveolar gas exchange.

2. What component of the respiratory system is most affected in emphysema, causing her to struggle with breathing?

   a. Nasal passageways are inflamed, and less air can move into and out of the respiratory tract.
   b. Bronchi are inflamed.
   c. Bronchioles are dilated.
   d. Damage to the alveoli has occurred.

3. Since physiologic dead space is increased, she would be exhibiting

   a. increased resistance during inhaling.
   b. smaller amounts of air entering her lungs.
   c. harder and deeper breathing that leaves her feeling tired.
   d. decreased blood P_{CO_2}.

4. Blood samples were also taken. Which results might be expected for her blood respiratory gases and blood pH?

   a. decrease in P_{O_2}, increase in P_{CO_2}, decrease in blood pH
   b. decrease in P_{O_2}, decrease in P_{CO_2}, decrease in blood pH
   c. decrease in P_{O_2}, increase in P_{CO_2}, increase in blood pH
   d. increase in P_{O_2}, decrease in P_{CO_2}, increase in blood pH

5. A 10-year-old boy named Michael is playing soccer and begins to have trouble breathing. His mother takes him to the pediatrician, who suspects that he has asthma. The pediatrician recommends that Michael see a respiratory specialist, and results from his pulmonary function tests indicate that Michael does have asthma. Michael's difficulty in breathing, as a result of the asthma, is caused by

   a. inflammation of his nasal passageways.
   b. inflammation and bronchoconstriction of his bronchioles.
   c. spastic closure of his epiglottis, temporarily closing off his trachea.
   d. damage to the alveoli, resulting in decreased surface area of the respiratory membrane.

Can You Synthesize What You've Learned?

1. Tiffany had returned to her college dorm and was having difficulty breathing. She knew she was having an asthma attack. What changes are occurring in her respiratory tract to cause her difficulty in breathing? What potential changes would you predict for her blood P_{O_2} and P_{CO_2}? What substance is generally given that would result in her bronchioles dilating?

2. The nerve to the sternocleidomastoid muscle was damaged during surgery. What type of breathing will be impaired— quiet inspiration, quiet expiration, forced inspiration, or forced expiration?

3. Mark is attempting his first serious mountain climb above 8000 feet. He begins to breathe harder during his ascent, feels light-headed, and has difficulty thinking clearly. What has stimulated him to breathe harder? What effect does this have on P_{CO_2}? What potential change in blood pH can occur? Why? Does more or less oxygen reach the brain? Explain.

chapter 24
Urinary System

Imagine a river that supplies drinking water to a town. The water in the river may become polluted with sediment, animal waste, and motorboat fuel, but the town has a water treatment plant that removes these wastes. In an analogous way, the cells of all body systems produce waste products, and these waste products end up in the blood. These unwanted substances are filtered from the blood by the kidneys to form urine, and the urine is then eliminated from the body by the ureters, urinary bladder, and urethra. ➜

Urologists are medical and surgical professionals who diagnose and treat individuals who have disorders of both the urinary system and reproductive organs in males. Conditions treated by urologists include kidney stones, stress incontinence, urinary tract infections, congenital abnormalities, benign prostatic hyperplasia, and various types of cancers. This photo shows a urologist viewing a video monitor during prostate surgery.

aprevealed.com

Module 13: Urinary System

Thus, the urinary system serves as the body's "water treatment plant."

Here we first introduce the urinary system and then discuss the details of kidney structure and its function in filtering blood and forming urine. The chapter ends with a description of the anatomic structures of the ureters, urinary bladder, and urethra, and their roles in transporting, storing, and eliminating urine.

24.1 Introduction to the Urinary System

LEARNING OBJECTIVES

1. Identify the structures that compose the urinary system, and provide a description of the general function of each.
2. List the functions of the kidneys.

The urinary (ūr'i-nār-ē) system is collectively composed of the kidneys, ureters, urinary bladder, and urethra (figure 24.1). One of the primary functions of the kidneys is to filter blood, removing waste products and converting the filtrate into urine. Urine is then transported by the ureters from the kidneys to the urinary bladder, which is an expandable muscular sac that stores as much as 1 liter (L) of urine until it is eliminated from the body through the urethra.

The kidneys perform other functions, however, in addition to their function in removing wastes. As you read through these functions, you may notice that many of these have been described in previous chapters. The other functions of the kidney include the following:

- **Formation of calcitriol.** The kidneys synthesize the final enzyme in calcitriol hormone formation. Calcitriol increases the absorption of calcium from the small intestine to increase blood calcium concentration (see section 7.6).

- **Production and release of erythropoietin.** As the kidneys are filtering the blood, they are also indirectly measuring the oxygen level of blood. In response to low blood oxygen levels, cells within the kidney secrete erythropoietin (EPO) hormone. EPO stimulates red bone marrow to increase its rate of erythrocyte formation (see section 18.3b). The greater numbers of erythrocytes transport additional oxygen from the lungs to systemic cells (see section 23.7a).

- **Regulation of ion levels and acid-base balance.** The kidneys help control the blood's inorganic ion balance, such as sodium ions (Na^+), potassium ions (K^+), calcium ions (Ca^{2+}), and phosphate ions (PO_4^{3-}). The kidneys also aid in maintaining acid-base balance by altering blood levels of both hydrogen ions (H^+) and bicarbonate ions (HCO_3^-).

- **Regulation of blood pressure.** The kidneys help regulate blood pressure by altering the amount of fluid lost in the urine. Regulating fluid lost in the urine helps to regulate blood volume. The kidneys also release renin enzyme, which is required for production of angiotensin II, a hormone that increases blood pressure (see section 20.5b). Arguably, blood pressure regulation is one of the kidneys most important functions and is described in detail in section 25.4.

- **Potential to engage in gluconeogenesis.** During prolonged fasting or starvation, the kidneys may engage in gluconeogenesis to produce glucose from noncarbohydrate sources; this helps to maintain normal blood glucose levels during periods of extreme nutrient deprivation (see section 17.7).

A general observation can be made about the various functions of the kidneys. Our kidneys take care of our blood. The kidneys remove unwanted materials from the blood, regulate the number of erythrocytes, maintain blood plasma concentration of ions (e.g., Ca^{2+}, Na^+, and K^+), help regulate blood pH (e.g., H^+ and HCO_3^- concentration), and can help maintain blood glucose with severe limitation on nutrient intake. Healthy blood is intimately dependent on healthy kidneys.

  ### WHAT DO YOU THINK?

❶ Which of the following would accompany a loss of kidney function: (a) accumulation of wastes, (b) anemia, (c) changes in blood pressure, or (d) pH imbalance?

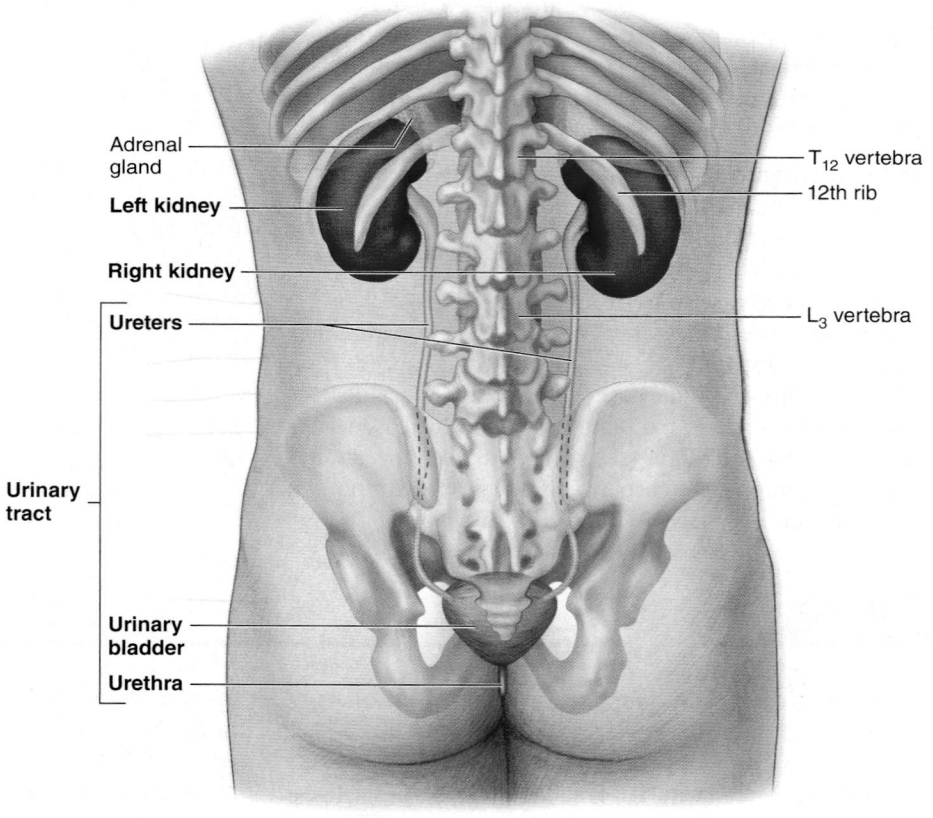

Diaphragm
Adrenal gland
Kidneys
Hilum
Renal artery
Renal vein
Inferior vena cava
Descending abdominal aorta

Ureters

Parietal peritoneum (cut)

**Urinary
bladder**

Urethra

(a) Anterior view

Adrenal
gland

Left kidney

Right kidney

Ureters

**Urinary
tract**

**Urinary
bladder**

Urethra

T₁₂ vertebra
12th rib

L₃ vertebra

(b) Posterior view

Figure 24.1 Urinary System. The urinary system is composed of two kidneys, two ureters, a single urinary bladder, and a single urethra, shown here in (*a*) anterior and (*b*) posterior views. (Components of urinary system are labeled in bold font.) AP|R

WHAT DID YOU LEARN?

1 Which structure of the urinary system forms urine, and which structure stores urine?

2 What are the two means that the kidney helps to regulate blood pressure?

24.2 Gross Anatomy of the Kidney

The kidneys are two symmetrical, bean-shaped, reddish-brown organs. Each kidney measures about 12 centimeters (4.7 inches) in length, 6.5 centimeters (2.5 inches) in width, and 2.5 centimeters (1 inch) in thickness, and is approximately the same size as your hand to the second knuckle. A kidney weighs approximately 100 grams (g). Each has a concave medial border called the **hilum** (hī'lŭm = a small bit), where vessels, nerves, and the ureter connect to the kidney. The kidney's lateral border is convex. An adrenal gland rests on the superior aspect of each kidney.

24.2a Location and Support

LEARNING OBJECTIVES

1. Describe the location of the kidneys in the body.
2. Name and describe the four tissue layers that surround and support the kidneys.

Kidneys are located along the posterior abdominal wall, lateral to the vertebral column (figure 24.1). The left kidney is between the level

of the T$_{12}$ and L$_3$ vertebrae, and the right kidney is about 2 centimeters inferior to the left kidney to accommodate the large size of the liver. Both kidneys are only partially protected by the rib cage, making them vulnerable to forceful blows to the inferior region of the back.

The kidneys are positioned posterior to the parietal peritoneum in the **retroperitoneal** (ret'rō-per'i-tō-nē'ăl; *retro* = back) **space** (figure 24.2). Thus, only the anterior surface of the kidneys is covered with parietal peritoneum.

Anterior

Stomach

Renal vein

Renal artery

Renal hilum

Left kidney

Spleen

Body of L$_2$ vertebra

Descending abdominal aorta

Inferior vena cava

Liver

Right kidney

Parietal peritoneum

Paranephric fat

Renal fascia

Perinephric fat

Fibrous capsule

Posterior

Figure 24.2 Position and Support of the Kidneys. A cross-sectional view shows that the kidneys lie on the posterior abdominal wall and are covered on their anterior surface by the parietal peritoneum and surrounded by four concentric tissue layers (from innermost to outermost): fibrous capsule, perinephric fat, renal fascia, and paranephric fat. AP|R

CLINICAL VIEW
Renal Ptosis

The loss of adipose connective tissue in very thin elderly people or individuals with anorexia nervosa may result in **renal ptosis** (tō'sēz), which is the "dropping" or inferior movement of the kidney within the abdominal cavity. Consequently, the ureter may kink, resulting in a decrease or blockage of urine flow from the kidney to the urinary bladder. Urine backs up into the kidney, a condition that may result in renal failure.

Each kidney is surrounded and supported by several tissue layers. From innermost (closest to the kidney) to outermost, these layers are the fibrous capsule, perinephric fat, renal fascia, and paranephric fat:

- The **fibrous capsule** (kap'sūl; *capsa* = box), or *renal capsule*, is directly adhered to the external surface of the kidney. It is composed of dense irregular connective tissue and maintains the kidney's shape, protects it from trauma, and helps prevent infectious pathogens from penetrating the kidney.
- The **perinephric** (*peri* = around) **fat** is also called the *perirenal fat*, or *adipose capsule*. It is external to the fibrous capsule and contains adipose connective tissue. It provides cushioning and support for the kidney.
- The **renal fascia** (rē'năl fash'ē-ă; *ren* = kidney) is external to the perinephric fat and is composed of dense irregular connective tissue. It anchors the kidney to surrounding structures.
- The **paranephric** (*para* = next to) **fat** is the outermost layer surrounding the kidney and is also known as *pararenal fat*, or the *paranephric body*. It is composed of adipose connective tissue and also provides cushioning and support for the kidney.

WHAT DID YOU LEARN?

3 What are the four tissue layers surrounding the kidneys (from innermost to outermost)?

24.2b Sectional Anatomy of the Kidney

LEARNING OBJECTIVES

3. Identify the two distinct regions of the kidney and the components of each.

4. Explain the relationship between minor calyces, major calyces, and renal pelvis.

When a kidney is sectioned along a coronal plane, the parenchyma or "functioning tissue" is visible. The two distinct regions of the parenchyma include an outer **renal cortex** and an inner **renal medulla** (**figure 24.3**).

Labels (left to right, top to bottom):
Renal cortex
Renal medulla
Renal column
Renal pyramid
Minor calyx
Corticomedullary junction
Renal papilla
Renal pelvis
Major calyx
Renal pyramid
Renal column
Renal lobe
Fibrous capsule
Ureter

Renal sinus contains:
Minor calyx
Major calyx
Renal pelvis
Renal artery
Renal vein
Ureter

Right kidney, coronal section

Figure 24.3 Kidney. A coronal cut through the right kidney reveals the parenchyma and urine drainage areas of the kidney. AP|R

Extensions of the cortex, called **renal columns,** project into the medulla and subdivide it into **renal pyramids** (also termed *medullary pyramids*) that appear striated or striped. An adult kidney typically contains 8 to 15 renal pyramids. The wide base of a renal pyramid lies at the external edge of the medulla, where it meets the cortex: This is called the **corticomedullary junction,** or *corticomedullary border*. The medially directed apex (or tip) of the renal pyramid is called the **renal papilla.**

The parenchyma of a human kidney can also be divided into 8 to 15 **renal lobes.** A renal lobe consists of a renal pyramid, portions of renal columns adjacent to either side of the renal pyramid, and the renal cortex external to the pyramid base.

Each kidney contains a medially located space called the **renal sinus,** in addition to the parenchyma. This space serves as the urine drainage area. It is organized into minor calyces, major calyces, and a renal pelvis. Each of the 8 to 15 funnel-shaped **minor calyces** (kāl'i-sēz, sing. calyx = cup of a flower) is associated with a renal pyramid. Several minor calyces merge to form a larger **major calyx.** Each kidney typically contains two or three major calyces. The major calyces merge to form a large, funnel-shaped **renal pelvis.** The renal pelvis merges at the medial edge of the kidney with the ureter. Housed within the space around the renal pelvis are the renal arteries, renal veins, lymph vessels, nerves, and a variable amount of fat. (Lymph vessels and nerves are not shown in figure 24.3.)

 WHAT DID YOU LEARN?

4 What are the regions of the kidney that drain urine?

24.2c Innervation of the Kidney

 LEARNING OBJECTIVE

5. Identify the nerve components of the renal plexus, and list the structures of the kidney innervated by the sympathetic nervous system.

Each kidney is innervated by the autonomic nervous system through the **renal plexus.** A renal plexus contains both sympathetic nerves from the T10–T12 segments of the spinal cord and parasympathetic nerves from CN X (vagus nerve) (section 15.3). Sympathetic axons extend to the blood vessels of the kidney (section 15.4), including the afferent and efferent arterioles, and also innervate the juxtaglomerular apparatus (these structures are described later). Pain from the kidneys is typically referred via the sympathetic pathway to the T10–T12 dermatomes (see figure 14.13). The effects of the parasympathetic innervation to the kidney are not known.

 WHAT DID YOU LEARN?

5 What three anatomic structures of the kidney are innervated by the sympathetic division of the autonomic nervous system?

24.3 Functional Anatomy of the Kidney

The functional anatomy of the kidneys encompasses structures that include nephrons, collecting tubules, collecting ducts, and their associated structures.

24.3a Nephron

 LEARNING OBJECTIVES

1. Describe the renal corpuscle and its components.

2. Identify the location, and describe the structure, of the three components of a renal tubule.

3. Name and compare the two types of nephrons and the functional differences between them.

The **nephron** (nef'ron: *nephros* = kidney) is the microscopic, functional filtration unit of the kidney. Each nephron consists of two major structures: a renal corpuscle and a renal tubule **(figure 24.4)**. All of the renal corpuscle and almost all of the renal tubules reside in the cortex (the exception being the nephron loop, which also extends into the medulla).

Renal Corpuscle

The **renal corpuscle** (kōr'pus-l; *corpus* = body, *cle* = tiny) is an enlarged, bulbous region of a nephron housed within the renal cortex. It is composed of two structures: the glomerulus and the glomerular capsule.

The **glomerulus** (glō-mer'yū-lŭs; *glomus* = ball of yarn, *ulus* = small) is a thick tangle of capillary loops called the *glomerular capillaries*. Blood enters the glomerulus by an **afferent** (af'er-ent; *aferrens* = to bring to) **arteriole** and exits by an **efferent** (ef'er-ent; *efferens* = to bring out) **arteriole**.

The **glomerular** (glō-mer'yū-lăr) **capsule** (*Bowman's capsule*) is formed by two layers: an internal permeable **visceral layer** that directly overlies the glomerular capillaries (described later in more detail), and an external impermeable **parietal layer** composed of simple squamous epithelium. Between these two layers is a **capsular space** that receives the filtrate (described later), which is then modified to form urine.

The renal corpuscle has two opposing poles: a **vascular pole,** where afferent and efferent arterioles attach to the glomerulus, and a **tubular pole,** where the renal tubule originates.

Renal Tubule

The **renal tubule** makes up the remaining part of a nephron. and it consists of three continuous parts: the proximal convoluted tubule, the nephron loop, and the distal convoluted tubule. The convoluted tubules reside in the cortex, while the nephron loop typically extends from the cortex into the medulla.

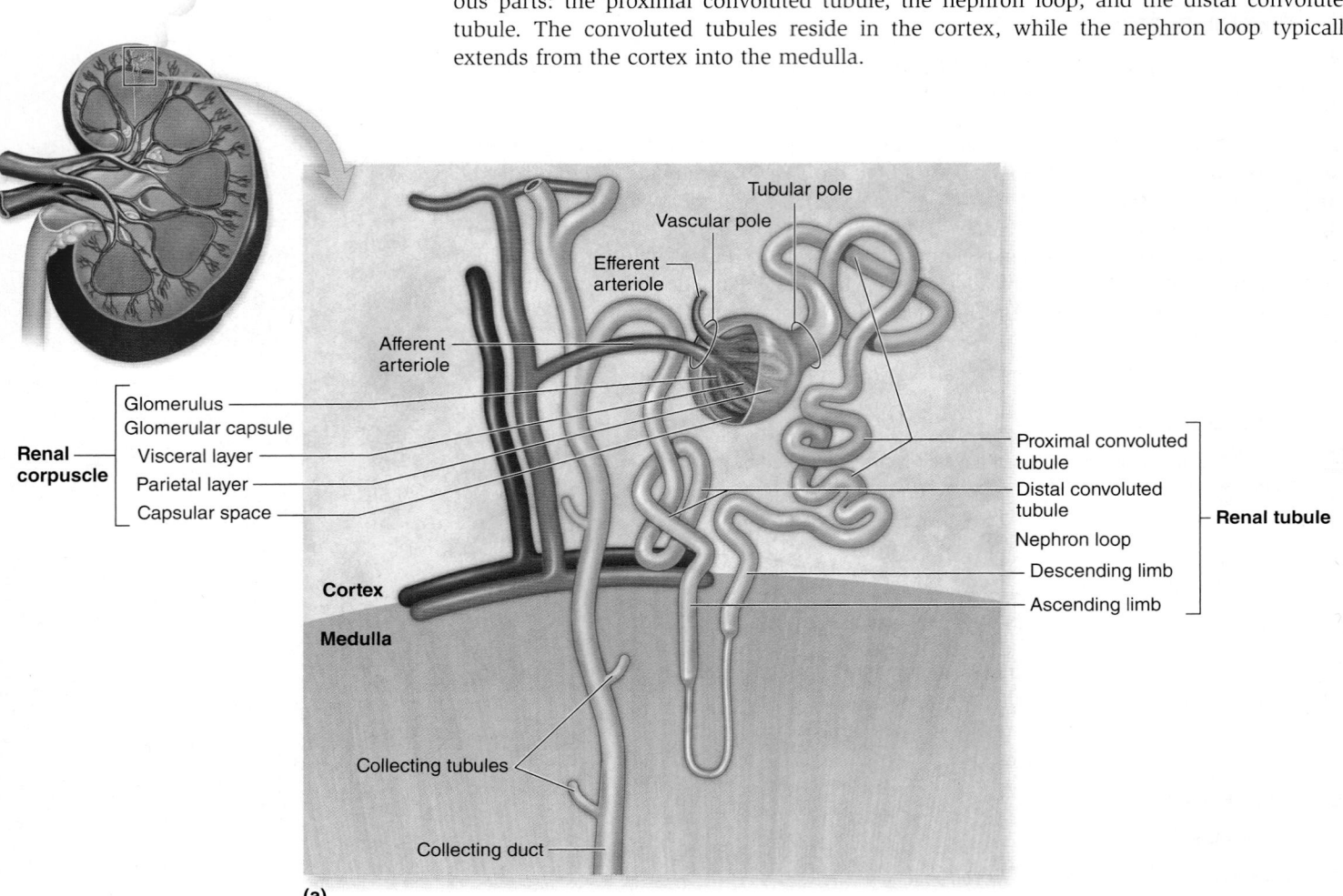

(a)

Figure 24.4 Nephron Structure. The nephron is composed of a renal corpuscle and renal tubule. (*a*) The nephron is shown in its anatomic orientation relative to its position in the cortex and medulla of the kidney. AP|R

The **proximal convoluted tubule (PCT)** is the first region of the renal tubule. It originates at the tubular pole of the renal corpuscle and is composed of a simple cuboidal epithelium with tall, apical microvilli that markedly increase its surface area and thus its reabsorption capacity. When viewed under a microscope, the lumen of the proximal convoluted tubule looks fuzzy due to the brush border formed by these tall microvilli.

The **nephron loop** (*loop of Henle*) originates at a sharp bend in the proximal convoluted tubule. Each nephron loop has two limbs: a descending limb and an ascending limb that connect at a "hairpin turn" within the medulla. The **descending limb** extends medially from the proximal convoluted tubule to the tip of the nephron loop; conversely, the **ascending limb** of the nephron loop returns to the renal cortex and terminates at the distal convoluted tubule. Portions of both limbs are classified as either thin or thick according to their lining epithelia. The **thin segments** of each limb are lined by a simple squamous epithelium, and **thick segments** of each limb have a simple cuboidal epithelium lining.

The **distal convoluted tubule (DCT)** originates in the renal cortex at the end of the nephron loop's thick ascending limb and extends to a collecting tubule. Like the proximal convoluted tubule, the distal convoluted tubule is lined with simple cuboidal epithelium. However, the distal convoluted tubule epithelial lining cells are smaller and have only sparse, short, apical microvilli. Thus, the distal convoluted tubule lumen appears clear and not fuzzy when observed under the microscope.

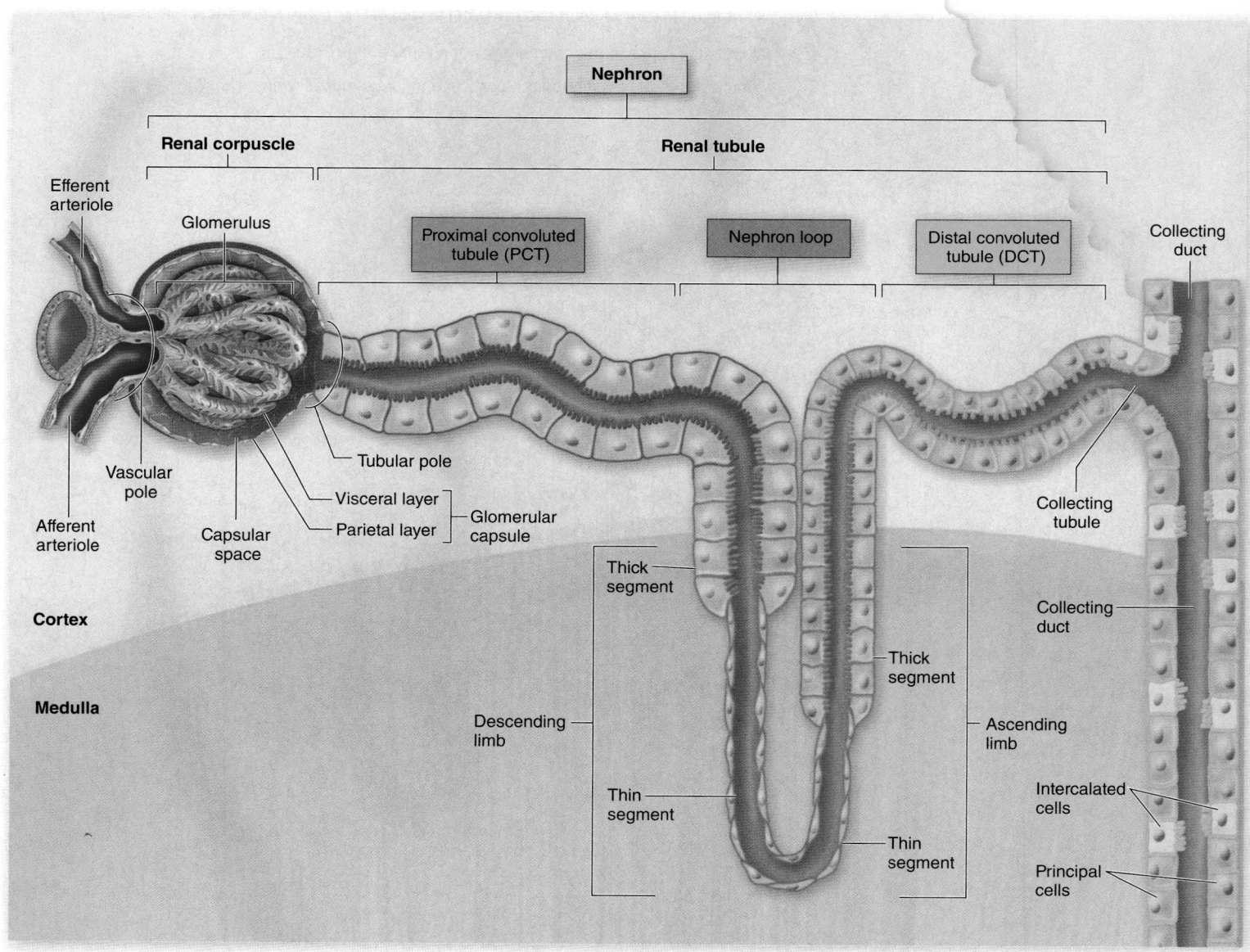

(b)

Figure 24.4 Nephron Structure *(continued).* (*b*) In this diagrammatic representation, the nephron has been straightened out, with each component color coded for clarity. Note that neither the collecting tubule nor the collecting duct are part of a nephron.

Two Types of Nephrons

The renal corpuscle and both the proximal and distal convoluted tubules are housed within the cortex; the nephron loops extend from the cortex medially toward or into the medulla, as previously described. The relative position of the nephron in the cortex and the length of the nephron loop are used to classify nephrons into two categories: cortical nephrons and juxtamedullary nephrons (figure 24.5).

Cortical nephrons are oriented with their renal corpuscles near the peripheral edge of the cortex and have a relatively short nephron loop that barely penetrates the medulla. Thus, the bulk of a cortical nephron resides within in the cortex. Approximately 85% of nephrons are cortical nephrons.

The remaining 15% of nephrons are called **juxtamedullary** (jŭks′tă-med′yŭ-lār-ē; *juxta* = near) **nephrons.** Their renal corpuscles lie adjacent to the corticomedullary junction, and they have relatively long nephron loops that extend deep into the medulla. Juxtamedullary nephrons are important in establishing a salt concentration gradient within the interstitial space that lies outside of the nephron loop, the collecting tubules, and the collecting ducts—thus allowing for the regulation of urine concentration by antidiuretic hormone (ADH) (a process described later).

WHAT DID YOU LEARN?

6 What two structures compose the renal corpuscle? Provide a brief description of each.

7 What is the order of the components of a renal tubule?

8 What differences exist between cortical and juxtamedullary nephrons?

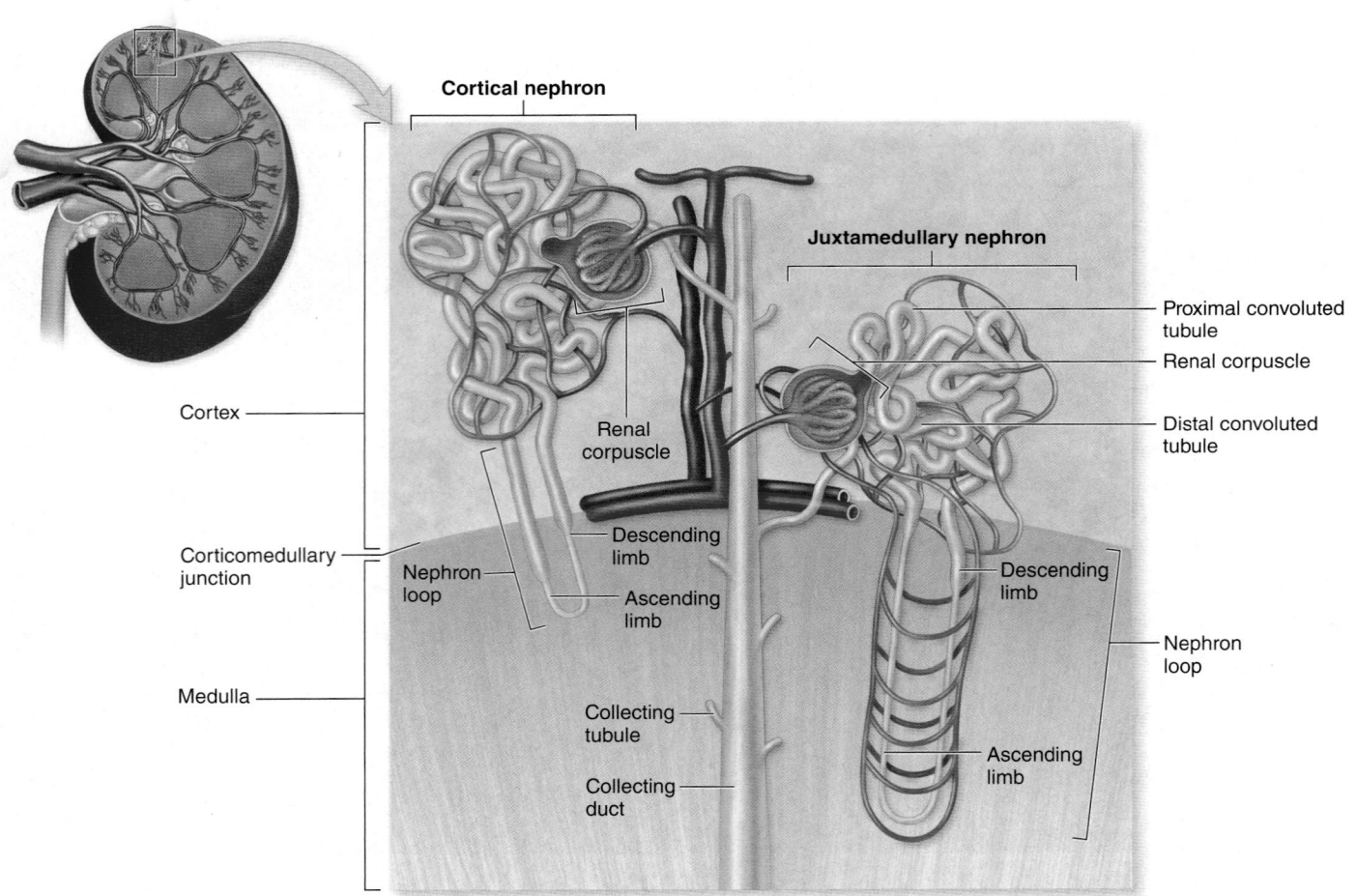

Figure 24.5 Two Types of Nephrons. Cortical nephrons are located almost completely in the cortex and have short nephron loops that barely penetrate into the medulla. Juxtamedullary nephrons, which lie close to the corticomedullary junction, have relatively long nephron loops that extend deeper into the medulla.

24.3b Collecting Tubules and Collecting Ducts

✓ LEARNING OBJECTIVES

4. State the relationship between collecting tubules and collecting ducts.

5. Identify the two types of specialized epithelial cells found within distal convoluted tubules and collecting tubules and ducts.

Each nephron drains into a **collecting tubule.** Each kidney contains thousands of collecting tubules, and a series of collecting tubules empty into larger **collecting ducts.** Both collecting tubules and collecting ducts project medially through the renal medulla toward the renal papilla. Numerous collecting ducts then empty into a **papillary duct** located within the renal papilla (see figure 24.9).

The epithelial cells of the collecting tubules are cuboidal-shaped, but the cells become very tall columnar cells in the collecting ducts near the renal papilla. The striations seen within the renal pyramid are formed collectively by the straight ascending and descending tubules of nephron loops, the collecting tubules, and collecting ducts.

The distal convoluted tubule, collecting tubules, and collecting ducts contain two types of specialized epithelial cells called principal cells and intercalated cells (see figure 24.4b). **Principal cells** are responsive to the hormones aldosterone (released from the adrenal cortex) and antidiuretic hormone (released from the posterior pituitary). **Intercalated cells** (types **A** and **B**) are specialized epithelial cells that help regulate urine pH and blood pH. Both types of cells are described in detail later in the chapter, but for now keep in mind that type A cells eliminate acid and type B cells eliminate base. Histologic images of the kidney are provided in **figure 24.6.**

💡 WHAT DID YOU LEARN?

9 What is the function of intercalated cells in the kidney?

Figure 24.6 Histology of Renal Cortex and Medulla. (*a*) A photomicrograph of a section through the cortex, which houses renal corpuscles and most of the tubule of a nephron. Proximal convoluted tubules stain more darkly and appear fuzzier than those of the distal convoluted tubules. (*b*) A photomicrograph of a transverse section through the medulla compares nephron loops and collecting ducts. AP|R

(a) Renal cortex

(b) Renal medulla

24.3c Juxtaglomerular Apparatus

LEARNING OBJECTIVES

6. Describe the location and structure of the juxtaglomerular apparatus.

7. Explain the two actions of granular cells.

8. Describe the function of cells of the macula densa.

The nephron was "stretched out" in figure 24.4b to more clearly view its components. A representation of the normal orientation of a nephron would show the distal convoluted tubule of the nephron contacting the afferent arteriole of that same nephron (**figure 24.7**). This accurate physical arrangement of the nephron allows us to understand the anatomic features of a specialized region of the nephron called the **juxtaglomerular (JG)** (jŭks′tă-glō-mer′ū-lăr; *juxta* = near to) **apparatus,** an important structure in regulating filtrate formation and blood pressure.

The primary components of the JG apparatus include both granular cells and a special group of cells that form the macula densa. **Granular cells** are also called *juxtaglomerular cells.* These are modified smooth muscle cells of the afferent arteriole located near its entrance into the renal corpuscle. Granular cells have two functions: (1) They contract when stimulated either by stretch or by the sympathetic division; and (2) they synthesize, store, and release **renin** enzyme. Renin is required in the production of angiotensin II hormone (see section 20.5b).

The **macula densa** (mak′ū-lă = spot, den′să = dense) is a group of modified epithelial cells in the wall of the distal convoluted tubule where it contacts the granular cells. The cells of the macula densa are located only on the tubule side next to the afferent arteriole, and they are narrower and taller than other distal convoluted tubule epithelial cells. The macula densa cells detect changes in the sodium chloride (NaCl) concentration of fluid within the lumen of the distal convoluted tubule. Macula densa cells signal granular cells to release renin through paracrine stimulation (see section 17.3b).

Extraglomerular mesangial cells, located just outside the glomerulus within the gap between the afferent arteriole and efferent arteriole, are also components of the JG apparatus. These cells communicate with the other cells of the JG apparatus via gap junctions and the release of paracrine hormones. Their specific function is not well understood.

WHAT DID YOU LEARN?

10. What are the two primary cellular components of the juxtaglomerular apparatus, and how is each stimulated?

24.4 Blood Flow and Filtered Fluid Flow

At least 20% to 25% of the resting cardiac output (or about 1 liter per minute [L/min]) normally flows through the kidneys for the purpose of removing unwanted substances. A filtrate is formed when blood flows through the glomerulus, and some components of the plasma enter the capsular space. As a result, two fluid flow patterns must be noted.

- The flow of blood into and out of the kidney
- The flow of filtrate, tubular fluid and urine through the nephron and other urinary system structures

24.4a Blood Flow Through the Kidney

LEARNING OBJECTIVES

1. Name the arteries that supply the kidney, in sequence from largest to smallest.

2. Describe the two capillary beds through which blood must pass in the kidney.

3. List the veins through which blood leaves the kidney, in sequence from smallest to largest.

Figure 24.7 Juxtaglomerular Apparatus. With the nephron in the normal orientation, there is physical contact between the afferent arteriole and the adjacent distal convoluted tubule (DCT) forming the juxtaglomerular apparatus. The juxtaglomerular apparatus is composed of granular cells of the afferent arteriole and macula densa cells of the distal convoluted tubule. The juxtaglomerular apparatus monitors blood pressure and releases renin into the blood in response to low blood pressure. AP|R

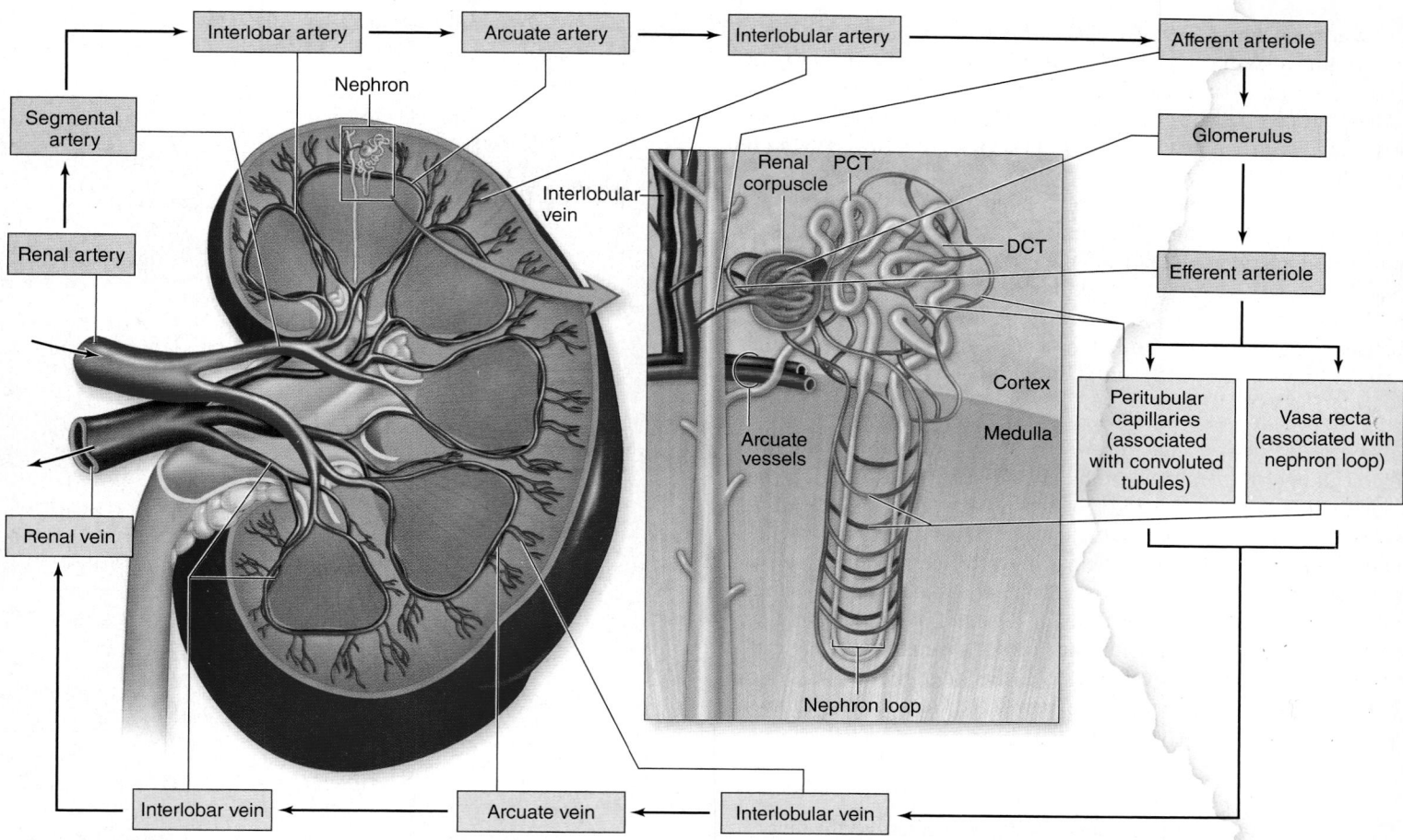

Figure 24.8 Blood Supply to the Kidneys. A coronal view depicts kidney circulation. An expanded view shows circulation to a nephron. Pink boxes indicate vessels with arterial blood; lavender boxes indicate vessels where reabsorbed materials reenter the blood; blue boxes indicate vessels returning blood to the general circulation.

The blood flow pathway is shown in **figure 24.8**. Be sure to refer back to this figure often as you read this section on blood flow through the kidney.

Arteries

Blood is delivered to each kidney by way of a **renal artery** that arises from the abdominal aorta, generally at the level of the first or second lumbar vertebra. Vascular subdivision begins immediately as **segmental arteries** branch from the renal artery within the renal sinus. While still in the renal sinus, the segmental arteries further ramify to form the **interlobar** (in-ter-lō'bar) **arteries.** Interlobar arteries travel through the renal columns toward the corticomedullary junction, where they branch to form **arcuate** (ar'kū-āt; *arcuatus* = bowed) **arteries.**

Arcuate arteries project parallel to the base of the medullary pyramid at the corticomedullary junction. The arcuate arteries extend branches called **interlobular** (in-ter-lob'ū-lăr) **arteries** (or *cortical radiate arteries)* that project peripherally into the cortex. As the interlobular arteries extend into the cortex, numerous small afferent arterioles branch from them.

Arterioles and Capillaries

Each **afferent arteriole** enters a renal corpuscle, forming a **glomerulus.** Some blood plasma is filtered at the renal corpuscle. After this filtration event, blood still remaining within the glomerulus exits the renal corpuscle through an **efferent arteriole.** Each efferent arteriole now branches into a second capillary network, either the **peritubular** (per″e-t̄u'bȳu-l̆ar; *peri* = around, *tubule* = small tube) **capillaries** or **vasa recta** (vā'să rek'tă). The peritubular capillaries are associated with, and intertwined around, both the proximal and distal convoluted tubules; thus, they primarily reside in the cortex of the kidney. In comparison, vasa recta capillaries are "straight vessels" associated with the nephron loop; thus, they primarily reside in the medulla of the kidney.

Notice that all blood moves through two capillary beds as it flows through the kidney. Blood first enters from the afferent arteriole into the glomerular capillaries, where it is filtered. When the blood reaches the second capillary bed of either the peritubular capillaries or the vasa recta, the exchange of gases, nutrients, and wastes occurs between the tissues of the kidney and the blood. The peritubular capillaries and vasa recta then drain into the network of veins.

Veins

Blood drains from both peritubular and vasa recta capillary beds into small veins. The smallest of these veins are the **interlobular veins** (or *cortical radiate veins*), which travel alongside the interlobular arteries. Interlobular veins merge to form **arcuate veins** at the base of the medullary pyramids, and these merge to form **interlobar veins** that travel through the renal columns. Interlobar veins merge in the renal sinus to form the **renal vein.** Note that there are no segmental veins; rather, the interlobar veins directly form the renal vein. The renal vein leaves the kidney at its hilum and drains into the inferior vena cava.

 WHAT DID YOU LEARN?

11 What is the pathway that blood follows as it enters via the renal artery and later leaves via the renal vein?

12 What are the three major types of capillaries associated with the nephron? Describe the location and general function of each.

24.4b Filtrate, Tubular Fluid, and Urine Flow

✔ LEARNING OBJECTIVES

4. Distinguish between filtrate, tubular fluid, and urine.

5. Trace the fluid from its formation at the renal corpuscle until it exits the body through the urethra.

The flow of fluid formed following filtration at the glomerulus, its movement through the microscopic structures of the kidney, and then the rest of the urinary system is integrated in **figure 24.9.** Be sure to refer to this figure as you read through this section.

When blood flows through the glomerulus, both water and solutes are filtered from the blood plasma, moving across the wall of the glomerular capillaries and into the capsular space to form **filtrate.** This filtrate then enters the proximal convoluted tubule, where it is now called **tubular fluid.** It flows through the proximal convoluted tubule, nephron loop, and distal convoluted tubule. Tubular fluid from several distal convoluted tubules enters into small collecting tubules that empty into larger collecting ducts.

Figure 24.9 Structures That Transport Fluids Through the Urinary System. (*a*) Microscopic view depicts flow of fluid through the nephron, and collecting tubules and ducts. (*b*) Macroscopic view depicts urine flow through the renal pelvis of the kidney and ureters, and then into the urinary bladder and expelled through the urethra.

Filtrate

1 Capsular space

Tubular fluid

2 Proximal convoluted tubule (PCT)

3 Descending limb of nephron loop

4 Ascending limb of nephron loop

5 Distal convoluted tubule (DCT)

6 Collecting tubules

7 Collecting duct

(a)

Urine

8 Papillary duct

9 Minor calyx

10 Major calyx

11 Renal pelvis

12 Ureter

13 Urinary bladder

14 Urethra

(b)

Tubular fluid has no further changes made to it after leaving the collecting ducts, and it is now called **urine**. It enters a papillary duct located within a renal papilla and then flows progressively through spaces within the renal sinus of the kidney. These spaces occur in the following order: minor calyx, major calyx, and renal pelvis. The renal pelvis conducts urine from the kidney into a ureter, and a ureter from each kidney conducts urine into the urinary bladder, where it is stored until it is excreted from the body through the urethra.

 WHAT DID YOU LEARN?

13 What is the pathway of fluid filtered by the kidney from the glomerulus to its eventual excretion?

24.5 Production of Filtrate Within the Renal Corpuscle

Filtrate production occurs within the renal corpuscle. Water and solutes cross the filtration membrane due to physiologic pressures, and enter into the capsular space. We first present a brief overview of the entire process of urine production and then consider details of filtrate production. The processes that occur within the tubules are discussed in the next section.

24.5a Overview of Urine Formation

LEARNING OBJECTIVE

1. Compare and contrast the renal processes of filtration, reabsorption, and secretion.

Urine is formed in the kidneys through three interrelated processes: filtration, reabsorption, and secretion (**figure 24.10**):

- **Filtration** passively separates some water and dissolved solutes from the blood plasma in the glomerular capillaries. Water and solutes enter into the capsular space of the renal corpuscle due to pressure differences across the filtration membrane. Collectively, this separated fluid is called filtrate.

- **Tubular reabsorption** occurs when components within the tubular fluid move by diffusion, osmosis, or active transport from the lumen of the renal tubules, collecting tubules, and collecting ducts across their walls and return to the blood within the peritubular capillaries and vasa recta. Generally, all vital solutes and most water that was in the filtrate are reabsorbed, while excess solutes, some water, and waste products remain within the tubular fluid.

- **Tubular secretion** is the movement of solutes, usually by active transport, out of the blood within the peritubular and vasa recta capillaries into the tubular fluid. Materials are moved selectively into the tubules to be eliminated or excreted from the body. Remember, "secretion results in excretion."

Notice that the processes of tubular reabsorption and tubular secretion involve the movement of materials in opposite directions. In tubular reabsorption, substances are moved from the tubular fluid into the blood, whereas in tubular secretion, substances are moved from the blood into the tubular fluid.

 WHAT DID YOU LEARN?

14 How does tubular reabsorption differ from tubular secretion?

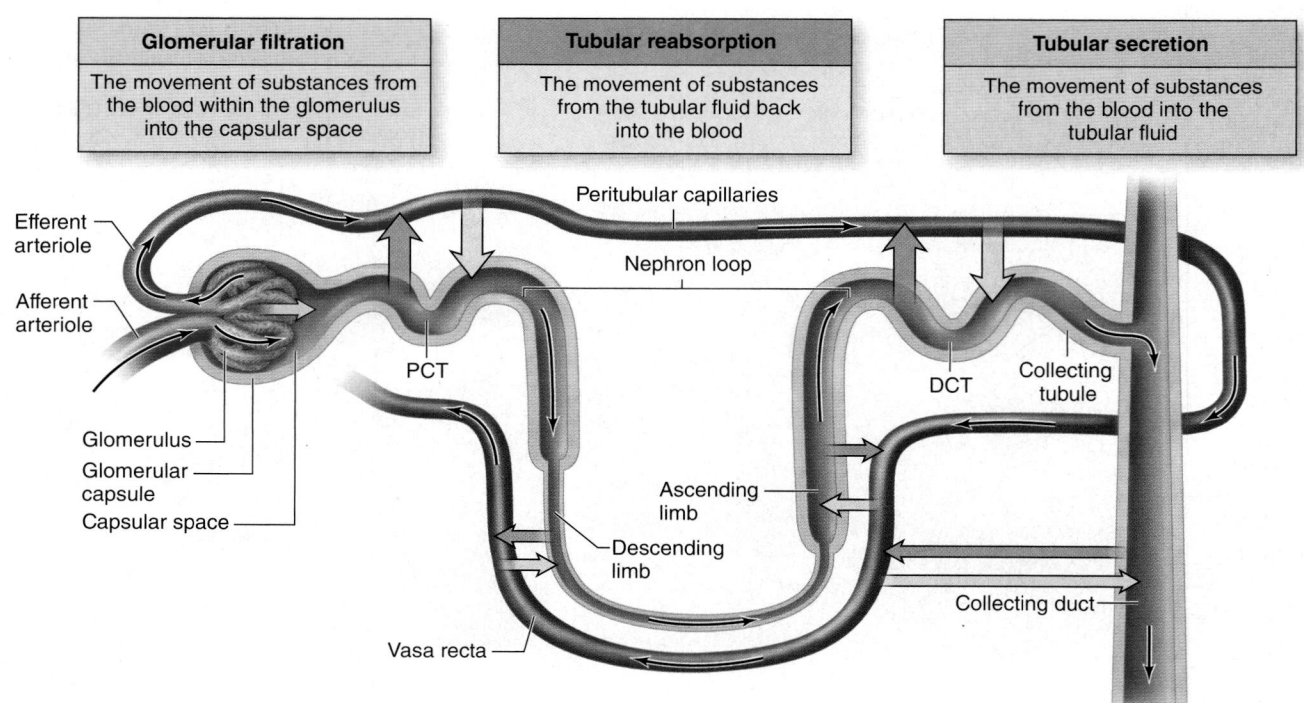

Glomerular filtration	Tubular reabsorption	Tubular secretion
The movement of substances from the blood within the glomerulus into the capsular space	The movement of substances from the tubular fluid back into the blood	The movement of substances from the blood into the tubular fluid

Figure 24.10 Overview of Processes of Urine Formation. The three major processes of urine formation include glomerular filtration, tubular reabsorption, and tubular secretion. AP|R

24.5b Filtration Membrane

✓ LEARNING OBJECTIVE

2. Describe the three layers that make up the glomerular filtration membrane.

The **filtration membrane** is a porous, thin (0.1 micrometer wide), and negatively charged structure that is formed by the glomerulus and visceral layer of the glomerular capsule **(figure 24.11)**. It is composed of three sandwiched layers. For a substance in the blood to become part of the filtrate, it must be able to pass through these three layers of the "filter," which are listed from innermost (closest to the lumen) to outermost:

1. **Endothelium of glomerulus.** The endothelium of the glomerulus is fenestrated (see types of capillaries in section 20.1c). It allows plasma and its dissolved substances to be filtered, while restricting the passage of large structures, such as the formed elements (erythrocytes, leukocytes, and platelets).

2. **Basement membrane of glomerulus.** The porous basement membrane is composed of glycoprotein and proteoglycan molecules. It restricts the passage of large plasma proteins such as albumin, while allowing smaller structures to pass through.

3. **Visceral layer of glomerular capsule.** The visceral layer of the glomerular capsule is composed of specialized cells called **podocytes** (pod'ō-sīt; *podos* = foot). They have long, "foot-like" processes called **pedicels** (ped'ĭ-sel; *pedicellus* = little foot) that wrap around the glomerular capillaries to support the capillary wall but do not completely ensheathe it. The pedicels are separated by thin spaces called **filtration slits** that

are covered with membrane. Pedicels of one podocyte interlock with pedicels of a different podocyte, similar to how the fingers of your hands can interlock. The membrane-covered filtration slits restrict the passage of most small proteins.

Mesangial (mes-an'jē-ăl) **cells** (or more specifically called *intra-glomerular mesangial cells*), are specialized cells positioned within and between the capillary loops of the glomerulus (not shown in figure 24.11). These cells have both phagocytic and contractile properties. These functions are described in detail later in this chapter.

❓ WHAT DO YOU THINK?

2. If a substance does not become part of the filtrate, does it remain a component of the blood? By what structure do these substances exit the glomerulus?

Figure 24.11 Filtration Membrane.

(a) Filtration membrane

(b) Substances filtered by filtration membrane

Filtrate is produced in the renal corpuscle when blood plasma is forced across the filtration membrane under pressure. (*a*) The filtration membrane is composed of three layers, including fenestrated capillary endothelium, basement membrane of the capillary, and filtration slits formed by podocytes of the visceral layer of the glomerular capsule. (*b*) Diagrammatic view of the three layers of the filtration membrane, including materials not filtered (left of membrane) and filtered (right of membrane). AP|R

WHAT DID YOU LEARN?

15 How are the components of the filtration membrane of the glomerulus arranged?

24.5c Formation of Filtrate and Its Composition

✓ LEARNING OBJECTIVES

3. Give examples of substances that are freely filtered, that are not filtered, and that are filtered in a limited way.
4. Describe the phagocytic function of mesangial cells.

An average of 180 L of filtrate is produced daily by the kidneys through the glomerular filtration membrane. However, because of the size of the openings in the membrane and the overall negative charge across the membrane, not all substances within the blood are filtered equally (figure 24.11*b*). Consequently, substances in the blood can be placed into one of three categories based on the degree to which the substance is filtered.

- **Freely filtered.** Small substances such as water, glucose, amino acids, ions, some hormones, vitamins B and C, and ketones can pass easily through the filtration membrane and become part of the filtrate.

- **Not filtered.** Formed elements (i.e., erythrocytes, leukocytes, and platelets) and large proteins are structures that cannot normally pass through the filtration membrane.

- **Limited filtration.** Proteins that are of intermediate size are generally not filtered. They are blocked from filtration either because their size prevents movement through the openings of the filtration membrane or because they are negatively charged and repelled by the membrane's negative charge.

Filtrate is characterized as filtered plasma with certain solutes and *minimal* amounts of protein. Filtrate is caught within the capsular space and then funneled into the proximal convoluted tubule. Components of blood exit the renal corpuscle through the efferent arteriole and then continue in the circulation through either the peritubular or vasa recta capillaries.

Some of the material being filtered becomes trapped within the basement membrane. One of the functions of the mesangial cells is to phagocytize macromolecules (e.g., immunoglobulins) that become caught within the basement membrane, thus helping to keep the filtration membrane clean.

WHAT DID YOU LEARN?

16 What is normally filtered across the glomerular membrane? What is not normally filtered?

17 Certain diseases eliminate the negative charge on the filtration membrane. What effect would this have on relative permeability of the membrane?

24.5d Pressures Associated with Glomerular Filtration

✓ LEARNING OBJECTIVES

5. Define glomerular hydrostatic pressure (HP$_g$), and explain why it is higher than the pressure in other capillaries.
6. Name two pressures that oppose HP$_g$.
7. Explain how to calculate the net filtration pressure.
8. Define glomerular filtration rate and the factors that influence it.

Filtrate is produced due to the difference between hydrostatic pressure of the blood in the glomerulus and the opposing pressures of both the osmotic blood pressure and fluid pressure in the capsular space of the renal corpuscle. This difference is termed the net filtration pressure.

Glomerular Hydrostatic (Blood) Pressure

Blood pressure in the glomerulus is called the **glomerular hydrostatic (blood) pressure (HP$_g$).** It is the driving force that "pushes" water and some dissolved solutes out of the glomerulus and into the capsular space of the renal corpuscle **(figure 24.12)**. It is the HP$_g$ that promotes filtration.

HP$_g$ has a higher value than the blood pressure of other systemic capillaries (60 mm Hg versus about 20 to 40 mm Hg; see section 20.2). This higher pressure is required for filtration to occur, and it is due to the relative diameter size difference in the afferent and efferent arterioles. The afferent arteriole has a larger internal diameter than the efferent arteriole. Consider that in this anatomic arrangement the "inflow pipe" is larger than the "outflow pipe." This creates a higher pressure in the intervening structures (i.e., the glomerular capillaries). As a consequence, these capillaries are more vulnerable to damage due to this relatively high blood pressure.

Pressures That Oppose Glomerular Hydrostatic Pressure

Two pressures oppose glomerular hydrostatic pressure and thus oppose filtration. They are the blood colloid osmotic pressure and capsular hydrostatic pressure.

Blood colloid osmotic pressure (OP$_g$) is the osmotic pressure exerted by the blood due to the dissolved solutes it contains. The most important of these solutes are the plasma proteins (colloid). Blood colloid osmotic pressure opposes filtration because it tends to pull or

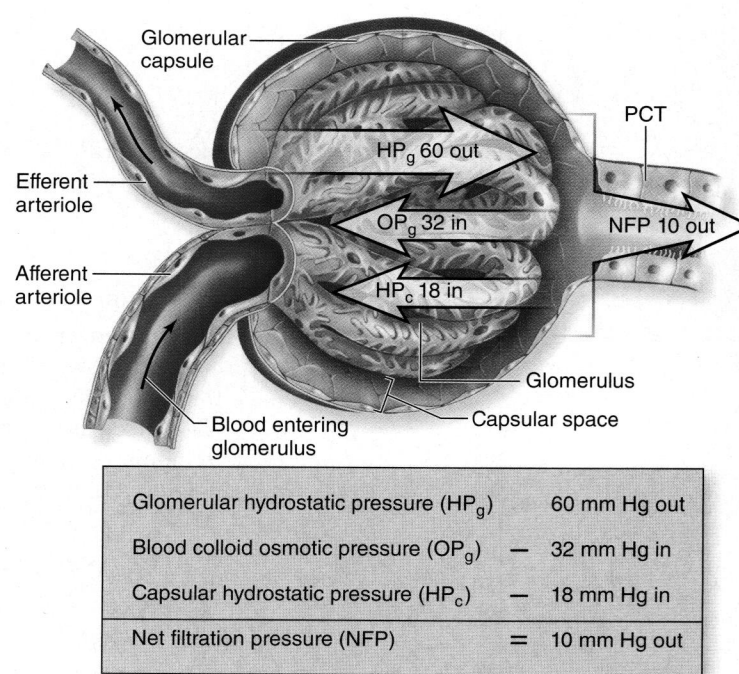

Glomerular hydrostatic pressure (HP$_g$)		60 mm Hg out
Blood colloid osmotic pressure (OP$_g$)	—	32 mm Hg in
Capsular hydrostatic pressure (HP$_c$)	—	18 mm Hg in
Net filtration pressure (NFP)	=	10 mm Hg out

Figure 24.12 Pressures That Determine Net Filtration Pressure. Blood colloid osmotic pressure and capsular hydrostatic pressure are subtracted from glomerular hydrostatic pressure to determine net filtration pressure. **AP|R**

draw fluids back into the glomerulus. The typical value is 32 mm Hg. This is very similar to the colloid osmotic pressure of 26 mm Hg within other systemic capillaries.

Capsular hydrostatic pressure (HP$_c$) is the pressure in the glomerular capsule due to the amount of filtrate already within the capsular space. The presence of this filtrate impedes the movement of additional fluid from the blood into the capsular space and thus it also opposes filtration. A typical value is 18 mm Hg.

Determining Net Filtration Pressure

Filtration occurs if the pressure that promotes filtration, HP$_g$, is greater than the sum of the pressures that oppose filtration (OP$_g$ and HP$_c$). The difference in these pressures is the **net filtration pressure (NFP)**. To determine NFP, use the following calculation:

$$HP_g - (OP_g + HP_c) = NFP$$
$$60 \text{ mm Hg} - (32 \text{ mm Hg} + 18 \text{ mm Hg}) = NFP$$
$$60 \text{ mm Hg} - 50 \text{ mm Hg} = 10 \text{ mm Hg}$$

 WHAT DO YOU THINK?

3 An individual with cirrhosis of the liver produces lower-than-normal amounts of plasma proteins. Which pressure is affected: HP$_g$, OP$_g$, or HP$_c$? What do you predict regarding net filtration pressure: Will it increase or decrease as a result? Will more or less filtrate be formed?

Variables Influenced by Net Filtration Pressure

The **glomerular filtration rate (GFR)** is an important variable influenced by net filtration pressure. It is defined as the rate at which the volume of filtrate is formed, and it is expressed as volume per unit time (usually 1 minute).

The net filtration pressure directly influences the GFR. As NFP increases, usually as the consequence of HP$_g$, the GFR also increases. Likewise, as NFP decreases, GFR decreases.

Net filtration pressure also influences other variables. As the NFP increases, and GFR increases more filtrate is produced. The increase in amount of filtrate results in increased fluid volume moving more rapidly through the tubules, so there is less time to reabsorb substances from the tubular fluid. Consequently, more substances remain in the tubular fluid and are excreted in the urine.

The relationship of these variables to an increase in NFP is shown here:

Increased HP$_g$ → Increased NFP

Increases
GFR
Solutes and water remaining in tubular fluid
Substances in urine

Decreases
Filtrate reabsorption

The significance of these relationships will be referred to throughout different sections of the chapter. Specifically, notice the direct relationship between HP$_g$ and the amount of solutes and water remaining in the tubular fluid. As HP$_g$ increases, substances in the filtrate, including NaCl, increase. As HP$_g$ decreases, substances in the filtrate, including NaCl, decrease. The level of NaCl is monitored by the macula densa of the JG apparatus to indirectly monitor blood pressure in the glomerulus. This concept is discussed in more detail in the following section.

 WHAT DID YOU LEARN?

18 What is the value of the NFP if the glomerular hydrostatic pressure (HP$_g$) is 65 mm Hg, OP$_g$ is 30 mm Hg, and HP$_c$ is 20 mm Hg?

19 Would the value of the NFP remain the same as in question 18 if the HP$_g$ increased from 65 mm Hg to 75 mm Hg?

20 If HP$_g$ increases, what is the effect on NFP? Is the relationship between HP$_g$ and NFP direct or inverse?

✓ LEARNING OBJECTIVES

9. Describe what is meant by intrinsic and extrinsic controls, and give examples of each.

10. Compare and contrast the myogenic mechanism and the tubuloglomerular feedback mechanism.

11. Explain the effects of sympathetic nervous system stimulation on the glomerular filtration rate.

12. Describe the effects of atrial natriuretic peptide on the glomerular filtration rate.

Glomerular filtration is highly regulated because of its influence on the amount of substances reabsorbed into the blood and the amount excreted in the urine. By being able to control glomerular filtration, the kidney is able to control urine production based on physiologic conditions, such as state of hydration.

Glomerular filtration is primarily influenced both by changing the luminal diameter of the afferent arteriole ("the inflow pipe") and by altering the surface area of the filtration membrane. The processes involved include (1) **intrinsic control** (within the kidney itself), which consists of *renal autoregulation* that maintains GFR at a normal level; and (2) **extrinsic controls** (external to the kidney) that involve neural or hormonal regulation, which may decrease or increase GFR, respectively.

Renal Autoregulation: Intrinsic Controls

Renal autoregulation is the intrinsic ability of the kidney to maintain a constant blood pressure and glomerular filtration rate despite changes in systemic arterial pressure. It functions by two mechanisms: the myogenic mechanism and the tubuloglomerular feedback mechanism (**figure 24.13**).

Renal autoregulation in response to systemic blood pressure

(a) Decrease in systemic blood pressure
Efferent arteriole
Glomerulus
Afferent arteriole vasodilates
Widened arteriole lumen allows more blood into glomerulus to offset a decrease in systemic blood pressure

(b) Normal systemic blood pressure
Efferent arteriole
Glomerulus
Afferent arteriole
Arteriole lumen
Normal systemic blood pressure

(c) Increase in systemic blood pressure
Efferent arteriole
Glomerulus
Afferent arteriole vasoconstricts
Narrowed arteriole lumen allows less blood into glomerulus to offset an increase in systemic blood pressure

(d)

Figure 24.13 Renal Autoregulation. Renal autoregulation is the intrinsic ability of the kidney to maintain a normal glomerular filtration rate despite changes in systemic blood pressure. The response to (*a*) a decrease in systemic blood pressure, (*b*) normal resting systemic blood pressure, and (*c*) an increase in systemic blood pressure. (*d*) Renal autoregulation is effective in maintaining normal glomerular filtration for mean arterial pressure (MAP) from 80 mm Hg to 180 mm Hg.

Myogenic Mechanism

The **myogenic** (mī′ō-jen′ik; *mys* = muscle, *genesis* = origin) **mechanism** involves contraction and relaxation of smooth muscle in the wall of the afferent arteriole. A decrease in systemic blood pressure results in a lower volume of blood entering the afferent arteriole, reducing the stretch of the smooth muscle in the arteriole wall. The smooth muscle cells in the vessel relax, resulting in vasodilation. The wider vessel lumen of the afferent arteriole allows more blood into the glomerulus, which compensates for the lower systemic blood pressure. Glomerular blood pressure and GFR remain normal (figure 24.13*a*).

In contrast, an increase in systemic blood pressure causes an additional volume of blood to enter the afferent arteriole, stretching the smooth muscle in the arteriole wall. The smooth muscle cells in the vessel contract, resulting in vasoconstriction. The narrower vessel lumen of the afferent arteriole allows less blood into the glomerulus, which compensates for the greater systemic blood pressure. Glomerular blood pressure and GFR remain normal (figure 24.13*c*).

Tubuloglomerular Feedback Mechanism

The juxtaglomerular apparatus also helps maintain a normal glomerular blood pressure through the **tubuloglomerular feedback mechanism,** which is based on detection of NaCl levels in the tubular fluid.

If the myogenic mechanism is not sufficient to maintain normal glomerular blood pressure in response to an increase in systemic blood pressure, then glomerular blood pressure increases and the amount of NaCl remaining in the tubular fluid increases (see preceding section showing this relationship). Ultimately, an increase in tubular fluid NaCl concentration is detected by macula densa cells in the juxtaglomerular apparatus. The macula densa cells respond by releasing a signaling molecule (most likely ATP is the signaling molecule) that binds to, and stimulates, smooth muscle cells in the afferent arteriole wall. This paracrine stimulation results in further vasoconstriction of the afferent arteriole and a decreased volume of blood entering the glomerulus. GFR and the amount of filtrate formed return to normal levels.

You might find it helpful to think of the tubuloglomerular feedback as a "backup mechanism" to the myogenic mechanism in response to increased systemic blood pressure.

Limitations to Maintaining GFR

It is possible to control GFR and the amount of urine formed by maintaining blood pressure in the glomerulus, as just described. However, there are limitations to this regulation. Renal autoregulation is effective in maintaining a normal glomerular blood pressure only if the systemic mean arterial blood pressure (MAP; see section 20.4a) remains between 80 and 180 mm Hg (figure 24.13*d*).

A decrease in systemic blood pressure results in vasodilation of the afferent arteriole, with maximal arteriole dilation being reached at a MAP of 80 mm Hg. Further decreases in MAP can bring no further arteriole dilation, resulting in a decrease in glomerular blood pressure and glomerular filtration rate. If systemic blood pressure is extremely low (e.g., resulting from a severe hemorrhage), filtration and the elimination of wastes in urine ceases, resulting in accumulation of toxic metabolic wastes in the blood.

If systemic blood pressure increases, then the converse occurs and the afferent arteriole vasoconstricts. The afferent arteriole vessels are maximally constricted at a MAP value of approximately 180 mm Hg. Further increases in systemic blood pressure can bring no further arteriole constriction, resulting in an increase in both glomerular blood pressure and glomerular filtration rate. Ultimately, the amount of urine increases.

Neural and Hormonal Control: Extrinsic Controls

While the intrinsic controls of renal autoregulation help to maintain the glomerular filtration rate within normal homeostatic limits, extrinsic controls involve physiologic processes to *change* GFR. GFR can be decreased with extensive sympathetic stimulation, and it can be increased with atrial natriuretic peptide stimulation. These processes alter urine production, as described next.

Decreasing GFR Through Sympathetic Stimulation

Activation of the sympathetic division as part of the "fight-or-flight" response results in a decrease in GFR through both vasoconstriction of the afferent arteriole and decreasing the surface area of the glomerulus.

The sympathetic division sends increased motor output to the kidneys during exercise or in an emergency (**figure 24.14*a***). Both afferent and efferent arterioles vasoconstrict as a result. Severe vasoconstriction of the afferent arteriole greatly reduces blood flow into the glomerulus. Glomerular blood pressure and GFR decrease.

Sympathetic stimulation also causes granular cells of the JG apparatus to release renin, with the subsequent production of angiotensin II hormone (see section 20.5b). Angiotensin II stimulates myofilaments within mesangial cells to contract. This results in a decrease in the surface area of the filtration membrane, and subsequently the GFR decreases.

Severe vasoconstriction of the afferent arteriole and contraction of mesangial cells both contribute to a decrease in GFR with an accompanying decrease in urine production. Fluid is retained within the blood, maintaining blood volume.

This is a critical adjustment that allows the body to conserve fluid under stressful conditions, such as extensive exertion (e.g., running a marathon on a hot day) or severe hemorrhaging.

Increasing GFR Through Atrial Natriuretic Peptide

Atrial natriuretic (nā′trē-yū-ret′ik) **peptide (ANP)** increases GFR to eliminate fluid. This peptide hormone is released from atrial cardiac muscle cells into the blood in response to distension of these chambers; this occurs when there is either an increase in blood volume return or an increase in blood pressure. ANP is transported in the blood to the kidney following its release from the heart. Atrial natriuretic peptide relaxes the afferent arteriole and inhibits the release of renin from the granular cells to ultimately cause relaxation of the mesangial cells to increase filtration membrane surface area (figure 24.14*b*). The net result is an increase in GFR that is accompanied by both an increase in urine volume and a decrease in blood volume.

The complex interrelationship of the urinary, nervous, and endocrine systems in controlling systemic blood volume and blood pressure is discussed in detail in chapter 25.

Summary of GFR Regulation

The glomerular filtration rate can be maintained, decreased, or increased by the following mechanisms:

- Renal autoregulation *maintains GFR* by altering the size of the afferent arteriole in response to changes in systemic blood pressure. The afferent arteriole vasoconstricts if systemic blood pressure increases, whereas the afferent arteriole vasodilates if systemic blood pressure decreases. Renal autoregulation is effective in maintaining GFR if MAP is within the range of 80 to 180 mm Hg (figure 24.13*d*).

- Direct stimulation by the sympathetic division, and the subsequent production of angiotensin II, *decreases* GFR by causing vasoconstriction of afferent arterioles, contraction of

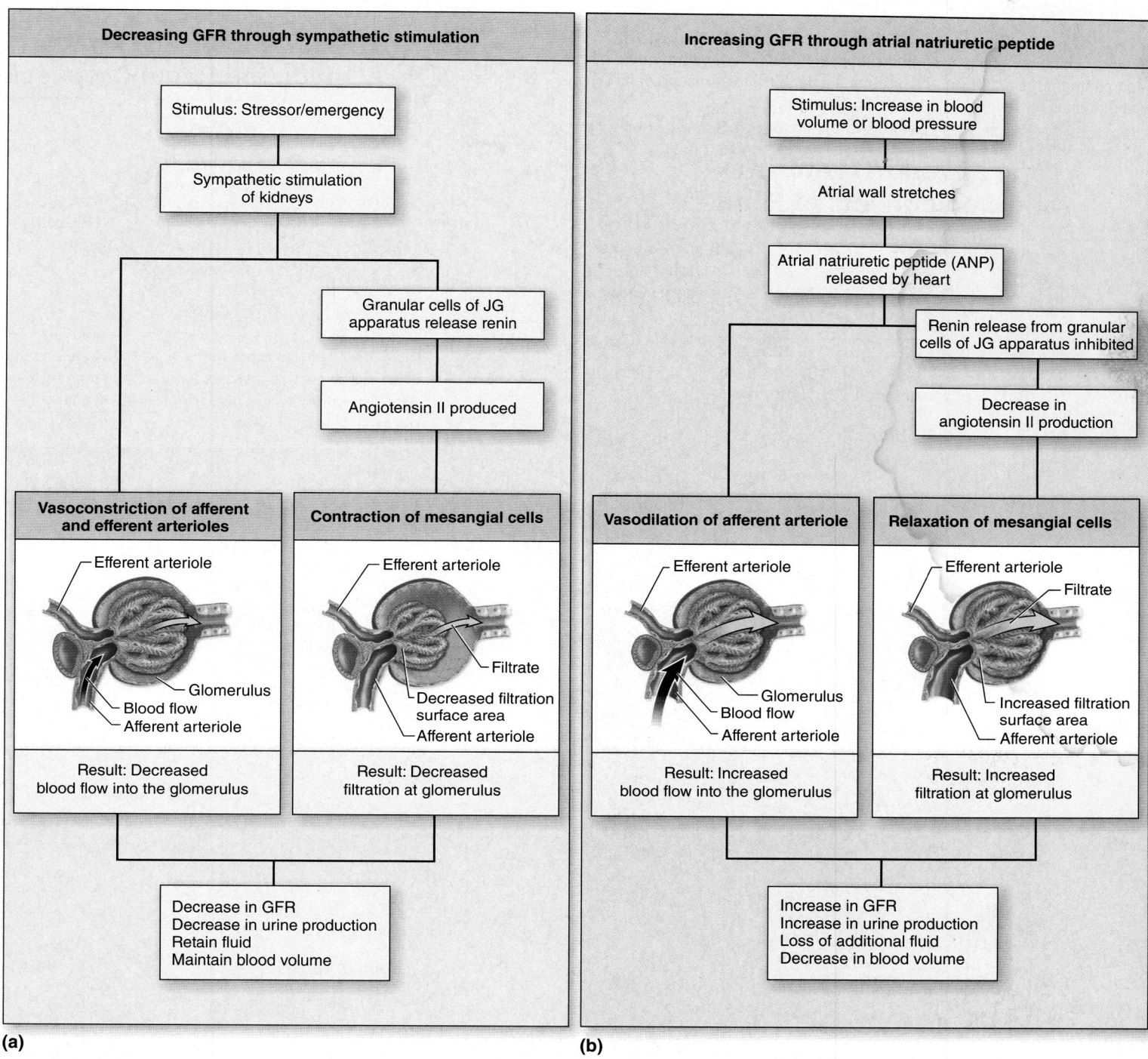

(a)

(b)

Figure 24.14 Extrinsic Mechanisms for Changing the Glomerular Filtration Rate (GFR) Through Nervous and Hormonal Control. Glomerular filtration can be (*a*) decreased by extensive sympathetic stimulation and (*b*) increased by atrial natriuretic peptide (ANP) stimulation.

mesangial cells that decrease the surface area of the glomerulus, or both.

- Atrial natriuretic peptide (ANP) *increases GFR* through vasodilation of the afferent arteriole, inhibition of renin release and the subsequent relaxation of mesangial cells that increase the surface area of the glomerulus, or both.

Figure 24.15 provides a visual summary of the structures and processes involved in glomerular filtration.

WHAT DID YOU LEARN?

21 Does urine production increase, decrease, or stay the same in response to an increase in glomerular filtration rate?

22 What are the three factors that regulate glomerular filtration rate? Do each of these increase, decrease, or maintain GFR?

23 Renal autoregulation is effective with a MAP between 80 and 180 mm Hg. Would renal autoregulation be effective in an individual with a blood pressure of 300/150 mm Hg? A pressure of 70/55 mm Hg? Explain.

Figure 24.15 **Glomerular Filtration and Its Regulation.**
A visual summary of glomerular filtration, including (*a*) the filtration membrane and components of filtrate, (*b*) determining net filtration pressure, and (*c*) the mechanisms for controlling glomerular filtration.

(a) Filtration Membrane and Components of Filtrate

Filtration membrane
Endothelium
Basement membrane

Filtration slit
Pedicel — Visceral layer

Filtrate includes water, glucose, amino acids, ions, urea, many hormones, vitamins B and C, ketones, and small amounts of protein

Not filtered
Erythrocytes
Leukocytes
Platelets
Proteins

Efferent arteriole

Juxtaglomerular apparatus (JGA)

Distal convoluted tubule (DCT)

Afferent arteriole

(b) Determining Net Filtration Pressure in the Renal Corpuscle

HP$_g$ 60 out
OP$_g$ 32 in
HP$_c$ 18 in
NFP 10 out

Glomerular hydrostatic pressure (HP$_g$)		60mm Hg out
Blood colloid osmotic pressure (OP$_g$)	−	32mm Hg in
Capsular hydrostatic pressure (HP$_c$)	−	18mm Hg in
Net filtration pressure (NFP)	=	10mm Hg out

Tubular fluid

Proximal convoluted tubule (PCT)

Filtrate

Leukocytes
Erythrocytes
Proteins
Solutes

Glomerulus

Capsular space

Glomerular capsule (parietal layer)

(c) Control of Glomerular Filtration Rate

MAINTAIN GFR

Afferent arteriole

Renal autoregulation maintains GFR despite changes in systemic blood pressure (BP):
- Decreased systemic BP results in vasodilation of afferent arteriole
- Increased systemic BP results in vasoconstriction of afferent arteriole

DECREASE GFR

Decreased filtration surface area

Vasoconstriction

The sympathetic division decreases GFR by:
- Afferent arteriole vasoconstriction
- Triggering mesangial cells to contract, which decreases filtration surface area

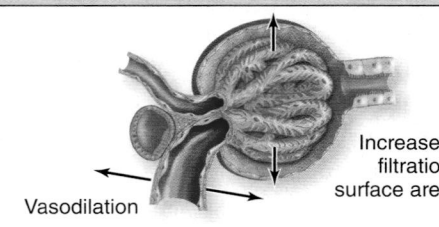

INCREASE GFR

Increased filtration surface area

Vasodilation

Atrial natriuretic peptide (ANP) increases GFR by:
- Afferent arteriole vasodilation
- Triggering mesangial cells to relax, which increases filtration surface area

24.6 Reabsorption and Secretion in Tubules and Collecting Ducts

Tubular fluid flows through the proximal convoluted tubule, nephron loop, distal convoluted tubule, and then into collecting tubules and collecting ducts, as described earlier. Substances are reabsorbed when they move from the tubular fluid back into the blood. Additionally, some substances that were not initially filtered in the glomerulus, but must be eliminated from the blood, become a component of urine through tubular secretion.

Here we provide an overview of transport processes, and consider transport maximum and renal threshold. We then consider the details of the substances reabsorbed and secreted. These are organized as follows:

- Substances reabsorbed completely
- Substances with regulated reabsorption (meaning some, but not all, of substance reabsorbed)
- Substances eliminated as waste products

Finally, we describe the establishment of a concentration gradient in the interstitial fluid, which drives the reabsorption of water controlled by ADH.

24.6a Overview of Transport Processes

LEARNING OBJECTIVE

1. Describe five characteristics and conditions that affect tubular reabsorption and secretion.

This section provides a general overview of important anatomic structures and physiologic conditions in the kidney that influence reabsorption and secretion of substances. Please refer to **figure 24.16** as you read through the following description:

1. The barrier that a substance must cross is the simple epithelium of the tubule wall.
2. Substances can either pass between the epithelial cells of the tubular wall by **paracellular** (păr′a-sel′yū-lăr; *para* = alongside) **transport,** or more commonly, move through the epithelial cells by **transcellular** (trănz′sel′yū-lăr; *trans* = across) **transport.**
3. During transcellular transport, a substance must cross two cell membranes: the **luminal membrane** that is in contact with tubular fluid and the **basolateral membrane** that rests on the basement membrane. The order in which the substance crosses these membranes depends upon whether it is being reabsorbed or secreted.

Figure 24.16 Convoluted Tubules and Peritubular Capillaries. The anatomic structures and physiologic conditions that influence tubular reabsorption and tubular secretion.

LEARNING STRATEGY

Movement of filtrate and tubular fluid through the nephron is analogous to movement of items along a conveyor belt. The fluid's path is like the conveyer belt, and substances are first loaded onto the beginning of the conveyor belt (filtration). Then, some of these substances are retrieved from the conveyor belt (tubular reabsorption). Additional substances not originally filtered can be added to the conveyor belt along its length (tubular secretion). Whatever is on the conveyor belt at the end represents the substances that make up urine.

CLINICAL VIEW
Glucosuria

Glucosuria (or *glycosuria*) is the excretion of glucose in urine. This occurs when the plasma glucose level exceeds approximately 220 milligrams per deciliter (mg/dL) and the transport maxiumum (T_m) rate for glucose of 320 milligrams per minute (mg/min) has been exceeded. Glucose molecules act as an osmotic diuretic, pulling water into the tubular fluid and causing loss of fluid in the urine. Glucosuria, along with frequent urination and thirst, are classical signs of diabetes mellitus (see Clinical View: "Conditions Resulting in Abnormal Blood Glucose Levels" in chapter 17).

4. Different transport proteins **(table 24.1)** are embedded within the two membranes. They control the movement of various substances using cellular processes that include simple or facilitated diffusion, osmosis, primary and secondary active transport, and vesicular transport (see section 4.3).

5. Peritubular capillaries have both low hydrostatic pressure (8 mm Hg), because of the loss of fluid during filtration in the glomerulus, and high colloid (oncotic) pressure exerted by protein, because most proteins remain in the blood during filtration. These two important properties facilitate reabsorption of substances through bulk flow (see section 20.2b).

Although reabsorption and secretion of substances occur along the entire length of the nephron tubule, collecting tubules, and collecting ducts, most reabsorption occurs in the proximal convoluted tubule, where the uptake processes are aided by the extensive microvilli on the cells' luminal surfaces that increase their surface area.

WHAT DID YOU LEARN?

24 What are the significant anatomic and physiologic factors that influence tubular reabsorption and tubular secretion?

24.6b Transport Maximum and Renal Threshold

LEARNING OBJECTIVES

2. Define the transport maximum of a substance.

3. Explain what is meant by renal threshold.

The **transport maximum (T_m)** is the maximum amount of a substance that can be reabsorbed (or secreted) across the tubule epithe-

lium in a given period of time (i.e., its rate of movement). This maximum is dependent upon the number of the transport proteins in the epithelial cell membrane specific for the substance.

For example, the T_m for glucose reabsorption by the glucose transport proteins is approximately 320 milligrams per minute (mg/min). As long as the tubular fluid contains no more than 320 mg of glucose passing through a region of the renal tubule every minute, all of it will be reabsorbed. If the tubular fluid level of glucose exceeds 320 mg/min, then the transport proteins are saturated, and the excess glucose is excreted in the urine.

The maximum *plasma concentration* of a substance that can be carried in the blood without eventually appearing in the urine is called the **renal threshold.** For example, the renal threshold for glucose is 220 milligrams per deciliter (mg/dL). Above this concentration, the substance is so concentrated in the plasma, and thus in the tubular fluid following filtration, that the transport proteins cannot reabsorb all of the substance from the fluid. The T_m is exceeded, and the substance remains within the tubule fluid and is excreted in the urine.

WHAT DID YOU LEARN?

25 What is the transport maximum of a substance? How is it different from the renal threshold of the substance?

24.6c Substances Reabsorbed Completely

LEARNING OBJECTIVES

4. Explain the reabsorption of nutrients such as glucose.

5. Describe the process by which protein is transported out of the filtrate and into the blood.

Some substances are not normal components of urine because 100% of the substance is reabsorbed from the tubular fluid back into the blood. The location for this reabsorption typically is in the proximal convoluted tubule. Two major types of substances fall into this category: nutrients (e.g., glucose, amino acids, lactate), and the small amount of filtered plasma proteins.

Nutrient Reabsorption

Nutrients are normally reabsorbed completely in the proximal convoluted tubule where each nutrient has its own specific transport

Table 24.1	Transport Proteins in Cells of the Nephron Tubule	
Pumps	**Carriers (Porters)**	**Channels**
Na$^+$/K$^+$ ATPase	Glucose uniporter	Na$^+$
Na$^+$/K$^+$/2 Cl$^-$	Na$^+$/glucose symporter	K$^+$
H$^+$ ATPase	Na$^+$/HCO$_3^-$ symporter	Aquaporins (H$_2$O channels)
Ca^{2+} ATPase	Na$^+$/H$^+$ antiporter	
	Cl$^-$/HCO$_3^-$ antiporter	

proteins. We use glucose as an example to describe how nutrients may be reabsorbed completely (figure 24.17).

Glucose is first transported into the tubule cell across the luminal membrane by Na$^+$/glucose symporter proteins. Energy from Na$^+$ moving down its concentration gradient into the tubule cell is used to move glucose up its concentration gradient into the tubule cell by secondary active transport (see section 4.3c). Glucose is then moved by glucose uniporters (carriers) out of the tubule cell down its concentration gradient via facilitated diffusion across the basolateral membrane.

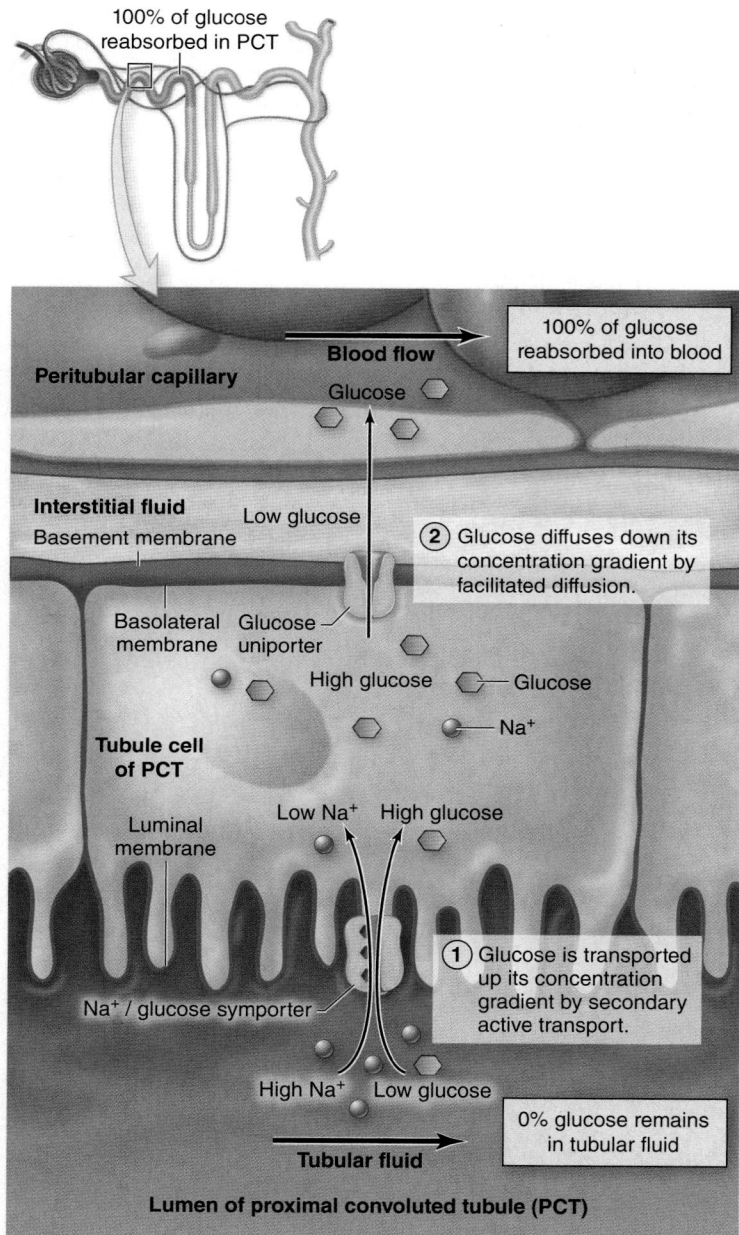

100% of glucose reabsorbed in PCT

100% of glucose reabsorbed into blood

Blood flow

Peritubular capillary

Glucose

Interstitial fluid
Basement membrane

Low glucose

(2) Glucose diffuses down its concentration gradient by facilitated diffusion.

Basolateral membrane | Glucose uniporter

High glucose — Glucose

 Na$^+$

Tubule cell of PCT

Luminal membrane

Low Na$^+$ | High glucose

(1) Glucose is transported up its concentration gradient by secondary active transport.

Na$^+$ / glucose symporter

High Na$^+$ | Low glucose

0% glucose remains in tubular fluid

Tubular fluid

Lumen of proximal convoluted tubule (PCT)

Figure 24.17 Glucose Reabsorption. Glucose reabsorption occurs in the proximal convoluted tubule. In a healthy individual, 100% of the glucose is reabsorbed. Glucose is transported 1) across the luminal membrane against its concentration gradient—this occurs by secondary active transport via Na$^+$/glucose symporters, and 2) across the basolateral membrane down its concentration gradient by facilitated diffusion via glucose uniporters.

Glucose ultimately is returned to the blood in the peritubular capillaries. As with many other substances that rely on membrane transport proteins, there is a maximum amount of glucose that can be reabsorbed per unit time.

Transport of Proteins

Although most proteins are not freely filtered in the glomerulus because of their size and negative charge, some small and medium-sized peptides, such as insulin and angiotensin, and limited amounts of large proteins (e.g., about 0.02% of albumin) may appear in the filtrate. Protein is transported from the tubular fluid in the proximal convoluted tubule back into the blood so as not to be excreted in the urine.

We use the general term "transported" here (instead of reabsorbed) because the proteins actually undergo transformational changes while being reabsorbed. Protein is moved across the luminal membrane by pinocytosis. Lysosomes in these tubule cells then digest the proteins into their amino acid building blocks. These amino acids are moved by facilitated diffusion across the basolateral membrane back into the blood. Very small peptides, such as angiotensin II, are degraded by peptidases within the luminal membrane and the amino acids are absorbed directly into the tubule cell. Thus, proteins and small peptides are first degraded into amino acids, which are then absorbed into the blood.

WHAT DID YOU LEARN?

26 How is glucose reabsorbed across the two membranes of the tubule cells?

27 Why are proteins said to be transported rather than simply reabsorbed in the proximal convoluted tubule?

24.6d Substances with Regulated Reabsorption

LEARNING OBJECTIVES

6. List substances for which reabsorption is regulated.

7. Describe the reabsorption of sodium, potassium, calcium, and phosphate.

8. Describe the reabsorption of water, and compare how it is regulated by the actions of aldosterone and antidiuretic hormone.

9. Describe how pH is regulated in the collecting tubules.

Some substances are recovered completely from the tubular fluid, while others are not completely reabsorbed, resulting in a variable and often small percentage of that substance being excreted into the urine. By varying the amount of a substance excreted, the nephron has a substantial role in regulating the blood level of that substance. A number of substances fall into the category of undergoing regulated reabsorption, including Na$^+$, water, K$^+$, HCO$_3^-$, and Ca^{2+}. We will see that the reabsorption of Na$^+$ plays a pivotal role in the reabsorption of many of these other substances.

WHAT DO YOU THINK?

4 If a substance in the blood is filtered, and not all of it is completely reabsorbed back into the blood, does its level in the blood increase, decrease, or stay the same? Explain.

Sodium (Na⁺) Reabsorption

The amount of Na⁺ reabsorbed from the tubular fluid can vary from 98% to 100%. Unlike glucose and other nutrients, Na⁺ is reabsorbed along the entire length of the nephron tubule, with the majority of the Na⁺ (about 65%) reabsorbed in the proximal convoluted tubule (figure 24.18a). Approximately 25% is reabsorbed in the nephron loop, and a varying (and regulated) amount in the distal convoluted tubule and collecting tubule and duct.

Sodium concentration is relatively low inside the tubule cell and relatively high within both the tubule lumen and interstitial fluid (figure 24.18b). (The Na⁺ concentration gradient is established by Na⁺/K⁺ pumps, as described shortly.) Thus, Na⁺ moves passively by facilitated diffusion down its electrochemical gradient across the luminal membrane into the tubular cell. The specific type of transport protein involved in

the movement across the luminal membrane varies with the different sections of the renal tubule.

Embedded in the basolateral membrane are Na⁺/K⁺ pumps. These pumps move Na⁺ from within the tubular cell into the interstitial fluid, while K⁺ is moved from the interstitial fluid into the tubular cell. This keeps the Na⁺ concentration relatively low within the tubule cells. The energy consumption of these pumps is substantial; they use approximately 80% of all energy invested in active transport within nephrons. The Na⁺ then enters into the peritubular and vasa recta capillaries through intercellular clefts.

Sodium reabsorption is regulated by hormones near the end of the tubule (figure 24.18c). If we consider that Na⁺ intake can vary from as little as 0.05 gram per day (g/day) if an individual is on a low-sodium diet to 20 g/day to 25 g/day, regulation of Na⁺ output is critical if blood Na⁺ levels are to be maintained within a normal homeostatic range.

~65% of Na⁺ reabsorbed in PCT

~25% of Na⁺ reabsorbed in nephron loop

Regulated percent of Na⁺ reabsorbed in DCT, CT, and CD

(a) Tubules

(b) Lumen of proximal convoluted tubule (PCT)

Blood flow

~65% of Na⁺ reabsorbed into the blood

Peritubular capillary

Na⁺

Interstitial fluid

High Na⁺   Low K⁺

Na⁺/K⁺ pump

② Na⁺ is moved up its concentration gradient by active transport.

Basolateral membrane

Low Na⁺   High K⁺

Tubule cell

① Na⁺ diffuses down its concentration gradient by facilitated diffusion.

Luminal membrane   Na⁺ transport protein

High Na⁺

~35% of Na⁺ remains in tubular fluid

Tubular fluid

(c) Lumen of the distal convoluted tubule (DCT), collecting tubule (CT), or collecting duct (CD)

Interstitial fluid

Tubular fluid

Blood flow

Luminal membrane

Basolateral membrane

Principal cell

High K⁺   K⁺   Na⁺/K⁺ pumps   Na⁺

Na⁺ channels

Low Na⁺   High Na⁺   H₂O

High Na⁺

H₂O   Osmosis

Aquaporin

Aldosterone increases both the number of Na⁺ channels and Na⁺/K⁺ pumps, resulting in an increase in Na⁺ reabsorption.

% of Na⁺ varies from 0–2%

Peritubular capillary

Figure 24.18 Sodium (Na⁺) Reabsorption. (a) Na⁺ reabsorption occurs along most of the length of the renal tubule. (b) The majority of Na⁺ is reabsorbed in the proximal convoluted tubule. Na⁺ is transported across the luminal membrane down its concentration gradient by facilitated diffusion via various types of Na⁺ transport proteins, and across the basolateral membrane against its concentration gradient by Na⁺/K⁺ pumps. (c) The amount of Na⁺ excreted in the urine is regulated in the distal convoluted tubule, collecting tubules, and collecting ducts by hormones. Aldosterone binds to principal cells, increasing both the number of Na⁺ carriers and Na⁺/K⁺ pumps. The net effect is that additional Na⁺ is reabsorbed, water follows by osmosis, and additional K⁺ is secreted.

The amount of Na⁺ that is excreted in urine ranges from 0% to 2% of the total filtered Na⁺. This amount is controlled by aldosterone and atrial natriuretic peptide hormones in the DCT, CT, and CD. **Aldosterone** (al-dos'tĕr-ōn) is a steroid hormone (see section 17.5a) produced by the adrenal cortex. It enters principal cells to bind with intracellular receptors to form a hormone-receptor complex that stimulates protein synthesis of Na⁺ channels and Na⁺/K⁺ pumps. These additional transport proteins become embedded in the plasma membranes of principal cells and Na⁺ reabsorption increases. Water follows the Na⁺ by osmosis, resulting in reabsorption of an isotonic fluid. Note that K⁺ is secreted into the tubular fluid during this process.

Atrial natriuretic peptide (ANP) inhibits both the reabsorption of Na⁺ in the proximal convoluted tubule and collecting tubules and the release of aldosterone (not shown in figure 24.18). Consequently, more Na⁺ and water (because water follows Na⁺ by osmosis) are excreted in urine. Recall that ANP increases GFR, a process that also increases urine output.

Water (H₂O) Reabsorption

Water movement occurs by osmosis. It is reabsorbed by paracellular transport between cells, or by transcellular transport through specific water transporter proteins called **aquaporins.** Of the approximately 180 L of water filtered daily, all except an average of approximately 1.5 L is reabsorbed. The exact amount of water reabsorbed depends upon both fluid intake and fluid excreted through other routes (e.g., sweating). The tubule varies in its permeability to water along its length, and the concentration of the tubular fluid changes as it moves through the different sections of the tubule.

Approximately 65% of the water in the tubular fluid is reabsorbed in the proximal convoluted tubule (**figure 24.19a**). The aquaporins here are permanent components of the luminal membrane and are relatively constant in number. The movement of water out of the proximal convoluted tubule follows Na⁺ by osmosis, and it is referred to as **obligatory water reabsorption.** This water movement is dependent upon the movement of Na⁺, so the water is "obliged" to follow Na⁺. The movement of Na⁺ and water is equivalent, and an isotonic tubular fluid is maintained as it moves through the proximal convoluted tubule.

In the nephron loop, only about 10% of the filtered water in the tubular fluid is reabsorbed. Water moves from the descending limb of the nephron loop into the vasa recta.

As tubular fluid moves through the distal convoluted tubules, and collecting tubules and ducts, water reabsorption is controlled primarily by aldosterone and antidiuretic hormone. Recall that aldosterone increases the number of Na⁺/K⁺ pumps and Na⁺ channels in principal cells, thus increasing both Na⁺ and water reabsorption.

Consequently, the concentration of tubular fluid is maintained (see figure 24.18). In contrast, antidiuretic hormone that is released from the posterior pituitary gland when we are dehydrated binds to receptors of principal cells to increase migration of vesicles containing aquaporins to the membrane. This action provides additional channels for water reabsorption (figure 24.19b).

The osmotic force caused by the concentration gradient within the interstitial fluid (described shortly) pulls water from the tubule. Thus, water reabsorption regulated by ADH near the end of the tubule is *independent* of Na⁺ reabsorption, and as a result solute concentration of the tubular fluid increases. Tubular reabsorption in response to ADH is referred to as **facultative water reabsorption.**

Regulated (facultative) water reabsorption in DCT, CT, and CD

~65% obligatory water reabsoption in PCT

10% of water reabsorbtion in nephron loop

(a) Tubules

Figure 24.19 Water Reabsorption. (*a*) Obligatory water reabsorption occurs in the proximal convoluted tubule (PCT: about 65%). In the nephron loop, approximately 10% of the water is reabsorbed. The amount excreted in the urine is regulated in the distal convoluted tubule (DCT), collecting tubules (CT), and collecting ducts (CD) in response to binding of antidiuretic hormone (ADH). (*b*) ADH binds to principal cells to increase the number of aquaporins. Water is "pulled" out of tubules by osmosis.

Tubular fluid

Blood flow

ADH

Principal cell

Aquaporins

Additional water is reabsorbed by osmosis due to increased numbers of aquaporins.

H₂O

Osmosis

H₂O

Interstitial fluid

H₂O

H₂O

H₂O

Luminal membrane

Basolateral membrane

Peritubular capillary

(b) Lumen of DCT, CT, and CD

ADH and Urine Production **Antidiuretic hormone (ADH)** increases water reabsorption from the filtrate into the blood, resulting in the production of a smaller volume of a more concentrated urine. Conditions of extreme dehydration result in subsequent high concentrations of ADH—thus, urine volume can be as little as about 0.5 L/day. Urine can be as concentrated as 1200 milliosmoles (mOsm), which is the same concentration as the interstitial fluid outside the tubules. Under these conditions, the urine generally appears noticeably darker yellow in color.

A decrease in ADH results in an increase in urine volume that is less concentrated. Urine volume can be several liters per day, and with the aid of pumps that move salt out of the tubular fluid, urine can be as dilute as 50 mOsm. Under these conditions, the urine will appear a light yellow to very pale yellow color.

Chapter 25 presents a detailed discussion of the effects of these hormones (aldosterone, ANP, and ADH) on electrolyte, fluid, and acid-base balance.

Movement of Potassium

Potassium is unlike other substances previously covered because it is both reabsorbed and secreted **(figure 24.20)**. The result may be a net reabsorption of K^+, with little being lost in urine, or a net secretion, with larger losses in the urine.

In the proximal convoluted tubule, 60% to 80% of the K^+ in the tubular fluid is reabsorbed by paracellular transport; it is dependent upon the movement of Na^+, as follows:

1. Sodium is reabsorbed across the luminal membrane.
2. Water follows the Na^+.
3. The concentration of the remaining solutes in the tubular fluid increases as water follows the movement of Na^+.
4. Consequently, the solute concentration of tubular fluid is greater than in the interstitial fluid, creating a gradient between the tubular fluid and interstitial fluid.
5. Potassium moves down its concentration gradient from the tubular fluid by the paracellular route.
6. These conditions also allow the passive reabsorption of other solutes, including other cations (Mg^{2+}, Ca^{2+}), phosphate ion (PO_4^{3-}), fatty acids, and urea.

Approximately 10% to 20% of the K^+ in tubular fluid is reabsorbed in the thick segment of the nephron loop ascending limb by both transcellular and paracellular transport.

Figure 24.20 Potassium Movement. Potassium is both reabsorbed and secreted along different segments of the renal tubule. The amount of K^+ lost in the urine is dependent upon the activity of principal cells in the collecting tubules in response to aldosterone.

Either a net reabsorption or net secretion of K$^+$ may occur in the collecting tubule. The two specialized cells in the collecting tubule, intercalated cells and principal cells, have opposite effects on K$^+$ movement. Type A intercalated cells reabsorb K$^+$ continuously, whereas principal cells secrete K$^+$ at varying rates based on aldosterone levels.

We have seen that aldosterone stimulates principal cells to secrete K$^+$, while Na$^+$ and water are reabsorbed. The most powerful stimulant to cause release of aldosterone from the adrenal cortex is an elevated K$^+$ blood level. Thus, this mechanism involves negative feedback to keep blood K$^+$ levels close to optimum values.

Calcium and Phosphate Balance

Calcium and PO$_4^{3-}$ are two substances generally considered together because 99% of the body calcium is stored in bone, and the majority is stored as calcium phosphate. Approximately 60% of the Ca^{2+} in blood becomes part of the filtrate and then the tubular fluid. The remainder of the Ca^{2+} is bound to protein in the blood and is prevented from being filtered. In comparison, 90% to 95% of the PO$_4^{3-}$ is filtered as blood passes through glomerular capillaries.

The amount of Ca^{2+} and PO$_4^{3-}$ excreted in the urine is regulated by parathyroid hormone (PTH), and thus it influences blood levels of both Ca^{2+} and PO$_4^{3-}$. Recall from section 7.6b that PTH is released from the parathyroid gland in response to decreased blood Ca^{2+}. One target of PTH is the kidney tubules **(figure 24.21)**. PTH inhibits PO$_4^{3-}$ reabsorption in the proximal convoluted tubule and it stimulates Ca^{2+} reabsorption in the distal convoluted tubule. As additional PO$_4^{3-}$ is eliminated via the urine, less PO$_4^{3-}$ is available to form calcium phosphate, the major calcium salt deposited in bone. Thus, Ca^{2+} redeposited in the bone decreases, and blood Ca^{2+} increases.

Bicarbonate Ions, Hydrogen Ions, and pH

The movement of bicarbonate ions (HCO$_3^-$, a weak base) and hydrogen ions (H$^+$, an acid) plays a significant role in regulating pH of both urine and the blood. Bicarbonate ions move freely across the filtration membrane, while only small amounts of H$^+$ are filtered with most remaining in the blood. The filtered HCO$_3^-$ must be reabsorbed to ensure blood pH does not

PTH inhibits reabsorption of PO$_4^{3-}$ in PCT.

PTH stimulates reabsorption of Ca^{2+} in DCT.

Result: Increased PO$_4^{3-}$ lost in urine

Figure 24.21 Calcium Ion and Phosphate Ion Reabsorption. Calcium and phosphate ions are both reabsorbed in various segments of the tubule. The amounts reabsorbed are regulated by parathyroid hormone (PTH), which both inhibits the reabsorption of PO$_4^{3-}$ in the proximal convoluted tubule (PCT) and stimulates Ca^{2+} reabsorption in the distal convoluted tubule (DCT).

(a) 80–90% HCO_3^- reclaimed in PCT

Regulated HCO_3^- and H^+ reabsorption and secretion in collecting tubules

10–20% HCO_3^- reclaimed in nephron loop

(a)

Blood flow

Peritubular capillary

HCO_3^- ④

Interstitial fluid

Basement membrane   **Tubule cell**

HCO_3^-

③ $CO_2 + H_2O \rightarrow H_2CO_3$

HCO_3^-

H^+

②

① $HCO_3^- + H^+ \rightarrow H_2CO_3 \rightarrow CO_2 + H_2O$

④ H^+

Tubular fluid

(b) Lumen of proximal convoluted tubule and nephron loop

① Within filtrate, HCO_3^- combines with H^+ to form carbonic acid (H_2CO_3), which is unstable and dissociates to form CO_2 and H_2O.

② CO_2 enters tubule cell by simple diffusion.

③ Within tubule cell, CO_2 combines with H_2O and the process is reversed to form HCO_3^- and H^+.

④ HCO_3^- is absorbed into the blood, and H^+ is secreted into the tubular fluid.

Net effect is "reclaiming" the HCO_3^- that was just filtered and "losing" H^+ in urine (this always occurs).

Blood flow

Peritubular capillary

HCO_3^- ③

Interstitial fluid

Type A intercalated cell

HCO_3^-

② $CO_2 + H_2O \rightarrow H_2CO_3$

H^+

① CO_2

③ H^+

Tubular fluid

(c) Lumen of collecting tubules: Type A intercalated cells

① CO_2 in tubular fluid enters tubule cell.

② CO_2 combines with H_2O to form HCO_3^- and H^+.

③ HCO_3^- is absorbed into the blood and H^+ is secreted into the tubular fluid.

Net effect is the "capturing" of newly formed HCO_3^- and "losing" H^+ in urine (occurs if in acidic state).

Figure 24.22 Bicarbonate Ion and Hydrogen Ion Movement. (*a*) Bicarbonate movement occurs along the entire length of the nephron. (*b*) In the proximal convoluted tubule (PCT), approximately 80–90% of the filtered HCO_3^- is "replaced" by an indirect mechanism. The remainder of filtered HCO_3^- is absorbed in the nephron loop (thick segment of ascending limb). (*c*) In the collecting tubules, when in an acidic state, type A intercalated cells synthesize a new molecule of HCO_3^- and an H^+. Bicarbonate ion is absorbed into blood, and H^+ is secreted into tubular fluid.

become too acidic (figure 24.22*a*). Approximately 80% to 90% of HCO_3^- is "reclaimed" from the tubular fluid, primarily in the proximal convoluted tubule. The remaining 10% to 20% is taken up from the thick segment of the ascending limb of the nephron loop. Thus, as the tubular fluid enters the distal convoluted tubule, usually 100% of the HCO_3^- originally in the filtrate has been reabsorbed. Note that filtered HCO_3^- is not specifically reabsorbed but rather is "replaced" by a process that is described in figure 24.22*b*.

The pH of urine, and consequently the pH of blood, are regulated in the collecting tubules. Exactly how this occurs depends upon the "pH state" of the individual—that is, "Is he or she in an acidic or alkaline state?" A person with a diet that includes animal protein and wheat (a typical American diet) is generally in an acidic state. As a result, newly synthesized HCO_3^- is reabsorbed into the blood, and H^+ is excreted within the filtrate, by *type A intercalated cells.* The result is an increase in blood pH (more alkaline) and a decrease in urine pH (more acidic), which averages a pH of about 6.0. The details of this process are described in figure 24.22*c*.

A person with a diet high in fruits and vegetables and little or no animal protein is more typically in an "alkaline state," and in this case *type B intercalated cells* are active (not shown in the figure). The action of type B cells is the reverse of that of type A cells. Think of type B intercalated cells as "flipped" type A cells: Type B cells secrete HCO_3^- and reabsorb H^+ to lower blood pH and increase urine pH.

The actions of the type A and type B intercalated cells in regulating blood pH are a significant component of how the body maintains pH balance (see section 25.5).

WHAT DID YOU LEARN?

28 How does Na^+ and water reabsorption occur? Which two hormones are involved?

29 What is the effect of parathyroid hormone on the reabsorption of both PO_4^{3-} and Ca^{2+}?

30 How are the movement of H^+ and HCO_3^- regulated by type A and type B intercalated cells?

24.6e Substances Eliminated as Waste Products

LEARNING OBJECTIVES

10. Identify the three nitrogenous waste products, and describe the fate of each.

11. Give examples of other materials eliminated by kidneys.

The urinary system prevents the accumulation of cellular waste, various hormones and their metabolites, and foreign substances (e.g., drugs and chemicals) by eliminating them in the urine. Materials to be excreted in the urine are both filtered at the glomerulus and secreted along the tubule pathway to ensure their elimination.

Elimination of Nitrogenous Waste

Nitrogenous waste is metabolic waste that contains nitrogen. The body's main nitrogenous waste products are (1) **urea,** a small, water-soluble molecule produced from protein breakdown in the liver; (2) **uric acid,** produced from nucleic acid breakdown primarily in the liver; and (3) **creatinine,** produced from metabolism of creatine in muscle tissue.

Urea and uric acid are both reabsorbed and secreted, whereas creatinine is only secreted. Here we describe the processing of urea. Urea levels in the blood range from 3 milliequivalents per liter (mEq/L) to 9 mEq/L and depend upon protein intake. Urea is freely filtered and is both reabsorbed and secreted in different areas of the tubules. Approximately half is reabsorbed at the proximal convoluted tubule by the paracellular movement but is then secreted back into the tubule at the nephron loop by urea uniporters. Thus, 100% of the filtered urea is present in the tubular fluid as it enters the distal convoluted tubules.

However, about 50% of the urea is then reabsorbed at the collecting tubules, leaving about 50% of the filtered urea to be excreted in the urine. In addition to being eliminated as a waste product, urea serves a functional role in the kidneys by helping to establish the concentration gradient in the interstitial fluid of the kidney (described later).

Elimination of Drugs and Bioactive Substances

The kidneys eliminate potentially harmful substances through both filtration and secretion in addition to eliminating nitrogenous wastes. Most secretion of these and other substances (except K^+, described earlier) occur in the proximal convoluted tubule and include the following:

- **Certain drugs.** Antibiotics including penicillin and sulfonamides, aspirin (salicylate), morphine, chemotherapy drugs, saccharin, and chemicals in marijuana are just a few examples of the drugs that are eliminated in the urine.
- **Other metabolic wastes.** Bilirubin (see section 18.3b) and hormone metabolites are examples of metabolic wastes that are eliminated in urine.
- **Certain hormones.** Human chorionic gonadotropin (hCG) is a hormone produced when a woman is pregnant: It is an example of a hormone that is eliminated in the urine. The presence of hCG can be used to verify the pregnancy with a pregnancy test completed at home or in the doctor's office (see section 29.2). Other examples of excreted hormones include epinephrine and prostaglandins.

WHAT DID YOU LEARN?

31 What are some substances eliminated as waste products?

24.6f Establishing the Concentration Gradient

LEARNING OBJECTIVES

12. Explain what is meant by the countercurrent multiplier that occurs within the nephron loop.

13. Describe the countercurrent exchange system that maintains the concentration gradient.

14. Discuss the contribution of urea cycling to the concentration gradient.

You previously learned that the action of antidiuretic hormone (ADH) is dependent upon the concentration gradient in the interstitial fluid surrounding nephron tubules. This concentration gradient is established by various solutes, including Na^+ and chloride ion (Cl^-), which progressively increase in concentration from the cortex into the medulla. The concentration gradient exerts osmotic pull to move more water from the tubular fluid into the interstitial fluid when ADH is present. The water then moves into the capillaries.

This section describes how the concentration gradient in the interstitial fluid is established and maintained by (1) the nephron loop via the countercurrent multiplier, (2) the vasa recta via the countercurrent exchange system, and (3) urea recycling.

The Nephron Loop

A positive feedback mechanism called the **countercurrent multiplier** involves the nephron loop and is partially responsible for establishing the salt concentration gradient within the interstitial fluid (figure 24.23). "Countercurrent" refers to the tubular fluid's "reversing" its relative direction as it moves first through the descending limb and then through the ascending limb of the loop. "Multiplier" refers to the positive feedback loop that increases the concentration of salts within the interstitial fluid. The juxtamedullary nephrons with their long nephron loops are primarily important in this process.

The *descending* limb is permeable to water. It is also impermeable to the movement of salts out of the tubule. Water is moved from the tubular fluid into the interstitial fluid as a result, while salts are retained within the tubular fluid. (Note that solute concentration in the tubule increases from 300 mOsm to as much as 1200 mOsm—by the loss of water and retaining of salt.)

In contrast to the descending limb, the *ascending* limb is impermeable to water, and it actively pumps salt out of the tubular fluid into the interstitial fluid. As a result, water is retained in the tubular fluid, and salt is moved from the tubular fluid into the interstitial fluid. (Note that the solute concentration becomes diluted from 1200 mOsm to 100 mOsm as it moves through the ascending limb.) Most importantly, however, is that the salt concentration in the interstitial fluid surrounding the tubules increases, which sets up a positive feedback loop.

Consider that as the salt concentration in the interstitial fluid increases (1) an even greater amount of water moves out of the descending limb, (2) this increases the salt concentration in the tubular fluid that flows into the ascending limb, which (3) allows even more salts to be pumped out of the ascending limb. Consequently, the concentration of salts in the interstitial fluid is increased or "multiplied" through this positive feedback loop.

Vasa Recta

The concentration gradient established in the interstitial fluid by the nephron loop is maintained or preserved by the unique anatomic arrangement and physiologic conditions of the

Figure 24.23 Interstitial Fluid Concentration Gradient. A visual representation of how the concentration gradient is established in the interstitial fluid surrounding the nephron loop. Countercurrent multiplier refers to the actions of the nephron loop. Countercurrent exchange system involves the processes of the vasa recta.

Within figure:

Establishing the concentration gradient

Less concentrated
Most concentrated

Descending limb
Ascending limb
300 mOsm
100 mOsm
Interstitial fluid
Cortex
Tubular fluid
Medulla
Blood

Descending limb loses water and the tubular fluid becomes more concentrated.

Ascending limb loses salts and the interstitial fluid becomes more concentrated.

Salts
Salts
Salts
Salts
Water

Nephron loop

Vasa recta lose salts, gain water.
Water
Vasa recta gain salts, lose water.

1200 mOsm

---

vasa recta (figure 24.23). The blood within the vasa recta travels in the *opposite* direction to the tubular fluid flow within the adjacent nephron loop. So, the blood flows deep into the medulla alongside the *ascending* limb of the nephron loop, and it then flows toward the cortex alongside the *descending* limb of the nephron loop.

The process by which the vasa recta help maintain the concentration gradient is termed the **countercurrent exchange system.** Recall that "countercurrent" refers to flow in opposite directions—in this case, blood flows in opposite directions within neighboring, parallel capillaries. The term "exchange" refers to the salts being exchanged for water.

The countercurrent exchange process occurs as follows:

- As the blood flows through the vasa recta deep into the renal medulla alongside the ascending limb, water diffuses out of these capillaries by osmosis.

- At the same time, salts in the interstitial fluid enter the vasa recta by diffusion down their concentration gradients. Thus, the blood in the vasa recta is losing water and gaining salts, and the concentration of total salt in the blood increases. (Note that this is opposite of what is occurring in the tubular fluid within the ascending limb of the nephron loop.)

- If the vasa recta were to continue deep into the medulla, these salts would be transported away in the blood. However, the path of the blood flow in the vasa recta makes a 180-degree turn and now runs alongside the descending limb of the nephron loop toward the cortex. Salts are now carried into a region in which osmotic and solute gradients reverse. Here, the salts diffuse back out of the blood into the interstitial fluid, while water moves into the vasa recta.

Thus, salts diffuse from the interstitial fluid into the vasa recta as blood is transported alongside of the ascending limb. The salts then diffuse in the reverse direction from the vasa recta into the interstitial fluid, as blood is transported alongside of the descending limb. In this way, solutes in the interstitial fluid are not diluted as blood moves through the vasa recta.

Urea Recycling

An important and additional contribution to maintaining the concentration gradient in the interstitial fluid occurs with **urea recycling.** Recycled urea in fact makes up approximately

Figure 24.24 Tubular Reabsorption and Tubular Secretion. Various reabsorption and secretion processes occur along the (a) proximal convoluted tubule, (b) nephron loop, (c) distal convoluted tubule and collecting tubules and ducts.

(a) Proximal Convoluted Tubule

Site for majority of reabsorption

Reabsorption	Secretion
The following substances move from the tubule into the blood: 100% of nutrients Majority of water Majority of ions PO_4^{3-} reabsorption is inhibited by PTH.	The following substances move from the blood into the tubule: Some drugs Nitrogenous wastes

Filtrate
Average daily
production: 180 L

Contents:

Ions   Water

Nutrients (i.e., glucose)

Trace amount
of proteins

Nitrogenous
wastes

Efferent arteriole

Afferent arteriole

Tubular fluid

Filtrate

(b) Nephron Loop and Vasa Recta

Site of countercurrent multiplier and countercurrent exchange

- Continues reabsorption of water and ions that begins in PCT.
- Nephron loops of juxtamedullary nephrons establish interstitial fluid concentration gradient (along with urea recycling).

Most concentrated

Nephron loop

Vasa recta

(c) Distal Convoluted Tubule, Collecting Tubule, and Collecting Ducts

Sites of regulation

- Na^+ reabsorption is regulated by aldosterone and ANP.
- Water reabsorption is regulated by aldosterone and ADH.
- Amount of K^+ secreted in the urine is dependent upon both intercalated cells and principal cells.
- Ca^{2+} reabsorption is increased by parathyroid hormone (PTH).
- pH is regulated by intercalated cells:
  Type A cells secrete acid (H^+) and retain base (HCO_3^-).
  Type B cells secrete base (HCO_3^-) and retain acid (H^+).

Peritubular capillary

Proximal convoluted tubule

Distal convoluted tubule

Collecting tubule

Collecting duct

Urea

Urea recycling

Less concentrated

Urine
Average daily urine
production: 1–1.5 L

Contents:

Ions   Water

Nitrogenous wastes and drugs

Some hormones

(No formed elements)

(No nutrients)

CLINICAL VIEW
Diuretics

Diuretics (dī-ū-ret'ik) are substances that increase excretion of urine and are a common treatment for hypertension. Diuretics are effective because by increasing urine output, both blood volume and blood pressure are decreased.

Diuretic drugs are grouped into different classes depending upon their mechanism of action. **Loop diuretics** such as furosemide (Lasix) and bumetinide target the transport protein ($Na^+/K^+/2\ Cl^-$ transporters) that pump the Na^+ salts within the nephron loop and lower the concentration gradient of the interstitial fluid, so less osmotic force is present to pull fluid out of the collecting tubule and collecting ducts, and more fluid is excreted in urine. **Thiazides** such as chlorothiazide and hydrochloro- thiazide interfere with Na^+ and water reabsorption in the distal convoluted tubule. Thus, less Na^+ and water are reabsorbed, increasing urine output.

one-half of the solutes of the interstitial fluid concentration gradient. Urea is removed from the tubular fluid in the collecting duct by urea uniporters as mentioned previously; it diffuses back into the tubular fluid in the thin segment of the ascending limb. Because both the thick segment of the ascending limb and DCT are not permeable to urea, urea remains within the tubular fluid until it reaches the collecting duct, where it is removed from the tubular fluid. Thus, urea is "cycled" between the collecting tubule and nephron loop. Some of this urea remains in the interstitial fluid, contributing to its concentration gradient.

Summary of Reabsorption and Secretion

The processes by which the nephron tubules, collecting tubules, and collecting ducts transform filtrate into urine in the different components of the nephron can be summarized and integrated, as follows (figure 24.24):

1. After filtration occurs, a majority of most other substances are either reabsorbed or secreted into the proximal convoluted tubules. Additional amounts of substances are reabsorbed as the tubular fluid moves through the nephron loop.

2. The nephron loop and the surrounding vasa recta are, along with the recycling of urea between the collecting duct and nephron loop, responsible for establishing the concentration gradient of the interstitial fluid. This gradient is necessary for the normal function of ADH.

3. The regulation of the amount of specific substances excreted in urine is controlled mainly by principal cells and by type A and type B intercalated cells within the distal convoluted tubule, collecting tubules, and collecting ducts. The fluid leaving the collecting ducts at the renal papilla is called urine.

4. Urine is composed of water and various dissolved substances including ions (e.g., Na^+, K^+, and Cl^-), various waste products, and perhaps drugs. Urine is drained into the renal sinus of the kidney to be excreted by the urinary tract. Under normal circumstances, urine does not contain either formed elements of the blood (erythrocytes, leukocytes, platelets) because they are not filtered or nutrients because they are 100% reabsorbed in the PCT.

WHAT DID YOU LEARN?

32 How is the concentration gradient that is essential for normal function of ADH in water reabsorption established and maintained?

33 Which substances are reabsorbed in tubular processing in the different regions of the nephron? Which are secreted? What are the general processes that occur in the different regions of the tubules: (a) PCT, (b) nephron loop, and (c) DCT, CT, and CD?

24.7 Evaluating Kidney Function

Some means of determining the effectiveness of kidney function is necessary, given the critical role the kidneys play in regulating concentrations of various substances within the blood and in eliminating wastes and foreign substances. This testing is especially crucial while monitoring and treating kidney disease.

24.7a Measuring Glomerular Filtration Rate

LEARNING OBJECTIVES

1. Describe the procedure for measuring the glomerular filtration rate.
2. Explain the formula for calculating the glomerular filtration rate.

One way to assess kidney function is to measure the rate filtrate is formed per unit time—that is, the glomerular filtration rate (GFR). To conduct this test, an individual is injected with *inulin*, a polysaccharide derived from plants that is freely filtered and neither reabsorbed nor secreted in the kidney. (Inulin should not be confused with the hormone insulin that regulates blood glucose levels.)

Enough inulin is injected into a subject to achieve a blood plasma concentration of 1 mg/mL. Urine is collected and measured for volume and concentration of the inulin. Additionally, blood is drawn and the plasma concentration of inulin is measured at given time intervals. Glomerular filtration rate is determined by the following formula:

$$GFR = \frac{UV}{P}$$

Where U = concentration of inulin in urine, V = volume of urine produced per minute, and P = concentration of inulin in plasma. For example, if the concentration of inulin in urine = 125 mg/mL, the volume of urine = 1 mL/min, and the concentration of inulin in plasma = 1 mg/mL, then

$$GFR = \frac{125\ mg/mL \times 1\ mL/min}{1\ mg/mL} = 125\ mL/min$$

Normal adult GFR is 125 mL/min. A lower glomerular filtration rate indicates a decrease in kidney function, and thus is more likely that nitrogenous wastes and other unwanted substances are accumulating in the blood.

WHAT DID YOU LEARN?

34 What is the purpose of measuring the glomerular filtration rate?

24.7b Measuring Renal Plasma Clearance

LEARNING OBJECTIVES

3. Define renal plasma clearance and its importance.
4. Identify the substance that may be measured to estimate the glomerular filtration rate.

CLINICAL VIEW
Renal Failure, Dialysis, and Kidney Transplant

Renal Failure

Renal failure refers to greatly diminished or absent renal functions caused by the destruction of about 90% of the kidney. Renal failure often results from a chronic disease that affects the glomerulus or the small blood vessels of the kidney, as a result of autoimmune conditions, high blood pressure, or diabetes. Once the kidney's structures have been destroyed, there is no chance they will regenerate or begin functioning again. Thus, the two main treatments are dialysis or kidney transplant.

Dialysis

The term **dialysis** (dī-al'i-sis) comes from a Greek word meaning "to separate agents or particles on the basis of their size." Two forms of dialysis are commonly used today: peritoneal dialysis and hemodialysis. In **peritoneal dialysis,** a catheter is permanently placed into the peritoneal cavity, to which a bag of dialysis fluid may be attached externally. A volume of a special dialysis fluid is introduced, and the harmful waste products in the blood are transferred, or dialyzed, into the fluid across the peritoneal membrane. After several hours, the fluid is drained from the peritoneal cavity and replaced with fresh fluid.

In **hemodialysis,** the patient's blood is cycled through a machine that filters the waste products across a specially designed membrane. A vascular connection is made between a conveniently located superficial artery and vein. This connection is called a shunt and is externally accessible. The patient must remain stationary for the time it takes to cycle the blood through the dialysis unit while metabolic waste products are removed. Hemodialysis must be performed three to four times a week and each treatment takes about 4 hours.

Kidney Transplant

A **kidney transplant** from a genetically similar person ("matched" for major histocompatability complex; see section 22.4c) may successfully restore

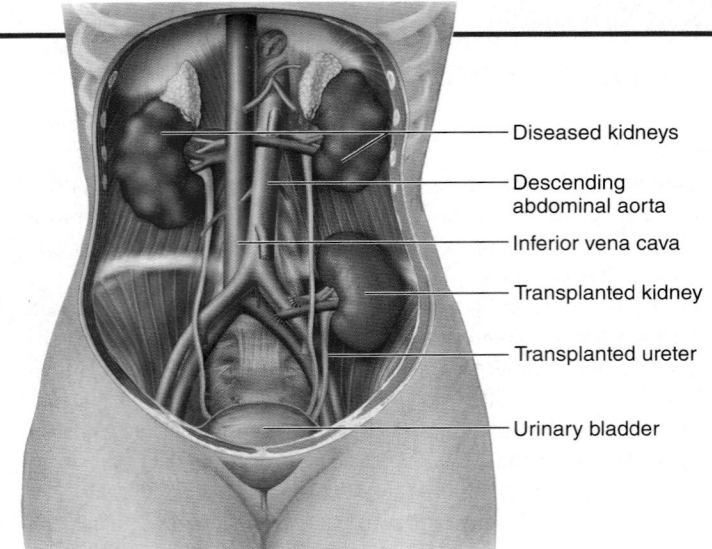

Location of a transplanted kidney in the abdominopelvic cavity.

- Diseased kidneys
- Descending abdominal aorta
- Inferior vena cava
- Transplanted kidney
- Transplanted ureter
- Urinary bladder

renal function. The kidney is generally removed from the donor by a laparoscopic procedure. A recent development for obtaining the kidney is to remove the kidney through the umbilicus (navel, or belly button) after making a single small incision. This decreases the donor's recovery time from approximately 3 months to just under a month.

The replacement kidney is attached to an artery and vein in the inferior abdominopelvic region, where it is relatively easy to establish a vascular connection. The new kidney rests either on the superior surface of, or immediately lateral to, the urinary bladder. Because a pelvic artery and vein connect the donor kidney to the patient's blood supply, having the kidney near the bladder means only a short segment of ureter is needed for the bladder connection. The diseased kidney is not removed.

The transplanted kidney is a foreign tissue. Therefore, immunosuppressant drugs are administered to suppress the immune system's activity. The recipient may need to take these drugs for the remainder of his or her life.

Another means of assessing kidney function is by measuring renal plasma clearance. The **renal plasma clearance** test measures the volume of plasma that can be completely cleared of a substance in a given period of time—usually in 1 minute. We may infer from this test whether a substance is reabsorbed or secreted. If a substance is neither reabsorbed nor filtered (like inulin), its renal plasma clearance is equal to the GFR (125 mL/min). However, if a substance is reabsorbed, its renal plasma clearance is lower than GFR because less of the substance is excreted, or "cleared," in the urine.

For example, the renal plasma clearance of urea is 70 mL/min. If urea is filtered at a 125 mL/min (the normal GFR), and only 70 mL/min is cleared, the rest (55 mL/min) is reabsorbed. In contrast, the renal plasma clearance of glucose is normally 0 mL/min because in a healthy individual 100% of the glucose is reabsorbed and none is excreted in the urine.

Substances that are filtered and secreted have renal plasma clearance values higher than the GFR. This occurs because addi-

tional amounts of the substance are secreted into the tubular fluid and excreted in the urine. For example, creatinine has a renal plasma clearance of 140 mL/min, indicating that the substance is both filtered and secreted.

Many medications also have renal plasma clearances higher than the GFR because they are secreted. For this reason, it is important to determine renal plasma clearance to know the amount and timing of drug dosage. The higher the renal plasma clearance, the more often the medications must be given to maintain therapeutic levels.

Note that in clinical practice, renal plasma clearance of creatinine can be used to approximate glomerular filtration rate because its clearance is only slightly higher than GFR. Measuring creatinine clearance avoids the need to inject inulin into the patient's blood.

WHAT DID YOU LEARN?

35 What information is gained by measuring the renal plasma clearance for a specific substance (e.g., medication)?

Table 24.2   Abnormal Urinalysis

Abnormal Urine Constituent	Clinical Term	Possible Cause(s)
Glucose	Glucosuria or glycosuria	Diabetes mellitus
Ketones (acetone, acetoacetic acid, beta-hydroxybutyric acid)	Ketonuria	Diabetes mellitus, starvation (including anorexia), low-carbohydrate diet (e.g., Atkins, South Beach)
Protein (Note that trace amounts of protein [5–10 mg/dL] are not clinically significant)	Proteinuria	Increased glomerular permeability caused by kidney trauma, heavy metals, bacterial toxins, exertion, hypertension, cold exposure, glomerular nephritis
Bile pigment	Bilirubinuria	Liver pathology (e.g., hepatitis or cirrhosis), obstructed bile duct due to gallstones
Erythrocytes	Hematuria	Glomerular damage, kidney trauma, pathology along the urinary tract (such as occurs with urinary tract stones), contamination from menstrual flow
Hemoglobin (Hb)	Hemoglobinuria	Accelerated rate of erythrocyte destruction (e.g., hemolytic anemia or a transfusion reaction), burns, renal damage, contamination from menstrual flow, heavy exercise (e.g., running a marathon)
Leukocytes	Pyuria	Urinary tract infection, acute glomerulonephritis, contamination from female reproductive tract
Nitrites	Nitrituria	Urinary tract infection because bacteria convert nitrates (NO_3^-) to nitrites (NO_2^-)

24.8 Urine Characteristics, Transport, Storage, and Elimination

Urine is the fluid that exits the kidneys and passes into the ureters. Thereafter, it is transported through the ureters into the urinary bladder, where it is stored until it can be eliminated from the body through the urethra. This process is referred to as micturition, or urination. Here we describe the characteristics of urine, the components of the urinary tract, and the process of micturition.

24.8a Characteristics of Urine

✓ LEARNING OBJECTIVES

1. Describe the composition of urine and its characteristics.
2. Explain what is meant by specific gravity.

Urine is the product of filtered and processed blood plasma. It typically is a sterile excretion unless contaminated with microbes in the kidney or urinary tract. Urine characteristics include its composition, volume, pH, specific gravity, color and turbidity, and smell.

Typical urine composition is approximately 95% water and 5% solutes. These solutes include salts (Na^+, Cl^-, K^+, Mg^{2+}, Ca^{2+}, SO_4^{2-}, $H_2PO_4^-$, and NH_4^+), nitrogenous wastes (e.g., urea, uric acid, and creatinine), some hormones, drugs, and small amounts of ketone bodies (a waste product of digesting fatty acids). **Table 24.2** lists some substances that should not normally be found within urine (i.e., they are abnormal constituents) and possible causes for their presence.

The average daily urine volume is normally 1–2 L. Variations occur due to many variables, including fluid intake, blood pressure, diet, body temperature, use of diuretics, diabetes, and the amount of fluid excreted by other means (e.g., heavy sweating, vomiting). A minimum of about 0.5 L of urine per day is required to eliminate the wastes from the body. If urine production drops below 0.40 L,

wastes will accumulate in the blood. **Table 24.3** list factors that influence urine volume output.

The normal pH for urine ranges between 4.5 and 8.0; the average value is 6.0, which is slightly acidic. The pH of urine may be affected by diet. It generally decreases to become more acidic when we consume proteins and wheat, and it tends to increase and become more basic with a diet high in fruits and vegetables. Urine pH can also be influenced by other factors, such as metabolism and bacterial infections.

Specific gravity is the density (g/mL) of a substance compared to the density (g/mL) of water. For example, if your urine were composed only of pure water, it would have a specific gravity of 1.000. The average specific gravity of urine is slightly higher, with levels ranging from 1.003 to 1.035 because solutes *are* normal components of urine. Levels vary due to time of day, amount of food and liquids consumed, and amount of exercise. Generally, if you are well hydrated, urine output increases and specific gravity values decrease.

Table 24.3   Factors That Influence Urine Volume

Decrease Urine Volume	Increase Urine Volume
Increase in antidiuretic hormone (ADH)	Decrease in ADH
Increase in aldosterone	Decrease in aldosterone
Decrease in atrial natriuretic peptide (ANP)	Increase in ANP
Decrease in fluid intake	Increase in fluid intake
Decrease in blood pressure	Increase in blood pressure
Increase in other fluid output (e.g., sweating, vomiting, diarrhea, hemorrhage)	Diabetes mellitus; Diuretics (medications, alcohol)

A specific gravity value below 1.010 indicates relative hydration, whereas a specific gravity value above 1.020 indicates relative dehydration.

The color of urine ranges from almost clear to dark yellow, depending upon the concentration of pigment from urobilin (bilirubin breakdown product; see section 18.3b). An increased volume of urine generally is lighter in color, and a decreased volume of urine is darker in color. However, intake of some substances (e.g., beets, certain vitamins) can change the color of urine. Normal vaginal secretions, excessive substances in urine (cellular material, protein), crystallization or precipitation of salts if collected and left standing, and bacteria will increase the turbidity (cloudiness) of the urine.

Urinoid is the term used for the normal smell of fresh urine. Urine may develop an ammonia smell if allowed to stand because bacteria convert urea to ammonia. Asparagus and certain other foods can alter the smell of urine. One of the indications that a person has diabetes mellitus is that the urine smells fruity (like acetone, which is found in fingernail polish) from the accelerated production of ketones from fatty acid metabolism (see section 3.4h).

 WHAT DID YOU LEARN?

36 What characteristics are used to describe urine? What conditions cause variation in pH of urine?

24.8b Urinary Tract (Ureters, Urinary Bladder, Urethra)

LEARNING OBJECTIVES

3. Describe the structure and function of the ureters.

4. Explain the structure of the urinary bladder.

5. List distinguishing characteristics of the female and male urethra.

The urinary tract consists of the ureters, urinary bladder, and urethra. The urinary tract is responsible for transporting the urine produced in the kidneys, storing the urine until the time and place are right for its elimination from the body, and transporting the urine from storage to the exterior of the body.

Ureters

The **ureters** (ū-rē′ter) are long, epithelial-lined, fibromuscular tubes that conduct urine from the kidneys to the urinary bladder **(figure 24.25)**. Each tube averages about 25 centimeters (about 10 inches) in length and is retroperitoneal. The ureters originate from the renal pelvis as it exits the hilum of the kidney and then extend inferiorly to enter the posterolateral wall of the base of the urinary bladder. The wall of the ureter is composed of three concentric tunics. From innermost to outermost, these tunics are the mucosa, muscularis, and adventitia. (Note that the ureter does not have a submucosa layer.)

(a) Ureter cross section

(b) Histology of ureter

Figure 24.25 Ureters. The ureters conduct urine from the kidneys to the urinary bladder for storage prior to voiding from the body. (*a*) Features of a ureter in cross-sectional view. (*b*) A photomicrograph of a ureter in cross section shows its mucosal folds and thick muscularis. AP|R

Minor calyx
Major calyx
Renal pelvis
Kidney

Ureter

Urinary bladder

Sometimes a physician needs to visualize the kidneys, ureters, and urinary bladder, especially when the flow of urine from one or both of the kidneys into the bladder becomes blocked. A physician may ask for an x-ray study known as an **intravenous pyelogram** (pī′el-ō-gram; *pyelos* = tub, *gram* = recording), which is produced by injecting a small amount of radiopaque dye into a vein. As the dye passes through the kidneys and is cleared into the urine, a series of sequential abdominal x-rays provide a "time lapse" view of urinary system flow.

An IV pyelogram is useful in diagnosing renal calculi, and may determine if there is abnormal dilation in any parts of the drainage system (including the calyces). If urine flow is normal, the entire pathway of the urinary tract should appear dark on the x-ray. However, if there is a blockage (as is the case with a renal calculus), the dark coloration will suddenly 'stop' at the area of the blockage.

A pyelogram enables physicians to visualize the urinary system organs and identify the location of any blockages within the urinary system.

The **mucosa** is formed by a transitional epithelium (see section 5.1c) that is both distensible and impermeable to the passage of urine. External to the transitional epithelium of the mucosa is the lamina propria, composed of a fairly thick layer of dense irregular connective tissue.

The middle **muscularis** consists of an inner longitudinal and an outer circular layer of smooth muscle cells. The presence of urine within the renal pelvis causes these muscle layers to contract rhythmically to propel the urine through the ureters into the urinary bladder. In areas where the ureter is not filled with urine, the mucosa folds to fill the lumen.

WHAT DO YOU THINK?

5 Why do the ureters use smooth muscle contraction to actively move urine to the urinary bladder? Why don't they rely on gravity to move the urine to the inferiorly located bladder?

The external layer of the ureter wall is the **adventitia.** It is composed of a dispersed array of collagen and elastic fibers within areolar connective tissue. Some extensions of this areolar connective tissue layer also anchor the ureter to the posterior abdominal wall.

The ureters project through the bladder wall obliquely, and some smooth muscle fibers of the inner longitudinal layer of the muscularis insert into the lamina propria of the bladder. Because of the oblique course of the ureters through the bladder wall, the ureter walls are compressed as the bladder distends, decreasing the likelihood of urine refluxing (backflowing) into the ureters from the bladder when it is emptying.

The ureters are innervated by the autonomic nervous system. Sympathetic axons extend from the T11–L2 segments of the spinal cord. Pain from the ureter (e.g., caused by a kidney stone lodged in the ureter) is referred to the T11–L2 dermatomes (see figure 16.5). These dermatomes are distributed along a "loin-to-groin" region, so "loin-to-groin" pain typically means ureter or kidney discomfort. The vagus nerve (CN X) innervates the superior region of the ureter, and the pelvic splanchnic nerves innervate the inferior region of the ureter. The effects of this parasympathetic stimulation are unknown.

Urinary Bladder

The **urinary bladder** is an expandable, muscular container that serves as a reservoir for urine. The bladder is positioned immediately posterior to the pubic symphysis. In females, the urinary bladder is anteroinferior to the uterus and directly anterior to the vagina (see figure 28.3); in males, the bladder is anterior to the rectum and superior to the prostate gland (see figure 28.14). The urinary bladder is a retroperitoneal organ, and only its superior surface is covered with the parietal peritoneum.

CLINICAL VIEW
Renal Calculi

A **renal calculus** (pl., *calculi*), or *kidney stone,* is formed from crystalline minerals that build up in the kidney. Causes and risk factors for kidney stone formation include inadequate fluid intake and dehydration, reduced urinary flow and volume, frequent urinary tract infections, and certain abnormal chemical or mineral levels in the urine. **Hypercalcuria,** a high level of calcium in the urine, can lead to calcium stones. In general, males tend to develop stones more often than females.

Very small renal calculi may be asymptomatic, and the person may excrete them without ever realizing it. However, a larger stone can become obstructed in the kidney, renal pelvis, or ureter. Symptoms include severe pain along the

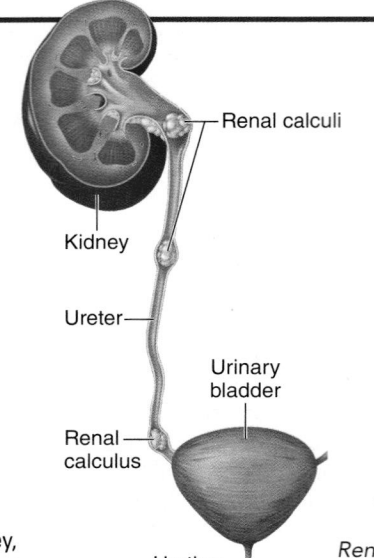

"loin-to-groin" region and possibly nausea and vomiting. Following the intake of plenty of water (2 to 3 quarts per day) to assist movement, most stones smaller than about 4 millimeters in diameter eventually pass through the urinary tract on their own. Administration of intravenous fluids may also assist this process.

If the stone is too large to pass on its own, one common treatment is **lithotripsy** (lith′ō-trip-sē; *lithos* = stone, *tresis* = boring), in which sonic shock waves are directed toward the stones to pulverize them into smaller particles that can be expelled in the urine. Alternatively, using **ureteroscopy,** a scope is inserted from the urethra into the urinary bladder and ureter to break up and remove the stone. If these treatments aren't viable, traditional surgery may be required.

Renal calculi may become lodged at various sites along the urinary tract.

When it is empty, the urinary bladder exhibits an inverted pyramidal shape (figure 24.26). As it fills with urine, the bladder distends superiorly until it assumes an oval shape.

A posteroinferior triangular area of the urinary bladder wall, called the **trigone** (trí′gōn; *trigonum* = triangle), is formed by imaginary lines connecting the two ureter openings and the urethral opening. The trigone remains immobile as the urinary bladder fills and evacuates. It functions as a funnel to direct urine into the urethra as the bladder wall contracts to evacuate the stored urine. Because the ureters and urethra form the three points of this triangular region, infections are more common within this area.

The four tunics that form the wall of the bladder are the mucosa, submucosa, muscularis, and adventitia. The innermost **mucosa** lines the bladder lumen; it is formed by a transitional epithelium that accommodates the shape changes occurring with distension, and by a highly vascularized lamina propria that supports the mucosa. Additionally, mucosal folds, called **mucosal folds** or *rugae* (rū′jē) allow

(a) Urinary bladder, anterior view

(b) Histology of the urinary bladder

(c) Urinary bladder, sagittal view

Figure 24.26 Urinary Bladder. (*a*) The urinary bladder is an expandable, muscular sac. This view depicts a female bladder. (*b*) Illustration and photomicrograph of the urinary bladder wall show its tunics. (*c*) Sagittal views show that the urinary bladder expands superiorly and becomes more oval in shape as it fills with urine. AP|R

(a) Female urethra

Figure 24.27 Urethra. The urethra conducts urine from the urinary bladder to the external urethral orifice. These coronal views compare (*a*) a female urethra and (*b*) a male urethra. AP|R

for even greater distension. Within the trigone region, the mucosa is smooth, thick, and lacking mucosal folds. The **submucosa** lies immediately external to the mucosa and is formed by dense irregular connective tissue that supports the urinary bladder wall.

The **muscularis** is formed by three layers of smooth muscle, collectively called the **detrusor** (dē-trū′ser, -sōr; *detrudo* = to drive away) **muscle.** These smooth muscle bundles exhibit such complex orientations that it is difficult to delineate individual layers in random histology sections. At the neck of the urinary bladder, an involuntary internal urethral sphincter is formed by the smooth muscle that encircles the urethral opening.

The **adventitia** is the outer layer of areolar connective tissue covering the urinary bladder. A peritoneal membrane covers only the superior surface of the urinary bladder, and in this superior region, the peritoneum plus the connective tissue forms a serosa.

Urethra

The **urethra** (ū-rē′thră) is an epithelial-lined fibromuscular tube that exits the urinary bladder through the urethral opening from its anteroinferior surface and conducts urine to the exterior of the body **(figure 24.27).** The luminal lining of the urethra is a protective mucous membrane that houses clusters of mucin-producing cells called urethral glands. Bundles of smooth muscle fibers surround the mucosa, and their contractions help propel urine to the outside of the body.

Two urethral sphincters restrict the release of urine until the pressure within the urinary bladder is high enough and both involuntary and voluntary activities are activated to release the urine. The **internal urethral sphincter** is the involuntary, superior sphincter. It is composed of smooth muscle and surrounds the neck of the bladder. It is controlled by the autonomic nervous system.

The **external urethral sphincter** is inferior to the internal urethral sphincter and is formed by skeletal muscle fibers of the urogenital diaphragm (see section 11.7). This sphincter is a voluntary

(b) Male urethra

sphincter controlled by the somatic nervous system (specifically, the frontal lobe of the cerebral cortex). This is the muscle children learn to control when they become "toilet-trained." The male and female urethras differ in length and morphology.

Female Urethra The female urethra has a single function: to transport urine from the urinary bladder to exterior of the body. The lumen of the female urethra is primarily lined with a stratified squamous epithelium. The urethra is approximately 4 centimeters (about 1.6 inches) long, and it opens to the outside of the body at the external urethral orifice located in the female perineum.

Male Urethra The male urethra has both urinary and reproductive functions because it serves as a passageway for urine and for semen (but not at the same time). It is approximately 19 centimeters long (7.5 inches) and is partitioned into three segments: the prostatic urethra, the membranous urethra, and the spongy urethra.

The **prostatic** (pros-tat′ik) **urethra** is approximately 3.5 centimeters (about 1.5 inches) in length and is the most dilatable portion of the urethra. It extends through the prostate gland immediately inferior to the male bladder, where multiple small prostatic ducts enter it. The urethra in this region is lined by a transitional epithelium. Two smooth muscle bundles surround the mucosa: an internal longitudinal bundle and an external circular bundle. The external circular muscular bundles are a continuation of the thickened circular region of the internal urethral sphincter at the bladder outlet.

The **membranous** (mem′bră-nus) **urethra** is the shortest and least dilatable portion of the male urethra. It extends from the inferior surface of the prostate gland through the urogenital diaphragm. As a result, it is surrounded by skeletal muscle fibers that form the external urethral sphincter of the urinary bladder. The epithelium in this region is often either stratified columnar or pseudostratified columnar.

The **spongy urethra** (or *penile urethra*) is the longest part of the male urethra at approximately 15 centimeters long (about 6 inches). It is encased within a cylinder of erectile tissue in the penis called the corpus spongiosum, and it extends to the **external urethral orifice.** The proximal part of the spongy urethra is lined by a pseudostratified columnar epithelium, while the distal part has a stratified squamous epithelial lining.

 WHAT DID YOU LEARN?

37 What are the major components of the urinary tract? What tunics are found in each of these?

38 How does the urethra of a male and female differ?

INTEGRATE

CLINICAL VIEW
Urinary Tract Infections

A **urinary tract infection (UTI)** occurs when either bacteria (most commonly *E. coli*) or fungi (e.g., yeast) enter and multiply within the urinary tract. Women are more prone to UTIs because they have a short urethra that is close to the anus, allowing bacteria from the gastrointestinal (GI) tract to more readily enter the urethra. Sexual intercourse or medical use of a urinary catheter also increase the risk of UTIs.

A UTI often develops first in the urethra, an inflammation called **urethritis** (ū-rē-thrī′tis). If the infection spreads to the urinary bladder, **cystitis** (sis-tī′tis) results. Occasionally, bacteria from an untreated UTI can spread up the ureters to the kidneys, a condition termed **pyelonephritis** (pī′ĕ-lō-ne-frī′tis). Symptoms of a UTI include difficult and painful urination, called **dysuria** (dis-ū′rē-ă; *dys* = bad, difficult), frequent urination, and a feeling of uncomfortable pressure in the pubic region. If the infection spreads to the kidneys, sharp back and flank pain, fever, and occasionally nausea and vomiting may occur. A UTI can be diagnosed through **urinalysis** (ū-ri-nal′i-sis), a test of the urine that can reveal the presence of leukocytes, blood, and bacteria or fungi. Appropriate antibiotic therapy cures most UTIs caused by bacteria.

24.8c Micturition

LEARNING OBJECTIVES

6. Define micturition.

7. Compare and contrast the storage reflex and the micturition reflex.

8. Explain conscious control over micturition.

The expulsion of urine from the bladder is called **micturition** (mik-chū-rish′ŭn; *micturio* = to desire to make water), *urination*, or *voiding*. Two reflexes are associated with the process of micturition: the storage reflex and the micturition reflex. These reflexes are regulated by the sympathetic and parasympathetic divisions of the autonomic nervous system, respectively.

Innervation of the Urinary Bladder and Urethral Sphincters

The urinary bladder has sympathetic, parasympathetic, and somatic innervation. Sympathetic axons extend from T11 to L2 segments of the spinal cord. Sympathetic stimulation causes contraction of the internal urethral sphincter and inhibits contraction of the detrusor muscle. Thus, stimulation by the sympathetic divison inhibits micturition. Innervation by the parasympathetic division is from the micturition center located in the pons, and extends from the spinal cord segments S2–S4 in the pelvic splanchnic nerves. The pelvic splanchnic nerves cause contraction of the detrusor muscle and relaxation of the internal urethral sphincter, so that urine can be expelled. Thus, the parasympathetic division stimulates micturition. The external urethral sphincter is composed of skeletal muscle. It is innervated by the somatic nervous system via the pudendal nerve (which is formed from the S2-S4 segments of the spinal cord). The pudendal nerve voluntarily contracts this sphincter to prevent urination.

Storage Reflex

The storage of urine in the urinary bladder is controlled by both the autonomic and somatic nervous system (**figure 24.28a**). During the filling of the urinary bladder, urine moves through the ureters from the kidneys. Continuous sympathetic stimulation causes (1) relaxation of the detrusor muscles of the urinary bladder wall to allow the bladder to accommodate the urine; and (2) stimulation of contraction of the internal urethral sphincter, so that urine is retained within the bladder.

This process is referred to as the **storage reflex.** The skeletal muscle of the external urethral sphincter is also continuously stimulated by nerve signals along the pudendal nerve so it remains contracted.

Micturition Reflex

The process of micturition is also controlled by both the autonomic and somatic nervous systems in a toilet-trained individual, and it usually proceeds as follows (figure 24.28b):

(1) When the volume of urine retained within the bladder reaches approximately 200 to 300 mL, the bladder becomes distended, and baroceptors in the bladder wall are activated.

(2) These baroceptors send nerve signals through visceral sensory neurons to stimulate the micturition reflex center within the pons.

(3) The micturition center alters nerve signals propagated down the spinal cord and through the pelvic splanchnic nerves (which are parasympathetic nerves).

Legend:
- Sensory input
- Sympathetic
- Parasympathetic
- Somatic

Cerebral cortex

Kidney

Ureter

Urinary bladder

T11
T12
L1
L2

S2
S3
S4

100 mL

Detrusor muscle (relaxed)

Internal urethral sphincter (contracted)

Urethra

Pudendal nerve

External urethral sphincter (contracted)

(a) Storage reflex

Micturition reflex center

Pelvic splanchnic nerves

Detrusor muscle contracts

300 mL

S2
S3
S4

Detrusor muscle stretched

Pudendal nerve

External urethral sphincter (relaxed)

Internal urethral sphincter (relaxed)

(b) Micturition reflex

Figure 24.28 Micturition. (*a*) The storage reflex allows urine to be held in the urinary bladder until it can be eliminated from the body. (*b*) The micturition reflex is the involuntary portion of eliminating urine. The relaxation of the external urethral sphincter permits voluntary control of micturitition. AP|R

④ Parasympathetic stimulation causes the smooth muscle cells composing the detrusor muscle to contract and internal urethral sphincter to relax. In infants, urination occurs at this point because they lack voluntary control of the external urethral sphincter.

The sensation of having to urinate is relayed along sensory axons to the cerebral cortex.

Conscious Control of Urination

An individual's conscious decision to urinate is due to altering nerve signals relayed from the cerebral cortex through the spinal cord and along the pudendal nerve to cause relaxation of the external urethral sphincter. Expulsion of urine is facilitated by both the voluntary contraction of muscles in the abdominal wall and expiratory muscles as part of the Valsalva maneuver (see section 23.3a). Upon emptying of the urinary bladder (all but about 10 mL), the detrusor muscle relaxes, and the neurons of the micturition reflex center are inactivated, while those of the storage reflex are activated.

If an individual does not urinate at the time of the first micturition reflex, the detrusor muscle relaxes as a consequence of the "stress-relaxation response" of smooth muscle (see section 10.10). The bladder continues to fill with urine, and the micturition reflex is initiated again after another 200–300 mL of urine is added. This cycle continues until there is between 500 mL and 600 mL. At this point, urination occurs without conscious control.

Additionally, an individual may choose to empty the bladder prior to the initiation of the micturition reflex by contracting the abdominal muscles as part of the Valsalva maneuver and compressing the bladder. This compression of the bladder initiates the micturition reflex as a consequence of stimulation of stretch receptors.

WHAT DID YOU LEARN?

39 What steps lead to micturition? At what point does the reflex overcome conscious control?

INTEGRATE

CLINICAL VIEW
Impaired Urination

Two common terms are associated with impaired urination: incontinence and retention. **Incontinence** (in-kon'ti-nens; *in* = not, *contineo* = to hold together) is the inability to voluntarily control urination. Incontinence may occur as a result of childbirth (stress incontinence), stronger than normal detrusor muscle contractions (urge incontinence), or the secondary result of medications. Uncontrolled urination may also occur when an individual is frightened, as nerve signals initiated in the limbic system are sent to the micturition center, causing urination.

Retention (rē-ten'shŭn) involves failure to eliminate urine normally. Causes include side effects following general anesthesia and an enlarged prostate in a male that impedes urine flow through the prostatic urethra. If necessary, a small tube called a *catheter* may be placed into the urethra to allow urine to flow out of the bladder.

- The urinary system is composed of the kidneys and the urinary tract (ureters, urinary bladder, and the urethra).

24.1 Introduction to the Urinary System 937

- The kidneys filter blood to produce urine, which is subsequently eliminated from the body through the ureters, urinary bladder, and urethra.
- The kidneys perform numerous functions, including eliminating waste products from the blood, forming calcitriol, producing and releasing erythropoietin, regulating ion and acid-base balance, regulating blood pressure, and having the potential to engage in gluconeogenesis to regulate blood glucose.

24.2 Gross Anatomy of the Kidney 939

24.2a Location and Support 939
- The kidneys are located along the posterior abdominal wall and are partially protected by the ribs.
- The kidneys are surrounded by a fibrous capsule, perinephric fat, renal fascia, and paranephric fat.

24.2b Sectional Anatomy of the Kidney 940
- Each kidney is composed of an outer cortex and an inner medulla, and the medulla is subdivided into 8 to 15 renal pyramids (or 8 to 15 renal lobes).
- Renal sinuses are spaces within the kidney and include the minor calyces, major calyces, and a single renal pelvis.

24.2c Innervation of the Kidney 941
- Sympathetic axons of the renal plexus innervate the afferent and efferent arterioles and the juxtaglomerular apparatus.

24.3 Functional Anatomy of the Kidney 941

- Nephrons, collecting tubules, collecting ducts, and associated structures form the functional anatomy of the kidney.

24.3a Nephron 941
- A nephron consists of a renal corpuscle, which is composed of a glomerulus plus glomerular capsule, and a renal tubule (proximal convoluted tubule, nephron loop, and distal convoluted tubule).

24.3b Collecting Tubules and Collecting Ducts 945
- Numerous nephrons drain into a collecting tubule, and numerous collecting tubules drain into a collecting duct.

24.3c Juxtaglomerular Apparatus 946
- The juxtaglomerular (JG) apparatus is composed of granular cells of the afferent arteriole and a macula densa of the distal convoluted tubule. It functions in the regulation of glomerular filtration rate and systemic blood pressure.

24.4 Blood Flow and Filtered Fluid Flow 946

- Filtrate is formed from blood as it flows through the glomerulus.

24.4a Blood Flow Through the Kidney 946
- Blood is transported to the kidneys in renal arteries, which divide into segmental arteries and then interlobar arteries. Branching off the interlobar arteries are arcuate arteries (at the corticomedullary junction) and then interlobular arteries, which supply the glomerulus via the afferent arteriole.
- Blood leaving the glomerulus follows this path: efferent arteriole, peritubular capillaries or vasa recta, interlobular veins, arcuate veins, interlobar veins, and a renal vein.

24.4b Filtrate, Tubular Fluid, and Urine Flow 948
- Filtrate is collected in the capsular space of the glomerular capsule.
- Tubular fluid flows through the proximal convoluted tubule, nephron loop, distal convoluted tubule, collecting tubules and ducts.
- Urine flows into the minor calyx, major calyx, renal pelvis, ureter, and urinary bladder (where it is stored), and excreted via the urethra.

24.5 Production of Filtrate Within the Renal Corpuscle 949

- The renal corpuscle is the site of filtrate production.

24.5a Overview of Urine Formation 949
- Filtration, reabsorption, and secretion are the three processes involved in urine formation.

24.5b Filtration Membrane 950
- The filtration membrane is composed of the fenestrated endothelium and basement membrane of the glomerulus and the visceral layer of the glomerular capsule.

24.5c Formation of Filtrate and Its Composition 951
- Filtrate is (essentially) protein-free filtered plasma.

24.5d Pressures Associated with Glomerular Filtration 951
- The three pressures that determine net filtration pressure are glomerular (blood) hydrostatic pressure (HP_g), which promotes filtration; and both blood colloid osmotic pressure (OP_g) and capsular hydrostatic pressure (HP_c), which oppose filtration.
- Net filtration pressure is determined by subtracting OP_g and HP_c from HP_g.

CHALLENGE YOURSELF

Do You Know the Basics?

_____ 1. All of following are functions of the kidney *except*

    a. gluconeogenesis, the formation of glucose from non-carbohydrate sources.

    b. release of erythropoietin to control erythrocyte production.

    c. control of blood pressure through the release of renin.

    d. production of plasma proteins to control blood volume.

_____ 2. When the kidneys are described as being retroperitoneal, this refers to the fact that the kidneys

    a. are within the peritoneal lining of the abdominal cavity.

    b. are posterior to the peritoneal lining of the abdominal cavity.

    c. are superior to the peritoneal lining of the abdominal cavity.

    d. have no protective covering.

_____ 3. Which of the following is in the renal medulla?

    a. collecting duct

    b. glomerulus

    c. renal corpuscle

    d. distal convoluted tubule

_____ 4. All of the following are capillaries *except*

    a. the glomerulus.

    b. the minor calyx.

    c. the vasa recta.

    d. peritubular capillaries.

_____ 5. Which of the following is a component of filtrate but not normally a component of urine?

    a. water

    b. erythrocytes

    c. nitrogenous waste

    d. glucose

_____ 6. If blood pressure in the glomerulus increases, then

    a. net filtration pressure decreases.

    b. the percentage of substances reabsorbed increases.

    c. urine production increases.

    d. renin is released.

_____ 7. Which hormone increases Na^+ and water reabsorption and K^+ secretion?

    a. antidiuretic hormone

    b. angiotensin II

    c. atrial natriuretic peptide

    d. aldosterone

_____ 8. If the tubular maximum is exceeded, then

    a. the carrier mechanism will work harder.

    b. the excess will be reabsorbed in the bladder.

    c. the excess will appear in the urine.

    d. its blood concentration will increase.

_____ 9. The function unique to the nephron loop is to

    a. regulate pH.

    b. excrete water.

    c. establish a concentration gradient in the medulla interstitial fluid.

    d. regulate the concentration of blood Ca^{2+}.

_____ 10. If antidiuretic hormone (ADH) concentration increases,

    a. urine volume increases.

    b. urine concentration decreases.

    c. urine volume decreases, and urine concentration increases.

    d. urine volume increases, and urine concentration decreases.

11. Trace blood flow into and out of the kidney. Identify the appropriate vessels.

12. Describe where filtrate, tubular fluid, and urine are found in the functioning kidney.

13. Describe the anatomic components of the juxtaglomerular apparatus.

14. Describe the filtration membrane, and explain the structures that do not normally pass through it.

15. Explain how glomerular filtration rate (GFR) is maintained by renal autoregulation, decreased by sympathetic stimulation, and increased by atrial natriuretic peptide.

16. Discuss the affect of aldosterone and antidiuretic hormone (ADH) on principal cells and their effect on urine production.

17. Explain how the concentration gradient in the medulla of the kidney is established and maintained.

18. Describe the significant differences between blood plasma, filtrate, and urine.

19. Identify all of the following that are functions of the kidney: (a) maintain blood pH; (b) regulate blood ion concentrations; (c) regulate blood volume and blood pressure; (d) eliminate wastes, some hormones, and certain drugs from the blood; (e) release renin; (f) release erythropoietin; and (g) stimulate the final step in calcitriol formation.

20. Explain the process of micturition.

Can You Apply What You've Learned?

Use the following paragraph to answer questions 1–3.

Maria is 8 months pregnant. When she goes to her doctor for her checkup, the nurse takes her blood pressure. It is unusually high: 200/100 mm Hg. The nurse also collects a urine sample and detects elevated levels of protein in her urine.

1. What can account for the protein in her urine?

    a. Protein is a normal component of urine and is no cause for concern.

    b. Excessive amounts of plasma proteins are filtered at the renal corpuscle.

    c. Tubular cells produce additional protein in response to the elevated blood pressure.

    d. The tubular cells have exocytosed protein into the tubular fluid.

2. What would you predict has happened to her plasma protein concentration?

    a. It has no effect.

    b. Plasma protein levels will have increased.

    c. Plasma protein levels will have decreased.

    d. Plasma proteins levels will have remained the same or increase.

3. What do you think has happened to her urine production? (Consider the pressures involved in determining net filtration pressure and osmotic force generated by solutes in the filtrate.)

    a. Urine production stays the same.

    b. Urine production increases.

    c. Urine production decreases.

    d. It is not possible to predict the effect on urine production.

4. Martin, a young man of 20, was in a car accident and is hemorrhaging. When he arrives by ambulance at the hospital, he is stabilized. However, they notice that over the next day he does not urinate. Which of the three variables for determining net filtration pressure has changed and can account for the lack of urine formation?

    a. Glomerular blood pressure has decreased.

    b. Capsular hydrostatic pressure has decreased.

    c. Blood colloidal osmotic pressure has decreased.

    d. Glomerular blood pressure has increased.

5. A 19-year-old male named Paul was in a diving accident and severed his spinal cord at the T1 segment. Which of the following describes one of the physiologic changes that he will experience?

    a. His kidneys will no longer be able to filter his blood and produce urine.

    b. His urinary bladder will no longer be able to contract to expel urine.

    c. His filtration membrane will contract, and filtration will no longer occur.

    d. He will no longer be able to consciously control urination.

Can You Synthesize What You've Learned?

1. A patient with cancer is treated with chemotherapy. This specific medication is eliminated by the kidney. Results from a renal plasma clearance test are higher than average. Will the medication need to be given more or less often? Explain.

2. Theoretically, which one of the following hormones could be administered to decrease blood volume: antidiuretic hormone, aldosterone, parathyroid hormone, or atrial natriuretic peptide? Explain.

3. Males who suffer from either benign prostatic hyperplasia (noncancerous prostate gland enlargement) or prostate cancer often have problems with urination. Based on your knowledge of the male urethra, hypothesize why these urination problems occur.

chapter 25
Fluid and Electrolytes

Our body's ability to maintain fluid balance is something most of us take for granted despite our sometimes erratic fluid intake. For example, we may drink several cups of coffee first thing in the morning, go the rest of the day without drinking fluid, perhaps run several miles in the evening, and then drink large quantities at the end of the day before retiring for the night. Fortunately, our body compensates for our inconsistent fluid intake by making physiologic adjustments throughout the day so that fluids are maintained within ➡

Medical laboratory technologists are healthcare professionals who examine and perform biological, chemical, and hematological tests on body fluids or specimens including urine, blood, stool, and pericardial fluid. Results are ensured for accuracy and reported to physicians. These medical care specialists typically earn a baccalaureate degree and are employed at hospitals, doctor's offices, and specialized medical laboratories.

aprevealed.com

Module 13: Urinary System

homeostatic limits. In a similar way, electrolyte levels, including those that determine pH, are being regulated to maintain electrolyte balance.

Fluid and electrolyte imbalances, however, can occasionally occur. Insufficient fluid intake, excessive sweating, vomiting, diarrhea, or abnormal changes in the function of an organ (e.g., kidney disease, congestive heart failure) all may tax the body to such an extent that fluid and electrolyte levels are driven out of balance. Here we describe the major concepts and mechanisms involved in fluid and electrolyte balance. These include the percentage, distribution, chemical composition, and movement of body fluid; maintenance of electrolyte levels; hormonal regulation of fluid balance and its influence on blood pressure; acid-base control and balance; and acid-base disturbances.

25.1 Body Fluids

We begin the discussion of fluid balance by describing the percentage of body fluid, the distribution of body fluid into two major fluid compartments, and how fluid moves between the fluid compartments within the body.

25.1a Percentage of Body Fluid

LEARNING OBJECTIVES

1. List the factors that influence the percentage of body fluid.
2. Explain the significance of percentage of body fluid relative to fluid balance.

The human body is composed of between 45% and 75% fluid by weight, with an average of about 65% (figure 25.1). The fluid percentage depends upon two variables: the age of an individual, and the relative amounts of adipose connective tissue and skeletal muscle tissue:

- **Age.** Infants have the highest percentage of fluid, at approximately 75% fluid by weight. In contrast, elderly individuals have the lowest percentage of fluid at 45%. Children and young and middle-aged adults are generally somewhere in between these two extremes, with a general trend of decreasing percentage of body fluid seen with increasing age.

- **Relative amounts of adipose connective tissue and skeletal muscle tissue.** The relative percentage of fluid in the body at each age depends upon the ratio of adipose connective tissue to skeletal muscle tissue because of the difference in water content of these tissues. Adipose connective tissue contains approximately 20% water, whereas skeletal muscle tissue is approximately 75% water. This accounts for the general differences in the percentage of body fluid that are noted between females and males of the same age after puberty.

  Lean adult females typically have more adipose connective tissue and are composed of 55% body fluid on average, whereas lean adult males have more skeletal muscle tissue and a slightly higher percentage of body fluid at approximately 60%. The relative percentage of fluid in both decreases as the percentage of body fat increases.

Most importantly, your body's water content influences how susceptible you are to a fluid imbalance; individuals that have a lower percentage of body fluid are more likely to experience a fluid imbalance. For example, one reason elderly individuals are more prone as a group to fluid imbalances than are young adults is because of their relatively smaller percentage of body fluid.

WHAT DID YOU LEARN?

1. If you gain weight (from increased adipose connective tissue), will your percentage of body fluid increase, decrease, or stay the same?

25.1b Fluid Compartments

LEARNING OBJECTIVES

3. Describe the two major body fluid compartments, and compare their compositions.
4. Explain how fluid moves between the major body fluid compartments.

The fluid in our body is partitioned into intracellular fluid and extracellular fluid compartments. **Intracellular fluid (ICF)** is the fluid within our cells. A majority or approximately two-thirds of the total

75%

65%

45%

Figure 25.1 Water Content of the Body. The percentage of water that composes the body varies from 45–75%, with an average of 65%.

LEARNING STRATEGY

The **"rule of thirds"** can help you to remember the distribution of fluid: intracellular fluid (ICF) = $2/3$ and extracellular fluid (ECF) = $1/3$. When only the extracellular fluid is considered, the distribution within the ECF is two-thirds interstitial fluid and one-third blood plasma.

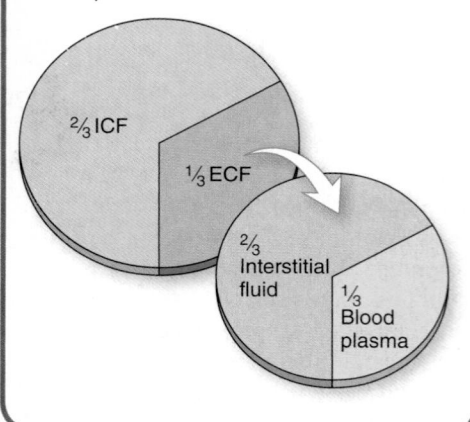

fluid is within our cells (**figure 25.2**). The barrier enclosing this fluid is the plasma membrane. The selectively permeable plasma membrane allows some, but not all, substances through it (see section 4.3).

The fluid outside of cells is referred to collectively as **extracellular fluid (ECF)**. Extracellular fluid includes both **interstitial fluid,** the fluid that surrounds and "bathes" the cells; and **blood plasma,** or *intravascular fluid,* the fluid within the blood vessels (see section 18.2).

Interstitial fluid composes approximately two-thirds of the extracellular fluid, and blood plasma about one-third. The barrier separating blood plasma from the interstitial fluid is the capillary vessel wall that consists of a single layer of simple squamous epithelium resting on a basement membrane (see section 20.1c). A capillary wall typically is more permeable than a plasma membrane. Consequently, the interstitial fluid and the blood plasma are more chemically similar to each other than they are to the intracellualr fluid (as described shortly).

Examples of specific extracellular fluids include cerebrospinal fluid of the brain and spinal cord, synovial fluid of joints, aqueous and vitreous humor of the eye, fluids of the inner ear (perilymph and endolymph), and serous fluid within body cavities (pleural, pericardial, and peritoneal). These extracellular fluids are not typically subject to significant daily gains and losses, and for this reason they are essentially ignored in this chapter. Only fluid in the two major compartments—and the factors that influence them, such as lymph return to blood—is addressed.

Composition of Body Fluids in the Two Compartments

Each fluid compartment is chemically distinct based upon the relative amounts of substances dissolved in it (figure 25.2b). Intracellular fluid is the most distinct compartment; it contains more potassium (K^+) and magnesium (Mg^{2+}) cations, phosphate anion (PO_4^{3-}), and negatively charged proteins than the extracellular fluid.

These differences in chemical composition reflect both processes within the cell and the regulatory activity of transport proteins within the plasma membrane that move substances into and out of the cell. For example, the relatively large amount of protein within intracellular fluid is a result of protein synthesis, whereas the relatively high concentration of intracellular K^+ occurs as a result of sodium-potassium (Na^+/K^+) pumps embedded within the plasma membrane that transports K^+ into a cell as Na^+ is transported out (see section 4.3).

In comparison, the two fluids composing the extracellular fluid—interstitial fluid and blood plasma—are both chemically distinct from intracellular fluid and similar in chemical composition to one another. Both interstitial fluid and blood plasma have a high concentration of these ions: sodium (Na^+) and calcium (Ca^{2+}) cations, and both chloride (Cl^-) and bicarbonate (HCO_3^-) anions.

Interstitial fluid and blood plasma exhibit one significant difference—namely, that protein is present in blood plasma, but very little protein is within the interstitial fluid. The similarity in ionic composition and the difference in protein composition reflect the relative

Figure 25.2 Fluid Compartments. (*a*) Fluid is contained within two major compartments: intracellular and extracellular. (*b*) K^+, Mg^{2+}, PO_4^{3-}, and proteins are more common in the intracellular fluid. The extracellular fluid is composed of both interstitial fluid and blood plasma, where Na^+, Ca^{2+}, Cl^-, and HCO_3^- are more prevalent than they are in the intracellular fluid. Within the extracellular fluid, significant amounts of protein are found within the blood plasma, with little or no protein in the interstitial fluid.

		Extracellular Fluid %	
Table 25.1	**Percentages of Solutes in Body Fluids[1]**		
Solutes	**Intracellular Fluid %**	**Interstitial Fluid %**	**Blood Plasma %**
CATIONS			
Potassium (K^+)	75	3	3
Magnesium (Mg^{2+})	17	1	1
Sodium (Na^+)	6	94	94
Calcium (Ca^{2+})	2	2	2
PROTEINS AND ANIONS			
Proteins	27	Trace	10
Phosphate (PO_4^{3-})	20	1	1
Bicarbonate (HCO_3^-)	6	18	16
Chloride (Cl^-)	2	77	69
Other	45	4	4

1. Values given are approximate percentages in skeletal muscle tissue.

permeability of the capillary wall: Proteins are generally too large to move out of the blood through the openings in the capillary wall to enter the interstitial fluid, whereas fluids and ions move freely. Therefore, during capillary exchange, blood plasma and all of its dissolved substances—except for most proteins—are filtered to become part of the interstitial fluid (see section 20.2). Specific percentages of the different substances in the intracellular fluid and extracellular fluid (both IF and blood plasma) are given in **table 25.1**.

Fluid Movement Between Compartments

Fluid movement between compartments occurs continuously in response to changes in relative osmolarity (concentration). This happens when the fluid concentration in one fluid compartment becomes either hypotonic or hypertonic (section 4.3b), with respect to another compartment; water immediately moves by osmosis between the two compartments until the water concentration is once again equal **(figure 25.3)**. You may recall from section 4.3b

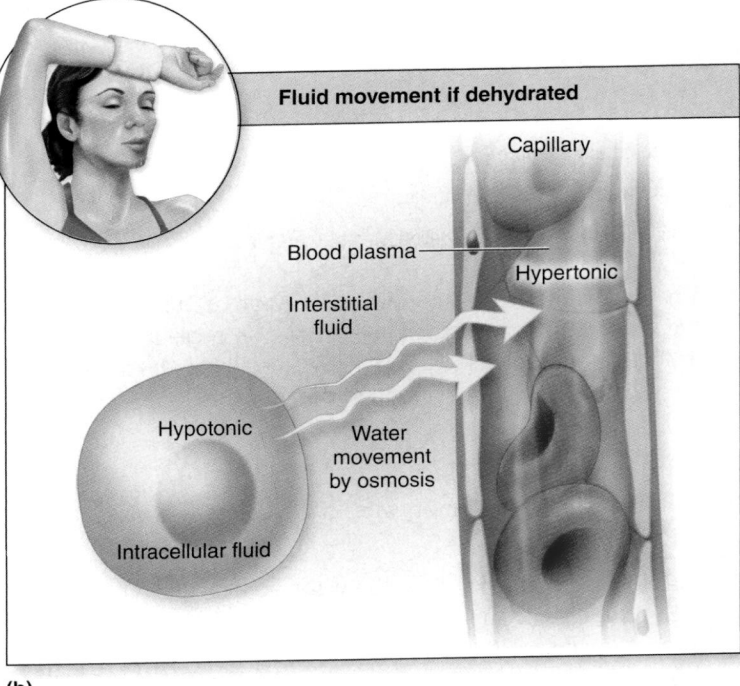

(a)   (b)

Figure 25.3 Fluid Movement Between Compartments. (*a*) A net movement of water from the blood plasma into the intracellular compartment (ICF) occurs following fluid intake. (*b*) A net movement of water from the intracellular compartment into the blood plasma occurs when one is dehydrated.

that water always moves by osmosis from the hypotonic solution to the hypertonic solution. This movement of water between the compartments is possible because the plasma membranes and the capillary wall are both permeable to water.

When you drink water, water enters your blood from the digestive system and becomes part of the blood plasma. Consequently, the plasma osmolarity decreases and blood plasma becomes hypotonic to the ICF. Thereafter, as blood moves through the capillaries, water first moves out of the blood plasma to become part of the interstitial fluid, and then moves from the interstitial fluid into cells (figure 25.3a). This means there is a net movement of water from the blood plasma into the cells. In contrast, if water is lost from the body without being replaced in a timely manner, then dehydration occurs. Blood plasma osmolarity increases, and blood plasma becomes hypertonic to both the interstitial fluid and the cells. Consequently, a net movement of water occurs from the cells into the blood plasma. It moves first into the interstitial fluid and then into the blood plasma (figure 25.3b).

WHAT DID YOU LEARN?

2 Which ions are more prevalent in the intracellular fluid? Which are more prevalent in the extracellular fluid?

3 What is the major distinction in the chemical composition of blood plasma and interstitial fluid?

4 When you are dehydrated, is the net movement of fluid from the blood plasma into the cells or from the cells into the blood plasma?

25.2 Fluid Balance

Many systems influence fluid balance, including the digestive, cardiovascular, lymphatic, integumentary, respiratory, urinary, nervous, and endocrine systems. Here we discuss how these systems help bring fluid into the body, are involved with movement of fluid within the body, participate in the loss of fluid from the body, and regulate the processes of fluid balance.

25.2a Fluid Intake and Fluid Output

LEARNING OBJECTIVES

1. Define fluid balance.
2. List the sources of fluid intake.
3. Distinguish between the categories of water loss.

Fluid balance exists when fluid intake is equal to fluid output, and a normal distribution of water and solutes is present in the two major fluid compartments. Our discussion begins by describing and comparing how fluid intake and fluid output occur.

Fluid Intake

Fluid intake is the addition of water to the body. It is divided into two categories (**figure 25.4**):

- **Preformed water** includes the water absorbed from food and drink taken into the gastrointestinal tract. On average, this is approximately 2300 milliliters (mL) of fluid intake per day.
- **Metabolic water** includes the water produced daily from aerobic cellular respiration (see section 3.4f) and dehydration reactions (see section 2.7). It is approximately 200 mL of fluid per day.

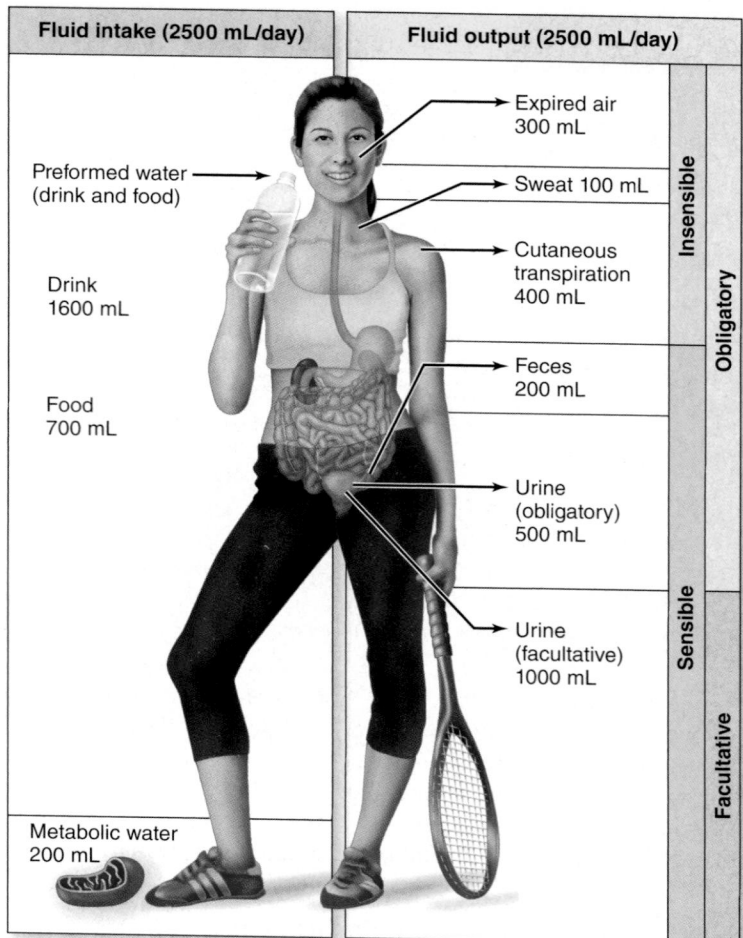

Figure 25.4 Fluid Intake and Fluid Output. Fluid balance is determined by relative amounts of fluid intake and fluid output. Fluid intake results from digestive tract absorption of ingested food and drink, as well as water produced by metabolic processes. Fluid output includes fluid lost from the body as a component of expired air, through the skin by both sweat and cutaneous transpiration, and in the feces and urine. Fluid output is called sensible if it is measurable or insensible if it is not. It may also be categorized as obligatory if is always lost, or facultative if the loss in the urine is regulated. (Values given are approximate averages.)

The sum of the average preformed water intake and metabolic water produced is 2500 mL. Given that fluid intake from both food and drink is approximately 2300 mL of the total 2500 mL, then the fluid absorbed from the digestive tract accounts for about 92% of daily fluid intake. A significant and perhaps obvious point is that normally the only way to significantly increase fluid in the body is through fluid intake from the food and drink that we consume (see Clinical View: "Intravenous [IV] Solution").

Fluid Output

Fluid output is the loss of water from the body. Fluid output must equal fluid intake to maintain fluid balance. Fluid is lost from the body through the normal mechanisms of

- Breathing
- Sweating
- Cutaneous transpiration (evaporation of water directly through the skin)
- Defecation
- Urination

CLINICAL VIEW

Intravenous (IV) Solution

A patient may be administered an **intravenous** (in'tră-vē'nŭs) **(IV) solution** as a clinical means of increasing fluid input directly into the blood. In this procedure, a needle is inserted into the individual's vein either in the hand or the antecubital region, with a tube extending from the needle to a bag.

The two most common IV solutions are a 0.9% saline solution and a 5% dextrose, or D5W, solution.

A **0.9% saline solution** is a solution containing 0.9 grams of sodium chloride to every 100 mL of sterile water. This solution is the standard IV solution for fluid replacement because it has a similar osmolarity to blood plasma. Thus, it will not cause a net shift of fluid between compartments following the addition of this fluid.

A **5% dextrose**, or **D5W**, solution is composed of 5 grams of dextrose sugar to every 100 mL of sterile water. However, this solution is a hypertonic solution (to blood plasma) when in the holding bag—but when infused into the body, the dextrose is metabolized, and the solution becomes hypotonic. This solution is used to supply the body with both water and an energy source (glucose).

The amount of water lost through these activities depends upon physical activity, environmental conditions, and internal conditions of the body. Average amounts for each type of fluid output are shown in figure 25.4. Notice that of the average fluid output, 1500 mL out of the 2500 mL (or approximately 60%) is lost in urine, and the remaining 40% of fluid is lost in expired air, through the skin by sweat and cutaneous transpiration, and in feces.

Water loss can be described in two ways: either as sensible and insensible water loss or as obligatory and facultative water loss.

Sensible and Insensible Water Loss   Sensible and insensible fluid loss reflects whether the fluid loss is measurable.

Sensible water loss is measurable, and it includes fluid lost through feces and urine. In contrast, **insensible water loss** is not measurable. It includes both fluid lost in expired air and fluid lost from the skin through sweat and cutaneous transpiration.

Obligatory and Facultative Water Loss   Water loss may also be described as either obligatory or facultative.

Obligatory water loss is a loss of water that always occurs, regardless of the state of hydration of the body. It includes water lost through breathing and through the skin (insensible water loss), as well as fluid lost in the feces and in the minimal amount of urine produced to eliminate wastes from the body, approximately 0.5 L (500 mL) per day.

Facultative (fak'ŭl-tā-tiv) **water loss** is controlled water loss. It is dependent upon the degree of hydration of the body and is hormonally regulated in the distal convoluted tubule, collecting tubules, and collecting ducts in nephrons of the kidney (see section 24.6d and later sections in this chapter).

Note that the only physiologic mechanism to control fluid output is through the hormonal regulation of urine output. When the body is overhydrated, hormonally controlled facultative water loss normally plays a significant role in eliminating excess fluid. In comparison, obligatory fluid output always occurs, regardless of the hydrated state of the body. Therefore, hormonal regulation of urine

output can decrease fluid loss when the body is dehydrated, but not inhibit it completely. Over time, the body continues to become more and more dehydrated unless fluids are replaced. Death may result in severe cases of dehydration.

WHAT DID YOU LEARN?

5 What are the two major sources of fluid intake? What are the different means of fluid output, and which one is regulated based on the hydrated state of the body?

25.2b Fluid Imbalance

✓ LEARNING OBJECTIVES

4. Name the different causes of fluid imbalance.

5. Compare and contrast the different types of fluid imbalances.

6. Explain what is meant by fluid sequestration.

A fluid imbalance occurs when fluid output does not equal fluid intake. Fluid imbalances can be organized into five categories that include volume depletion, volume excess, dehydration, hypotonic hydration, and fluid sequestration. The first four of these categories can be differentiated using two criteria:

1. Does the fluid imbalance change the osmolarity (concentration) of body fluid?

2. Is the fluid imbalance caused by an excess or deficiency of body fluid?

Fluid Imbalance with Constant Osmolarity

Fluid imbalances with constant osmolarity occur when isotonic fluid is lost or gained. **Volume depletion** occurs when isotonic fluid loss is greater than isotonic fluid gain. Examples of conditions that result in volume depletion include hemorrhage, severe burns, chronic vomiting, diarrhea, or the hyposecretion of aldosterone (a hormone that stimulates both Na^+ and water reabsorption in the kidney; see section 24.6d).

Volume excess occurs when isotonic fluid gain is greater than isotonic fluid loss. This typically results when fluid intake is normal, but there is decreased fluid loss through the kidneys (e.g., from either renal failure or aldosterone hypersecretion). In both volume depletion and volume excess, there is no change is osmolarity. Consequently, there is no net movement of water between fluid compartments.

Fluid Imbalance with Changes in Osmolarity

Certain types of fluid imbalance involve fluid loss or gain that is not isotonic. **Dehydration** can result from profuse sweating, diabetes mellitus, hyposecretion of antidiuretic hormone (ADH—a hormone that stimulates water reabsorption in the kidney; see section 24.6d), insufficient water intake, or overexposure to cold weather. In each case, the water loss is greater than the loss of solutes, and the blood plasma becomes hypertonic. Consequently, water shifts between fluid compartments with a net movement of water from the cells into the interstitial fluid and then into blood plasma. Body cells may become dehydrated as a result (see figure 25.3b).

Hypotonic hydration is also called *water intoxication*, or *positive water balance*. It can result from ADH hypersecretion, but it is generally caused from drinking a large amount of plain water following excessive sweating. An example would be some amateur athletes who run marathons, and drink plain water instead of using an electrolyte-enhanced solution. Both Na^+ and water are

CLINICAL VIEW
Dehydration in Infants and the Elderly

Both infants and the elderly are more vulnerable to dehydration than are young and middle-aged adults.

Infants are especially vulnerable to dehydration for the following reasons:

- Infants have a greater ratio of skin surface area to volume in comparison to adults, and thus lose more fluid via sweating and transpiration.
- They have immature kidneys that cannot effectively concentrate urine; therefore, more water is required to eliminate wastes.
- They have a higher metabolic rate, which produces more metabolic waste to be eliminated.
- They do not have a completely developed homeostatic mechanism for temperature regulation; thus, they develop fevers that are both

higher and longer lasting. As a result, additional water is required to cool the body.

In comparison, the elderly are also susceptible to dehydration, but for different reasons:

- Due to the loss of skeletal muscle tissue and other changes, elderly people are on average composed of 45% water by weight. Smaller losses in water thus may result in a fluid imbalance.
- The kidneys become less effective at concentrating and diluting urine as we age, so more fluid is lost in the urine.
- Cutaneous loss of fluid increases due to decreased thickness of the skin and loss of subcutaneous tissue.
- Fluid replacement may not occur with regularity because the thirst mechanism is less effective. Some elderly people, especially nonambulatory individuals, may also voluntarily restrict fluid intake due to concerns of incontinence.
- Elders are at greater risk for hyperglycemia, with the elevated glucose causing the loss of additional water from the body.

---

lost during sweating, and drinking water replaces only the water, but not the solutes. The blood plasma then becomes hypotonic to the other fluid compartments. Fluid moves from blood plasma into the interstitial fluid, and then into the cells (see figure 25.3a). Cells may become swollen with fluid.

One of the consequences of extreme hypotonic hydration is cerebral edema. Brain cells become impaired as they swell with excess fluid. The person may experience headaches, nausea, or both. Convulsions, coma, or death may result in severe cases. In addition, some individuals have died after having been forced or enticed to drink excessive amounts of water (e.g., fraternity hazings and water-drinking contests).

Fluid Sequestration

Fluid sequestration (sē'kwes-trā'shŭn; *sequestro* = to lay aside) differs from the other fluid imbalances because total body fluid may be normal, but it is distributed abnormally. Fluid accumulates in a particular location, and it is not available for use elsewhere.

Edema is an example of fluid sequestration in which fluid accumulates in the interstitial space around cells, and is characterized by puffiness or swelling **(figure 25.5)**. Anatomic or physi-

ologic changes that can result in edema are listed in **table 25.2**. Notice as you review the contents of this table that edema is generally a result of abnormal changes in the cardiovascular system (heart or blood vessels), blood composition, or changes to lymph vessels (the vessels that return fluid to the cardiovascular system). These

Figure 25.5 Edema.
Edema occurs when excess fluid accumulates in the interstitial space around cells.

Table 25.2	Conditions That Result in Edema
Changes That Influence Fluid Movement	**Causes**
Increased interstitial fluid formation from blood capillaries	Increased hydrostatic blood pressure resulting from increased blood volume, congestive heart failure (either on the right side, which can result in systemic edema, or on the left side, which can result in pulmonary edema), incompetent heart valves, or poor venous return due to faulty valves
	Increased capillary leakage due to histamine release, presence of bacterial toxins, or increased age
Decreased fluid removal from interstitial space back into capillaries	Decreased blood colloid osmotic pressure caused by the reduced ability of the liver to produce albumin and other plasma proteins as a consequence of liver cirrhosis or malnutrition, or excessive loss of protein by the kidneys
Decreased fluid removal by lymph vessels	Surgical removal of lymph nodes (e.g., following mastectomy), obstruction of lymph vessels (e.g., elephantiasis)

CONCEPT CONNECTION

You learned in section 20.2 that capillary dynamics are determined by the **net filtration pressure (NFP).** NFP is determined by subtracting the net colloid osmotic pressure from the net hydrostatic pressure. On the arterial end of the capillary, capillary hydrostatic pressure is sufficient to push fluid out of the capillary with an NFP of approximately 14 mm Hg. Fluid exits the blood into the interstitial space, but most plasma proteins remain within the blood.

In contrast, at the venous end of capillaries, the NFP is approximately − 5 mm Hg. This relatively negative pressure causes fluid to be pulled in the opposite direction from the interstitial space back into the blood. However, most but not all of the fluid returns to the blood on the venous end. The excess fluid remaining in the interstitial space, which is approximately 15% of what was originally filtered, is taken up by the lymphatic system. Changes to either NFP or lymph transport can result in edema (see table 25.2).

changes alter the net filtration pressure (NFP) at systemic capillaries (see section 20.2c), causing additional fluid to either leave the capillaries or remain in the interstitial space.

Other examples of fluid sequestration include hemorrhage, ascites, and pleural effusion. *Ascites* (ā-sī'tēz) is the accumulation of fluid within the peritoneal cavity, and *pleural effusion* is the accumulation of fluid, sometimes up to several liters, in the pleural cavity as a consequence of lung infections. Pleural effusion is a condition that can lead to suffocation.

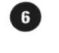 **WHAT DID YOU LEARN?**

6 How would you distinguish fluid deficiency from dehydration in terms of changes in total body fluid, changes in blood osmolarity, and fluid movement between compartments?

25.2c Regulation of Fluid Balance

 LEARNING OBJECTIVES

7. Describe the stimuli that increase fluid intake.

8. Explain the conditions and stimuli that decrease fluid intake.

9. Name the four hormones that are involved in regulating fluid output.

Maintaining fluid balance involves the regulation of both fluid intake and fluid output to prevent fluid imbalances. Because no receptors directly monitor water volume or grams of dissolved solutes, such as Na$^+$ or K$^+$, the mechanisms for monitoring fluid are indirect. Fluid balance is regulated by monitoring blood volume, blood pressure, and blood plasma osmolarity (concentration of solutes in blood plasma). The relationships between these variables can be described as follows:

- **Fluid intake increases blood volume.** The additional volume of blood has two consequences: Blood pressure increases, and if water gain exceeds solute gain, then blood osmolarity decreases.

- **Fluid output decreases blood volume.** Therefore, blood pressure is lower, and if more water is lost than solutes, blood osmolarity increases.

Fluid intake and fluid output regulation generally occur in response to the fluctuation of these variables discussed in the following sections.

Regulating Fluid Intake

Fluid intake is regulated by various stimuli that either activate or inhibit the **thirst center** located within the hypothalamus (see section 13.4c).

Stimuli to Turn on the Thirst Center Stimuli for activating the thirst center, which occurs when fluid intake is less than fluid output, include the following:

- **Decreased salivary secretions.** Saliva production decreases, and mucous membranes are not as moist, when less fluid is available. Sensory input is relayed from sensory receptors in the mucous membranes of the mouth and throat to the thirst center.

- **Increased blood osmolarity.** This occurs most commonly from insufficient water intake and dehydration. The increase in blood osmolarity stimulates sensory receptors in the thirst center directly, and also stimulates the hypothalamus to initiate nerve signals to the posterior pituitary to release antidiuretic hormone (ADH) (see section 17.8b). ADH also stimulates the thirst center. This stimulation of the thirst center occurs with as little as a 2–3% increase in ADH.

- **Decreased blood pressure.** When fluid intake is less than fluid output, blood volume decreases with an accompanying decrease in blood pressure. Renin is released from the kidney in response to a lower blood pressure (see section 20.5). Renin initiates the conversion of angiotensinogen to angiotensin II. An increase of 10–15% in the concentration of angiotensin II within the blood stimulates the thirst center. This mechanism is especially important when extreme volume depletion occurs; for example, when an individual is hemorrhaging.

When the thirst center is activated, nerve signals are relayed to the cerebral cortex, and we then become conscious of our thirst. If we take fluid into the body by drinking or eating, water is absorbed from the digestive system into the blood, and the water then moves into the interstitial space and ultimately into the cells (see figure 25.3a).

Stimuli to Turn off the Thirst Center Stimuli for inhibiting the thirst center are produced when fluid intake is greater than fluid output. All of these stimuli (except distension of the stomach, described here) oppose stimuli that activate the thirst center. These include the following:

- **Increased salivary secretions.** When body fluid level is high, salivary secretions increase, and the mucous membranes of the mouth and throat become moist. Sensory input to the thirst center decreases.

- **Distension of the stomach.** Fluid entering the stomach causes it to stretch, and inhibitory sensory impulses are relayed to the thirst center. (Note that an empty stomach does not stimulate the thirst center; rather, only a stretched stomach wall will inhibit the thirst center.)

- **Decreased blood osmolarity.** Blood osmolarity decreases when additional fluid enters the blood. In response, the thirst center is no longer stimulated directly, and the hypothalamus decreases stimulation of ADH release from the posterior pituitary.

- **Increased blood pressure.** Blood volume and blood pressure increase with the addition of fluid. This rise in blood pressure inhibits the kidney from releasing renin, and the subsequent production of angiotensin II decreases. A decrease in angiotensin II results in a reduced stimulation of the thirst center.

The stimuli that inhibit the thirst center can be divided into two categories, depending upon both the time required to inhibit the thirst center and their level of accuracy in reflecting the hydrated state of the body. Stimuli that immediately inhibit the thirst center,

but are less accurate concerning the hydrated state, include both the moistening of the mucous membranes and distension of the stomach. Signals from these stimuli will inhibit the thirst center for approximately 30 to 45 minutes, which is long enough for the absorption of fluids from the digestive system into the blood plasma.

Once fluids are absorbed, blood osmolarity decreases (with an accompanying decrease in ADH release), and both blood volume and blood pressure increase (with an accompanying decrease in renin release and production of angiotensin II). These are less immediate stimuli but more accurately reflect the body's state of hydration.

WHAT DO YOU THINK?

1 Many times during a long-distance race, water stations are positioned along the side of the road so that runners may rehydrate during the race. Sometimes a runner will take a drink, swirl it around in the mouth, and then spit the water back out instead of swallowing it. Do you think this practice should be encouraged? Explain in terms of the effect on the thirst center and the hydrated state of the body.

Regulating Fluid Output

Recall that fluid output is regulated through the kidneys by controlling urine output. Four major hormones are involved in regulating urine output: angiotensin II, antidiuretic hormone (ADH), aldosterone, and atrial natriuretic peptide (ANP).

Angiotensin II, ADH, and aldosterone help decrease urine output. These three hormones function to maintain both blood volume and blood pressure. In contrast, ANP increases urine output to decrease both blood volume and blood pressure. The specific mechanisms employed by each of these hormones in regulating fluid output in the kidneys also function in regulating some electrolytes (e.g., Na^+). Thus, it is more appropriate to describe the details of these hormones at the end of the next section on electrolytes.

WHAT DID YOU LEARN?

7 What stimuli activate the thirst center?

8 Which of these four hormones—angiotensin II, antidiuretic hormone, aldosterone, and atrial natriuretic peptide—increases urine output?

25.3 Electrolyte Balance

Water movement between fluid compartments is caused by a relative difference in the concentration of solutes in those compartments. The greater the difference in the number of solutes, the greater the osmotic pressure (see section 4.3b). Because it is the number of solutes that determines the osmotic pressure, solutes are differentiated into nonelectrolytes and electrolytes. Nonelectrolytes and electrolytes were first introduced in section 2.4c.

25.3a Nonelectrolytes and Electrolytes

LEARNING OBJECTIVES

1. Describe the difference between a nonelectrolyte and an electrolyte.

2. Explain the general role of electrolytes in fluid balance.

Molecules that do not dissociate (or come apart) in solution are called **nonelectrolytes.** Most of these substances are covalently bonded organic molecules (e.g., glucose, urea, and creatinine). In

---

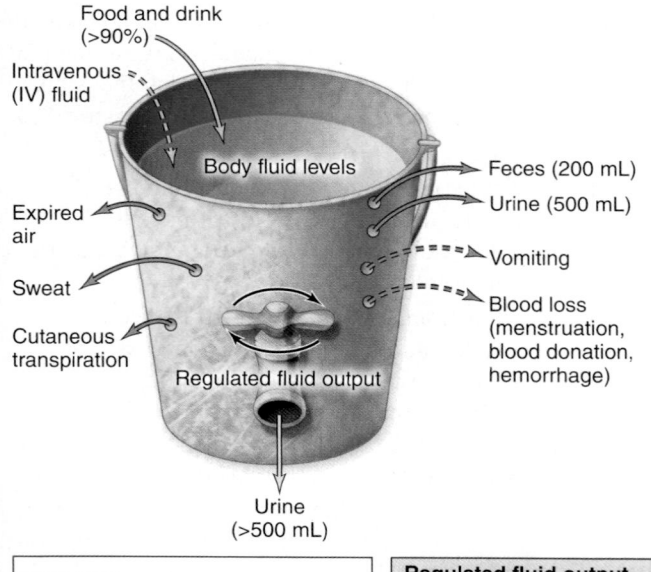

contrast, an **electrolyte** is any substance that dissociates in solution to form cations and anions. Electrolytes include salts, acids, bases, and some negatively charged proteins. The term electrolyte refers directly to the ability of these substances, when dissolved and dissociated in solution, to conduct an electric current. Examples of electrolytes and the dissociated ions they produce when placed into an aqueous solution (aq) include the following:

Salts: $NaCl$ (aq) $\longrightarrow$ Na^+ + Cl^- or $CaCl_2$ (aq) $\longrightarrow$ Ca^{2+} + 2 Cl^-
Acid: HCl (aq) $\longrightarrow$ H^+ + Cl^-
Base: $NaOH$ (aq) $\longrightarrow$ Na^+ + OH^-

$NaCl$ dissociates into two ions, Na^+ and Cl^-. Because osmotic pressure is dependent upon the *number* of solutes, $NaCl$ exerts twice the osmotic pressure of the same concentration of a nonelectrolyte, such as glucose, which does not dissociate into ionic forms. Further, $CaCl_2$ in solution dissociates into three components, Ca^{2+} and two Cl^-, and exerts three times the osmotic pressure compared to that of glucose.

To account for this difference in osmotic pressure, the concentration of electrolytes in solution is commonly expressed in milliequivalents per liter (mEq/L), which reflects the amount or equivalent number of electrical charges in 1 liter of solution. (Milliequivalents is a measure of either the amount of H^+ an anion can bind, or the amount of bicarbonate ion (HCO_3^-) a cation can bind, in 1 liter of solution.)

 WHAT DID YOU LEARN?

9 Why do electrolytes exert a greater osmotic pressure than nonelectrolytes?

25.3b Major Electrolytes: Location, Functions, and Regulation

LEARNING OBJECTIVES

3. List the six major electrolytes found in body fluids, other than H^+ and HCO_3^-.

4. Explain why Na^+ is a critical electrolyte in the body.

5. Describe the variables that influence K^+ distribution.

6. Identify the main location, functions, and the means of regulation for each electrolyte.

The human body fluids contain common electrolytes, both cations such as Na^+ and K^+, and anions such as Cl^- and HCO_3^-, as described previously. Each electrolyte has unique functions in the body in addition to its general function of contributing to the exertion of osmotic pressure. To carry out these functions effectively, each electrolyte must be maintained within a normal concentration range in the blood plasma (see table 18.3).

Regulating normal concentration of the different electrolytes in the blood plasma requires maintaining input equal to output, similar to what we discussed with respect to water balance. Here we present a description of the location, functions, and regulation of the major electrolytes, with the exception of H^+ and HCO_3^-, which are covered later in the section on acid-base balance.

Sodium Ion (Na^+)

Approximately 99% of Na^+ is in the ECF and only 1% in the ICF, a gradient that is maintained by Na^+/K^+ pumps. Sodium is the principal cation in the ECF. It is usually present in the form of either sodium bicarbonate ($NaHCO_3$) or sodium chloride ($NaCl$) and exerts the greatest osmotic pressure in the ECF.

Sodium functions in a number of physiologic processes, many of which have been presented in previous chapters (e.g., neuromuscular functions and cotransport in kidney tubules). We now describe how Na^+ concentration is regulated to maintain its balance, and how it functions in determining plasma osmolarity and regulating fluid balance.

Sodium Balance Our normal blood plasma Na^+ concentration is 135–145 mEq/L (**figure 25.6a**). We obtain Na^+ from our diet. Although the daily dietary requirement for Na^+ is only 1.5 to 2.3 grams per day (g/day), our intake may vary from as little as 0.5 g on a low-sodium diet to as high as 20–25 g with high Na^+

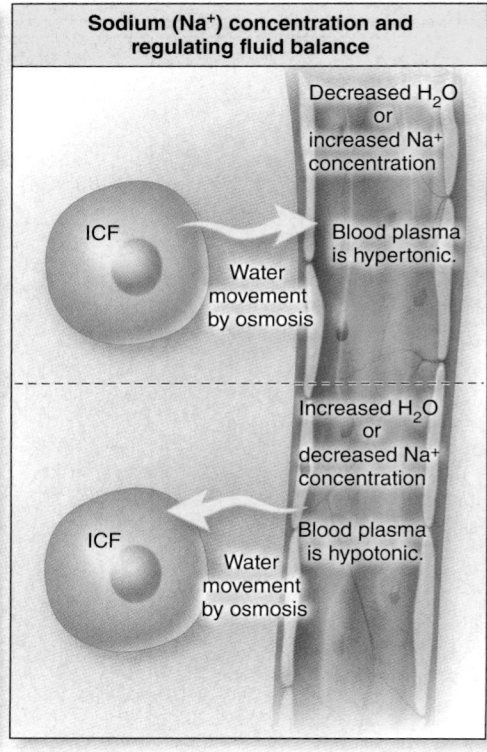

(a) **(b)**

Figure 25.6 Sodium Balance. Sodium is the principal cation in the extracellular fluid (ECF). (*a*) Normal blood plasma Na^+ concentration is between 135 mEq/L and 145 mEq/L and is important in maintaining fluid balance. Sodium level increases through the diet and decreases through urine, feces, and sweating. Sodium content and concentration are regulated by aldosterone, antidiuretic hormone (ADH), and atrial natriuretic peptide (ANP). (*b*) Changes in Na^+ concentration cause movement of water between fluid compartments.

intake. A typical American diet averages 3–7 g of Na^+ per day. Most of our Na^+ comes from table salt and processed foods such as canned soups. Sodium loss is through urine, feces, and sweat. The amount of Na^+ lost in urine is regulated by three hormones, namely aldosterone, ADH, and ANP. These hormones also indirectly help in regulating fluid balance and are described in detail later in this chapter.

WHAT DO YOU THINK?

2. Discuss why physicians might recommend a diet low in Na^+ for individuals with high blood pressure.

Sodium's Role in Blood Plasma Osmolarity   As the most common cation in the ECF—composing approximately 90% of the solute concentration in the ECF—Na^+ is therefore the most important electrolyte in determining blood plasma osmolarity and in regulating fluid balance. The ECF becomes temporarily hypertonic if Na^+ concentration increases from either elevated Na^+ content or decreased water content. Consequently, water moves from the other compartments into the blood plasma in an attempt to reestablish the normal Na^+ concentration (figure 25.6b).

The ECF becomes temporarily hypotonic if Na^+ concentration decreases either as a consequence of decreased Na^+ content or increased water content. Water then moves from the plasma into the cells until the normal Na^+ concentration is reestablished.

Note that changes in plasma volume directly influence both blood volume and blood pressure. Thus, retention of Na^+ and water increases both blood volume and blood pressure, whereas the loss of Na^+ and water causes both a decrease in blood volume and blood pressure. For this reason, individuals with high blood pressure may be instructed by their physician to restrict their sodium intake. Although high blood pressure has many causes, and individuals retain Na^+ to varying degrees, studies have shown that decreasing dietary intake of Na^+ is effective in lowering blood pressure in most individuals.

Sodium imbalance is one of the most common types of electrolyte imbalances. A Na^+ imbalance occurs when the Na^+ concentration is either above the normal levels (**hypernatremia;** hī'per-nă-trē'mē-ă) or below normal levels (**hyponatremia;** hī'pō-nă-trē'mē-ă). Any condition that alters Na^+ intake or output, or any condition that alters water intake or output, may cause a change in Na^+ plasma concentration. Most occurrences result from changes in water content. The causes, effects, and symptoms of electrolyte imbalances are included in **table 25.3** on p. 994.

Potassium Ion (K^+)

In contrast to Na^+, approximately 98% of **potassium** is in the ICF and only 2% is in the ECF. This gradient is also maintained by the Na^+/K^+ pump. Potassium is the principal cation to exert intracellular osmotic pressure because it is the most abundant cation in the ICF. Potassium is required for normal neuromuscular physiologic activities, and it has a significant role in controlling heart rhythm.

Potassium Balance   Although the vast majority of the total body K^+ is located within the ICF, it is only the approximate 2% of the K^+ in the ECF that is continually regulated. The normal plasma value for K^+ in the ECF is between 3.5 mEq/L and 5.0 mEq/L (**figure 25.7a**). Small changes in blood plasma K^+ levels can readily lead to a K^+ imbalance—the *most lethal* of the electrolyte imbalances. Neuromuscular changes are the most significant effects of a K^+ imbalance. These can lead to either cardiac or respiratory arrest.

Both the total body K^+ and the distribution of K^+ must be regulated in order to maintain K^+ balance in our body fluids. **Total body potassium** is regulated by K^+ intake and output. The daily dietary requirement for K^+ is 40 mEq/L, although it may vary from 40–150 mEq/L. Potassium is generally obtained from fruits and vegetables, but input is increased with salt substitutes that contain K^+.

Only small amounts of K^+ are lost from the body through sweat and in feces. Most K^+ (approximately 80–90%) is lost in urine. Some

Figure 25.7 Potassium Balance. Potassium is the principal cation in the intracellular fluid (ICF). (*a*) Normal blood plasma K^+ concentration is 3.5–5.0 mEq/L. Potassium balance is dependent upon both total K^+ and its distribution in the fluid compartments. Total K^+ levels are a function of intake from the diet and loss through urine, feces, and sweat. (*b*) Potassium distribution changes in response to changing levels of K^+ in the extracellular fluid (ECF), changes in H^+ blood plasma concentration, and to the presence of specific hormones (e.g., insulin).

(a)

(b)

K^+ is always being lost because the body has no means to conserve all of its K^+. The amount of K^+ lost in the urine fluctuates, and greater amounts are lost during conditions of high blood plasma K^+, increased aldosterone secretion, and high blood pH (see section 26.4d).

Potassium distribution is the ratio of K^+ in the ICF to that in the ECF. This ratio is dependent upon both the level of activity of Na^+/K^+ pumps that actively pump K^+ into the cell, and the K^+ leak channels that allow K^+ to flow back out of the cell. Variables that influence K^+ distribution are described next.

Potassium Shifts   Potassium can redistribute between compartments under certain conditions that include changing blood plasma K^+ concentration, changing blood plasma H^+ concentration, and the presence of specific hormones in the blood (figure 25.7b).

Changes in blood plasma K^+ concentration cause shifts in K^+ between the ECF and ICF. An increase in blood plasma K^+ results in K^+ moving from the ECF into the ICF, whereas a decrease in blood plasma K^+ results in the movement of K^+ from the ICF into the ECF. Thus, the ICF serves as a reservoir for blood plasma K^+ levels, taking on excess K^+ in response to elevated blood plasma K^+ concentration and releasing K^+ when blood plasma K^+ concentration begins to decline.

Changes in blood plasma H^+ concentration also cause a shift in K^+ between the ECF and ICF. When H^+ increases (decrease in pH) in the ECF, excess H^+ moves from the ECF into the ICF in an attempt to reestablish acid-base balance (described later in this chapter). At the same time, K^+ moves in the opposite direction, from the ICF into the ECF, to prevent the development of an electrostatic gradient. The reverse movement of both H^+ and K^+ occurs if H^+ decreases (causing an increase in pH). A primary reason an acid-base imbalance can be lethal is because of these shifts in K^+ that occur in response to pH changes.

Certain hormones also induce shifts in K^+ between the ECF and ICF; insulin is one important example. Insulin is typically released following a meal and decreases not only blood glucose (as described in section 17.10) but also blood K^+. Insulin decreases blood plasma K^+ by stimulating the activity of Na^+/K^+ pumps in cells, thus increasing the transport of K^+ from the ECF into the ICF. Physiologists reason that this helps prevent elevated K^+ in the blood plasma (**hyperkalemia**; hī′per-kă-lē′mē-ă) that could potentially occur as K^+ is absorbed into the blood following a meal. Interestingly, individuals exhibiting hyperkalemia may be treated with the administration of insulin (along with glucose).

WHAT DO YOU THINK?

3   Body builders have been known to inject insulin to increase muscle mass because it stimulates protein anabolism. What is one of the risks associated with this practice in terms of K^+ levels: elevated blood plasma K^+ (hyperkalemia) or decreased blood plasma K^+ (hypokalemia)? Can the practice of injecting insulin to increase muscle mass be fatal?

Chloride Ion (Cl⁻)

Chloride is a common anion that is normally associated with Na^+. It is the most abundant anion in the ECF. Chloride ions are found in the lumen of stomach as hydrochloric acid (see section 26.2d), and they also participate in the chloride shift within erythrocytes for transport of carbon dioxide in the form of HCO_3^- (see figure 23.27).

Normal blood plasma Cl^- concentration is 96–106 mEq/L. Chloride is obtained in the diet, primarily from table salt and processed foods. Chloride is normally lost in the sweat, stomach secretions, and urine. The amount lost in urine is primarily dependent upon

blood plasma Na^+. Chloride levels are directly correlated with Na^+ levels, because Cl^- follows Na^+ by electrostatic interactions and is regulated by the same mechanisms as Na^+.

Calcium Ion (Ca²⁺)

Calcium is the most abundant electrolyte in bone and teeth. Approximately 99% of all body Ca^{2+} (most commonly as calcium phosphate, $Ca_3[PO_4]_2$), is stored within the extracellular matrix of these structures causing them to harden. To prevent hardening or calcification of other tissue, Ca^{2+} is normally moved by Ca^{2+} pumps either out of cells or into the sarcoplasmic reticulum. This prevents Ca^{2+} from binding to the abundant PO_4^{3-} within cells. In addition to hardening of both bones and teeth, Ca^{2+} is needed to initiate muscle contraction and release neurotransmitters; it also serves as a second messenger, and participates in blood clotting.

Normal blood plasma Ca^{2+} concentration is approximately 5 mEq/L. In blood plasma, Ca^{2+} can exist either bound to protein such as albumin (about 35%), associated with anions such as PO_4^{3-} (about 15%), or in an ionized or unbound state (about 50%). Only the ionized form is physiologically active. Calcium is obtained in the diet from yogurt, milk, soy products, cheese, sardines, and green leafy vegetables (such as broccoli and collard greens). Calcium is lost from the body in urine, feces, and sweat. (The regulation of Ca^{2+} by parathyroid hormone, calcitriol, and calcitonin is discussed in sections 7.6 and 24.4d.)

Phosphate Ion (PO₄³⁻)

Phosphate ions (PO_4^{3-}) occur as both hydrogen phosphate (HPO_4^{2-}) and dihydrogen phosphate ($H_2PO_4^-$). Phosphate is the most abundant anion in the ICF. Approximately 85% is stored in the extracellular matrix of bone and teeth as calcium phosphate, $Ca_3(PO_4)_2$. Phosphate is also a component of nucleotides of DNA and RNA and of phospholipid molecules within plasma membranes. It serves as an intracellular buffer against pH changes (described later) and is a common buffer in urine.

Normal blood plasma concentration of PO_4^{3-} ranges from 1.8–2.9 mEq/L. Most PO_4^{3-} is ionized (about 90%) in blood plasma and the rest is bound to plasma proteins such as albumin. Phosphorus is obtained in the diet from milk, meat, and fish. In addition, many food additives (used to prevent spoilage) and most soft drinks contain PO_4^{3-}. Phosphate is regulated by many of the same mechanisms as Ca^{2+}; this is because as just described 99% of body calcium is stored in bone, with the majority stored as calcium phosphate.

Magnesium Ion (Mg²⁺)

Magnesium is primarily located within bone or within cells. After K^+, Mg^{2+} is the most abundant cation in the ICF. Magnesium participates in over 300 enzymatic reactions including ATP synthesis, the synthesis of protein, and enzymatic reactions involving carbohydrate metabolism. It also assists in the movement of Na^+ and K^+ across the plasma membrane by the Na^+/K^+ pump, and it is important in muscle relaxation.

Normal blood plasma concentration of Mg^{2+} ranges from 1.4–2.1 mEq/L. Because most Mg^{2+} is located within cells, this represents only a small fraction of total body Mg^{2+}. In blood plasma, Mg^{2+} is either in a free, ionized form or bound to protein. The ionized form is physiologically active. Magnesium is obtained in the diet from beans and peas, leafy green vegetables, and other sources, and is lost from the body in sweat and urine. Magnesium blood plasma levels are regulated through the kidney.

Table 25.3	Blood Electrolyte Imbalances		
Condition	**Causes**	**Effects**	**Symptoms**
Hypernatremia ($Na^+ > 145$ mEq/L)	Dehydration, diabetes insipidus (hyposecretion of ADH), administration of intravenous (IV) saline	Cell shrinkage, resulting in neurologic impairment; may result in excess fluid causing high blood pressure or edema	Confusion, coma, paralysis of breathing muscles, death
Hyponatremia ($Na^+ < 135$ mEq/L)	Excessive water intake, hypersecretion of antidiuretic hormone (ADH), diuretic abuse, severe diarrhea, burns, hyposecretion of aldosterone, excessive sweating	Cell swelling and decrease in blood volume and blood pressure	Nausea, lethargy, confusion, headache, muscle cramps, seizures, coma, death
Hyperkalemia ($K^+ > 5.0$ mEq/L)	Aldosterone hyposecretion, renal failure, acidosis, decreased insulin, extensive cellular trauma from a crushing injury or burn, transfusion of outdated blood, hemolytic anemia	A fast rise in K^+ results in K^+ diffusing into cells, altering the resting membrane potential; interferes with an action potential A slow rise in K^+ inactivates Na^+ channels; action potentials impaired, with muscles and nerves being less excitable	Nausea, vomiting, diarrhea, skeletal muscle weakness, tingling of skin, numbness of hands or feet, and irregular heartbeat that can lead to cardiac arrest[1] Can be asymptomatic, or an individual may have nausea, fatigue, muscle weakness
Hypokalemia ($K^+ < 3.5$ mEq/L)	Diuretic abuse, aldosterone hypersecretion, chronic vomiting, diarrhea, excessive laxative or enema use, heavy sweating, alkalosis, increased insulin, or formation of new tissue since K^+ is the predominant intracellular fluid (ICF) cation	Cells become hyperpolarized, interfering with neuron and muscle function	Nausea, vomiting; nervous and muscle tissue are less excitable, resulting in numbness, muscle weakness, decreased tone of smooth muscle, flaccid paralysis; decreased and irregular heart rate that may lead to cardiac arrest; muscle weakness can be severe enough to cause paralysis of diaphragm, leading to respiratory arrest
Hyperchloremia ($Cl^- > 107$ mEq/L)	Excess Cl^- in diet, intravenous (IV) solution containing NaCl, diarrhea, hyperaldosteronism, hyperparathyroidism, kidney disease; usually associated with metabolic acidosis	Decreased nerve excitability; causes changes in concentration of other ions	May be asymptomatic or the individual may have irregular breathing, weakness, and intense thirst; symptoms generally arise from other conditions associated with hyperchloremia
Hypochloremia ($Cl^- < 97$ mEq/L)	Heavy sweating, vomiting, gastrointestinal (GI) suction, kidney disease, metabolic alkalosis	Increased nerve excitability; causes changes in concentration of other ions	Many individuals are asymptomatic, but may experience tetany, hyperactive reflexes, muscle cramps; if severe—arrhythmias, seizures, coma, or respiratory arrest
Hypercalcemia ($Ca^{2+} > 5.2$ mEq/L)	Hyperparathyroidism, hypothyroidism (decreased calcitonin), bone loss from cancer, immobilization, excessive intake of vitamin D or calcium antacids, renal failure	Interferes with normal muscle and nerve function and causes underexcitability of muscles and nerves	May be asymptomatic; muscle weakness, fatigue, depression, confusion, loss of appetite, nausea, vomiting, constipation, and abnormal heart rhythms; severe calcification of soft tissue
Hypocalcemia ($Ca^{2+} < 4.5$ mEq/L)	Vitamin D deficiency, diarrhea, pregnancy, lactation; less calcium released from bone due to hypoparathyroidism, or hyperthyroidism (increased calcitonin)	Overexcitability of muscles and nerves due to hypocalcemia	Numbness, tingling, muscle spasms, increased heart rate; skeletal muscle also more excitable and can go into tetany, causing laryngospasms and suffocation
Hyperphosphatemia ($PO_4^{3-} > 2.9$ mEq/L)	Kidney impairment; increased dietary intake of supplements; laxatives or enemas; respiratory acidosis, cellular damage	Precipitation of Ca^{2+}, resulting in hypocalcemia	Generally asymptomatic by itself; however, may lead to hypocalcemia as PO_4^{3-} binds with Ca^{2+}; symptoms affect muscles, nerves, and bone calcification
Hypophosphatemia ($PO_4^{3-} < 1.8$ mEq/L)	Insufficient PO_4^{3-} intake; hyperparathyroidism; respiratory alkalosis	Many effects due to decreased production of ATP	Weakness and dysfunction of nervous system and both skeletal and cardiac muscle
Hypermagnesemia ($Mg^{2+} > 2.1$ mEq/L)	Kidney impairment, high intake of Mg^{2+}, such as in antacids or enemas	Changes in neuromuscular, cardiovascular, and central nervous system	Depressed neuromuscular activity, hypotension, cardiac arrest, weakness, lethargy, and respiratory depression
Hypomagnesemia ($Mg^{2+} < 1.4$ mEq/L)	Impaired absorption from the GI tract; increased loss in kidneys, or redistribution of Mg^{2+}; chronic alcoholism	Changes in neuromuscular, cardiovascular, and central nervous system	Muscle twitches, tremors, hyperactive reflexes, mental confusion and depression

1. Lethal injections for euthanizing animals and for capital punishment include high doses of K^+, causing cardiac arrest.

WHAT DID YOU LEARN?

10 What is the net direction of K^+ movement in response to a decrease in pH? Explain.

25.4 Hormonal Regulation

Four hormones play a major role in homeostatic regulation of both fluid and electrolytes: angiotensin II, antidiuretic hormone, aldosterone, and atrial natriuretic peptide. We look closely at the details of regulatory mechanisms for each hormone, including the stimulus for its release and its subsequent effects on numerous variables, such as fluid intake, fluid output, blood volume, blood pressure, and blood osmolarity.

Before reading this section, recall that an increase in fluid intake increases blood volume and systemic blood pressure, and may decrease blood osmolarity if more water that solutes are taken in. The reverse occurs with a decrease in fluid intake.

25.4a Angiotensin II

LEARNING OBJECTIVES

1. Explain the means by which angiotensin II formation can be triggered.
2. List the four primary effects of angiotensin II.

Angiotensin II is an oligopeptide hormone that is unique among the four hormones that affect fluid balance because (1) it has two significantly different means of stimulation for its formation, and (2) when produced, it stimulates the most diverse effects (**figure 25.8**).

Figure 25.8 Renin-Angiotensin System. Angiotensin II production is initiated when renin enzyme is released into the blood from the kidney in response to decreased blood pressure. The effect of angiotensin II is to increase peripheral resistance, and increase blood volume and blood pressure to within normal homeostatic limits. APR

We first described angiotensin II as a potent vasoconstrictor that helps regulate blood pressure (see section 20.5b). Recall that angiotensinogen is an inactive hormone synthesized and released continuously from the liver. Its activation, which occurs within the blood, is initiated by the enzyme renin. Renin is released from the juxtaglomerular (JG) apparatus of the kidneys in response to either (1) low blood pressure (as detected by decreased stretch of baroreceptors within granular cells, or by decreased NaCl detected by chemoreceptors within macula densa cells; see section 24.3c); or (2) stimulation by the sympathetic division. The sequential action of renin and angiotensin converting enzyme (ACE) cause the formation of angiotensin II (the active form of the hormone).

Angiotensin II has a number of effectors (target organs), and it initiates the following changes when it binds to these structures:

- **Blood vessels.** Stimulates vasoconstriction of systemic blood vessels to increase total peripheral resistance (see section 20.5b), which increases systemic blood pressure.
- **Kidneys.** Decreases urine output from the kidneys as a result of decreased glomerular filtration rate (GFR) in the nephrons by stimulating vasoconstriction of afferent arterioles and contraction of the mesangial cells within the glomerulus (see section 24.5c). This decreases urine output and helps to maintain systemic blood volume, and thus blood pressure.
- **Thirst center.** Stimulates the thirst center in the hypothalamus. If fluid intake occurs, this increases blood volume, which increases systemic blood pressure.
- **Hypothalamus and adrenal cortex.** Stimulates both the hypothalamus to activate the posterior pituitary to release ADH and adrenal cortex to release aldosterone (both described shortly).

The formation and action of angiotensin II can be summarized as follows: It is synthesized either when blood pressure is low or the sympathetic division is activated. It causes an increase in resistance, decrease in fluid output (which helps to maintain blood volume and blood pressure), and an increase in blood volume (if fluid intake occurs). Consequently, blood pressure increases. Increasing blood pressure is aided by the release of both ADH and aldosterone. As blood pressure returns to within normal homeostatic levels, both renin release and angiotensin II synthesis are decreased by negative feedback.

 WHAT DID YOU LEARN?

11 How does angiotensin II alter fluid output and potentially alter fluid intake?

25.4b Antidiuretic Hormone (ADH)

LEARNING OBJECTIVES

3. Explain how release of antidiuretic hormone (ADH) occurs from the posterior pituitary.

4. Describe the three actions of antidiuretic hormone.

Antidiuretic hormone (ADH) (also called *vasopressin*) is released from the posterior pituitary in response to nerve signals from the hypothalamus (figure 25.9). ADH is an oligopeptide that is synthesized by the hypothalamus and then transported to the posterior pituitary, where it is stored and released (see section 17.8b).

Three primary types of stimuli—low blood pressure, low blood volume, or an increase in blood osmolarity—signal the need to retain fluid:

- Angiotensin II binds with receptors of cells of the hypothalamus, having been released in response to low blood pressure, as just described.
- Nerve stimulation from baroreceptors within the atria of the heart and aorta and carotid blood vessels stimulate the hypothalamus. A decrease in this nerve stimulation is initiated in response to decreased stretch of baroreceptors within the atria, aorta, and carotid; the decrease in stretch is caused by low blood volume in the vasculature (see section 20.5a). Please note that this decrease in sensory nerve input from the heart and blood vessels to the hypothalamus is critical under conditions of severe blood loss.

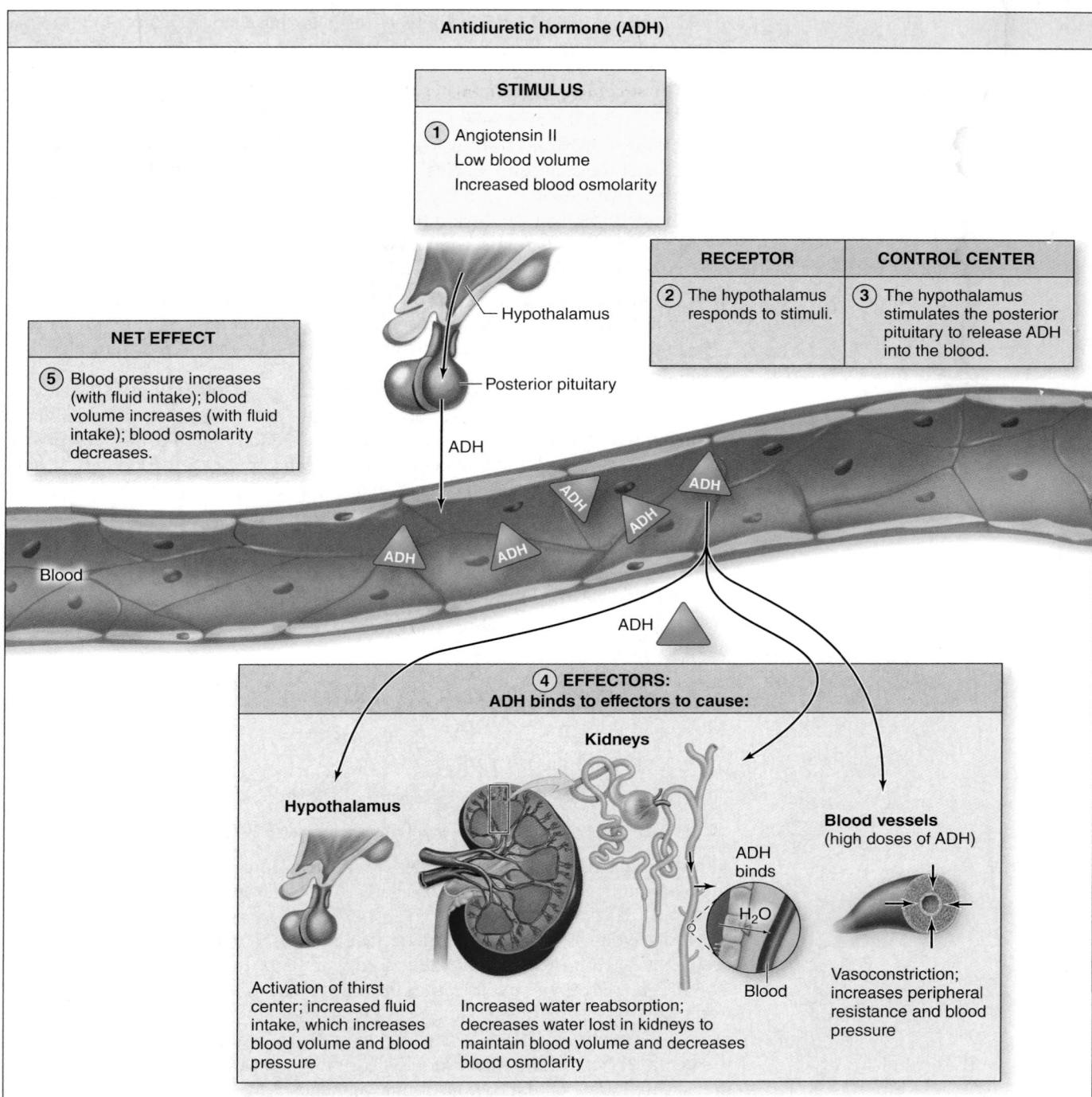

Figure 25.9 Actions and Effects of Antidiuretic Hormone. Antidiuretic hormone (ADH) is released in response to various stimuli, including angiotensin II, low blood volume, and high blood osmolarity. The effect of ADH on target organs is to raise blood volume and blood pressure, and decrease blood osmolarity to within normal homeostatic limits.

- Chemoreceptors within the hypothalamus detect an increase in blood osmolarity as blood is transported through the capillaries of the hypothalamus. Increased blood osmolarity is the primary stimulus for release of ADH.

In response to any of these stimuli, the hypothalamus increases release of ADH from the posterior pituitary: The larger the change in these stimuli, the greater the amount of ADH released.

ADH travels in the blood and initiates the following changes when it binds to these various effectors:

- **Thirst center.** ADH stimulates the thirst center in the hypothalamus. If fluid intake occurs, blood volume and blood pressure increase, and blood osmolarity decreases.

- **Kidneys.** ADH increases water reabsorption in the kidneys. ADH binds to principal cells of the collecting tubules and ducts, stimulating these cells to increase the number of aquaporins in the tubular membrane. Additional water is reabsorbed through these aquaporins in response to the osmotic gradient of the interstitial fluid (as described in section 24.6d). This helps to both maintain blood volume by decreasing fluid loss in urine and decrease blood osmolarity.

- **Blood vessels.** High doses of ADH cause vasoconstriction of systemic blood vessels, which increases peripheral resistance. This action is the reason that ADH is also referred to as vasopressin. Systemic blood pressure increases as a result.

The release and action of ADH can be summarized as follows: ADH is released under conditions of low blood pressure (action of angiotensin II), low blood volume (detected by stretch receptors in the heart and blood vessels), and high blood osmolarity (dehydration) to stimulate both fluid intake and water reabsorption in the kidneys. If fluid intake occurs, then blood pressure increases, blood osmolarity is further decreased, and blood volume increases. As the stimuli return to within normal homeostatic levels, ADH release is decreased through negative feedback.

 WHAT DID YOU LEARN?

12 How does the homeostatic system involving ADH function? Include how it is released and its actions.

25.4c Aldosterone

 LEARNING OBJECTIVES

5. List three conditions that lead to aldosterone release.

6. Describe the changes that occur in response to binding of aldosterone by kidney cells.

Aldosterone (ALDO) is normally released from the adrenal cortex in response to angiotensin II hormone, decreased blood plasma Na^+ levels, or most importantly, increased blood plasma K^+ levels (**figure 25.10**).

Aldosterone is a steroid hormone that is transported within the blood plasma and eventually binds to receptors within principal cells of the kidney, as described in section 24.6d. Its binding to these cells causes increased reabsorption and retention of both Na^+ and water, and increased secretion and then excretion of K^+. Aldosterone increases the number of Na^+/K^+ pumps and Na^+ channels, so more Na^+ is reabsorbed from the filtrate back into the blood. Water naturally follows the Na^+ movement by osmosis. Fluid retention results in decreased urine output. Because equal amounts of Na^+ and water are reabsorbed, blood osmolarity remains constant.

Note that K^+ excretion is normally increased except under conditions of low pH. In acidic conditions, as Na^+ and water are reabsorbed from the tubule into the blood, H^+ (instead of K^+) is secreted from the blood into the tubule. This loss of excess H^+ assists in returning blood pH to within normal homeostatic limits.

In summary, low blood pressure and changes in Na^+ and K^+ blood plasma levels cause aldosterone release. Blood volume and blood pressure are maintained through the reabsorption of both Na^+ and water in the kidneys, with no change to osmolarity. K^+ secretion is increased (unless there is an increase in H^+). As blood volume, blood pressure, and both Na^+ and K^+ blood plasma levels return to normal ranges, aldosterone release is decreased. Thus, as with angiotensin II and ADH, aldosterone release and its effects are regulated by negative feedback.

 WHAT DID YOU LEARN?

13 How does aldosterone influence the contents and volume of fluid output?

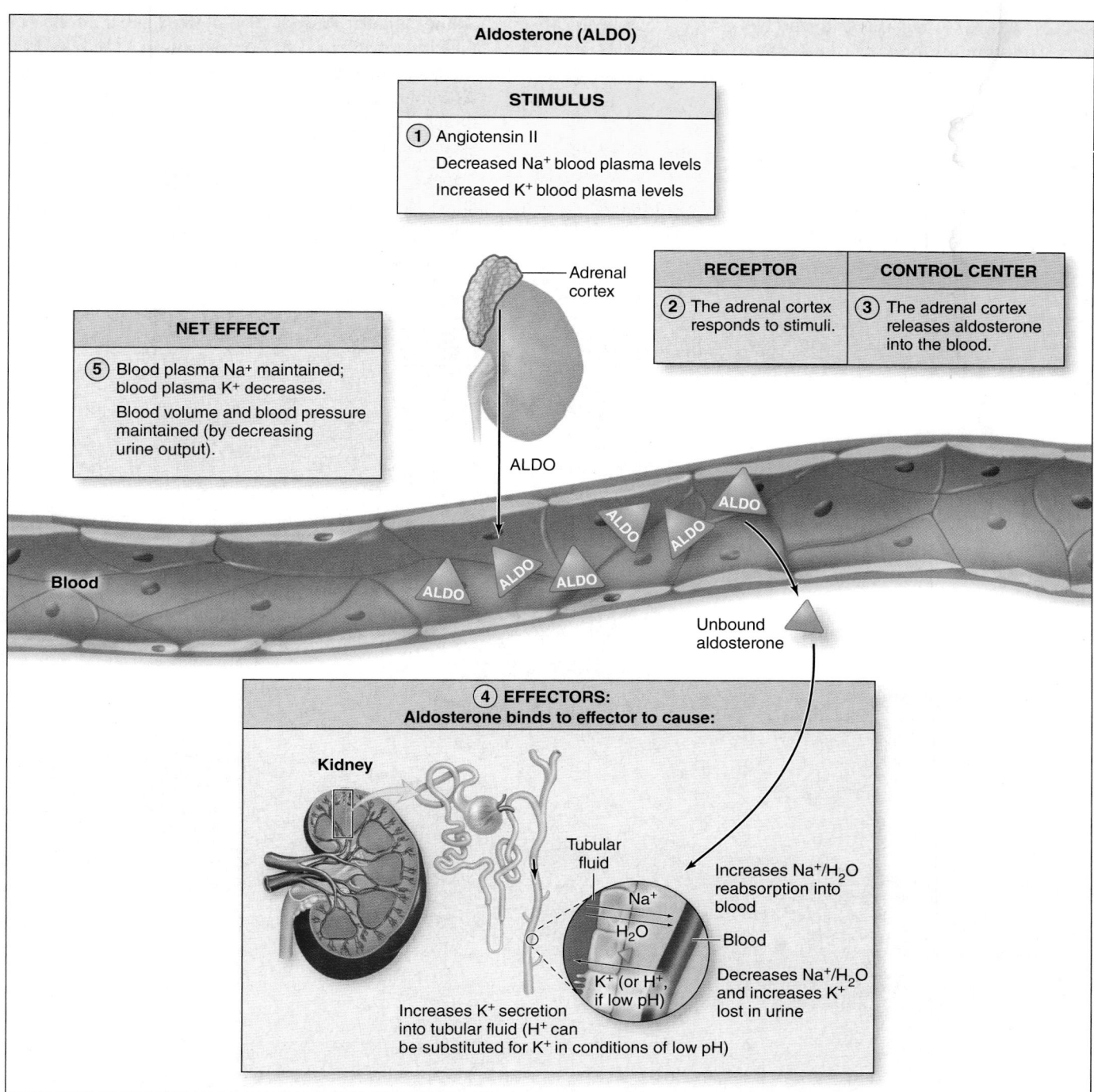

Aldosterone (ALDO)

STIMULUS

① Angiotensin II

Decreased Na⁺ blood plasma levels

Increased K⁺ blood plasma levels

Adrenal cortex

RECEPTOR	**CONTROL CENTER**
② The adrenal cortex responds to stimuli.	③ The adrenal cortex releases aldosterone into the blood.

NET EFFECT

⑤ Blood plasma Na⁺ maintained; blood plasma K⁺ decreases.

Blood volume and blood pressure maintained (by decreasing urine output).

ALDO

ALDO

Blood

Unbound aldosterone

④ **EFFECTORS:**
Aldosterone binds to effector to cause:

Kidney

Tubular fluid

Na⁺

H₂O

Increases Na⁺/H₂O reabsorption into blood

Blood

K⁺ (or H⁺, if low pH)

Increases K⁺ secretion into tubular fluid (H⁺ can be substituted for K⁺ in conditions of low pH)

Decreases Na⁺/H₂O and increases K⁺ lost in urine

Figure 25.10 Actions and Effects of Aldosterone. Aldosterone is released from the adrenal cortex in response to various stimuli, including angiotensin II, decreased blood plasma levels of Na⁺, or increased blood plasma levels of K⁺. The effect of aldosterone is to decrease urine output to maintain blood volume, and alter blood plasma concentration of Na⁺ and K⁺ to within normal homeostatic limits.

25.4d Atrial Natriuretic Peptide (ANP)

✔ LEARNING OBJECTIVES

7. Describe the stimulus for the release of atrial natriuretic peptide (ANP) and its three actions.

8. Explain the ways in which the effects of atrial natriuretic peptide differ from the effects of ADH, aldosterone, and angiotensin II.

Atrial natriuretic (nā′trē-yū-ret′ik; *natrium* = sodium, *uresis* = urination) **peptide (ANP)** is a polypeptide hormone that opposes the actions of the three hormones just discussed

(figure 25.11). ANP is released into the blood from cells in the heart atria. The stimulus for its release is increased stretch of these chambers, which is an indication of both increased blood volume and blood pressure.

ANP decreases both blood volume and blood pressure by binding to these target organs and causing the following responses:

- **Blood vessels.** Dilates systemic blood vessels, resulting in decreased total peripheral resistance. Systemic blood pressure decreases as a result.

- **Kidneys.** Causes vasodilation of the afferent arterioles in the kidneys and relaxation of mesangial cells; both increase the glomerular filtration rate (see section 24.5c). Additionally, ANP inhibits Na^+ and water reabsorption by nephron tubules, resulting in additional loss of Na^+ and water (see section 24.6d). These changes increase urine output. Blood volume and systemic blood pressure decreases.

In addition, atrial natriuretic peptide inhibits the release of renin, the action of angiotensin II, and the release of ADH and aldosterone, thus preventing the actions of these hormones.

Figure 25.11 Actions and Effects of Atrial Natriuretic Peptide. Atrial natriuretic peptide (ANP) is released in response to increased stretch in atria as a consequence of high blood volume and high blood pressure. The effect of ANP is to decrease peripheral resistance and blood volume with a resultant decrease in blood pressure to within normal homeostatic limits.

CONCEPT CONNECTION

Blood pressure is one of the most fascinating and complex physiologic variables of the body. Blood pressure is similar to body temperature because it has a set point that is maintained through a variety of mechanisms. Three major variables influence blood pressure, as described in other chapters:

- Cardiac output (see section 19.9)
- Resistance within blood vessels (see section 20.4)
- Blood volume (see section 20.5b)

In this chapter, we have discussed and integrated how various hormones regulate both blood volume and resistance to alter blood pressure.

CONCEPT CONNECTION

Recall from section 2.8b that normal three-dimensional folding of protein is pH dependent. If pH changes occur, the protein may permanently unfold or denature. Under acidic conditions, H^+ binds to the protein; under alkaline conditions, H^+ is released from the protein. In either case, the weak intermolecular bonds that hold the shape of a protein are broken, and it loses its three-dimensional shape and ability to function. Because most enzymes are proteins, one of the most serious consequences of acid-base imbalance is decreased enzymatic activity in metabolic pathways. If severe enough, these disruptions can be fatal.

These four hormones that regulate fluid balance, blood volume, and blood pressure are summarized in appendix table B.7.

 WHAT DID YOU LEARN?

 14 How does ANP influence fluid output, blood volume, and systemic blood pressure?

25.5 Acid-Base Balance

Acid-base balance is also called *pH balance*. It requires the regulation of hydrogen ion (H^+) concentration in body fluids in order to maintain a slightly alkaline arterial blood pH that is between 7.35 and 7.45. The regulation of H^+ concentration is under the same constraints as other electrolytes; that is, the input must equal output. However, there are some unique considerations to acid-base regulation. Hydrogen ion concentration is altered by the input and output of both acids and bases, by the respiratory rate, and by chemical buffers. We describe here the details of each of the factors that influence acid-base balance.

25.5a Categories of Acid

 LEARNING OBJECTIVES

1. Distinguish between the two categories of acids in the body.
2. Name the two buffering systems that regulate each category.

You first encountered the concepts of acidity, alkalinity, and pH in section 2.5, and you've seen how maintaining a proper pH balance is critical to body functions. The pH of a solution was shown to be inversely related to H^+ concentration. Adding an acid increases the H^+ concentration, resulting in a lower pH; adding a base reduces the amount of H^+ in solution and results in a higher pH.

Two major categories of acid are present in the body; fixed acid and volatile acid. **Fixed acid** is also called *metabolic acid,* since it is produced from metabolic wastes (other than from carbon dioxide). Examples of fixed acids include lactic acid from anaerobic cellular respiration, phosphoric acid from nucleic acid metabolism, and ketoacids from metabolism of fat.

Volatile (vol′ă-til; to evaporate quickly) **acid** is carbonic acid produced when carbon dioxide combines with water, as shown

$$CO_2 + H_2O \longleftrightarrow H_2CO_3$$

This reaction occurs readily in the presence of the enzyme carbonic anhydrase; H_2CO_3 then dissociates into H^+ and HCO_3^-. The entire chemical reaction is as follows:

$$CO_2 + H_2O \longleftrightarrow H_2CO_3 \longleftrightarrow H^+ + HCO_3^-$$

The term "volatile acid" refers to the fact that carbonic acid is produced from a gas that is normally expired (or "evaporated"). Because CO_2 is readily converted to carbonic acid in the presence of carbonic anhydrase, CO_2 itself is often referred to as the volatile acid.

The level of each acid is regulated by two separate *physiologic* buffering systems:

- Fixed acid is regulated by the kidney through the reabsorption and elimination of HCO_3^- and H^+.
- Volatile acid is regulated by the respiratory system through the regulation of the respiratory rate.

We first consider the sources of fixed acids along with the regulation of acid-base balance by the kidney, and later we explore the regulation of volatile acids through the respiratory system.

 WHAT DID YOU LEARN?

15 What is meant by acid-base balance?

16 How are fixed acids distinguished from volatile acids?

25.5b The Kidneys and Regulation of Fixed Acids

LEARNING OBJECTIVES

3. List the various sources of fixed acid.
4. Describe how the kidneys counteract excess blood H^+.
5. Explain how the kidneys function with decreasing blood H^+.

Daily input of fixed acid and base varies, and the net effect can tend to either decrease or increase the body's pH. As a general rule, the daily processes that influence acid-base balance tend to increase blood H^+ concentration, thus decreasing blood's pH. Maintaining acid-base balance requires that the normal excretion processes eliminate the excess H^+. We examine these typical conditions looking first at input and then how pH is maintained.

Typical Conditions That Cause Blood H^+ Concentration to Increase

The input of acid into the blood, except that produced from CO_2, occurs from two major sources: nutrients absorbed by the gastrointestinal (GI) tract and body cells (**figure 25.12a**). Typically, more acid is absorbed from the GI tract because most individuals, at least in the United States, consume a diet rich in animal protein and wheat. These various ingested items contribute H^+ to the blood. Cells also contribute acid as waste products from metabolic processes. These products include lactic acid, phosphoric acid, and ketoacids. Acidic conditions may also result from the excessive loss of HCO_3^- (a weak base) as a consequence of diarrhea. (HCO_3^- is normally lost in the feces, but excess amounts can be lost when an individual has diarrhea.)

The additional H^+ must be eliminated to maintain acid-base balance. Recall from section 24.6d that kidney tubules respond to increased blood H^+ concentration, as follows:

- Reabsorb all filtered HCO_3^- along the length of the nephron tubule
- Synthesize and absorb new HCO_3^- while excreting H^+ into the filtrate through type A intercalated cells in the distal convoluted tubule and collecting tubules

Thus, under conditions when blood H^+ concentration is increasing, kidneys help to maintain a normal blood pH by both eliminating excess H^+ and synthesizing and reabsorbing HCO_3^-.

Less Typical Conditions That Cause Blood H^+ Concentration to Decrease

Although the general daily input of acid tends to decrease pH, some conditions tend to increase pH as a result of excess retention of base or loss of acid (figure 25.12b). Substances that increase blood pH also enter the blood from the GI tract. For example, this may occur if an individual regularly eats a vegetarian diet (that is rich in fruits and vegetables and low in animal protein), or regularly ingests antacids. These increase the absorption of alkaline substances into the blood, and blood H^+ concentration decreases. Alkaline conditions may also be caused by the abnormal loss of HCl as a result of vomiting.

When alkaline conditions are present, renal tubules responsd in the following way:

- Do not reabsorb all of the filtered HCO_3^- along the length of the nephron tubule
- Secrete HCO_3^- from the blood into the filtrate, while reabsorbing H^+ in exchange through type B intercalated cells

Some of the filtered HCO_3^- (which is not reabsorbed) and secreted HCO_3^- is lost in the urine, while H^+ is reabsorbed. Blood plasm H^+ concentration increases, and blood pH decreases, returning to normal.

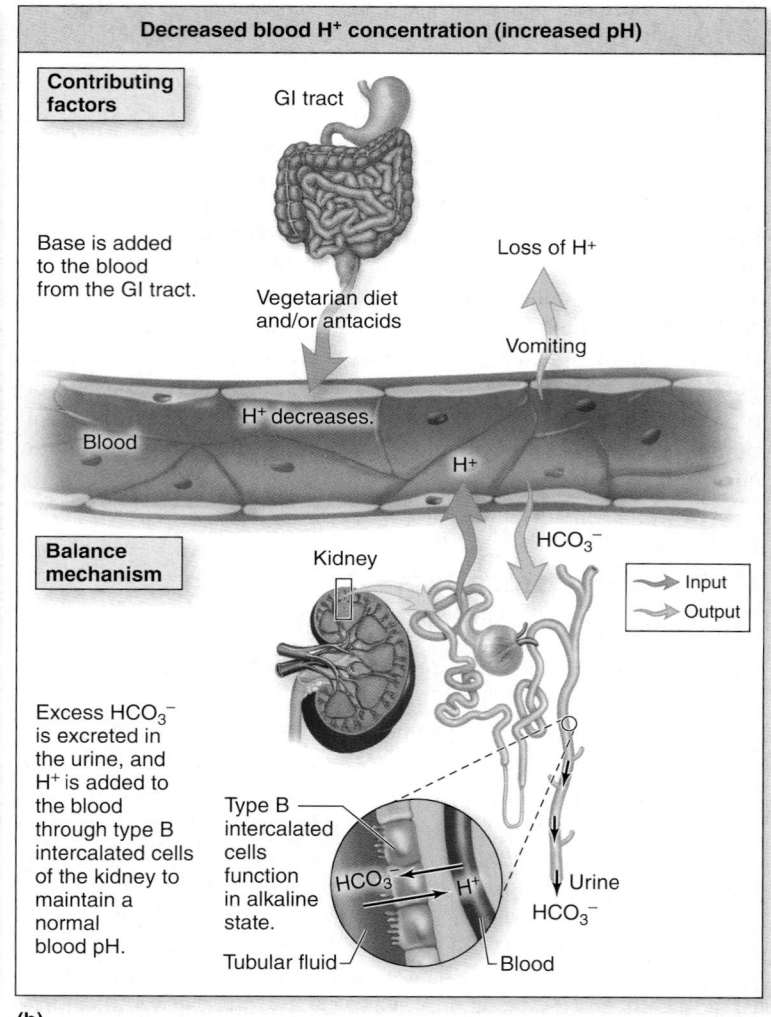

Figure 25.12 Altered Blood H^+ Concentration and Adjustments by the Kidneys. (*a*) Acid is normally added to the blood from the gastrointestinal (GI) tract as a result of diets rich in animal protein and wheat, and cellular metabolic wastes that include lactic acid from anaerobic respiration, phosphoric acid from nucleic acid metabolism, and ketoacids from fat metabolism. Excessive loss of HCO_3^- as a consequence of diarrhea further increases blood H^+ concentration. The kidney adjusts blood plasma H^+ concentration as it eliminates excess H^+ and synthesizes and reabsorbs HCO_3^- through action of type A cells. (*b*) A vegetarian diet, high intake of antacids, or the loss of acid from vomiting decreases blood H^+ concentration. The kidney adjusts blood H^+ concentration as it eliminates HCO_3^- and reabsorbs H^+ through action of type B cells. **AP|R**

CLINICAL VIEW

How Does Vomiting or Diarrhea Alter Blood H⁺ Concentration?

Although different regions of the gastrointestinal (GI) tract may contribute either acid or base to the blood, the overall effect of these secretions is generally neutral in pH. This balance changes, however, with vomiting and diarrhea.

Vomiting, or *emesis* (em′e′sis; *emeo* = to vomit), is the ejection of the contents of the stomach through the mouth that occurs by involuntary spasms of the stomach and forceful contraction of the abdominal muscles. The ejected material is referred to as *vomitus* and contains hydrochloric acid (HCl). The loss of HCl triggers cells of the epithelial lining of the stomach to replace the

lost H⁺. These cells are similar to the type A intercalated cells of the kidney; they excrete H⁺ into the lumen of the stomach and simultaneously transport HCO_3^- into the blood. The addition of HCO_3^- to the blood increases blood pH. If severe enough, it can result in metabolic alkalosis.

Diarrhea is an excessive amount of watery stool. Severe cases of diarrhea are potentially life-threatening because of the excessive loss of HCO_3^- in the feces. The HCO_3^- loss triggers epithelial lining cells of the intestine to replace the lost HCO_3^-. These cells are similar to the type B intercalated cells of the kidney, and they both excrete HCO_3^- into the lumen of the intestine and simultaneously transport H⁺ into the blood. Consequently, blood pH decreases. Severe cases can result in metabolic acidosis.

Metabolic alkalosis and acidosis are described in later sections.

The kidneys therefore act as a physiologic buffering system to eliminate either excess acid or base from the body. The process is relatively slow, taking from several hours to days; however, this is the only way to eliminate fixed acid or base, and it provides the most powerful means of maintaining blood H⁺ concentration and preventing pH changes.

💡 WHAT DID YOU LEARN?

17 How do the kidneys regulate fixed acids to help maintain blood pH in response to increased blood H⁺ concentration?

25.5c Respiration and Regulation of Volatile Acid

✅ LEARNING OBJECTIVE

6. Explain the relationship between breathing rate and blood pH.

Like the kidneys, the respiratory system serves as a physiologic buffering system to maintain acid-base balance, but does so by regulating the level of the volatile carbonic acid (H_2CO_3).

The respiratory system normally eliminates CO_2 from the lungs at rates that are equivalent to the production of CO_2. Recall that chemoreceptors detect changes in H⁺, CO_2, and O_2 and relay to the respiratory center to alter breathing rate, and the most significant variable is changes in CO_2 (section 23.5c). Blood levels of CO_2 are normally maintained such that the partial pressure of CO_2 (P_{CO_2}) is between 35 and 45 mm Hg. Given that H_2CO_3 production is dependent upon CO_2 levels:

$$CO_2 + H_2O \longleftrightarrow H_2CO_3 \longleftrightarrow H^+ + HCO_3^-$$

the respiratory system also maintains the volatile acid H_2CO_3 within a normal homeostatic range (H_2CO_3 = 3 micromoles per deciliter [μmol/dL]). Consequently, H_2CO_3 does not usually have daily fluctuations that affect acid-base balance.

An abnormal increase or decrease in the respiratory rate, however, that occurs independently of changes in the P_{CO_2} may affect acid-base balance. The following changes occur within several minutes **(figure 25.13)**:

- **Increasing the respiratory rate** causes elevated levels of CO_2 to be expired, resulting in decreasing blood CO_2 concentration

---

Abnormal increases in respiratory rate	Abnormal decreases in respiratory rate

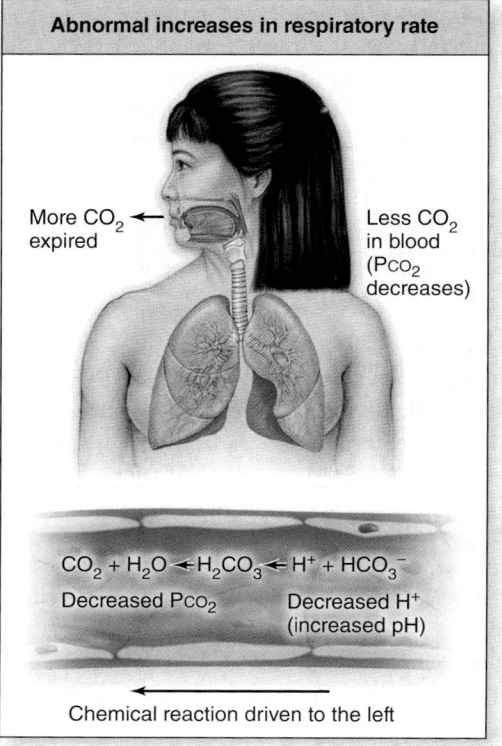

More CO_2 expired ←   Less CO_2 in blood (P_{CO_2} decreases)

$CO_2 + H_2O \leftarrow H_2CO_3 \leftarrow H^+ + HCO_3^-$

Decreased P_{CO_2} Decreased H⁺ (increased pH)

← Chemical reaction driven to the left

(a)

Less CO_2 expired ←   More CO_2 in blood (P_{CO_2} increases)

$CO_2 + H_2O \rightarrow H_2CO_3 \rightarrow H^+ + HCO_3^-$

Increased P_{CO_2} Increased H⁺ (decreased pH)

Chemical reaction driven to the right →

(b)

Figure 25.13 Respiration Rate and Blood pH. The respiratory system normally eliminates CO_2 at the same rate that cells produce it; thus, blood P_{CO_2} of 35–45 mm Hg is maintained under normal conditions. (*a*) An abnormal increase in respiratory rate decreases blood P_{CO_2}, driving the chemical reaction to the left. Subsequently, blood H⁺ concentration decreases, increasing blood pH. (*b*) An abnormal decrease in respiratory rate increases blood P_{CO_2}, driving the chemical reaction to the right. Subsequently blood H⁺ concentration increases, decreasing blood pH.

CONCEPT CONNECTION

The respiratory center receives sensory nerve signals from both central and peripheral chemoreceptors (see section 23.5c). These chemoreceptors are stimulated by increased H^+, and they initiate sensory input to the medullary respiratory center. Respiration rate and depth are increased to rid the body of more CO_2. Conversely, a decrease in H^+ reduces stimulation of chemoreceptors, causing a reduction in breathing rate and depth to retain more CO_2. Under normal conditions, adjustments in the respiratory rate maintain the partial pressure of carbon dioxide (P_{CO_2}) within a range of 35 to 45 mm Hg.

(blood P_{CO_2} decreases). The decreased level of blood CO_2 drives the chemical reaction (as shown in the equation) to the left (figure 25.13a). Blood H^+ concentration decreases, and blood pH goes up.

- **Decreasing the respiratory rate** results in an increase in the amount of CO_2 retained, thus elevating blood CO_2 (blood P_{CO_2} increases). The increased levels of blood CO_2 drive the equation to the right (figure 25.13b). Blood H^+ concentration increases, and blood pH goes down.

WHAT DID YOU LEARN?

18 Describe the change (increase, decrease, or stays the same) for each of the following variables if an individual hyperventilates (breathes at a higher than normal breathing rate): (a) blood CO_2, (b) blood H^+ concentration, and (c) blood pH.

25.5d Chemical Buffers

LEARNING OBJECTIVES

7. Describe the components of the protein buffering system.

8. Explain the reactions of the phosphate buffering system.

9. Discuss how the bicarbonate buffering system maintains acid-base balance in the ECF.

The physiologic buffering systems previously described are extremely effective in helping to maintain body fluid pH. The physiologic processes within the kidneys occur over several hours to several days, while those of the respiratory system require only a few minutes to respond.

In contrast, **chemical buffering systems** act quickly (and temporarily) to help prevent pH changes that would occur in response to the addition of acid or base, such as happens shortly after a meal, or as a result of abnormal loss of acid or base.

Chemical buffering systems are composed of one or two types of molecules that can bind and release H^+ within a fraction of a second to prevent large pH changes. The molecule, or molecules, of chemical buffering systems are composed of both a weak base that can bind

LEARNING STRATEGY

You can think of chemical buffering systems as "sponges" for H^+. When pH decreases, the chemical buffering system soaks up H^+, and when pH increases, the chemical buffering system releases H^+. In this way, the H^+ concentration in solution may be kept within normal range, helping to prevent pH changes.

excess H^+ and a weak acid that can release H^+. Remember that chemical buffers cause both temporary and limited adjustments until the body can eliminate the excess acid or base through physiologic buffering systems (namely, the kidneys or the respiratory system).

The three most important chemical buffering systems include the following:

- The protein buffering system within both cells and the blood
- The phosphate (PO_4^{3-}) buffering system within cells
- The bicarbonate (HCO_3^-) buffering system within the ECF, particularly the blood

Although similar in the mechanism that buffers both acid and base, the three chemical buffering systems differ in their locations and in the molecules that compose them.

Protein Buffering System

The **protein buffering system** is a chemical buffering system that is composed of proteins within cells and in blood plasma. It accounts for about three-quarters of the chemical buffering in body fluids. The **amine group (—NH₂)** of amino acids acts as a weak base to buffer acid, while the **carboxylic acid (—COOH)** of amino acids acts as a weak acid to buffer base (see section 2.8 for a review of protein structure). The chemical change to each group is shown here:

$$\underset{\text{(weak base)}}{-NH_2} + \underset{\text{(strong acid)}}{H^+} \longrightarrow \underset{\text{(weak acid)}}{NH_3^+} \qquad (1)$$

$$\underset{\text{(weak acid)}}{-COOH} + \underset{\text{(strong base)}}{OH^-} \longrightarrow \underset{\text{(weak base)}}{COO^-} + H_2O \quad (2)$$

With the addition of strong acid, shown in equation (1), the weak base (—NH₂) of the protein buffering system binds the H^+ that was added to the solution. This weak base becomes a weak acid (NH_3^+) as a result. The net effect is elimination of a strong acid (H^+) and the production of a weak acid (NH_3^+). In comparison, the addition of strong base, as in equation (2), causes the weak acid (—COOH) of the protein buffering system to release H^+, and as it does so, it becomes a weak base (COO^-). The net effect is removal of a strong base (OH^-) and the production of a weak base (COO^-).

Proteins are components within both cells and blood, and their buffering systems help minimize pH changes throughout the body. The most notable exception is in the cerebrospinal fluid (CSF), where there are no proteins. Proteins that help buffer pH changes include both intracellular proteins, plasma proteins, and hemoglobin in erythrocytes.

CONCEPT CONNECTION

The addition of either a strong acid or strong base causes greater changes in pH than the addition of a weak acid or a weak base.

A **strong acid**, such as HCl, dissociates completely in solution, whereas a **weak acid**, such as H_2CO_3, only partially dissociates in solution. As a result, a strong acid releases more H^+ into solution, causing greater decreases in pH.

In a similar way, a **strong base**, such as NaOH, dissociates completely in solution, and a **weak base**, such as $NaHCO_3$, only partially dissociates. As a result, a strong base binds more H^+ from the solution, resulting in larger increases in pH.

By independently binding and releasing H^+, buffers help limit pH changes by converting strong acids to weak acids and strong bases to weak bases.

Phosphate Buffering System

The **phosphate buffering system** is found in intracellular fluid (ICF). It is especially effective in buffering metabolic acid produced by cells because phosphate (PO_4^{3-}) is the most common anion within cells. The phosphate buffering system is also composed of both a weak base and a weak acid. Here **hydrogen phosphate (HPO_4^{2-})** is the weak base and **dihydrogen phosphate ($H_2PO_4^-$)** is the weak acid. The chemical change to HPO_4^{2-} and $H_2PO_4^-$ is shown here:

$$\underset{\text{(weak base)}}{HPO_4^{2-}} + \underset{\text{(strong acid)}}{H^+} \longrightarrow \underset{\text{(weak acid)}}{H_2PO_4^-} \qquad (3)$$

$$\underset{\text{(weak acid)}}{H_2PO_4^-} + \underset{\text{(strong base)}}{OH^-} \longrightarrow \underset{\text{(weak base)}}{HPO_4^{2-}} + H_2O \quad (4)$$

The addition of acid, shown in equation (3), is buffered by the weak base (HPO_4^{2-}) that binds the H^+ to become a weak acid ($H_2PO_4^-$). In contrast, the addition of base, as in equation (4), causes the weak acid $H_2PO_4^-$ to release H^+. As it does so, it becomes the weak base HPO_4^{2-}, and water is formed. As with the protein buffering system, the net result is either a strong acid buffered to produce a weak acid or a strong base buffered to produce a weak base.

Bicarbonate Buffer System

The **bicarbonate buffering system** in the blood is the most important buffering system in the ECF. Bicarbonate ion and carbonic acid are the key components of this buffering system. **Bicarbonate (HCO_3^-)** serves as a weak base, while **carbonic acid (H_2CO_3)** acts as a weak acid. The chemical change to HCO_3^- and H_2CO_3 is shown here:

$$\underset{\text{(weak base)}}{HCO_3^-} + \underset{\text{(strong acid)}}{H^+} \longrightarrow \underset{\text{(weak acid)}}{H_2CO_3} \qquad (5)$$

$$\underset{\text{(weak acid)}}{H_2CO_3} + \underset{\text{(strong base)}}{OH^-} \longrightarrow \underset{\text{(weak base)}}{HCO_3^-} + H_2O \quad (6)$$

The addition of acid is buffered in equation (5) by the weak base HCO_3^-. Bicarbonate binds the excess H^+ and becomes the weak acid H_2CO_3. In comparison, with the addition of base as in equation (6), the weak acid H_2CO_3 releases H^+. As it does so, it becomes a weak base (HCO_3^-), and water is formed. The net result again is that a strong acid is buffered to produce a weak acid, or a strong base is buffered to produce a weak base.

In summary, the phosphate buffering system is important in buffering against pH changes within cells, whereas the bicarbonate buffering system buffers against pH changes in the blood. Proteins buffer in both cells (intracellular proteins) and within the blood plasma (plasma proteins, hemoglobin).

The moderation of pH changes by chemical buffers usually allows time for the kidneys to alter the excretion of H^+ or HCO_3^-, or

INTEGRATE

CONCEPT CONNECTION

Recall that following systemic gas exchange, CO_2 enters erythrocytes and binds to water, and then it dissociates from the water to produce H^+ and HCO_3^-. The HCO_3^- shifts out of the erythrocyte to be carried in the blood plasma, whereas the H^+ attaches to hemoglobin protein within the erythrocyte (see section 23.7b). This process then reverses when the blood reaches the lungs for alveolar gas exchange. During this process, hemoglobin acts as a buffer (first binding and then releasing H^+) to help maintain the concentration of free H^+ within both erythrocytes and blood plasma.

for the respiratory system to adjust the expiration of CO_2. All the chemical buffering systems, however, are limited in the amount of acid or base that they can buffer. If the buffering capacity is exceeded, then pH levels may decrease or increase beyond normal limits. These changes in pH are referred to as acid-base disturbances and are described in the next section.

The body's buffering systems—both the chemical buffering systems and physiologic buffering systems—that are involved in maintaining acid-base balance are integrated in **figure 25.14**.

WHAT DID YOU LEARN?

19 What are the three chemical buffering systems, and where do they function?

20 What is the general amount of time required to maintain pH by (a) the chemical buffering systems, (b) the respiratory system, and (c) the kidneys?

25.6 Disturbances to Acid-Base Balance

Severe vomiting, diarrhea, diabetes, emphysema, pneumonia, brainstem trauma, renal failure, congestive heart failure, climbing to high altitude, and diuretic abuse all have something in common: All of these conditions can cause an acid-base disturbance. **Acidosis,** or *acidemia*, is an arterial blood pH reading below 7.35, whereas **alkalosis,** or *alkalemia*, is an arterial blood pH reading above 7.45.

Before describing the different types of acid-base disturbances, we begin by describing some relevant terminology, including acid-base disturbance, compensation, and acid-base imbalance.

25.6a Overview of Acid-Base Imbalances

LEARNING OBJECTIVE

1. Explain acid-base disturbance, compensation, and acid-base imbalance.

An **acid-base disturbance** occurs when the buffering capacity of chemical buffering systems is exceeded, and there is a transient or temporary change in blood H^+ concentration, resulting in a change in blood pH beyond the normal range of 7.35 to 7.45. In response to a transient acid-base disturbance, the physiologic buffering system of the kidneys, the respiratory system, or both together operate to offset the disturbance. The response of physiologic buffering systems to acid-base disturbances that results in the return of blood pH to normal is called **compensation.**

If these physiologic buffering systems are not effective in returning the pH to normal, then pH disturbance is referred to as **uncompensated** (or *partially uncompensated*). When an uncompensated, temporary pH disturbance results in a persistent pH change, it is referred to as an **acid-base imbalance.** An acid-base imbalance for any extended period of time is life-threatening. Without intervention, an acid-base imbalance continues to worsen, and if the pH reaches values below 7.0 or above 7.7, it is fatal within a few hours.

Four major types of acid-base disturbances are distinguished based on two criteria: whether the primary disturbance is respiratory or metabolic in nature; and whether the pH change is acidic or alkaline. The four categories are respiratory acidosis, respiratory alkalosis, metabolic acidosis, and metabolic alkalosis. We examine each of these in terms of the cause of the primary disturbance, and then we describe the compensation made by the physiologic buffering system that helps prevent an acid-base imbalance.

Figure 25.14 Maintaining Acid-Base Balance. Buffering systems help maintain normal body pH. (*a*) Chemical buffering systems are located within cells and the blood, and they function within seconds to correct imbalances. (*b*) Physiologic buffering systems include both the respiratory system, which buffers within minutes, and the kidneys, which buffer within hours to days.

(a) Chemical Buffering Systems

Chemical buffers help minimize pH changes by temporarily binding and releasing H^+ within seconds.

PHOSPHATE BUFFERING SYSTEM:
Buffers within cells

HPO_4^{2-} buffers acid to form $H_2PO_4^-$.
$H_2PO_4^-$ buffers base to form HPO_4^{2-}.

Cell

Works within seconds

→ Input
→ Output

PROTEIN BUFFERS:
Buffers within both cells and blood

—NH_2 groups buffer addition of acid to form NH_3^+. —$COOH$ groups buffer addition of base to form COO^-.

BICARBONATE BUFFERING SYSTEM:
Buffers in blood

HCO_3^- buffers the addition of acid to form H_2CO_3.
H_2CO_3 buffers the addition of base to form HCO_3^-.

CO_2
H^+
H^+
Blood
CO_2

$CO_2 + H_2O \rightarrow H_2CO_3$ → H^+ (binds with hemoglobin)
→ HCO_3^-

HCO_3^-

(b) Physiologic Buffering Systems

Physiologic buffers maintain pH by eliminating excess acid or base from the body; these processes may take minutes to days.

H^+ and HCO_3^-

RESPIRATORY SYSTEM

Increased respiratory rate:
• Decreases blood CO_2
• Decreases H^+, which increases blood pH

Decreased respiratory rate:
• Increases blood CO_2
• Increases H^+, which decreases blood pH

CO_2

Works within minutes

Works within hours or days

H^+ or HCO_3^-
Blood

Tubular fluid
HCO_3^-
H^+
Blood
Type A intercalated cell

Tubular fluid
HCO_3^-
H^+
Blood
Type B intercalated cell

KIDNEY

Type A intercalated cells:
• Eliminate excess H^+
• Synthesize and reabsorb HCO_3^-
• Blood pH increases

Type B intercalated cells:
• Reabsorb H^+
• Secrete HCO_3^-
• Blood pH decreases

21 How does a compensated acid-base imbalance differ from an uncompensated acid-base imbalance?

25.6b Respiratory-Induced Acid-Base Disturbances

LEARNING OBJECTIVES

2. Define respiratory acidosis, and identify some of the causes of this type of acid-base imbalance.

3. Explain why infants are more susceptible to respiratory acidosis.

4. Define respiratory alkalosis, and identify some of the causes of this type of acid-base imbalance.

Respiratory acid-base disturbances occur when changes in respiratory function result in either increased or decreased blood P_{CO_2} that is outside the normal range of 35 to 45 mm Hg, with the subsequent change in H_2CO_3 levels.

Respiratory Acidosis

The most common acid-base disturbance occurs because of impaired elimination of CO_2 by the respiratory system. **Respiratory acidosis** is defined as occurring when the P_{CO_2} in the arterial blood becomes elevated above 45 mm Hg. Causes include the following:

- Injury to the respiratory center, perhaps caused by trauma or by poliovirus infections
- Disorders of the nerves or muscles involved with breathing, such as the loss of muscle strength associated with muscular dystrophy
- Airway obstruction
- Decreased gas exchange due to reduced respiratory surface area or thickened width of the respiratory membrane (these two conditions are associated with emphysema or pulmonary edema, respectively)

Continued impairment results in the accumulation of CO_2 in the blood that ultimately causes an increase in blood H_2CO_3 and a subsequent increase in H^+ concentration.

Infants are more susceptible to respiratory acidosis because their smaller lungs and lower residual volume (see section 23.5f) do not eliminate CO_2 as effectively. CO_2 accumulates in the blood, with a subsequent increase in carbonic acid (H_2CO_3).

Respiratory Alkalosis

Respiratory alkalosis occurs when the P_{CO_2} decreases to levels below 35 mm Hg due to an increase in respiration. Faster breathing (hyperventilation) may occur in response to the following:

- Severe anxiety
- Any condition in which an individual is not receiving sufficient oxygen (e.g., as might occur when climbing to a high altitude where there is a decrease in the partial pressure of oxygen [P_{O_2}]; during congestive heart failure; as a result of severe anemia; or due to low blood pressure)
- Aspirin overdose (a condition that stimulates the respiratory center)

Continued elimination of CO_2 results in decreased levels of blood CO_2 that in turn cause a decrease in blood H_2CO_3 and lowered H^+ concentration.

 WHAT DID YOU LEARN?

22 How does hyperventilation bring about respiratory alkalosis?

25.6c Metabolic-Induced Acid-Base Disturbances

LEARNING OBJECTIVES

5. Explain how metabolic acid-base disturbances differ from respiratory acid-base disturbances.

6. Define both metabolic acidosis and metabolic alkalosis, and identify some of the causes of each type of acid-base imbalance.

Metabolic disturbances are reflected by blood plasma HCO_3^- concentration that is outside its normal range of 22–26 mEq/L. This condition may occur either from the loss or gain of H^+ (except for H_2CO_3 produced from CO_2), or the loss or gain of HCO_3^-. These disturbances involve physiologic processes other than respiratory function changes.

Metabolic Acidosis

The most common metabolic acid-base disturbance occurs as a result of a decrease in HCO_3^-. This decrease may result from an excessive loss of HCO_3^-, but more generally it occurs when there is an accumulation of fixed acid. The excess H^+ binds with HCO_3^- to form H_2CO_3; thus, HCO_3^- levels in the blood decrease. **Metabolic acidosis** occurs when arterial blood levels of HCO_3^- fall below 22 mEq/L. This condition is usually caused by unhealthy changes in physiologic processes that were described earlier in the chapter (see figure 25.12a). These include the following:

- Increased production of metabolic acids, such as ketoacidosis from diabetes mellitus, increased lactic acid from anaerobic respiration, or excessive production of acetic acid from excessive intake of alcohol
- Decreased elimination of acid due to renal dysfunction
- Increased elimination of HCO_3^- as a result of severe diarrhea

Infants are especially vulnerable to this condition also, because they produce larger amounts of acidic metabolic wastes due to a higher metabolic rate.

INTEGRATE

CLINICAL VIEW

Lactic Acidosis and Ketoacidosis

When insufficient oxygen is available (called *ischemia*), cells are forced to shift from aerobic to anaerobic cellular respiration (with increased production of lactic acid). This occurs during prolonged intense exercise or when the cardiovascular system is impaired, such as in congestive heart failure. Blood pH drops as a result. If substantial amounts of lactic acid are produced, acid-base balance is disturbed, resulting in the condition called **lactic acidosis.**

During conditions of insufficient cellular glucose uptake, cells are forced to shift from glucose metabolism to fat metabolism for their ATP production (ketoacids are a by-product). Individuals who have diabetes mellitus type 1 experience this condition because insufficient insulin is produced (see Clinical View: "Conditions Resulting in Abnormal Blood Glucose Levels" in chapter 17). Glucose is unable to enter most cells without insulin. This forces cells to use fat for ATP production. The greater the deficiency of insulin, the greater the degree of fat metabolism, and the larger the amount of ketoacids formed. If substantial amounts of ketoacids are produced, a disturbance in the acid-base balance may occur that is called **ketoacidosis.**

Ketoacidosis may also occur if blood glucose levels are too low, and the body cells must metabolize fat for ATP production. Ketoacidosis is one of the risks of very-low-carbohydrate diets (VLCDs) that are not medically monitored.

CLINICAL VIEW

Arterial Blood Gas (ABG) and Diagnosing Different Types of Acid-Base Disturbances

Measurements of **arterial blood gas (ABG)** are used to diagnose and monitor an acid-base disturbance and its compensation. These measurements include pH, Pa_{CO_2} (arterial P_{CO_2}), and HCO_3^-. Changes in these values can help formulate a diagnosis, differentiate between the four types of acid-base disturbances, determine whether compensation is occurring—and if so, whether it is complete or partial.

Normal Conditions

First, consider the ABG results if an individual is in pH balance (no disturbance or compensation):

- Blood pH is within the normal range of 7.35 to 7.45.
- Pa_{CO_2} is 35 to 45 mm Hg, which reflects a normal respiratory rate and elimination of CO_2. By maintaining Pa_{CO_2}, an H_2CO_3 concentration of approximately a value of 3 μmol/dL is also regulated.
- Blood HCO_3^- concentration is 22–26 mEq/L, reflecting the effectiveness of the kidney in retaining or excreting HCO_3^-.

When an individual is in acid-base balance, a normal ratio between H_2CO_3 concentration and HCO_3^- concentration of 1:20 exists. A "balance" of acid and base with a normal ratio of 1:20 can be represented with a scale.

Normal Values

pH = 7.35–7.45
Pa_{CO_2} = 35–45 mm Hg
H_2CO_3 = 3 μmol/dL
HCO_3^- = 22–26 mEq/L

Acid-Base Disturbances and Compensation

Now consider what occurs to both ABG values and the ratio of H_2CO_3 to HCO_3^- in each of the four types of acid-base disturbances and the resulting compensation. When compensation is complete, pH returns to normal, but altered blood levels of HCO_3^- and CO_2 are seen in the ABG. These changes and their compensation are visually represented with scales. Each primary disturbance and the accompanying compensation are presented in a separate box. Each box contains two figures; the left figure represents the primary disturbance and the right figure represents compensation.

Respiratory acidosis with renal compensation.

In respiratory acidosis, respiratory rate decreases and blood CO_2 increases. This drives the chemical equation to the right ($CO_2 + H_2O \longrightarrow H_2CO_3$), and H_2CO_3 increases. This increase in H_2CO_3 is represented with a "tipped" scale. The kidneys compensate with increased secretion of H^+ and increased reabsorption of HCO_3^-. The increase in blood HCO_3^- from renal compensation reestablishes acid-base balance. However, although blood pH is returned to normal and the ratio of H_2CO_3 to HCO_3^- is returned to 1:20, notice that blood levels of H_2CO_3 and HCO_3^- are both greater than normal.

Respiratory alkalosis with renal compensation.

In respiratory alkalosis, respiratory rate increases and blood CO_2 decreases. This drives the chemical equation to the left ($CO_2 + H_2O \longleftarrow H_2CO_3$), and H_2CO_3 decreases. Again, this decrease in H_2CO_3 is shown with a "tipped" scale. The kidneys compensate with increased secretion of HCO_3^- and increased reabsorption of H^+. The decrease in blood HCO_3^- from renal compensation reestablishes acid-base balance. However, although blood pH is returned to normal and the ratio of H_2CO_3 to HCO_3^- is returned to 1:20, both H_2CO_3 and HCO_3^- are lower than normal.

Metabolic acidosis with respiratory compensation.

In metabolic acidosis, blood H^+ increases, driving the chemical equation to the left ($CO_2 + H_2O \longleftarrow H_2CO_3 \longleftarrow H^+ + HCO_3^-$), and HCO_3^- decreases. The respiratory system compensates with an increased respiratory rate, and CO_2 (and H_2CO_3) decrease. The decrease in blood H_2CO_3 from respiratory compensation reestablishes acid-base balance. However, although blood pH is returned to normal and the ratio of H_2CO_3 to HCO_3^- is returned to 1:20, again notice that both H_2CO_3 and HCO_3^- are lower than normal.

Metabolic alkalosis with respiratory compensation.

In metabolic alkalosis, blood H^+ has decreased, driving the chemical equation to the right ($CO_2 + H_2O \longrightarrow H_2CO_3 \longrightarrow H^+ + HCO_3^-$), and HCO_3^- increases. The respiratory system compensates with a decreased respiratory rate, and CO_2 (and H_2CO_3) increase. The increase in blood H_2CO_3 from respiratory compensation reestablishes acid-base balance. However, although blood pH is returned to normal and the ratio of H_2CO_3 to HCO_3^- is returned to 1:20, again notice that both H_2CO_3 and HCO_3^- are greater than normal.

Notice that if compensation occurs, both respiratory acidosis and metabolic alkalosis have similar outcomes: an increase in H_2CO_3 and an increase in HCO_3^-. In a like manner, both respiratory alkalosis and metabolic acidosis have similar results if compensation occurs: a decrease in H_2CO_3 and a decrease in HCO_3^-. To differentiate between the pH imbalances that have similar lab results, you would need further information.

If compensation is not complete, you will be able to differentiate based on pH. For example, to distinguish respiratory acidosis from metabolic alkalosis, a low pH would occur if the primary disturbance was caused by respiratory acidosis, and a high pH would occur from metabolic alkalosis. It would also be possible to differentiate between these based on the diagnosis of the individual's condition. For example, you would most likely conclude that the pH imbalance was respiratory acidosis if the individual had emphysema, or that it was metabolic alkalosis if the person was taking diuretics to treat high blood pressure. Similar analysis could be used to differentiate respiratory alkalosis and metabolic acidosis.

Metabolic Alkalosis

Metabolic alkalosis is defined as arterial blood levels of HCO_3^- that exceed 26 mEq/L. A loss of H^+ or an increase in HCO_3^- can bring about this condition (see figure 25.12b). Causes include the following:

- Vomiting (the most common cause)
- Increased loss of acids by the kidneys with overuse of diuretics (medications that increase urine output)
- Increased alkaline input from consuming large amounts of antacid tablets

 WHAT DID YOU LEARN?

23 What is the primary cause of metabolic alkalosis?

25.6d Compensation

 LEARNING OBJECTIVE

7. Describe renal and respiratory compensation.

It is possible for both the kidneys and the respiratory system to make adjustments to compensate for changes in H^+ and HCO_3^- in an attempt to return blood pH to within its normal range. However, it is important to remember that both the initial disturbance *and* the system compensation are reflected in abnormal (low or high) concentrations of CO_2 and HCO_3^- in lab results that measure these variables. These changes in blood levels may be monitored with arterial blood gas (ABG) lab results (see Clinical View: "Arterial Blood Gas [ABG] and Diagnosing Different Types of Acid-Base Disturbances").

Renal Compensation

Renal compensation (physiologic adjustments of the kidney to changes in pH) occurs in response to elevated blood H^+ concentration due to a cause other than a renal dysfunction. We know that the normal physiologic activities of type A intercalated cells result in excretion of H^+ and reabsorption of HCO_3^- (see figure 25.12a). However, during renal compensation, this occurs to a greater degree than normal. Consequently, higher than normal levels of H^+ are excreted, and higher than normal amounts of HCO_3^- are synthesized and reabsorbed into the blood. Renal compensation results in elevated values for blood HCO_3^-. As expected, urine pH is lower than normal.

In comparison, renal compensation in response to a decrease in blood H^+ concentration involves the normal response of type B intercalated cells to excrete HCO_3^- and reabsorb H^+ (see figure 25.12b). During renal compensation, this activity occurs to a greater degree than normal; higher than normal levels of H^+ are reabsorbed into the blood, and higher amounts of HCO_3^- are excreted. Renal compensation results in lower than normal values for blood HCO_3^-. Urine pH in this case is higher than normal.

Renal compensation is generally effective in neutralizing acid-base disturbances that are not due to renal dysfunction, and in returning the pH back to normal. However, impaired renal function immediately places an individual at higher risk for an acid-base imbalance. Renal function decreases as we age, and because of this, the elderly are at greater risk for pH imbalances.

Respiratory Compensation

The respiratory system attempts to compensate for metabolic acidosis (e.g., a complication of uncontrolled diabetes mellitus). Respiratory rate increases as a result of increased H^+ concentration (see figure 25.13a). During respiratory compensation, higher than normal amounts of CO_2 are expired, as evidenced by a lower than normal blood P_{CO_2} value.

Changes in the respiratory rate also may compensate for metabolic alkalosis, such as occurs with vomiting. The normal response of decreasing respiratory rate in response to decreased blood H^+ concentration occurs during respiratory compensation (see figure 25.13b). However, during respiratory compensation, this occurs to a greater degree than normal, resulting in lower than normal amounts of CO_2 expired. The evidence is in the higher than normal blood CO_2 values that are measured.

Generally, respiratory compensation is less effective in addressing metabolic acid-base disturbances than renal compensation. The ability to decrease respiratory rate in response to metabolic alkalosis is limited by the development of hypoxia. As the respiratory rate decreases, P_{O_2} levels also decrease. When P_{O_2} levels decrease below critical values, the respiratory rate is stimulated to increase. This may prevent complete compensation for metabolic alkalosis.

Acid-base imbalances are summarized in **table 25.4**.

 WHAT DID YOU LEARN?

24 How does renal compensation affect blood plasma levels of HCO_3^-? How does respiratory compensation affect blood P_{CO_2}?

Table 25.4	Acid-Base Imbalances				
Variable	**Normal Values**	**Respiratory Acidosis**	**Respiratory Alkalosis**	**Metabolic Acidosis**	**Metabolic Alkalosis**
PRIMARY DISTURBANCE					
pH	7.35–7.45	< 7.35	> 7.45	< 7.35	> 7.45
P_{aCO_2}	35–45 mm Hg	**> 45 mm Hg (high)**	**< 35 mm Hg (low)**	Normal	Normal
HCO_3^-	22–26 mEq/L	Normal	Normal	**< 22 mEq/L (low)**	**> 26 mEq/L (high)**
COMPENSATION[1]					
pH	7.35–7.45	Normal	Normal	Normal	Normal
P_{aCO_2}	35–45 mm Hg	> 45 mm Hg (high)	< 35 mm Hg (low)	**< 35 mm Hg (low)**	**> 45 mm Hg (high)**
HCO_3^-	22–26 mEq/L	**> 26 mEq/L (high)**	**< 22 mEq/L (low)**	< 22 mEq/L (low)	> 26 mEq/L (high)

1. If completely compensated, pH returns to normal. The ratio of H_2CO_3 to HCO_3^- is once again 1:20.

CHAPTER SUMMARY

- Normal homeostatic levels of fluid and electrolytes are usually maintained despite sometimes erratic fluid intake.

25.1 Body Fluids   983
- The percentage of fluid that composes our body varies between individuals.

25.1a Percentage of Body Fluid   983
- Your total body water content is dependent upon your age, gender, and your percentage of body fat.

25.1b Fluid Compartments   983
- The two major fluid compartments are intracellular fluid (fluid inside of a cell) and extracellular fluid (fluid outside of a cell). Extracellular fluid is composed of interstitial fluid (fluid around cells) and fluid within the blood plasma.

25.2 Fluid Balance   986
- Maintaining fluid balance involves the interaction of many systems.

25.2a Fluid Intake and Fluid Output   986
- Fluid intake includes preformed water in our food and drink, and metabolic water that is produced within the body.
- Fluid output includes losses when we expire air, through our skin, feces, and urine.
- Fluid output is categorized as sensible or insensible, depending upon if it is measurable; or as obligatory or facultative, depending upon if the loss is regulated based on state of hydration.

25.2b Fluid Imbalance   987
- A fluid imbalance occurs when fluid output does not equal fluid intake.
- Fluid imbalances can be organized into five categories including volume depletion, volume excess, dehydration, hypotonic hydration, and fluid sequestration.

25.2c Regulation of Fluid Balance   989
- Fluid intake is regulated through the thirst center by stimuli that turn on and turn off the thirst center.
- Fluid output is hormonally regulated by altering the amount of fluid lost in urine (facultative water loss); is decreased by the renin-angiotensin system, aldosterone, and antidiuretic hormone; and is increased by atrial natriuretic peptide.

25.3 Electrolyte Balance   990
- Solutes are differentiated into nonelectrolytes and electrolytes.

25.3a Nonelectrolytes and Electrolytes   990
- Nonelectrolytes do not dissociate in solution. Electrolytes are substances that conduct an electric current and dissociate in solution, and include salts, acids, bases, and some negatively charged proteins.

25.3b Major Electrolytes: Location, Functions, and Regulation   991
- Major electrolytes include sodium ion (Na^+), potassium ion (K^+), chloride ion (Cl^-), calcium ion (Ca^{2+}), phosphate ion (PO_4^{3-}), and magnesium ion (Mg^{2+}). Each is normally maintained within homeostatic levels.

25.4 Hormonal Regulation   995
- Hormonal regulation of fluid and electrolyte balance occurs primarily through: angiotensin II, antidiuretic hormone, aldosterone, and atrial natriuretic peptide.

25.4a Angiotensin II   995
- Angiotensin II stimulates vasoconstriction to increase blood pressure, decreases fluid output by the kidney to maintain blood volume, activates the thirst center, and stimulates the release of aldosterone and antidiuretic hormone.

25.4b Antidiuretic Hormone (ADH)   996
- Antidiuretic hormone (ADH) stimulates the thirst center to increase fluid intake, decreases fluid output from the kidney to maintain blood volume, and decreases blood osmolarity. In high doses, ADH is a vasoconstrictor.

25.4c Aldosterone   998
- Aldosterone (ALDO) stimulates reabsorption of both Na^+ and water to maintain blood volume and blood pressure. However, blood osmolarity is unchanged. Potassium ions are normally secreted except under conditions of low pH; then excess H^+ is excreted.

25.4d Atrial Natriuretic Peptide (ANP)   999
- Atrial natriuretic peptide (ANP) decreases blood volume and blood pressure by causing vasodilation and increasing fluid output—both processes that occur from stimulation of ANP directly—and through the inhibition of renin-angiotensin system, antidiuretic hormone, and aldosterone.

25.5 Acid-Base Balance   1001
- Acid-base balance requires regulating H^+ concentration in body fluids to maintain arterial blood pH between 7.35 and 7.45.

25.5a Categories of Acid   1001
- Acid can be classified as fixed or volatile. Fixed acid is acid from a source other than CO_2, and volatile acid is produced from CO_2.

25.5b The Kidneys and Regulation of Fixed Acids   1001
- Acidic and alkaline input occurs through the diet with absorption of foods from the gastrointestinal (GI) tract. Acidic input also occurs through by-products of metabolism. Adjustments are made to maintain acid-base balance by the output of the kidney as it alters its secretion and reabsorption of H^+ and HCO_3^-.

(continued on next page)

25.5 Acid-Base Balance (continued)	**25.5c Respiration and Regulation of Volatile Acid** 1003
	• Along with the kidneys, the respiratory system is a physiologic buffering system. Altering the respiratory rate affects H^+ concentration as a result of this chemical process: $CO_2 + H_2O \longleftrightarrow H_2CO_3 \longleftrightarrow H^+ + HCO_3^-$.
	• Increasing respiratory rate decreases Pco_2, decreases H^+, increasing pH. Decreasing respiratory rate increases Pco_2, increases H^+, decreasing pH.
	25.5d Chemical Buffers 1004
	• Chemical buffers help prevent pH changes within fractions of a second and include proteins, the phosphate system, and the bicarbonate system until the kidney or respiratory system can alter the blood pH through physiologic mechanisms.
25.6 Disturbances to Acid-Base Balance 1005	• A transient acid-base disturbance, in which the buffering capacity of chemical buffers is temporarily exceeded, is usually compensated for by the kidneys or respiratory system to prevent permanent acid-base imbalances.
	25.6a Overview of Acid-Base Imbalances 1005
	• There are four types of acid-base imbalances, including respiratory acidosis, respiratory alkalosis, metabolic acidosis, and metabolic alkalosis.
	25.6b Respiratory-Induced Acid-Base Disturbances 1007
	• Respiratory acidosis is the most common acid-base disturbance and occurs due to impaired respiratory function. Pco_2 is above 45 mm Hg, causing a decrease in pH.
	• Respiratory alkalosis occurs when Pco_2 is below 35 mm Hg due to an increase in respiratory rate, resulting in an increase in pH.
	25.6c Metabolic-Induced Acid-Base Disturbances 1007
	• Metabolic acidosis is the most common metabolic acid-base disturbance and occurs when HCO_3^- is below 22 mEq/L, resulting in a decrease in pH.
	• Metabolic alkalosis occurs when HCO_3^- is above 26 mEq/L, resulting in an increase in pH.
	25.6d Compensation 1010
	• Renal compensation eliminates excess H^+ and reabsorbs HCO_3^- in response to low pH, or eliminates excess HCO_3^- and reabsorbs H^+ in response to high pH. Blood HCO_3^- levels will be higher or lower than normal, respectively.
	• Respiratory compensation eliminates additional CO_2 in response to metabolic acidosis, or decreases the elimination of CO_2 in response to metabolic alkalosis. Blood CO_2 (and H_2CO_3) will be lower or higher than normal, respectively.

CHALLENGE YOURSELF

Do You Know the Basics?

_____ 1. Which of the following individuals is most likely to contain the largest percentage of water?

   a. a frail 76-year-old woman

   b. a chunky 52-year-old male athlete

   c. a healthy 88-year-old man

   d. a lean 35-year-old male athlete

_____ 2. The fluid compartment with the largest percentage of fluid is

   a. intracellular.   c. plasma.

   b. interstitial.   d. extracellular.

_____ 3. Which of the following would result in fluid moving from the blood into the interstitial space?

   a. dehydration

   b. increased blood pressure

   c. burns

   d. vomiting

_____ 4. If an individual has decreased saliva production, increased blood osmotic pressure, decreased blood volume, and decreased blood pressure, he or she is experiencing

   a. edema.   c. hypotonic hydration.

   b. dehydration.   d. acidosis.

_____ 5. Which hormone decreases total body fluid, blood volume, and blood pressure?

   a. antidiuretic hormone (ADH)

   b. aldosterone

   c. atrial natriuretic peptide (ANP)

   d. angiotensin II

_____ 6. Which of the following describes an electrolyte? An electrolyte

   a. does not conduct an electric current.

   b. is covalently bonded and usually contains carbon.

   c. does not dissociate in solution.

   d. plays a significant role in regulating fluid balance.

_____ 7. The major role of this electrolyte is to maintain osmotic pressure in the extracellular fluid (ECF).

   a. HCO_3^- c. Na^+

   b. Ca^{2+} d. K^+

_____ 8. An increase in blood CO_2 levels is followed by a(n) _____ in blood H^+ levels and a(n) _____ in blood pH.

   a. decrease; decrease   c. decrease; increase

   b. increase; increase   d. increase; decrease

_____ 9. Which of the following is *not* a buffer system in the body?

    a. carbohydrate   c. phosphate

    b. protein   d. hemoglobin

_____ 10. The kidney can act to buffer the blood by

    a. secreting H^+.

    b. reabsorbing H^+.

    c. producing HCO_3^-.

    d. All of these are correct.

11. List the three variables that determine the percentage of total water in the body.

12. Describe the movement of water between the compartments after taking a drink of water.

13. List the stimuli that turn on, and turn off, the thirst center.

14. Explain the homeostatic system involving the renin angiotensin system, ADH, and aldosterone.

15. Describe how ANP is regulated and how it opposes the action of the other three hormones (angiotensin II, ADH, and aldosterone).

16. Describe the functions of Na^+ and how it is regulated.

17. Describe what occurs in the kidney to maintain acid-base balance when there is an increase in blood plasma H^+.

18. Explain how increasing breathing rate increases blood pH.

19. List the three chemical buffers, and describe how and where they buffer pH.

20. Describe one example of an acid-base disturbance and its compensation.

Can You Apply What You've Learned?

1. Maria brings her baby to the emergency room. She reports that her daughter Sophia has had a fever for 2 days. She has also been vomiting and had diarrhea, and refuses to drink any fluid. Sophia is at risk for

    a. volume excess.   c. dehydration.

    b. volume depletion.   d. hypotonic hydration.

2. A young man has burns over 25% of his body, destroying his cells. This electrolyte is released from the damaged cells, resulting in elevated blood plasma levels. Results from the lab would indicate elevated levels of this common intracellular electrolyte.

    a. Ca^{2+} c. Na^+

    b. K^+ d. Cl^-

3. Harriet, a young, poor, single mother, brings her baby to the emergency room because the baby is crying constantly. She reports that she is unable to buy formula and has been unable to breastfeed. Instead she has been giving the baby a bottle with only water. What is the potential fluid imbalance this infant might be experiencing?

    a. volume excess   c. volume depletion

    b. dehydration   d. hypotonic hydration

4. Harold has been suffering from diabetes mellitus for approximately 15 years. As a result of having recently lost his job and being under a great deal of stress, he has not been adequately managing his diabetes. His breath smells sweet, a sign of producing ketoacids. Harold is most likely suffering from which type of pH imbalance?

    a. respiratory acidosis   c. respiratory alkalosis

    b. metabolic acidosis   d. metabolic alkalosis

5. Harold's blood lab results would most likely show _____ caused by the primary disturbance and _____ caused by compensation.

    a. decreased HCO_3^-; decreased P_{CO_2}

    b. decreased HCO_3^-; increased P_{CO_2}

    c. increased HCO_3^-; decreased P_{CO_2}

    d. increased HCO_3^-; increased P_{CO_2}

Can You Synthesize What You've Learned?

1. Morgan is a nurse at the local hospital. She received the lab results back from a patient that said the patient has hyperaldosteronism, a high level of aldosterone. Based on this diagnosis, explain why this patient has elevated blood Na^+ and low K^+.

2. Ms. Taylor, 68 years old, has been vomiting for 2 days. On the day of admission to the hospital, she feels agitated and anxious. Her lab results, and normal lab values, are given in the following table. What is the primary disturbance: respiratory acidosis, respiratory alkalosis, metabolic acidosis, or metabolic alkalosis? How is her body attempting to compensate, and is it successful? Explain.

Variable	Patient's Lab Results	Normal Values
Blood pH	7.38	7.35–7.45
HCO_3^-	30 mEq/L	22–26 mEq/L
P_{CO_2}	60 mm Hg	35–45 mm Hg

chapter 26

Digestive System

Each time we eat a meal and drink fluids, our body takes in the nutrients required for our survival. However, these nutrients are typically unusable by us in their original forms. The **digestive system** provides the means to break down ingested nutrients and then absorb them.

Here we present the many organs and processes associated with the digestive system. We begin with an introduction to the system and its organs, and then ➤

A gastroenterologist specializes in both the diagnosis and treatment of gastrointestinal (GI) tract disorders, as well as disorders of the pancreas, liver, and gall bladder. These medical specialists treat several common malfunctions of the digestive system including gastroesophageal reflux (heartburn), peptic ulcers, irritable bowel syndrome, hepatitis, colitis, colon polyps, and cancer. Colonoscopy is a noninvasive technique used to examine the digestive tract. Gastroenterologists performing this procedure must have knowledge of the anatomy and histology of the digestive tract.

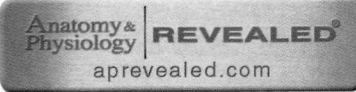

Module 12: Digestive System

we explore each part of this system in more detail: the upper gastrointestinal (GI) tract, lower GI tract, and the accessory organs associated with them. The chapter concludes with a review of both the major nutrients and the details of their digestion and absorption, including the portions of the digestive system in which these functions occur. This will provide you with an opportunity to view the "big picture" of enzyme pathways that occur in the different organs for each type of molecule—an approach that integrates form and function.

26.1 Introduction to the Digestive System

The **digestive system** includes the organs that ingest the food, mix and propel the ingested materials, add secretions to facilitate digestion of these materials into smaller usable components, absorb the necessary nutrients into the blood or lymph, and expel the waste products from the body.

26.1a General Functions of the Digestive System

 LEARNING OBJECTIVE

1. List and describe the six general functions of the digestive system.

The digestive system performs six main functions: ingestion, motility, secretion, digestion, absorption, and elimination of wastes.

- **Ingestion** (in-jes'chŭn; *ingero* = to carry in) is the introduction of solid and liquid nutrients into the oral cavity (*mouth*). It is the first step in the process of digesting and absorbing nutrients.
- **Motility** (mō-til'i-tē) is a general term describing both voluntary and involuntary muscular contractions for mixing and moving materials through the gastrointestinal tract.
- **Secretion** (se-krē'shŭn) is the process of producing and releasing fluid products such as digestive enzymes, acid, and bile into the gastrointestinal tract. These secretions facilitate digestion.
- **Digestion** is the breakdown of ingested food into smaller structures that may be absorbed from the gastrointestinal tract. **Mechanical digestion** occurs when ingested material is physically broken down into smaller units by chewing and mixing without changing their chemical structure. **Chemical digestion** involves specific enzymes to break chemical bonds to change larger complex molecules into smaller molecules that can then be absorbed.
- **Absorption** (ab-sōrp'shŭn) involves both passive movement and active transport of digested molecules, electrolytes, vitamins, and water from the gastrointestinal tract into the blood or lymph.

- **Elimination** is the expulsion of indigestible components that are not absorbed.

 WHAT DID YOU LEARN?

1 What is the primary difference between mechanical digestion and chemical digestion?

26.1b Organization of the Digestive System

 LEARNING OBJECTIVES

2. Identify the six organs that make up the gastrointestinal (GI) tract.
3. List the accessory organs and structures involved in the digestive process.

The digestive system has two separate categories of organs: those composing the gastrointestinal tract, and the accessory digestive organs (**figure 26.1**). The **gastrointestinal** (gas'trō-in-tes'tin-ăl; *gastro* = the stomach) **(GI) tract** is also called either the *digestive tract,* or *alimentary* (al-i-men'ter-ē; *alimentum* = nourishment) *canal.* The GI tract organs essentially form a continuous tube that includes the oral cavity, pharynx (throat), esophagus, stomach, small intestine, and large intestine, and ends at the anus. It is typically about 30 feet in length in an adult cadaver—although, due to smooth muscle tone, it is significantly shorter in a living individual. Within the confines of the GI tract, food is broken down into smaller components that can then be absorbed along its length. Note that materials within the lumen of the GI tract are not considered part of the body until they are absorbed.

Accessory digestive organs assist in the digestion of food. Accessory digestive glands produce secretions that empty into the GI tract and include the salivary glands, liver, and pancreas. Other accessory digestive organs are not glands. They include the teeth and tongue, which participate in the chewing and swallowing of food, and the gallbladder, which concentrates and stores the secretions of the liver.

WHAT DID YOU LEARN?

2 How is the gastrointestinal (GI) tract distinguished from accessory digestive organs?

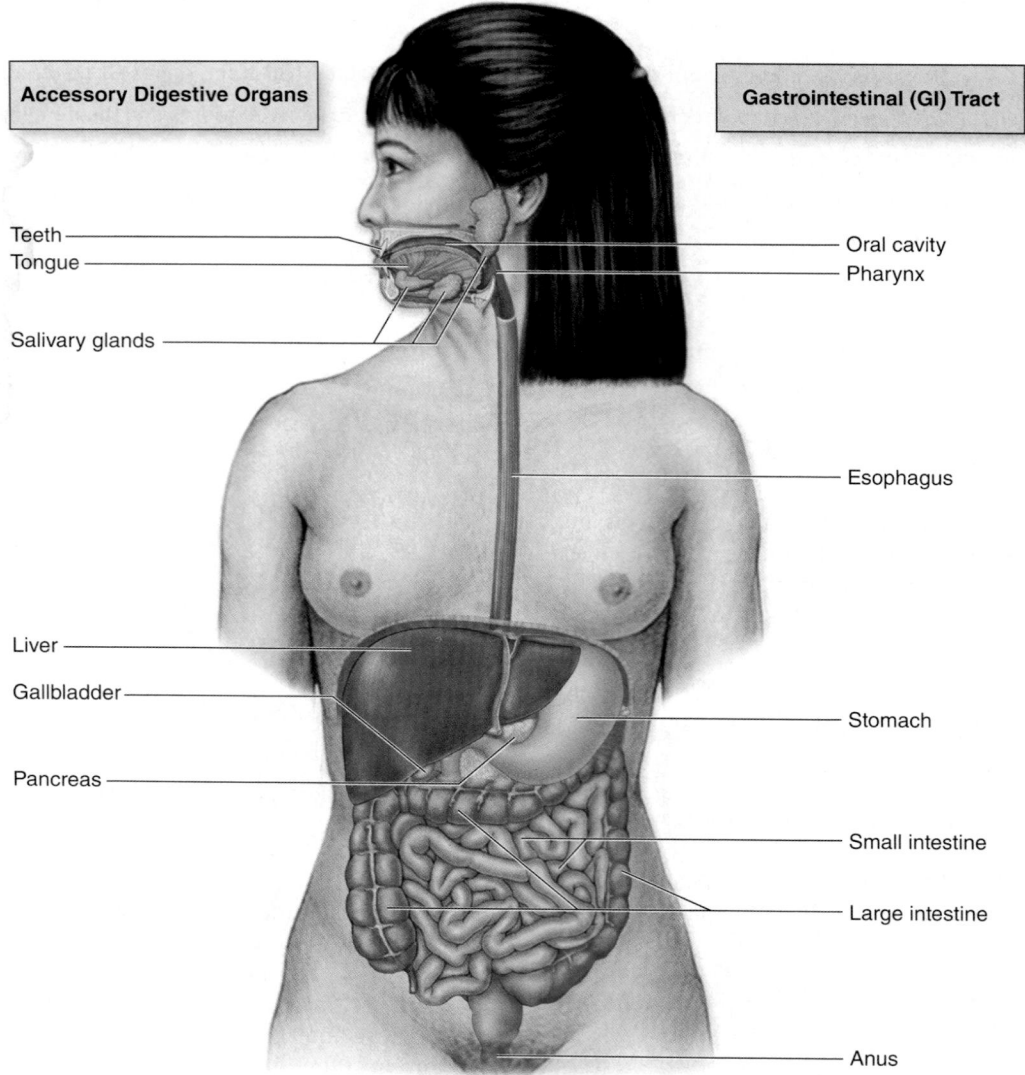

Accessory Digestive Organs

Gastrointestinal (GI) Tract

Teeth

Tongue

Salivary glands

Liver

Gallbladder

Pancreas

Oral cavity

Pharynx

Esophagus

Stomach

Small intestine

Large intestine

Anus

Figure 26.1 Digestive System. The digestive system is composed of the gastrointestinal (GI) tract and accessory digestive organs that assist the GI tract in the process of digestion. AP|R

26.1c Gastrointestinal Tract Wall

LEARNING OBJECTIVES

4. List and describe the four tunics (layers) that make up the gastrointestinal wall.

5. Briefly describe the general process of absorption.

6. Explain the action of the muscularis.

The GI tract from the esophagus through the large intestine is a hollow tube composed of four concentric layers, called **tunics.** From innermost (adjacent to the lumen) to outermost, the four general tunics are the mucosa, submucosa, muscularis, and adventitia or serosa **(figure 26.2).**

Mucosa

The **mucosa** (mū-kō′sa) is the inner-lining mucous membrane. It typically consists of an epithelium, an underlying lamina propria, and a thin layer of muscularis mucosae.

The **epithelium** is in contact with the contents within the lumen. It is a simple columnar epithelium for most of the GI tract (stomach, small intestine, large intestine). Recall from section 5.1 that this type of epithelium allows for secretion and absorption. The

portions of the GI tract that must withstand abrasion (such as the esophagus) are lined by a nonkeratinized, stratified squamous epithelium.

The underlying **lamina propria** is composed of areolar connective tissue that contains small blood vessels and nerves. Absorption occurs when substances are moved through the epithelial cells that line the GI tract wall, and are absorbed into blood or lymphatic capillaries located within the lamina propria (figure 26.2b).

The **muscularis mucosae** is a thin layer of smooth muscle deep to the lamina propria. Contractions of this layer of smooth muscle cause slight movements in the mucosa, which (1) facilitate the release of secretions from the mucosa into the lumen, and (2) increase contact of materials in the lumen with the mucosa. In other words, the muscularis mucosae gently "shakes things up."

Submucosa

The **submucosa** is composed of areolar and dense irregular connective tissue, the relative amounts of each vary depending on the specific region of the GI tract. Many large blood vessels, lymph vessels, and nerves are within the submucosa. Fine branches of the nerves extend into the mucosa and along with their associated ganglia are collectively referred to as the **submucosal nerve plexus,** or

(a) Tunics

Mucosa
- Epithelium
- Lamina propria
- Muscularis mucosae

Submucosa

Submucosal nerve plexus

Lumen

Muscularis
- Inner circular layer
- Myenteric nerve plexus
- Outer longitudinal layer

Serosa

Vein, artery, lymph vessel (within mesentery)

Absorption

Digested substances are transported from the lumen of the GI tract through the epithelium

Lumen

Microvilli

Epithelium

Basement membrane

Lamina propria

Lymphatic capillary

Capillary

Most nutrients are absorbed into the blood capillaries

Large lipids and lipid-soluble vitamins are absorbed into the lymph

(b) Mucosa: Absorption

Motility

Peristalsis	Mixing

Wave of contraction — Wall of GI tract — Lumen

Relaxation

Mixing

Bolus

Further mixing

(c) Muscularis: Motility

Figure 26.2 Tunics of the Abdominal GI Tract. The wall of the abdominal GI tract has four tunics. (*a*) From the lining of its lumen to the external covering, the tunics are the mucosa, submucosa, muscularis, and adventitia or serosa. (*b*) Substances need only to cross the epithelium of the mucosa through cellular transport processes to be absorbed into the blood capillaries or lymphatic capillaries within the lamina propria. (*c*) Peristalsis is the coordinated contraction and relaxation of the muscularis layer to propel material through the lumen of the GI tract. "Mixing" is any type of muscular contraction that facilitates the blending of materials within the GI tract. AP|R

Meissner plexus. These nerves innervate both the smooth muscle and glands of the mucosa and submucosa.

The areolar connective tissue of both the lamina propria of the mucosa and the submucosa house mucosa-associated lymphatic tissue (MALT). In the last region of the small intestine (the ileum), larger aggregates of lymphatic nodules in the submucosa are called **Peyer patches.** The presence of MALT helps prevent ingested microbes from crossing the GI tract wall and entering the body (see section 21.4d).

Muscularis

The **muscularis** (mŭs-kū-lā′ris) usually contains two layers of smooth muscle. The smooth muscle cells of the inner layer are ori-

ented circumferentially around the GI tract and are called the **inner circular layer.** The cells of the outer layer are oriented lengthwise along the GI tract and are called the **outer longitudinal layer.** The axons and the associated ganglia located between these two layers of smooth muscle control its contractions and are collectively referred to as the **myenteric** (mī-en-ter′ik; *mys* = muscle, *enteron* = intestine) **nerve plexus,** or *Auerbach plexus.*

Both the submucosal nerve plexus and the myenteric nerve plexus together compose the **enteric nervous system.** Sensory neurons within these plexuses detect both changes in the GI tract wall (e.g., stretch) and chemical makeup of the contents of the lumen. Thus, this system is composed of both sensory and motor neurons of the autonomic nervous system (see chapter 15). It is interesting to note that some researchers consider the enteric nervous system a completely separate nervous system from the central nervous system because of both the number of neurons that compose it and the fact that it can function independently of the central nervous system.

The inner circular muscle layer is greatly thickened at several locations along the GI tract to form a **sphincter.** A sphincter closes off the lumen at some point along the GI tract, and in so doing it can control the movement of materials into the next section of the GI tract.

The function of the muscularis is to mix and propel the contents within the GI tract. If you think of the GI tract as a hollow tube, then contractions of the circular layer constrict the lumen of the tube, while contractions of the longitudinal layer shorten the tube. Contractions of these smooth muscle layers are associated with two primary types of motility: peristalsis and mixing (figure 26.2c):

- **Peristalsis** (per'i-stal'sis; *stalsis* = constriction) is the alternating contraction sequence of both the inner circular and outer longitudinal muscle layers for the purpose of propelling ingested materials through the GI tract.
- **Mixing** is the "back-and-forward," or kneading, motion that occurs at any point in time within different regions but lacks directional movement. Mixing is for the purpose of blending ingested materials with the secretions within the GI tract.

Adventitia or Serosa

The outermost tunic may be either an adventitia or a serosa. An **adventitia** (ad-ven-tish'ă) is composed of areolar connective tissue with dispersed collagen and elastic fibers and is found outside the peritoneal cavity (described shortly). A **serosa** (se-rō'să) has the same composition as the adventitia, but it is completely covered by a visceral peritoneum and is found within the peritoneal cavity.

Some GI organs deviate from the typical pattern of the tunics just described. For example, the esophagus has a stratified squamous nonkeratinized epithelium in its mucosa to protect its lining, and the stomach has three layers of smooth muscle in the muscularis. Being familiar with the basic tunic pattern, and then discovering how an organ may deviate from this pattern, provides clues as to the organ's function.

WHAT DID YOU LEARN?

3 What specific layer(s) must substances cross to enter the blood or lymphatic capillaries during their absorption?

4 What purpose is served by muscular sphincters at various locations along the length of the GI tract?

5 How does peristalsis differ from mixing?

26.1d Serous Membranes of the Abdominal Cavity

LEARNING OBJECTIVES

7. Describe the structure of the serous membranes associated with the digestive tract.
8. Distinguish between intraperitoneal and retroperitoneal organs.
9. Explain the function of the mesentery, and describe the five individual mesenteries of the abdominopelvic cavity.

Two serous membranes are associated with the abdominal cavity (see section 1.4e). The serous membrane that lines the inside surface of the body wall is called the **parietal peritoneum** (per'i-tō-nē'ŭm; *periteino* = to stretch over). The portion of the serous membrane that reflects over and covers the surface of internal organs is called

the **visceral peritoneum.** Between these two layers is the thin **peritoneal cavity.** It is a potential space in which both peritoneal layers secrete a lubricating serous fluid. This small volume of fluid in the peritoneal cavity lubricates both the internal body wall and the external organ surfaces. It allows the abdominal organs to move freely and reduces friction resulting from this movement.

Organs within the abdomen that are completely surrounded by visceral peritoneum are called **intraperitoneal** (in'tr̆a-per'i-t̆o-n̆e'̆al) **organs.** They include the stomach, most of the small intestine, and parts of the large intestine. **Retroperitoneal** (re-tr̄o-per'i-t̄o-n̄e'̆al) **organs** typically lie directly against the posterior abdominal wall, so only their anterolateral portions are covered with peritoneum. Retroperitoneal digestive organs include most of the duodenum (the first part of the small intestine), the pancreas, ascending and descending colon (parts of the large intestine), and the rectum (see figure 1.9).

Mesentery

The general term **mesentery** (mes'en-ter-ē) refers to the double-layer of peritoneum that supports, suspends, and stabilizes the intraperitoneal GI tract organs. Blood vessels, lymph vessels, and nerves are sandwiched between the two folds and supply the digestive organs. Several terms are used to identify the individual mesenteries associated with specific organs (**figure 26.3**; see also figure 1.9):

- The **greater omentum** (ō-men'tŭm) extends inferiorly like an apron from the inferolateral surface of the stomach (greater curvature) and covers most of the abdominal organs. It often accumulates large amounts of adipose connective tissue, thus it is referred to as the "fatty apron."

Liver
Falciform ligament
Round ligament of the liver
Lesser omentum
Stomach

Greater omentum

(a) Omenta

Greater omentum (reflected)

Transverse colon

Transverse mesocolon

Mesentery proper

Small intestine

(b) Mesentery proper and mesocolon

Figure 26.3 Serous Membranes. Many abdominal organs are held in place by double-layered serous membranes called mesenteries, which include (*a*) the greater and lesser omenta, and (*b*) the mesentery proper and some of the mesocolon.

- The **lesser omentum** connects the superomedial surface of the stomach (lesser curvature) and the proximal end of the duodenum to the liver.
- The **falciform** (fal'si-fōrm; *falx* = sickle) **ligament** is a peritoneal fold that attaches the liver to the internal surface of the anterior abdominal wall.
- The **mesentery proper,** which is sometimes referred to as the *mesentery,* is a fan-shaped fold of peritoneum that suspends most of the small intestine (the jejunum and the ileum) from the internal surface of the posterior abdominal wall.

- The **mesocolon** (mez'ō-kō'lon) is a fold in the peritoneum that attaches parts of the large intestine to the internal surface of the posterior abdominal wall. The mesocolon has several distinct sections, each named for the portion of the colon it suspends. For example, transverse mesocolon is associated with the transverse colon, whereas sigmoid mesocolon is associated with the sigmoid colon.

WHAT DID YOU LEARN?

6 What is the difference between intraperitoneal and retroperitoneal organs? List the digestive organs that are intraperitoneal organs.

7 Where is the greater omentum located?

26.1e Regulation of Digestive System Processes

LEARNING OBJECTIVES

10. Identify the type and location of the two main receptors of the digestive system.

11. Describe and compare long reflexes and short reflexes.

12. List the major hormones that regulate the processes of digestion.

Regulation of digestion involves receptors that monitor changes associated with the GI tract and its contents. Stimulation of these receptors brings about both nervous system and hormonal responses.

Receptors

Two major types of general receptors (see section 16.1) are embedded throughout the mucosa and submucosa of the GI tract length: **mechanoreceptors** within the wall of the GI tract that detect either stretch or pressure of a particular region of the GI tract as the contents move through, and **chemoreceptors** that detect the presence of specific chemicals of the passing contents within the lumen.

Nervous Control

Sensory input from both mechanoreceptors and chemoreceptors is relayed to the central nervous system (CNS) in response to stimulation. Autonomic motor output is then relayed through three cranial nerves (the facial, glossopharyngeal, and vagus nerves; see sections 13.9 and 15.3a) to different digestive system effectors, such as salivary glands, the pancreas, and the muscularis layers in the GI tract wall. The result is coordinated secretory and smooth muscle contractions involved in digestive responses. These autonomic interactions of the CNS are described as **long reflexes**.

Some digestive reflexes do not involve the CNS. Instead, they are local and occur only within the neurons of the enteric nervous system that are housed within the GI tract wall. These are called **short reflexes.** The details of reflexes are described in later sections that discuss specific regions of the GI tract.

Hormonal Control

Three primary hormones participate in the regulation of the processes of digestion: gastrin that is released from the stomach; and secretin and cholecystokinin that are released from the small intestine. The specific functions of these hormones are described in later sections.

Now that an overview of the main functions and features of the GI tract has been presented, we are ready to proceed with a more detailed exploration through the system, beginning with the upper GI tract.

WHAT DID YOU LEARN?

8 Does a long reflex involve the central nervous system?

9 What three primary hormones regulate digestive processes?

26.2 Upper Gastrointestinal Tract

The upper gastrointestinal tract is where initial processing by both mechanical and chemical means takes place.

26.2a Overview of the Upper Gastrointestinal Tract Organs

LEARNING OBJECTIVE

1. Describe the components of the upper gastrointestinal tract.

A superficial view of the upper GI tract organs and accessory structures helps integrate their general structures with their digestive activities and functions (see figure 26.1):

- **Oral cavity and salivary glands.** Mechanical digestion (mastication) begins in the oral cavity. Saliva is secreted from the salivary glands in response to food being present within the oral cavity. It is mixed with the ingested materials to form a wet mass called a bolus. One component of saliva is salivary amylase, a hydrolytic enzyme that initiates the chemical digestion of starch (amylose).

- **Pharynx.** The bolus is moved into the pharynx, where swallowing occurs. Mucus secreted in saliva and in the superior part of the esophagus facilitates swallowing.

- **Esophagus.** The bolus is transported from the pharynx through the esophagus into the stomach. Mucus secretion by the esophagus lubricates the passage of the bolus.

- **Stomach.** The bolus is mixed with gastric secretions as smooth muscle in the stomach wall contracts. These secretions are produced by epithelial cells of the stomach mucosa and include acid (hydrochloric acid [HCl]), digestive enzymes, and mucin. The mixing continues as an acidic "purée" called chyme is formed.

Note that the first part of the small intestine is the duodenum. It is also included in the upper GI tract; however, it will be described with the rest of the small intestine later in the chapter.

WHAT DID YOU LEARN?

10 What structures are considered part of the upper gastrointestinal tract?

26.2b Oral Cavity and Salivary Glands

LEARNING OBJECTIVES

2. Identify the anatomic structures in the oral cavity.
3. Describe the structure and function of salivary glands and how the release of saliva is regulated.
4. Explain the process of mastication.
5. Discuss the structure and development of the teeth.

The Oral Cavity

The **oral cavity,** or *mouth,* is the entrance to the GI tract **(figure 26.4)**. Food is ingested into the oral cavity, where it undergoes the initial processes of mechanical and chemical digestion.

Gross Anatomy   The oral cavity has two distinct spatial regions: The vestibule (or buccal cavity) is the space between the gums, lips, and cheeks, and the oral cavity proper lies central to the teeth. The oral cavity is bounded laterally by the cheeks, anteriorly by the teeth and lips, and it leads posteriorly into the oropharynx.

The cheeks are covered externally by the integument and contain the buccinator muscles (see figure 11.5). These muscles compress the cheeks against the teeth to hold solid materials in place during mastication (chewing). The cheeks terminate at the fleshy **lips** (or *labia*) that are formed primarily by the orbicularis oris muscle. Lips have a reddish hue because of their abundant supply of superficial blood vessels and the reduced amount of keratin within their outer skin. The internal surfaces of both the superior and inferior lips each are attached to the gingivae (gums) by a thin mucosa fold in the midline, called the **labial frenulum** (lā′bē-ăl; *labium* = lip; fren′ū-lŭm; *frenum* = bridle).

The **palate** (pal′ăt) forms the superior boundary, or "roof," of the oral cavity and acts as a barrier to separate it from the nasal cavity. The anterior two-thirds of the palate is hard and bony (called the hard palate), while the posterior one-third is soft and muscular (called the soft palate). The **hard palate** is formed by the palatine processes of the maxillae and the horizontal plates of the palatine bones (see section 8.2b). It exhibits prominent **transverse**

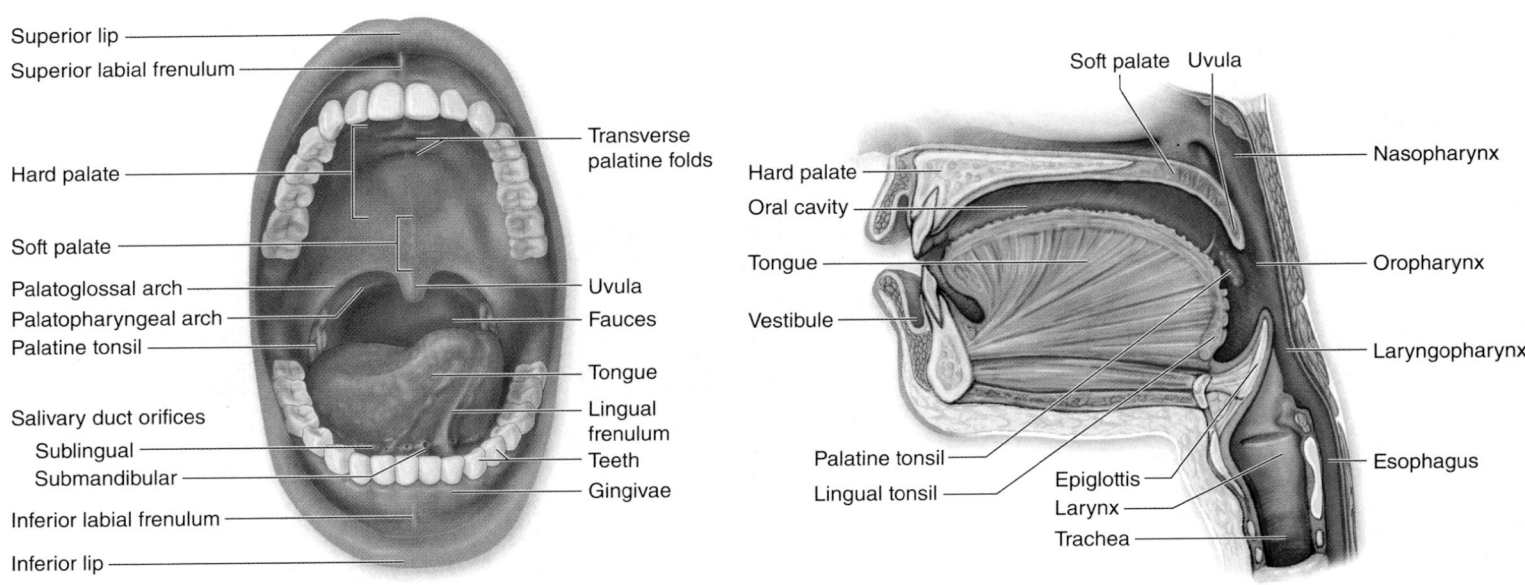

(a) Oral cavity, anterior view

(b) Oral cavity and pharynx, sagittal section

Figure 26.4 Oral Cavity. Ingested food and drink enter the GI tract through the oral cavity and move into the pharynx. (*a*) An anterior view shows the structures of the oral cavity. (*b*) A sagittal section shows the structures of both the oral cavity and the pharynx. AP|R palatine folds, or *friction ridges,* that assist the tongue in manipulating ingested materials prior to swallowing. Extending inferiorly from the posterior part of the soft palate is a conical median projection called the **uvula** (ū'vū-lă). When you swallow, the soft palate and the uvula elevate to close off the posterior entrance into the nasopharynx and prevent ingested materials from entering the nasal region.

The **fauces** (faw'sēz) represent the opening between the oral cavity and the oropharynx. The fauces are bounded by paired muscular folds: the **palatoglossal** (păl'a-tō-glos'ăl) **arch** (anterior fold) and the **palatopharyngeal** (păl'a-tō-fa-rin'jē-ăl) **arch** (posterior fold). The palatine tonsils are housed inferiorly between the arches. These tonsils serve as an "early line of defense" as they monitor ingested food and drink for foreign antigens and initiate an immune response when necessary (see section 21.4c).

The inferior surface, or floor, of the oral cavity houses the tongue. The **tongue** is formed primarily from skeletal muscle. Both extrinsic and intrinsic muscles move the tongue (see section 11.3c). Numerous small projections called **papillae** (pă-pil'ē; sing., *papilla, papula* = pimple) cover the superior (dorsal) surface of the tongue and are involved in the sense of taste (see section 16.3b). The posteroinferior region of the tongue also contains round masses of lymphatic tissue called the lingual tonsils. The inferior surface of the

tongue attaches to the floor of the oral cavity by a thin vertical mucous membrane, the **lingual frenulum.** The tongue manipulates and mixes ingested materials during chewing and helps compress the partially digested materials against the palate to assist in mechanical digestion. The tongue also performs important functions in both swallowing and in speech production. The teeth and gums are described in detail at the end of this section.

Histology   The epithelial lining of the oral cavity is a stratified squamous epithelium that protects against the abrasive activities associated with mechanical digestion. The nonkeratinized type of epithelium lines most of the oral cavity; the keratinized type lines the lips, portions of the tongue, and a small region of the hard palate.

Salivary Glands

The oral cavity continually receives serous and mucus secretions from unicellular exocrine glands within the oral cavity. Numerous unicellular glands associated with the structures of the oral cavity, including the buccal glands of the cheek, lingual glands of the tongue, and labial glands of the lips, are collectively referred to as **intrinsic salivary glands.** These small glands contribute to the production of **saliva** (să-lī'vă). The secretions of intrinsic salivary glands include **lingual lipase** enzyme. Most saliva, however, is produced from multicellular exocrine glands outside the oral cavity called **extrinsic salivary glands.**

Gross Anatomy   Three pairs of multicellular salivary glands are located external to the oral cavity: the parotid, submandibular, and sublingual glands (**figure 26.5a**).

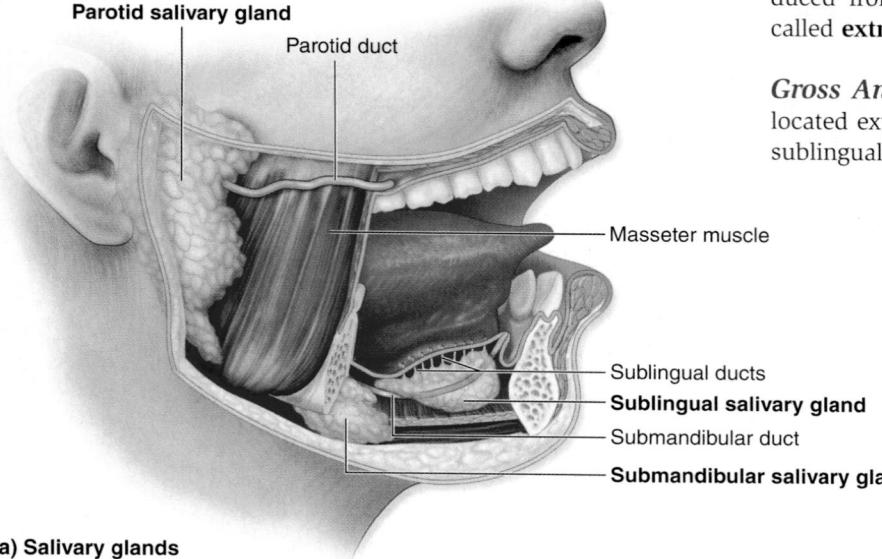

Parotid salivary gland

Parotid duct

— Masseter muscle

— Sublingual ducts
Sublingual salivary gland
— Submandibular duct
Submandibular salivary gland

(a) Salivary glands

Figure 26.5 Salivary Glands. Saliva is produced by three paired extrinsic salivary glands. (*a*) The relative locations of the parotid, submandibular, and sublingual salivary glands are shown in a side view. (*b*) Serous and mucous alveoli are shown in a diagrammatic representation of salivary gland histology. (*c*) A photomicrograph reveals the histologic detail of the submandibular salivary gland. AP|R

Mucous cell
Salivary duct

Mucous alveolus —

Mixed alveolus —

— Duct epithelium

— Serous alveolus

Serous cell

(b) Salivary gland histology

Salivary duct   Mucous cells

Serous cells

LM 200x

(c) Submandibular salivary gland

The **parotid** (pă-rot′id; *para* = beside; *ot* = ear) **salivary glands** are the largest salivary glands. Each parotid gland is located anterior and inferior to the ear, partially overlying the masseter muscle. The parotid salivary glands produce about 25–30% of the saliva, which is conducted through the **parotid duct** to the oral cavity. The parotid duct extends from the gland, across the external surface of the masseter muscle, before penetrating the buccinator muscle and opening into the vestibule of the oral cavity near the second upper molar. Infection of the parotid glands by a specific virus (*myxovirus*) causes *mumps*. Children are vaccinated against mumps when immunized with the MMR (measles, mumps, and rubella) vaccine.

The **submandibular salivary glands** are both inferior to the floor of the oral cavity and medial to the body of the mandible as their name suggests. The submandibular salivary glands produce most of the saliva (about 60–70%). A **submandibular duct** opens from each gland through a papilla in the floor of the oral cavity on the lateral sides of the lingual frenulum.

The **sublingual** (sŭb-ling′gwăl) **salivary glands** are inferior to the tongue, medial and anterior to the submandibular salivary glands, and internal to the oral cavity mucosa. Each sublingual salivary gland extends multiple tiny sublingual ducts that open onto the inferior surface of the oral cavity, posterior to the submandibular duct papilla. These tiny glands contribute only about 3–5% of the total saliva.

Histology   Two types of secretory cells are housed within the large paired salivary glands and collectively produce the components of saliva: mucous cells and serous cells (figure 26.5b, c). Mucous cells secrete mucin, which forms mucus upon hydration, while serous cells secrete a watery fluid containing electrolytes and salivary amylase. The proportion of mucous cells to serous cells varies among the three types of salivary glands. The parotid glands produce only serous secretions, whereas the submandibular and sublingual glands produce both mucus and serous secretions. The structure and secretions of salivary glands are summarized in **table 26.1**.

Saliva   The volume of saliva secreted daily ranges between 1.0 and 1.5 liters. Most saliva is produced during mealtime, but smaller amounts are produced continuously to ensure that the oral cavity mucous membrane remains moist. Saliva is composed of 99.5% water and a mixture of solutes. Saliva is formed as water and electrolytes are filtered from capillaries through cells (acini) of a salivary gland. Other components are added by acinar cells, including salivary amylase, mucin, and lysozyme. These components permit saliva to participate in various functions:

- Moistens ingested food and helps it become a **bolus** (bō′lŭs; *bolos* = lump), a globular wet mass of partially digested material that is more easily swallowed
- Initiates the chemical breakdown of starch in the oral cavity because of the salivary amylase it contains
- Acts as a watery medium into which food molecules are dissolved so taste receptors may be stimulated
- Cleanses the oral cavity structures
- Helps inhibit bacterial growth in the oral cavity because it contains antibacterial substances including lysozyme and antibodies (IgA) (IgA is formed by plasma cells in the lamina propria and transported across the epithelial cells.)

Regulation of Salivary Secretions   The salivary nuclei within the brainstem (section 13.5) regulate salivation. A basal level of salivation in response to parasympathetic stimulation ensures that the oral cavity remains moist. Input to the salivary nuclei is received from chemoreceptors or mechanoreceptors in the upper GI tract. These receptors detect various types of stimuli, including the introduction of substances into the oral cavity, especially those that are acidic, such as a lemon; and arrival of foods into the stomach lumen, especially foods that are spicy or acidic. If one eats spoiled food, bacterial toxins within the stomach stimulate receptors that initiate sensory nerve signals to the salivary nuclei. Input is also received by the salivary nuclei from the higher brain centers in response to the thought, smell, or sight of food. Stimulation of the salivary nuclei results in increased parasympathetic output relayed along the facial nerve to the submandibular and sublingual salivary glands and glossopharyngeal nerve to the parotid salivary glands, and additional saliva is released.

Sympathetic stimulation, which occurs during exercise or when an individual is excited or anxious (section 15.4), results in a more viscous saliva by decreasing the water content of saliva. (This occurs because sympathetic stimulation constricts the capillaries of the salivary gland and decreases the fluid added to saliva.)

 WHAT DO YOU THINK?

1 Research suggests that a dry mouth (inadequate production of saliva) is correlated with an increase in dental problems, such as cavities. What are the possible reasons for this correlation?

Table 26.1	Salivary Glands and Secretions		
SALIVARY GLANDS			
Gland	**Structure and Location**	**Types of Secretion**	**Percentage of Saliva Produced**
Parotid	Largest salivary gland; located anterior and inferior to ears; parotid duct opens into vestibule near second molar	Only serous secretions	25–30%
Submandibular	Located inferior to the floor of the oral cavity; duct opens lateral to lingual frenulum	Both serous and mucus secretions	60–70%
Sublingual	Smallest salivary gland; located inferior to tongue; ducts open into floor of oral cavity	Both serous and mucus secretions	3–5%
SALIVA CHARACTERISTICS			
Production Rate	**Solute Components**	**pH Range and Composition**	
1–1.5 liters per day	Salivary amylase, lingual lipase (from intrinsic salivary glands), mucin, ions (Na^+, K^+, Cl^-, HCO_3^-), lysozyme (antibacterial enzyme), immunoglobulin A (from plasma cells)	Slightly acidic (pH 6.4–6.8): 99.5% water, 0.5% solutes	

Mechanical Digestion: Mastication

Mechanical digestion in the oral cavity is called **mastication** (mas'tĭ-kā'shŭn; *mastico* = to chew) or *chewing*. It requires the coordinated activities of teeth, skeletal muscles in lips, tongue, cheeks, and jaws that are controlled by nuclei within the medulla oblongata and pons, collectively called the **mastication center.**

The primary function in chewing the food is to mechanically reduce its bulk into smaller particles to facilitate swallowing. Actual digestion and absorption are affected very little by chewing, except that the surface area of the food is increased, which facilitates exposure to and action by digestive enzymes. Mastication also promotes salivation to help soften and moisten the food to form a bolus.

Note that medications composed of small, nonpolar molecules (e.g., nitroglycerin) may be absorbed in the mouth. When these medications are placed under the tongue, they pass through the oral cavity epithelium by simple diffusion and are absorbed into the blood.

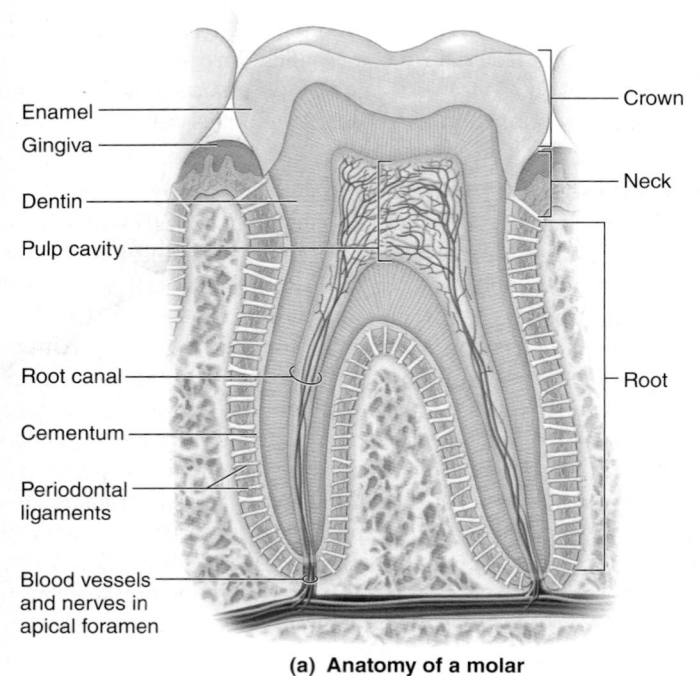

(a) **Anatomy of a molar**

Enamel
Gingiva
Dentin
Pulp cavity
Root canal
Cementum
Periodontal ligaments
Blood vessels and nerves in apical foramen

Crown
Neck
Root

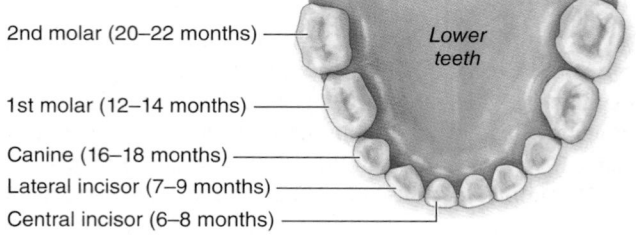

(b) **Deciduous teeth**

Central incisor (7–9 months)
Lateral incisor (9–11 months)
Canine (18–20 months)
1st molar (14–16 months)
2nd molar (24–30 months)

Upper teeth

2nd molar (20–22 months)
1st molar (12–14 months)
Canine (16–18 months)
Lateral incisor (7–9 months)
Central incisor (6–8 months)

Lower teeth

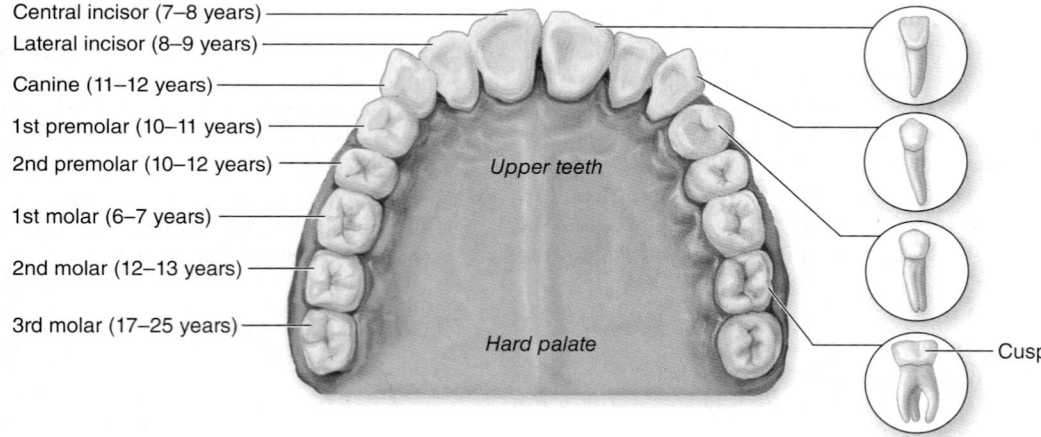

Central incisor (7–8 years)
Lateral incisor (8–9 years)
Canine (11–12 years)
1st premolar (10–11 years)
2nd premolar (10–12 years)
1st molar (6–7 years)
2nd molar (12–13 years)
3rd molar (17–25 years)

Upper teeth

Hard palate

Cusp

3rd molar (17–25 years)
2nd molar (11–13 years)
1st molar (6–7 years)
2nd premolar (11–12 years)
1st premolar (10–12 years)
Canine (9–10 years)
Lateral incisor (7–8 years)
Central incisor (6–7 years)

Lower teeth

(c) **Permanent teeth**

Figure 26.6 Teeth. Ingested food is chewed by the teeth in the oral cavity. (*a*) Anatomy of a molar. (*b, c*) Comparison of the average dentition of deciduous and permanent teeth, including the approximate age at eruption for each tooth. AP|R

Teeth

The **teeth** are collectively known as the **dentition** (den-tish'ŭn; *dentition* = teething). Teeth are responsible for mastication. A tooth has an exposed **crown,** a constricted **neck,** and one or more **roots** that anchor it to the jaw **(figure 26.6a)**. The roots of the teeth fit tightly into dental alveoli, which are sockets within the alveolar processes of both the maxillae and the mandible. Collectively, the roots, the dental alveoli, and the periodontal ligament that binds the roots to the alveolar processes form a gomphosis joint (described in section 9.2a).

Dentin (den'tin; *dens* = tooth) forms the primary mass of a tooth. Dentin is comparable to bone but harder. On the external surface of the dentin, a tough, durable layer of **enamel** (ē-nam'ĕl) forms the crown of the tooth. Enamel is the hardest substance in the body and is primarily composed of calcium phosphate crystals. The center of the tooth is a **pulp cavity** that contains a connective tissue called **pulp.**

A **root canal** is continuous with the pulp cavity and opens into the connective tissue surrounding the root through an opening called the apical foramen. Blood vessels and nerves housed in the pulp pass through the apical foramen. Each root of a tooth is ensheathed within hardened material called **cementum** (se-men'tŭm).

Deciduous and Permanent Teeth

Two sets of teeth develop and erupt during a normal lifetime (figure 26.6b, c). In an infant, 20 **deciduous** (dē-sid'ū-ŭs; *deciduus* = falling off) **teeth,** also called *milk teeth,* erupt between 6 months and 30 months after birth. These teeth are eventually lost and replaced by 32 **permanent teeth.** As figure 26.6b shows, the more anteriorly placed permanent teeth tend to appear first, followed by the posteriorly placed teeth. (The major exception to this rule is the first molars, which appear at about age 6 and sometimes are referred to as the *6-year molars.*) The last teeth to erupt are the third molars, often called *wisdom teeth,* in the late teens or early 20s. The jaw often lacks space to accommodate these final molars, and they may either emerge only partially or grow at an angle and become impacted (wedged against another structure). Impacted teeth cannot erupt properly because of the angle of their growth.

The most anteriorly placed permanent teeth are called **incisors** (in-sī'zōr; *incido* = to cut into). They are shaped like a chisel and have a single root. They are designed for slicing or cutting into food. Immediately posterolateral to the incisors are the **canines** (kā'nīn; *canis* = dog) that have a pointed tip for puncturing and tearing food. **Premolars** (prē-mō'lăr) are located posterolateral to the canines and anterior to the molars. They have flat crowns with prominent ridges called **cusps** that are used to crush and grind ingested materials. Premolars may have one or two roots. The **molars** (mō'lăr) are the thickest and most posteriorly placed teeth. They have large, broad, flat crowns with distinctive cusps, and three or more roots. Molars are also adapted for grinding and crushing ingested materials. If the oral cavity is divided into quadrants, each quadrant contains the following number of permanent teeth: two incisors, one canine, two premolars, and three molars.

The **gingivae** (jin'ji-vă, -vē) are the *gums.* They are composed of dense irregular connective tissue, with an overlying nonkeratinized stratified squamous epithelium that covers the alveolar processes of the upper and lower jaws and surrounds the neck of the teeth.

💡 WHAT DID YOU LEARN?

11 What are the roles of the tongue, teeth, and salivary glands in forming a bolus?

26.2c Pharynx and Esophagus

✔ LEARNING OBJECTIVE

6. Discuss the anatomy of the pharynx and esophagus and their complementary activities in the process of swallowing.

The pharynx and the esophagus connect the oral cavity to the stomach **(figure 26.7a)**.

Gross Anatomy of the Pharynx

The pharynx was previously described in detail in section 23.2c. It is a funnel-shaped, muscular passageway with distensible lateral walls that serves as the passageway for both air and food. Three skeletal

(a) Pharynx and esophagus

Mucosa
Submucosa
Muscularis
Circular layer
Longitudinal layer
Adventitia
Lumen

Oropharynx
Laryngopharynx
Superior esophageal sphincter
Esophagus
Esophageal hiatus
Inferior esophageal sphincter
Diaphragm
Stomach

(b) Esophagus, transverse section

LM 11x

Figure 26.7 The Esophagus. (*a*) The esophagus extends inferiorly from the pharynx and conducts the swallowed bolus and drink to the stomach. (*b*) A photomicrograph of a transverse section through the esophagus identifies the tunics in its wall. AP|R muscle pairs called the superior, middle, and inferior **pharyngeal constrictors** form the wall of the pharynx (see section 11.3c). The oropharynx and laryngopharynx are lined with nonkeratinized stratified squamous epithelium that provides protection against the abrasive activities associated with swallowing ingested materials.

Gross Anatomy of the Esophagus

The **esophagus** (ĕ-sof′ă-gŭs) is a normally collapsed, tubular passageway. It is about 25 centimeters (10 inches) long in an adult and begins at approximately the level of the cricoid cartilage of the larynx, with most of its length within the thorax. This tube is directly anterior to the vertebral bodies, until it passes through the diaphragm. The inferior region of the esophagus connects to the stomach, where it passes through an opening in the diaphragm called the **esophageal hiatus** (hī-ā′tŭs; to yawn). Only the last 1.5 centimeters (slightly more than one-half inch) of the esophagus is located in the abdomen.

The **superior esophageal sphincter** (or *pharyngoesophageal sphincter*) is a contracted ring of circular skeletal muscle at the superior end of the esophagus. It is the area where the esophagus and the pharynx meet. This sphincter is closed during inhalation of air, so air does not enter the esophagus and instead enters the larynx and trachea.

The **inferior esophageal sphincter** (*esophageal gastric*, or *cardiac sphincter*) is a contracted ring of circular smooth muscle at the inferior end of the esophagus. This sphincter isn't strong enough alone to prevent materials from refluxing back into the esophagus; instead, the muscles of the diaphragm at the esophageal opening contract to help prevent materials from regurgitating from the stomach into the esophagus.

Histology

The mucosa of the esophagus is lined with a nonkeratinized stratified squamous epithelium like the oropharynx and laryngopharynx (figure 26.7b). Because the pharynx and esophagus do not absorb any nutrients, this thicker, protective epithelium supports their function.

The submucosa of the esophagus is thick and composed of abundant elastic fibers that permit distension during swallowing. It also houses numerous mucous glands that provide thick, lubricating mucus for the epithelium. The ducts of these glands project through the mucosa and open into the lumen.

The muscularis of the esophagus is unique in that it contains a blend of both skeletal and smooth muscle. The two layers of muscle in the superior one-third of the esophageal muscularis are skeletal, rather than smooth, to ensure that the swallowed material moves rapidly out of the pharynx and into the esophagus before the next respiratory cycle begins. (Remember that smooth muscle contracts more slowly than does skeletal muscle; see section 10.10c.) Skeletal muscle and smooth muscle cells intermingle in the middle one-third of the esophageal muscularis, and only smooth muscle is found within the wall of the inferior one-third of this muscularis. This transition marks the beginning of a continuous smooth muscle muscularis that extends throughout the stomach and the small and large intestines to the anus. The outermost layer of the esophagus is an adventitia.

Motility: The Swallowing Process

Swallowing is called *deglutition* (dē-glū-tish′ŭn). It is the process of moving ingested materials from the oral cavity to the stomach. Swallowing has three phases: the voluntary phase, the pharyngeal phase, and the esophageal phase (**figure 26.8**).

The **voluntary phase** occurs after ingestion. It is controlled by the cerebral cortex (primarily the temporal lobes, limbic system, and motor cortex of the frontal lobe). Ingested materials and saliva mix in the oral cavity. Chewing forms a bolus that is mixed and manipulated by the tongue and then pushed superiorly against the hard palate. Transverse palatine folds in the hard palate help direct the bolus posteriorly toward the oropharynx.

The arrival of the bolus at the entryway to the oropharynx initiates the swallowing reflex of the **pharyngeal phase.** The pha-

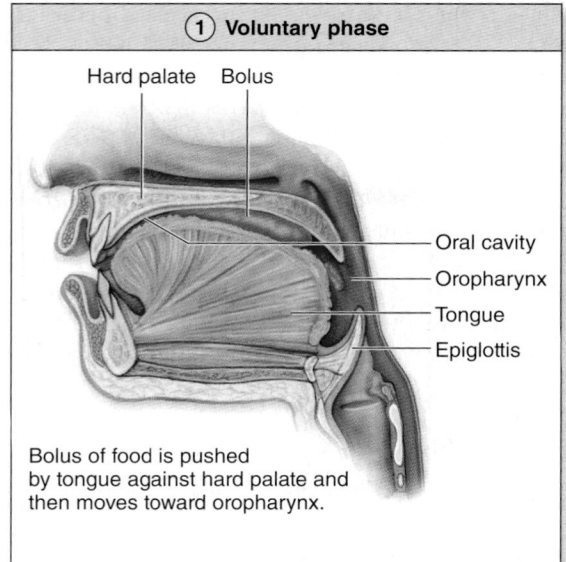

① Voluntary phase

Hard palate Bolus

Oral cavity
Oropharynx
Tongue
Epiglottis

Bolus of food is pushed by tongue against hard palate and then moves toward oropharynx.

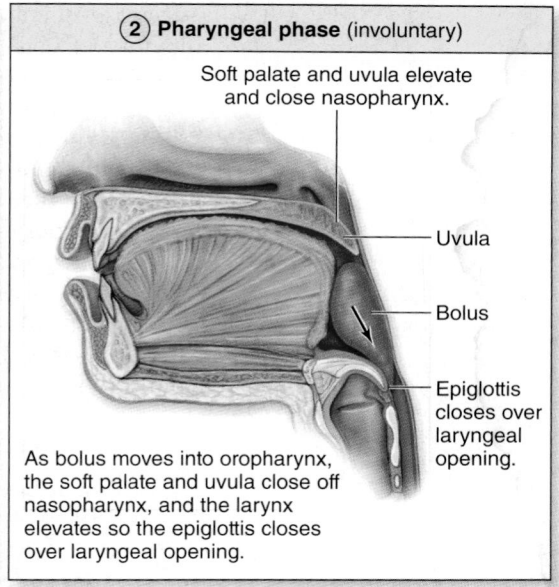

② Pharyngeal phase (involuntary)

Soft palate and uvula elevate and close nasopharynx.

Uvula

Bolus

Epiglottis closes over laryngeal opening.

As bolus moves into oropharynx, the soft palate and uvula close off nasopharynx, and the larynx elevates so the epiglottis closes over laryngeal opening.

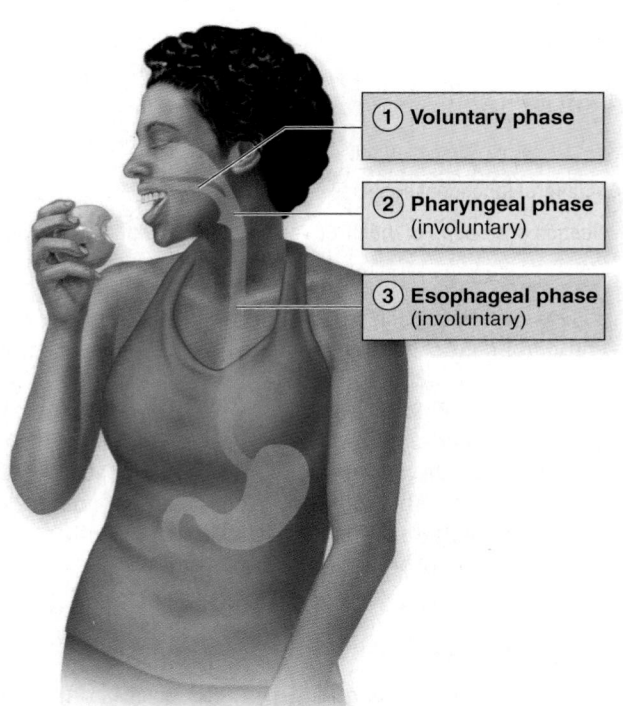

③ Esophageal phase (involuntary)

Soft palate, uvula, and epiglottis return to preswallowing position.

Superior esophageal sphincter closes.

Esophagus
Bolus

Bolus passes through esophagus and enters into the stomach.

Inferior esophageal sphincter opens.

Peristaltic contractions of esophageal muscle push bolus toward stomach.

① Voluntary phase

② Pharyngeal phase (involuntary)

③ Esophageal phase (involuntary)

Figure 26.8 Phases of Swallowing. Swallowing occurs as a result of coordinated muscular activities that force the bolus from the oral cavity into the stomach. The process is organized into three phases: (1) voluntary phase, (2) pharyngeal phase, and (3) esophageal phase.

ryngeal phase is involuntary. Tactile sensory receptors around the fauces are stimulated by the bolus and initiate sensory input to the **swallowing center** (or *deglutition center*) in the medulla oblongata. Nerve signals are then relayed to effectors to cause the following response:

- Entry of the bolus into the oropharynx
- Elevation of the soft palate and uvula to block the passageway between the oropharynx and nasopharynx

- Elevation of the larynx by the hyoid muscles in the neck to move the epiglottis to cover the laryngeal opening; this prevents ingested material from entering the larynx and trachea
- Inhibition of the respiratory center in the medulla oblongata to assure that a breath is not taken during swallowing

During this time, the bolus passes quickly and involuntarily through the pharynx to the esophagus—about 1 second elapses in this phase. Sequential contraction of the pharyngeal constrictors decreases the diameter of the pharynx, beginning at its superior end and moving toward its inferior end. This creates a pressure difference, forcing swallowed material from the pharynx into the esophagus.

The **esophageal phase** is also involuntary. It is the time during which the bolus passes through the esophagus and into the stomach—about 5 to 8 seconds. The presence of the bolus within the lumen of the esophagus stimulates sequential peristaltic waves of muscular contraction that assist in propelling the bolus toward the stomach. Higher pressure occurs in the superior region of the esophagus relative to the inferior region.

The superior and inferior esophageal sphincters are normally closed at rest. When the bolus is swallowed, these sphincters relax to allow it to pass through the esophagus. Nerve signals to the inferior esophageal sphincter after passage of the bolus cause it to contract, preventing reflux of materials and fluids from the stomach into the esophagus.

💡 WHAT DID YOU LEARN?

12 How do the esophageal tunics differ from the "default" tunic pattern in both the mucosa and muscularis?

13 How is the bolus moved from the oral cavity into the stomach, as described in the three phases of swallowing?

26.2d Stomach

✓ LEARNING OBJECTIVES

7. Describe the gross anatomy and histology of the stomach.

8. Explain the two general functional activities of the stomach.

9. Describe the initiation and action of the three reflexes that regulate motility and secretion in the stomach.

The **stomach** (stŭm′ŭk) is a holding sac in the superior left quadrant of the abdomen immediately inferior to the diaphragm, where mechanical and chemical digestion continues on the bolus. Specifically, the chemical digestion of protein and fat begin in the stomach. Under normal conditions, between 3 and 4 liters of food, drink, and saliva enter the stomach daily. Ingested nutrients generally spend between 2 and 6 hours in the stomach, depending upon the amount and composition of the ingested material. Fatty substances tend to take longer to be emptied from the stomach. Absorption in the stomach is limited to small, nonpolar substances that are in contact with the mucosa of the stomach. Both alcohol and aspirin are examples of substances that are absorbed in the stomach.

Gross Anatomy of the Stomach

The stomach is a muscular J-shaped organ **(figure 26.9)**. It has both a larger convex inferolateral surface called the **greater curvature** and a smaller concave superomedial surface called the **lesser curvature.** This organ is composed of four regions:

- The **cardia** (kar′dē-ă) is a small, narrow, superior entryway into the stomach lumen from the esophagus. The internal opening where the cardia meets the esophagus is called the **cardiac orifice.**

- The **fundus** (fŭn′dŭs; bottom) is the dome-shaped region lateral and superior to the esophageal connection with the stomach. Its superior surface contacts the diaphragm.

- The **body** is the largest region of the stomach; it is inferior to the cardiac orifice and the fundus and extends to the pylorus.

- The **pylorus** (pī-lōr′ŭs; *pylorus* = gatekeeper) is a narrow, medially directed, funnel-shaped pouch that forms the terminal region of the stomach. Its opening into the duodenum of the small intestine is called the **pyloric orifice.** Surrounding this pyloric orifice is a thick ring of circular smooth muscle called the **pyloric sphincter.** The pyloric sphincter regulates the entry of material into the small intestine.

The internal stomach lining is composed of numerous **gastric folds,** or *rugae* (rū′jē; *ruga* = wrinkle). These gastric folds are seen only when the stomach is empty. They allow the

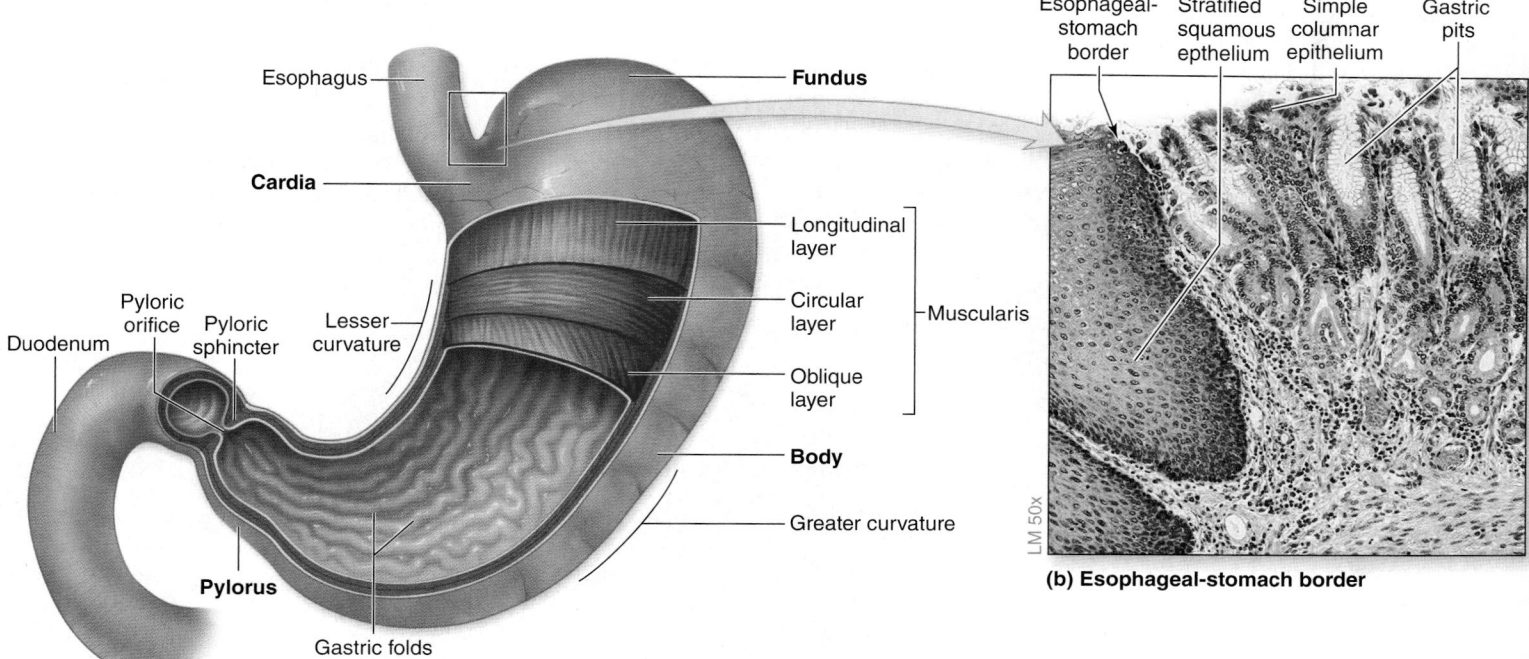

Esophageal-stomach border   Stratified squamous epthelium   Simple columnar epithelium   Gastric pits

Esophagus   Fundus

Cardia

Longitudinal layer

Pyloric orifice   Pyloric sphincter   Lesser curvature   Circular layer   } Muscularis

Duodenum

Oblique layer

Body

Pylorus

Greater curvature

Gastric folds

(a) Stomach regions, anterior view

LM 50x

(b) Esophageal-stomach border

Liver (cut)   Lesser curvature   Diaphragm

Esophagus
Cardiac orifice

Gastric folds

Body of stomach
Pylorus of stomach
Greater curvature

(c) Gross anatomy of stomach (cut open)

Figure 26.9 Gross Anatomy of the Stomach. The stomach is a muscular sac where mechanical and chemical digestion of the bolus occurs. (*a*) The major regions of the stomach are the cardia, the fundus, the body, and the pylorus. Three layers of smooth muscle make up the muscularis tunic. (*b*) A photomicrograph of the abrupt transition from stratified squamous epithelium in the esophagus to simple columnar in the stomach. (*c*) A cadaver photo shows an anterior, open section of the stomach, revealing the gastric folds and the cardiac orifice. AP|R

stomach to expand greatly when it fills with food and drink and then return to its normal J-shape when it empties.

Two serous membranes are associated with the stomach: the *greater omentum* and the *lesser omentum,* which were described previously. The greater omentum extends inferiorly from the greater curvature of the stomach, forming the fatty apron that covers the anterior surface of abdominal organs. The lesser omentum extends superiorly from the lesser curvature of the stomach and duodenum to the liver.

Histology

The mucosa of the stomach is only 1.5 millimeters at its thickest region (about the thickness of a nickel). This inner lining has three significant features (figure 26.10):

- It is lined by a simple columnar epithelium supported by lamina propria. The transition from stratified squamous in the superior regions of the upper GI tract to simple columnar epithelium in the stomach is abrupt. (See figure 26.9b.)

- The lining is indented by numerous depressions called **gastric pits.**

- Several **gastric glands** extend deep into the mucosa from the base of each gastric pit. The muscularis mucosae partially surround the gastric glands and helps expel gastric gland secretions when it contracts.

(a) Stomach wall, sectional view

(b) Stomach mucosa

(c) Gastric pit and gland

Figure 26.10 Histology of the Stomach Wall. (*a*) The stomach wall contains invaginations within the mucosa called gastric pits that lead into gastric glands. (*b*) A photomicrograph shows the cells lining the gastric pit and gastric glands. (*c*) A diagrammatic section of a gastric gland shows its structure and the distribution of different secretory cells. AP|R

The muscularis of the stomach varies from the general GI tract pattern in that it is composed of three smooth muscle layers instead of two: an inner oblique layer, a middle circular layer, and an outer longitudinal layer. The oblique layer is most developed at the cardia and the body of the stomach. The presence of a third layer of smooth muscle assists the continued churning and blending of the swallowed bolus to help mechanically digest the food. The muscularis becomes increasingly thicker as it progresses from the body to the pylorus.

The outermost layer is a serosa called the visceral peritoneum because the stomach is intraperitoneal.

WHAT DO YOU THINK?

2 The stomach secretes highly acidic gastric juices that facilitate the breakdown of food. What prevents the gastric juices from eating away at the stomach itself?

Gastric Secretions

Five types of secretory cells of the gastric epithelium are integral contributors to the process of digestion (figure 26.10c). Four of these cell types produce the approximate 3 liters per day of **gastric juice** associated with the stomach. The fifth type of cell secretes a hormone into the blood.

Surface Mucous Cells   **Surface mucous cells** line the stomach lumen and extend into the gastric pits. They continuously secrete an alkaline product containing mucin onto the gastric surface. Mucin becomes hydrated, producing a 1- to 3-millimeter mucus layer. This mucus layer, along with a high rate of cell turnover in the mucosa, helps to prevent ulceration of the stomach lining upon exposure to both the high acidity of the gastric fluid and gastric enzymes.

Mucous Neck Cells   **Mucous neck cells** are located immediately deep to the base of the gastric pit and are interspersed among the parietal cells (described next). These cells produce an acidic mucin that differs structurally and functionally from the alkaline mucin secreted by the surface mucous cells. The acidic mucin helps maintain the acidic conditions resulting from the secretion of hydrochloric acid by parietal cells. The mucus produced from mucin secretion by both types of mucous cells has lubricating properties to protect the stomach lining from abrasion or mechanical injury.

Parietal Cells   **Parietal cells** (also called *oxyntic cells*) are responsible for the addition of two substances into the lumen of the stomach:

- **Intrinsic factor.** The production of this glycoprotein is the *only* essential function performed by the stomach. Intrinsic factor is required for absorption of vitamin B_{12} in the ileum (final portion of the small intestine). B_{12} is necessary for production of normal erythrocytes. A critical decrease or absence of B_{12} results in pernicious anemia (see Clinical View: "Erythrocyte Volume Disorders" in chapter 18).

- **Hydrochloric acid (HCl).** HCl is not formed within the parietal cell; it would destroy the cell. Instead, it forms from the H^+ and Cl^- secreted across the parietal cells' surface. The details of this process are described in **figure 26.11**. HCl is responsible for the low pH of between 1.5 and 2.5 within the stomach.

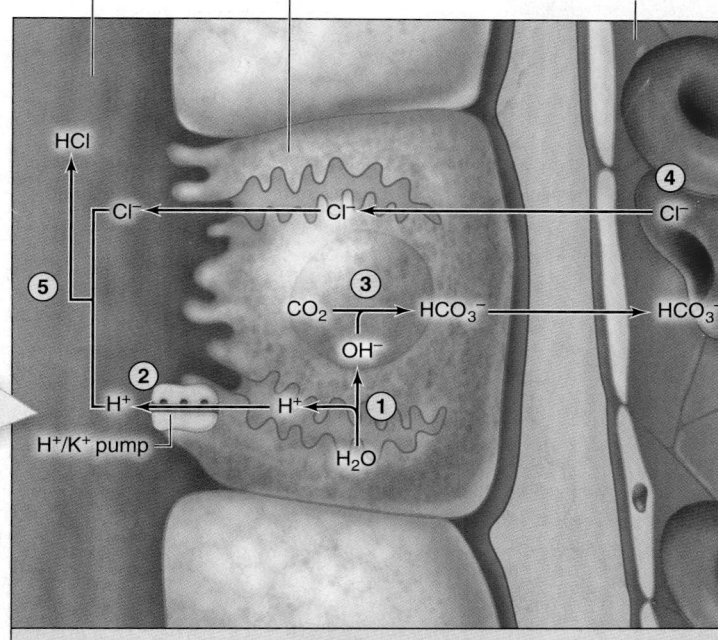

① Water (H_2O) within the parietal cell is split into a hydrogen ion (H^+) and hydroxide ion (OH^-).

② H^+ is pumped into the lumen of the gastric pit by an H^+/K^+ pump.

③ OH^- bonds with carbon dioxide (CO_2) to form bicarbonate ion (HCO_3^-).

④ An exchange occurs as HCO_3^- is transported out of the parietal cell (HCO_3^- then enters the blood), while chloride ion (Cl^-) is transported into the parietal cell; Cl^- then enters the lumen of the gastric gland.

⑤ Within the lumen of the gastric gland, Cl^- combines with H^+ to form hydrochloric acid (HCl).

Figure 26.11 Formation of HCl from Parietal Cells.
H^+ and HCO_3^- are produced in epithelial cells of the stomach. The net movement is H^+ into the lumen of the stomach and HCO_3^- into the blood. Additionally, Cl^- is transferred from the blood into the stomach lumen, where it combines with H^+ to form hydrochloric acid (HCl). AP|R

Hydrochloric acid has several functions in the digestive processes of the stomach:

- It converts the inactive enzyme pepsinogen into active pepsin and provides the optimal pH environment for pepsin activity.

- It kills most microorganisms that enter the stomach (most cannot survive in the extremely low pH).

- It contributes to the breakdown of plant cell walls and animal connective tissue.

- It denatures proteins (see section 2.8b) by causing them to unfold, thus facilitating chemical digestion by enzymes.

Chief Cells   **Chief cells** (also called *zymogenic cells*, or *peptic cells*) are the most numerous secretory cells within the gastric glands, hence the name "chief" cells. These cells produce and secrete packets of zymogen granules primarily containing pepsinogen. Pepsinogen is the inactive precursor of the proteolytic enzyme pepsin. Pepsin must be produced in this inactive form to prevent the destruction of chief cell proteins.

Pepsinogen is activated following its release into the stomach. It is activated by both HCl and other active pepsin molecules already present in the stomach. The pepsin chemically digests denatured proteins in the stomach into smaller peptide fragments (oligopeptides).

CLINICAL VIEW
Peptic Ulcers

Normally a balance exists in the stomach between the acidic gastric juices and the protective, regenerative nature of the mucosa lining. When this balance is thrown off, the stage is set for the development of a **peptic ulcer**—a chronic, solitary erosion of a portion of the lining of either the stomach or the duodenum. Annually, over 4 million people in the United States are diagnosed with an ulcer.

Gastric ulcers are peptic ulcers that occur in the stomach, whereas **duodenal ulcers** are peptic ulcers that occur in the superior part of the duodenum, the first segment of the small intestine. Duodenal ulcers are common because the first part of the duodenum receives the acidic chyme from the stomach but has yet to receive the alkaline bile and pancreatic juice that may neutralize chyme's acidic content.

Symptoms of an ulcer include a gnawing, burning pain in the epigastric region, which may be worse after eating a meal; nausea; vomiting; and extreme belching. Bleeding also may occur, and the partially digested blood results in dark, tarlike stools. If left untreated, an ulcer may erode the entire organ wall and cause **perforation,** which is a medical emergency.

Irritation of the gastric mucosa **(gastritis)** has been linked to many cases of peptic ulcer. Nonsteroidal anti-inflammatory drugs (NSAIDs), such as ibuprofen and aspirin, are a common cause of gastritis, and these drugs also impair healing of the gastric lining. However, the major player in peptic ulcer formation is a bacterium called *Helicobacter pylori*, which is present in over 70% of gastric ulcer cases and well over 90% of duodenal ulcer cases. *H. pylori* resides in the stomach and produces enzymes that break down the components in the gastric mucus, weakening its protective effects. As leukocytes enter the stomach to destroy the bacteria, they also destroy the mucous neck cells. This further irritates the stomach lining and creates an ideal environment for continued *H. pylori* colonization. Thus, the bacteria initiate a cascade of events that lead to erosion of the gastric lining and eventual perforation of the stomach wall, if not treated.

Categories of medications that help are an antibiotic taken for 2 weeks to eradicate *H. pylori,* and treatments that are similar for gastric reflux, including antacids, proton-pump inhibitors, and a histamine (H_2) blocker.

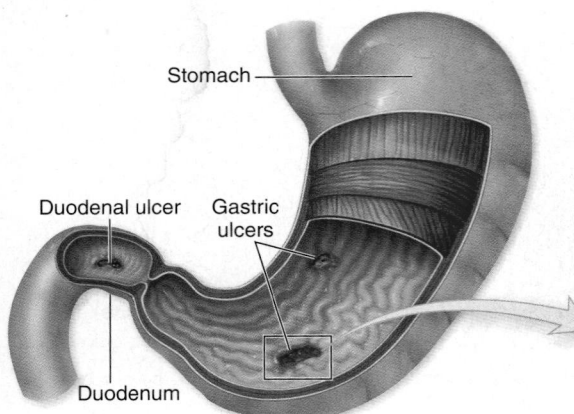

Common locations of gastric and duodenal ulcers.

Mucosa
Submucosa
Muscularis
Serosa

Perforated gastric ulcer

Chief cells also produce **gastric lipase,** an enzyme that has a limited role in fat digestion (digests about 10–15% of the ingested fat).

G-Cells
G-cells are **enteroendocrine** (en′ter-ō-en′dō-krin; *enteron* = gut, intestine) **cells** that are widely distributed in the gastric glands of the stomach. G-cells secrete gastrin hormone into the blood. **Gastrin** stimulates stomach secretions and motility. Other enteroendocrine cells (there are at least eight types) produce other hormones, such as somatostatin, a peptide hormone that modulates the function of nearby enteroendocrine and exocrine cells.

The five types of secretory cells and their products are summarized in **figure 26.12.**

Motility in the Stomach
Smooth muscle activity in the stomach wall has two primary functions: (1) mixing the bolus with gastric juice to form chyme, and (2) emptying chyme from the stomach into the small intestine.

Gastric mixing is a form of mechanical digestion that changes the semidigested bolus into **chyme** (kīm; *chymos* = juice). Chyme has the consistency of a pastelike soup. Contractions of the stomach's thick muscularis layer churn and mix the bolus with the gastric secretions, leading to a reduction in the size of swallowed particles.

Gastric emptying is the movement of acidic chyme from the stomach through the pyloric sphincter into the duodenum, which is facilitated by the progressive thickening of the muscularis layer in the pylorus region. As a wave of peristaltic muscular contraction moves through the pylorus toward the pyloric sphincter, a pressure gradient is established that drives the stomach contents toward the small intestine.

The interaction here is unique: The peristaltic wave establishes a greater pressure on the contents in the pylorus than the pressure exerted by the pyloric sphincter to stay closed and prevent movement. Consequently, a few milliliters (about 3 milliliters) of chyme are emptied into the small intestine. After the peristaltic wave has moved past the pyloric sphincter, the pressure of the sphincter is

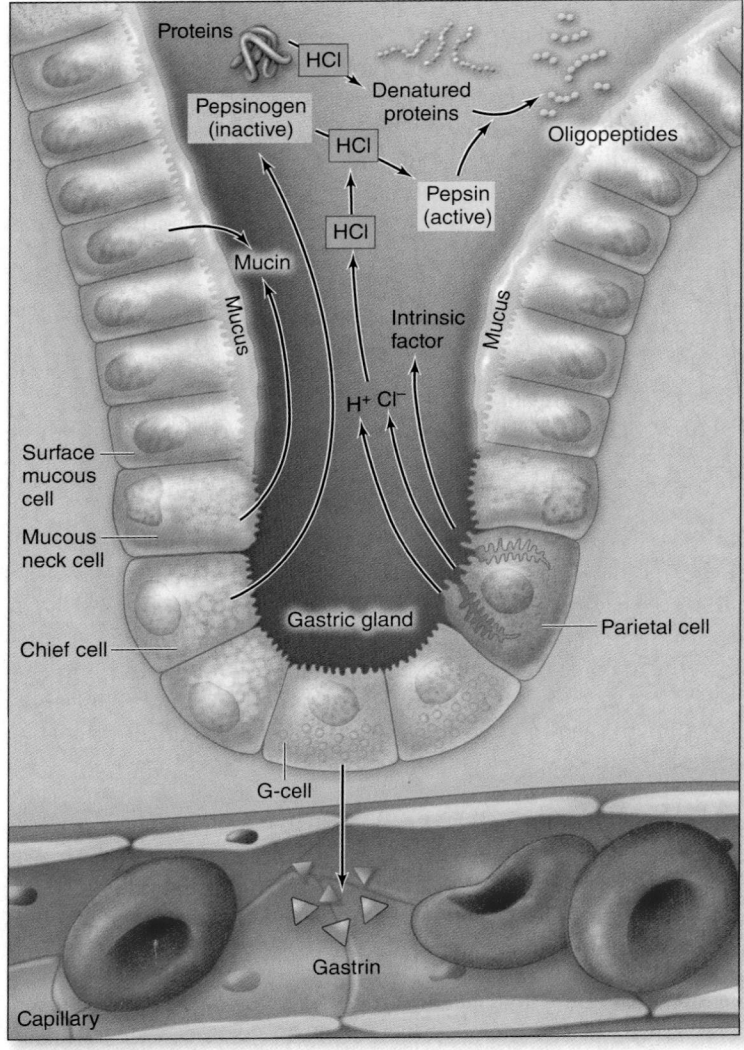

Figure 26.12 Gastric Secretions. Secretory cells and their products are identified. Secretions enter the lumen of the stomach, except the hormone gastrin, which enters the blood.

once again greater than the pressure on the contents, and the pyloric sphincter closes. As this sphincter closes, stomach contents are squeezed back toward the stomach body. This reverse flow event is called **retropulsion.** Retropulsion not only results in the prevention of further chyme moving into the small intestine, but it also contributes to additional mixing of the stomach contents to further reduce size of food particles. The processes of both gastric mixing and gastric emptying are summarized in **figure 26.13**.

Regulation of the Digestive Processes in the Stomach

The stomach is essentially a holding bag for partially digested food until it enters the small intestine, where its digestion will be completed. This process is highly regulated.

INTEGRATE

CLINICAL VIEW
Gastric Content Expulsion by Vomiting

Vomiting is the rapid expulsion of gastric contents through the oral cavity. Prior to vomiting, heart rate and sweating increase, nausea is felt, and a noticeable increase in saliva production occurs. The vomiting reflex is a complicated act that is controlled by the vomiting center in the medulla oblongata. This brainstem region responds to head injury, inner ear motion sickness, infection, toxicity, or food irritation in the stomach and intestines.

Vomiting is initiated following a deep inspiration and the closure of both nasal passages and the glottis. Skeletal muscle contraction (abdominal muscles and diaphragm) increase intragastric pressure and thus supply the primary force for expulsion of digestive tract contents. As the pressure increases in the stomach, the acidic gastric contents are forced into and through the esophagus and out of the oral cavity.

Care must be taken that vomit is not aspirated into the respiratory tract; a risk for a semiconscious or unconscious individual. Thus, it is critical that individuals undergoing surgical procedures have an empty stomach and small intestine because general anesthesia has an associated risk of inducing nausea and vomiting.

① Contractions of smooth muscle in stomach wall mix bolus with gastric secretions to form chyme.

② Peristaltic wave results in pressure gradient that moves stomach contents toward the pylorus region.

③ Pressure gradient increases force in pylorus against pyloric sphincter.

④ Pyloric sphincter opens, and a small volume of chyme enters the duodenum.

⑤ Pyloric sphincter closes, and retropulsion occurs.

(a) Gastric mixing

(b) Gastric emptying

Figure 26.13 Gastric Mixing and Emptying. (*a*) Chyme is formed in the stomach as the bolus is mixed with gastric secretions. (*b*) A small volume is then forced into the duodenum through the partially open pyloric sphincter.

Pacemaker cells (interstitial cells of Cajal) in the stomach wall spontaneously depolarize less than four times per minute and establish its basic rhythm of muscular contraction in this organ. Electrical signals spread through the smooth muscle cells in the muscularis layer of the stomach via gap junctions. Muscular contractions by the stomach wall are regulated by both nervous reflexes and hormones, which alter the force but not rate of contraction, which is constant. Secretory activity of gastric glands is also altered. How this occurs is organized into three phases: cephalic phase, gastric phase, and intestinal phase. The cephalic and gastric reflexes operate most strongly before and during a meal, and the intestinal reflex is more active after a meal, as the ingested materials are being digested.

Cephalic Phase   The cephalic phase primarily involves the *cephalic reflex*, which is a nervous system reflex initiated by the thought, smell, sight, or taste of food. Nerve signals from the higher regions of the brain are sent to the hypothalamus, which then relays nerve signals to the medulla oblongata. The medulla oblongata increases vagal stimulation of the stomach (by increasing parasympathetic output along the vagus nerve to the stomach), causing both an increase in contractile force in the gastric wall (increases motility) and secretory activity of the gastric glands. Sometimes you become aware of these processes when your stomach "growls."

Gastric Phase   The gastric phase involves the processes following the bolus reaching the stomach. This phase is regulated by both the nervous system via the gastric reflex and the endocrine system through the release of gastrin hormone. The *gastric reflex* is initiated as food enters the stomach. Baroreceptors in the wall of the stomach detect increased distension in the stomach wall, and chemoreceptors detect both protein and an increase in pH of gastric contents. (Proteins buffer H^+ and increase pH.) Nerve signals are relayed directly to the medulla oblongata, resulting in the same effects as described in the cephalic reflex—an increase in both stomach motility and secretory activity of gastric cells.

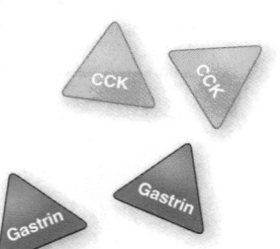

The presence of food (especially protein) in the stomach also causes release of gastrin from enteroendocrine cells. Gastrin enters the blood and circulates back to the stomach to further stimulate the contractile activity of muscle in the gastric wall and to primarily increase release of HCl from parietal cells. Gastrin also stimulates contraction of the pyloric sphincter to slow stomach emptying, thereby allowing sufficient time for completion of digestive activities associated with the stomach.

Intestinal Phase   The intestinal phase involves the processes following the chyme reaching the small intestine, a phase that is also regulated by both the nervous system and the endocrine system. The intestinal phase involves both the intestinal reflex and the release of two significant hormones: cholecystokinin (CCK) and secretin. The *intestinal reflex* opposes the other two reflexes (cephalic reflex and gastric reflex). It protects the small intestine from being overloaded with chyme. The intestinal reflex is initiated with entry of acidic chyme into the duodenum which initiates inhibitory nerve signals to the medulla oblongata. Consequently, vagal stimulation to the stomach is decreased with a concomitant decrease in both motility and secretory activity of the stomach.

Cholecystokinin and secretin, both released from the small intestine, are hormones that decrease both stomach motility and secretory activity, and inhibit the release of gastrin. This slows down the emptying of the stomach, thus allowing the small intestine to continue its digestive processes before additional chyme is added. Both hormones also influence the digestive processes in the lower GI tract and are discussed in more detail later in the chapter. (Note that researchers initially believed an additional hormone released from the small intestine named *gastric inhibitory peptide* regulated stomach activity. However, this hormone is now thought to primarily regulate the release of insulin in response to increased glucose concentration in the contents of the small intestine. To better reflect its role, it has been renamed **glucose-insulinotropic peptide (GIP).**

 WHAT DID YOU LEARN?

14   List the secretory cell types in the stomach, their products, and the function of the products.

15   Which neural reflex is initiated by food in the stomach and what does it control?

26.3 Lower Gastrointestinal Tract

The lower gastrointestinal (GI) tract continues the processes of digestion and importantly functions in the absorption of nutrients. Material that cannot be digested and absorbed is then eliminated.

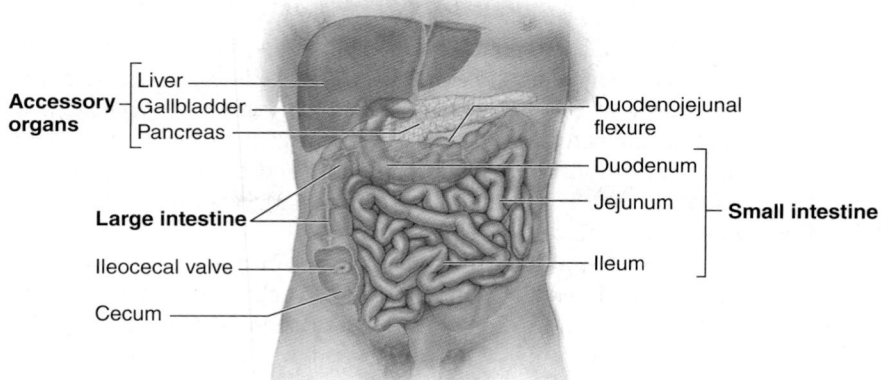

Accessory organs
- Liver
- Gallbladder
- Pancreas

Duodenojejunal flexure

Duodenum
Jejunum — **Small intestine**
Ileum

Large intestine

Ileocecal valve

Cecum

Figure 26.14 Gross Anatomy of the Lower GI Tract Organs and Accessory Organs The three regions of the small intestine—duodenum, jejunum, and ileum—are continuous and framed within the abdominal cavity by the large intestine. Accessory organs release secretions into the duodenum.

26.3a Overview of the Lower Gastrointestinal Tract Organs

 LEARNING OBJECTIVE

1. Describe the three components of the lower gastrointestinal tract.

First, we take a superficial view of the lower GI tract organs and accessory organs to help integrate their structures with their digestive activities and functions (**figure 26.14**):

- **Small intestine.** The small intestine is divided into three continuous regions (duodenum, jejunum, and ileum). Recall that the duodenum is considered part of the upper GI tract, but it is described in this section on the lower GI tract organs. The small intestine receives chyme from the stomach that is then mixed with accessory organ secretions. Most chemical digestion and absorption occurs in this organ.
- **Accessory organs.** Accessory organ secretions include bile and pancreatic juice. Bile is produced by the liver and then stored, concentrated, and released by the gallbladder. Pancreatic juice contains numerous digestive enzymes and is produced and released by the pancreas.
- **Large intestine.** The large intestine continues absorption, primarily of water, electrolytes, and vitamins (including vitamins B and K produced by bacteria within the large intestine). The digestive process is completed as feces is produced and then eliminated through the anus.

 WHAT DID YOU LEARN?

16 What organs are considered part of the lower GI tract?

26.3b Small Intestine

 LEARNING OBJECTIVES

2. Describe the anatomy of the small intestine.
3. List the glands found in the small intestine and their secretions.
4. Explain motility within the small intestine.

The **small intestine** is a long tube that is inferior to the stomach and located medially in the abdominal cavity. Generally, about 9 to 10 liters of ingested food, water, and digestive system secretions enter the small intestine daily. Ingested nutrients typically spend at least 12 hours in the small intestine. The small intestine finishes the chemical digestion process and is responsible for absorbing most of the nutrients and a large percentage of the water and electrolytes. Vitamins ingested in the diet are also absorbed by the small intestine. Fat-soluble vitamins are absorbed with lipids, and water-soluble vitamins are absorbed through various transport mechanisms. (Recall from our discussion on parietal cells that vitamin B_{12} requires intrinsic factor that is produced by the stomach to be absorbed.)

Gross Anatomy of the Small Intestine

The **small intestine** is also called the *small bowel.* It is a coiled, thin-walled tube about 6 meters (20 feet) in length in the unembalmed cadaver. (It is much shorter in a living individual due to muscle tone.) It extends from the pylorus of the stomach to the cecum of the large intestine; thus, it occupies a significant portion of the abdominal cavity. The small intestine consists of three specific segments: the duodenum, jejunum, and ileum.

The **duodenum** (dū-ō-dē′nŭm, dū-od′ĕ-nŭm; breadth of twelve fingers) forms the first segment of the small intestine. It is approximately 25 centimeters (10 inches) long and originates at the pyloric sphincter (see figure 26.9). The duodenum is arched into a C-shape around the head of the pancreas and becomes continuous with the jejunum at the **duodenojejunal flexure** (flek′sher; *fleksura* = bend). Most of the duodenum is retroperitoneal, although the very proximal part is intraperitoneal and is connected to the liver by the lesser omentum. The duodenum receives accessory gland secretions from the liver, gallbladder, and pancreas.

The **jejunum** (jĕ-jū′nŭm; *jejunus* = empty) is the middle region of the small intestine (figure 26.14). Extending approximately 2.5 meters (7.5 feet), it makes up about two-fifths of the small intestine's total length. The jejunum is the primary region within the small intestine for chemical digestion and nutrient absorption.

The **ileum** (il′ē-ŭm; *eiles* = twisted) is the last region of the small intestine. At about 3.6 meters (10.8 feet) in length, the ileum forms approximately three-fifths of the small intestine. Its distal end terminates at the **ileocecal** (il′ē-ō-sē′kăl) **valve,** a sphincter that controls the entry of materials into the large intestine. Both the jejunum and the ileum are intraperitoneal and suspended within the abdomen by the mesentery (see figure 26.3). Absorption of digested materials continues in the ileum.

The mucosal and submucosal tunics of the small intestine are thrown into internal **circular folds** (also called *plicae* [plī′sē] *circulares*) that extend inward toward the lumen **(figure 26.15)**. Circular folds are easily seen by the naked eye: They help increase the surface area through which nutrients are absorbed. They also act like "speed bumps" to slow down the movement of chyme and ensure that it remains within the small intestine for maximal nutrient absorption. Circular folds are more numerous in the duodenum and jejunum and least numerous in the ileum.

Figure 26.15 Histology of the Small Intestine. (*a*) The wall of the small intestine is formed by four tunics: mucosa, submucosa, muscularis, and serosa. (*b*) Circular folds are inward projections of both the mucosa and submucosa, whereas villi are fingerlike projections of only the mucosa. Both circular folds and villi increase the surface area of the small intestine. (*c*) The epithelial cells covering the surface of each villus have microvilli to further increase the surface area. The lamina propria within each villus houses both blood capillaries and lymphatic capillaries (lacteals). AP|R

WHAT DO YOU THINK?

③ Why are the circular folds much more numerous in the duodenum and least numerous in the ileum? How does the abundance of circular folds relate to the main functions of the duodenum?

Histology

In the small intestine, the length of the muscularis mucosae is shorter than the two layers internal to it, forcing these two inner layers into folds to form small fingerlike projections of the mucosa called **villi.**

Villi are larger and most numerous in the jejunum. The epithelium and lamina propria of each villus appears analogous to a glove (epithelium) covering a finger (lamina propria). These villi, along with the circular folds described earlier, help increase the surface area for absorption and secretion. Each villus contains an arteriole, a rich capillary network, and a venule. The capillaries absorb most nutrients. A **lacteal** is a type of lymphatic capillary also within the villus (described in section 21.1a). A lacteal is responsible for absorbing lipids and lipid-soluble vitamins that are too large to be absorbed by the blood capillaries.

Microvilli (mī-krō-vil′ī; *micros* = small) are extensions of the plasma membrane of the simple columnar epithelial cells lining the small intestine. Microvilli further increase the surface area of the small intestine. Individual microvilli are not clearly visible in light micrographs of the small intestine; instead, they appear as a fuzzy edge of the simple columnar cells called the **brush border.** Embedded within this brush border are various enzymes that complete the chemical digestion of most nutrients immediately before absorption. Collectively these are called **brush border enzymes.** Located in close proximity and also embedded within the membrane are the required proteins for transport of digestion products. Histologic images of both villi and microvilli are shown in **figure 26.16.**

Small Intestine Secretions

Between the intestinal villi are invaginations of mucosa called **intestinal glands** (also known as *intestinal crypts,* or *crypts of Lieberkühn*); these mucosal cells secrete **intestinal juice.** These glands extend to the base of the mucosa and slightly resemble the anatomy of the gastric glands of the stomach (figure 26.15c).

- **Goblet cells** produce mucin that when hydrated form mucus, which lubricates and protects the intestinal lining. These cells increase in number from the duodenum to the ileum, because more lubrication is needed as digested materials are absorbed and undigested materials are left behind.
- **Unicellular gland cells** synthesize **enteropeptidase,** an enzyme described later in this chapter.
- The enteroendocrine cells release hormones such as CCK and GIP. We have already discussed the stomach-associated functions of these hormones. Several other functions are described later.

Another type of gland housed within the submucosa layer and found only in the proximal duodenum is called a **submucosal,** or **duodenal, gland** (*Brunner gland*). This gland produces a viscous, alkaline mucus secretion that protects the duodenum from the acidic chyme.

Motility of the Small Intestine

Smooth muscle activity in the small intestine wall has three primary functions: (1) mixing chyme with accessory gland secretions, (2) moving the chyme continually against new areas of the brush border, and (3) propelling the contents through the small intestine toward the large intestine.

All these functions facilitate chemical digestion and absorption, employing the processes of segmentation and peristalsis. When

(a) Intestinal villi

Villi
Intestinal lumen
Simple columnar epithelium
Lamina propria
Goblet cells
LM 70x

Simple columnar cell
Brush border (microvilli)
Intestinal lumen
TEM 18,000x
(b) Microvilli

Figure 26.16 Microvilli. Photomicrographs show (*a*) the internal structure of villi projecting into the intestinal lumen, and (*b*) microvilli along the plasma membrane of the epithelium's apical surface.

chyme first enters the small intestine, segmentation is more prevalent than peristalsis. **Segmentation** mixes chyme with accessory gland secretion through a "back-and-forward" motion.

Peristalsis then propels material within the GI lumen by alternating contraction of the circular and longitudinal muscle layers in small regions. The rhythm of muscular contractions is more frequent in the duodenum than the ileum, thus the net movement of intestinal contents is toward the large intestine.

The **gastroileal** (gas′trō-il′ē-ăl) **reflex** moves the contents from the ileum into the cecum in response to food entering the stomach. Although the ileocecal sphincter is usually constricted, increased muscular activity in the ileum during digestion is accompanied by ileocecal sphincter relaxation, allowing small intestine contents to enter the large intestine. Then, contraction of the sphincter closes the passage to decrease backflow into the ileum.

WHAT DID YOU LEARN?

17 What are the three anatomic structures that increase the surface area of the small intestine? Describe each.

18 Which type of motility is primarily responsible for mixing the chyme and accessory gland secretions within the small intestine—segmentation or peristalsis?

26.3c Accessory Organs and Ducts

LEARNING OBJECTIVES

5. Describe the accessory digestive organs associated with the small intestine and the contributions of each to digestive processes.

6. Explain how blood and bile flow through the liver.

7. Discuss the regulation of the accessory glands associated with the small intestine.

Three accessory digestive organs release secretions into the duodenum: the liver, the gallbladder, and the pancreas. Here we examine the ducts from each organ to the duodenum, the anatomy and histology of each organ, and their products conveyed to the small intestine that contribute to the digestion of the chyme arriving from the stomach. The accessory organs are summarized in **table 26.2**.

Accessory Organ Ducts

A series of ducts deliver secretions to the duodenum of the small intestine (**figure 26.17**). These ducts include the biliary apparatus from the liver and gallbladder, and the pancreatic duct from the pancreas.

The **biliary** (bil′ē-ăr-ē) **apparatus** is a network of thin ducts that include the left and right hepatic ducts, which drain the left and right lobes of the liver, respectively. The **left** and **right hepatic ducts** merge to form a single **common hepatic duct.** The union of the **cystic duct** from the gallbladder and the common hepatic duct forms the **common bile duct** that extends inferiorly to the duodenum.

The **hepatopancreatic ampulla** (or *ampulla of vater*) is a swelling on the posterior duodenal wall, where the common bile duct and **main pancreatic duct** from the pancreas merge and pierce the duodenal wall. Bile (secretions released from the liver and gallbladder) and pancreatic juice (from the pancreas) mix in the hepatopancreatic ampulla prior to emptying into the duodenum. Associated with the hepatopancreatic ampulla is the **hepatopancreatic sphincter** that regulates movement of bile and pancreatic juice into the duodenum. Within the duodenum, the **major duodenal papilla** is a projection where the duct penetrates the wall, and both bile and pancreatic juice enter the duodenum. An

Table 26.2	Accessory Organs Associated with the Duodenum	
Organ	**Description**	**Functions**
Liver	Largest internal organ	Primary digestive function is to produce and release bile into the duodenum
Gallbladder	Small muscular sac on inferior side of liver	Stores, concentrates, and releases bile into the duodenum
Pancreas	Mixed gland with endocrine and exocrine functions	Exocrine functions produce and release digestive enzymes, and HCO_3^- is released from pancreatic ducts to form a mixture called "pancreatic juice" into the duodenum

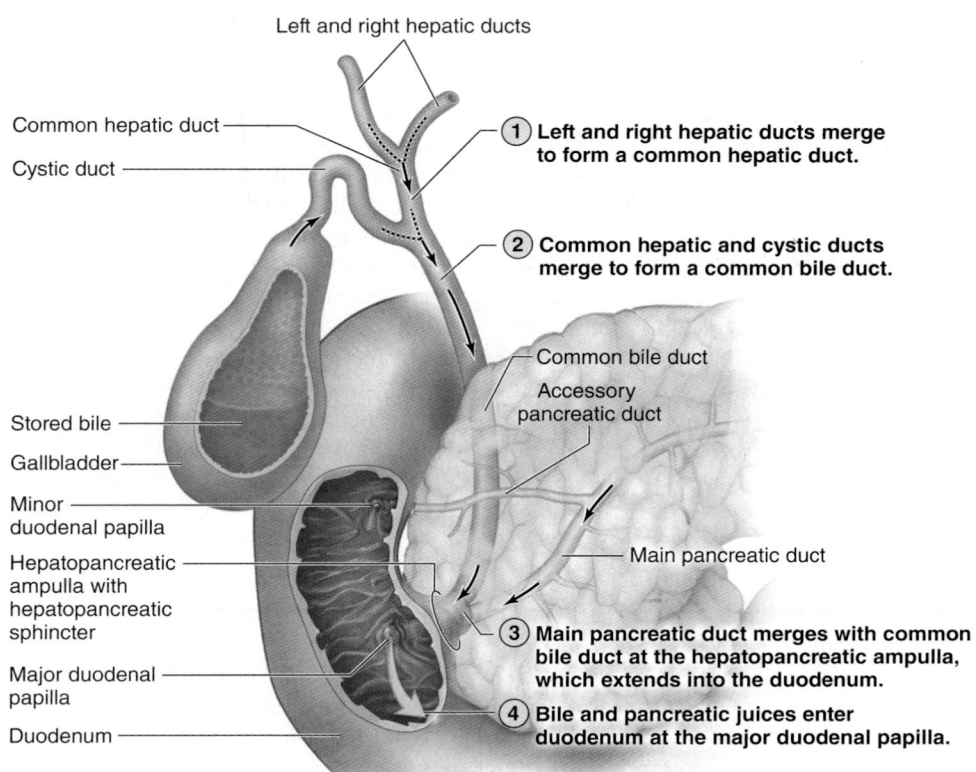

Left and right hepatic ducts

Common hepatic duct

Cystic duct

① **Left and right hepatic ducts merge to form a common hepatic duct.**

② **Common hepatic and cystic ducts merge to form a common bile duct.**

Common bile duct

Accessory pancreatic duct

Stored bile

Gallbladder

Minor duodenal papilla

Hepatopancreatic ampulla with hepatopancreatic sphincter

Major duodenal papilla

Duodenum

Main pancreatic duct

③ **Main pancreatic duct merges with common bile duct at the hepatopancreatic ampulla, which extends into the duodenum.**

④ **Bile and pancreatic juices enter duodenum at the major duodenal papilla.**

alternative way that a small amount of pancreatic juice may also enter the duodenum is through an **accessory pancreatic duct.** This duct penetrates the duodenal wall, forming the **minor duodenal papilla.**

Liver

The **liver** is an accessory digestive organ. It is located in the right upper quadrant of the abdomen, immediately inferior to the diaphragm (see figure 26.1). It has numerous functions (described in section 27.4), but its main function in digestion is the production of bile.

Gross Anatomy of the Liver   The liver is the largest internal organ, weighing 1 to 2 kilograms (2 to 4 pounds), and it constitutes approximately 2% of an adult's body weight. The liver is covered by a connective tissue capsule and a layer of visceral peritoneum, except for a small region on its diaphragmatic surface called the bare area **(figure 26.18).**

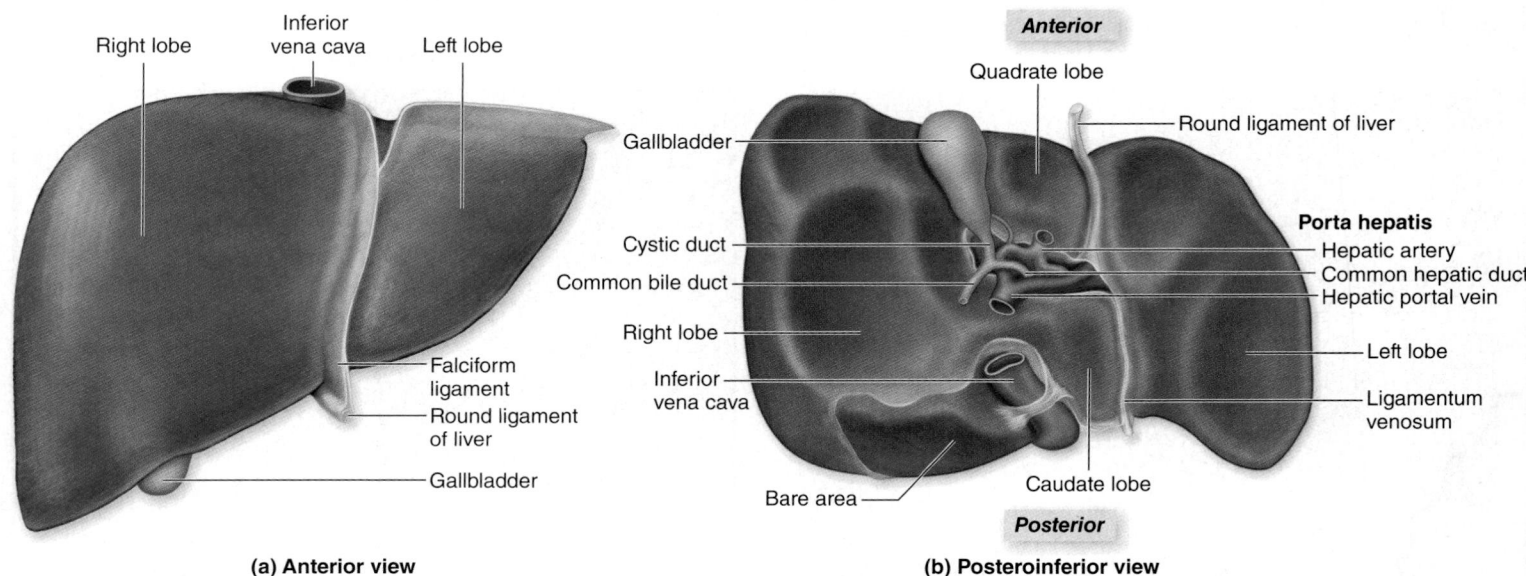

Right lobe

Inferior vena cava

Left lobe

Gallbladder

Cystic duct

Common bile duct

Right lobe

Inferior vena cava

Falciform ligament

Round ligament of liver

Gallbladder

(a) Anterior view

Anterior

Quadrate lobe

Round ligament of liver

Porta hepatis
Hepatic artery
Common hepatic duct
Hepatic portal vein

Left lobe

Ligamentum venosum

Caudate lobe

Bare area

Posterior

(b) Posteroinferior view

Figure 26.18 Gross Anatomy of the Liver. The liver is in the upper right quadrant of the abdomen. (*a*) Anterior and (*b*) posteroinferior views show the four lobes of the liver. AP|R

INTEGRATE

CONCEPT CONNECTION

The hepatic portal system is a venous network that drains the digestive organs and shunts the blood to the liver (see section 20.10d). The blood exits the liver through hepatic veins that merge with the inferior vena cava.

The GI tract absorbs digested nutrients. These nutrients must be transported to and processed within the liver. The liver also detoxifies any potentially harmful agents that have been absorbed into the GI blood vessels. It is much more efficient to carry blood containing these materials first to the liver via the hepatic portal system for processing, before it is distributed throughout the body.

The liver is composed of four partially separated lobes and is supported by two ligaments. The major lobes are the **right lobe** and the **left lobe.** The right lobe is separated from the smaller left lobe by the falciform ligament, a peritoneal fold that secures the liver to the anterior abdominal wall. In the inferior free edge of the falciform ligament lies the **round ligament of the liver** (*ligamentum teres*), which represents the remnant of the fetal umbilical vein. Within the right lobe are the **caudate** (kaw'dāt; *cauda* = tail) **lobe** and the **quadrate** (kwah'drāt; *quadrates* = square) **lobe.** The caudate lobe is adjacent to the inferior vena cava, and the quadrate lobe is adjacent to the gallbladder.

Along the inferior surface of the liver are several structures that collectively resemble the letter H. The gallbladder and the round ligament of the liver form the vertical superior parts of the H; the **inferior vena cava** and the **ligamentum venosum** form the vertical inferior parts. (Recall from section 20.12 that the ligamentum venosum is a

INTEGRATE

CLINICAL VIEW
Cirrhosis of the Liver

Liver cirrhosis (sir-rō'sis; *kirrhos* = yellow) results when hepatocytes have been destroyed and are replaced by fibrous scar tissue. This scar tissue, which results from collagen synthesis by reticuloendothelial cells in the liver, often surrounds isolated nodules of regenerating hepatocytes. The fibrous scar tissue also compresses both the blood vessels resulting in **hepatic portal hypertension** (high blood pressure in the hepatic portal venous system) and bile ducts in the liver, which impedes bile flow.

Liver cirrhosis is caused by chronic injury to the hepatocytes, as may result from chronic alcoholism, liver diseases, or certain drugs or toxins. Chronic hepatitis (hep-ă-tī'tis) is a long-term inflammation of the liver that leads to necrosis of liver tissue. Most frequently, viral infections from either **hepatitis B** or **hepatitis C** produce chronic hepatitis. Other disorders that result in liver cirrhosis include some inherited diseases, chronic biliary obstruction, and biliary cirrhosis.

Early stages of liver cirrhosis may be asymptomatic. However, once liver function begins to falter, the patient complains of fatigue, weight loss, and nausea, and may have pain in the right upper quadrant. During an exam, a doctor may palpate an abnormally small and hard liver. To confirm the

diagnosis, a liver biopsy is done to obtain a small portion of liver tissue through a needle passed into the liver; the cells are then examined microscopically. The fibrosis and scarring of liver cirrhosis are irreversible. However, further scarring may be slowed or prevented by treating the cause of the cirrhosis (e.g., hepatitis, alcoholism).

Advanced liver cirrhosis may have a variety of complications :

- **Jaundice** (yellowing of the skin and sclerae of the eyes) occurs when the liver's ability to eliminate bilirubin is impaired.
- **Edema** (e-dē'mă), the accumulation of fluid in body tissues, is evident due to reduced formation and release of albumin.
- **Ascites** (ă-sī'tēz; fluid accumulation in the abdomen) develops because of decreased albumin production.
- Intense itching occurs when bile products are deposited in the skin.
- Toxins in the blood and brain accumulate because the liver cannot effectively process them.
- Hepatic portal hypertension may lead to dilated veins of the inferior esophagus (esophageal varices).

End-stage liver cirrhosis may be treated only with a liver transplant. Otherwise, death results either from progressive liver failure or from the complications.

This gross specimen depicts a type of nodular cirrhosis of the liver.

Fibrous scar tissue

LM 100x

Normal hepatocytes

A photomicrograph shows how fibrous scar tissue infiltrates and replaces hepatocytes.

remnant of the ductus venosus in the embryo. This vessel shunted blood from the umbilical vein to the inferior vena cava.) Finally, the **porta hepatis** (pōr′tă, = gate; hep′ă-tis), the horizontal crossbar of the H, is the site at which blood and lymph vessels, bile ducts, and nerves (not shown) enter and leave the liver. In particular, the hepatic portal vein and branches of the hepatic artery proper enter at the porta hepatis.

The cells of the liver are served by a dual blood supply; one is oxygenated and the other is deoxygenated. The **hepatic artery** is a branch of the celiac trunk that carries oxygenated blood to the liver. The **hepatic portal vein,** as part of the hepatic portal system (see

section 20.10d) carries blood from the capillary beds of the GI tract, spleen, and pancreas. It brings approximately 75% of the blood volume to the liver. This blood is rich in nutrients and other absorbed substances but relatively poor in oxygen. Blood from branches of these two vessels mixes as it passes into and through the hepatic lobules (described next).

Histology The liver's connective tissue capsule branches throughout the organ and forms septa that partition the liver into thousands of small, polyhedral **hepatic lobules** that are the structural and functional units of the liver (**figure 26.19**). Within hepatic lobules are

Figure 26.19 Histology of the Liver.
(a) The functional units of the liver are called hepatic lobules.
(b) A central vein projects through the center of a hepatic lobule, and several portal triads define its periphery.
(c) A photomicrograph depicts a liver lobule and portal triad.
(d) Diagram of the hepatic portal system. AP|R

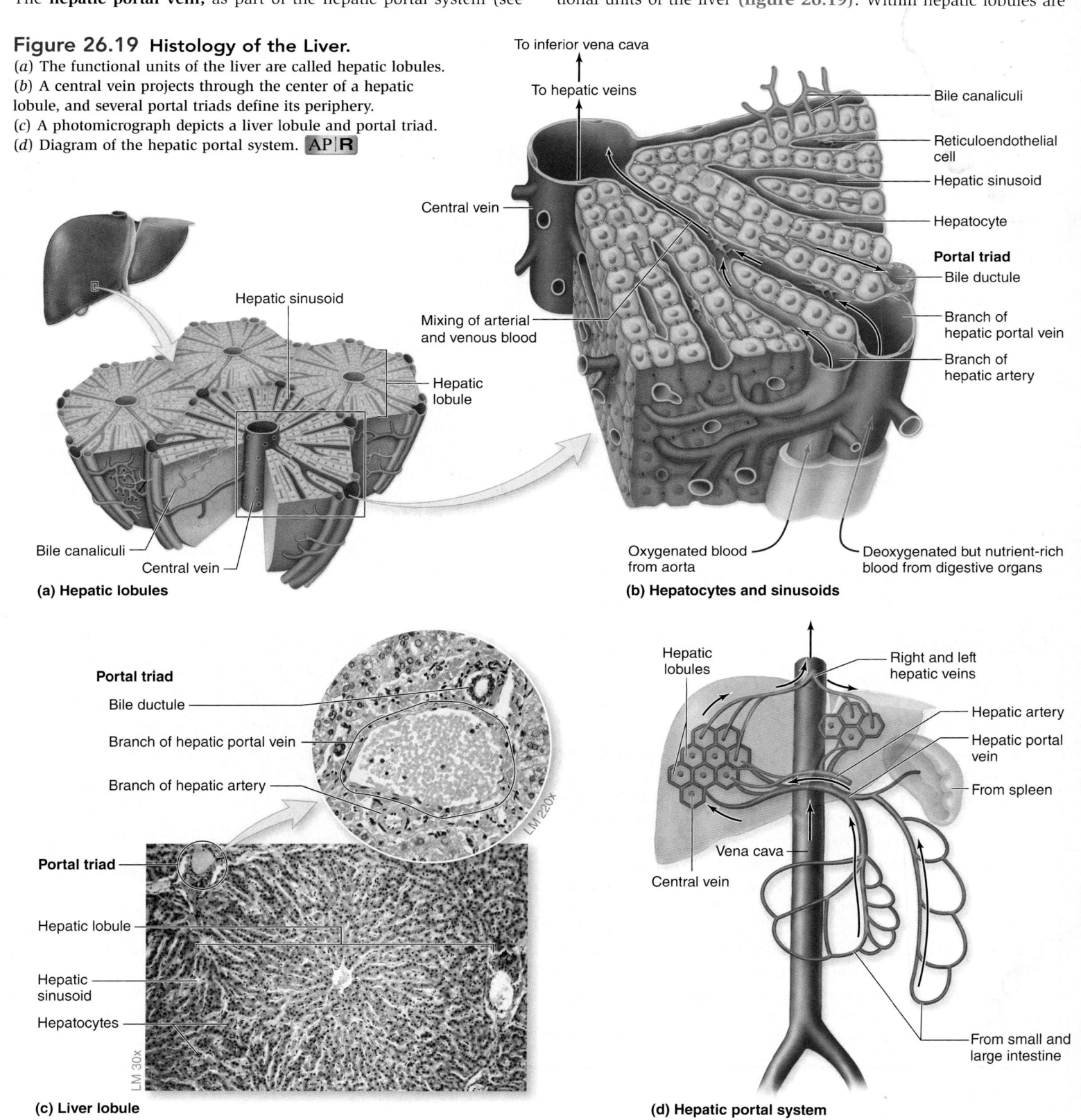

(a) Hepatic lobules

(b) Hepatocytes and sinusoids

(c) Liver lobule

(d) Hepatic portal system

liver cells called **hepatocytes** (hep'ă-tō-sīt). At the periphery of each lobule are several **portal triads,** composed of a hepatic duct bile ductule, and *branches* of the hepatic portal vein and the hepatic artery. At the center of each lobule is a **central vein** that drains the blood flow from the lobule. Central veins collect the blood and merge throughout the liver to form numerous **hepatic veins** that eventually empty into the inferior vena cava.

In cross section, a hepatic lobule looks like a side view of a bicycle wheel. The central vein is like the hub of the wheel. At the circumference of the wheel (where the tire would be) are the portal triads that are usually equidistant apart. Cords of hepatocytes make up the numerous spokes of the wheel, and they are bordered by **hepatic sinusoids** (sī'nŭ-soyd; *sinus* = cavity).

Hepatic sinusoids are thin-walled capillaries with large gaps between these cells, which make the sinusoids more permeable than other capillaries. Venous blood of the hepatic portal system (figure 26.19b) and arterial blood are mixed within hepatic sinusoids and then flow slowly toward the central vein (figure 26.19*b*). Nutrients are absorbed from the sinusoids and enter the hepatocytes. Additionally, the sinusoids are lined with stellate (star-shaped) cells called **reticuloendothelial cells** (*Kupffer cells*). These cells are macrophages that are normally responsible for engulfing potentially harmful substances (e.g., microbes) as the blood travels through the liver sinusoids.

Sandwiched between each cord of hepatocytes is a **bile canaliculus** (kan'ă-lik-yū-lŭs). This is a small channel that conducts bile produced by hepatocytes to the hepatic duct in the portal triad.

Bile   The liver secretes bile, an alkaline fluid containing mostly water, bicarbonate ions (HCO_3^-), bile salts (formed from cholesterol), bile pigments (e.g., bilirubin), cholesterol, lecithin (a phospholipid) and mucin. The liver produces bile at a rate of 0.5 to 1 liter per day. Bile salts and lecithin function in the mechanical digestion of lipids, allowing more efficient chemical digestion of triglycerides.

Gallbladder

Attached to the inferior surface of the liver (see figure 26.18), the **gallbladder** (or *cholecyst*) is a saclike organ that stores, concentrates,

and releases bile that the liver produces. The gallbladder has three tunics: an inner mucosa, a middle muscularis, and an external serosa. The mucosa is thrown into folds that permit distension of the wall as the gallbladder fills with bile. Earlier we learned that the **cystic** (sis'tik; *cysto* = bladder) **duct** connects the gallbladder to the common bile duct.

At the neck of the gallbladder, a sphincter valve controls the flow of bile into and out of the gallbladder. Bile enters the gallbladder when the hepatopancreatic sphincter associated with the hepatopancreatic ampulla is closed. It backs up through both the common bile duct and cystic duct into the gallbladder. The gallbladder can hold approximately 40 to 60 milliliters of concentrated bile. Concentrated bile then travels back from the gallbladder through the cystic duct and then the common bile duct for conduction to the small intestine.

 WHAT DO YOU THINK?

4 If your gallbladder were surgically removed, how would this affect your digestion of fatty meals? What diet alterations might you have to make after this surgery?

Pancreas

The **pancreas** has both endocrine and exocrine functions. Endocrine cells produce and secrete hormones such as insulin and glucagon (see section 17.10). Exocrine cells (also called acinar cells) produce pancreatic juice to assist with digestive activities.

Gross Anatomy of the Pancreas   The pancreas is a retroperitoneal organ that extends horizontally from the left lateral edge of the duodenum toward the left side of the abdominal cavity, where it touches the spleen. The pancreas exhibits a wide **head** adjacent to the curvature of the duodenum; a central, elongated **body** projecting toward the left lateral abdominal wall; and a **tail** that tapers as it approaches the spleen **(figure 26.20)**.

Histology   The pancreas contains modified simple cuboidal epithelial cells called **acinar** cells that are arranged in saclike **acini**

INTEGRATE

CLINICAL VIEW
Gallstones (Cholelithiasis)

Concentration of materials in the bile may lead to the eventual formation of **gallstones.** Gallstones occur twice as frequently in women as in men and are more prevalent in developed countries. Obesity, increasing age, female sex hormones, Caucasian ethnicity, and lack of physical activity are all risk factors for developing gallstones.

The term **cholelithiasis** (kō'lē-li-thī'ă-sis) refers to the presence of gallstones in either the gallbladder or the biliary apparatus. Gallstones are typically formed from condensations of either cholesterol or calcium and bile salts. These stones may vary from the tiniest grains to almost golf-ball-sized. The majority of gallstones are asymptomatic until a gallstone becomes lodged in the neck of the cystic duct, causing the gallbladder to become inflamed (**cholecystitis**) and dilated. The most common symptom is severe pain (called biliary colic) perceived in the right hypochondriac region or sometimes between the shoulder blades or in the area of the right shoulder.

A photograph of gallstones in a gallbladder.

Nausea and vomiting may occur, along with indigestion and bloating. Symptoms are typically worse after eating a fatty meal. Treatment consists of surgical removal of the gallbladder, called **cholecystectomy** (kō'lē-sis-tek'tō-mē; *chol* = bile, *kystis* = bladder, *ektome* = excision).

Following surgery, the liver continues to produce bile, even in the absence of the gallbladder, but concentrating bile no longer occurs, so no more gallstones are produced.

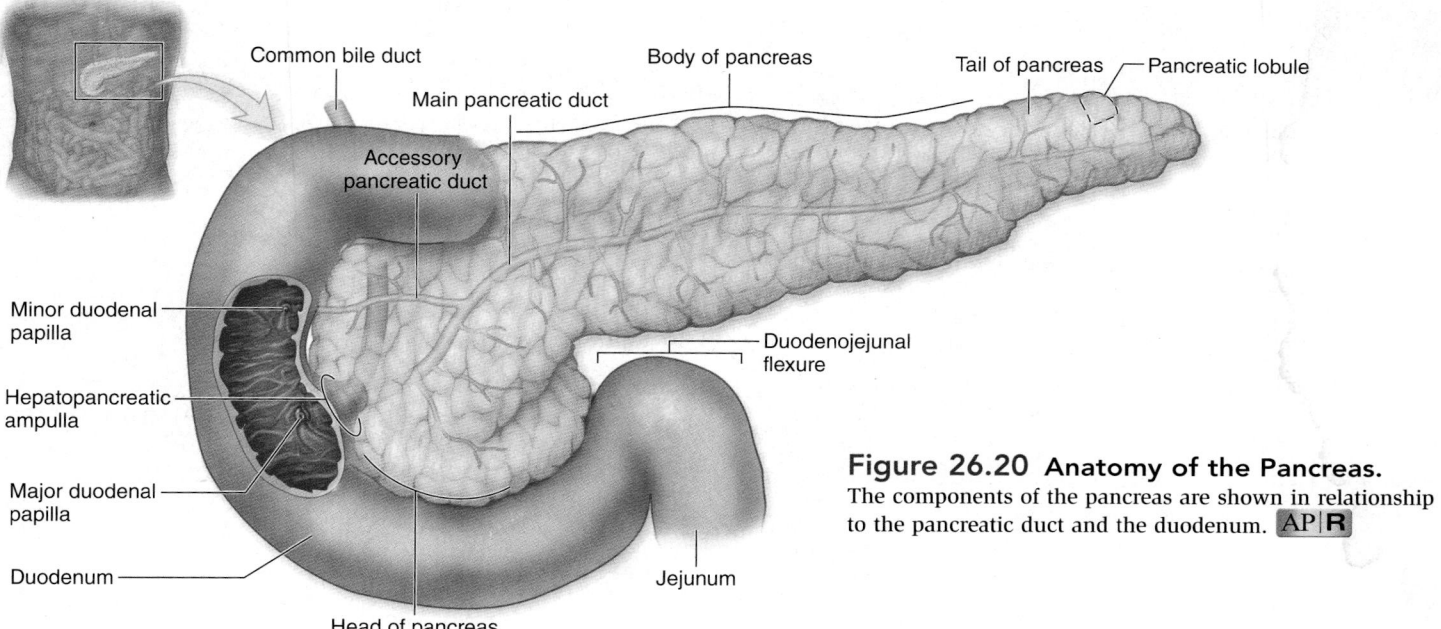

Figure 26.20 Anatomy of the Pancreas.
The components of the pancreas are shown in relationship to the pancreatic duct and the duodenum. AP|R

(sing., *acinus* = grape) **(figure 26.21)**. These cells are organized into large clusters termed **lobules**. Acinar cells produce and release hydrolytic enzymes. Small ducts lead from each acinus into larger ducts that empty into larger pancreatic ducts that lead to the duodenum (as described earlier). The simple cuboidal epithelial cells lining the pancreatic ducts have the important function of secreting alkaline HCO_3^- fluid.

Pancreatic Juice Together, secretions of acinar cells and cells that line the pancreatic ducts form **pancreatic juice**. Pancreatic juice (approximately 1 to 1.5 liters per day) is an alkaline fluid containing mostly water, HCO_3^-, and a versatile mixture of hydrolytic enzymes that are described in detail later in the chapter. These enzymes include the following:

- Pancreatic amylase to digest starch
- Pancreatic lipase for the digestion of fats
- Inactive proteases (trypsinogen, chymotrypsinogen, and procarboxypeptidase) that, when activated, digest protein
- Nucleases for the digestion of nucleic acids (DNA and RNA)

Regulation of Accessory Structures Several of the same processes that regulate stomach secretions and motility control the release of secretions from the accessory organs. Vagal stimulation (see section 15.3a) during the cephalic and gastric phase, in addition to stimulating stomach motility and secretion, also activates the pancreas to release pancreatic juice.

Cholecystokinin (CCK) (ko′lē-sis-to-kī′nin; *chole* = bile; *cyst* = sac, *kinin* = to move) is a hormone released from the small intestine primarily in response to fatty chyme. One of the primary functions of cholecystokinin (and from which its name is derived) is stimulation of the smooth muscle in the gallbladder wall to strongly contract, causing the release of concentrated bile. Other functions of CCK include stimulating the pancreas to release enzyme-rich pancreatic juice, and relaxing the smooth muscle within the hepatopancreatic ampulla, allowing entry of the bile and pancreatic juice into the small intestine. CCK also inhibits both stomach motility and release of gastric secretions (as described earlier).

Secretin (se-krē′tin) is released from the small intestine primarily in response to an increase in chyme acidity. Secretin primarily causes the release of an alkaline solution that contains HCO_3^- from both the liver and ducts of the pancreas. Upon entering the small intestine, this alkaline

Figure 26.21 Histology of the Pancreas. Photomicrographs show the histology of pancreatic islets and pancreatic acini.

Alpha cell (secretes glucagon)
Beta cell (secretes insulin)
Arteriole
Venule
Pancreatic islet
LM 75x
Pancreatic acini
Pancreatic islet
Acinar cell
LM 200x
Pancreatic acinus
Acinar cell (secretes amylase, lipase, proteases, and nucleases)
Duct cell (secretes HCO_3^-)
Pancreatic acinus

Table 26.3   Hormones That Control Digestion

Hormone	Secreted by	Stimulus for Release	Primary Target(s) and Effects
Gastrin	G-cells in stomach	Bolus in the stomach—especially if the bolus contains proteins	Parietal cells (primarily): Stimulates secretion of hydrochloric acid (HCl) Chief cells: Stimulates secretion of pepsinogen Pyloric sphincter: Stimulates contraction
Cholecystokinin (CCK)	Enteroendocrine cells of small intestine	Chyme containing amino acids and fatty acids entering small intestine	Stomach: Inhibits stomach motility and gastric secretion Gallbladder: Stimulates release of bile Pancreas: Stimulates release of enzyme-rich pancreatic juice Hepatopancreatic sphincter: Causes relaxation
Secretin	Enteroendocrine cells of small intestine	Primarily with increase in acidity of chyme entering the small intestine	Stomach: Inhibits gastric secretion and stomach motility Pancreas: Stimulates secretion of alkaline solution from pancreatic ducts Liver: Stimulates secretion of alkaline solution

fluid helps neutralize the acidic chyme. Secretin also inhibits gastric secretions and motility. Hormones that regulate digestion are summarized in **table 26.3**.

 WHAT DID YOU LEARN?

19 Where do deoxygenated, nutrient-rich blood and oxygenated blood first come together within a liver lobule?

20 Does the liver produce digestive enzymes? If not, what substance does it produce that assists in digestion?

21 What are the primary functions of pancreatic juice?

26.3d Large Intestine

 LEARNING OBJECTIVES

8. Name the three major regions of the large intestine and four segments of the colon of the large intestine.

9. Explain the distinguishing histologic features of the large intestine.

10. Describe the bacterial action that takes place in the large intestine.

The **large intestine** is called the *large bowel* and it is a relatively wide tube that is significantly shorter than the small intestine. It is located

---

INTEGRATE

CLINICAL VIEW
Appendicitis

Inflammation of the appendix is called **appendicitis** (ă-pen-di-sī′tis). Most cases of appendicitis occur because fecal matter obstructs the appendix, although sometimes an appendix becomes inflamed without any obstruction. As the tissue becomes inflamed, the appendix swells, the blood supply is compromised, and bacteria may proliferate in the wall. Untreated, the appendix may burst and spew its contents into the peritoneum, causing a massive and potentially deadly infection called peritonitis.

During the early stages of acute appendicitis, the smooth muscle wall contracts and goes into spasms. Because this smooth muscle is innervated by the autonomic nervous system, pain is referred to the T10 dermatome around the umbilicus.

As the inflammation worsens and the parietal peritoneum becomes inflamed as well, the pain becomes sharp and localized to the right lower quadrant of the abdomen. Individuals with appendicitis typically experience nausea or vomiting, abdominal tenderness in the inferior right quadrant, a low fever, and an elevated leukocyte count. An inflamed appendix is surgically removed in a procedure called an *appendectomy*.

Inflammed appendix

within the abdominal pelvic cavity and called the "large" intestine because its diameter is greater than that of the small intestine.

About 1 liter of digested material passes from the small intestine to the large intestine daily. Most nutrients have been absorbed within the small intestine. The large intestine absorbs water and electrolytes (primarily sodium [Na^+] and chloride [Cl^-] ions) from the remaining digested material that enters into it from the small intestine. It is estimated that only 100 milliliters of the water entering the colon daily is lost in feces. Thus, the watery chyme that first enters the large intestine (including all of the undigested materials as well as the waste products secreted by the accessory organs (e.g., bilirubin by the liver) soon solidifies and is compacted into **feces** (fē'cēz; *faex* = dregs), or fecal material. The large intestine then stores this fecal material until it is eliminated through defecation.

Gross Anatomy of the Large Intestine

The large intestine has a diameter of 6.5 centimeters (2.5 inches) and an approximate length of 1.5 meters (5 feet) from its origin at the ileocecal junction to its termination at the anus (**figure 26.22**).

Three major regions comprise the large intestine: the cecum, the colon, and the rectum.

Cecum The **cecum** (sē'kŭm; *caecus* = blind) is a blind sac. It is the first portion of the large intestine and located in the right lower abdominal quadrant. This pouch extends inferiorly from the ileocecal valve. Chyme enters the cecum from the ileum. Projecting inferiorly from the posteromedial region of the cecum is the **vermiform appendix** (ver'mi-fōrm; *vermis* = worm; ă-pen'diks; appendage), a thin, hollow, fingerlike sac lined by lymphocyte-filled lymphatic nodules. Both the cecum and the vermiform appendix are intraperitoneal organs. Research studies suggest that the appendix may harbor bacteria that are beneficial to the function of the colon.

Colon At the level of the ileocecal valve, the second region of the large intestine, the **colon**, begins and forms an inverted U-shaped arch. The colon is partitioned into four segments: the ascending colon, transverse colon, descending colon, and sigmoid colon.

The **ascending colon** originates at the ileocecal valve and extends superiorly from the superior edge of the cecum along the

Figure 26.22 Gross Anatomy of the Large Intestine. (*a*) Anterior view of the large intestine that forms the distal end of the GI tract. (*b*) Details of the anal canal. AP|R

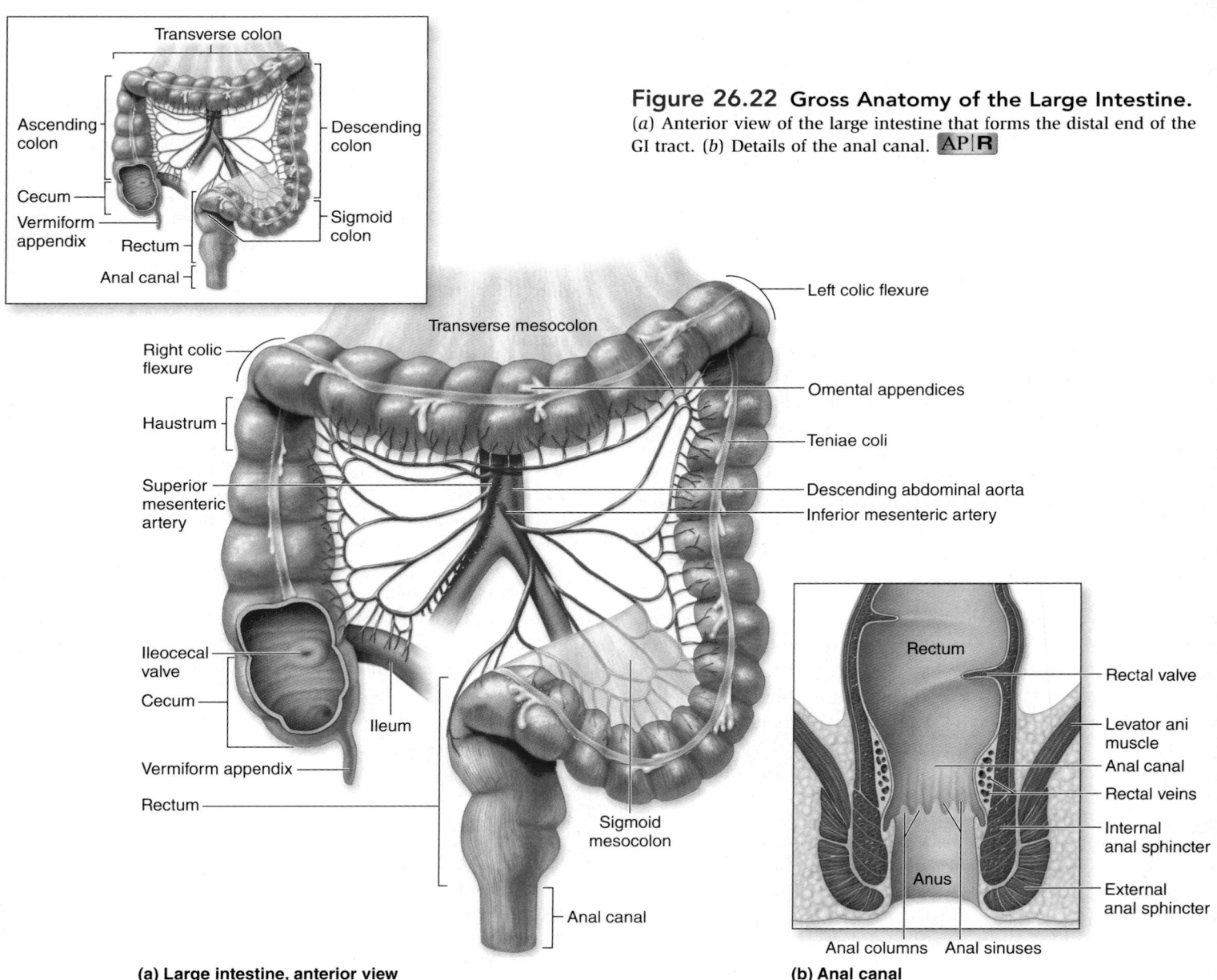

(a) Large intestine, anterior view

(b) Anal canal

CLINICAL VIEW
Colorectal Cancer

Colorectal cancer is the second most common type of cancer in the United States, with over 140,000 cases occurring annually and 60,000 of those resulting in death. The term **colorectal cancer** refers to a malignant growth anywhere along the large intestine (colon) or rectum. The majority of colorectal cancers appear in the distal descending colon, sigmoid colon, and rectum, which are the segments of the large intestine that have the longest contact with fecal matter before it is expelled from the body. Most colorectal cancers arise from **polyps** (pol'ip), which are outgrowths from the colon mucosa. Note, however, that colon polyps are very common, and most of them never become cancerous. Low-fiber diets have also been implicated in increasing the risk of colon cancer, because decreased dietary fiber leads to decreased stool bulk and longer time for stools to remain in the large

intestine. Theoretically, this condition exposes the large intestine mucosa to toxins in the stools for longer periods of time. Other risk factors include a family history of colorectal cancer, personal history of ulcerative colitis, and increased age (most patients are over the age of 40).

Initially, most patients are asymptomatic. Later, they may notice rectal bleeding (often evidenced as blood in the stool or on the toilet paper) and a persistent change in bowel habits (typically constipation). Eventually, the person may experience abdominal pain, fatigue, unexplained weight loss, and anemia.

The cancerous growth must be removed surgically, and sometimes radiation or chemotherapy are used as well. Colorectal cancers that are limited to the mucosa have a 5-year survival rate, but the prognosis is poor for cancers that have spread into deeper colon wall tunics or metastasized to the lymph nodes.

The key to an increased survival rate for colorectal cancer is early detection. If caught early, colorectal cancer is very treatable. An individual

---

right lateral border of the abdominal cavity. The ascending colon is retroperitoneal, since its posterior wall directly adheres to the posterior abdominal wall, and only its anterior surface is covered with peritoneum. As it approaches the inferior surface of the liver, the ascending colon makes a 90-degree turn toward the left side and anterior region of the abdominal cavity. This bend in the colon is called the **right colic** (kol'ik) **flexure,** or the *hepatic flexure.*

The **transverse colon** originates at the right colic flexure and curves slightly anteriorly as it projects horizontally to the left across the anterior region of the abdominal cavity. The transverse colon is intraperitoneal. As the transverse colon approaches the spleen in the left upper quadrant of the abdomen, it makes a 90-degree turn inferiorly and posteriorly. The resulting bend in the colon is called the **left colic flexure,** or the *splenic flexure.*

The **descending colon** is retroperitoneal and located along the left side of the abdominal cavity and slightly posterior. It originates at the left colic flexure and descends vertically to the sigmoid colon.

The **sigmoid** (sig'moyd; resembling letter S) **colon** originates at the **sigmoid flexure** and turns inferomedially into the pelvic cavity. The sigmoid colon, like the transverse colon, is intraperitoneal. The sigmoid colon terminates at the rectum. Recall that a type of mesentery, called the mesocolon, attaches each section of the colon to the posterior abdominal wall, with the mesocolon of each region specifically named (e.g., ascending mesocolon, transverse mesocolon).

Rectum The **rectum** (rek'tŭm; *rectus* = straight) is the third major region of the large intestine. It is a retroperitoneal structure that connects to the sigmoid colon. The rectum is a muscular tube that readily expands to store accumulated fecal material prior to defecation. Three thick transverse folds of the rectum, called **rectal valves,** ensure that fecal material is retained during the passing of gas.

The **anal** (ā'nǎl) **canal** makes up the terminal few centimeters of the large intestine. The anal canal is lined by a stratified squamous epithelium, and it passes through an opening in the levator ani muscles of the pelvic floor (see section 11.7) and terminates at the anus. The internal lining of the anal canal contains relatively thin longitudinal ridges, called **anal columns,** between which are small depressions termed **anal sinuses.** As fecal material passes through the anal canal during defecation, pressure exerted on the anal sinuses causes their cells to release mucin to form mucus. The extra mucus lubricates the anal canal during defecation. At the base of the anal canal are the involuntary smooth muscle **internal anal sphincter** and voluntary

skeletal muscle **external anal sphincter,** which generally close off the opening to the anal canal. They relax (open) during defecation.

Specialized Structures of the Large Intestine

Several features are unique to the large intestine including teniae coli, haustra, and epiploic appendages. **Teniae coli** (tē'nē-ē; ribbons, band; kō'lī) are thin, distinct, longitudinal bundles of smooth muscle. The teniae coli act like elastic in a waistband—they help bunch up the large intestine into many sacs, collectively called **haustra** (haw'strǎ; sing., *haustrum; haustus* = to drink up). Hanging off the external surface of the haustra are lobules of fat called **omental appendices,** or *epiploic* (e-pi-plō'ik; membrane-covered) *appendages.*

Histology

The mucosa of the large intestine is lined by a simple columnar epithelium with numerous goblet cells (**figure 26.23**). Unlike the small intestine, the large intestine mucosa is smooth and lacks intestinal villi, yet it resembles the small intestine in that it has transporting epithelial cells and numerous **intestinal glands** (or crypts) that extend inward toward the muscularis mucosae. The glands' mucous cells secrete mucin to lubricate the undigested material and facilitate its passage through the large intestine. Many lymphatic nodules and lymphatic cells occupy the lamina propria of the large intestine.

The muscularis of the cecum and colon has two layers of smooth muscle, but the outer longitudinal layer is discontinuous and does not completely surround the colon and cecum. Instead, these longitudinal smooth muscle fibers form the teniae coli, just described.

CONCEPT CONNECTION

Recall that heme is broken down into bilirubin and absorbed from the blood in the liver (see section 18.3b). Bilirubin is then released as a component of bile into the small intestine. It is either reabsorbed back into the blood and eliminated as urobilin in the urine, or it continues through the GI tract into the large intestine, where bacteria convert it to stercobilin. Stercobilin is a brown pigment that accounts for the normal color of feces.

should see their doctor if rectal bleeding or any persistent change in bowel habits is experienced. By age 50 (or earlier, for those that have symptoms or a family history of colorectal cancer), the following screening methods are recommended:

1. A yearly **fecal occult** (ō-kŭlt´, ok´ŭlt) **blood test,** which checks for the presence of blood in the stools.

2. A **sigmoidoscopy** (sig´moy-dos´kŏ-pē; *skopeo* = to view) every 5 years. In this procedure, which is done in the doctor's office, an endoscope is inserted into the rectum and sigmoid colon to check for polyps or cancer.

3. A **colonoscopy** (kō-lon-os´kŏ-pē) every 10 years. A colonoscopy is more extensive than a sigmoidoscopy. The endoscope is inserted into the large intestine at least up to the right colic flexure of the colon, and sometimes as far proximally as the ileocecal valve.

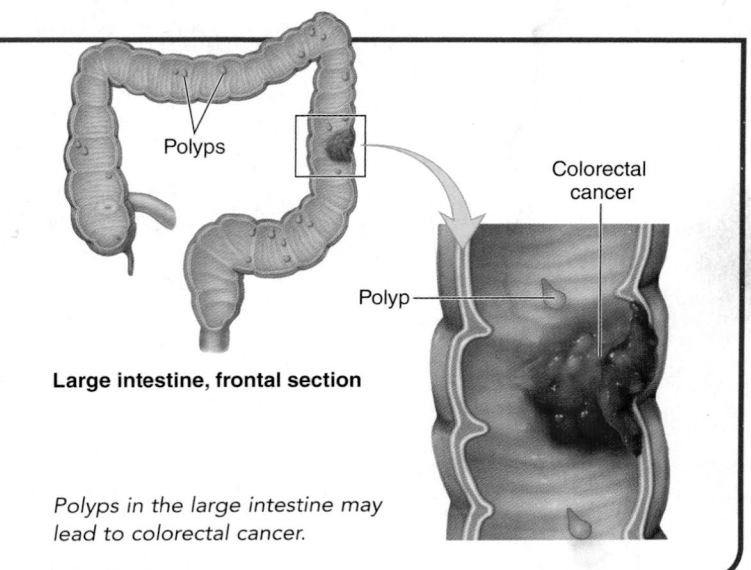

Large intestine, frontal section

Polyps in the large intestine may lead to colorectal cancer.

Bacterial Action in the Large Intestine

Numerous normal bacterial flora inhabit the large intestine; they are termed the *indigenous microbiota.* These bacteria are responsible for the chemical breakdown of complex carbohydrates, proteins, and lipids that remain in the chyme after it has passed through the small intestine. Bacterial actions produce carbon dioxide, H^+, hydrogen sulfide, methane, indoles, and skatoles. Some of these substances account for the odor of feces. Additionally, B vitamins and vitamin K are produced by the bacterial flora, which are then absorbed from the large intestine into the blood. (Note that these vitamins are also absorbed in the small intestine from the foods that we eat.)

Motility and Regulation of the Large Intestine

Several types of movements are observed in the large intestine:

- **Peristaltic movements** of the large intestine are usually weak and sluggish, but otherwise they resemble those that occur in the wall of the small intestine.

- **Haustral churning** occurs after a relaxed haustrum fills with digested or fecal material until its distension stimulates reflex contractions in the muscularis. These contractions increase churning and move the material to more distal haustra.

- **Mass movements** are powerful, peristaltic-like contractions involving the teniae coli, which propel fecal material toward the rectum. A wave of contraction begins in the middle of the transverse colon, forcing a large amount of fecal matter into the descending colon, sigmoid colon, and the rectum. Generally, mass movements occur two or three times a day, often during or immediately after a meal.

(a) Large intestine tunics

(b) Large intestine mucosa and submucosa

Figure 26.23 Histology of the Large Intestine. (*a*) The luminal wall of the large intestine is composed of four tunics: mucosa, submucosa, muscularis, and serosa. (*b*) A photomicrograph shows the histology of the mucosa and submucosa of the large intestine wall.

CLINICAL VIEW
Diverticulosis and Diverticulitis

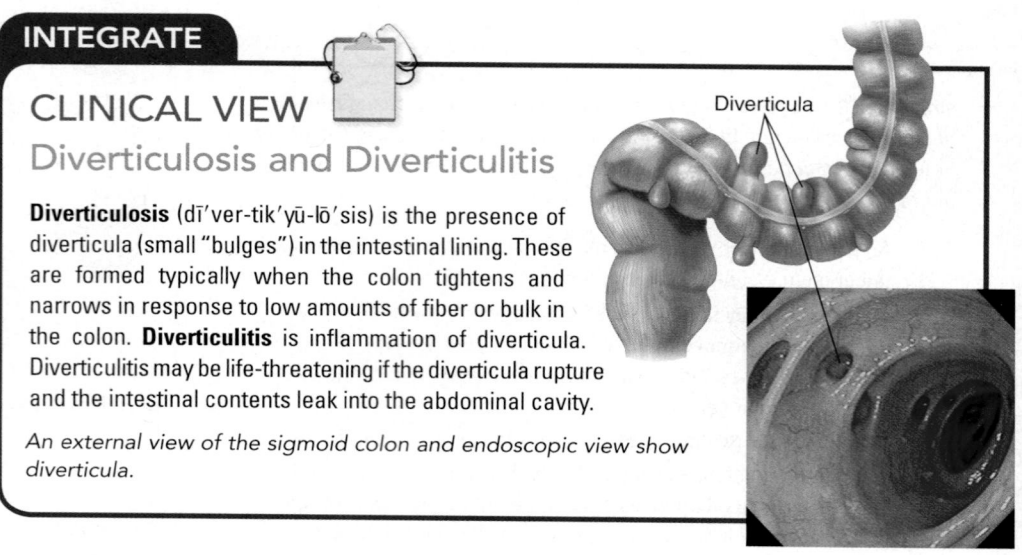

Diverticulosis (dī′ver-tik′yū-lō′sis) is the presence of diverticula (small "bulges") in the intestinal lining. These are formed typically when the colon tightens and narrows in response to low amounts of fiber or bulk in the colon. **Diverticulitis** is inflammation of diverticula. Diverticulitis may be life-threatening if the diverticula rupture and the intestinal contents leak into the abdominal cavity.

An external view of the sigmoid colon and endoscopic view show diverticula.

Two major reflexes are associated with motility in the large intestine:

- The **gastrocolic** (gas′trō-kol′ik) **reflex** is initiated by stomach distension to cause a mass movement (motility in the large intestine just described).
- The **defecation reflex.** The elimination of feces from the GI tract by the process of **defecation** (def-ĕ-kā′shŭn; *defaeco* = to remove the dregs) **(figure 26.24)**. Filling of the rectum initiates the urge to defecate. This stimulus results in transmission of

Figure 26.24 Elimination. The defecation reflex involves sensory perception of stretch in the rectum that initiates a spinal reflex that stimulates muscles in the rectal wall to contract and the internal anal sphincter to relax. Conscious regulation of defecation requires the relaxation of the external anal sphincter and the Valsalva maneuver.

nerve signals from the receptors to the spinal cord. In response, parasympathetic output increases to both the sigmoid colon and rectum, while it decreases to the internal (involuntary) anal sphincter. (The defecation reflex is an example of a monosynaptic reflex; see section 14.6b.)

Voluntary elimination of feces from the body typically is learned sometime after age 3 years. The conscious decision to defecate involves both the Valsalva maneuver (see section 23.3) and relaxation of the external (voluntary) anal sphincter.

WHAT DID YOU LEARN?

22 What is the pathway of chyme from its entry into the large intestine until feces is eliminated?

23 What are the general functions of bacteria within the large intestine?

24 Which substances are typically absorbed by the large intestine?

26.4 Nutrients and Their Digestion

The term **essential nutrients** indicates substances that must constitute part of the diet for survival. The six essential nutrients are carbohydrates, lipids, proteins, minerals, vitamins, and water. These nutrients and their functions in the body are described in depth in section 27.1.

This section discusses the chemical digestion of the foods that we eat. In addition to the mechanism of their breakdown, we describe their absorption and general use by the body. We describe the breakdown of carbohydrates, lipids, and proteins, as well as nucleic acids, which are not an essential nutrient. All are digested by the process of *hydrolysis*, the breaking of chemical bonds with an accompanying addition of a water molecule (see section 2.7a).

26.4a Carbohydrate Digestion

LEARNING OBJECTIVES

1. Name the three classes of carbohydrates.
2. Explain the processing in the oral cavity that initiates carbohydrate digestion.
3. Describe the chemical digestion of carbohydrates that occurs in the small intestine.

Carbohydrates are organized based upon the number of repeating units of simple sugars. You learned in section 2.7c that carbohydrates may be classified as **monosaccharides** (e.g., glucose, fructose, and galactose), **disaccharides** (e.g., sucrose, maltose, and lactose), and **polysaccharides** (e.g., starch and cellulose). Chemical digestion of carbohydrates consists of: (1) the breakdown of starch into individual glucose molecules, and (2) the breakdown of disaccharides into the individual monosaccharides that compose them. The oral cavity and small intestine are the main sites of carbohydrate digestion.

Carbohydrate Breakdown in the Oral Cavity

Digestion of starch begins in the oral cavity. It is catalyzed by **salivary amylase** that is synthesized and released from the salivary glands. Salivary amylase breaks the chemical bonds between glucose molecules, within the starch molecule, to partially digest the starch molecule. The extent of starch digestion is dependent upon the length of time the salivary amylase is allowed to act on the starch.

Salivary amylase is inactivated by the low pH of the stomach when the bolus is swallowed. This inactivation typically occurs within 15 to 20 minutes after the bolus enters the stomach. The larger the meal, the longer salivary amylase remains active. This extended activity reveals that it takes longer for the swallowed bolus to be mixed with the low pH of the gastric juices that inactivate the salivary amylase. This is more likely when the bolus is within the fundus of the stomach, where smooth muscle contractions are the weakest and the pH is the highest. No new enzymes for carbohydrate digestion are introduced in the stomach.

Carbohydrate Breakdown in the Small Intestine

Pancreatic amylase is synthesized and released by the pancreas as a component of pancreatic juice into the small intestine through the main or accessory pancreatic duct (**figure 26.25**). This enzyme continues the digestion of starch into shorter strands of glucose (5 to 25 glucose molecules, oligosaccharides), maltose (disaccharide of two glucose molecules), and individual glucose molecules.

The completion of starch breakdown is accomplished by brush border enzymes embedded within the epithelial lining of the small intestine. These enzymes include **dextrinase** and **glucoamylase,** which break the bonds between glucose subunits of oligosaccharides, and **maltase** that breaks the bond between the two glucose molecules that compose maltose.

The digestion of other ingested disaccharides, such as lactose (milk sugar) and sucrose (table sugar), requires only one enzyme each. Each enzyme is specifically named for the substrate it digests. **Lactase** digests lactose to glucose and galactose, and **sucrase** digests sucrose to glucose and fructose. These enzymes are brush border enzymes. Individuals with either a reduced amount or lack of lactase enzyme are referred to as being **lactose intolerant** (see Clinical View: "Lactose Intolerance" in chapter 3).

The monosaccharides released in these enzymatic reactions include glucose, fructose, and galactose. They are absorbed across the small intestinal epithelial lining into the blood. All venous blood from

Partially digested starch

Lactose and sucrose

(1) Pancreatic amylase is produced by the pancreas and secreted into the small intestine.

Pancreatic amylase

(2) Pancreatic amylase continues digestion of starch that began in the oral cavity by salivary amylase.

(3) Brush border enzymes complete the breakdown of starch to individual glucose molecules, and are responsible for the digestion of disaccharides.

Brush border enzymes

(a) Duodenum and pancreas

Figure 26.25 Carbohydrate Digestion in the Small Intestine. (*a*) Pancreatic amylase is produced by the pancreas and secreted into the small intestine. (*b*) Pancreatic amylase continues digestion of starch that began in the oral cavity, and brush border enzymes complete the breakdown of starch to individual glucose molecules. (*c*) Lactose and sucrose disaccharides are each digested by a specific brush border enzyme. AP|R

Brush border enzymes*

Lactose — Lactase → Glucose + Galactose

Sucrose — Sucrase → Glucose + Fructose

*Only brush border enzymes are required to digest lactose and sucrose (i.e., amylases are not required)

(c) Digestion of other disaccharides

Partially digested starch — Pancreatic amylase → Oligosaccharides / Maltose / Glucose — Brush border enzymes Dextrinase Glucoamylase Maltase → Glucose molecules

(b) Digestion of starch

Table 26.4	Digestion of Macromolecules			
Location	**Carbohydrates**	**Proteins**	**Lipids**	**Nucleic Acids**
Oral cavity (saliva)	Starch—*salivary amylase*⟶ partially digested starch	No protein digestion	*Lingual lipase* added but activated in low pH of stomach	No nucleic acid digestion
Stomach (gastric juice)	No additional enzymes added	Protein—*pepsin*⟶ polypeptide and peptide fragments	Triglyceride—*lingual lipase*⟶ monoglyceride and fatty acids (limited amounts) Triglyceride—*gastric lipase*⟶ monoglyceride and fatty acids (limited amounts)	No nucleic acid digestion
Small intestine (pancreatic juice secreted into duodenum)	Partially digested starch—*pancreatic amylase*⟶ oligosaccharides, maltose, and glucose	Protein—*trypsin*⟶ polypeptide and peptide fragments Protein—*chymotrypsin*⟶ polypeptide and peptide fragments Protein—*carboxypeptidase*⟶ amino acids from carboxy-end of peptides	Triglyceride—*pancreatic lipase*⟶ monoglyceride and fatty acids (within micelles)	DNA—*deoxyribonuclease*⟶ deoxyribonucleotides RNA—*ribonuclease*⟶ ribonucleotides
Small intestine (brush border enzymes)	Oligosaccharides—*dextrinase* and *glucoamylase*⟶ maltose, glucose Maltose—*maltase*⟶ glucose Lactose—*lactase*⟶ glucose, galactose Sucrose—*sucrase*⟶ glucose, fructose	Dipeptides—*dipeptidase*⟶ amino acids Peptides—*aminopeptidase*⟶ amino acids from amino end of peptides	No brush border enzymes are required for completing lipid digestion	Nucleotides—*phosphatase*⟶ nucleosides and phosphate Nucleosides—*nucleosidase*⟶ nitrogenous base and sugar (ribose or deoxyribose)

the small intestine is transported through the hepatic portal vein to the liver, where fructose and galactose will be converted into glucose. Glucose has different fates. It can become part of the blood glucose, be taken up by any cell for energy use, be taken up by liver cells and muscle cells and synthesized into glycogen and stored, or converted into fat (triglycerides) and stored in adipose connective tissue.

Cellulose is a carbohydrate that is a component of plant cell walls. Cellulose is not chemically digested because we lack the enzymes required to break the bonds between its glucose molecules. Thus, cellulose, along with other indigestible substances, is fiber that adds "bulk" to the contents of the lumen and facilitates its moving through the GI tract. A summary of carbohydrate digestion is included in **table 26.4**.

 **WHAT DID YOU LEARN?**

25 What enzymes are required to completely break down starch? Name the specific source of each of these enzymes.

26.4b Protein Digestion

 LEARNING OBJECTIVES

4. Identify the enzyme that initiates protein digestion in the stomach, and explain its activation and action.

5. Explain why the proteolytic enzymes of the stomach and pancreas are synthesized in inactive forms.

6. Describe the chemical digestion of proteins that occurs in the small intestine.

Proteins are polymers composed of amino acid subunits linked by peptide bonds (see section 2.7e). Digestion releases the individual amino acids so that the body may use them to build its own proteins.

Proteins are broken down into their substituent amino acids by enzymes that either target peptide bonds between specific adjacent amino acids within the protein, or nonspecifically release amino acids from either end of a protein. All enzymes that digest protein are released as inactive enzymes and must be activated (e.g., pepsinogen is activated to pepsin within the low pH of the stomach). This is because the proteolytic enzymes would destroy the proteins within the cells that produce them. This also prevents proteolytic enzymes produced in the pancreas from "eating away" the cells lining the main and accessory pancreatic ducts as they pass through the ducts.

Protein Breakdown in the Stomach

Protein hydrolysis begins within the stomach lumen with the enzyme pepsin. **Pepsin** is formed from pepsinogen, an inactive precursor released by chief cells. Hydrochloric acid that is released from parietal cells causes a low pH within the stomach that both activates pepsinogen to pepsin and denatures proteins to facilitate their chemical breakdown (as described earlier).

Protein Breakdown in the Small Intestine

The high pH of the small intestine inhibits further action by pepsin on protein shortly following the entry of chyme into the small intestine. Three of the enzymes that continue the digestion of

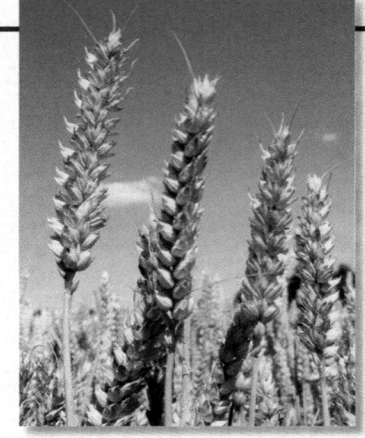

Celiac disease (also known as *gluten-sensitive enteropathy*) is an autoimmune disorder that affects up to 1% of the population in the United States. Gluten—a protein common in wheat, rye, and barley (but not rice or corn)—stimulates an immune response in affected individuals that damages the villi of the small intestine, which interferes with absorption. Common foods that contain gluten include breads, pizza, and pasta. Symptoms include abdominal pain and chronic diarrhea, which leads to nutrient deficiencies because of malabsorption. Although there is no cure for celiac disease, it can be effectively managed by following a gluten-free diet.

protein are synthesized and released from the pancreas into the small intestine in inactive forms—trypsinogen, chymotrypsinogen, and procarboxypeptidase **(figure 26.26)**. Once these inactive forms of the enzymes reach the small intestine, the enzyme **enteropeptidase** (previously called *enterokinase*), is an enzyme synthesized by the small intestine and released into the lumen of the small intestine. Enteropeptidase activates trypsinogen to **trypsin**. Trypsin in turn activates additional molecules of trypsinogen to trypsin, as well as chymotrypsinogen to **chymotrypsin** and procarboxypeptidase to **carboxypeptidase.**

Trypsin and chymotrypsin break the bonds between specific amino acids within the protein to produce smaller strands of amino acids called peptides. (Trypsin cleaves a protein specifically at positively charged amino acids of arginine and lysine, whereas chymotrypsin cleaves specifically at hydrophobic amino acids including phenylalanine, tryptophan, and tyrosine; see figure 2.26, which shows the 20 different amino acids.) Carboxypeptidase is restricted to breaking the bond only between an amino acid on the carboxyl end and the remaining protein (it releases one amino acid at a time). Dipeptides and free amino acids are the breakdown products of carboxypeptidase.

The brush border enzyme **dipeptidase** breaks the final bond between the two amino acids of a dipeptide so that both may be absorbed. The brush border enzyme **aminopeptidase** generates free amino acids from the amino end of peptides.

Free amino acids are absorbed across the small intestine epithelial lining and enter into the blood. Amino acids can be used as building blocks of new proteins by cells, or if excess amino acids are absorbed, they are converted either into glucose (by gluconeogenesis in the liver primarily or kidney). A summary of protein digestion is included in table 26.4.

 **WHAT DID YOU LEARN?**

26 How are proteolytic enzymes activated in the stomach and in the small intestine? Explain why this is necessary.

26.4c Lipid Digestion

 LEARNING OBJECTIVES

7. Explain the role of bile salts in lipid digestion.
8. Discuss the process by which lipids are absorbed.

Lipids are highly variable structures that contain different arrangements of their building blocks (see section 2.7b). Lipids have one unifying property, which is that they are not water-soluble. Two major ingested lipids are triglycerides (or neutral fats) and cholesterol. Triglycerides are composed of a glycerol molecule and three fatty acids bonded to the

(b)

(a)

Figure 26.26 Protein Digestion in the Small Intestine. (*a*) Pancreatic enzymes for protein digestion are produced and secreted into the small intestine in an inactive form. After reaching the small intestine, these enzymes are activated. (*b*) The locations where different protein-digesting enzymes break peptide bonds are highlighted in purple.

glycerol, and enzymes are required to break the bonds between glycerol and fatty acids. Digestion of cholesterol is not required for its absorption.

Lipid Breakdown in the Stomach

Lingual lipase (produced by intrinsic salivary glands in the mouth) is a component of saliva in the oral cavity. The optimal pH of this enzyme (4.5 to 5.4), however, means it is not activated until it reaches the stomach. Once in the stomach, triglycerides undergo limited digestion by both lingual lipase and gastric lipase (an enzyme produced by chief cells of the stomach). These "acidic lipases" digest approximately 30% of the triglycerides to diglyceride and fatty acid. Neither of these lipase enzymes requires the participation of bile salts (see next section).

Lipid Breakdown in the Small Intestine

The majority of triglyceride digestion occurs in the small intestine and is facilitated by **pancreatic lipase,** an enzyme produced by the pancreas and released into the duodenum. Pancreatic lipase digests each triglyceride into a monoglyceride and two free fatty acids. However, because triglycerides are lipids and do not dissolve in the luminal fluids of the digestive system, triglycerides form relatively large lipid masses. For example, when butter is added to water, the butter does not stay mixed with the water but remains separate.

For pancreatic lipase to effectively digest the fat, the large lipid droplets must first be mechanically separated into smaller droplets; this process is called **emulsification** (**figure 26.27**). Emulsification occurs by the action of **bile salts,** which are part of bile. Bile is produced by the liver and stored, concentrated, and released from the gallbladder. Bile salts are amphipathic molecules composed of a polar head and a nonpolar tail. The nonpolar tails position themselves around the fat with the polar heads next to the aqueous fluid in the lumen (like an inverted spiked ball with the fat in the center). This structure is called a **micelle.** Thus, the function of bile salts is to emulsify fats so that pancreatic lipase has greater "access" to the triglyceride molecules and may more effectively chemically digest the fat. (Note that the process of emulsification is facilitated by lecithin, phospholipid molecules within bile.) Cholesterol is also within the micelle, but it is not chemically digested. No brush border enzymes are required in the breakdown of triglycerides.

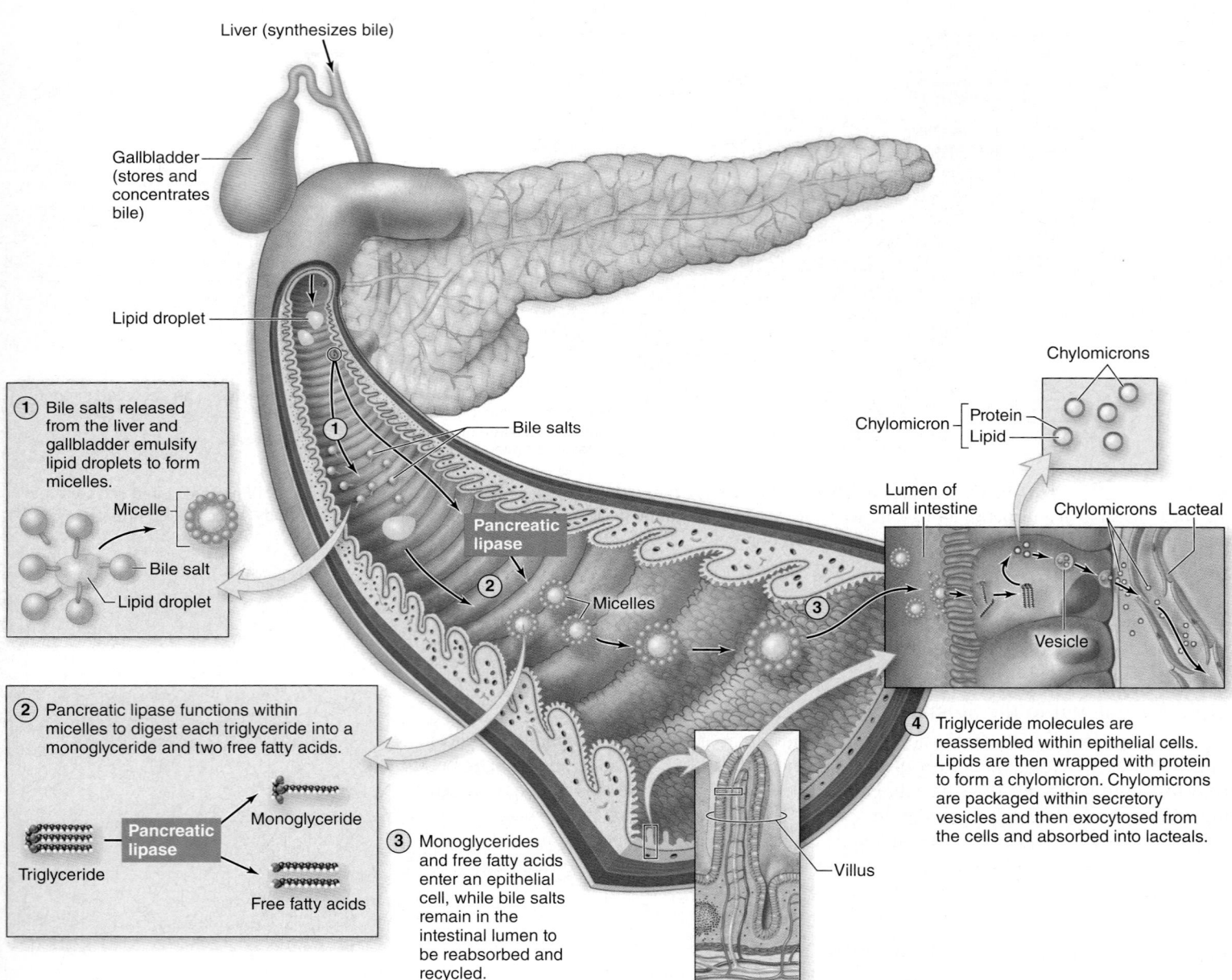

Liver (synthesizes bile)

Gallbladder (stores and concentrates bile)

Lipid droplet

(1) Bile salts released from the liver and gallbladder emulsify lipid droplets to form micelles.

Micelle

Bile salt

Lipid droplet

Bile salts

Pancreatic lipase

(2)

Micelles

(2) Pancreatic lipase functions within micelles to digest each triglyceride into a monoglyceride and two free fatty acids.

Triglyceride

Pancreatic lipase

Monoglyceride

Free fatty acids

(3) Monoglycerides and free fatty acids enter an epithelial cell, while bile salts remain in the intestinal lumen to be reabsorbed and recycled.

Villus

Chylomicrons

Chylomicron — Protein / Lipid

Lumen of small intestine

Chylomicrons   Lacteal

(3)

Vesicle

(4) Triglyceride molecules are reassembled within epithelial cells. Lipids are then wrapped with protein to form a chylomicron. Chylomicrons are packaged within secretory vesicles and then exocytosed from the cells and absorbed into lacteals.

Figure 26.27 Lipid Digestion and Absorption in the Small Intestine. Bile salts emulsify lipids within the small intestine, forming micelles to facilitate fat digestion by pancreatic lipase. After the pancreatic lipase has digested the fat, fatty acids and monoglycerides are taken into an epithelial cell where triglycerides are re-formed, then wrapped along with other lipids within protein to form a chylomicron. Chylomicrons are released from the epithelial cells and then enter a lacteal in the lamina propria of the small intestine wall.

Eventually, in the last portion of the ileum, bile salts are recovered by active transport and ultimately recycled to the liver for reuse. New bile salts are synthesized by hepatocytes to replace those inevitably lost during elimination of feces. Table 26.4 summarizes lipid digestion.

Lipid Absorption

Digested triglycerides (monoglycerides and free fatty acids), cholesterol, other lipids (e.g., lecithin), and fat-soluble vitamins are contained within micelles. Micelles transport lipids to the simple columnar epithelial lining of the small intestine. Here, the lipids enter the epithelial cells, while the bile salts remain in the small intestine lumen to be recycled and reused.

Once inside the epithelial cells, the fatty acids are reattached to the monoglyceride to re-form triglycerides. Triglycerides, cholesterol, and other lipid molecules are then "wrapped" with protein to form a **chylomicron** (kī′lō-mī′kron; *chylos* = juice; *micros* = small). The Golgi apparatus (see section 4.5a) packages chylomicrons into secretory vesicles. The chylomicrons are released from the epithelial cells by exocytosis. Chylomicrons are too large to pass through blood capillary walls but instead enter the lacteals, the lymphatic capillaries of the small intestine. The overlapping endothelial cells of the lacteals act like one-way valves to permit entry of chylomicrons.

Recall that all lymph enters the blood at the junction of the jugular vein and the subclavian vein (see section 21.1). Chylomicrons enter the blood and deliver lipids to the liver and other tissues (e.g., adipose connective tissue, skeletal muscle tissue, and cardiac muscle).

  WHAT DID YOU LEARN?

27 What is the function of bile salts in lipid digestion? Is this considered chemical digestion or mechanical digestion?

26.4d Nucleic Acid Digestion

 LEARNING OBJECTIVE

9. Describe the digestion of nucleic acids.

Nucleic acids are polymers of nucleotides. The two types of nucleic acid polymers are deoxyribonucleic acid (DNA) and ribonucleic acid (RNA). A nucleotide monomer is composed of three components: sugar (either deoxyribose or ribose), a phosphate group, and a nitrogenous base (see section 2.7d).

Nucleic Acid Breakdown in the Small Intestine

Nucleic acid digestion occurs in the small intestine. The nucleases (**deoxyribonuclease** and **ribonuclease**), synthesized and released by the pancreas, begin the digestion of nucleic acids. Each breaks the phosphodiester bond between the individual nucleotides of DNA and RNA, respectively.

The breakdown of the nucleotides is further accomplished by brush border enzymes embedded in the epithelial lining of the small intestine. These enzymes include (1) **phosphatase,** which breaks the bond holding the phosphate to the rest of the nucleotide (without the phosphate, this molecule is called a *nucleoside*); and (2) **nucleosidase,** which breaks the bond between the sugar and the nitrogenous base of the nucleoside, releasing the sugar and nitrogenous base.

All nucleic acid component building blocks are absorbed across the epithelium of the small intestine into the blood. These include phosphate, the sugar (ribose or deoxyribose), and the nitrogenous bases (thymine, adenine, guanine, cytosine, and uracil). Table 26.4 summarizes nucleic acid digestion. A summary of all digestive processes is presented in figure 26.28.

  WHAT DID YOU LEARN?

28 Where does nucleic acid digestion occur?

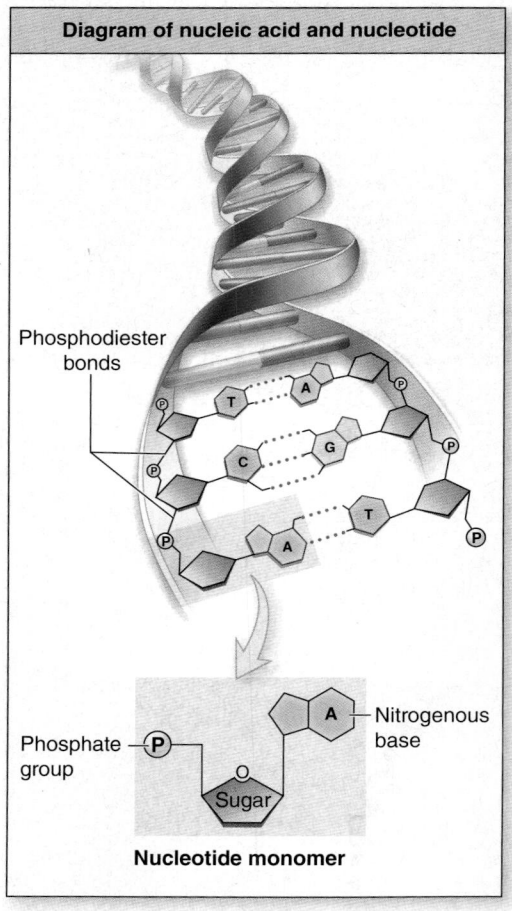

Diagram of nucleic acid and nucleotide

Phosphodiester bonds

Phosphate group

Sugar

Nitrogenous base

Nucleotide monomer

Figure 26.28 **Structures and Functions of the Digestive System.** Chemical digestion of nutrients occurs in the (*a*) oral cavity, (*b*) stomach, and (*c*) small intestine. Undigested substances are modified by bacteria within the *(d)* large intestine before being eliminated as feces. (Mechanical digestion and digestion of nucleic acids are not shown.)

(a) Oral Cavity

Addition of saliva to food in the mouth and formation of a bolus

Starch is partially digested by salivary amylase.

Mouth

Bolus

(b) Stomach

Release of gastric secretions and formation of chyme

HCl denatures protein and activates pepsinogen to pepsin.

Pepsin partially digests protein.

Intrinsic factor is released for absorption of vitamin B$_{12}$, which occurs in the ileum.

Lingual lipase (from intrinsic salivary glands) and gastric lipase begin limited digestion of triglycerides.

Stomach

Chyme

(d) Large Intestine

Bacteria act on remaining undigested material

Bacteria produce vitamins B and K as they act on undigested material.

Bacteria (normal flora)

Large intestine

Small intestine

(c) Small Intestine and Accessory Organs

Legend:
- Carbohydrate digestion
- Protein digestion
- Lipid digestion

Liver

Gallbladder

Pancreas

Inactive proteolytic enzymes are released from the pancreas into the duodenum.

Trypsinogen Chymotrypsinogen Procarboxypeptidase

Enterokinase

Enterokinase produced in the small intestine initiates enzyme activation.

Pancreatic amylase continues digestion of starch.

Protein

Bile salts released from the liver and gallbladder into the small intestine emulsify lipids, forming micelles.

Pancreatic lipase digests triglycerides into monoglyceride and free fatty acids within micelles.

Pancreatic lipase

Starch

Pancreatic amylase

Oligosaccharides

Maltose   Glucose

Lactase digests lactose into glucose and galactose.

Sucrase digests sucrose into glucose and fructose.

Sucrose

Lactose

Sucrase

Trypsin, chymotrypsin, and carboxypeptidase break down protein into amino acids within the lumen of the small intestine.

Bile

Lactase

Glucose   Fructose

Trypsin Chymotrypsin Carboxypeptidase

Brush border enzymes complete digestion of starch to individual glucose molecules.

Glucose   Galactose

Triglyceride

Pancreatic lipase

Glucoamylase Dextrinase Maltase

Glucose, fructose, and galactose are absorbed into the blood.

Brush border enzymes complete the breakdown of proteins into amino acids.

Micelle

Monoglyceride   Free fatty acids

Aminopeptidase Dipeptidase

Cholesterol is unchanged

Glucose molecules

Individual amino acids are absorbed into the blood.

Villus

Micelles transport lipid to the epithelium, where triglycerides are reassembled and lipid molecules are wrapped in protein to form chylomicrons.

Water and electrolytes are also absorbed.

Lacteal

Lumen of small intestine   Epithelium   Chylomicrons are absorbed into lacteals.

CHAPTER SUMMARY

26.1 Introduction to the Digestive System 1015

- The digestive system provides the means to process, break down, and absorb nutrients needed for our survival.

26.1a General Functions of the Digestive System 1015
- The digestive system performs six major functions: ingestion, motility, secretion, digestion, absorption, and elimination.

26.1b Organization of the Digestive System 1015
- The gastrointestinal (GI) tract includes the oral cavity, pharynx, esophagus, stomach, small intestine, and large intestine.
- Accessory digestive organs are connected to the GI tract: salivary glands, liver, gallbladder, and pancreas. Teeth and tongue also assist in digestion activities.

26.1c Gastrointestinal Tract Wall 1016
- The GI tract tunics—from adjacent to the tube lumen to the outer wall—are the mucosa, submucosa, muscularis, and serosa or adventitia.

26.1d Serous Membranes of the Abdominal Cavity 1018
- Components of serous membranes are either parietal (inside wall of body cavity) or visceral (layer covering the organ); a peritoneal cavity is between them with a lubricating serous fluid. Organs completely wrapped by the membrane are intraperitoneal; those only partially covered are retroperitoneal.
- Serous membranes suspend and stabilize some GI tract organs. They are called the greater omentum, lesser omentum, falciform ligament, mesentery proper, and mesocolon.

26.1e Regulation of Digestive System Processes 1019
- Major receptors throughout the GI tract include mechanoreceptors and chemoreceptors. Motor reflex outputs are associated with either long reflexes (involving the central nervous system) or short reflexes among nerve cells in the GI tract wall.
- Hormones that participate in regulating digestive processes include gastrin, which is released from the stomach, and secretin and cholecystokinin, which are released from the small intestine.

26.2 Upper Gastrointestinal Tract 1020

26.2a Overview of the Upper Gastrointestinal Tract Organs 1020
- Digestion begins in upper GI tract organs. Its organs include the oral cavity, pharynx, esophagus, stomach, and the initial part of small intestine (duodenum).

26.2b Oral Cavity and Salivary Glands 1021
- The oral cavity is where ingested food is immediately exposed to mechanical digestion (mastication) by actions of the teeth and compression of materials by the tongue against the hard palate.
- Both serous and mucus secretions constitute saliva produced by three sets of glands: parotid, submandibular, and sublingual. Saliva helps form a wet mass called a bolus and initiates chemical digestion of starch by salivary amylase.

26.2c Pharynx and Esophagus 1025
- The pharynx and esophagus connect the oral cavity to the stomach.
- Swallowing occurs in three phases: (1) voluntary phase, (2) pharyngeal phase, and (3) esophageal phase.
- After the bolus passes into the stomach, nervous stimulation of the lower esophageal sphincter causes the sphincter to contract, preventing backflow.

26.2d Stomach 1028
- Both mechanical and chemical digestion activities continue in the stomach.
- The tunica mucosa has a simple columnar epithelium, indentations (gastric pits) to increase its surface area, and deep penetrations (gastric glands) that house unique secretory cells.
- Gastric juice is composed of secretions from mucous cells (mucin) to protect the stomach lining. Parietal cells release intrinsic factor (to help absorb vitamin B_{12}) and hydrochloric acid (to activate pepsinogen to pepsin, kill most microorganisms, contribute to the breakdown of plant cell walls and animal connective tissue, and denature proteins). Chief cells release pepsinogen (the precursor of pepsin, a proteolytic enzyme).
- G-cells in the stomach secrete gastrin, a hormone that stimulates release of secretions from both parietal and chief cells, and increases the activity of smooth muscle in the stomach wall for mixing and mechanical digestion activities.
- Pacemaker cells of the stomach control motility.
- Three reflexes alter stomach activity. The cephalic reflex is stimulated by the thought, smell, sight, or taste of food. The gastric reflex is stimulated by arrival of a bolus in the stomach. Both increase activity of the stomach. The intestinal reflex is stimulated by chyme in the small intestine; it opposes the other reflexes.

26.3 Lower Gastrointestinal Tract 1034

26.3a Overview of the Lower Gastrointestinal Tract Organs 1035
- The lower GI tract organs include most of the small intestine (ileum and jejunum), accessory organs (liver, gallbladder, and pancreas), and the large intestine.

26.3b Small Intestine 1035
- The small intestine has three parts: duodenum, jejunum, and ileum.
- Small intestine motility has three primary functions: (1) mixing chyme with accessory gland secretions, (2) continuing to expose the chyme to different regions of the brush border, and (3) moving small intestine contents toward the large intestine.

26.3c Accessory Organs and Ducts   1038

- Accessory organ ducts include hepatic ducts, cystic ducts, and pancreatic ducts. Secretions from the liver and pancreas enter the small intestine through these ducts.

- The liver produces bile to facilitate mechanical digestion of triglycerides.

- The gallbladder stores and concentrates bile produced by the liver.

- Exocrine cells of the pancreas secrete pancreatic enzymes, and cells of the pancreatic duct secrete bicarbonate ion; both secretions enter the duodenum. Pancreatic juice is an alkaline "cocktail" of hydrolytic enzymes, affecting major digestive activities in the ingested nutrients.

- Nervous system reflexes and endocrine secretions (gastrin, cholecystokinin, and secretin) control stomach activity, small intestine motility, and secretions from accessory organs.

26.3d Large Intestine   1044

- Only the last portion of absorption occurs in the large intestine—primarily consisting of water and electrolytes. Once these materials have been removed, the remnants solidify to become feces.

- The large intestine is composed of three regions: ileum, colon, and rectum.

- Movements in the large intestine include peristaltic movement, haustral churning, and mass movements. Reflexes associated with the large intestine include the gastrocolic reflex, and the defecation reflex.

26.4 Nutrients and Their Digestion 1049

- The six essential nutrients are carbohydrates, proteins, lipids, minerals, vitamins, and water.

26.4a Carbohydrate Digestion   1049

- Only monosaccharides may be directly absorbed. These are also called simple sugars and include glucose, fructose, and galactose.

- Starch must first be digested into smaller units by amylase (from the oral cavity) and then by specific pancreatic and brush border enzymes into smaller structures. Digestion is accompanied by absorption into the blood.

- Disaccharides (lactose and sucrose) only require one brush border enzyme each to be digested.

26.4b Protein Digestion   1051

- Denaturation of proteins by exposure to hydrochloric acid [HCl] accelerates the breakdown of proteins.

- All general proteases are released in an inactive state to prevent digestion of our body proteins.

- Pepsin, trypsin, chymotrypsin, and carboxypeptidase breaks down larger proteins into smaller fragments within the stomach and small intestine.

- Some specific brush border proteases (dipeptidases and aminopeptidases) finish the digestion of proteins into amino acids.

26.4c Lipid Digestion   1052

- Triglyceride digestion is facilitated by an interaction with bile salts that emulsify lipids to form micelles.

- Within micelles, pancreatic lipase breaks down triglyceride molecules into a monoglyceride and free fatty acids.

- Digested triglycerides are reassembled into triglycerides within epithelial cells and then along with other lipids are wrapped in proteins to form a chylomicron; chylomicrons then are absorbed into lacteals (lymphatic capillaries of the small intestine).

26.4d Nucleic Acid Digestion   1055

- Deoxyribonucleases and ribonucleases break apart DNA and RNA, respectively. Brush border enzymes break the bonds within the nucleotide, which are subsequently absorbed into the blood.

CHALLENGE YOURSELF

Do You Know the Basics?

_____ 1. Which organ is located in the right upper quadrant of the abdomen?

    a. liver

    b. spleen

    c. descending colon

    d. appendix

_____ 2. The _____ cells of the stomach secrete hydrochloric acid (HCl).

    a. chief

    b. parietal

    c. mucous

    d. G-

_____ 3. Which of the following is an unregulated process in the digestive tract?

    a. secretion of cholecystokinin (CCK) by the duodenal mucosa

    b. absorption of amino acids across epithelium of the small intestine

    c. release of bicarbonate ion (HCO_3^-) by pancreatic duct cells

    d. peristalsis in the stomach

_____ 4. Which organ (or part of an organ) is retroperitoneal?

    a. stomach

    b. transverse colon

    c. descending colon

    d. ileum

_____ 5. Pancreatic juice contains

   a. HCO_3^- and digestive enzymes.
   b. bile.
   c. bile and digestive enzymes.
   d. gastrin hormone.

_____ 6. Bile is conducted through the

   a. lacteals.
   b. accessory pancreatic duct.
   c. cystic duct.
   d. teniae coli.

_____ 7. Digestion of proteins begins in the

   a. oral cavity.
   b. stomach.
   c. small intestine.
   d. large intestine.

_____ 8. Micelles help promote

   a. denaturation of proteins.
   b. digestion and absorption of lipids.
   c. storage of digested carbohydrates.
   d. increased degradation of carbohydrates.

_____ 9. Hydrolytic enzymes that chemically digest most of our ingested food are secreted by the

   a. liver.
   b. small intestine.
   c. pancreas.
   d. salivary glands.

_____ 10. Most of the absorption of our digested food occurs within the

   a. large intestine.
   b. pancreas.
   c. small intestine.
   d. esophagus.

11. The GI tract from the esophagus to the anal canal is composed of four tunics. Describe the general histology of the tunics and the specific features of the esophageal tunics.

12. Discuss the reason why the involuntary sequence of contraction in the pharyngeal phase of swallowing involves skeletal muscle.

13. Explain why intrinsic factor release is the only essential function of the stomach.

14. Compare the structure of the circular folds, villi, and microvilli (the three structures that increase the surface area of the small intestine).

15. Discuss why the tunica mucosa in the colon has a high percentage of goblet cells to produce mucin.

16. Why is it necessary for proteases to be secreted in an inactive form?

17. What is the role of the gallbladder in digestion?

18. Describe the different forms of mechanical digestion in the oral cavity, stomach, and small intestine.

19. Describe the chemical digestive processes that occur in the stomach.

20. Explain the absorption of lipids.

Can You Apply What You've Learned?

1. Maria was diagnosed with stomach cancer and had to have her stomach surgically removed. Following the removal of her stomach, Maria must obtain shots of which substance?

   a. pepsinogen
   b. B_{12}
   c. HCl
   d. gastrin

2. Harold had his gallbladder removed (cholecystectomy). What advice is given concerning his diet that directly relates to the removal of his gallbladder?

   a. Eat a diet low in protein.
   b. Avoid meals high in fat.
   c. Consume a diet low in carbohydrates.
   d. Eat large meals once a day.

3. What component of the digestive tract can you not live without because almost all absorption of nutrients occurs here?

   a. small intestine
   b. large intestine
   c. stomach
   d. gallbladder

4. The pancreatic ducts are blocked with a thick, sticky mucus in individuals with the genetic condition called cystic fibrosis. What difficulties will these individuals experience?

   a. inability to produce mucin
   b. inability to produce HCl
   c. insufficient digestive enzymes
   d. excess production of bile

5. Mark was rushed to the hospital when his appendix ruptured. This condition is life-threatening due to

   a. entrance of bacteria into the abdominal cavity.
   b. serous fluid entering the GI tract.
   c. leaking of intestinal enzymes into the abdominal cavity.
   d. leaking of HCl into the abdominal cavity.

Can You Synthesize What You've Learned?

1. Alexandra experienced vomiting and diarrhea and was diagnosed with gastroenteritis (stomach flu). What specific digestive system organs were affected by the illness, and how did the illness interfere with each organ's function?

2. A key event in the chemical digestion processes that occur within the stomach is the formation of HCl by parietal cells in the gastric glands. Explain how these cells are able to produce HCl that is a million times more acidic than blood without destroying the cells themselves.

3. Most cases of colorectal cancer occur in the most distal part of the large intestine (the rectum, sigmoid colon, and descending colon). Why does the proximal part of the large intestine tend to have fewer instances of colon cancer? Include the anatomy and function of the colon structures in your explanation.

chapter 27

Nutrition and Metabolism

Many individuals express the desire to "eat healthy." Given the amount of media coverage regarding dietary intake, most of us are aware that eating healthy includes eating a diet with plenty of fruits, vegetables, and whole grains, which also includes small portions of protein, and is low in fat and sodium. By eating healthy we provide our bodies with the nutrients required for both the synthesis of new molecules and the energy for maintenance, growth, and repair, and we avoid foods that may cause us harm. ➔

Dietitians and nutritionists are health care professionals who are concerned with proper nutrition to maintain good health. They evaluate and assess the needs of individual patients and help develop appropriate nutritional programs. Often they recommend modifications of the diet to help prevent or treat illnesses. Dietitians manage and provide nutritional services to nursing care facilities, schools, and hospitals.

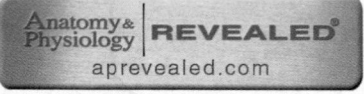

Anatomy & Physiology | REVEALED®
aprevealed.com

Module 12: Digestive System

Here we describe nutrients, how they are obtained through the food we eat, and how the body regulates nutrient levels in the blood during and following a meal. We also examine the functions of the liver including its essential role in regulating nutrient blood levels, the central role of cellular respiration in nutrient metabolism, the production of heat from metabolic processes, and the regulation of body temperature.

27.1 Nutrients

Nutrients include most biomolecules (see section 2.7), vitamins, and minerals. These substances are obtained through the diet by the processes of the digestive system. **Nutrition** is the study of the means by which living organisms acquire the nutrients they need to grow and sustain life.

Water is considered by some to be a nutrient because 2 to 3 liters of it are required daily by the body. Water and its properties are described in section 2.4, and water balance is discussed in section 25.2. The different essential nutrients and their general functions are summarized in **table 27.1**.

27.1a Nutrient Biomolecules

LEARNING OBJECTIVES

1. Name and briefly describe the three major nutrient biomolecules.
2. Distinguish between essential and nonessential amino acids, and compare proteins that are complete with those that are incomplete.

Nutrient biomolecules include carbohydrates, lipids, and proteins. Nucleic acids, the other major biomolecule described in section 2.7, are not considered nutrients because they are not required in our diet for survival:

- **Carbohydrates** are composed of simple sugar monomers called **monosaccharides; disaccharides** that have two monosaccharides; and **polysaccharides** formed from chains of monosaccharides (see section 2.7c).

- **Lipids** are a diverse group of biologically active, hydrophobic molecules that include triglycerides, phospholipids, steroids, and eicosanoids. **Triglycerides** are an important energy source (see section 2.7b).

- **Proteins** are formed by 20 different amino acids and contain nitrogen in the amine group (see section 2.8). The body is able to synthesize some, but not all, of the amino acids needed to produce a protein. **Nonessential amino acids** may be made in the body, while **essential amino acids** (8 out of the 20) must come from the diet. Proteins may be categorized as **complete proteins,** which supply all of our essential amino acids, and **incomplete proteins,** which do not.

WHAT DID YOU LEARN?

1. What are the three major categories of nutrient biomolecules?
2. What is the basis for identifying amino acids as essential or nonessential?

27.1b Vitamins

LEARNING OBJECTIVES

3. Distinguish between water-soluble and fat-soluble vitamins.
4. Describe the difference between essential and nonessential vitamins.
5. List examples of how vitamins function in the body.

Vitamins are organic molecules required for normal metabolism, yet they are present in only small amounts in food. Vitamins are categorized in two ways: (1) water-soluble vitamins or fat-soluble vitamins

Table 27.1	Essential Nutrients and Their Functions	
Nutrient	**Description**	**Functions**
Carbohydrates	Carbohydrates are classified as monosaccharides, disaccharides, and polysaccharides	Glucose is broken down to generate energy for life processes; glycogen is a polymer of glucose molecules that are stored in the liver and skeletal muscle tissue
Lipids	Lipids are a diverse group of hydrophobic biomolecules that include triglycerides, steroids, phospholipids, and eicosanoids	Triglycerides serve as a form of energy storage (gram for gram, triglycerides provide more energy than carbohydrates); phospholipids compose cell membranes; steroids are components of plasma membranes, serve as hormones, and are precursors for synthesis of bile salts; eicosanoids are local hormones
Proteins	Proteins are polymers composed of amino acids	Proteins are both structural and functional components of the body
Vitamins	Organic nutrients	Serve as coenzymes in chemical reactions; participate in connective tissue synthesis, part of visual pigment in eye; enhance calcium absorption, and aid in bone formation
Minerals	Inorganic nutrients	Minerals are required, for example, in bone formation, nerve and muscle function; component of nucleic acids, adenosine triphosphate [ATP], and part of hemoglobin
Water	The biological solvent of life that composes two-thirds of the body	Unique properties to support life including exhibiting cohesion, adhesion, surface tension, high specific heat, high heat of vaporization

and (2) essential vitamins or nonessential vitamins. **Table 27.2** lists the water-soluble and fat-soluble vitamins and their sources, functions, and deficiency symptoms.

 WHAT DO YOU THINK?

1 Predict what happens to the level of fat-soluble vitamins stored in adipose connective tissue as a result of megadoses of vitamins.

Water-Soluble and Fat-Soluble Vitamins

Water-soluble vitamins dissolve in water: They include both the B vitamins and vitamin C. These vitamins are easily absorbed into the blood from the digestive tract. If dietary intake of water-soluble vitamins exceeds what is needed by the body, the excess is excreted into the urine. Some water-soluble vitamins function as coenzymes to assist with normal enzyme function (see section 3.3). Examples include vitamin B_3, also called niacin, a necessary hydrogen carrier in mitochondria during adenosine triphosphate (ATP) synthesis (see section 3.4).

Fat-soluble vitamins dissolve in fat (not in water) and include vitamins A, D, E, and K. They are absorbed from the gastrointestinal tract within the lipid of micelles and ultimately enter into the lymphatic capillaries (lacteals) (see section 26.4c). If dietary intake of fat-soluble vitamins exceeds body requirements, the excess is stored within the body fat and may reach toxic levels (hypervitaminosis).

The functions of fat-soluble vitamins vary.

- Vitamin A (retinol) is a precursor molecule for the formation of the visual pigment retinal (see section 16.4c).
- Vitamin D (calciferol) is modified to form calcitriol: This is a hormone that increases calcium absorption from the gastrointestinal tract (see section 7.6).
- Vitamin E (tocopherol) helps stabilize and prevent damage of cell membranes that are described in section 4.2.
- Vitamin K is required for synthesis of specific blood clotting proteins (see section 18.4c).

Essential and Nonessential Vitamins

Vitamins are also categorized based upon their requirement in the diet. Essential vitamins must be provided in the diet. If an essential vitamin is lacking in our intake, or its absorption is impaired, then

Table 27.2	**Vitamins Required by Humans**		
Vitamin	**Source**	**Function**	**Deficiency Symptoms**
WATER-SOLUBLE VITAMINS			
B-complex vitamins			
Vitamin B_1 (thiamine)	Meats, nuts, and grains	Coenzyme in cellular respiration to assist with carbon dioxide (CO_2) removal	Weakened heart, beriberi, edema
Vitamin B_2 (riboflavin)	Numerous food types	Portion of coenzyme (flavin adenine dinucleotide [FAD]), which is required in aerobic cellular respiration	Inflammation and breakdown of skin
Vitamin B_3 (niacin)	Lean meats, liver	Portion of coenzyme (nicotinamide adenine dinucleotide [NAD^+]); helps increase high-density lipoprotein (HDL)	Nerve inflammation, pellagra
Vitamin B_5 (pantothenic acid)	Numerous food types	Portion of coenzyme A (CoA), which functions in aerobic cellular respiration	Fatigue, decreased coordination
Vitamin B_6 (pyridoxine)	Meats, vegetables	Coenzyme in amino acid metabolism	Anemia, convulsions
Vitamin B_{12} (cyanocobalamin)	Dairy products, red meats	Coenzyme in synthesis of nucleic acid building blocks	Pernicious anemia
Biotin (Vitamin B_7)	Vegetables, meats	Coenzyme in amino acid metabolism and fat synthesis	Nausea, depression
Folate (folic acid; B_9)	Many green vegetables	Coenzyme in nucleic acid and amino acid metabolism	Risk of neural tube defects to unborn child if mother is deficient during pregnancy
Vitamin C	Leafy green vegetables, fruit	Synthesis of collagen, which is an important component of connective tissue, and is needed for development of a healthy nervous system	Scurvy, breakdown of blood vessels and skin
FAT-SOLUBLE VITAMINS			
Vitamin A (retinol)	Liver, milk products, green vegetables	Formed from beta-carotene obtained from plants; precursor molecule to form retinal that is part of visual pigment, and retinoic acid that serves as a second messenger	Night blindness, dry and flaky skin
Vitamin D (calciferol)	Cod liver oil, dairy products; UV rays (when synthesized by keratinocytes of epidermis)	Calcium absorption	Rickets, bone abnormalities
Vitamin E (tocopherol)	Leafy green vegetables, seeds, margarine, butter	Cell membrane and fatty acid protection from oxidation	Rare
Vitamin K	Leafy green vegetables	Needed for blood clotting	Abnormal bleeding

a vitamin deficiency disease results (avitaminosis). The vitamins in table 27.2 are all essential vitamins.

Nonessential vitamins are cofactors that the body is able to produce and recycle as needed. Examples are the NADH and FADH$_2$ that occur in the citric acid cycle (see section 3.4d).

 WHAT DID YOU LEARN?

3 Which vitamins are water-soluble? Which are fat-soluble? Which of these groups may be dangerous in excess?

27.1c Minerals

 LEARNING OBJECTIVES

6. Define minerals, and list examples of how minerals absorbed in the small intestine function in the body.

7. Distinguish between major minerals and trace minerals.

Minerals are inorganic ions such as iron, calcium, sodium, potassium, iodine, zinc, magnesium, and phosphorus. Minerals have diverse functions in the body. For example:

- **Iron** is present both in hemoglobin within erythrocytes, where it binds oxygen (section 18.3b), and within the mitochondria in the electron transport system to bind electrons (section 3.4e).

- **Calcium** is required for formation and maintenance of the skeleton (section 7.2e), for blood clotting (section 18.4c), and for exocytosis of neurotransmitters (section 12.8d).
- **Sodium** and **potassium** function to maintain a resting membrane potential in excitable cells, and are required in the generation of an action potential (section 12.7).
- **Iodine** is needed to produce thyroid hormone (section 17.9b).
- **Zinc** has roles in both protein synthesis (section 4.7) and wound healing.

All minerals are obtained from the diet. We have a daily requirement for all minerals, and the amount required places minerals into one of two categories: **major minerals,** which are needed at levels greater than 100 milligrams per day, and **trace minerals,** which are required at less than 100 milligrams per day. Major minerals include calcium, chlorine, cobalt, magnesium, manganese, phosphorus, potassium, sodium, and sulfur; trace minerals include chromium, copper, fluorine, iodine, iron, seleneium, and zinc.

Minerals absorbed from the digestive system are stored to varying degrees within the body. These reserves are "hedges" against unexpected decreases in availability; however, if stored minerals are depleted, clinical problems may occur. **Table 27.3** lists the minerals, their sources, functions, and deficiency symptoms.

 WHAT DID YOU LEARN?

4 What are the major minerals? The trace minerals? How are these two groups distinguished?

Table 27.3	Minerals Required by Humans		
Mineral	**Source**	**Functions**	**Deficiency Symptoms**
MAJOR MINERALS			
Calcium (Ca)	Green vegetables, dairy products	Bone and tooth formation, exocytosis, blood clotting, intracellular signaling	Loss of bone mass, muscle weakness, depressed nerve activity
Chlorine (Cl)	Cured meats, table salt (NaCl)	Acid-base balance, osmotic pressure	Muscle cramps
Cobalt (Co)	Fish, green vegetables, nuts	Component of vitamin B$_{12}$	Anemia
Magnesium (Mg)	Green leafy vegetables, grains (whole)	Complexes with coenzyme for ATP synthesis	Muscle weakness, nervous system disturbances
Manganese (Mn)	Vegetables, nuts, tea, fruits	Cofactor for enzymes including oxidoreductases, transferases, hydrolases, lyases, isomerases	Behavioral changes, abnormal bone formation
Phosphorus (P)	Meats, nuts, dairy products, grains	Bone and tooth formation	Weakness
Potassium (K)	Meats, fruits, grains, vegetables, dairy products, salt substitutes	Muscle contraction, nerve function, osmotic pressure	Muscle weakness, abnormal cardiac function
Sodium (Na)	Table salt (NaCl), canned foods	Muscle contraction, nerve function, osmotic pressure	Neuromuscular disturbances, hypertension
Sulfur (S)	Kale, cauliflower, cabbage	Specific amino acids (cysteine, methionine) contain sulfur	Symptoms associated with protein deficiency
MINOR (TRACE) MINERALS			
Chromium (Cr)	Whole grains, meats, cereals	Metabolism of carbohydrates, proteins, and fats; role in insulin function	Impaired glucose tolerance associated with insulin resistance
Copper (Cu)	Seafood, legumes, liver, nuts	Enzyme cofactor	Anemia
Fluorine (F)	Fluorinated water, fish, tea	Required in structure of bone and teeth	Increased risk of dental caries (cavities)
Iodine (I)	Iodized table salt	Component of thyroid hormone	Goiter
Iron (Fe)	Red meat, poultry, fish, dark green leafy vegetables, nuts, whole grains	Structural component of hemoglobin and cytochromes	Anemia, weakness, fatigue, pale skin, headaches, sensitivity to cold
Selenium (Se)	Cereals, nuts, meats	Cofactor of certain enzymes	Rare
Zinc (Zn)	Meat, seeds	Protein synthesis; wound healing	Changes in skin, eyes; hair loss; diarrhea

CLINICAL VIEW
Iron Deficiency

Iron (Fe) has several critical functions within the body: (1) It is required in the structure of hemoglobin in erythrocytes and myoglobin in muscle cells; (2) Iron is a component of specific electron transport proteins (cytochromes) within mitochondria; (3) It is required for some enzymes in the synthesis of certain hormones, neurotransmitters, and amino acids.

Iron is obtained in the diet from diverse sources including red meat, poultry, fish, dark green leafy vegetables, nuts, and whole grains. Although it is an essential mineral, iron is toxic in its free or unattached form. The toxic effects of iron are avoided by having it bound to specific proteins. **Mucosal ferritin** binds iron within epithelial cells in the small intestine lining following its absorption from the gastrointestinal (GI) tract. When iron is needed in the body, mucosal ferritin transfers iron to **mucosal transferrin** (of epithelial cells of the small intestine) that then transfers it to blood transferrin. **Blood transferrin** (a plasma protein) delivers iron to tissues throughout the body, including red bone marrow for hemoglobin synthesis, or to the liver for storage. Within the liver, iron is bound to **hemosiderin** and **ferritin**.

Iron deficiency is one of the most common nutritional deficiencies. Symptoms of iron deficiency typically include fatigue, weakness, pale skin, headaches, and sensitivity to cold temperatures. It results from insufficient intake of iron based on loss of iron from the body. Iron is obtained in the diet. How much is obtained is dependent upon the quantities present in the consumed food and the amount absorbed from the GI tract. Heme iron (iron obtained in eating animal flesh of meats, poultry, and fish) is absorbed much more readily than nonheme iron (iron not associated with heme, which is obtained by eating iron-rich plants such as spinach and beans). Absorption may be altered by other food substances that are also present in the GI tract. For example, vitamin C increases the absorption of iron, whereas tea, which contains tannic acid, interferes with absorption of iron. In fact, high intake of tea may lead to iron deficiency. Changes to the intestinal lining that accompany certain diseases, such as Crohn disease (an inflammatory disease) or celiac sprue (an autoimmune disorder) also interfere with iron absorption.

Iron is lost in feces (from the cells of the intestinal lining), urine, and sweat. Excessive loss of iron from bleeding (e.g., heavy or frequent menses, internal bleeding, trauma, blood donation) also may lead to an iron deficiency. Women are more prone to iron deficiencies because of the loss of blood with each menses. Pregnant women and women that are breast-feeding have an even higher risk because of the extra demands for iron placed on them.

27.2 Obtaining Nutrients from Food

Here we discuss dietary requirements and guidelines for adequate nutrition.

27.2a Meeting Dietary Requirements

✓ LEARNING OBJECTIVES

1. List dietary sources for carbohydrates, lipids, proteins, vitamins, and minerals.
2. Compare how a nonvegetarian and a vegetarian meet their dietary needs for essential amino acids.
3. Explain nitrogen balance, including the difference between a positive and negative nitrogen balance.

As described in the first section of this chapter, the nutrient biomolecules include carbohydrates, lipids, and proteins. Here we look at the sources of these molecules in the diet.

Carbohydrates

The major carbohydrate that provides energy is glucose. It is obtained in the diet from various sources (or is converted from either galactose or fructose by hepatocytes following their delivery to the liver via the hepatic portal system; see section 26.4a). Examples of dietary sources of carbohydrates include the following:

- Starch, a polysaccharide polymer of glucose that is a component of foods such as potatoes, breads, rice, and other grains
- Lactose, a disaccharide composed of glucose and galactose, found in milk and termed milk sugar
- Sucrose, a disaccharide containing both glucose and fructose that occurs in table sugar, maple syrup, and fruits
- Various other disaccharides (e.g., maltose found in cereals), monosaccharides (e.g., fructose and glucose found in honey and agave nectar), and high fructose corn syrup (manufactured from cornstarch)

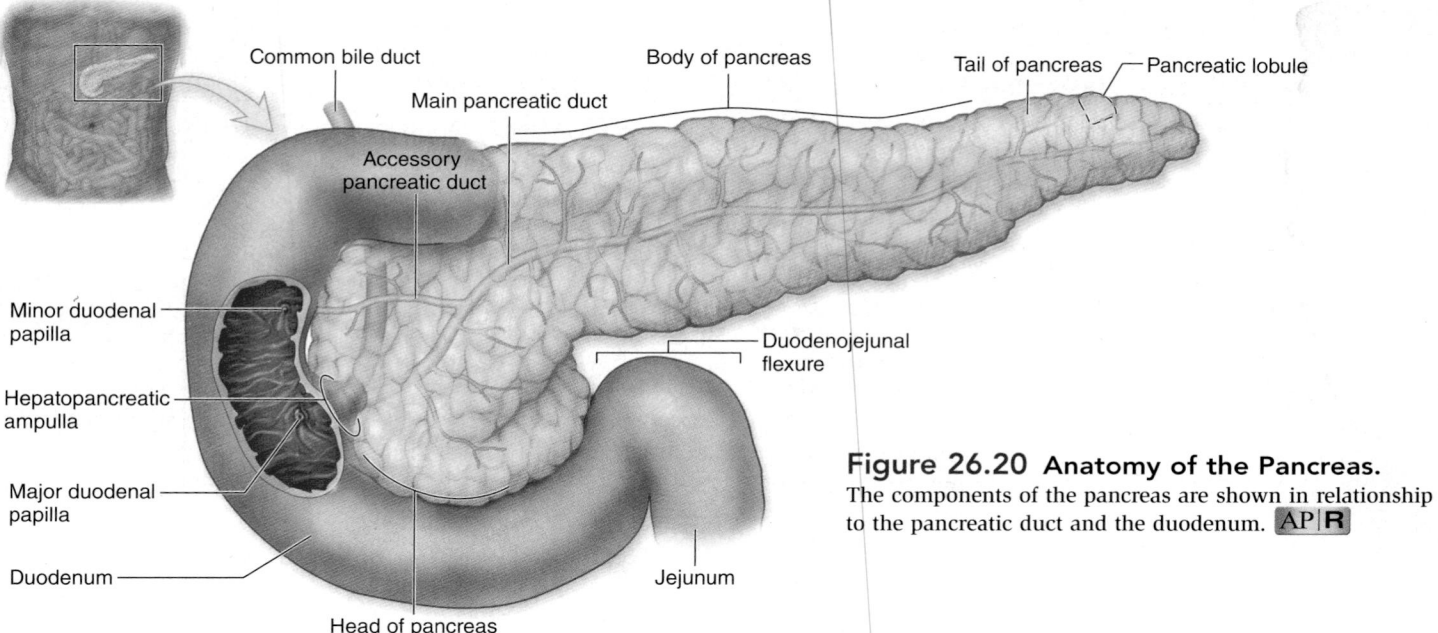

Common bile duct
Body of pancreas
Tail of pancreas
Pancreatic lobule
Main pancreatic duct
Accessory pancreatic duct
Minor duodenal papilla
Hepatopancreatic ampulla
Major duodenal papilla
Duodenum
Duodenojejunal flexure
Jejunum
Head of pancreas

Figure 26.20 Anatomy of the Pancreas.
The components of the pancreas are shown in relationship to the pancreatic duct and the duodenum. AP|R

(sing., *acinus* = grape) (**figure 26.21**). These cells are organized into large clusters termed **lobules.** Acinar cells produce and release hydrolytic enzymes. Small ducts lead from each acinus into larger ducts that empty into larger pancreatic ducts that lead to the duodenum (as described earlier). The simple cuboidal epithelial cells lining the pancreatic ducts have the important function of secreting alkaline HCO_3^- fluid.

Pancreatic Juice   Together, secretions of acinar cells and cells that line the pancreatic ducts form **pancreatic juice.** Pancreatic juice (approximately 1 to 1.5 liters per day) is an alkaline fluid containing mostly water, HCO_3^-, and a versatile mixture of hydrolytic enzymes that are described in detail later in the chapter. These enzymes include the following:

- Pancreatic amylase to digest starch
- Pancreatic lipase for the digestion of fats
- Inactive proteases (trypsinogen, chymotrypsinogen, and procarboxypeptidase) that, when activated, digest protein
- Nucleases for the digestion of nucleic acids (DNA and RNA)

Regulation of Accessory Structures   Several of the same processes that regulate stomach secretions and motility control the release of secretions from the accessory organs. Vagal stimulation (see section 15.3a) during the cephalic and gastric phase, in addition to stimulating stomach motility and secretion, also activates the pancreas to release pancreatic juice.

   Cholecystokinin (CCK) (ko′lē-sis-to-kī′nin; *chole* = bile; *cyst* = sac, *kinin* = to move) is a hormone released from the small intestine primarily in response to fatty chyme. One of the primary functions of cholecystokinin (and from which its name is derived) is stimulation of the smooth muscle in the gallbladder wall to strongly contract, causing the release of concentrated bile. Other functions of CCK include stimulating the pancreas to release enzyme-rich pancreatic juice, and relaxing the smooth muscle within the hepatopancreatic ampulla, allowing entry of the bile and pancreatic juice into the small intestine. CCK also inhibits both stomach motility and release of gastric secretions (as described earlier).

   Secretin (se-krē′tin) is released from the small intestine primarily in response to an increase in chyme acidity. Secretin primarily causes the release of an alkaline solution that contains HCO_3^- from both the liver and ducts of the pancreas. Upon entering the small intestine, this alkaline

Alpha cell (secretes glucagon)
Beta cell (secretes insulin)
Arteriole
Venule
Pancreatic islet
LM 75x
Pancreatic acini
Pancreatic islet
LM 200x
Acinar cell
Pancreatic acinus
Acinar cell (secretes amylase, lipase, proteases, and nucleases)
Duct cell (secretes HCO_3^-)
Pancreatic acinus

Figure 26.21 Histology of the Pancreas. Photomicrographs show the histology of pancreatic islets and pancreatic acini.

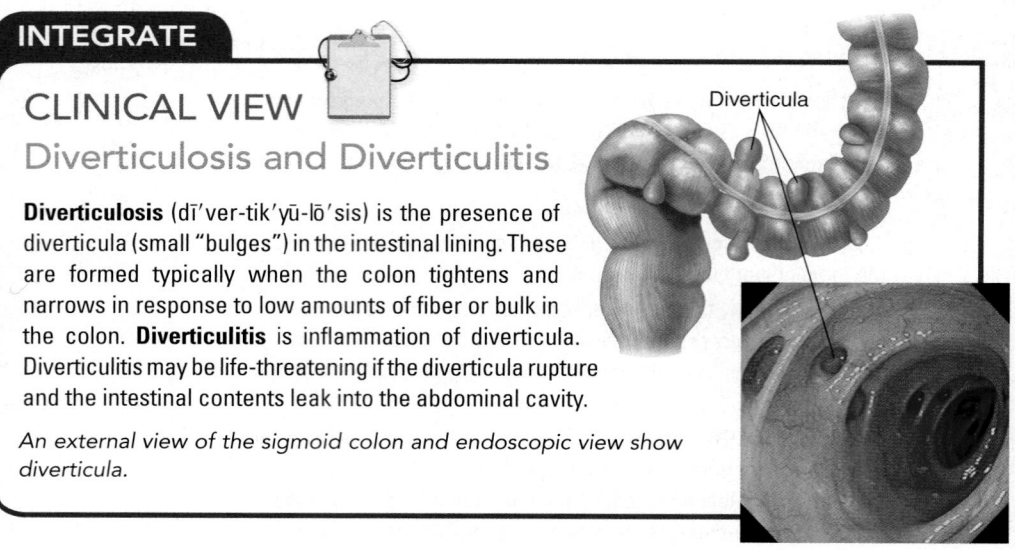
Two major reflexes are associated with motility in the large intestine:

- The **gastrocolic** (gas′trō-kol′ik) **reflex** is initiated by stomach distension to cause a mass movement (motility in the large intestine just described).
- The **defecation reflex.** The elimination of feces from the GI tract by the process of **defecation** (def-ĕ-kā′shŭn; *defaeco* = to remove the dregs) **(figure 26.24)**. Filling of the rectum initiates the urge to defecate. This stimulus results in transmission of

Nerve signals from cerebral cortex

② Sensory input initiated by baroreceptors in rectum is relayed to the spinal cord.

Sensory neurons

Parasympathetic motor neurons

① Rectum contents stimulate baroreceptors in rectal wall.

③ Motor output along parasympathetic axons is altered.

Stretch baroreceptors

④ Increased motor output to smooth muscle of rectum; rectum contracts, squeezing the contents. Decreased motor output to internal anal sphincter causes sphincter relaxation.

Rectum

Anal canal

Internal anal sphincter

External anal sphincter

Somatic motor axons

⑤ The conscious decision to defecate is controlled by the cerebral cortex. External anal sphincter relaxes and Valsalva maneuver is initiated, eliminating the feces.

Figure 26.24 Elimination. The defecation reflex involves sensory perception of stretch in the rectum that initiates a spinal reflex that stimulates muscles in the rectal wall to contract and the internal anal sphincter to relax. Conscious regulation of defecation requires the relaxation of the external anal sphincter and the Valsalva maneuver.

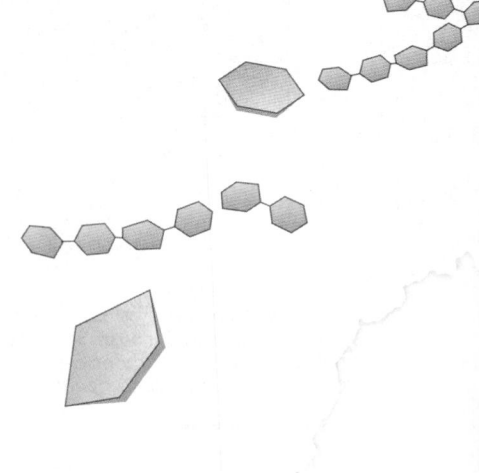

(b)

1. Proteolytic enzymes are released from pancreas.

Trypsinogen
Chymotrypsinogen
Procarboxypeptidase
Enteropeptidase

2. Enteropeptidase activates trypsinogen to trypsin; trypsin then activates other proteolytic enzymes.

Trypsin
Chymotrypsin
Carboxypeptidase

Inactive enzyme
Active enzyme

Partially digested proteins

Peptides

3. Activated pancreatic proteolytic enzymes break proteins into peptides and amino acids.

Epithelial cell
Brush border
Villus

Brush border   Epithelial cell   Blood capillary

Peptidases (dipeptidase, aminopeptidase)

Amino acids

4. Brush border peptidases break peptides into single amino acids to be absorbed through epithelial cell into blood.

(a)

Figure 26.26 Protein Digestion in the Small Intestine. (*a*) Pancreatic enzymes for protein digestion are produced and secreted into the small intestine in an inactive form. After reaching the small intestine, these enzymes are activated. (*b*) The locations where different protein-digesting enzymes break peptide bonds are highlighted in purple.

glycerol, and enzymes are required to break the bonds between glycerol and fatty acids. Digestion of cholesterol is not required for its absorption.

Lipid Breakdown in the Stomach

Lingual lipase (produced by intrinsic salivary glands in the mouth) is a component of saliva in the oral cavity. The optimal pH of this enzyme (4.5 to 5.4), however, means it is not activated until it reaches the stomach. Once in the stomach, triglycerides undergo limited digestion by both lingual lipase and gastric lipase (an enzyme produced by chief cells of the stomach). These "acidic lipases" digest approximately 30% of the triglycerides to diglyceride and fatty acid. Neither of these lipase enzymes requires the participation of bile salts (see next section).

Lipid Breakdown in the Small Intestine

The majority of triglyceride digestion occurs in the small intestine and is facilitated by **pancreatic lipase,** an enzyme produced by the pancreas and released into the duodenum. Pancreatic lipase digests each triglyceride into a monoglyceride and two free fatty acids. However, because triglycerides are lipids and do not dissolve in the luminal fluids of the digestive system, triglycerides form relatively large lipid masses. For example, when butter is added to water, the butter does not stay mixed with the water but remains separate.

2. A key event in the chemical digestion processes that occur within the stomach is the formation of HCl by parietal cells in the gastric glands. Explain how these cells are able to produce HCl that is a million times more acidic than blood without destroying the cells themselves.

3. Most cases of colorectal cancer occur in the most distal part of the large intestine (the rectum, sigmoid colon, and descending colon). Why does the proximal part of the large intestine tend to have fewer instances of colon cancer? Include the anatomy and function of the colon structures in your explanation.

INTEGRATE

ONLINE STUDY TOOLS
www.mhhe.com/mckinleyap

Clinical Case Study: A Teenage Boy with Abdominal Pain and Weight Loss

Interactive Questions: This chapter's content is served up in a number of multimedia question formats for student study.

LearnSmart: Topics and terminology include introduction to the digestive system; upper gastrointestinal tract; lower gastrointestinal tract; nutrients and their digestion

Anatomy & Physiology Revealed: Topics include digestive system overview; oral cavity and pharynx; salivary glands; teeth; esophagus; stomach; HCL production; small intestine; duodenum; liver; biliary ducts; abdominal cavity; hydrolysis of sucrose

Animations: Topics include organs of digestion; digestive system overview; stomach; hydrochloric acid production of the stomach; hormones and gastric secretion; three phases of gastric secretions; liver; reflexes in the colon

Certain carbohydrates contribute to our fiber intake. For example, cellulose is a plant polymer composed of glucoses bonded together in a different way than they are in starch. Our digestive system does not produce enzymes that can chemically digest these bonds. Consequently, cellulose remains in the gastrointestinal (GI) tract as fiber, facilitating the movement of the contents through the GI tract and its ultimate elimination as a component of feces. In other words, cellulose and other forms of fiber help to "keep you regular."

Lipids

Triglycerides are another major energy-providing molecule obtained from the diet in fats (e.g., butter, animal fat, milk, and cheese) and oils (e.g., vegetable oils and fish oils). As mentioned, the absorption of fat-soluble vitamins requires the absorption of fat.

Cholesterol is another type of lipid that is a component of all animal-based products (e.g., meats, eggs, and milk) because it is within the plasma membrane of animal cells. (Plant cell plasma membranes do not contain cholesterol.) Cholesterol is also produced through metabolic pathways in liver cells that synthesize cholesterol (described later). Thus, cholesterol is made available through both its intake in the diet and its synthesis by the liver. Cholesterol is also the precursor molecule for the formation of steroid hormones, bile salts, and fat-soluble vitamins.

Proteins

Adequate dietary intake of protein provides the amino acids to synthesize new protein to replace protein structures that have worn out. Protein is obtained from meat, dairy products, poultry, fish, beans, and nuts. A **vegetarian** is an individual who does not eat meat, fish, or poultry. **Lacto-ovo vegetarians** do not eat animal flesh but do eat milk, eggs, and cheese. **Vegans** do not eat any animal products. **Pescatarians** do not eat most animal flesh but do eat fish.

A major concern for vegetarians is that plant-based protein sources are often individually incomplete. These individuals must be sure to obtain the essential amino acids from a variety of complementary protein sources. For example, legumes such as beans provide the essential amino acid lysine, whereas brown rice provides methionine. Another combination would be whole wheat bread with hummus (made from chickpeas). These balanced food combinations do not need to be eaten in the same meal, but if eaten regularly, they may supply the necessary amino acids.

Proteins are also a source of nitrogen (each amino acid contains an —NH_2 functional-group; see section 2.7e). Nitrogen is needed for synthesizing other nitrogen-containing molecules, such as nitrogenous bases of nucleic acids (DNA, RNA), and porphyrin (a component of heme in hemoglobin, see section 18.3b). Adequate availability of nitrogen is expressed as nitrogen balance.

Nitrogen balance occurs when equilibrium exists between its dietary intake and its loss in urine and feces. Input of nitrogen must equal output of nitrogen to maintain a nitrogen balance. A **positive nitrogen balance** occurs when an individual absorbs more nitrogen than is excreted, such as occurs in individuals who are growing, pregnant, or recovering from injury. A **negative nitrogen balance** occurs when more nitrogen is excreted than is absorbed; a condition that might result from malnutrition or blood loss, for example. An individual in sustained negative nitrogen balance has insufficient nitrogen to synthesize nitrogen-containing molecules, and a decrease in as little as a few hundred grams of total nitrogen may be fatal.

Vitamins and Minerals

Vitamins and minerals are primarily obtained in the foods that we eat. Each type of food may contain a variety of vitamins and minerals, but no one food contains all that are required. Consequently, it is necessary to have variety in the diet to meet the body's needs. The various dietary sources of vitamins and minerals are included in tables 27.2 and 27.3.

WHAT DID YOU LEARN?

5 What are some dietary sources for carbohydrates, fats, cholesterol, and proteins?

6 How may a vegetarian obtain all of the essential amino acids?

7 Is an individual more likely to have a positive nitrogen balance or negative nitrogen balance with insufficient protein intake?

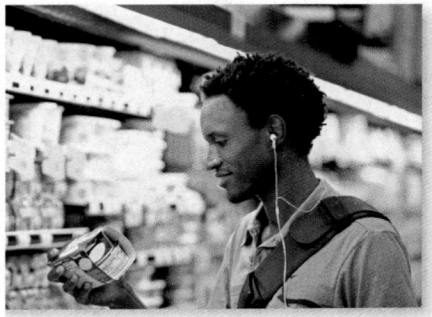

27.2b Guidelines for Adequate Nutrition

LEARNING OBJECTIVES

4. Explain the meaning of recommended daily allowance (RDA).
5. Describe MyPlate, which was developed by the USDA to help people eat healthy.
6. Identify the items that are included on a food label.

The amount of each type of nutrient biomolecule, vitamin, and mineral required by the body is not the same for all individuals; rather, it is dependent upon a number of factors, including an individual's age, sex, body mass, level of physical activity, health, and whether an individual is pregnant. A number of guidelines (recommended daily allowance, the USDA MyPlate, and required nutritional labels on packaged foods) have been provided or are required by scientific governmental agencies in the United States.

Recommended Daily Allowance

Federal government agencies have established values for nutrients called the **recommended daily allowances (RDAs).** These were originally established by the Food and Nutrition Board (FNB) as directed by the National Academy of Sciences (NAS), and they are reviewed and updated periodically based on additional continuing nutrition studies. RDA information may be accessed online at the USDA's food and nutrition information center (http://fnic.nal.usda.gov).

These government-established values are used for food planning, food labeling, clinical dietetics, food programs, and educational programs on nutrition. Although RDA values are currently based on population studies, in the future these RDA levels could be established for each individual based upon their specific genetic makeup.

MyPlate

Not only may malnutrition be avoided, but an individual's state of health may be maximized when all of the nutrients are obtained at appropriate levels in the diet. Previously, food groups were organized by the United States Department of Agriculture (USDA) into a food guide pyramid that consisted of breads/grains, vegetables, fruits, dairy, proteins, and fats/oils/sweets. This organization provided a general approach for the number of servings that should be consumed daily from each category.

In 2011, the USDA revised the pyramid to **MyPlate (figure 27.1)**. This visual of a divided plate helps us to see at a glance the relative proportions of the types of foods we need to stay healthy. One half of the plate is vegetables and fruit and the other half is protein and cereals, with dairy off to the side. Examples of each category of food include the following:

- **Vegetables**—broccoli, lettuce, peppers, and carrots
- **Fruits**—apples, blueberries, bananas, and oranges
- **Protein**—poultry, fish, beans, eggs, and nuts
- **Grains**—bread, cereals, rice, and pasta
- **Milk**—skim milk, yogurt, and cheese

You will notice several additional recommendations listed if you go to the USDA website (www.choosemyplate.gov). These include the suggestion to balance calories by eating less, switch from whole milk to low-fat or no-fat milk, reduce the intake of foods that are high in salt (e.g., canned soup), and cut back on sugary drinks by drinking water instead.

Nutritional Food Labels

Specific details on the composition of prepackaged items are made available on food labels. These labels are required by law and include servings per container, serving size, calories, total fat, cholesterol, sodium, carbohydrates, proteins, vitamins, some minerals, and product ingredients **(figure 27.2)**.

This information may be helpful for those who are interested in eating a healthy diet, those who are meal planning for weight-loss programs, and individuals who are restricting intake of nutrients such as sugar or sodium.

Figure 27.1 MyPlate. MyPlate shows the relative proportions of fruits, vegetables, grains, protein, and dairy for eating healthy.

WHAT DID YOU LEARN?

8 What is meant by the RDA of nutrients?

9 What four categories of food are shown on the USDA MyPlate? Which food category takes up the largest portion of the plate?

10 What is the purpose of the requirement for nutritional labeling on packaged foods?

Figure 27.2 Food Label.
A food label is included on prepackaged foods and provides serving size, calories, and nutrient information.

27.3 Regulating Blood Levels of Nutrients

Recall that blood is composed of plasma and formed elements. Plasma contains water, proteins, electrolytes, nutrients, respiratory gases, and waste products (see section 18.2). The percentage of these substances is regulated by several processes, many of which have been described in the preceding chapters. Here we limit our discussion to regulation of levels of nutrients as they vary during the day relative to the intake of meals. Generally, regulation of blood nutrients is dependent upon the length of time since you have eaten. These conditions are referred to as the absorptive state and the postabsorptive state.

27.3a Absorptive State

✓ LEARNING OBJECTIVE

1. Explain when the absorptive state occurs and how nutrient levels are regulated during this time.

The **absorptive state** includes the time you are eating, digesting, and absorbing nutrients. It usually lasts approximately 4 hours after a given meal. If you eat three meals spread throughout the day, you typically spend about 12 hours daily in the absorptive state. During the absorptive state, the concentrations of glucose, triglycerides, and amino acids are increasing within the blood as they are absorbed from the GI tract **(figure 27.3)**. The

Figure 27.3 Absorptive State.
During the absorptive state, nutrients are being digested, absorbed into the blood, and then removed from the blood and stored in various body tissues. Insulin is the primary regulatory hormone of the absorptive state.

body's challenge is to maintain homeostatic levels of these nutrients during this time—primarily while maintaining homeostatic blood glucose levels to within the range of 70 to 110 milligrams per deciliter (mg/dL).

Insulin (discussed in detail in section 17.10b) is the major regulatory hormone that is released during the absorptive state. Its release from the pancreas occurs in response to an increase in blood glucose levels. A few of the responses initiated by insulin that alter blood nutrient levels are listed here:

- Stimulates both liver cells and muscle cells to form the polysaccharide glycogen from glucose by increasing glycogenesis
- Causes adipose connective tissue to increase uptake of triglycerides from the blood and decreases the breakdown of triglycerides by stimulating lipogenesis and inhibiting lipolysis
- Stimulates most cells (especially muscle cells) to increase amino acid uptake that causes an accelerated rate in protein synthesis

Consequently, the release of insulin results in a decrease in all energy-releasing molecules (glucose, triglycerides, and amino acids) in the blood, an increase in the storage of glycogen and triglycerides, and the formation of protein within body tissues. Note that excess amino acids are not "stored" as protein. The amino acids become structural and functional components of the body.

 WHAT DID YOU LEARN?

 11 How does the storage of nutrient molecules change during the absorptive state?

27.3b Postabsorptive State

 LEARNING OBJECTIVE

2. Explain when the postabsorptive state occurs, and how nutrient levels are regulated during this time.

The **postabsorptive state** is the time between meals when the body relies on its stores of nutrients because no further absorption of nutrients is occurring **(figure 27.4)**. Assuming that an individual eats three meals spread out through the day, and spends 12 hours in the absorptive state, the other 12 hours are spent in the postabsorptive state. The challenge is to maintain homeostatic levels of many nutrients (e.g., monosaccharides, triglycerides, and amino acids) as these substances are decreasing in the blood.

Glucagon (discussed in detail in section 17.10b) is the major regulatory hormone that is released during the postabsorptive state. The pancreas releases glucagon in response to decreasing blood glucose levels. Glucagon has several effects, including the following:

- Stimulates liver cells to engage in catabolism of glycogen to glucose by increasing glycogenolysis. Glucagon may also increase the formation of glucose from noncarbohydrate sources by stimulating gluconeogenesis
- Causes adipose connective tissue to break down triglycerides to glycerol and fatty acids by stimulating lipolysis

Glucose is released from the liver, and fatty acids (and glycerol) are released from fat storage in response to glucagon stimulation. The levels of these molecules increase in the blood.

There is no storage form of either amino acids or proteins in cells; thus, glucagon has no effect on body proteins. The physiologic significance of this becomes apparent when you realize that a hormone released on a regular basis (i.e., during periods between meals) is not tearing down the structural and functional protein components of the body to maintain blood glucose levels.

 WHAT DID YOU LEARN?

 12 What is the major regulatory hormone in the postabsorptive state, and what are its functions?

INTEGRATE

CONCEPT CONNECTION

Insulin and glucagon, as well as cortisol, thyroid hormone, and growth hormone participate in regulating nutrient levels in the blood. These five hormones are described in detail in the discussion and examination of the endocrine system (see sections 17.8 to 17.10).

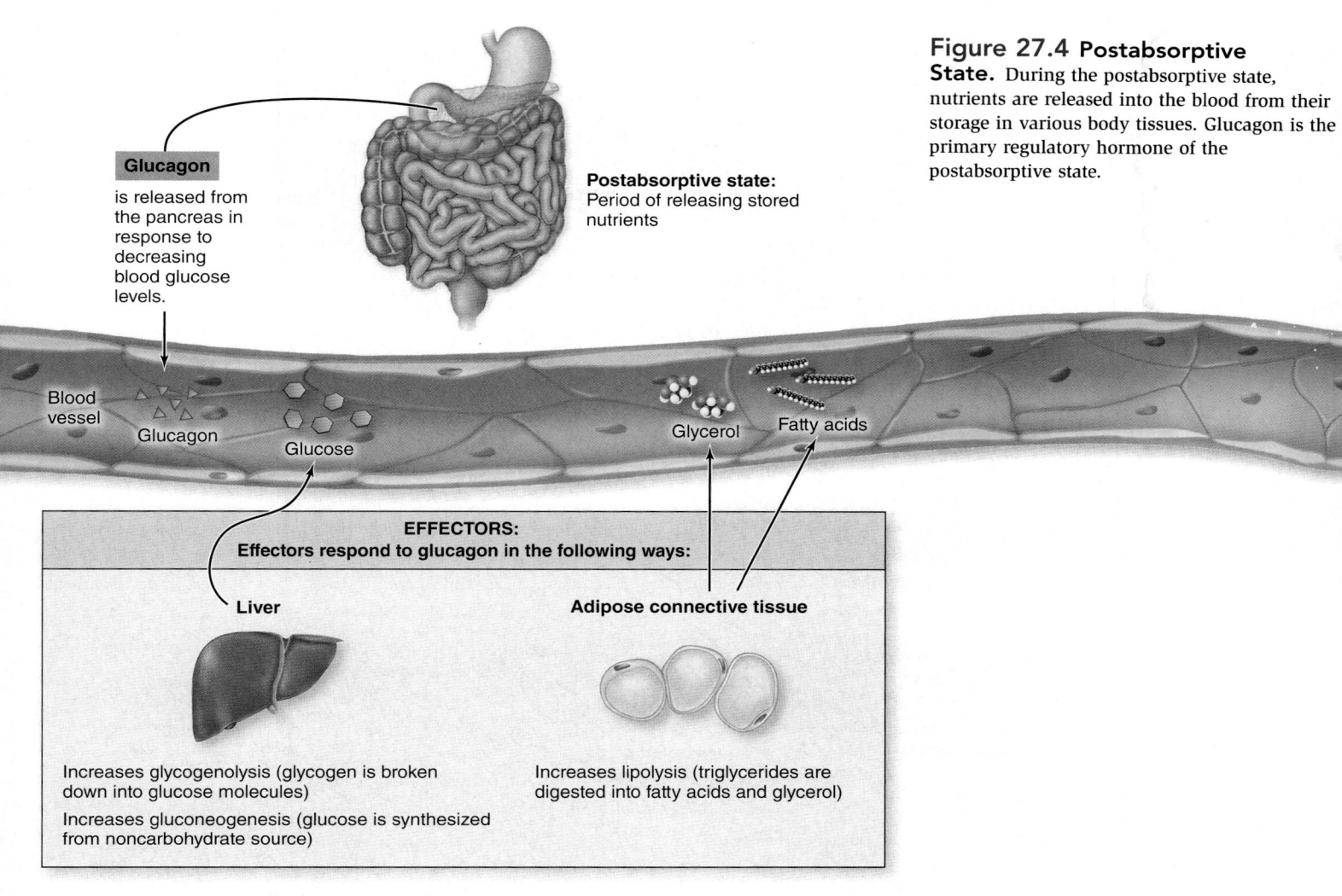

Figure 27.4 Postabsorptive State. During the postabsorptive state, nutrients are released into the blood from their storage in various body tissues. Glucagon is the primary regulatory hormone of the postabsorptive state.

Glucagon is released from the pancreas in response to decreasing blood glucose levels.

Postabsorptive state: Period of releasing stored nutrients

Blood vessel

Glucagon

Glucose

Glycerol

Fatty acids

EFFECTORS:
Effectors respond to glucagon in the following ways:

Liver

Adipose connective tissue

Increases glycogenolysis (glycogen is broken down into glucose molecules)

Increases gluconeogenesis (glucose is synthesized from noncarbohydrate source)

Increases lipolysis (triglycerides are digested into fatty acids and glycerol)

27.4 Functions of the Liver

The liver is the largest internal organ. We described the details of both its anatomic and histologic structure in section 26.3c. This amazing organ is estimated to have several hundred different functions. Several of these have been described in earlier chapters, including (1) the formation of plasma proteins (e.g., albumin and clotting proteins) (see section 18.2a); (2) removal of bilirubin from blood, following breakdown of hemoglobin as part of erythrocyte destruction (see section 18.3b); and (3) formation and release of bile into the small intestine for emulsification of lipids (see section 26.4c). We just described its role in regulating blood glucose in the absorptive and postabsorptive states by serving as a "glucose bank," a concept first introduced in section 17.7.

Here we first review the histologic structure of liver lobules and then examine more closely liver function in both the synthesis of cholesterol and the transport of lipids in the blood. We conclude this section by integrating the structure and the various functions of the liver that have been described throughout the text.

27.4a Anatomy of Liver Lobules

✓ LEARNING OBJECTIVE

1. Describe the anatomic arrangement of liver lobules, including the central vein, hepatocytes, sinusoids, and bile canaliculi.

Liver lobules are the functional unit of the liver (as described in section 26.3c). These microscopic structures are composed of cords of hepatocytes that radiate out from a

(a) Liver lobule

(b) Cholesterol synthesis

Figure 27.5 The Liver and Cholesterol Synthesis. (a) Both deoxygenated blood (which is nutrient-rich) and oxygenated blood flow through the sinusoids of liver lobules toward the central vein. Hepatocytes produce bile that is released into bile canaliculi that moves toward microscopic bile ducts. These ducts merge to form larger ducts that ultimately release bile into the small intestine. (b) Cholesterol is synthesized within individual hepatocytes that compose liver lobules. Following their synthesis, cholesterol molecules are released either into the blood of the liver sinusoids or synthesized into bile salts and released as a component of bile. AP|R central vein (**figure 27.5a**). Sinusoids (modified capillaries) are located between the cords of hepatocytes.

Both oxygenated blood from branches of the hepatic artery and deoxygenated (nutrient-rich) blood delivered from branches of the hepatic portal vein travel simultaneously through the liver sinusoids toward the central vein (sections 20.10d and 26.3c). This blood then flows out of the liver via several hepatic veins into the inferior vena cava (IVC). The bile canaliculi are sandwiched between each cord of hepatocytes and receive bile synthesized by hepatocytes. Bile then drains through a series of progressively larger ducts until it enters the small intestine.

 WHAT DID YOU LEARN?

13 What is the path of blood flow through a liver lobule?

27.4b Cholesterol Synthesis

 LEARNING OBJECTIVE

   2. Explain the relationship of dietary intake of cholesterol and level of cholesterol synthesis in the liver.

We previously stated that cholesterol is obtained from animal products as dietary sources, such as meat, milk, and eggs. Hepatocytes also contain metabolic pathways that synthesize cholesterol (figure 27.5b).

Cholesterol Synthesis

Fatty acids transported within the blood move from a liver sinusoid to enter a hepatocyte. Fatty acids are broken down into a series of two-carbon units to form acetyl CoA through a process called beta oxidation. Acetyl CoA molecules are used to synthesize cholesterol in an enzymatic pathway that includes a specific enzyme called HMG-CoA (3-hydroxy-3-methylglutaryl CoA) reductase. (This enzyme is the target for cholesterol-lowering statin drugs; see Clinical View: "Blood Cholesterol Levels.")

The liver produces cholesterol at a basal level that varies among individuals. An individual's basal level is adjusted inversely to his or her dietary intake of cholesterol. A low dietary intake results in lower blood cholesterol and less cholesterol entering hepatocytes. Thus, cholesterol synthesis by the liver increases. In contrast, a high dietary intake of cholesterol increases blood cholesterol with more cholesterol entering hepatocytes. Consequently, cholesterol synthesis decreases.

Following its formation, cholesterol is either (1) released into the blood as a component of very-low-density lipoproteins (VLDLs), which are described in the next section, or (2) synthesized into bile salts (bile acids) and released as a component of bile into the small intestine (see section 26.4c). A majority of the bile salts are reabsorbed back into the blood primarily while moving through the ileum (and to a limited extent while moving through the large intestine). A small amount of bile salts (about 10%) continue into the large intestine and are removed from the body as a component of feces. This provides a means of eliminating excess cholesterol from the body and lowering blood cholesterol levels.

 WHAT DID YOU LEARN?

14 Is cholesterol synthesis increased or decreased in response to high dietary intake of cholesterol? What are the two fates of cholesterol following its synthesis?

27.4c Transport of Lipids

 LEARNING OBJECTIVE

   3. Describe the transport of lipids within the blood.

Lipids are hydrophobic molecules and are insoluble in blood. Their transportation within the blood requires that they are first wrapped in a water-soluble protein. The lipid and the protein "wrap" are collectively called a **lipoprotein:** These are a general category of structures that contain triglycerides, cholesterol, and phospholipids within the "confines" of a protein.

We previously discussed one group of lipoproteins—chylomicrons (see section 26.4c). Recall that the absorption of lipids from the small intestine requires the formation of chylomicrons within epithelial cells lining the small intestine. A chylomicron is mostly composed of triglycerides and some cholesterol enveloped in protein. After its formation, it is absorbed into a lacteal and transported within the lymph until it enters into venous blood at the junction of the jugular and subclavian vein (see section 21.1b). Chylomicrons deliver lipids to the liver and other tissues (e.g., adipose connective tissue for storage and skeletal muscle and cardiac muscle for energy use). Chylomicron remnants are then taken up by the liver.

Various other lipoproteins are formed within the liver. The relative density of these structures is used to classify these lipoproteins. (This is possible because lipids are less dense than protein.) The three broad categories of lipoproteins are (1) very-low-density lipoproteins (VLDL), which contain the most lipid; (2) low-density lipoproteins (LDL) with somewhat less lipid; and (3) high-density lipoproteins (HDL) with the least amount of lipid. These function in transport of lipids between the liver and peripheral tissues.

Transport from the Liver to Peripheral Tissues

Both very-low-density lipoproteins and low-density lipoproteins are associated with transport of lipids from the liver to the peripheral tissues (**figure 27.6**):

- **Very-low-density lipoproteins (VLDLs)** contain various types of lipids (e.g., triglycerides and cholesterol) packaged with protein. VLDLs are assembled within the liver and then released into the blood. These "lipid delivery vehicles" circulate in the blood to release triglycerides to all cells of peripheral tissues, but primarily to adipose connective tissue. A change in density accompanies the release of triglycerides from these structures, and the lipoprotein is then called a low-density lipoprotein.

- **Low-density lipoproteins (LDLs)** contain relatively high amounts of cholesterol. LDLs deliver cholesterol to cells. LDLs bind to LDL receptors displayed within the plasma membrane of a cell and are subsequently engulfed into the cell by receptor-mediated endocytosis (see section 4.3c). Cholesterol is incorporated into the plasma membrane of all cells or is used by certain tissues (e.g., testes, ovaries, and the adrenal cortex) to produce steroid hormones.

Transport from Peripheral Tissues to the Liver

High-density lipoproteins (HDLs) are associated with the transport of lipid from the peripheral tissues to the liver. These structures are produced in stages and have a function that opposes both VLDLs and LDLs. The proteins are formed in the liver and are released into the blood without the addition of lipid (i.e., these structures are "empty" HDLs). HDL molecules circulate throughout the blood and "fill" with lipids (e.g., cholesterol and triglycer-

Figure 27.6 Lipid Transport.

Very-low-density lipoproteins (VLDLs), which become low-density lipoproteins (LDLs), participate in transporting lipid from the liver to the peripheral tissues. In contrast, high-density lipoproteins (HDLs) transport lipid from peripheral tissues to the liver.

CLINICAL VIEW
Blood Cholesterol Levels

Blood cholesterol levels are tested to determine blood levels for total cholesterol, low density lipoproteins (LDLs), and high density lipoproteins (HDLs). An important comparison also includes the relative levels of HDLs and LDLs. The results are clinically significant because high blood levels for either total cholesterol or LDLs, as well as low blood levels for HDLs are considered risk factors for cardiovascular disease.

A total cholesterol value above 200 mg/dL is considered "high." A normal value for LDL blood levels for a healthy adult is less than 100 mg/dL, and for those at risk for cardiovascular disease an acceptable value is below 70 mg/dL. In comparison, a normal value for HDL blood levels is between 40 and 50 mg/dL for adult males and between 50 and 60 mg/dL for adult females. A healthy ratio of HDL to LDL is considered to be above 0.3, or even better above 0.4.

A healthy ratio of HDL to LDL is a more accurate reading than total cholesterol because of the difference in the function of LDLs and HDLs. LDLs are considered to be the "bad cholesterol" because excess cholesterol not needed by peripheral tissue is deposited on the inner arterial walls, an event that may lead to development of plaque and arteriosclerosis (a risk factor for heart attacks and strokes). HDLs are considered the "good cholesterol" because they transport lipid (e.g., cholesterol, triglycerides)

from the arterial wall to the liver for eventual elimination from the body through the GI tract.

Dietary intake of various types of fats influences blood cholesterol levels. The omega-3 fatty acids found in some cold-water fish, for example, lower total blood cholesterol levels. In comparison, high intake of saturated fats (especially the trans fats) has been shown to decrease HDL blood levels and increase LDL blood levels. Other risks factors correlated with elevated blood cholesterol include cigarette smoking, caffeine intake, and stress.

Statin drugs (e.g., Zocor, Lipitor, Crestor) were developed for the purpose of lowering blood cholesterol. They are typically prescribed for individuals with LDL blood levels higher than 130 mg/dL. Statin drugs act as a competitive inhibitor for HMG-CoA (3-hydroxy-3-methyglutaryl CoA) reductase, a specific enzyme within the metabolic pathway for cholesterol synthesis. Thus, these drugs help decrease cholesterol synthesis. Subsequently, liver cells increase their uptake of cholesterol, which lowers blood cholesterol levels.

Please note that blood cholesterol is only one of many risks factors for developing cardiovascular disease. Given that cardiovascular disease is the cause of death in approximately 50% of disease-related deaths in the United States, research continues in determining the most accurate risk factors and how to help individuals to lower their risk.

---

ides) from peripheral tissue and the inner lining of arterial walls. HDLs then transport these lipids to the liver. Excess cholesterol is converted to bile salts within the liver and released into the small intestine as a component of bile (recall that this is the means of eliminating cholesterol from the body). Note that HDLs, like LDLs, make cholesterol available to steroid-producing tissues. However, in contrast to LDLs, HDLs have cholesterol removed without being engulfed by the cell (not shown in figure).

WHAT DO YOU THINK?

2 Which lab test result is more informative: (a) one that gives total cholesterol or (b) one that provides the levels of both LDL and HDL? Explain.

WHAT DID YOU LEARN?

15 Which of these molecular structures (VLDLs, LDLs, or HDLs) is responsible for transporting cholesterol from peripheral tissues to the liver?

27.4d Integration of Liver Structure and Function

LEARNING OBJECTIVE

4. Identify and briefly describe the numerous roles of the liver in metabolism.

The liver is responsible for many different metabolic processes. Its structure and some of its many functions are integrated, visually represented, and described in **figure 27.7**. A summary of liver functional categories include the following:

- Carbohydrate metabolism
- Protein metabolism
- Lipid metabolism
- Transport of lipids
- Other functions (e.g., storage and drug detoxification)

WHAT DID YOU LEARN?

16 Choose one of the functions of the liver. How does this function help keep us healthy?

Figure 27.7 **Liver Structure and Function.** (*a*) Liver lobules are the microscopic functional units of the liver. Liver functions include (*b*) carbohydrate metabolism, (*c*) protein metabolism, (*d*) lipid metabolism, (*e*) lipid transport, and (*f*) various other functions. (Numbers included for each function do not indicate sequential steps.)

(a) Liver Lobule | The Functional Unit

Lobule

Blood flow

Central vein

Hepatocytes

Sinusoid

Bile canaliculi

Blood flow

Bile ductule

Branch of hepatic artery

Branch of hepatic portal vein

Monosaccharides

Noncarbohydrates

Glucose

Glucose   Fructose   Galactose   Glycerol   Amino acids

Blood

(b) Carbohydrate Metabolism

① Monosaccharides are absorbed from the small intestine into the blood and then enter hepatocytes. Fructose and galactose are converted to glucose.

② Noncarbohydrates are converted to glucose by gluconeogenesis.

③ Glucose molecules are bonded together to form glycogen by glycogenesis.

④ Glucose molecules are released from glycogen by glycogenolysis.

①

②

Gluconeogenesis

Glucose

Hepatocyte

③ Glycogenesis   ④ Glycogenolysis

Glycogen

Amino acids

③ Transamination

Amino acids

② Protein synthesis

① Deamination

NH_2 Remaining components

Urea cycle   Cellular respiration

Urea transported to kidney and excreted

Plasma proteins

(c) Protein Metabolism

① Deamination: Amine group removed from amino acids

NH₂ is converted to urea and urea enters blood (urea eliminated by kidney)

Remaining components oxidized in cellular respiration to generate ATP from the liver

② Amino acids used to form proteins, including plasma proteins

③ Transamination: Amino acids converted from one form to another

Blood →

VLDLs

Ketone bodies

Bile

VLDLs

Bile

⑤

Bile salts ← Cholesterol ← Acetyl CoA → Ketone bodies

Glycerol

③ Beta oxidation

① Lipogenesis

Triglycerides

② Lipolysis   Fatty acids

(d) Lipid Metabolism

① Fatty acids joined with glycerol to form triglycerides (lipogenesis)

② Fatty acids released from triglycerides (lipolysis)

③ Fatty acids broken down into acetyl CoA (beta oxidation)

④ Acetyl CoA changed to ketone bodies (water-soluble molecules); ketone bodies released into blood, transported to other cells, where they can be oxidized in cell respiration pathways

⑤ Acetyl CoA used in cholesterol synthesis; cholesterol released into blood within VLDLs, and some used to form bile salts and released as a component of bile

Blood

(e) Lipid Transport

Transport both triglycerides and cholesterol (within VLDLs and LDLs) from the liver to peripheral tissues

"Empty" HDLs released to pick up lipids (e.g., cholesterol) from peripheral tissues and blood vessels; return as "full" HDL to the liver

(f) Other Liver Functions

Bilirubin

Vitamins and minerals

Drugs   Hormones

Absorption of bilirubin (derived from heme of hemoglobin); eliminated as a component of bile

Bile

Storage site for vitamins (A, D, B₁₂) and minerals (Fe, Zn, Cu, Mg, Mn)

Detoxification of drugs

Hormone breakdown

VLDLs   "Empty" HDLs   "Full" HDLs

VLDL

Cholesterol + Triglycerides

"Full" HDLs

We first introduced the details of cellular respiration early in the text in section 3.4. This information provided the necessary background to understand later sections including muscle metabolism in section 10.4, muscle fiber types in section 10.5, and metabolism of cardiac muscle in section 19.3. We also discussed how cellular respiration is supported by the general processes of respiration, and how an individual's ability to produce sufficient energy (ATP) is dependent on both a healthy respiratory and cardiovascular system.

27.5 Central Role of Cellular Respiration

The biochemical pathways of cellular respiration were discussed in detail in section 3.4 for the oxidation of glucose to generate ATP. Here we first review ATP generation through the metabolic pathways of cellular respiration. We then discuss how these pathways are also used to oxidize other nutrient molecules (e.g., fatty acids and amino acids) both to generate ATP and to interconvert between various biomolecules and their building blocks.

27.5a ATP Generation

✓ LEARNING OBJECTIVES

1. Describe where the following nutrient molecules enter the metabolic pathway of cellular respiration: glucose, the breakdown products of triglycerides, and amino acids.
2. Explain deamination of proteins.

Recall from our discussion of cellular respiration that it involves four stages (figure 27.8):

(1) **Glycolysis** is an anaerobic metabolic pathway that occurs in the cytoplasm of a cell. Glucose is oxidized to two pyruvate molecules. Two ATP molecules are formed (by substrate-level phosphorylation), and hydrogen is transferred to 2 NAD^+ molecules to form 2 NADH molecules during this process. If insufficient oxygen is available to the cell, then the pyruvate is converted to lactate (lactic acid). The other steps in cell respiration are aerobic and occur within the mitochondria.

(2) The **intermediate stage** is a multienzyme step during which pyruvate is converted to acetyl CoA, and a molecule of carbon dioxide (CO_2) is formed by decarboxylation. One molecule of NADH is produced.

(3) The **citric acid cycle** is the metabolic pathway in which acetyl CoA binds to oxaloacetic acid (OAA) to form citric acid. Thereafter, two carbons are released as part of CO_2 by decarboxylation. One ATP molecule, 1 $FADH_2$ molecule, and 3 NADH molecules are produced per "turn" of the cycle. Remember that both the intermediate stage and the citric acid cycle occur twice because there are two pyruvate molecules formed from oxidation of each glucose molecule entering glycolysis.

(4) The **electron transport system** involves the transfer of hydrogen and an electron from the coenzymes NADH and $FADH_2$. ATP formation subsequently occurs through oxidative phosphorylation.

Glycerol and Fatty Acids

The building blocks of triglycerides are glycerol and fatty acids. They may enter into the pathway at certain stages of cellular respiration to release their chemical energy to generate ATP. Glycerol specifically enters the pathway of glycolysis. Glycerol is converted to glucose through gluconeogenesis within the liver. The carbons of fatty acids are removed two at a time to form acetyl CoA (through beta oxidation). Acetyl CoA molecules enter the citric acid cycle.

Amino Acids

The amino acids that compose a protein may be used at various stages of cellular respiration to generate ATP. However, recall that amino acids contain nitrogen in an amine group (—NH_2). The amine group is removed by a process called **deamination** (dē-am'i-nā'shŭn; *de* = remove, *aminate* = to combine with ammonia) within hepatocytes of the liver. You might find it helpful to think of the amine group as a "contaminant" that must be removed in order for amino acids to be used in cellular respiration to generate ATP.

The remaining portion of the amino acid following deamination enters the metabolic pathway of cellular respiration at different steps, depending upon the specific amino acid. They may enter (1) into the pathway of glycolysis, (2) at the intermediate stage, or (3) at specific points within the citric acid cycle. The amine group (—NH_2) is converted to urea (urea cycle) and is eliminated through the kidney as a component of urine.

WHAT DID YOU LEARN?

 Where in the biochemical pathway of cellular respiration (glycolysis, intermediate stage, or citric acid cycle) does each of the following enter: (a) glycerol, (b) fatty acids, and (c) deaminated amino acids?

Figure 27.8 Cellular Respiration: Generation of ATP Molecules and Interconversion of Nutrient Molecules. The metabolic pathways of cellular respiration serve to both generate ATP molecules through the oxidation of glucose, triglycerides, and proteins, and provide a means of converting one type of nutrient biomolecule to another.

27.5b Interconversion of Nutrient Biomolecules and Their Building Blocks

 LEARNING OBJECTIVE

3. Describe the physiologic advantages of the ability to interconvert nutrient biomolecules.

Individuals who eat excess amounts of carbohydrates, including sweets, can deposit additional triglycerides into their adipose connective tissue and gain weight. How is consumed sugar turned into fat? Some weight-loss plans advocate following a low-carbohydrate diet (e.g., the Atkins diet). Considering that nervous tissue primarily uses glucose, how is it possible that individuals on low-carbohydrate diets are able to provide the cells of the nervous tissue with the needed glucose?

Interconversion of nutrient biomolecules, which is the changing of one nutrient biomolecule to another, is possible because of the biochemical pathways that are associated with cellular respiration. Notice in figure 27.8 how the three nutrient biomolecules can be converted to each other through pathways that involve cellular respiration. This is indicated with arrows extending in both directions between the different pathways. For example, if energy is not needed, glucose can be broken down to acetyl CoA that is then synthesized into triglycerides and stored, instead of entering the citric acid cycle. Likewise, the protein and fat that are consumed in a low-carbohydrate diet may be converted to glucose by reversal of the biochemical pathways of cellular respiration.

 WHAT DID YOU LEARN?

18 How is excess sugar (glucose) converted to fat (triglycerides)?

27.6 Energy and Heat

In chapter 3 we discussed how energy may be converted from one form to another. For example, the chemical energy in food is first converted into ATP (another form of chemical energy) that is used to generate the mechanical energy of muscle contraction that occurs as we walk. We have previously stated that energy conversions result in the production of heat (according to the second law of thermodynamics). Here we describe how heat is related to metabolic rate and how we regulate body temperature, which has normal variations among individuals.

27.6a Metabolic Rate

 LEARNING OBJECTIVES

1. Define metabolic rate.
2. Explain how both basal metabolic rate and total metabolic rate are measured, and the variables that influence each.

The **metabolic rate** is the measure of energy used in a given period of time. There are two means of expressing metabolic rate: basal metabolic rate and total metabolic rate.

Basal Metabolic Rate

Basal metabolic rate (BMR) is the amount of energy used when an individual is at rest (and not eating). Resting conditions are determined as follows: The individual has not eaten for 12 hours, is reclining and relaxed, and is exposed to specific environmental conditions, including a room temperature between 20°C and 25°C.

BMR may be measured by either of two methods:

- A **calorimeter,** which is a water-filled chamber into which an individual is placed. Heat released from the person's body alters the temperature of the water, and the change in temperature is measured. This is considered a direct method because heat is directly measured.
- A **respirometer,** which is an instrument to measure oxygen consumption. It is used to indirectly measure BMR because a relationship exists between oxygen consumption and heat production. Oxygen is used to produce ATP in aerobic cellular respiration, and ATP is utilized in metabolic processes that produce heat. Typically, for every liter of oxygen consumed, 4.8 kilocalories of heat are produced. This is considered an indirect method because the amount of heat produced is inferred from oxygen consumption.

The BMR of individuals varies because of their age, sex, stress, and blood levels of various hormones. The most important variable in BMR, however, is body surface area. The reason is that heat is lost through the surface of the skin. The greater the surface area of the skin, the more heat that is lost. Heat lost through the surface is offset by the metabolic rate of cells, within limits. The more heat that is being lost, the more metabolically active body cells must be to maintain body temperature.

 WHAT DO YOU THINK?

3 Which individual would you predict to have a higher basal metabolic rate, a man who is 6 feet tall weighing 200 pounds, or a man who is 5 feet, 9 inches tall weighing 160 pounds? Explain your answer.

Total Metabolic Rate

Total metabolic rate (TMR) is the amount of energy used by the body, including energy needed for physical activity. Thus, TMR is the BMR plus metabolism associated with physical activity. The TMR varies widely, depending upon several factors:

- **The amount of skeletal muscle and its activity.** For example, a rapid elevation in TMR occurs during vigorous exercise and stays elevated for several hours after exercise.
- **Food intake.** Metabolic rate increases following ingestion of a meal but decreases after the absorption of nutrients has been completed.
- **Changing environmental conditions.** Metabolic rate increases, for example, when one is exposed to cold temperatures.

 WHAT DID YOU LEARN?

19 Would your total metabolic rate increase when you exit your home on a cold winter day? Explain.

27.6b Temperature Regulation

 LEARNING OBJECTIVES

3. Define core body temperature, and explain why it must be maintained.
4. Explain the neural and hormonal controls of temperature regulation.

We have just seen that a direct relationship exists between the metabolic rate of an individual and heat production—as the metabolic rate increases, more heat is produced. Because metabolic rate fluctuations are influenced by level of activity, food intake, and environmental temperature, the amount of heat produced also varies.

Consequently, it is imperative that body temperature be maintained within certain physiologic limits in response to these changes. Homeostatic mechanisms usually keep our body temperature near the normal value of 98.6°F (37°C). This temperature regulation is accomplished through a balance of heat production and heat loss, and it occurs through both neural and hormonal controls.

One of the critical aspects of regulating body temperature is maintaining **core body temperature,** which is the temperature of the vital portions of the body, or *core,* that consists of the head and torso. The temperature of these regions is kept relatively constant, or stable, to assure that life is maintained. This generally occurs by allowing fluctuations in the temperature of peripheral regions, such as the limbs. (Regulation of body temperature is first discussed in section 1.5c.)

Nervous System Control

Nervous system control of body temperature is mediated primarily through the hypothalamus (see section 13.4c). Motor pathways extend from the hypothalamus to the sweat glands in the skin, skeletal muscles, and peripheral blood vessels **(figure 27.9)**. The hypothalamus detects changes in body temperature either by monitoring the temperature of blood as it passes through the hypothalamus or nerve signals received from the skin.

An increase in metabolic rate causes a subsequent increase in body temperature, and heat must be released. The hypothalamus responds by stimulating sweat glands to release sweat onto the surface of the body to draw heat away, and stimulating vasodilation of peripheral blood vessels to bring heat to the skin surface.

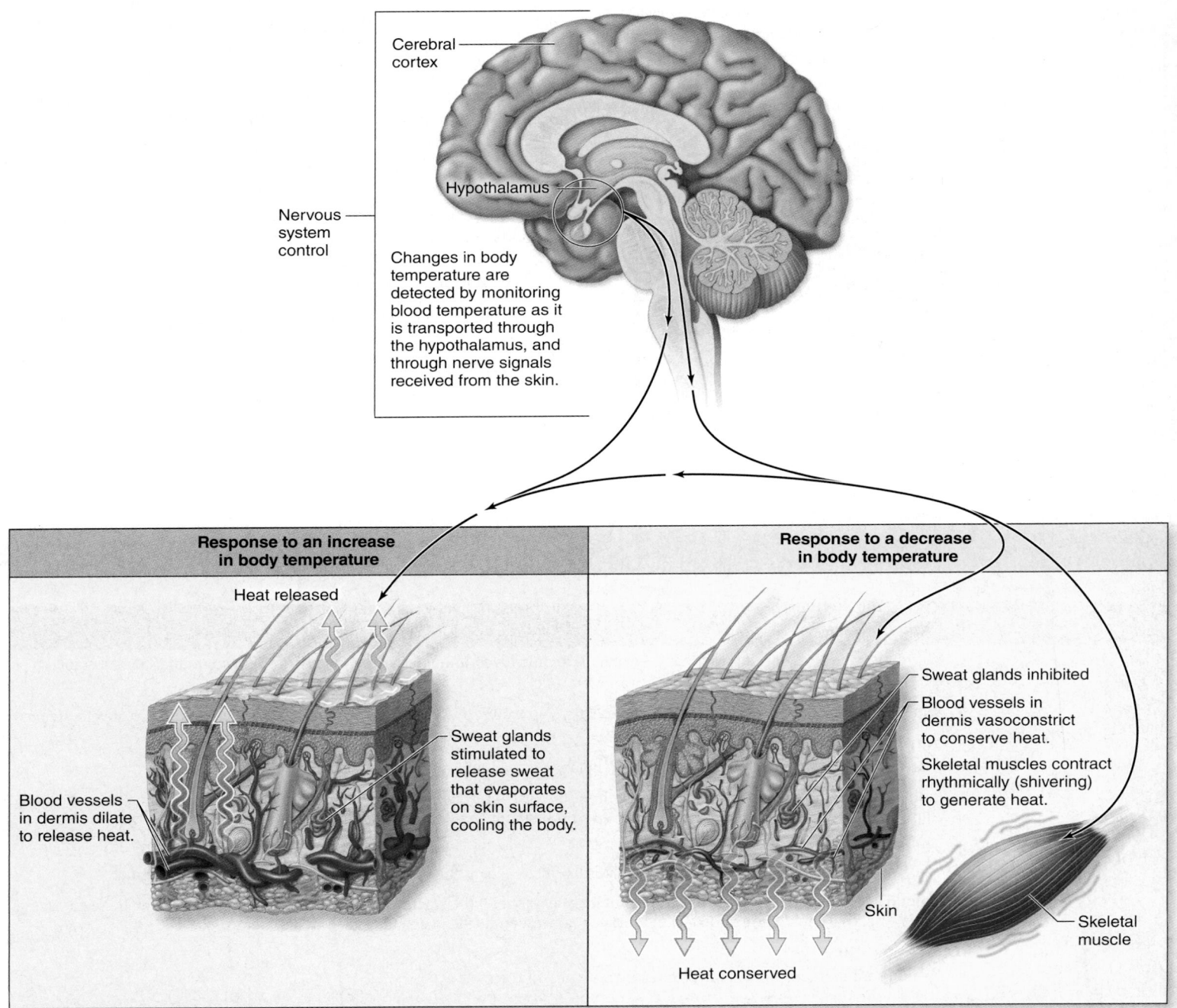

Figure 27.9 Nervous System Control of Body Temperature. The hypothalamus regulates body temperature by controlling sweat glands, vasoconstriction and vasodilation of blood vessels, and the involuntary skeletal muscle contractions of shivering.

In contrast, when metabolic rate decreases, it causes a subsequent decrease in body temperature, and additional heat must be generated. Now the hypothalamus inhibits sweat gland activity, stimulates constriction of peripheral blood vessels, thereby reducing blood circulation and heat loss at the periphery, and induces skeletal muscle contraction through shivering to generate heat. With extreme cold, the result of vasoconstriction to the peripheral regions may be frostbite, leading to dry gangrene (see Clinical View: "Frostbite and Dry Gangrene").

Conscious changes in behavior that are initiated by the cerebral cortex can help regulate body temperature. When we are hot, heat release is expedited by the removal of clothing, stopping work to rest, going inside where it is air-conditioned, or jumping into a pool; but when cold we attempt to both conserve heat by putting on additional clothing or curling up under a blanket, and we generate additional heat by becoming more active.

Hormonal Control

Temperature regulation is also mediated by hormone secretion, including thyroid hormone, epinephrine and norepinephrine, growth hormone, and testosterone. The most significant is thyroid hormone. Recall from section 17.9b, that thyroid hormone establishes the metabolic rate, causing us to produce a certain amount of heat to keep the body warm. As your body temperature begins to drop, the hypothalamus releases thyrotropin-releasing hormone (TRH); TRH stimulates the anterior pituitary to release thyroid-stimulating hormone (TSH); and TSH stimulates the thyroid gland to release the thyroid hormones(T_3 and T_4). Thyroid hormone is able to help maintain body temperature by increasing the metabolic rate of almost all cells, especially neurons. Neurons are specifically stimulated to increase their number of sodium-potassium (Na^+/K^+) pumps. Because there are more Na^+/K^+ pumps, more energy is converted as the pumps use ATP to move the ions, then more heat is produced, and body temperature is maintained.

 WHAT DID YOU LEARN?

20 What is the core body temperature, and why must it be maintained?

21 What are the nervous system and hormonal controls operating on body temperature?

CLINICAL VIEW

Frostbite and Dry Gangrene

Frostbite is damage to superficial cells due to exposure to extreme cold. The skin appears white and may be blistered. Loss of sensation may also occur. It may lead to dry gangrene in severe cases. **Dry gangrene** (necrosis or pathologic death) is a form of gangrene in which the involved body part is desiccated (loss of water), sharply demarcated (distinct change in coloration), and shriveled. These changes are usually due to extensive and prolonged vasoconstriction of blood vessels as a result of exposure to extreme cold. This results in oxygen deprivation and death of the tissue.

Photo of frostbite and dry gangrene.

CHAPTER SUMMARY

	• Nutrition is the study of the way living organisms acquire everything necessary to grow and maintain life; the substances we must acquire are called nutrients.
27.1 Nutrients 1063	• Nutrients include biomolecules, vitamins, minerals, and water; they are obtained through the diet via the digestive system.
	27.1a Nutrient Biomolecules 1063
	• Nutrient biomolecules include carbohydrates, lipids, and proteins.
	• Amino acids are either essential (must come from the diet) or nonessential (made by the body); proteins are either complete (supply all essential amino acids) or incomplete (do not supply all essential amino acids).
	27.1b Vitamins 1063
	• Vitamins are organic molecules required for normal metabolism; they are present in small amounts in our food.
	• Vitamins are categorized as either water-soluble or fat-soluble; their necessity in the diet results in their being labeled as either essential (must be provided in the diet) or nonessential (may be synthesized by the body).
	27.1c Minerals 1065
	• Minerals are inorganic ions, and all must be obtained in the diet.

(continued on next page)

27.6 Energy and Heat 1080	• The amount of heat produced by the body is related to metabolic rate.
	• Physiologic mechanisms maintain normal body temperature in response to changes in heat produced and environmental conditions.

27.6a Metabolic Rate 1080

- The metabolic rate is the rate that energy is used in a given period of time.
- Basal metabolic rate (BMR) is the amount of energy used when an individual is at rest and can be measured directly with a calorimeter and indirectly with a respirometer. The BMR of individuals varies, depending upon their age, sex, stress, hormone levels, and body surface area.
- Total metabolic rate is the total amount of energy used by an individual and varies, depending upon amount of skeletal muscle, level of physical activity, food intake, and changing environmental conditions.

27.6b Temperature Regulation 1080

- A direct relationship exists between an individual's metabolic rate and heat production.
- Temperature regulation is accomplished through a balance of heat production and heat loss, and occurs through both nervous system and hormonal controls.

CHALLENGE YOURSELF

Do You Know the Basics?

____ 1. Which of the following is a nutrient?

    a. proteins

    b. minerals

    c. vitamins

    d. All of these are correct.

____ 2. Which of these vitamins is water-soluble?

    a. vitamin D

    b. vitamin E

    c. vitamin C

    d. vitamin A

____ 3. What is the major nutrient biomolecule in a potato?

    a. carbohydrate

    b. protein

    c. triglyceride

    d. vitamin A

____ 4. During the absorptive state

    a. blood glucose is initially decreasing.

    b. glucagon is released.

    c. insulin is released.

    d. several hours (more than 4 hours) have passed since the last meal.

____ 5. When the pancreas releases insulin, it causes

    a. amino acid uptake in muscle.

    b. hepatocytes to form glycogen from glucose.

    c. lipogenesis in adipocytes.

    d. All of these are correct.

____ 6. Which of the following nutrient biomolecules can be oxidized in biochemical pathways of cellular respiration to generate ATP?

    a. glucose

    b. amino acids

    c. fatty acids

    d. All of these are correct.

____ 7. Which of the following conditions is *not* applicable to measuring basal metabolic rate?

    a. reclining

    b. the time immediately after a meal

    c. room temperature

    d. resting

____ 8. Total metabolic rate increases under which condition?

    a. warm weather

    b. starvation

    c. being confined to bed

    d. eating a meal

____ 9. Which structure of the brain regulates body temperature?

    a. hypothalamus

    b. cerebrum

    c. cerebellum

    d. brainstem

____ 10. Thyroid hormone is the primary hormone that regulates body temperature. It does so by

    a. stimulating muscle contraction.

    b. increasing the number of Na^+/K^+ pumps in neurons.

    c. vasoconstriction of peripheral blood vessels.

    d. sweating.

11. Define nutrition.

12. Describe the general function of most water-soluble vitamins.

13. Distinguish between nonessential and essential amino acids.

14. Explain the risk of excessive intake of fat-soluble vitamins.

15. Define minerals, and give examples of their functions in the body.

16. Define nitrogen balance, and compare positive nitrogen balance and negative nitrogen balance.

17. Define the postabsorptive state. What is the major hormone that regulates blood nutrients during this time, and what is its role?

18. Explain the function of the liver in the transport of lipid in the blood.

19. Briefly describe the role of the liver in carbohydrate metabolism, protein metabolism, and lipid metabolism.

20. Explain neural and hormonal induced changes when you are cold.

Can You Apply What You've Learned?

1. An individual has recently adopted a vegetarian lifestyle. She has been on this type of diet for approximately 6 months and admits that she has not been conscientious about making healthy food choices. She is feeling weak, appears gaunt, and is losing body mass. What type of nutrient biomolecule is most likely missing from her diet?

   a. nonessential amino acids
   b. essential amino acids
   c. fats (triglycerides)
   d. carbohydrates

2. A young man explains to his doctor that he has been having headaches and fluctuations in body temperature, going from shivering to sweating, that are not induced by changes in his environment. After a great deal of diagnostic work, the physician orders a magnetic resonance imaging (MRI) scan. A mass is most likely detected in which area of his brain?

   a. hypothalamus
   b. pons
   c. thalamus
   d. medulla oblongata

3. Derrick is a young man who lifts weights for several hours a day. He explains that remaining physically fit is very important to him and has been taking megadoses of vitamins as part of maintaining his health. You are concerned about

   a. reduced carbohydrate intake that may result in ketoacidosis.
   b. toxic buildup of water-soluble vitamins.
   c. loss of protein mass.
   d. toxic buildup of fat-soluble vitamins.

4. An elderly gentleman has recently been diagnosed with cirrhosis of the liver. He admits to being a heavy drinker. This man is your patient. Given the damage to his liver, you would have concerns about all of the following *except*

   a. regulating his ability to maintain body temperature, because of decreased thyroid hormone levels.
   b. internal bleeding, because he has impaired ability to synthesize clotting proteins.
   c. edema, because of impaired synthesis of plasma proteins (e.g., albumin).
   d. jaundice, because his liver is less efficient at removing bilirubin from the blood.

5. Howard is a middle-aged man and has been slowly gaining weight after reaching the age of 30. He has decided to lose weight by following a low-carbohydrate diet. What physiologic process allows his brain to still have sufficient glucose to function normally?

   a. maintaining nitrogen balance
   b. hypothalamus regulation
   c. gluconeogenesis
   d. transamination

Can You Synthesize What You've Learned?

1. As a dietician in the hospital, explain to a patient the new MyPlate.

2. Explain the challenge in meeting dietary requirements to an individual who has adopted a vegetarian lifestyle.

3. Explain to a patient who is being admitted to the hospital with frostbite what has occurred.

INTEGRATE

ONLINE STUDY TOOLS
www.mhhe.com/mckinleyap

Clinical Case Study: A Young Man with Lung Disease and Bruising

Interactive Questions: This chapter's content is served up in a number of multimedia question formats for student study.

LearnSmart: Topics and terminology include nutrients; obtaining nutrients from food; regulating blood levels of nutrients; functions of the liver; central role of cellular respiration; energy and heat

Anatomy & Physiology Revealed: Topic includes liver

Animations: Topics include B vitamins; complementary proteins; anatomy of a food label

chapter 28

Reproductive System

The female and male reproductive systems provide the means for both the sexual maturation of each individual and the production of special cells necessary to propagate the next generation. Here we first discuss the general similarities between the two reproductive systems. Gametogenesis (the formation of gametes) and the process of meiosis (sex cell division) are discussed and examined before we describe the structures and functions of both the female and male reproductive systems. Our discussion concludes with a description of reproductive system development.

An ultrasound technician is trained in the medical field of sonography, which uses sound waves to visualize internal organs. In addition to a general knowledge of anatomy and physiology, these health care professionals receive additional training in the use of the ultrasound equipment. This individual must be able to accurately locate internal organs and recognize potential abnormalities. Here, an ultrasound technician is examining the female reproductive organs and determining the viability of an early pregnancy.

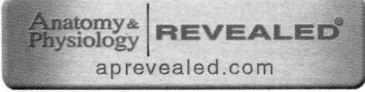

Anatomy & Physiology | REVEALED®
aprevealed.com

Module 14: Reproductive System

28.1 Overview of Female and Male Reproductive Systems

The female and male reproductive systems have obvious differences, and yet they share several general characteristics. For example, some mature reproductive system structures in both sexes are derived from common developmental structures called primordia and serve a common function in adults. Such structures are called **homologues** (hōm′ō-log; *homo* = same, alike, *logos* = relation). They are compared in **table 28.1** and are described in detail later in the chapter.

28.1a Common Elements of the Two Systems

 LEARNING OBJECTIVE

1. List the similarities between the female and male reproductive systems.

Both reproductive systems have elements in common, including the general processes that produce the gametes, the production of hormones, and the maturation of reproductive capability:

- Both females and males have primary reproductive organs called **gonads** (gō′nad; *gone* = seed): These are ovaries in females and testes in males. The gonads produce sex cells called **gametes** (gam′ēt; husband or wife), which unite at fertilization to initiate the formation of a new individual.
- The gonads also produce relatively large amounts of **sex hormones,** which affect maturation, development, and changes in the activity of the reproductive system organs.
- Both sexes also exhibit **accessory reproductive organs,** including ducts to carry gametes away from the gonads toward the site of fertilization (in females) or to the outside of the body (in males).

The sexual union between a female and a male is known as **copulation** (kop-ū-lā′shŭn; *copulatio* = a joining), **coitus** (kōi′-tŭs; to come together), or **sexual intercourse.** If fertilization occurs, then the support, protection, and nourishment of the developing human occurs within the female reproductive tract.

 WHAT DID YOU LEARN?

❶ What general components make up the reproductive systems in both females and males?

28.1b Sexual Maturation in Females and Males

 LEARNING OBJECTIVE

2. Name the hormones responsible for initiating puberty in females and males.

INTEGRATE

LEARNING STRATEGY

A simplified flowchart of the endocrine pathway in puberty is as follows:

GnRH (from hypothalamus) ⟶ **FSH and LH** (from anterior pituitary) ⟶ Sex hormone release and gamete maturation (in the gonads)

Both the female and male reproductive systems are primarily non-functional and dormant until a time in adolescence known as puberty. At **puberty** (pū′ber-tē; *puber* = grown up), external sex characteristics become more prominent, such as breast enlargement in females, pubic hair growth in both sexes, and fully functional reproductive organs in both sexes. Gametes begin to mature, and the gonads start to secrete their sex hormones.

Puberty is initiated when the hypothalamus begins secreting **gonadotropin-releasing hormone (GnRH)** (see section 17.8c and table 17.4). GnRH acts on specific endocrine cells in the anterior pituitary and stimulates them to release the gonadotropins **follicle-stimulating hormone (FSH)** and **luteinizing hormone (LH).** (Prior to puberty, FSH and LH are virtually nonexistent in girls and boys.) As levels of FSH and LH increase, the gonads produce significant levels of sex hormones and start the processes of both gamete and sexual maturation.

Although both reproductive systems produce gametes, the female typically produces and releases only a single gamete, termed an oocyte (ō′ō-sīt′; *oon* = egg), monthly, whereas the male produces large numbers of gametes, or sperm, daily—about 100 million per day. These male gametes are stored for a short time, and if they are not expelled from the body within that period, they are resorbed.

 WHAT DID YOU LEARN?

❷ What hormones begin to be secreted at puberty, and what are their general functions?

28.1c Anatomy of the Perineum

 LEARNING OBJECTIVE

3. Compare the components of the perineum in females and males.

The **perineum** (per′i-nē′ŭm) is a diamond-shaped area between the thighs in both females and males that is bounded anteriorly by the pubic symphysis, laterally by the ischial tuberosities, and posteriorly

Table 28.1	Reproductive System Homologues	
Female Organ	**Male Organ Homologue**	**Common Function**
Ovary	Testis	Produces gametes and sex hormones
Clitoris	Glans of penis	Contains erectile tissue that stimulates feelings of arousal and sexual climax
Labia majora	Scrotum	Protect and cover some reproductive structures
Greater vestibular gland	Bulbourethral gland	Secretes mucin for lubrication

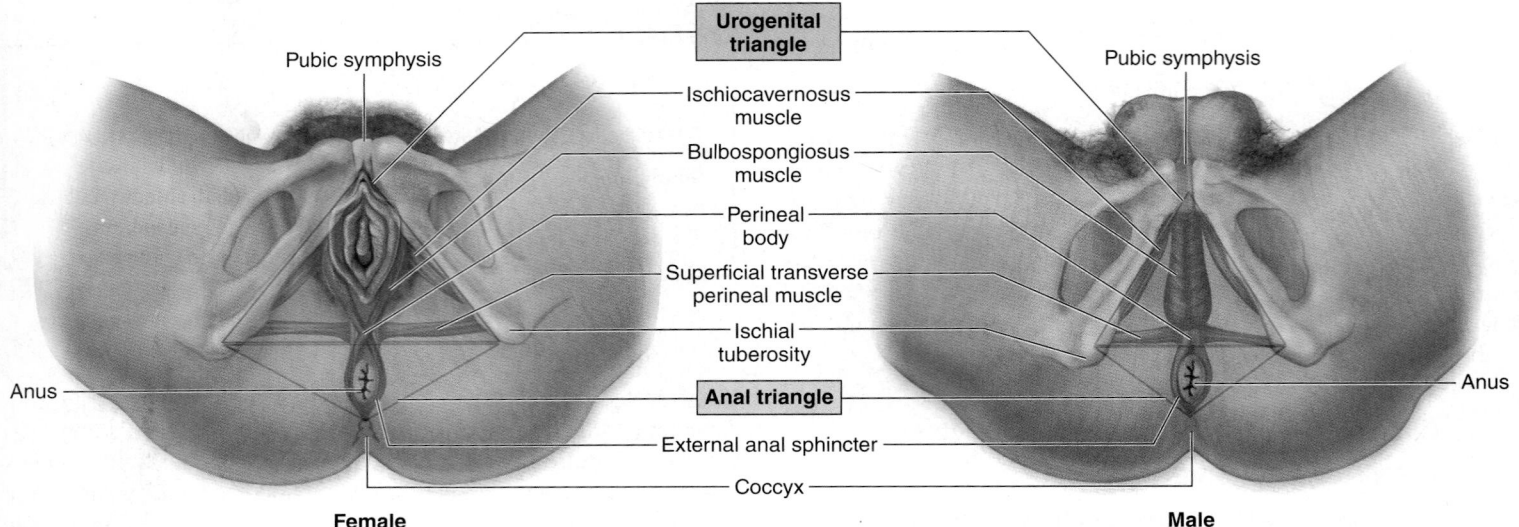

Pubic symphysis

Urogenital triangle

Pubic symphysis

Ischiocavernosus muscle

Bulbospongiosus muscle

Perineal body

Superficial transverse perineal muscle

Ischial tuberosity

Anus

Anal triangle

Anus

External anal sphincter

Coccyx

Female

Male

Figure 28.1 Perineum. In both females and males, the perineum is the diamond-shaped area between the thighs, extending from the pubis anteriorly to the coccyx posteriorly, and bordered laterally by the ischial tuberosities. An imaginary horizontal line extending from the ischial tuberosities subdivides the perineum into a urogenital triangle anteriorly and an anal triangle posteriorly. AP|R

by the coccyx (**figure 28.1**). It is an area that may be partially torn during childbirth, due to the extensive stretching needed to expel the baby. (Sometimes, this region may have to be surgically cut during birth if there is difficulty expelling the baby, see section 29.6d.) Two distinct triangle bases are formed by an imaginary horizontal line extending between the ischial tuberosities of the ossa coxae. Both triangles house specific structures in the floor of the pelvis:

- The anterior triangle, called the **urogenital triangle,** contains the urethral and vaginal orifices in females and the base of the penis and the scrotum in males. Within the urogenital triangle are the muscles that surround the external genitalia, called the ischiocavernosus, bulbospongiosus, and superficial transverse perineal muscles.

- The posterior triangle, called the **anal triangle,** is the location of the anus in both sexes. Surrounding the anus is the external anal sphincter.

The external anal sphincter, bulbospongiosus, and superficial transverse perineal muscles are partly anchored by a dense connective tissue structure called the perineal body. Review table 11.12 and figure 11.17 when learning these structures.

 WHAT DID YOU LEARN?

 What are the components of the urogenital triangles in females and males?

28.2 Gametogenesis

Gametogenesis (gam′ĕ-tō-jen′ĕ-sis; *gameto* = gamete, *genesis* = beginning) is the process of forming human sex cells, called gametes. Female gametes are secondary oocytes (commonly referred to as "eggs"), whereas male gametes are sperm. The process of gametogenesis begins with a specific type of cell division called meiosis. The events of meiosis generally are similar in both females and males, with a few differences. Here we describe the basics of heredity and meiosis; sex-specific differences are described later in this chapter.

28.2a A Brief Review of Heredity

 LEARNING OBJECTIVES

1. Distinguish between autosomes and sex chromosomes.
2. Explain why somatic cells contain 2*n* chromosomes, but gametes must contain *n* chromosomes.

Humans pass on their traits to a new individual when they reproduce. This hereditary information is carried on chromosomes. Human somatic (body) cells contain 23 pairs of chromosomes—22 pairs of autosomes and one pair of sex chromosomes, for a total of 46 chromosomes:

- **Autosomes** contain genes that code for cellular functions. These genes also help determine most human characteristics, such as eye color, hair color, height, and skin pigmentation. A pair of matching autosomes are called **homologous chromosomes** (hō-mol'ō-gŭs; *homos* = same, *logos* = relation).
- The pair of **sex chromosomes** consists of either two X chromosomes or an X and a Y chromosome. These chromosomes primarily determine whether an individual is female (two X chromosomes) or male (one X chromosome and one Y chromosome), although they also contain genes that code for cellular functions.

One member of each pair of chromosomes is inherited from each parent. In other words, if you examined one of your body cells, you would discover that 23 of the chromosomes came from your mother, and the other 23 chromosomes in this same cell came from your father. A cell that contains 23 pairs of chromosomes is said to be **diploid** (dip'loyd; *diploos* = double) and to have $2n$ chromosomes, where n is the unpaired chromosome number.

If the gametes were diploid, then each new individual would receive two sets of paired chromosomes, or $4n$. This situation is not what happens in nature, and it is not compatible in life. The gametes from either sex are **haploid** (hap'loyd; *haplos* = simple, *eidos* = appearance) because they contain 23 chromosomes only, not 23 pairs, and thus their chromosome number is designated as $1n$, or just n. (Heredity is discussed in more detail in section 29.9.)

 WHAT DID YOU LEARN?

4 How do sex chromosomes differ from autosomes?

5 Why do gametes have to be haploid instead of diploid?

28.2b An Overview of Meiosis

LEARNING OBJECTIVES

3. Compare and contrast meiosis and mitosis.
4. Describe events during interphase, before cell division begins.

Meiosis (mī-ō'sis; *meiosis* = lessening) is a type of sex cell division that starts off with a diploid parent cell and produces haploid daughter cells called gametes. Mitosis (somatic cell division, described in section 4.8) and meiosis (sex cell division) differ in the following ways:

- Mitosis produces *two* daughter cells that are genetically *identical* to the parent cell. In contrast, meiosis produces *four* daughter cells that are genetically *different* from the parent cell.
- Mitosis produces daughter cells that are *diploid*, whereas meiosis produces daughter cells that are *haploid.*
- Meiosis includes a process called **crossing over,** whereby genetic material is exchanged between homologous chromosomes.

Crossing over helps "shuffle the genetic deck of cards," so to speak. Thus, crossing over is a means of combining different genes from both parents on one of the homologous chromosomes. Crossing over does not occur in mitosis.

Meiosis begins with a diploid parent cell located in the gonad (ovary or testis). In this cell, 23 chromosomes came from the organism's mother (23 maternal chromosomes), and 23 from the father (23 paternal chromosomes). To produce haploid gametes, this parent cell must undergo meiosis.

The cell phase called interphase occurs prior to meiosis. During interphase, the DNA in each chromosome is replicated, or duplicated exactly, in the parent cell. These **replicated chromosomes** (also known as *double-stranded chromosomes*) are composed of two identical structures called **sister chromatids** (krō'mă-tid; *chromo* = color, *id* = resembling). Each sister chromatid contains an identical copy of DNA at this point. The sister chromatids are attached at a specialized region termed the **centromere.**

Note that sister chromatids are *not* the same as a "pair" of chromosomes. A chromosome composed of sister chromatids resembles a written letter X, whereas a homologous *pair* of chromosomes is composed of a matching maternal chromosome and paternal

LEARNING STRATEGY

Meiosis I (the first meiotic division) randomly separates maternal and paternal *pairs* of replicated (double-stranded) chromosomes, whereas meiosis II (the second meiotic division) separates replicated chromosomes into single chromosomes. Also, meiosis II is very similar to mitosis. Thus, if you remember the steps of mitosis, you can figure out the steps of meiosis II.

Table 28.2   Cell Division Terminology

Term	Definition	Image
Replicated chromosome (also known as a *double-stranded chromosome, duplicated chromosome*)	A chromosome that initially has two identical sister chromatids joined at the centromere (Note: once crossing over occurs, the sister chromatids are no longer identical.)	Sister chromatids / Centromere
Pair of chromosomes	A homologous maternal chromosome and a paternal chromosome	
Single chromosome (also known as a *single-stranded chromosome*)	A chromosome consisting of a single chromatid and a centromere	

chromosome, which are not attached at a centromere. Therefore, after interphase, there are 23 pairs of replicated chromosomes. To assist you with this terminology, please refer to **table 28.2**.

Once the DNA is replicated in interphase, the phases of meiosis begin **(figure 28.2)**. Meiosis is comprised of two separate sequential events: meiosis I and meiosis II.

WHAT DID YOU LEARN?

6 In what ways do mitosis and meiosis differ?

7 What events must occur in interphase to prepare for cell division?

28.2c Meiosis I: Reduction Division

LEARNING OBJECTIVES

5. Explain the difference between homologous chromosome pairs and sister chromatids.

6. Discuss why meiosis I is termed reduction division.

During **meiosis I** (also known as the *first meiotic division*), the homologous pairs of chromosomes are separated when the cell divides. The result is two cells, each of which contains 23 chromosomes only (not 23 pairs) that consist of duplicated sister chromatids held together at a centromere. Because meiosis I results in the reduction of the number of chromosomes in the daughter cells, it is also called *reduction division*. Meiosis I consists of four phases plus cytokinesis, described next.

MEIOSIS I

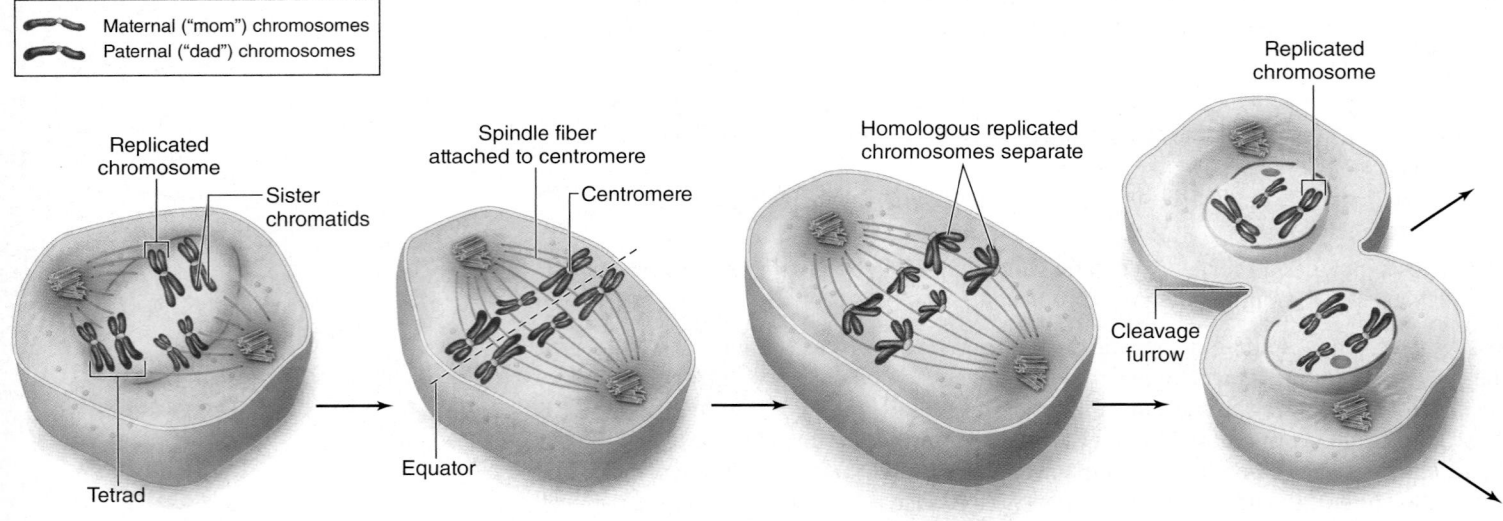

Prophase I
Homologous maternal and paternal replicated chromosomes (each composed of sister chromatids) pair up (synapsis), and the pair forms a tetrad. Crossing over occurs between homologous maternal and paternal chromosomes, ensuring genetic diversity.

Metaphase I
Homologous replicated chromosomes line up above and below the equator of the cell, forming a double line of chromosomes. Spindle fibers attach to the centromeres.

Anaphase I
Maternal and paternal pairs of replicated chromosomes are separated and pulled to the opposite ends of the cell, a process called reduction division. Note that the sister chromatids remain attached in each replicated chromosome.

Telophase I and Cytokinesis
Nuclear division finishes and nuclear envelopes re-form. The cytoplasm divides and two new cells are produced, each containing 23 replicated chromosomes only. The replicated chromosomes are still composed of sister chromatids.

Figure 28.2 Meiosis. Meiosis is a type of cell division that results in the formation of gametes (sex cells). In meiosis I, homologous pairs of chromosomes are separated after synapsis and crossing over occurs. In meiosis II, sister chromatids are separated in a sequence of phases that resembles the steps of mitosis. AP|R

Prophase I

Homologous replicated chromosomes in the parent cell pair up to form a **tetrad.** (Keep in mind that each chromosome here consists of two sister chromatids.) The process by which homologous chromosomes pair up is called **synapsis** (si-nap'sis; *syn* = together).

As the maternal and paternal chromosomes come close together, crossing over occurs. The homologous chromosomes within each tetrad exchange genetic material at this time. A portion of the genetic material in a sister chromatid of a maternal chromosome is exchanged with the same portion of genetic material in a sister chromatid of a paternal chromosome. This shuffling of the genetic material ensures continued genetic diversity in new organisms. (Note that after crossing over, the sister chromatids in a replicated chromosome are no longer identical.) Prophase I ends with the breakdown of the nuclear envelope.

Metaphase I

The homologous pairs of each tetrad line up on either side of the midline or equator of the cell, forming a double line of chromosomes. This alignment of paired chromosomes is random with respect to whether the original maternal or paternal chromosome of a pair is on one side of the equator or the other. For example, some maternal chromosomes may be to the left of the equator, and other maternal chromosomes may be to the right. This random alignment of homologous chromosomes is called **independent assortment.**

Spindle fibers formed by microtubules extend from centrioles at opposite ends of the cell and attach to the centromere of each homologous replicated chromosome.

Anaphase I

The homologous pairs of chromosomes separate and are pulled to the opposite ends of the cell. Thus, a maternal chromosome consisting of two sister chromatids is pulled to one side of the cell, while the homologous paternal chromosome is pulled to the opposite side. The process by which maternal and paternal chromosome pairs are separated and move to opposite ends of the cell is referred to as **reduction division,** because each daughter cell receives only one-half the starting number of chromosomes (only 23 chromosomes of the original 23 pairs). Note that the pairs of chromosomes are no longer together; however, each replicated chromosome still consists of two sister chromatids.

Telophase I and Cytokinesis

The replicated chromosomes arrive at opposite ends of the cell, and then a nuclear membrane may re-form around these chromosomes. A cleavage furrow forms in the cell, and the cell cytoplasm divides (cytokinesis) to produce two new cells. Each daughter cell now contains 23 replicated chromosomes only, but each replicated chromosome is still composed of two sister chromatids bound together.

The two cells formed in this stage must undergo another round of cell division, meiosis II, to separate the sister chromatids.

WHAT DID YOU LEARN?

8 What is the difference between sister chromatids and paired homologous chromosomes?

9 Why is a reduction division necessary in production of gametes?

MEIOSIS II

Sister chromatids separate

Sister chromatids separate

Cells separate into four haploid daughter cells

Single chromosomes

Prophase II
Nuclear envelope breaks down, and replicated chromosomes cluster together. (There is no crossing over in prophase II.)

Metaphase II
Spindle fibers extend from the centrioles to each sister chromatid in each chromosome and align the replicated chromosomes along the equator of the cell.

Anaphase II
Sister chromatids of each replicated chromosome are pulled apart at the centromere. Sister chromatids (now called single chromosomes) migrate to opposite ends of the cell.

Telophase II and Cytokinesis
Nuclear division finishes, and the nuclear envelopes re-form. The four new daughter cells that are produced each contain 23 single chromosomes only.

28.2d Meiosis II: Separation of Sister Chromatids

✓ LEARNING OBJECTIVE

7. Describe the events of meiosis II and the final outcome of the two stages of meiosis.

After meiosis I, the two daughter cells formed each contain 23 replicated chromosomes consisting of two connected sister chromatids. In **meiosis II** (also known as the *second meiotic division*), these chromatids separate and become single chromosomes in haploid cells.

Prophase II

The second prophase event of meiosis resembles the prophase stage of mitosis. In each of the two new cells, the nuclear envelope breaks down, and the chromosomes collect together. However, crossing over does not occur in this phase because no homologous chromosome pairs are present; they were separated in anaphase I.

Metaphase II

Spindle fibers extend from the centrioles to the centromere of each chromatid. The replicated chromosomes (composed of sister chromatids) are aligned to form a single line along the equator in the middle of the cell.

Anaphase II

The sister chromatids of each replicated chromosome are pulled apart at the centromere and are now separated. Each sister chromatid is now called a single chromosome (or *single-stranded chromosome*) and is pulled to the opposite pole of the cell.

Telophase II and Cytokinesis

The single chromosomes arrive at opposite ends of the cell. Nuclear membranes re-form, a cleavage furrow forms, and the cytoplasm in both cells divides.

These meiotic processes produce four daughter cells from the original single cell. These daughter cells are haploid, because they contain 23 chromosomes only, not 23 pairs. Twenty-two of these are autosomes, and one is a sex chromosome, either X or Y.

These daughter cells mature into secondary oocytes in females, and they mature into sperm in males. These processes are described in more detail later in this chapter.

💡 WHAT DID YOU LEARN?

10. At what point during meiosis do the daughter cells become haploid?

INTEGRATE

CLINICAL VIEW
Nondisjunction

Normally, the two members of a homologous chromosome pair separate during meiosis I, and paired sister chromatids separate during meiosis II. In **nondisjunction**, these entities fail to separate properly, and both members of a homologous chromosome pair move into one cell, or both sister chromatids move into one cell. As a result of nondisjunction, one gamete may receive two copies of a single chromosome and thus have 24 chromosomes, while the other gamete would receive no copy of a specific chromosome and would have only 22 chromosomes. If either of these cells unites with a normal gamete at fertilization, the resulting individual will have either 47 chromosomes **(trisomy)** or 45 chromosomes **(monosomy)**. Trisomy means the individual has three copies of a

chromosome, whereas monosomy means an individual has only one copy of a chromosome.

Most trisomies and monosomies are lethal to the embryo, but a few trisomies that involve smaller chromosomes allow survival. A trisomy disorder is named according to the specific chromosome that has three copies. The most well-known of these is **trisomy 21,** also known as **Down syndrome.** A person with trisomy 21 typically has some form of intellectual disability, slanting epicanthal folds (eye creases), heart defects, poor muscle tone, and short stature. Many, but not all, cases of Down syndrome occur due to nondisjunction in the formation of the oocyte. The incidence of Down syndrome increases with the mother's age, suggesting that nondisjunction problems may occur as the mother (and her sex cells) age; however, cases are known in which the nondisjunction occurs in formation of sperm. (A less common cause of Down syndrome is the result of part of chromosome 21 translocating [attaching] to chromosome 14.)

(a) Nondisjunction during meiosis can lead to abnormalities in chromosome number.
(b) Down syndrome (trisomy 21) is one possible consequence of nondisjunction. Individuals with Down syndrome have certain characteristic facial features as well as mental and physical abnormalities.

Meiosis

Nondisjunction

Gametes

| 24 chromosomes **(trisomy)** | 22 chromosomes **(monosomy)** | 23 chromosomes (normal) | 23 chromosomes (normal) |

(a)

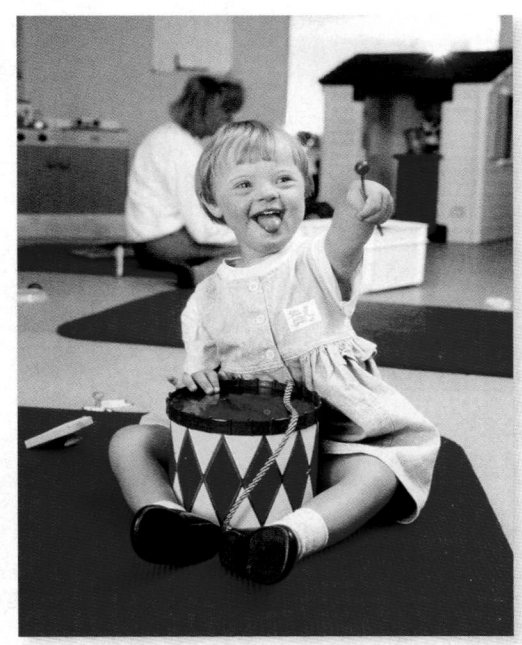

(b)

28.3 Female Reproductive System

A sagittal section through the female pelvis illustrates the internal reproductive structures and their relationships to the urinary bladder and rectum (figure 28.3). As the peritoneum folds around the various pelvic organs, it produces two major dead-end recesses, or pouches. The anterior **vesicouterine** (ves′i-kō-ū′ter-in) **pouch** forms the space between the urinary bladder and the uterus, and the posterior **rectouterine** (rek-tō-ū′ter-in) **pouch** forms the space between the rectum posteriorly and the uterus anteriorly.

The primary reproductive organs of the female are the ovaries. The accessory reproductive organs include the uterine tubes, uterus, vagina, clitoris, and mammary glands.

(a) Sagittal view

Ureter
Uterine tube
Ovary
Fimbriae of uterine tube

Uterus

Rectouterine pouch

Vesicouterine pouch
Urinary bladder
Pubic symphysis

Cervix of uterus

Rectum

Urethra
Clitoris

Vagina

External urethral orifice
Vaginal orifice
Labium minus
Labium majus

Anus

(b) Anterosuperior view

Fimbriae
Ovaries

Uterine tube

Uterus
Broad ligament

Urinary bladder

Round ligament

Mons pubis

Figure 28.3 Female Pelvic Region. (*a*) A sagittal section of the female pelvis illustrates the position of the uterus with respect to the rectum and urinary bladder. (*b*) A cadaver photo provides an anterosuperior view of the female pelvis and reproductive organs. AP|R

28.3a Ovaries

LEARNING OBJECTIVES

1. Describe the gross and microscopic anatomy of the ovary.
2. Compare the different types of ovarian follicles that form in the ovary.

Here we consider the anatomy of the ovaries, and more specifically, the types of ovarian follicles observed in a mature ovary. The ovarian follicles are the site of oocyte production and release of sex hormones.

Anatomy of Ovaries

The **ovaries** are paired, oval organs located within the pelvic cavity lateral to the uterus **(figure 28.4)**. In an adult, the ovaries are slightly larger than an almond—about 2 to 3 centimeters (cm) long, 2 cm wide, and 1 to 1.5 cm thick. Their size usually varies during each menstrual cycle as well as during pregnancy.

The ovaries are anchored within the pelvic cavity by specific cords and sheets of connective tissue. A double fold of peritoneum, called the **mesovarium** (mez′ō-vā′rē-ūm), attaches to each ovary at its **hilum,** which is the anterior surface of the ovary where its blood vessels and nerves enter and leave the organ. The mesovarium secures each ovary to a **broad ligament,** which is a drape of peritoneum that hangs over the uterus. Each ovary is anchored to the posterior aspect of the broad ligament by an **ovarian ligament,** which is the superior portion of the round ligament of the uterus. Finally, a **suspensory ligament** attaches to the lateral edge of each ovary and projects superolaterally to the pelvic wall. The ovarian blood vessels and nerves are housed within each suspensory ligament, and they join the ovary at its hilum.

Each ovary is supplied by both an **ovarian artery** and an **ovarian vein.** The ovarian arteries are direct branches off the aorta, immediately inferior to the renal vessels. The ovarian veins exit the ovary and drain into either the inferior vena cava or one of the renal veins. Traveling with the ovarian artery and vein are autonomic nerves (see sections 15.3 and 15.4). Sympathetic axons come from the T10 segments of the spinal cord, whereas parasympathetic axons come from CN X (vagus).

When an ovary is sectioned and viewed microscopically, many features are visible (figure 28.4*b*). Surrounding the ovary is a thin, simple cuboidal epithelial layer called the **germinal epithelium,** so named because early anatomists erroneously thought it was the origin of the female germ (sex) cells. Deep to the germinal epithelium is a dense connective tissue capsule called the **tunica albuginea** (al-bū-jin′ē-ă; *albugo* = white spot). Deep to the tunica albuginea, the ovary can be partitioned into an outer **cortex** and an inner **medulla.** The cortex contains ovarian follicles (described next), while the medulla is composed of areolar connective tissue and contains branches of the ovarian blood vessels, lymph vessels, and nerves.

Ovarian Follicles

Within the cortex are thousands of **ovarian follicles.** Ovarian follicles consist of an **oocyte** surrounded by **follicle cells** (or *granulosa cells*), which support the oocyte. There are several different types of ovarian follicles, each representing a different stage of development; here we describe the six main types **(figure 28.5):**

1. A **primordial follicle** is the most primitive type of ovarian follicle. Each primordial follicle consists of a **primary oocyte**

(a) Posterior view

Figure 28.4 Internal Organs of the Female Reproductive System. (*a*) A posterior view shows the internal organs of the female reproductive system, including the ovaries, uterine tubes, uterus, and vagina. (*b*) A lateral sectional view of the ovary shows the mesovarium in relation to the mesosalpinx (a specific part of the broad ligament that overlies the uterine tubes). AP|R

(b) Lateral sectional view

(b) Primordial follicles

Primordial follicles · Primary oocyte · Follicle cells

(c) Primary follicle

Thecal cells · Primary oocyte · Granulosa cells · Primary follicle

(d) Secondary follicle

Thecal cells · Primary oocyte · Zona pellucida · Corona radiata · Granulosa cells · Antrum · Secondary follicle · Cumulus oophorus

Secondary follicle

Primary follicles

Medulla

Primordial follicles

Tunica albuginea

Germinal epithelium

Suspensory ligament of ovary

Vesicular follicle

Corona radiata
Zona pellucida
Ovulated secondary oocyte

Ovarian ligament

Corpus albicans · **Corpus luteum** · Developing corpus luteum · Cortex

(a) Cross section of ovary

(g) Corpus albicans

Corpus albicans

(f) Corpus luteum

Corpus luteum

(e) Vesicular follicle

Cumulus oophorus · Antrum · Corona radiata · Zona pellucida · Secondary oocyte

Figure 28.5 Ovary. The ovary produces and releases both female gametes (secondary oocytes) and sex hormones. (*a*) A coronal view of the ovary contents depicts the different stages of follicle maturation, ovulation, and corpus luteum development and degeneration. Note that all of the follicles and structures shown in this image would appear at different times during the ovarian cycle—they do not occur simultaneously. Further, the follicles do not migrate through the ovary; rather, all follicles are shown together merely for comparative purposes. (*b–e*) The stages of follicle development, ending with the vesicular follicle, which ruptures during ovulation. After ovulation, the remnant of the vesicular follicle forms (*f*) the corpus luteum, which then degenerates into (*g*) the corpus albicans. AP|R surrounded by a single layer of *flattened* follicle cells. A primary oocyte is an oocyte that is arrested in the first meiotic prophase. About 1.5 million of these types of follicles are present in both ovaries at birth.

2. A **primary follicle** forms from a maturing primordial follicle. Each primary follicle consists of a primary oocyte surrounded by one or more layers of *cuboidal* follicular cells, which are now called **granulosa cells.** Each primary follicle secretes **estrogen** (es'trō-jen; *oistrus* = estrus, *gen* = producing) as it continues to mature, which stimulates changes in the uterine lining. Some connective tissue derived cells, called **thecal cells,** are located around and on the periphery of the ovarian follicle. These cells help initiate and control follicle development by influencing hormone production. Specifically, the thecal cells secrete androgens, which are converted to estrogen by the granulosa cells.

3. A **secondary follicle** forms from a primary follicle. Each secondary follicle contains a primary oocyte, many layers of granulosa cells, and a fluid-filled space called an **antrum.** Within the antrum, serous fluid accumulates and increases in volume as ovulation nears. The oocyte is forced toward one side of the follicle, where it is surrounded by a cluster of follicle cells termed the **cumulus** (kū'mū-lŭs; heap) **oophorus** (ō-of'ōr-ŭs; *phorus* = bearing).

   Surrounding the primary oocyte are two protective structures, the zona pellucida and the corona radiata. The **zona pellucida** (zō'nă; zone) (pe-lū'sĭ d-ă; *pellucidus* = allowing the passage of light) is a translucent structure that contains glycoproteins. External to the zona pellucida is the **corona radiata** (kō-rō'nă; crown) (rā-dē-ă'tă; radiating), which is the innermost layer of cumulus oophorus cells.

4. A **vesicular follicle** (also called a *mature follicle,* or *Graafian follicle*) forms from a secondary follicle. A vesicular follicle becomes quite large, and contains a **secondary oocyte** (surrounded by a zona pellucida and the corona radiata), numerous layers of granulosa cells, and a large, fluid-filled, crescent-shaped antrum. A secondary oocyte has completed meiosis I and is arrested in the second meiotic metaphase. Typically, only one vesicular follicle forms each month.

5. When a vesicular follicle ruptures and expels its oocyte (a process called ovulation), the remnants of the follicle in the ovary turn into a yellowish structure called the **corpus luteum** (lū-tē'ŭm; *luteus* = saffron yellow). The corpus luteum secretes the sex hormones **progesterone** (prō-jes'ter-ōn; *pro* = before; gestation) and estrogen. These hormones stimulate and support the continuing buildup of the uterine lining and prepare the uterus for possible implantation of a fertilized oocyte.

6. When a corpus luteum undergoes regression (breaks down), it turns into a white connective tissue scar called the **corpus albicans** (al'bi-kanz; white). Most corpus albicans structures are completely resorbed, and only a few may remain within an ovary.

Table 28.3 summarizes the different structures that develop during a female's monthly cycle.

 WHAT DID YOU LEARN?

11 What are the broad ligament, ovarian ligament, and suspensory ligament of an ovary?

12 How are the primordial, primary, secondary, and vesicular follicles similar? How are they different?

Table 28.3	Ovarian Follicles and Structures That Develop in the Ovary		
Ovarian Structure	**Type of Oocyte**	**Anatomic Characteristics**	**Time of First Appearance**
Primordial follicle	Primary oocyte	Single layer of flattened follicular cells surround an oocyte	Fetal period
Primary follicle	Primary oocyte	Single or multiple layers of cuboidal granulosa cells surround an oocyte	Puberty
Secondary follicle	Primary oocyte	Multiple layers of granulosa cells surround the oocyte and a small, fluid-filled antrum	Puberty
Vesicular follicle	Secondary oocyte	Many layers of granulosa cells surround the oocyte and a very large antrum	Puberty
Corpus luteum	No oocyte	Yellowish, collapsed folds of granulosa cells	Puberty
Corpus albicans	No oocyte	Whitish connective tissue scar, remnant of a degenerated corpus luteum	Puberty

28.3b Oogenesis and the Ovarian Cycle

✔ LEARNING OBJECTIVES

3. List the hormones responsible for oogenesis, and explain each hormone's effect on oogenesis.
4. Identify the ovarian follicles that develop before birth and those that form after puberty.
5. Describe the three phases of the ovarian cycle.

Oogenesis is the maturation of a primary oocyte to a secondary oocyte. We describe this process as it relates to the life stages of a female; it is illustrated in **figure 28.6**.

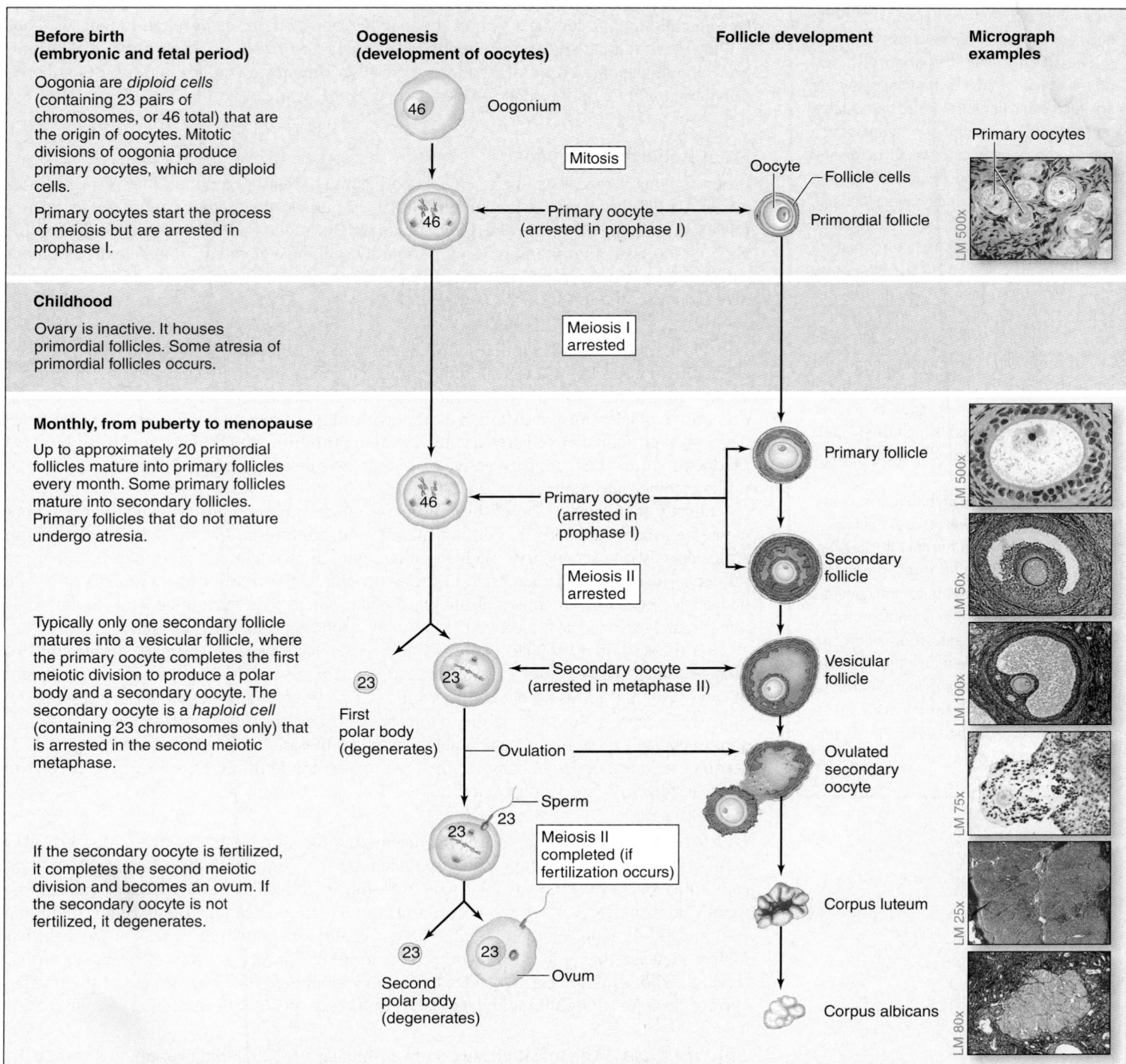

Figure 28.6 Oogenesis. Oogenesis begins in a female fetus, when primary oocytes form in primordial follicles. The ovary and these follicles remain inactive in childhood. At puberty, a select number of primordial follicles each month undergoes maturation and produces a female gamete (secondary oocyte).

Before Birth

The process of oogenesis begins in a female fetus before birth. At this time, the ovary contains primordial germ cells called **oogonia** (ō-ō-gō′nē-ă; sing., *oogonium; oon* = egg), which are diploid cells (they have 23 pairs of chromosomes). During the fetal period, the oogonia divide by mitosis to produce primary oocytes. Primary oocytes are the structures that start the process of meiosis, but they are arrested in prophase I. At this point, the cells are the primary oocytes described in the preceding section. At birth, the ovaries of a female child are estimated to contain a total of approximately 1.5 million primordial follicles within its cortex. The primary oocytes in the primordial follicles remain arrested in prophase I until after puberty.

Childhood

During childhood, a female's ovaries are inactive, and no follicles develop. In fact, the continuing event that occurs during childhood is **atresia** (ă-trē′zē-ă; *a* = not, *tresis* = a perforation), in which some primordial follicles regress. By the time a female child reaches puberty, only about 400,000 primordial follicles remain in the ovaries.

From Puberty to Menopause

When a female reaches puberty, the hypothalamus releases gonadotropin-releasing hormone (GnRH) in a pulsatile manner. GnRH stimulates the anterior pituitary to release follicle-stimulating hormone (FSH) and luteinizing hormone (LH). The levels of FSH and LH vary in a cyclical pattern and produce a monthly sequence of events in follicle development called the **ovarian cycle.** The three phases of the ovarian cycle are the follicular phase, ovulation, and the luteal phase **(figure 28.7)**.

Follicular Phase   The **follicular phase** occurs during days 1–13 of an approximate 28-day ovarian cycle. At the beginning of the follicular phase, FSH and LH stimulate up to about 20 primordial follicles to mature into primary follicles. It is unclear why some of the primordial follicles are stimulated to mature while the rest remain unaffected. As the follicles develop, their follicular cells release the hormone **inhibin,** which helps inhibit further FSH production, thus preventing excessive ovarian follicle development and allowing the current primary follicles to mature.

Shortly thereafter, a few of these primary follicles mature and become secondary follicles. The primary follicles that do not mature undergo atresia. Late in the follicular phase, typically only one secondary follicle in an ovary matures into a vesicular follicle. Under the influence of LH, the volume of fluid increases within the antrum of this follicle, and the oocyte is forced toward one side of the follicle, where it is surrounded by the cumulus oophorus. The innermost layer of the cumulus oophorus cells is the corona radiata.

As the secondary follicle matures into a vesicular follicle, its primary oocyte finishes meiosis I, and two cells form (see figure 28.6). One of these cells receives a minimal amount of cytoplasm and forms a **polar body,** which is a nonfunctional cell that later regresses. The other cell receives the bulk of the cytoplasm and becomes the secondary oocyte, which continues to develop and reaches metaphase II of meiosis before it is arrested again. This secondary oocyte does not complete meiosis unless it is fertilized by a sperm. If the oocyte is not fertilized, it breaks down and regresses about 24 hours later.

Ovulation   **Ovulation** (ov′ū-lā′shŭn) occurs on day 14 of a 28-day ovarian cycle and is defined as the release of the secondary oocyte from a vesicular follicle (figure 28.7). Typically, only one ovary ovulates each month—that is, typically the left ovary ovulates one month, and the right ovary ovulates the next. Ovulation is induced only when there is a peak in LH secretion. As the time of ovulation approaches, the follicle cells in the vesicular follicle increase their rate of fluid secretion, forming a larger antrum and causing further swelling within the follicle. The edge of the follicle that continues to expand at the ovarian surface becomes quite thin and eventually ruptures, expelling the secondary oocyte.

Luteal Phase   The **luteal phase** occurs during days 15–28 of the ovarian cycle, when the remaining follicle cells in the ruptured vesicular follicle become the corpus luteum.

The corpus luteum is essentially a temporary endocrine gland. It secretes progesterone and estrogen that stabilize and build up the uterine lining, and prepare for possible implantation of a fertilized oocyte. The corpus luteum has a life span of about 10 to 13 days if the

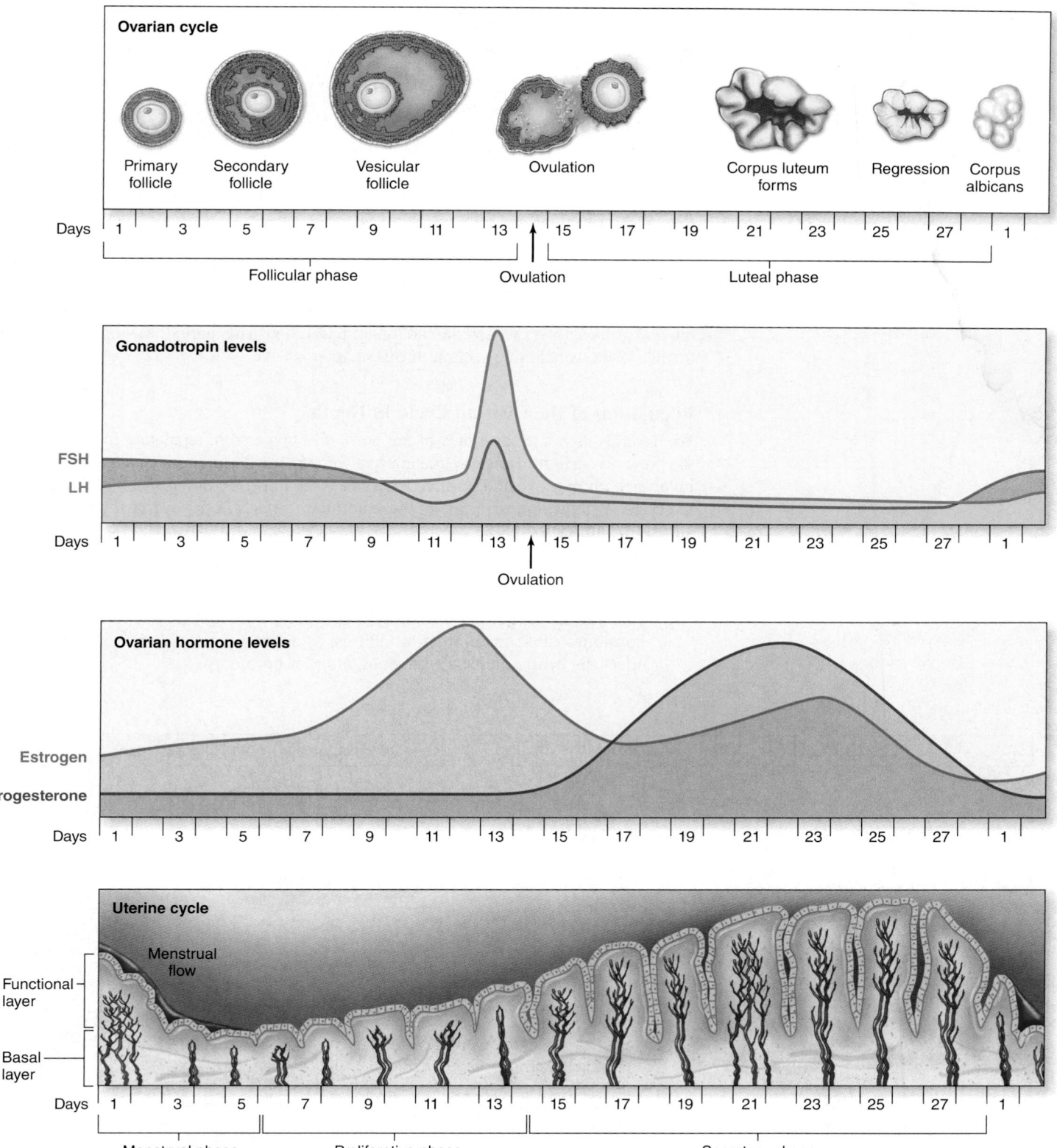

Figure 28.7 Hormonal Changes in the Female Reproductive System. Follicle-stimulating hormone (FSH) stimulates development of ovarian follicles during the follicular phase of the ovarian cycle. Estrogen stimulates the proliferative phase in the uterine cycle, while a peak in luteinizing hormone (LH) promotes ovulation. The corpus luteum becomes functional after ovulation, and it produces both progesterone and estrogen to promote uterine lining development. AP|R

secondary oocyte is not fertilized. After this time, the corpus luteum regresses and becomes a corpus albicans. As the corpus luteum regresses, its levels of secreted progesterone and estrogen drop, causing the uterine lining to be shed in a process called **menstruation** (men-strū-ā′shŭn). The shed lining is called **menses** or a *period*. This marks the end of the luteal phase. A female's first menstrual cycle, called **menarche** (me-nar′kē; *men* = month, *arche* = beginning), indicates the culmination of female puberty and typically occurs around age 11–12.

1 If a woman has one ovary surgically removed, can she still become pregnant? Why or why not?

After Menopause

When a woman has stopped having monthly menstrual cycles for 1 year and is not pregnant, or has a medical condition that leads to a cessation of menstruation—such as extremely low body fat or in cases of anorexia nervosa—she is said to be in **menopause** (men'ō-pawz; *pauses* = cessation).

The age at normal onset of menopause varies considerably, but typically it is between 45 and 55 years. The reason a woman reaches menopause is that either there are no more ovarian follicles remaining, or ovarian follicle maturation has halted. As a result, significant amounts of estrogen and progesterone are no longer being secreted. Thus, a woman's uterine lining does not grow, and she no longer has a menstrual period. Menopause is discussed further in the concluding section of this chapter.

Regulation of the Ovarian Cycle in Depth

We have given you an overview of the hormones involved in regulating the ovarian cycle in the previous sections. However, the interplay among the hormones is much more intricate and involves both negative and positive feedback mechanisms in order to complete a single ovarian cycle. A stepwise description of these hormonal effects in the ovarian cycle are listed here and shown in **figure 28.8**:

1 **The hypothalamus initiates the ovarian cycle by secreting GnRH,** which stimulates the anterior pituitary to secrete FSH and LH.

2 **FSH and LH target the ovaries and stimulate follicular development.** These hormones cause maturation of follicles, as described earlier, and both hormones also affect the ovarian follicle's secretion of other hormones.

Figure 28.8 Hormonal Interactions in the Ovarian Cycle. The ovarian cycle is initiated when the hypothalamus secretes gonadotropin-releasing hormone (GnRH), which stimulates the anterior pituitary to secrete follicle-stimulating hormone (FSH) and luteinizing hormone (LH). The cascade of events that occur during the cycle is illustrated.

(3) **The maturing ovarian follicles secrete inhibin and estrogen.** These hormones have a negative feedback effect on the hypothalamus and anterior pituitary. Specifically, inhibin helps inhibit FSH release by the anterior pituitary; low levels of estrogen inhibit production of GnRH, FSH, and LH.

(4) **Estrogen also assists with the development of the dominant (vesicular) ovarian follicle.** A secondary follicle matures into a vesicular follicle under the influence of estrogen.

(5) **The vesicular follicle, once it develops, produces a larger threshold amount of estrogen.** Paradoxically, higher levels of estrogen have a stimulatory effect on the hypothalamus and anterior pituitary, and thus a positive feedback loop is initiated.

(6) **The positive feedback loop results in an LH surge from the anterior pituitary, which induces ovulation.** Without this surge in LH, the vesicular follicle would not ovulate (expel its secondary ooctye). Most oral contraceptives regulate estrogen and progesterone levels, which in turn prevent this LH surge (see Clinical View: "Contraception Methods"). Estrogen levels decline slightly right after ovulation, presumably because ovulation damaged some of the estrogen-secreting follicular cells in the vesicular follicle.

(7) **A corpus luteum forms from the ovulated follicle.** After ovulation, LH induces the remaining follicular cells in the ovary to develop into the corpus luteum—hence the name "luteinizing."

(8) **The corpus luteum secretes large amounts of estrogen, progesterone, and inhibin.** This combination inhibits both the hypothalamus and anterior pituitary and builds the uterine lining. The corpus luteum degenerates in 10 to 13 days (if the oocyte is not fertilized), which results in decreases in some hormone levels.

(9) **The ovarian cycle repeats.** (Step 9 not shown in figure 28.8.) Unless the oocyte is fertilized, the negative feedback events described in step 8 serve to reduce LH levels, resulting in the degeneration of the corpus luteum. Consequently, the levels of estrogen, progesterone, and inhibin drop, and the hypothalamus again is able to secrete GnRH to initiate the cycle.

If the secondary oocyte is fertilized, and if it successfully implants in the uterine lining, this fertilized structure, now called a pre-embryo, starts secreting **human chorionic gonadotropin (hCG),** a hormone that enters the mother's blood and acts on the corpus luteum (see section 29.2). Essentially, hCG mimics the effects of LH and continues to stimulate the corpus luteum. As a result, the corpus luteum continues producing progesterone and estrogen, which maintains and continues building the uterine lining. After 3 months, the placenta of the developing fetus starts producing its own progesterone and estrogen. Thus, typically by the end of the third month the corpus luteum has usually regressed and formed a corpus albicans.

WHAT DID YOU LEARN?

(13) What follicles are present at birth? What follicles are present at puberty?

(14) What are the specific effects of FSH and LH on the ovarian cycle?

(15) What are the three phases of the ovarian cycle, and what main events occur in each phase?

28.3c Uterine Tubes, Uterus, and Vagina

LEARNING OBJECTIVES

6. Describe the anatomy and function of the uterine tubes.

7. List the functions of the uterus, and compare its three tunics.

8. Explain the gross anatomy of the vagina.

The uterine tubes, uterus, and vagina are accessory reproductive organs responsible for the transport and implantation of the fertilized oocyte, and the eventual expulsion of the developing human.

Uterine Tubes

The **uterine tubes,** also called the *fallopian* (fa-lō′pē-an) *tubes* or *oviducts* (ō′vi-dŭkt; *duco* = to lead), extend laterally from both sides of the uterus toward the ovaries (figure 28.9). The uterine tubes are small in diameter, and reach their maximum length of between 10 and 12 centimeters after puberty. These tubes are covered and suspended by the **mesosalpinx** (mez′ō-sal′pinks; *salpinx* = trumpet), a specific superior part of the broad ligament of the uterus (see figure 28.4*a*). Each uterine tube is composed of the following contiguous segments:

- The **infundibulum** (in-fŭn-dib′ū-lŭm; funnel) is the free, funnel-shaped, lateral margin of the uterine tube. Its

numerous fingerlike folds are called **fimbriae** (fim′brē-ē; fringes). The fimbriae of the infundibulum enclose the ovary only at the time of ovulation.

- The **ampulla** (am-pul′lă; two-handled bottle) is the expanded region medial to the infundibulum. Fertilization of an oocyte typically occurs there.
- The **isthmus** (is′mus) extends medially from the ampulla toward the lateral wall of the uterus. It forms about one-third of the length of the uterine tube.

Figure 28.9 Uterine Tubes and the Uterus. The uterine tubes are paired passageways that capture the ovulated secondary oocyte, provide the site for fertilization, and transport the oocyte to the uterus. (*a*) The relationship between a uterine tube and the uterus is shown in a partially cutaway diagram. Photomicrographs show (*b*) a cross section of the uterine tube and (*c*) the layers of the endometrium and part of the myometrium in the wall of the uterus. AP|R

CLINICAL VIEW

Tubal Pregnancy

An *ectopic pregnancy* refers to a fertilized oocyte implanting in a location other than the uterine endometrium. In a **tubal pregnancy** (one specific type of ectopic pregnancy), the fertilized oocyte implants in the uterine tube rather than the uterus. The uterine tube is unable to expand as the embryo grows, so the embryo can remain viable no later than week 8, at which time it has become too large for the confines of the uterine tube. The woman experiences severe cramping, and the uterine tube will rupture if the embryo is not surgically removed. Rupture of the uterine tube results in a massive hemorrhage into the abdominopelvic cavity that may endanger the life of the mother. No current method is available to treat a tubal pregnancy that can spare the developing embryo.

Tubal pregnancy

Uterus

Tubal pregnancy

Embryo   Placenta   Uterine tube

Uterus

The **uterus** (u′ter-ŭs; womb) is a pear-shaped, thick-walled muscular organ within the pelvic cavity. It has a lumen (internal space) that connects to the uterine tubes superolaterally and to the vagina inferiorly (figure 28.9a). Normally, the uterus is angled anterosuperiorly across the superior surface of the urinary bladder, a position referred to as **anteverted** (an-te-vert′ed; *ante* = before, *versio* = a turning). In figure 28.3, the uterus is shown in an anteverted position. If the uterus is positioned posterosuperiorly, so that it is projecting toward the rectum, this position is called **retroverted** (re′trō-ver-ted). The uterus may shift from an anteverted to a retroverted position in older women.

The uterus serves many functions. Following fertilization, the pre-embryo makes contact with the uterine lining and implants in the inner uterine wall. The uterus then supports, protects, and nourishes the developing embryo/fetus by forming a vascular connection that later develops into the placenta. The uterus ejects the fetus at birth after maternal oxytocin levels increase to initiate the uterine contractions of labor. If an oocyte is not fertilized, the muscular wall of the uterus contracts and sheds its inner lining as menstruation.

The uterus and uterine tubes receive their blood supply from the uterine arteries (branches of the internal iliac arteries; see section 20.10e), which branch into smaller vessels that supply the inner lining of the uterus.

The uterus is partitioned into the following regions:

- The **fundus** (fŭn′dŭs) is the broad, curved superior region extending between the lateral attachments of the uterine tubes.
- The middle region, called the **body,** is the major part of the organ and is composed of a thick wall of smooth muscle.
- The **isthmus** is the narrow, constricted inferior region of the body that is superior to the cervix.
- The **cervix** is the narrow inferiormost portion of the uterus that projects into the vagina.

A narrow channel within the cervix that is called the **cervical canal** connects to the vagina inferiorly. The superior opening of this canal is the **internal os** (*os* = mouth). The inferior opening of the cervix into the lumen of the vagina is the **external os.** The external os is covered with nonkeratinized stratified squamous epithelium. The cervix contains mucin-secreting glands that help form a thick mucus plug at the external os. This mucus plug is suspected to be a physical barrier that prevents pathogens from invading the uterus from the vagina. The mucus plug thins considerably around the time of ovulation, so that sperm may more easily enter the uterus.

Several structures support the uterus and help hold it in place:

- The muscles of the pelvic floor (**pelvic diaphragm** and **urogenital diaphragm;** see figure 11.17) hold the uterus and vagina in place and help resist intra-abdominal pressure exerted inferiorly on the pelvis.
- The **round ligaments** (figure 28.9a) extend from the lateral sides of the uterus, traverse through the inguinal canal and attach to the labia majora.
- The **transverse cervical ligaments,** or *cardinal ligaments,* run from the sides of the cervix and superior vagina laterally to the pelvic wall.
- The **uterosacral ligaments,** or *sacrocervical ligaments,* connect the inferior portion of the uterus posteriorly to the sacrum.

Many of these ligaments travel between the folds of the broad liga-ment. Weakness in either the pelvic floor muscles or these ligaments can lead to **prolapse** (prō-laps′; *prolapsus* = a failing) of the uterus, in which the uterus starts to protrude through the vagina. Despite its name, the broad ligament is not a strong support for the uterus, but rather is a peritoneal drape over the uterus.

The uterine wall is composed of three concentric tunics: the perimetrium, myometrium, and endometrium (figure 28.9). The outer tunic is a serosa called the **perimetrium** (per-i-me′trē-ŭm;

---

and penetrates the wall of the uterus.

The wall of the uterine tube consists of a mucosa, a muscularis, and a serosa. The **mucosa** is formed from a simple ciliated columnar epithelium and an underlying layer of areolar connective tissue. The mucosa is thrown into linear folds, which reduce the size of the uterine tube lumen. After ovulation, the cilia on the apical surface of the epithelial cells of both the infundibulum and the ampulla begin to beat in the direction of the uterus. This causes a slight current in the fluid within the uterine tube lumen, drawing the oocyte into the uterine tube and moving it toward the uterus.

The **muscularis** is composed of an inner circular layer and an outer longitudinal layer of smooth muscle. Some peristaltic contrac-tions in the muscularis help propel the oocyte, or pre-embryo if fertil-ization has occurred, through the uterine tube toward the uterus. The **serosa** is the external serous membrane covering the uterine tube.

- The **uterine part** is also called the *intramural part,* or *interstitial segment,* and it extends medially from the isthmus

Cervical Cancer

Cervical cancer is one of the most common malignancies of the female reproductive system. The most important risk factor is previous human papillomavirus (HPV) infection. Researchers have developed a vaccine (Gardasil) for the four most common types of HPV that cause cervical cancer. However, for the vaccine to be effective, it must be given to girls who are not yet sexually active, so the recommended age range for the vaccine is 11 to 13 years.

The **Papanicolaou (Pap) smear** has become a very effective method of detecting cervical cancer in its early and curable stage. A health-care professional inserts a metal or plastic instrument called a **speculum** (spek'ū-lŭm; mirror) into the vagina to keep the vagina open in order to examine the cervix. Epithelial cells are scraped from the edge of the cervix and examined for any abnormal cellular development (termed **dysplasia**).

Normal epithelial cells

Normal Pap smear — LM 140x

Normal epithelial cells

Dysplastic cells

Abnormal Pap smear — LM 160x

If dysplastic cells are detected, the health-care professional will likely request a follow-up Pap smear and possibly a biopsy. Sometimes, dysplastic cells are a result of irritation, infection, or some undetermined cause, and are not cancerous. If cervical cancer is present, a portion of the cervix may be removed, a procedure known as a **cone biopsy.** Invasive cancer is treated with the removal of the entire uterus, called a **hysterectomy** (his-ter-ek'tō-mē; *hystera* = womb).

---

metra = uterus). The perimetrium is continuous with the broad ligament. The **myometrium** (mī'ō-mē'trē-ŭm; *mys* = muscle) is the thick, middle tunic of the uterine wall formed from three intertwining layers of smooth muscle. The innermost tunic of the uterus, called the **endometrium** (en'dō-mē'trē-ŭm), is an intricate mucosa composed of a simple columnar epithelium and an underlying lamina propria. The lamina propria is filled with compound tubular glands (also called **uterine glands**), which enlarge during the uterine cycle.

Two distinct layers form the endometrium. The deeper layer is the **basal layer,** also called the *stratum basalis* (bă-sā'lis). The basal layer is immediately adjacent to the myometrium and is a permanent layer that undergoes few changes during each uterine cycle. The more superficial of the two endometrial layers is the **functional layer,** or *stratum functionalis* (fŭnk'shŭn-ăl'is). Beginning at puberty, the functional layer grows from the basal layer under the influence of estrogen and progesterone secreted from the ovarian follicles. If fertilization and implantation do not occur, the functional layer is shed as menses. The basal layer gives rise to a new functional layer after the end of each menses.

Vagina

The **vagina** (vă-jī'nă) is a thick-walled, fibromuscular tube that forms the inferiormost region of the female reproductive tract and measures about 10 centimeters in length in an adult female (figure 28.3a). The vagina connects the uterus with the outside of the body and functions as the birth canal. The vagina is also the copulatory organ of the female, as it receives the penis during intercourse, and it serves as the passageway for menstruation.

Arterial supply comes from the vaginal arteries (branches of the internal iliac arteries), and venous drainage is via vaginal veins. The lumen of the vagina is flattened anteroposteriorly. The vagina's relatively thin, distensible wall consists of three tunics: an inner mucosa, a middle muscularis, and an outer adventitia (figure 28.10). The **mucosa** consists of a nonkeratinized stratified squamous epithelium (after puberty; prior to puberty the epithelium is relatively thin) and a highly vascularized lamina propria. Vaginal epithelial cells produce an acidic secretion that helps prevent bacterial and other pathogenic infection. The inferior region of the vaginal mucosa contains numerous transverse folds, or rugae. Near the external opening of the vagina, called the **vaginal orifice,** these mucosal folds project into the lumen to form a vascularized, membranous barrier called the **hymen** (hī'men; membrane). The hymen typically is perforated during the first instance of sexual intercourse, but also may be perforated by tampon use, medical exams, or very strenuous physical activity. The **muscularis** of the vagina has both outer and inner layers of smooth

Endometriosis

Endometriosis (en'dō-mē-trē-ō'sis) occurs when part of the endometrium is displaced onto the external surface of organs within the abdominopelvic cavity. Scientists think that during the regular uterine (menstrual) cycle of some women, some endometrial tissue may be expelled from the uterine tubes and become implanted on the surface of various abdominal and pelvic organs. This displaced endometrium may grow under the influence of hormones, but it cannot be expelled in a normal fashion. Thus, the ensuing hemorrhage and breakdown of the displaced endometrium may cause considerable pain and scarring that often leads to deformities of the uterine tubes. Treatments include the use of hormones designed to retard the growth and cycling of the displaced endometrial tissue, as well as surgical removal of the ectopic endometrium.

Uterus

Ectopic endometrial tissue

Intestines

The pelvic organs show extensive endometrial tissue attachments.

muscle. The **adventitia** contains some inner elastic fibers and an outer layer of areolar connective tissue.

💡 **WHAT DID YOU LEARN?**

16 What are the four contiguous segments of the uterine tubes, and what major events occur with each?

17 How do the three tunics of the uterus contribute to its function?

18 What are the main functions of the vagina, and how does its structure support these functions?

Figure 28.10
Histology of the Vagina. The epithelial lining of the vagina in a mature female is a stratified squamous epithelium. AP|R

Table 28.4	Comparison of Ovarian and Uterine Cycle Phases	
Day¹	**Ovarian Cycle Phase**	**Uterine Cycle Phase**
1–5	Follicular phase	Menstrual phase
6–13	Follicular phase	Proliferative phase
14	Ovulation	Proliferative phase
15–28	Luteal phase	Secretory phase

1. This table assumes a 28-day cycle between menstrual periods. If a woman has a longer or shorter cycle, the day ranges for the follicular, menstrual, and proliferative phases will vary.

28.3d Uterine (Menstrual) Cycle and Menstruation

✓ **LEARNING OBJECTIVES**

9. Compare the three phases of the uterine cycle.

10. List and explain what hormones influence the events in each part of the ovarian cycle.

11. Explain how the ovarian cycle and the uterine cycle are interrelated.

The cyclical changes in the endometrial lining occur under the influence of estrogen and progesterone secreted by the developing follicles and the corpus luteum. The **uterine cycle** (or *menstrual cycle*) consists of three distinct phases of endometrium development: the menstrual phase, proliferative phase, and secretory phase (see figure 28.7, *bottom*). The length of the uterine cycle may vary greatly among females; the timeline listed in the following paragraphs represents a typical 28-day uterine cycle. Note that the uterine cycle could be shorter (21 days or less) or longer (35 days or more).

❓ **WHAT DO YOU THINK?**

2 What factors could influence the length and timing of a woman's monthly uterine cycle?

The **menstrual** (men′stru-ăl; *menstrualis* = monthly) **phase** occurs approximately during days 1–5 of the cycle. This phase is marked by sloughing of the functional layer and lasts through the period of menstrual bleeding. The **proliferative** (prō-lif′er-ă-tiv; *proles* = offspring, *fero* = to bear) **phase** follows, spanning approximately days 6–14. The initial development of the new functional layer of the endometrium overlaps the time of follicle growth and estrogen secretion by the ovary. The last phase is the **secretory** (se-krēt′ĕ-rē, sē′krĕ-tōr-ē) **phase,** which occurs at approximately days 15–28. During the secretory phase, increased progesterone secretion from the corpus luteum results in increased vascularization and development of uterine glands.

The corpus luteum degenerates and progesterone level drops dramatically if fertilization does not occur. Without significant levels of progesterone, the functional layer lining sloughs off, and the next uterine cycle begins with the menstrual phase.

Table 28.4 and figure 28.7 compare the uterine cycle with the ovarian cycle discussed previously, and **table 28.5** summarizes the hormones that influence the ovarian and uterine cycles. **Figure 28.11** illustrates how the hormones, ovarian cycle, and uterine cycle are interrelated and follow a cyclical process.

Table 28.5	Influence of Hormones on the Ovarian and Uterine Cycles	
Hormone	**Primary Source of Hormone**	**Effects**
Gonadotropin-releasing hormone (GnRH)	Hypothalamus	Stimulates anterior pituitary to produce and secrete FSH and LH
Follicle-stimulating hormone (FSH)	Anterior pituitary	Stimulates development and maturation of ovarian follicles
Luteinizing hormone (LH)	Anterior pituitary	Stimulates ovulation (when there is a peak in LH)
Estrogen	Ovarian follicles (before ovulation), corpus luteum (after ovulation), or placenta (during pregnancy)	Initiates and maintains growth of the functional layer of the endometrium
Progesterone	Corpus luteum or placenta (during pregnancy)	Primary hormone responsible for functional layer growth after ovulation; causes increase in blood vessel distribution, uterine gland size, and nutrient production
Inhibin	Ovarian follicles	Inhibits FSH secretion so as to prevent excessive follicular development

Figure 28.11 **The Interrelationships Between Hormones, the Ovarian Cycle, and the Uterine (Menstrual) Cycle.** (*a*) Days 1–5 include menstruation and new follicular development. (*b*) Days 6–12 begin the proliferative phase of the uterine cycle and the development of a vesicular follicle. (*c*) Days 13–14 begin with a peak in LH and end with ovulation. (*d*) Days 15–28 include development of the corpus luteum and continued buildup of the uterine lining.

(a) Days 1–5 | Ovarian cycle: Follicular phase / Uterine cycle: Menstrual phase

GnRH stimulates FSH and LH secretion: Some ovarian follicles develop and produce estrogen. Functional layer of the endometrium is shed.

(d) Days 15–28 | Ovarian cycle: Luteal phase / Uterine cycle: Secretory phase

Corpus luteum forms and secretes large amounts of estrogen, progesterone, and inhibin. Combined, these inhibit GnRH, FSH, and LH secretion. Progesterone stimulates uterine lining growth. If the oocyte is not fertilized, the corpus luteum regresses and hormone levels drop.

(b) Days 6–12 | Ovarian cycle: Follicular phase
Uterine cycle: Proliferative phase

Estrogen and inhibin inhibit the hypothalamus and anterior pituitary, causing a drop in FSH. One follicle continues to mature and produce estrogen. Functional layer of the endometrium is rebuilding.

Gonadotropin levels

FSH
LH

Days 7 9 11

Ovarian hormone levels

Estrogen

Progesterone

Days 7 9 11

Uterine cycle

Functional layer
Basal layer

Days 7 9 11

Hypothalamus

Anterior pituitary

Inhibin, estrogen (low levels)

Estrogen (low levels)

Secondary follicle

Vesicular follicle

(c) Days 13–14 | Ovarian cycle: Follicular phase, ovulation
Uterine cycle: Proliferative phase

The increase in estrogen above threshold stimulates the hypothalamus and anterior pituitary, causing an LH surge. The LH surge induces ovulation.

Gonadotropin levels

LH
FSH

Days 12 13 14

Ovulation

Ovarian hormone levels

Estrogen

Progesterone

Days 12 13 14

Uterine cycle

Functional layer

Basal layer

Days 12 13 14

Hypothalamus

Anterior pituitary

Estrogen

LH

Vesicular follicle

Ovulation

The menstrual and proliferative phases of the menstrual cycle occur in conjunction with the follicular and ovulation phases of the ovarian cycle. The secretory phase of the menstrual cycle occurs at the same time as the luteal phase of the ovarian cycle.

The day ranges listed in the figures assume that the woman has a 28-day cycle, meaning she ovulates at day 14 and has a menstrual period about every 28 days. If a woman has a longer cycle, her menstrual phase or her proliferative phase is longer than average. Typically, a woman ovulates 14 days before menstruation (regardless of the length of her cycle), so the secretory phase day ranges do not vary as much.

WHAT DID YOU LEARN?

19 What are the three phases of the uterine cycle, and what major events occur in each?

20 Compare and contrast the ovarian and uterine cycles. How are they interrelated?

28.3e External Genitalia

✔ LEARNING OBJECTIVE

12. Describe the components of the female external genitalia.

The external reproductive organs of the female are termed the **external genitalia,** or **vulva** (vŭl′vă; a covering) **(figure 28.12).** The **mons pubis** (monz; mountain) is an expanse of skin and subcutaneous connective tissue immediately anterior to the pubic symphysis. The mons pubis is covered with pubic hair in postpubescent females. The **labia majora** (lā′bē-ă mă-jŏr′ă; sing., *labium majus; labium* = lip, *majus* = larger) are paired, thickened folds of skin and connective tissue. The labia majora are homologous to the scrotum of the male. In adulthood, their outer surface is covered with coarse pubic hair; they contain numerous sweat and sebaceous glands. The **labia minora** (mī-nŏr′ă; sing., *labium minus; minus* = smaller) are paired folds immediately internal to the labia majora. They are devoid of hair and contain a highly vascular layer of areolar connective tissue. Sebaceous glands are located within these

folds, as are numerous melanocytes, resulting in enhanced pigmentation of the folds.

The space between the labia minora is called the **vestibule.** Within the vestibule are the **urethral opening** and the vaginal orifice. On either side of the vaginal orifice is an erectile body called the **bulb of the vestibule,** which engorges with blood and increases in sensitivity during sexual intercourse. A pair of **greater vestibular glands** (previously called *glands of Bartholin*) are housed within the posterolateral walls of the vestibule and secrete mucin, which forms mucus to act as a lubricant for the vagina. Secretion increases during sexual intercourse, when additional lubrication is needed. These secretory structures are homologous to the male bulbourethral glands (which are discussed with the male reproductive system).

The **clitoris** (klit′ō-ris) is a small erectile body, usually less than 2 centimeters in length, located at the anterior regions of the labia minora. It is homologous to the penis of the male. Two small erectile bodies called **corpora cavernosa** form the **body** of the clitoris. The corpora cavernosa become engorged with blood and increase in sensitivity during sexual intercourse. Extending from each of these bodies posteriorly are elongated masses, each called the **crus** (krūs) of the clitoris, which attach to the pubic arch. Capping the body of the clitoris is the **glans** (glanz; acorn). The many specialized sensory nerve receptors housed in the clitoris provide pleasure to the female during sexual intercourse. The **prepuce** (prē′pūs; foreskin) is an external fold of the labia minora that forms a hoodlike covering over the clitoris.

WHAT DID YOU LEARN?

21 What are the individual components of the female external genitalia and their functions?

28.3f Mammary Glands

✔ LEARNING OBJECTIVES

13. Explain the gross anatomy of the mammary glands.

14. Compare the hormones responsible for milk production and milk ejection.

Glans of clitoris — Mons pubis — Prepuce

Urethral opening
Vestibule
Vaginal orifice
Openings for greater vestibular glands

Labia minora

Labia majora

Perineum

Anus

(a) Superficial structures of external genitalia

Pubic symphysis
Body of clitoris
Crus of clitoris
Bulb of the vestibule
Greater vestibular gland

(b) Deep structures of external genitalia

Figure 28.12 Female External Genitalia. (*a*) Inferior view of the external genitalia, illustrating the urethral opening and the vaginal opening, which are within the vestibule and bounded by the labia minora. (*b*) Deep structures associated with the external genitalia.

Each **mammary gland,** or *breast,* is located within the anterior thoracic wall and is composed of a compound tubuloalveolar exocrine gland (**figure 28.13**). The gland's secretory product is called breast milk and it contains proteins, fats, and a lactose sugar to provide nutrition to infants.

The **nipple** is a cylindrical projection on the center of the breast. It contains multiple tiny openings of the excretory ducts that transport breast milk. The **areola** (ă-rē'ō-lă; small area) is the pigmented, rosy or brownish ring of skin around the nipple. Its surface often appears uneven and grainy due to the numerous sebaceous glands, called **areolar glands,** immediately internal to the surface. The color of the areola may vary, depending upon whether or not a woman has given birth. In a **nulliparous** (nŭl-ip'ă-rŭs; *nullus* = none, *pario* = to bear) woman, one who has never given birth, the areola is rosy or light brown in color. In a **parous** (par'ŭs) woman, one who has given birth, the areola may change to a darker color.

Internally, the breasts are supported by fibrous connective bands called **suspensory ligaments.** These thin bands extend from the skin and attach to the deep fascia overlying the pectoralis major muscle. Thus, the breast and the pectoralis major muscle are structurally linked.

The mammary glands are subdivided into **lobes,** which are further subdivided into smaller compartments called **lobules.** Lobules contain secretory units termed **alveoli** that produce milk in the lactating female. Alveoli become more numerous and larger during pregnancy. Tiny ducts drain milk from the alveoli and lobules. The tiny ducts of the lobules merge and form 10 to 20 larger channels called **lactiferous** (lak-tif'er-ŭs; *lact* = milk, *fero* = to bear) **ducts.** A lactiferous duct drains breast milk from a single lobe. As each lactiferous duct approaches the nipple, its lumen expands to form a **lactiferous sinus,** a space where milk is stored prior to release from the nipple.

(a) Anteromedial view

(b) Sagittal view

Figure 28.13 Mammary Glands. The mammary glands are composed of glandular tissue and a variable amount of fat. (*a*) An anterior view is partially cut away to reveal internal structures. (*b*) A diagrammatic sagittal section of a mammary gland shows the distribution of alveoli within lobules and the extension of ducts to the nipple. AP|R

CLINICAL VIEW
Contraception Methods

The term **contraception** (kon-tră-sep'shun) refers to birth control, or the prevention of pregnancy. A wide range of birth control methods are available, and they have varying degrees of effectiveness.

Abstinence (ab'sti-nens; *abstineo* = to hold back) means refraining from sexual intercourse. Abstinence is the only 100% proven way to prevent pregnancy.

The **rhythm method** requires avoiding sexual intercourse during the time when a woman is ovulating. Because sperm can live for several days in the female reproductive tract, it is best to avoid intercourse both a few days prior and a few days after ovulating. The rhythm method requires that a woman know when she is ovulating, which may be difficult to determine since there is great variation in ovarian cycles. As a result, this method has a high failure rate.

The **withdrawal method,** also known as the *pull-out method,* is where the male pulls his penis out of the vagina before he ejaculates. This method has a high failure rate, in part because it may be difficult to predict the point prior to ejaculation. Additionally, it may be possible for pre-ejaculate (emissions secreted prior to ejaculation) to collect enough sperm in the urethra from a prior ejaculation to impregnate a female.

Barrier methods of birth control use a physical barrier to prevent sperm from reaching the uterine tubes. Barrier methods include the following:

- **Condoms,** when used properly, collect the sperm and prevent them from entering the female reproductive tract. They are also the only birth control method that helps protect against sexually transmitted infections (STIs), such as human papillomavirus (HPV), herpes, and HIV. Condoms for males fit snugly on the erect penis, while **vaginal condoms** are placed in the vagina prior to sexual intercourse.

- **Spermicidal foams and gels** are chemical barrier methods that kill sperm before they travel to the uterine tubes. They are inserted into the vagina or placed on the penis prior to sexual intercourse. Foams and gels are not the most effective method of birth control; rather, they should be used in conjunction with a physical barrier method.

- **Diaphragms** and **cervical caps** are circular, rubbery structures that are inserted into the vagina and placed over the cervix prior to sexual intercourse. Spermicidal gel is used around the edges to help prevent sperm from entering the cervix. Some women find it difficult to correctly place the diaphragm or cervical cap, and incorrect placement can result in sperm entering the uterus.

Lactation is the production of milk for nursing a baby, and it can prevent ovulation and menstruation for several to many months after childbirth *if* a woman nurses her child constantly (i.e., much more than five times a day). Frequent lactation sends signals to the hypothalamus to prevent follicle-stimulating hormone (FSH) and luteinizing hormone (LH) from being secreted, thus preventing ovulation. If a woman is lactating, she should always use another form of birth control as well, because she will not know when her ovulation cycle begins again until many weeks later, when she begins menstruating again.

Intrauterine devices (IUDs) are T-shaped, flexible plastic structures inserted into the uterus by a health-care provider. Once in place, the IUD prevents fertilization from occurring, although researchers aren't sure specifically how. Some IUDs may contain copper or a synthetic progestin, both of which help prevent implantation. An IUD containing copper may stay in place for up to 10 years, whereas one with progestin must be removed

(a) Condoms

(b) Spermicidal foams

(c) Diaphragm

(d) Intrauterine device (IUD)

(e) Oral contraceptive

Uterine tubes are tied off and cut.

(f) Tubal ligation

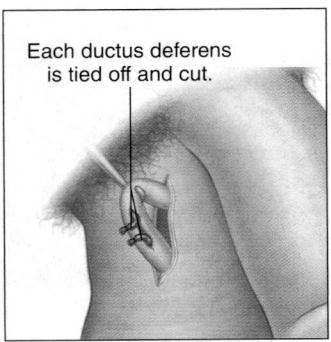

Each ductus deferens is tied off and cut.

(g) Vasectomy

Contraception includes barrier, chemical, and surgical methods.

and replaced each year. Rarely, the IUD may be expelled from the uterus or displaced, in which case a pregnancy can occur.

Chemical methods of birth control are very effective if used properly. They include the following:

- **Oral contraceptives** are commonly called *birth control pills* and typically come in 28-day packets. The first 21 days of pills contain low levels of estrogen and progestins, and the last 7 days are sugar pills. (Progesterone is one type of progestin.) The low levels of estrogen and progestins prevent the LH "spike" needed for ovulation. Thus, oral contraceptives prevent ovulation. During the 7 days of sugar pills, the circulating levels of estrogen and progestins drop, and menstruation occurs. Menstrual flow typically is much lighter when a woman takes oral contraceptives because the circulating levels of hormones were low to begin with, so the uterine lining does not build up as much. Oral contraceptives require a woman to take a pill a day, at about the same time each day. If she misses one or more days of pills, ovulation may occur. In addition, some medications (such as antibiotics) may interfere with their effectiveness, so a backup method of contraception should be used when taking these medications.

- **Estrogen/progestin** (prō-jes'tin; *pro* = before; gestation) **patches** are alternatives to the daily oral contraceptive. A patch placed on the body delivers a regular amount of estrogen and progestin through the skin (transdermally). The patch is replaced each week.

- **Implanted/injected progestins** help prevent pregnancy by preventing ovulation and thickening the mucus around the cervix (thus creating a slight physical barrier to the sperm). Medroxyprogesterone (Depo-Provera) is an injectable contraceptive given once every 3 months, while etonogestrel (Implanon) is an implantable contraceptive that lasts for up to 3 years. The drawback is that ovulation may not occur for many months after stopping the injections.

- **Morning-after pills** containing levonorgestrel (e.g., Plan B One-Step) can be taken within 72 hours after having unprotected intercourse. These pills work by inhibiting ovulation, altering the menstrual cycle to delay ovulation, or irritating the uterine lining to prevent implantation. The U.S. Food and Drug Administration approved pharmacies to sell this medication over the counter (without a prescription) for women over age 18, while those younger than 18 must get a prescription for the medication.

- **Mifepristone** (Mifeprex in the United States; RU-486 in Europe) may be used during the first 7 weeks of pregnancy. Mifepristone blocks progesterone receptors, so progesterone cannot attach to these receptors and thereby maintain a pregnancy. When taken with a prostaglandin drug, mifepristone induces a miscarriage. Mifepristone's availability and use is very politically charged, with each side of the abortion debate arguing for or against it.

Surgical methods of contraception are both **tubal ligation** for women and **vasectomy** (va-sek'tō-mē) for men. A tubal ligation requires that uterine tubes are cut and the ends are tied off or cauterized shut to prevent both sperm from reaching the oocyte and the oocyte from reaching the uterus. The uterine tubes are ligated either laparoscopically (shown in the adjacent figure) or via entry through the uterus (which is a much more difficult procedure for the surgeon.) A vasectomy is an outpatient procedure whereby each ductus deferens is cut, a short segment is removed, and then the ends are tied off. Sperm cannot leave the testis and thus are broken down and resorbed. Both surgeries are effective birth control methods, but they are usually permanent and irreversible, so they are not options for people who wish to have more children.

Breast milk is released by a process called **lactation** (laktā'shŭn; *lactatio* = to suckle), which occurs in response to a complex sequence of internal and external stimuli. Normally, a woman starts to produce breast milk when she has recently given birth. Recall from section 17.8c that the hormone **prolactin** is produced in the anterior pituitary and is responsible for milk production. Thus, when the amount of prolactin increases, the mammary gland grows and forms more expanded and numerous alveoli. The hormone **oxytocin,** produced by the hypothalamus and released from the posterior pituitary, is responsible for milk ejection.

 WHAT DID YOU LEARN?

22 What is the relationship between lobes, suspensory ligaments, and lactiferous ducts in the breast?

23 What are the effects of prolactin and oxytocin on the female mammary gland?

28.3g Female Sexual Response

LEARNING OBJECTIVE

15. Explain how the female sexual response and orgasm is elicited.

The female sexual response refers to a series of anatomic and physiologic events that occur during stimulation of the female reproductive organs. The response begins with the **excitement phase,** where reproductive organs such as the mammary glands, clitoris, vaginal wall, bulbs of the vestibule, and labia become engorged with blood. The nipples become erect as a result of the blood engorgement in the mammary glands. The vestibular glands and the glands within the vaginal wall both produce mucus for lubrication. The uterus shifts from an anteverted position to a more erect position within the pelvic cavity.

As the excitement phase continues, the erectile tissue of the clitoris swells as it engorges with blood and becomes very sensitive to tactile stimuli. The inferior part of the vaginal wall constricts slightly. The woman's heart rate, blood pressure, and respiratory rate increase during this time as orgasm nears. Both divisions of the autonomic nervous system control many of these physiologic responses, and the excitement phase also is facilitated by somatosensory signals, such as the sensation of the penis in the vagina or the caressing of parts of the body.

Orgasm refers to the time period where there are intense feelings of pleasure, a feeling of a release of tension, perhaps a feeling of warmth, and some pelvic throbbing. The vagina and uterus contract rhythmically for a period of many seconds.

INTEGRATE

CONCEPT CONNECTION

The male and female sexual response each requires an intricate interplay among various body systems beyond the reproductive system. The nervous system (both autonomic and somatic parts) is involved with orchestrating the entire event and controlling an array of physiologic processes. The cardiovascular system is responsible for the engorgement of erectile tissue with blood and increases heart rate and blood pressure just prior to orgasm. In addition, the respiratory system is involved as breathing rate increases prior to orgasm. For the male, there is an additional step as the internal urethral sphincter (part of the urinary system) is contracted so no urine enters the urethra during ejaculation.

The **resolution phase** follows orgasm. The uterus returns to its original position and the vaginal wall relaxes at this time. The excess blood leaves the other reproductive organs. The cycle may begin again. Unlike men, women do not have a refractory period, which is a period of time where the body cannot have another orgasm; thus, women have the potential to have multiple orgasms during a single sexual experience.

WHAT DID YOU LEARN?

24 What are the three phases of female sexual response?

28.4 Male Reproductive System

The primary reproductive organs in the male are the **testes** (tes′tēz; sing., *testis*). The accessory reproductive organs include a complex set of ducts and tubules leading from the testes to the penis, a group of male accessory glands, and the penis, which is the organ of copulation **(figure 28.14)**.

28.4a Scrotum

LEARNING OBJECTIVE

1. Describe the gross anatomy and function of the scrotum.

The ideal temperature for producing and storing sperm is about 2–3°C lower than internal body temperature. The **scrotum** (skrō′tŭm), a skin-covered sac between the thighs, provides the cooler environment needed for normal sperm development and maturation **(figure 28.15)**. The scrotum is homologous to the labia majora in the female.

Externally, the scrotum contains a distinct, ridgelike seam at its midline, called the **raphe** (rā′fē; *rhaphe* = seam). The raphe extends in an anterior direction along the inferior surface of the penis and in a posterior direction to the anus. The wall of the scrotum is composed of an external layer of skin, a thin layer of superficial fascia immediately internal to the skin, and a layer of smooth muscle, the **dartos** (dar′tos; skinned) **muscle,** immediately internal to the fascia.

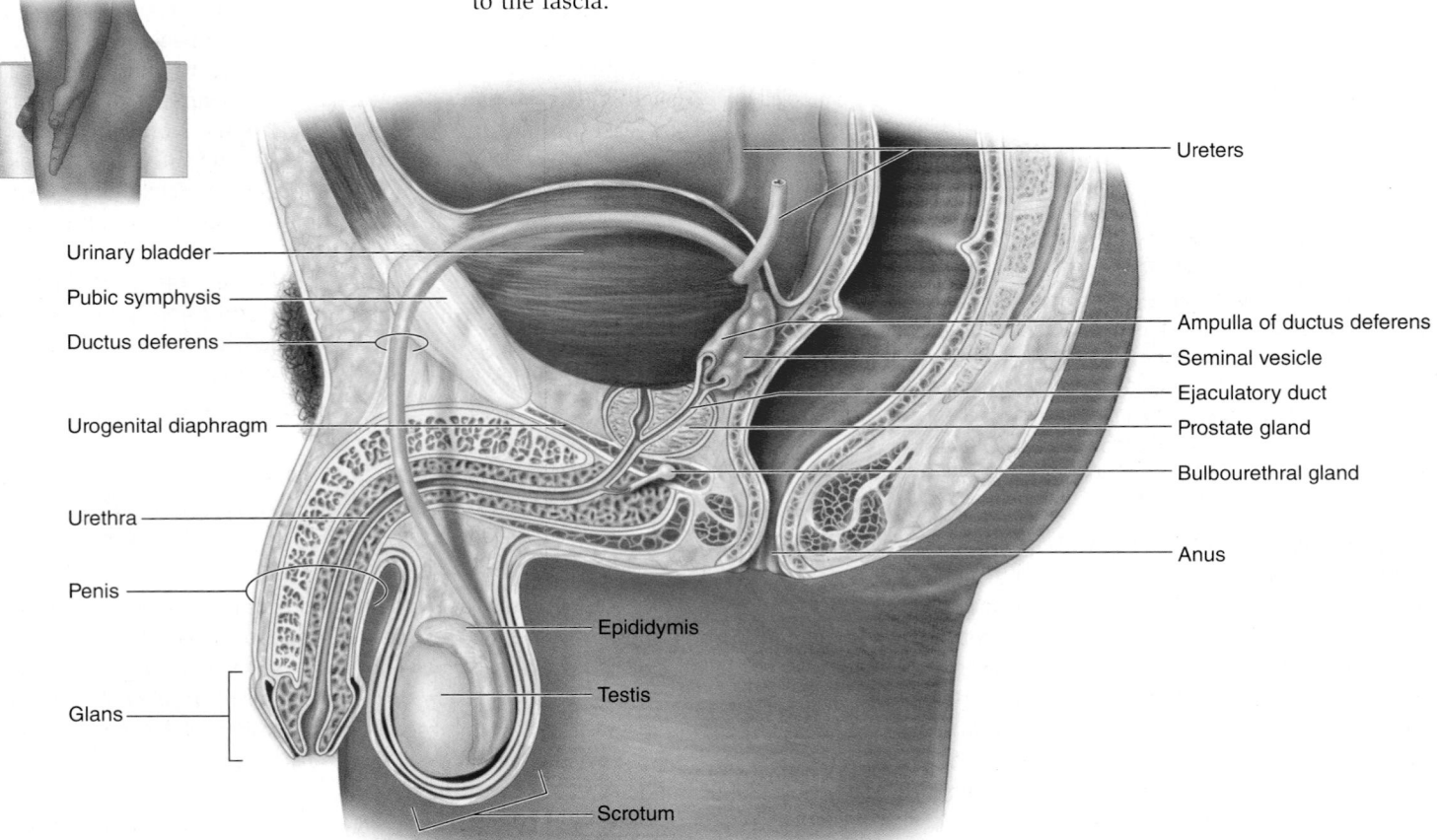

- Ureters
- Urinary bladder
- Pubic symphysis
- Ductus deferens
- Ampulla of ductus deferens
- Seminal vesicle
- Ejaculatory duct
- Urogenital diaphragm
- Prostate gland
- Bulbourethral gland
- Urethra
- Anus
- Penis
- Epididymis
- Testis
- Glans
- Scrotum

Figure 28.14 Male Pelvic Region. A sagittal diagrammatic section shows the location and relationship of the male pelvic structures. AP|R

The blood vessels and nerves supplying each testis travel from within the abdomen to the scrotum in a multilayered structure called the **spermatic cord**. The spermatic cord originates in the **inguinal canal,** a tubelike passageway through the inferior abdominal wall. The spermatic cord wall consists of three layers:

- An **internal spermatic fascia** is formed from fascia deep to the abdominal muscles.
- The **cremaster** (krē-mas'ter; a suspender) **muscle** and **cremasteric fascia** are formed from muscle fiber extensions of the internal oblique muscle and its aponeurosis, respectively.
- An **external spermatic fascia** is formed from the aponeurosis of the external oblique muscle.

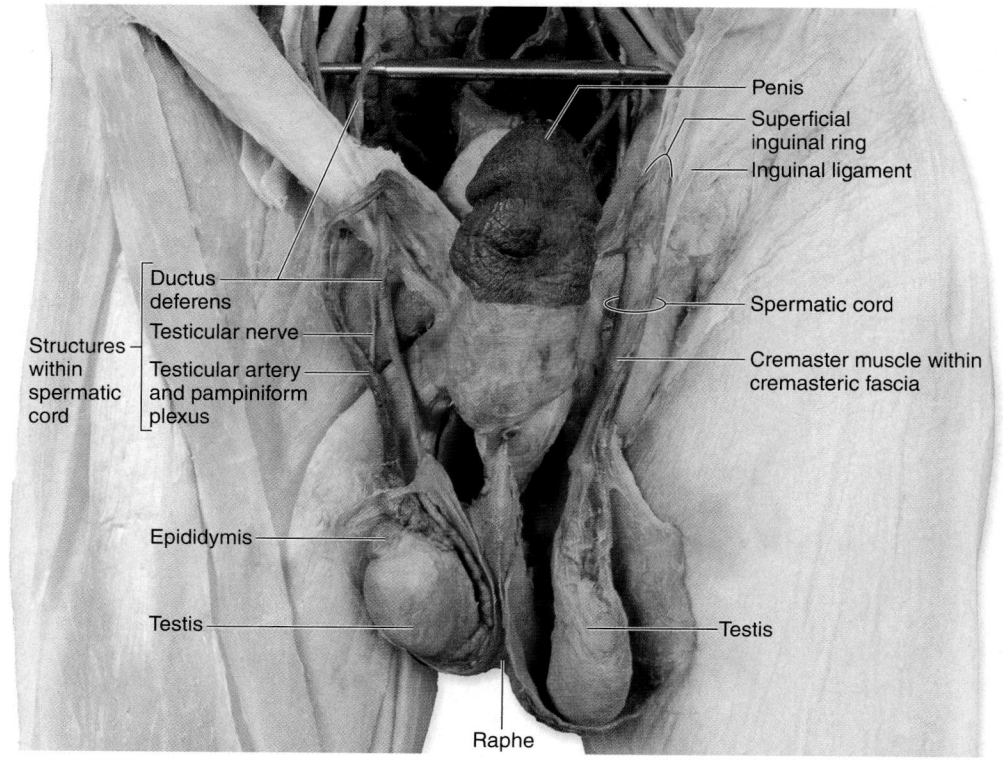

Figure 28.15 Scrotum and Testes. Anterior view and cadaver photo show the scrotum, a skin-covered sac that houses the testes. A multilayered spermatic cord houses the blood vessels, nerves, and a sperm-carrying duct (ductus deferens) for each testis. AP|R

Within the spermatic cord is a singular **testicular artery** that is a direct branch from the abdominal aorta. The testicular artery is surrounded by a plexus of veins called the **pampiniform** (pam-pin'i-form; *pampinus* = tendril, *forma* = form) **plexus.** This venous plexus is a means to provide thermoregulation by pre-cooling arterial blood prior to its reaching the testes. Autonomic nerves travel with these vessels and innervate each testis.

When the testes are exposed to elevated temperatures, the dartos muscle relaxes, which unwrinkles the skin of the scrotum and allows the testes to move inferiorly further away from the body. This movement away from the body cools the testes. At the same time, the cremaster muscle also relaxes to allow the testes to move inferiorly away from the body. The opposite occurs if the testes are exposed to cold. In this case, both the dartos and cremaster muscles contract, pulling the testes and scrotum closer to the body in order to conserve heat.

WHAT DID YOU LEARN?

25 How does the scrotum help regulate the temperature of the testes?

28.4b Testes and Spermatogenesis

✓ LEARNING OBJECTIVES

2. Describe the gross anatomy and microscopic anatomy of the testes.

3. Explain the process of spermatogenesis and spermiogenesis.

4. Compare and contrast spermatogenesis with oogenesis.

In the adult human male, the testes are relatively small, oval organs housed within the scrotum (see figures 28.14 and 28.15). Each weighs approximately 10 to 12 grams, and displays average dimensions of 4 centimeters (cm) in length, 2 cm in width, and 2.5 cm in anteroposterior diameter. The testes produce sperm and androgens (male sex hormones).

WHAT DO YOU THINK?

3 If a man's testes were removed, would he still be able to produce androgens?

Each testis is covered anteriorly and laterally by a serous membrane, the **tunica vaginalis** (văj-in-ăl'ĭs; ensheathing) **(figure 28.16a;** see also figure 28.15). This membrane is derived from the peritoneum of the abdominal cavity. The tunica vaginalis has an outer **parietal layer** and an inner **visceral layer** that are separated by a cavity filled with serous fluid. A thick, whitish, fibrous capsule called the **tunica albuginea** covers the testis and lies immediately deep to the visceral layer of the tunica vaginalis. At the posterior margin of the testis, the tunica albuginea thickens and projects into the interior of the organ as the **mediastinum testis.** Blood vessels, a system of ducts, lymph vessels, and some nerves enter or leave each testis through the mediastinum testis.

The tunica albuginea projects internally into the testis and forms delicate connective tissue **septa,** which subdivide the internal space into about 250 separate **lobules.** Each lobule contains up to four extremely convoluted, thin and elongated **seminiferous** (sem'in-if'er-ŭs; *semen* = seed, *fero* = to carry) **tubules.** The seminiferous tubules contain two types of cells: (1) a group of nondividing support cells called the **sustentacular** (sŭs-ten-tak'ū-lăr; *sustento* = to hold upright) **cells,** which also are termed *Sertoli cells,* or *nurse cells*; and (2) a population of dividing germ cells that continuously produce sperm beginning at puberty.

The sustentacular cells provide a protective environment for the developing sperm, and their cytoplasm helps nourish the developing sperm (figure 28.16b). In addition, sustentacular cells release the hormone **inhibin** when sperm count is high. Inhibin inhibits FSH secretion and thus regulates sperm production. (Conversely, when sperm count declines, inhibin secretion decreases.)

The sustentacular cells are secured together by tight junctions, which form a **blood-testis barrier** that is similar to the blood-brain

Figure 28.16 Testes and Seminiferous Tubules.

(*a*) The gross anatomy of a testis is shown diagrammatically in a cutaway, partial sagittal section. (*b*) A photomicrograph reveals a seminiferous tubule in the testis. AP|R

(a) Testis

(b) Seminiferous tubule, cross section

barrier. The blood-testis barrier helps protect developing sperm from materials in the blood. It also protects the sperm from the body's leukocytes, which may perceive the sperm as foreign since they have different chromosome numbers and proteins. (In contrast, the female oocyte likely is protected from materials in the blood by the ovarian follicle structures that surround the oocyte.)

The spaces surrounding the seminiferous tubules are called **interstitial spaces.** Within these spaces reside the **interstitial cells** (or *Leydig cells*). Luteinizing hormone stimulates the interstitial cells to produce hormones called **androgens** (an'drō-jen; *andros* = male human). There are several types of androgens, the most common one being testosterone. Although the adrenal cortex secretes a small amount of androgens, the vast majority of androgen release is via the interstitial cells in the testis, beginning at puberty.

Hormonal Regulation of Androgen Production and Sperm Development

Like the hormone interactions involved in the ovarian cycle, the interplay among the hormones involved in regulating the spermatogenesis and androgen production is intricate and involves several negative feedback mechanisms. A stepwise description of these hormonal effects are listed here and shown in **figure 28.17**:

① **The hypothalamus initiates spermatogenesis by secreting GnRH,** which stimulates the anterior pituitary to secrete FSH and LH.

② **FSH and LH target the testes and stimulate both spermatogenesis and androgen production.** Specifically, LH stimulates interstitial cells in the testis to secrete testosterone,

and FSH stimulates the sustentacular cells to secrete androgen-binding protein (ABP). ABP binds to androgens, which allows these hormones to become more concentrated in the seminiferous tubule and ensures that testosterone levels remain high in the testes. Therefore, the testis and its cells are the effectors, and they release stimuli (testosterone and ABP) in this cycle.

③ **The increased levels of testosterone have various immediate effects on the body.** The high testosterone levels facilitate spermatogenesis. However, this same circulating testosterone inhibits GnRH secretion and reduces anterior pituitary sensitivity to GnRH. Thus, rising levels of testosterone have a negative feedback effect on the entire cycle.

④ **Sustentacular cells respond to rising sperm count levels and secrete inhibin.** Inhibin primarily causes inhibition of FSH secretion from the anterior pituitary, and it serves as an additional negative feedback mechanism on the cycle.

⑤ **Circulating testosterone stimulates libido (sex drive) and development of secondary sex characteristics.** Testosterone acts on the brain so there is an increased desire for and sensitivity to sexual stimulation. Secondary sex characteristics include growth and development of hair in the pubic and axillary regions, a deeper voice (because testosterone affects larynx development), and the growth of facial hair.

Note that sperm development and androgen production are controlled by negative feedback only, whereas the ovarian cycle uses both positive and negative feedback mechanisms.

Figure 28.17 Hormonal Regulation of Spermatogenesis and Androgen Production. The hypothalamus secretes gonadotropin-releasing hormone (GnRH), which stimulates the anterior pituitary to release follicle-stimulating hormone (FSH) and luteinizing hormone (LH). FSH and LH stimulate spermatogenesis and androgen production, as shown in this image.

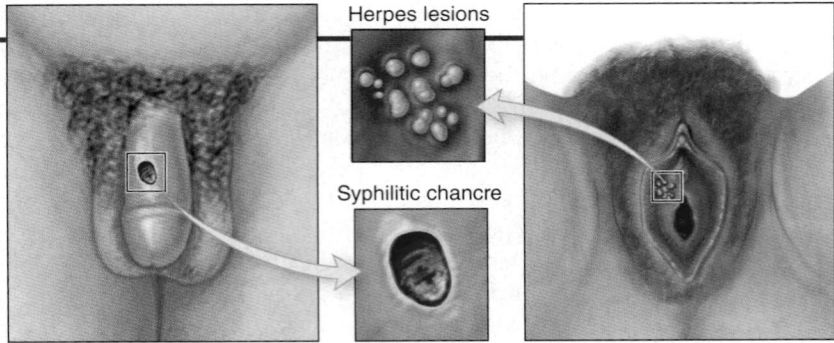
Development of Sperm: Spermatogenesis and Spermiogenesis

Spermatogenesis (sper′mă-tō-jen′ĕ-sis; *genesis* = origin) is the process of sperm development that occurs within the seminiferous tubule of the testis. Spermatogenesis does not begin until puberty, when significant levels of FSH and LH stimulate the testis to begin gamete development.

The process of spermatogenesis is shown in **figure 28.18a.** All sperm develop from primordial germ (stem) cells called **spermatogonia** (sper′mă-tō-gō′nē-ă; sing., s*permatogonium; sperma* = seed, *gone* = generation). Spermatogonia are diploid cells (meaning they have 23 pairs of chromosomes for a total of 46). These cells lie near the base of the seminiferous tubule, surrounded by the cytoplasm of a sustentacular cell. To produce sperm, spermatogonia first divide by mitosis. One of the cells produced is a new spermatogonium (a new germ cell), to ensure that the numbers of spermatogonia never become depleted, and the other cell is a committed cell called **primary spermatocyte.** Primary spermatocytes are diploid and are the cells that undergo meiosis.

When a primary spermatocyte undergoes meiosis I, the two cells produced are called **secondary spermatocytes.** Secondary spermatocytes are haploid cells, meaning they each have 23 chromosomes only. These cells are still surrounded by the sustentacular cell cytoplasm, but they are relatively closer to the lumen of the seminiferous tubule as opposed to the base of the seminiferous tubule.

Secondary spermatocytes complete meiosis II to form **spermatids** (sper′mă-tid). A spermatid is a haploid cell and is surrounded by the sustentacular cell cytoplasm, very near to the lumen of the seminiferous tubule. The spermatids still have a circular appearance, rather than the sleek shape of mature sperm.

In the final stage of spermatogenesis, a process called **spermiogenesis,** the newly formed spermatids differentiate to become anatomically mature **spermatozoa** (sing., *spermatozoon;* sper′mă-to-zo′on) or **sperm** (figure 28.18b). During spermiogenesis, the spermatid sheds excess cytoplasm and its nucleus elongates. A structure called the **acrosome cap** (ak′rō-sōm; *akros* = tip, *soma* = body) forms over the nucleus. This structure contains digestive enzymes that help penetrate the secondary oocyte for fertilization. As the spermatid elongates, a **tail,** also called the *flagellum,* forms from the organized microtubules within the cell. The tail is attached to a **midpiece** or *neck* region containing mitochondria and a centriole. These mitochondria provide the energy to move the tail.

Although the sperm look mature, they do not yet have all of the characteristics needed to successfully travel through the female reproductive tract and fertilize an oocyte. The sperm must leave the seminiferous tubule through a network of ducts (described

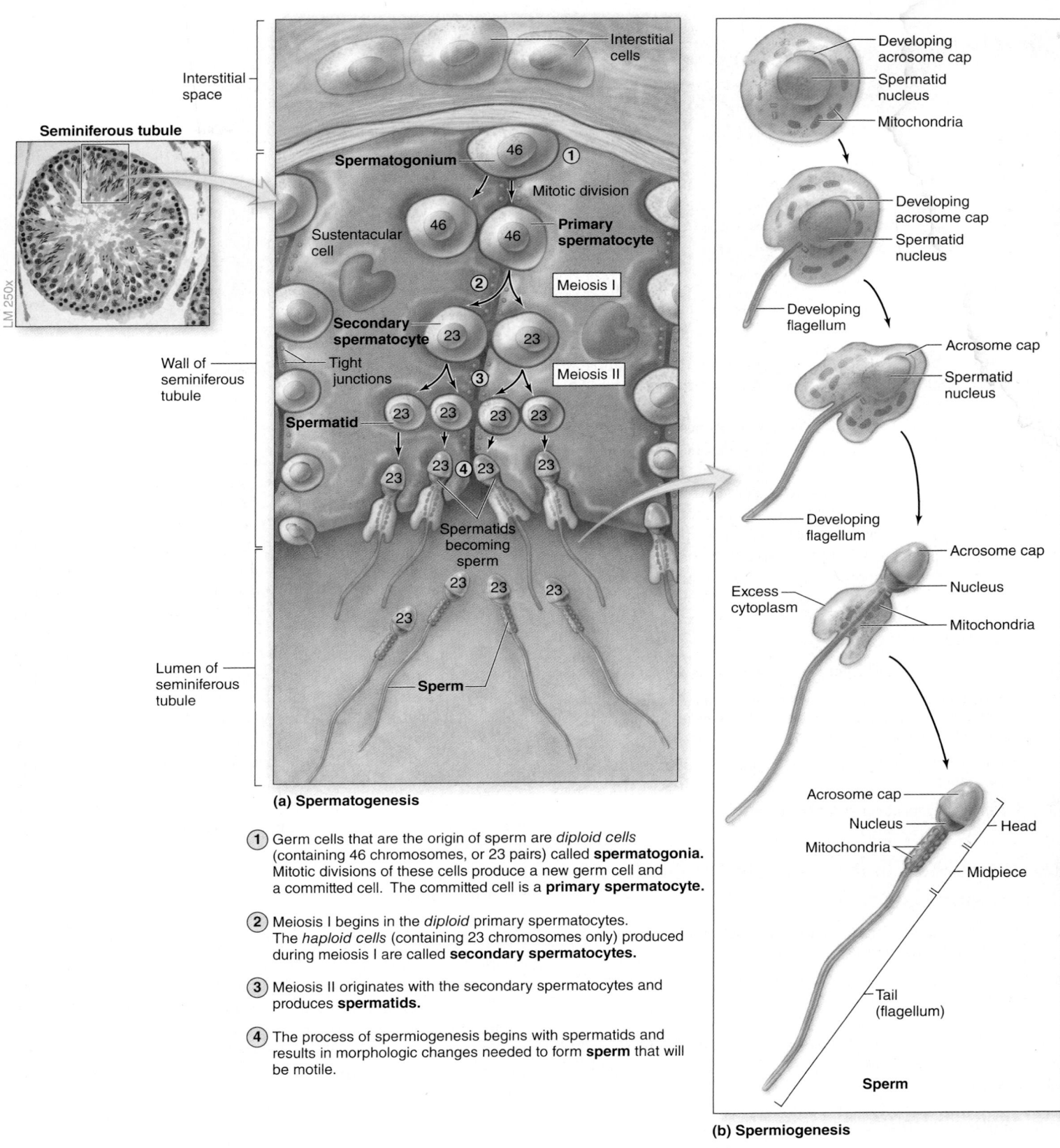

(a) Spermatogenesis

(b) Spermiogenesis

(1) Germ cells that are the origin of sperm are *diploid cells* (containing 46 chromosomes, or 23 pairs) called **spermatogonia.** Mitotic divisions of these cells produce a new germ cell and a committed cell. The committed cell is a **primary spermatocyte.**

(2) Meiosis I begins in the *diploid* primary spermatocytes. The *haploid cells* (containing 23 chromosomes only) produced during meiosis I are called **secondary spermatocytes.**

(3) Meiosis II originates with the secondary spermatocytes and produces **spermatids.**

(4) The process of spermiogenesis begins with spermatids and results in morphologic changes needed to form **sperm** that will be motile.

Figure 28.18 Spermatogenesis and Spermiogenesis. (*a*) The processes of spermatogenesis and spermiogenesis take place within the wall of the seminiferous tubule. (*b*) Structural changes occur during spermiogenesis as a sperm forms from a spermatid. APR

Table 28.6	Stages of Spermatogenesis		
Cell Type	Number of Chromosomes	Haploid or Diploid	Action
Spermatogonium	23 pairs (46)	Diploid	Divides by mitosis to produce a new spermatogonium and a primary spermatocyte
Primary spermatocyte	23 pairs (46)	Diploid	Completes meiosis I to produce secondary spermatocytes
Secondary spermatocyte	23 only	Haploid	Completes meiosis II to produce spermatids
Spermatid	23 only	Haploid	Undergoes spermiogenesis, where most of its cytoplasm is shed and a midpiece, tail, and head form
Spermatozoon (sperm)	23 only	Haploid	Leaves seminiferous tubule and matures in epididymis

next) and reside in the epididymis for a period of time in order to become fully motile. **Table 28.6** summarizes the stages of spermatogenesis.

Note that both female and male gametogenesis events share some similarities and have some notable differences. Both female and male gametes undergo meiosis, but only a single viable secondary oocyte is produced, whereas four sperm are produced. All female oocytes have initiated (and then become arrested in) meiosis prior to the female being born. In contrast, male spermatogonia do not undergo spermatogenesis until puberty, but after this time they can divide and produce spermatocytes throughout a male's adult lifetime.

 WHAT DID YOU LEARN?

26. What are the major cell types in the seminiferous tubules?

27. What hormones are produced by the interstitial cells and the sustentacular cells, and how do these hormones affect the hypothalamus and anterior pituitary?

28. How does a spermatogonium divide to produce spermatozoa? Give specific steps.

29. What main events occur in spermiogenesis?

28.4c Duct System in the Male Reproductive Tract

LEARNING OBJECTIVES

5. Explain the function of each component of the ducts associated with the male reproductive system.

6. Trace the pathway that sperm travel through the testes and duct system.

The left and right testes each have their own set of ducts. These ducts store and transport sperm as they mature and pass out of the male body (**figure 28.19**).

Ducts Within the Testis

The **rete** (rē′tē; net) **testis** is a meshwork of interconnected channels in the mediastinum testis that receive sperm from the seminiferous tubules. The rete testis is lined by simple cuboidal epithelium with short microvilli covering its luminal surface. The channels of the rete testis merge to form the efferent ductules (see figure 28.16a).

Approximately 12 to 15 **efferent ductules** (duk′tūl) connect the rete testis to the epididymis. They are lined with both ciliated columnar epithelia that gently propel the sperm toward the epididymis and nonciliated columnar epithelia that absorb excess fluid secreted by

the seminiferous tubules. The efferent ductules drain into the epididymis.

Epididymis

The **epididymis** (ep-i-did′i-mis; pl., *epididymides*; *epi* = upon, *didymis* = twin) is a comma-shaped structure composed of an internal duct and an external covering of connective tissue. Its **head** lies on the superior surface of the testis, while the **body** and **tail** are on the posterior surface of the testis (see figure 28.16a). Internally, the epididymis contains a long, convoluted **duct of the epididymis,** which is approximately 4 to 5 meters in length and lined with pseudostratified columnar epithelium that contains stereocilia (long microvilli) (figure 28.19d).

The epididymis stores sperm until they are fully mature and capable of being motile. Just as a newborn has the superficial anatomic characteristics of an adult, but cannot move as an adult, the sperm that first enter the epididymis look like mature sperm but can't move like mature sperm. If they are expelled too soon, they lack the ability to be motile, which is necessary to travel through the female reproductive tract and fertilize a secondary oocyte. If sperm are not ejected from the male reproductive system in a timely manner, the old sperm degenerate and are resorbed by cells lining the duct of the epididymis.

Ductus Deferens

When sperm leave the epididymis, they enter the **ductus deferens** (děf′er-ens; carry away), also called the *vas deferens*. The ductus deferens is a thick-walled tube that travels within the spermatic cord, through the inguinal canal (figure 28.15), and then within the pelvic cavity before it nears the prostate gland (figure 28.19a). The ductus deferens wall is composed of an inner **mucosa** (lined by a pseudostratified ciliated columnar epithelium), a middle **muscularis,** and an outer **adventitia** (figure 28.19c). The muscularis contains three layers of smooth muscle: an inner longitudinal, middle circular, and outer longitudinal layer. Contraction of the muscularis is necessary to move sperm through the ductus deferens, since sperm do not exhibit motility until they are ejaculated from the penis.

When the ductus deferens travels through the inguinal canal and enters the pelvic cavity, it separates from the other spermatic cord components and extends posteriorly along the superolateral surface of the bladder. It then travels inferiorly and terminates close to the region where the bladder and prostate gland meet. As the ductus deferens approaches the superoposterior edge of the prostate gland, it enlarges and forms the **ampulla** of the ductus deferens (figure 28.19a). The ampulla of the ductus deferens

Urinary bladder

Ureter

Ampulla

Seminal vesicle

Ejaculatory duct

Prostate gland

Prostatic urethra

Bulbourethral gland

Urogenital diaphragm

Ductus deferens

Epididymis

Testis

Penis

LM 80x

Tubuloalveolar glands in prostate gland

(b) Prostate gland

Muscularis

Adventitia

Mucosa

LM 32x

(c) Ductus deferens

Membranous urethra

Bulb

Crus

Corpus cavernosum

Corpus spongiosum

Spongy urethra

Glans

Section of duct of epididymis

Sperm in lumen of duct of epididymis

LM 50x

(d) Epididymis

(a) Posterior view

Figure 28.19 Duct System and Accessory Glands in Male Reproductive Tract. (*a*) A posterior view depicts the structural components of the male reproductive ducts and accessory glands. Micrographs show cross sections through the (*b*) prostate gland, (*c*) ductus deferens, and (*d*) epididymis. AP|R

unites with the proximal region of the seminal vesicle to form the terminal portion of the reproductive duct system, called the ejaculatory duct.

Ejaculatory Duct

Each **ejaculatory duct** is between 1 and 2 centimeters long. The epithelium of the ejaculatory duct is a pseudostratified ciliated columnar epithelium. The ejaculatory duct conducts sperm (from the ductus deferens) and a component of seminal fluid (from the seminal vesicle) toward the urethra. Each ejaculatory duct opens into the prostatic urethra.

Urethra

The **urethra** transports semen from both ejaculatory ducts to the outside of the body. Recall from section 24.8b that the urethra is subdivided into a **prostatic** (pros-tat′ik) **urethra** that extends from the bladder through the prostate gland, a **membranous urethra** that continues through the urogenital diaphragm, and a **spongy urethra** that extends through the penis.

 WHAT DID YOU LEARN?

 What is the sequence of ducts through which male gametes pass?

28.4d Accessory Glands and Semen Production

LEARNING OBJECTIVES

7. Describe the anatomy and function of the accessory glands.

8. Compare and contrast sperm, seminal fluid, and semen.

9. List the major components of semen and which accessory gland produces each component.

Recall from earlier in this chapter that the vagina has a highly acidic environment to prevent bacterial growth. Sperm cannot survive in this type of environment, so an alkaline secretion called **seminal** (sem'i-nal) **fluid** is needed to neutralize the acidity of the vagina. In addition, as the sperm travel through the female reproductive tract (a process that can take hours to several days), they are nourished by nutrients within the seminal fluid. The components of seminal fluid are produced by the accessory glands that include the seminal vesicles, the prostate gland, and the bulbourethral glands.

Seminal Vesicles

The paired **seminal vesicles** are located on the posterior surface of the urinary bladder lateral to the ampulla of the ductus deferens. Each seminal vesicle is an elongated, hollow organ approximately 5 to 8 centimeters long. The wall of each vesicle contains mucosal folds of pseudostratified columnar epithelium. The medial (proximal) portion of the seminal vesicle merges with a ductus deferens to form the ejaculatory duct.

The seminal vesicles secrete a viscous, whitish-yellow, alkaline fluid containing both fructose and prostaglandins. Fructose nourishes the sperm as they travel through the female reproductive tract. Prostaglandins are hormonelike substances that promote the widening and slight dilation of the external os of the cervix, which facilitates sperm entry into the uterus.

Prostate Gland

The **prostate** (pros'tāt; one who stands before) **gland** is a compact, encapsulated organ that weighs about 20 grams and is shaped like a walnut, measuring approximately 2 cm by 3 cm by 4 cm. It is located immediately inferior to the bladder. The prostate gland includes submucosal glands that produce mucin and more than 30 tubuloalveolar glands that open directly through numerous ducts into the prostatic urethra (figure 28.19b). Together, this aggregate of secretory structures contributes a component to the seminal fluid.

The prostate gland secretes a slightly milky fluid that is weakly acidic and rich in citric acid, seminalplasmin, and **prostate-specific antigen (PSA).** The citric acid is a nutrient for sperm health, the seminalplasmin is an antibiotic that combats urinary tract infections in the male, and the PSA acts as an enzyme to help liquify semen following ejaculation. (Note that the slightly acidic prostate secretion of the prostate is not sufficient to cause seminal fluid to be acidic, and thus seminal fluid is still alkaline and functions to neutralize the acidity of the vagina.)

Bulbourethral Glands

Paired, pea-shaped **bulbourethral** (bŭl'bō-ū-rē'thrăl) **glands** (or *Cowper glands*) are located within the urogenital diaphragm on each side of the membranous urethra (figure 28.19a; see also figure 28.14). Each gland has a short duct that projects into the bulb (base) of the penis and enters the spongy urethra. Bulbourethral glands are tubuloalveolar glands that have a simple columnar and pseudostratified columnar epithelium. Their secretory product is a clear, viscous mucin that forms mucus. As a component of the seminal fluid, this mucus protects the urethra and serves as a lubricant during sexual intercourse.

Semen

Seminal fluid from the accessory glands combines with sperm from the testes to make up **semen** (sē'men; seed). When released during intercourse, semen is called **ejaculate** (ē-jak'ū-lāt), and it normally measures about 3 to 5 milliliters in volume and contains approximately 200 to 500 million spermatozoa. In a sexually active male, the average transit time of human spermatozoa—from their release into the lumen of the seminiferous tubules, passage through the duct system, and presence in the ejaculate—is about 2 weeks. Since semen is composed primarily of seminal fluid, a male who is very

INTEGRATE

CLINICAL VIEW

Benign Prostatic Hyperplasia and Prostate Cancer

Benign prostatic hyperplasia (BPH) is a noncancerous enlargement of the prostate gland. BPH is a common disorder in older men, and hormonal changes in aging males are the cause of the enlargement.

In BPH, large nodules form within the prostate and compress the prostatic urethra. Thus, the patient has difficulty starting and stopping a stream of urine, and often complains of **nocturia** (frequent urinating at night), **polyuria** (more frequent urination), and **dysuria** (painful urination). Some drug regimens help inhibit hormones that cause prostate enlargement, but when medications are no longer effective, surgical removal of the prostatic enlargement is indicated. The most commonly performed surgical procedure is called a **TURP (transurethral resection of the prostate),** in which an instrument called a **resectoscope** (rē-sek'tō-skōp) is inserted into the urethra to cut away the problematic enlargement.

Prostate cancer is one of the most common malignancies among men over 50, and the risk of developing it increases with age. Prostate cancer forms hard, solid nodules, most often in the posterior part of the prostate gland. Early stages of the cancer are generally asymptomatic, but as it progresses, urinary symptoms may develop.

Benign prostatic hyperplasia

Prostate cancer

A very effective screening tool is a **digital rectal exam,** whereby a physician inserts a gloved finger into the rectum and palpates adjacent structures (including the prostate gland). Additionally, most physicals for men over the age of 50 now include a test for prostate-specific antigen (PSA) in the blood. An elevated PSA level may indicate either benign prostatic hyperplasia or prostate cancer.

For earlier stages of prostate cancer, radiation therapy may be beneficial—either traditional external-beam radiation or **interstitial radiotherapy,** in which radioactive palladium or iodine "seeds" are permanently implanted in the prostate. For patients with a more aggressive cancer, the entire prostate and some surrounding structures are surgically removed, a procedure called a **radical prostatectomy.**

active sexually may have a reduced sperm count because there are fewer sperm to be released from the epididymis; however, the total semen volume remains close to normal for that individual.

WHAT DO YOU THINK?

4 If a man has a vasectomy, is he still able to produce sperm? If so, what happens to those sperm? How is the composition of semen changed in an individual who has had a vasectomy?

WHAT DID YOU LEARN?

31 What are the specific functions of the accessory glands?

32 How is seminal fluid different from semen?

28.4e Penis

LEARNING OBJECTIVE

10. Describe the structure and functions of the penis.

The **penis** (pē′nis; tail) and the scrotum form the external genitalia in males **(figure 28.20)**. Internally, the attached portion of the penis is the **root,** which is dilated internal to the body surface, form-

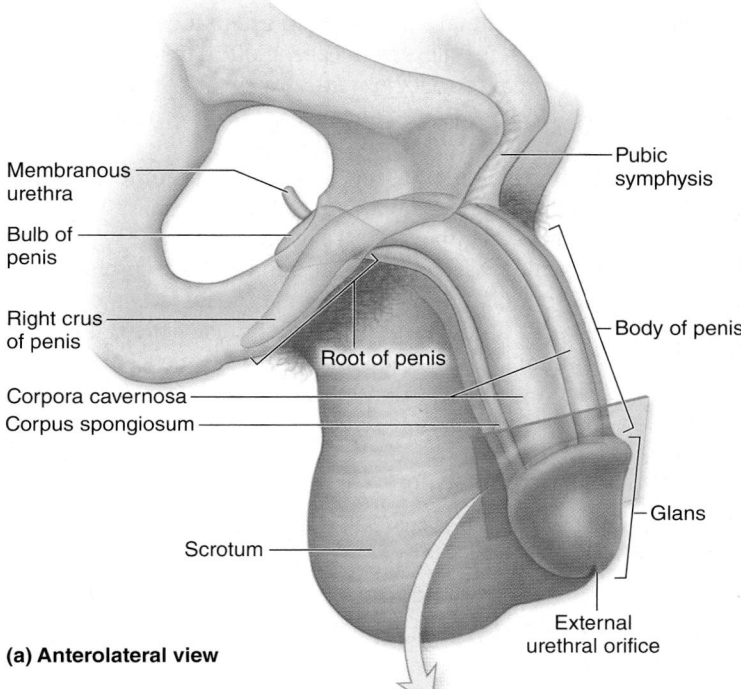

(a) Anterolateral view

Membranous urethra —
Bulb of penis —
Right crus of penis —
Corpora cavernosa —
Corpus spongiosum —
Scrotum —
Pubic symphysis —
Root of penis —
Body of penis —
Glans —
External urethral orifice —

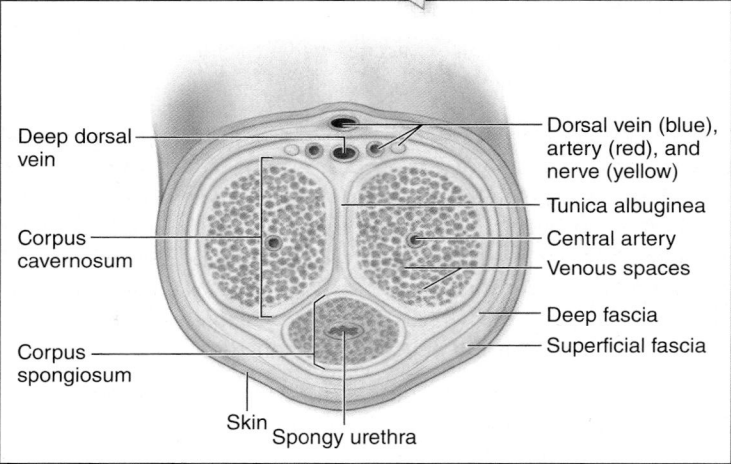

(b) Cross section

Deep dorsal vein —
Corpus cavernosum —
Corpus spongiosum —
Dorsal vein (blue), artery (red), and nerve (yellow) —
Tunica albuginea —
Central artery —
Venous spaces —
Deep fascia —
Superficial fascia —
Skin —
Spongy urethra —

Prepuce

(c) Uncircumcised penis

ing both the **bulb** and the **crus** of the penis. The bulb attaches the penis to the bulbospongiosus muscle in the urogenital triangle, and the crus attaches the penis to the pubic arch. The **body,** or *shaft,* of the penis is the elongated, movable portion. The tip of the penis is called the **glans,** and it contains the **external urethral orifice.** The skin of the penis is thin and elastic. At the distal end of the penis, the skin is attached to the raised edge of the glans and forms a circular fold called the **prepuce,** or *foreskin.*

Within the shaft of the penis are three cylindrical erectile bodies. The paired **corpora cavernosa** (kav′er-nō-sa′; sing., *corpus cavernosum; caverna* = grotto) are located dorsolaterally. Ventral to them in the midline is the single **corpus spongiosum** (spŭn′jē-ō-sŭm), which contains the spongy urethra. Each corpus cavernosum terminates in the shaft of the penis, while the corpus spongiosum continues within the glans. The erectile bodies are ensheathed by the **tunica albuginea**, which also provides an attachment to the skin over the shaft of the penis.

WHAT DID YOU LEARN?

33 What are the similarities and differences between the corpora cavernosa and the corpus spongiosum of the penis?

Figure 28.20 Anatomy of the Penis. (*a*) An anterolateral view of the penis. The dorsum of the penis faces anteriorly, while the ventral surface is adjacent to the scrotum. (*b*) A diagrammatic, cross section shows the arrangement of the erectile bodies. (*c*) An uncircumcised penis.

28.4f Male Sexual Response

⟩✓⟨ LEARNING OBJECTIVES

11. Compare and contrast the processes of erection and ejaculation.

12. Explain how the male sexual response (and ejaculation) is elicited.

The male sexual response begins with an excitement phase. The erectile bodies of the penis are composed of a complex network of **venous spaces** surrounding a central artery. During sexual excitement, blood enters the erectile bodies and fills the venous spaces. As these venous spaces become engorged with blood, the erectile bodies become rigid, a process called **erection** (ē-rek′shŭn; *erecto* = to set up). The rigid erectile bodies compress the veins that drain blood away from the venous spaces. Thus, the spaces fill with blood, but the blood cannot leave the erectile bodies until the sexual excitement ceases. Parasympathetic innervation (through the pelvic splanchnic nerves; see section 15.3b) is responsible for increased blood flow and thus the erection of the penis. Specifically, the parasympathetic innervation facilitates local release of nitric oxide (NO) into the tissues, which assists with erection. (Recall from section 20.3b that NO is a vasodilator.) Near the end of the excitement phase but before orgasm, increases occur in heart rate, blood pressure, and respiratory rate.

Orgasm refers to the time period during which there are intense feelings of pleasure, a feeling of a release of tension, and expulsion of semen. In the beginning phases of orgasm, the ductus deferens undergoes peristalsis and moves the sperm towards the urethra. Later in this phase, the accessory glands secrete their components of seminal fluid, which combine with the sperm to form semen. The internal urethral sphincter of the urinary bladder contracts to ensure that no urine enters the urethra at this time. **Ejaculation** (ē-jak-ū-lā′shŭn; *eiaculatus* = to shoot out) typically occurs at the ending stage of an orgasm and is the process by which semen is expelled from the penis with the help of rhythmic contractions of the smooth muscle in the wall of the urethra. Sympathetic innervation (from the lumbar splanchnic nerves; see section 15.4a) is responsible for ejaculation.

Although in most body systems sympathetic and parasympathetic innervation tend to perform opposite functions, the male reproductive system is an exception. Here, parasympathetic innervation is necessary to achieve an erection, while sympathetic innervation promotes ejaculation. Relaxation of autonomic activity after sexual excitement reduces blood flow to the erectile bodies and shunts most of the blood to other veins, thereby returning the penis to its flaccid condition.

Following an orgasm, there is a resolution phase, which is marked by feelings of intense relaxation. The sympathetic division is stimulated to contract the central artery of the penis and contract small muscles around the erectile tissue, which serves to expel the engorged blood. Gradually, the penis becomes soft and flaccid again. Resolution in men is followed by a **refractory period,** during which the man cannot attain another erection. This period may last for many minutes or for hours. This refractory period becomes longer as men age. (Women, in contrast, have no refractory period and thus have the potential to experience multiple orgasms in a single sexual experience.)

⟩♡⟨ WHAT DID YOU LEARN?

34 How do erection and ejaculation differ?

35 How do both parasympathetic and sympathetic innervation contribute to penile function during sexual arousal?

28.5 Development and Aging of the Female and Male Reproductive Systems

The female and male reproductive structures originate from the same basic embryonic primordia, but they differentiate into either female or male structures, depending upon the molecular signals the primordia receive. To better explain this process, we must first distinguish between the genetic and phenotypic sex of an individual.

28.5a Genetic versus Phenotypic Sex

⟩✓⟨ LEARNING OBJECTIVES

1. Compare and contrast genetic versus phenotypic sex.

2. List the gene(s) responsible for producing a phenotypic male.

Genetic sex is also called *genotypic sex,* and it refers to the sex of an individual based on the sex chromosomes inherited. An individual with two X chromosomes is a genetic female, whereas an individual with one X and one Y chromosome is a genetic male. Genetic sex is determined at fertilization.

In contrast, **phenotypic** (fē′nō-tip-ik, fen′ō-) **sex** refers to the appearance of an individual's internal and external genitalia. A person with ovaries and female external genitalia (labia) is a phenotypic female, whereas a person with testes and male external genitalia (penis, scrotum) is a phenotypic male. Phenotypic sex starts to become apparent after the seventh week of development.

How does the primordial tissue know whether to develop into female reproductive organs or male reproductive organs? In males, the **sex-determining region Y (SRY) gene** is located within the larger testis-determining factor (TDF) region on the Y chromosome. If the Y chromosome is present and the *SRY* gene is appropriately expressed, this gene produces proteins to stimulate the production of androgens that initiate male phenotypic development. If a Y chromosome is absent, or if the Y chromosome is either lacking or has an abnormal *SRY* gene, a female phenotypic sex results.

⟩♡⟨ WHAT DID YOU LEARN?

36 What gene normally present on the Y chromosome is responsible for a male phenotypic sex?

28.5b Formation of Indifferent Gonads and Genital Ducts

⟩✓⟨ LEARNING OBJECTIVE

3. Describe what anatomic structures are formed from the mesonephric and paramesonephric ducts.

Early in the fifth week of embryonic development, paired **genital ridges,** also called *gonadal ridges,* form from **intermediate mesoderm.** The genital ridges will form the gonads. These longitudinal ridges are medial to the developing kidneys at about the level of the tenth thoracic vertebra (**figure 28.21**, *top*). Between weeks 5 and 6, primordial **germ cells** migrate from the yolk sac to the genital ridges. These germ cells will form the future gametes (either oocytes or sperm). Shortly thereafter, two sets of duct systems are formed.

- The **mesonephric** (mez-ō-nef′rik) **ducts,** also known as *Wolffian ducts,* form most of the male duct system.

Figure 28.21 Embryonic Development of the Female and Male Reproductive Tracts. Through the first 6 weeks of development, the embryo is termed "sexually indifferent." Thereafter, genetic expression determines sex differentiation.

The mesonephric ducts also connect the mesonephros to the developing urinary bladder.

- The **paramesonephric ducts,** or *Müllerian ducts,* form most of the female duct system, including the uterine tubes, uterus, and superior part of the vagina. These ducts appear lateral to the mesonephric ducts.

All human embryos develop both duct systems, but only one of the duct systems remains in the fetus. If the embryo is female, the paramesonephric ducts develop, and the mesonephric ducts degenerate. If the embryo is male, the mesonephric ducts grow and differentiate into male reproductive structures, while the paramesonephric ducts degenerate.

 WHAT DID YOU LEARN?

37 Which duct system persists in female embryos? In male embryos?

28.5c Internal Genitalia Development

✓ **LEARNING OBJECTIVES**

4. Describe the events that cause the female internal reproductive organs to develop.
5. Name the hormone responsible for inducing paramesonephric duct degeneration, and identify the cells responsible for secreting this hormone.

The development of the female internal reproductive structures is traced in figure 28.21, *left.* Because no SRY proteins are produced in the developing female, the mesonephric ducts degenerate. Between weeks 8 and 20 of development, the paramesonephric ducts develop and differentiate. The caudal (inferior) ends of the paramesonephric ducts fuse, forming the uterus and the superior part of the vagina. The cranial (superior) parts of the paramesonephric ducts remain separate and form two uterine tubes. The remaining inferior part of the vagina is formed from the urogenital sinus, which also forms the urinary bladder and urethra.

By about week 7 of development in the male, the *SRY* gene on the Y chromosome begins influencing the indifferent gonad to become a testis, which then forms sustentacular cells and interstitial cells. Once the sustentacular cells form, they begin secreting **anti-Müllerian hormone (AMH)** (also known as *Müllerian inhibiting substance*), which inhibits the development of the paramesonephric ducts (see figure 28.21, *right*). These paramesonephric ducts degenerate, and between weeks 8 and 12, the mesonephric ducts begin to form the male duct system—efferent ductules, epididymides, vasa deferens, seminal vesicles, and ejaculatory ducts.

The prostate and bulbourethral glands do not form from the mesonephric ducts. Instead, they begin to form as endodermal "buds" or outgrowths of the developing urethra between weeks 10 and 13. As the prostate gland and bulbourethral glands develop, they incorporate mesoderm into their structures as well.

Finally, note that the indifferent gonad originates near the level of the T_{10} vertebra. Throughout prenatal development, the developing testis descends inferiorly from the abdominal region toward the developing scrotum. A thin band of connective tissue called the **gubernaculum** (gū′ber-nak′ū-lŭm; helm) attaches to the testis and assists the testis descent from the abdomen, through the developing inguinal canal, to its placement in the scrotum (not shown in figure 28.21). As the embryo grows (but the gubernaculums remains the same length), the testis is passively pulled into the scrotum. This process is slow, beginning in the third month and not completed until the ninth month. It is common for premature male babies to have undescended testes because they were born before the testes had fully descended into the scrotum. Their testes usually descend shortly after birth.

 WHAT DID YOU LEARN?

38 What is the fate of the paramesonephric ducts in a female embryo?

39 What hormone do the sustentacular cells secrete in the male embryo, and how does this affect internal genitalia development?

28.5d External Genitalia Development

 LEARNING OBJECTIVE

6. List the common primordial external genitalia structures, and compare their development in females and males.

As with the internal genitalia, both female and male external genitalia develop from the same primordial structures **(figure 28.22)**. By the sixth week of development, the following external structures are seen:

- The **urogenital folds** (or *urethral folds*) are paired, elevated structures on either side of the urogenital membrane, a thin partition separating the urogenital sinus from the outside of the body.

INTEGRATE

CLINICAL VIEW

Intersex Conditions (Disorders of Sex Development)

Intersex conditions, or *disorders of sex development,* refer to a series of disorders where there is a discrepancy between a person's genotype (and gonad development) and their external genitalia. (The previous term to describe this condition is *hermaphrodite* (her-maf′rō-dīt), which is derived from the Greek name Hermaphroditus, the mythological son of the Greek god Hermes and the goddess Aphrodite.) **True gonadal intersex,** also known as *true hermaphroditism,* refers to an individual with both ovarian and testicular structures (which typically does not have the potential for fertility) and ambiguous (or female) external genitalia. The person may be a genetic male (XY) or a genetic female (XX). True hermaphroditism is very rare.

Pseudohermaphroditism (sū′dō-her-maf′rō-dī-tizm; *pseudes* = false) refers to an individual whose genetic sex and phenotypic sex do not match. A **46 XY intersex** individual, previously known as a *male pseudohermaphrodite,* is a genetic male (XY) whose external genitalia resemble those of a female (female phenotypic sex). Male pseudohermaphroditism usually results from either a reduction or lack of male hormones (e.g., testosterone) during development.

A **46 XX intersex** individual, previously known as a *female pseudohermaphrodite,* is a genetic female (XX) with external genitalia that resemble those of a male (male phenotypic sex). The clitoris enlarges to look like a small penis, and the two labia may become partially fused to resemble a scrotum. Female pseudohermaphroditism may result if the female fetus is exposed to excessive androgens (e.g., if the pregnant mother was given certain medications to help prevent miscarriage). More commonly, it is caused by **congenital adrenal hyperplasia,** in which the fetus's adrenal glands produce excessive amounts of androgens.

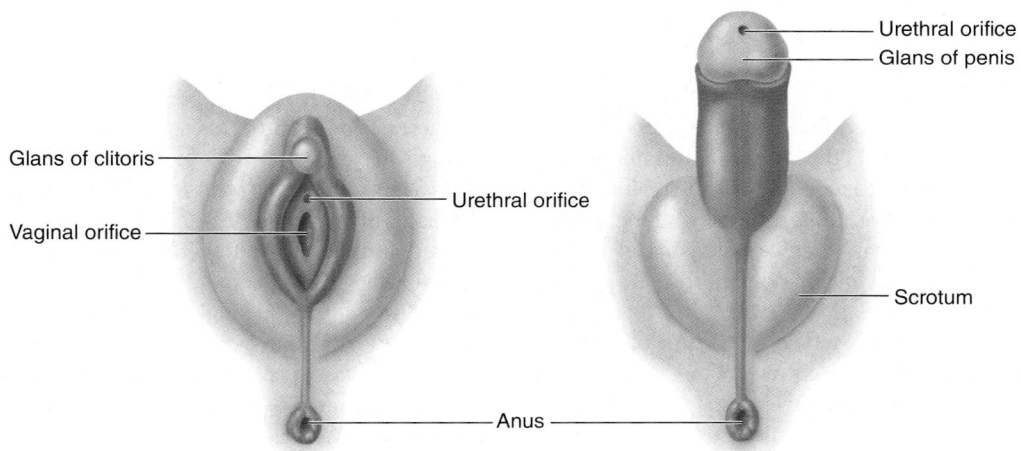

(a) Week 6

Female

Developing clitoris

Labia minora

Labia majora

Anus

Male

Developing glans of penis

Anus

(b) Week 12: Urogenital folds begin to fuse in the male

Glans of clitoris

Vaginal orifice

Urethral orifice

Anus

Urethral orifice

Glans of penis

Scrotum

Anus

(c) Week 20: External genitalia well differentiated

Genital tubercle

Urogenital fold

Labioscrotal swelling

Sexually indifferent stage

Figure 28.22 Development of External Genitalia. (*a*) At 6 weeks of development, the external genitalia are undifferentiated. (*b*) By 12 weeks, the urogenital folds begin to fuse in the male and remain open in the female. (*c*) By 20 weeks, external genitalia are well differentiated.

- The **genital tubercle** is a rounded structure anterior to the urogenital folds.
- The **labioscrotal swellings** (or *genital swellings*) are paired elevated structures lateral to the urethral folds.

The external genitalia appear very similar in both females and males until about week 12 of development: They do not become clearly differentiated until about week 20. In the absence of testosterone, female external genitalia develop. The genital tubercle becomes the clitoris. The urogenital folds do not fuse, but become the labia minora. Finally, the labioscrotal folds also remain unfused and become the labia majora.

Production and circulation of testosterone in the male cause the primitive external structures to differentiate. The genital tubercle enlarges and elongates, forming the glans of the penis and part of the dorsal side of the penis. The urogenital folds grow and fuse around the developing urethra and form the ventral side of the penis. Finally, the labioscrotal swellings fuse at the midline, forming the scrotum.

WHAT DID YOU LEARN?

40 What causes the differentiation of tissues into male structures?

28.5e Puberty

Recall that both the female and male reproductive systems are primarily nonfunctional and "dormant" until puberty. **Puberty** (pū′ber-tē; *puber* = grown up) is a period in adolescence where the reproductive organs become fully functional and the external sex characteristics become more prominent, such as breast enlargement in females and pubic hair in both sexes. The timing of puberty may be affected by genetics, environmental factors, and overall health of the individual.

Puberty is initiated when the hypothalamus begins secreting GnRH, which stimulates the anterior pituitary to release the gonadotropins FSH and LH). Prior to puberty, FSH and LH are virtually nonexistent in girls and boys. As levels of FSH and LH increase, the gonads produce significant levels of sex hormones and start the processes of gamete maturation and sexual maturation.

The earliest signs of puberty are the development of breast buds in girls and the appearance of pubic and axillary hair in both boys and girls. Menarche is one of the later events of puberty, and tends to occur about 2 years after the first signs appear. Boys experience growth in the testicles and penis, and they may begin to get erections at this time and experience ejaculations during the night. Male voices start to change and become lower in pitch, as the increase in testosterone causes rapid growth of the laryngeal structures.

The timing of puberty differs between females and males and varies among different populations. Girls generally reach puberty about 2 years prior to boys. African American girls tend to experience puberty about 1 year earlier than their Caucasian counterparts. Additionally, children in better economic conditions experience puberty earlier than children who are underprivileged, presumably because the former group experience better nutrition and heath care. Over the past 100 years, the age of puberty has dropped, so current-day children are starting puberty about 2 years earlier than children in the past. Currently, puberty typically begins between ages 8 and 12 for girls and between ages 9 and 14 for boys (although puberty may occur much later in either population).

Precocious puberty is apparent when the signs of puberty develop much earlier than normal—such as at the ages of 7 to 8 for girls, or age 9 for boys. Precocious puberty may be idiopathic (no known cause) or due to brain injury or infection, or a tumor in the pituitary or gonads. If a child experiences signs of precocious puberty, he or she should be taken to a pediatrician for an evaluation to see if any treatment is needed.

💡 WHAT DID YOU LEARN?

41 What factors affect the age that menarche first occurs?

28.5f Menopause and Male Climacteric

After reaching sexual maturity, the female and male reproductive systems exhibit marked differences in their response to aging.

Female Menopause

Gametes typically stop maturing in females by their 40s or 50s, and menopause occurs. The time when a woman is nearing menopause is called **perimenopause.** During perimenopause, estrogen levels begin to drop, and a woman may experience irregular periods, skip some periods, or have very light periods. Recall that when a woman has stopped having monthly menstrual cycles for 1 year and is not pregnant, she is said to be in **menopause** (men′ō pawz; *pauses* = cessation). The age at normal onset of menopause varies considerably, but typically is between 45 and 55 years. A reduction in hormone production that accompanies menopause causes some atrophy of the reproductive organs and the breasts. The vaginal wall thickness decreases, as do glandular secretions for maintaining a moist, lubricated lining. The uterus shrinks and atrophies, becoming much smaller than it was before puberty. The woman's endometrial lining does not grow, and she no longer has a menstrual period.

The lack of significant amounts of estrogen and progesterone in a menopausal woman also affects other organs and body systems. Women may experience "hot flashes," in which their bodies perceive periodic elevations in body temperature, and they may develop thinning scalp hair and an increase in facial hair. Menopausal women are at greater risk for osteoporosis and heart disease due to the drop in estrogen and progesterone levels.

Formerly, **hormone replacement therapy (HRT)** in the form of estrogen and progesterone supplements was routinely offered to menopausal women to help diminish these symptoms and risks. However, recent studies indicate that the risks associated with HRT (e.g., increased risk of breast cancer and lack of protection against heart disease) may outweigh the benefits in older women. As a result, many physicians have stopped prescribing HRT for menopausal symptoms, although some women still choose to receive HRT if their symptoms are severe.

Male Climacteric

In contrast to females, males do not experience the relatively abrupt change in reproductive system function that females do. A slight decrease in the size of the testes parallels a reduction in the size of the seminiferous tubules and the number of interstitial cells. As a consequence of the reduced number of interstitial cells, decreased testosterone levels in men in their 50s signal a change called the **male climacteric** (klī-mak′ter-ik, klī-mak-ter′ik). Most men experience few symptoms, but some may experience mood swings, decreased sex drive, and hot flashes and sweating episodes. However, men generally do not stop producing gametes as women do following menopause. Additionally, while men experience a reduction in testosterone levels, this reduction is gradual and not as steep or sudden as the estrogen and progesterone drop seen in menopausal women.

Most men experience prostate enlargement (either benign or cancerous) as they age. This prostate enlargement can interfere with sexual and urinary functions. Also associated with aging are **erectile dysfunction** and **impotence,** which refer to the inability to achieve or maintain an erection. Besides aging, other risk factors for this condition include heart disease, diabetes, smoking, and prior prostate surgery. Recently, many drugs (e.g., sildenafil [Viagra]) have entered the market that treat erectile dysfunction by prolonging vasodilation of the penile arteries and thus inhibit relaxation of the erectile bodies.

💡 WHAT DID YOU LEARN?

42 How do the female and male reproductive systems differ with respect to aging?

CHAPTER SUMMARY

28.1 Overview of Female and Male Reproductive Systems 1087

- The female and male reproductive systems function to propogate the next generation.

28.1a Common Elements of the Two Systems 1087

- Both reproductive systems have gonads that produce gametes (sex cells) and sex hormones and a duct system to transport the gametes.

28.1b Sexual Maturation in Females and Males 1087

- Sexual maturation begins at puberty when the hypothalamus begins secreting gonadotropin-releasing hormone (GnRH). This hormone stimulates the anterior pituitary to release follicle-stimulating hormone (FSH) and luteinizing hormone (LH).
- FSH and LH stimulate the gonads to release sex hormones and produce gametes.

28.1c Anatomy of the Perineum 1087

- The perineum is a diamond-shaped area between the thighs that houses the urogenital and anal triangles.

28.2 Gametogenesis

- Gametogenesis is the process of forming sex cells.

28.2a A Brief Review of Heredity 1088

- Humans have 22 pairs of autosomes and 1 pair of sex chromosomes in the body's diploid cells. The sex chromosomes, termed X and Y, determine gender: XX is female, and XY is male.
- The gametes, or sex cells, are haploid cells; they contain 22 chromosomes and 1 sex chromosome, not pairs of chromosomes. When gametes unite in fertilization, the diploid condition is restored.

28.2b An Overview of Meiosis 1089

- Meiosis is sex cell division that produces haploid gametes from diploid parent cells.
- Meiosis involves two rounds of division: meiosis I and meiosis II. As a result of these two rounds of division, one diploid cell gives rise to four haploid cells.

28.2c Meiosis I: Reduction Division 1090

- Chromosomes become replicated prior to meiosis I so that each chromosome consists of two sister chromatids held together by a single centromere.
- The pairs of homologous chromosomes separate during meiosis I. The stages are prophase I, metaphase I, anaphase I, and telophase I and cytokinesis.
- Crossing over and exchange between homologous chromosomes occurs in prophase I and helps produce gametes that are genetically different from the parent cell.

28.2d Meiosis II: Separation of Sister Chromatids 1092

- The replicated sister chromatids separate in meiosis II. The stages are prophase II, metaphase II, anaphase II, and telophase II and cytokinesis.
- The result of the two sequences of meiosis is that four haploid cells are produced that may go on to form gametes.

28.3 Female Reproductive System 1093

- Female internal reproductive organs include paired ovaries and uterine tubes, a uterus, and a vagina.

28.3a Ovaries 1094

- The cortex of the ovary houses ovarian follicles that consist of an oocyte surrounded by follicle (or granulosa) cells.

28.3b Oogenesis and the Ovarian Cycle 1097

- GnRH stimulates release of FSH and LH, which bring about follicle maturation. As the follicles mature, they release estrogen, and when these levels reach a threshold, the estrogen positively stimulates the hypothalamus and anterior pituitary to release more of their hormones.
- Changing levels of FSH and LH cause a primordial follicle to mature into a primary follicle. A secondary follicle matures from a primary follicle, and a vesicular follicle matures from a secondary follicle.
- A peak in LH causes the secondary oocyte to be released from the vesicular follicle at ovulation; remaining follicular cells become the hormone-producing corpus luteum.
- The ovarian cycle consists of the follicular phase, ovulation, and the luteal phase.

28.3c Uterine Tubes, Uterus, and Vagina 1101

- The uterine tubes are the site of fertilization.
- The uterus is a thick-walled muscular organ that functions as the site of pre-embryo implantation, supports and nourishes the embryo/fetus, and is the site of menstruation.
- The uterine wall consists of an inner mucosa, the endometrium; a thick-walled middle muscular layer, the myometrium; and an outer serosa, the perimetrium.
- The vagina is an epithelial-lined fibromuscular tube that serves as the birth canal for the fetus, a receptacle for the penis during intercourse, and the passageway for menstrual discharge.

28.3d Uterine (Menstrual) Cycle and Menstruation 1105

- The endometrium has a functional layer that is sloughed off as menses and a deeper basal layer that regenerates a new functional layer during the next uterine cycle.
- The menstrual and proliferative phases of the menstrual cycle occur in conjunction with the follicular and ovulation phases of the ovarian cycle. The secretory phase of the menstrual cycle occurs at the same time as the luteal phase of the ovarian cycle.

(continued on next page)

28.3 Female Reproductive System *(continued)*	**28.3e External Genitalia** 1108
	• The external female reproductive organs, collectively called the vulva, include the mons pubis, labia majora and minora, and the clitoris.

28.3f Mammary Glands 1108

• The female mammary glands produce breast milk.

• Prolactin is responsible for milk production; oxytocin is responsible for milk ejection.

28.3g Female Sexual Response 1111

• The female sexual response begins with the excitement phase, where reproductive organs become engorged with blood and the vaginal wall constricts slightly.

• Orgasm refers to the time period where there are intense feelings of pleasure, a feeling of a release of tension, perhaps a feeling of warmth, and some pelvic throbbing.

• Following orgasm is the resolution phase, where the uterus returns to its original position and the vaginal wall relaxes.

28.4 Male Reproductive System 1112

• The primary male reproductive system organs are the testes; accessory reproductive organs include ducts, male accessory glands, and the penis.

28.4a Scrotum 1112

• The scrotum houses the testes outside the body, where the lower temperature is needed to form functional sperm.

28.4b Testes and Spermatogenesis 1114

• The testes contain seminiferous tubules (coiled tubes that house developing sperm and sustentacular cells) and interstitial cells, which produce androgens.

• Spermatogenesis is the meiotic process that forms haploid spermatids, while spermiogenesis is the process by which spermatids differentiate into sperm.

• The hypothalamus secretes GnRH, which stimulates the anterior pituitary to secrete FSH and LH, which stimulates spermatogenesis and testosterone production.

• Rising levels of testosterone and inhibin inhibit both GnRH production and anterior pituitary sensitivity to GnRH, resulting in a negative feedback loop.

28.4c Duct System in the Male Reproductive Tract 1118

• The ducts store and transport sperm and include the rete testis, efferent ductules, epididymis, ductus deferens, and the ejaculatory duct.

• The male urethra transports either urine or semen at any one time.

28.4d Accessory Glands and Semen Production 1120

• The accessory glands produce seminal fluid, which is a nutrient-rich fluid that supports sperm.

• Accessory glands include seminal vesicles, the prostate gland, and bulbourethral glands.

• Semen is a mixture of seminal fluid and sperm.

28.4e Penis 1121

• The penis is the male copulatory organ, and contains three parallel erectile bodies plus the urethra.

28.4f Male Sexual Response 1122

• Erection is the process by which the erectile tissue (in the corpora cavernosa and spongiosum) fills with blood and the penis enlarges. This process is primarily controlled by the parasympathetic division of the autonomic nervous system (ANS).

• Ejaculation is the process by which the penis expels semen and is primarily controlled by the sympathetic division of the ANS.

• After orgasm, men experience a refractory period where they can't have another erection for several minutes or hours later.

28.5 Development and Aging of the Female and Male Reproductive Systems 1122

• Both female and male reproductive structures originate from the same basic primordia . Gene expression determines how they differentiate.

28.5a Genetic versus Phenotypic Sex 1122

• Genetic sex is based on chromosome type; phenotypic sex refers to the appearance of the internal and external genitalia.

28.5b Formation of Indifferent Gonads and Genital Ducts 1122

• Genital ridges in embryonic development form from intermediate mesoderm. Primordial germ cells migrate from the yolk sac to the genital ridges and form the future gametes.

28.5c Internal Genitalia Development 1124

• In the absence of a Y-chromosome (and thus the absence of the sex-determining region [*SRY*] gene), the female reproductive pattern develops. The male pattern develops as a result of the SRY protein.

28.5d External Genitalia Development 1124

• The external genitalia appear very similar until about week 12; external genitalia become fully differentiated by about week 20.

28.5e Puberty 1126

• Puberty is the time when the reproductive system begins to become fully functional and starts producing gametes and sex hormones.

• The timing for puberty varies, but it typically occurs earlier in girls than boys.

- Menopause is when a woman stops ovulating and having menstrual periods for 1 year. As a result, estrogen levels decline markedly at this time.

- Some women may experience additional symptoms such as hot flashes, thinner scalp hair, growth of darker facial hair, and increased risk for osteoporosis.

- Men may experience a male climacteric, which is the result of decreased testosterone levels. However, men continue to produce gametes throughout their lifetime.

CHALLENGE YOURSELF

Do You Know the Basics?

_____ 1. The female homologue to the penis is the
  a. labia majora.
  b. labia minora.
  c. clitoris.
  d. vagina.

_____ 2. Ovulation occurs due to a dramatic "peak" of which hormone?
  a. progesterone
  b. LH (luteinizing hormone)
  c. FSH (follicle-stimulating hormone)
  d. prolactin

_____ 3. Which statement is accurate about the uterus?
  a. The endometrium basal layer is shed each month as menses.
  b. The myometrium has several layers of skeletal muscle.
  c. The cervix projects into the vagina.
  d. The round ligament is peritoneum that drapes over the uterus.

_____ 4. Which structure contains a primary oocyte, several layers of granulosa cells, and an antrum?
  a. primordial follicle
  b. primary follicle
  c. secondary follicle
  d. vesicular follicle

_____ 5. In the male, what cells produce androgens?
  a. spermatogonia
  b. interstitial cells
  c. sustentacular cells
  d. All of these are correct.

_____ 6. All of the following organs produce a component of seminal fluid _except_ the
  a. bulbourethral glands.
  b. testes.
  c. seminal vesicles.
  d. prostate gland.

_____ 7. Spermatogonia divide by mitosis to form a new spermatogonium and
  a. a sperm.
  b. spermatids.
  c. a primary spermatocyte.
  d. zygotes.

_____ 8. Sperm are stored in the _____, where they remain until they are fully mature and capable of motility.
  a. epididymis
  b. seminiferous tubule
  c. ductus deferens
  d. rete testis

_____ 9. Which statement is accurate about the ovarian cycle?
  a. GnRH inhibits the anterior pituitary from secreting FSH and LH.
  b. Progesterone stimulates the follicle cells to mature.
  c. Estrogen production ceases when the secondary oocyte is ovulated.
  d. High levels of estrogen stimulate the anterior pituitary to secrete FSH and LH.

_____ 10. The paramesonephric ducts in the embryo form which of the following?
  a. uterine tubes and uterus
  b. ovary
  c. ductus deferens
  d. seminal vesicle

11. What are some anatomic similarities between the male and female reproductive systems? What are the anatomic homologues between these systems?

12. What hormones are associated with the female reproductive system, and what is the function of each hormone?

13. Describe the differences among a primary follicle, secondary follicle, and vesicular follicle.

14. List the uterine wall layers, and describe the basic anatomy of each layer.

15. Compare and contrast the ovarian cycle phases and the uterine cycle phases. When do they occur? What specific events are associated with each phase?

16. Describe the relationship among the hypothalamus, anterior pituitary, and the testis with regard to sperm and androgen production. What hormones initiate the cycle? What hormones inhibit the feedback loop?

17. What is the function of sustentacular cells in the production of spermatozoa?

18. Describe the process of spermatogenesis, including which cells are diploid and which are haploid.

19. How do erection and ejaculation occur in the male?

20. What structures are formed from the paramesonephric ducts? From the mesonephric ducts?

Can You Apply What You've Learned?

Use the following paragraph to answer questions 1–5.

Luisa and Victor are a young married couple trying to start a family but are having trouble conceiving. They make an appointment with a fertility clinic to determine what the problem may be. The physicians take blood samples from Luisa and Victor and ask them a series of questions. The physicians learn that Victor likes to take long hot baths each evening, as a way to unwind, and that Luisa has had an irregular menstrual cycle since her early 20s.

1. The physicians tell Victor that the long hot baths he takes may be interfering with them conceiving. Based on your knowledge of the reproductive system, why do you think this would be the case?
   a. Soaking the penis in the hot water prevents the penis from becoming fully erect.
   b. The autonomic axons responsible for erection and ejaculation become singed in the bath.
   c. The testes' temperature rises in the hot water, preventing successful spermatogenesis.
   d. The long hot baths prevent the hypothalamus from secreting GnRH to begin the hormonal cycle for sperm development.

2. Luisa tells the physician that her periods are irregular, but most recently she had a 35-day cycle (meaning 35 days elapsed from day 1 of menses to the next menstrual period). Given this particular menstrual cycle, what day of this cycle would be the most likely time Luisa and Victor could conceive?
   a. day 5   c. day 21
   b. day 14   d. day 28

3. The physicians review Luisa's and Victor's blood work. They discover that Victor has low levels of circulating luteinizing hormone (LH). How could this specifically affect Victor's fertility?
   a. The interstitial cells would not be producing enough testosterone for spermatogenesis.

b. The sustentacular cells are secreting too much inhibin.
   c. Spermatids are degenerating into primary spermatocytes.
   d. The sustentacular cells are unable to produce enough androgen-binding protein (ABP) for sperm development.

4. Victor and Luisa are questioned about their past sexual history. Specifically, they are asked if they ever tested positive for any sexually transmitted infection (STI) or experienced symptoms of an STI before. Why would this information be helpful?
   a. This information is not necessary for analysis of their fertility—useful only if they carry a child to term.
   b. Some STIs cause pelvic inflammatory disease, which can affect fertility.
   c. Syphilitic chancres are associated with a drop in sperm count.
   d. Women with herpes sores have difficulty ovulating.

5. The physicians give Luisa a fertility medication that mimics the effects of follicle-stimulating hormone (FSH). This medication would be expected to
   a. facilitate sperm traveling to the uterine tube for easy fertilization.
   b. cause a greater number of ovarian follicles to mature.
   c. build up the uterine lining for successful implantation.
   d. extend the time of ovulation.

Can You Synthesize What You've Learned?

1. Jennifer is a 44-year-old woman who just gave birth to a son. The son has poor muscle tone, slanting eye creases, and a heart defect. What is the likely cause of the son's characteristics? Does Jennifer's age have anything to do with her son's condition? Why or why not?

2. Caitlyn had unprotected sex with her fiancé approximately 2 weeks after her last period and is worried that she might have become pregnant. She asks her physician if there are times during her monthly menstrual cycle when she might be more likely to become pregnant. She also asks how birth control pills prevent a woman from becoming pregnant. What will the physician tell Caitlyn?

3. If parents wish to know the sex of their unborn baby, they usually have to wait until weeks 18–22 of development before a sonogram determining the sex can be performed. Based on your knowledge of reproductive system development, explain why the sex of the unborn baby can't be determined easily with a sonogram before this time.

chapter 29

Development, Pregnancy, and Heredity

Humans are like all other organisms in that they undergo **development,** a series of progressive changes that leads to the formation and organization of the diverse cell types in the body. In this chapter we focus primarily on the developmental events that occur prior to birth, a discipline known as **embryology** (em-brē-ol'ō-jē; *embryon* = a young one, *logos* = study). Embryology encompasses the developmental events that occur during the prenatal period, the first 38 weeks of human development culminating at birth. ➡

An obstetrician/gynecologist (OB/GYN) is a physician whose medical training is focused on the female reproductive system, pregnancy, labor, and the postpartum period (the period following birth). An OB/GYN must be aware of the anatomic and physiologic changes that occur to the mother during pregnancy, and have a thorough understanding of key developmental events for the fetus. The OB/GYN not only assists the woman during birth, but also will see the new mother in the weeks following giving birth, as the mother's body returns to its pre-pregnancy state.

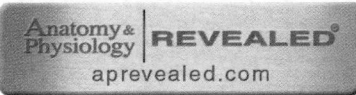

Module 14: Reproductive System

As the embryo, and later the fetus, is developing, the body of the expectant mother undergoes a series of remarkable changes. We describe the anatomic and physiologic changes of pregnancy and explain the processes that must occur during parturition, or childbirth. We then explore postpartum (post-birth) changes and feeding of the newborn. This chapter concludes with an overview of heredity, the transmission of genetic traits from parent to newborn.

29.1 Overview of the Prenatal Period

LEARNING OBJECTIVE

1. Define embryogenesis, and identify the three stages that occur during this process.

The **prenatal period** begins with fertilization, when a secondary oocyte (see section 28.3b) and sperm unite, and it ends approximately 38 weeks later with birth.[1] The general term for the new organism is a conceptus, but you will see that different terms are used during specific parts of the prenatal period.

The prenatal period is broken down into three shorter periods (**Figure 29.1**):

- The **pre-embryonic period** is the first 2 weeks of development (the first 2 weeks after fertilization), when the single cell produced by fertilization (the zygote) becomes a spherical, multicellular structure (a blastocyst). This period ends when the blastocyst implants in the lining of the uterus.
- The **embryonic period** includes the third through eighth weeks of development. It is a remarkably active time during which rudimentary versions of the major organ systems appear in the body, which is now called an embryo.
- The **fetal period** includes the remaining 30 weeks of development prior to birth, when the organism is called a **fetus** (fē′tus; offspring). During the fetal period, the fetus continues to grow, and its organs increase in complexity.

Figure 29.1 Developmental History of a Human.
The stages of development from fertilization through the embryonic period are known collectively as embryogenesis. The fetal period follows embryogenesis. Maturation continues after birth. Gametogenesis occurs in the sexually mature adult.

In the next sections, we describe the developmental processes that occur in the pre-embryonic and embryonic periods, which are known collectively as **embryogenesis.**

WHAT DID YOU LEARN?

1. What distinguishes the pre-embryonic period from the embryonic period? The embryonic period from the fetal period?

1. Some physicians refer to a 40-week gestation period, or pregnancy. This time frame is measured from a woman's last period to the birth of the newborn, so fertilization does not occur until week 2 (when a woman ovulates). Physicians may use this reference because a woman knows when her last period was, but she may not know the day on which she ovulated and had a secondary oocyte fertilized.

29.2 Pre-Embryonic Period

The pre-embryonic period in human development begins with fertilization, when the male's sperm and the female's secondary oocyte unite to form a single diploid cell called the **zygote** (zī'gōt; *zygotes* = yoked). The zygote is the same size as the secondary oocyte, which typically is between 100 and 120 micrometers (μm) in diameter. During the first 2 weeks, the zygote undergoes mitotic cell divisions, and the number of cells increases, forming a **pre-embryo.** The pre-embryonic stage of development spans the time from fertilization in the uterine tube through completion of implantation (burrowing and embedding) into the wall of the mother's uterus. **Table 29.1** traces the sequence of these events.

Table 29.1	Chronology of Events in Pre-Embryonic Development		
Developmental Stage or Process	**Time of Occurrence**	**Location**	**Events**
Fertilization — Ovum pronucleus — Sperm pronucleus ⊢— 120 μm —⊣	Within 12–24 hours after ovulation	Ampulla of uterine tube	Sperm penetrates secondary oocyte; secondary oocyte completes meiosis and becomes an ovum; ovum and sperm plasma membranes fuse
Zygote — Nucleus ⊢— 120 μm —⊣	At the end of fertilization	Ampulla of uterine tube	Diploid cell produced when ovum and sperm pronuclei fuse
Cleavage ⊢— 120 μm —⊣ ⊢— 120 μm —⊣ 4-cell stage 8-cell stage	30 hours to day 3 post-fertilization	Uterine tube	Zygote undergoes cell division by mitosis to increase cell number, but overall size of structure remains constant
Morula ⊢— 120 μm —⊣ Morula	Days 3–4 post-fertilization	Uterine tube	Structure formed resembles a solid ball of cells; 16 or more cells are present, but there is no change in diameter from original zygote
Blastocyst Embryoblast — Trophoblast — ⊢— 120 μm —⊣	Days 5–6	Uterus	Hollow ball of cells; outer ring formed by trophoblast; inner cell mass (embryoblast) is a cell cluster inside blastocyst
Implantation Cytotrophoblast — Embryoblast — Syncytiotrophoblast —	Begins late first week and is complete by end of second week	Functional layer of endometrium of uterus	Blastocyst adheres to functional layer of uterus; trophoblast cells and functional layer together begin to form the placenta

29.2a Fertilization

LEARNING OBJECTIVES

1. Describe the events of fertilization.
2. Explain capacitation of sperm and its relationship to fertilization.

Fertilization is the process by which two gametes (sex cells) fuse to form a new diploid cell containing genetic material derived from both parents. Besides combining the male and female genetic material, fertilization restores the diploid number of chromosomes, determines the sex of the organism, and initiates cleavage (discussed later in this section). Fertilization typically occurs in the widest part of the uterine tube, called the ampulla. Following ovulation, the secondary oocyte remains viable in the female reproductive tract for no more than 24 hours, whereas sperm remain viable for an average of 3 to 4 days after ejaculation from the male.

Upon arrival in the female reproductive tract, sperm are not yet capable of fertilizing the secondary oocyte. Sperm must undergo **capacitation** (kă-pas'i-tā'shun; *capacitas* = capable of), which is a physiologic conditioning, before they can accomplish fertilization. Capacitation occurs in the female reproductive tract, and typically lasts several hours. During this time, a glycoprotein coat and some proteins are removed from the sperm plasma membrane that overlies the acrosomal region of the sperm.

Normally, millions of sperm are deposited in the vagina of the female reproductive tract during intercourse. However, many sperm leak out of the vagina, and some are not completely motile (able to swim). Other sperm do not survive the acidic environment of the vagina, and still more lose direction as they move through the uterus and get "churned" by its muscular contractions (which may occur as a result of sexual intercourse). Thus, while the male releases millions of sperm during sexual intercourse, only a few hundred have a chance at fertilization.

The oocyte cytoplasm releases chemotaxic signals (chemicals) to attract the sperm to its location. Cumulus cells around the oocyte also release progesterone, which binds to specific channels found on the flagella of sperm and cause an influx of calcium ions (Ca^{2+}). The influx of Ca^{2+} is necessary for calcium-dependent actions such as capacitation, the acrosome reaction (discussed next), and fertilization.

When sperm reach the secondary oocyte, they attempt fertilization. Only the first sperm to enter the secondary oocyte is able to fertilize it; the remaining sperm are prevented from penetrating the oocyte.

WHAT DO YOU THINK?

1. Rarely, two sperm may penetrate a secondary oocyte. Do you think this fertilized cell will survive for long? Why or why not?

The phases of fertilization are corona radiata penetration, zona pellucida penetration, and fusion of the sperm and oocyte plasma membranes (**figure 29.2**).

Corona Radiata Penetration

The sperm that successfully reach the secondary oocyte are initially prevented entry by both the corona radiata and the zona pellucida. When sperm reach the corona radiata, their motility allows the sperm to push through the cell layers. Once the sperm have penetrated the corona radiata, they then encounter the more solid zona pellucida.

Zona Pellucida Penetration

After the sperm have made a pathway through the corona radiata, they release digestive enzymes from their acrosomes to penetrate the zona pellucida. This release of enzymes (primarily hyaluronidase and acrosin) from the acrosome is known as the **acrosome reaction.** When the

SEM 4700x

(a)

Sperm

Oocyte

Figure 29.2 Fertilization of a Secondary Oocyte in Humans. A secondary oocyte is ovulated in a "developmentally arrested" state at metaphase II in meiosis. (*a*) Scanning electron micrograph of sperm surrounding the secondary oocyte. (*b*) Schematic representation of the three phases of fertilization.

Secondary oocyte in metaphase II

First polar body

Zona pellucida

Corona radiata

Sperm pronucleus

Polar bodies

Ovum pronucleus

Phase 1	**Phase 2**	**Phase 3**
Sperm penetrates corona radiata.	Sperm undergoes acrosome reaction and penetrates zona pellucida.	Sperm and oocyte plasma membranes fuse.

(b) Phases of fertilization

first sperm successfully penetrates the zona pellucida and its nucleus enters the secondary oocyte, immediate changes occur to both the zona pellucida and the oocyte, so that no other sperm can enter. In essence, the zona pellucida hardens, preventing other sperm from binding to and ultimately digesting their way through this layer. This process is necessary to ensure that only one sperm fertilizes the oocyte.

On very rare occasions, two or more sperm cell nuclei simultaneously enter the secondary oocyte, a phenomenon called **polyspermy** (pol'ē-sper-mē; *poly* = many). Polyspermy is immediately fatal because it causes the fertilized oocyte to have 23 triplets (if two sperm enter) or 23 quadruplets (if three sperm enter) of chromosomes, instead of the normal 23 pairs of chromosomes.

Fusion of Sperm and Oocyte Plasma Membranes and Nuclei

When the sperm and oocyte plasma membranes come into contact, they immediately fuse. Only the nucleus of the sperm enters the cytoplasm of the secondary oocyte. When the nucleus of the sperm enters the secondary oocyte, the secondary oocyte completes the second meiotic division and forms an ovum (see section 28.3b). The nucleus of the sperm and the nucleus of the ovum are called **pronuclei** (*pro* = before, precursor of) because they have a haploid number of chromosomes. These pronuclei come together and fuse, forming a single nucleus that contains a diploid number (23 pairs) of chromosomes. The single diploid cell formed is the zygote.

WHAT DID YOU LEARN?

2 What are some factors or events that can prevent sperm from reaching the secondary oocyte?

3 What are the three events that occur during fertilization?

29.2b Cleavage

LEARNING OBJECTIVES

3. Define cleavage, and explain when it occurs.

4. Compare and contrast the structures of the zygote, morula, and blastocyst.

Following fertilization, the zygote begins the process of becoming a multicellular organism. After the zygote divides once and reaches the 2-cell stage, a series of mitotic divisions called **cleavage** (klēv′ij) results in an increase in cell number, but not an increase in the overall size of the structure. The diameter of the structure remains about 120 μm, so the mitotic divisions produce greater numbers of smaller cells to fit in this structure. The structure will not increase in *size* until it implants in the uterine wall and derives a source of nourishment from the mother (**figure 29.3**).

Before the 8-cell stage, cells are not tightly bound together, but after the third cleavage division, the cells become tightly compacted into a ball. The process by which contact between cells is increased to the maximum is called **compaction.** These cells now divide again,

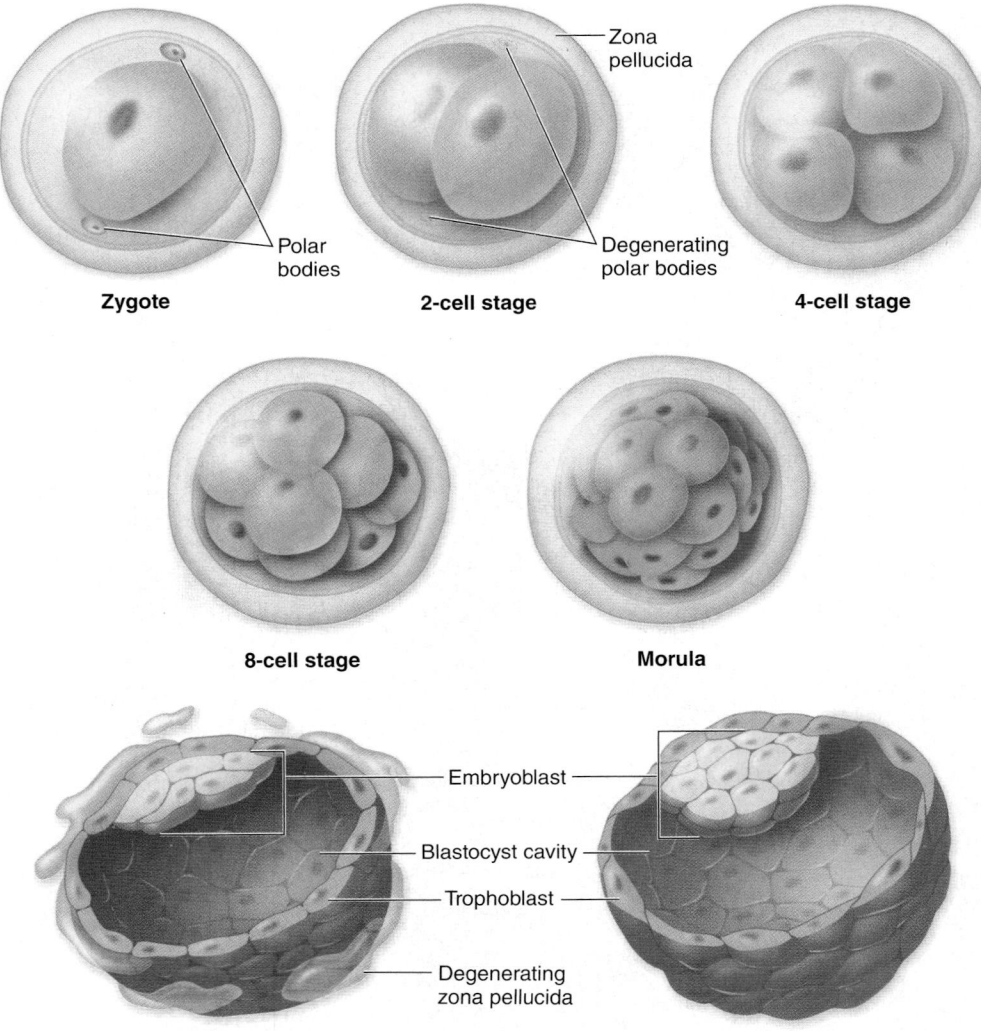

Zygote

2-cell stage

Zona pellucida

4-cell stage

Polar bodies

Degenerating polar bodies

8-cell stage

Morula

Embryoblast

Blastocyst cavity

Trophoblast

Degenerating zona pellucida

Early blastocyst

Late blastocyst

Figure 29.3 Cleavage in the Pre-Embryo. Shortly after fertilization, the zygote begins to undergo a series of cell divisions, termed cleavage. Divisions increase the number of cells, but the pre-embryo remains the same size. During each succeeding division, the cells are smaller than those in the previous generation, until they reach the size of most cells of the body.

forming a 16-cell stage, the **morula** (mōr'ū-lă; *morus* = mulberry). The cells of the morula continue to divide further.

Shortly after the morula enters the lumen of the uterus, fluid begins to leak through the degenerating zona pellucida surrounding the morula. As a result, a fluid-filled cavity, called the **blastocyst cavity,** develops within the morula. The pre-embryo at this stage of development is known as a **blastocyst** (blas'tō-sist; *blastos* = germ), and it has two distinct components:

- The **trophoblast** (trof'ō-blast; *trophe* = nourishment) is an outer ring of cells surrounding the fluid-filled cavity. These cells will form the chorion, one of the extraembryonic membranes discussed later in this section.
- The **embryoblast,** or *inner cell mass,* is a tightly packed group of cells located only within one side of the blastocyst. The embryoblast will form the embryo proper. These early cells are **pluripotent** (plū-rip'ō-tent; *pluris* = multi, *potentia* = power), which means they have the power to differentiate into any cell or tissue type in the body. (For more information about pluripotent cells, see Clinical View: "Stem Cells" in chapter 5.)

An overview of fertilization and cleavage, including the movement of the pre-embryo from the uterine tube into the uterus, is given in **figure 29.4**.

WHAT DID YOU LEARN?

4 How many cells are present initially in the morula?

5 What are the two cell layers of the blastocyst?

Figure 29.4 Transit of the Pre-Embryo Through the Uterine Tube: Fertilization Through Implantation. Sequential illustrations characterize the changes in the pre-embryo from the first cleavage division of the zygote in the uterine tube through the formation of the blastocyst in the uterus. AP|R

Development, Pregnancy, and Heredity

29.2c Implantation

LEARNING OBJECTIVES

5. Define implantation, and explain when it occurs.

6. Explain the physiologic significance of the syncytiotrophoblast's production of hCG.

By the end of the first week after fertilization, the blastocyst enters the lumen of the uterus. The zona pellucida around the blastocyst begins to break down as the blastocyst prepares to invade the functional layer of the uterus. **Implantation** is the process by which the blastocyst burrows into and embeds within the endometrium.

The blastocyst begins the implantation process by about day 7 (the end of the first week of development), when trophoblast cells begin to invade the functional layer of the endometrium (figure 29.5). Simultaneously, the trophoblast subdivides into two layers: a **cytotrophoblast** (sī′-tō-trō′fō-blast; *kytos* = cell), which is the inner cellular layer of the trophoblast, and a **syncytiotrophoblast** (sin-sish′ē-ō-trō′fō-blast), which is the outer, thick layer of the trophoblast where no plasma membranes are visible. Over the next few days, the syncytiotrophoblast cells burrow into the functional layer of the endometrium and bring with them the rest of the blastocyst.

By day 9, the blastocyst has completely burrowed into the uterine wall and makes contact with the pools of nutrients in the uterine glands. Thus, implantation begins during the first week of development and is not complete until the second week.

The syncytiotrophoblast is responsible for producing a hormone called **human chorionic gonadotropin (hCG).** Recall from section 28.3 that hCG signals the female reproductive system that fertilization and implantation have occurred. Thus, the corpus luteum does not degenerate but rather persists for another 3 months, producing large amounts of estrogen and progesterone that build the uterine lining.

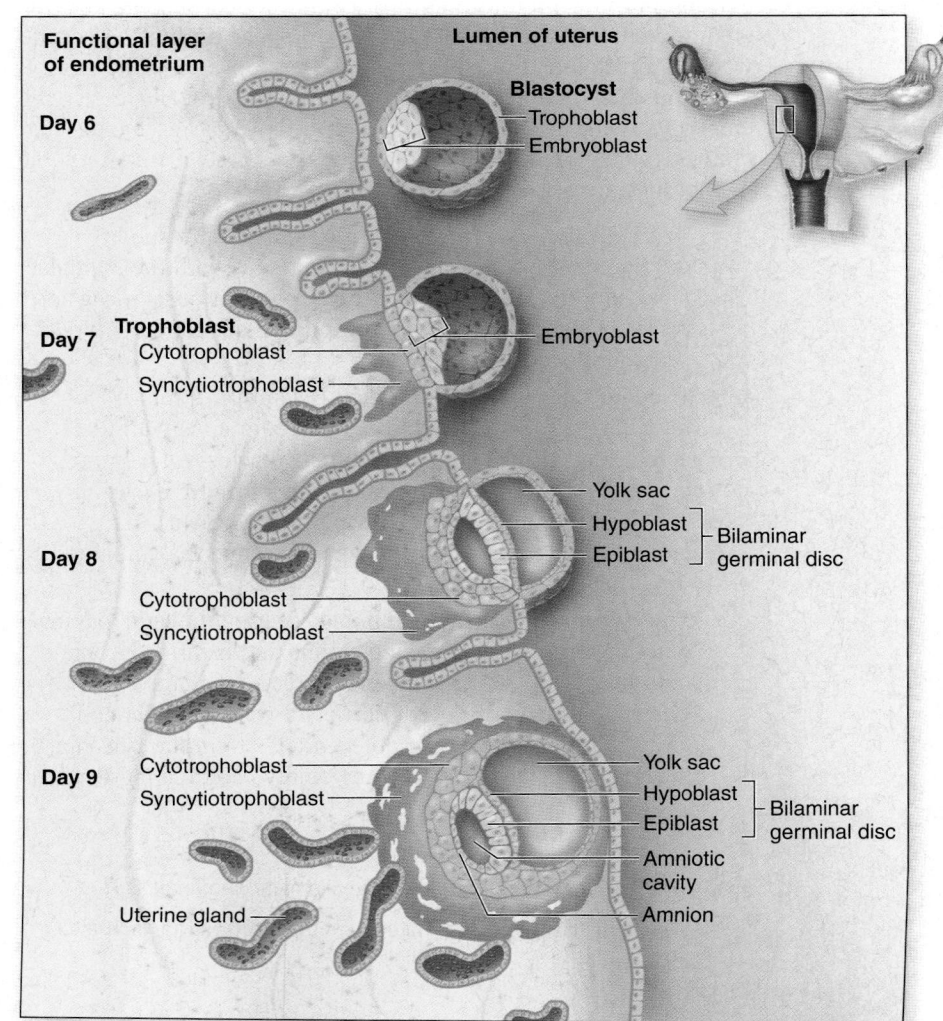

Figure 29.5 Implantation of the Blastocyst. The pre-embryo becomes a blastocyst in the uterine lumen prior to implantation. Contact between the blastocyst and the uterine wall begins the process of implantation about day 7. The implanting blastocyst makes contact with the maternal blood supply (via uterine glands) about day 9.

CLINICAL VIEW
Chromosomal Abnormalities and Spontaneous Abortion

Abnormalities in chromosome number or form occur regularly during gametogenesis, fertilization, or cleavage. If chromosomal abnormalities are severe enough, they result in the spontaneous abortion (miscarriage) of the blastocyst or embryo. Many of these spontaneous abortions occur early in pregnancy (within 2 to 3 weeks after fertilization), so a woman often spontaneously aborts without ever realizing she was pregnant.

Some estimates propose that approximately 50% of all pregnancies terminate as a result of spontaneous abortion; perhaps half of these are caused by chromosomal abnormalities in the developing organism. Thus, while 2–3% of all infants are born with some type of birth defect, this percentage would be much higher if not for the high frequency of spontaneous abortions very early in pregnancy.

By the end of the second week of development, sufficient quantities of hCG are produced to be detected in a woman's urine (**figure 29.6**). The presence of hCG in urine indicates a woman is pregnant, and thus hCG is the basis for most modern-day pregnancy tests. For the first 3 months of pregnancy, hCG levels remain high, but after that they decline. When hCG declines, the corpus luteum

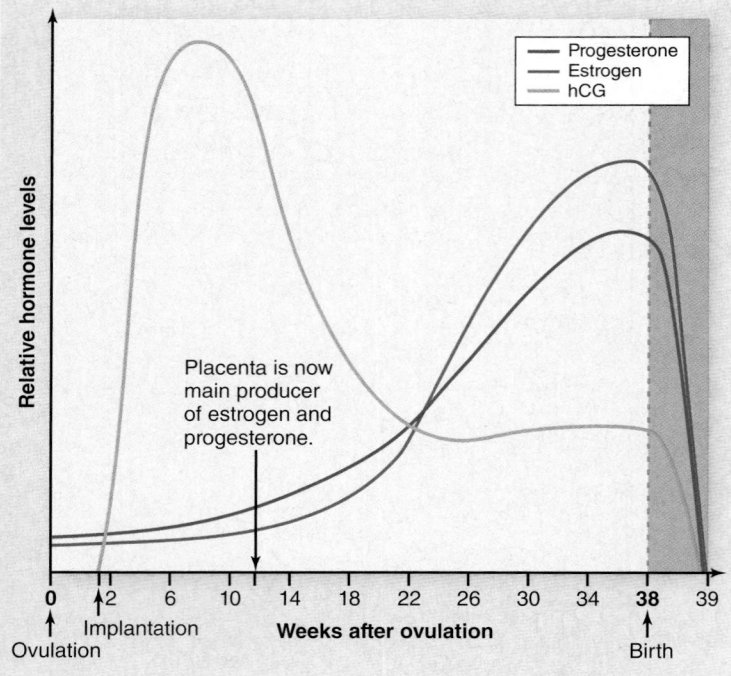

Figure 29.6 Hormone Levels During Pregnancy.
When the pre-embryo implants, it secretes human chorionic gonadotropin (hCG), which sustains the corpus luteum for 12 weeks (3 months). After the twelfth week, levels of hCG drop and the corpus luteum degenerates, and the placenta becomes the main producer of the estrogen and progesterone.

degenerates as well. However, by this time, the corpus luteum is no longer needed because the placenta is producing its own estrogen to maintain the pregnancy.

 WHAT DID YOU LEARN?

6 What would happen if a mutation prevented development of the syncytiotrophoblast cell layer?

7 Why is detection of significant levels of hCG a reliable test for pregnancy?

29.2d Formation of the Bilaminar Germinal Disc and Extraembryonic Membranes

LEARNING OBJECTIVES

7. Describe the development of the bilaminar germinal disc.

8. Name the three extraembryonic membranes, and summarize their functions.

During the second week of development, as the blastocyst is undergoing implantation, changes also occur to the embryoblast portion of the blastocyst (the inner cell mass described earlier). By day 8, the cells of the embryoblast begin to differentiate into two layers. A layer of small, cuboidal cells adjacent to the blastocyst cavity is termed the **hypoblast** layer, and a layer of columnar cells adjacent to the amniotic cavity is called the **epiblast** layer (see figure 29.5). Together, these layers form a flat disc termed a **bilaminar germinal disc,** or *blastodisc.*

The bilaminar germinal disc and trophoblast also produce **extraembryonic membranes** to mediate between them and the environment (**figure 29.7**). They first appear during the second week of development and continue to develop during the embryonic and fetal periods. They protect the embryo and assist the embryo in vital functions such as nutrition, gas exchange, and removal and storage of waste materials. These extraembryonic membranes are as follows:

- The **yolk sac** is the first extraembryonic membrane to develop. It is formed from and continuous with the hypoblast layer. In humans, it does not store yolk as it does in eggs of birds and reptiles, but it is an important site for early blood cell and blood vessel formation.

- The **amnion** (am'nē-on; *amnios* = lamb) is a thin membrane that is formed from and continuous with the epiblast layer. The amnion eventually encloses the entire embryo in a fluid-filled sac called the **amniotic cavity** to protect the embryo from desiccation (drying out). The amniotic membrane is specialized to secrete the amniotic fluid that bathes the embryo.

- The **chorion** (kō'rē-on; membrane covering the fetus) is the outermost extraembryonic membrane and is formed from both the rapidly growing cytotrophoblast cells and syncytiotrophoblast. These cells blend with the functional layer of the endometrium and eventually form the placenta, the site of exchange between the embryo and the mother.

 WHAT DID YOU LEARN?

8 What are the two cell layers of the bilaminar germinal disc?

9 Which cell layers give rise to each of the three extraembryonic membranes?

Figure 29.7 Formation of Extraembryonic Membranes. The extraembryonic membranes (yolk sac, amnion, and chorion) first appear during the second week of development. Their changes in growth and form are shown at (*a*) week 3, (*b*) early week 4, and (*c*) late week 4 of development.

Connecting stalk (future umbilical cord)

Yolk sac

Amniotic cavity

Amnion

Embryo

Chorion

Functional layer of uterus

Placenta

(a) Week 3

Connecting stalk

Yolk sac

Amniotic cavity

Amnion

Embryo

Chorion

Functional layer of uterus

Placenta

(b) Early week 4

Maternal artery

Maternal vein

Maternal blood

Trophoblast cells

Umbilical vein (carries oxygenated blood to embryo)

Umbilical artery (carries deoxygenated blood to placenta)

Placenta

Chorionic villus (in placenta)

Umbilical cord

Umbilical vein

Umbilical arteries

Yolk sac

Amniotic cavity

Amnion

Embryo

(c) Late week 4

LEARNING STRATEGY

The *second week* of development may be thought of as the "period of twos," because many paired structures develop.

- A *two-layered* (epiblast and hypoblast) germinal disc forms.
- *Two membranes* (the yolk sac and the amnion) develop on either side of the bilaminar germinal disc.
- The placenta develops from *two* components that merge (the chorion and the functional layer of the endometrium of the uterus).

29.2e Development of the Placenta

✓ LEARNING OBJECTIVES

9. Compare the maternal and fetal portions of the placenta.

10. Describe the main functions of the placenta, and name the hormones that promote its development.

Recall that the blastocyst is approximately the same size as the initial zygote, but the blastocyst contains many more cells than the zygote. In order to develop into an embryo and fetus, the blastocyst must receive nutrients and respiratory gases from the maternal blood supply. The connection between the embryo or fetus and the mother is the richly vascular **placenta** (plă-cen′tă; a cake). The main functions of the placenta are as follows:

- Exchange of nutrients, waste products, and respiratory gases between the maternal and fetal blood
- Transmission of maternal antibodies to the developing embryo or fetus (see section 22.8)
- Production of estrogen and progesterone to maintain and build the uterine lining

The placenta begins to form during the second week of development. The fetal portion of the placenta develops from the chorion, while the maternal portion of the placenta forms from the functional layer of the uterus. The early organism is connected to the placenta via a structure called the **connecting stalk** (figure 29.7a, b). This connecting stalk eventually contains the umbilical arteries and veins that distribute blood through the embryo or fetus. The connecting stalk is the precursor to the future **umbilical cord** (figure 29.7c).

Figure 29.7 illustrates how the components of the placenta become better defined during the embryonic period. Fingerlike structures called **chorionic villi** form from the chorion. The chorionic villi contain branches of the umbilical vessels. Adjacent to the chorionic villi is the functional layer of the endometrium, which contains maternal blood. Note that fetal blood and maternal blood do not mix; however, the bloodstreams are so close to one another that exchange of gases and nutrients can occur. The concentration of O_2 and nutrients is higher in the maternal blood, and therefore these diffuse into the fetal blood. Conversely, the concentration of CO_2 and waste products is higher in the fetal blood, so these materials diffuse from the fetal blood into the maternal circulation.

Although the placenta first forms during the pre-embryonic period, most of its growth and development occur during the fetal period. When the placenta matures, it is disc shaped and adheres firmly to the wall of the uterus. Immediately after the baby is born, the placenta is also expelled from the uterus. The expelled placenta is often called the *afterbirth*.

The placenta may be thought of as a selectively permeable structure. Certain materials enter freely through the placenta into the fetal blood, while other substances are effectively blocked. For example, respiratory gases and nutrients may freely cross the placental barrier, but certain microorganisms and high levels of maternal hormones are prevented from crossing this barrier into the developing fetus. Unfortunately, a number of undesirable substances, such as many viruses (e.g., HIV and rubella) and bacteria (e.g., *Treponema*, the bacterium that causes syphilis) *can* cross the placental barrier, infecting the fetus and sometimes causing birth defects or death. Most drugs, alcohol, and the toxins from smoking can pass through the placental barrier as well.

Some fetuses may be more susceptible to materials that cross the placental barrier than other fetuses. Additionally, the *dose* of the material crossing the placental barrier and the timing of this crossing both affect fetus susceptibility. These facts help explain why some newborns are strongly affected by materials that cross the placental barrier, while other newborns are relatively unaffected.

INTEGRATE

LEARNING STRATEGY

The *third week* of development produces an embryo with *three* primary germ layers: ectoderm, mesoderm, and endoderm.

Prior to implantation, the blastocyst is not harmed by undesirable substances because it does not yet have a connection with the mother's uterine lining. However, once implantation begins and the placenta starts to form, the developing organism is exposed to most of the chemicals and other substances to which the mother is exposed. For these reasons, pregnant women are strongly urged to quit smoking and to refrain from taking drugs and drinking alcohol during their pregnancies.

 WHAT DID YOU LEARN?

10 What are the main functions of the placenta?

29.3 Embryonic Period

The embryonic period begins in week 3 with the establishment of the three primary germ layers through the process of gastrulation. Subsequent interactions and rearrangements among the cells of the three layers prepare for the formation of specific tissues and organs, a process called organogenesis. By week 4 the embryo has a beating heart, and by the end of the embryonic period (week 8), the main organ systems have been established, and the major features of the external body form are recognizable. **Table 29.2** summarizes the events that occur during the embryonic period.

Table 29.2	Events in Embryonic Development
Developmental Week	**Events**
Week 3 1.5 mm Superior/dorsal view *(Future head region, Neural groove, Neural fold, Primitive streak labeled)*	Primitive streak appears Three primary germ layers form Notochord develops Neurulation begins Length: 1.5 millimeters (mm)
Week 4 4.0 mm Lateral view *(Head, Heart, Umbilical cord, Limb buds labeled)*	Cephalocaudal and lateral folding produce a cylindrical embryo Basic human body plan is established Derivatives of the three germ layers begin to form Limb buds appear Crown-rump length: 4.0 mm
Weeks 5–8 30 mm Lateral view	Head enlarges Eyes, ears, and nose appear Major organ systems are formed by the end of week 8 (although some may not be fully functional yet) Crown-rump length by the end of week 8: 30 mm

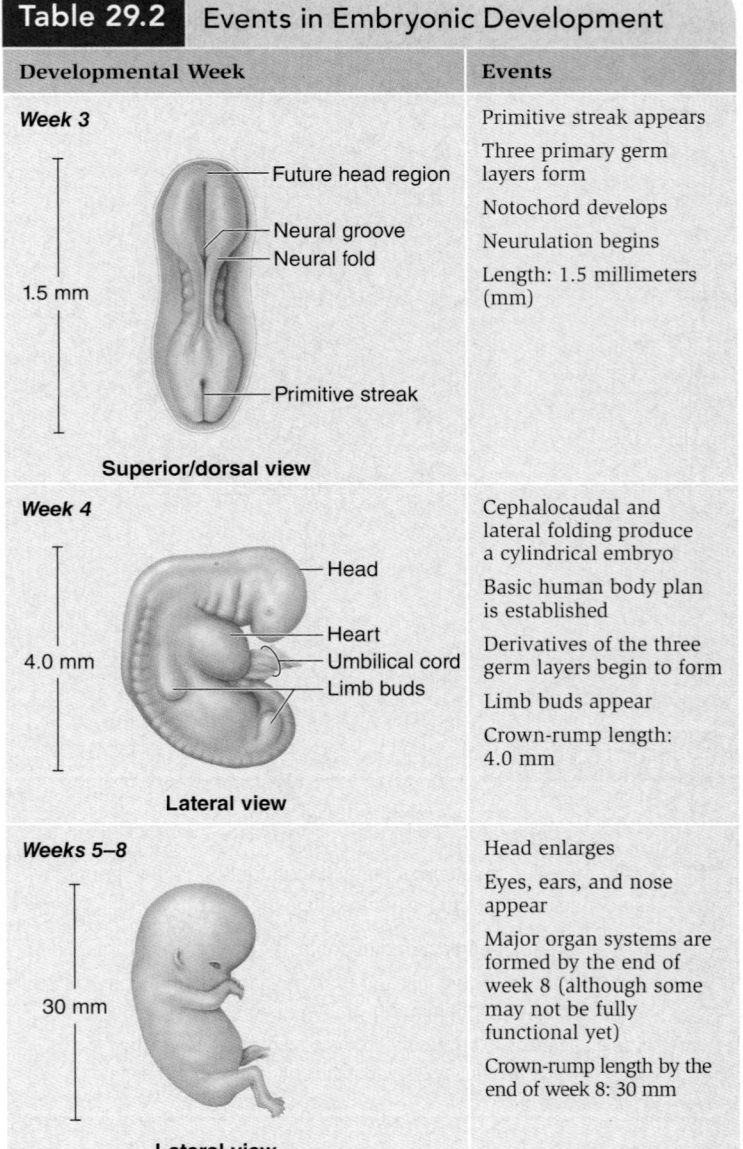

29.3a Gastrulation and Formation of the Primary Germ Layers

✓ LEARNING OBJECTIVES

1. Describe the process of gastrulation.
2. List the three primary germ layers that compose the embryo.

Gastrulation (gas-trū-lā′shŭn; *gaster* = belly) occurs during the third week of development immediately after implantation, and is one of the most critical periods in the development of the embryo. Gastrulation is a process by which the cells of the epiblast migrate and form the three **primary germ layers,** which are the cells from which all body tissues develop. The three primary germ layers are called ectoderm, mesoderm, and endoderm. Once these three layers have formed, the developing trilaminar (three-layered) structure may be called an **embryo.**

Gastrulation begins with formation of the **primitive streak,** a thin depression on the surface of the epiblast **(figure 29.8a, b).** The cephalic (head) end of the streak, known as the **primitive node,** consists of a slightly elevated area surrounding a small **primitive pit.**

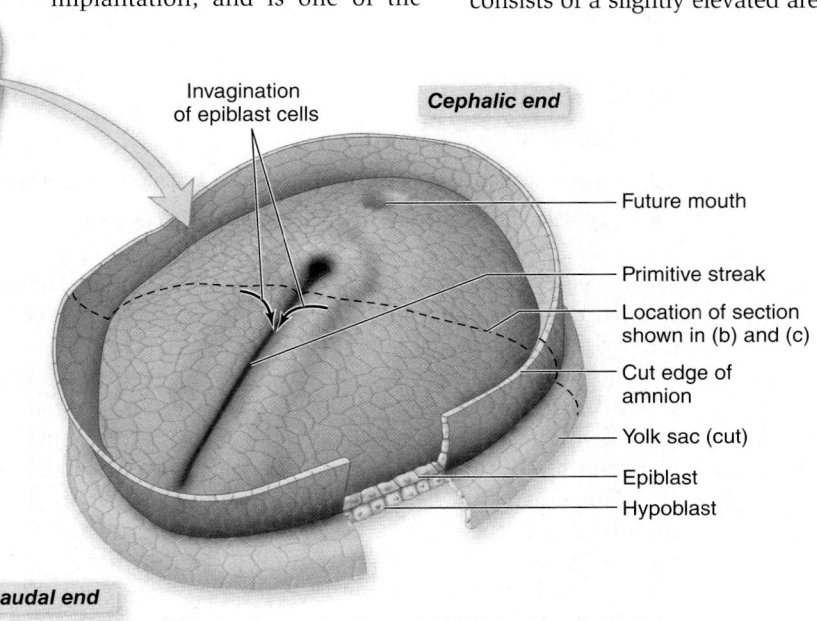

(a) Early week 3, superolateral view

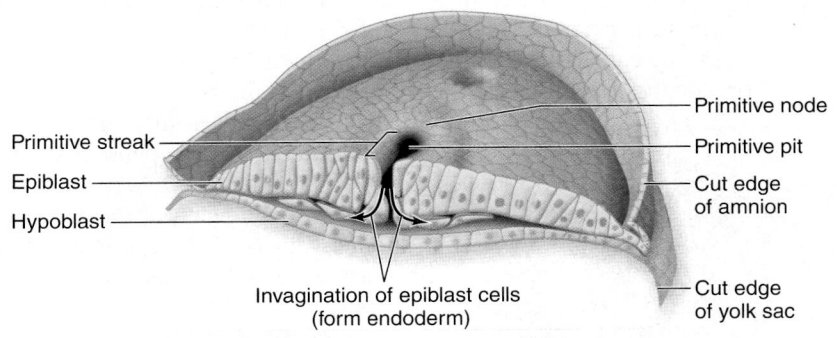

(b) Early week 3, cross-sectional view

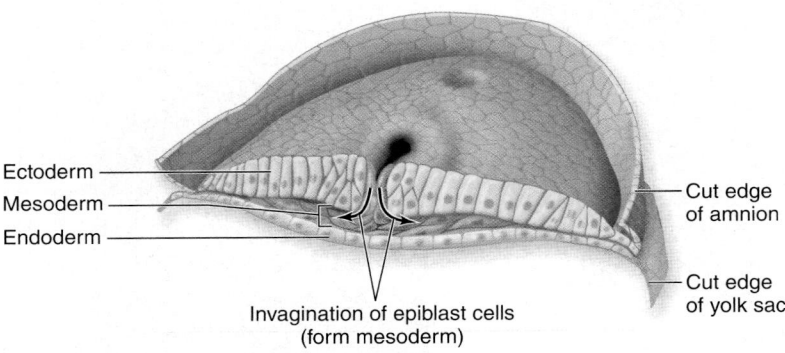

(c) Late week 3, cross-sectional view

Figure 29.8 The Role of the Primitive Streak in Gastrulation. (*a*) The primitive streak is a raised groove on the epiblast surface of the bilaminar germinal disc that appears early in the third week. (*b, c*) During gastrulation, epiblast cells migrate toward the primitive streak, where some become embryonic endoderm, and others form mesoderm between the epiblast and the new endoderm. Thus, the epiblast forms all three primary germ layers.

Cells detach from the epiblast layer and migrate through the primitive streak between the epiblast and hypoblast layers. This inward movement of cells is known as **invagination.** The layer of cells that forms between these two layers becomes the primary germ layer known as **mesoderm** (mez'ō-derm; *meso* = middle, *derma* = skin). Other migrating cells eventually displace the hypoblast and form the **endoderm** (en'dō-derm; *endo* = inner). Cells remaining in the epiblast then form the **ectoderm** (ek'tō-derm; *ektos* = outside). Thus, the epiblast, through the process of gastrulation, is the source of the three primary germ layers from which all body tissues and organs eventually derive (figure 29.8c).

WHAT DID YOU LEARN?

11 What events occur during gastrulation? What are the locations of the three germ layers?

29.3b Folding of the Embryonic Disc

LEARNING OBJECTIVES

3. Explain the process and the purpose of the folding of the embryonic disc.
4. Describe how the three primary germ layers differentiate.

The 3-week embryo is a flattened, disc-shaped structure. For this reason, the structure is also referred to as an **embryonic disc (figure 29.9).** So how does this flattened structure turn into a three-dimensional human?

The shape transformation begins during the late third and fourth weeks of development, when certain regions of the embryo grow faster than others. As a result of this differential growth, the embryonic disc starts to fold on itself and become more cylindrical. **Figure 29.10** illustrates the two types of folding that occur: cephalocaudal folding and transverse folding.

Cephalocaudal (sef'ă-lō-kaw'dăl) **folding** occurs in the cephalic (head) and caudal (tail) regions of the embryo. Essentially, the embryonic disc and amnion grow very rapidly, but the yolk sac does not grow at all. This differential growth causes the head and tail regions to fold on themselves.

Transverse folding (or *lateral folding*) occurs when the left and right sides of the embryo curve and migrate toward the midline. As these sides come together, they restrict and start to pinch off the yolk sac. Eventually, the sides of the embryonic disc fuse in the midline and create a cylindrical embryo. Thus, the ectoderm is now solely along the entire exterior of the embryo, while the endoderm is confined to the internal region of the embryo. As this midline fusion occurs, the yolk sac pinches off from most of the endoderm (with the exception of one small region of communication called the *vitelline duct*).

Thus, cephalocaudal folding helps create the future head and buttocks region of the embryo, while transverse folding creates a cylindrical trunk or torso region of the embryo. We now examine the specific derivatives of these primary germ layers (which were previously introduced in section 5.6a).

Cross-sectional view

Amnion
Amniotic cavity
Ectoderm
Mesoderm — **Embryonic disc**
Endoderm
Yolk sac
Notochord

Figure 29.9 Embryonic Disc. Gastrulation produces a trilaminar embryonic disc (outlined in pink) that contains three primary germ layers: endoderm, mesoderm, and ectoderm.

Figure 29.10 Folding of the Embryonic Disc. During the third and fourth weeks of development, the flat embryo undergoes both (*a*) cephalocaudal folding and (*b*) transverse folding.

Differentiation of Ectoderm

After the embryo undergoes cephalocaudal and transverse folding, the ectoderm is located on the external surface of the now-cylindrical embryo. The ectoderm is responsible for forming nervous system tissue in a process called *neurulation* (see section 13.1b). The ectodermal cells covering the embryo after neurulation form the epidermis. Ectoderm also forms the sweat and mammary glands, hair, nails, tooth enamel, and sense organs. It forms the adrenal medulla and lens of the eye. With a few exceptions, ectoderm gives rise to those organs and structures that maintain contact with the outside world (**figure 29.11**).

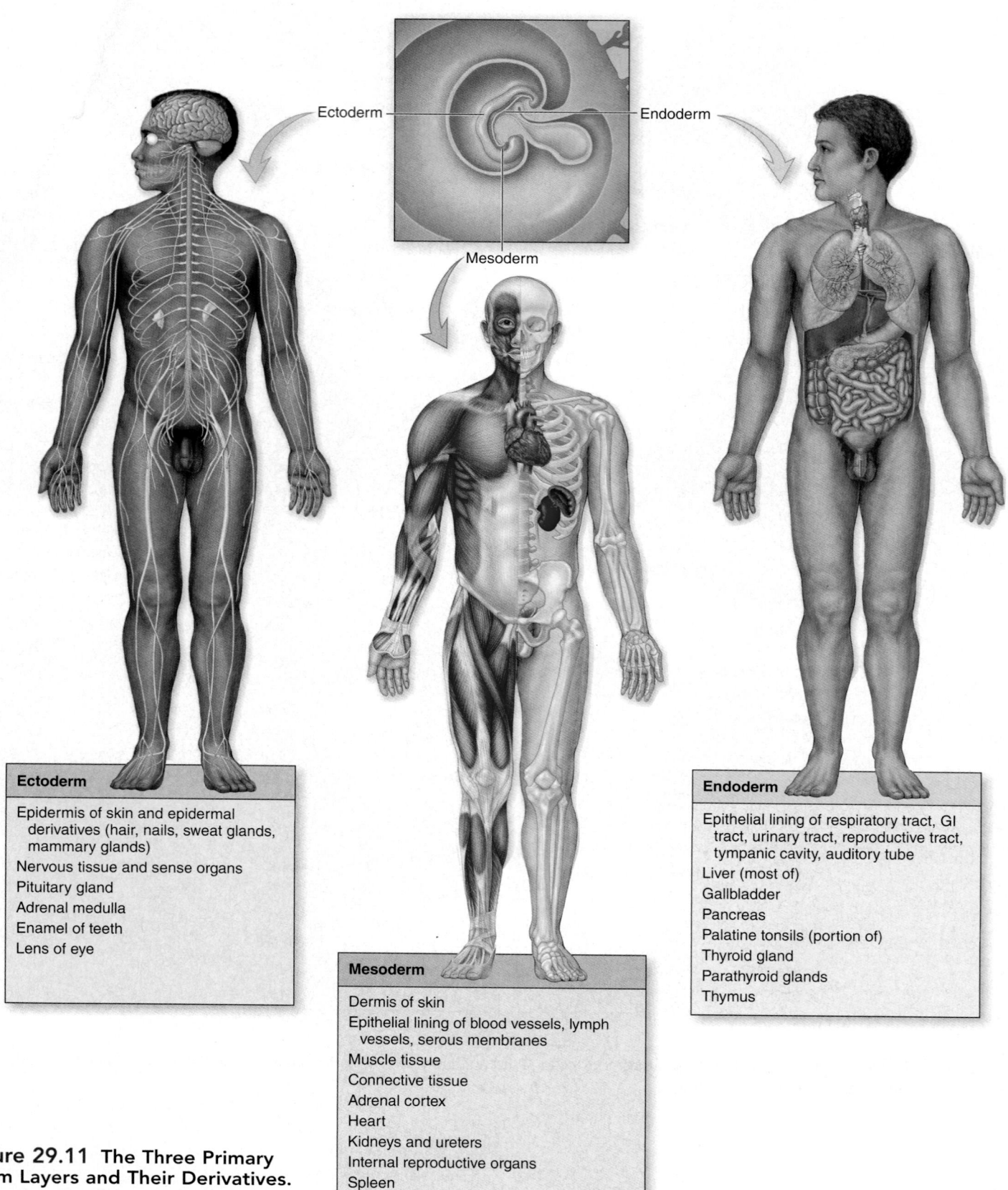

Ectoderm

Endoderm

Mesoderm

Ectoderm

Epidermis of skin and epidermal derivatives (hair, nails, sweat glands, mammary glands)
Nervous tissue and sense organs
Pituitary gland
Adrenal medulla
Enamel of teeth
Lens of eye

Mesoderm

Dermis of skin
Epithelial lining of blood vessels, lymph vessels, serous membranes
Muscle tissue
Connective tissue
Adrenal cortex
Heart
Kidneys and ureters
Internal reproductive organs
Spleen

Endoderm

Epithelial lining of respiratory tract, GI tract, urinary tract, reproductive tract, tympanic cavity, auditory tube
Liver (most of)
Gallbladder
Pancreas
Palatine tonsils (portion of)
Thyroid gland
Parathyroid glands
Thymus

Figure 29.11 The Three Primary Germ Layers and Their Derivatives.
Ectoderm, mesoderm, and endoderm give rise to all of the tissues in the body.

Differentiation of Mesoderm

Mesoderm subdivides into the following five categories (figure 29.12):

- The tightly packed midline group of mesodermal cells, also called *chordamesoderm*, forms the **notochord.** The notochord serves as the basis for the central body axis and the axial skeleton, and induces the formation of the neural tube, as previously described in section 13.1b.

- **Paraxial mesoderm** is found on both sides of the neural tube. The paraxial mesoderm then forms **somites** (sō′mīt; *soma* = body), which are blocklike masses responsible for the formation of the axial skeleton, most muscle (including limb musculature), and most of the cartilage, dermis, and connective tissues of the body.

- Lateral to the paraxial mesoderm are cords of **intermediate mesoderm,** which forms most of the kidneys, ureters, and the reproductive system.

- The most lateral layers of mesoderm on both sides of the neural tube remain thin and are called the **lateral plate mesoderm.** These give rise to the spleen, adrenal cortex, most of the components of the cardiovascular system, the serous membranes of the body cavities, and all the connective tissue components of the limbs.

- The last region of mesoderm, called the **head mesenchyme** (mez′en-kīm), forms connective tissues and musculature of the face (not shown in figure).

The derivatives of the mesoderm are listed and illustrated in figure 29.11.

Differentiation of Endoderm

Endoderm becomes the innermost tissue when the embryo undergoes transverse folding. Among the structures formed by embryonic endoderm are the linings of the gastrointestinal (GI), respiratory, urinary, and reproductive tracts (see figure 29.11). It forms the tympanic cavity (middle ear) and the auditory tube. Endoderm also forms the thyroid gland, parathyroid glands, thymus, and portions of the palatine tonsils, as well as most of the liver, gallbladder, and pancreas.

 WHAT DID YOU LEARN?

12 How are the results of cephalocaudal folding and transverse folding different?

13 What structures form from each of the three germ layers? Give specific examples.

29.3c Organogenesis

Figure 29.12 Differentiation of Mesoderm. By early week 4 of development, the notochord, paraxial mesoderm, intermediate mesoderm, and lateral plate mesoderm are seen.

LEARNING OBJECTIVE

5. Explain the meaning of teratogen and describe the potential effects of teratogens.

Once the three primary germ layers have formed and the embryo has undergone cephalocaudal and transverse folding, the process of **organogenesis** (ōr′gă-nō-jen-ĕ-sis), or organ development, can begin. The upper and lower limbs attain their adult shapes, and the rudimentary forms of most organ systems have developed by week 8 of development.

By the end of the embryonic period, the embryo is slightly longer than 2.5 centimeters (1 inch), and yet it already has the outward appearance of a human (figure 29.1). During the embryonic period, the embryo is particularly sensitive to **teratogens** (ter′ă-tō-jen, te-ră′tō-jen; *teras* = monster, *gen* = producing), substances that can cause birth defects or the death of the embryo. Teratogens include alcohol, tobacco smoke, drugs, some viruses, and even some seemingly benign medications, such as aspirin. Because the embryonic period includes organogenesis, exposure to teratogens at this time can result in the malformation of some or all organ systems.

Although rudimentary versions of most organ systems have formed during the embryonic period, different organ systems undergo "peak development" periods at different times. For example, the peak development for limb maturation is weeks 4–8, while peak development of the external genitalia begins in the late embryonic period and continues through the early fetal period. Teratogens cause the most harm to an organ system during its peak development period. So, a drug such as thalidomide (which causes limb defects) causes the most limb development damage if taken by the mother during weeks 4–8 (see Clinical View: "Limb Malformations" in chapter 8).

 WHAT DID YOU LEARN?

14 Why is it important for a pregnant woman to consult with her physician before using any medication?

29.4 Fetal Period

 LEARNING OBJECTIVE

1. Describe the major events that occur during the fetal stage of development.

The fetal period extends from the beginning of the third month of development (week 9) to birth. It is characterized by maturation of tissues and organs, and rapid growth of the body. Fetal length increases dramatically in months 3 to 5. The length of the fetus is usually measured in centimeters, either as the crown-rump length (CRL) or the crown-heel length (CHL). The 2.5-centimeter (1 inch) embryo will grow in the fetal period to an average length of 53 centimeters (21 inches).

Fetal weight increases steadily as well, although the weight increase is most striking in the last 2 months of pregnancy. The average weight of a full-term fetus ranges from 2.5 to 4.5 kilograms (5.5–9.9 pounds). The major events that occur during the fetal period are listed in table 29.3.

WHAT DID YOU LEARN?

15 The fetal period is characterized by what changes?

Table 29.3	Fetal Stage of Development
Time Period	**Major Events**
Weeks 9–12 CRL: 9 cm	Primary ossification centers appear in most bones Reproductive organs begin to develop Coordination between nerves and muscles for movement of limbs occurs Brain enlarges Body elongates Epidermis and dermis of the skin become more fully developed Permanent kidney develops Palate (roof of mouth) develops Average crown-rump length at 12 weeks: 9 centimeters (cm) Average weight: 28 grams (g)
Weeks 13–16 CRL: 14 cm	Body grows rapidly Ossification in the skeleton continues Limbs become more proportionate in length to body Brain and skull continue to enlarge Average crown-rump length at 16 weeks: 14 cm Average weight: 170 g
Weeks 17–20 CRL: 19 cm	Muscle movements become stronger and more frequent Lanugo covers skin Vernix caseosa covers skin Limbs near final proportions Brain and skull continue to enlarge Average crown-rump length at 20 weeks: 19 cm Average weight: 454 g
Weeks 21–38 CRL: 36 cm	Body gains major amount of weight Subcutaneous fat is deposited Eyebrows and eyelashes appear Eyelids open Testes descend into scrotum (month 9) Blood cells form in marrow only Average crown-rump length at 38 weeks: 36 cm Average *total* length at 38 weeks: 53 cm Average weight: 2.5–4.5 kilograms (kg)

CLINICAL VIEW
Infertility and Infertility Treatments

Infertility refers to the inability to conceive and maintain a pregnancy. Typically, it is defined medically as the inability to conceive after at least 1 year of regular sexual intercourse without protection.

Contrary to popular belief, the causes of infertility are equally split between females and males. One of the most common causes of infertility in women is blocked uterine tubes due to pelvic inflammatory disease or complications from endometriosis (see Clinical View: "Endometriosis" and Clinical View: "Sexually Transmitted Infections" in chapter 28). Ovulation disorders (e.g., abnormal follicle-stimulating hormone [FSH] and luteinizing hormone [LH]) secretion or polycystic ovarian syndrome) are another common cause of female infertility. Some men (and more rarely, some women) develop **anti-sperm antibodies,** substances that mark and target the sperm for destruction by the immune system. Other male-related causes of infertility include low sperm count, morphologically abnormal sperm, or impaired sperm delivery. Obesity, alcohol intake, drug use, smoking, exposure to certain environmental chemicals, and higher levels of stress have been associated with an increased risk of infertility in both sexes. In some cases, the cause for infertility remains unknown.

Several potential treatments are available for infertility, depending upon the initial cause:

- **Intrauterine insemination,** also known as *artificial insemination,* consists of injection of specially prepared sperm directly into the uterus through the vagina. Prior to injection, the sperm are prepared in the lab and stimulated to undergo capacitation.
- **Clomiphene citrate** (Clomid) is an oral medication that competes for estrogen receptors in the hypothalamus, pituitary, and ovaries—and in so doing, it reduces the negative feedback effects of the body's own estrogens on the ovarian cycle. Thus, follicular development and ovulation is stimulated. Clomid sometimes is associated with multiple pregnancies and ovarian hyperstimulation.
- **Human menopausal gonadotropins** (e.g., Repronex, Menopur, and Pergonal) and pure **follicle-stimulating hormone (FSH)** (Gonal-F) are injected medications that stimulate follicular development. These medications may have multiple adverse effects, including multiple pregnancy (from too many follicles being stimulated), ectopic pregnancy, miscarriages, and ovarian hyperstimulation syndrome.
- **Bromocriptine** (Parlodel) is an oral medication used to treat high prolactin levels seen in some infertile women. When prolactin levels drop, normal follicular development may ensue.

If pregnancy does not ensue after about 6 months of treatment with medications, or with multiple intrauterine insemination attempts, a couple may wish to explore the more complex **assisted reproductive technologies (ARTs).** These technologies may cost tens of thousands of dollars and have variable success rates. Among the ARTs are the following:

- **In vitro fertilization (IVF)** is a procedure by which pre-ovulatory oocytes are surgically extracted from the ovaries and each is injected with a prepared sperm in the lab. Prior to this process, the woman often takes medications (such as the ones previously listed) to stimulate the ovaries to produce multiple vesicular

Some infertility treatments have a greater likelihood of multiple births, which can be risky for both mother and the developing fetuses.

In vitro fertilization (IVF) is a procedure where a sperm is injected directly into the secondary oocyte.

follicles. One or more fertilized oocytes (now multicellular pre-embryos) are then surgically implanted in the uterus, and any remaining fertilized pre-embryos are cryopreserved (frozen) for future use. This procedure may have a success rate ranging from 10–35%, depending upon the age of the mother and other factors. One complication of IVF is multiple pregnancies, due to the fact that usually two or more pre-embryos are transferred during any one procedure.

- **Donor oocytes** may be retrieved from a female donor surgically. The oocytes may be fertilized with sperm in vitro and then placed in the future mother's uterus. Alternatively, the donor oocytes may be injected into the future mother's uterine tube with sperm (a process referred to as **gamete intrafallopian transfer**), in the hopes that the sperm will fertilize one or more of the donor oocytes.
- Likewise, **donor embryos** may be given to, and used by, an infertile couple. These embryos often were cryopreserved from another couple who may have undergone IVF.

Some infertile couples have chosen to have a **surrogate mother.** This surrogate may be impregnated with a pre-embryo from the infertile couple, or she may use her own oocyte and the male's donated sperm. However, the use of surrogates is fraught with ethical and legal complications; for example, the surrogate and the couple may fight for legal rights to the baby, or the couple may have issues with respect to how the surrogate is caring for herself during the pregnancy.

Many of these infertility treatments have come under ethical and legal scrutiny. For example, is it ethical to impregnate a woman with multiple pre-embryos? Who has legal rights to cryopreserved embryos, and who decides about their fate if the mother and father disagree? If a couple uses a surrogate mother, and that same couple later divorces, could the father claim sole custody because he is the only parent biologically related to the child? The medical advances of infertility treatments have outpaced their regulation and oversight, and medical ethicists will continue to debate these issues for years to come.

29.5 Effects of Pregnancy on the Mother

Pregnancy is an approximately nine-month process that, if all goes well, leads to the birth of a healthy baby. In the previous sections we discussed how the developing embryo/fetus undergoes a variety of changes within these 9 months. However, pregnancy also has dramatic anatomic and physiologic effects on the mother. Some of these changes can be very demanding, as the mother's body adapts to caring for itself and that of the developing fetus.

Here we discuss some of the typical anatomic and physiologic changes a woman experiences throughout her pregnancy. However, one very important thing to keep in mind is that great variation exists in how women experience pregnancy.

29.5a The Course of Pregnancy

LEARNING OBJECTIVE

1. Compare and contrast the first, second, and third trimesters of pregnancy.

As mentioned earlier, the length of the pregnancy is subdivided into trimesters:

- The **first trimester** encompasses the first 3 months of pregnancy (or the first 12 weeks of development of the embryo and fetus). During this time period, the zygote develops into an embryo and then into an early fetus.

- The **second trimester** includes months 4 to 6 of pregnancy and is marked by growth of the fetus and expansion of maternal tissues.

- The **third trimester** encompasses months 7 to 9 of pregnancy. During this time period, the fetus grows most rapidly and gains weight, and the mother's body prepares for the eventual labor and delivery.

Women's experience of pregnancy varies greatly. For example, some women may have little or no "morning sickness" during pregnancy, while others may have to be hospitalized due to extreme nausea and vomiting that lasts well past the first trimester. Some women may have little weight gain, while others may gain a significant amount of weight. Even the *length* of the pregnancy isn't the same for everyone—some women may deliver well before their projected due dates, while some may need to have labor induced because they are well past the due date.

In addition, one woman may have different pregnancy experiences for each of her children. One pregnancy may be uneventful, whereas another may have medical complications; or one birth may be long and difficult while another is relatively quick. As you read this section about the typical anatomic and physiologic changes that occur, please keep in mind that every pregnancy, and how it is experienced by the mother, is unique.

WHAT DID YOU LEARN?

16. How would you describe the differences between the first trimester and the second trimester? Between the second trimester and the third?

29.5b Hormonal Changes

LEARNING OBJECTIVES

2. Discuss the critical effects of estrogen and progesterone during pregnancy.

3. Identify other hormones whose levels are altered during pregnancy.

A wide array of hormonal changes occurs during pregnancy. We do not go into detail about all hormonal changes here; instead, we summarize the major alterations.

Recall that when the blastocyst implants in the uterus, its syncytiotrophoblast begins secreting large amounts of human chorionic gonadotropin (hCG), which signals the female reproductive system to maintain and build the uterine lining. During the first trimester of pregnancy, hCG levels remain high, but after that they decline (see figure 29.6). When hCG declines, the corpus luteum degenerates as well—but by this time, the corpus luteum is no longer needed because the placenta is producing its own estrogen and progesterone to maintain the pregnancy.

In the second and third trimesters of pregnancy, the placenta is the major producer of estrogen and progesterone, which are responsible for the majority of effects we discuss later in this section. The high levels of estrogen and progesterone suppress FSH and LH secretion, so the ovarian cycle and additional follicular development is arrested during the pregnancy. They facilitate uterine enlargement, mammary gland enlargement, and fetal growth.

Estrogen and progesterone have a dramatic effect on the integumentary system; many pregnant women report faster-growing and stronger nails, and their hair tends to be fuller and thicker in response to these hormones (because the hormones prevent normal cyclical hair loss, and a greater percentage of hair follicles remain in the resting stage). In addition, estrogen is primarily responsible for relaxation of many ligamentous joints, such as the sacroiliac joints and pubic symphysis, in preparation for labor. Progesterone is responsible for functional layer growth and the prevention of menstruation during pregnancy.

Another hormone called **relaxin** is secreted by the corpus luteum and placenta. Despite its name, research suggests that this hormone is not responsible for the ligament relaxation seen in pregnancy. Rather, relaxin appears to promote blood vessel growth in the uterus. The placenta also becomes a major secretor of **corticotropin-releasing hormone (CRH).** Recall from section 17.9c that small amounts of CRH are produced by the hypothalamus and stimulate the anterior pituitary to secrete adrenocorticotropic hormone (ACTH), which acts on the adrenal cortex. In comparison to the hypothalamus, the placenta secretes large amounts of CRH during pregnancy, and this hormone is believed to play a role in the length of pregnancy and the timing of childbirth. CRH also is responsible for the rise in aldosterone in the mother, which promotes fluid retention (see sections 24.6d and 25.4c) and an overall increase in blood volume during pregnancy. (Recall that aldosterone regulates sodium and potassium levels.)Thus, a woman may experience **edema** (e-dē′mă; swelling) during the later stages of pregnancy.

The placenta secretes **human chorionic thyrotropin (HCT),** which is similar to thyroid-stimulating hormone and thus stimulates the thyroid gland. As a result, a pregnant woman's metabolic rate increases.

Human placental lactogen (HPL), also known as *human chorionic somatomammotropin* (*hCS*), is secreted by the developing placenta—specifically, by the syncytiotrophoblast cells. The levels of this hormone rise linearly beginning the fifth week to maximum levels by the thirty-sixth week of development. Although this hormone is named for its effects on inducing lactation in mammals generally,

its effects on human lactation have not been demonstrated. Specifically, HPL does affect how the pregnant woman metabolizes certain nutrients—the mother metabolizes more fatty acids instead of glucose, leaving greater glucose reserves for the fetus. HPL also inhibits the effects of insulin (see section 17.10b), so there are greater circulating levels of glucose in the blood (again, for the use of the fetus).

Other hormones whose levels increase include prolactin and oxytocin. You learned in section 28.3 that oxytocin is produced by the hypothalamus and is involved in uterine contractions as well as milk expulsion from the mammary glands. Oxytocin levels increase in the second and third trimesters, in response to rising estrogen levels, and peak during labor. Prolactin is produced by the anterior pituitary and is responsible for milk production. Prolactin levels increase ten-fold during pregnancy to ensure that lactation occurs after giving birth.

WHAT DID YOU LEARN?

17 How do estrogen and progesterone act to sustain pregnancy?

18 What are the actions of CRH, HPL, oxytocin, and prolactin during pregnancy?

29.5c Uterine and Mammary Gland Changes

LEARNING OBJECTIVES

4. Explain the changes to the uterus in a pregnant woman.

5. Describe the hormones that affect mammary gland development during pregnancy.

The uterus undergoes a dramatic metamorphosis during pregnancy. **Figure 29.13** illustrates how both the uterus and the mammary glands change shape throughout the entire pregnancy.

Recall from section 28.3 that prior to pregnancy, the uterus is approximately 8 cm by 5 cm and situated within the pelvic cavity. Once implantation occurs, the uterus begins to enlarge and expand as its muscle cells hypertrophy and undergo hyperplasia. Uterine enlargement can be detected during a vaginal exam by 4 weeks after fertilization, and by 12 weeks (the end of the first trimester) the uterus is just superior to the level of the pubic symphysis and is about the size and shape of a large grapefruit. As the uterus expands, it impinges on the space occupied by

(a) **Before conception**
Uterus the size of a fist and resides in pelvis

— Umbilicus
— Uterus
— Pubic symphysis

(b) **4 months**
Fundus of uterus between pubic symphysis and umbilicus

(c) **7 months**
Fundus superior to the umbilicus

(d) **9 months**
Fundus at level of xiphoid process of sternum

— Diaphragm
— Xiphoid process
— Pubic symphysis

Figure 29.13 Uterine and Mammary Gland Changes During Pregnancy. The uterus enlarges dramatically, reaching the xiphoid process of the sternum by the ninth month of pregnancy. The mammary glands increase in size as well, as they prepare to produce breast milk.

the urinary bladder, so more frequent urination during this trimester is a common complaint. Recall that the developing fetus has a crown-to-rump length of only 9 cm at this time, so the bulk of the enlargement is due to myometrium muscle hypertrophy and hyperplasia, placental growth, and amniotic fluid production.

By 16 weeks (4 months) (figure 29.13b) the uterus has expanded into the abdominal cavity and its fundus typically is at a midpoint level between the pubic symphysis and umbilicus. The uterus continues to expand and reaches the level of the umbilicus by about week 22. During this second trimester, the superior growth of the uterus temporarily decreases pressure on the urinary bladder, so the need to frequently urinate may lessen during this trimester.

The expansion continues during the third trimester, as now the fetus is preparing for its own rapid growth sequence. By about 28 weeks (7 months) the fundus of the uterus is superior to the umbilicus, and by the ninth month the fundus of the uterus is at the level of the xiphoid process of the sternum (figure 29.13d). The enlarged uterus pushes against the diaphragm and compresses many of the abdominopelvic organs, resulting in certain gastrointestinal (GI) ailments (described in the next section). In addition, now the uterus is so large that it impinges on the bladder, so frequent urination becomes a common complaint again.

WHAT DO YOU THINK?

2 Some pregnant women experience difficulty with deep breathing during the last trimester. Can you think of any reasons as to why deep breathing (versus shallow breathing) is more difficult during this time?

The mammary glands typically are tender and sore during the first trimester due to the increasing levels of estrogen and progesterone. The placenta secretes **melanocyte-stimulating hormone (MSH)**, which is in part responsible for the darkening of the areolae and nipples during this time (figure 29.13d). MSH also is responsible for a darkening of the linea alba, the ligamentous connection between left and right rectus sheaths, turning it into a temporary vertical dark line called the **linea nigra** (nī′gră; *niger* = black). Mammary glandular tissue grows and additional acini develop, especially under the influence of prolactin. It is typical for a pregnant woman to increase one bra cup size during this time due to the mammary gland growth. Further discussion of lactation occurs later in this chapter.

WHAT DID YOU LEARN?

19 What impact does the growth of the uterus during pregnancy have on other organs of the abdomen?

20 What hormones affect the mammary glands of a pregnant woman?

29.5d Digestive System, Nutrient, and Metabolic Changes

LEARNING OBJECTIVES

6. Describe the effects of HPL and other hormones on the pregnant woman's ability to utilize glucose.

7. List some common GI complaints and conditions that occur during pregnancy and their causes.

You read earlier that human placental lactogen (HPL) affects how the mother metabolizes certain nutrients, so that she metabolizes more fatty acids instead of glucose, leaving the glucose for the developing fetus. The increased levels of corticosteroids, estrogen, progesterone, and human placental lactogen also result in increased insulin

resistance in the pregnant mother. This increased insulin resistance in some cases can lead to gestational diabetes in the mother.

Many expectant mothers may experience **morning sickness** during the first trimester of their pregnancy. Contrary to its name, morning sickness does not occur just in the morning, although typically symptoms tend to be most severe then. Symptoms may vary dramatically among women—some may experience a little nausea for a few months only, while others may have dehydrating vomiting that lasts throughout their pregnancy and may be debilitating. In the most severe cases, a woman may need to be hospitalized and replenished with IV fluids until the pregnancy comes to term.

There are several hypotheses about the cause of morning sickness, but none have been definitively proven. One suggests that the high levels of circulating hormones, especially hCG, are the cause. However, several research studies have not been able to demonstrate this. Others have suggested that morning sickness is an evolutionary adaptation to protect the developing fetus from harmful toxins in the food. Women with morning sickness tend to prefer bland carbohydrates (which may be less likely to be spoiled or have toxins) and may have aversions to meat and eggs (which may be more likely to have toxins or be spoiled with pathogens).

The higher circulating levels of progesterone result in relaxed smooth muscle and thus slowed intestinal motility, so digested materials remain in the GI tract for longer periods of time. In the later stages of pregnancy, the expanding uterus compresses the abdominal organs and may impinge on part of the intestines. All of these factors may result in heartburn and indigestion; mothers also may experience constipation (see section 26.3d). Chronic constipation, as well as problems with venous circulation (caused by compression of the lower veins by the fetus) also can lead to hemorrhoids (see Clinical View: "Varicose Veins" in chapter 20).

A pregnant woman typically needs about 300 extra calories daily to supply both herself and her fetus. Adequate levels of folic acid, calcium, protein, and iron are especially important during pregnancy. A woman experiences weight gain during pregnancy, but only about 20 pounds of this weight gain is due to the fetus, placenta, breast and uterine enlargement, and fluid retention. Any additional weight gain typically is additional adipose tissue, fluid retention, or both.

WHAT DID YOU LEARN?

21 Why is it important to check a woman's blood glucose levels during pregnancy?

22 What conditions other than overeating might explain weight gain during pregnancy?

CLINICAL VIEW
Preeclampsia

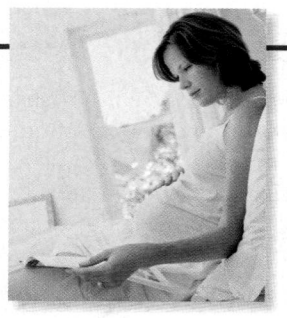

Preeclampsia (prē-ē-klamp'sē-ă), also known as *toxemia* or *pregnancy-induced hypertension,* is high blood pressure that occurs by the second half of pregnancy and is marked by protein in the urine (proteinuria). It occurs in about 2–6% of all pregnancies, and risk factors include maternal obesity, diabetes, advanced age, and having a previous preeclampsic birth. The cause is unknown, but researchers suspect that endothelial cell injury, due to a poorly perfused placenta, initiates the disorder. The high blood pressure carries with it the risks of general hypertension for the mother, and the poor perfusion of the placenta means the fetus may not get an adequate supply of nutrients. The only cure for preeclampsia is giving birth, so depending upon when symptoms occur, a woman may be put on bedrest and medications (to keep blood pressure levels lower), or labor may be induced if the baby is close to term.

Eclampsia is high blood pressure that causes seizures or convulsions in the mother and is a medical emergency. The concern for every preeclampsia patient is to make sure her symptoms do not develop into full-blown eclampsia.

29.5e Cardiovascular and Respiratory System Changes

LEARNING OBJECTIVES

8. List the cardiovascular changes a woman typically exhibits during pregnancy.

9. Explain the changes to the respiratory system during pregnancy.

Because of the needs of both the mother and the embryo/fetus, the cardiovascular system undergoes dramatic changes throughout pregnancy. Respiratory system function also becomes altered to meet increased requirements for gas exchange.

Cardiovascular System

The cardiovascular system must distribute respiratory gases and nutrients to both the mother and the growing fetus. More blood is needed, so plasma volume increases by about 50% throughout pregnancy. The increased blood volume needs an increased cardiac output to pump this blood through the circulation. Cardiac output increases 30–50% beginning at week 6 of pregnancy and peaks about weeks 24–28 of pregnancy, before dropping slightly. To increase cardiac output, the body increases both heart rate (on average from 70 to 90 beats per minute) and stroke volume.

The increase in blood volume may initially cause an increase in blood pressure during the first trimester. However, by the second trimester the blood pressure drops because of a decrease in peripheral vascular resistance that results from both a decrease in blood viscosity (a pregnant woman has a lower hematocrit than a nonpregnant female) and a decreased sensitivity to the hormone angiotensin (see sections 20.5b and 25.4a).

By the third trimester, the uterus and fetus compress the abdominal blood vessels, so venous return from the lower part of the body may be impaired. As a result, some pregnant women may develop varicose veins, hemorrhoids, and edema in the lower limbs.

Respiratory System

Earlier we mentioned that in the later part of pregnancy, the expanding uterus prevents the diaphragm from fully descending and the lungs from fully expanding with air. **Dyspnea** (disp'nē-a) is the uncomfortable awareness of breathing and may occur during periods of exertion. Increased estrogen levels may cause the nasal mucosa to become fluid-filled, have increased blood circulation, and congestion. The expectant mother also may experience **epistaxis** (nosebleeds) due to the increased circulation.

Progesterone increases the brainstem chemoreceptors' sensitivity to blood CO_2 levels, ultimately functioning to lower the blood CO_2 levels. These lower blood CO_2 levels facilitate the diffusion of gases across the placenta. To lower the blood CO_2 levels, the tidal volume and pulmonary ventilation levels (see section 23.5a) increase by 30–40%. Respiratory rate increases slightly as well. Additionally, the mother's oxygen consumption increases about 20–30% to meet the oxygen demands of both mother and fetus. Thus, all of these alterations serve to provide enough oxygen to mother and fetus, as well as facilitate gas exchange between the placenta and the maternal blood.

WHAT DID YOU LEARN?

23 Is a woman's cardiovascular system under stress during pregnancy? Explain your answer.

24 Why is it beneficial for CO_2 receptor sensitivity to be increased when a woman is pregnant?

29.5f Urinary System Changes

LEARNING OBJECTIVE

10. Describe the effects of pregnancy on the mother's urinary system.

The pregnant woman's urinary system is responsible for eliminating not only her own metabolic waste products but also the waste products of her fetus. In addition, up to 50% more plasma volume must be filtered by the kidneys. Glomerular filtration rate (GFR; see section 24.5d) thus increases about 30–50% during pregnancy and urine output increases slightly.

Recall that compression by the expanding uterus can lead to frequent urination in both the first and third trimesters. In contrast, the uterus places relatively less pressure on the bladder during the second trimester.

Progesterone causes smooth muscle relaxation in the ureters, which may cause uretal and renal pelvic dilation. This dilation and the increased urine volume may result in urine stasis (slowing or stopping) anywhere along its path. In addition, compression of the ureter or kidney by the uterus can result in urine drainage issues. All of these factors put pregnant women at much greater risk for urinary tract infections (UTIs), which are perhaps the most common type of bacterial infection during pregnancy.

WHAT DID YOU LEARN?

25 What factors make pregnant women more likely to get urinary tract infections?

29.6 Labor (Parturition) and Delivery

Labor is also known as *parturition* (par-tūr-ĭsh'ŭn; *parturitio* = to be in labor) and is the physical expulsion of the fetus and placenta from the uterus. True labor typically occurs at 38 weeks for a full-term pregnancy, but not all uterine contractions lead to true labor. We first consider factors that initiate labor, and then compare the contractions of false labor with those of true labor; we conclude with a description of the three stages of labor.

29.6a Factors That Lead to Labor

 LEARNING OBJECTIVE

1. Explain the physiologic processes that initiate labor.

Throughout the pregnancy, as the uterus enlarges and stretches, the uterine myometrium prepares itself for uterine contractions. In the later stages of pregnancy, the increasing levels of estrogen counteract the calming influence of progesterone on the uterine myometrium, and increase the uterine myometrium sensitivity. In addition, the rising levels of estrogen stimulate the production of oxytocin receptors on the uterine myometrium, so as the levels of oxytocin also rise, more receptors are available on the uterus for binding this hormone.

All of these factors result in the uterine myometrium becoming more sensitive and "irritable" in the later stages of pregnancy, and contractions begin to occur. These contractions typically are weak and irregular, but as levels of estrogen and oxytocin continue to rise in the later stages, they become more intense and frequent. Thus, weak contractions may occur and be noticed as soon as the second trimester of pregnancy.

Premature labor refers to labor that occurs prior to 38 weeks. Premature labor (and giving birth to a premature infant) is not desirable because the infant's body systems, especially the lungs, may not be fully developed. Very premature infants are at greater risk for morbidity and mortality due to their underdeveloped organ systems. Thus, the ideal outcome is for labor to begin as close as possible to term.

WHAT DID YOU LEARN?

26 How do progesterone, estrogen, and oxytocin interact to eventually bring about labor?

29.6b False Labor

 LEARNING OBJECTIVE

2. List the signs and characteristics of false labor.

False labor is defined as uterine contractions that do *not* result in the three stages of labor and the expulsion of the fetus. The contractions of false labor are known as **Braxton-Hicks contractions,** named for a nineteenth-century gynecologist. It may be difficult for a woman to know whether she is experiencing Braxton-Hicks contractions or true labor contractions, and it is not uncommon for a woman to mistakenly think she is about to give birth.

In general, Braxton-Hicks contractions have the following characteristics:

- They tend to be irregularly spaced and do not become more frequent as time passes.
- They tend to be relatively weak, do not increase in intensity, and may stop entirely if the woman changes position or activity (e.g., goes for a walk).
- The pain from these contractions is usually limited to the lower abdomen and pelvic region, instead of radiating through the entire abdominal region and back (as with true labor contractions).
- The pain from the contractions may stop or change in response to movement.
- They do not lead to the cervical changes seen in the three stages of labor (described later in this chapter).

WHAT DID YOU LEARN?

27 What are five signs of false labor?

29.6c Initiation of True Labor

✓ LEARNING OBJECTIVES

3. Explain the signs and characteristics of true labor.
4. Describe the positive feedback mechanism of true labor.

True labor is defined as uterine contractions that increase in intensity and regularity, and that result in changes to the cervix. The mother and the fetus both have an active role in initiating true labor.

As the pregnancy nears term, the mother's hypothalamus secretes increasing levels of oxytocin, as described earlier. In addition, the fetus's hypothalamus secretes its own oxytocin near the beginning of true labor. Both sources of oxytocin stimulate the placenta to secrete **prostaglandins** (pros-tă-glan′dĭn), which are fatty acids and hormonelike substances that also stimulate smooth muscle contraction, most notably uterine muscle contraction (see section 17.3b for a review of prostaglandins and other types of eicosanoids). Prostaglandins are also responsible for the softening and dilating of the cervix. The combined action of maternal oxytocin, fetal oxytocin, and the rising levels of prostaglandins initiate the rhythmic contractions of true labor.

In comparison to Braxton-Hicks contractions, true labor contractions have the following characteristics:

- They tend to increase in frequency over time, so a woman who starts with contractions that occur roughly every 15 minutes eventually will have contractions that occur about every 5 minutes.
- Contractions increase in intensity as labor progresses.
- The pain from the contractions tends to radiate from the upper abdomen inferiorly to the lower back (or vice versa), instead of being localized in the lower abdomen or groin (as with Braxton-Hicks contractions).
- The pain from the contractions does not go away or change in response to movement.
- The contractions facilitate cervical dilation and expulsion of the fetus and placenta.

True labor also initiates a positive feedback mechanism **(figure 29.14)**. The more intense uterine contractions result in the fetus's head pushing against the cervix, stimulating the

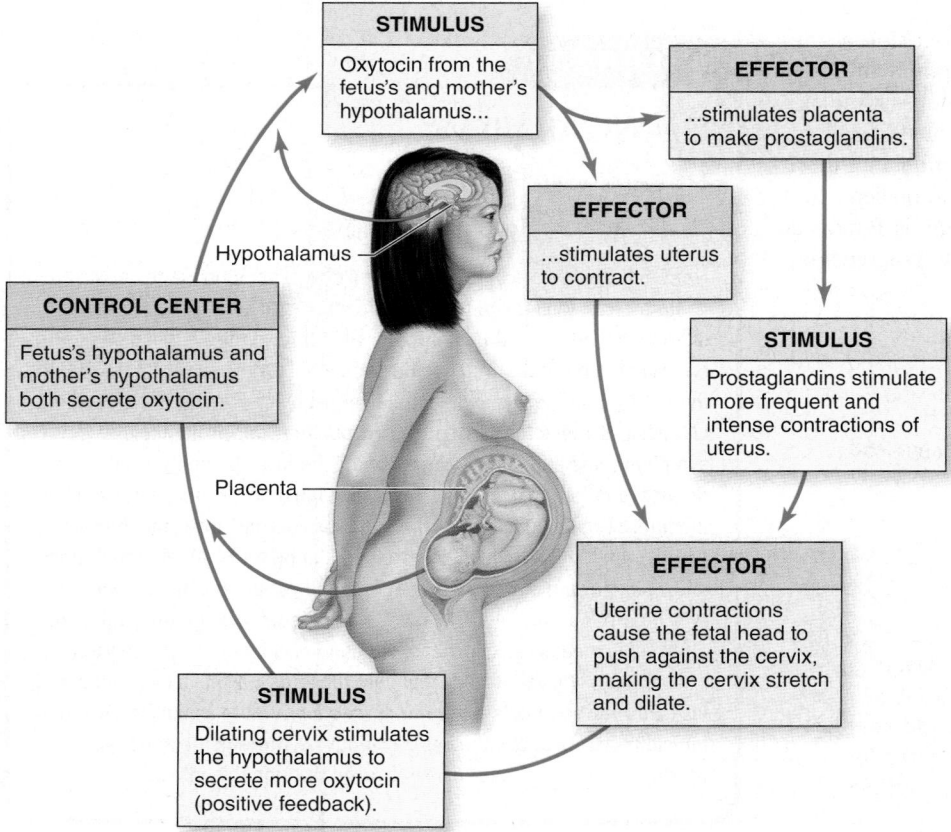

STIMULUS
Oxytocin from the fetus's and mother's hypothalamus...

EFFECTOR
...stimulates placenta to make prostaglandins.

EFFECTOR
...stimulates uterus to contract.

Hypothalamus

CONTROL CENTER
Fetus's hypothalamus and mother's hypothalamus both secrete oxytocin.

STIMULUS
Prostaglandins stimulate more frequent and intense contractions of uterus.

Placenta

EFFECTOR
Uterine contractions cause the fetal head to push against the cervix, making the cervix stretch and dilate.

STIMULUS
Dilating cervix stimulates the hypothalamus to secrete more oxytocin (positive feedback).

Figure 29.14 Positive Feedback Mechanism of True Labor. Rising levels of maternal and fetal oxytocin together initiate the positive feedback mechanism of true labor. Oxytocin stimulates uterine contractions as well as the release of prostaglandins, which promote cervical stretching and also facilitate uterine contractions. Uterine contractions are detected by the hypothalamus, which in turn stimulates production and release of more oxytocin. The process escalates until the fetus is expelled from the uterus.

CLINICAL VIEW

Anesthetic Procedures to Facilitate True Labor

Uterine contractions can be quite painful and discomforting for the expectant mother. While some women may choose not to have any pain medication and have what is referred to as a *natural childbirth,* others may select oral pain medication or a variety of anesthetic procedures.

A **pudendal nerve block** numbs the pudendal nerve, which is the main sensory nerve of the perineum and also innervates the perineal muscles. This type of anesthesia numbs the lower part of the vagina as well as the skin and muscles of the perineum, but the woman can still feel uterine contractions and some vaginal stretching. The obstetrician places the needle in the vagina and puts his or her finger above the needle and below the fetus's head, so the needle will not injure the fetus. A pudendal nerve block may be given during the second stage of labor, in conjunction with an episiotomy (described later in the chapter), or after labor if repairs to torn tissue are needed.

An **epidural nerve block** for labor is placed in the epidural space, usually somewhere between the L_1 and L_4 vertebrae. As the anesthetic traverses the lower part of the epidural space, it bathes the outer covering of the lower thoracic, lumbar, and sacral nerves. Thus, all of the nerves involved with the uterus, vagina, and perineum are numbed, as well as the lower limbs to some extent (depending upon the type of epidural anesthetic used.) It relieves the pain associated with uterine labor contractions, but usually does not interfere with the contractions themselves. However, some women who receive an epidural may also need an IV of synthetic oxytocin (Pitocin) to ensure uterine contractions progress well.

A **spinal nerve block** currently is typically reserved for cesarean sections. In this case, the needle is placed in the subarachnoid space, typically between the T_{10} and L_1 vertebrae. The placement of the anesthetic here ensures that the anterior abdominal wall is numbed, prior to its incision. The lower limbs and pelvis are completely numbed as well as a consequence of the procedure. Side effects from spinal anesthetic include nausea and a headache, perhaps from the loss of some CSF from the injection site.

Comparisons are shown for the placement of pudendal anesthesia, epidural anesthesia, and spinal anesthesia.

stretching and dilation of the cervix. This manual stretching of the cervix and uterine contractions both signal the hypothalamus to secrete more oxytocin. In addition, uterine contractions stimulate the placenta to secrete more prostaglandins, which also result in more intensive uterine contractions. Thus, true labor intensifies until the fetus is expelled from the uterus. Once the fetus and placenta are expelled (and thus the major source of prostaglandins is removed from the body), the uterus and cervix are no longer fully stretched, oxytocin levels drop, and labor ceases.

WHAT DID YOU LEARN?

28 What are the five signs of true labor?

29 How does the positive feedback mechanism of true labor lead to birth of the fetus?

29.6d Stages of True Labor

LEARNING OBJECTIVE

5. List the three stages of true labor and events of each stage.

True labor involves three stages: the dilation stage, the expulsion stage, and the placental stage **(figure 29.15)**. The lengths for each stage are discussed next, but note that the timing may vary greatly among different women.

CLINICAL VIEW

Fetal Positioning and the Dilation Stage

Normally, the fetus is in a **vertex** (head down) position in the cervix, and its face is toward the sacrum. This position is the ideal position for both dilating the cervix and pushing the fetus through the vagina. If a fetus is in **breech** (buttocks first) position, the head is not in a position to dilate the cervix, and there may be a delay or problems with cervical dilation. Likewise, if the fetus is head-down but the face is facing the pubic symphysis instead of the sacrum, the head is positioned such that cervical dilation is not optimal. Instead, each uterine contraction causes the fetal head to push against the mother's sacrum more than the cervix, which can result in a delay in cervical dilation and cause more intense labor pain for the mother. For both of these variant positions, there also may be greater difficulties in expelling the fetus through the vagina and alternative means (e.g., forceps, vacuum) may be needed to extract the baby through the vagina. Alternatively, the fetus may have to be delivered via **cesarean section** (se-zā'rē-ăn; *C-section*), where a midline horizontal incision is made above the pubic symphysis, through the abdominal and uterine walls, and the fetus is delivered through this incision.

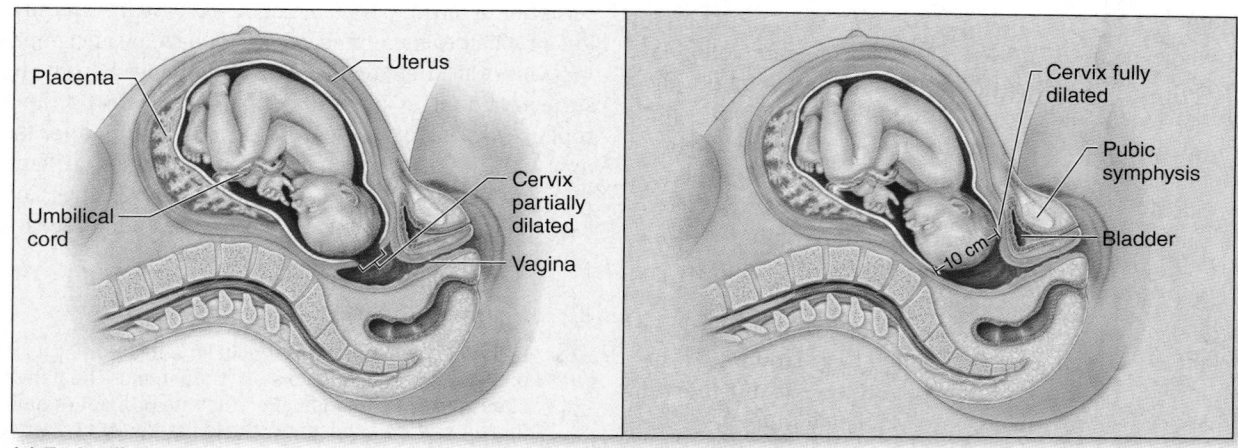

(a) Early dilation stage

(b) Late dilation stage

(c) Expulsion stage

(d) Placental stage

Figure 29.15 Stages of True Labor and Childbirth. The dilation stage begins (*a*) with a distension of the cervix, due to the manual forces exerted by the fetal head. (*b*) Late in the dilation stage, the cervix will dilate to 10 cm in diameter. The expulsion stage (*c*) is where the fetus is pushed out of the uterus, and is followed by (*d*) the placental stage, where the placenta is expelled.

Dilation Stage

The **dilation stage** (figure 29.15*a*, *b*) begins with the onset of regular uterine contractions and ends when the cervix is **effaced** (thinned) and **dilated** (expanded) to 10 centimeters in diameter. This is the longest of the three stages and is the stage marked by the greatest variability. **Nulliparous women** (those who have never given birth before) generally experience a longer dilation stage—on average, 8 to 24 hours—than do **parous women** (those who have given birth previously); the dilation stage in parous women may range from 4 to about 12 hours.

The dilation stage starts with regularly spaced uterine contractions that increase in intensity and frequency. Each time the uterus contracts, the baby's head pushes against the cervix and causes it to efface and dilate slightly, until the cervix dilates from 1 cm to 10 cm in diameter.

This stage is also marked by the rupture of the amniotic sac and the release of amniotic fluid, also commonly known as the "water breaking." If the amniotic sac doesn't rupture on its own by the end of this stage, the physician or other birth practitioner will manually rupture the sac in preparation for the expulsion stage.

Expulsion Stage

The **expulsion stage** (figure 29.15c) begins with the complete dilation of the cervix and ends with the expulsion of the fetus from the mother's body. This stage may last as little as several minutes but typically takes 30 minutes to several hours. As with the dilation stage, nulliparous women typically have a longer expulsion stage than parous women. The uterine contractions help push the fetus through the vagina and may be facilitated if the woman "bears down" (i.e., uses the Valsalva maneuver to increase abdominal pressure as she pushes) with each contraction.

When the first part of the baby's calvarium (i.e., skullcap; see section 8.2) distends the vagina, this is referred to as **crowning.** The head is then followed by the rest of the body. If there is difficulty in expelling the baby from the vagina, then an **episiotomy** (e-piz-ē-ot'ō-mē; *episeion* = pundenda, *tome* = incision) may be performed, which is where the perineal muscles are surgically incised to create a wider opening for the baby to pass through. (This cut is sutured after the birth.) When the baby's body is fully expelled, the umbilical cord is clamped and tied off.

Placental Stage

The **placental stage** (figure 29.15d) occurs after the baby is expelled. The uterus continues to contract, and these contractions help compress the uterine blood vessels and also help displace the placenta from the uterine wall. The placenta and remaining fetal membranes (e.g., the amnion) collectively are referred to as the **afterbirth.** The expulsion of the afterbirth typically is completed within 30 minutes. The obstetrician or other birth practitioner carefully examines the afterbirth to make sure all portions of the placenta have been expelled from the uterus, because fragments of placenta left in the uterus can lead to extensive bleeding or other postpartum complications.

 WHAT DID YOU LEARN?

30 What are the three stages of labor?

31 Why is the placental stage a critical part of labor?

29.7 Postnatal Changes for the Newborn

 LEARNING OBJECTIVES

1. Describe the respiratory events that occur as the newborn adjusts to life outside of the uterus.

2. Compare and contrast the fetal circulatory pattern with the newborn circulatory pattern.

Once the fetus is expelled from the uterus, it is now known as a newborn, or **neonate** (nē'ō-nāt; *neo* = new, *natalis* = relating to birth). A variety of respiratory and cardiovascular changes must occur quickly after birth in order for the neonate to adjust to life outside of the uterus.

Prior to birth, respiratory gases were exchanged between maternal and fetal circulation at the placenta. The fetal lungs are not fully inflated because they are not yet fully functional. However, within about 10 seconds after being born, the neonate typically takes its first breath. This first breath is believed to be caused by central nervous system reactions to the change in environment and temperature. This process may be facilitated by a general respiratory acidosis (caused by clamping of the umbilical vessels and constriction of the umbilical ves-

sels prior to birth), but note that the first breath typically occurs regardless of whether the umbilical vessels have been clamped or not.

Once this first breath is taken, the lungs become inflated and the surfactant that is present in the alveoli keeps the alveoli patent (open) (see section 23.3d). Thus, every breath after the first is easier now that the alveoli remain patent. Premature infants born earlier than 28 weeks are not producing sufficient levels of surfactant to keep their alveoli patent, so these infants may need to placed on a ventilator until their lungs mature.

 WHAT DO YOU THINK?

 In the past, obstetricians would lift a neonate by its feet and slap it on the back, allegedly to start it breathing. The baby's crying was supposed to be an indication that the procedure had worked. Was this procedure necessary? Could it actually be harmful?

The fetal circulatory pattern was described in detail in section 20.12a. Recall that because the fetal lungs are not functional, multiple pathways (e.g., ductus arteriosus, foramen ovale) shunt blood away from the nonfunctional lungs and directly to the fetal circulation. As a result, the fetal cardiovascular system has some structures that are modified or that cease to function once the fetus is born.

At birth, the fetal circulation begins to change into the postnatal pattern. When the neonate takes its first breath, pulmonary resistance drops, and the pulmonary arteries dilate. As a result, pressure on the right side of the heart decreases and the pressure is then greater on the left side of the heart, which handles the systemic circulation. The specific changes are described in section 20.12b.

 WHAT DID YOU LEARN?

 What event must occur when the neonate takes its first breath?

 How does the fetal circulation change once the neonate begins breathing?

29.8 Changes in the Mother After Delivery

Postpartum refers to the time period after giving birth. It is a time when a woman's body must undergo further transformative changes to both feed the neonate and return to pre-pregnancy form and function. Here we describe most of the postpartum changes that typically occur over the first 6 weeks after giving birth.

29.8a Hormonal Changes

 LEARNING OBJECTIVE

1. Compare and contrast the hormonal levels of a woman prior to birth and after birth.

Within a few days after giving birth, estrogen and progesterone levels plummet, because the uterine lining no longer needs to be maintained for pregnancy. Many experts believe this precipitous drop in sex hormone levels may account for the *baby blues*, feelings of varying degrees of sadness and depression immediately after giving birth.

As estrogen and progesterone levels plummet, the integumentary system is affected. Recall that high levels of these hormones prevented the normal cyclical hair loss. After giving birth, the hair reverts back to its normal cyclical growth and hair loss cycle. And in fact, some of the hair that was prevented from falling out during pregnancy may fall out rather abruptly after giving birth for some women. A peak in hair loss may be experienced by some women about 3 to 4 months after delivery, and it may take up to 12 months for the normal cyclical hair growth and loss cycle to resume. Thus, many new mothers may experience temporary hair thinning during this time.

The decrease in progesterone also affects the respiratory system. Without the high levels of progesterone, the chemoreceptors are less sensitive to CO_2 levels. As a result, respiratory rate, tidal volume, and pulmonary ventilation return to pre-pregnancy levels.

Additionally, the levels of corticotropin-releasing hormone (CRH) drop dramatically, now that there is no longer a placenta producing copious amounts of this hormone. Recent research has suggested that high levels of CRH during pregnancy are associated with an increased risk of **postpartum depression,** a serious disorder in which the mother experiences severe depression and possibly suicidal thoughts; unlike baby blues, this condition should be treated as soon as possible.

Prolactin levels and oxytocin levels drop after birth as well. However, because both of these hormones are involved in lactation, periodic surges occur in these hormone levels each time a baby nurses. These surges are described in greater detail in a later section.

  WHAT DID YOU LEARN?

34 Which hormone levels drop in a postpartum woman, and what are the effects of this reduction in hormone levels?

29.8b Blood Volume and Fluid Changes

 LEARNING OBJECTIVE

2. List the various ways that the mother loses the excess fluids gained during pregnancy.

A pregnant woman retains a great deal of fluid throughout the 9 months of pregnancy. In addition to the fluid retained in the amniotic sac and some excess fluid found in the interstitial spaces, most additional fluid is due to the increased blood volume acquired during pregnancy. After a woman gives birth, she no longer has need for this additional fluid and must expel it in a relatively quick and efficient manner. The amniotic fluid is quickly expelled by the end of the first stage of labor. But what about the rest?

A portion of the blood volume, as well as mucus and hypertrophied endometrial tissue, is released from the uterus as **lochia** (lō′kē-ă; *lochos* = childbirth). Lochia is similar to a menstrual period, in that blood and some endometrial tissue is expelled from the uterus via the vagina. However, lochia results in much heavier bleeding than a typical menstrual period, because the uterine lining buildup occurred over a 9-month period, instead of a typical 28-day cycle. Thus, the first 5 days of lochia typically results in very heavy bleeding, after which it lightens but progresses for at least 2 to 3 weeks. For some women, it may take 4 to 6 weeks before the flow finally stops. As the blood volume decreases, the woman's cardiac output returns to pre-pregnancy levels.

A woman also may expel excess fluids via increased urination. The decline in CRH after birth results in a decline in aldosterone (see section 25.4c), which precipitates the overall drop in blood volume and interstitial fluid levels. The lymphatic system cycles some of the excess interstitial fluid into the blood circulation, where it may be filtered by the kidneys and secreted as urine. Within about 24 hours after giving birth, most women experience copious, frequent urination, the result of the kidneys "working overtime," so to speak, in filtering out this excess fluid. Urination levels typically return to normal by the end of the first week after birth.

Another common symptom new mothers experience is profuse sweating for the first 2 weeks after giving birth. This abundant sweating is yet another way the body expels the excess fluid gained during pregnancy.

  WHAT DID YOU LEARN?

35 What are four ways by which excess fluid is eliminated from a postpartum woman's body?

29.8c Lactation

 LEARNING OBJECTIVE

3. Describe the process by which lactation occurs.

Lactation (lak-tā′shŭn; *lactatio* = suckle) refers to the production and release of breast milk from the mammary glands. Prolactin is produced by the anterior pituitary and is responsible for milk production (see section 17.8c). In nonpregnant women and in men, the secretion of significant amounts of prolactin is inhibited by dopamine secreted by cells in the hypothalamus.

High levels of estrogen positively influence the secretion of prolactin, so as estrogen levels rise during pregnancy, so do prolactin levels. Both estrogen and prolactin cause mammary gland acini proliferation and branching of the lactiferous ducts. Paradoxically, the high levels of estrogen and progesterone are also responsible for preventing breast milk secretion until after birth. It isn't until levels of estrogen and progesterone drop that prolactin works unopposed to stimulate breast milk production.

During late pregnancy and for the first few days after birth, the substance produced by the mammary glands isn't breast milk per se. It is a watery, yellowish milklike substance called **colostrum** (kō-los′trŭm; *foremilk*), and it has lower concentrations of fat than true breast milk but is rich in immunoglobulins, especially immunoglobulin A (IgA). By drinking colostrum, the infant acquires passive immunity from the mother. IgA resists breakdown in the infant's stomach and is believed to protect the infant against ingested pathogens. Colostrum also has a laxative effect, and facilitates the infant having its first bowel movement shortly after birth.

A few days postpartum, the true breast milk starts to be produced. It has a higher fat content than colostrum, and it contains several growth factors, essential fatty acids (needed for optimal brain growth and development), specific enzymes to aid in digestion of the milk, and an array of immunoglobulins. Breast milk typically is more easily

---

INTEGRATE

CONCEPT CONNECTION

Many organ systems work in tandem to help bring the mother's body back to a pre-pregnancy homeostasis. Excess fluids are removed from the cardiovascular system and excreted by both the urinary system and the integumentary system. The endocrine system secretes oxytocin to promote uterine contractions and shrinkage to a pre-pregnancy state. The immune system produces immunoglobulins that are found in abundance in the newly-produced breast milk. Many of the pregnancy digestive system challenges, such as heartburn, constipation, and morning sickness, resolve once the baby is born. Finally, if the mother is breastfeeding, the skeletal system will be called upon to supply calcium for the breast milk.

digestible for an infant than other types of breast milk substitutes (e.g., cow's milk, soy "milk") and it remains the optimal source of nutrition for an infant, if the mother is able to breastfeed. One vitamin that is *not* abundant in breast milk is vitamin D, and recently physicians have recommended that infants of breastfeeding mothers receive a vitamin D supplement.

WHAT DO YOU THINK?

4 The recommendation that breastfeeding infants receive vitamin D supplementation is a recent one. Can you think of any recent change in behaviors that may have made this recommendation necessary? (Hint: How does the body produce vitamin D?)

Lactation requires the hormones prolactin for breast milk production and oxytocin for breast milk secretion (see section 28.3f). Although prolactin levels drop after birth by about 50%, surges in prolactin continue as long as the baby continues to breastfeed. Thus, the continual production and release of breast milk is a positive feedback mechanism that is maintained by regular breastfeeding (**figure 29.16a**).

(a)

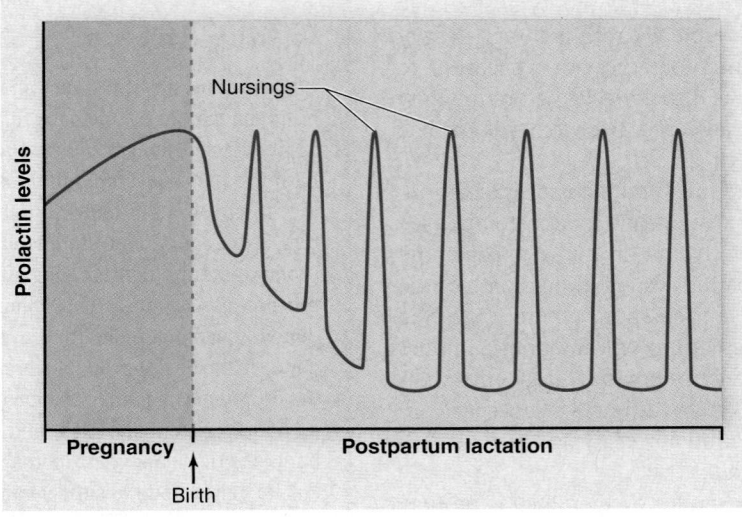

(b)

Figure 29.16 Lactation.
(*a*) Positive feedback mechanism of lactation. (*b*) Prolactin levels during lactation. After parturition, prolactin levels drop by about 50%. However, each time the infant nurses, prolactin levels spike, thus ensuring that milk production will continue for the next feeding.

The release of breast milk is referred to as **milk letdown,** or the *letdown reflex,* because it involves this positive feedback mechanism. When the infant suckles at the breast, mechanoreceptors in the nipple and areola are stimulated, and they send sensory impulses to the hypothalamus. The hypothalamus is stimulated to produce oxytocin, and the posterior pituitary releases this oxytocin into the bloodstream. The oxytocin targets special cells in the mammary glands called **myoepithelial cells,** which surround the mammary gland acini. Specifically, oxytocin stimulates the myoepithelial cells to contract, thereby releasing breast milk from the acini. As milk is released from the breast, the infant may continue to nurse. Milk will continue to be released from the breast as long as the infant continues to nurse. Once the infant stops suckling (and the nipple and areola are no longer being mechanically stimulated), oxytocin levels drop and milk letdown stops.

The milk letdown reflex may be initiated in some mothers simply in response to hearing a baby cry. Note that since a baby usually cries when it is hungry, the mother's milk letdown response may have adapted to prepare for the eventual feeding of this baby.

Note in figure 29.16*a* that as the infant breastfeeds, dopamine release is inhibited by the hypothalamus. This inhibition of dopamine secretion stimulates the anterior pituitary to secrete large amounts of prolactin. Figure 29.16*b* illustrates that spikes or peaks in prolactin production occur each time a baby breastfeeds. This prolactin promotes new breast milk production, so a new supply of breast milk will be available to the baby at the next feeding.

Most women who regularly breastfeed (i.e., more than four to five feedings a day) often do not ovulate at this time. Researchers believe that either the hormones or the sensory stimuli involved with breastfeeding inhibit release of gonadotropin-releasing hormone (GnRH) from the hypothalamus. If GnRH is not released, then FSH and LH won't be released by the anterior pituitary, and so ovulation is prevented. This mechanism may have evolved as a way of spacing births, so that a nursing mother's body won't be additionally taxed by a new pregnancy. However, breastfeeding is not a reliable form of birth control because ovulation can and does occur in breastfeeding mothers, especially those that may have reduced numbers of breastfeedings, and it is difficult to determine that ovulation has occurred. Thus, most lactating women are encouraged to use some form of birth control if they do not want to become pregnant again at that time.

  WHAT DID YOU LEARN?

36 How does the positive feedback mechanism in breastfeeding ensure that the infant receives breast milk?

29.8d Uterine Changes

 LEARNING OBJECTIVE

4. Explain the mechanisms by which the uterus returns close to its pre-pregnancy size.

The uterus spends the 9 months of pregnancy undergoing hyperplasia and hypertrophy. It takes 6 weeks following birth for the uterus to shrink to close to its pre-pregnancy size. Oxytocin facilitates this shrinkage by stimulating uterine contractions. These contractions tend to be most severe the first week after giving birth and are referred to as **afterpains.** Afterpains may be most severe and noticeable when a woman breastfeeds, since oxytocin is involved in milk ejection. After the first week, these contractions will continue but typically will be less noticeable.

The spike in oxytocin that occurs each time a woman breastfeeds not only expels the milk but stimulates uterine contractions. Thus, regular breastfeeding facilitates rapid, efficient shrinkage of the uterus. Although these contractions occur in women who don't breastfeed, they may not be as frequent or as efficient, and the uterus may not return to its pre-pregnancy size as quickly.

The changes that occur in the mother to both accommodate a pregnancy and return the body back to normal are quite remarkable. Refer to **figure 29.17** to review these processes.

  WHAT DID YOU LEARN?

37 How are prolactin and oxytocin related to both the uterine changes and lactation?

INTEGRATE CONCEPT OVERVIEW

Figure 29.17 **Anatomic and Physiologic Changes That Occur in the Mother.** (*a*) During pregnancy and (*b*) postpartum (after birth).

(a) Pregnancy

Anterior pituitary secretes prolactin, which stimulates mammary glandular tissue to grow and develop.

Uterus hypertrophies, reaching the level of the xiphoid process by the ninth month.

Hair and nails become thicker and stronger during pregnancy due to increased levels of estrogen and progesterone (which slow hair loss).

Placenta produces many hormones. There is an increase in CRH, hCG, estrogen, and progesterone levels.

Placenta is now main producer of estrogen and progesterone.

Increase in blood volume causes resulting increase in cardiac output.

Progesterone increases chemoreceptors' sensitivity to CO_2, so tidal volume, respiratory rate, and pulmonary ventilation levels increase.

Weight gain occurs.

Constipation, hemorrhoids, heartburn, and morning sickness may occur.

Spine exhibits lordosis to accommodate carrying additional weight.

Uterine compression of the bladder results in frequent urination.

Graph legend:
— Progesterone
— Estrogen
— hCG

Relative hormone levels (y-axis)

Weeks after ovulation (x-axis): 0 2 6 10 14 18 22 26 30 34

Lactation occurs: Suckling infant stimulates oxytocin release and thus milk ejection, while spikes in prolactin occur to ensure new milk production.

Nursings

Prolactin levels

Postpartum lactation

CRH, hCG, estrogen, and progesterone levels drop dramatically days after giving birth.

— Progesterone
— Estrogen
— hCG

Relative hormone levels

26 30 34 **38** 39
↑
Birth
Weeks after ovulation

Blood volume and cardiac output decrease to pre-pregnancy levels.

Under the influence of oxytocin, the uterus returns to close to its pre-pregnancy size by 6 weeks postpartum.

Due to the drop in estrogen and progesterone at around the third month after birth, hair falls out in larger than normal quantities.

Drop in hormone levels may account for "baby blues" experienced by the mother.

Decrease in progesterone results in less sensitivity of chemoreceptors to CO_2 levels, so respiratory rate, pulmonary ventilation, and tidal volume return to pre-pregnancy levels.

Lochia is discharged for several weeks after labor.

Fluid loss occurs through copious sweating and urination shortly after birth.

130

Mother may lose some or all of the weight gained during pregnancy.

29.9 Heredity

Heredity is the transmission of genetic characteristics from parent to child. **Genetics** is the field of biology that studies heredity and its transmission patterns. Here we provide a basic overview of human genetics and introduce you to some of the concepts and vocabulary necessary to understand patterns of inheritance.

29.9a Overview of Human Genetics

✓ LEARNING OBJECTIVE

1. Become familiar with common genetic terminology.

We have already discussed the mechanisms of somatic and sex cell division in previous chapters (see sections 4.8 and 28.2, respectively). Recall that human cells have 23 pairs of chromosomes. The display of the chromosome pairs, which are ordered and arranged by similar features, banding patterns and size, is called the **karyotype** (kar′ē-ō-tīp; *karyon* = nucleus) **(figure 29.18)**. Recall from section 28.2 that the paired chromosomes are called **homologous chromosomes** (or *homologues*), as they contain genes for equivalent biological characteristics, such as eye color. Twenty-two of these pairs of chromosomes are called **autosomes;** they have no genes that determine the sex of the individual. The last two chromosomes are called the **sex chromosomes,** which contain genes that specify the sex of an individual. (In mammals, two X chromosomes occur in females, and an X and a Y are found in males.)

Figure 29.18 Karyotype. A karyotype is a conventional representation of pairs of homologous chromosomes as they appear in metaphase of the cell cycle.

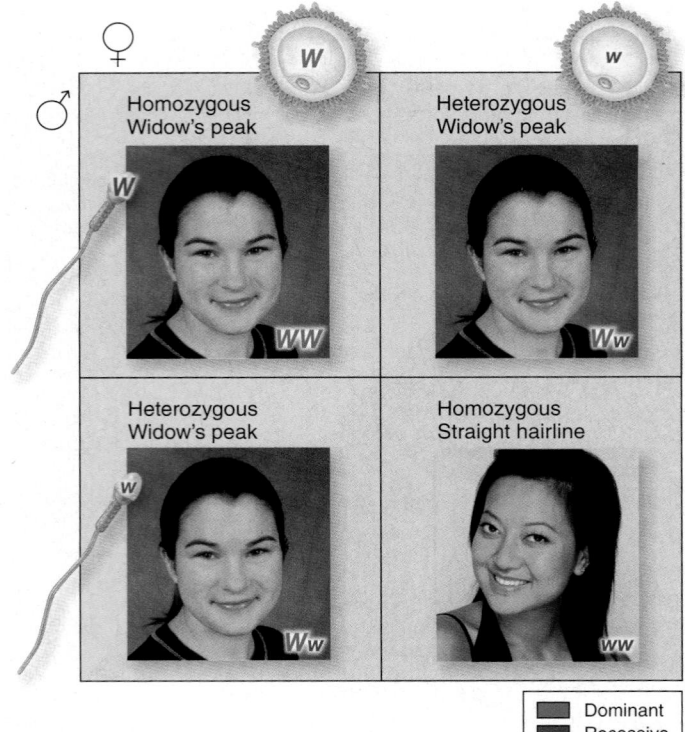

Figure 29.19 Dominant Versus Recessive Alleles. A widow's peak is a dominant trait, and the allele for this trait is designated as *W*. A straight hairline allele is designated as *w*. The Punnett square illustrates the probabilities that two parents who are heterozygous for the widow's peak trait will have offspring that also have a widow's peak. There is a 1 in 4 chance that a child born to these parents will have a straight hairline, and a 3 in 4 chance that a child will have a widow's peak.

Recall from section 4.6b that genes are discrete units of DNA that provide the instructions for the production of specific proteins. Genes are located on chromosomes; the specific place where each gene is located on a chromosome is called its **locus** (lō′kŭs; pl. = *loci*). Variants of one gene found at the same locus on homologous chromosomes are called **alleles** (ă-lēl′; *allelon* = reciprocally). You inherit from your parents a combination of two alleles that determines the expression of a particular trait. For example, the two alleles at a locus may determine whether you have the A or O blood type, or whether your hair is straight or wavy.

How do two alleles code for one trait? In the most straightforward situation, one allele is **dominant,** and the other allele is **recessive.** The dominant allele **expresses,** or physically shows, the trait (e.g., blood type), while the recessive trait is masked. The recessive allele is expressed only if it is present on both homologous chromosomes.

Typically, a dominant allele is expressed by a capital letter, and the recessive allele is represented by a lowercase letter. For example, having a widow's peak, in which the hairline on the forehead comes to a point or V in the center, is a dominant trait. So the allele for a widow's peak would be shown as *W*. The recessive allele for a strait forehead hairline would be represented by a *w*. **Figure 29.19** illustrates how these two traits would be expressed. The box used to sort out the alleles is called a **Punnett square,** and it shows the specific gene combinations resulting from two parents. The Punnett square can also give the probability that a particular gene combination can occur.

If identical alleles are present, the individual is said to be **homozygous** (hō-mō-zī′gŭs; *homos* = same, *zygotes* = yoke) for the trait. So in this example, *WW* (widow's peak) and *ww* (straight hairline) are both homozygous, because the alleles are identical. Individuals who are **heterozygous** for a trait have both a dominant allele and a recessive allele (e.g., *Ww*), but only the dominant allele is expressed. Expression of the recessive allele may appear to skip generations, because its phenotype is masked by the dominant allele.

In a mating between heterozygous individuals, or heterozygotes, there is a 1 in 4 chance (or 25%) the child would be homozygous for a widow's peak, a 2 in 4 chance (50%) of being heterozygous for a widow's peak, and a 1 in 4 chance (25%) the child would have a straight hairline. If we simply look at how the children may appear, then there is a 3 in 4 chance (75%) that a child would have a widow's peak (includes both *WW* and *Ww*), and a 1 in 4 chance (25%) that a child would have a straight hairline (*ww*).

The genetic makeup of an individual is called the **genotype** (jen′ō-tīp; *genos* = birth). So in this example, individuals may have the genotype *WW, Ww,* or *ww*. The physical expression of the genotype, however, is called the **phenotype** (fē′nō-tīp; *phaino* = to appear, show forth). The phenotype for a *WW* and a *Ww* genotype is to exhibit a widow's peak, whereas the phenotype for a *ww* genotype is a straight hairline. Thus, genotype and phenotype describe the difference between the genetic constitution and the actual observed traits of an individual.

 WHAT DID YOU LEARN?

 38   What would be the results in terms of the genotype and phenotype if one parent is heterozygous for the widow's peak and the other parent is homozygous for a straight hairline?

29.9b Patterns of Inheritance

LEARNING OBJECTIVE

2.   Compare and contrast the types of inheritance patterns.

Not all types of inheritance follow the relatively simple pattern just described. In fact, inheritance of most traits involves the interaction of multiple genes. Here we describe some of the typical patterns of inheritance.

Strict dominant-recessive inheritance has been illustrated in figure 29.19. This type of inheritance is also referred to as *Mendelian inheritance* after Gregor Mendel, who first described this pattern. The dominant allele is always expressed in the phenotype, regardless of whether the individual is homozygous or heterozygous for that trait. Examples of traits that follow this strict dominant-recessive inheritance are found in **table 29.4**. Relatively few human traits follow this pattern of inheritance, but instead may involve the interaction of multiple genes (and thus multiple alleles). In addition, the expression of many traits may be affected by environmental factors.

For some traits, the phenotype of two heterozygous alleles is intermediate between the phenotypes of homozygous dominant or recessive alleles. This trait is said to exhibit **incomplete dominance.** Thus, three phenotypes are possible: (1) the phenotype produced by homozygous dominant alleles, (2) the phenotype produced by homozygous recessive alleles, and (3) the phenotype produced by heterozygous alleles.

One example of incomplete dominance is the sickle cell trait, which affects the shape of erythrocytes. Most individuals have two identical alleles (each designated *A*) that code for the normal hemoglobin A in erythrocytes. The sickling allele (designated *s*) produces an abnormal form of hemoglobin, hemoglobin S. This hemoglobin

Table 29.4	Traits That Follow a Strict Dominant-Recessive Inheritance
Dominant Trait	**Recessive Trait**
Dimples in cheeks	Absence of dimples
Cleft chin	Uncleft chin
Widow's peak	Straight hairline
Normal skin and hair pigmentation	Albinism (absence of skin and hair pigmentation)
Huntington disease (leads to progressive neurodegeneration and death)	Absence of Huntington disease
Astigmatism	Nondistorted vision
Achondroplasia (a type of dwarfism)	Normal endochondral ossification of bones
Rh$^+$ blood type (e.g., O$^+$)	Rh$^-$ blood type (e.g., O$^-$)
Free earlobes	Attached earlobes
Polydactyly (extra digits)	Normal number of digits
Extensive flexibility in thumb joints ("hitchhiker's thumb")	Inability to extend distal phalanx of thumb past 180 degrees

crystallizes when oxygen levels are low and results in the erythrocyte becoming brittle and forming a sickle-shape. The sickling allele is recessive, and individuals who are homozygous recessive exhibit **sickle cell disease,** also known as *sickle cell anemia* (see Clinical View: "Erythrocyte Volume Disorders," in Chapter 18). Erythrocytes in these individuals are inefficient; they may fragment in blood vessels and obstruct them, and they don't have as long as life span as normal erythrocytes. Individuals with sickle cell anemia may experience greater morbidity and mortality than individuals who code for normal hemoglobin A.

Heterozygous individuals are said to carry the **sickle cell trait,** whereby under very low oxygen conditions, some (but not all) of their erythrocytes may develop this sickle shape. Researchers have found that individuals with the sickle cell trait experience less mortality from malaria than do individuals without the trait, so the sickle cell trait is somewhat adaptive for individuals who live in malaria-prone environments.

 INTEGRATE

CLINICAL VIEW
Familial Hypercholesteremia

Another example of incomplete dominance in humans is the condition **familial hypercholesterolemia (FH).** In this clinical disorder, a person who has two abnormal alleles lacks receptors for low-density lipoprotein (LDL) and cannot transport LDL from the blood; thus, the individual has very high serum cholesterol and often develops heart disease early in life. In contrast, the heterozygote for this condition has about half the number of receptors for LDL. This individual exhibits some LDL transport-related problems related to slightly elevated cholesterol blood levels, but usually these levels are not life-threatening.

In some cases, two or more alleles appear to be equally dominant, and the trait is said to exhibit **codominant inheritance.** Both alleles are expressed in the phenotype. An example of codominance is the ABO blood group. Blood types A and B are codominant, so if an individual receives an *A* allele from one parent and a *B* allele from the other parent, the individual will have an AB blood type. A third allele, *i*, is recessive; the combination *ii* results in the O blood type (see section 18.3b).

Polygenic inheritance, also known as *multiple gene inheritance,* occurs when multiple genes interact to produce a phenotypic trait. These multiple genes may be on the same chromosome or on different chromosomes. Most human traits are the result of polygenic inheritance. For example, eye color was originally believed to be a strict dominant-recessive inheritance involving a single gene, but we now know that eye color is the result of interactions of many genes. Other traits such as height, skin color, predisposition to certain diseases, and many others, are traits under polygenic influence.

 WHAT DID YOU LEARN?

39 How does codominant inheritance differ from incomplete dominance?

29.9c Sex-Linked Inheritance

 LEARNING OBJECTIVE

3. Describe sex-linked inheritance and give a clinical example of this type of inheritance.,

Sex-linked traits are traits expressed by genes on the X or Y chromosomes. You can see from figure 29.18 that the X and Y chromosomes are physically different—and these differences are also represented in the number of genes each carries. The National Institutes of Health estimates there are between 900 and 1400 genes on the X chromosome, while the Y chromosome contains somewhere between 70 and 200 genes. Further, since only males have a Y chromosome, most of the Y chromosome genes code for male-specific development. In contrast, most of the genes on the X chromosome are not involved in sex determination. Thus, although either sex chromosome may be responsible for a sex-linked trait, it is far more common for the X chromosome to be involved.

X-linked traits may be recessive or dominant. An **X-linked recessive trait** is always expressed in a male, because he has only one X chromosome. In contrast, an X-linked recessive trait is expressed in a female *only* if she has two recessive alleles for that trait; typically, the probability of this occurring is very low. A woman is said to be a **carrier** if she has one X-linked recessive allele only and does not exhibit any phenotypic effects. This carrier may pass on the X-linked recessive allele to her offspring; if she passes it on to a female child, the female child also will be a carrier. If she passes the allele to a male child, he is assured of expressing the X-linked trait.

One example of an X-linked recessive trait is *color blindness,* where in the most common form an individual has trouble distinguishing among different shades of red and green (see Clinical View: "Color Blindness" in chapter 16). Women are rarely color-blind, because they would have to inherit a recessive allele each from their mother and their father. More often, a woman may be a carrier for the red-green color-blindness allele, but her other, normal allele (on her second X chromosome) allows her to see colors normally. In contrast, if a man inherits a red-green color-blindness allele, he will be color-blind because he has only one X chromosome (and thus, no additional normal allele to counteract the color-blindness allele).

Another example of an X-linked recessive trait is hemophilia A, which is a disorder of blood clotting (see Clinical View: "Bleeding and Blood Clotting Disorders" in chapter 18). Individuals with this disorder bleed profusely after an injury and may die from this extensive bleeding. The normal allele is typically designated *H* and the hemophilic allele is designated *h,* as illustrated in **figure 29.20.** Females may be carriers, in that they will have one *h* allele and one normal *H* allele. Thus, while they do not have hemophilia, they could pass the hemophilic gene to their offspring. A male child who inherits the *h* allele is guaranteed to develop hemophilia, because he has only one X chromosome.

X-linked dominant traits are relatively rare. An X-linked dominant is expressed in both males and females who carry it; however, men typically are more severely affected because they have no normal recessive allele to counteract the effects of the dominant allele. In fact, many male zygotes or embryos with an X-linked dominant disorder are spontaneously aborted (miscarried) because a high rate of lethality is present with these disorders.

 WHAT DID YOU LEARN?

40 If a woman homozygous for color blindness has children with a man having normal vision, what would be the genotypes and phenotypes of her offspring?

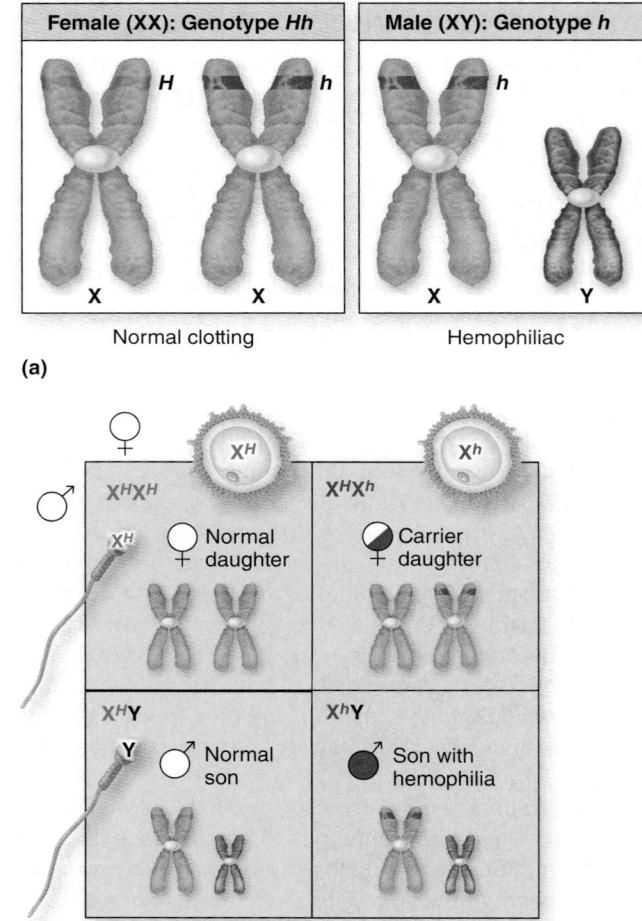

Figure 29.20 Hemophilia A. (*a*) Hemophilia A is an X-linked recessive trait that leads to abnormal blood clotting and severe bleeding. (*b*) A Punnett square illustrates the possible transmission paths from a heterozygous female and a normal male to their male and female offspring.

29.9d Penetrance and Environmental Influences on Heredity

LEARNING OBJECTIVE

4. Explain how the environment may influence genetic expression.

The expression of the genotype may be influenced by a variety of factors, inheritance patterns notwithstanding. Sometimes an individual does not display a particular phenotype, despite having the expected genotype for that phenotypical pattern. The term **penetrance** refers to the percentage of a population with a particular genotype that exhibits the expected phenotype. For example, the autosomal dominant disorder *hereditary pancreatitis* has a penetrance level of 80%. This means that 20% of individuals having this genotype will experience none of the symptoms seen in hereditary pancreatitis.

The environment has variable influence on many genetic traits, especially during embryonic and fetal development. If a pregnant woman is exposed to teratogens such as radiation, drugs, viruses, or alcohol, any of these teratogens have the potential to cause harm to the fetus and interfere with its normal phenotypic development. Mothers that ingest large amounts of alcohol while pregnant are more likely to give birth to children with **fetal alcohol syndrome,** which is characterized by mental retardation and distinctive facial features. The alcohol was a teratogen that affected the phenotypic pattern of the fetus. However, these changes do not occur in the gametes of offspring, and thus they do not get passed on.

The environment continues to affect phenotype well after birth. Poor nutrition, an environmental effect, may negatively affect an individual's brain development and growth patterns. In the early twentieth century, researchers studied identical twins who were raised in separate households beginning at a young age. Twins with significant environmental differences (e.g., one child received adequate nutrition and an enriched environment, while the other had deficiencies in the environment) displayed phenotypic differences such as dramatic differences in height. Also, some individuals may have alleles associated with a risk of developing certain cancers (e.g., individuals with a mutation of the *BRCA1* gene are at greater risk of developing breast cancer; see Clinical View: "Breast Cancer" in chapter 28). However, just because an individual has that mutant allele does not guarantee she (or he) will develop cancer. It is the combination of the genetics plus the individual's environment that determine whether an individual will develop cancer. Thus, while our genotype may be determined prior to birth, the phenotypic expression of these genes may be affected by a variety of external factors.

WHAT DID YOU LEARN?

 How would nutrition affect growth where hereditary factors are equal?

CHAPTER SUMMARY

29.1 Overview of the Prenatal Period 1132	• Embryology is the study of development between the fertilization of the secondary oocyte and birth.
	• The prenatal period is subdivided into the pre-embryonic period (the 2 weeks after fertilization), the embryonic period (between 3 and 8 weeks after fertilization), and the fetal period (the remaining 30 weeks prior to birth).
29.2 Pre-Embryonic Period 1133	• A pre-embryo develops during the first 2 weeks after fertilization.

29.2a Fertilization 1134
- Fertilization is the process whereby two sex cells fuse to form a zygote, which is the first cell of a new organism.
- The phases of fertilization are corona radiata penetration, zona pellucida penetration, and fusion of the sperm and oocyte plasma membranes.
- When a sperm penetrates the secondary oocyte, the secondary oocyte completes meiosis II and becomes an ovum.
- The pronuclei of the ovum and sperm fuse and form a single diploid cell called a zygote.

29.2b Cleavage 1135
- The series of mitotic divisions of the zygote is called cleavage. Once the zygote starts dividing, it is referred to as a pre-embryo.
- At the 16-cell stage, the ball of cells is called a morula.
- Upon arrival in the uterine lumen, the morula has developed into a single central fluid-filled cavity and is called a blastocyst.
- Cells within the blastocyst form the embryoblast (inner cell mass), which gives rise to the embryo proper. The outer ring of cells forms the trophoblast, which contributes to the placenta.

29.2c Implantation 1137
- Implantation consists of attachment and embedding of the blastocyst into the endometrial wall, and cell changes in the trophoblast and uterine epithelium.

29.2d Formation of the Bilaminar Germinal Disc and Extraembryonic Membranes 1138
- During the implantation of the blastocyst into the endometrium of the uterus, cells of the embryoblast differentiate into two layers: the hypoblast and the epiblast. Together, these two layers form a flat disc called a bilaminar germinal disc.
- The extraembryonic membranes provide support to the embryo and fetus.

29.2e Development of the Placenta 1139
- The main functions of the placenta are the exchange of metabolic products and respiratory gases between fetal and maternal blood, transmission of maternal antibodies, and hormone production.

(continued on next page)

29.3 Embryonic Period 1140

- The embryonic period extends from week 3 to week 8.

29.3a Gastrulation and Formation of the Primary Germ Layers 1141

- Gastrulation produces three primary germ layers: ectoderm, mesoderm, and endoderm.
- Derivatives of the ectoderm include the nervous system, most exocrine glands, tooth enamel, epidermis, and sense organs.
- Mesoderm forms most muscle, connective tissue, much of the cardiovascular system, urinary system, and reproductive system.
- Endoderm gives rise to the inner lining of the digestive, respiratory, and urinary tracts as well as the thyroid, parathyroid, and thymus glands, portions of the palatine tonsils, and most of the liver, gallbladder, and pancreas.

29.3b Folding of the Embryonic Disc 1142

- The embryonic disc undergoes cephalocaudal and transverse folding, beginning late in the third week.

29.3c Organogenesis 1146

- Almost all of organogenesis (organ development) occurs during the embryonic period.
- During the embryonic period, the embryo is very sensitive to teratogens, substances that can cause birth defects or the death of the embryo.

29.4 Fetal Period 1145

- The time from the beginning of the third month to birth is known as the fetal period. It is characterized by maturation of tissues and organs and rapid growth.

29.5 Effects of Pregnancy on the Mother 1148

- Although certain anatomic and physiologic changes typically occur in a pregnant woman, a great deal of variation exists in how individual women experience pregnancy.

29.5a The Course of Pregnancy 1148

- During the first trimester, the zygote develops into an embryo and then into an early fetus.
- During the second trimester, the fetus grows and the mother's tissues undergo expansion.
- During the third trimester, the fetus undergoes rapid growth, and the mother's body prepares for eventual labor and delivery.

29.5b Hormonal Changes 1148

- Human chorionic gonadotropin peaks during the first trimester and then its levels drop thereafter.
- Levels of estrogen, progesterone, and human placental lactogen (HPL) increase dramatically during the second and third trimesters.
- Prolactin and oxytocin levels rise in the later months of pregnancy.

29.5c Uterine and Mammary Gland Changes 1149

- The uterus enlarges throughout pregnancy, reaching the level of the xiphoid process by the ninth month. The uterine lining grows and proliferates throughout the pregnancy.
- The mammary glands enlarge, and the acini begin producing milk in the later months of pregnancy.

29.5d Digestive System, Nutrient, and Metabolic Changes 1150

- The hormone HPL is responsible for the mother metabolizing fatty acids versus glucose, so more glucose remains in the blood for the fetus.
- Some women may experience heartburn, constipation, and morning sickness during part or all of their pregnancy.

29.5e Cardiovascular and Respiratory System Changes 1151

- Cardiac output, plasma volume, stroke volume, and heart rate increase during pregnancy.
- Tidal volume increases during pregnancy, although respiratory rate increases only slightly.

29.5f Urinary System Changes 1151

- Glomerular filtration rate (GFR) increases during pregnancy, and during parts of pregnancy, urination may become more frequent.

29.6 Labor (Parturition) and Delivery 1152

- Labor is the expulsion of the fetus and placenta from the uterus.

29.6a Factors That Lead to Labor 1152

- Rising estrogen levels counteract the calming influence of progesterone on the uterine myometrium, and stimulate the production of oxytocin receptors on the myometrium. Both events facilitate uterine irritability and uterine contractions.

29.6b False Labor 1152

- False labor is irregular uterine contractions that do *not* result in the three stages of labor and the expulsion of the fetus.

29.6c Initiation of True Labor 1153

- True labor is defined as uterine contractions that increase in intensity and regularity and result in changes to the cervix.
- The fetus and the mother secrete oxytocin, which stimulates uterine contractions and also causes the placenta to release prostaglandins, which further stimulate uterine contractions.
- A positive feedback cycle is initiated, whereby the uterine contractions stimulate cervical stretching, which causes increased release of oxytocin and more intense and frequent uterine contractions.

29.6d Stages of True Labor 1154

- The dilation stage begins with the onset of rhythmic uterine contractions and is complete when the cervix dilates to 10 centimeters in diameter.

- The expulsion stage begins when the cervix is fully dilated and ends when the baby is expelled from the mother's body.

- The placental stage is where the placenta and fetal membranes are expelled from the uterus.

29.7 Postnatal Changes for the Newborn 1156

- The first breath is initiated by changes in the environment and temperature, which stimulate the neonate's central nervous system.

- The fetal cardiovascular system contains some structures that are modified or cease to function once the baby is born.

29.8 Changes in the Mother After Delivery 1156

- After a woman gives birth, a variety of anatomic and physiologic changes occur to accommodate lactation and bring the mother's body back to its pre-pregnancy form.

29.8a Hormonal Changes 1156

- Estrogen, progesterone, and corticotropin-releasing hormone (CRH) levels all decrease after pregnancy.

- Prolactin levels decrease significantly after pregnancy, but prolactin levels will spike each time the baby nurses.

29.8b Blood Volume and Fluid Changes 1157

- Blood volume decreases after pregnancy, as the mother expels excess fluids.

- The mother loses excess fluids via the expulsion of amniotic fluid (during labor), discharge of lochia, frequent urination, and copious sweating.

29.8c Lactation 1157

- Lactation occurs via a positive feedback mechanism: The infant suckling stimulates the mother's hypothalamus to release oxytocin, which facilitates milk ejection.

- Breastfeeding stimulates the hypothalamus, which stimulates the anterior pituitary to release prolactin, so new milk will be produced for the next feeding.

29.8d Uterine Changes 1159

- Within the first 6 weeks postpartum, the uterus shrinks to close to its pre-pregnancy size.

- Oxytocin facilitates uterine contractions that help the uterus shrink.

29.9 Heredity 1162

- Heredity is the transmission of genetic characteristics from parent to child.

29.9a Overview of Human Genetics 1162

- Humans have 23 pairs of chromosomes: 22 pairs are autosomes and one pair is the sex chromosomes.

- Alternate forms of a gene are called alleles.

- A dominant allele is one that is expressed if present; a recessive allele is expressed only if present in both alleles.

- A homozygous trait has two identical alleles for the trait; a heterozygous trait has two different alleles for the trait.

- The genetic makeup of an individual comprises the genotype; the physical expression of the genotype is called the phenotype.

29.9b Patterns of Inheritance 1163

- Strict dominant-recessive inheritance is where the dominant phenotype is expressed, unless the individual is homozygous recessive.

- Incomplete dominance is where there are multiple phenotypes, depending upon whether the individual is homozygous dominant, heterozygous dominant, or homozygous recessive.

- Codominance is where two alleles are equally dominant, and both are expressed in the phenotype.

- Polygenic inheritance is where multiple genes interact to produce a phenotypic trait. Most human traits fall under polygenic inheritance.

29.9c Sex-Linked Inheritance 1164

- Sex-linked traits are traits expressed by genes on the X or Y chromosomes.

- X-linked recessive traits are always expressed in a male offspring, whereas a female offspring is typically a carrier and does not exhibit any phenotypic effects.

- X-linked dominant traits may be exhibited in both males and females, but typically males experience more severe effects.

29.9d Penetrance and Environmental influences on Heredity 1165

- Penetrance is the percentage of a population with a particular genotype that exhibits the expected phenotype.

- The environment has a variable influence on many genetic traits, especially during embryonic and fetal development.

Do You Know the Basics?

____ 1. The outer layer of the blastocyst that attaches to the wall of the uterus at implantation is called the
   a. amnion.
   b. yolk sac.
   c. embryoblast.
   d. trophoblast.

____ 2. At about day 3 after fertilization, the cells of the pre-embryo adhere tightly to each other and increase their surface contact in a process called
   a. implantation.
   b. compaction.
   c. gastrulation.
   d. neurulation.

____ 3. During gastrulation, cells from the _____ layer of the bilaminar germinal disc migrate and form the three primary germ layers.
   a. notochord
   b. hypoblast
   c. epiblast
   d. mesoblast

____ 4. The cells of the embryoblast differentiate into the _____ and the _____ .
   a. epiblast; hypoblast
   b. cytotrophoblast; syncytiotrophoblast
   c. amnioblast; epiblast
   d. epiblast; cytotrophoblast

____ 5. Which of the following is *not* an extraembryonic membrane?
   a. amnion   c. chorion
   b. mesoderm   d. yolk sac

____ 6. All of the following cardiovascular events occur during pregnancy *except*
   a. plasma volume increases.
   b. blood pressure increases during the second trimester.
   c. cardiac output increases by 30–50%.
   d. stroke volume increases.

____ 7. After a woman gives birth, what happens to her levels of estrogen, progesterone, and prolactin?
   a. Progesterone, estrogen, and prolactin levels all decrease.
   b. Progesterone and prolactin levels decrease, and estrogen levels increase.
   c. Progesterone, estrogen, and prolactin levels all increase.
   d. Estrogen and prolactin levels increase, and progesterone levels decrease.

____ 8. Freckles are considered to be a dominant trait. If a mother without freckles and a father without freckles have a child, what are the odds that the child will have freckles ?
   a. 1 in 4 chance (25%)
   b. 2 in 4 chance (50%)
   c. 3 in 4 chance (75%)
   d. it is impossible for the child to be born with freckles (0% chance).

____ 9. Hair color is a trait that is determined by
   a. strict dominant-recessive inheritance.
   b. incomplete dominant inheritance.
   c. codominant inheritance.
   d. polygenic inheritance.

____ 10. A woman is a carrier for the color-blindness gene, found on the X chromosome. She does not have color blindness, however. What are the chances that her female child will also inherit this gene?
   a. no chance (0%)   c. 2 in 4 chance (50%)
   b. 1 in 4 chance (25%)   d. 100% chance

11. Briefly describe the process of fertilization, mentioning a hallmark event that occurs in each phase.

12. List the five regions of the mesoderm, and identify some major body parts derived from each region.

13. Explain why teratogens are especially harmful to the developing organism during the embryonic period. What events occur during this period?

14. Describe the differences between the embryonic period and the fetal period.

15. List the major hormone levels that change during pregnancy and their major functions during pregnancy.

16. List the three phases of labor, and describe a major event that occurs in each phase.

17. Explain the positive feedback mechanism involved with lactation and milk letdown, and describe the function of the hormones oxytocin and prolactin during this process.

18. Describe the various ways by which the mother's body expels the excess fluids gained during pregnancy.

19. Compare and contrast strict dominant-recessive inheritance, incomplete dominance, codominance, and polygenic inheritance, and give an example of each.

20. Explain the difference between X-linked recessive traits and X-linked dominant traits. What are the possibilities that a female child will be affected and express each of the traits?

Can You Apply What You've Learned?

Use the following paragraph to answer questions 1–5.

Ashley is a 29-year-old pregnant woman who is in the second trimester of her pregnancy. At her regular OB/GYN checkup, the doctor records the following about Ashley:

Heart rate: 92

Urinalysis: Negative for bacteria and protein in urine

Weight gain since beginning of pregnancy: 15 pounds

Blood pressure: 125/81 mm Hg

Uterine fundus height: At a midpoint between the umbilicus and the xiphoid process of the sternum

Blood glucose level: 95

1. Which of the following medical assessments is abnormal and would be of concern for the physician?

   a. Blood pressure is too high.

   b. Urinalysis results are abnormal.

   c. Ashley's blood glucose levels are too high.

   d. All of the medical findings are within normal ranges for a pregnant woman.

2. The physician determines that Ashley is in her twentieth week of pregnancy. Which of the following best describes the fetus development at this time (refer to Table 29.3)?

   a. The crown-rump length is 19 centimeters.

   b. The heart and lungs have fully developed, but the GI tract has yet to form.

   c. The testes have descended into the scrotum.

   d. The average weight of the fetus at this time is about 2.5 kilograms.

3. Months pass as Ashley has an uneventful pregnancy. Eventually, Ashley goes into labor and goes to the hospital to give birth. As Ashley progresses through the first stage of labor, all of the following occur *except*

   a. the fetus's head pushes against the cervix, promoting the cervical dilation.

   b. oxytocin levels decrease as labor progresses.

   c. the amniotic sac may rupture.

   d. contractions become more frequent and more intense.

4. Ashley gives birth to a 7.5-pound baby boy. In the first few weeks after giving birth, Ashley notices she develops cramping in the pelvic region whenever she breastfeeds her child. What is the likely cause of the cramping?

   a. The suckling stimulates oxytocin production, which both releases the milk and causes uterine contractions.

   b. Breastfeeding results in a rise in prolactin, which also causes cramping of the abdominal muscles.

   c. The drop in estrogen and progesterone levels causes the pelvic cramping.

   d. The tugging on the breast (caused by the suckling) pulls on the abdominal muscles, causing the cramping.

5. As Ashley cares for her son, she notices some problems in his development. During one of the baby's checkups, Ashley voices her concerns to the pediatrician. The pediatrician performs a series of assessments on the baby and orders a genetic workup. The genetic test results demonstrate that the baby has Duchenne muscular dystrophy, which is an X-linked recessive trait.

   Based on your knowledge of heredity, if the baby boy has Duchenne muscular dystrophy, then what else must be true?

   a. The baby's father is a carrier of the Duchenne muscular dystrophy allele and passed along this trait to the baby.

   b. Duchenne muscular dystrophy is an autosomal-dominant disorder.

   c. Ashley is a carrier of the Duchenne muscular dystrophy allele but does not display symptoms because she has two X chromosomes, one of which is normal.

   d. If Ashley had a baby girl (instead of a baby boy), the baby girl would be at equal risk for having Duchenne muscular dystrophy.

Can You Synthesize What You've Learned?

1. In the late 1960s, a number of pregnant women in Europe and Canada were prescribed a drug called thalidomide. Many of these women gave birth to children with amelia (no limbs) or meromelia (malformed upper and/or lower limbs). It was later discovered that thalidomide is a teratogen that can cause limb defects in an unborn baby. Based on this information, during what period of their pregnancy (pre-embryonic, embryonic, or fetal) do you think these women took thalidomide? During which of these periods would thalidomide cause the most harm to limb development?

2. A 22-year-old woman consumes large quantities of alcohol at a party and loses consciousness. Three weeks later, she misses her second consecutive period, and a pregnancy test is positive. Should she be concerned about the effects of her binge-drinking episode on her baby?

3. Simon and Carla are siblings who recently discovered that their father was diagnosed with Huntington disease. This disease is autosomal dominant and results in gradual neurologic degeneration and death, usually within 5 years of diagnosis. There is no cure for the disease. Their mother does not have the disease. Both Simon and Carla discuss the possibility of getting tested to see if they will develop Huntington disease as well. Based on your knowledge of heredity and genetics, what is the likelihood that Simon or Carla will develop Huntington disease?

INTEGRATE

ONLINE STUDY TOOLS
www.mhhe.com/mckinleyap

Clinical Case Study: Queen Victoria's Family Tree

Interactive Questions: This chapter's content is served up in a number of multimedia question formats for student study.

LearnSmart: Topics and terminology include overview of prenatal development; pre-embryonic period; embryonic period; fetal period; effects of pregnancy on the mother; labor (parturition) and delivery; postnatal changes for the newborn; changes to the mother after delivery; heredity

Anatomy & Physiology Revealed: Ovulation through implantation

Animations: Fetal development and risk

Answers to "What Do You Think?"

CHAPTER 1

1. When you digest a meal, you are utilizing primarily catabolic chemical reactions, because the main goal is to break down larger molecules (such as starches in bread) into smaller molecules (such as simple sugars) that can be absorbed.

2. If you didn't have the lubricating serous fluid, there would be increased friction and it would be quite painful whenever your organs moved. For example, the illness *pleurisy* (inflammation of the pleura) makes it very painful to breathe, because the pleural membranes are inflamed and the serous fluid cannot appropriately lubricate the membranes.

CHAPTER 2

1. $^{16}_{8}O$

2. Magnesium is in column IIA. The atomic structures of the elements in column IIA all contain two electrons in the outer shell. Consequently, a magnesium ion will donate two electrons and will develop a $(+2)$ charge, written as Mg^{2+}.

3. The partial charges assigned to the nitrogen and hydrogen that results from a polar covalent bond formed between them would be: $^{\delta-}N-H^{\delta+}$ because nitrogen is more electronegative than hydrogen $(O > N > C > H)$.

4. A fatty acid is a nonpolar molecule because it contains predominantly C–C and C–H covalent nonpolar bonds. Nonpolar molecules are hydrophobic and do not dissolve in water.

5. On a humid day there is more water vapor in the air causing the rate of evaporation to slow down. So, sweating has less of a cooling effect on the body during humid days.

6. Stomach acid with a pH of 2 is 10^5 or 100,000 times more acidic than pure water with a pH of 7. Without protection (a mucus coating and rapid turn-over of cells lining the stomach), the stomach wall would be destroyed.

7. Protein function is dependent on the retention of their normal 3-dimensional shape. An increase in temperature can weaken the intramolecular attractions between the amino acids in the primary structure of the protein strand causing the protein to unfold or denature such that it can no longer function normally.

CHAPTER 3

1. NAD^+ is reduced to become NADH because NAD^+ has gained electrons (2 e⁻ and H^+) to become NADH.

2. An isomerase converts a molecule to one of its isomers (different forms) by rearranging the atoms within the molecule. Recall from section 2.3a that isomers are molecules that contain the same number and kind of atoms, but in a different arrangement.

3. During glycolysis, there is a net of 2 ATP molecules formed (4 ATP generated at steps 7 and 10 that occur twice, and 2 ATP "invested" in steps 1 and 3), and 2 NADH (step 6 that occurs twice).

4. The enzymatic pathway of the citric acid cycle is considered a "cycle" because it begins and ends with oxaloacetic acid.

5. Glycolysis:
ATP total: 6 ATP: 2 ATP and 2 NADH (converted to 6 ATP with a cost of 2 ATP for shipping) (Only 2 ATP are produced if insufficient oxygen.)
Intermediate Stage and Citric Acid Cycle:
ATP total: 30 ATP (8 NADH, 2 FADH, and 2 ATP = 30 ATP).
Total ATP: 36 ATP

CHAPTER 4

1. A cell with 0.9% solute is 99.1% water. Both the pure water and the 0.2% NaCl solution are hypotonic to the cell. Thus, there will be a net movement of water by osmosis into the cell when placed into either liquid. However, the pure water would exert greater osmotic pressure on the cell, as there is not any solute present and thus there is a steeper gradient.

2. The function of lysosomes is to digest unwanted or unneeded organic molecules within the cell. Without lysosomes these substances would accumulate and interfere with normal cell function. A cell cannot survive without lysosomes. There are several inherited lysosomal storage diseases that can occur if the lysosomal enzymes do not function properly. Lastly, a cell that lacked a lysosome would be unable to undergo autophagy or autolysis.

3. If a gene is mutated, the mRNA that is produced during transcription will have a different ribonucleotide sequence. The abnormal mRNA may result in the production of a protein during translation with an abnormal amino acid sequence. Because the chemistry of the amino acids influences the folding and ultimate 3-dimensional shape of the protein, and because its function is dependent on its shape, the protein may not function normally.

4. During transcription only segments of the DNA are opened and "read." Ribonucleotides are used to form the new RNA molecule. In contrast, DNA replication involves all DNA being copied. Deoxyribonucleotides are used to form the new DNA molecule.

CHAPTER 5

1. If epithelium contained blood vessels, the "gatekeeper" function of selective permeability would be compromised. Materials would be able to enter the body by entering the blood without passing through the epithelial cells.

2. All types of stratified epithelium (stratified squamous, stratified columnar, stratified cuboidal) and transitional epithelium are suited for protection, because they have multiple layers of cells.

3. You've damaged dense regular connective tissue when you sprain your ankle.

4. The striations in skeletal and cardiac muscle indicate the organized pattern of protein filaments in sarcomeres. Smooth muscle has these same protein filaments, but they are not arranged in the same ordered pattern. Thus, smooth muscle lacks striations.

CHAPTER 6

1. Thick skin is found on the palms of the hands and soles of the feet. Secretions from sebaceous glands would make these areas slippery, which would interfere with grasping items and walking. The presence of hair in these areas would similarly interfere with these functions.

2. When we are frightened or nervous, the sympathetic division of the autonomic nervous system is stimulated, which in turn stimulates sweat production and secretion. This is why our palms and other regions of the epidermis may become moist in nervous or frightening situations.

3. These children already were not getting enough vitamin D in their diet, and they were spending all of their daylight hours indoors. Since the children were not exposed to much sunlight, their skin could not synthesize vitamin D from the UV rays of the sun. Without adequate amounts of vitamin D, the children developed rickets. Rickets is on the rise in the U.S. again among poor urban children who spend little time outdoors and who drink soda instead of milk.

CHAPTER 7

1. The numerous complex steps in endochondral bone formation ensure that a working bone may be formed for a newborn and later develop into a working adult bone. Having a periosteal bone collar, epiphyseal plates, and constant bone remodeling ensures that the bone can reshape itself, grow in both width and length, and develop a medullary cavity so that it will not weigh too much.

2. A physician will look for active epiphyseal plates (indicating the bones are still growing in length). The epiphyseal plate becomes ossified once an individual reaches maturity. Presence of an epiphyseal line indicates that lengthwise bone growth is complete.

3. Testosterone initially accelerates bone growth. However, bone deposition by osteoblasts occurs at a greater rate than cartilage growth within the epiphyseal plate. This ultimately results in the premature closure of the growth plate. Because the young boy was taking anabolic steroids prior to puberty his growth plates fused at a younger age than would have occurred if he had not taken them. Consequently, he is shorter than he would have been.

4. Milk is supplemented with vitamin D because following its absorption into the body it is converted to calcitriol. Calcitriol, the active form of vitamin D_3, increases the absorption of calcium that is present in the milk from the small intestine.

CHAPTER 8

1. The shape of the skull is very complex, and it would be unlikely for a single bone to be formed in this shape. Multiple bones connected by sutures allow the size of the skull to increase as the child grows. If the skull were a single bone, it would be very difficult for it to change shape and increase in size during growth.

2. Male sex hormones and increased growth beginning at puberty cause the skull to become more robust, have more prominent bony features and a more squared-off jaw.

3. A typical cervical vertebra (C_3-C_6) has transverse foramina and a bifid spinous process. Both the lumbar and thoracic vertebra lack the bifid spinous process and transverse foramina.

4. The acetabulum of the os coxae is deeper than the glenoid cavity of the scapula. Consequently, the pelvic girdle maintains a stronger, more tightly fitting bony connection with the femur of the lower limbs than the pectoral girdle (scapula and clavicle) does with the humerus of the upper limbs.

5. The medial and lateral malleoli of the leg are similar to the styloid processes of the radius and ulna.

CHAPTER 9

1. A synchondrosis is a synarthrosis because as the bone ends are growing, they must not be allowed to move in relation to one another. For example, if the epiphysis and diaphysis move along the epiphyseal plate, bone growth is compromised and the bone may become misshapen.

2. The plane joint, also called a gliding joint, is the least mobile of the two joints. The uniaxial gliding joint occurs where two bones have limited side-to-side movements in a single plane. This is more stable than the multiaxial ball-and-socket joint that consists of a bone with a spherical head articulating in a shallow cuplike socket.

3. When sitting upright in a chair, both the hip joints and knee joints are flexed. Flexion is defined as a decrease in the angle between the bones in an anterior-posterior plane.

CHAPTER 10

1. A skeletal muscle fiber typically is very long, and its cellular demands (such as for synthesizing proteins) are too much for a single nucleus. Multiple nuclei are beneficial for maintaining normal cell function.

2. If the muscle is contracted: (a) the width of the A band remains the same as it represents the length of the myosin filaments, which do not change in length; (b) the width of the H zone shortens as the actin and myosin myofilaments slide past one another; (c) the Z discs in one sarcomere move closer together as the sarcomere shortens, and (d) the width of the I band decreases.

3. As long as excess calcium ions are present, the cell would stay contracted. ATP is needed to release the myosin head from the actin binding sites that would allow the muscle to return to a relaxed state.

4. There is a direct relationship between the extent of muscle tissue damage and the blood level of creatine kinase. The greater the damage to muscle tissue, the higher the blood level of creatine kinase.

5. The duration of a muscle twitch of an extrinsic eye muscle is shorter than it is in the gastrocnemius muscle because the extrinsic eye muscle is composed predominantly of fast glycolytic fibers and the gastrocnemius is composed of a mixture of fast glycolytic fibers and slow oxidative fibers.

CHAPTER 11

1. Since the omohyoid attaches to the scapula (which is part of the shoulder), the prefix *omo-* means "shoulder."

2. When you breathe deeply, the diaphragm contracts and pushes inferiorly on the GI tract (abdominal viscera). If these viscera are bulging with food, the diaphragm has less room to contracting fully, making it hard to take deep breaths.

3. The brachialis is an anterior arm muscle. Because anterior arm muscles tend to flex the elbow joint, we can surmise that the brachialis flexes the elbow joint.

4. Remember that there are leg muscles that also move the toes. In this case, the extensor digitorum longus (a leg muscle) attaches to toes 2–5 and helps move them all.

CHAPTER 12

1. The opening of Na^+ channels results in Na^+ diffusing into the neuron as Na^+ moves down its concentration gradient from where there is more Na^+ outside the neuron to where there is less Na^+ inside the neuron. Consequently, the membrane potential becomes more positive.

2. The generation of IPSPs, which are produced either by the loss of K^+ or the gain of Cl^-, make it less likely that a nerve signal will be sent because the membrane potential has moved away from the threshold (the value that must be reached for a nerve signal to be initiated).

CHAPTER 13

1. While all the meningeal layers give some support and protection to the brain, the dura mater provides the most support. This layer is the thickest and most durable, and it also forms the cranial dural septa that support the brain components.

2. Cutting the corpus callosum dramatically reduces communication between the right and left cerebral hemispheres, but some communication is maintained between the hemispheres via the much smaller anterior and posterior commissures.

3. If there were no thalamus, the cerebrum would still receive sensory stimuli, but the information would not be decoded first. So, the cerebrum would not be able to distinguish taste information from touch or vision information. In addition, there would be no filtering of sensory information so the person would experience sensory overload.

4. Severe injury to the medulla oblongata would most likely cause death, because the medulla oblongata is responsible for basic reflex and life functions, including breathing and heartbeat.

CHAPTER 14

1. The two layers of the cranial dura mater split to form the dural venous sinuses, which are large veins that drain blood away from the brain. The spinal cord lacks dural venous sinuses, so it does not need two layers of dura.

2. An anterior ramus is larger than a posterior ramus because the posterior rami only innervate deep back muscles and the skin of the back, while the anterior rami innervate almost all other body structures (e.g., the limbs and the anterior and lateral trunk).

3. A nerve plexus houses axons from several different spinal nerves. Thus, damage to a single segment of the spinal cord or damage to a single spinal nerve generally does not result in complete loss of innervation to a particular muscle or region of skin.

CHAPTER 15

1. The pterygopalatine ganglion is nicknamed the "hay fever ganglion" because when it is overstimulated, it causes some of the classic allergic reactions, including watery eyes, runny and itchy nose, sneezing, and scratchy throat.

2. Sympathetic innervation causes vasoconstriction of most blood vessels. When blood vessels are constricted, it takes more force and pressure to pump blood through the vessels, so blood pressure rises.

3. Nicotine binds to nictotinic receptors. Many neurons in the brain and peripheral nervous system are affected, but the overall effect usually is an increase in blood pressure and heart rate, and vasoconstriction (in other words, a general stimulation of the sympathetic division). Nicotine also works on the reward centers of the brain, stimulating a release of the neurotransmitter dopamine, which is responsible for the pleasurable, relaxed sensations most smokers get while lighting up. These effects are short lived, so a smoker must smoke fairly continuously to continue to get the increased dopamine in his or her system.

CHAPTER 16

1. Olfaction plays a major role in detecting tastes. Most taste is due to our perception of the odor, rather than the taste, of the food. If your nose is stuffed up and you can't smell the food, your taste perception is impaired as well.

2. When a person cries, tears flood the lacrimal apparatus. The lacrimal puncta are unable to collect all the tears, which then flow over the lower eyelids. In addition, the nasolacrimal duct pours many more tears than normal into the nasal cavity where they mix with mucus, resulting in the runny nose.

3. Air pressure increases when the airplane descends, which is why you may feel greater pressure outside your ears. The "popping" noise results from your auditory tubes opening and equalizing the pressure on either side of the tympanic membrane.

CHAPTER 17

1. Malfunction of the liver and kidneys can result in an imbalance of hormones. One would predict an increase in blood concentration of a hormone given the role of the liver and kidneys in eliminating hormones, wastes and other metabolites.

2. If a drug binds to a specific hormone receptor of a cell to initiate its affect, the cell will down regulate receptors. Over time, more of the drug will be required for the same response.

3. Increased lipolysis is caused by growth hormone. This results in loss of stored adipose connective tissue and the "thinning out" experienced by many during puberty.

4. Iodine is absorbed into the blood and ultimately used for thyroid hormone synthesis.

5. The affected individual with hyperthyroidism would have a high temperature, elevated pulse, elevated breathing rate, and a thin body.

6. Elevated insulin levels typically results in decreased levels of all nutrients in the blood and an increase in the storage form of these molecules within the cells of the body. Thus, elevated serum insulin leads to protein anabolism in the muscle cells resulting in increased muscle bulk. An insulin overdose may lead to dangerously low serum glucose levels and ATP levels. If ATP cannot be generated at the rate needed, death could result. (It also can result in a potassium imbalance as described in chapter 25.)

CHAPTER 18

1. A woman who has 5 L of blood would donate approximately 10% of her blood. Low weight individuals are not allowed to donate blood because these individuals have relatively less blood volume, and by donating 1 pint of blood they would be donating much more than 10% of their total blood volume.

2. By losing its nucleus and other organelles the erythrocyte has more space for hemoglobin, enabling the erythrocyte to bind to and transport greater amounts of O_2 and CO_2 more efficiently. Because the erythrocyte has lost its nucleus it will no longer be able to synthesize proteins or divide via mitosis. The oxygen being transported in an erythrocyte will not be used up by aerobic cellular respiration (since erythrocytes don't have mitochondria).

3. A person with type O⁻ blood is considered a "universal donor" because his or her erythrocytes have no surface antigens. Without surface antigens, the type O⁻ erythrocytes will not be destroyed through agglutination and hemolysis by antibodies in the recipient's plasma. Likewise, a person with type AB⁺ blood is considered a "universal recipient" because his or her blood plasma has no antibodies to the ABO or Rh blood types. Thus, the AB⁺ recipient may receive any type of blood and not worry about the donor's erythrocytes being destroyed.

4. The formation of the platelet plug is an example of positive feedback. The platelets release chemicals that stimulate more platelets to arrive at the site of injury and release their chemicals.

5. An individual who is confined to a wheelchair may have impaired blood flow, as the skeletal muscle pump is less effective. If blood is not moving through the blood vessels properly and begins to pool in the vessels, the clotting cascade may be initiated.

CHAPTER 19

1. The aorta and pulmonary veins are the vessels that contain oxygenated blood. The aorta is an artery and the pulmonary veins are veins.

2. Coronary arteries are compressed more often as heart rate increases.

3. Slow Na^+ channels are unique to nodal cells. These channels open and Na^+ gradually enters the nodal cells. When threshold is reached, Ca^{2+} voltage-gated channels open and Ca^{2+} enters the cells and causes depolarization.

4. Ca^{2+} channel blockers decrease the intracellular calcium in a cardiac muscle cell, thus decreasing the contractility of the heart. Ca^{2+} channel blockers may also block calcium movement into conduction cells, decreasing heart rate.

5. The plateau delays repolarization to allow time for cardiac muscle cells to contract and relax; thus, it prevents a sustained contraction (tetany).

CHAPTER 20

1. A decrease in hydrostatic pressure decreases filtration with less fluid being filtered into the interstitial space of the surrounding tissue. If hydrostatic pressure decreases significantly, capillary exchange can cease to occur.

2. A smoker likely would have elevated blood pressure, since nicotine increases cardiac output and causes vasoconstriction.

3. ACE-inhibitors are a medication given to treat high-blood pressure (hypertension). These medications interfere with the production of angiotensin II (a potent vasoconstrictor). Angiotensin II also regulates blood volume by influencing urine production. A decrease in angiotensin II would increase fluid loss from the blood, thus preventing an escalation in high blood pressure.

4. If the left ulnar artery were cut, the left hand and fingers could still receive blood via the left radial artery, since both vessels contribute to the superficial and deep palmar arches.

CHAPTER 21

1. The removal of lymph nodes interferes with the drainage of fluid from specific regions of the body and will result in lymphedema.

2. The spleen, located in the left upper quadrant, is a soft organ that could easily be ruptured by the pressure of the seatbelt pushing against the abdomen in an automobile accident. Most individuals who have their spleens removed can fight off illness and infections effectively, because the other lymphatic tissues and organs take over the immune functions previously handled by the spleen. However, the risk for severe bacterial infection is greater, because there is no spleen to filter bacteria from the blood. For this reason, individuals who have undergone splenectomies may need to be vaccinated against certain bacteria and undergo long-term (years or even lifelong) antibiotic therapy.

CHAPTER 22

1. Inflammation can be observed if the area is red and swollen. It also may feel warm to the touch.

2. If an antigen mutates it is likely that it will not be recognized by the same lymphocytes. Each lymphocyte recognizes a specific molecular shape of an antigen. An example of a virus that mutates often is HIV, the virus that causes AIDS. It is for this reason that vaccines have not been produced against HIV.

3. Helper T cells play an essential role in both the innate and adaptive immune responses. These cells function to activate B cells, cytotoxic T cells as well as macrophages and NK cells. Without the proper functioning of all of these cells, an individual is highly susceptible to infection.

CHAPTER 23

1. A deviated nasal septum is off-center so one side of the nasal cavity is larger than the other. This alters the normal flow of air through the nose, and if the narrower side becomes blocked, nasal congestion and sinus problems may result.

2. The epithelium changes because a stratified squamous epithelium is more sturdy and protective against smoke than a pseudostratified, ciliated columnar epithelium. Unfortunately, since a stratified squamous epithelium lacks both goblet cells and cilia, there is less mucus produced, and no cilia are present to propel particles away from the bronchi towards the pharynx. Thus, the main way to eliminate the particles is by coughing, leading to the chronic "smoker's cough."

3. The phrenic nerves extend from each cervical plexus to the diaphragm. Since the cervical plexus includes axons of C2-C4, spinal cord injuries above C2-C4 prevent nerve stimulation of the diaphragm, and breathing stops. Spinal cord injuries between C2-C4 and T12 result in nerve signals being sent along the phrenic nerves but not along all intercostal nerves. The degree of loss will depend on where the level of injury has occurred. The further down the spinal cord, the closer the breathing will be to normal (since additional intercostal nerves will be functioning). Spinal cord injuries below T12 should not normally interfere with normal quiet breathing, because these represent injuries that do not interfere with nerve signals being relayed along the phrenic or intercostal nerves.

4. Epinephrine causes bronchodilation, consequently resistance is decreased with a subsequent increase in airflow.

5. No, not all of the air that we breathe in is available for gas exchange. Only the air that reaches the alveoli is available for gas exchange.

6. Blood PO_2 is lower in systemic capillaries than when it left pulmonary capillaries, because bronchial veins dump small amounts of deoxygenated blood into the pulmonary veins prior to the blood being returned to the heart and subsequently pumped by the left ventricle through the systemic circuit.

7. Since hemoglobin is 98% saturated with oxygen if $PO_2 = 104$ mm Hg (normal value at sea level), additional administered oxygen can only increase the % saturation of hemoglobin 2%. This can occur only with an increase from 1 atm to 3 atm, pressures that are only generally reached in hyperbaric oxygen chambers. (In addition, the limiting factor is usually not the ability to load oxygen in the lungs but the ability to deliver the oxygen to the body's tissues.)

8. During exercise, the PO_2 decreases as cells engage in elevated levels of cellular respiration. The decrease in PO_2 results in more oxygen delivered to the cells. As a result the oxygen reserve (the amount remaining attached to hemoglobin) is lower.

9. Exercise increases venous return of blood and lymph by the action of both the muscular pump and respiratory pump. Subsequently, more blood enters the atria triggering the atrial (Bainbridge) reflex that causes increased sympathetic output from the cardiac center to the SA node, thus increasing heart rate.

CHAPTER 24

1. A loss of kidney function could: (a) impair the ability of the kidneys to filter and eliminate wastes; (b) induce anemia as erythropoietin production may be altered; (c) decrease urine production with an accompanying increase in blood volume and blood pressure; (d) lead to a disruption of the normal pH balance in the blood as the kidneys play a role in maintaining acid-base (pH) balance.

2. A filtered substance enters the nephron and becomes part of the filtrate. A substance that is not filtered remains in the blood and exits the glomerulus by the efferent arteriole.

3. Cirrhosis of the liver may lead to a drop of blood colloid osmotic pressure (OP_g). OP_g opposes the filtration pressure and draws fluid back into the glomerulus. A decrease in OP_g will induce less reabsorption of fluid and therefore more filtrate will be formed.

4. If a substance in the blood is filtered and not all of it is completely reabsorbed back into the blood, the level of the substance in the blood decreases. One of the critical functions of the kidney is to regulate blood levels of specific substances.

5. When we are lying down, gravity is unable to passively transport urine to the urinary bladder. Thus, peristalsis is needed so that urine can be pumped actively from the ureters to the urinary bladder, no matter what position the body is in.

CHAPTER 25

1. It is possible to "fool" the thirst center that you are hydrated simply by taking fluid into the mouth without swallowing the fluid (or even by having an inflated balloon in the stomach, as was done experimentally with rats). This will only last for a short time (30–45 minutes) since the long-term stimuli from the detection of blood osmolarity and blood volume will again stimulate the thirst center if fluid is not absorbed into the blood.

2. If the individual retains the sodium by not effectively eliminating it in the urine, blood osmolarity increases causes fluid retention. Increased fluid in the intravascular space increases blood volume and blood pressure.

3. Since insulin increases K^+ uptake by cells, insulin injection could result in low blood K^+ (hypokalemia). Severe hypokalemia could be life threatening (fatal), as potassium is required for cells, especially nerve and muscle cells, to function normally.

CHAPTER 26

1. Saliva cleanses the mouth in a variety of ways. As saliva washes over the tongue and teeth, it helps remove foreign materials and buildup. Lysozyme in saliva is an antibacterial enzyme. A person who has a dry mouth is not able to cleanse the mouth well and is more likely to develop dental problems as a result of build-up of bacterial and foreign material.

2. The stomach is lined with specialized surface mucous cells that secrete an alkaline mucus onto the lining. This mucus prevents the acid from eating away the stomach wall. In addition, the stomach epithelial lining is constantly regenerating to replace any cells that are damaged.

3. The duodenum has many circular folds so that the digested materials can be slowed down and adequately mixed with pancreatic juice and bile. The jejunum also has many circular folds because the slowing down of the materials aids in absorbing the maximum amount of nutrients. By the time chyme reaches the distal ileum, most nutrient absorption has occurred, and so the circular folds are not as essential.

4. When the gallbladder is removed, bile is still produced by the liver, but it is secreted in a "slow drip." A fatty meal requires much more bile for digestion than the amount supplied by a "slow drip," causing the patient to experience gas, pain, bloating, and diarrhea. Thus, surgical patients are initially told to limit their fat intake. The body gradually adjusts so that more bile is secreted, and thus a person may eventually be able to introduce more fat back into his or her diet.

CHAPTER 27

1. Water soluble vitamins (ADEK) are the B-complex vitamins and vitamin C. Fat-soluble vitamins are stored in body fat. Excessive consumption of fat-soluble vitamins may induce toxicity (hypervitaminosis).

2. A lipid profile that includes both HDL and LDL levels is more informative than a total cholesterol count. HDLs function to transport lipids to the liver for elimination. LDLs function to transport cholesterol to the cells for storage or use within the cell. LDL is considered "bad" cholesterol as some of this lipid tends to be deposited on the inner walls of arteries increasing risk for heart disease and high blood pressure.

3. A man that is 6 feet tall and 200 pounds would have a higher BMR than a man that is 5 feet 9 inches tall weighing 160 pounds. BMR is the amount of energy that an individual uses when their body is at rest. One of the most important variables in determining BMR is body surface area. A larger individual has a greater surface area of skin and thus loses more energy as heat. When more heat is lost, the body must increase its metabolic rate to maintain body temperature.

CHAPTER 28

1. A woman can become pregnant as long as she has one remaining functioning ovary. However, she may not ovulate every month, since the ovaries typically "take turns" ovulating each month.

2. Stress, age, medications, and body weight all can affect a woman's monthly uterine (menstrual) cycle. Stress and excessively lean body mass can lead to amenorrhea (absence of periods).

3. If a man's testes were removed, the adrenal glands could still produce a small amount of androgens. However, because the testes produce the overwhelming majority of androgens, the small amount produced by the adrenal glands would have little effect.

4. If a man has a vasectomy, sperm still form in the seminiferous tubule and then mature in the epididymis. However, since the sperm are not ejaculated, they die, and their components are broken down and resorbed in the epididymis. An individual who has had a vasectomy ejaculates seminal fluid only, not semen (which contains sperm).

1. If two sperm penetrate the secondary oocyte, the condition called polyspermy occurs. In this case, the fertilized cell contains 23 triplets of chromosomes, instead of the normal 23 pairs of chromosomes. In humans, a cell with 69 chromosomes (3 sets of 23 chromosomes) will not survive.

2. In the last trimester, the uterus continues to expand and compress abdominal organs. The uterus also prevents the diaphragm from moving too far inferiorly, such as is needed when one takes a deep breath. The uterus and fetus are physical barriers that prevent full lung expansion, and thus deep breathing, for some women.

3. It is unnecessary to slap newborns to "make" them breathe, because the breathing reflex generally occurs in about 10 seconds in response to the change in environment and temperature. It can be harmful because crying may actually make the baby's breathing more difficult, to say nothing of the shock and fear response that could occur.

4. As parents have become more diligent about protecting infants' skin from sun exposure, one potential negative effect is that these infants cannot synthesize vitamin D from the UV rays. Because breast milk is low in vitamin D, and these infants aren't synthesizing enough vitamin D from sunlight, supplementation of this vitamin is recommended.

MAJOR REGULATORY HORMONES OF THE HUMAN BODY

These tables provide a succinct reference for the major regulatory hormones of the human body. They are organized by the general variable or process regulated by each hormone or group of hormones. Each table includes the name of the hormone(s), source of the hormone(s), its chemical structure, primary stimulus for its release, whether it is bound or unbound as it is transported in the blood, its primary target organs and the cellular responses that it initiates, the net result or summary of its effect, whether it is regulated by negative feedback or positive feedback, an example of a related disease or condition, and the chapter reference in the text where the hormone is discussed in detail.

Table B.1	Regulating Blood Glucose with Pancreatic Hormones	
Hormone	**Insulin**	**Glucagon**
Source	Pancreatic beta (β) cells	Pancreatic alpha (α) cells
Chemical structure	Polypeptide (51 amino acids); water-soluble	Polypeptide (29 amino acids); water-soluble
Primary stimulus for release	Increased blood glucose levels	Decreased blood glucose levels
Transport in the blood	Unbound	Unbound
Primary target organs and cellular changes	Liver: Increased glycogenesis, decreased glycogenolysis and gluconeogenesis Adipose connective tissue: Increased lipogenesis, decreased lipolysis Muscle cells: Increased glycogenesis, increased uptake of potassium—through increased number of sodium-potassium (Na^+/K^+) pumps All target cells: Increased amino acid uptake and utilization in protein anabolism and increased glucose uptake (through increased number of glucose transport proteins)	Liver: Increased glycogenolysis, followed by increased gluconeogenesis as glycogen stores are depleted, decreased glycogenesis Adipose connective tissue: Increased lipolysis, decreased lipogenesis Muscle cells: Increased glycogenolysis; glucose is not released in the blood but oxidized in cellular respiration to produce ATP
Net result	Decreased blood levels of fuel molecules (glucose, fatty acids, and amino acids) and increased synthesis/storage of fuel molecules (glycogen, fat, and protein)	Increased blood levels of glucose and fatty acids and decreased storage of glycogen and fat
Regulation	Negative feedback	Negative feedback
Related diseases or conditions	Diabetes mellitus	Hypoglycemia
Text reference	Chapter 17	Chapter 17

Table B.2	Regulating Blood Calcium with Parathyroid Hormone and Calcitonin	
Hormone	**Parathyroid Hormone (PTH)**	**Calcitonin**
Source	Parathyroid gland	Thyroid gland (parafollicular cells)
Chemical structure	Polypeptide (84 amino acids); water-soluble	Polypeptide (32 amino acids); water-soluble
Primary stimulus for release	Decreased blood calcium	Increased blood calcium
Transport in the blood	Unbound	Unbound
Primary target organs and cellular changes	Bone: Increased osteoclast activity Kidney: Decreased loss of calcium ions (Ca^{2+}) and increased loss of hydrogen phosphate (HPO_4^{2-}) in urine; increased number of enzymes that convert calcidiol (inactive hormone in blood formed from vitamin D) to calcitriol, a hormone which increases absorption of Ca^{2+} from small intestine	Bone: Primarily decreased activity of osteoclasts (especially in children) Kidney: Increased loss of Ca^{2+} in urine
Net result	Increased blood Ca^{2+}	Decreased blood Ca^{2+}
Regulation	Negative feedback	Negative feedback
Related diseases or conditions	Hyperparathyroidism; hypoparathyroidism	Hyperthyroidism; hypothyroidism
Text reference	Chapter 7	Chapter 7

Table B.3	Regulating Growth with Growth Hormone (and Insulin-like growth factor)
Hormone	**Growth Hormone (GH)**
Source	Anterior pituitary
Chemical structure	Polypeptide (191 amino acids); water-soluble
Primary stimulus for release	Variables that regulate the release of **growth hormone–releasing hormone (GHRH)** include age (GH decreases beginning in the mid-twenties), time of day (peak levels in earlier stages of sleep), reproductive hormones (increases release, especially during puberty), change in fuel molecules in blood (increases with an increase in amino acids or decrease in glucose within the blood), and stress (increases with moderate levels of stress). GHRH is transported in the hypophyseal portal veins to the anterior pituitary and stimulates the anterior pituitary to release **growth hormone (GH)**. GH stimulates the release of **insulin-like growth factor (IGF)** from the liver.
Transport in the blood	Unbound
Primary target organs and cellular changes*	Together growth hormone and IGF interact with the following: • All cells, especially cartilage, bone, and muscle: Increased mitosis, protein synthesis, and cell differentiation • Liver: Increased glycogenolysis and gluconeogenesis • Adipose connective tissue: Increased lipolysis
Net result	Cellular growth and protein synthesis; release of glucose and fatty acids into the blood (provide necessary fuel molecules needed for growth)
Regulation	Negative feedback
Related diseases or conditions	Pituitary dwarfism, gigantism, acromegaly
Text reference	Chapter 17

*Other effects of growth hormone include increased hunger; skin development, including nails and hair; development of skeletal, muscular and nervous system; increased metabolic rate in mother and fetus during pregnancy; enhanced development of mammary glands during pregnancy; insulin antagonist; increased reabsorption of sodium ions (Na^+), potassium ions (K^+), and chlorine ions (Cl^-) by the kidneys; increased absorption of Ca^{2+} by the small intestine; and increased uptake of sulfur for synthesis of chondroitin sulfate by chondrocytes.

Table B.4	Regulating Metabolism with Thyroid Hormone
Hormone	**Thyroid Hormone (TH)**
Source	Thyroid gland
Chemical structure	Biogenic amine (monoamine); lipid-soluble
Primary stimulus for release	Variables that regulate the release of **thyrotropin-releasing hormone (TRH)** include decreased thyroid hormone level, cold weather, pregnancy, an increase in altitude, and hypoglycemia. TRH is transported in the hypophyseal portal veins to the anterior pituitary and stimulates the anterior pituitary to release **thyroid-stimulating hormone (TSH)** into the general circulation. TSH binds to cellular receptors of the thyroid gland, stimulating the release of **thyroid hormone (TH)—triiodothyronine (T3)** and **tetraiodothyronine (T$_4$).**
Transport in the blood	Bound to thyroxine-binding globulin, transthyretin, albumin, or alpha-globulin
Primary target organs and cellular changes*	All cells, especially neurons: Increased metabolic rate; increased amino acid uptake and protein anabolism Liver: Stimulation of glycogenolysis and gluconeogenesis Adipose connective tissue: Increased lipolysis Heart: Increased heart rate and force of contraction (through increased number of receptors for epinephrine and norepinephrine)
Net result	Increased metabolism (results in increased production of ATP, increased body temperature [calorigenic effect] and oxygen consumption); increased release of glucose and fatty acids into the blood (provide necessary fuel molecules needed for increased metabolic rate)
Regulation	Negative feedback
Related diseases or conditions	Hyperthyroidism; hypothyroidism
Text reference	Chapter 17

*Other effects of thyroid hormone include increased respiratory rate, increased appetite; increased alertness; bone growth and remodeling; skin development, including nails and hair; skeletal, muscular, and nervous system development; increased metabolic rate in mother and fetus during pregnancy; insulin antagonist; and release of GH from the anterior pituitary.

Table B.5	Regulating the Stress Response with Catecholamines and Glucocorticoids	
Hormone	Catecholamines: Epinephrine and Norepinephrine	Glucocorticoids: Cortisol and Corticosterone
Source	Adrenal medulla	Adrenal cortex (zona fasciculata)
Chemical structure	Biogenic amine (monoamine); water-soluble	Steroid hormones; lipid-soluble
Primary stimulus for release	Sympathetic division stimulation causes release of epinephrine (85%) and norepinephrine (15%)	Variables that increase the release of **corticotropin-releasing hormone (CRH)** include decreased cortisol, time of day (peak levels in the early morning), eating, and stress. CRH is transported in the hypophyseal portal veins to the anterior pituitary and stimulates the anterior pituitary to release **adrenocorticotropic hormone (ACTH)** into the general circulation. ACTH binds to cellular receptors of the adrenal cortex, stimulating the release of **glucocorticoids (e.g., cortisol).**
Transport in the blood	Unbound	Bound (transcortin or albumin)
Primary target organs and cellular changes*	Increases all effects of the sympathetic division of the autonomic nervous system (see table 15.5)	Liver: Increased gluconeogenesis Adipose connective tissue: Increased lipolysis All cells, especially muscle: Increased protein catabolism Immune system: Increased anti-inflammatory effect
Net result	Increased level of response and increased duration of response (about 30 minutes) that is initiated by the sympathetic division of the autonomic nervous system	Increased all fuel molecules in blood especially glucose (decreased storage of fuel molecules); anti-inflammatory
Regulation	Sympathetic division of the autonomic nervous system	Negative feedback
Related diseases or conditions	Stress	Cushing syndrome, Addison disease
Text reference	Chapter 15	Chapter 17

*Other effects of glucocorticoids include impaired connective tissue repair (decreased fibroblasts, and decreased protein synthesis of connective tissue matrix formation); atrophy of muscle, atrophy of skin, decrease in bone tissue; decreased lymphatic tissue (thymus, lymph nodes, spleen), decreased white blood cells (eosinophils, lymphocytes, and macrophages); decreased production of antibodies; decreased response by cell-mediated immunity and blocked production of fever; increased Na^+ and water retention; permissive effects for epinephrine and norepinephrine (catecholamines) that enhance vasoconstriction and increase cardiac output; increased gastric secretion; and inhibited release of luteinizing hormone, estrogen, and possibly testosterone.

Cortisol-like drugs are administered as treatment for inflammation (e.g., rheumatoid arthritis, eczema, asthma). High doses can result in side effects that include edema, muscle weakness, osteoporosis, thin skin, suppressed immune response, and infertility.

Table B.6	Regulating Erythrocyte Concentration in the Blood
Hormone	**Erythropoietin (EPO)**
Source	Kidney (primarily) and liver
Chemical structure	Glycoprotein; water-soluble
Primary stimulus for release	Decreased blood O_2; testosterone
Transport in the blood	Unbound
Primary target organs and cellular changes	Red bone marrow: Increases rate of production of erythrocytes, cells that transport oxygen
Net result	Increased O_2-carrying capacity of blood
Regulation	Negative feedback
Related diseases or conditions	Anemia; polycythemia
Text reference	Chapter 18

Table B.7 Regulating Fluid Balance, Blood Volume, and Blood Pressure

Hormone	Angiotensin II (Ang II)	Antidiuretic Hormone (ADH)	Aldosterone (ALDO)	Atrial Natriuretic Peptide (ANP)*
Source	Liver (produces and releases inactive angiotensinogen into the blood); activated in the blood in the presence of renin (released from kidney when stimulated) and angiotensin-converting enzymes (ACE) (endothelial layer of blood vessels, especially those in the lungs)	Produced by the hypothalamus and stored in the posterior pituitary (release is controlled by hypothalamus)	Adrenal cortex (zona glomerulosa)	Atrial chambers of the heart
Chemical structure	Oligopeptide (8 amino acids); water-soluble	Oligopeptide (9 amino acids); water-soluble	Steroid hormone; lipid-soluble	Polypeptide (28 amino acids); water-soluble
Primary stimulus for release	Release of renin from juxtaglomerular apparatus of kidney stimulated by the following: • Decreased blood pressure • Sympathetic division stimulation	Hypothalamus is stimulated by the following: • Angiotensin II • Increased blood osmolarity • Decreased nerve signals initiated by baroreceptors in atria, aorta, and carotid arteries in response to decrease in stretch	Angiotensin II Increased blood K^+ Decreased blood Na^+	Increased stretch of atrial wall (reflects increase in blood volume and blood pressure)
Transport in the blood	Unbound	Unbound	Bound	Unbound
Primary target organs and cellular changes	Blood vessels: Potent vasoconstrictor, increases vascular resistance Kidney: Decreases urine output by decreasing GFR to maintain blood volume Thirst center: Stimulation Hypothalamus: Releases ADH from posterior pituitary Adrenal cortex: Releases aldosterone	Kidney: Decreases H_2O excreted in urine Thirst center: Stimulation Blood vessels: Vasoconstrictor in high doses (why it is also called vasopressin)	Kidney: Decreases Na^+ and H_2O excreted in urine; increases K^+ excretion (except under conditions of low pH when H^+ is excreted instead)	Kidney: Increases GFR; increases Na^+ and H_2O excreted in urine; inhibits release of renin Blood vessels: Vasodilation, decreases vascular resistance Hypothalamus: Inhibits release of ADH from posterior pituitary Adrenal cortex: Inhibits release of aldosterone
Net result	Increased resistance, increased blood pressure; maintaining blood volume and blood pressure	Increased retention of water; maintaining blood volume and blood pressure	Maintenance of blood Na^+ and blood K^+ levels; maintaining blood volume and pressure by decreasing urine output	Increased urine output; decreased resistance, decreased blood volume and blood pressure
Regulation	Negative feedback	Negative feedback	Negative feedback	Negative feedback
Related diseases or conditions	Blood pressure homeostasis	Diabetes insipidus	Hyperaldosteronism Hypoaldosteronism	Blood pressure homeostasis
Text reference	Chapters 20, 24, and 25	Chapters 24 and 25	Chapters 24 and 25	Chapters 24 and 25

*Other names include atrial natriuretic factor (ANF), atrial natriuretic hormone (ANH), and atriopeptin.

Table B.8	Regulating the Digestive System		
Hormone	Gastrin	Secretin	Cholecystokinin (CCK)
Source	Stomach and duodenum (enteroendocrine G cells)	Duodenal enteroendocrine cells	Duodenal enteroendocrine cells
Chemical structure	Three forms of polypeptides (34, 17, 14 amino acids); water-soluble	Polypeptide (27 amino acids); water-soluble	Polypeptide (varying numbers of amino acids); water-soluble
Primary stimulus for release	Thought, smell, sight of food; parasympathetic division (vagal) stimulation; presence of partially digested protein in stomach; stretch of stomach wall, caffeine, increase in stomach pH	Acidic chyme entering small intestine	Chyme high in lipids and protein entering small intestine (duodenum)
Transport in the blood	Unbound	Unbound	Unbound
Primary target organs and cellular changes	Stomach: Parietal cells release HCl and intrinsic factor, chief cells release pepsinogen; increased motility Gallbladder: Contraction causing release of bile into small intestine Pancreas: Secretion of pancreatic juice Small intestine: Contraction of wall Large intestine: Mass movements Pyloric sphincter: Relaxes Ileocecal valve: Relaxes	Stomach: Decreased secretions and motility Liver and pancreas: Increased secretion of bicarbonate ion (weak base) in bile and pancreatic juice	Stomach: Decreased secretions and motility Pancreas: Secretion of pancreatic juice containing pancreatic digestive enzymes Liver: Secretion of bile Gallbladder: Contraction causing release of bile into small intestine Hepatopancreatic sphincter: Relaxes
Net result	Increased secretions and motility of stomach; preparation of small intestine for arrival of chyme by relaxing pyloric sphincter and stimulating accessory gland secretions; movement of contents through the large intestine	Inhibited stomach activity; buffering of acidic chyme entering duodenum	Most important in increasing ability of small intestine to digest fat by decreasing stomach motility, and increasing secretions from accessory glands (liver, gallbladder, and pancreas) into small intestine
Regulation	Negative feedback	Negative feedback	Negative feedback
Related diseases or conditions	Zollinger-Ellison syndrome	Low levels are associated with *Helicobacter pylori* infection	Change in release of CCK is associated with gallstones
Text reference	Chapter 26	Chapter 26	Chapter 26

Table B.9	Regulating the Female Reproductive System			
Hormone	**Estrogen**	**Progesterone**	**Prolactin**	**Oxytocin**
Source	Ovary (developing follicle)	Ovary (corpus luteum)	Anterior pituitary	Posterior pituitary
Chemical structure	Steroid hormone; lipid-soluble	Steroid hormone; lipid-soluble	Polypeptide (198 amino acids); water-soluble	Oligopeptide (9 amino acids); water-soluble
Primary stimulus for release	At the beginning of the female cycle, decreased levels of estrogen and progesterone stimulate the release of **gonadotropin-releasing hormone (GnRH)** from the hypothalamus; GnRH travels in the hypophyseal portal veins to stimulate the release of **follicle-stimulating hormone (FSH)** from the anterior pituitary into general circulation; FSH stimulates the development of follicles (in the ovary) and developing follicles produce **estrogen**	Hypothalamus is stimulated in the middle of female cycle; an increase in estrogen stimulates the release of **GnRH** from the hypothalamus; GnRH travels in the hypophyseal portal veins to stimulate the release of **luteinizing hormone (LH)** from the anterior pituitary into general circulation; LH triggers ovulation and the production of the corpus luteum; the corpus luteum produces **progesterone**	Hypothalamus releases **prolactin-releasing hormone (PRH)** beginning at about week 5 of pregnancy; PRH travels in the hypophyseal portal veins to stimulate the release of prolactin (PRL) from the anterior pituitary into general circulation (Prolactin release is normally inhibited by the release of **prolactin-inhibiting hormone [PIH]** from the hypothalamus)	Hypothalamus sends a nerve signal along the hypothalamo-hypophyseal tract to the posterior pituitary in response to sensory nerve signals from contractions of uterus or suckling of breast, to stimulate release of **oxytocin**
Transport in the blood	Bound	Bound	Unbound	Unbound
Primary target organs and cellular changes	Uterus: Builds endometrial lining Hypothalamus: Moderate levels inhibit release of GnRH and FSH; high levels stimulate release of GnRH and FSH Breast: Stimulates development of mammary gland Kidney: Retention of Na+ and water All cells: Increases protein anabolism	Uterus: Builds and maintains endometrial lining Mammary glands: Prepares for secretion of milk Kidney: Decreases retention of Na+ and water	Breast: Development of mammary ducts and glands	Uterus: Stimulates uterine contraction during delivery (and after delivery to expel the placenta, and continues to cause contractions to firm up the uterus) Breast: Stimulates ejection of milk from mammary glands Brain: Increases feelings of emotional bonding between individuals
Net result	Assists in ovarian follicle (oocyte) development, regulation of female cycle; anabolic hormone; development of female characteristics; retention of Na+ and water	Regulates second half of uterine cycle; prepares mammary glands for milk production; eliminates Na+ and water	Stimulates development of mammary ducts and glands within the breast for milk production	Stimulates contraction of smooth muscle of uterus and breast
Regulation	Estrogen levels fluctuate throughout the female cycle	When corpus luteum becomes corpus albicans, it no longer produces progesterone	Positive feedback	Positive feedback
Related diseases or conditions	Infertility	Infertility	Prolactinomas	Severe cases of autism are associated with low levels of oxytocin
Text reference	Chapters 28 and 29	Chapters 28 and 29	Chapters 28 and 29	Chapters 28 and 29

Table B.10	Regulating the Male Reproductive System
Hormone	**Testosterone**
*Source**	Testes (interstitial cells or Leydig cells)
Chemical structure	Steroid hormone; lipid-soluble
Primary stimulus for release	Decreased levels of testosterone result in release of **gonadotropin-releasing hormone (GnRH)** from hypothalamus into hypophyseal portal veins; GnRH stimulates anterior pituitary to release both **luteinizing hormone (LH)** and **follicle-stimulating hormone (FSH)**; LH stimulates testes (interstitial cells) to release **testosterone;** FSH stimulates release of **androgen-binding protein (ABP)** and release of **inhibin** from sustentacular cells
Transport in the blood	Bound
*Primary target organs and cellular changes**	Testes: With ABP, testosterone stimulates sperm production Hypothalamus: Inhibits GnRH All cells with testosterone receptors: Increases protein anabolism Bone: Stimulates osteoblasts Kidney: Increases production of erythropoietin Secondary sex characteristics Increases libido (sex drive)
Net result	Assists in sperm production, regulation of male cycle; anabolic hormone; increases erythrocytes; development of male characteristics
Regulation	Negative feedback: Increased levels of testosterone inhibit release of GnRH from hypothalamus and the response of the anterior pituitary to GnRH and inhibits release of LH; Inhibin inhibits release of FSH from anterior pituitary
Related diseases or conditions	Androgen insensitivity, infertility
Text reference	Chapters 28 and 29

*In both males and females, **dehydroepiandrosterone (DHEA)** is produced from adrenal cortex and is converted to testosterone (this is the only source of testosterone in females).

glossary

Pronunciation Key

Pronouncing a word correctly is as important as knowing its spelling and its contextual meaning. The mastery of all three allows a student to take ownership of the word. The system employed in this text is basic and consists of the following conventions:

1. Vowels marked with a line above the letter are pronounced as follows:
   ā   day, base
   ē   be, feet
   ī   pie, ivy
   ō   so, pole
   ū   unit, cute

2. Vowels marked with the breve (˘) are pronounced as follows:
   ă   above, about
   ĕ   genesis, bet
   ĭ   it, sip
   ŏ   collide
   ŭ   cut, bud

3. Vowels not marked are pronounced as follows:
   a   mat
   o   not, ought
   e   term

4. Other phonetic symbols used include the following:
   ah   father
   aw   fall
   oo   food
   ow   cow
   oy   void

5. For consonants, the following key was employed:
   b   bad
   ch   child
   d   dog
   dh   this
   f   fit
   g   got
   h   hit
   j   jive
   k   keep
   ks   tax
   kw   quit
   l   learn
   m   mice
   n   no
   ng   ring
   p   put
   r   right
   s   so
   sh   shoe
   t   tight
   th   thin
   v   very
   w   wet
   y   yes
   z   zero
   zh   measure

6. The principal stressed syllables are followed by a prime ('); single-syllable words do not have a stress mark. Nonstressed syllables are separated by a hyphen.

7. Acceptable alternate pronunciations are given as needed.

A

abduction (ab-dŭk′shŭn) Movement of a body part away from the median plane of the body.

absolute refractory (rē-frak′tō r-ē) **period** Time period when an excitable cell cannot be restimulated to respond.

absorption (ab-sōrp-shŭn) Process of moving substances, such as products of digestion, into the blood or lymph.

accommodation (ā-kom′ŏ-dā′shŭn) Changing the lens shape in order to focus on a nearby object.

acetylcholine (a-sē′til-kō′lēn) **(ACh)** Neurotransmitter produced by the central and peripheral nervous systems.

acid Substance that releases a hydrogen ion when added to a solution.

acid-base balance Maintaining hydrogen ion concentration of body fluids within normal limits; also called pH balance.

acidosis (as-i-dō′sis) Condition in which the pH of arterial blood is below 7.35.

acrosome (ak′rō-sōm) A cap-like structure on the anterior two-thirds of the sperm nucleus that contains digestive enzymes for penetrating an oocyte.

actin (ak′-tin) Contractile protein forming the major part of the thin filaments in a sarcomere.

action potential Self-propagating change in membrane potential occurring in excitable cells (e.g., neurons, muscle cells).

active immunity (i-myū′ni-tē) Activation of the immune system by a vaccine or by exposure to the naturally occurring infectious agent. Offers long-term protection because memory cells are formed. *Compare to passive immunity.*

active site Region of an enzyme where substrate binds.

active transport Method of transporting a substance across the membrane, against its concentration gradient.

acute (ă-kyūt′) Takes place over a short period of time. *Compare to chronic.*

adaptation (ad-ap-tā′shŭn) Advantageous change of an organ or tissue to meet new conditions.

adduction (ăd-dŭk′shŭn) Medial movement of a body part toward the midline.

adenosine triphosphate (ă-den′ō-sēn trī-fos′fāt) **(ATP)** Stores and releases chemical energy in a cell; composed of adenine, ribose, and three phosphate groups.

adipocyte (ad′i-pō-sīt) Fat storage cell.

adrenergic (ad-rĕ-ner′jik) Relating to nerve cells that release norepinephrine neurotransmitter.

adventitia (ad-ven-tish′ă) Outermost covering of an organ.

aerobic (ār-o′-bik) **respiration** Breakdown of glucose or other nutrients to produce ATP, water, and carbon dioxide. The process requires oxygen.

afferent (af′er-ent) Inflowing or going toward a center.

agglutination (ă-glū-ti-nā′shŭn) Process by which cells clump due to cross-linking by antibodies.

agonist (ag′on-ist) Muscle that contracts to produce a particular movement; also called prime mover.

albumin (al-bū′min) Plasma protein important in regulating fluid balance.

alimentary (al-i-men′ter-ē) Relating to food or nutrition.

alkalosis (al-kă-lō′-sis) Condition in which the pH of arterial blood is above 7.45.

allele (ă-lēl′) Variation of a gene found on the same locus of homologous chromosomes.

allergen (al′er-gen) Noninfectious substance that elicits an excessive response by the immune system (allergic reaction).

active site Region of an enzyme where substrate binds.

alveolus (al-vē′ō-lŭs; pl., alveoli, -ō-lī) Small cavity. Air sac in the lungs; also, a milk-secreting portion of a mammary gland.

amino (ă-mē′nō) **acid** Organic molecule used to build proteins; contains both an amine group and carboxyl group.

amnion (am′nē-on) Extraembryonic membrane that envelops the embryo.

amphiarthrosis (am′fē-ar-thrō′sis) A slightly movable joint.

amphipathic (am-fē-path′ik) Molecule that contains a hydrophobic region and a hydrophilic region.

ampulla (am-pul′lă; pl., ampullae, -lē) Saccular dilation of a canal or duct, such as the ductus deferens in the male reproductive system.

anabolism (ă-nab′ō-lizm) Formation of large, complex molecules from simple molecules.

anaerobic (an-ār-ō′bik) Process that does not require oxygen.

anastomosis (ă-nas′tō-mō′sis; pl., anastomoses, -sēz) Union of two structures, such as blood vessels, to supply the same region.

anatomic (ă-na-tom′ik) **position** Standing upright, arms at the sides with palms forward and feet flat on the floor; reference position for naming body regions.

anatomy (ă-nat′ŏ-mē) Study of structures in the human body.

androgen (an′drō-jen) Generic term for a hormone that stimulates the activity of accessory male sex organs or the development of male sex characteristics.

anemia (ă-nē′mē-ă) Any condition in which the number of erythrocytes is below normal.

aneurysm (an′ū-rizm) Ballooning of an artery due to a weakened vessel wall; it is susceptible to rupture, leading to severe bleeding.

angiogenesis (an′jē-ō-jen′ĕ-sis) Process of forming new blood vessels.

angioplasty (an′jē-ō-plas′tē) The reopening of a blood vessel through a variety of means.

angiotensin II (an′jē-ō-ten′sin) A peptide hormone, derived from angiotensin I, that increases blood pressure.

anion (an′ī-on) Negatively charged ion; e.g., Cl⁻.

antagonist (an-tag′ō-nist) Muscle (or hormone) that opposes or resists the action of another.

antebrachium (an-te-brā′kē-ŭm) Forearm.

anterior Toward the front of the body.

antibody (an′tē-bod-ē) Immunoglobulin that binds to a specific antigen; released by plasma cells (activated B lymphocytes).

anticodon (antē-kō′don) Group of three nucleotide bases on a transfer RNA molecule; base pairs with a complementary codon on messenger RNA.

antidiuretic (an′tē-dī-ū-ret′-ik) **hormone (ADH)** Hormone released by the posterior pituitary gland; increases water reabsorption in the kidney and reduces urine production.

antigen (an′ti-jen) Substance that causes a state of sensitivity or responsiveness and reacts with antibodies or immune cells of the affected subject.

antigen-presenting cell (APC) Immune cell that presents (displays) an antigen to T-lymphocytes; e.g., a macrophage.

aorta (ā-ōr′tă) Main trunk of the systemic arterial system, beginning at the left ventricle and ending when it forks at its inferior end to form the common iliac arteries.

aortic (ā-ōr′tik) **body** Structure composed of neurons sensitive to changing levels of blood pH, O₂, and CO₂; located in the aortic arch.

aperture (ap′er-chūr) Open gap or hole.

apex (ā′peks) Extremity of a conical or pyramidal structure; e.g., the inferior, conical end of the heart.

apical (ap′i-kăl) Related to the tip or extremity of a conical or pyramidal structure; opposite of basal.

apnea (ap′nē ă) Cessation of breathing while sleeping.

apocrine (ap′ō-krin) **gland** Gland that releases a substance by pinching off the apical membrane of a cell and a portion of its cytoplasm; e.g., apocrine sweat glands.

aponeurosis (ap′ō-nū-rō′sis; pl., aponeuroses, -sēz) Fibrous sheet or flat, expanded tendon.

apoptosis (ap′op-tō′sis) Programmed cell death.

appendicular (ap′en-dik′-ū-lăr) Relating to an appendage or limb; e.g., the appendicular skeleton.

appositional (ap-ō-zish′ŭn-ăl) Being placed or fitted together; e.g., appositional growth of bone.

aquaporins (ak′wă-pōr-in) Protein channels in the plasma membrane allowing the passage of water.

arachnoid mater (ă-rak′noyd mah′ter) Spider weblike meningeal layer; located between the dura mater and the pia mater.

arcuate (ar′kū-āt) Having a shape that is arched or bowed.

arteriole (ar-tēr′ē-ōl) The smallest type of artery.

artery (ar′ter-ē) Blood vessel conveying blood away from the heart.

articular (ar-tik′ū-lăr) Relating to a joint.

articulation (ar-tik-ū-lā′shŭn) Joint or connection between bones.

astrocyte (as′trō-sīt) Largest and most abundant glial cell of the nervous system.

atherosclerosis (ath′er-ō-skler-ō′sis) Disease in which an artery wall thickens, leaving a smaller lumen for blood flow.

atlas (at′las) The first cervical vertebra.

atom The smallest particle that displays properties of an element; composed of electrons, protons, and neutrons (except in hydrogen).

atomic mass unit (AMU) Mass of a specific atom.

atomic number Indicates the number of protons in one atom of a specific element. Value appears above each atomic symbol in the periodic table.

ATP (adenosine triphosphate) Chemical that transfers energy within a cell.

atrioventricular node (ā′trē-ō-ven-trik′ū-lar nōd) **(AV)** Group of specialized heart cells, located in the inferior right atrium, that sends action potentials to the AV bundle.

atrium (ā′trē-ŭm; pl., atria, ā′trē-ă) Chamber or cavity to which are connected other chambers or passageways; e.g., the heart has both a right atrium and a left atrium that are thin-walled, superior chambers that receive blood returning to the heart.

atrophy (at′rō-fē) Wasting of tissues, organs, or the entire body.

auricle (aw′ri-kl) The external ear; also called the pinna. Also, flaplike extensions on the anterior part of each atrium.

autoimmune (aw-tō-i-mūn′) **disease** Disease in which the immune system attacks self-antigens as if they were foreign.

autolysis (aw-tol′i-sis) Digestion of cells by enzymes present within the cell itself.

autonomic (aw-tō-nom′ik) **nervous system** The part of the nervous system that regulates processes that occur below the conscious level; e.g., the activity of cardiac muscle, smooth muscle, and glands.

autophagy (aw-tof′ā-jē) Segregation and disposal of damaged organelles within a cell.

autoregulation Intrinsic ability of an organ to regulate its activity.

axial (ak′sē-ăl) Relating to or situated in the central part of the body—the head, neck, and trunk; e.g., the axial skeleton.

axis (ak′sis) The second cervical vertebra.

axolemma (ak′sō-lem′ă) Plasma membrane of an axon.

axon (ak′son) Process of a nerve cell that conducts a nerve signal away from the cell body.

axoplasm (ak′sō-plazm) Cytoplasm within the axon.

B

B-lymphocyte (lim′fō-sīt) Cell involved in humoral immunity; matures into a plasma cell.

baroreceptor (bar′ō-rē-sep′ter, -tōr) Any sensor of pressure changes.

basal nuclei (nū′klē′ ī) *See cerebral nuclei.*

base Substance that accepts a hydrogen ion.

basement membrane Thin layer at the basal surface of epithelial tissue that helps to attach it to underlying connective tissue.

basophil (bā′sō-fil) The least common of the white blood cells. Basophils release proinflammatory agents (e.g., histamine, heparin).

benign (bē-nīn′) Term that denotes the mild character of an illness or the nonmalignant character of a neoplasm.

bile (bīl) Fluid secreted by the liver, stored and discharged from the gallbladder into the duodenum.

bilirubin (bil-i-rū′bin) Waste product derived from the breakdown of hemoglobin and excreted in bile.

blood-brain barrier Structure formed by capillary endothelial cells and astrocytes that regulates what can enter the interstitial fluid in the brain: helps prevent transport of harmful substances from the blood into the brain.

blood pressure Measure of the force of blood pushing against the blood vessel wall; commonly measured in the brachial artery.

bolus (bō′lŭs) A single quantity of something, such as a mass of food swallowed.

brachial (brā′kē-ăl) Relating to the region between the shoulder and the elbow.

bradycardia (brad-ē-kar′dē-ă) A resting heart rate below 60 beats per minute.

brainstem Brain region composed of the mibrain, pons, and medulla oblongata.

bronchiole (brong′kē-ōl) Small tubules that branch from bronchi in the lungs.

bronchus (brong′kŭs) Airways that deliver air from the trachea to the bronchioles.

buffer Substance that minimizes a change in pH even after an acid or base is added.

bursa (ber′să; pl., bursae, ber′sē) Closed, fluid-filled sac lined with a synovial membrane; usually found in areas subject to friction.

C

calcification (kal′si-fi-kā′shŭn) Process in which structures in the body become hardened as a result of deposited calcium salts; normally occurs only in the formation of bone and teeth.

callus (kal′ŭs) Composite mass of cells and extracellular matrix that forms at a fracture site to establish continuity between the bone ends.

calorie The amount of energy required to raise the temperature of 1 g of water by 1°C.

calyx (kā′liks; pl., calyces or calices, kal′i-sēz) Cup-shaped structure.

canaliculus (kan-ă-lik′ū-lŭs; pl., canaliculi, -lī) Small canal or channel.

cancer Disease involving a malignant neoplasm that can metastasize (spread to other organs).

capacitation (kă-pas′i-tā′shŭn) A period of conditioning whereby the sperm cell membrane is modified while in the female reproductive tract prior to being able to fertilize the secondary oocyte.

capillary (kap′i-lār-ē) The smallest blood vessel, its thin walls allow movement of substances between blood and interstitial fluid.

carbohydrate An organic molecule composed of carbon, hydrogen, and oxygen.

cardiac cycle Events taking place in the heart during one heart beat.

cardiac output (CO) Volume of blood ejected by the ventricle in 1 minute; calculated by multiplying heart rate times stroke volume.

carotene (kar′ō-tēn) Class of yellow-red pigments widely distributed in plants and animals.

carotid (ka-ro′tid) **body** Contains neurons sensitive to changing levels of blood pH, CO_2, and O_2; located in the common carotid artery.

carotid sinus (sī′nŭs) Structure composed of neurons sensitive to changes in blood pressure; located in the internal carotid arteries.

carpal (kar′păl) Relating to the wrist.

carrier Protein that bonds to a molecule then alters its shape in order to transport the molecule across the plasma membrane; also, a person with one recessive mutant allele (when in a homozygous form causes a phenotypical change) who does not express the trait but can pass the mutation on to their offspring.

cartilaginous (kar-ti′laj′i-nŭs) Relating to or consisting of cartilage.

catabolism (kă-tab′ō-lizm) Breakdown of complex molecules into simple molecules.

catalyst (kat′ă-list) Substance that speeds up a chemical reaction.

cataract (kat′ă-rakt) Complete or partial opacity of the lens.

catecholamines (kat-ĕ-kōl′ă-mēnz) Class of neurotransmitters (includes epinephrine, norepinephrine, and dopamine).

cation (kat′-ī-on) Ion with a positive charge; (e.g., Na^+).

cauda equina (kaw′dă ē-kwī′nă) Spinal nerve roots within the vertebral canal inferior to the tapered inferior end of the spinal cord proper.

cecum (sē′kŭm) Blind pouch forming the first part of the large intestine.

cell Basic structural and functional unit of a living organism.

cell-mediated immunity Immune response involving T lymphocytes.

cellular respiration Multistep metabolic pathway in which organic molecules are disassembled in a controlled manner by a series of enzymes to eventually form ATP.

central nervous system (CNS) Composed of the brain and spinal cord.

centriole (sen′trē-ōl) Organelle that participates in the separation of chromosome pairs during cell division.

centromere (sen′trō-mēr) The nonstaining constriction of a chromosome that is the point of attachment of the spindle fiber.

cephalic (se-fal′ik) Relating to the head area.

cerebellum (ser-e-bel′ŭm) The second largest part of the brain; develops posteriorly to the pons in the metencephalon.

cerebral cortex (se-rē′bral kor′teks) Superficial layer of gray matter in the cerebrum.

cerebral nuclei Paired irregular masses of gray matter buried deep within central white matter in the basal region of the cerebral hemispheres inferior to the floor of the lateral ventricle.

cerebrospinal (sĕ-rē′brō-spī-năl) **fluid (CSF)** A clear, colorless fluid that circulates in the ventricles and subarachnoid space to protect and support the brain and spinal cord; fluid produced by ependymal cells.

cerebrovascular (sĕ-rē′brō-vas′kū-lăr) **accident (CVA)** Altered brain activity caused by reduced blood supply to the brain. It may result in permanent damage.

cerebrum (ser′ē-brŭm, ser′ĕ-brŭm) The largest, most superior part of the brain; composed of the left and right cerebral hemispheres; location of conscious thought processes and origin of all complex intellectual functions.

cerumen (sĕ-rū′men) Soft, waxy secretion of the ceruminous gland; found in the external auditory meatus.

cervical (ser′vĭ-kal) Relating to the neck.

chemical energy Energy stored in the chemical bonds of a molecule.

chemical equilibrium (ē-kwi-lib′rē-ŭm) State of a chemical reaction in which there is no net change in formation of products or reactants.

chemical reaction Process during which chemical bonds of a molecule are broken or new ones are formed.

chemical synapse (sin′aps) Junction between two communicating cells (neurons, and neurons and effectors): neurotransmitter molecule travels across this type of synapse.

chemoreceptor (kē′mō-rē-sep′tor) Cell that detects specific chemicals in a fluid; e.g., taste receptors.

chemotaxis (kē-mo-tak′sis) Movement in response to chemicals.

cholecalciferol (kō′lē-kal-sif′er-ol) Vitamin D.

cholecystokinin (kō′lē-sis-to-kī′nin) **(CCK)** Hormone released from the duodenum in response to lipid-rich chyme; stimulates secretion from the pancreas and gallbladder.

cholesterol Type of steroid found in the plasma membrane.

cholinergic (kol-in-er′jik) Relating to neurons that use acetylcholine as their neurotransmitter.

chondroblast (kon′drō-blast) Actively mitotic form of a matrix-forming cell found in developing and growing cartilage.

chondrocyte (kon′drō-sīt) Mature, nondividing cartilage cell.

chorion (kō′rē-on) Multilayered, outermost extraembryonic membrane; together with the functional layer of the endometrium it forms the placenta, the site through which nourishment and waste are exchanged between mother and developing fetus; attachment to the uterus.

chromatid (krō′mă-tid) One of the two strands of a chromosome joined by a centromere.

chromatin (krō′ma-tin) Genetic material of the nucleus in a nondividing cell.

chromosome (krō′mō-sōm) The most organized level of genetic material; a single long molecule of DNA and associated proteins; becomes visible only when the cell is dividing.

chronic (krŏn′ik) Takes place over a long period of time. *Compare to acute.*

chronic obstructive pulmonary disease (COPD) Group of respiratory diseases involving obstruction of the airways.

chyle (kīl) Chylomicron-containing lymph drained from gastrointestinal tract.

chyme (kīm) Mixture of partially digested food and gastric juice that is pastelike.

cilium (sil′ē-ŭm; pl., cilia, -ă) Motile extension of a cell surface containing cytoplasm and microtubules.

circumduction (ser-kŭm-dŭk′shŭn) Movement of a body part in a circular direction.

cisterna (sis-ter′nă; pl., cisternae, -ter′nē) Enclosed microscopic space (e.g., between the parallel membranes of the Golgi apparatus).

citric acid cycle A cyclic metabolic pathway that occurs in the matrix of mitochondria during which energy in the bonds of acetyl CoA is transferred to form ATP, NADH, and FADH.

cleavage (klēv′ij) Series of mitotic cell divisions occurring in the zygote immediately following its fertilization.

climacteric (klī-mak′ter-ik, klī-mak-ter′ik) Changes occurring in the male and female reproductive systems, beginning at around 50 years, resulting in altered levels of reproductive hormones.

coagulation (kō-ag-yū-lā′-shŭn) Formation of a blood clot.

codon (kō′don) Group of three nucleotide bases in a messenger RNA molecule.

coenzyme (kō-en′zīm) Organic chemical assisting in enzyme function.

cofactor Chemical that aids in enzyme function.

cognition (kog-ni′shŭn) Mental activities associated with thinking, learning, and memory.

coitus (kō-i′tŭs; koy′tus) Sexual union between a male and a female.

collagen (kol′lă-jen) **fibers** Strong, flexible protein found in many connective tissues.

colloid (kol′oyd) Opaque mixture composed of water and solute (usually protein); substance within thyroid follicles.

columnar (kol-ŭm′năr) Relating to epithelial cells that are taller than they are wide.

commissure (kom′i-shūr) Bundle of axons passing from one side to the other in the brain or spinal cord.

complement (kom′plĕ-ment) Group of plasma proteins working together during an innate immune response; may lead to increased inflammation and cytolysis of the invading cell.

concentration gradient (grā′dē-ent) Difference in the concentration of a substance between two areas.

conducting zone Respiratory system passageways transporting air from the nose to the terminal bronchioles. *Compare to respiratory zone.*

conductivity (kon-dŭk-tiv′i-tē) Property of sending an electrical change along the cell membrane.

cone Cone-shaped cell in the retina that provides color vision; works best in bright light.

congenital (kon-jen′i-tăl) Present at birth.

conjunctiva (kon-jŭnk-tī′vă) Mucous membrane covering the anterior surface of the eyeball and the posterior surface of the eyelids.

contralateral (kon-tră-lat′er-ăl) Relating to the opposite side.

control center Structure in a feedback cycle interpreting information from a receptor and sending information to an effector to produce a response.

cornea (kōr′nē-ă) Transparent structure that forms the anterior surface of the eye.

coronal (kōr′ō-năl) A vertical plane that divides the body into anterior and posterior parts; also called frontal plane.

coronary (kōr′o-nār-ē) Denoting the blood vessels or other structures and activities related to the heart.

cortex (kor′teks) Outer region of an organ; (e.g., cerebral cortex or adrenal cortex).

corticosteroid (kōr-ti-kō-stēr′-oyd) Hormones secreted by the adrenal cortex (e.g., cortisol).

costal (kos′tăl) Relating to a rib.

covalent (kō-vāl′ent) **bond** Chemical bond formed when nearby atoms share electrons.

cranial (krā′nē-ăl) Relating to the skull.

cranium (krā′nē-ŭm) Region of the skull composed of the frontal, parietal, temporal, occipital, ethmoid, and sphenoid bone.

creatine (krē′-ă-tēn; -tin) Chemical providing muscle cells with energy; present as creatine phosphate.

creatinine (krē-at′i-nēn) Nitrogenous waste product resulting from the breakdown of creatine and excreted in urine. Used to estimate glomerular filtration rate since it is not reabsorbed by the kidney.

cross-section Transverse section.

cubital (kū′bi-tal) Relating to the elbow.

cuboidal (kū-boy′dăl) Relating to cells that are cube-shaped.

current Movement of charged particles, such as ions.

cutaneous (kū-tā′nē-ŭs) Relating to the skin.

cyclic adenosine monophosphate (sī′klik ă-den′ō-sēn mon-ō-fos′-făt) **(cAMP)** A second messenger used when some hormones act on a target cell. Formed when adenylate cyclase reacts with ATP.

cytokine (sī′tō-kīn) Protein that regulates the intensity and duration of the immune system.

cytokinesis (sī′tō-ki-nē′sis) Division of the cytoplasm during cell division.

cytology (sī-tol′ō-jē) Study of cells.

cytoplasm (sī′tō-plazm) All cellular contents contained between the plasma membrane and the nucleus; includes cytosol, organelles, and inclusions.

cytoskeleton (sī-tō-skel′ĕ-ton) Organized network of protein filaments and hollow tubules that provide organization, support, and movement throughout the cell.

cytosol (sī′tō-sol) The viscous, syruplike fluid medium with dissolved solutes in the cytoplasm.

cytotoxic T (T$_C$) lymphocyte (sī′tō-tok′-sik līm′fō′sīt) A class of T-lymphocytes that releases chemicals toxic to cells; also called CD8 cells.

D

deamination (dē-am-i-nā′shŭn) Process of removing the amine group of an amino acid.

deciduous (dē-sid′ū-ŭs) Not permanent; e.g., deciduous teeth.

decussation (dē-kŭ-sā′shŭn) Any crossing over or intersection of parts.

defecation (def-ĕ-kā′shŭn) Discharge of feces from the rectum.

deglutition (dē-glū-tish′ŭn) Swallowing.

dehydration synthesis Chemical reaction in which water is formed during formation of a complex molecule.

denaturation (dē-nā-tū-rā′shŭn) A change in a protein's complex three-dimensional shape into a simpler shape; may occur with changes in pH or increased temperature.

dendrite (den′drīt) Process of a neuron that receives and conducts graded potentials toward the cell body.

dendritic (den-dri′tik) **cell** Phagocytic cells of the skin and mucous membranes.

dentition (den-tish′ŭn) Natural teeth in the dental arch, considered collectively.

deoxyribonucleic (dē-oks′ē-rībō-nū-klēic′) **acid (DNA)** A double-stranded nucleic acid, composed of deoxyribonucleotide monomers; directs protein synthesis.

depolarization (dē-pō′lăr-i-zā-shŭn) Change in membrane potential or voltage to a more positive value.

depression (dē-presh′ŭn) Downward or inward displacement of a body part.

dermatome (der′mă-tōm) Specific segment of skin supplied by a single spinal nerve. Also, during embryonic development, the cells that form the connective tissue of the skin.

dermis (der′mis) Connective tissue layer of skin internal to the epidermis; contains blood and lymph vessels, nerves and nerve endings, glands, and usually hair follicles.

desmosome (dez′mō-sōm) One type of adhesion between two epithelial cells; a type of intercellular junction that holds cells together at a single point (like a button).

detrusor (dē-trū′ser, -sōr) Muscle that acts to expel urine from the bladder.

diabetes (dī-ă-bē′tēz) **insipidus** Disease involving reduced ADH release or reduced kidney response to ADH; leads to excessive urine production.

diabetes mellitus (me-lī′tŭs) Disease involving reduced insulin release or reduced tissue response to insulin; leads to elevated blood and urine glucose levels.

diapedesis (dī′ă-pĕ-dē′sis) Passage of blood or its formed elements through the intact blood vessel wall.

diaphragm Muscle that separates the thoracic cavity and abdominopelvic cavity; aids in breathing.

diaphysis (dī-af′i-sis; pl., diaphyses, -sēz) Elongated, usually cylindrical part of a long bone between its two ends; the shaft of a long bone.

diarthrosis (dī-ar-thrō′sis; pl., diarthroses, -sēz) A freely movable (synovial) joint.

diastole (dī-as′tō-lē) The relaxation phase of a heart chamber.

diastolic pressure (dī-ă-stol′ik) Blood pressure measured in an artery during diastole.

diencephalon (dī-en-sef′ă-lon) Brain region deep to the cerebrum; contains the thalamus, hypothalamus, and epithalamus.

diffusion (di-fū′zhŭn) Random movement of molecules or particles down their concentration gradient.

diploë (dip′lō-ē) Central layer of spongy bone between the two layers of compact bone (outer and inner plates) of the flat cranial bones.

diploid (dip′loyd) State of a cell containing pairs of homologous chromosomes. In humans, the diploid number of chromosomes is 46 (23 pairs).

disaccharide (dī-sak′ă-rīd) Carbohydrate composed of two monosaccharides; e.g., sucrose.

dislocation (dis-lō-kā′shŭn) Complete displacement of an organ (e.g., a bone) from its normal position.

distal (dis′tăl) Far from the point of attachment at the trunk.

diuretic (dī-ū-ret′ik) Agent that increases the excretion of urine.

diverticulum (dī′ver-tik′yū-lŭm; pl., diverticula) A pouch or sac opening from a tubular or saccular organ, such as the gut or bladder; small bulge in the intestinal wall.

dorsal (dōr′săl) Toward the back.

dorsiflexion (dōr-si-flek′shŭn) Upward movement of the foot or toes, or of the hand or fingers.

duodenum (dū-ō-dē′nŭm, dū-od′ĕ-nŭm) First section of small intestine.

dura mater (dū′ră mah′ter) Tough, fibrous membrane forming the outer covering of the central nervous system.

E

ectoderm (ek′tō-derm) Outermost of the three primary germ layers of the embryo.

ectopic (ek-top′ik) Out of place; e.g., in an ectopic pregnancy, the pre-embryo implants in the uterine tube rather than in the uterus.

edema (e-dē′mă) Localized swelling of a tissue.

effector (ē-fek′tŏr, -tōr) Peripheral tissue or organ that responds to nervous or hormonal stimulation.

efferent (ef′er-ent) Outgoing or moving away from a center.

eicosanoids (ī'kō'-să-noydz) Local hormones derived from fatty acids.

ejaculation (ē-jak-ū-lā'shŭn) Expulsion of semen from the penis.

elastic fiber Protein that allows tissues to stretch and return to their original shape; found in connective tissues.

electrical energy Movement of charged particles (such as ions).

electrical synapse (sin'aps) Junction between two communicating cells. Signal travels across this type of synapse by moving through gap junctions.

electrochemical gradient Electrical charge difference across a membrane.

electrolyte (ē-lek'trō-līt) Chemical that dissociates when added to water and can conduct an electrical current; includes salts, bases, and acids.

electrolyte balance Maintenance of the appropriate levels of electrolytes (such as sodium ions) in body fluids.

electron Subatomic particle with a negative charge; found orbiting the nucleus of an atom.

element Substance composed of only one type of atom.

elevation (el-ĕ-vā'shŭn) Superior movement of a body part.

embolus (em-bō'lŭs) Dislodged blood clot or air bubble traveling through the blood.

embryo (em'brē-ō) Organism in the early stages of development; in humans, the embryonic stage extends from the third to the eighth week of development.

embryology (em-brē-ol'ō-jē) Study of the origin and development of the organism, from fertilization of the secondary oocyte until birth.

end diastolic (dī-ă-stol'ik) **volume (EDV)** Volume of blood in the ventricle at the end of diastole (relaxation).

end systolic volume (ESV) Volume of blood in the ventricle at the end of systole (contraction).

endergonic (en'der-gon'ik) **reaction** Chemical reaction that requires the input of energy.

endocardium (en-dō-kar'dē-ŭm) Covering of the internal surface of the heart wall and external surface of heart valves.

endochondral ossification (en-dō-kon'drăl os'i-fi-kā'shŭn) Bone formation that takes place within hyaline cartilage; used to form most bones of the body.

endocrine (en'dō-krin) Hormonal secretions that are transported by the blood. *Compare to exocrine.*

endocytosis (en'dō-sī-tō'sis) Movement of substances from the extracellular environment into the cell through the formation of a vesicle.

endoderm (en'dō-derm) Innermost of the three primary germ layers of the embryo.

endolymph (en'dō-limf) Fluid within the membranous labyrinth of the inner ear.

endometrium (en'dō-mē'trē-ŭm) Mucous membrane forming the inner layer of the uterine wall.

endomysium (en'dō-miz'ē-ŭm, -mis'ē-ŭm) Areolar connective tissue layer surrounding a muscle fiber.

endoneurium (en-dō-nū'rē-ŭm) Areolar connective tissue of a peripheral nerve that surrounds the axons.

endoplasmic reticulum (en'-dō-plas'mik re-tik'ū-lum) **(ER)** Organelle composed of an extensive network of connected membranes; involved in synthesis, transport, and storage of macromolecules, and detoxification of drugs: present as smooth ER or rough ER.

endosteum (en-dos'tē-ŭm) Layer of cells lining the inner surface of bone in the medullary cavity.

endothelium (en-dō-thē'lē-ŭm) The simple squamous epithelium that lines the lumen of blood vessels, lymphatic vessels, and heart chambers and valves.

energy Capacity to do work.

enzyme (en'zīm) Protein that catalyzes a chemical reaction by lowering the activation energy.

eosinophil (ē-ō-sin'ō-fil) White blood cell that destroys parasitic worms and phagocytizes antibody-antigen complexes.

ependymal (ep-en'di-mal) Relating to the cellular lining of the brain ventricles and central canal of the spinal cord; assists in production and circulation of CSF.

epicardium (ep-i-kar'dē-ŭm) The visceral (outermost) layer of the heart; also called the serous pericardium.

epidermis (ep-i-derm'is) The epithelium (keratinized, stratified squamous) of the integument.

epimysium (ep-i-mis'ē-ŭm) A layer of dense, irregular connective tissue surrounding a skeletal muscle.

epinephrine (ep'i-nef'rin) Hormone released by the adrenal medulla during activation of the sympathetic nervous system.

epineurium (ep-i-nū'rē-ŭm) Outermost supporting connective tissue layer of peripheral nerves.

epiphyseal (ep-i-fiz'ē-ăl) **line** The remnant of the epiphyseal plate that remains when long bone growth ceases; thin, defined area of compact bone.

epiphyseal plate Layer of hyaline cartilage located between a long bone diaphysis and epiphysis; allows longitudinal growth of the bone.

epiphysis (e-pif'i-sis; pl., epiphyses, -sēz) Expanded, knobby region at the end of a long bone.

erection (ē-rek'shŭn) Erectile tissues in the penis fill with blood and cause the penis to enlarge and become firm.

erythrocyte (ĕ-rith'rō-sīt) Mature red blood cell.

erythropoiesis (ĕ-rith'rō-poy-ē'sis) Formation of erythrocytes.

erythropoietin (ĕ-rith-rō-poy'ē-tin) Protein that stimulates erythropoiesis.

esophagus (ē-sof'ă-gŭs) Portion of the gastrointestinal tract between the pharynx and the stomach.

excitability The ability of a cell to respond to a stimulus with an action potential.

excretion (eks-krē'-shŭn) Process of removing waste products from the body.

exergonic (ek'ser-gon'ik) **reaction** Chemical reaction in which chemical energy is released.

exocrine (ek'sō-krin) Glandular secretions delivered to an apical or luminal surface through a duct.

exocytosis (ek'sō-sī-to'sis) Process whereby secreting granules or droplets are released from a cell.

exon (ek'-son) A portion of a DNA molecule; that codes for a section of the future messenger RNA molecule; these "coding" regions in pre-messenger RNA are joined together to form mature messenger RNA.

expiration (eks-pi-rā'shŭn) To breathe out; exhalation.

extension (eks-ten'shŭn) Movement that increases the articulating angle.

exteroceptor (eks'ter-ō-sep'ter, -tōr) Peripheral end organ of the afferent nerves in the skin or mucous membrane that responds to external stimulation.

extracellular (eks-tră-sel'ū-lăr) **fluid (ECF)** Fluid located outside of cells.

extracellular matrix (mā'triks) Protein fibers and ground substance in the extracellular space of connective tissue.

extrinsic (eks-trin'sik) Originates outside of an organ (e.g., extrinsic eye muscles).

F

facet (fas'et, fă-set') Small, flat, shallow articulating surface; smooth area on a bone.

facilitated diffusion Passive transport process using carrier proteins or channel proteins to move a chemical across the plasma membrane.

falciform (fal'si-fōrm) Having a crescent or sickle shape (e.g., falciform ligament).

falx cerebri (falks se-rē'brē) Portion of the dura mater septa that projects into the longitudinal fissure between the right and left hemispheres of the brain.

fascia (fash'ē-ă; pl., fasciae, -ē-ē) Sheath of fibrous connective tissue that envelops the body internal to the skin; encloses muscles, and separates their various layers or groups.

fascicle (fas'i-kl) Band or bundle of muscle or nerve fibers.

fauces (faw'sēz) Space between the oral cavity and the pharynx.

feces (fē'sēz) Material discharged from the GI tract during defecation.

fertilization (fer'til-i-zā'shŭn) Process of sperm penetration of the secondary oocyte.

fetal (fē'tăl) Relating to the fetus; in humans, the fetal period extends from the eighth week after conception until birth.

fibrin (fī'brin) Fibrous protein that creates a web during blood clot formation.

fibroblast (fī'brō-blast) Large, flat, connective tissue cells with tapered ends that produce the fibers and ground substance components of the extracellular matrix.

fibrosis (fī-brō'sis) Formation of fibrous connective tissue as a repair or reactive process.

filtrate (fil'trāt) The materials that pass through a filter.

fimbria (fim'brē-ă; pl., fimbriae, -brē-ē) Any fringelike structure (e.g., the fimbriae of the infundibulum enclose the ovary at the time of ovulation).

fissure (fish'ur) Deep furrow, cleft, or slit.

flagellum (flă-jel'-ŭm; pl., flagella, -ă) Whiplike locomotory organelle that arises from within the cell and extends outside it; permits a sperm cell to move.

flexion (flek'shŭn) Movement that decreases the angle between the articulating bones.

flexure (flek'sher) Bend in an organ or structure.

follicle Roughly spherical group of cells enclosing a cavity.

fontanelle (fon'tă-nel') One of several membranous intervals at the margins of the cranial bones in an infant.

foramen (fō-rā'men) Hole in a bone (e.g., foramen magnum, obturator foramen).

formed elements Erythrocytes, leukocytes, and platelets found in blood.

fornix (fōr'niks; pl., fornices, -ni-sēz) Arch-shaped structure.

fossa (fos'ă; pl., fossae, -fos'ē) Depression, often more or less longitudinal in shape, below the level of the surface of a part.

G

G protein Specific protein that acquires its energy from guanosine triphosphate; when activated by a membrane receptor, it relays the signal to another membrane protein and alters the activity of that protein.

gamete (gam'ēt) A sex cell with the haploid number of chromosomes.

gametogenesis (gam'ě-tō-jen'ě-sis) Formation and development of gametes (sex cells).

ganglion (gang'glē-on; pl., ganglia, -glē-ă) Group of nerve cell bodies in the peripheral nervous system.

gastric (gas'trik) Relating to the stomach.

gastrulation (gas-trū-lā'shŭn) Formation of the three primary germ layers.

gene Segment of DNA containing information to direct synthesis of a specific protein; functional unit of DNA.

genotype (jen'ō-tīp) The genetic constitution of an individual that, along with environmental influences, contributes to the phenotype.

gestation (jes-tā'shŭn) Pregnancy.

gland Organ or individual cells that secrete a substance.

glomerulus (glō-mer'yū-lŭs) A capillary network within the renal corpuscle in a kidney.

glucocorticoid (glū-kō-kōr'ti-kōyd) Group of hormones released from the adrenal cortex; help regulate glucose levels (e.g., cortisol, corticosteroid).

gluconeogenesis (glū'kō-nē'ō-jen'ěsis) Formation of glucose from a noncarbohydrate source.

glucose (glū'kōs) Primary nutrient source for producing cellular energy; one of the monosaccharides.

glycerol (glis'er-ol) Chemical component of a triglyceride molecule.

glycocalyx (glī-kō-kā'liks) Filamentous coating on the apical surface of certain types of cells.

glycogen (glī'kō-jen) Polysaccharide formed from glucose monomers.

glycogenesis (glī'kō-jen'ě-sis) Formation of glycogen from glucose.

glycogenolysis (glī'kō-je-nol'i-sis) Breakdown of glycogen into glucose.

glycolipid (glī-kō-lip'id) Lipid with an attached carbohydrate group found on the extracellular side of the plasma membrane.

glycolysis (glī-kol'i-sis) Stage of cellular respiration in which glucose is partially catabolized to form pyruvic acid and to form ATP molecules (also called anaerobic cellular respiration).

glycosuria (glī-kō-sū'rē-ă) Presence of glucose in urine; symptom of diabetes mellitus (also called glucosuria).

goblet cells Unicellular glands that secrete mucin.

Golgi (gol'jē) **apparatus** Series of saclike membranes that act as a center to package, sort, and modify molecules arriving from the endoplasmic reticulum in a transport vesicle.

gonad (gō'nad) Organ that produces sex cells and sex hormones; the ovaries in a female and the testes in a male.

gonadocorticoids (gō-na'dō-kōr'ti-kōyd) Group of sex hormones including estrogen and androgen.

graded potential Small deflection in the resting membrane potential that decreases in intensity as it travels; may be a depolarization or hyperpolarization.

gradient A difference from one area to another; e.g., concentration gradient, pressure gradient.

gray matter Brain or spinal cord tissue composed of neuron cell bodies, dendrites, and unmyelinated axons.

gustation (gŭs-tā'shŭn) Sense of taste.

gyrus (jī'rŭs; pl., gyri, -rī) Prominent rounded surface elevation that helps form the cerebral hemispheres.

H

hair cell Specialized sensory cell in the inner ear.

half-life Time required to reduce substance by one-half of its original quantity.

haploid (hap'loyd) The number of chromosomes in a sperm or secondary oocyte. In humans, the haploid number is 23.

hapten (hap'ten) Small substance that attaches to another molecule to initiate an immune reaction.

helper T (T$_H$) lymphocyte (lim'fō-sīt) A T-lymphocyte that releases cytokines to regulate humoral immunity and cellular immunity as well as cells of innate immunity; also called CD4 cells.

hematocrit (hē'mă-tō-krit, hem'ă-) Percentage of whole blood attributed to erythrocytes.

hematoma (hē-mă-tō'mă) Mass of blood outside of the blood vessels (e.g., subdural hematoma).

heme (hēm) Portion of a hemoglobin molecule that transports oxygen.

hemocytoblast (hē'mō-sī'tō-blast) Immature cells that produce all types of formed elements in blood.

hemoglobin (hē-mō-glō'bin) A red-pigmented protein that transports oxygen and carbon dioxide; responsible for characteristic bright red color of arterial blood.

hemolysis (hē-mol'i-sis) The process of rupture and destruction of erythrocytes.

hemopoiesis (hē'mō-poy-ē'sis) Formation and development of blood cells.

hemorrhage (hem'ŏ-rij) Abnormal escape of blood from a blood vessel.

hemostasis (hē'mō-stā'sīs) Process of stopping bleeding; steps include vascular spasm, platelet plug formation, and coagulation.

heparin (hep'a-rĭn) Chemical that prevents blood clot formation; released by basophils and mast cells.

hepatic (he-pat'ik) Relating to the liver.

gray matter Brain or spinal cord tissue composed of neuron cell bodies, dendrites, and unmyelinated axons.

hernia (her'nē-ă) Protrusion of a part through the structures normally surrounding or containing it.

heterozygous (het'er-ō-zī'gŭs) Having both dominant and recessives alleles for a trait.

hiatus (hī-ā'tŭs) Opening.

hillock (hil'lok) Any small elevation or prominence.

hilum (hī'lŭm) The part of an organ where structures such as blood vessels, nerves, and lymph vessels enter or leave.

histamine (his'tă-mēn) Chemical that increases capillary permeability and causes vasodilation; released by mast cells and basophils.

histology (his-tol'ō-jē) Study of tissues formed by cells and cell products.

homeostasis (hō'mē-ō-stā'sis, -os'tă-sis) State of equilibrium in the body with respect to various functions and the chemical composition of fluids and tissues.

homologous (hŏ-mol'ō-gŭs) Alike in certain critical attributes.

homozygous (hō-mō-zī'gŭs) Having two identical alleles for a trait.

hormone (hōr'mōn) Chemical formed in one part of the body and carried by the blood to another part of the body where it can affect cellular activity.

humoral (hyū'mōr-ăl) **immunity** Immune response involving B-lymphocytes; involves release of antibodies from plasma cells.

hyaline (hī'a-lin, -lēn) Clear, homogeneous substance; a type of cartilage.

hydrogen bond A weak attraction formed when a hydrogen atom of one molecule is attracted to a slightly negative atom within either the same molecule or a different molecule.

hydrolysis (hī-drol'i-sis) Chemical reaction in which water is used during the breakdown of a complex molecule.

hydrophilic (hī-drō-fil'ik) **molecule** Substance that does dissolve in water.

hydrophobic (hī-drō-fōb'ik) **molecule** Substance that does not dissolve in water.

hydroxyapatite (hī-drok'sē-ap-ă-tīt) Natural mineral structure that the crystal lattice of bone and teeth closely resembles.

hyperextension (hī'per-eks-ten'shŭn) Extension of a body part beyond 180 degrees.

hyperplasia (hī-per-plā′zhē-ă) Increase in the number of cells in a tissue.

hyperpolarization (hī′pĕr-pō′lăr-i-zā-shŭn) Change in the membrane potential to a value more negative than the resting potential.

hypertension (hī′pĕr-ten′shŭn). Persistently elevated blood pressure.

hypertonic (hī′pĕr-ton′ik) **solution** Solution with a lower water concentration and higher solute concentration than that of the cytosol.

hypertrophy (hī-pĕr′trō-fē) Increase in the size of cells in a tissue.

hyperventilation (hī-pĕr-ven′ti-lā′shŭn) Increase in the breathing rate or depth.

hypodermis (hī-pō-der′mis) Subcutaneous layer of tissue internal to and not part of the integument.

hypogastric (hī-pō-gas′trik) Relating to the hypogastrium, or pubic region.

hypothalamus (hī′pō-thal′ă-mŭs) Region of the brain in the diencephalon; regulates body temperature, autonomic nervous system, and endocrine system.

hypotonic (hī′pō-ton′ik) **solution** Solution with a lower solute concentration and a higher water concentration than that of the cytosol.

hypoventilation Decrease in the breathing rate or depth.

hypoxia (hī-pok′sē-ă) Decreased oxygen level.

I

idiopathic (id′ē-ō-path′ik) Describing a disease of unknown cause.

immunity (i-myū′ni-tē) Ability of the body to protect itself against foreign cells and chemicals; includes humoral immunity and innate immunity.

immunocompetence (im′ū-nō-kom′pĕ-tens) Ability of immune cells to recognize and bind to an antigen.

immunoglobulin (im′ū-nō-glob′ū-lin) **(Ig)** *See antibody.*

implantation Embedding of the pre-embryo in the uterine wall.

inclusion A temporary store of molecules in the cytosol.

infarction (in-fark′shŭn) Tissue death resulting from reduced or absent blood supply; e.g., myocardial infarction.

inferior Toward the feet.

inflammation A nonspecific, localized immune response to tissue injury.

infundibulum (in-fŭn-dib′ū-lŭm) Funnel-shaped structure or passage.

ingestion (in-jes′chŭn) Introduction of food and drink into the GI tract.

inguinal (ing′gwi-năl) Relating to the groin area.

innervation (in-er-vā′shŭn) Supply of axons functionally connected with a structure of the body.

inorganic Chemical substance that is not organic (e.g., water, acids, bases).

insertion (in-ser′shŭn) The usually distal and more movable attachment of a muscle.

inspiration (in-spi-rā′shŭn) To breathe in; inhalation.

integument (in-teg′ū-ment) Cover enveloping the body; includes the epidermis, dermis, and all derivatives of the epidermis; also called skin or the cutaneous membrane.

intercalated disc (in-ter′kă-lā-ted disk) Complex junction that interconnects cardiac muscle cells in the heart wall to mechanically and electrically link these cells.

interneuron (in′ter-nū′ron) Type of neuron that resides within the CNS and coordinates activity between sensory and motor neurons.

interoceptor (in′ter-ō-sep′ter) Small sensory receptors within the walls of the viscera.

interphase First phase of the cell cycle during which the cell carries out normal activities and prepares for cell division.

interstitial (in-ter-stish′ăl) Relating to spaces within a tissue or organ, but not a body cavity; e.g., interstitial fluid occupies the extracellular environment of the cells.

intervertebral (in-ter-ver′te-brăl) Between vertebrae.

intracellular fluid (ICF) *See cytosol.*

intramembranous (in′tră-mem′brā-nŭs) **ossification** Bone formation that takes place within a membrane; the formation of flat bones.

intraperitoneal (in′tră-per′i-tō-nē′ăl) Location of a structure or organ that is completely covered with visceral peritoneum.

intrinsic (in-trin′sik) Originates inside of an organ; e.g., intrinsic muscles of the hand.

intrinsic factor Chemical, produced by stomach cells, required for absorption of vitamin B$_{12}$.

intron (in′tron) A portion of DNA that lies between two exons; noncoding regions in pre-messenger RNA. These are removed during pre-messenger RNA processing.

invaginate (in-vaj′i-nāt) To infold or insert a structure within itself.

ion (ī′on) An atom with a net positive or negative charge.

ionic bond Chemical bond formed when a cation is electrostatically attracted to an anion.

ipsilateral (ip-si-lat′er-ăl) Relating to the same side.

ischemia (is-kē′mē-ă) Reduced blood flow; may lead to hypoxia.

isomer (ī′sō-mer) Molecules composed of the same number and types of atoms but with a different arrangement; e.g., glucose and galactose.

isometric (ī-sō-met′rik) **contraction** Muscle contraction during which its length does not change because tension does not exceed resistance (load).

isotonic (ī-sō-ton′ik) **contraction** Muscle contraction during which tension exceeds the resistance and the muscle fibers shorten, resulting in movement.

isotonic solution Contains the same relative solute and water concentration as the cytosol.

isotope (ī′sō-tōp) Atoms of an element that have a different number of neutrons.

K

keratin (ker′ă-tin) Protein that strengthens the epidermis, hair, and nails; produced by keratinocytes.

keratinization (ker′ă-tin-i-zā′shŭn) Development of a horny layer due to cells filled with the protein keratin.

keratinocyte (ke-rat′i-nō-sīt) The most abundant cell type in the epidermis and found throughout the epidermis; cells that produce keratin.

ketone (kē′tōn) **bodies** Waste product of fatty acid breakdown; also called ketoacids.

ketoacidosis (kē′tō-as-i-dō′sis) Accumulation of ketone bodies in the blood; a symptom of diabetes mellitus.

kinase (kī′nās) Type of enzyme that transfers a phosphate group from one molecule to another.

kinetic (ki-net′ik) **energy** Energy of movement. *Compare to potential energy.*

L

labia (lā′bē-ă; sing. labium) Tissue fold having the appearance of a lip.

lacrimal (lak′ri-măl) Relating to tears.

lactation (lak-tā′shŭn) Production of milk.

lacteal (lak′tē-al) Tiny vessel that transports lymph with lipids and lipid-soluble vitamins from the small intestine.

lactic acid Chemical produced during glycolysis.

lacuna (lă-kū′nă; pl., lacunae, -kū′nē) Small space, cavity, or depression.

lamella (lă-mel′ă; pl., lamellae, -mel′ē) Layer of bone connective tissue; forms concentric rings.

lamina (lam′i-nă) Thin layer (i.e., epithelial tissue basal lamina).

lanugo (lă-nū′gō) Fine, soft, unpigmented fetal hair.

larynx (lar′ingks) Organ of voice production that lies between the pharynx and the trachea.

lateral (lat′er-ăl) Away from the midline.

lateralization (lat′er-al-ī-zā′shŭn) Process whereby certain asymmetries of structure and function occur.

lemniscus (lem-nis′kŭs; pl., lemnisci, -nis′ī) Bundle of axons ascending from sensory relay nuclei to the thalamus.

lesion (lē′zhŭn) Pathologic change in a tissue.

lethargy (leth′ar-jē) Mild impairment of consciousness characterized by reduced awareness and alertness.

leukocyte (lū′kō-sīt) Any one of several types of white blood cells.

leukopoiesis (lū′kō-poy-ē′sis) Formation and development of leukocytes.

ligament (lig′ă-ment) Band or sheet of dense regular fibrous tissue that connects structures; usually bones.

ligand (lig′and, lī′gand) Chemical released from one cell that binds to receptors on another cell.

lingual (lin′gwăl) Relating to the tongue.

lipase (lip′ās) Enzyme that digests triglycerides.

lipid Group of organic molecules including triglycerides, phospholipids, steroids, and ecosanoids.

lipogenesis (lĭp′o-jĕn′e-sis) Formation of triglyercides from glycerol and fatty acids.

lipolysis (li-pol′i-sis) Breakdown of triglycerides to glycerol and fatty acids.

lobe (lōb) Subdivision of an organ, bounded by some structural demarcation.

lumbar (lŭm′bar) Relating to the lower back.

lumen (lū′men) The space inside a structure, such as where blood is transported within a blood vessel.

lymph (limf) Usually transparent fluid found in lymph vessels; derived from interstitial fluid.

lymphocyte (lim′fō-sīt) White blood cell involved in immune responses (i.e. T lymphocyte, B lymphocyte).

lysosome (lī′sō-sōm) Organelle containing digestive enzymes.

lysozyme (lī′-sō-zīm) Enzyme that attacks the bacterial cell wall. Present in saliva, tears, sweat, and nasal secretions.

M

macromolecules Large complex molecules (e.g., carbohydrates, nucleic acids, proteins).

macrophage (mak′rō-fāj) Phagocytic cell derived from monocytes and can activate the immune system.

major histocompatibility (his′tō-kom-pat′i-bil′i-tē) **complex (MHC)** Plasma membrane proteins used to mark cells as self and to present antigens.

malignant (mă-lig′nant) In reference to a neoplasm, having the property of invasiveness and spread.

mass number Total number of neutrons and protons in the nucleus of an atom.

mast cells Resident cells that secrete heparin and histamine during inflammation; often found near blood vessels.

mastication (mas-ti-kā′shŭn) Chewing ingested food in preparation for swallowing.

matrix (mā′triks; pl., matrices, mā′tri-sēz) Surrounding substance within which cells or structures are contained or embedded.

meatus (mē-ā′tŭs) Passageway traveling through a bone (i.e., external acoustic meatus).

mechanoreceptor (mek′ă-nō-rē-sep′tŏr) Sensory receptor that responds to touch, vibration, pressure, or distortion.

medial (mē′dē-ăl) Toward the midline.

mediastinum (me′dē-as-tī′nŭm) Median space of the thoracic cavity between the lungs.

medulla (me-dŭl′ă) Inner region of an organ; e.g., adrenal medulla.

medulla oblongata (ob-long-gah′tă) Brain region that transmits information between the spinal cord and higher brain centers; controls heart rate, blood pressure, breathing.

meiosis (mī-ō′sis) Process of sex cell division that results in four gametes, each with the haploid number of chromosomes.

melanin (mel′ă-nin) Any of the dark brown-black pigments or yellow-red pigments that occur in the skin, hair, and retina.

melanocyte (mel′ă-nō-sīt) Pigment-producing cell in the basal layer of the epidermis.

membrane potential Difference in charges across the plasma membrane.

memory cells Lymphocytes that produce a strong, rapid response during the second exposure to an invader.

menarche (me-nar′kē) Time of the first menstrual period.

meninx (mē′ninks; pl., meninges, -jēz) Any one of the membranes covering the brain and spinal cord.

meniscus (mě-nis′kŭs; pl., menisci, mě-nis′sī) Crescent-shaped fibrocartilage found in certain joints.

menopause (men′ō-pawz) Permanent cessation of menses.

menses (men′sēz) Periodic physiologic hemorrhage from the uterine mucous membrane; commonly referred to as the menstrual period.

menstruation (men-strū-ā′shŭn) Cyclic endometrial shedding and discharge of bloody fluid.

mesenchyme (mez′en-kīm) An embryonic connective tissue.

mesentery (mes′en-ter-ē) Fan-shaped fold of peritoneum attaching the small intestine to the posterior abdominal wall; may refer to other membranes associated with organs of the abdominal cavity.

mesoderm (mez′ō-derm) The middle of the three primary germ layers of the embryo.

mesothelium (mez-ō-thē′lē-ŭm) The simple squamous epithelium that lines serous cavities.

metabolic acid Acid produced as a byproduct of metabolism (e.g., ketoacid).

metabolic rate Amount of energy used in a given time period.

metabolic water Water formed during dehydration reactions and during aerobic respiration; contributes approximately 8% of total fluid intake.

metabolism (mě-tab′ō-li-zem) All chemical reactions taking place in the body, including both anabolic and catabolic reactions.

metaphysis (mě-taf′i-sis; pl., metaphyses, -sēz) Section of a long bone between the epiphysis and the diaphysis.

metaplasia (met-ă-plā′zē-ă) Abnormal change in a tissue.

metastasis (mě-tas′tă-sis) The movement or spread of malignant cells from one part of the body to another.

microfilament (mī-krō-fil′ă-ment) Smallest structural protein of the cytoskeleton.

microglia (mī-krog′lē-ă) Category of small glial cells in the central nervous system; wander and exhibit phagocytic activity.

microscopy (mī-kros′kŏ-pē) Investigation of very small objects by means of a microscope.

microtubule (mī-krō-too′būl) Hollow cylinders of tublin protein that are part of the cytoskeleton; able to lengthen and shorten.

microvilli (mī-krō-vil′ī; sing., microvillus -vil′ŭs) Microscopic extensions of the plasma membrane that increase the surface area for secretion or absorption.

micturition (mik-chū-rish′ŭn) Urination.

midsagittal (mid-saj′-i-tăl) Vertical plane cutting the body or body part into an even left and right half.

mineralocorticoid (min′er-al-ō-kōr′ti-kōyd) Group of hormones released from the adrenal cortex that help regulate electrolyte levels in the body.

mitochondrion (mī-tō-kon′drē-on; pl., mitochondria, -ă) Organelle associated with the production of ATP.

mitosis (mī-tō′sis) Process of somatic cell division.

mixed nerve Nerve composed of both sensory and motor neurons.

molarity (mō-lar′i-tē) Number of moles in 1 liter of solution.

mole Unit composed of 6.023 × 10^{23} particles; its mass in grams is equal to the element's atomic mass or the compound's molecular mass.

molecule Composed of atoms or ions held together by an attraction or chemical bond.

monocyte (mon′ō-sīt) White blood cell that develops into a macrophage and phagocytizes bacteria and viruses.

monosaccharide (mon-ō-sak′ă-rīd) The simplest carbohydrate molecules; e.g., glucose, ribose.

mons (monz) Anatomic prominence or slight elevation above the general level of the surface; e.g., mons pubis.

motor (efferent) nerves Composed of neurons that take information away from the central nervous system.

motor unit One motor neuron and all the muscle cells it innervates.

mucin (mū′sin) An often protective secretion containing carbohydrate-rich glycoproteins that forms mucus when hydrated.

mucosa (mū-kō′să) Mucous membrane that lines various body structures.

multipotent (mŭl-tip′ŏ-tent) **stem cells** Adult stem cell that can differentiate into a few specific cell types.

muscle fiber Muscle cell.

muscularis (mŭs-kū-lā′ris) Muscular layer in the wall of a hollow organ or tubular structure.

mutation An alteration in a segment of DNA; may lead to production of an abnormal protein.

myelin (mī′ě-lin) Lipoproteinaceous material of the myelin sheath.

myoblast (mī′ō-blast) Undifferentiated muscle cell with the potential of becoming a muscle fiber.

myocardium (mī-ō-kar′dē-ŭm) Middle layer of the heart wall, consisting of cardiac muscle.

myofibril (mī-ō-fī′bril) Bundles of myofilaments within skeletal and cardiac muscle cells.

myofilament (mī-ō-fil′ă-ment) A protein filament that makes up the myofibrils in skeletal muscle.

myoglobin (mī-ō-glō′bin) Oxygen-carrying and -storing molecule in muscle.

myometrium (mī-ō-mē′trē-ŭm) Middle tunic (muscular wall) of the uterus.

N

naris (nā′ris; pl., nares, -res) Anterior opening to the nasal cavity.

necrosis (nĕ-krō′sis) Pathologic death of cells or a portion of a tissue or organ.

negative feedback Control mechanism that keeps a variable within normal levels (limits amount of product formed). *Compare to positive feedback*

neoplasia (nē-ō-plā′zē-ă) Process that results in the formation of a neoplasm or abnormal growth.

neoplasm (nē′ō-plazm) An abnormal tissue that grows by cell proliferation more rapidly than normal.

nephron (nef′ron) Functional filtration unit in the kidney; composed of a renal corpuscle, a proximal and distal convoluted tubule, and nephron loop.

nerve A bundle of peripheral nervous system axons.

nerve plexus (plek′sŭs) Group of interconnecting spinal nerves (e.g., brachial plexus, lumbar plexus).

nerve signal Propagation or conduction of an action potential along a neuron.

net filtration pressure The aggregate pressure that causes fluid to move out across a blood capillary wall; calculated by subtracting net osmotic pressure from net hydrostatic pressure.

neurilemma (nūr-i-lem′a) The delicate outer membrane sheath around an axon.

neurofibril (nūr-o-fi′bril) Filamentous protein structure in a neuron composed of neurofilaments and microtubules.

neurofilament (nūr-o-fil′a-ment) Group of intermediate-sized filaments in a neuron.

neuroglia (nū-rog′lē-a) Nervous system cells that support neurons.

neuromuscular (nūr-ō-mus′ku-lar) Relationship between a nerve and a muscle; e.g., a neuromuscular junction where a neuron and a muscle cell interface.

neuron (nūr′on) Functional unit of the nervous system.

neurotoxin (nūr-ō-tok′sin) Chemical that alters normal activity of a neuron.

neurotransmitter (nū′rō-trans-mit′er) Chemical released from a neuron that delivers information to another cell.

neurulation (nū′rū-lā′shun) Formation of the neural plate and its closure to form the neural tube.

neutron (nū′tron) Subatomic particle with a neutral charge; found in the nucleus of an atom.

neutrophil (nū′trō-fil) The most common of the white blood cells. Cells that phagocytize bacteria.

nociceptor (nō-si-sep′ter, -tōr) Peripheral sensory receptor for the detection of painful stimuli.

nonpolar molecules Molecules containing nonpolar covalent chemical bonds.

norepinephrine (nōr-ep-i-nef′rin) Neurotransmitter released by the sympathetic nervous system; hormones released from adrenal medulla.

nucleic acid (nū-klē′ik) An organic molecule composed of nucleotide monomers; in DNA and RNA. These store genetic information in the cell.

nucleolus (nū′klē′ō-lŭs; pl., nucleoli, -lī) Spherical, dark body within the nucleus where subunits of ribosomes are made.

nucleotide (nū′klē-ō-tīd) Building blocks of DNA and RNA; composed of a nitrogenous base, a phosphate group, and a sugar.

nucleus (nū′klē-ŭs) Cellular organelle housing DNA or a group of cell bodies in the central nervous system.

nutrient Chemicals obtained from food that are necessary for normal function in cells.

O

oblique (ob-lēk′) Slanted, at an angle.

occult (ŏ-kŭlt′, ok′ult) Hidden or concealed.

octet rule Tendency of atoms to maintain an outer shell with eight electrons.

olfaction (ol-fak′shŭn) Sense of smell.

oligodendrocyte (ol′i-gō-den′drō-sīt) Category of large glial cells in the central nervous system that wrap around and insulate axons.

omentum (ō-men′tŭm) Fold of peritoneum from the stomach to either cover the region between the liver and stomach, or extends to cover most abdominal organs on their anterior surface.

oocyte (ō′-ō-sīt) Female gamete released from the ovary during ovulation.

oogenesis (ō-ō-jen′ĕ-sis) Formation and development of oocytes.

oogonium (ō-ō-gō′nē-ŭm; pl., oogonia) Primitive germ cell of the oocyte.

opposition (op′pō-si′shŭn) Movement of the thumb across the palm to touch the palmar side of the fingertips.

optic Relating to the eye.

orbit Bony socket housing the eye.

organ Composed of two or more tissue types that perform a specific function for the body.

organ system A group of organs working together to coordinate and perform specific function(s).

organelle (or′gă-nel) Complex, organized structures in the cytoplasm of a cell with unique characteristic shapes; called "little organs."

organic molecule Molecule containing carbon atoms; e.g., carbohydrates, proteins, lipids.

organism A living being.

organogenesis (ōr′gă-nō-jen′ĕ-sis) Formation of organs during development.

orifice (or′i-fis) Aperture or opening.

origin (ōr′i-jin) The usually proximal and less movable of the two points of attachment of a muscle.

os (os; pl., ossa, os′ă) An opening into a hollow organ or canal.

osmosis (os-mō′sis) Process by which water moves through a semipermeable membrane from a hypotonic solution to a hypertonic one.

osmotic pressure Pressure exerted by water movement across a membrane as it moves toward an area of lower water concentration.

osseous (os′ē-ŭs) Bony.

ossicle (os′i-kl) Small bone within the ear.

ossification (os′i-fi-kā′shŭn) Bone formation; also called osteogenesis.

osteoblast (os′tē-ō-blast) Bone-forming cell.

osteoclast (os′tē-ō-klast) Large cell type that functions in the absorption and removal of bone connective tissue.

osteocyte (os′tē-ō-sīt) Bone cell in a lacuna within bone matrix.

osteogenesis (os′tē-ō-jen′ĕ-sis) Production of new bone.

osteon (os′tē-on) Functional unit of compact bone tissue; also called a Haversian system.

osteopenia (os′tē-ō-pē′nē-ă) Decreased calcification or density of bone.

osteoporosis (os′tē-ō-pō-rō′sis) Medical condition characterized by decreased bone mass and increased susceptibility to fracture.

osteoprogenitor (os′tē-ō-prō-jen′i-ter) Precursor to bone cells.

ovulation (ov′ū-lā′shŭn) Release of a secondary oocyte from the ovarian follicle.

ovum (ō′vŭm; pl., ova, -vă) Female sex cell that has been fertilized and has completed meiosis II.

oxidation (ok-si-dā′shŭn) Occurs when a chemical loses an electron.

oxidation-reduction reaction Exchange reaction involving transfer of electrons from one chemical to another; also called a redox reaction.

oxidative phosphorylation (ok-si-dā-tiv fos′fōr-i-lā′shŭn) Process of forming ATP by using coenzymes to transfer energy.

P

palate (pal′ăt) Partition between the oral and nasal cavities; the roof of the mouth.

palpation (pal-pā′shŭn) Using the sense of touch to identify or examine internal body structures.

papilla (pă-pil′ă; pl., papillae, -pil′ē) Small, nipplelike process.

paracrine (par′a-krīn) Hormonal secretions that stimulate neighboring cells; also called a local hormone (does not enter the blood). *Compare to endocrine.*

parietal (pă-rī′ĕ-tăl) Relating to the wall of any ventral body cavity.

partial pressure Pressure exerted by a gas in a mixture of gases.

passive immunity Activation of the immune system by administration of antibodies produced by another individual; offers short-term protection since memory cells are not formed. *Compare to active immunity.*

patent (pa′tent, pā′tent) Open or unblocked.

pathogen (path′ō-jen) Disease-causing substance or organism.

pathologic (path-ō-loj′-ik) Pertaining to disease.

pectoral (pek′tŏ-răl) Relating to the chest area.

pedal (ped′ăl) Relating to the foot.

peptide (pep′tīd) **bond** Chemical bond joining amino acid monomers.

perfusion (per-fyū′zhŭn) Blood flow through a tissue; measured in milliliters per minute per gram (mL/min/g).

pericardium (per-i-kar′dē-ŭm) Fibroserous membrane covering the heart.

perichondrium (per′i-kon′drē-ŭm) Layer of dense irregular connective tissue around the surface of cartilage.

perilymph (per′i-limf) Fluid within the osseous labyrinth that surrounds and protects the membranous labyrinth.

perimetrium (per-i-mē′trē-ŭm) Serous coat of the uterus.

perimysium (per-i-mis′ē-ŭm, -miz′ē-ŭm) Fibrous sheath enveloping each of the fascicles of skeletal muscle fibers.

perineurium (per-i-nū′rē-ŭm) Fibrous sheath of peripheral nerves that surrounds the nerve fascicles.

periosteum (per-ē-os′tē-ŭm) Thick, fibrous membrane covering the entire external surface of a bone, except for the articular cartilage on the epiphyses.

peripheral (pĕ-rif′-ē-răl) **nervous system (PNS)** Composed of neurons and neuroglial cells found outside of the central nervous system.

peristalsis (per-i-stal′sis) Rhythmic contractions that propel material through tubes in the gastrointestinal tract.

peritoneum (per′i-tō-nē′ŭm) Serous sac that lines the abdominopelvic cavity and covers most of the viscera within.

permeability (per′mē-ă-bil′i-tē) Capacity of a membrane to allow passage of a substance.

peroxisome (per-ok′si-sōm) Membrane-bound organelle containing oxidative enzymes.

pH Value indicating the relative hydrogen ion (H$^+$) and hydroxyl ion (OH$^-$) concentrations of a solution.

phagocytosis (fāg′ō-sī-tō′sis) A form of endocytosis by which cells ingest and digest solid substances.

phalanx (fā′langks; pl., phalanges, -jēz) Long bone of a digit.

pharynx (far′ingks) Funnel-shaped muscular tube extending from the posterior nasal cavity to the esophagus and larynx; composed of the nasopharynx, oropharynx, and laryngopharynx.

phenotype (fē′nō-tīp) Observable characteristics of an individual.

phospholipid (fos-fō-lip′id) Lipid that forms bilayers of the plasma membrane.

phosphorylation (fos′fōr-i-lā′shŭn) Process of adding a phosphate group to another chemical.

photoreceptor Specialized receptor cells in the eye that detect light. *See rod; cone.*

physiology (fiz-ē-ol′ō-jē) Study of how body parts function together.

pinocytosis (pin′ō-sī-tō′sis) A form of endocytosis by which cells ingest liquid.

placenta (plă-sen′tă) Organ of exchange between the embryo or fetus and the mother.

plasma (plaz′mă) The liquid portion of blood.

plasma cell Cell that produces and releases specific antibodies; derived from B-lymphocytes.

plasma membrane Barrier separating the intracellular fluid from the interstitial fluid.

platelet (plāt′let) Irregularly shaped cell fragment that participates in blood clotting.

pleura (plūr′ă; pl., pleurae, ploor′ē) Serous membranes enveloping the lungs and lining the internal walls of the thoracic cavity.

pleuripotent (plūr′i′pŏ-tent) **cells** Embryonic stem cells that can differentiate into any cell type (except cells of the placenta).

plexus (plek′sŭs) Network of nerves, blood vessels, or lymph vessels.

polar (po′lăr) **molecule** Refers to partial electrical charges on different portions of a molecule .

polycythemia (pol′ē-sī-thē′mē-ă) More than the normal number of erythrocytes.

polymer (pol′-i-mer) Molecule composed of many repeating subunits.

polypeptide (pol-ē-pep′tīd) Chain of 21–199 amino acids linked by peptide bonds.

polysaccharide (pol-ē-sak′ă-rīd) Class of carbohydrates composed of three or more monosaccharide monomers; e.g., glycogen.

portal (pōr′tăl) **system** Unique organization of blood vessels sending blood from a capillary bed through a vein to another capillary bed.

positive feedback Control mechanism that increases the original change in a variable. *Compare to negative feedback.*

posterior Toward the back of the body.

postsynaptic (pōst-si-nap′tik) On the distal side of a synaptic cleft.

potential energy Stored energy.

pressure gradient Difference in pressure between two adjacent areas.

presynaptic (prē-si-nap′tik) On the proximal side of a synaptic cleft.

prion (prī′on) Small disease-causing protein.

pronation (prō-nā′shŭn) Rotational movement of the forearm such that the hand faces posteriorly or inferiorly.

proprioceptor (prō′prē-ō-sep′ter) Sensory receptor that detects position change or state of contraction.

prostaglandin (pros-tă-glan′din) Local hormone derived from a fatty acid.

protein Organic molecule composed of one or more chains of amino acid monomers.

proton (prō′ton) Subatomic particle with a positive charge; found in the nucleus of an atom.

protraction (prō-trak′shun) Movement of a body part anteriorly in a horizontal plane (i.e., thrusting out of the mandible [chin]).

protuberance (prō-tū′ber-ans) Swelling or knoblike outgrowth.

proximal (prok′si-măl) Near the point of attachment to the trunk.

puberty Time period when reproductive organs become fully functional and secondary sex characteristics become more prominent.

pulmonary (pŭl′mō-nār-ē) Relating to the lung.

pulse (pŭls) Rhythmic dilation of an artery resulting from passage of increased blood volume during heart contraction.

pupil (pū′pl) Circular hole in the center of the iris of the eye.

pus (pŭs) Substance composed of dead pathogens, white blood cells, and cellular debris.

pyrogen (pī′rō-jen) Fever-producing substance.

R

radioactivity Emission of high energy radiation from a radioisotope.

radioisotope (rā′dē-ō-ī′sō-tōp) Unstable isotope that emits high energy radiation (e.g., gamma rays) until it decays into a stable isotope.

ramus (rā′mŭs; pl., rami, rā′mī) One of the primary divisions of a nerve or blood vessel. Also, part of an irregularly shaped bone that forms an angle.

raphe (rā′fē) Line of union between two contiguous, bilaterally symmetrical structures; e.g., the raphe of the scrotum.

receptor Structure that detects a stimulus.

reduction Occurs when a chemical gains an electron.

referred pain Pain sensed, not from the organ, but from an unrelated region of the body.

reflex Fast, predetermined response to a stimulus.

refraction (rē-frak′shŭn) Bending of light waves as they pass through a material.

refractory (rē-frak′tōr-ē) **period** Time period when a cell is either unresponsive or less responsive to a stimulus.

renal (rē′năl) Relating to the kidney.

repolarization (rē′pō-lăr-i-zā′shŭn) Change in membrane potential from a depolarized value back to the resting value.

respiration Exchange of O_2 and CO_2 between air and body cells.

respiratory zone Respiratory system passageways transporting air from respiratory bronchioles to the alveoli; airways that participate in gas exchange. *Compare to conducting zone.*

resting membrane potential (RMP) Voltage measured across the plasma membrane of an excitable cell at rest.

reticular (re-tik′ū-lăr) **fibers** Proteins that form a flexible network in tissues; found in some connective tissues.

reticulocyte (re-tik′ū-lō-sīt) Immature erythrocyte.

retroperitoneal (re′trō-per′i-tō nē′ăl) External or posterior to the peritoneum.

ribonucleic (rī′bō-nū-klē′ik) **acid (RNA)** Nucleic acid composed of ribonucleotide monomers; used to direct protein synthesis based on instructions in DNA. *See messenger RNA, ribosomal RNA, and transfer RNA.*

ribosome (rī′bō-sōm) Ribonucleoprotein structure that is the site of protein synthesis; organelle in the cytoplasm.

rod Rod-shaped cell in retina that detects light and can work even in dim light.

rotation (rō-tā′shŭn) Movement of a part around its axis.

rouleau (rū-lō′; pl., rouleaux) Aggregation of erythrocytes in single file.

ruga (rū′gă; pl., rugae, rū′gē) Fold, ridge, or crease.

S

sacroiliac (sā-krō-il′ē-ak) Pertaining to the sacrum and the ilium (e.g., sacroiliac joint).

sacrum (sā′krŭm) Next-to-last group of bones in the vertebral column; formed of five fused vertebrae.

sagittal (saj′i-tăl) Relating to a plane cutting the body into a left and a right part.

salt Substance formed by an ionic bond.

saltatory (sal′tă-tōr-ē) **conduction** Transmission of an action potential along the plasma membrane of a myelinated axon.

sarcolemma (sar′kō-lem′ă) Plasma membrane of a muscle cell.

sarcomere (sar′kō-mēr) Functional unit of skeletal muscle.

sarcoplasm (sar′kō-plazm) Cytoplasm of a muscle cell.

sarcoplasmic reticulum (sar-ko′-plaz′mik re-tik′ū-lŭm) **(SR)** Endoplasmic reticulum found in muscle cells; stores calcium ions required for contraction.

sclera (skler′ă) Portion of the fibrous layer forming the outer covering of the eyeball, except for the cornea; 'white' of the eye.

scoliosis (skō-lē-ō′sis) Abnormal lateral and rotational curvature of the vertebral column.

sebum (sē′bŭm) Secretion of a sebaceous gland.

second messenger Intracellular chemical modifying activity within a cell after a first messenger binds to the plasma membrane.

selective permeability Ability to regulate what can cross a membrane.

semen (sē′men) Secretion composed of sperm and seminal fluid.

semipermeable (sem′ē-per′mē-ă-bl) Freely permeable to some molecules, but relatively impermeable to other molecules.

sensation (sen-sā′shun) Conscious perception of a stimulus.

sensory (afferent) nerve Nerves sending information to the central nervous system.

septum (sep′tŭm; pl., septa) Wall of tissue separating nearby chambers; e.g., nasal septum.

serosa (se-rō′să) Outermost coat of a visceral structure that lies in a closed body cavity.

serous (sēr′ŭs) Producing a substance that has a watery consistency.

serum (sēr′ŭm) Clear, watery fluid that remains after clotting proteins are removed from plasma.

set point Normal value of a variable.

simple diffusion Passive transport process used when a chemical slips between plasma membrane phospholipids to enter or leave a cell.

sinoatrial (sī′nō-ā′trē-ăl) **(SA) node** Group of cells in right atrium that set the heart rate.

sinus (sī′nŭs) Cavity or hollow space; also, a channel for the passage of blood or lymph.

sinusoid (sī′nŭ-soyd) Resembling a sinus; extremely permeable capillary in certain organs, such as the liver or the spleen.

skeleton (skel′ĕ-tŏn) Bony framework of the body; collectively, all the bones of the body.

solute (sol′ūt) Substance dissolving in a solvent.

solution A homogeneous mixture composed of a solvent and a solute.

solvent (sol′vent) Substance (e.g., water) holding a solute in solution.

somite (sō′mīt) One of the paired segments consisting of cell masses formed in the early embryonic mesoderm on the sides of the neural tube.

sonography (sŏ-nog′ră-fē) Radiographic technique using ultrasound waves.

sperm (spermatozoon) Male gamete produced in the testes.

spermatogenesis (sper′mă-tō-jen′ĕ-sis) Process by which stem cells called spermatogonia become sperm.

sphincter (sfingk′ter) Muscle that encircles a duct, tube, or orifice such that its contraction constricts the lumen or orifice and restricts movement through the tube.

sphygmomanometer (sfig′mō-mă-nom′ĕ-ter) Instrument for measuring arterial blood pressure.

splanchnic (splangk′nik) Relating to the viscera.

sprain Tearing or overstretching ligaments without fracturing the nearby bone; results in localized pain and swelling.

squamous (skwā′mŭs) Referring to cell or area that is flat.

stem cells Unspecialized, immature cells.

stenosis (ste-nō′sis) Inability of a tube or valve to open completely; e.g., valvular stenosis.

steroid (stēr′oyd, ster′oyd) Group of lipids including bile salts, cholesterol, and some hormones; molecule is composed of four attached hydrocarbon rings.

stimulus Change in a regulated variable; event that provokes a cellular response.

stria (strī′ă; pl., striae, strī′ē) Stripes, bands, streaks, or lines distinguished by a difference in color, texture, or elevation from surrounding tissue.

stupor (stū′per) State of impaired consciousness from which the individual can be aroused only by continual stimulation.

subcutaneous (sŭb-kū-tā′nē-ŭs) Immediately internal to the integument.

subluxation (sŭb-lŭk-sā′shŭn) Incomplete dislocation of a body part from its normal position.

substrate (sŭb′strāt) Substance binding to the active site of an enzyme; reactant in a chemical reaction.

sulcus (sŭl′kŭs; pl., sulci, sŭl′sī) Groove or furrow (e.g., on the surface of the brain).

summation (sŭm-ā′shŭn) Accumulation of stimuli occurring in neurons or muscle cells; e.g., wave summation.

superficial (sū-per-fish′ăl) Toward the surface.

supination (sū′pi-nā′shŭn) Rotation of the forearm such that the hand faces anteriorly or superiorly.

suspension Mixture of a solvent with large materials that do not dissolve (e.g., blood).

suture (sū′chūr) Synarthrosis in which cranial bones are united by a dense regular connective tissue membrane.

symphysis (sim′fi-sis; pl., symphyses, -sēz) Cartilaginous joint in which the two bones are separated by a pad of fibrocartilage.

synapse (sin′aps) Functional contact of a nerve cell with another nerve cell, effector, or receptor.

synaptic vesicle (si-nap′tik ves′i-kl) Package of plasma membrane enclosing neurotransmitter molecules in the synaptic knob.

syndesmosis (sin′dez-mō′sis; pl., syndesmoses, -sēz) Fibrous joint in which the opposing surfaces of articulating bones are united by ligaments.

synergist (sin′er-jist) Structure, muscle, agent, or process that aids the action of another.

synostosis (sin-os-tō′sis; pl., synostoses, -sēz) Osseous union between two bones that were initially separate.

system Group of interacting structures working as a whole entity.

systemic (sis-tem′ik) Relating to the entire organism as opposed to any of its individual parts.

systole (sis′tō-lē) Contraction of the heart.

systolic (sis-tol′ik) **pressure** Blood pressure measured in an artery during systole.

T

T-lymphocyte (lim′fō-sīt) Immune cell that matures in the thymus gland. *See TC lymphocyte* and *TH lymphocyte.*

tachycardia (tak′i-kar′dē-ă) Resting heart rate above 100 beats per minute.

tactile (tak′til) Relating to touch.

tendon (ten′dŏn) Cord of dense regular connective tissue that connects muscle to bone.

teratogen (ter′ă-tō-jen, te-ră′tō-jēn) Substance that may cause death or malformation of an embryo.

testis (tes′tis; pl., testes, -tēz) Male organ for producing gametes and androgens.

tetanus (tet′ă-nŭs) Sustained contraction that may lead to spastic paralysis.

thalamus (thal′ă-mŭs) Region of the brain in the diencephalon involved in motor control and relaying sensory information to higher brain centers.

thermoreceptor (ther′mō-rē-sep′ter, -tōr) Receptor that is sensitive to heat.

thoracic (thō-ras′ik) Relating to the thorax, the area between the neck and the abdomen.

thrombopoiesis (throm′bō-poy-ē′sis) Formation of blood platelets.

thrombus (throm′bŭs) Blood clot formed within a blood vessel during hypercoagulation; may become an embolus if dislodged.

tissue Groups of similar types of cells performing a common function for the body.

tomography (tō-mog′ră-fē) A radiographic image of a plane constructed by means of reciprocal linear or curved motion of the x-ray tube and film cassette; used in producing a CT scan.

totipotent (tō-tip′ŏ-tent) **cells** Embryonic stem cells that can differentiate into any cell of the body or placenta.

trabecula (tră-bek′ū-lă; pl., trabeculae, -lē) Meshwork; (e.g., trabeculae within spongy bone)

tract (trakt) Bundle of central nervous system axons travelling along the same path.

transcription (tran-skrip′shŭn) Copying information from DNA to form an RNA molecule.

transducer (tranz-dū′sĕr) Device or organ designed to convert energy from one form to another.

translation Process involving RNA and ribosomes to produce a new protein.

transverse (trans-vers′) Relating to a plane cutting a structure into a superior and inferior portion.

transverse (T) tubule (tū′būl) Invaginations of the sarcolemma that allow action potentials to approach and stimulate the sarcoplasmic reticulum.

triglyceride (trī-glis′er-īd) Lipid providing long-term energy storage in adipose connective tissue; composed of glycerol and three fatty acids.

trophoblast (trof′ō-blast, trō′fō-blast) Cell layer covering the blastocyst that will allow the embryo to receive nourishment from the mother.

tubercle (tū′ber-kl) Nodule or slight elevation from the surface of a bone that allows attachment of a tendon or ligament.

tuberosity (tū′ber-os′i-tē) Large tubercle or rounded elevation, as on the surface of a bone.

tumor Mass of new tissue cells resulting from abnormal cell division.

tunic (tū′nik) One of the covering layers of a body part, such as a blood vessel or muscle.

U

ultrastructure (ŭl-tră-strŭk′chūr) Cell structure viewable via the electron microscope.

umbilical (ŭm-bil′i-kăl) Relating to the umbilicus (navel).

unipotent (ū-ni′pŏ-tent) **stem cells** Adult stem cell that can differentiate into only one specific cell type.

unmyelinated (ŭn-mī′ĕ-li-nā-ted) Not covered by a myelin sheath.

urea (ū-rē′ă) A nitrogenous waste product produced by amino acid metabolism and eliminated in urine.

ureter (ū-rē′ter, ū′rē-ter) Tubes that connect the kidney to the urinary bladder.

urethra (ū-rē′thră) Tube that extends from the bladder and conducts urine to the exterior of the body.

uric (ūr′ik) **acid** Waste product of nucleic acid metabolism eliminated in urine.

urinalysis (ū-ri-nal′i-sis) Analysis of the urine to help assess the state of a person's health.

urine (ūr′in) Fluid and dissolved substances excreted by the kidney.

V

vaccine A weakened pathogen, or part of a pathogen, used to stimulate the immune system and produce memory cells; provides artificially acquired active immunity.

varicose (var′i-kōs) **vein** Vein that is extremely dilated and follows a twisting path due to poorly functioning venous valves.

vascular (vas′kū-lăr) Relating to blood vessels.

vasoconstriction (vā′sō-kon-strik′shŭn) Narrowing of blood vessel lumen.

vasodilation (vā′sō-dī-lā′shŭn) Increased blood vessel lumen.

vein (vān) Blood vessel carrying blood toward the heart.

vellus (vel′ŭs) Fine, nonpigmented hair covering most of the fetal body.

ventral (ven′trăl) Toward the belly.

ventricle (ven′tri-kl) Cavity within an organ such as the heart or the brain.

venules (ven′ūl) The smallest veins.

vertebra (ver′tĕ-bră; pl., vertebrae, -brā) Segment of the vertebral column.

vertebral (ver′tĕ-brăl) Relating to a vertebra or the vertebral column.

vesicle (ves′i-kl) Closed cellular structure within the cytoplasm surrounded by a single membrane.

vestibule (ves′ti-byūl) Small space near the entryway of a canal (e.g., nasal vestibule, inner ear vestibule)

viscera (vis′er-ă) Internal organs of the body; especially those in the thoracic and abdominopelvic cavities.

viscosity (vis-kos′i-tē) Thickness of a solution; provides resistance to fluid flow.

volatile (vol′ă-til) **acid** In the body, an acid produced from carbon dioxide (e.g., carbonic acid).

voltage Measure of potential energy in separated charges; expressed in volts.

vulva (vŭl′vă) External genitalia of the female.

W

white matter Brain or spinal cord tissue that derives its color from myelin in myelinated axons.

Y

yolk sac Extraembryonic membrane; site of early blood cell formation in the embryo.

Z

zygote (zī′gōt) Diploid cell resulting from the union of a sperm and a secondary oocyte.

credits

PHOTOGRAPHS

Chapter 1

Opener: © Jupiterimages/Getty Images RF; p. 4(top left): © Dennis Kunkel Microscopy, Inc./Phototake; p. 4(top right): © Dennis Kunkel Microscopy, Inc./Visuals Unlimited; p. 4(bottom left): © Dr. Gopal Murti/Visuals Unlimited; p. 4(bottom right): © EM Research Services, Newcastle University; 1.4a: © The McGraw-Hill Companies, Inc./Eric Wise, photographer; 1.4b: © James Cavallini/Photo Researchers, Inc.; 1.4c: © Trevor Lush/Getty Images; 1.4d: © ISM/Phototake; p. 24(top left): © Ralph T. Hutchings/Visuals Unlimited; p. 24(top right): © SIU BioMed/Custom Medical Stock Photo; p. 24(bottom): © ATL/Photo Researchers, Inc.; p. 25(top): © Athenais/Phototake; p. 25(bottom left): © Alfred Pasieka/SPL/Photo Researchers, Inc.; p. 25(bottom right): © Hank Morgan/Photo Researchers, Inc.

Chapter 2

Opener: USDA ARS/Photo by Scott Bauer; p.32: © Frédéric Astier/Photo Researchers, Inc.

Chapter 3

Opener: CDC/Maryam I. Daneshvar, Ph.D.; p. 85: © Creatas/PunchStock RF

Chapter 4

Opener: © Science Photo Library/www.agefotostock. com RF; 4.1a: © The McGraw-Hill Companies, Inc./Al Telser, photographer; 4.1b: © VVG/SPL/Photo Researchers, Inc.; 4.1c: © Eye of Science/Photo Researchers, Inc.; 4.5b: © Don W. Fawcett/Photo Researchers, Inc.; 4.12a-4.21a: © Dennis Kunkel Microscopy, Inc./Phototake; 4.22: © David M. Phillips/Visuals Unlimited; 4.23: © D. Friend and Donald Fawcett/Visuals Unlimited; 4.24: © Donald Fawcett/Visuals Unlimited; 4.25b: © Gopal Murti/Visuals Unlimited; 4.27: © Donald Fawcett/Visuals Unlimited; 4.28: © Edward P. Morris; 4.29: © Don W. Fawcett/Photo Researchers, Inc.; 4.31a: © Donald Fawcett/Visuals Unlimited; 4.38a: © Michael Abbey/Photo Researchers, Inc.; 4.38b-d: © Carolina Biological Supply Company/Phototake; 4.38e: © Michael Abbey/Photo Researchers, Inc.

Chapter 5

Opener: © Antenna/Getty Images RF; Tbl 5.2a: © Dr. Thomas Caceci, Virginia-Maryland Regional College of Veterinary Medicine; Tbl 5.2b-c: © The McGraw-Hill Companies, Inc./Al Telser, photographer; Tbl 5.2d: © Ed Reschke; Tbl 5.3(top): © The McGraw-Hill Companies, Inc./Al Telser, photographer; Tbl 5.3 (bottom): © Alfred Owczarzak/Biological Photo Service; Tbl 5.4a-e(top): © The McGraw-Hill Companies, Inc./Al Telser, photographer; Tbl 5.4e(bottom): © Victor P. Eroschenko; p. 157: © Leonard Lessin/SPL/Photo Researchers, Inc.; p. 162: © Comstock/Jupiterimages RF; Tbl 5.5a: © The McGraw-Hill Companies, Inc./Al Telser, photographer; Tbl 5.5b: © Ed Reschke; p. 166: © National Marfan Foundation; Tbl. 5.6a-c: © The McGraw-Hill Companies, Inc./Al Telser, photographer; Tbl 5.7a: © Ed Reschke; Tbl 5.7b: © The McGraw-Hill Companies, Inc./Dennis Strete, photographer; Tbl 5.7c: © The McGraw-Hill Companies, Inc./Al Telser, photographer; Tbl 5.8a: © Ed Reschke/Peter Arnold Images/Photolibrary Group; Tbl 5.8b: © Ed Reschke; Tbl 5.8c: © The McGraw-Hill Companies, Inc./Al Telser, photographer; Tbl 5.9: © The McGraw-Hill Companies, Inc./Dennis Strete, photographer; Tbl 5.10-Tbl 5.11c: © The McGraw-Hill Companies, Inc./Al Telser, photographer; Tbl 5.12: © Carolina Biological Supply Company/Phototake; p. 179(top): © Dr P. Marazzi/Photo Researchers, Inc.; p. 179(bottom): © Stevie Grand/Photo Researchers, Inc.

Chapter 6

Opener: © agefotostock/SuperStock; 6.2a: © Ed Reschke/Peter Arnold Images/Photolibrary Group; p. 187: © Steve Cole/Getty Images RF; 6.3a-b: © Carolina Biological Supply Company/Phototake; 6.4b: © John Burbidge/Photo Researchers, Inc.; p. 189: © The McGraw-Hill Companies, Inc./Jill Braaten, photographer; p. 191: © Ingram Publishing RF; p. 194(left): © Dr. P. Marazzi/Photo Researchers, Inc.; p. 194(center left): © Logical Images, Inc.; p. 194(center right): © John Radcliffe Hospital/Photo Researchers, Inc.; p. 194(right): © Dr. P. Marazzi/Photo Researchers, Inc.; 6.9a-b: © The McGraw-Hill Companies, Inc./Al Telser, photographer; 6.10b: © Collection CNRI/Phototake; 6.10c: © G.W. Willis, MD/Visuals Unlimited; 6.10d: © The McGraw-Hill Companies, Inc./Al Telser, photographer; p. 202: © Dr. Zara/Photo Researchers, Inc.; p. 204(left): © Sheila Terry/Photo Researchers, Inc.; p. 204(center): © Dr. P. Marazzi/Photo Researchers, Inc.; p. 204(right): © John Radcliffe Hospital/Photo Researchers, Inc.; p. 206(top): © Science Photo Library RF/Getty Images; Tbl 6.2(top)-(center): © Dr. P. Marazzi/Photo Researchers, Inc.; Tbl 6.2(bottom): © James Stevenson/Photo Researchers, Inc.

Chapter 7

Opener: © AJPhoto/Hôpital Américain/Photo Researchers, Inc.; 7.4: © Susumu Nishinaga/Photo Researchers, Inc.; 7.5b: Credit: Dr. M. Laurent, University Hospitals Leuven, Belgium. Image is available under a creative commons attribution license; 7.6c: © The McGraw-Hill Companies, Inc./Al Telser, photographer; p. 217: © SPL/Photo Researchers, Inc.; p. 219(top left): © C Squared Studios/Getty Images RF; 7.8a: © Carolina Biological Supply Company/Phototake; 7.8b: © Dr. Richard Kessel & Dr. Randy Kardon/Tissues and Organs/Visuals Unlimited; 7.8c: © Leonard Lessin/SPL/Photo Researchers, Inc.; 7.9(top): © The McGraw-Hill Companies, Inc./Al Telser, photographer; p. 223: © David Hunt/Smithsonian Institution; p. 224(left): © Science VU/Visuals Unlimited; p. 224(center): © Tissuepix/Photo Researchers, Inc.; p. 224(right): © MShieldsPhotos/Alamy; p. 225(left): © Bone Clones; p. 225(right): © ZEPHYR/SPL/Getty Images RF; 7.12a: © The McGraw-Hill Companies, Inc./Al Telser, photographer; 7.12b: © Image Shop/Phototake; p. 230: © Dr. LR/Photo Researchers, Inc.; p. 232a: © SPL/Photo Researchers, Inc.; p. 232b: © P. Motta/Photo Researchers, Inc.; 7.16(top): © Mediscan/Visuals Unlimited; 7.16(center): © ISM/Phototake; 7.16(bottom): © Wellcome Photo Library, Wellcome Images; p. 234 (left): © Simon Fraser/Medical Physics, RVI, Newcastle upon Tyne/Photo Researchers, Inc.; p. 234(right): John Pape/MedPix™. Website: rad.usuhs.edu/medpix

Chapter 8

Opener: © Dennis MacDonald/PhotoEdit; 8.4-8.6: © The McGraw-Hill Companies, Inc./Christine Eckel, photographer; p. 255(top): © Dr. M. A. Ansary/SPL/Photo Researchers, Inc.; p. 255(bottom): © NMSB/Custom Medical Stock Photo; p. 257(left)-(center): Courtesy of Dr. John A. Jane, Sr., David D. Weaver Professor of Neurosurgery, Department of Neurological Surgery, University of Virginia Health System, Charlottesville, Virginia; p. 257(right): Used with permission and copyright of Cranial Technologies, Inc.; 8.12b:

© The McGraw-Hill Companies, Inc./Photo and Dissection by Christine Eckel; Tbl 8.4 (top left)-(bottom right): © Ralph T. Hutchings/Visuals Unlimited; 8.16b-8.26d: © The McGraw-Hill Companies, Inc./Christine Eckel, photographer; 8.28b: © Mediscan/Visuals Unlimited; Tbl 8.6(top left): © David Hunt/Smithsonian Institution; Tbl 8.6(bottom left): © L. Bassett/Visuals Unlimited; Tbl 8.6(top right): © David Hunt/Smithsonian Institution; Tbl 8.6(bottom right): © L. Bassett/Visuals Unlimited; 8.33a-b: © The McGraw-Hill Companies, Inc./Christine Eckel, photographer; p. 288(top left): © Dr. P. Marazzi/Photo Researchers, Inc.; p. 288(top center): © SPL/Photo Researchers, Inc.; p. 288(top right): © Mediscan/Visuals Unlimited; p. 288(bottom left): © Bart's Medical Library/Phototake; p. 288(bottom right): © ISM/Phototake; p. 292: © Science Photo Library/Photo Researchers, Inc.

Chapter 9

Opener: © Russell Illig/Getty Images RF; 9.8a: © The McGraw-Hill Companies, Inc./Eric Wise, photographer; 9.8b-c: © The McGraw-Hill Companies, Inc./JW Ramsey, photographer; 9.8d: © The McGraw-Hill Companies, Inc./Eric Wise, photographer; 9.8e-9.9c: © The McGraw-Hill Companies, Inc./JW Ramsey, photographer; 9.9d(left)-(right): © The McGraw-Hill Companies, Inc./Eric Wise, photographer; 9.10a-9.11d(right): © The McGraw-Hill Companies, Inc./JW Ramsey, photographer; 9.12a(left)-(right): © The McGraw-Hill Companies, Inc./Eric Wise, photographer; 9.12b-c(bottom): © The McGraw-Hill Companies, Inc./JW Ramsey, photographer; 9.12d(top)-9.12e: © The McGraw-Hill Companies, Inc./Eric Wise, photographer; p. 316(left): © & Courtesy of Dr. Mike Langran/www.ski-injury.com; p. 316(right): © Science Photo Library/Phototake; 9.15a: © The McGraw-Hill Companies, Inc./Photo and Dissection by Christine Eckel; p. 318: © sot/Photodisc/Getty Images RF; 9.17d: © The McGraw-Hill Companies, Inc./Photo and Dissection by Christine Eckel; p.326(left): © John Watney/Photo Researchers, Inc.; p. 326(right): © CNRI/Photo Researchers, Inc.

Chapter 10

Opener: © Tony McConnell/Photo Researchers, Inc.; 10.6b: © Dr. Thomas Caceci, Virginia-Maryland Regional College of Veterinary Medicine; 10.12a(right)-b(right): © Dr. H. E. Huxley; 10.17: © Gladden Willis/Visuals Unlimited; p. 357: © Ed Scott/agefotostock RF; p. 358: © George Doyle/Getty Images RF; p. 359: © Ingram Publishing RF; 10.24(top): © Christine Eckel; 10.24(2nd from top): © Dr. Gladden Willis/Visuals Unlimited; 10.24(3rd from top): © Victor P. Eroschenko; 10.24(4th from top): © The McGraw-Hill Companies, Inc./Al Telser, photographer; 10.24(bottom): © Educational Images/Custom Medical Stock Photo

Chapter 11

Opener: © Nova stock/www.agefotostock.com; p. 376: © Dr. P. Marazzi/SPL/Photo Researchers, Inc.; 11.6(top left)-(bottom right): © The McGraw-Hill Companies, Inc./JW Ramsey, photographer; p. 389: Photo courtesy of SC Photo; 11.15b-11.16b: © The McGraw-Hill Companies, Inc./Photo and Dissection by Christine Eckel; 11.22(left): © Elsa/Getty Images; 11.22(right): © Brita Meng Outzen/AP Photo; 11.22(bottom): © Mike Fiala/Getty Images; p. 409: © Karl Weatherly/Getty Images RF; 11.27a(right): © The McGraw-Hill Companies, Inc./Photo and Dissection by Christine Eckel; 11.28: © The McGraw-Hill Companies, Inc./JW Ramsey, photographer; 11.29a(right): © The McGraw-Hill Companies, Inc./Photo and Dissection by Christine Eckel; p. 424:

Humoral immunity, 856, 856t
Hunchback, 263
Huntington disease, 507
Hydration, hypotonic, 987–988
Hydrocarbons, 50
Hydrocephalus, 492
Hydrochloric acid (HCl), 1031
secretion of, 1030f
Hydrogen bonds, 40, 40f, 131f
Hydrogen ions, 34t, 963–965, 964f
Hydrogen phosphate, 1005
Hydrolase, 82t
Hydrolysis, 51, 51f
Hydrophilic substances, 43f
Hydrophobic exclusion, 44
Hydrophobic interactions, 40, 44
Hydrophobic substances, 43f
Hydrostatic pressure (HP), 780. *See also* Blood pressure
Hydroxyapatite, 217
Hydroxyl group, 50f
Hymen, 1104
Hyperbaric oxygen chambers, 920
Hypercalcemia, 994t
Hypercalcuria, 974
Hypercapnia, 931
Hyperchloremia, 994t
Hypercholesterolemia, 773
Hypercoagulation, 718
Hyperemesis gravidarum (HG), 1150
Hyperextension, 307t, 308, 308f
Hyperkalemia, 993, 994t
Hypermagnesemia, 994t
Hypernatremia, 992, 994t
Hyperopia, 622
Hyperphosphatemia, 994t
Hyperplasia, 170, 358, 682
Hyperpnea, 931
Hyperpolarization, and return to resting membrane potential, 465
Hypersensitivities, 877
acute, 877
allergies, 877
Hypertension, 773, 792
hepatic portal, 1040
pregnancy-induced, 1151
Hyperthyroidism, 678
Hypertonic solutions, 112, 112f
Hypertrophic heart, 738
Hypertrophy, 179
Hyperventilation, effect on cardiovascular function, 930–931
Hypoblast, 1137f
Hypocalcemia, 230, 994t
Hypocapnia, 931
Hypochloremia, 994t
Hypochondriac region, 1042
Hypodermis. *See* Subcutaneous layer
Hypogastric region, 17
Hypoglossal canal, 243t, 247, 248f, 249f, 251t
Hypoglycemia, 673, 688
Hypokalemia, 993, 994t
Hypomagnesemia, 994t
Hyponatremia, 992, 994t
Hyponychium, 193f, 194
Hypophosphatemia, 994t
Hypophysectomy, 672
Hypopnea, 931
Hypotension, 792
orthostatic, 792
Hypothalamic-pituitary-thyroid axis, 678, 683

Hypothalamo-hypophyseal portal system, 670
Hypothalamo-hypophyseal tract, 670
Hypothalamus, 464t, 483f, 505–506f, 508–509, 508f, 669–685
and angiotensin II, 996
control of autonomic functions, 597, 597f
control of endocrine system, 654, 1100
functions of, 464t, 508
interactions with the anterior pituitary gland, 671–672, 672t
interactions with the posterior pituitary gland, 670–671
relationship to the pituitary gland, 669–670, 669f
thirst center within, 989
Hypothyroidism, 228, 678
Hypotonic solutions, 112, 112f
Hypoventilation, 931
effect on cardiovascular function, 930–931
Hypoxia, 708, 931
Hypoxic drive, 912
Hysterectomy, 1104

I

I bands, 337f
Identity markers, 108, 108f
Ileum, 1035f, 1036, 1045f
Iliac region, 17
Iliotibial band, 371f
Iliotibial tract, 420, 421f, 426f
Imaging procedures, medical, 24–25
Immune cells, structures that house, 843–844, 844f
Immune complex elimination, 850, 850f
Immune function
of connective tissue, 165
of epidermis, 201
Immune privilege, 857
Immune response, 856
Immune surveillance, 849
Immune system, 842–883
lymphatic structures that assist, 837f
overview of, 843–846, 845f, 879
relationship of lymphatic system to, 837
Immunity, 842
active and passive, 876–878
adaptive, 845–846, 845f, 856–863, 872–873, 879
antibody-mediated, 856
cell-mediated, 856, 856t
humoral, 856, 856t, 875f
and immunologic memory, 874–878
innate, 845–856, 845f, 848f, 854, 879
Immunogen, 856
Immunogenicity, 856
Immunoglobulins (Ig), 869–874, 880
classes of, 871, 871t
IgA, 871, 871t
IgD, 871, 871t
IgE, 871, 871t
IgG, 871, 871t
IgM, 871, 871t
structure of, 869
Immunologic memory, 874–875

initial exposure, 874–875
measure of, 874–875
primary response, 874–875, 875f
lag (latent) phase, 874–875
production of antibody, 875
secondary response, 874–875, 875f
lag (latent) phase, 875
production of antibody, 875
Immunosuppressant drugs, 180
Impaired urination, 977
Implantation, 1133f, 1136–1137f, 1137–1138, 1165
Implanted/injected progestins, 1111
Impotence, 1126
In vitro fertilization (IVF), 1147
Incisors, 1024f, 1025
Inclusions, 105f, 106, 123t, 124f
Incomplete tetanus, 356
Incontinence, 977
Independent assortment, 1091
Indirect pathway, 546
Inducing labor, 1152
Infants
dehydration in, 988
skull of, 262, 262f
Infarction, 743
Infection site, effector response at, 868–869
Infectious agents
categories of, 842–843t
diseases caused by, 842–883
preventing entry of, 846–848, 847t
Inferior (direction), 13
Inferior angle, of scapula, 275, 275f
Infertility and infertility treatments, 1147
Inflammation, 850–851f, 850–853
acute, applying ice for, 852
cardinal signs of, 852
heat, 852
loss of function, 852
pain, 852
redness, 852
swelling, 852
chemicals of, 851t
effects of, 852
events of, 850–851f, 850–853
chemotaxis, 851f, 852
diapedesis, 851f, 852
margination, 851f, 852
Information
collecting, 438
initiating response to, 438
processing and evaluating, 438
model of, 519f
Infraorbital margin, 254t
Infundibular stalk, 670
Infundibulum
of brain, 482f, 506f, 508f, 509f, 521f, 670
of uterine tube, 1102f
Ingestion, 1015
Inguinal canal, 1113
Inguinal ring, superficial, 397, 1113f
Inheritance
codominant, 1164
dominant-recessive, 1163–1164, 1163t
patterns of, 1163–1164
polygenic, 1164
sex-linked, 1164
Inhibin, 1098, 1100f, 1114
Inhibiting hormones (IHs), 671

Inhibitors, 84
Inhibitory postsynaptic potentials (IPSPs), generation of, 461f, 462
Inner cell mass. *See* Embryoblast
Innervation
of dermis, 192–193
dual, 590–591, 594
antagonistic effects, 590–591
cooperative effects, 594
of heart, 744–746, 745f
of joints, 303
of kidneys, 941
of muscles, 333, 339–340
of respiratory system, 904
Inorganic molecules, 49
Inotropic agents, 760, 761f
Inspiratory capacity (IC), 916, 917f, 917t
Inspiratory reserve volume (IRV), 916, 917f, 917t
Insula, 497t, 505f
Insulin, 687–688, 1070
diabetes mellitus, 688
regulation and action of, 687f
Insulin-like growth factor 1 (IGF-1), 672, 675
Insulin-like growth factor 2 (IGF-2), 672, 675
Integument, 185f. *See also* Dermis; Epidermis; Skin
aging of, 205–206, 208
composition of, 185–193, 207
dermis, 190–191f, 190–193, 207
development of, 204–205, 208
epidermal accessory organs, 193–197, 207
epidermis, 186–190, 188f, 207
form influencing function in, 198–199
functions of, 197–201, 207
repair and regeneration of, 202–204, 208
structure of, 185f
subcutaneous layer of, 185f, 190f, 192t, 193, 207
Integumentary structures, derived from epidermis, 193–197, 207
Integumentary system, 185–193, 185–210, 207
overview of, 8f
Intercalated discs, 174–175, 174t, 359f, 740f, 741
Intercellular clefts, 774
Intercellular structures, 741
desmosomes, 741
gap junctions, 741
Interferons (IFNs), 848
effects of, 848f
Intermediate filaments, 124t, 128f
Intermolecular attractions, 40, 66
Internal capsule, 502, 505f, 524f
Internal genitalia, development of, 1123f, 1124
Internal os, 1102f, 1103
Interoceptors, 604t, 605
Interosseous borders, 278, 286, 287f
Interosseous membrane, 277f, 278, 300f, 301
Interphase, 140–142, 140–147, 140f, 141t, 142–143f, 142f
Intersex conditions, 1124
Interstitial cells, 1115, 1117f